PEARSON   ALWAYS LEARNING

Jane B. Reece • Lisa A. Urry • Michael L. Cain
Steven A. Wasserman • Peter V. Minorsky • Robert B. Jackson

Campbell Biology
Volume II

Custom Edition for Houston Community College

Taken from:
Campbell Biology, Tenth Edition
by Jane B. Reece, Lisa A. Urry, Michael L. Cain, Steven A. Wasserman,
Peter V. Minorsky, Robert B. Jackson

Pearson Learning Solutions, 501 Boylston Street, Suite 900, Boston, MA 02116
A Pearson Education Company
www.pearsoned.com

Printed in the United States of America

5 6 7 8 9 10 V0UD 19 18 17 16 15

000200010271882946

AL/MB

ISBN 10: 1-269-75797-0
ISBN 13: 978-1-269-75797-3

The Tenth Edition author team's contributions reflect their biological expertise as researchers and their teaching sensibilities gained from years of experience as instructors at diverse institutions. The team's highly collaborative style continues to be evident in the cohesiveness and consistency of the Tenth Edition.

Jane B. Reece

Jane Reece was Neil Campbell's longtime collaborator, and she has participated in every edition of *CAMPBELL BIOLOGY*. Earlier, Jane taught biology at Middlesex County College and Queensborough Community College. She holds an A.B. in biology from Harvard University, an M.S. in microbiology from Rutgers University, and a Ph.D. in bacteriology from the University of California, Berkeley. Jane's research as a doctoral student at UC Berkeley and postdoctoral fellow at Stanford University focused on genetic recombination in bacteria. Besides her work on *CAMPBELL BIOLOGY*, she has been a coauthor on *Campbell Biology in Focus, Campbell Biology: Concepts & Connections, Campbell Essential Biology*, and *The World of the Cell*.

Lisa A. Urry

Lisa Urry is Professor of Biology and Chair of the Biology Department at Mills College in Oakland, California, and a Visiting Scholar at the University of California, Berkeley. After graduating from Tufts University with a double major in biology and French, Lisa completed her Ph.D. in molecular and developmental biology at the Massachusetts Institute of Technology (MIT) in the MIT/Woods Hole Oceanographic Institution Joint Program. She has published a number of research papers, most of them focused on gene expression during embryonic and larval development in sea urchins. Lisa has taught a variety of courses, from introductory biology to developmental biology and senior seminar. As a part of her mission to increase understanding of evolution, Lisa also teaches a nonmajors course called Evolution for Future Presidents and is on the Teacher Advisory Board for the Understanding Evolution website developed by the University of California Museum of Paleontology. Lisa is also deeply committed to promoting opportunities in science for women and underrepresented minorities. Lisa is also a coauthor of *Campbell Biology in Focus*.

Michael L. Cain

Michael Cain is an ecologist and evolutionary biologist who is now writing full-time. Michael earned a joint degree in biology and math at Bowdoin College, an M.Sc. from Brown University, and a Ph.D. in ecology and evolutionary biology from Cornell University. As a faculty member at New Mexico State University and Rose-Hulman Institute of Technology, he taught a wide range of courses, including introductory biology, ecology, evolution, botany, and conservation biology. Michael is the author of dozens of scientific papers on topics that include foraging behavior in insects and plants, long-distance seed dispersal, and speciation in crickets. In addition to his work on *CAMPBELL BIOLOGY* and *Campbell Biology in Focus*, Michael is the lead author of an ecology textbook.

Steven A. Wasserman

Steve Wasserman is Professor of Biology at the University of California, San Diego (UCSD). He earned his A.B. in biology from Harvard University and his Ph.D. in biological sciences from MIT. Through his research on regulatory pathway mechanisms in the fruit fly *Drosophila*, Steve has contributed to the fields of developmental biology, reproduction, and immunity. As a faculty member at the University of Texas Southwestern Medical Center and UCSD, he has taught genetics, development, and physiology to undergraduate, graduate, and medical students. He currently focuses on teaching introductory biology. He has also served as the research mentor for more than a dozen doctoral students and more than 50 aspiring scientists at the undergraduate and high school levels. Steve has been the recipient of distinguished scholar awards from both the Markey Charitable Trust and the David and Lucile Packard Foundation. In 2007, he received UCSD's Distinguished Teaching Award for undergraduate teaching. Steve is also a coauthor of *Campbell Biology in Focus*.

Peter V. Minorsky

Peter Minorsky is Professor of Biology at Mercy College in New York, where he teaches introductory biology, evolution, ecology, and botany. He received his A.B. in biology from Vassar College and his Ph.D. in plant physiology from Cornell University. He is also the science writer for the journal *Plant Physiology*. After a postdoctoral fellowship at the University of Wisconsin at Madison, Peter taught at Kenyon College, Union College, Western Connecticut State University, and Vassar College. His research interests concern how plants sense environmental change. Peter received the 2008 Award for Teaching Excellence at Mercy College. Peter is also a coauthor of *Campbell Biology in Focus*.

Robert B. Jackson

Rob Jackson is the Douglas Professor of Environment and Energy in the Department of Environmental Earth System Science at Stanford University. Rob holds a B.S. in chemical engineering from Rice University, as well as M.S. degrees in ecology and statistics and a Ph.D. in ecology from Utah State University. While a biology professor at Duke University, Rob directed the university's Program in Ecology and was Vice President of Science for the Ecological Society of America. He has received numerous awards, including a Presidential Early Career Award in Science and Engineering from the National Science Foundation. Rob is a Fellow of both the Ecological Society of America and the American Geophysical Union. He also enjoys popular writing, having published a trade book about the environment, *The Earth Remains Forever*, and two books of poetry for children, *Animal Mischief* and *Weekend Mischief*. Rob is also a coauthor of *Campbell Biology in Focus*.

Neil A. Campbell

Neil Campbell (1946–2004) combined the investigative nature of a research scientist with the soul of an experienced and caring teacher. He earned his M.A. in zoology from the University of California, Los Angeles, and his Ph.D. in plant biology from the University of California, Riverside, where he received the Distinguished Alumnus Award in 2001. Neil published numerous research articles on desert and coastal plants and how the sensitive plant (*Mimosa*) and other legumes move their leaves. His 30 years of teaching in diverse environments included introductory biology courses at Cornell University, Pomona College, and San Bernardino Valley College, where he received the college's first Outstanding Professor Award in 1986. Neil was a visiting scholar in the Department of Botany and Plant Sciences at the University of California, Riverside.

We are honored to present the Tenth Edition of CAMPBELL BIOLOGY. For the last quarter century, CAMPBELL BIOLOGY has been the leading college text in the biological sciences. It has been translated into more than a dozen languages and has provided millions of students with a solid foundation in college-level biology. This success is a testament not only to Neil Campbell's original vision but also to the dedication of thousands of reviewers, who, together with editors, artists, and contributors, have shaped and inspired this work. Although this Tenth Edition represents a milestone, science and pedagogy are not static—as they evolve, so does CAMPBELL BIOLOGY.

Our goals for the Tenth Edition include:

- helping students **make connections visually** across the diverse topics of biology
- giving students a strong foundation in **scientific thinking and quantitative reasoning skills**
- inspiring students with the excitement and relevance of modern biology, particularly in the realm of **genomics**

Our starting point, as always, is our commitment to crafting text and visuals that are accurate, are current, and reflect our passion for teaching and learning about biology.

New to This Edition

Here we provide an overview of the new features that we have developed for the Tenth Edition; we invite you to explore pages x–xxvi for more information and examples.

- **Make Connections Figures** draw together topics from different chapters to show how they are all related in the "big picture." By reinforcing fundamental conceptual connections throughout biology, these figures help overcome students' tendencies to compartmentalize information.
- **Scientific Skills Exercises** in every chapter use real data and guide students in learning and practicing data interpretation, graphing, experimental design, and math skills. All 56 Scientific Skills Exercises have assignable, automatically graded versions in **MasteringBiology®**.

- **Interpret the Data Questions** throughout the text engage students in scientific inquiry by asking them to interpret data presented in a graph, figure, or table. The Interpret the Data Questions can be assigned and automatically graded in **MasteringBiology**.
- The impact of genomics across biology is explored throughout the Tenth Edition with examples that reveal how our ability to rapidly sequence DNA and proteins is transforming all areas of biology, from molecular and cell biology to phylogenetics, physiology, and ecology. Chapter 5 provides a launching point for this feature in a new Key Concept, "Genomics and proteomics have transformed biological inquiry and applications." Illustrative examples are distributed throughout later chapters.
- **Synthesize Your Knowledge Questions** at the end of each chapter ask students to synthesize the material in the chapter and demonstrate their big-picture understanding. A striking photograph with a thought-provoking question helps students see how material they learned in the chapter connects to their world and provides insight into natural phenomena.
- The Tenth Edition provides a range of new practice and assessment opportunities in **MasteringBiology.** Besides the Scientific Skills Exercises and Interpret the Data Questions, Solve It Tutorials in MasteringBiology engage students in a multistep investigation of a "mystery" or open question. Acting as scientists, students must analyze real data and work through a simulated investigation. In addition, Adaptive Follow-Up Assignments provide coaching and practice that continually adapt to each student's needs, making efficient use of study time. Students can use the Dynamic Study Modules to study anytime and anywhere with their smartphones, tablets, or computers.
- Learning Catalytics™ allows students to use their smartphones, tablets, or laptops to respond to questions in class.
- As in each new edition of CAMPBELL BIOLOGY, the Tenth Edition incorporates **new content** and **organizational improvements**. These are summarized on pp. viii–ix, following this Preface.

Our Hallmark Features

Teachers of general biology face a daunting challenge: to help students acquire a conceptual framework for organizing an ever-expanding amount of information. The hallmark features of CAMPBELL BIOLOGY provide such a framework, while promoting a deeper understanding of biology and the process of science.

To help students distinguish the "forest from the trees," each chapter is organized around a framework of three to seven carefully chosen **Key Concepts**. The text, Concept Check Questions, Summary of Key Concepts, and MasteringBiology all reinforce these main ideas and essential facts.

CAMPBELL BIOLOGY also helps students organize and make sense of what they learn by emphasizing **evolution and other unifying themes** that pervade biology. These themes are introduced in Chapter 1 and are integrated throughout the book. Each chapter includes at least one Evolution section that explicitly focuses on evolutionary aspects of the chapter material, and each chapter ends with an Evolution Connection Question and a Write About a Theme Question.

Because text and illustrations are equally important for learning biology, **integration of text and figures** has been a hallmark of this text since the First Edition. In addition to the new Make Connections Figures, our popular Exploring Figures on selected topics epitomize this approach: Each is a learning unit of core content that brings together related illustrations and text. Another example is our Guided Tour Figures, which use descriptions in blue type to walk students through complex figures as an instructor would. Visual Organizer Figures highlight the main parts of a figure, helping students see key categories at a glance. And Summary Figures visually recap information from the chapter.

To encourage **active reading** of the text, CAMPBELL BIOLOGY includes numerous opportunities for students to stop and think about what they are reading, often by putting pencil to paper to draw a sketch, annotate a figure, or graph data. Active learning questions include Make Connections Questions, What If? Questions, Figure Legend Questions, Draw It Questions, Summary Questions, and the new Synthesize Your Knowledge and Interpret the Data Questions.

Finally, CAMPBELL BIOLOGY has always featured **scientific inquiry**, an essential component of any biology course. Complementing stories of scientific discovery in the text narrative and the unit-opening interviews, our standard-setting Inquiry Figures deepen the ability of students to understand how we know what we know. Scientific Inquiry Questions give students opportunities to practice scientific thinking, along with the new Scientific Skills Exercises and Interpret the Data Questions.

MasteringBiology®

MasteringBiology, the most widely used online assessment and tutorial program for biology, provides an extensive library of homework assignments that are graded automatically. In addition to the new Scientific Skills Exercises, Interpret the Data Questions, Solve It Tutorials, Adaptive Follow-Up Assignments, and Dynamic Study Modules, MasteringBiology offers BioFlix® Tutorials with 3-D Animations, Experimental Inquiry Tutorials, Interpreting Data Tutorials, BLAST Tutorials, Make Connections Tutorials, Video Tutor Sessions, Get Ready for Biology, Activities, Reading Quiz Questions, Student Misconception Questions, 4,500 Test Bank Questions, and MasteringBiology Virtual Labs. MasteringBiology also includes the CAMPBELL BIOLOGY eText, Study Area, and Instructor Resources. See pages xviii–xxi and www.masteringbiology.com for more details.

Our Partnership with Instructors and Students

A core value underlying our work is our belief in the importance of a partnership with instructors and students. One primary way of serving instructors and students, of course, is providing a text that teaches biology well. In addition, Pearson Education offers a rich variety of instructor and student resources, in both print and electronic form (see pp. xviii–xxiii). In our continuing efforts to improve the book and its supplements, we benefit tremendously from instructor and student feedback, not only in formal reviews from hundreds of scientists, but also via e-mail and other avenues of informal communication.

The real test of any textbook is how well it helps instructors teach and students learn. We welcome comments from both students and instructors. Please address your suggestions to any of us:

Jane Reece
    janereece@cal.berkeley.edu
Lisa Urry (Chapter 1 and Units 1–3)
    lurry@mills.edu
Michael Cain (Units 4 and 5)
    mcain@bowdoin.edu
Peter Minorsky (Unit 6)
    pminorsky@mercy.edu
Steven Wasserman (Unit 7)
    stevenw@ucsd.edu
Rob Jackson (Unit 8)
    rob.jackson@stanford.edu

This section highlights selected new content and organizational changes in *CAMPBELL BIOLOGY*, Tenth Edition.

CHAPTER 1 **Evolution, the Themes of Biology, and Scientific Inquiry**

To help students focus on the big ideas of biology, we now emphasize five themes: Organization, Information, Energy and Matter, Interactions, and the core theme of Evolution. The new Figure 1.8 on gene expression equips students from the outset with an understanding of how gene sequences determine an organism's characteristics. Concept 1.3 has been reframed to more realistically reflect the scientific process, including a new figure on the complexity of the practice of science (Figure 1.23). A new case study in scientific inquiry (Figures 1.24 and 1.25) deals with evolution of coloration in mice.

  The Chemistry of Life

New chapter-opening photos and introductory stories engage students in learning this foundational material. Chapter 2 has a new Evolution section on radiometric dating. In Chapter 5, there is a new Key Concept section, "Genomics and proteomics have transformed biological inquiry and applications" (Concept 5.6), and a new Make Connections Figure, "Contributions of Genomics and Proteomics to Biology" (Figure 5.26).

  The Cell

Our main goal for this unit was to make the material more accessible to students. We have streamlined coverage of the cytoskeleton in Chapter 6 and historical aspects of the membrane model in Chapter 7. We have revised the photosynthesis summary figure (Figure 10.22) to incorporate a big-picture view of photosynthesis. The new Make Connections Figure 10.23 integrates the cellular activities covered in Chapters 5–10 in the context of a single plant cell. Concept 12.3 has been streamlined, with a new Figure 12.17 that covers the M checkpoint as well as the G_1 checkpoint.

  Genetics

In Chapters 13–17, we have incorporated changes that help students make connections between the more abstract concepts of genetics and their molecular underpinnings. For example, Chapter 13 includes a new figure (Figure 13.9) detailing the events of crossing over during prophase. Figure 14.4, showing alleles on chromosomes, has been enhanced to show the DNA sequences of both alleles, along with their biochemical and phenotypic consequences. A new figure on sickle-cell disease also connects these levels (Figure 14.17). In Chapter 17, material on coupled transcription and translation in bacteria has been united with coverage of polyribosomes.

Chapters 18–21 are extensively updated, driven by exciting new discoveries based on high-throughput sequencing. Chapter 18 includes a new figure (Figure 18.15) on the role of siRNAs in chromatin remodeling. A new Make Connections Figure (Figure 18.27) describes four subtypes of breast cancer that have recently been proposed, based on gene expression in tumor cells. In Chapter 20, techniques that are less commonly used have been pruned, and the chapter has been reorganized to emphasize the important role of sequencing. A new figure (Figure 20.4) illustrates next-generation sequencing. Chapter 21 has been updated to reflect new research, including the ENCODE project, the Cancer Genome Atlas, and the genome sequences of the gorilla and bonobo. A new figure (Figure 21.15) compares the 3-D structures of lysozyme and α-lactalbumin and their amino acid sequences, providing support for their common evolutionary origin.

  Mechanisms of Evolution

One goal of this revision was to highlight connections among fundamental evolutionary concepts. Helping meet this goal, new material connects Darwin's ideas to what can be learned from phylogenetic trees, and a new figure (Figure 25.13) and text illustrate how the combined effects of speciation and extinction determine the number of species in different groups of organisms. The unit also features new material on nucleotide variability within genetic loci, including a new figure (Figure 23.4) that shows variability within coding and noncoding regions of a gene. Other changes enhance the storyline of the unit. For instance, Chapter 25 includes new text on how the rise of large eukaryotes in the Ediacaran period represented a monumental transition in the history of life—the end of a microbe-only world. Updates include revised discussions of the events and underlying causes of the Cambrian explosion and the Permian mass extinction, as well as new figures providing fossil evidence of key evolutionary events, such as the formation of plant-fungi symbioses (Figure 25.12). A new Make Connections Figure (Figure 23.17) explores the sickle-cell allele and its impact from the molecular and cellular levels to organisms to the evolutionary explanation for the allele's global distribution in the human population.

UNIT 5 The Evolutionary History of Biological Diversity

In keeping with our Tenth Edition goals, we have expanded the coverage of genomic and other molecular studies and how they inform our understanding of phylogeny. Examples include a new Inquiry Figure (Figure 34.49) on the Neanderthal genome and presentation of new evidence that mutualistic interactions between plants and fungi are ancient. In addition, many phylogenies have been revised to reflect recent miRNA and genomic data. The unit also contains new material on tree-thinking, such as a new figure (Figure 26.11) that distinguishes between paraphyletic and polyphyletic taxa. We continue to emphasize evolutionary events that underlie the diversity of life on Earth. For example, a new section in Chapter 32 discusses the origin of multicellularity in animal ancestors. A new Make Connections Figure (Figure 33.9) explores the diverse structural solutions for maximizing surface area that have evolved across different kingdoms.

UNIT 6 Plant Form and Function

In developing the Tenth Edition, we have continued to provide students with a basic understanding of plant anatomy and function while highlighting dynamic areas of plant research and the many important connections between plants and other organisms. To underscore the relevance of plant biology to society, there is now expanded coverage of plant biotechnology and the development of biofuels in Chapter 38. Other updates include expanded coverage of bacterial components of the rhizosphere (Figure 37.9), plant mineral deficiency symptoms (Table 37.1), evolutionary trends in floral morphology (Chapter 38), and chemical communication between plants (Chapter 39). The discussion of plant defenses against pathogens and herbivores has been extensively revised and now includes a Make Connections Figure that examines how plants deter herbivores at numerous levels of biological organization, ranging from the molecular level to the community level (Figure 39.27).

UNIT 7 Animal Form and Function

In revising this unit, we strove to enhance student appreciation of the core concepts and ideas that apply across diverse organisms and varied organ systems. For example, a new Make Connections Figure (Figure 40.22) highlights challenges common to plant and animal physiology and presents both shared and divergent solutions to those challenges; this figure provides both a useful summary of plant physiology and an introduction to animal physiology. To help students recognize the central concept of homeostasis, figures have been revised across six chapters to provide a consistent organization that facilitates interpretation of individual hormone pathways as well as the comparison of pathways for different hormones. Homeostasis and endocrine regulation are highlighted by new and engaging chapter-opening photos and stories on the desert ant (Chapter 40) and on sexual dimorphism (Chapter 45), a revised presentation of the variation in target cell responses to a hormone (Figure 45.8), and a new figure integrating art and text on human endocrine glands and hormones (Figure 45.9). Many figures have been reconceived to emphasize key information, including new figures introducing the classes of essential nutrients (Figure 41.2) and showing oxygen and carbon dioxide partial pressures throughout the circulatory system (Figure 42.29). A new Make Connections Figure (Figure 44.17) demonstrates the importance of concentration gradients in animals as well as all other organisms. Throughout the unit, new state-of-the-art images and material on current and compelling topics—such as the human stomach microbiome (Figure 41.18) and the identification of the complete set of human taste receptors (Chapter 50)—will help engage students and encourage them to make connections beyond the text.

UNIT 8 Ecology

For the Tenth Edition, the ecology unit engages students with new ideas and examples. Chapter 52 highlights the discovery of the world's smallest vertebrate species. New text and a figure use the saguaro cactus to illustrate how abiotic and biotic factors limit the distribution of species (Figure 52.15). Greater emphasis is placed on the importance of disturbances, such as the effects of Hurricane Katrina on forest mortality. Chapter 53 features the loggerhead turtle in the chapter opener, Concept 53.1 (reproduction), and Concept 53.4 (evolution and life history traits). The chapter also includes new molecular coverage: how ecologists use genetic profiles to estimate the number of breeding loggerhead turtles (Figure 53.7) and how a single gene influences dispersal in the Glanville fritillary. In Chapter 54, new text and a figure highlight the mimic octopus, a recently discovered species that illustrates how predators use mimicry (Figure 54.6). A new Make Connections Figure ties together population, community, and ecosystem processes in the arctic tundra (Figure 55.13). Chapter 55 also has a new opening story on habitat transformation in the tundra. Chapter 56 highlights the emerging fields of urban ecology and conservation biology, including the technical and ethical challenges of resurrecting extinct species. It also examines the threat posed by pharmaceuticals in the environment. The book ends on a hopeful note, charging students to use biological knowledge to help solve problems and improve life on Earth.

KEY CONCEPTS

Each chapter is organized around a framework of 3 to 7 Key Concepts that focus on the big picture and provide a context for the supporting details.

KEY CONCEPTS

41.1 An animal's diet must supply chemical energy, organic molecules, and essential nutrients

41.2 The main stages of food processing are ingestion, digestion, absorption, and elimination

41.3 Organs specialized for sequential stages of food processing form the mammalian digestive system

41.4 Evolutionary adaptations of vertebrate digestive systems correlate with diet

41.5 Feedback circuits regulate digestion, energy storage, and appetite

▲ Figure 41.1 **How does a crab help an otter make fur?**

The Need to Feed

Dinnertime has arrived for the sea otter in Figure 41.1 (and for the crab, though in quite a different sense). The muscles and other organs of the crab will be chewed into pieces, broken down by acid and enzymes in the otter's digestive system, and finally absorbed as small molecules into the body of the otter. Such a process is what is meant by animal **nutrition**: food being taken in, taken apart, and taken up.

Although dining on fish, crabs, urchins, and abalone is the sea otter's specialty, all animals eat other organisms—dead or alive, piecemeal or whole. Unlike plants, animals must consume food for both energy and the organic molecules used to assemble new molecules, cells, and tissues. Despite this shared need, animals have diverse diets. **Herbivores**, such as cattle, sea slugs, and caterpillars, dine mainly on plants or algae. **Carnivores**, such as sea otters, hawks, and spiders, mostly eat other animals. Rats and other **omnivores** (from the Latin *omnis*, all) don't in fact eat everything, but they do regularly consume animals as well as plants or algae. We humans are typically omnivores, as are cockroaches and crows.

The terms *herbivore, carnivore,* and *omnivore* represent the kinds of food an animal usually eats. Keep in mind, however, that most animals are opportunistic feeders, eating foods outside their standard diet when their usual foods aren't available.

◀ Every chapter opens with a visually dynamic photo accompanied by an intriguing question that invites students into the chapter.

▲ The List of Key Concepts introduces the big ideas covered in the chapter.

After reading a Key Concept section, students can check their understanding using the Concept Check Questions.

◀ Questions throughout the chapter encourage students to read the text actively.

CONCEPT CHECK 41.1

1. All 20 amino acids are needed to make animal proteins. Why aren't they all essential to animal diets?

2. **MAKE CONNECTIONS** Considering the role of enzymes in metabolic reactions (see Concept 8.4), explain why vitamins are required in very small amounts in the diet.

3. **WHAT IF?** If a zoo animal eating ample food shows signs of malnutrition, how might a researcher determine which nutrient is lacking in its diet?

Make Connections Questions ▶ ask students to relate content in the chapter to material presented earlier in the course.

What if? Questions ask students ▶ to apply what they've learned.

The **Summary of Key Concepts** refocuses students on the main points of the chapter.

▲ **Summary Figures** recap key information in a visual way. **Summary of Key Concepts Questions** check students' understanding of a key idea from each concept.

▼ **Test Your Understanding Questions** at the end of each chapter are organized into three levels based on **Bloom's Taxonomy:**

- Level 1: Knowledge/Comprehension
- Level 2: Application/Analysis
- Level 3: Synthesis/Evaluation

Test Bank questions and multiple-choice questions in MasteringBiology® are also categorized by Bloom's Taxonomy.

◄ **NEW!** Synthesize Your Knowledge Questions ask students to apply their understanding of the chapter content to explain an intriguing photo.

THEMES

To help students focus on the big ideas of biology, five themes are introduced in Chapter 1 and woven throughout the text:

- Evolution
- Organization
- Information
- Energy and Matter
- Interactions

Every chapter has a section ▶ explicitly relating the chapter content to evolution, the fundamental theme of biology.

▲ To reinforce the themes, every chapter ends with an **Evolution Connection Question** and a **Write About a Theme Question.**

The Evolutionary Origins of Mitochondria and Chloroplasts

EVOLUTION Mitochondria and chloroplasts display similarities with bacteria that led to the **endosymbiont theory,** illustrated in **Figure 6.16**. This theory states that an early ancestor of eukaryotic cells engulfed an oxygen-using non-photosynthetic prokaryotic cell. Eventually, the engulfed

Make Connections Visually

Make Connections Figures pull together content from different chapters, providing a visual representation of "big picture" relationships.

Make Connections Figures include:

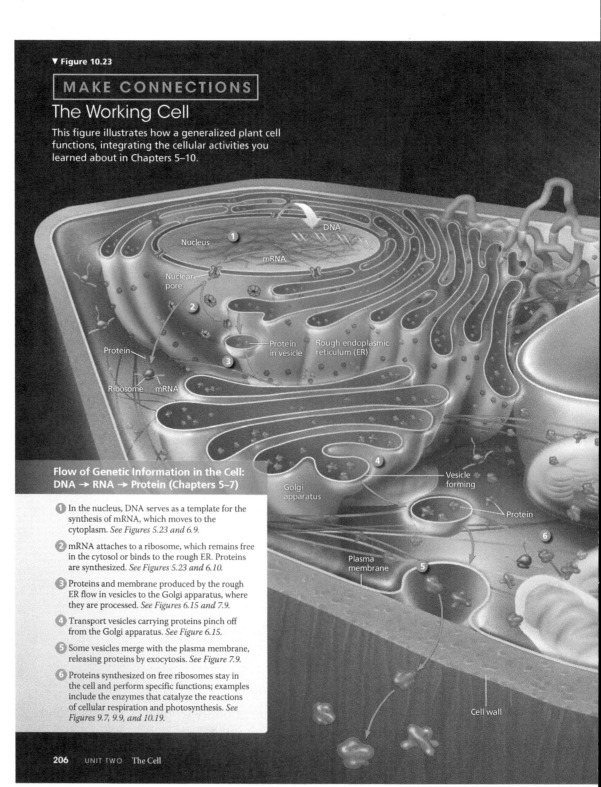

▼ Figure 10.23

MAKE CONNECTIONS

The Working Cell

This figure illustrates how a generalized plant cell functions, integrating the cellular activities you learned about in Chapters 5–10.

Flow of Genetic Information in the Cell: DNA → RNA → Protein (Chapters 5–7)

1. In the nucleus, DNA serves as a template for the synthesis of mRNA, which moves to the cytoplasm. *See Figures 5.23 and 6.9.*

2. mRNA attaches to a ribosome, which remains free in the cytosol or binds to the rough ER. Proteins are synthesized. *See Figures 5.23 and 6.10.*

3. Proteins and membrane produced by the rough ER flow in vesicles to the Golgi apparatus, where they are processed. *See Figures 6.15 and 7.9.*

4. Transport vesicles carrying proteins pinch off from the Golgi apparatus. *See Figure 6.15.*

5. Some vesicles merge with the plasma membrane, releasing proteins by exocytosis. *See Figure 7.9.*

6. Proteins synthesized on free ribosomes stay in the cell and perform specific functions; examples include the enzymes that catalyze the reactions of cellular respiration and photosynthesis. *See Figures 9.7, 9.9, and 10.19.*

206 UNIT TWO The Cell

Energy Transformations in the Cell: Photosynthesis and Cellular Respiration (Chapters 8–10)

7 In chloroplasts, the process of photosynthesis uses the energy of light to convert CO_2 and H_2O to organic molecules, with O_2 as a by-product. *See Figure 10.22.*

8 In mitochondria, organic molecules are broken down by cellular respiration, capturing energy in molecules of ATP, which are used to power the work of the cell, such as protein synthesis and active transport. CO_2 and H_2O are by-products. *See Figures 8.9–8.11, 9.2, and 9.16.*

Movement Across Cell Membranes (Chapter 7)

9 Water diffuses into and out of the cell directly through the plasma membrane and by facilitated diffusion through aquaporins. *See Figure 7.1.*

10 By passive transport, the CO_2 used in photosynthesis diffuses into the cell and the O_2 formed as a by-product of photosynthesis diffuses out of the cell. Both solutes move down their concentration gradients. *See Figures 7.10 and 10.22.*

11 In active transport, energy (usually supplied by ATP) is used to transport a solute against its concentration gradient. *See Figure 7.16.*

Exocytosis (shown in step 5) and endocytosis move larger materials out of and into the cell. *See Figures 7.9 and 7.19.*

Vacuole

7 Photosynthesis in chloroplast

CO_2

H_2O

Organic molecules

O_2

ATP

ATP

ATP

8 Cellular respiration in mitochondrion

ATP

Transport pump

11

10

9

O_2

CO_2

H_2O

MAKE CONNECTIONS *The first enzyme that functions in glycolysis is hexokinase. In this plant cell, describe the entire process by which this enzyme is produced and where it functions, specifying the locations for each step. (See Figures 5.18, 5.23, and 9.9.)*

ANIMATION *BioFlix* Visit the Study Area in **MasteringBiology** for BioFlix 3-D Animations in Chapters 6, 7, 9, and 10. BioFlix Tutorials can also be assigned in MasteringBiology.

◀ **Make Connections Questions**
Ask students to relate content in the chapter to material presented earlier in the course. Every chapter has at least three Make Connections Questions.

Practice Scientific Skills

NEW! Scientific Skills Exercises in every chapter use real data to build key skills needed for biology, including data interpretation, graphing, experimental design, and math skills.

▼ Photos provide visual interest and context.

Each Scientific Skills Exercise ▶ is based on an experiment related to the chapter content.

Most Scientific Skills Exercises ▶ use data from published research.

Questions build in difficulty, ▶ walking students through new skills step by step and providing opportunities for higher-level critical thinking.

SCIENTIFIC SKILLS EXERCISE

Interpreting a Scatter Plot with a Regression Line

How Does the Carbonate Ion Concentration of Seawater Affect the Calcification Rate of a Coral Reef? Scientists predict that acidification of the ocean due to higher levels of atmospheric CO will lower the concentration of dissolved carbonate ions, which living corals use to build calcium carbonate reef structures. In this exercise, you will analyze data from a controlled experiment that examined the effect of carbonate ion concentration ([CO]) on calcium carbonate deposition, a process called calcification.

How the Experiment Was Done The Biosphere 2 aquarium in Arizona contains a large coral reef system that behaves like a natural reef. For several years, a group of researchers measured the rate of calcification by the reef organisms and examined how the calcification rate changed with differing amounts of dissolved carbonate ions in the seawater.

Data from the Experiment The black data points in the graph form a scatter plot. The red line, known as a linear regression line, is the best-fitting straight line for these points.

Interpret the Data

1. When presented with a graph of experimental data, the first step in analysis is to determine what each axis represents. (a) In words, explain what is being shown on the x-axis. Be sure to include the units. (b) What is being shown on the y-axis (including units)? (c) Which variable is the independent variable—the variable that was *manipulated* by the researchers? (d) Which variable is the dependent variable—the variable that responded to or depended on the treatment, which was *measured* by the researchers? (For additional information about graphs, see the Scientific Skills Review in Appendix F and in the Study Area in MasteringBiology.)

2. Based on the data shown in the graph, describe in words the relationship between carbonate ion concentration and calcification rate.

3. (a) If the seawater carbonate ion concentration is 270 µmol/kg, what is the approximate rate of calcification, and approximately how many days would it take 1 square meter of reef to accumulate 30 mmol of

calcium carbonate (CaCO)? (b) If the seawater carbonate ion concentration is 250 µmol/kg, what is the approximate rate of calcification, and approximately how many days would it take 1 square meter of reef to accumulate 30 mmol of calcium carbonate? (c) If carbonate ion concentration decreases, how does the calcification rate change, and how does that affect the time it takes coral to grow?

4. (a) Referring to the equations in Figure 3.11, determine which step of the process is measured in this experiment. (b) Are the results of this experiment consistent with the hypothesis that increased atmospheric [CO] will slow the growth of coral reefs? Why or why not?

Data from C. Langdon et al., Effect of calcium carbonate saturation state on the calcification rate of an experimental coral reef, *Global Biogeochemical Cycles* 14:639–654 (2000).

(MB) A version of this Scientific Skills Exercise can be assigned in MasteringBiology.

▲ Each Scientific Skills Exercise cites the published research.

Every chapter has a Scientific Skills Exercise

NEW! All **56 Scientific Skills Exercises** from the text have assignable, interactive versions in MasteringBiology® that are automatically graded.

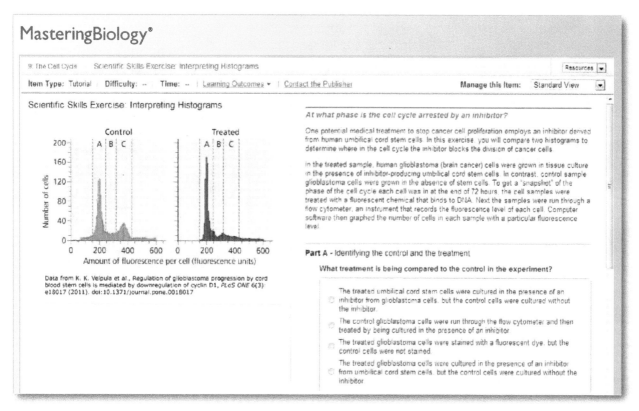

MasteringBiology®

MasteringBiology®

9: The Cell Cycle   Scientific Skills Exercise: Interpreting Histograms

Item Type: Tutorial   Difficulty: --   Time: -- | Learning Outcomes ▾ | Contact the Publisher   Manage this Item: Standard View

Scientific Skills Exercise: Interpreting Histograms

At what phase is the cell cycle arrested by an inhibitor?

One potential medical treatment to stop cancer cell proliferation employs an inhibitor derived from human umbilical cord stem cells. In this exercise, you will compare two histograms to determine where in the cell cycle the inhibitor blocks the division of cancer cells.

In the treated sample, human glioblastoma (brain cancer) cells were grown in tissue culture in the presence of inhibitor-producing umbilical cord stem cells. In contrast, control sample glioblastoma cells were grown in the absence of stem cells. To get a "snapshot" of the phase of the cell cycle each cell was in at the end of 72 hours, the cell samples were treated with a fluorescent chemical that binds to DNA. Next the samples were run through a flow cytometer, an instrument that records the fluorescence level of each cell. Computer software then graphed the number of cells in each sample with a particular fluorescence level.

Part A - Identifying the control and the treatment

What treatment is being compared to the control in the experiment?

○ The treated umbilical cord stem cells were cultured in the presence of an inhibitor from glioblastoma cells, but the control cells were cultured without the inhibitor.

○ The control glioblastoma cells were run through the flow cytometer and then treated by being cultured in the presence of an inhibitor.

○ The treated glioblastoma cells were stained with a fluorescent dye, but the control cells were not stained.

○ The treated glioblastoma cells were cultured in the presence of an inhibitor from umbilical cord stem cells, but the control cells were cultured without the inhibitor.

Data from K. K. Velpula et al., Regulation of glioblastoma progression by cord blood stem cells is mediated by downregulation of cyclin D1, *PLoS ONE* 6(3): e18017 (2011). doi:10.1371/journal.pone.0018017

MasteringBiology®

To learn more, visit www.masteringbiology.com

CAMPBELL BIOLOGY, Tenth Edition, and MasteringBiology®
offer a wide variety of ways for students to move beyond
memorization and think like a scientist.

◀ NEW! Interpret the Data
Questions throughout the
text ask students to analyze
a graph, figure, or table.

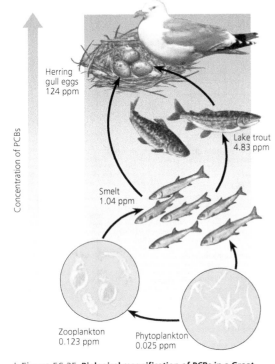

▲ Figure 56.25 **Biological magnification of PCBs in a Great Lakes food web.** (ppm = parts per million)

INTERPRET THE DATA *If a typical smelt weighs 225 g, what is the total mass of PCBs in a smelt in the Great Lakes? If an average lake trout weighs 4,500 g, what is the total mass of PCBs in a trout in the Great Lakes? Assume that a lake trout from an unpolluted source is introduced into the Great Lakes and smelt are the only source of PCBs in the trout's diet. The new trout would have the same level of PCBs as the existing trout after eating how many smelt? (Assume that the trout retains 100% of the PCBs it consumes.)*

▲ NEW! Every Interpret the
Data Question from the text is
assignable in MasteringBiology.

MasteringBiology®

Learn more at
www.masteringbiology.com

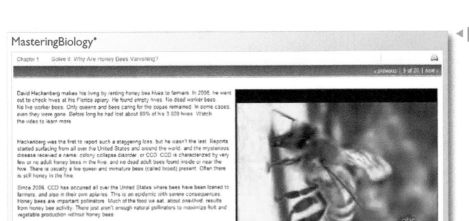

◀ NEW! Solve It Tutorials engage
students in a multi-step investigation of
a "mystery" or open question in which
they must analyze real data. These are
assignable in MasteringBiology.

Topics include:

- Is It Possible to Treat Bacterial Infections Without Traditional Antibiotics?
- Are You Getting the Fish You Paid For?
- Why Are Honey Bees Vanishing?
- Which Biofuel Has the Most Potential to Reduce our Dependence on Fossil Fuels?
- Which Insulin Mutations May Result in Disease?
- What is Causing Episodes of Muscle Weakness in a Patient?

Throughout the Tenth Edition, new examples show students how our ability to sequence DNA and proteins rapidly and inexpensively is transforming every subfield of biology, from cell biology to physiology to ecology.

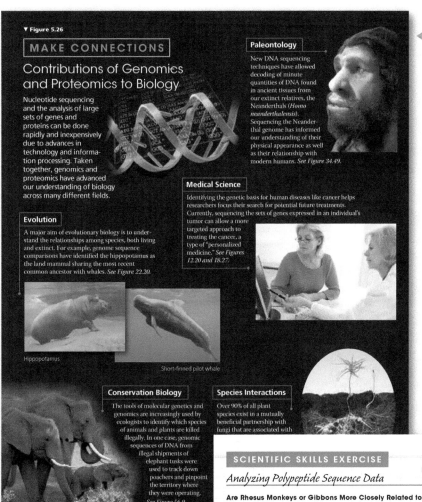

◀ Figure 5.26

MAKE CONNECTIONS

Contributions of Genomics and Proteomics to Biology

Nucleotide sequencing and the analysis of large sets of genes and proteins can be done rapidly and inexpensively due to advances in technology and information processing. Taken together, genomics and proteomics have advanced our understanding of biology across many different fields.

Evolution

A major aim of evolutionary biology is to understand the relationships among species, both living and extinct. For example, genome sequence comparisons have identified the hippopotamus as the land mammal sharing the most recent common ancestor with whales. *See Figure 22.20.*

Hippopotamus

Short-finned pilot whale

Paleontology

New DNA sequencing techniques have allowed decoding of minute quantities of DNA found in ancient tissues from our extinct relatives, the Neanderthals (*Homo neanderthalensis*). Sequencing the Neanderthal genome has informed our understanding of their physical appearance as well as their relationship with modern humans. *See Figure 34.49.*

Medical Science

Identifying the genetic basis for human diseases like cancer helps researchers focus their search for potential future treatments. Currently, sequencing the sets of genes expressed in an individual's tumor can allow a more targeted approach to treating the cancer, a type of "personalized medicine." *See Figures 12.20 and 18.27.*

Conservation Biology

The tools of molecular genetics and genomics are increasingly used by ecologists to identify which species of animals and plants are killed illegally. In one case, genomic sequences of DNA from illegal shipments of elephant tusks were used to track down poachers and pinpoint the territory where they were operating. *See Figure 56.9.*

Species Interactions

Over 90% of all plant species exist in a mutually beneficial partnership with fungi that are associated with

88   The Chemistry of Life

◀ This new Make Connections Figure in Chapter 5 previews some examples of how genomics and proteomics have helped shed light on diverse biological questions. These examples are explored in greater depth later in the text.

SCIENTIFIC SKILLS EXERCISE

Analyzing Polypeptide Sequence Data

▶ Human   ▶ Rhesus monkey   ▶ Gibbon

Are Rhesus Monkeys or Gibbons More Closely Related to Humans? DNA and polypeptide sequences from closely related species are more similar to each other than are sequences from more distantly related species. In this exercise, you will look at amino acid sequence data for the β polypeptide chain of hemoglobin, often called β-globin. You will then interpret the data to hypothesize whether the monkey or the gibbon is more closely related to humans.

How Such Experiments Are Done Researchers can isolate the polypeptide of interest from an organism and then determine the amino acid sequence. More frequently, the DNA of the relevant gene is sequenced, and the amino acid sequence of the polypeptide is deduced from the DNA sequence of its gene.

Data from the Experiments In the data below, the letters give the sequence of the 146 amino acids in β-globin from humans, rhesus

monkeys, and gibbons. Because a complete sequence would not fit on one line here, the sequences are broken into three segments. The sequences for the three different species are aligned so that you can compare them easily. For example, you can see that for all three species, the first amino acid is V (valine) and the 146th amino acid is H (histidine).

Interpret the Data

1. Scan the monkey and gibbon sequences, letter by letter, circling any amino acids that do not match the human sequence. (a) How many amino acids differ between the monkey and the human sequences? (b) Between the gibbon and human?

2. For each nonhuman species, what percent of its amino acids are identical to the human sequence of β-globin?

3. Based on these data alone, state a hypothesis for which of these two species is more closely related to humans. What is your reasoning?

4. What other evidence could you use to support your hypothesis?

A version of this Scientific Skills Exercise can be assigned in MasteringBiology.

Data from Human: http://www.ncbi.nlm.nih.gov/protein/AAA21113.1; rhesus monkey: http://www.ncbi.nlm.nih.gov/protein/122634; gibbon: http://www.ncbi.nlm.nih.gov/protein/122616

Species	Alignment of Amino Acid Sequences of β-globin
Human	1 VHLTPEEKSA VTALWGKVNV DEVGGEALGR LLVVYPWTQR FFESFGDLST
Monkey	1 VHLTPEEKNA VTTLWGKVNV DEVGGEALGR LLLVYPWTQR FFESFGDLSS
Gibbon	1 VHLTPEEKSA VTALWGKVNV DEVGGEALGR LLVVYPWTQR FFESFGDLST
Human	51 PDAVMGNPKV KAHGKKVLGA FSDGLAHLDN LKGTFATLSE LHCDKLHVDP
Monkey	51 PDAVMGNPKV KAHGKKVLGA FSDGLNHLDN LKGTFAQLSE LHCDKLHVDP
Gibbon	51 PDAVMGNPKV KAHGKKVLGA FSDGLAHLDN LKGTFAQLSE LHCDKLHVDP
Human	101 ENFRLLGNVL VCVLAHHFGK EFTPPVQAAY QKVVAGVANA LAHKYH
Monkey	101 ENFKLLGNVL VCVLAHHFGK EFTPQVQAAY QKVVAGVANA LAHKYH
Gibbon	101 ENFRLLGNVL VCVLAHHFGK EFTPQVQAAY QKVVAGVANA LAHKYH

◀ Selected Scientific Skills Exercises involve working with DNA or protein sequences.

MasteringBiology®

eTEXT

Access the complete
textbook online!

▲ The Pearson eText gives students access to the text whenever and wherever
they can access the Internet. The eText can be viewed on PCs, Macs, and
tablets, including iPad® and Android.® The eText includes powerful interactive
and customization functions:

- Write notes
- Highlight text
- Bookmark pages
- Zoom

- Click hyperlinked words
  to view definitions
- Search
- Link to media activities and quizzes

Instructors can even write notes for the class and highlight important materials
using a tool that works like an electronic pen on a whiteboard.

STUDY AREA

Students can access the Study Area for
use on their own or in a study group.

BioFlix® 3-D Animations ▶
explore the most
difficult biology topics,
reinforced with tutorials,
quizzes, and more.

▲ Get Ready for Biology helps
students get up to speed for
their course by covering study
skills, basic math, terminology,
chemistry, and biology basics.

◀ Practice Tests help students
assess their understanding of
each chapter, providing feedback
for right and wrong answers.

The Study Area also includes:
Cumulative Test, MP3 Tutor
Sessions, Videos, Activities,
Investigations, Lab Media, Audio
Glossary, Word Roots, Key Terms,
Flashcards, and Art.

DYNAMIC STUDY MODULES

NEW! Dynamic Study Modules, designed to enable students to study effectively on their own, help students quickly access and learn the information they need to be more successful on quizzes and exams.

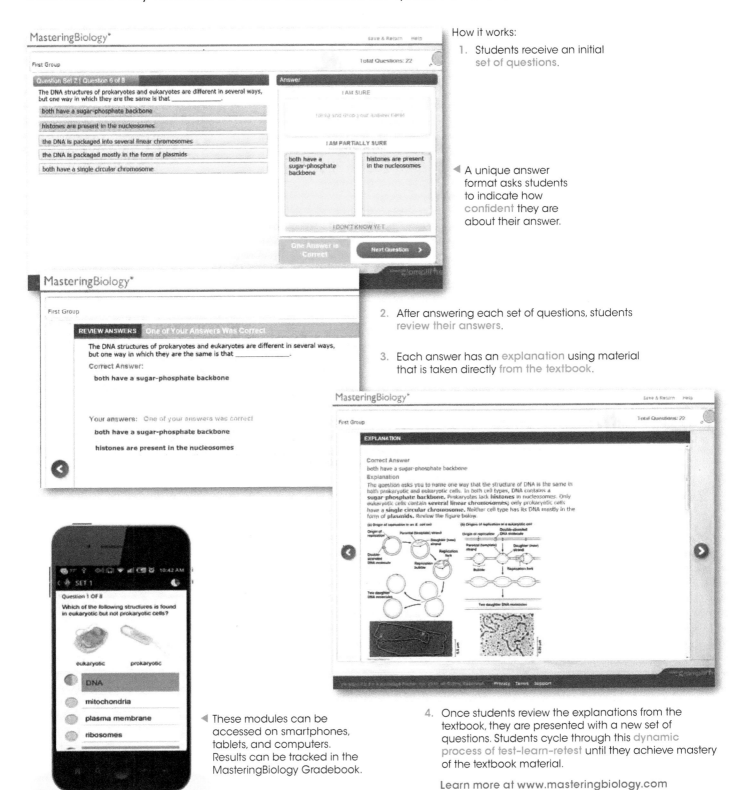

How it works:

1. Students receive an initial set of questions.

◄ A unique answer format asks students to indicate how confident they are about their answer.

2. After answering each set of questions, students review their answers.

3. Each answer has an explanation using material that is taken directly from the textbook.

◄ These modules can be accessed on smartphones, tablets, and computers. Results can be tracked in the MasteringBiology Gradebook.

4. Once students review the explanations from the textbook, they are presented with a new set of questions. Students cycle through this dynamic process of test-learn-retest until they achieve mastery of the textbook material.

Learn more at www.masteringbiology.com

Instructors can assign self-paced MasteringBiology® tutorials that provide students with individualized coaching with specific hints and feedback on the toughest topics in the course.

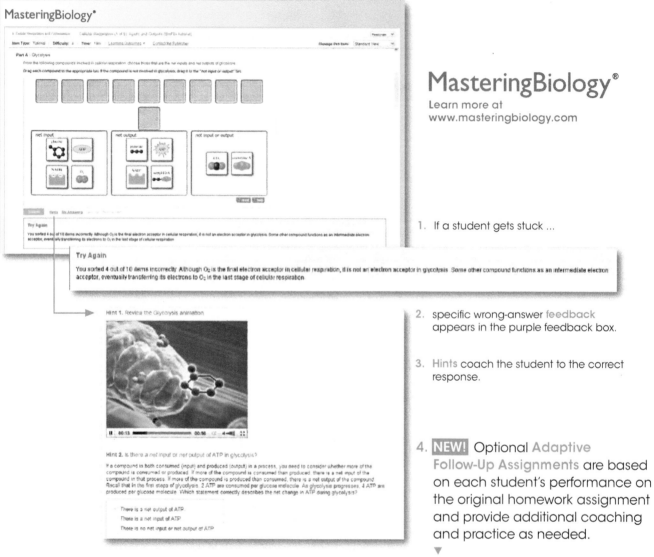

MasteringBiology®

Learn more at
www.masteringbiology.com

1. If a student gets stuck ...

2. specific wrong-answer feedback appears in the purple feedback box.

3. Hints coach the student to the correct response.

4. NEW! Optional Adaptive Follow-Up Assignments are based on each student's performance on the original homework assignment and provide additional coaching and practice as needed.

Question sets in the Adaptive Follow-Up Assignments continuously adapt to each student's needs, making efficient use of study time.

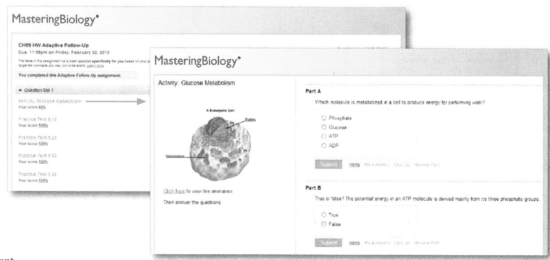

The MasteringBiology® Gradebook provides instructors with quick results and easy-to-interpret insights into student performance. Every assignment is automatically graded. Shades of red highlight vulnerable students and challenging assignments.

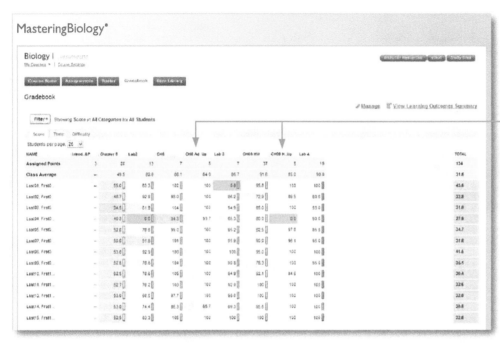

NEW! Student scores on the optional Adaptive Follow-Up Assignments are recorded in the gradebook and offer additional diagnostic information for instructors to monitor learning outcomes and more.

MasteringBiology offers a wide variety of tutorials that can be assigned as homework. For example, BioFlix Tutorials use 3-D, movie-quality Animations and coaching exercises to help students master tough topics outside of class. Animations can also be shown in class.

BioFlix Tutorials and 3-D Animations include:

- A Tour of the Animal Cell
- A Tour of the Plant Cell
- Membrane Transport
- Cellular Respiration
- Photosynthesis
- Mitosis

- Meiosis
- DNA Replication
- Protein Synthesis
- Mechanisms of Evolution
- Water Transport in Plants
- Homeostasis: Regulating Blood Sugar

- Gas Exchange
- How Neurons Work
- How Synapses Work
- Muscle Contraction
- Population Ecology
- The Carbon Cycle

Supplements

FOR INSTRUCTORS

NEW! Learning Catalytics™ allows students to use their smartphone, tablet, or laptop to respond to questions in class. Visit www.learningcatalytics.com.

Instructor's Resource DVD (IRDVD) Package
978-0-321-83494-2 / 0-321-83494-1

The instructor resources for **CAMPBELL BIOLOGY, Tenth Edition,** are combined into one chapter-by-chapter resource that includes DVDs of all chapter visual resources. Assets include:

- Editable figures (art and photos) and tables from the text in PowerPoint®
- Prepared PowerPoint Lecture Presentations for each chapter, with lecture notes, editable figures, tables, and links to animations and videos
- 250+ Instructor Animations and Videos, including BioFlix® 3-D Animations and *ABC News* Videos
- JPEG Images, including labeled and unlabeled art, photos from the text, and extra photos
- Digital Transparencies
- Clicker Questions in PowerPoint
- Quick Reference Guide
- Test Bank questions in TestGen® software and Microsoft® Word

Instructor Resources Area in MasteringBiology®

This area includes:

- Art and Photos in PowerPoint
- PowerPoint Lecture Presentations
- Videos and Animations, including BioFlix®
- JPEG Images
- Digital Transparencies
- Clicker Questions
- Test Bank Files
- Lecture Outlines
- Learning Objectives
- Pre-Tests, Post-Tests, and Strategies for Overcoming Common Student Misconceptions
- Instructor Guides for Supplements
- Rubric and Tips for Grading Short-Answer Essays
- Suggested Answers for Scientific Skills Exercises and Short-Answer Essay Questions
- Lab Media

▲ Clicker Questions can be used to stimulate effective classroom discussions (for use with or without clickers).

Instructor Resources for Flipped Classrooms

- Lecture videos can be posted on MasteringBiology for students to view before class.
- Homework can be assigned in MasteringBiology so students come to class prepared.
- In-class resources: Learning Catalytics, Clicker Questions, Student Misconception Questions, end-of-chapter essay questions, and activities and case studies from the student supplements.

▲ Customizable PowerPoints provide a jumpstart for each lecture.

▲ All of the art, graphs, and photos from the book are provided with customizable labels. More than 1,600 photos from the text and other sources are included.

Printed Test Bank
978-0-321-82371-7 / 0-321-82371-0

This invaluable resource contains more than 4,500 questions, including scenario-based questions and art, graph, and data interpretation questions. In addition to a print version, the Test Bank is available electronically in MasteringBiology, on the Instructor's Resource DVD Package, within the Blackboard course management system, and at www.pearsonhighered.com.

Course Management Systems

Content is available in **Blackboard**. Also, **MasteringBiology New Design** offers the usual Mastering features plus:

- Blackboard integration with single sign-on
- Temporary access (grace period)
- Discussion boards
- Email
- Chat and class live (synchronous whiteboard presentation)
- Submissions (Dropbox)

FOR STUDENTS

Study Guide, Tenth Edition
by Martha R. Taylor, *Ithaca, New York*
978-0-321-83392-1 / 0-321-83392-9
This popular study aid provides concept maps, chapter summaries, word roots, and a variety of interactive activities including multiple-choice, short-answer essay, art labeling, and graph-interpretation questions.

Inquiry in Action: Interpreting Scientific Papers, Third Edition *
by Ruth Buskirk, *University of Texas at Austin,*
and Christopher M. Gillen, *Kenyon College*
978-0-321-83417-1 / 0-321-83417-8
This guide helps students learn how to read and understand primary research articles. Part A presents complete articles accompanied by questions that help students analyze the article. Related Inquiry Figures are included in the supplement. Part B covers every part of a research paper, explaining the aim of the sections and how the paper works as a whole.

Practicing Biology: A Student Workbook, Fifth Edition *
by Jean Heitz and Cynthia Giffen, *University of Wisconsin, Madison*
978-0-321-87705-5 / 0-321-87705-5
This workbook offers a variety of activities to suit different learning styles. Activities such as modeling and concept mapping allow students to visualize and understand biological processes. Other activities focus on basic skills, such as reading and drawing graphs.

Biological Inquiry: A Workbook of Investigative Cases,
Fourth Edition *
by Margaret Waterman, *Southeast Missouri State University,* and Ethel Stanley, *BioQUEST Curriculum Consortium and Beloit College*
978-0-321-83391-4 / 0-321-83391-0
This workbook offers ten investigative cases. Each case study requires students to synthesize information from multiple chapters of the text and apply that knowledge to a real-world scenario as they pose hypotheses, gather new information, analyze evidence, graph data, and draw conclusions. A link to a student website is in the Study Area in MasteringBiology.

Study Card, Tenth Edition
978-0-321-83415-7 / 0-321-83415-1
This quick-reference card provides students with an overview of the entire field of biology, helping them see the connections among topics.

Spanish Glossary, Tenth Edition
by Laura P. Zanello, *University of California, Riverside*
978-0-321-83498-0 / 0-321-83498-4
This resource provides definitions in Spanish for glossary terms.

Into the Jungle: Great Adventures in the Search for Evolution
by Sean B. Carroll, *University of Wisconsin, Madison*
978-0-321-55671-4 / 0-321-55671-2
These nine short tales vividly depict key discoveries in evolutionary biology and the excitement of the scientific process. Online resources available at www.aw-bc.com/carroll.

Get Ready for Biology
978-0-321-50057-1 / 0-321-50057-1
This engaging workbook helps students brush up on important math and study skills and get up to speed on biological terminology and the basics of chemistry and cell biology.

A Short Guide to Writing About Biology, Eighth Edition
by Jan A. Pechenik, *Tufts University*
978-0-321-83386-0 / 0-321-83386-4
This best-selling writing guide teaches students to think as biologists and to express ideas clearly and concisely through their writing.

An Introduction to Chemistry for Biology Students, Ninth Edition
by George I. Sackheim, *University of Illinois, Chicago*
978-0-8053-9571-6 / 0-8053-9571-7
This text/workbook helps students review and master all the basic facts, concepts, and terminology of chemistry that they need for their life science course.

FOR LAB

Investigating Biology Laboratory Manual, Eighth Edition
by Judith Giles Morgan, *Emory University,* and M. Eloise Brown Carter, *Oxford College of Emory University*
978-0-321-83899-5 / 0-321-83899-8
Now in full color! With its distinctive investigative approach to learning, this best-selling laboratory manual is now more engaging than ever, with full-color art and photos throughout. As always, the lab manual encourages students to participate in the process of science and develop creative and critical-reasoning skills.

The Eighth Edition includes major revisions that reflect new molecular evidence and the current understanding of phylogenetic relationships for plants, invertebrates, protists, and fungi. A new lab topic, "Fungi," has been added, providing expanded coverage of the major fungi groups. The "Protists" lab topic has been revised and expanded with additional examples of all the major clades. In the new edition, population genetics is covered in one lab topic with new problems and examples that connect ecology, evolution, and genetics.

Annotated Instructor Edition for Investigating Biology Laboratory Manual, Eighth Edition
by Judith Giles Morgan, *Emory University,* and M. Eloise Brown Carter, *Oxford College of Emory University*
978-0-321-83497-3 / 0-321-83497-6

Preparation Guide for Investigating Biology Laboratory Manual, Eighth Edition
by Judith Giles Morgan, *Emory University,* and M. Eloise Brown Carter, *Oxford College of Emory University*
978-0-321-83445-4 / 0-321-83445-3

Symbiosis: The Pearson Custom Laboratory Program for the Biological Sciences
www.pearsoncustom.com/database/symbiosis/bc.html

MasteringBiology® Virtual Labs
www.masteringbiology.com
This online environment promotes critical thinking skills using virtual experiments and explorations that may be difficult to perform in a wet lab environment due to time, cost, or safety concerns. Designed to supplement or substitute for existing wet labs, this product offers students unique learning experiences and critical thinking exercises in the areas of microscopy, molecular biology, genetics, ecology, and systematics.

*An Instructor Guide is available for download in the Instructor Resources Area in MasteringBiology.

Featured Figures

Research Method Figures

*The Inquiry Figure, original research paper, and a worksheet to guide you through the paper are provided in *Inquiry in Action: Interpreting Scientific Papers*, Third Edition.
†A related Experimental Inquiry Tutorial can be assigned in MasteringBiology.®

Acknowledgments

The authors wish to express their gratitude to the global community of instructors, researchers, students, and publishing professionals who have contributed to the Tenth Edition of CAMPBELL BIOLOGY.

As authors of this text, we are mindful of the daunting challenge of keeping up to date in all areas of our rapidly expanding subject. We are grateful to the many scientists who helped shape this text by discussing their research fields with us, answering specific questions in their areas of expertise, and sharing their ideas about biology education. We are especially grateful to the following, listed alphabetically: Monika Abedin, John Archibald, Chris Austin, Kristian Axelsen, Jamie Bascom, Ethan Bier, Barbara Bowman, Daniel Boyce, Jean DeSaix, Amy Dobberteen, Ira Greenbaum, Ken Halanych, Robert Hebbel, Erin Irish, Duncan Irschick, Azarias Karamanlidis, Patrick Keeling, Nikos Kyrpides, Teri Liegler, Gene Likens, Tom Owens, Kevin Peterson, Michael Pollock, Amy Rappaport, Andrew Roger, Andrew Roth, Andrew Schaffner, Thomas Schneider, Alastair Simpson, Doug Soltis, Pamela Soltis, Anna Thanukos, Elisabeth Wade, Phillip Zamore, and Christine Zardecki. In addition, the biologists listed on pages xxviii–xxxi provided detailed reviews, helping us ensure the text's scientific accuracy and improve its pedagogical effectiveness. We thank Marty Taylor, author of the Study Guide, for her many contributions to the accuracy, clarity, and consistency of the text; and we thank Carolyn Wetzel, Ruth Buskirk, Joan Sharp, Jennifer Yeh, and Charlene D'Avanzo for their contributions to the Scientific Skills Exercises.

Thanks also to the other professors and students, from all over the world, who contacted the authors directly with useful suggestions. We alone bear the responsibility for any errors that remain, but the dedication of our consultants, reviewers, and other correspondents makes us confident in the accuracy and effectiveness of this text.

Interviews with prominent scientists have been a hallmark of CAMPBELL BIOLOGY since its inception, and conducting these interviews was again one of the great pleasures of revising the book. To open the eight units of this edition, we are proud to include interviews with Venki Ramakrishnan, Haifan Lin, Charles Rotimi, Hopi Hoekstra, Nicole King, Jeffery Dangl, Ulrike Heberlein, and Monica Turner.

The value of CAMPBELL BIOLOGY as a learning tool is greatly enhanced by the supplementary materials that have been created for instructors and students. We recognize that the dedicated authors of these materials are essentially writing mini (and not so mini) books. We appreciate the hard work and creativity of all the authors listed, with their creations, on page xxiii. We are also grateful to Kathleen Fitzpatrick and Nicole Tunbridge (PowerPoint® Lecture Presentations); Scott Meissner, Roberta Batorsky, Tara Turley Stoulig, Lisa Flick, and Bryan Jennings (Clicker Questions); Ed Zalisko, Melissa Fierke, Rebecca Orr, and Diane Jokinen (Test Bank); Natalie Bronstein, Linda Logdberg, Matt McArdle, Ria Murphy, Chris Romero, and Andy Stull (Dynamic Study Modules); and Eileen Gregory, Rebecca Orr, and Elena Pravosudova (Adaptive Follow-up Assignments).

MasteringBiology® and the other electronic accompaniments for this text are invaluable teaching and learning aids. We thank the hardworking, industrious instructors who worked on the revised and new media: Beverly Brown, Erica Cline, Willy Cushwa, Tom Kennedy, Tom Owens, Michael Pollock, Frieda Reichsman, Rick Spinney, Dennis Venema, Carolyn Wetzel, Heather Wilson-Ashworth, and Jennifer Yeh. We are also grateful to the many other people—biology instructors, editors, and production experts—who are listed in the credits for these and other elements of the electronic media that accompany the text.

CAMPBELL BIOLOGY results from an unusually strong synergy between a team of scientists and a team of publishing professionals.

Our editorial team at Pearson Education again demonstrated unmatched talents, commitment, and pedagogical insights. Our Senior Acquisitions Editor, Josh Frost, brought publishing savvy, intelligence, and a much appreciated level head to leading the whole team. The clarity and effectiveness of every page owe much to our extraordinary Supervising Editors Pat Burner and Beth Winickoff, who worked with a top-notch team of Developmental Editors in Mary Ann Murray, John Burner, Matt Lee, Hilair Chism, and Andrew Recher (Precision Graphics). Our unsurpassed Executive Editorial Manager Ginnie Simione Jutson, Executive Director of Development Deborah Gale, Assistant Editor Katherine Harrison-Adcock, and Editor-in-Chief Beth Wilbur were indispensable in moving the project in the right direction. We also want to thank Robin Heyden for organizing the annual Biology Leadership Conferences and keeping us in touch with the world of AP Biology.

You would not have this beautiful text if not for the work of the production team: Director of Production Erin Gregg; Managing Editor Michael Early; Project Manager Shannon Tozier; Senior Photo Editor Donna Kalal; Photo Researcher Maureen Spuhler; Copy Editor Joanna Dinsmore; Proofreader Pete Shanks; Text Permissions Project Managers Alison Bruckner and Joe Croscup; Text Permissions Manager Tim Nicholls; Senior Project Editor Emily Bush, Paging Specialist Donna Healy, and the rest of the staff at S4Carlisle; Art Production Manager Kristina Seymour, Artist Andrew Recher, and the rest of the staff at Precision Graphics; Design Manager Marilyn Perry; Art/Design Specialist Kelly Murphy; Text Designer tani hasegawa; Cover Designer Yvo Riezebos; and Manufacturing Buyer Jeffery Sargent. We also thank those who worked on the text's supplements: Susan Berge, Brady Golden, Jane Brundage, Phil Minnitte, Katherine Harrison-Adcock, Katie Cook, Melanie Field, Kris Langan, Pete Shanks, and John Hammett. And for creating the wonderful package of electronic media that accompanies the text, we are grateful to Tania Mlawer (Director of Content Development for MasteringBiology), Sarah Jensen, J. Zane Barlow, Lee Ann Doctor, Caroline Ross, Taylor Merck, and Brienn Buchanan, as well as Director of Media Development Lauren Fogel and Director of Media Strategy Stacy Treco.

For their important roles in marketing the text and media, we thank Christy Lesko, Lauren Harp, Scott Dustan, Chris Hess, Jane Campbell, Jessica Perry, and Jennifer Aumiller. For her market development support, we thank Michelle Cadden. We are grateful to Paul Corey, President of Pearson Science, for his enthusiasm, encouragement, and support.

The Pearson sales team, which represents CAMPBELL BIOLOGY on campus, is an essential link to the users of the text. They tell us what you like and don't like about the text, communicate the features of the text, and provide prompt service. We thank them for their hard work and professionalism. David Theisen, national director for Key Markets, tirelessly visits countless instructors every year, providing us with meaningful editorial guidance. For representing our text to our international audience, we thank our sales and marketing partners throughout the world. They are all strong allies in biology education.

Finally, we wish to thank our families and friends for their encouragement and patience throughout this long project. Our special thanks to Paul, Dan, Maria, Armelle, and Sean (J.B.R.); Lillian Alibertini Urry and Ross, Lily, and Alex (L.A.U.); Debra and Hannah (M.L.C.); Harry, Elga, Aaron, Sophie, Noah, and Gabriele (S.A.W.); Natalie (P.V.M.); and Sally, Will, David, and Robert (R.B.J.). And, as always, thanks to Rochelle, Allison, Jason, McKay, and Gus.

Jane B. Reece, Lisa A. Urry, Michael L. Cain,
Steven A. Wasserman, Peter V. Minorsky, and Robert B. Jackson

Reviewers

Tenth Edition Reviewers

John Alcock, *Arizona State University*
Rodney Allrich, *Purdue University*
Teri Balser, *University of Wisconsin, Madison*
David Bos, *Purdue University*
Scott Bowling, *Auburn University*
Beverly Brown, *Nazareth College*
Warren Burggren, *University of North Texas*
Dale Burnside, *Lenoir-Rhyne University*
Mickael Cariveau, *Mount Olive College*
Jung Choi, *Georgia Institute of Technology*
Steve Christensen, *Brigham Young University*
Reggie Cobb, *Nashville Community College*
Sean Coleman, *University of the Ozarks*
Deborah Dardis, *Southeastern Louisiana University*
Melissa Deadmond, *Truckee Meadows Community College*
Jean DeSaix, *University of North Carolina, Chapel Hill*
Jason Douglas, *Angelina College*
Anna Edlund, *Lafayette College*
Kurt Elliott, *North West Vista College*
Rob Erdman, *Florida Gulf Coast College*
Dale Erskine, *Lebanon Valley College*
Margaret Folsom, *Methodist College*
Robert Fowler, *San Jose State University*
Kim Fredericks, *Viterbo University*
Craig Gatto, *Illinois State University*
Kristen Genet, *Anoka Ramsey Community College*
Phil Gibson, *University of Oklahoma*
Eric Gillock, *Fort Hayes State University*
Edwin Ginés-Candelaria, *Miami Dade College*
Eileen Gregory, *Rollins College*
Bradley Griggs, *Piedmont Technical College*
Edward Gruberg, *Temple University*
Carla Guthridge, *Cameron University*
Carla Haas, *Pennsylvania State University*
Pryce Pete Haddix, *Auburn University*
Heather Hallen-Adams, *University of Nebraska, Lincoln*
Monica Hall-Woods, *St. Charles Community College*
Bill Hamilton, *Washington & Lee University*
Dennis Haney, *Furman University*
Jean Hardwick, *Ithaca College*
Luke Harmon, *University of Idaho*
Chris Haynes, *Shelton State Community College*
Jean Heitz, *University of Wisconsin, Madison*
Albert Herrera, *University of Southern California*
Chris Hess, *Butler University*
Kendra Hill, *San Diego State University*
Laura Houston, *Northeast Lakeview College*
Harry Itagaki, *Kenyon College*
Kathy Jacobson, *Grinnell College*
Roishene Johnson, *Bossier Parish Community College*
The-Hui Kao, *Pennsylvania State University*
Judy Kaufman, *Monroe Community College*
Thomas Keller, *Florida State University*
Janice Knepper, *Villanova University*
Charles Knight, *California Polytechnic State University*
Jacob Krans, *Western New England University*
Barb Kuemerle, *Case Western Reserve University*
Jani Lewis, *State University of New York*
Nancy Magill, *Indiana University*
Charles Mallery, *University of Miami*
Mark Maloney, *University of South Mississippi*
Darcy Medica, *Pennsylvania State University*
Mike Meighan, *University of California, Berkeley*
Jan Mikesell, *Gettysburg College*
Sarah Milton, *Florida Atlantic University*
Linda Moore, *Georgia Military College*
Karen Neal, *Reynolds University*
Ross Nehm, *Ohio State University*
Eric Nielsen, *University of Michigan*
Gretchen North, *Occidental College*
Margaret Olney, *St. Martin's College*
Rebecca Orr, *Spring Creek College*

Matt Palmtag, *Florida Gulf Coast University*
Eric Peters, *Chicago State University*
Larry Peterson, *University of Guelph*
Deb Pires, *University of California, Los Angeles*
Crima Pogge, *San Francisco Community College*
Michael Pollock, *Mount Royal University*
Jason Porter, *University of the Sciences, Philadelphia*
Elena Pravosudova, *University of Nevada, Reno*
Eileen Preston, *Tarrant Community College Northwest*
Pushpa Ramakrishna, *Chandler-Gilbert Community College*
David Randall, *City University Hong Kong*
Robert Reavis, *Glendale Community College*
Todd Rimkus, *Marymount University*
John Rinehart, *Eastern Oregon University*
Diane Robins, *University of Michigan*
Deb Roess, *Colorado State University*
Suzanne Rogers, *Seton Hill University*
Glenn-Peter Saetre, *University of Oslo*
Sanga Saha, *Harold Washington College*
Kathleen Sandman, *Ohio State University*
Andrew Schaffner, *Cal Poly San Luis Obispo*
Duane Sears, *University of California, Santa Barbara*
Joan Sharp, *Simon Fraser University*
Eric Shows, *Jones County Junior College*
John Skillman, *California State University, San Bernardino*
Doug Soltis, *University of Florida, Gainesville*
Mike Toliver, *Eureka College*
Victoria Turgeon, *Furman University*
Amy Volmer, *Swarthmore College*
James Wandersee, *Louisiana State University*
James Wee, *Loyola University*
Murray Wiegand, *University of Winnipeg*
Kimberly Williams, *Kansas State University*
Shuhai Xiao, *Virginia Polytechnic Institute*

Reviewers of Previous Editions

Kenneth Able, *State University of New York, Albany*; Thomas Adams, *Michigan State University*; Martin Adamson, *University of British Columbia*; Dominique Adriaens, *Ghent University*; Ann Aguanno, *Marymount Manhattan College*; Shylaja Akkaraju, *Bronx Community College of CUNY*; Marc Albrecht, *University of Nebraska*; John Alcock, *Arizona State University*; Eric Alcorn, *Acadia University*; George R. Aliaga, *Tarrant County College*; Richard Almon, *State University of New York, Buffalo*; Bonnie Amos, *Angelo State University*; Katherine Anderson, *University of California, Berkeley*; Richard J. Andren, *Montgomery County Community College*; Estry Ang, *University of Pittsburgh, Greensburg*; Jeff Appling, *Clemson University*; J. David Archibald, *San Diego State University*; David Armstrong, *University of Colorado, Boulder*; Howard J. Arnott, *University of Texas, Arlington*; Mary Ashley, *University of Illinois, Chicago*; Angela S. Aspbury, *Texas State University*; Robert Atherton, *University of Wyoming*; Karl Aufderheide, *Texas A&M University*; Leigh Auleb, *San Francisco State University*; Terry Austin, *Temple College*; P. Stephen Baenziger, *University of Nebraska*; Brian Bagatto, *University of Akron*; Ellen Baker, *Santa Monica College*; Katherine Baker, *Millersville University*; Virginia Baker, *Chipola College*; William Barklow, *Framingham State College*; Susan Barman, *Michigan State University*; Steven Barnhart, *Santa Rosa Junior College*; Andrew Barton, *University of Maine Farmington*; Rebecca A. Bartow, *Western Kentucky University*; Ron Basmajian, *Merced College*; David Bass, *University of Central Oklahoma*; Bonnie Baxter, *Westminster College*; Tim Beagley, *Salt Lake Community College*; Margaret E. Beard, *College of the Holy Cross*; Tom Beatty, *University of British Columbia*; Chris Beck, *Emory University*; Wayne Becker, *University of Wisconsin, Madison*; Patricia Bedinger, *Colorado State University*; Jane Beiswenger, *University of Wyoming*; Anne Bekoff, *University of Colorado, Boulder*; Marc Bekoff, *University of Colorado, Boulder*; Tania Beliz, *College of San Mateo*; Adrianne Bendich, *Hoffman-La Roche, Inc.*; Marilee Benore, *University of Michigan, Dearborn*; Barbara Bentley, *State University of New York, Stony Brook*; Darwin Berg, *University of California, San Diego*; Werner Bergen, *Michigan State University*; Gerald Bergstrom, *University of Wisconsin, Milwaukee*; Anna W. Berkovitz, *Purdue University*; Dorothy Berner, *Temple University*; Annalisa Berta, *San Diego State University*; Paulette Bierzychudek, *Pomona College*; Charles Biggers, *Memphis State University*; Kenneth Birnbaum, *New York University*; Catherine Black, *Idaho State University*; Michael W. Black, *California Polytechnic State University, San Luis Obispo*; William Blaker, *Furman University*; Robert Blanchard, *University of New Hampshire*; Andrew R. Blaustein, *Oregon State University*; Judy Bluemer, *Morton*

College; Edward Blumenthal, *Marquette University*; Robert Blystone, *Trinity University*; Robert Boley, *University of Texas, Arlington*; Jason E. Bond, *East Carolina University*; Eric Bonde, *University of Colorado, Boulder*; Cornelius Bondzi, *Hampton University*; Richard Boohar, *University of Nebraska, Omaha*; Carey L. Booth, *Reed College*; Allan Bornstein, *Southeast Missouri State University*; David Bos, *Purdue University*; Oliver Bossdorf, *State University of New York, Stony Book*; James L. Botsford, *New Mexico State University*; Lisa Boucher, *University of Nebraska, Omaha*; J. Michael Bowes, *Humboldt State University*; Richard Bowker, *Alma College*; Robert Bowker, *Glendale Community College, Arizona*; Scott Bowling, *Auburn University*; Barbara Bowman, *Mills College*; Barry Bowman, *University of California, Santa Cruz*; Deric Bownds, *University of Wisconsin, Madison*; Robert Boyd, *Auburn University*; Sunny Boyd, *University of Notre Dame*; Jerry Brand, *University of Texas, Austin*; Edward Braun, *Iowa State University*; Theodore A. Bremner, *Howard University*; James Brenneman, *University of Evansville*; Charles H. Brenner, *Berkeley, California*; Lawrence Brewer, *University of Kentucky*; Donald P. Briskin, *University of Illinois, Urbana*; Paul Broady, *University of Canterbury*; Chad Brommer, *Emory University*; Judith L. Bronstein, *University of Arizona*; Danny Brower, *University of Arizona*; Carole Browne, *Wake Forest University*; Mark Browning, *Purdue University*; David Bruck, *San Jose State University*; Robb T. Brumfield, *Louisiana State University*; Herbert Bruneau, *Oklahoma State University*; Gary Brusca, *Humboldt State University*; Richard C. Brusca, *University of Arizona, Arizona-Sonora Desert Museum*; Alan H. Brush, *University of Connecticut, Storrs*; Howard Buhse, *University of Illinois, Chicago*; Arthur Buikema, *Virginia Tech*; Beth Burch, *Huntington University*; Al Burchsted, *College of Staten Island*; Meg Burke, *University of North Dakota*; Edwin Burling, *De Anza College*; William Busa, *Johns Hopkins University*; Jorge Busciglio, *University of California, Irvine*; John Bushnell, *University of Colorado*; Linda Butler, *University of Texas, Austin*; David Byres, *Florida Community College, Jacksonville*; Guy A. Caldwell, *University of Alabama*; Jane Caldwell, *West Virginia University*; Kim A. Caldwell, *University of Alabama*; Ragan Callaway, *The University of Montana*; Kenneth M. Cameron, *University of Wisconsin, Madison*; R. Andrew Cameron, *California Institute of Technology*; Alison Campbell, *University of Waikato*; Iain Campbell, *University of Pittsburgh*; Patrick Canary, *Northland Pioneer College*; W. Zacheus Cande, *University of California, Berkeley*; Deborah Canington, *University of California, Davis*; Robert E. Cannon, *University of North Carolina, Greensboro*; Frank Cantelmo, *St. John's University*; John Capeheart, *University of Houston, Downtown*; Gregory Capelli, *College of William and Mary*; Cheryl Keller Capone, *Pennsylvania State University*; Richard Cardullo, *University of California, Riverside*; Nina Caris, *Texas A&M University*; Jeffrey Carmichael, *University of North Dakota*; Robert Carroll, *East Carolina University*; Laura L. Carruth, *Georgia State University*; J. Aaron Cassill, *University of Texas, San Antonio*; Karen I. Champ, *Central Florida Community College*; David Champlin, *University of Southern Maine*; Brad Chandler, *Palo Alto College*; Wei-Jen Chang, *Hamilton College*; Bruce Chase, *University of Nebraska, Omaha*; P. Bryant Chase, *Florida State University*; Doug Cheeseman, *De Anza College*; Shepley Chen, *University of Illinois, Chicago*; Giovina Chinchar, *Tougaloo College*; Joseph P. Chinnici, *Virginia Commonwealth University*; Jung H. Choi, *Georgia Institute of Technology*; Steve Christensen, *Brigham Young University, Idaho*; Geoffrey Church, *Fairfield University*; Henry Claman, *University of Colorado Health Science Center*; Anne Clark, *Binghamton University*; Greg Clark, *University of Texas*; Patricia J. Clark, *Indiana University-Purdue University, Indianapolis*; Ross C. Clark, *Eastern Kentucky University*; Lynwood Clemens, *Michigan State University*; Janice J. Clymer, *San Diego Mesa College*; William P. Coffman, *University of Pittsburgh*; Austin Randy Cohen, *California State University, Northridge*; J. John Cohen, *University of Colorado Health Science Center*; James T. Colbert, *Iowa State University*; Jan Colpaert, *Hasselt University*; Robert Colvin, *Ohio University*; Jay Comeaux, *McNeese State University*; David Cone, *Saint Mary's University*; Elizabeth Connor, *University of Massachusetts*; Joanne Conover, *University of Connecticut*; Gregory Copenhaver, *University of North Carolina, Chapel Hill*; John Corliss, *University of Maryland*; James T. Costa, *Western Carolina University*; Stuart J. Coward, *University of Georgia*; Charles Creutz, *University of Toledo*; Bruce Criley, *Illinois Wesleyan University*; Norma Criley, *Illinois Wesleyan University*; Joe W. Crim, *University of Georgia*; Greg Crowther, *University of Washington*; Karen Curto, *University of Pittsburgh*; William Cushwa, *Clark College*; Anne Cusic, *University of Alabama, Birmingham*; Richard Cyr, *Pennsylvania State University*; Marymegan Daly, *The Ohio State University*; W. Marshall Darley, *University of Georgia*; Cynthia Dassler, *The Ohio State University*; Shannon Datwyler, *California State University, Sacramento*; Marianne Dauwalder, *University of Texas, Austin*; Larry Davenport, *Samford University*; Bonnie J. Davis, *San Francisco State University*; Jerry Davis, *University of Wisconsin, La Crosse*; Michael A. Davis, *Central Connecticut State University*; Thomas Davis, *University of New Hampshire*; John Dearn, *University of Canberra*; Maria E. de Bellard, *California State University, Northridge*; Teresa DeGolier, *Bethel College*; James Dekloe, *University of California, Santa Cruz*; Eugene Delay, *University of Vermont*; Patricia A. DeLeon, *University of Delaware*; Veronique Delesalle, *Gettysburg College*; T. Delevoryas, *University of Texas, Austin*; Roger Del Moral, *University of Washington*; Charles F. Delwiche, *University of Maryland*; Diane C. DeNagel, *Northwestern University*; William L. Dentler, *University of Kansas*; Daniel DerVartanian, *University of Georgia*; Jean DeSaix, *University of North Carolina, Chapel Hill*; Janet De Souza-Hart, *Massachusetts College of Pharmacy & Health Sciences*; Biao Ding, *Ohio State University*; Michael Dini, *Texas Tech University*; Andrew Dobson, *Princeton University*; Stanley Dodson, *University of Wisconsin, Madison*; Mark Drapeau, *University of California, Irvine*; John Drees, *Temple University School of Medicine*; Charles Drewes, *Iowa State University*; Marvin Druger, *Syracuse University*; Gary Dudley, *University of Georgia*; Susan Dunford, *University of Cincinnati*; Kathryn A. Durham, *Lorain Community College*; Betsey Dyer, *Wheaton College*; Robert Eaton, *University of Colorado*; Robert S. Edgar, *University of California, Santa Cruz*; Douglas J. Eernisse, *California State University, Fullerton*; Betty J. Eidemiller, *Lamar University*; Brad Elder, *Doane College*; Curt Elderkin, *College of New Jersey*; William D. Eldred, *Boston University*; Michelle Elekonich, *University of Nevada, Las Vegas*; George Ellmore, *Tufts University*; Mary Ellard-Ivey, *Pacific Lutheran University*; Norman Ellstrand, *University of California, Riverside*; Johnny El-Rady, *University of South Florida*; Dennis Emery, *Iowa State University*; John Endler, *University of California, Santa Barbara*; Margaret T. Erskine, *Lansing Community College*; Gerald Esch, *Wake Forest University*; Frederick B. Essig, *University of South Florida*; Mary Eubanks, *Duke University*; David Evans, *University of Florida*; Robert C. Evans, *Rutgers University, Camden*; Sharon Eversman, *Montana State University*; Olukemi Fadayomi, *Ferris State University*; Lincoln Fairchild, *Ohio State University*; Peter Fajer, *Florida State University*; Bruce Fall, *University of Minnesota*; Sam Fan, *Bradley University*; Lynn Fancher, *College of DuPage*; Ellen H. Fanning, *Vanderbilt University*; Paul Farnsworth, *University of New Mexico*; Larry Farrell, *Idaho State University*; Jerry F. Feldman, *University of California, Santa Cruz*; Lewis Feldman, *University of California, Berkeley*; Myriam Alhadeff Feldman, *Cascadia Community College*; Eugene Fenster, *Longview Community College*; Russell Fernald, *University of Oregon*; Rebecca Ferrell, *Metropolitan State College of Denver*; Kim Finer, *Kent State University*; Milton Fingerman, *Tulane University*; Barbara Finney, *Regis College*; Teresa Fischer, *Indian River Community College*; Frank Fish, *West Chester University*; David Fisher, *University of Hawaii, Manoa*; Jonathan S. Fisher, *St. Louis University*; Steven Fisher, *University of California, Santa Barbara*; David Fitch, *New York University*; Kirk Fitzhugh, *Natural History Museum of Los Angeles County*; Lloyd Fitzpatrick, *University of North Texas*; William Fixsen, *Harvard University*; T. Fleming, *Bradley University*; Abraham Flexer, *Manuscript Consultant, Boulder, Colorado*; Kerry Foresman, *University of Montana*; Norma Fowler, *University of Texas, Austin*; Robert G. Fowler, *San Jose State University*; David Fox, *University of Tennessee, Knoxville*; Carl Frankel, *Pennsylvania State University, Hazleton*; Robert Franklin, *College of Charleston*; James Franzen, *University of Pittsburgh*; Art Fredeen, *University of Northern British Columbia*; Bill Freedman, *Dalhousie University*; Matt Friedman, *University of Chicago*; Otto Friesen, *University of Virginia*; Frank Frisch, *Chapman University*; Virginia Fry, *Monterey Peninsula College*; Bernard Frye, *University of Texas, Arlington*; Jed Fuhrman, *University of Southern California*; Alice Fulton, *University of Iowa*; Chandler Fulton, *Brandeis University*; Sara Fultz, *Stanford University*; Berdell Funke, *North Dakota State University*; Anne Funkhouser, *University of the Pacific*; Zofia E. Gagnon, *Marist College*; Michael Gaines, *University of Miami*; Cynthia M. Galloway, *Texas A&M University, Kingsville*; Arthur W. Galston, *Yale University*; Stephen Gammie, *University of Wisconsin, Madison*; Carl Gans, *University of Michigan*; John Gapter, *University of Northern Colorado*; Andrea Gargas, *University of Wisconsin, Madison*; Lauren Garner, *California Polytechnic State University, San Luis Obispo*; Reginald Garrett, *University of Virginia*; Patricia Gensel, *University of North Carolina*; Chris George, *California Polytechnic State University, San Luis Obispo*; Robert George, *University of Wyoming*; J. Whitfield Gibbons, *University of Georgia*; J. Phil Gibson, *Agnes Scott College*; Frank Gilliam, *Marshall University*; Simon Gilroy, *University of Wisconsin, Madison*; Alan D. Gishlick, *Gustavus Adolphus College*; Todd Gleeson, *University of Colorado*; Jessica Gleffe, *University of California, Irvine*; John Glendinning, *Barnard College*; David Glenn-Lewin, *Wichita State University*; William Glider, *University of Nebraska*; Tricia Glidewell, *Marist School*; Elizabeth A. Godrick, *Boston University*; Jim Goetze, *Laredo Community College*; Lynda Goff, *University of California, Santa Cruz*; Elliott Goldstein, *Arizona State University*; Paul Goldstein, *University of Texas, El Paso*; Sandra Gollnick, *State University of New York, Buffalo*; Roy Golsteyn, *University of Lethbridge*; Anne Good, *University of California, Berkeley*; Judith Goodenough, *University of Massachusetts, Amherst*; Wayne Goodey, *University of British Columbia*; Barbara E. Goodman, *University of South Dakota*; Robert Goodman, *University of Wisconsin, Madison*; Ester Goudsmit, *Oakland University*; Linda Graham, *University of Wisconsin, Madison*; Robert Grammer, *Belmont University*; Joseph Graves, *Arizona State University*; Phyllis Griffard, *University of Houston, Downtown*; A. J. F. Griffiths, *University of British Columbia*; William Grimes, *University of Arizona*; David Grise, *Texas A&M University, Corpus Christi*; Mark Gromko, *Bowling Green State University*; Serine Gropper, *Auburn University*; Katherine L. Gross, *Ohio State University*; Gary Gussin, *University of Iowa*; Mark Guyer, *National Human Genome Research Institute*; Ruth Levy Guyer, *Bethesda, Maryland*; R. Wayne Habermehl, *Montgomery County Community College*; Mac Hadley, *University of Arizona*; Joel Hagen, *Radford University*; Jack P. Hailman, *University of Wisconsin*; Leah Haimo, *University of California, Riverside*; Ken Halanych, *Auburn University*; Jody Hall, *Brown University*; Douglas Hallett, *Northern Arizona University*; Rebecca Halyard, *Clayton State College*; Devney Hamilton, *Stanford University* (student); E. William Hamilton, *Washington and Lee University*; Matthew B. Hamilton, *Georgetown University*; Sam Hammer, *Boston University*; Penny Hanchey-Bauer, *Colorado State University*; William F. Hanna, *Massasoit Community College*; Laszlo Hanzely, *Northern Illinois University*; Jeff Hardin, *University of Wisconsin, Madison*; Lisa Harper, *University of California, Berkeley*; Jeanne M. Harris, *University of Vermont*; Richard Harrison, *Cornell University*; Stephanie Harvey, *Georgia Southwestern State University*; Carla Hass, *Pennsylvania State University*; Chris Haufler, *University of Kansas*; Bernard A. Hauser, *University of Florida*; Chris Haynes,

29 Plant Diversity I: How Plants Colonized Land 612

30 Plant Diversity II: The Evolution of Seed Plants 630

31 Fungi 648

32 An Overview of Animal Diversity 667

33 An Introduction to Invertebrates 680

34 The Origin and Evolution of Vertebrates 712

UNIT 6 PLANT FORM AND FUNCTION 751

35 Plant Structure, Growth, and Development 752

36 Resource Acquisition and Transport in Vascular Plants 778

37 Soil and Plant Nutrition 799

42 Circulation and Gas Exchange 915

43 The Immune System 946

44 Osmoregulation and Excretion 971

45 Hormones and the Endocrine System 993

46 Animal Reproduction 1013

47 Animal Development 1037

UNIT 8 ECOLOGY 1157

52 An Introduction to Ecology and the Biosphere 1158

53 Population Ecology 1184

54 Community Ecology 1208

55 Ecosystems and Restoration Ecology 1232

56 Conservation Biology and Global Change 1254

UNIT 4 MECHANISMS OF EVOLUTION

AN INTERVIEW WITH

Hopi Hoekstra

Meet the queen of the beach mice: Hopi Hoekstra, the Alexander Agassiz Professor of Zoology at Harvard University. Dr. Hoekstra received her B.A. in integrative biology from the University of California, Berkeley, and her Ph.D. in zoology from the University of Washington, Seattle. She is interested in the genetic basis of adaptation and speciation in vertebrates and has published dozens of ground-breaking papers on organisms ranging from rodents to lizards to birds of prey.

How did you first become interested in biology?

My family is from Holland, and I thought I wanted to be a political science major—my goal was to become the ambassador to Holland. But I quickly realized that wasn't my cup of tea. This led me to consider, "What do I get most excited about?" I had always been captivated by the natural world, and I wondered how what I observed in nature could all come to be. So I started taking biology courses, and eventually I worked in a lab where I was running cockroaches on treadmills. This is not glamorous, you know. But even so, this was where I fell in love with research, with the idea of discovery, of designing experiments and testing them. I was hooked.

> " By performing experiments in the wild along with molecular genetic studies in the lab, we can tell a more complete story about how organisms evolve.... "

Much of your research concerns beach mice in the genus *Peromyscus.* What drew you to these mice?

Well, they're adorable, aren't they? Just look at the picture!

But they are also related closely enough to lab mice that we can borrow the many genetic and genomic tools that have been developed for those mice. In addition, they breed in the lab just like lab mice, so we can do well-controlled experiments. And third, and probably most importantly, biologists have studied these species in the wild for many years, dating back to the late 1800s. As a result, we have an incredible wealth of information about their ecology, reproductive biology, physiology, and behavior.

Tell us about the work you and your students are currently doing.

We're trying to uncover the genetic basis of traits that affect survival and reproduction in nature. Typically, we begin with a particular phenotype, such as coat color in beach mice, and we perform experiments in the wild to test whether the phenotype really does affect the organism's ability to survive or reproduce. Then we try to find the gene or genes that code for this trait. But we don't stop there. Once we have found the genes, we examine how particular changes in those genes affect development to produce the variation in the trait that we see in the wild—such as the different colors we see in a population of beach mice. By performing experiments in the wild along with molecular genetic studies in the lab, we can tell a more complete story about how organisms evolve in response to the challenges they face in nature.

You have a very busy laboratory, filled with students and postdoctoral researchers. What are your thoughts about mentoring students?

My day-to-day job is all about discovery. For example, we recently had a lab meeting where several students described a project they had been working on for some time, and now they were moving towards an answer to their initial question. There's something so satisfying about that. Science is like a treasure hunt. It is thrilling to ask questions that we find interesting, and then have our results contribute to our understanding of evolution. Mentoring students is about passing along that enthusiasm, that sense of wonder about how nature works. Seeing the enthusiasm of my students as they describe what they did and what it tells us—I can't think of anything more fun to do with my day!

▶ Beach mouse (*Peromyscus polionotus*).

(MB) For an extended interview and video clip, go to the Study Area in MasteringBiology.

22

Descent with Modification: A Darwinian View of Life

▲ Figure 22.1 **How is this caterpillar protecting itself from predators?**

Endless Forms Most Beautiful

A hungry bird would have to look very closely to spot this caterpillar of the moth *Synchlora aerata*, which blends in well with the flowers on which it feeds. The disguise is enhanced by the caterpillar's flair for "decorating"—it glues pieces of flower petals to its body, transforming itself into its own background (Figure 22.1).

This distinctive caterpillar is a member of a diverse group, the more than 120,000 species of lepidopteran insects (moths and butterflies). All lepidopterans go through a juvenile stage characterized by a well-developed head and many chewing mouthparts: the ravenous, efficient feeding machines we call caterpillars. As adults, all lepidopterans share other features, such as three pairs of legs and two pairs of wings covered with small scales. But the many lepidopterans also differ from one another. How did there come to be so many different moths and butterflies, and what causes their similarities and differences? The self-decorating caterpillar and its many close relatives illustrate three key observations about life:

- the striking ways in which organisms are suited for life in their environments*
- the many shared characteristics (unity) of life
- the rich diversity of life

*Here and throughout this text, the term *environment* refers to other organisms as well as to the physical aspects of an organism's surroundings.

More than a century and a half ago, Charles Darwin was inspired to develop a scientific explanation for these three broad observations. When he published his hypothesis in his book *The Origin of Species*, Darwin ushered in a scientific revolution—the era of evolutionary biology.

For now, we will define **evolution** as *descent with modification*, a phrase Darwin used in proposing that Earth's many species are descendants of ancestral species that were different from the present-day species. Evolution can also be defined more narrowly as a change in the genetic composition of a population from generation to generation (see Chapter 23).

We can also view evolution in two related but different ways: as a pattern and as a process. The *pattern* of evolutionary change is revealed by data from many scientific disciplines, including biology, geology, physics, and chemistry. These data are facts—they are observations about the natural world. The *process* of evolution consists of the mechanisms that produce the observed pattern of change. These mechanisms represent natural causes of the natural phenomena we observe. Indeed, the power of evolution as a unifying theory is its ability to explain and connect a vast array of observations about the living world.

As with all general theories in science, we continue to test our understanding of evolution by examining whether it can account for new observations and experimental results. In this and the following chapters, we'll examine how ongoing discoveries shape what we know about the pattern and process of evolution. To set the stage, we'll first retrace Darwin's quest to explain the adaptations, unity, and diversity of what he called life's "endless forms most beautiful."

CONCEPT 22.1

The Darwinian revolution challenged traditional views of a young Earth inhabited by unchanging species

What impelled Darwin to challenge the prevailing views about Earth and its life? Darwin developed his revolutionary proposal over time, influenced by the work of others and by his travels (Figure 22.2). As we'll see, his ideas also had deep historical roots.

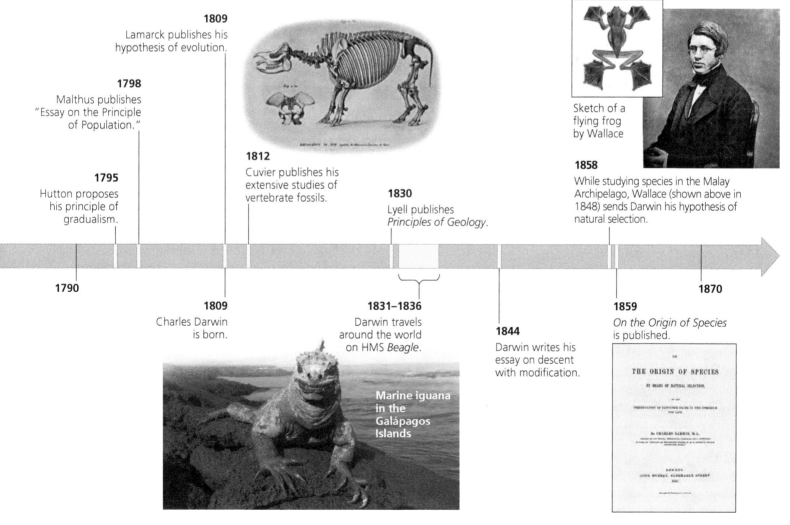

1809 Lamarck publishes his hypothesis of evolution.

1798 Malthus publishes "Essay on the Principle of Population."

1795 Hutton proposes his principle of gradualism.

1812 Cuvier publishes his extensive studies of vertebrate fossils.

1830 Lyell publishes *Principles of Geology*.

Sketch of a flying frog by Wallace

1858 While studying species in the Malay Archipelago, Wallace (shown above in 1848) sends Darwin his hypothesis of natural selection.

1790

1870

1809 Charles Darwin is born.

1831–1836 Darwin travels around the world on HMS *Beagle*.

Marine iguana in the Galápagos Islands

1844 Darwin writes his essay on descent with modification.

1859 *On the Origin of Species* is published.

THE ORIGIN OF SPECIES

▲ Figure 22.2 **The intellectual context of Darwin's ideas.**

Scala Naturae and Classification of Species

Long before Darwin was born, several Greek philosophers suggested that life might have changed gradually over time. But one philosopher who greatly influenced early Western science, Aristotle (384–322 BCE), viewed species as fixed (unchanging). Through his observations of nature, Aristotle recognized certain "affinities" among organisms. He concluded that life-forms could be arranged on a ladder, or scale, of increasing complexity, later called the *scala naturae* ("scale of nature"). Each form of life, perfect and permanent, had its allotted rung on this ladder.

These ideas were generally consistent with the Old Testament account of creation, which holds that species were individually designed by God and therefore perfect. In the 1700s, many scientists interpreted the often remarkable match of organisms to their environment as evidence that the Creator had designed each species for a particular purpose.

One such scientist was Carolus Linnaeus (1707–1778), a Swedish physician and botanist who sought to classify life's diversity, in his words, "for the greater glory of God." Linnaeus developed the two-part, or *binomial*, format for naming species (such as *Homo sapiens* for humans) that is still used today. In contrast to the linear hierarchy of the *scala naturae*, Linnaeus adopted a nested classification system, grouping similar species into increasingly general categories. For example, similar species are grouped in the same genus, similar genera (plural of genus) are grouped in the same family, and so on (see Figure 1.12).

Linnaeus did not ascribe the resemblances among species to evolutionary kinship, but rather to the pattern of their creation. A century later, however, Darwin argued that classification should be based on evolutionary relationships. He also noted that scientists using the Linnaean system often grouped organisms in ways that reflected those relationships.

Ideas About Change over Time

Among other sources of information, Darwin drew from the work of scientists studying **fossils**, the remains or traces of organisms from the past. Many fossils are found in sedimentary rocks formed from the sand and mud that settle to the bottom of seas, lakes, and swamps (**Figure 22.3**). New layers of sediment cover older ones and compress them into superimposed layers of rock called **strata** (singular, *stratum*). The fossils in a particular stratum provide a glimpse of some of the organisms that populated Earth at the time that layer formed. Later, erosion may carve through upper (younger) strata, revealing deeper (older) strata that had been buried.

Paleontology, the study of fossils, was developed in large part by French scientist Georges Cuvier (1769–1832). In

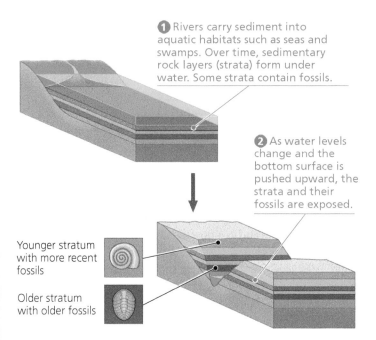

❶ Rivers carry sediment into aquatic habitats such as seas and swamps. Over time, sedimentary rock layers (strata) form under water. Some strata contain fossils.

❷ As water levels change and the bottom surface is pushed upward, the strata and their fossils are exposed.

Younger stratum with more recent fossils

Older stratum with older fossils

▲ Figure 22.3 **Formation of sedimentary strata with fossils.**

examining strata near Paris, Cuvier noted that the older the stratum, the more dissimilar its fossils were to current life-forms. He also observed that from one layer to the next, some new species appeared while others disappeared. He inferred that extinctions must have been a common occurrence, but he staunchly opposed the idea of evolution. Cuvier speculated that each boundary between strata represented a sudden catastrophic event, such as a flood, that had destroyed many of the species living in that area. Such regions, he reasoned, were later repopulated by different species immigrating from other areas.

In contrast, other scientists suggested that profound change could take place through the cumulative effect of slow but continuous processes. In 1795, Scottish geologist James Hutton (1726–1797) proposed that Earth's geologic features could be explained by gradual mechanisms, such as valleys being formed by rivers. The leading geologist of Darwin's time, Charles Lyell (1797–1875), incorporated Hutton's thinking into his proposal that the same geologic processes are operating today as in the past, and at the same rate.

Hutton and Lyell's ideas strongly influenced Darwin's thinking. Darwin agreed that if geologic change results from slow, continuous actions rather than from sudden events, then Earth must be much older than the widely accepted age of a few thousand years. It would, for example, take a very long time for a river to carve a canyon by erosion. He later reasoned that perhaps similarly slow and subtle processes could produce substantial biological change. Darwin was not the first to apply the idea of gradual change to biological evolution, however.

Lamarck's Hypothesis of Evolution

Although some 18th-century naturalists suggested that life evolves as environments change, only one proposed a mechanism for *how* life changes over time: French biologist Jean-Baptiste de Lamarck (1744–1829). Alas, Lamarck is primarily remembered today *not* for his visionary recognition that evolutionary change explains patterns in fossils and the match of organisms to their environments, but for the incorrect mechanism he proposed.

Lamarck published his hypothesis in 1809, the year Darwin was born. By comparing living species with fossil forms, Lamarck had found what appeared to be several lines of descent, each a chronological series of older to younger fossils leading to a living species. He explained his findings using two principles that were widely accepted at the time. The first was *use and disuse*, the idea that parts of the body that are used extensively become larger and stronger, while those that are not used deteriorate. Among many examples, he cited a giraffe stretching its neck to reach leaves on high branches. The second principle, *inheritance of acquired characteristics*, stated that an organism could pass these modifications to its offspring. Lamarck reasoned that the long, muscular neck of the living giraffe had evolved over many generations as giraffes stretched their necks ever higher.

Lamarck also thought that evolution happens because organisms have an innate drive to become more complex. Darwin rejected this idea, but he, too, thought that variation was introduced into the evolutionary process in part through inheritance of acquired characteristics. Today, however, our understanding of genetics refutes this mechanism: Experiments show that traits acquired by use during an individual's life are not inherited in the way proposed by Lamarck (Figure 22.4).

▲ **Figure 22.4 Acquired traits cannot be inherited.** This bonsai tree was "trained" to grow as a dwarf by pruning and shaping. However, seeds from this tree would produce offspring of normal size.

Lamarck was vilified in his own time, especially by Cuvier, who denied that species ever evolve. In retrospect, however, Lamarck did recognize that the match of organisms to their environments can be explained by gradual evolutionary change, and he did propose a testable explanation for how this change occurs.

CONCEPT CHECK 22.1

1. How did Hutton's and Lyell's ideas influence Darwin's thinking about evolution?
2. **MAKE CONNECTIONS** Scientific hypotheses must be testable (see Concept 1.3). Applying this criterion, are Cuvier's explanation of the fossil record and Lamarck's hypothesis of evolution scientific? Explain your answer in each case.

For suggested answers, see Appendix A.

CONCEPT 22.2

Descent with modification by natural selection explains the adaptations of organisms and the unity and diversity of life

As the 19th century dawned, it was generally thought that species had remained unchanged since their creation. A few clouds of doubt about the permanence of species were beginning to gather, but no one could have forecast the thundering storm just beyond the horizon. How did Charles Darwin become the lightning rod for a revolutionary view of life?

Darwin's Research

Charles Darwin (1809–1882) was born in Shrewsbury, in western England. Even as a boy, he had a consuming interest in nature. When he was not reading nature books, he was fishing, hunting, riding, and collecting insects. However, Darwin's father, a physician, could see no future for his son as a naturalist and sent him to medical school in Edinburgh. But Charles found medicine boring and surgery before the days of anesthesia horrifying. He quit medical school and enrolled at Cambridge University, intending to become a clergyman. (At that time, many scholars of science belonged to the clergy.)

At Cambridge, Darwin became the protégé of John Henslow, a botany professor. Soon after Darwin graduated, Henslow recommended him to Captain Robert FitzRoy, who was preparing the survey ship HMS *Beagle* for a long voyage around the world. Darwin would pay his own way and serve as a conversation partner to the young captain. FitzRoy, who was himself an accomplished scientist, accepted Darwin because he was a skilled naturalist and because they were of similar age and social class.

The Voyage of the Beagle

Darwin embarked from England on the *Beagle* in December 1831. The primary mission of the voyage was to chart poorly known stretches of the South American coastline. Darwin, however, spent most of his time on shore, observing and collecting thousands of plants and animals. He described features of organisms that made them well suited to such diverse environments as the humid jungles of Brazil, the expansive grasslands of Argentina, and the towering peaks of the Andes. He also noted that the plants and animals in temperate regions of South America more closely resembled species living in the South American tropics than species living in temperate regions of Europe. Furthermore, the fossils he found, though clearly different from living species, distinctly resembled the living organisms of South America.

Darwin also spent much time thinking about geology. Despite repeated bouts of seasickness, he read Lyell's *Principles of Geology* during the voyage. He experienced geologic change firsthand when a violent earthquake shook the coast of Chile, and he observed afterward that rocks along the coast had been thrust upward by several feet. Finding fossils of ocean organisms high in the Andes, Darwin inferred that the rocks containing the fossils must have been raised there by many similar earthquakes. These observations reinforced what he had learned from Lyell: Physical evidence did not support the traditional view that Earth was only a few thousand years old.

Darwin's interest in the species (or fossils) found in an area was further stimulated by the *Beagle*'s stop at the Galápagos, a group of volcanic islands located near the equator about 900 km west of South America (Figure 22.5). Darwin was fascinated by the unusual organisms there. The birds he collected included several kinds of mockingbirds. These mockingbirds, though similar to each other, seemed to be different species. Some were unique to individual islands, while others lived on two or more adjacent islands. Furthermore, although the animals on the Galápagos resembled species living on the South American mainland, most of the Galápagos species were not known from anywhere else in the world. Darwin hypothesized that the Galápagos had been colonized by organisms that had strayed from South America and then diversified, giving rise to new species on the various islands.

Darwin's Focus on Adaptation

During the voyage of the *Beagle*, Darwin observed many examples of **adaptations**, inherited characteristics of organisms that enhance their survival and reproduction in specific environments. Later, as he reassessed his observations, he began to perceive adaptation to the environment and the origin of new species as closely related processes. Could a new species arise from an ancestral form by the gradual accumulation of adaptations to a different environment? From studies made years after Darwin's voyage, biologists have concluded that this is indeed what happened to a diverse

▲ Figure 22.5 **The voyage of HMS *Beagle* (December 1831–October 1836).**

group of finches found on the Galápagos Islands (see Figure 1.20). The finches' various beaks and behaviors are adapted to the specific foods available on their home islands (Figure 22.6). Darwin realized that explaining such adaptations was essential to understanding evolution. His explanation of how adaptations arise centered on **natural selection**, a process in which individuals that have certain inherited traits tend to survive and reproduce at higher rates than other individuals *because of* those traits.

By the early 1840s, Darwin had worked out the major features of his hypothesis. He set these ideas on paper in 1844, when he wrote a long essay on descent with modification and its underlying mechanism, natural selection. Yet he was still reluctant to publish his ideas, in part because he anticipated the uproar they would cause. During this time, Darwin continued to compile evidence in support of his hypothesis. By the mid-1850s, he had described his ideas to Lyell and a few others. Lyell, who was not yet convinced of evolution, nevertheless urged Darwin to publish on the subject before someone else came to the same conclusions and published first.

In June 1858, Lyell's prediction came true. Darwin received a manuscript from Alfred Russel Wallace (1823–1913), a British naturalist working in the South Pacific islands of the Malay Archipelago (see Figure 22.2). Wallace had developed a hypothesis of natural selection nearly identical to Darwin's. He asked Darwin to evaluate his paper and forward it to Lyell if it merited publication. Darwin complied, writing to Lyell: "Your words have come true with a vengeance. . . . I never saw a more striking coincidence . . . so all my originality, whatever it may amount to, will be smashed." On July 1, 1858, Lyell and a colleague presented Wallace's paper, along with extracts from Darwin's unpublished 1844 essay, to the Linnean Society of London. Darwin quickly finished his book, titled *On the Origin of Species by Means of Natural Selection* (commonly referred to as *The Origin of Species*), and published it the next year. Although Wallace had submitted his ideas for publication first, he admired Darwin and thought that Darwin had developed the idea of natural selection so extensively that he should be known as its main architect.

Within a decade, Darwin's book and its proponents had convinced most scientists of the time that life's diversity is the product of evolution. Darwin succeeded where previous evolutionists had failed, mainly by presenting a plausible scientific mechanism with immaculate logic and an avalanche of evidence.

The Origin of Species

In his book, Darwin amassed evidence that three broad observations about nature—the unity of life, the diversity of life, and the match between organisms and their environments—resulted from descent with modification by natural selection.

Descent with Modification

In the first edition of *The Origin of Species*, Darwin never used the word *evolution* (although the final word of the book is "evolved"). Rather, he discussed *descent with modification*, a phrase that summarized his view of life. Organisms share many characteristics, leading Darwin to perceive unity in life. He attributed the unity of life to the descent of all organisms from an ancestor that lived in the remote past. He also thought that as the descendants of that ancestral organism lived in various habitats, they gradually accumulated diverse modifications, or adaptations, that fit them to

(a) **Cactus-eater.** The long, sharp beak of the cactus ground finch (*Geospiza scandens*) helps it tear and eat cactus flowers and pulp.

(b) **Insect-eater.** The green warbler finch (*Certhidea olivacea*) uses its narrow, pointed beak to grasp insects.

(c) **Seed-eater.** The large ground finch (*Geospiza magnirostris*) has a large beak adapted for cracking seeds found on the ground.

▲ **Figure 22.6 Three examples of beak variation in Galápagos finches.** The Galápagos Islands are home to more than a dozen species of closely related finches, some found only on a single island. A striking difference among them is their beaks, which are adapted for specific diets.

MAKE CONNECTIONS *Review Figure 1.20. To which of the other two species shown above is the cactus-eater more closely related (that is, with which does the cactus-eater share a more recent common ancestor)?*

▶ **Figure 22.7 "I think. . . ." In this 1837 sketch, Darwin envisioned the branching pattern of evolution.** Branches that end in twigs labeled A–D represent particular groups of living organisms; all other branches represent extinct groups.

specific ways of life. Darwin reasoned that over a long period of time, descent with modification eventually led to the rich diversity of life we see today.

Darwin viewed the history of life as a tree, with multiple branchings from a common trunk out to the tips of the youngest twigs (**Figure 22.7**). In his diagram, the tips of the twigs that are labeled A–D represent several groups of organisms living in the present day, while the unlabeled branches represent groups that are extinct. Each fork of the tree represents the most recent common ancestor of all the lines of evolution that subsequently branch from that point. Darwin reasoned that such a branching process, along with past extinction events, could explain the large morphological gaps that sometimes exist between related groups of organisms.

As an example, let's consider the three living species of elephants: the Asian elephant (*Elephas maximus*) and two species of African elephants (*Loxodonta africana* and *L. cyclotis*). These closely related species are very similar because they shared the same line of descent until a relatively recent split from their common ancestor, as shown in the tree diagram in **Figure 22.8**. Note that seven lineages related to elephants have become extinct over the past 32 million years. As a result, there are no living species that fill the morphological gap between the elephants and their nearest relatives today, the hyraxes and manatees. Such extinctions are not uncommon. In fact, many evolutionary branches, even some major ones, are dead ends: Scientists estimate that over 99% of all species that have ever lived are now extinct. As in Figure 22.8, fossils of extinct species can document the divergence of present-day groups by "filling in" gaps between them.

Artificial Selection, Natural Selection, and Adaptation

Darwin proposed the mechanism of natural selection to explain the observable patterns of evolution. He crafted his argument carefully, hoping to persuade even the most skeptical readers. First he discussed familiar examples of selective breeding of domesticated plants and animals. Humans

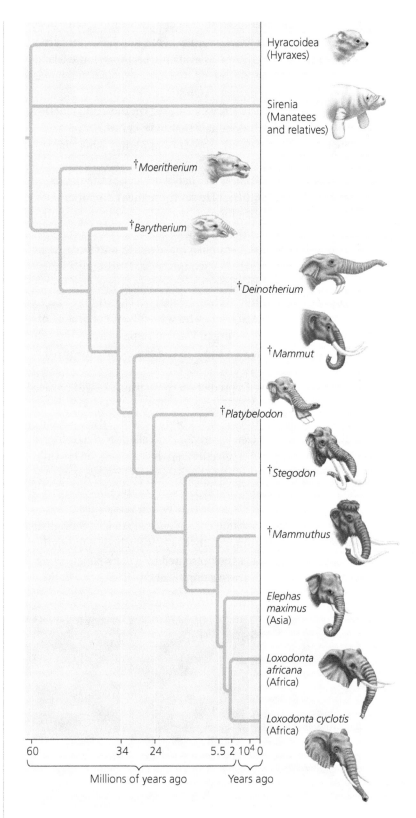

▲ **Figure 22.8 Descent with modification.** This evolutionary tree of elephants and their relatives is based mainly on fossils—their anatomy, order of appearance in strata, and geographic distribution. Note that most branches of descent ended in extinction (denoted by the dagger symbol †). (Time line not to scale.)

? *Based on the tree shown here, approximately when did the most recent ancestor shared by* Mammuthus *(woolly mammoths), Asian elephants, and African elephants live?*

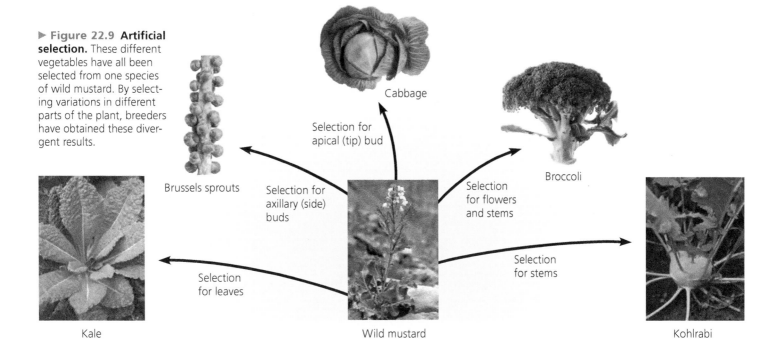

▶ **Figure 22.9 Artificial selection.** These different vegetables have all been selected from one species of wild mustard. By selecting variations in different parts of the plant, breeders have obtained these divergent results.

Cabbage

Selection for apical (tip) bud

Broccoli

Brussels sprouts

Selection for axillary (side) buds

Selection for flowers and stems

Selection for leaves

Selection for stems

Kale

Wild mustard

Kohlrabi

have modified other species over many generations by selecting and breeding individuals that possess desired traits, a process called **artificial selection (Figure 22.9)**. As a result of artificial selection, crops, livestock animals, and pets often bear little resemblance to their wild ancestors.

Darwin then argued that a similar process occurs in nature. He based his argument on two observations, from which he drew two inferences:

Observation #1: Members of a population often vary in their inherited traits **(Figure 22.10)**.

Observation #2: All species can produce more offspring than their environment can support **(Figure 22.11)**, and many of these offspring fail to survive and reproduce.

Inference #1: Individuals whose inherited traits give them a higher probability of surviving and reproducing in a given environment tend to leave more offspring than other individuals.

Inference #2: This unequal ability of individuals to survive and reproduce will lead to the accumulation of favorable traits in the population over generations.

As these two inferences suggest, Darwin saw an important connection between natural selection and the capacity of organisms to "overreproduce." He began to make this connection after reading an essay by economist Thomas Malthus, who contended that much of human suffering—disease, famine, and war—resulted from the human population's potential to increase faster than food supplies and other resources. Similarly, Darwin realized that the capacity to overreproduce was characteristic of all species. Of the many eggs laid, young born, and seeds spread, only a tiny fraction complete their development and leave offspring of

▲ **Figure 22.10 Variation in a population.** Individuals in this population of Asian ladybird beetles vary in color and spot pattern. Natural selection may act on these variations only if (1) they are heritable and (2) they affect the beetles' ability to survive and reproduce.

▶ **Figure 22.11 Overproduction of offspring.** A single puffball fungus can produce billions of offspring. If all of these offspring and their descendants survived to maturity, they would carpet the surrounding land surface.

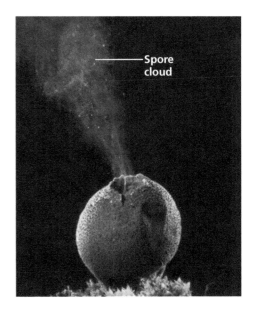

Spore cloud

their own. The rest are eaten, starved, diseased, unmated, or unable to tolerate physical conditions of the environment such as salinity or temperature.

An organism's heritable traits can influence not only its own performance, but also how well its offspring cope with environmental challenges. For example, an organism might have a trait that gives its offspring an advantage in escaping predators, obtaining food, or tolerating physical conditions. When such advantages increase the number of offspring that survive and reproduce, the traits that are favored will likely appear at a greater frequency in the next generation. Thus, over time, natural selection resulting from factors such as predators, lack of food, or adverse physical conditions can lead to an increase in the proportion of favorable traits in a population.

How rapidly do such changes occur? Darwin reasoned that if artificial selection can bring about dramatic change in a relatively short period of time, then natural selection should be capable of substantial modification of species over many hundreds of generations. Even if the advantages of some heritable traits over others are slight, the advantageous variations will gradually accumulate in the population, and less favorable variations will diminish. Over time, this process will increase the frequency of individuals with favorable adaptations and hence refine the match between organisms and their environment.

Natural Selection: *A Summary*

Let's now recap the main ideas of natural selection:

- Natural selection is a process in which individuals that have certain heritable traits survive and reproduce at a higher rate than other individuals because of those traits.
- Over time, natural selection can increase the match between organisms and their environment (Figure 22.12).
- If an environment changes, or if individuals move to a new environment, natural selection may result in adaptation to these new conditions, sometimes giving rise to new species.

One subtle but important point is that although natural selection occurs through interactions between individual organisms and their environment, *individuals do not evolve.* Rather, it is the population that evolves over time.

A second key point is that natural selection can amplify or diminish only those heritable traits that differ among the individuals in a population. Thus, even if a trait is heritable, if all the individuals in a population are genetically identical for that trait, evolution by natural selection cannot occur.

Third, remember that environmental factors vary from place to place and over time. A trait that is favorable in one place or time may be useless—or even detrimental—in other places or times. Natural selection is always operating, but

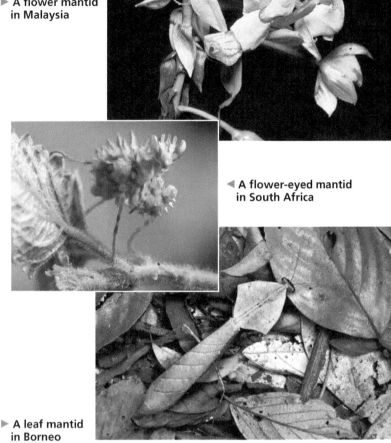

▶ A flower mantid in Malaysia

◀ A flower-eyed mantid in South Africa

▶ A leaf mantid in Borneo

▲ **Figure 22.12 Camouflage as an example of evolutionary adaptation.** Related species of the insects called mantids have diverse shapes and colors that evolved in different environments.

? *Explain how these mantids demonstrate the three key observations about life introduced at the beginning of the chapter: the match between organisms and their environments, unity, and diversity.*

which traits are favored depends on the context in which a species lives and mates.

Next, we'll survey the wide range of observations that support a Darwinian view of evolution by natural selection.

CONCEPT CHECK 22.2

1. How does the concept of descent with modification explain both the unity and diversity of life?
2. **WHAT IF?** If you discovered a fossil of an extinct mammal that lived high in the Andes, would you predict that it would more closely resemble present-day mammals from South American jungles or present-day mammals that live high in African mountains? Explain.
3. **MAKE CONNECTIONS** Review the relationship between genotype and phenotype (see Figures 14.4 and 14.6). Suppose that in a particular pea population, flowers with the white phenotype are favored by natural selection. Predict what would happen over time to the frequency of the *p* allele in the population, and explain your reasoning.

For suggested answers, see Appendix A.

Evolution is supported by an overwhelming amount of scientific evidence

In *The Origin of Species*, Darwin marshaled a broad range of evidence to support the concept of descent with modification. Still—as he readily acknowledged—there were instances in which key evidence was lacking. For example, Darwin referred to the origin of flowering plants as an "abominable mystery," and he lamented the lack of fossils showing how earlier groups of organisms gave rise to new groups.

In the last 150 years, new discoveries have filled many of the gaps that Darwin identified. The origin of flowering plants, for example, is much better understood (see Chapter 30), and many fossils have been discovered that signify the origin of new groups of organisms (see Chapter 25). In this section, we'll consider four types of data that document the pattern of evolution and illuminate how it occurs: direct observations, homology, the fossil record, and biogeography.

Direct Observations of Evolutionary Change

Biologists have documented evolutionary change in thousands of scientific studies. We'll examine many such studies throughout this unit, but let's look at two examples here.

Natural Selection in Response to Introduced Species

Animals that eat plants, called herbivores, often have adaptations that help them feed efficiently on their primary food sources. What happens when herbivores switch to a new food source with different characteristics?

An opportunity to study this question in nature is provided by soapberry bugs, which use their "beak," a hollow, needlelike mouthpart, to feed on seeds located within the fruits of various plants. In southern Florida, the soapberry bug (*Jadera haematoloma*) feeds on the seeds of a native plant, the balloon vine (*Cardiospermum corindum).* In central Florida, however, balloon vines have become rare. Instead, soapberry bugs in that region now feed on the seeds of the goldenrain tree (*Koelreuteria elegans*), a species recently introduced from Asia.

Soapberry bugs feed most effectively when their beak length closely matches the depth at which seeds are found within the fruit. Goldenrain tree fruit consists of three flat lobes, and its seeds are much closer to the fruit surface than are the seeds of the plump, round fruit of the native balloon vine. These differences led researchers to predict that in populations that feed on goldenrain tree, natural selection would result in beaks that are *shorter* than those in populations that feed on balloon vine **(Figure 22.13)**. Indeed, beak

▼ Figure 22.13 | Inquiry

Can a change in a population's food source result in evolution by natural selection?

Field Study Soapberry bugs feed most effectively when the length of their "beak" closely matches the depth of the seeds within the fruit. Scott Carroll and his colleagues measured beak lengths in soapberry bug populations feeding on the native balloon vine. They also measured beak lengths in populations feeding on the introduced goldenrain tree. The researchers then compared the measurements with those of museum specimens collected in the two areas before the goldenrain tree was introduced.

Soapberry bug with beak inserted in balloon vine fruit

Results Beak lengths were shorter in populations feeding on the introduced species than in populations feeding on the native species, in which the seeds are buried more deeply. The average beak length in museum specimens from each population (indicated by red arrows) was similar to beak lengths in populations feeding on native species.

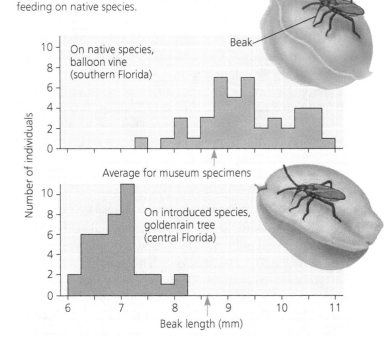

Conclusion Museum specimens and contemporary data suggest that a change in the size of the soapberry bug's food source can result in evolution by natural selection for matching beak size.

Source: S. P. Carroll and C. Boyd, Host race radiation in the soapberry bug: natural history with the history, *Evolution* 46:1052–1069 (1992).

WHAT IF? *Data from additional studies showed that when soapberry bug eggs from a population fed on balloon vine fruits were reared on goldenrain tree fruits (or vice versa), the beak lengths of the adult insects matched those in the population from which the eggs were obtained. Interpret these results.*

lengths are shorter in the populations that feed on golden-rain tree.

Researchers have also studied beak length evolution in soapberry bug populations that feed on plants introduced to Louisiana, Oklahoma, and Australia. In each of these locations, the fruit of the introduced plants is larger than the fruit of the native plant. Thus, in populations feeding on introduced species in these regions, researchers predicted that natural selection would result in the evolution of *longer* beak length. Again, data collected in field studies upheld this prediction.

The observed changes in beak lengths had important consequences: In Australia, for example, the increase in beak length nearly doubled the success with which soapberry bugs could eat the seeds of the introduced species. Furthermore, since historical data show that the goldenrain tree reached central Florida just 35 years before the scientific studies were initiated, the results demonstrate that natural selection can cause rapid evolution in a wild population.

The Evolution of Drug-Resistant Bacteria

An example of ongoing natural selection that dramatically affects humans is the evolution of drug-resistant pathogens (disease-causing organisms and viruses). This is a particular problem with bacteria and viruses because resistant strains of these pathogens can proliferate very quickly.

Consider the evolution of drug resistance in the bacterium *Staphylococcus aureus*. About one in three people harbor this species on their skin or in their nasal passages with no negative effects. However, certain genetic varieties (strains) of this species, known as methicillin-resistant *S. aureus* (MRSA), are formidable pathogens. The past decade has seen an alarming increase in virulent forms of MRSA such as clone USA300, a strain that can cause "flesh-eating disease" and potentially fatal infections **(Figure 22.14)**. How did clone USA300 and other strains of MRSA become so dangerous?

The story begins in 1943, when penicillin became the first widely used antibiotic. Since then, penicillin and other antibiotics have saved millions of lives. However, by 1945, more than 20% of the *S. aureus* strains seen in hospitals were already resistant to penicillin. These bacteria had an enzyme, penicillinase, that could destroy penicillin. Researchers responded by developing antibiotics that were not destroyed by penicillinase, but some *S. aureus* populations developed resistance to each new drug within a few years.

Then, in 1959, doctors began using the powerful antibiotic methicillin. But within two years, methicillin-resistant strains of *S. aureus* appeared. How did these resistant strains emerge? Methicillin works by deactivating a protein that bacteria use to synthesize their cell walls. However, different *S. aureus* populations exhibited variations in how strongly their members were affected by the drug. In particular, some individuals were able to synthesize their cell walls using a different protein that was not affected by methicillin. These individuals survived the methicillin treatments and

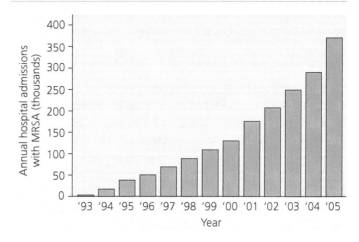

(a) Most MRSA infections are caused by recently appearing strains such as clone USA300. Resistant to multiple antibiotics and highly contagious, this strain and its close relatives can cause lethal infections of the skin, lungs, and blood. As shown here, researchers have identified key areas of the USA300 genome that code for adaptations that cause its virulent properties.

(b) MRSA infections severe enough to result in hospital admission have proliferated greatly in the past few decades.

▲ **Figure 22.14 The rise of methicillin-resistant *Staphylococcus aureus* (MRSA).**

WHAT IF? *Some drugs being developed specifically target and kill* S. aureus; *others slow the growth of MRSA but do not kill it. Based on how natural selection works and on the fact that bacterial species can exchange genes, explain why each of these strategies might be effective.*

reproduced at higher rates than did other individuals. Over time, these resistant individuals became increasingly common, leading to the spread of MRSA.

Initially, MRSA could be controlled by antibiotics that work differently from the way methicillin works. But this has become less effective because some MRSA strains are resistant to multiple antibiotics—probably because bacteria can exchange genes with members of their own and other species. Thus, the multidrug-resistant strains of today may have emerged over time as MRSA strains that were resistant to different antibiotics exchanged genes.

The *S. aureus* and soapberry bug examples highlight two key points about natural selection. First, natural selection is a process of editing, not a creative mechanism. A drug does not *create* resistant pathogens; it *selects for* resistant individuals that are already present in the population. Second, natural selection depends on time and place. It favors those characteristics in a genetically variable population that provide advantage in the current, local environment. What is beneficial in one situation may be useless or even harmful in another. Beak lengths that match the size of the typical fruit eaten by members of a particular soapberry bug population are favored by selection. However, a beak length suitable for fruit of one size can be disadvantageous when the bug is feeding on fruit of another size.

Homology

A second type of evidence for evolution comes from analyzing similarities among different organisms. As we've discussed, evolution is a process of descent with modification: Characteristics present in an ancestral organism are altered (by natural selection) in its descendants over time as they face different environmental conditions. As a result, related species can have characteristics that have an underlying similarity yet function differently. Similarity resulting from common ancestry is known as **homology**. As we'll describe in this section, an understanding of homology can be used to make testable predictions and explain observations that are otherwise puzzling.

Anatomical and Molecular Homologies

The view of evolution as a remodeling process leads to the prediction that closely related species should share similar features—and they do. Of course, closely related species share the features used to determine their relationship, but they also share many other features. Some of these shared features make little sense except in the context of evolution. For example, the forelimbs of all mammals, including humans, cats, whales, and bats, show the same arrangement of bones from the shoulder to the tips of the digits, even though the appendages have very different functions: lifting,

Humerus
Radius
Ulna
Carpals
Metacarpals
Phalanges

Human   Cat   Whale   Bat

▲ **Figure 22.15 Mammalian forelimbs: homologous structures.** Even though they have become adapted for different functions, the forelimbs of all mammals are constructed from the same basic skeletal elements: one large bone (purple), attached to two smaller bones (orange and tan), attached to several small bones (gold), attached to several metacarpals (green), attached to approximately five digits, each of which is composed of phalanges (blue).

walking, swimming, and flying (**Figure 22.15**). Such striking anatomical resemblances would be highly unlikely if these structures had arisen anew in each species. Rather, the underlying skeletons of the arms, forelegs, flippers, and wings of different mammals are **homologous structures** that represent variations on a structural theme that was present in their common ancestor.

Comparing early stages of development in different animal species reveals additional anatomical homologies not visible in adult organisms. For example, at some point in their development, all vertebrate embryos have a tail located posterior to (behind) the anus, as well as structures called pharyngeal (throat) arches (**Figure 22.16**). These homologous throat arches ultimately develop into structures with

Pharyngeal arches

Post-anal tail

Chick embryo (LM)   Human embryo

▲ **Figure 22.16 Anatomical similarities in vertebrate embryos.** At some stage in their embryonic development, all vertebrates have a tail located posterior to the anus (referred to as a post-anal tail), as well as pharyngeal (throat) arches. Descent from a common ancestor can explain such similarities.

very different functions, such as gills in fishes and parts of the ears and throat in humans and other mammals.

Some of the most intriguing homologies concern "left-over" structures of marginal, if any, importance to the organism. These **vestigial structures** are remnants of features that served a function in the organism's ancestors. For instance, the skeletons of some snakes retain vestiges of the pelvis and leg bones of walking ancestors. Another example is provided by eye remnants that are buried under scales in blind species of cave fishes. We would not expect to see these vestigial structures if snakes and blind cave fishes had origins separate from other vertebrate animals.

Biologists also observe similarities among organisms at the molecular level. All forms of life use essentially the same genetic code, suggesting that all species descended from common ancestors that used this code. But molecular homologies go beyond a shared code. For example, organisms as dissimilar as humans and bacteria share genes inherited from a very distant common ancestor. Some of these homologous genes have acquired new functions, while others, such as those coding for the ribosomal subunits used in protein synthesis (see Figure 17.17), have retained their original functions. It is also common for organisms to have genes that have lost their function, even though the homologous genes in related species may be fully functional. Like vestigial structures, it appears that such inactive "pseudogenes" may be present simply because a common ancestor had them.

Homologies and "Tree Thinking"

Some homologous characteristics, such as the genetic code, are shared by all species because they date to the deep ancestral past. In contrast, homologous characteristics that evolved more recently are shared only within smaller groups of organisms. Consider the *tetrapods* (from the Greek *tetra*, four, and *pod*, foot), the vertebrate group that consists of amphibians, mammals, and reptiles (including birds—see Figure 22.17). All tetrapods have limbs with digits (see Figure 22.15), whereas other vertebrates do not. Thus, homologous characteristics form a nested pattern: All life shares the deepest layer, and each successive smaller group adds its own homologies to those it shares with larger groups. This nested pattern is exactly what we would expect to result from descent with modification from a common ancestor.

Biologists often represent the pattern of descent from common ancestors with an **evolutionary tree**, a diagram that reflects evolutionary relationships among groups of organisms. We will explore in detail how evolutionary trees are constructed in Chapter 26, but for now, let's consider how we can interpret and use such trees.

Figure 22.17 is an evolutionary tree of tetrapods and their closest living relatives, the lungfishes. In this diagram, each branch point represents the common ancestor of all species that descended from it. For example, lungfishes and all tetrapods descended from ancestor ❶, whereas mammals, lizards and snakes, crocodiles, and birds all descended from ancestor ❸. As expected, the three homologies shown on the tree—limbs with digits, the amnion (a protective embryonic membrane), and feathers—form a nested pattern. Limbs with digits were present in common ancestor ❷ and hence are found in all of the descendants of that ancestor (the tetrapods). The amnion was present only in ancestor ❸ and hence is shared only by some tetrapods (mammals and reptiles). Feathers were present only in common ancestor ❻ and hence are found only in birds.

To explore "tree thinking" further, note that in Figure 22.17, mammals are positioned closer to amphibians than to birds. As a result, you might conclude that mammals are more closely related to amphibians than they are to birds. However, mammals are actually more closely related to birds than to amphibians because mammals and birds share a more recent

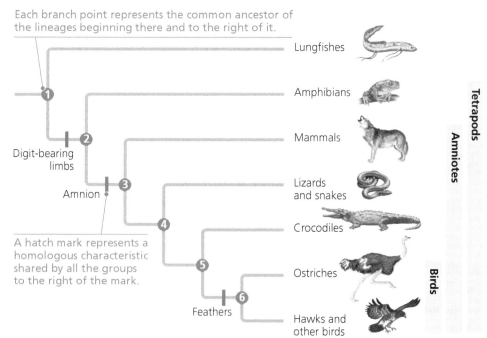

Each branch point represents the common ancestor of the lineages beginning there and to the right of it.

A hatch mark represents a homologous characteristic shared by all the groups to the right of the mark.

▲ **Figure 22.17 Tree thinking: information provided in an evolutionary tree.** This evolutionary tree for tetrapods and their closest living relatives, the lungfishes, is based on anatomical and DNA sequence data. The purple bars indicate the origin of three important homologies, each of which evolved only once. Birds are nested within and evolved from reptiles; hence, the group of organisms called "reptiles" technically includes birds.

? *Are crocodiles more closely related to lizards or birds? Explain your answer.*

common ancestor (ancestor ❸) than do mammals and amphibians (ancestor ❷). Ancestor ❷ is also the most recent common ancestor of birds and amphibians, making mammals and birds equally related to amphibians. Finally, note that the tree in Figure 22.17 shows the relative timing of events but not their actual dates. Thus, we can conclude that ancestor ❷ lived before ancestor ❸, but we do not know when that was.

Evolutionary trees are hypotheses that summarize our current understanding of patterns of descent. Our confidence in these relationships, as with any hypothesis, depends on the strength of the supporting data. In the case of Figure 22.17, the tree is supported by many different data sets, including both anatomical and DNA sequence data. As a result, biologists are confident that it accurately reflects evolutionary history. Scientists can use such well-supported evolutionary trees to make specific and sometimes surprising predictions about organisms (see Chapter 26).

A Different Cause of Resemblance: Convergent Evolution

Although organisms that are closely related share characteristics because of common descent, distantly related organisms can resemble one another for a different reason: **convergent evolution**, the independent evolution of similar features in different lineages. Consider marsupial mammals, many of which live in Australia. Marsupials are distinct from another group of mammals—the eutherians—few of which live in Australia. (Eutherians complete their embryonic development in the uterus, whereas marsupials are born as embryos and complete their development in an external pouch.) Some Australian marsupials have eutherian look-alikes with superficially similar adaptations. For instance, a forest-dwelling Australian marsupial called the sugar glider is superficially very similar to flying squirrels, gliding eutherians that live in North American forests (Figure 22.18). But the sugar glider has many other characteristics that make it a marsupial, much more closely related to kangaroos and other Australian marsupials than to flying squirrels or other eutherians. Once again, our understanding of evolution can explain these observations. Although they evolved independently from different ancestors, these two mammals have adapted to similar environments in similar ways. In such examples in which species share features because of convergent evolution, the resemblance is said to be **analogous**, not homologous. Analogous features share similar function, but not common ancestry, while homologous features share common ancestry, but not necessarily similar function.

▲ **Figure 22.18 Convergent evolution.** The ability to glide through the air evolved independently in these two distantly related mammals.

The Fossil Record

A third type of evidence for evolution comes from fossils. The fossil record documents the pattern of evolution, showing that past organisms differed from present-day organisms and that many species have become extinct. Fossils also show the evolutionary changes that have occurred in various groups of organisms. To give one of hundreds of possible examples, researchers found that the pelvic bone in fossil stickleback fish became greatly reduced in size over time in a number of different lakes. The consistent nature of this change suggests that the reduction in the size of the pelvic bone may have been driven by natural selection.

Fossils can also shed light on the origins of new groups of organisms. An example is the fossil record of cetaceans, the mammalian order that includes whales, dolphins, and porpoises. Some of these fossils (Figure 22.19) provided an

Most mammals   **Cetaceans and even-toed ungulates**

(a) *Canis* (dog)   (b) *Pakicetus*   (c) *Sus* (pig)   (d) *Odocoileus* (deer)

▲ **Figure 22.19 Ankle bones: one piece of the puzzle.** Comparing fossils and present-day examples of the astragalus (a type of ankle bone) indicates that cetaceans are closely related to even-toed ungulates. **(a)** In most mammals, the astragalus is shaped like that of a dog, with a double hump on one end (red arrows) but not at the opposite end (blue arrow). **(b)** Fossils show that the early cetacean *Pakicetus* had an astragalus with double humps at both ends, a shape otherwise found only in pigs **(c)**, deer **(d)**, and all other even-toed ungulates.

unexpected line of support for a hypothesis based on DNA sequence data: that cetaceans are closely related to even-toed ungulates, a group that includes deer, pigs, camels, and cows.

What else can fossils tell us about cetacean origins? The earliest cetaceans lived 50–60 million years ago. The fossil record indicates that prior to that time, most mammals were terrestrial. Although scientists had long realized that whales and other cetaceans originated from land mammals, few fossils had been found that revealed how cetacean limb structure had changed over time, leading eventually to the loss of hind limbs and the development of flippers and tail flukes. In the past few decades, however, a series of remarkable fossils have been discovered in Pakistan, Egypt, and North America. These fossils document steps in the transition from life on land to life in the sea, filling in some of the gaps between ancestral and living cetaceans (Figure 22.20).

▲ *Diacodexis*, an early even-toed ungulate

Collectively, the recent fossil discoveries document the origin of a major new group of mammals, the cetaceans. These discoveries also show that cetaceans and their close living relatives (hippopotamuses, pigs, and other even-toed ungulates) are much more different from each other than were *Pakicetus* and early even-toed ungulates, such as *Diacodexis*. Similar patterns are seen in fossils documenting the origins of other major new groups of organisms, including mammals (see Chapter 25), flowering plants (see Chapter 30), and tetrapods (see Chapter 34). In each of these cases, the fossil record shows that over time, descent with modification produced increasingly large differences among related groups of organisms, ultimately resulting in the diversity of life we see today.

Biogeography

A fourth type of evidence for evolution comes from **biogeography**, the scientific study of the geographic distributions of species. The geographic distributions of organisms are influenced by many factors, including *continental drift*, the slow movement of Earth's continents over time. About 250 million years ago, these movements united all of Earth's landmasses into a single large continent called **Pangaea** (see Figure 25.16). Roughly 200 million years ago, Pangaea began to break apart; by 20 million years ago, the continents we know today were within a few hundred kilometers of their present locations.

We can use our understanding of evolution and continental drift to predict where fossils of different groups of organisms might be found. For example, scientists have constructed evolutionary trees for horses based on anatomical data. These trees and the ages of fossils of horse ancestors suggest that the genus that includes present-day horses (*Equus*) originated 5 million years ago in North America. At that time, North and South America were close to their present locations, but they were not yet connected, making it difficult for horses to travel between them. Thus, we would predict that the oldest *Equus* fossils

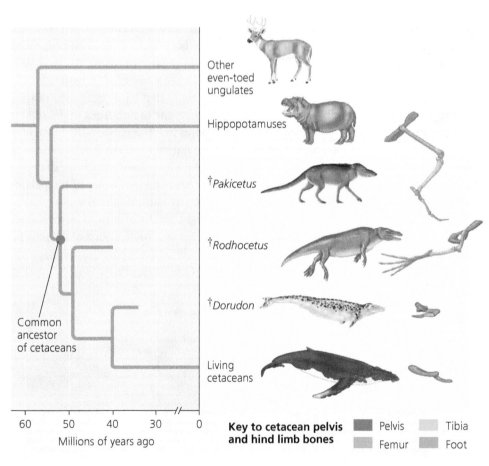

Other even-toed ungulates

Hippopotamuses

†*Pakicetus*

†*Rodhocetus*

†*Dorudon*

Living cetaceans

Common ancestor of cetaceans

60   50   40   30   0
Millions of years ago

Key to cetacean pelvis and hind limb bones   ■ Pelvis   □ Tibia   ■ Femur   □ Foot

▲ **Figure 22.20 The transition to life in the sea.** Cetacean lineages are highlighted in yellow in the above evolutionary tree diagram. Multiple lines of evidence support the hypothesis that cetaceans evolved from terrestrial mammals. Fossils document the reduction over time in the pelvis and hind limb bones of extinct cetacean ancestors, including *Pakicetus, Rodhocetus,* and *Dorudon*. DNA sequence data support the hypothesis that cetaceans are most closely related to hippopotamuses.

? *Which happened first during the evolution of cetaceans: changes in hind limb structure or the origin of tail flukes? Explain.*

should be found only on the continent on which the group originated—North America. This prediction and others like it for different groups of organisms have been upheld, providing more evidence for evolution.

We can also use our understanding of evolution to explain biogeographic data. For example, islands generally have many plant and animal species that are **endemic** (found nowhere else in the world). Yet, as Darwin described in *The Origin of Species*, most island species are closely related to species from the nearest mainland or a neighboring island. He explained this observation by suggesting that islands are colonized by species from the nearest mainland. These colonists eventually give rise to new species as they adapt to their new environments. Such a process also explains why two islands with similar environments in distant parts of the world tend to be populated not by species that are closely related to each other, but rather by species related to those of the nearest mainland, where the environment is often quite different.

What Is Theoretical About Darwin's View of Life?

Some people dismiss Darwin's ideas as "just a theory." However, as we have seen, the *pattern* of evolution—the observation that life has evolved over time—has been documented directly and is supported by a great deal of evidence. In addition, Darwin's explanation of the *process* of evolution—that natural selection is the primary cause of the observed pattern of evolutionary change—makes sense of massive amounts of data. The effects of natural selection also can be observed and tested in nature. Once such experiment is described in the Scientific Skills Exercise.

What, then, is theoretical about evolution? Keep in mind that the scientific meaning of the term *theory* is very different from its meaning in everyday use. The colloquial use of the word *theory* comes close to what scientists mean by a hypothesis. In science, a theory is more comprehensive

---

SCIENTIFIC SKILLS EXERCISE

Making and Testing Predictions

Can Predation Result in Natural Selection for Color Patterns in Guppies? What we know about evolution changes constantly as new observations lead to new hypotheses—and hence to new ways to test our understanding of evolutionary theory. Consider the wild guppies (*Poecilia reticulata*) that live in pools connected by streams on the Caribbean island of Trinidad. Male guppies have highly varied color patterns, which are controlled by genes that are only expressed in adult males. Female guppies choose males with bright color patterns as mates more often than they choose males with drab coloring. But the bright colors that attract females also make the males more conspicuous to predators. Researchers observed that in pools with few predator species, the benefits of bright colors appear to "win out," and males are more brightly colored than in pools where predation is more intense.

One guppy predator, the killifish, preys on juvenile guppies that have not yet displayed their adult coloration. Researchers predicted that if guppies with drab colors were transferred to a pool with only killifish, eventually the descendants of these guppies would be more brightly colored (because of the female preference for brightly colored males).

How the Experiment Was Done Researchers transplanted 200 guppies from pools containing pike-cichlid fish, intense guppy predators, to

pools containing killifish, less active predators that prey mainly on juvenile guppies. They tracked the number of bright-colored spots and the total area of those spots on male guppies in each generation.

Data from the Experiment After 22 months (15 generations), researchers compared the color pattern data for the source and transplanted populations.

Interpret the Data

1. Identify the following elements of hypothesis-based science in this example: (a) question, (b) hypothesis, (c) prediction, (d) control group, and (e) experimental group. (For additional information about hypothesis-based science, see Chapter 1 and the Scientific Skills Review in Appendix F and the Study Area of MasteringBiology.)

2. Explain how the types of data the researchers chose to collect enabled them to test their prediction.

3. (a) What conclusion would you draw from the data presented above? (b) What additional questions might you ask to determine the strength of this conclusion?

4. Predict what would happen if, after 22 months, guppies from the transplanted population were returned to the source pool. Describe an experiment to test your prediction.

(MB) A version of this Scientific Skills Exercise can be assigned in MasteringBiology.

Data from J. A. Endler, Natural selection on color patters in *Poecilia reticulata*, *Evolution* 34:76–91 (1980).

Guppies transplanted

Pools with pike-cichlids and guppies

Pools with killifish, but no guppies prior to transplant

than a hypothesis. A theory, such as the theory of evolution by natural selection, accounts for many observations and explains and integrates a great variety of phenomena. Such a unifying theory does not become widely accepted unless its predictions stand up to thorough and continual testing by experiment and additional observation (see Chapter 1). As the rest of this unit demonstrates, this has certainly been the case with the theory of evolution by natural selection.

The skepticism of scientists as they continue to test theories prevents these ideas from becoming dogma. For example, although Darwin thought that evolution was a very slow process, we now know that new species sometimes form in relatively short periods of time: a few thousand years or less (see Chapter 24). Furthermore, evolutionary biologists now recognize that natural selection is not the only mechanism responsible for evolution. Indeed, the study of evolution today is livelier than ever as scientists make new discoveries using a wide range of experimental approaches and genetic analyses; you can read about one such biologist, Dr. Hopi Hoekstra, and her work in the interview before this chapter.

Although Darwin's theory attributes life's diversity to natural processes, the diverse products of evolution are nevertheless elegant and inspiring. As Darwin wrote in the final sentence of *The Origin of Species*, "There is grandeur in this view of life . . . [in which] endless forms most beautiful and most wonderful have been, and are being, evolved."

CONCEPT CHECK 22.3

1. Explain how the following statement is inaccurate: "Antibiotics have created drug resistance in MRSA."
2. How does evolution account for (a) the similar mammalian forelimbs with different functions shown in Figure 22.15 and (b) the similar forms of the two distantly related mammals shown in Figure 22.18?
3. **WHAT IF?** Dinosaurs originated 250–200 million years ago. Would you expect the geographic distribution of early dinosaur fossils to be broad (on many continents) or narrow (on one or a few continents only)? Explain.

For suggested answers, see Appendix A.

22 Chapter Review

SUMMARY OF KEY CONCEPTS

CONCEPT 22.1

The Darwinian revolution challenged traditional views of a young Earth inhabited by unchanging species (pp. 463–465)

- Darwin proposed that life's diversity arose from ancestral species through natural selection, a departure from prevailing views.
- Cuvier studied fossils but denied that evolution occurs; he proposed that sudden catastrophic events in the past caused species to disappear from an area.
- Hutton and Lyell thought that geologic change could result from gradual mechanisms that operated in the past in the same manner as they do today.
- Lamarck hypothesized that species evolve, but the underlying mechanisms he proposed are not supported by evidence.

? *Why was the age of Earth important for Darwin's ideas about evolution?*

CONCEPT 22.2

Descent with modification by natural selection explains the adaptations of organisms and the unity and diversity of life (pp. 465–470)

- Darwin's experiences during the voyage of the *Beagle* gave rise to his idea that new species originate from ancestral forms through the accumulation of **adaptations**. He refined his theory for many years and finally published it in 1859 after learning that Wallace had come to the same idea.

- In *The Origin of Species*, Darwin proposed that over long periods of time, descent with modification produced the rich diversity of life through the mechanism of **natural selection**.

Observations

Individuals in a population vary in their heritable characteristics.	Organisms produce more offspring than the environment can support.

Inferences

Individuals that are well suited to their environment tend to leave more offspring than other individuals.

and

Over time, favorable traits accumulate in the population.

? *Describe how overreproduction and heritable variation relate to evolution by natural selection.*

CONCEPT 22.3

Evolution is supported by an overwhelming amount of scientific evidence (pp. 471–478)

- Researchers have directly observed natural selection leading to adaptive evolution in many studies, including research on soapberry bug populations and on MRSA.
- Organisms share characteristics because of common descent (**homology**) or because natural selection affects independently

evolving species in similar environments in similar ways (**convergent evolution**).

- Fossils show that past organisms differed from living organisms, that many species have become extinct, and that species have evolved over long periods of time; fossils also document the origin of major new groups of organisms.
- Evolutionary theory can explain biogeographic patterns.

? *Summarize the different lines of evidence supporting the hypothesis that cetaceans descended from land mammals and are closely related to even-toed ungulates.*

TEST YOUR UNDERSTANDING

LEVEL 1: KNOWLEDGE/COMPREHENSION

1. Which of the following is *not* an observation or inference on which natural selection is based?
   a. There is heritable variation among individuals.
   b. Poorly adapted individuals never produce offspring.
   c. Species produce more offspring than the environment can support.
   d. Only a fraction of an individual's offspring may survive.

2. Which of the following observations helped Darwin shape his concept of descent with modification?
   a. Species diversity declines farther from the equator.
   b. Fewer species live on islands than on the nearest continents.
   c. Birds live on islands located farther from the mainland than the birds' maximum nonstop flight distance.
   d. South American temperate plants are more similar to the tropical plants of South America than to the temperate plants of Europe.

LEVEL 2: APPLICATION/ANALYSIS

3. Within six months of effectively using methicillin to treat *S. aureus* infections in a community, all new *S. aureus* infections were caused by MRSA. How can this best be explained?
   a. A patient must have become infected with MRSA from another community.
   b. In response to the drug, *S. aureus* began making drug-resistant versions of the protein targeted by the drug.
   c. Some drug-resistant bacteria were present at the start of treatment, and natural selection increased their frequency.
   d. *S. aureus* evolved to resist vaccines.

4. The upper forelimbs of humans and bats have fairly similar skeletal structures, whereas the corresponding bones in whales have very different shapes and proportions. However, genetic data suggest that all three kinds of organisms diverged from a common ancestor at about the same time. Which of the following is the most likely explanation for these data?
   a. Forelimb evolution was adaptive in people and bats, but not in whales.
   b. Natural selection in an aquatic environment resulted in significant changes to whale forelimb anatomy.
   c. Genes mutate faster in whales than in humans or bats.
   d. Whales are not properly classified as mammals.

5. DNA sequences in many human genes are very similar to the sequences of corresponding genes in chimpanzees. The most likely explanation for this result is that
   a. humans and chimpanzees share a relatively recent common ancestor.
   b. humans evolved from chimpanzees.
   c. chimpanzees evolved from humans.
   d. convergent evolution led to the DNA similarities.

LEVEL 3: SYNTHESIS/EVALUATION

6. **EVOLUTION CONNECTION**
   Explain why anatomical and molecular features often fit a similar nested pattern. In addition, describe a process that can cause this not to be the case.

7. **SCIENTIFIC INQUIRY**
   DRAW IT Mosquitoes resistant to the pesticide DDT first appeared in India in 1959, but now are found throughout the world. (a) Graph the data in the table below. (b) Examining the graph, hypothesize why the percentage of mosquitoes resistant to DDT rose rapidly. (c) Suggest an explanation for the global spread of DDT resistance.

Month	0	8	12
Mosquitoes Resistant* to DDT	4%	45%	77%

   Source: C. F. Curtis et al., Selection for and against insecticide resistance and possible methods of inhibiting the evolution of resistance in mosquitoes, *Ecological Entomology* 3:273–287 (1978).

   *Mosquitoes were considered resistant if they were not killed within 1 hour of receiving a dose of 4% DDT.

8. **WRITE ABOUT A THEME: INTERACTIONS**
   Write a short essay (about 100–150 words) evaluating whether changes to an organism's physical environment are likely to result in evolutionary change. Use an example to support your reasoning.

9. **SYNTHESIZE YOUR KNOWLEDGE**

This honeypot ant (genus *Myrmecocystus*) can store liquid food inside its expandable abdomen. Consider other ants you are familiar with, and explain how a honeypot ant exemplifies three key features of life: adaptation, unity, and diversity.

For selected answers, see Appendix A.

MasteringBiology®

23
The Evolution of Populations

▲ Figure 23.1 **Is this finch evolving?**

The Smallest Unit of Evolution

One common misconception about evolution is that individual organisms evolve. It is true that natural selection acts on individuals: Each organism's traits affect its survival and reproductive success compared with those of other individuals. But the evolutionary impact of natural selection is only apparent in the changes in a *population* of organisms over time.

Consider the medium ground finch (*Geospiza fortis*), a seed-eating bird that inhabits the Galápagos Islands **(Figure 23.1)**. In 1977, the *G. fortis* population on the island of Daphne Major was decimated by a long period of drought: Of some 1,200 birds, only 180 survived. Researchers Peter and Rosemary Grant observed that during the drought, small, soft seeds were in short supply. The finches mostly fed on large, hard seeds that were more plentiful. Birds with larger, deeper beaks were better able to crack and eat these larger seeds, and they survived at a higher rate than finches with smaller beaks. Since beak depth is an inherited trait in these birds, the average beak depth in the next generation of *G. fortis* was greater than it had been in the pre-drought population **(Figure 23.2)**. The finch population had evolved by natural selection. However, the *individual* finches did not evolve. Each bird had a beak of a particular size, which did not grow larger during the drought. Rather, the proportion of large beaks in the population increased from generation to generation: The population evolved, not its individual members.

► **Figure 23.2 Evidence of selection by food source.** The data represent adult beak depth measurements of medium ground finches hatched in the generations before and after the 1977 drought. In one generation, natural selection resulted in a larger average beak size in the population.

(MB) *A related Experimental Inquiry Tutorial can be assigned in MasteringBiology.*

▲ **Figure 23.3 Phenotypic variation in horses.** In horses, coat color varies along a continuum and is influenced by multiple genes.

Focusing on evolutionary change in populations, we can define evolution on its smallest scale, called **microevolution**, as a change in allele frequencies in a population over generations. As you will see in this chapter, natural selection is not the only cause of microevolution. In fact, there are three main mechanisms that can cause allele frequency change: natural selection, genetic drift (chance events that alter allele frequencies), and gene flow (the transfer of alleles between populations). Each of these mechanisms has distinctive effects on the genetic composition of populations. However, only natural selection consistently improves the match between organisms and their environment (adaptation). Before we examine natural selection and adaptation more closely, let's revisit a prerequisite for these processes in a population: genetic variation.

CONCEPT 23.1

Genetic variation makes evolution possible

In *The Origin of Species*, Darwin provided abundant evidence that life on Earth has evolved over time, and he proposed natural selection as the primary mechanism for that change. He observed that individuals differ in their inherited traits and that selection acts on such differences, leading to evolutionary change. Although Darwin realized that variation in heritable traits is a prerequisite for evolution, he did not know precisely how organisms pass heritable traits to their offspring.

Just a few years after Darwin published *The Origin of Species*, Gregor Mendel wrote a groundbreaking paper on inheritance in pea plants (see Chapter 14). In that paper, Mendel proposed a model of inheritance in which organisms transmit discrete heritable units (now called genes) to their offspring. Although Darwin did not know about genes, Mendel's paper set the stage for understanding the genetic differences on which evolution is based. Here we'll examine such genetic differences and how they are produced.

Genetic Variation

Individuals within a species vary in their specific characteristics. Among humans, you can easily observe phenotypic variation in facial features, height, and voice. Indeed, individual variation occurs in all species. And though you cannot identify a person's blood group (A, B, AB, or O) from his or her appearance, this and many other molecular traits also vary extensively among individuals.

Such phenotypic variations often reflect **genetic variation**, differences among individuals in the composition of their genes or other DNA sequences. Some heritable phenotypic differences occur on an "either-or" basis, such as the flower colors of Mendel's pea plants: Each plant had flowers that were either purple or white (see Figure 14.3). Characters that vary in this way are typically determined by a single gene locus, with different alleles producing distinct phenotypes. In contrast, other phenotypic differences vary in gradations along a continuum. Such variation usually results from the influence of two or more genes on a single phenotypic character. In fact, many phenotypic characters are influenced by multiple genes, including coat color in horses **(Figure 23.3)**, seed number in maize (corn), and height in humans.

How much do genes and other DNA sequences vary from one individual to another? Genetic variation at the whole-gene level (*gene variability*) can be quantified as the average percentage of loci that are heterozygous. (Recall that a heterozygous individual has two different alleles for a given locus, whereas a homozygous individual has two identical alleles for that locus.) As an example, on average the fruit fly *Drosophila melanogaster* is heterozygous for about 1,920 of its 13,700 loci (14%) and homozygous for all the rest.

Considerable genetic variation can also be measured at the molecular level of DNA (*nucleotide variability*). But little of this variation results in phenotypic variation. The reason is that many of the differences occur within *introns*, noncoding segments of DNA lying between *exons*, the regions retained

Base-pair substitutions are shown in orange.

A red arrow indicates an insertion site.

The substitution at this site results in the translation of a different amino acid.

A deletion of 26 base pairs occurred here.

1   500   1,000   1,500   2,000   2,500

Exon   Intron

▲ **Figure 23.4 Extensive genetic variation at the molecular level.** This diagram summarizes data from a study comparing the DNA sequence of the alcohol dehydrogenase (*Adh*) gene in several fruit flies (*Drosophila melanogaster*). The *Adh* gene has four exons (dark blue) separated by introns (light blue);

the exons include the coding regions that are ultimately translated into the amino acids of the *Adh* enzyme (see Figure 5.1). Only one substitution has a phenotypic effect, producing a different form of the *Adh* enzyme.

MAKE CONNECTIONS *Review Figures 17.5 and 17.10. Explain how a base-pair substitution that alters a coding region of the* Adh *locus could have no effect on amino acid sequence. Then explain how an insertion in an exon could have no effect on the protein produced.*

in mRNA after RNA processing (see Figure 17.11). And of the variations that occur within exons, most do not cause a change in the amino acid sequence of the protein encoded by the gene. For example, in the sequence comparison shown in **Figure 23.4**, there are 43 nucleotide sites with variable base pairs (where substitutions have occurred), as well as several sites where insertions or deletions have occurred. Although 18 variable sites occur within the four exons of the *Adh* gene, only one of these variations (at site 1,490) results in an amino acid change. Note, however, that this single variable site is enough to cause genetic variation at the level of the gene—and hence two different forms of the *Adh* enzyme are produced.

It is important to bear in mind that some phenotypic variation does not result from genetic differences among individuals (**Figure 23.5** shows a striking example in a caterpillar of the southwestern United States). Phenotype is the product of an inherited genotype and many environmental influences (see Concept 14.3). In a human example, bodybuilders alter their phenotypes dramatically but do not pass their huge muscles on to the next generation. In general, only the genetically determined part of phenotypic variation can have evolutionary consequences. As such, genetic variation provides the raw material for evolutionary change: Without genetic variation, evolution cannot occur.

Sources of Genetic Variation

The genetic variation on which evolution depends originates when mutation, gene duplication, or other processes produce new alleles and new genes. Genetic variants can be produced rapidly in organisms with short generation times. Sexual reproduction can also result in genetic variation as existing genes are arranged in new ways.

Formation of New Alleles

New alleles can arise by *mutation*, a change in the nucleotide sequence of an organism's DNA. A mutation is like a shot in the dark—we cannot predict accurately which segments of DNA will be altered or how. In multicellular organisms, only mutations in cell lines that produce gametes can be passed to offspring. In plants and fungi, this is not as limiting as it may sound, since many different cell lines can produce gametes. But in most animals, the majority of mutations occur in somatic cells and are not passed to offspring.

A change of as little as one base in a gene—a "point mutation"—can have a significant impact on phenotype, as in sickle-cell disease (see Figure 17.25). Organisms reflect many generations of past selection, and hence their phenotypes tend to be well matched to their environments. As a result, most new mutations that alter a phenotype are at least slightly harmful. In some cases, natural selection quickly removes such harmful alleles. In diploid organisms, however, harmful alleles that are recessive can be hidden from selection. Indeed, a harmful recessive allele can persist for generations by propagation in heterozygous individuals (where its harmful effects are masked by the more favorable dominant allele). Such "heterozygote protection" maintains a huge pool of alleles that might not be favored under present conditions, but that could be beneficial if the environment changes.

(a)   (b)

▲ **Figure 23.5 Nonheritable variation.** These caterpillars of the moth *Nemoria arizonaria* owe their different appearances to chemicals in their diets, not to differences in their genotypes. **(a)** Caterpillars raised on a diet of oak flowers resemble the flowers, whereas **(b)** their siblings raised on oak leaves resemble oak twigs.

While many mutations are harmful, many others are not. Recall that much of the DNA in eukaryotic genomes does not encode proteins (see Figure 21.6). Point mutations in these noncoding regions generally result in **neutral variation**, differences in DNA sequence that do not confer a selective advantage or disadvantage. The redundancy in the genetic code is another source of neutral variation: even a point mutation in a gene that encodes a protein will have no effect on the protein's function if the amino acid composition is not changed. And even where there is a change in the amino acid, it may not affect the protein's shape and function. Finally, as you will see later in this chapter, a mutant allele may on rare occasions actually make its bearer better suited to the environment, enhancing reproductive success.

Altering Gene Number or Position

Chromosomal changes that delete, disrupt, or rearrange many loci are usually harmful. However, when such large-scale changes leave genes intact, they may not affect the organisms' phenotype. In rare cases, chromosomal rearrangements may even be beneficial. For example, the translocation of part of one chromosome to a different chromosome could link genes in a way that produces a positive effect.

A key potential source of variation is the duplication of genes due to errors in meiosis (such as unequal crossing over), slippage during DNA replication, or the activities of transposable elements (see Concept 21.5). Duplications of large chromosome segments, like other chromosomal aberrations, are often harmful, but the duplication of smaller pieces of DNA may not be. Gene duplications that do not have severe effects can persist over generations, allowing mutations to accumulate. The result is an expanded genome with new genes that may take on new functions.

Such increases in gene number appear to have played a major role in evolution. For example, the remote ancestors of mammals had a single gene for detecting odors that has since been duplicated many times. As a result, humans today have about 350 functional olfactory receptor genes, and mice have 1,000. This dramatic proliferation of olfactory genes probably helped early mammals, enabling them to detect faint odors and to distinguish among many different smells.

Rapid Reproduction

Mutation rates tend to be low in plants and animals, averaging about one mutation in every 100,000 genes per generation, and they are often even lower in prokaryotes. But prokaryotes have many more generations per unit of time, so mutations can quickly generate genetic variation in their populations. The same is true of viruses. For instance, HIV has a generation span of about two days. It also has an RNA genome, which has a much higher mutation rate than a typical DNA genome because of the lack of RNA repair mechanisms in host cells (see Chapter 19). For this reason,

single-drug treatments are unlikely to be effective against HIV; mutant forms of the virus that are resistant to a particular drug would tend to proliferate in relatively short order. The most effective AIDS treatments to date have been drug "cocktails" that combine several medications. It is less likely that a set of mutations that together confer resistance to *all* the drugs will occur in a short time period.

Sexual Reproduction

In organisms that reproduce sexually, most of the genetic variation in a population results from the unique combination of alleles that each individual receives from its parents. Of course, at the nucleotide level, all the differences among these alleles have originated from past mutations. Sexual reproduction then shuffles existing alleles and deals them at random to produce individual genotypes.

Three mechanisms contribute to this shuffling: crossing over, independent assortment of chromosomes, and fertilization (see Chapter 13). During meiosis, homologous chromosomes, one inherited from each parent, trade some of their alleles by crossing over. These homologous chromosomes and the alleles they carry are then distributed at random into gametes. Then, because myriad possible mating combinations exist in a population, fertilization brings together gametes that are likely to have different genetic backgrounds. The combined effects of these three mechanisms ensure that sexual reproduction rearranges existing alleles into fresh combinations each generation, providing much of the genetic variation that makes evolution possible.

CONCEPT CHECK 23.1

1. Explain why genetic variation within a population is a prerequisite for evolution.
2. Of all the mutations that occur in a population, why do only a small fraction become widespread?
3. MAKE CONNECTIONS If a population stopped reproducing sexually (but still reproduced asexually), how would its genetic variation be affected over time? Explain. (See Concept 13.4.)

For suggested answers, see Appendix A.

CONCEPT 23.2

The Hardy-Weinberg equation can be used to test whether a population is evolving

Although the individuals in a population must differ genetically for evolution to occur, the presence of genetic variation does not guarantee that a population will evolve. For that to happen, one of the factors that cause evolution must be at work. In this section, we'll explore one way to test whether evolution is occurring in a population. First, let's clarify what we mean by a population.

Gene Pools and Allele Frequencies

A **population** is a group of individuals of the same species that live in the same area and interbreed, producing fertile offspring. Different populations of a species may be isolated geographically from one another, exchanging genetic material only rarely. Such isolation is common for species that live on widely separated islands or in different lakes. But not all populations are isolated (Figure 23.6). Still, members of a population typically breed with one another and thus on average are more closely related to each other than to members of other populations.

We can characterize a population's genetic makeup by describing its **gene pool**, which consists of all copies of every type of allele at every locus in all members of the population. If only one allele exists for a particular locus in a population, that allele is said to be *fixed* in the gene pool, and all individuals are homozygous for that allele. But if there are two or more alleles for a particular locus in a population, individuals may be either homozygous or heterozygous.

For example, imagine a population of 500 wildflower plants with two alleles, C^R and C^W, for a locus that codes for flower pigment. These alleles show incomplete dominance; thus, each genotype has a distinct phenotype. Plants homozygous for the C^R allele ($C^R C^R$) produce red pigment and have red flowers; plants homozygous for the C^W allele ($C^W C^W$) produce no red pigment and have white flowers; and heterozygotes ($C^R C^W$) produce some red pigment and have pink flowers.

 $C^R C^R$

 $C^W C^W$

$C^R C^W$

Each allele has a frequency (proportion) in the population. For example, suppose our population has 320 plants with red flowers, 160 with pink flowers, and 20 with white flowers. Because these are diploid organisms, these 500 individuals have a total of 1,000 copies of the gene for flower color. The C^R allele accounts for 800 of these copies ($320 \times 2 = 640$ for $C^R C^R$ plants, plus $160 \times 1 = 160$ for $C^R C^W$ plants). Thus, the frequency of the C^R allele is $800/1,000 = 0.8$ (80%).

When studying a locus with two alleles, the convention is to use p to represent the frequency of one allele and q to represent the frequency of the other allele. Thus, p, the frequency of the C^R allele in the gene pool of this population, is $p = 0.8$ (80%). And because there are only two alleles for this gene, the frequency of the C^W allele, represented by q, must be $q = 1 - p = 0.2$ (20%). For loci that have more than two alleles, the sum of all allele frequencies must still equal 1 (100%).

Porcupine herd

Fortymile herd

▲ **Figure 23.6 One species, two populations.** These two caribou populations in the Yukon are not totally isolated; they sometimes share the same area. Still, members of either population are most likely to breed within their own population.

Next we'll see how allele and genotype frequencies can be used to test whether evolution is occurring in a population.

The Hardy-Weinberg Equation

One way to assess whether natural selection or other factors are causing evolution at a particular locus is to determine what the genetic makeup of a population would be if it were *not* evolving at that locus. We can then compare that scenario with the data we actually observed for the population. If there are no differences, we can conclude that the population is not evolving. If there are differences, this suggests that the population may be evolving—and then we can try to figure out why.

Hardy-Weinberg Equilibrium

In a population that is not evolving, allele and genotype frequencies will remain constant from generation to generation, provided that only Mendelian segregation and recombination of alleles are at work. Such a population is said to be in **Hardy-Weinberg equilibrium**, named for the British mathematician and German physician, respectively, who independently developed this idea in 1908.

To determine whether a population is in Hardy-Weinberg equilibrium, it is helpful to think about genetic crosses in a new way. Previously, we used Punnett squares to determine the genotypes of offspring in a genetic cross (see Figure 14.5). Here, instead of considering the possible allele combinations from one cross, we'll consider the combination of alleles in *all* of the crosses in a population.

Imagine that all the alleles for a given locus from all the individuals in a population are placed in a large bin (Figure 23.7). We can think of this bin as holding the population's gene pool for that locus. "Reproduction" occurs by selecting alleles at random from the bin; somewhat similar events occur in nature when fish release sperm and eggs into the water or when pollen (containing plant

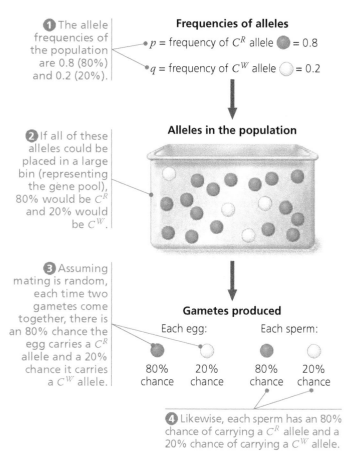

① The allele frequencies of the population are 0.8 (80%) and 0.2 (20%).

Frequencies of alleles

p = frequency of C^R allele ● = 0.8

q = frequency of C^W allele ○ = 0.2

② If all of these alleles could be placed in a large bin (representing the gene pool), 80% would be C^R and 20% would be C^W.

Alleles in the population

③ Assuming mating is random, each time two gametes come together, there is an 80% chance the egg carries a C^R allele and a 20% chance it carries a C^W allele.

Gametes produced

Each egg:

80% chance   20% chance

Each sperm:

80% chance   20% chance

④ Likewise, each sperm has an 80% chance of carrying a C^R allele and a 20% chance of carrying a C^W allele.

▲ **Figure 23.7 Selecting alleles at random from a gene pool.**

sperm) is blown about by the wind. By viewing reproduction as a process of randomly selecting and combining alleles from the bin (the gene pool), we are in effect assuming that mating occurs at random—that is, that all male-female matings are equally likely.

Let's apply the bin analogy to the hypothetical wildflower population discussed earlier. In that population of 500 flowers, the frequency of the allele for red flowers (C^R) is $p = 0.8$, and the frequency of the allele for white flowers (C^W) is $q = 0.2$. In other words, a bin holding all 1,000 copies of the flower-color gene in the population would contain 800 C^R alleles and 200 C^W alleles. Assuming that gametes are formed by selecting alleles at random from the bin, the probability that an egg or sperm contains a C^R or C^W allele is equal to the frequency of these alleles in the bin. Thus, as shown in Figure 23.7, each egg has an 80% chance of containing a C^R allele and a 20% chance of containing a C^W allele; the same is true for each sperm.

Using the rule of multiplication (see Figure 14.9), we can now calculate the frequencies of the three possible genotypes, assuming random unions of sperm and eggs. The probability that two C^R alleles will come together is $p \times p = p^2 = 0.8 \times 0.8 = 0.64$. Thus, about 64% of the plants in the next generation will have the genotype $C^R C^R$. The frequency of $C^W C^W$ individuals is expected to be about $q \times q = q^2 =$

Gametes for each generation are drawn at random from the gene pool of the previous generation:

80% C^R ($p = 0.8$)   20% C^W ($q = 0.2$)

Sperm

C^R $p = 0.8$ C^W $q = 0.2$

Eggs

C^R $p = 0.8$

0.64 (p^2) $C^R C^R$ 0.16 (pq) $C^R C^W$

C^W $q = 0.2$

0.16 (qp) $C^R C^W$ 0.04 (q^2) $C^W C^W$

If the gametes come together at random, the genotype frequencies of this generation are in Hardy-Weinberg equilibrium:

64% $C^R C^R$, 32% $C^R C^W$, and 4% $C^W C^W$

Gametes of this generation:

64% C^R (from $C^R C^R$ plants) + 16% C^R (from $C^R C^W$ plants) = 80% C^R = 0.8 = p

4% C^W (from $C^W C^W$ plants) + 16% C^W (from $C^R C^W$ plants) = 20% C^W = 0.2 = q

With random mating, these gametes will result in the same mix of genotypes in the next generation:

64% $C^R C^R$, 32% $C^R C^W$, and 4% $C^W C^W$ plants

▲ **Figure 23.8 The Hardy-Weinberg principle.** In our wildflower population, the gene pool remains constant from one generation to the next. Mendelian processes alone do not alter frequencies of alleles or genotypes.

? *If the frequency of the C^R allele is 0.6, predict the frequencies of the $C^R C^R$, $C^R C^W$, and $C^W C^W$ genotypes.*

$0.2 \times 0.2 = 0.04$, or 4%. $C^R C^W$ heterozygotes can arise in two different ways. If the sperm provides the C^R allele and the egg provides the C^W allele, the resulting heterozygotes will be $p \times q = 0.8 \times 0.2 = 0.16$, or 16% of the total. If the sperm provides the C^W allele and the egg the C^R allele, the heterozygous offspring will make up $q \times p = 0.2 \times 0.8 = 0.16$, or 16%. The frequency of heterozygotes is thus the sum of these possibilities: $pq + qp = 2pq = 0.16 + 0.16 = 0.32$, or 32%.

As shown in **Figure 23.8**, the genotype frequencies in the next generation must add up to 1 (100%). Thus, the equation for Hardy-Weinberg equilibrium states that at a locus with two alleles, the three genotypes will appear in the following proportions:

$$\underset{\substack{\text{Expected}\\\text{frequency}\\\text{of genotype}\\C^R C^R}}{p^2} + \underset{\substack{\text{Expected}\\\text{frequency}\\\text{of genotype}\\C^R C^W}}{2pq} + \underset{\substack{\text{Expected}\\\text{frequency}\\\text{of genotype}\\C^W C^W}}{q^2} = 1$$

Note that for a locus with two alleles, only three genotypes are possible (in this case, $C^R C^R$, $C^R C^W$, and $C^W C^W$). As a result, the sum of the frequencies of the three genotypes must equal 1 (100%) in *any* population—regardless of whether the population is in Hardy-Weinberg equilibrium. A population is in Hardy-Weinberg equilibrium only if the genotype frequencies are such that the actual frequency of one homozygote is p^2, the actual frequency of the other homozygote is q^2, and the actual frequency of heterozygotes is $2pq$. Finally, as suggested by Figure 23.8, if a population such as our wildflowers is in Hardy-Weinberg equilibrium and its members continue to mate randomly generation after generation, allele and genotype frequencies will remain constant. The system operates somewhat like a deck of cards: No matter how many times the deck is reshuffled to deal out new hands, the deck itself remains the same. Aces do not grow more numerous than jacks. And the repeated shuffling of a population's gene pool over the generations cannot, in itself, change the frequency of one allele relative to another.

Conditions for Hardy-Weinberg Equilibrium

The Hardy-Weinberg approach describes a hypothetical population that is not evolving. But in real populations, the allele and genotype frequencies often *do* change over time. Such changes can occur when at least one of the following five conditions of Hardy-Weinberg equilibrium is not met:

1. **No mutations.** The gene pool is modified if mutations alter alleles or if entire genes are deleted or duplicated.
2. **Random mating.** If individuals tend to mate within a subset of the population, such as their near neighbors or close relatives (inbreeding), random mixing of gametes does not occur, and genotype frequencies change.
3. **No natural selection.** Differences in the survival and reproductive success of individuals carrying different genotypes can alter allele frequencies.
4. **Extremely large population size.** The smaller the population, the more likely it is that allele frequencies will fluctuate by chance from one generation to the next (a process called genetic drift).
5. **No gene flow.** By moving alleles into or out of populations, gene flow can alter allele frequencies.

Departure from these conditions usually results in evolutionary change, which, as we've already described, is common in natural populations. But it is also common for natural populations to be in Hardy-Weinberg equilibrium for specific genes. This can occur if selection alters allele frequencies at some loci but not others. In addition, some populations evolve so slowly that the changes in their allele and genotype frequencies are difficult to distinguish from those predicted for a non-evolving population.

Applying the Hardy-Weinberg Equation

The Hardy-Weinberg equation is often used as an initial test of whether evolution is occurring in a population (Concept Check 23.2, question 3 is an example). The equation also has medical applications, such as estimating the percentage of a population carrying the allele for an inherited disease. For example, consider phenylketonuria (PKU), a metabolic disorder that results from homozygosity for a recessive allele and occurs in about one out of every 10,000 babies born in the United States. Left untreated, PKU results in mental disability and other problems. (As described in Concept 14.4, newborns are now tested for PKU, and symptoms can be largely avoided with a diet very low in phenylalanine.)

To apply the Hardy-Weinberg equation, we must assume that no new PKU mutations are being introduced into the population (condition 1) and that people neither choose their mates on the basis of whether or not they carry this gene nor generally mate with close relatives (condition 2). We must also ignore any effects of differential survival and reproductive success among PKU genotypes (condition 3) and assume that there are no effects of genetic drift (condition 4) or of gene flow from other populations into the United States (condition 5). These assumptions are reasonable: The mutation rate for the PKU gene is low, inbreeding and other forms of nonrandom mating are not common in the United States, selection occurs only against the rare homozygotes (and then only if dietary restrictions are not followed), the U.S. population is very large, and populations outside the country have PKU allele frequencies similar to those seen in the United States.

If all these assumptions hold, then the frequency of individuals in the population born with PKU will correspond to q^2 in the Hardy-Weinberg equation (q^2 = frequency of homozygotes). Because the allele is recessive, we must estimate the number of heterozygotes rather than counting them directly as we did with the pink flowers. Since we know there is one PKU occurrence per 10,000 births ($q^2 = 0.0001$), the frequency (q) of the recessive allele for PKU is

$$q = \sqrt{0.0001} = 0.01$$

and the frequency of the dominant allele is

$$p = 1 - q = 1 - 0.01 = 0.99$$

The frequency of carriers, heterozygous people who do not have PKU but may pass the PKU allele to offspring, is

$$2pq = 2 \times 0.99 \times 0.01 = 0.0198$$
(approximately 2% of the U.S. population)

Remember, the assumption of Hardy-Weinberg equilibrium yields an approximation; the real number of carriers may differ. Still, our calculations suggest that harmful recessive alleles at this and other loci can be concealed in a population because they are carried by healthy heterozygotes. The Scientific Skills Exercise provides another opportunity for you to apply the Hardy-Weinberg equation to allele data.

CONCEPT CHECK 23.2

1. A population has 700 individuals, 85 of genotype *AA*, 320 of genotype *Aa*, and 295 of genotype *aa*. What are the frequencies of alleles *A* and *a*?

2. The frequency of allele *a* is 0.45 for a population in Hardy-Weinberg equilibrium. What are the expected frequencies of genotypes *AA*, *Aa*, and *aa*?

3. **WHAT IF?** A locus that affects susceptibility to a degenerative brain disease has two alleles, *V* and *v*. In a population, 16 people have genotype *VV*, 92 have genotype *Vv*, and 12 have genotype *vv*. Is this population evolving? Explain.

For suggested answers, see Appendix A.

Natural selection, genetic drift, and gene flow can alter allele frequencies in a population

Note again the five conditions required for a population to be in Hardy-Weinberg equilibrium. A deviation from any of these conditions is a potential cause of evolution. New mutations (violation of condition 1) can alter allele frequencies, but because mutations are rare, the change from one generation to the next is likely to be very small. Non-random mating (violation of condition 2) can affect the frequencies of homozygous and heterozygous genotypes but by itself has no effect on allele frequencies in the gene pool. (Allele frequencies can change if individuals with certain inherited traits are more likely than other individuals to obtain mates. However, such a situation not only causes a deviation from random mating, but also violates condition 3, no natural selection.)

For the rest of this section we will focus on the three mechanisms that alter allele frequencies directly and cause most evolutionary change: natural selection, genetic drift, and gene flow (violations of conditions 3–5).

SCIENTIFIC SKILLS EXERCISE

Using the Hardy-Weinberg Equation to Interpret Data and Make Predictions

Is Evolution Occurring in a Soybean Population? One way to test whether evolution is occurring in a population is to compare the observed genotype frequencies at a locus with those expected for a non-evolving population based on the Hardy-Weinberg equation. In this exercise, you'll test whether a soybean population is evolving at a locus with two alleles, C^G and C^Y, that affect chlorophyll production and hence leaf color.

How the Experiment Was Done Students planted soybean seeds and then counted the number of seedlings of each genotype at day 7 and again at day 21. Seedlings of each genotype could be distinguished visually because the C^G and C^Y alleles show incomplete dominance: $C^G C^G$ seedlings have green leaves, $C^G C^Y$ seedlings have green-yellow leaves, and $C^Y C^Y$ seedlings have yellow leaves.

Data from the Experiment

Time (days)	Number of Seedlings			
	Green ($C^G C^G$)	Green-yellow ($C^G C^Y$)	Yellow ($C^Y C^Y$)	Total
7	49	111	56	216
21	47	106	20	173

Interpret the Data
1. Use the observed genotype frequencies from the day 7 data to calculate the frequencies of the C^G allele (*p*) and the C^Y allele (*q*).

2. Next, use the Hardy-Weinberg equation ($p^2 + 2pq + q^2 = 1$) to calculate the expected frequencies of genotypes $C^G C^G$, $C^G C^Y$, and $C^Y C^Y$ for a population in Hardy-Weinberg equilibrium.

3. Calculate the observed frequencies of genotypes $C^G C^G$, $C^G C^Y$, and $C^Y C^Y$ at day 7. Compare these frequencies to the expected frequencies calculated in step 2. Is the seedling population in Hardy-Weinberg equilibrium at day 7, or is evolution occurring? Explain your reasoning and identify which genotypes, if any, appear to be selected for or against.

4. Calculate the observed frequencies of genotypes $C^G C^G$, $C^G C^Y$, and $C^Y C^Y$ at day 21. Compare these frequencies to the expected frequencies calculated in step 2 and the observed frequencies at day 7. Is the seedling population in Hardy-Weinberg equilibrium at day 21, or is evolution occurring? Explain your reasoning and identify which genotypes, if any, appear to be selected for or against.

5. Homozygous $C^Y C^Y$ individuals cannot produce chlorophyll. The ability to photosynthesize becomes more critical as seedlings age and begin to exhaust the supply of food that was stored in the seed from which they emerged. Develop a hypothesis that explains the data for days 7 and 21. Based on this hypothesis, predict how the frequencies of the C^G and C^Y alleles will change beyond day 21.

(MB) A version of this Scientific Skills Exercise can be assigned in MasteringBiology.

Natural Selection

The concept of natural selection is based on differential success in survival and reproduction: Individuals in a population exhibit variations in their heritable traits, and those with traits that are better suited to their environment tend to produce more offspring than those with traits that are not as well suited (see Chapter 22).

In genetic terms, selection results in alleles being passed to the next generation in proportions that differ from those in the present generation. For example, the fruit fly *D. melanogaster* has an allele that confers resistance to several insecticides, including DDT. This allele has a frequency of 0% in laboratory strains of *D. melanogaster* established from flies collected in the wild in the early 1930s, prior to DDT use. However, in strains established from flies collected after 1960 (following 20 or more years of DDT use), the allele frequency is 37%. We can infer that this allele either arose by mutation between 1930 and 1960 or was present in 1930, but very rare. In any case, the rise in frequency of this allele most likely occurred because DDT is a powerful poison that is a strong selective force in exposed fly populations.

As the *D. melanogaster* example suggests, an allele that confers resistance to an insecticide will increase in frequency in a population exposed to that insecticide. Such changes are not coincidental. By consistently favoring some alleles over others, natural selection can cause **adaptive evolution** (evolution that results in a better match between organisms and their environment). We'll explore this process in more detail later in this chapter.

Genetic Drift

If you flip a coin 1,000 times, a result of 700 heads and 300 tails might make you suspicious about that coin. But if you flip a coin only 10 times, an outcome of 7 heads and 3 tails would not be surprising. The smaller the number of coin flips, the more likely it is that chance alone will cause a deviation from the predicted result. (In this case, the prediction is an equal number of heads and tails.) Chance events can also cause allele frequencies to fluctuate unpredictably from one generation to the next, especially in small populations—a process called **genetic drift**.

Figure 23.9 models how genetic drift might affect a small population of our wildflowers. In this example, drift leads to the loss of an allele from the gene pool, but it is a matter of chance that the C^W allele is lost and not the C^R allele. Such unpredictable changes in allele frequencies can be caused by chance events associated with survival and reproduction. Perhaps a large animal such as a moose stepped on the three $C^W C^W$ individuals in generation 2, killing them and increasing the chance that only the C^R allele would be passed to the next generation. Allele frequencies can also be affected by chance events that occur during fertilization. For example, suppose two individuals of genotype $C^R C^W$ had a small number of offspring. By chance alone, every egg and sperm pair that generated offspring could happen to have carried the C^R allele and not the C^W allele.

Certain circumstances can result in genetic drift having a significant impact on a population. Two examples are the founder effect and the bottleneck effect.

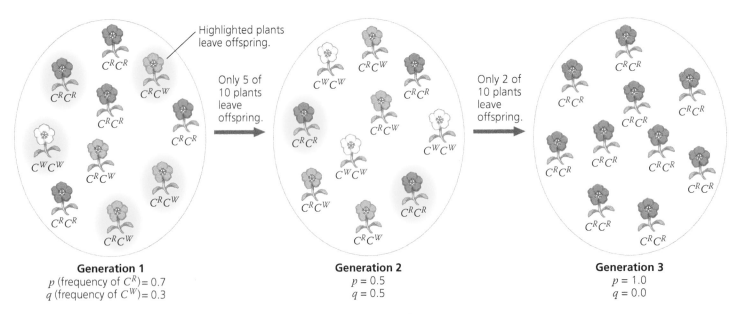

Generation 1
p (frequency of C^R)= 0.7
q (frequency of C^W)= 0.3

Generation 2
$p = 0.5$
$q = 0.5$

Generation 3
$p = 1.0$
$q = 0.0$

▲ **Figure 23.9 Genetic drift.** This small wildflower population has a stable size of ten plants. Suppose that by chance only five plants of generation 1 (those highlighted in yellow) produce fertile offspring. (This could occur, for example, if only those plants happened to grow in a location that provided enough nutrients to support the production of offspring.) Again by chance, only two plants of generation 2 leave fertile offspring. As a result, by chance the frequency of the C^W allele first increases in generation 2, then falls to zero in generation 3.

ANIMATION **BioFlix** Visit the Study Area in **MasteringBiology** for the BioFlix® 3-D Animation on Mechanisms of Evolution.

The Founder Effect

When a few individuals become isolated from a larger population, this smaller group may establish a new population whose gene pool differs from the source population; this is called the **founder effect**. The founder effect might occur, for example, when a few members of a population are blown by a storm to a new island. Genetic drift, in which chance events alter allele frequencies, will occur in such a case if the storm indiscriminately transports some individuals (and their alleles), but not others, from the source population.

The founder effect probably accounts for the relatively high frequency of certain inherited disorders among isolated human populations. For example, in 1814, 15 British colonists founded a settlement on Tristan da Cunha, a group of small islands in the Atlantic Ocean midway between Africa and South America. Apparently, one of the colonists carried a recessive allele for retinitis pigmentosa, a progressive form of blindness that afflicts homozygous individuals. Of the founding colonists' 240 descendants on the island in the late 1960s, 4 had retinitis pigmentosa. The frequency of the allele that causes this disease is ten times higher on Tristan da Cunha than in the populations from which the founders came.

The Bottleneck Effect

A sudden change in the environment, such as a fire or flood, may drastically reduce the size of a population. A severe drop in population size can cause the **bottleneck effect**, so named because the population has passed through a "bottleneck" that reduces its size (**Figure 23.10**). By chance alone, certain alleles may be overrepresented among the survivors, others may be underrepresented, and some may be absent altogether. Ongoing genetic drift is likely to have substantial effects on the gene pool until the population becomes large enough that chance events have less impact. But even if a population that has passed through a bottleneck ultimately

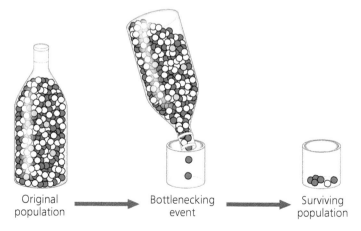

▲ **Figure 23.10 The bottleneck effect.** Shaking just a few marbles through the narrow neck of a bottle is analogous to a drastic reduction in the size of a population. By chance, blue marbles are overrepresented in the surviving population and gold marbles are absent.

recovers in size, it may have low levels of genetic variation for a long period of time—a legacy of the genetic drift that occurred when the population was small.

Human actions sometimes create severe bottlenecks for other species, as the following example shows.

Case Study: Impact of Genetic Drift on the Greater Prairie Chicken

Millions of greater prairie chickens (*Tympanuchus cupido*) once lived on the prairies of Illinois. As these prairies were converted to farmland and other uses during the 19th and 20th centuries, the number of greater prairie chickens plummeted (**Figure 23.11a**). By 1993 fewer than 50 birds remained. These few surviving birds had low levels of genetic variation, and less than 50% of their eggs hatched, compared with much higher hatching rates of the larger populations in Kansas and Nebraska (**Figure 23.11b**).

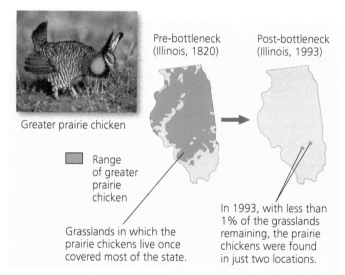

(a) The Illinois population of greater prairie chickens dropped from millions of birds in the 1800s to fewer than 50 birds in 1993.

Location	Population size	Number of alleles per locus	Percentage of eggs hatched
Illinois			
1930–1960s	1,000–25,000	5.2	93
1993	<50	3.7	<50
Kansas, 1998 (no bottleneck)	750,000	5.8	99
Nebraska, 1998 (no bottleneck)	75,000–200,000	5.8	96

(b) In the small Illinois population, genetic drift led to decreases in the number of alleles per locus and the percentage of eggs hatched.

▲ **Figure 23.11 Genetic drift and loss of genetic variation.**

These data suggest that genetic drift during the bottleneck may have led to a loss of genetic variation and an increase in the frequency of harmful alleles. To investigate this hypothesis, researchers extracted DNA from 15 museum specimens of Illinois greater prairie chickens. Of the 15 birds, 10 had been collected in the 1930s, when there were 25,000 greater prairie chickens in Illinois, and 5 had been collected in the 1960s, when there were 1,000 greater prairie chickens in Illinois. By studying the DNA of these specimens, the researchers were able to obtain a minimum, baseline estimate of how much genetic variation was present in the Illinois population *before* the population shrank to extremely low numbers. This baseline estimate is a key piece of information that is not usually available in cases of population bottlenecks.

The researchers surveyed six loci and found that the 1993 population had fewer alleles per locus than the pre-bottleneck Illinois or the current Kansas and Nebraska populations (see Figure 23.11b). Thus, as predicted, drift had reduced the genetic variation of the small 1993 population. Drift may also have increased the frequency of harmful alleles, leading to the low egg-hatching rate. To counteract these negative effects, 271 birds from neighboring states were added to the Illinois population over four years. This strategy succeeded: New alleles entered the population, and the egg-hatching rate improved to over 90%. Overall, studies on the Illinois greater prairie chicken illustrate the powerful effects of genetic drift in small populations and provide hope that in at least some populations, these effects can be reversed.

Effects of Genetic Drift: *A Summary*

The examples we've described highlight four key points:

1. **Genetic drift is significant in small populations.** Chance events can cause an allele to be disproportionately over- or underrepresented in the next generation. Although chance events occur in populations of all sizes, they tend to alter allele frequencies substantially only in small populations.

2. **Genetic drift can cause allele frequencies to change at random.** Because of genetic drift, an allele may increase in frequency one year, then decrease the next; the change from year to year is not predictable. Thus, unlike natural selection, which in a given environment consistently favors some alleles over others, genetic drift causes allele frequencies to change at random over time.

3. **Genetic drift can lead to a loss of genetic variation within populations.** By causing allele frequencies to fluctuate randomly over time, genetic drift can eliminate alleles from a population. Because evolution depends on genetic variation, such losses can influence how effectively a population can adapt to a change in the environment.

4. **Genetic drift can cause harmful alleles to become fixed.** Alleles that are neither harmful nor beneficial can be lost or become fixed by chance through genetic drift. In very small populations, genetic drift can also cause alleles that are slightly harmful to become fixed. When this occurs, the population's survival can be threatened (as in the case of the greater prairie chicken).

Gene Flow

Natural selection and genetic drift are not the only phenomena affecting allele frequencies. Allele frequencies can also change by **gene flow**, the transfer of alleles into or out of a population due to the movement of fertile individuals or their gametes. For example, suppose that near our original hypothetical wildflower population there is another population consisting primarily of white-flowered individuals ($C^W C^W$). Insects carrying pollen from these plants may fly to and pollinate plants in our original population. The introduced C^W alleles would modify our original population's allele frequencies in the next generation. Because alleles are transferred between populations, gene flow tends to reduce the genetic differences between populations. In fact, if it is extensive enough, gene flow can result in two populations combining into a single population with a common gene pool.

Alleles transferred by gene flow can also affect how well populations are adapted to local environmental conditions. Researchers studying the songbird *Parus major* (great tit) on the small Dutch island of Vlieland noted survival differences between two populations on the island. The survival rate of females born in the eastern population is twice that of females born in the central population, regardless of where the females eventually settle and raise offspring (**Figure 23.12**). This finding suggests that females born in the eastern population are better adapted to life on the island than females born in the central population. But field studies also showed that the two populations are connected by high levels of gene flow (mating), which should reduce genetic differences between them. So how can the eastern population be better adapted to life on Vlieland than the central population?

The answer lies in the unequal amounts of gene flow from the mainland. In any given year, 43% of the first-time breeders in the central population are immigrants from the mainland, compared with only 13% in the eastern population. Birds with mainland genotypes survive and reproduce poorly on Vlieland, and in the eastern population, selection reduces the frequency of these genotypes. In the central population, however, gene flow from the mainland is so high that it overwhelms the effects of selection. As a result, females born in the central population have many immigrant genes, reducing the degree to which members of that population are adapted to life on the island. Researchers are currently investigating why gene flow is so much higher in the

Parus major

© 2005 Macmillan Publishers Ltd.

▲ **Figure 23.12 Gene flow and local adaptation.** In *Parus major* populations on Vlieland, the yearly survival rate of females born in the central population is lower than that of females born in the eastern population. Gene flow from the mainland is much higher to the central population than it is to the eastern population, and birds from the mainland are selected against in both populations. These data suggest that gene flow from the mainland has prevented the central population from adapting fully to its local conditions.

central population and why birds with mainland genotypes survive and reproduce poorly on Vlieland.

Gene flow can also transfer alleles that improve the ability of populations to adapt to local conditions. For example, gene flow has resulted in the worldwide spread of several insecticide-resistance alleles in the mosquito *Culex pipiens*, a vector of West Nile virus and other diseases. Each of these alleles has a unique genetic signature that allowed researchers to document that it arose by mutation in only one or a few geographic locations. In their population of origin, these alleles increased because they provided insecticide resistance. These alleles were then transferred to new populations, where again, their frequencies increased as a result of natural selection.

Finally, gene flow has become an increasingly important agent of evolutionary change in human populations. Humans today move much more freely about the world than in the past. As a result, mating is more common between members of populations that previously had very little contact, leading to an exchange of alleles and fewer genetic differences between those populations.

CONCEPT CHECK 23.3

1. In what sense is natural selection more "predictable" than genetic drift?

2. Distinguish genetic drift from gene flow in terms of (a) how they occur and (b) their implications for future genetic variation in a population.

3. **WHAT IF?** Suppose two plant populations exchange pollen and seeds. In one population, individuals of genotype *AA* are most common (9,000 *AA*, 900 *Aa*, 100 *aa*), while the opposite is true in the other population (100 *AA*, 900 *Aa*, 9,000 *aa*). If neither allele has a selective advantage, what will happen over time to the allele and genotype frequencies of these populations?

For suggested answers, see Appendix A.

CONCEPT 23.4

Natural selection is the only mechanism that consistently causes adaptive evolution

Evolution by natural selection is a blend of chance and "sorting": chance in the creation of new genetic variations (as in mutation) and sorting as natural selection favors some alleles over others. Because of this favoring process, the outcome of natural selection is *not* random. Instead, natural selection consistently increases the frequencies of alleles that provide reproductive advantage, thus leading to adaptive evolution.

Natural Selection: *A Closer Look*

In examining how natural selection brings about adaptive evolution, we'll begin with the concept of relative fitness and the different ways that an organism's phenotype is subject to natural selection.

Relative Fitness

The phrases "struggle for existence" and "survival of the fittest" are commonly used to describe natural selection, but these expressions are misleading if taken to mean direct competitive contests among individuals. There *are* animal species in which individuals, usually the males, lock horns or otherwise do combat to determine mating privilege. But reproductive success is generally more subtle and depends on many factors besides outright battle. For example, a barnacle that is more efficient at collecting food than its neighbors may have greater stores of energy and hence be able to produce a larger number of eggs. A moth may have more offspring than other moths in the same population because its body colors more effectively conceal it from predators, improving its chance of surviving long enough to produce more offspring. These examples illustrate how in a given environment, certain traits can lead to greater **relative fitness**: the contribution an individual makes to the gene pool of the next generation *relative to* the contributions of other individuals.

Although we often refer to the relative fitness of a genotype, remember that the entity that is subjected to natural selection is the whole organism, not the underlying genotype. Thus, selection acts more directly on the phenotype than on the genotype; it acts on the genotype indirectly, via how the genotype affects the phenotype.

Directional, Disruptive, and Stabilizing Selection

Natural selection can alter the frequency distribution of heritable traits in three ways, depending on which phenotypes in a population are favored. These three modes of selection are called directional selection, disruptive selection, and stabilizing selection.

Directional selection occurs when conditions favor individuals exhibiting one extreme of a phenotypic range, thereby shifting a population's frequency curve for the phenotypic character in one direction or the other **(Figure 23.13a)**.

Directional selection is common when a population's environment changes or when members of a population migrate to a new (and different) habitat. For instance, an increase in the relative abundance of large seeds over small seeds led to an increase in beak depth in a population of Galápagos finches (see Figure 23.2).

Disruptive selection **(Figure 23.13b)** occurs when conditions favor individuals at both extremes of a phenotypic range over individuals with intermediate phenotypes. One example is a population of black-bellied seedcracker finches in Cameroon whose members display two distinctly different beak sizes. Small-billed birds feed mainly on soft seeds, whereas large-billed birds specialize in cracking hard seeds. It appears that birds with intermediate-sized bills are relatively inefficient at cracking both types of seeds and thus have lower relative fitness.

Stabilizing selection **(Figure 23.13c)** acts against both extreme phenotypes and favors intermediate variants. This mode of selection reduces variation and tends to maintain the status quo for a particular phenotypic character. For example, the birth weights of most human babies lie in the range of 3–4 kg (6.6–8.8 pounds); babies who are either much smaller or much larger suffer higher rates of mortality.

Regardless of the mode of selection, however, the basic mechanism remains the same. Selection favors individuals whose heritable phenotypic traits provide higher reproductive success than do the traits of other individuals.

▶ **Figure 23.13 Modes of selection.** These cases describe three ways in which a hypothetical deer mouse population with heritable variation in fur coloration from light to dark might evolve. The graphs show how the frequencies of individuals with different fur colors change over time. The large white arrows symbolize selective pressures against certain phenotypes.

MAKE CONNECTIONS *Review Figure 22.13. Which mode of selection has occurred in soapberry bug populations that feed on the introduced goldenrain tree? Explain.*

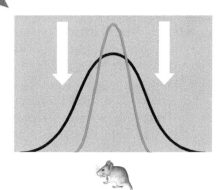

(a) Directional selection shifts the overall makeup of the population by favoring variants that are at one extreme of the distribution. In this case, lighter mice are selected against because they live among dark rocks, making it harder for them to hide from predators.

(b) Disruptive selection favors variants at both ends of the distribution. These mice have colonized a patchy habitat made up of light and dark rocks, with the result that mice of an intermediate color are selected against.

(c) Stabilizing selection removes extreme variants from the population and preserves intermediate types. If the environment consists of rocks of an intermediate color, both light and dark mice will be selected against.

The Key Role of Natural Selection in Adaptive Evolution

The adaptations of organisms include many striking examples. Certain octopuses, for example, have the ability to change color rapidly, enabling them to blend into different backgrounds. Another example is the remarkable jaws of snakes **(Figure 23.14)**, which allow them to swallow prey much larger than their own head (a feat analogous to a person swallowing a whole watermelon). Other adaptations, such as a version of an enzyme that shows improved function in cold environments, may be less visually dramatic but just as important for survival and reproduction.

Such adaptations can arise gradually over time as natural selection increases the frequencies of alleles that enhance survival and reproduction. As the proportion of individuals that have favorable traits increases, the match between a species and its environment improves; that is, adaptive evolution occurs. However, the physical and biological components of an organism's environment may change over time. As a result, what constitutes a "good match" between an organism and its environment can be a moving target, making adaptive evolution a continuous, dynamic process.

And what about genetic drift and gene flow? Both can, in fact, increase the frequencies of alleles that improve the match between organisms and their environment, but neither does so consistently. Genetic drift can cause the frequency of a slightly beneficial allele to increase, but it also can cause the frequency of such an allele to decrease.

Similarly, gene flow may introduce alleles that are advantageous or ones that are disadvantageous. Natural selection is the only evolutionary mechanism that consistently leads to adaptive evolution.

Sexual Selection

Charles Darwin was the first to explore the implications of **sexual selection**, a form of natural selection in which individuals with certain inherited characteristics are more likely than other individuals to obtain mates. Sexual selection can result in **sexual dimorphism**, a difference in secondary sexual characteristics between males and females of the same species **(Figure 23.15)**. These distinctions include differences in size, color, ornamentation, and behavior.

How does sexual selection operate? There are several ways. In **intrasexual selection**, meaning selection within the same sex, individuals of one sex compete directly for mates of the opposite sex. In many species, intrasexual selection occurs among males. For example, a single male may patrol a group of females and prevent other males from mating with them. The patrolling male may defend his status by defeating smaller, weaker, or less fierce males in combat. More often, this male is the psychological victor in ritualized displays that discourage would-be competitors but do not risk injury that would reduce his own fitness (see Figure 51.16). Intrasexual selection also occurs among females in a variety of species, including ring-tailed lemurs and broad-nosed pipefish.

In **intersexual selection**, also called *mate choice*, individuals of one sex (usually the females) are choosy in selecting their mates from the other sex. In many cases, the female's choice depends on the showiness of the male's appearance or behavior (see Figure 23.15). What intrigued Darwin about mate choice is that male showiness may not seem adaptive in any other way and may in fact pose some risk. For

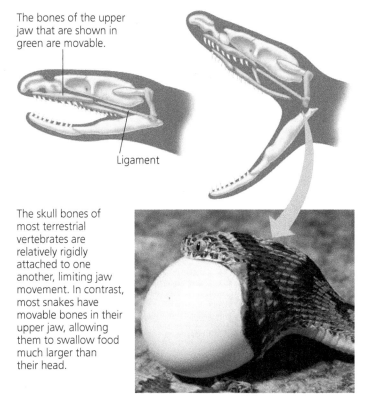

The bones of the upper jaw that are shown in green are movable.

Ligament

The skull bones of most terrestrial vertebrates are relatively rigidly attached to one another, limiting jaw movement. In contrast, most snakes have movable bones in their upper jaw, allowing them to swallow food much larger than their head.

▲ Figure 23.14 **Movable jaw bones in snakes.**

▲ Figure 23.15 **Sexual dimorphism and sexual selection.** Peacocks (above left) and peahens (above right) show extreme sexual dimorphism. There is intrasexual selection between competing males, followed by intersexual selection when the females choose among the showiest males.

example, bright plumage may make male birds more visible to predators. But if such characteristics help a male gain a mate, and if this benefit outweighs the risk from predation, then both the bright plumage and the female preference for it will be reinforced because they enhance overall reproductive success.

How do female preferences for certain male characteristics evolve in the first place? One hypothesis is that females prefer male traits that are correlated with "good genes." If the trait preferred by females is indicative of a male's overall genetic quality, both the male trait and female preference for it should increase in frequency. **Figure 23.16** describes one experiment testing this hypothesis in gray tree frogs.

Other researchers have shown that in several bird species, the traits preferred by females are related to overall male health. Here, too, female preference appears to be based on traits that reflect "good genes," in this case alleles indicative of a robust immune system.

Balancing Selection

As we've seen, genetic variation is often found at loci affected by selection. What prevents natural selection from reducing the variation at those loci by culling all unfavorable alleles? As mentioned earlier, in diploid organisms, many unfavorable recessive alleles persist because they are hidden from selection when in heterozygous individuals. In addition, selection itself may preserve variation at some loci, thus maintaining two or more forms in a population. Known as **balancing selection**, this type of selection includes heterozygote advantage and frequency-dependent selection.

Heterozygote Advantage

If individuals who are heterozygous at a particular locus have greater fitness than do both kinds of homozygotes, they exhibit **heterozygote advantage**. In such a case, natural selection tends to maintain two or more alleles at that locus. Note that heterozygote advantage is defined in terms of *genotype*, not phenotype. Thus, whether heterozygote advantage represents stabilizing or directional selection depends on the relationship between the genotype and the phenotype. For example, if the phenotype of a heterozygote is intermediate to the phenotypes of both homozygotes, heterozygote advantage is a form of stabilizing selection.

An example of heterozygote advantage occurs at the locus in humans that codes for the β polypeptide subunit of hemoglobin, the oxygen-carrying protein of red blood cells. In homozygous individuals, a certain recessive allele at that locus causes sickle-cell disease. The red blood cells of people with sickle-cell disease become distorted in shape, or *sickled*, under low-oxygen conditions (see Figure 5.19), as occurs in the capillaries. These sickled cells can clump together and block the flow of blood in the capillaries, resulting in serious

▼ Figure 23.16 | Inquiry

Do females select mates based on traits indicative of "good genes"?

Experiment Female gray tree frogs (*Hyla versicolor*) prefer to mate with males that give long mating calls. Allison Welch and colleagues, at the University of Missouri, tested whether the genetic makeup of long-calling (LC) males is superior to that of short-calling (SC) males. The researchers fertilized half the eggs of each female with sperm from an LC male and fertilized the remaining eggs with sperm from an SC male. In two separate experiments (one in 1995, the other in 1996), the resulting half-sibling offspring were raised in a common environment and their survival and growth were monitored.

Results

Offspring Performance	1995	1996
Larval survival	LC better	NSD
Larval growth	NSD	LC better
Time to metamorphosis	LC better (shorter)	LC better (shorter)

NSD = no significant difference; LC better = offspring of LC males superior to offspring of SC males.

Conclusion Because offspring fathered by an LC male outperformed their half-siblings fathered by an SC male, the team concluded that the duration of a male's mating call is indicative of the male's overall genetic quality. This result supports the hypothesis that female mate choice can be based on a trait that indicates whether the male has "good genes."

Source: A. M. Welch et al., Call duration as an indicator of genetic quality in male gray tree frogs, *Science* 280:1928–1930 (1998).

Inquiry in Action *Read and analyze the original paper in* Inquiry in Action: Interpreting Scientific Papers.

WHAT IF? *Why did the researchers split each female frog's eggs into two batches for fertilization by different males? Why didn't they mate each female with a single male frog?*

damage to organs such as the kidney, heart, and brain. Although some red blood cells become sickled in heterozygotes, not enough become sickled to cause sickle-cell disease.

Heterozygotes for the sickle-cell allele are protected against the most severe effects of malaria, a disease caused by a parasite that infects red blood cells (see Figure 28.16). One reason for this partial protection is that the body destroys sickled red blood cells rapidly, killing the parasites they harbor. Protection against malaria is important in tropical regions where the disease is a major killer. In such regions, selection favors heterozygotes over homozygous dominant individuals, who are more vulnerable to the effects of malaria, and also over homozygous recessive individuals, who develop sickle-cell disease. As we explore further in **Figure 23.17**, on the next two pages, these selective pressures have caused the frequency of the sickle-cell allele to reach relatively high levels in areas where the malaria parasite is common.

Frequency-Dependent Selection

In **frequency-dependent selection**, the fitness of a phenotype depends on how common it is in the population. Consider the scale-eating fish (*Perissodus microlepis*) of Lake Tanganyika, in Africa. These fish attack other fish from behind, darting in to remove a few scales from the flank of their prey. Of interest here is a peculiar feature of the scale-eating fish: Some are "left-mouthed" and some are "right-mouthed." Simple Mendelian inheritance determines these phenotypes, with the right-mouthed allele being dominant to the left-mouthed allele. Because their mouth twists to the left, left-mouthed fish always attack their prey's right flank (**Figure 23.18**). (To see why, twist your lower jaw and lips to the left and imagine trying to take a bite from the left side of a fish, approaching it from behind.) Similarly, right-mouthed fish always attack from the left. Prey species guard against attack from whatever phenotype of scale-eating fish is most common in the lake. Thus, from year to year, selection favors whichever mouth phenotype is least common. As a result, the frequency of left- and right-mouthed fish oscillates over time, and balancing selection (due to frequency dependence) keeps the frequency of each phenotype close to 50%.

Why Natural Selection Cannot Fashion Perfect Organisms

Though natural selection leads to adaptation, nature abounds with examples of organisms that are less than ideally suited for their lifestyles. There are several reasons why.

1. **Selection can act only on existing variations.** Natural selection favors only the fittest phenotypes among those currently in the population, which may not be the ideal traits. New advantageous alleles do not arise on demand.

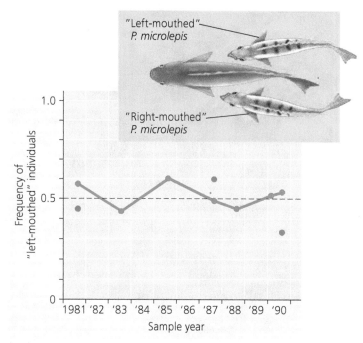

▲ **Figure 23.18 Frequency-dependent selection.** In a population of the scale-eating fish, *Perissodus microlepis*, the frequency of left-mouthed individuals (red data points) rises and falls in a regular manner. The frequency of left-mouthed individuals among adults that reproduced was also recorded in three sample years (green data points).

INTERPRET THE DATA *For 1981, 1987, and 1990, compare the frequency of left-mouthed individuals among breeding adults to the frequency of left-mouthed individuals in the entire population. What do the data suggest about when natural selection favors left-mouthed individuals over right-mouthed individuals (or vice versa)? Explain.*

2. **Evolution is limited by historical constraints.** Each species has a legacy of descent with modification from ancestral forms. Evolution does not scrap the ancestral anatomy and build each new complex structure from scratch; rather, evolution co-opts existing structures and adapts them to new situations. We could imagine that if a terrestrial animal were to adapt to an environment in which flight would be advantageous, it might be best just to grow an extra pair of limbs that would serve as wings. However, evolution does not work this way; instead, it operates on the traits an organism already has. Thus, in birds and bats, an existing pair of limbs took on new functions for flight as these organisms evolved from nonflying ancestors.

3. **Adaptations are often compromises.** Each organism must do many different things. A seal spends part of its time on rocks; it could probably walk better if it had legs instead of flippers, but then it would not swim nearly as well. We humans owe much of our versatility and athleticism to our prehensile hands and flexible limbs, but these also make us prone to sprains, torn ligaments, and dislocations: Structural reinforcement has been compromised for agility.

MAKE CONNECTIONS

The Sickle-Cell Allele

This child has sickle-cell disease, a genetic disorder that strikes individuals that have two copies of the sickle-cell allele. This allele causes an abnormality in the structure and function of hemoglobin, the oxygen-carrying protein in red blood cells. Although sickle-cell disease is lethal if not treated, in some regions the sickle-cell allele can reach frequencies as high as 15–20%. How can such a harmful allele be so common?

Events at the Molecular Level

- Due to a point mutation, the sickle-cell allele differs from the wild-type allele by a single nucleotide. *See Figure 17.25.*
- The resulting change in one amino acid leads to hydrophobic interactions between the sickle-cell hemoglobin proteins under low-oxygen conditions.
- As a result, the sickle-cell proteins bind to each other in chains that together form a fiber.

Consequences for Cells

- The abnormal hemoglobin fibers distort the red blood cell into a sickle shape under low-oxygen conditions, such as those found in blood vessels returning to the heart.

Sickle-cell allele on chromosome

Template strand

An adenine replaces a thymine in the template strand of the sickle-cell allele, changing one codon in the mRNA produced during transcription. This change causes an amino-acid change in sickle-cell hemoglobin: A valine replaces a glutamic acid at one position. *See Figure 5.19.*

Sickle-cell hemoglobin

Fiber

Low-oxygen conditions

Sickled red blood cell

Wild-type allele

Normal hemoglobin (does not aggregate into fibers)

Normal red blood cell

Infected mosquitos spread malaria when they bite people. *See Figure 28.16.*

Evolution in Populations

- Homozygotes with two sickle-cell alleles are strongly selected against because of mortality caused by sickle-cell disease. In contrast, heterozygotes experience few harmful effects from sickling yet are more likely to survive malaria than are homozygotes.
- In regions where malaria is common, the net effect of these opposing selective forces is heterozygote advantage. This has caused evolutionary change in populations—the products of which are the areas of relatively high frequencies of the sickle-cell allele shown in the map below.

Effects on Individual Organisms

- The formation of sickled red blood cells causes homozygotes with two copies of the sickle-cell allele to have sickle-cell disease.
- Some sickling also occurs in heterozygotes, but not enough to cause the disease; they have sickle-cell trait. *See Figure 14.17.*

The sickled blood cells of a homozygote block small blood vessels, causing great pain and damage to organs such as the heart, kidney, and brain.

Normal red blood cells are flexible and are able to flow freely through small blood vessels.

Key
Frequencies of the sickle-cell allele

- 3.0–6.0%
- 6.0–9.0%
- 9.0–12.0%
- 12.0–15.0%
- >15.0%

Distribution of malaria caused by *Plasmodium falciparum* (a parasitic unicellular eukaryote)

MAKE CONNECTIONS *In a region free of malaria, would individuals who are heterozygous for the sickle-cell allele be selected for or selected against? Explain.*

4. Chance, natural selection, and the environment interact. Chance events can affect the subsequent evolutionary history of populations. For instance, when a storm blows insects or birds hundreds of kilometers over an ocean to an island, the wind does not necessarily transport those individuals that are best suited to the new environment. Thus, not all alleles present in the founding population's gene pool are better suited to the new environment than the alleles that are "left behind." In addition, the environment at a particular location may change unpredictably from year to year, again limiting the extent to which adaptive evolution results in a close match between the organism and current environmental conditions.

With these four constraints, evolution does not tend to craft perfect organisms. Natural selection operates on a "better than" basis. We can, in fact, see evidence for evolution in the many imperfections of the organisms it produces.

CONCEPT CHECK **23.4**

1. What is the relative fitness of a sterile mule? Explain.
2. Explain why natural selection is the only evolutionary mechanism that consistently leads to adaptive evolution.
3. **WHAT IF?** Consider a population in which heterozygotes at a certain locus have an extreme phenotype (such as being larger than homozygotes) that confers a selective advantage. Does such a situation represent directional, disruptive, or stabilizing selection? Explain.

For suggested answers, see Appendix A.

23 Chapter Review

SUMMARY OF KEY CONCEPTS

CONCEPT 23.1

Genetic variation makes evolution possible (pp. 481–483)

- **Genetic variation** refers to genetic differences among individuals within a population.
- The nucleotide differences that provide the basis of genetic variation originate when mutation and gene duplication produce new alleles and new genes. New genetic variants are produced rapidly in organisms with short generation times. In sexually reproducing organisms, most of the genetic differences among individuals result from crossing over, the independent assortment of chromosomes, and fertilization

> ? *Typically, most of the nucleotide variability that occurs within a genetic locus does not affect the phenotype. Explain why.*

CONCEPT 23.2

The Hardy-Weinberg equation can be used to test whether a population is evolving (pp. 483–487)

- A **population**, a localized group of organisms belonging to one species, is united by its **gene pool**, the aggregate of all the alleles in the population.
- For a population in **Hardy-Weinberg equilibrium**, the allele and genotype frequencies will remain constant if the population is large, mating is random, mutation is negligible, there is no gene flow, and there is no natural selection. For such a population, if p and q represent the frequencies of the only two possible alleles at a particular locus, then p^2 is the frequency of one kind of homozygote, q^2 is the frequency of the other kind of homozygote, and $2pq$ is the frequency of the heterozygous genotype.

> ? *Is it circular reasoning to calculate p and q from observed genotype frequencies and then use those values of p and q to test if the population is in Hardy-Weinberg equilibrium? Explain your answer.*

CONCEPT 23.3

Natural selection, genetic drift, and gene flow can alter allele frequencies in a population (pp. 487–491)

- In natural selection, individuals that have certain inherited traits tend to survive and reproduce at higher rates than other individuals *because of* those traits.
- In **genetic drift**, chance fluctuations in allele frequencies over generations tend to reduce genetic variation.
- **Gene flow**, the transfer of alleles between populations, tends to reduce genetic differences between populations over time.

> ? *Would two small, geographically isolated populations in very different environments be likely to evolve in similar ways? Explain.*

CONCEPT 23.4

Natural selection is the only mechanism that consistently causes adaptive evolution (pp. 491–498)

- One organism has greater **relative fitness** than another organism if it leaves more fertile descendants. The modes of natural selection differ in their effect on phenotype:

Original population   Evolved population

Directional selection   Disruptive selection   Stabilizing selection

- Unlike genetic drift and gene flow, natural selection consistently improves the match between organisms and their environment.
- **Sexual selection** influences change in secondary sex characteristics that can give individuals advantages in mating.
- **Balancing selection** occurs when natural selection maintains two or more forms in a population.

- There are constraints to evolution: Natural selection can act only on available variation; structures result from modified ancestral anatomy; adaptations are often compromises; and chance, natural selection, and the environment interact.

? *How might secondary sex characteristics differ between males and females in a species in which females compete for mates?*

TEST YOUR UNDERSTANDING

LEVEL 1: KNOWLEDGE/COMPREHENSION

1. Natural selection changes allele frequencies because some _____ survive and reproduce better than others.
   a. alleles   b. loci   c. species   d. individuals

2. No two people are genetically identical, except for identical twins. The main source of genetic variation among humans is
   a. new mutations that occurred in the preceding generation.
   b. genetic drift.
   c. the reshuffling of alleles in sexual reproduction.
   d. environmental effects.

LEVEL 2: APPLICATION/ANALYSIS

3. If the nucleotide variability of a locus equals 0%, what is the gene variability and number of alleles at that locus?
   a. gene variability = 0%; number of alleles = 0
   b. gene variability = 0%; number of alleles = 1
   c. gene variability = 0%; number of alleles = 2
   d. gene variability > 0%; number of alleles = 2

4. There are 25 individuals in population 1, all with genotype *AA*, and there are 40 individuals in population 2, all with genotype *aa*. Assume that these populations are located far from each other and that their environmental conditions are very similar. Based on the information given here, the observed genetic variation most likely resulted from
   a. genetic drift.   c. nonrandom mating.
   b. gene flow.   d. directional selection.

5. A fruit fly population has a gene with two alleles, *A1* and *A2*. Tests show that 70% of the gametes produced in the population contain the *A1* allele. If the population is in Hardy-Weinberg equilibrium, what proportion of the flies carry both *A1* and *A2*?
   a. 0.7   b. 0.49   c. 0.42   d. 0.21

LEVEL 3: SYNTHESIS/EVALUATION

6. **EVOLUTION CONNECTION**
   Using at least two examples, explain how the process of evolution is revealed by the imperfections of living organisms.

7. **SCIENTIFIC INQUIRY**
   INTERPRET THE DATA Researchers studied genetic variation in the marine mussel *Mytilus edulis* around Long Island, New York. They measured the frequency of a particular allele (*lap⁹⁴*) for an enzyme involved in regulating the mussel's internal saltwater balance. The researchers presented their data as a series of pie charts linked to sampling sites within Long Island Sound, where the salinity is highly variable, and along the coast of the open ocean, where salinity is constant.
   Create a data table for the 11 sampling sites by estimating the frequency of *lap⁹⁴* from the pie charts. (*Hint*: Think of each pie chart as a clock face to help you estimate the proportion of the shaded area.) Then graph the frequencies for sites 1–8 to show how the frequency of this allele changes with increasing salinity in Long Island Sound (from southwest to northeast). How do the data from sites 9–11 compare with the data from the sites within the Sound? Construct a hypothesis that explains the patterns you observe in the data and that accounts for the two observations listed below the map.

Salinity increases toward the open ocean

Data from R. K. Koehn and T. J. Hilbish, The adaptive importance of genetic variation, *American Scientist* 75:134–141 (1987).

(1) The *lap⁹⁴* allele helps mussels maintain osmotic balance in water with a high salt concentration but is costly to use in less salty water; and (2) mussels produce larvae that can disperse long distances before they settle on rocks and grow into adults.

8. **WRITE ABOUT A THEME: ORGANIZATION**
   Heterozygotes at the sickle-cell locus produce both normal and abnormal (sickle-cell) hemoglobin (see Concept 14.4). When hemoglobin molecules are packed into a heterozygote's red blood cells, some cells receive relatively large quantities of abnormal hemoglobin, making these cells prone to sickling. In a short essay (approximately 100–150 words), explain how these molecular and cellular events lead to emergent properties at the individual and population levels of biological organization.

9. **SYNTHESIZE YOUR KNOWLEDGE**

This kettle lake formed 14,000 years ago when a glacier that covered the surrounding area melted. Initially devoid of animal life, over time the lake was colonized by invertebrates and other animals. Hypothesize how mutation, natural selection, genetic drift, and gene flow may have affected populations that colonized the lake.

For suggested answers, see Appendix A.

MasteringBiology®

Students Go to **MasteringBiology** for assignments, the eText, and the Study Area with practice tests, animations, and activities.

Instructors Go to **MasteringBiology** for automatically graded tutorials and questions that you can assign to your students, plus Instructor Resources.

24

The Origin of Species

▲ Figure 24.1 **How did this flightless bird come to live on the isolated Galápagos Islands?**

That "Mystery of Mysteries"

When Darwin came to the Galápagos Islands, he noted that these volcanic islands were teeming with plants and animals found nowhere else in the world (Figure 24.1). Later he realized that these species had formed relatively recently. He wrote in his diary: "Both in space and time, we seem to be brought somewhat near to that great fact—that mystery of mysteries—the first appearance of new beings on this Earth."

The "mystery of mysteries" that captivated Darwin is **speciation**, the process by which one species splits into two or more species. Speciation fascinated Darwin (and many biologists since) because it has produced the tremendous diversity of life, repeatedly yielding new species that differ from existing ones. Speciation also helps to explain the many features that organisms share (the unity of life). When one species splits into two, the species that result share many characteristics because they are descended from this common ancestor. At the DNA sequence level, for example, such similarities indicate that the flightless cormorant (*Phalacrocorax harrisi*) in Figure 24.1 is closely related to flying cormorants found in the Americas. This suggests that the flightless cormorant originated from an ancestral cormorant species that flew from the mainland to the Galápagos.

◄ **Galápagos giant tortoise, another species unique to the islands**

Speciation also forms a conceptual bridge between **microevolution**, changes over time in allele frequencies in a population, and **macroevolution**, the broad pattern of evolution above the species level. An example of macroevolutionary change is the origin of new groups of organisms, such as mammals or flowering plants, through a series of speciation events. We examined microevolutionary mechanisms in Chapter 23, and we'll turn to macroevolution in Chapter 25. In this chapter, we'll explore the "bridge" between microevolution and macroevolution—the mechanisms by which new species originate from existing ones. First, let's establish what we actually mean by a "species."

CONCEPT 24.1

The biological species concept emphasizes reproductive isolation

The word *species* is Latin for "kind" or "appearance." In daily life, we commonly distinguish between various "kinds" of organisms—dogs and cats, for instance—from differences in their appearance. But are organisms truly divided into the discrete units we call species, or is this classification an arbitrary attempt to impose order on the natural world? To answer this question, biologists compare not only the morphology (body form) of different groups of organisms but also less obvious differences in physiology, biochemistry, and DNA sequences. The results generally confirm that morphologically distinct species are indeed discrete groups, differing in many ways besides their body forms.

The Biological Species Concept

The primary definition of species used in this textbook is the **biological species concept**. According to this concept, a **species** is a group of populations whose members have the potential to interbreed in nature and produce viable, fertile offspring—but do not produce viable, fertile offspring with members of other such groups (Figure 24.2). Thus, the members of a biological species are united by being reproductively compatible, at least potentially. All human beings, for example, belong to the same species. A businesswoman in Manhattan may be unlikely to meet a dairy farmer in Mongolia, but if the two should happen to meet and mate, they could have viable babies who develop into fertile adults. In contrast, humans and chimpanzees remain distinct biological species even where they live in the same region, because many factors keep them from interbreeding and producing fertile offspring.

What holds the gene pool of a species together, causing its members to resemble each other more than they resemble members of other species? Recall the evolutionary mechanism of *gene flow*, the transfer of alleles between populations (see Chapter 23). Typically, gene flow occurs

(a) Similarity between different species. The eastern meadowlark (*Sturnella magna*, left) and the western meadowlark (*Sturnella neglecta*, right) have similar body shapes and colorations. Nevertheless, they are distinct biological species because their songs and other behaviors are different enough to prevent interbreeding should they meet in the wild.

(b) Diversity within a species. Although diverse in appearance, all humans belong to a single biological species (*Homo sapiens*), defined by our capacity to interbreed successfully.

▲ **Figure 24.2 The biological species concept is based on the potential to interbreed, not on physical similarity.**

between the different populations of a species. This ongoing exchange of alleles tends to hold the populations together genetically. As we'll explore in this chapter, the absence of gene flow is important in the formation of new species.

Reproductive Isolation

Because biological species are defined in terms of reproductive compatibility, the formation of a new species hinges on **reproductive isolation**—the existence of biological factors (barriers) that impede members of two species from interbreeding and producing viable, fertile offspring. Such barriers block gene flow between the species and limit the formation of **hybrids**, offspring that result from an interspecific mating. Although a single barrier may not prevent all gene flow, a combination of several barriers can effectively isolate a species' gene pool.

Clearly, a fly cannot mate with a frog or a fern, but the reproductive barriers between more closely related species are not so obvious. As described in **Figure 24.3**, these barriers

▼ Figure 24.3
Exploring Reproductive Barriers

Prezygotic barriers impede mating or hinder fertilization if mating does occur

Habitat Isolation	Temporal Isolation	Behavioral Isolation	Mechanical Isolation

Individuals of different species → ⊘ ⊘ ⊘ **MATING ATTEMPT** ⊘

Two species that occupy different habitats within the same area may encounter each other rarely, if at all, even though they are not isolated by obvious physical barriers, such as mountain ranges.

Species that breed during different times of the day, different seasons, or different years cannot mix their gametes.

Courtship rituals that attract mates and other behaviors unique to a species are effective reproductive barriers, even between closely related species. Such behavioral rituals enable mate recognition—a way to identify potential mates of the same species.

Mating is attempted, but morphological differences prevent its successful completion.

Example: Two species of garter snakes in the genus *Thamnophis* occur in the same geographic areas, but one lives mainly in water (a) while the other is primarily terrestrial (b).

Example: In North America, the geographic ranges of the eastern spotted skunk (*Spilogale putorius*) (c) and the western spotted skunk (*Spilogale gracilis*) (d) overlap, but *S. putorius* mates in late winter and *S. gracilis* mates in late summer.

Example: Blue-footed boobies, inhabitants of the Galápagos, mate only after a courtship display unique to their species. Part of the "script" calls for the male to high-step (e), a behavior that calls the female's attention to his bright blue feet.

Example: The shells of two species of snails in the genus *Bradybaena* spiral in different directions: Moving inward to the center, one spirals in a counterclockwise direction (f, left), the other in a clockwise direction (f, right). As a result, the snails' genital openings (indicated by arrows) are not aligned, and mating cannot be completed.

(a)

(b)

(c)

(d)

(e)

(f)

| Gametic Isolation | Reduced Hybrid Viability | Reduced Hybrid Fertility | Hybrid Breakdown |

FERTILIZATION → VIABLE, FERTILE OFFSPRING

Sperm of one species may not be able to fertilize the eggs of another species. For instance, sperm may not be able to survive in the reproductive tract of females of the other species, or biochemical mechanisms may prevent the sperm from penetrating the membrane surrounding the other species' eggs.

Example: Gametic isolation separates certain closely related species of aquatic animals, such as sea urchins (g). Sea urchins release their sperm and eggs into the surrounding water, where they fuse and form zygotes. It is difficult for gametes of different species, such as the red and purple urchins shown here, to fuse because proteins on the surfaces of the eggs and sperm bind very poorly to each other.

The genes of different parent species may interact in ways that impair the hybrid's development or survival in its environment.

Example: Some salamander subspecies of the genus *Ensatina* live in the same regions and habitats, where they may occasionally hybridize. But most of the hybrids do not complete development, and those that do are frail (h).

Even if hybrids are vigorous, they may be sterile. If the chromosomes of the two parent species differ in number or structure, meiosis in the hybrids may fail to produce normal gametes. Since the infertile hybrids cannot produce offspring when they mate with either parent species, genes cannot flow freely between the species.

Example: The hybrid offspring of a male donkey (i) and a female horse (j) is a mule (k), which is robust but sterile. A "hinny" (not shown), the offspring of a female donkey and a male horse, is also sterile.

(i)

Some first-generation hybrids are viable and fertile, but when they mate with one another or with either parent species, offspring of the next generation are feeble or sterile.

Example: Strains of cultivated rice have accumulated different mutant recessive alleles at two loci in the course of their divergence from a common ancestor. Hybrids between them are vigorous and fertile (l, left and right), but plants in the next generation that carry too many of these recessive alleles are small and sterile (l, center). Although these rice strains are not yet considered different species, they have begun to be separated by postzygotic barriers.

(g)

(h)

(j)

(k)

(l)

can be classified according to whether they contribute to re-productive isolation before or after fertilization. **Prezygotic barriers** ("before the zygote") block fertilization from oc-curring. Such barriers typically act in one of three ways: by impeding members of different species from attempting to mate, by preventing an attempted mating from being com-pleted successfully, or by hindering fertilization if mating is completed successfully. If a sperm cell from one species overcomes prezygotic barriers and fertilizes an ovum from another species, a variety of **postzygotic barriers** ("after the zygote") may contribute to reproductive isolation after the hybrid zygote is formed. Developmental errors may reduce survival among hybrid embryos. Or problems after birth may cause hybrids to be infertile or decrease their chance of surviving long enough to reproduce.

Limitations of the Biological Species Concept

One strength of the biological species concept is that it di-rects our attention to a way by which speciation can occur: by the evolution of reproductive isolation. However, the number of species to which this concept can be usefully ap-plied is limited. There is, for example, no way to evaluate the reproductive isolation of fossils. The biological species concept also does not apply to organisms that reproduce asexually all or most of the time, such as prokaryotes. (Many prokaryotes do transfer genes among themselves, as we will discuss in Chapter 27, but this is not part of their reproduc-tive process.) Furthermore, in the biological species concept, species are designated by the *absence* of gene flow. But there are many pairs of species that are morphologically and eco-logically distinct, and yet gene flow occurs between them. An example is the grizzly bear (*Ursus arctos*) and polar bear (*Ursus maritimus*), whose hybrid offspring have been dubbed "grolar bears" **(Figure 24.4)**. As we'll discuss, natu-ral selection can cause such species to remain distinct even though some gene flow occurs between them. Because of the limitations to the biological species concept, alternative species concepts are useful in certain situations.

Other Definitions of Species

While the biological species concept emphasizes the *separ-ateness* of species from one another due to reproductive bar-riers, several other definitions emphasize the *unity within* a species. For example, the **morphological species concept** distinguishes a species by body shape and other structural features. The morphological species concept can be applied to asexual and sexual organisms, and it can be useful even without information on the extent of gene flow. In practice, scientists often distinguish species using morphological criteria. A disadvantage of this approach, however, is that it relies on subjective criteria; researchers may disagree on which structural features distinguish a species.

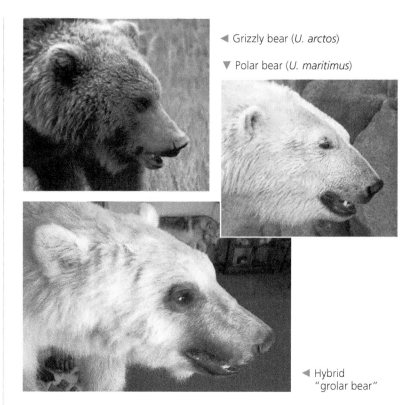

◄ Grizzly bear (*U. arctos*)

▼ Polar bear (*U. maritimus*)

◄ Hybrid "grolar bear"

▲ **Figure 24.4 Hybridization between two species of bears in the genus *Ursus*.**

The **ecological species concept** defines a species in terms of its ecological niche, the sum of how members of the species interact with the nonliving and living parts of their environment (see Concept 54.1). For example, two spe-cies of oak trees might differ in their size or in their ability to tolerate dry conditions, yet still occasionally interbreed. Because they occupy different ecological niches, these oaks would be considered separate species even though they are connected by some gene flow. Unlike the biological species concept, the ecological species concept can accommodate asexual as well as sexual species. It also emphasizes the role of disruptive natural selection as organisms adapt to differ-ent environments.

The **phylogenetic species concept** defines a species as the smallest group of individuals that share a common ancestor, forming one branch on the tree of life. Biologists trace the phylogenetic history of a species by comparing its characteristics, such as morphology or molecular sequences, with those of other organisms. Such analyses can distinguish groups of individuals that are sufficiently different to be considered separate species. Of course, the difficulty with this species concept is determining the degree of difference required to indicate separate species.

In addition to those discussed here, more than 20 other species definitions have been proposed. The usefulness of each definition depends on the situation and the research questions being asked. For our purposes of studying how species originate, the biological species concept, with its focus on reproductive barriers, is particularly helpful.

CONCEPT CHECK 24.1

1. (a) Which species concept(s) could you apply to both asexual and sexual species? (b) Which would be most useful for identifying species in the field? Explain.

2. **WHAT IF?** Suppose you are studying two bird species that live in a forest and are not known to interbreed. One species feeds and mates in the treetops and the other on the ground. But in captivity, the birds can interbreed and produce viable, fertile offspring. What type of reproductive barrier most likely keeps these species separate in nature? Explain.

For suggested answers, see Appendix A.

CONCEPT 24.2

Speciation can take place with or without geographic separation

Having discussed what constitutes a unique species, let's return to the process by which such species arise from existing species. We'll describe this process by focusing on the geographic setting in which gene flow is interrupted between populations of the existing species—in allopatric speciation the populations are geographically isolated, while in sympatric speciation they are not **(Figure 24.5)**.

Allopatric ("Other Country") Speciation

In **allopatric speciation** (from the Greek *allos*, other, and *patra*, homeland), gene flow is interrupted when a

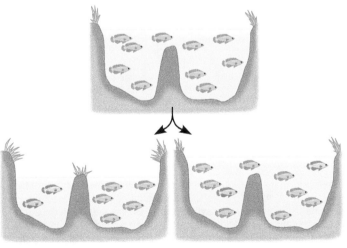

(a) **Allopatric speciation.** A population forms a new species while geographically isolated from its parent population.

(b) **Sympatric speciation.** A subset of a population forms a new species without geographic separation.

▲ Figure 24.5 **The geography of speciation.**

population is divided into geographically isolated subpopulations. For example, the water level in a lake may subside, resulting in two or more smaller lakes that are now home to separated populations (see Figure 24.5a). Or a river may change course and divide a population of animals that cannot cross it. Allopatric speciation can also occur without geologic remodeling, such as when individuals colonize a remote area and their descendants become geographically isolated from the parent population. The flightless cormorant shown in Figure 24.1 most likely originated in this way from an ancestral flying species that reached the Galápagos Islands.

The Process of Allopatric Speciation

How formidable must a geographic barrier be to promote allopatric speciation? The answer depends on the ability of the organisms to move about. Birds, mountain lions, and coyotes can cross rivers and canyons—as can the windblown pollen of pine trees and the seeds of many flowering plants. In contrast, small rodents may find a wide river or deep canyon a formidable barrier.

Once geographic separation has occurred, the separated gene pools may diverge. Different mutations arise, and natural selection and genetic drift may alter allele frequencies in different ways in the separated populations. Reproductive isolation may then evolve as a by-product of the genetic divergence that results from selection or drift.

Figure 24.6 describes an example. On Andros Island, in the Bahamas, populations of the mosquitofish *Gambusia hubbsi* colonized a series of ponds that later became isolated from one another. Genetic analyses indicate that little or no gene flow currently occurs between the ponds. The environments of these ponds are very similar except that some contain many predatory fishes, while others do not. In the "high-predation" ponds, selection has favored the evolution of a mosquitofish body shape that enables rapid bursts of speed (see Figure 24.6a). In low-predation ponds, selection

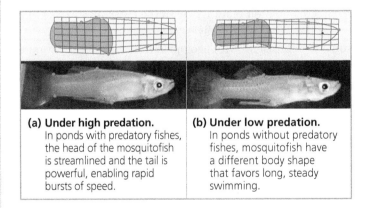

(a) **Under high predation.** In ponds with predatory fishes, the head of the mosquitofish is streamlined and the tail is powerful, enabling rapid bursts of speed.

(b) **Under low predation.** In ponds without predatory fishes, mosquitofish have a different body shape that favors long, steady swimming.

▲ Figure 24.6 **Reproductive isolation as a by-product of selection.** Bringing together mosquitofish from different ponds indicates that selection for traits that enable mosquitofish in high-predation ponds to avoid predators has isolated them reproductively from mosquitofish in low-predation ponds.

has favored a different body shape, one that improves the ability to swim for long periods of time (see Figure 24.6b). How have these different selective pressures affected the evolution of reproductive barriers? Researchers studied this question by bringing together mosquitofish from the two types of ponds. They found that female mosquitofish prefer to mate with males whose body shape is similar to their own. This preference establishes a behavioral barrier to reproduction between mosquitofish from high-predation and low-predation ponds. Thus, as a by-product of selection for avoiding predators, reproductive barriers have started to form in these allopatric populations.

Evidence of Allopatric Speciation

Many studies provide evidence that speciation can occur in allopatric populations. For example, laboratory studies show that reproductive barriers can develop when populations are isolated experimentally and subjected to different environmental conditions (Figure 24.7).

Field studies indicate that allopatric speciation also can occur in nature. Consider the 30 species of snapping shrimp in the genus *Alpheus* that live off the Isthmus of Panama, the land bridge that connects South and North America (Figure 24.8). Fifteen of these species live on the Atlantic side of the isthmus, while the other 15 live on the Pacific side. Before the isthmus formed, gene flow could occur between the Atlantic and Pacific populations of snapping shrimp. Did the species on different sides of the isthmus originate by allopatric speciation? Morphological and genetic data group these shrimp into 15 pairs of *sister species*, pairs whose member species are each other's closest relative. In each of these 15 pairs, one of the sister species lives on the Atlantic side of the isthmus, while the other lives on the Pacific side, strongly suggesting that the two species arose as a consequence of geographic separation. Furthermore, genetic analyses indicate that the *Alpheus* species originated from 9 to 3 million years ago, with the sister species that live in the deepest water diverging first. These divergence times are consistent with geologic evidence that the isthmus formed gradually, starting 10 million years ago, and closing completely about 3 million years ago.

The importance of allopatric speciation is also suggested by the fact that regions that are isolated or highly subdivided by barriers typically have more species than do otherwise similar regions that lack such features. For example, many unique plants and animals are found on the geographically isolated Hawaiian Islands (we'll return to the origin of Hawaiian species in Chapter 25). Field studies also show that reproductive isolation between two populations generally increases as the geographic distance between them increases, a finding consistent with allopatric speciation. In the Scientific Skills Exercise, you will analyze data from one such study that examined reproductive isolation

▼ Figure 24.7 | Inquiry

Can divergence of allopatric populations lead to reproductive isolation?

Experiment A researcher divided a laboratory population of the fruit fly *Drosophila pseudoobscura*, raising some flies on a starch medium and others on a maltose medium. After one year (about 40 generations), natural selection resulted in divergent evolution: Populations raised on starch digested starch more efficiently, while those raised on maltose digested maltose more efficiently. The researcher then put flies from the same or different populations in mating cages and measured mating frequencies. All flies used in the mating preference tests were reared for one generation on a standard cornmeal medium.

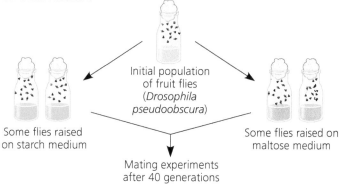

Initial population of fruit flies (*Drosophila pseudoobscura*)

Some flies raised on starch medium

Some flies raised on maltose medium

Mating experiments after 40 generations

Results Mating patterns among populations of flies raised on different media are shown below. When flies from "starch populations" were mixed with flies from "maltose populations," the flies tended to mate with like partners. But in the control group (shown on the right), flies from different populations adapted to starch were about as likely to mate with each other as with flies from their own population; similar results were obtained for control groups adapted to maltose.

		Female	
		Starch	Maltose
Male	Starch	22	9
	Maltose	8	20

Number of matings in experimental group

		Female	
		Starch population 1	Starch population 2
Male	Starch population 1	18	15
	Starch population 2	12	15

Number of matings in control group

Conclusion In the experimental group, the strong preference of "starch flies" and "maltose flies" to mate with like-adapted flies indicates that a reproductive barrier was forming between these fly populations. Although this reproductive barrier was not absolute (some mating between starch flies and maltose flies did occur), after 40 generations isolation appeared to be increasing. This barrier may have been caused by differences in courtship behavior that arose as an incidental by-product of differing selective pressures as these allopatric populations adapted to different sources of food.

Source: D. M. B. Dodd, Reproductive isolation as a consequence of adaptive divergence in *Drosophila pseudoobscura, Evolution* 43:1308–1311 (1989).

WHAT IF? *Why were all flies used in the mating preference tests reared on a standard medium (rather than on starch or maltose)?*

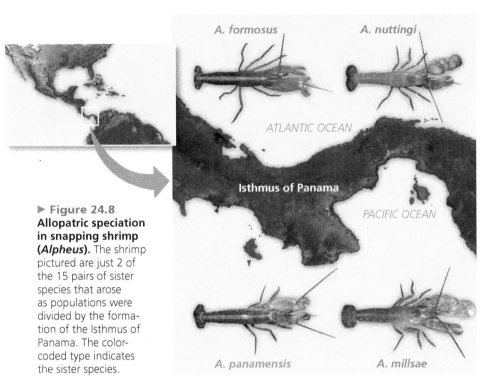

► **Figure 24.8
Allopatric speciation in snapping shrimp (*Alpheus*).** The shrimp pictured are just 2 of the 15 pairs of sister species that arose as populations were divided by the formation of the Isthmus of Panama. The color-coded type indicates the sister species.

in geographically separated salamander populations.

Note that while geographic isolation prevents interbreeding between members of allopatric populations, physical separation is not a biological barrier to reproduction. Biological reproductive barriers such as those described in Figure 24.3 are intrinsic to the organisms themselves. Hence, it is biological barriers that can prevent interbreeding when members of different populations come into contact with one another.

Sympatric ("Same Country") Speciation

In **sympatric speciation** (from the Greek *syn*, together), speciation occurs in populations that live in the same geographic area (see Figure 24.5b). How can reproductive barriers form between sympatric populations while

---

SCIENTIFIC SKILLS EXERCISE

Identifying Independent and Dependent Variables, Making a Scatter Plot, and Interpreting Data

Does Distance Between Salamander Populations Increase Their Reproductive Isolation? Allopatric speciation begins when populations become geographically isolated, preventing mating between individuals in different populations and thus stopping gene flow. It is logical that as distance between populations increases, so will their degree of reproductive isolation. To test this hypothesis, researchers studied populations of the dusky salamander (*Desmognathus ochrophaeus*) living on different mountain ranges in the southern Appalachians.

How the Experiment Was Done The researchers tested the reproductive isolation of pairs of salamander populations by leaving one male and one female together and later checking the females for the presence of sperm. Four mating combinations were tested for each pair of populations (A and B)—two *within* the same population (female A with male A and female B with male B) and two *between* populations (female A with male B and female B with male A).

Data from the Experiment The researchers used an index of reproductive isolation that ranged from a value of 0 (no isolation) to a value of 2 (full isolation). The proportion of successful matings for each mating combination was measured, with 100% success = 1 and no success = 0. The reproductive isolation value for two populations is the sum of the proportion of successful matings of each type within populations (AA + BB) minus the sum of the proportion of successful matings of each type between populations (AB + BA). The table provides distance and reproductive isolation data for 27 pairs of dusky salamander populations.

Interpret the Data

1. State the researchers' hypothesis, and identify the independent and dependent variables in this study. Explain why the researchers used four mating combinations for each pair of populations.

2. Calculate the value of the reproductive isolation index if (a) *all* of the matings within a population were successful, but *none* of the matings between populations were successful; (b) salamanders are equally successful in mating with members of their own population and members of another population.

3. Make a scatter plot to help you visualize any patterns that might indicate a relationship between the variables. Plot the independent variable on the *x*-axis and the dependent variable on the *y*-axis. (For additional information about graphs, see the Scientific Skills Review in Appendix F and the Study Area of MasteringBiology.)

4. Interpret your graph by (a) explaining in words any pattern indicating a possible relationship between the variables and (b) hypothesizing the possible cause of such a relationship.

(MB) A version of this Scientific Skills Exercise can be assigned in MasteringBiology.

Data from S. G. Tilley, A. Verrell, and S. J. Arnold, Correspondence between sexual isolation and allozyme differentiation: a test in the salamander *Desmognathus ochrophaeus, Proceedings of the National Academy of Sciences USA* 87:2715–2719 (1990).

Geographic Distance (km)	15	32	40	47	42	62	63	81	86	107	107	115	137	147
Reproductive Isolation Value	0.32	0.54	0.50	0.50	0.82	0.37	0.67	0.53	1.15	0.73	0.82	0.81	0.87	0.87
Distance (continued)	137	150	165	189	219	239	247	53	55	62	105	179	169	
Isolation (continued)	0.50	0.57	0.91	0.93	1.5	1.22	0.82	0.99	0.21	0.56	0.41	0.72	1.15	

their members remain in contact with each other? Although such contact (and the ongoing gene flow that results) makes sympatric speciation less common than allopatric speciation, sympatric speciation can occur if gene flow is reduced by such factors as polyploidy, sexual selection, and habitat differentiation. (Note that these factors can also promote allopatric speciation.)

Polyploidy

A species may originate from an accident during cell division that results in extra sets of chromosomes, a condition called **polyploidy**. Polyploid speciation occasionally occurs in animals; for example, the gray tree frog *Hyla versicolor* (see Figure 23.16) is thought to have originated in this way. However, polyploidy is far more common in plants. Botanists estimate that more than 80% of the plant species alive today are descended from ancestors that formed by polyploid speciation.

Two distinct forms of polyploidy have been observed in plant (and a few animal) populations. An **autopolyploid** (from the Greek *autos*, self) is an individual that has more than two chromosome sets that are all derived from a single species. In plants, for example, a failure of cell division could double a cell's chromosome number from the original number (2*n*) to a tetraploid number (4*n*).

A tetraploid can produce fertile tetraploid offspring by self-pollinating or by mating with other tetraploids. In addition, the tetraploids are reproductively isolated from 2*n* plants of the original population, because the triploid (3*n*) offspring of such unions have reduced fertility. Thus, in just one generation, autopolyploidy can generate reproductive isolation without any geographic separation.

A second form of polyploidy can occur when two different species interbreed and produce hybrid offspring. Most such hybrids are sterile because the set of chromosomes from one species cannot pair during meiosis with the set of chromosomes from the other species. However, an infertile hybrid may be able to propagate itself asexually (as many plants can do). In subsequent generations, various mechanisms can change a sterile hybrid into a fertile polyploid called an **allopolyploid** (Figure 24.9). The allopolyploids are fertile when mating with each other but cannot interbreed with either parent species; thus, they represent a new biological species.

Cell division error
2*n* = 6 → Tetraploid cell 4*n*
Meiosis
2*n*
2*n*
Gametes produced by tetraploids
New species (4*n*)

▲ Autopolyploid speciation

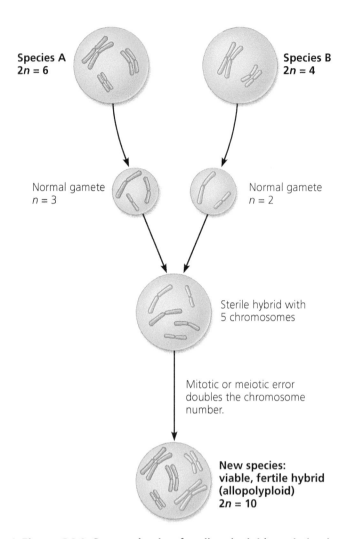

▲ **Figure 24.9 One mechanism for allopolyploid speciation in plants.** Most hybrids are sterile because their chromosomes are not homologous and cannot pair during meiosis. However, such a hybrid may be able to reproduce asexually. This diagram traces one mechanism that can produce fertile hybrids (allopolyploids) as new species. The new species has a diploid chromosome number equal to the sum of the diploid chromosome numbers of the two parent species.

Species A 2*n* = 6
Species B 2*n* = 4
Normal gamete *n* = 3
Normal gamete *n* = 2
Sterile hybrid with 5 chromosomes
Mitotic or meiotic error doubles the chromosome number.
New species: viable, fertile hybrid (allopolyploid) 2*n* = 10

Although it can be challenging to study speciation in the field, scientists have documented at least five new plant species that have originated by polyploid speciation since 1850. One of these examples involves the origin of a new species of goatsbeard plant (genus *Tragopogon*) in the Pacific Northwest. *Tragopogon* first arrived in the region when humans introduced three European species in the early 1900s: *T. pratensis, T. dubius,* and *T. porrifolius.* These three species are now common weeds in abandoned parking lots and other urban sites. In 1950, a new *Tragopogon* species was discovered near the Idaho-Washington border, a region where all three European species also were found. Genetic analyses revealed that this new species, *Tragopogon miscellus*, is a hybrid of two of the European species (Figure 24.10). Although the *T. miscellus* population grows mainly by reproduction of its own members, additional

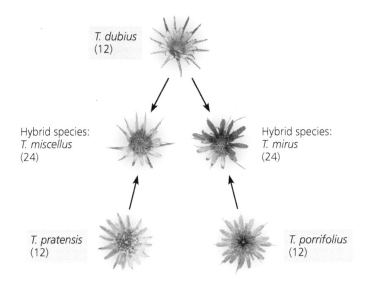

▲ **Figure 24.10 Allopolyploid speciation in *Tragopogon*.** The gray boxes indicate the three parent species. The diploid chromosome number of each species is shown in parentheses.

episodes of hybridization between the parent species continue to add new members to the *T. miscellus* population. Later, scientists discovered another new *Tragopogon* species, *T. mirus*—this one a hybrid of *T. dubius* and *T. porrifolius* (see Figure 24.10). The *Tragopogon* story is just one of several well-studied examples in which scientists have observed speciation in progress.

Many important agricultural crops—such as oats, cotton, potatoes, tobacco, and wheat—are polyploids. The wheat used for bread, *Triticum aestivum*, is an allohexaploid (six sets of chromosomes, two sets from each of three different species). The first of the polyploidy events that eventually led to modern wheat probably occurred about 8,000 years ago in the Middle East as a spontaneous hybrid of an early cultivated wheat species and a wild grass. Today, plant geneticists generate new polyploids in the laboratory by using chemicals that induce meiotic and mitotic errors. By harnessing the evolutionary process, researchers can produce new hybrid species with desired qualities, such as a hybrid that combines the high yield of wheat with the hardiness of rye.

Sexual Selection

There is evidence that sympatric speciation can also be driven by sexual selection. Clues to how this can occur have been found in cichlid fish from one of Earth's hot spots of animal speciation, East Africa's Lake Victoria. This lake was once home to as many as 600 species of cichlids. Genetic data indicate that these species originated within the last 100,000 years from a small number of colonizing species that arrived from other lakes and rivers. How did so many species—more than double the number of freshwater fish species known in all of Europe—originate within a single lake?

One hypothesis is that subgroups of the original cichlid populations adapted to different food sources and the resulting genetic divergence contributed to speciation in Lake Victoria. But sexual selection, in which (typically) females select males based on their appearance (see Concept 23.4), may also have been a factor. Researchers have studied two closely related sympatric species of cichlids that differ mainly in the coloration of breeding males: Breeding *Pundamilia pundamilia* males have a blue-tinged back, whereas breeding *Pundamilia nyererei* males have a red-tinged back (**Figure 24.11**). The studies' results suggest that mate choice based on male breeding coloration is the main reproductive barrier that normally keeps the gene pools of these two species separate.

▼ **Figure 24.11** | **Inquiry**

Does sexual selection in cichlids result in reproductive isolation?

Experiment Researchers placed males and females of *Pundamilia pundamilia* and *P. nyererei* together in two aquarium tanks, one with natural light and one with a monochromatic orange lamp. Under normal light, the two species are noticeably different in male breeding coloration; under monochromatic orange light, the two species are very similar in color. The researchers then observed the mate choices of the females in each tank.

Results Under normal light, females of each species strongly preferred males of their own species. But under orange light, females of each species responded indiscriminately to males of both species. The resulting hybrids were viable and fertile.

Conclusion The researchers concluded that mate choice by females based on male breeding coloration is the main reproductive barrier that normally keeps the gene pools of these two species separate. Since the species can still interbreed when this prezygotic behavioral barrier is breached in the laboratory, the genetic divergence between the species is likely to be small. This suggests that speciation in nature has occurred relatively recently.

Source: O. Seehausen and J. J. M. van Alphen, The effect of male coloration on female mate choice in closely related Lake Victoria cichlids (*Haplochromis nyererei* complex), *Behavioral Ecology and Sociobiology* 42:1–8 (1998).

WHAT IF? *Suppose that female cichlids living in the murky waters of a polluted lake could not distinguish colors well. In such waters, how might the gene pools of these species change over time?*

Habitat Differentiation

Sympatric speciation can also occur when a subpopulation exploits a habitat or resource not used by the parent population. Consider the North American apple maggot fly (*Rhagoletis pomonella*), a pest of apples. The fly's original habitat was the native hawthorn tree, but about 200 years ago, some populations colonized apple trees that had been introduced by European settlers. Apple maggot flies usually mate on or near their host plant. This results in a prezygotic barrier (habitat isolation) between populations that feed on apples and populations that feed on hawthorns. Furthermore, as apples mature more quickly than hawthorn fruit, natural selection has favored apple-feeding flies with rapid development. These apple-feeding populations now show temporal isolation from the hawthorn-feeding *R. pomonella*, providing a second prezygotic barrier to gene flow between the two populations. Researchers also have identified alleles that benefit the flies that use one host plant but harm the flies that use the other host plant. Natural selection operating on these alleles has provided a postzygotic barrier to reproduction,

▲ *R. pomonella* **feeding on a hawthorn berry**

further limiting gene flow. Altogether, although the two populations are still classified as subspecies rather than separate species, sympatric speciation appears to be well under way.

Allopatric and Sympatric Speciation: A Review

Now let's recap the processes by which new species form. In allopatric speciation, a new species forms in geographic isolation from its parent population. Geographic isolation severely restricts gene flow. Intrinsic barriers to reproduction with the parent population may then arise as a by-product of genetic changes that occur within the isolated population. Many different processes can produce such genetic changes, including natural selection under different environmental conditions, genetic drift, and sexual selection. Once formed, reproductive barriers that arise in allopatric populations can prevent interbreeding with the parent population even if the populations come back into contact.

Sympatric speciation, in contrast, requires the emergence of a reproductive barrier that isolates a subset of a population from the remainder of the population in the same area. Though rarer than allopatric speciation, sympatric speciation can occur when gene flow to and from the isolated subpopulation is blocked. This can occur as a result

of polyploidy, a condition in which an organism has extra sets of chromosomes. Sympatric speciation also can result from sexual selection. Finally, sympatric speciation can occur when a subset of a population becomes reproductively isolated because of natural selection that results from a switch to a habitat or food source not used by the parent population.

Having reviewed the geographic context in which species originate, we'll next explore in more detail what can happen when new or partially formed species come into contact.

CONCEPT CHECK 24.2

1. Summarize key differences between allopatric and sympatric speciation. Which type of speciation is more common, and why?
2. Describe two mechanisms that can decrease gene flow in sympatric populations, thereby making sympatric speciation more likely to occur.
3. **WHAT IF?** Is allopatric speciation more likely to occur on an island close to a mainland or on a more isolated island of the same size? Explain your prediction.
4. **MAKE CONNECTIONS** Review the process of meiosis in Figure 13.8. Describe how an error during meiosis could lead to polyploidy.

For suggested answers, see Appendix A.

CONCEPT 24.3

Hybrid zones reveal factors that cause reproductive isolation

What happens if species with incomplete reproductive barriers come into contact with one another? One possible outcome is the formation of a **hybrid zone**, a region in which members of different species meet and mate, producing at least some offspring of mixed ancestry. In this section, we'll explore hybrid zones and what they reveal about factors that cause the evolution of reproductive isolation.

Patterns Within Hybrid Zones

Some hybrid zones form as narrow bands, such as the one depicted in **Figure 24.12** for the yellow-bellied toad (*Bombina variegata*) and its close relative, the fire-bellied toad (*B. bombina*). This hybrid zone, represented by the red line on the map, extends for 4,000 km but is less than 10 km wide in most places. The hybrid zone occurs where the higher-altitude habitat of the yellow-bellied toad meets the lowland habitat of the fire-bellied toad. Across a given "slice" of the zone, the frequency of alleles specific to yellow-bellied toads typically decreases from close to 100% at the edge where only yellow-bellied toads are found, to 50% in the central portion of the zone, to 0% at the edge where only fire-bellied toads are found.

Hybrid zone (red line) occurs where the habitats of the two species meet.

Fire-bellied toad range

Hybrid zone

Yellow-bellied toad range

Fire-bellied toad, *Bombina bombina*: lives at lower altitudes

Yellow-bellied toad, *Bombina variegata*: lives at higher altitudes

© 1993 Oxford University Press, Inc.

Yellow-bellied toad range

Hybrid zone

Fire-bellied toad range

Frequency of *B. variegata*-specific allele

Distance from hybrid zone center (km)

▲ **Figure 24.12 A narrow hybrid zone for *Bombina* toads in Europe.** The graph shows the pattern of species-specific allele frequencies across the width of the zone near Krakow, Poland. Individuals with frequencies close to 1 are yellow-bellied toads, individuals with frequencies close to 0 are fire-bellied toads, and individuals with intermediate frequencies are considered hybrids.

? *Does the graph indicate that gene flow is spreading fire-bellied toad alleles into the range of the yellow-bellied toad? Explain.*

What causes such a pattern of allele frequencies across a hybrid zone? We can infer that there is an obstacle to gene flow—otherwise, alleles from one parent species would also be common in the gene pool of the other parent species. Are geographic barriers reducing gene flow? Not in this case, since the toads can move throughout the hybrid zone. A more important factor is that hybrid toads have increased rates of embryonic mortality and a variety of morphological abnormalities, including ribs that are fused to the spine and malformed tadpole mouthparts. Because the hybrids have poor survival and reproduction, they produce few viable offspring with members of the parent species. As a result, hybrid individuals rarely serve as a stepping-stone from which alleles are passed from one species to the other. Outside the hybrid zone, additional obstacles to gene flow may be provided by natural selection in the different environments in which the parent species live.

Hybrid zones typically are located wherever the habitats of the interbreeding species meet. Those regions often resemble a group of isolated patches scattered across the landscape—more like the complex pattern of spots on a Dalmatian than the continuous band shown in Figure 24.12. But regardless of whether they have complex or simple spatial patterns, hybrid zones form when two species lacking complete barriers to reproduction come into contact. Once formed, how does a hybrid zone change over time?

Hybrid Zones over Time

Studying a hybrid zone is like observing a naturally occurring experiment on speciation. Will the hybrids become reproductively isolated from their parents and form a new species, as occurred by polyploidy in the goatsbeard plant of the Pacific Northwest? If not, there are three possible outcomes for the hybrid zone over time: reinforcement of

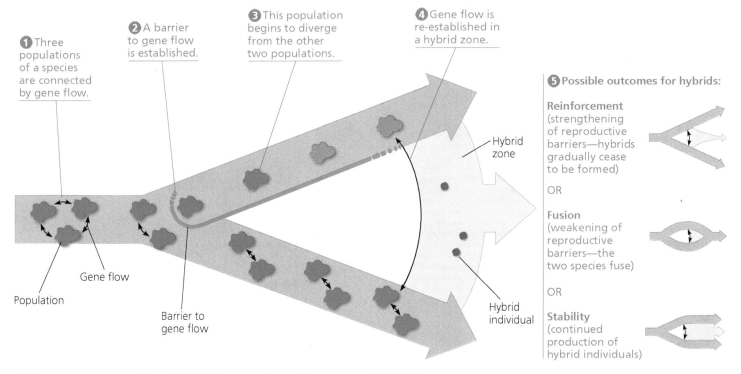

① Three populations of a species are connected by gene flow.

② A barrier to gene flow is established.

③ This population begins to diverge from the other two populations.

④ Gene flow is re-established in a hybrid zone.

⑤ Possible outcomes for hybrids:

Reinforcement (strengthening of reproductive barriers—hybrids gradually cease to be formed)

OR

Fusion (weakening of reproductive barriers—the two species fuse)

OR

Stability (continued production of hybrid individuals)

Hybrid zone

Gene flow

Population

Barrier to gene flow

Hybrid individual

▲ **Figure 24.13 Formation of a hybrid zone and possible outcomes for hybrids over time.** The thick colored arrows represent the passage of time.

WHAT IF? *Predict what might happen if gene flow were re-established at step 3 in this process.*

barriers, fusion of species, or stability (**Figure 24.13**). Let's examine what studies suggest about these possibilities.

Reinforcement: Strengthening Reproductive Barriers

Hybrids often are less fit than members of their parent species. In such cases, natural selection should strengthen prezygotic barriers to reproduction, reducing the formation of unfit hybrids. Because this process involves *reinforcing* reproductive barriers, it is called **reinforcement**. If reinforcement is occurring, a logical prediction is that barriers to reproduction between species should be stronger for sympatric populations than for allopatric populations.

As an example, we'll examine evidence for reinforcement in two species of European flycatcher, the pied flycatcher and the collared flycatcher. In allopatric populations of these birds, males of the two species closely resemble one another. But in sympatric populations, the males of the two species look very different: Male pied flycatchers are a dull brown, whereas male collared flycatchers have enlarged patches of white. Female pied and collared flycatchers do not select males of the other species when given a choice between males from sympatric populations, but they frequently do make mistakes when selecting between males from allopatric populations (**Figure 24.14**). Thus, barriers to reproduction are stronger in birds from sympatric populations than in birds from allopatric populations, as you would predict if reinforcement is occurring. Similar results have been

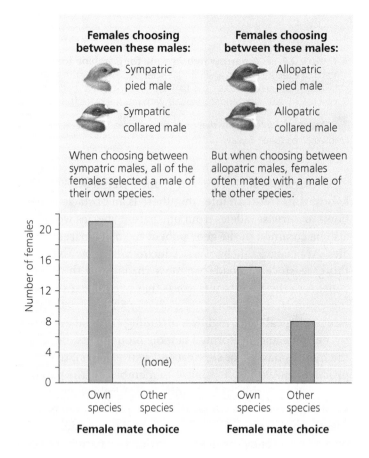

Females choosing between these males:
Sympatric pied male
Sympatric collared male

When choosing between sympatric males, all of the females selected a male of their own species.

Females choosing between these males:
Allopatric pied male
Allopatric collared male

But when choosing between allopatric males, females often mated with a male of the other species.

Number of females

(none)

Own species / Other species
Female mate choice

Own species / Other species
Female mate choice

▲ **Figure 24.14 Reinforcement of barriers to reproduction in closely related species of European flycatchers.**

observed in a number of organisms, including fishes, insects, plants, and other birds.

Fusion: Weakening Reproductive Barriers

Next let's consider the case in which two species contact one another in a hybrid zone, but the barriers to reproduction are not strong. So much gene flow may occur that reproductive barriers weaken further and the gene pools of the two species become increasingly alike. In effect, the speciation process reverses, eventually causing the two hybridizing species to fuse into a single species.

Such a situation may be occurring among Lake Victoria cichlids. In the past 30 years, about 200 of the former 600 species of these cichlids have vanished. Some were driven to extinction by an introduced predator, the Nile perch. But many species not eaten by Nile perch also have disappeared—perhaps by species fusion. Many pairs of ecologically similar cichlid species are reproductively isolated because the females of one species prefer to mate with males of one color, while females of the other species prefer to mate with males of a different color (see Figure 24.11). Results from field and laboratory studies indicate that murky waters caused by pollution have hampered females in distinguishing males of their own species from males of closely related species. In some polluted waters, many hybrids have been produced, leading to fusion of the parent species' gene pools and a loss of species (Figure 24.15).

Pundamilia nyererei

Pundamilia pundamilia

Pundamilia "turbid water,"
hybrid offspring from a location with turbid water

▲ **Figure 24.15 Fusion: The breakdown of reproductive barriers.** Increasingly cloudy water in Lake Victoria over the past 30 years may have weakened reproductive barriers between *P. nyererei* and *P. pundamilia*. In areas of cloudy water, the two species have hybridized extensively, causing their gene pools to fuse.

Stability: Continued Formation of Hybrid Individuals

Many hybrid zones are stable in the sense that hybrids continue to be produced. In some cases, this occurs because the hybrids survive or reproduce better than members of either parent species, at least in certain habitats or years. But stable hybrid zones have also been observed in cases where the hybrids are selected *against*—an unexpected result.

For example, hybrids continue to form in the *Bombina* hybrid zone even though they are strongly selected against. One explanation relates to the narrowness of the *Bombina* hybrid zone (see Figure 24.12). Evidence suggests that members of both parent species migrate into the zone from the parent populations located outside the zone, thus leading to the continued production of hybrids. If the hybrid zone were wider, this would be less likely to occur, since the center of the zone would receive little gene flow from distant parent populations located outside the hybrid zone.

Sometimes the outcomes in hybrid zones match our predictions (European flycatchers and cichlid fishes), and sometimes they don't (*Bombina*). But whether our predictions are upheld or not, events in hybrid zones can shed light on how barriers to reproduction between closely related species change over time. In the next section, we'll examine how interactions between hybridizing species can also provide a glimpse into the speed and genetic control of speciation.

CONCEPT CHECK **24.3**

1. What are hybrid zones, and why can they be viewed as "natural laboratories" in which to study speciation?

2. **WHAT IF?** Consider two species that diverged while geographically separated but resumed contact before reproductive isolation was complete. Predict what would happen over time if the two species mated indiscriminately and (a) hybrid offspring survived and reproduced more poorly than offspring from intraspecific matings or (b) hybrid offspring survived and reproduced as well as offspring from intraspecific matings.

For suggested answers, see Appendix A.

CONCEPT 24.4

Speciation can occur rapidly or slowly and can result from changes in few or many genes

Darwin faced many questions when he began to ponder that "mystery of mysteries"—speciation. He found answers to some of those questions when he realized that evolution by natural selection helps explain both the diversity of life and the adaptations of organisms (see Concept 22.2). But biologists since Darwin have continued to ask fundamental questions about speciation. How long does it take for new species to form? And how many genes change when one species splits into two? Answers to these questions are also emerging.

The Time Course of Speciation

We can gather information about how long it takes new species to form from broad patterns in the fossil record and from studies that use morphological data (including fossils) or molecular data to assess the time interval between speciation events in particular groups of organisms.

Patterns in the Fossil Record

The fossil record includes many episodes in which new species appear suddenly in a geologic stratum, persist essentially unchanged through several strata, and then disappear. For example, there are dozens of species of marine invertebrates that make their debut in the fossil record with novel morphologies, but then change little for millions of years before becoming extinct. Paleontologists Niles Eldredge and Stephen Jay Gould coined the term **punctuated equilibria** to describe these periods of apparent stasis punctuated by sudden change (Figure 24.16a). Other species do not show a punctuated pattern; instead, they appear to have changed more gradually over long periods of time (Figure 24.16b).

What might punctuated and gradual patterns tell us about how long it takes new species to form? Suppose that a species survived for 5 million years, but most of the morphological changes that caused it to be designated a new species occurred during the first 50,000 years of its existence—just 1% of its total lifetime. Time periods this short (in geologic terms) often cannot be distinguished in fossil strata, in part because the rate of sediment accumulation may be too slow to separate layers this close in time. Thus, based on its fossils, the species would seem to have appeared suddenly and then lingered with little or no change before becoming extinct. Even though such a species may have originated more slowly than its fossils suggest (in this case taking up to 50,000 years), a punctuated pattern indicates that speciation occurred relatively rapidly. For species whose fossils changed much more gradually, we also cannot tell exactly when a new biological species formed, since information about reproductive isolation does not fossilize. However, it is likely that speciation in such groups occurred relatively slowly, perhaps taking millions of years.

Speciation Rates

The existence of fossils that display a punctuated pattern suggests that once the process of speciation begins, it can be completed relatively rapidly—a suggestion supported by a growing number of studies.

For example, rapid speciation appears to have produced the wild sunflower *Helianthus anomalus*. Genetic evidence indicates that this species originated by the hybridization of two other sunflower species, *H. annuus* and *H. petiolaris*. The hybrid species *H. anomalus* is ecologically distinct and reproductively isolated from both parent species (Figure 24.17). Unlike the outcome of allopolyploid speciation, in which there is a change in chromosome number after hybridization, in these sunflowers the two parent species and the hybrid all have the same number of chromosomes ($2n = 34$). How, then, did speciation occur? To study this question, researchers performed an experiment designed to mimic events in nature (Figure 24.18). Their results indicated that natural selection could produce extensive genetic changes in hybrid populations over short periods of time. These changes appear to have caused the hybrids to diverge reproductively from their parents and form a new species, *H. anomalus*.

The sunflower example, along with the apple maggot fly, Lake Victoria cichlid, and fruit fly examples discussed earlier, suggests that new species can arise rapidly *once divergence begins*. But what is the total length of time between speciation events? This interval consists of the time that elapses before populations of a newly formed species start to

(a) In a punctuated model, new species change most as they branch from a parent species and then change little for the rest of their existence.

Time

(b) In a gradual model, species diverge from one another more slowly and steadily over time.

▲ Figure 24.16 **Two models for the tempo of speciation.**

▲ **Figure 24.17 A hybrid sunflower species and its dry sand dune habitat.** The wild sunflower *Helianthus anomalus* originated via the hybridization of two other sunflowers, *H. annuus* and *H. petiolaris*, which live in nearby but moister environments.

diverge from one another plus the time it takes for speciation to be complete once divergence begins. It turns out that the total time between speciation events varies considerably. In a survey of data from 84 groups of plants and animals, speciation intervals ranged from 4,000 years (in cichlids of Lake Nabugabo, Uganda) to 40 million years (in some beetles). Overall, the time between speciation events averaged 6.5 million years and was rarely less than 500,000 years.

These data suggest that on average, millions of years may pass before a newly formed plant or animal species will itself give rise to another new species. As we'll see in Chapter 25, this finding has implications for how long it takes life on Earth to recover from mass extinction events. Moreover, the extreme variability in the time it takes new species to form indicates that organisms do not have an internal "speciation clock" causing them to produce new species at regular intervals. Instead, speciation begins only after gene flow between populations is interrupted, perhaps by changing environmental conditions or by unpredictable events, such as a storm that transports a few individuals to a new area. Furthermore, once gene flow is interrupted, the populations must diverge genetically to such an extent that they become reproductively isolated—all before other events cause gene flow to resume, possibly reversing the speciation process (see Figure 24.15).

Studying the Genetics of Speciation

Studies of ongoing speciation (as in hybrid zones) can reveal traits that cause reproductive isolation. By identifying the genes that control those traits, scientists can explore a fundamental question of evolutionary biology: How many genes influence the formation of new species?

In some cases, the evolution of reproductive isolation results from the effects of a single gene. For example, in Japanese snails of the genus *Euhadra*, a change in a single gene results in a mechanical barrier to reproduction. This gene controls the direction in which the shells spiral. When their shells spiral in different directions, the snails' genitalia

▼ **Figure 24.18** | Inquiry

How does hybridization lead to speciation in sunflowers?

Experiment Loren Rieseberg and his colleagues crossed the two parent sunflower species, *H. annuus* and *H. petiolaris*, to produce experimental hybrids in the laboratory (for each gamete, only two of the $n = 17$ chromosomes are shown).

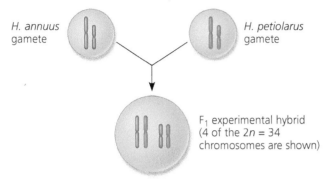

Note that in the first (F_1) generation, each chromosome of the experimental hybrids consisted entirely of DNA from one or the other parent species. The researchers then tested whether the F_1 and subsequent generations of experimental hybrids were fertile. They also used species-specific genetic markers to compare the chromosomes in the experimental hybrids with the chromosomes in the naturally occurring hybrid *H. anomalus*.

Results Although only 5% of the F_1 experimental hybrids were fertile, after just four more generations the hybrid fertility rose to more than 90%. The chromosomes of individuals from this fifth hybrid generation differed from those in the F_1 generation (see above) but were similar to those in *H. anomalus* individuals from natural populations:

■ Comparison region containing *H. annuus*-specific marker
■ Comparison region containing *H. petiolarus*-specific marker

Conclusion Over time, the chromosomes in the population of experimental hybrids became similar to the chromosomes of *H. anomalus* individuals from natural populations. This suggests that the observed rise in the fertility of the experimental hybrids may have occurred as selection eliminated regions of DNA from the parent species that were not compatible with one another. Overall, it appeared that the initial steps of the speciation process occurred rapidly and could be mimicked in a laboratory experiment.

Source: L. H. Rieseberg et al., Role of gene interactions in hybrid speciation: evidence from ancient and experimental hybrids, *Science* 272:741–745 (1996). Reprinted with permission from AAAS.

WHAT IF? *The increased fertility of the experimental hybrids could have resulted from natural selection for thriving under laboratory conditions. Evaluate this alternative explanation for the result.*

are oriented in a manner that prevents mating (Figure 24.3f shows a similar example). Recent genetic analyses have uncovered other single genes that cause reproductive isolation in fruit flies or mice.

A major barrier to reproduction between two closely related species of monkey flower, *Mimulus cardinalis* and *M. lewisii*, also appears to be influenced by a relatively small number of genes. These two species are isolated by several prezygotic and postzygotic barriers. Of these, one prezygotic barrier, pollinator choice, accounts for most of the isolation: In a hybrid zone between *M. cardinalis* and *M. lewisii*, nearly 98% of pollinator visits were restricted to one species or the other.

The two monkey flower species are visited by different pollinators: Hummingbirds prefer the red-flowered *M. cardinalis*, and bumblebees prefer the pink-flowered *M. lewisii*. Pollinator choice is affected by at least two loci in the monkey flowers, one of which, the "yellow upper," or *yup*, locus, influences flower color (Figure 24.19). By crossing the two parent species to produce F$_1$ hybrids and then performing repeated backcrosses of these F$_1$ hybrids to each parent species, researchers succeeded in transferring the *M. cardinalis* allele at this locus into *M. lewisii*, and vice versa. In a field experiment, *M. lewisii* plants with the *M. cardinalis yup* allele received 68-fold more visits from hummingbirds than did wild-type *M. lewisii*. Similarly, *M. cardinalis* plants with the *M. lewisii yup* allele received 74-fold more visits from bumblebees than did wild-type *M. cardinalis*. Thus, a mutation at a single locus can influence pollinator preference and hence contribute to reproductive isolation in monkey flowers.

In other organisms, the speciation process is influenced by larger numbers of genes and gene interactions. For example, hybrid sterility between two subspecies of the fruit fly *Drosophila pseudoobscura* results from gene interactions among at least four loci, and postzygotic isolation in the sunflower hybrid zone discussed earlier is influenced by at least 26 chromosome segments (and an unknown number of genes). Overall, studies suggest that few or many genes can influence the evolution of reproductive isolation and hence the emergence of a new species.

From Speciation to Macroevolution

As you've seen, speciation may begin with differences as small as the color on a cichlid's back. However, as speciation occurs again and again, such differences can accumulate and become more pronounced, eventually leading to the formation of new groups of organisms that differ greatly from their ancestors (as in the origin of whales from terrestrial mammals; see Figure 22.20). Moreover, as one group of organisms increases in size by producing many new species, another group of organisms may shrink, losing species to extinction. The cumulative effects of many such speciation and extinction events have helped shape the sweeping

(a) Typical *Mimulus lewisii*   **(b) *M. lewisii* with an *M. cardinalis* flower-color allele**

(c) Typical *Mimulus cardinalis*   **(d) *M. cardinalis* with an *M. lewisii* flower-color allele**

▲ **Figure 24.19 A locus that influences pollinator choice.** Pollinator preferences provide a strong barrier to reproduction between *Mimulus lewisii* and *M. cardinalis*. After transferring the *M. lewisii* allele for a flower-color locus into *M. cardinalis* and vice versa, researchers observed a shift in some pollinators' preferences.

WHAT IF? *If* M. cardinalis *individuals that had the* M. lewisii yup *allele were planted in an area that housed both monkey flower species, how might the production of hybrid offspring be affected?*

evolutionary changes that are documented in the fossil record. In the next chapter, we turn to such large-scale evolutionary changes as we begin our study of macroevolution.

CONCEPT CHECK 24.4

1. Speciation can occur rapidly between diverging populations, yet the time between speciation events is often more than a million years. Explain this apparent contradiction.

2. Summarize evidence that the *yup* locus acts as a prezygotic barrier to reproduction in two species of monkey flowers. Do these results demonstrate that the *yup* locus alone controls barriers to reproduction between these species? Explain.

3. **MAKE CONNECTIONS** Compare Figure 13.11 with Figure 24.18. What cellular process could cause the hybrid chromosomes in Figure 24.18 to contain DNA from both parent species? Explain.

For suggested answers, see Appendix A.

24 Chapter Review

SUMMARY OF KEY CONCEPTS

CONCEPT 24.1

The biological species concept emphasizes reproductive isolation (pp. 501–505)

- A biological **species** is a group of populations whose individuals may interbreed and produce viable, fertile offspring with each other but not with members of other species. The **biological species concept** emphasizes reproductive isolation through prezygotic and postzygotic barriers that separate gene pools.
- Although helpful in thinking about how speciation occurs, the biological species concept has limitations. For instance, it cannot be applied to organisms known only as fossils or to organisms that reproduce only asexually. Thus, scientists use other species concepts, such as the **morphological species concept**, in certain circumstances.

? *Explain the role of gene flow in the biological species concept.*

CONCEPT 24.2

Speciation can take place with or without geographic separation (pp. 505–510)

- In **allopatric speciation**, gene flow is reduced when two populations of one species become geographically separated from each other. One or both populations may undergo evolutionary change during the period of separation, resulting in the establishment of prezygotic or postzygotic barriers to reproduction.
- In **sympatric speciation**, a new species originates while remaining in the same geographic area as the parent species. Plant species (and, more rarely, animal species) have evolved sympatrically through polyploidy. Sympatric speciation can also result from sexual selection and habitat shifts.

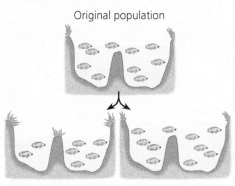

Original population

Allopatric speciation   Sympatric speciation

? *Can factors that cause sympatric speciation also cause allopatric speciation? Explain.*

CONCEPT 24.3

Hybrid zones reveal factors that cause reproductive isolation (pp. 510–513)

- Many groups of organisms form **hybrid zones** in which members of different species meet and mate, producing at least some offspring of mixed ancestry.

- Many hybrid zones are *stable*, in that hybrid offspring continue to be produced over time. In others, **reinforcement** strengthens prezygotic barriers to reproduction, thus decreasing the formation of unfit hybrids. In still other hybrid zones, barriers to reproduction may weaken over time, resulting in the *fusion* of the species' gene pools (reversing the speciation process).

? *What factors can support the long-term stability of a hybrid zone if the parent species live in different environments?*

CONCEPT 24.4

Speciation can occur rapidly or slowly and can result from changes in few or many genes (pp. 513–516)

- New species can form rapidly once divergence begins—but it can take millions of years for that to happen. The time interval between speciation events varies considerably, from a few thousand years to tens of millions of years.
- New developments in genetics have enabled researchers to identify specific genes involved in some cases of speciation. Results show that speciation can be driven by few or many genes.

? *Is speciation something that happened only in the distant past, or are new species continuing to arise today? Explain.*

TEST YOUR UNDERSTANDING

LEVEL 1: KNOWLEDGE/COMPREHENSION

1. The *largest* unit within which gene flow can readily occur is a
   a. population.   c. genus.
   b. species.   d. hybrid.

2. Males of different species of the fruit fly *Drosophila* that live in the same parts of the Hawaiian Islands have different elaborate courtship rituals. These rituals involve fighting other males and making stylized movements that attract females. What type of reproductive isolation does this represent?
   a. habitat isolation
   b. temporal isolation
   c. behavioral isolation
   d. gametic isolation

3. According to the punctuated equilibria model,
   a. given enough time, most existing species will branch gradually into new species.
   b. most new species accumulate their unique features relatively rapidly as they come into existence, then change little for the rest of their duration as a species.
   c. most evolution occurs in sympatric populations.
   d. speciation is usually due to a single mutation.

LEVEL 2: APPLICATION/ANALYSIS

4. Bird guides once listed the myrtle warbler and Audubon's warbler as distinct species. Recently, these birds have been classified as eastern and western forms of a single species, the yellow-rumped warbler. Which of the following pieces of evidence, if true, would be cause for this reclassification?
   a. The two forms interbreed often in nature, and their offspring survive and reproduce well.
   b. The two forms live in similar habitats and have similar food requirements.
   c. The two forms have many genes in common.
   d. The two forms are very similar in appearance.

5. Which of the following factors would *not* contribute to allopatric speciation?
   a. The separated population is small, and genetic drift occurs.
   b. The isolated population is exposed to different selection pressures than the ancestral population.
   c. Different mutations begin to distinguish the gene pools of the separated populations.
   d. Gene flow between the two populations is extensive.

6. Plant species A has a diploid chromosome number of 12. Plant species B has a diploid number of 16. A new species, C, arises as an allopolyploid from A and B. The diploid number for species C would probably be
   a. 14.   b. 16.   c. 28.   d. 56.

LEVEL 3: SYNTHESIS/EVALUATION

7. Suppose that a group of male pied flycatchers migrated from a region where there were no collared flycatchers to a region where both species were present (see Figure 24.14). Assuming events like this are very rare, which of the following scenarios is *least* likely?
   a. The frequency of hybrid offspring would increase.
   b. Migrant pied males would produce fewer offspring than would resident pied males.
   c. Migrant males would mate with collared females more often than with pied females.
   d. The frequency of hybrid offspring would decrease.

8. SCIENTIFIC INQUIRY
   DRAW IT In this chapter, you read that bread wheat (*Triticum aestivum*) is an allohexaploid, containing two sets of chromosomes from each of three different parent species. Genetic analysis suggests that the three species pictured following this question each contributed chromosome sets to *T. aestivum*. (The capital letters here represent sets of chromosomes rather than individual genes, and the diploid chromosome number for each species is shown in parentheses.) Evidence also indicates that the first polyploidy event was a spontaneous hybridization of the early cultivated wheat species *T. monococcum* and a wild *Triticum* grass species. Based on this information, draw a diagram of one possible chain of events that could have produced the allohexaploid *T. aestivum*.

Ancestral species:

| AA | BB | DD |

Triticum monococcum (14)   Wild *Triticum* (14)   Wild *T. tauschii* (14)

Product:

AA BB DD

T. aestivum (bread wheat) (42)

9. EVOLUTION CONNECTION
   What is the biological basis for assigning all human populations to a single species? Can you think of a scenario by which a second human species could originate in the future?

10. SCIENCE, TECHNOLOGY, AND SOCIETY
    In the United States, the rare red wolf (*Canis lupus*) has been known to hybridize with coyotes (*Canis latrans*), which are much more numerous. Although red wolves and coyotes differ in terms of morphology, DNA, and behavior, genetic evidence suggests that living red wolf individuals are actually hybrids. Red wolves are designated as an endangered species and hence receive legal protection under the Endangered Species Act. Some people think that their endangered status should be withdrawn because the remaining red wolves are hybrids, not members of a "pure" species. Do you agree? Why or why not?

11. WRITE ABOUT A THEME: INFORMATION
    In sexually reproducing species, each individual begins life with DNA inherited from both parent organisms. In a short essay (100–150 words), apply this idea to what occurs when organisms of two species that have homologous chromosomes mate and produce (F_1) hybrid offspring. What percentage of the DNA in the F_1 hybrids' chromosomes comes from each parent species? As the hybrids mate and produce F_2 and later-generation hybrid offspring, describe how recombination and natural selection may affect whether the DNA in hybrid chromosomes is derived from one parent species or the other.

12. SYNTHESIZE YOUR KNOWLEDGE

Suppose that females of one population of strawberry poison dart frogs (*Dendrobates pumilio*) prefer to mate with males that have a bright red and black coloration. In a different population, the females prefer males with yellow skin. Propose a hypothesis to explain how such differences could have arisen in allopatric versus sympatric populations.

For selected answers, see Appendix A.

MasteringBiology®

Students Go to **MasteringBiology** for assignments, the eText, and the Study Area with practice tests, animations, and activities.

Instructors Go to **MasteringBiology** for automatically graded tutorials and questions that you can assign to your students, plus Instructor Resources.

25

The History of Life on Earth

▲ Figure 25.1 **On what continent did these dinosaurs roam?**

Lost Worlds

Early Antarctic explorers encountered one of Earth's harshest, most barren environments, a land of extreme cold and almost no liquid water. Antarctic life is sparse and small—the largest fully terrestrial animal is a fly 5 mm long. But even as they struggled to survive, some of these explorers made an astonishing discovery: fossil evidence that life once thrived where it now barely exists. Fossils reveal that 500 million years ago, the ocean around Antarctica was warm and teeming with tropical invertebrates. Later, the continent was covered in forests for hundreds of millions of years. At various times, diverse animals stalked through these forests, including 3-m-tall predatory "terror birds" and giant dinosaurs such as the voracious *Cryolophosaurus* (Figure 25.1), a 7-m-long relative of *Tyrannosaurus rex*.

Fossils discovered in other parts of the world tell a similar story: Past organisms were very different from those presently living. The sweeping changes in life on Earth as revealed by fossils illustrate **macroevolution**, the broad pattern of evolution above the species level. Examples of macroevolutionary change include the emergence of terrestrial vertebrates through a series of speciation events, the impact of mass extinctions on biodiversity, and the origin of key adaptations such as flight.

Taken together, such changes provide a grand view of the evolutionary history of life. We'll begin by examining hypotheses regarding the origin of life. This is the most speculative topic of the entire unit, for no fossil evidence of that seminal

◄ *Cryolophosaurus* skull

519

episode exists. We will then turn to evidence from the fossil record about major events in the history of life and the factors that have shaped the rise and fall of different groups of organisms over time.

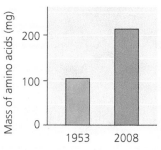

▲ **Figure 25.2 Amino acid synthesis in a simulated volcanic eruption.** In addition to his classic 1953 study, Miller also conducted an experiment simulating a volcanic eruption. In a 2008 reanalysis of those results, researchers found that far more amino acids were produced under simulated volcanic conditions than were produced in the conditions of the original 1953 experiment.

MAKE CONNECTIONS *How could more than 20 amino acids have been produced in the 2008 experiment? (See Concept 5.4.)*

CONCEPT 25.1

Conditions on early Earth made the origin of life possible

Direct evidence of life on early Earth comes from fossils of microorganisms that lived 3.5 billion years ago. But how did the first living cells appear? Observations and experiments in chemistry, geology, and physics have led scientists to propose one scenario that we'll examine here. They hypothesize that chemical and physical processes could have produced simple cells through a sequence of four main stages:

1. The abiotic (nonliving) synthesis of small organic molecules, such as amino acids and nitrogenous bases
2. The joining of these small molecules into macromolecules, such as proteins and nucleic acids
3. The packaging of these molecules into **protocells**, droplets with membranes that maintained an internal chemistry different from that of their surroundings
4. The origin of self-replicating molecules that eventually made inheritance possible

Though speculative, this scenario leads to predictions that can be tested in the laboratory. In this section, we'll examine some of the evidence for each stage.

Synthesis of Organic Compounds on Early Earth

Our planet formed 4.6 billion years ago, condensing from a vast cloud of dust and rocks that surrounded the young sun. For its first few hundred million years, Earth was bombarded by huge chunks of rock and ice left over from the formation of the solar system. The collisions generated so much heat that all of the available water was vaporized, preventing the formation of seas and lakes.

This massive bombardment ended about 4 billion years ago, setting the stage for the origin of life on our young planet. The first atmosphere had little oxygen and was probably thick with water vapor, along with various compounds released by volcanic eruptions, including nitrogen and its oxides, carbon dioxide, methane, ammonia, and hydrogen. As Earth cooled, the water vapor condensed into oceans, and much of the hydrogen escaped into space.

During the 1920s, Russian chemist A. I. Oparin and British scientist J. B. S. Haldane independently hypothesized that Earth's early atmosphere was a reducing (electron-adding) environment, in which organic compounds could have formed from simpler molecules. The energy for this synthesis could have come from lightning and UV radiation.

Haldane suggested that the early oceans were a solution of organic molecules, a "primitive soup" from which life arose.

In 1953, Stanley Miller, working with Harold Urey at the University of Chicago, tested the Oparin-Haldane hypothesis by creating laboratory conditions comparable to those that scientists at the time thought existed on early Earth (see Figure 4.2). His apparatus yielded a variety of amino acids found in organisms today, along with other organic compounds. Many laboratories have since repeated Miller's classic experiment using different recipes for the atmosphere, some of which also produced organic compounds.

However, some evidence suggests that the early atmosphere was made up primarily of nitrogen and carbon dioxide and was neither reducing nor oxidizing (electron removing). Recent Miller-Urey-type experiments using such "neutral" atmospheres have also produced organic molecules. In addition, small pockets of the early atmosphere, such as those near the openings of volcanoes, may have been reducing. Perhaps the first organic compounds formed near volcanoes. In a 2008 test of this hypothesis, researchers used modern equipment to reanalyze molecules that Miller had saved from one of his experiments. The 2008 study found that numerous amino acids had formed under conditions that simulated a volcanic eruption (**Figure 25.2**).

Another hypothesis is that organic compounds were first produced in deep-sea **hydrothermal vents**, areas on the seafloor where heated water and minerals gush from Earth's interior into the ocean. Some of these vents, known as "black smokers," release water so hot (300–400°C) that organic compounds formed there may have been unstable. But other deep-sea vents, called **alkaline vents**, release water that has a high pH (9–11) and is warm (40–90°C) rather than hot, an environment that may have been more suitable for the origin of life (**Figure 25.3**).

Studies related to the volcanic-atmosphere and alkaline-vent hypotheses show that the abiotic synthesis of organic molecules is possible under various conditions. Another

◄ **Figure 25.3 Did life originate in deep-sea alkaline vents?** The first organic compounds—and indeed, the first cells—may have arisen in warm alkaline vents similar to this one from the 40,000-year-old "Lost City" vent field in the mid-Atlantic Ocean. These vents contain hydrocarbons and are full of tiny pores (inset) lined with iron and other catalytic minerals. Early oceans were acidic, and so a pH gradient would have formed between the interior of the vents and the surrounding ocean water. Energy for the synthesis of organic compounds could have been harnessed from this pH gradient.

source of organic molecules may have been meteorites. For example, fragments of the Murchison meteorite, a 4.5-billion-year-old rock that landed in Australia in 1969, contain more than 80 amino acids, some in large amounts. These amino acids cannot be contaminants from Earth because they consist of an equal mix of D and L isomers (see Chapter 4). Organisms make and use only L isomers, with a few rare exceptions. Recent studies have shown that the Murchison meteorite also contained other key organic molecules, including lipids, simple sugars, and nitrogenous bases such as uracil.

Abiotic Synthesis of Macromolecules

The presence of small organic molecules, such as amino acids and nitrogenous bases, is not sufficient for the emergence of life as we know it. Every cell has many types of macromolecules, including enzymes and other proteins and the nucleic acids needed for self-replication. Could such macromolecules have formed on early Earth? A 2009 study demonstrated that one key step, the abiotic synthesis of RNA monomers, can occur spontaneously from simple precursor molecules. In addition, by dripping solutions of amino acids or RNA nucleotides onto hot sand, clay, or rock, researchers have produced polymers of these molecules. The polymers formed spontaneously, without the help of enzymes or ribosomes. Unlike proteins, the amino acid polymers are a complex mix of linked and cross-linked amino acids. Still, it is possible that such polymers acted as weak catalysts for a variety of chemical reactions on early Earth.

Protocells

All organisms must be able to carry out both reproduction and energy processing (metabolism). DNA molecules carry

genetic information, including the instructions needed to replicate themselves accurately during reproduction. But DNA replication requires elaborate enzymatic machinery, along with an abundant supply of nucleotide building blocks provided by the cell's metabolism. This suggests that self-replicating molecules and a metabolism-like source of building blocks may have appeared together in early protocells. The necessary conditions may have been met in *vesicles*, fluid-filled compartments enclosed by a membrane-like structure. Recent experiments show that abiotically produced vesicles can exhibit certain properties of life, including simple reproduction and metabolism, as well as the maintenance of an internal chemical environment different from that of their surroundings **(Figure 25.4)**.

For example, vesicles can form spontaneously when lipids or other organic molecules are added to water. When this occurs, the hydrophobic molecules in the mixture organize into a bilayer similar to the lipid bilayer of a plasma membrane. Adding substances such as *montmorillonite*, a soft mineral clay produced by the weathering of volcanic ash, greatly increases the rate of vesicle self-assembly (see Figure 25.4a). This clay, which is thought to have been common on early Earth, provides surfaces on which organic molecules become concentrated, increasing the likelihood that the molecules will react with each other and form vesicles. Abiotically produced vesicles can "reproduce" on their own (see Figure 25.4b), and

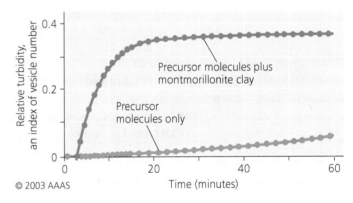

© 2003 AAAS

(a) Self-assembly. The presence of montmorillonite clay greatly increases the rate of vesicle self-assembly.

(b) Reproduction. Vesicles can divide on their own, as in this vesicle "giving birth" to smaller vesicles (LM).

(c) Absorption of RNA. This vesicle has incorporated montmorillonite clay particles coated with RNA (orange).

▲ **Figure 25.4 Features of abiotically produced vesicles.**

they can increase in size ("grow") without dilution of their contents. Vesicles also can absorb montmorillonite particles, including those on which RNA and other organic molecules have become attached (see Figure 25.4c). Finally, experiments have shown that some vesicles have a selectively permeable bilayer and can perform metabolic reactions using an external source of reagents—another important prerequisite for life.

Self-Replicating RNA

The first genetic material was most likely RNA, not DNA. RNA plays a central role in protein synthesis, but it can also function as an enzyme-like catalyst (see Chapter 17). Such RNA catalysts are called **ribozymes**. Some ribozymes can make complementary copies of short pieces of RNA, provided that they are supplied with nucleotide building blocks.

Natural selection on the molecular level has produced ribozymes capable of self-replication in the laboratory. How does this occur? Unlike double-stranded DNA, which takes the form of a uniform helix, single-stranded RNA molecules assume a variety of specific three-dimensional shapes mandated by their nucleotide sequences. In a particular environment, RNA molecules with certain nucleotide sequences may have shapes that enable them to replicate faster and with fewer errors than other sequences. The RNA molecule with the greatest ability to replicate itself will leave the most descendant molecules. Occasionally, a copying error will result in a molecule with a shape that is even more adept at self-replication than the ancestral sequence. Similar selection events may have occurred on early Earth. Thus, life as we know it may have been preceded by an "RNA world," in which small RNA molecules were able to replicate and to store genetic information about the vesicles that carried them.

A vesicle with self-replicating, catalytic RNA would differ from its many neighbors that lacked such molecules. If that vesicle could grow, split, and pass its RNA molecules to its daughters, the daughters would be protocells. Although the first such protocells likely carried only limited amounts of genetic information, specifying only a few properties, their inherited characteristics could have been acted on by natural selection. The most successful of the early protocells would have increased in number because they could exploit their resources effectively and pass their abilities on to subsequent generations.

Once RNA sequences that carried genetic information appeared in protocells, many additional changes would have been possible. For example, RNA could have provided the template on which DNA nucleotides were assembled. Double-stranded DNA is a more chemically stable repository for genetic information than is the more fragile RNA. DNA also can be replicated more accurately. Accurate replication was advantageous as genomes grew larger through gene duplication and other processes and as more properties of the protocells became coded in genetic information. Once DNA appeared, the stage was set for a blossoming of new forms of life—a change we see documented in the fossil record.

CONCEPT CHECK 25.1

1. What hypothesis did Miller test in his classic experiment?
2. How would the appearance of protocells have represented a key step in the origin of life?
3. **MAKE CONNECTIONS** In changing from an "RNA world" to today's "DNA world," genetic information must have flowed from RNA to DNA. After reviewing Figures 17.3 and 19.8, suggest how this could have occurred. Is such a flow a common occurrence today?

For suggested answers, see Appendix A.

CONCEPT 25.2

The fossil record documents the history of life

Starting with the earliest traces of life, the fossil record opens a window into the world of long ago and provides glimpses of the evolution of life over billions of years. In this section, we'll examine fossils as a form of scientific evidence: how fossils form, how scientists date and interpret them, and what they can and cannot tell us about changes in the history of life.

The Fossil Record

Sedimentary rocks are the richest source of fossils. As a result, the fossil record is based primarily on the sequence in which fossils have accumulated in sedimentary rock layers, called *strata* (see Figure 22.3). Useful information is also provided by other types of fossils, such as insects preserved in amber (fossilized tree sap) and mammals frozen in ice.

The fossil record shows that there have been great changes in the kinds of organisms on Earth at different points in time (**Figure 25.5**). Many past organisms were unlike organisms living today, and many organisms that once were common are now extinct. As we'll see later in this section, fossils also document how new groups of organisms arose from previously existing ones.

As substantial and significant as the fossil record is, keep in mind that it is an incomplete chronicle of evolutionary change. Many of Earth's organisms did not die in the right place at the right time to be preserved as fossils. Of those fossils that were formed, many were destroyed by later geologic processes, and only a fraction of the others have been discovered. As a result, the known fossil record is biased in favor of species that existed for a long time, were abundant and widespread in certain kinds of environments, and had hard shells, skeletons, or other parts that facilitated their

▼ **Figure 25.5 Documenting the history of life.** These fossils illustrate representative organisms from different points in time. Although prokaryotes and unicellular eukaryotes are shown only at the base of the diagram, these organisms continue to thrive today. In fact, most organisms on Earth are unicellular.

Present

100 million years ago

▼ *Rhomaleosaurus victor*, a plesiosaur. These large marine reptiles were important predators from 200 million to 65.5 million years ago.

▼ *Dimetrodon*, the largest known carnivore of its day, was more closely related to mammals than to reptiles. The spectacular "sail" on its back may have functioned in temperature regulation.

0.5 m

1 m

175

▶ *Tiktaalik*, an extinct aquatic organism that is the closest known relative of the four-legged vertebrates that went on to colonize land

200

270

300

4.5 cm

▲ *Coccosteus cuspidatus*, a placoderm (fishlike vertebrate) that had a bony shield covering its head and front end

375

▶ *Hallucigenia*, a member of a morphologically diverse group of animals found in the Burgess Shale fossil bed in the Canadian Rockies

1 cm

400

▲ Some prokaryotes bind thin films of sediments together, producing layered rocks called stromatolites, such as these in Shark Bay, Australia.

500

510

◀ *Dickinsonia costata*, a member of the Ediacaran biota, an extinct group of soft-bodied organisms

2.5 cm

560

▲ A section through a fossilized stromatolite

600

▶ *Tappania*, a unicellular eukaryote thought to be either an alga or a fungus

1,500

3,500

fossilization. Even with its limitations, however, the fossil record is a remarkably detailed account of biological change over the vast scale of geologic time. Furthermore, as shown by the recently unearthed fossils of whale ancestors with hind limbs (see Figures 22.19 and 22.20), gaps in the fossil record continue to be filled by new discoveries.

How Rocks and Fossils Are Dated

Fossils are valuable data for reconstructing the history of life, but only if we can determine where they fit in that unfolding story. While the order of fossils in rock strata tells us the sequence in which the fossils were laid down—their relative ages—it does not tell us their actual (absolute) ages. Examining the relative positions of fossils is like peeling off layers of wallpaper in an old house. You can infer the sequence in which the layers were applied, but not the year each layer was added.

How can we determine the absolute age of a fossil? (Note that "absolute" does not mean errorless, but that an age is given in years rather than relative terms such as *before* and *after*.) One of the most common techniques is **radiometric dating**, which is based on the decay of radioactive isotopes (see Chapter 2). In this process, a radioactive "parent" isotope decays to a "daughter" isotope at a characteristic rate. The rate of decay is expressed by the **half-life**, the time required for 50% of the parent isotope to decay (Figure 25.6). Each type of radioactive isotope has a characteristic half-life, which is not affected by temperature, pressure, or other environmental variables. For example, carbon-14 decays relatively quickly; its half-life is 5,730 years. Uranium-238 decays slowly; its half-life is 4.5 billion years.

Fossils contain isotopes of elements that accumulated in the organisms when they were alive. For example, a living organism contains the most common carbon isotope, carbon-12, as well as a radioactive isotope, carbon-14. When the organism dies, it stops accumulating carbon, and the amount of carbon-12 in its tissues does not change over time. However, the carbon-14 that it contains at the time of death slowly decays into another element, nitrogen-14. Thus, by measuring the ratio of carbon-14 to carbon-12 in a fossil, we can determine the fossil's age. This method works for fossils up to about 75,000 years old; fossils older than that contain too little carbon-14 to be detected with current techniques. Radioactive isotopes with longer half-lives are used to date older fossils.

Determining the age of these older fossils in sedimentary rocks is challenging. Organisms do not use radioisotopes with long half-lives, such as uranium-238, to build their bones or shells. In addition, the sedimentary rocks themselves tend to consist of sediments of differing ages. So while we may not be able to date these older fossils directly, an indirect method can be used to infer the age of fossils that are sandwiched between two layers of volcanic rock. As lava

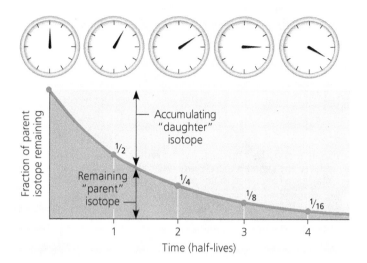

© Pearson Education, Inc.

▲ **Figure 25.6 Radiometric dating.** In this diagram, each division of the clock face represents a half-life.

> **DRAW IT** *Relabel the x-axis of this graph in years to illustrate the radioactive decay of uranium-238 (half-life = 4.5 billion years).*

cools into volcanic rock, radioisotopes from the surrounding environment become trapped in the newly formed rock. Some of the trapped radioisotopes have long half-lives, allowing geologists to estimate the ages of ancient volcanic rocks. If two volcanic layers surrounding fossils are determined to be 525 million and 535 million years old, for example, then the fossils are roughly 530 million years old.

The Origin of New Groups of Organisms

Some fossils provide a detailed look at the origin of new groups of organisms. Such fossils are central to our understanding of evolution; they illustrate how new features arise and how long it takes for such changes to occur. We'll examine one such case here: the origin of mammals.

Along with amphibians and reptiles, mammals belong to the group of animals called *tetrapods* (from the Greek *tetra*, four, and *pod*, foot), named for having four limbs. Mammals have a number of unique anatomical features that fossilize readily, allowing scientists to trace their origin. For example, the lower jaw is composed of one bone (the dentary) in mammals but several bones in other tetrapods. In addition, the lower and upper jaws in mammals hinge between a different set of bones than in other tetrapods. Mammals also have a unique set of three bones that transmit sound in the middle ear, the hammer, anvil, and stirrup, whereas other tetrapods have only one such bone, the stirrup (see Chapter 34). Finally, the teeth of mammals are differentiated into incisors (for tearing), canines (for piercing), and the multi-pointed premolars and molars (for crushing and grinding). In contrast, the teeth of other tetrapods usually consist of a row of undifferentiated, single-pointed teeth.

As detailed in **Figure 25.7**, the fossil record shows that the unique features of mammalian jaws and teeth evolved

▼ **Figure 25.7**

Exploring The Origin of Mammals

Over the course of 120 million years, mammals originated gradually from a group of tetrapods called synapsids. Shown here are a few of the many fossil organisms whose morphological features represent intermediate steps between living mammals and their synapsid ancestors. The evolutionary context of the origin of mammals is shown in the tree diagram at right (the dagger symbol † indicates extinct lineages).

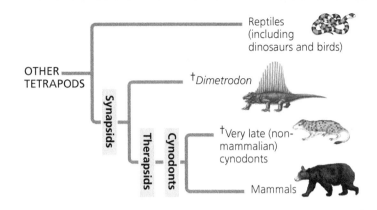

Key to skull bones

▨ Articular	▨ Dentary
▨ Quadrate	▨ Squamosal

Synapsid (300 mya)

Synapsids had multiple bones in the lower jaw and single-pointed teeth. The jaw hinge was formed by the articular and quadrate bones. Synapsids also had an opening called the temporal fenestra behind the eye socket. Powerful cheek muscles for closing the jaws probably passed through the temporal fenestra. Over time, this opening enlarged and moved in front of the hinge between the lower and upper jaws, thereby increasing the power and precision with which the jaws could be closed (much as moving a doorknob away from the hinge makes a door easier to close).

Therapsid (280 mya)

Later, a group of synapsids called therapsids appeared. Therapsids had large dentary bones, long faces, and the first examples of specialized teeth, large canines. These trends continued in a group of therapsids called cynodonts.

Early cynodont (260 mya)

In early cynodont therapsids, the dentary was the largest bone in the lower jaw, the temporal fenestra was large and positioned forward of the jaw hinge, and teeth with several cusps first appeared (not visible in the diagram). As in earlier synapsids, the jaw had an articular-quadrate hinge.

Later cynodont (220 mya)

Later cynodonts had teeth with complex cusp patterns and their lower and upper jaws hinged in two locations: They retained the original articular-quadrate hinge and formed a new, second hinge between the dentary and squamosal bones. (The temporal fenestra is not visible in this or the below cynodont skull at the angles shown.)

Very late cynodont (195 mya)

In some very late (non-mammalian) cynodonts and early mammals, the original articular-quadrate hinge was lost, leaving the dentary-squamosal hinge as the only hinge between the lower and upper jaws, as in living mammals. The articular and quadrate bones migrated into the ear region (not shown), where they functioned in transmitting sound. In the mammal lineage, these two bones later evolved into the familiar hammer (malleus) and anvil (incus) bones of the ear.

© 2001 AAAS

gradually over time, in a series of steps. As you study , bear in mind that it includes just a few examples of the fossil skulls that document the origin of mammals. If all the known fossils in the sequence were arranged by shape and placed side by side, their features would blend smoothly from one group to the next. Some of these fossils would reflect how the features of a group that dominates life today, the mammals, gradually arose in a previously existing group, the cynodonts. Others would reveal side branches on the tree of life—groups of organisms that thrived for millions of years but ultimately left no descendants that survive today.

CONCEPT CHECK 25.2

1. Your measurements indicate that a fossilized skull you unearthed has a carbon-14/carbon-12 ratio about $1/16$ that of the skulls of present-day animals. What is the approximate age of the fossilized skull?

2. Describe an example from the fossil record that shows how life has changed over time.

3. **WHAT IF?** Suppose researchers discover a fossil of an organism that lived 300 million years ago but had mammalian teeth and a mammalian jaw hinge. What inferences might you draw from this fossil about the origin of mammals and the evolution of novel skeletal structures? Explain.

For suggested answers, see Appendix A.

CONCEPT 25.3

Key events in life's history include the origins of unicellular and multicellular organisms and the colonization of land

The study of fossils has helped geologists establish a **geologic record**: a standard time scale that divides Earth's history into four eons and further subdivisions (**Table 25.1**). The first three eons—the Hadean, Archaean, and Proterozoic—together lasted about 4 billion years. The Phanerozoic eon, roughly the last half billion years, encompasses most of the time that animals have existed on Earth. It is divided into three eras: the Paleozoic, Mesozoic, and Cenozoic. Each era represents a distinct age in the history of Earth and its life. For example, the Mesozoic era is sometimes called the "age of reptiles" because of its abundance of reptilian fossils, including those of dinosaurs. The boundaries between the eras correspond to major extinction events seen in the fossil record, when many forms of life disappeared and were replaced by forms that evolved from the survivors.

As we've seen, the fossil record provides a sweeping overview of the history of life over geologic time. Here we will focus on a few major events in that history, returning to study the details in Unit Five.

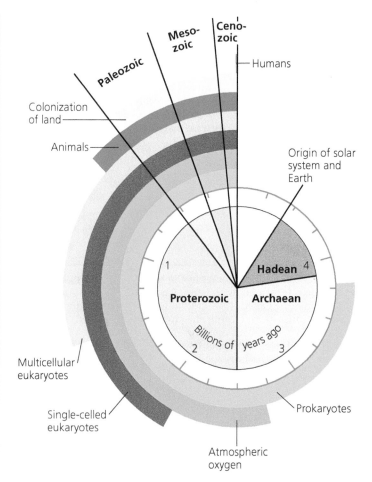

▲ **Figure 25.8 Clock analogy for some key events in Earth's history.** The clock ticks down from the origin of Earth 4.6 billion years ago to the present.

Figure 25.8 uses the analogy of a clock to place these events in the context of the geologic record. This clock will reappear at various points in this section as a quick visual reminder of when the events we are discussing took place.

The First Single-Celled Organisms

The earliest direct evidence of life, dating from 3.5 billion years ago, comes from fossilized stromatolites (see Figure 25.5). **Stromatolites** are layered rocks that form when certain prokaryotes bind thin films of sediment together. Present-day stromatolites are found in a few shallow marine bays. Stromatolites and other early prokaryotes were Earth's sole inhabitants for more than 1.5 billion years. As we will see, these prokaryotes transformed life on our planet.

Table 25.1 The Geologic Record

Relative Duration of Eons	Era	Period	Epoch	Age (Millions of Years Ago)	Some Important Events in the History of Life
Phan-erozoic	**Cenozoic**	Quaternary	Holocene	0.01	Historical time
			Pleistocene	2.6	Ice ages; origin of genus *Homo*
		Neogene	Pliocene	5.3	Appearance of bipedal human ancestors
			Miocene	23	Continued radiation of mammals and angiosperms; earliest direct human ancestors
		Paleogene	Oligocene	33.9	Origins of many primate groups
			Eocene	55.8	Angiosperm dominance increases; continued radiation of most present-day mammalian orders
			Paleocene	65.5	Major radiation of mammals, birds, and pollinating insects
Proter-ozoic	**Mesozoic**	Cretaceous		145.5	Flowering plants (angiosperms) appear and diversify; many groups of organisms, including most dinosaurs, become extinct at end of period
		Jurassic		199.6	Gymnosperms continue as dominant plants; dinosaurs abundant and diverse
		Triassic		251	Cone-bearing plants (gymnosperms) dominate landscape; dinosaurs evolve and radiate; origin of mammals
	Paleozoic	Permian		299	Radiation of reptiles; origin of most present-day groups of insects; extinction of many marine and terrestrial organisms at end of period
		Carboniferous		359	Extensive forests of vascular plants form; first seed plants appear; origin of reptiles; amphibians dominant
		Devonian		416	Diversification of bony fishes; first tetrapods and insects appear
		Silurian		444	Diversification of early vascular plants
		Ordovician		488	Marine algae abundant; colonization of land by diverse fungi, plants, and animals
Archaean		Cambrian		542	Sudden increase in diversity of many animal phyla (Cambrian explosion)
		Ediacaran		635	Diverse algae and soft-bodied invertebrate animals appear
				1,800	Oldest fossils of eukaryotic cells appear
				2,500	
				2,700	Concentration of atmospheric oxygen begins to increase
Hadean				3,500	Oldest fossils of cells (prokaryotes) appear
				3,850	Oldest known rocks on Earth's surface
				Approx. 4,600	Origin of Earth

Photosynthesis and the Oxygen Revolution

—Atmospheric oxygen

Most atmospheric oxygen gas (O_2) is of biological origin, produced during the water-splitting step of photosynthesis. When oxygenic photosynthesis first evolved, the free O_2 it produced probably dissolved in the surrounding water until it reached a high enough concentration to react with elements dissolved in water, including iron. This would have caused the iron to precipitate as iron oxide, which accumulated as sediments. These sediments were compressed into banded iron formations, red layers of rock containing iron oxide that are a source of iron ore today. Once all of the dissolved iron had precipitated, additional O_2 dissolved in the water until the seas and lakes became saturated with O_2. After this occurred, the O_2 finally began to "gas out" of the water and enter the atmosphere. This change left its mark in the rusting of iron-rich terrestrial rocks, a process that began about 2.7 billion years ago. This chronology implies that bacteria similar to today's cyanobacteria (oxygen-releasing, photosynthetic bacteria) originated before 2.7 billion years ago.

The amount of atmospheric O_2 increased gradually from about 2.7 to 2.4 billion years ago, but then shot up relatively rapidly to between 1% and 10% of its present level (Figure 25.9). This "oxygen revolution" had an enormous impact on life. In certain of its chemical forms, oxygen attacks chemical bonds and can inhibit enzymes and damage cells. As a result, the rising concentration of atmospheric O_2 probably doomed many prokaryotic groups. Some species survived in habitats that remained anaerobic, where we find their descendants living today (see Chapter 27). Among

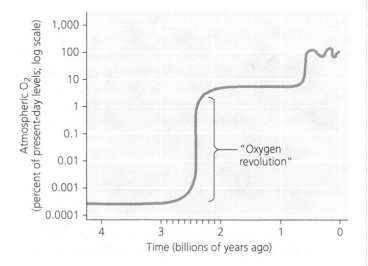

▲ **Figure 25.9 The rise of atmospheric oxygen.** Chemical analyses of ancient rocks have enabled this reconstruction of atmospheric oxygen levels during Earth's history.

other survivors, diverse adaptations to the changing atmosphere evolved, including cellular respiration, which uses O_2 in the process of harvesting the energy stored in organic molecules.

The rise in atmospheric O_2 levels left a huge imprint on the history of life. A few hundred million years later, another fundamental change occurred: the origin of the eukaryotic cell.

The First Eukaryotes

Single-celled eukaryotes

The oldest widely accepted fossils of eukaryotic organisms are 1.8 billion years old. Recall that eukaryotic cells have more complex organization than prokaryotic cells: Eukaryotic cells have a nuclear envelope, mitochondria, endoplasmic reticulum, and other internal structures that prokaryotes lack. Also, unlike prokaryotic cells, eukaryotic cells have a well-developed cytoskeleton, a feature that enables eukaryotic cells to change their shape and thereby surround and engulf other cells.

How did such eukaryotic features evolve from prokaryotic cells? Much evidence supports the **endosymbiont theory**, which posits that mitochondria and plastids (a general term for chloroplasts and related organelles) were formerly small prokaryotes that began living within larger cells. The term *endosymbiont* refers to a cell that lives within another cell, called the *host cell*. The prokaryotic ancestors of mitochondria and plastids probably entered the host cell as undigested prey or internal parasites. Though such a process may seem unlikely, scientists have directly observed cases in which endosymbionts that began as prey or parasites developed a mutually beneficial relationship with the host in as little as five years.

By whatever means the relationship began, we can hypothesize how the symbiosis could have become beneficial. For example, in a world that was becoming increasingly aerobic, a host that was itself an anaerobe would have benefited from endosymbionts that could make use of the oxygen. Over time, the host and endosymbionts would have become a single organism, its parts inseparable. Although all eukaryotes have mitochondria or remnants of these organelles, they do not all have plastids. Thus, the hypothesis of **serial endosymbiosis** supposes that mitochondria evolved before plastids through a sequence of endosymbiotic events (Figure 25.10).

A great deal of evidence supports the endosymbiotic origin of mitochondria and plastids:

- The inner membranes of both organelles have enzymes and transport systems that are homologous to those found in the plasma membranes of living prokaryotes.

- Mitochondria and plastids replicate by a splitting process that is similar to that of certain prokaryotes. In addition, each of these organelles contains circular DNA molecules that, like the chromosomes of bacteria, are not associated with histones or large amounts of other proteins.
- As might be expected of organelles descended from free-living organisms, mitochondria and plastids also have the cellular machinery (including ribosomes) needed to transcribe and translate their DNA into proteins.
- Finally, in terms of size, RNA sequences, and sensitivity to certain antibiotics, the ribosomes of mitochondria and plastids are more similar to prokaryotic ribosomes than they are to the cytoplasmic ribosomes of eukaryotic cells.

In Chapter 28, we'll return to origin of eukaryotes, focusing on what genomic data have revealed about the prokaryotic lineages that gave rise to the host and endosymbiont cells.

The Origin of Multicellularity

An orchestra can play a greater variety of musical compositions than a violin soloist can; the increased complexity of the orchestra makes more variations possible. Likewise, the appearance of structurally complex eukaryotic cells sparked the evolution of greater morphological diversity than was possible for the simpler prokaryotic cells. After the first eukaryotes appeared, a great range of unicellular forms evolved, giving rise to the diversity of single-celled eukaryotes that continue to flourish today. Another wave of diversification also occurred: Some single-celled eukaryotes gave rise to multicellular forms, whose descendants include a variety of algae, plants, fungi, and animals.

Early Multicellular Eukaryotes

The oldest known fossils of multicellular eukaryotes that can be resolved taxonomically are of relatively small red algae that lived 1.2 billion years ago; even older fossils, dating to 1.8 billion years ago, may also be of small, multicellular eukaryotes. Larger and more diverse multicellular eukaryotes do not appear in the fossil record until about 600 million years ago (see Figure 25.5). These fossils, referred to as the Ediacaran biota, were of soft-bodied organisms—some over 1 m long—that lived from 600 to 535 million years ago. The Ediacaran biota included both algae and animals, along with various organisms of unknown taxonomic affinity.

The rise of large eukaryotes in the Ediacaran period represents an enormous change in the history of life. Before that time, Earth was a microbial world: Its only inhabitants

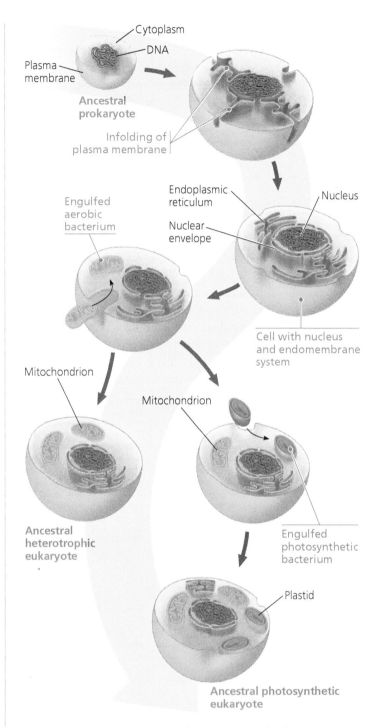

▲ **Figure 25.10 A hypothesis for the origin of eukaryotes through serial endosymbiosis.** The proposed ancestors of mitochondria were aerobic, heterotrophic prokaryotes (meaning that they used oxygen to metabolize organic molecules obtained from other organisms). The proposed ancestors of plastids were photosynthetic prokaryotes. In this figure, the arrows represent change over evolutionary time.

were single-celled prokaryotes and eukaryotes, along with an assortment of microscopic, multicellular eukaryotes. As the diversification of the Ediacaran biota came to a close about 535 million years ago, the stage was set for another, even more spectacular burst of evolutionary change.

The Cambrian Explosion

Many present-day animal phyla appear suddenly in fossils formed 535–525 million years ago, early in the Cambrian period. This phenomenon is referred to as the **Cambrian explosion**. Fossils of several animal groups—sponges, cnidarians (sea anemones and their relatives), and molluscs (snails, clams, and their relatives)—appear in even older rocks dating from the late Proterozoic **(Figure 25.11)**.

Prior to the Cambrian explosion, all large animals were soft-bodied. The fossils of large pre-Cambrian animals reveal little evidence of predation. Instead, these animals appear to have been grazers (feeding on algae), filter feeders, or scavengers, not hunters. The Cambrian explosion changed all of that. In a relatively short period of time (10 million years), predators over 1 m in length emerged that had claws and other features for capturing prey; simultaneously, new defensive adaptations, such as sharp spines and heavy body armor, appeared in their prey (see Figure 25.5).

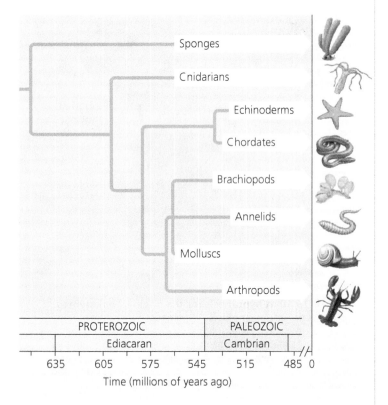

▲ **Figure 25.11 Appearance of selected animal groups.** The white bars indicate earliest appearances of these animal groups in the fossil record.

DRAW IT *Circle the branch point that represents the most recent common ancestor of chordates and annelids. What is a minimum estimate of that ancestor's age?*

Although the Cambrian explosion had an enormous impact on life on Earth, it appears that many animal phyla originated long before that time. Recent DNA analyses suggest that sponges, an early-diverging animal group, had evolved by 700 million years ago; such analyses also indicate that the common ancestor of arthropods, chordates, and other animal phyla that radiated during the Cambrian explosion lived 670 million years ago. Researchers have unearthed 710-million-year-old fossils containing steroids indicative of a particular group of sponges—a finding that supports the molecular data. In contrast, the oldest fossil assigned to an extant animal phylum is that of the mollusc *Kimberella*, which lived 560 million years ago. Overall, molecular and fossil data indicate that the Cambrian explosion had a "long fuse"—at least 25 million years long based on the age of *Kimberella* fossils, and over 100 million years long based on some DNA analyses. We'll explore factors that may have triggered the Cambrian explosion in Chapter 32.

The Colonization of Land

The colonization of land was another milestone in the history of life. There is fossil evidence that cyanobacteria and other photosynthetic prokaryotes coated damp terrestrial surfaces well over a billion years ago. However, larger forms of life, such as fungi, plants, and animals, did not begin to colonize land until about 500 million years ago. This gradual evolutionary venture out of aquatic environments was associated with adaptations that made it possible to reproduce on land and that helped prevent dehydration. For example, many land plants today have a vascular system for transporting materials internally and a waterproof coating of wax on their leaves that slows the loss of water to the air. Early signs of these adaptations were present 420 million years ago, at which time small plants (about 10 cm high) existed that had a vascular system but lacked true roots or leaves. By 40 million years later, plants had diversified greatly and included reeds and treelike plants with true roots and leaves.

Plants colonized land in the company of fungi. Even today, the roots of most plants are associated with fungi that aid in the absorption of water and minerals from the soil (see Chapter 31). These root fungi (or *mycorrhizae*), in turn, obtain their organic nutrients from the plants. Such mutually beneficial associations of plants and fungi are evident in some of the oldest fossilized plants, dating this relationship back to the early spread of life onto land **(Figure 25.12)**.

Although many animal groups are now represented in terrestrial environments, the most widespread and diverse land

Zone of arbuscule-containing cells

100 nm

▲ **Figure 25.12 An ancient symbiosis.** This 405-million-year-old fossil stem (cross section) documents mycorrhizae in the early land plant *Aglaophyton major*. The inset shows an enlarged view of a cell containing a branched fungal structure called an arbuscule; the fossil arbuscule resembles those seen in plant cells today.

animals are arthropods (particularly insects and spiders) and tetrapods. Arthropods were among the first animals to colonize land, roughly 450 million years ago. The earliest tetrapods found in the fossil record lived about 365 million years ago and appear to have evolved from a group of lobe-finned fishes (see Chapter 34). Tetrapods include humans, although we are late arrivals on the scene. The human lineage diverged from other primates around 6–7 million years ago, and our species originated only about 195,000 years ago. If the clock of Earth's history were rescaled to represent an hour, humans appeared less than 0.2 second ago.

CONCEPT CHECK 25.3

1. The first appearance of free oxygen in the atmosphere likely triggered a massive wave of extinctions among the prokaryotes of the time. Why?

2. What evidence supports the hypothesis that mitochondria preceded plastids in the evolution of eukaryotic cells?

3. **WHAT IF?** What would a fossil record of life today look like?

For suggested answers, see Appendix A.

CONCEPT 25.4

The rise and fall of groups of organisms reflect differences in speciation and extinction rates

From its beginnings, life on Earth has been marked by the rise and fall of groups of organisms. Anaerobic prokaryotes originated, flourished, and then declined as the oxygen content of the atmosphere rose. Billions of years later, the first tetrapods emerged from the sea, giving rise to several major

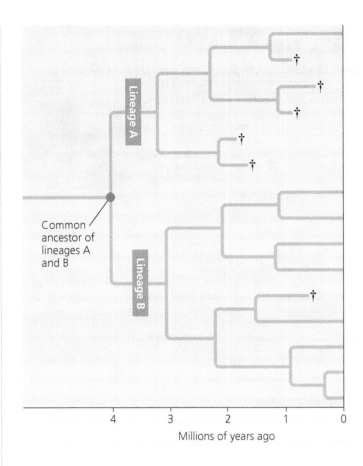

Common ancestor of lineages A and B

Lineage A

Lineage B

Millions of years ago

▲ **Figure 25.13 How speciation and extinction affect diversity.** The species diversity of an evolutionary lineage will increase when more new member species originate than are lost to extinction. In this hypothetical example, by 2 million years ago both lineage A and lineage B have given rise to four species, and no species have become extinct (denoted by a dagger symbol). By time 0, however, lineage A contains only one species while lineage B contains eight species.

INTERPRET THE DATA *Consider the period from 2 million years ago to time 0. For each lineage, determine how many speciation and extinction events occurred during that time.*

new groups of organisms. One of these, the amphibians, went on to dominate life on land for 100 million years, until other tetrapods (including dinosaurs and, later, mammals) replaced them as the dominant terrestrial vertebrates.

The rise and fall of these and other major groups of organisms have shaped the history of life. Narrowing our focus, we can also see that the rise or fall of any particular group is related to the speciation and extinction rates of its member species (**Figure 25.13**). Just as a population increases in size when there are more births than deaths, the rise of a group of organisms occurs when more new species are produced than are lost to extinction. The reverse occurs when a group is in decline. In the Scientific Skills Exercise, you will interpret data from the fossil record about changes in a group of snail species in the early Paleogene period. Such changes in the fates of groups of organisms have been influenced by large-scale processes such as plate tectonics, mass extinctions, and adaptive radiations.

Estimating Quantitative Data from a Graph and Developing Hypotheses

Do Ecological Factors Affect Evolutionary Rates? Researchers studied the fossil record to investigate whether differing modes of larval dispersal might explain species longevity within one taxon of marine snails, the family Volutidae. Some of the snail species had nonplanktonic larvae: They developed directly into adults without a swimming stage. Other species had planktonic larvae: They had a swimming stage and could disperse very long distances. The adults of these planktonic species tended to have broad geographic distributions, whereas nonplanktonic species tended to be more isolated.

How the Research Was Done The researchers studied the stratigraphic distribution of volutes in outcrops of sedimentary rocks located along North America's Gulf coast. These rocks, which formed from 65 to 37 million years ago, early in the Paleogene period, are an excellent source of well-preserved snail fossils. The researchers were able to classify each fossil species of volute snail as having planktonic or nonplanktonic larvae based on features of the earliest formed whorls of the snail's shell. Each bar in the graph shows how long one species of snail persisted in the fossil record.

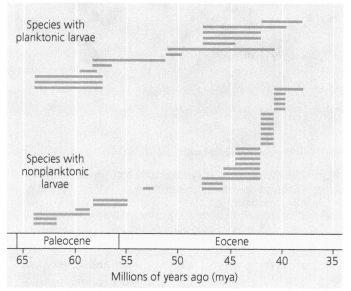

© 1978 AAAS

Interpret the Data

1. You can estimate quantitative data (fairly precisely) from a graph. The first step is to obtain a conversion factor by measuring along an axis that has a scale. In this case, 25 million years (my; from 65 to 40 million years ago (mya) on the *x*-axis is represented by a distance of 7.0 cm. This yields a conversion factor (a ratio) of 25 my/7.0 cm = 3.6 my/cm. To estimate the time period represented by a horizontal bar on this graph, measure the length of that bar in centimeters and multiply that measurement by the conversion factor, 3.6 my/cm. For example, a bar that measures 1.1 cm on the graph represents a persistence time of 1.1 cm × 3.6 my/cm = 4 million years.

2. Calculate the mean (average) persistence times for species with planktonic larvae and species with nonplanktonic larvae.

3. Count the number of new species that form in each group beginning at 60 mya (the first three species in each group were present around 64 mya, the first time period sampled, so we don't know when those species first appear in the fossil record).

4. Propose a hypothesis to explain the differences in longevity of snail species with planktonic and nonplanktonic larvae.

(MB) A version of this Scientific Skills Exercise can be assigned in MasteringBiology.

Data from: T. A. Hansen, Larval dispersal and species longevity in Lower Tertiary gastropods, *Science* 199:885–887 (1978). Reprinted with permission from AAAS.

Plate Tectonics

If photographs of Earth were taken from space every 10,000 years and spliced together to make a movie, it would show something many of us find hard to imagine: The seemingly "rock solid" continents we live on move over time. Over the past 1.5 billion years, there have been three occasions (1.1 billion, 600 million, and 250 million years ago) when most of the landmasses of Earth came together to form a supercontinent, then later broke apart. Each time, this breakup yielded a different configuration of continents. Looking into the future, some geologists have estimated that the continents will come together again and form a new supercontinent roughly 250 million years from now.

According to the theory of **plate tectonics**, the continents are part of great plates of Earth's crust that essentially float on the hot, underlying portion of the mantle (**Figure 25.14**). Movements in the mantle cause the plates to move over time in a process called *continental drift*. Geologists can measure the rate at which the plates are moving now, usually only a few centimeters per year. They can also infer the past locations of the continents using the magnetic signal recorded in rocks at the time of their formation. This method works because as a continent shifts its position over time, the direction of magnetic north recorded in its newly formed rocks also changes.

Earth's major tectonic plates are shown in **Figure 25.15**. Many important geologic processes, including the formation of mountains and islands, occur at plate boundaries. In some cases, two plates are moving away from each other, as are the North American and Eurasian plates, which are currently drifting apart at a rate of about 2 cm per year.

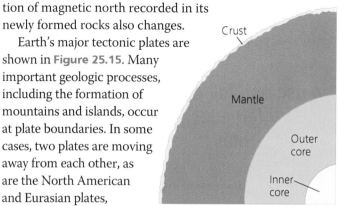

▲ **Figure 25.14 Cutaway view of Earth.** The thickness of the crust is exaggerated here.

In other cases, two plates are sliding past each other, forming regions where earthquakes are common. California's infamous San Andreas Fault is part of a border where two plates slide past each other. In still other cases, two plates collide, producing violent upheavals and forming new mountains along the plate boundaries. One spectacular example of this occurred 45 million years ago, when the Indian plate crashed into the Eurasian plate, starting the formation of the Himalayan mountains.

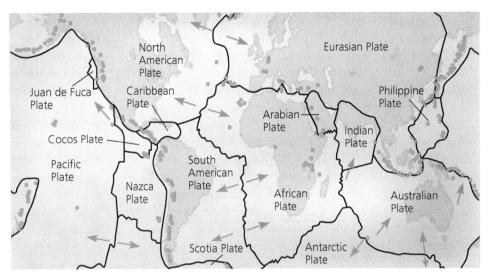

▲ Figure 25.15 **Earth's major tectonic plates.** The arrows indicate direction of movement. The reddish orange dots represent zones of violent tectonic activity.

Consequences of Continental Drift

Plate movements rearrange geography slowly, but their cumulative effects are dramatic. In addition to reshaping the physical features of our planet, continental drift also has a major impact on life on Earth.

One reason for this is that continental drift alters the habitats in which organisms live. Consider the changes shown in **Figure 25.16**. About 250 million years ago, plate movements brought previously separated landmasses together into a supercontinent named **Pangaea**. Ocean basins became deeper, which lowered sea levels and drained shallow coastal seas. At that time, as now, most marine species inhabited shallow waters, and the formation of Pangaea destroyed much of that habitat. Pangaea's interior was cold and dry, probably an even more severe environment than that of central Asia today. Overall, the formation of Pangaea greatly altered the physical environment and climate, which drove some species to extinction and provided new opportunities for groups of organisms that survived the crisis.

Organisms are also affected by the climate change that results when a continent shifts its location. The southern tip of Labrador, Canada, for example, once was located in the tropics but has moved 40° to the north over the last 200 million years. When faced with the changes in climate that such shifts in position entail, organisms adapt, move to a new location, or become extinct (this last outcome occurred for many organisms stranded on Antarctica).

Continental drift also promotes allopatric speciation on a grand scale. When supercontinents break apart, regions that once were connected become isolated. As the continents drifted apart over the last 200 million years, each became a separate evolutionary arena, with lineages of plants and animals that diverged from those on other continents.

Finally, continental drift can help explain puzzles about the geographic distribution of extinct organisms, such as why fossils of the same species of Permian freshwater reptiles have been discovered in both Brazil and the West African nation of Ghana. These two parts of the world, now separated by 3,000 km of ocean, were joined together when

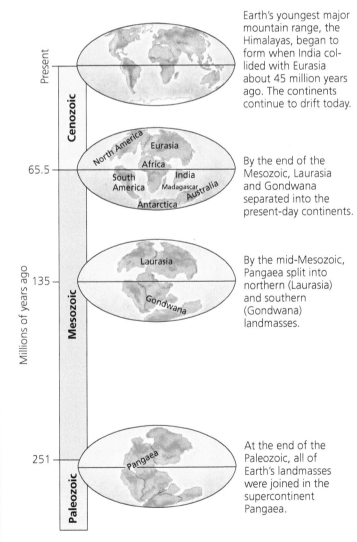

Earth's youngest major mountain range, the Himalayas, began to form when India collided with Eurasia about 45 million years ago. The continents continue to drift today.

By the end of the Mesozoic, Laurasia and Gondwana separated into the present-day continents.

By the mid-Mesozoic, Pangaea split into northern (Laurasia) and southern (Gondwana) landmasses.

At the end of the Paleozoic, all of Earth's landmasses were joined in the supercontinent Pangaea.

▲ Figure 25.16 **The history of continental drift during the Phanerozoic eon.**

? *Is the Australian plate's current direction of movement (see Figure 25.15) similar to the direction it traveled over the past 65 million years?*

these reptiles were living. Continental drift also explains much about the current distributions of organisms, such as why Australian fauna and flora contrast so sharply with those of the rest of the world. Marsupial mammals fill ecological roles in Australia analogous to those filled by eutherians (placental mammals) on other continents (see Figure 22.18). Fossil evidence suggests that marsupials originated in what is now Asia and reached Australia via South America and Antarctica while the continents were still joined. The subsequent breakup of the southern continents set Australia "afloat," like a giant raft of marsupials. In Australia, marsupials diversified, and the few eutherians that lived there became extinct; on other continents, most marsupials became extinct, and the eutherians diversified.

Mass Extinctions

The fossil record shows that the overwhelming majority of species that ever lived are now extinct. A species may become extinct for many reasons. Its habitat may have been destroyed, or its environment may have changed in a manner unfavorable to the species. For example, if ocean temperatures fall by even a few degrees, species that are otherwise well adapted may perish. Even if physical factors in the environment remain stable, biological factors may change—the origin of one species can spell doom for another.

Although extinction occurs regularly, at certain times disruptive changes to the global environment have caused the rate of extinction to increase dramatically. The result is a **mass extinction**, in which large numbers of species become extinct worldwide.

The "Big Five" Mass Extinction Events

Five mass extinctions are documented in the fossil record over the past 500 million years (Figure 25.17). These events are particularly well documented for the decimation of hard-bodied animals that lived in shallow seas, the organisms for which the fossil record is most complete. In each mass extinction, 50% or more of marine species became extinct.

Two mass extinctions—the Permian and the Cretaceous—have received the most attention. The Permian mass extinction, which defines the boundary between the Paleozoic and Mesozoic eras (251 million years ago), claimed about 96% of marine animal species and

drastically altered life in the ocean. Terrestrial life was also affected. For example, 8 out of 27 known orders of insects were wiped out. This mass extinction occurred in less than 500,000 years, possibly in just a few thousand years—an instant in the context of geologic time.

The Permian mass extinction occurred during the most extreme episode of volcanism in the past 500 million years. Geologic data indicate that 1.6 million km² (roughly half the size of western Europe) in Siberia was covered with lava hundreds of meters thick. The eruptions are thought to have produced enough carbon dioxide to warm the global climate by an estimated 6°C, harming many temperature-sensitive species. The rise in atmospheric CO_2 levels would also have led to ocean acidification, thereby reducing the availability of calcium carbonate, which is required by reef-building corals and many shell-building species (see Figure 3.11). The explosions would also have added nutrients such as phosphorous to ecosystems, stimulating the growth of microorganisms. Upon their deaths, these microorganisms would have provided food for bacterial decomposers. Bacteria use oxygen as they decompose the bodies of dead organisms, thus causing oxygen concentrations to drop. This would have harmed oxygen-breathers and promoted the growth of anaerobic bacteria that emit a poisonous metabolic by-product,

▲ **Figure 25.17 Mass extinction and the diversity of life.** The five generally recognized mass extinction events, indicated by red arrows, represent peaks in the extinction rate of marine animal families (red line and left vertical axis). These mass extinctions interrupted the overall increase in the number of marine animal families over time (blue line and right vertical axis).

INTERPRET THE DATA *96% of marine animal species became extinct in the Permian mass extinction. Explain why the blue curve shows only a 50% drop at that time.*

hydrogen sulfide (H_2S) gas. Overall, the volcanic eruptions appear to have triggered a series of catastrophic events that together resulted in the Permian mass extinction.

The Cretaceous mass extinction occurred 65.5 million years ago. This event extinguished more than half of all marine species and eliminated many families of terrestrial plants and animals, including all dinosaurs (except birds, which are members of the same group; see Chapter 34). One clue to a possible cause of the Cretaceous mass extinction is a thin layer of clay enriched in iridium that dates to the time of the mass extinction (about 65 million years ago). Iridium is an element that is very rare on Earth but common in many of the meteorites and other extraterrestrial objects that occasionally fall to Earth. As a result, researchers proposed that this clay is fallout from a huge cloud of debris that billowed into the atmosphere when an asteroid or large comet collided with Earth. This cloud would have blocked sunlight and severely disturbed the global climate for several months.

Is there evidence of such an asteroid or comet? Research has focused on the Chicxulub crater, a 65-million-year-old scar beneath sediments off the coast of Mexico **(Figure 25.18)**.

▼ **Figure 25.18 A trauma for Cretaceous life.** Beneath the Caribbean Sea, the 65-million-year-old Chicxulub crater measures 180 km across. The horseshoe shape of the crater and the pattern of debris in sedimentary rocks indicate that an asteroid or comet struck at a low angle from the southeast. This drawing represents the impact and its immediate effect: a cloud of hot vapor and debris that could have killed many of the plants and animals in North America within hours.

The crater is the right size to have been caused by an object with a diameter of 10 km. Critical evaluation of this and other hypotheses for mass extinctions continues.

Is a Sixth Mass Extinction Under Way?

As you will read further in Chapter 56, human actions, such as habitat destruction, are modifying the global environment to such an extent that many species are threatened with extinction. More than a thousand species have become extinct in the last 400 years. Scientists estimate that this rate is 100 to 1,000 times the typical background rate seen in the fossil record. Is a sixth mass extinction now in progress?

This question is difficult to answer, in part because it is hard to document the total number of extinctions occurring today. Tropical rain forests, for example, harbor many undiscovered species. As a result, destroying tropical forest may drive species to extinction before we even learn of their existence. Such uncertainties make it hard to assess the full extent of the current extinction crisis. Even so, it is clear that losses to date have not reached those of the "big five" mass extinctions, in which large percentages of Earth's species became extinct. This does not in any way discount the seriousness of today's situation. Monitoring programs show that many species are declining at an alarming rate due to habitat loss, introduced species, overharvesting, and other factors. Recent studies on a variety of organisms, including lizards, pine trees, and polar bears, suggest that climate change may hasten some of these declines. The fossil record also highlights the potential importance of climate change: Over the last 500 million years, extinction rates have tended to increase when global temperatures were high **(Figure 25.19)**.

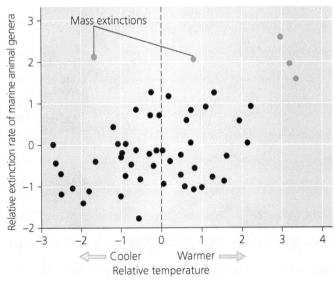

© 2008 The Royal Society

▲ **Figure 25.19 Fossil extinctions and temperature.** Extinction rates increased when global temperatures were high. Temperatures were estimated using ratios of oxygen isotopes and converted to an index in which 0 is the overall average temperature.

Overall, the evidence suggests that unless dramatic actions are taken, a sixth, human-caused mass extinction is likely to occur within the next few centuries or millennia.

Consequences of Mass Extinctions

Mass extinctions have significant and long-term effects. By eliminating large numbers of species, a mass extinction can reduce a thriving and complex ecological community to a pale shadow of its former self. And once an evolutionary lineage disappears, it cannot reappear. The course of evolution is changed forever. Consider what would have happened if the early primates living 66 million years ago had died out in the Cretaceous mass extinction. Humans would not exist, and life on Earth would differ greatly from what it is today.

The fossil record shows that it typically takes 5–10 million years for the diversity of life to recover to previous levels after a mass extinction. In some cases, it has taken much longer than that: It took about 100 million years for the number of marine families to recover after the Permian mass extinction (see Figure 25.17). These data have sobering implications. If current trends continue and a sixth mass extinction occurs, it will take millions of years for life on Earth to recover.

Mass extinctions can also alter ecological communities by changing the types of organisms residing there. For example, after the Permian and Cretaceous mass extinctions, the percentage of marine organisms that were predators increased substantially (Figure 25.20). A rise in the number of predators can increase both the risks faced by prey and the competition among predators for food. In addition, mass extinctions can curtail lineages with novel and advantageous features. For example, in the late Triassic a group of gastropods (snails and their relatives) arose that could drill through the shells of bivalves (such as clams) and feed on the animals inside. Although shell drilling provided access

to a new and abundant source of food, this newly formed group was wiped out during the mass extinction at the end of the Triassic (about 200 million years ago). Another 120 million years passed before another group of gastropods (the oyster drills) exhibited the ability to drill through shells. As their predecessors might have done if they had not originated at an unfortunate time, oyster drills have since diversified into many new species. Finally, by eliminating so many species, mass extinctions can pave the way for adaptive radiations, in which new groups of organisms proliferate.

Adaptive Radiations

The fossil record shows that the diversity of life has increased over the past 250 million years (see blue line in Figure 25.17). This increase has been fueled by **adaptive radiations**, periods of evolutionary change in which groups of organisms form many new species whose adaptations allow them to fill different ecological roles, or niches, in their communities. Large-scale adaptive radiations occurred after each of the big five mass extinctions, when survivors became adapted to the many vacant ecological niches. Adaptive radiations have also occurred in groups of organisms that possessed major evolutionary innovations, such as seeds or armored body coverings, or that colonized regions in which they faced little competition from other species.

Worldwide Adaptive Radiations

Fossil evidence indicates that mammals underwent a dramatic adaptive radiation after the extinction of terrestrial dinosaurs 65.5 million years ago (Figure 25.21). Although mammals originated about 180 million years ago, the mammal fossils older than 65.5 million years are mostly small and not morphologically diverse. Many species appear to have been nocturnal based on their large eye sockets, similar to those in living nocturnal mammals. A few early mammals were intermediate in size, such as *Repenomamus giganticus*, a 1-m-long predator that lived 130 million years ago—but none approached the size of many dinosaurs. Early mammals may have been restricted in size and diversity because they were eaten or outcompeted by the larger and more diverse dinosaurs. With the disappearance of the dinosaurs (except for birds), mammals expanded greatly in both diversity and size, filling the ecological roles once occupied by terrestrial dinosaurs.

The history of life has also been greatly altered by radiations in which groups of organisms increased in diversity as they came to play entirely new

▲ Figure 25.20 **Mass extinctions and ecology.** The Permian and Cretaceous mass extinctions (indicated by red arrows) altered the ecology of the oceans by increasing the percentage of marine genera that were predators.

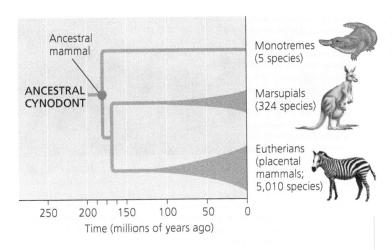

ANCESTRAL
CYNODONT

Ancestral
mammal

Monotremes
(5 species)

Marsupials
(324 species)

Eutherians
(placental
mammals;
5,010 species)

250   200   150   100   50   0

Time (millions of years ago)

▲ **Figure 25.21 Adaptive radiation of mammals.**

ecological roles in their communities. Examples include the rise of photosynthetic prokaryotes, the evolution of large predators in the Cambrian explosion, and the radiations following the colonization of land by plants, insects, and

tetrapods. Each of these last three radiations was associated with major evolutionary innovations that facilitated life on land. The radiation of land plants, for example, was associated with key adaptations, such as stems that support plants against gravity and a waxy coat that protects leaves from water loss. Finally, organisms that arise in an adaptive radiation can serve as a new source of food for still other organisms. In fact, the diversification of land plants stimulated a series of adaptive radiations in insects that ate or pollinated plants, one reason that insects are the most diverse group of animals on Earth today.

Regional Adaptive Radiations

Striking adaptive radiations have also occurred over more limited geographic areas. Such radiations can be initiated when a few organisms make their way to a new, often distant location in which they face relatively little competition from other organisms. The Hawaiian archipelago is one of the world's great showcases of this type of adaptive radiation (**Figure 25.22**). Located about 3,500 km from the

Close North American relative,
the tarweed *Carlquistia muirii*

Dubautia laxa

Argyroxiphium sandwicense

KAUAI
5.1
million
years

OAHU
3.7
million
years

MOLOKAI

LANAI

MAUI

1.3
million
years

N

HAWAII
0.4
million
years

Dubautia waialealae

Dubautia scabra

Dubautia linearis

▲ **Figure 25.22 Adaptive radiation on the Hawaiian Islands.** Molecular analysis indicates that these remarkably varied Hawaiian plants, known collectively as the "silversword alliance," are all descended from an ancestral tarweed that arrived on the islands about 5 million years ago from North America. Members of the silversword alliance have since spread into different habitats and formed new species with strikingly different adaptations.

nearest continent, the volcanic islands are progressively older as one follows the chain toward the northwest; the youngest island, Hawaii, is less than a million years old and still has active volcanoes. Each island was born "naked" and was gradually populated by stray organisms that rode the ocean currents and winds either from far-distant land areas or from older islands of the archipelago itself. The physical diversity of each island, including immense variation in elevation and rainfall, provides many opportunities for evolutionary divergence by natural selection. Multiple invasions followed by speciation events have ignited an explosion of adaptive radiation in Hawaii. As a result, most of the thousands of species that inhabit the islands are found nowhere else on Earth.

CONCEPT CHECK 25.4

1. Explain the consequences of plate tectonics for life on Earth.

2. What factors promote adaptive radiations?

3. **WHAT IF?** Suppose that an invertebrate species was lost in a mass extinction caused by a sudden catastrophic event. Would the last appearance of this species in the fossil record necessarily be close to when the extinction actually occurred? Would the answer to this question differ depending on whether the species was common (abundant and widespread) or rare? Explain.

For suggested answers, see Appendix A.

CONCEPT 25.5

Major changes in body form can result from changes in the sequences and regulation of developmental genes

The fossil record tells us what the great changes in the history of life have been and when they occurred. Moreover, an understanding of plate tectonics, mass extinction, and adaptive radiation provides a picture of how those changes came about. But we can also seek to understand the intrinsic biological mechanisms that underlie changes seen in the fossil record. For this, we turn to genetic mechanisms of change, paying particular attention to genes that influence development.

Effects of Developmental Genes

As you read in Chapter 21, "evo-devo"—research at the interface between evolutionary biology and developmental biology—is illuminating how slight genetic differences can produce major morphological differences between species. In particular, large morphological differences can result from genes that alter the rate, timing, and spatial pattern of change in an organism's form as it develops from a zygote into an adult.

Chimpanzee infant — Chimpanzee adult

Chimpanzee fetus — Chimpanzee adult

Human fetus — Human adult

▲ **Figure 25.23 Relative skull growth rates.** In the human evolutionary lineage, mutations slowed the growth of the jaw relative to other parts of the skull. As a result, in humans the skull of an adult is more similar to the skull of an infant than is the case for chimpanzees..

Changes in Rate and Timing

Many striking evolutionary transformations are the result of **heterochrony** (from the Greek *hetero*, different, and *chronos*, time), an evolutionary change in the rate or timing of developmental events. For example, an organism's shape depends in part on the relative growth rates of different body parts during development. Changes to these rates can alter the adult form substantially, as seen in the contrasting shapes of human and chimpanzee skulls **(Figure 25.23)**. Other examples of the dramatic evolutionary effects of heterochrony include how increased growth rates of finger bones yielded the skeletal structure of wings in bats (see Figure 22.15) and how slowed growth of leg and pelvic bones led to the reduction and eventual loss of hind limbs in whales (see Figure 22.20).

Heterochrony can also alter the timing of reproductive development relative to the development of nonreproductive organs. If reproductive organ development accelerates compared to other organs, the sexually mature stage of a species may retain body features that were juvenile structures in an ancestral species, a condition called **paedomorphosis** (from the Greek *paedos*, of a child, and *morphosis*, formation). For example, most salamander species have

Gills

▲ **Figure 25.24 Paedomorphosis.** The adults of some species retain features that were juvenile in ancestors. This salamander is an axolotl, an aquatic species becomes a sexually mature adult while retaining certain larval (tadpole) characteristics, including gills.

aquatic larvae that undergo metamorphosis in becoming adults. But some species grow to adult size and become sexually mature while retaining gills and other larval features (Figure 25.24). Such an evolutionary alteration of developmental timing can produce animals that appear very different from their ancestors, even though the overall genetic change may be small. Indeed, recent evidence indicates that a change at a single locus was probably sufficient to bring about paedomorphosis in the axolotl salamander, although other genes may have contributed as well.

Changes in Spatial Pattern

Substantial evolutionary changes can also result from alterations in genes that control the spatial organization of body parts. For example, master regulatory genes called **homeotic genes** (described in Chapters 18 and 21) determine such basic features as where a pair of wings and legs will develop on a bird or how a plant's flower parts are arranged.

The products of one class of homeotic genes, the *Hox* genes, provide positional information in an animal embryo. This information prompts cells to develop into structures appropriate for a particular location. Changes in *Hox* genes or in how they are expressed can have a profound impact on morphology. For example, among crustaceans, a change in the location where two *Hox* genes (*Ubx* and *Scr*) are expressed correlates with the conversion of a swimming appendage to a feeding appendage. Similarly, when comparing plant species, changes to the expression of homeotic genes known as *MADS-box* genes can produce flowers that differ dramatically in form (see Chapter 35).

The Evolution of Development

The 560-million-year-old fossils of Ediacaran animals in Figure 25.5 suggest that a set of genes sufficient to produce complex animals existed at least 25 million years *before* the Cambrian explosion. If such genes have existed for so long, how can we explain the astonishing increases in diversity seen during and since the Cambrian explosion?

Adaptive evolution by natural selection provides one answer to this question. As we've seen throughout this unit, by sorting among differences in the sequences of protein-encoding genes, selection can improve adaptations rapidly. In addition, new genes (created by gene duplication events) can take on new metabolic and structural functions, as can existing genes that are regulated in new ways.

Examples in the previous section suggest that developmental genes may have been particularly important. Thus, we'll turn next to how new morphological forms can arise from changes in the nucleotide sequences or regulation of developmental genes.

Changes in Genes

New developmental genes arising after gene duplication events very likely facilitated the origin of novel morphological forms. But since other genetic changes also may have occurred at such times, it can be difficult to establish causal links between genetic and morphological changes that occurred in the past.

This difficulty was sidestepped in a study of developmental changes associated with the divergence of six-legged insects from crustacean-like ancestors that had more than six legs. In insects, such as *Drosophila*, the *Ubx* gene is expressed in the abdomen, while in crustaceans, such as *Artemia*, it is expressed in the main trunk of the body (Figure 25.25). When expressed, the *Ubx* gene suppresses leg formation in insects but not in crustaceans. To examine the workings of this gene, researchers cloned the *Ubx* gene from *Drosophila* and *Artemia*. Next, they genetically engineered fruit fly embryos to express either the *Drosophila Ubx* gene or the *Artemia Ubx* gene throughout their bodies. The *Drosophila* gene suppressed 100% of the limbs in the embryos, as expected, whereas the *Artemia* gene suppressed only 15%.

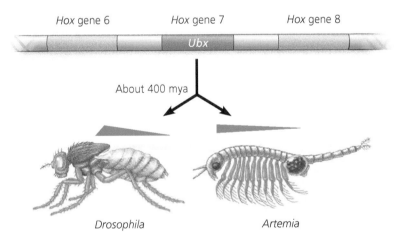

Hox gene 6   Hox gene 7   Hox gene 8

Ubx

About 400 mya

Drosophila   Artemia

▲ **Figure 25.25 Origin of the insect body plan.** Expression of the *Hox* gene *Ubx* suppresses the formation of legs in fruit flies (*Drosophila*) but not in brine shrimp (*Artemia*), thus helping to build the insect body plan. Fruit fly and brine shrimp *Hox* genes have evolved independently for 400 million years. The green triangles indicate the relative amounts of *Ubx* expression in different body regions.

The researchers then sought to uncover key steps involved in the evolutionary transition from a crustacean *Ubx* gene to an insect *Ubx* gene. Their approach was to identify mutations that would cause the *Artemia Ubx* gene to suppress leg formation, thus making the crustacean gene act more like an insect *Ubx* gene. To do this, they constructed a series of "hybrid" *Ubx* genes, each of which contained known segments of the *Drosophila Ubx* gene and known segments of the *Artemia Ubx* gene. By inserting these hybrid genes into fruit fly embryos (one hybrid gene per embryo) and observing their effects on leg development, the researchers were able to pinpoint the exact amino acid changes responsible for the suppression of additional limbs in insects. In so doing, this study provided evidence linking a particular change in the nucleotide sequence of a developmental gene to a major evolutionary change: the origin of the six-legged insect body plan.

Changes in Gene Regulation

A change in the nucleotide sequence of a gene may affect its function wherever the gene is expressed, while changes in the regulation of gene expression can be limited to one cell type (see Chapter 18). Thus, a change in the regulation of a developmental gene may have fewer harmful side effects than a change to the sequence of the gene. This reasoning has prompted researchers to suggest that changes in the form of organisms may often be caused by mutations that affect the regulation of developmental genes—not their sequences.

This idea is supported by studies of a variety of species, including threespine stickleback fish. These fish live in the open ocean and in shallow, coastal waters. In western Canada, they also live in lakes formed when the coastline receded during the past 12,000 years. Marine stickleback fish have a pair of spines on their ventral (lower) surface, which deter some predators. These spines

▼ **Figure 25.26** **Inquiry**

What causes the loss of spines in lake stickleback fish?

Experiment Marine populations of the threespine stickleback fish (*Gasterosteus aculeatus*) have a set of protective spines on their lower (ventral) surface; however, these spines have been lost or reduced in some lake populations of this fish. Working at Stanford University, Michael Shapiro, David Kingsley, and colleagues performed genetic crosses and found that most of the reduction in spine size resulted from the effects of a single developmental gene, *Pitx1*. The researchers then tested two hypotheses about how *Pitx1* causes this morphological change.

▲ **Threespine stickleback (*Gasterosteus aculeatus*)**

Hypothesis A: A change in the DNA sequence of *Pitx1* had caused spine reduction in lake populations. To test this idea, the team used DNA sequencing to compare the coding sequence of the *Pitx1* gene between marine and lake stickleback populations.

Hypothesis B: A change in the regulation of the expression of *Pitx1* had caused spine reduction. To test this idea, the researchers monitored where in the developing embryo the *Pitx1* gene was expressed. They conducted whole-body *in situ* hybridization experiments (see Chapter 20) using *Pitx1* DNA as a probe to detect *Pitx1* mRNA in the fish.

Results

Test of Hypothesis A:	Are there differences in the coding sequence of the *Pitx1* gene in marine and lake stickleback fish?	**Result: No**	The 283 amino acids of the *Pitx1* protein are identical in marine and lake stickleback populations.
Test of Hypothesis B:	Are there any differences in the regulation of expression of *Pitx1*?	**Result: Yes**	Red arrows (⟶) indicate regions of *Pitx1* gene expression in the photographs below. *Pitx1* is expressed in the ventral spine and mouth regions of developing marine stickleback fish butonly in the mouth region of developing lake stickleback fish.

Marine stickleback embryo

Close-up of mouth

Close-up of ventral surface

Lake stickleback embryo

Conclusion The loss or reduction of ventral spines in lake populations of threespine stickleback fish appears to have resulted primarily from a change in the regulation of *Pitx1* gene expression, not from a change in the gene's sequence.

Source: M. D. Shapiro et al., Genetic and developmental basis of evolutionary pelvic reduction in three-spine sticklebacks, *Nature* 428:717–723 (2004).

WHAT IF? *Describe the set of results that would have led researchers to the conclusion that a change in the coding sequence of the* Pitx1 *gene was more important than a change in regulation of gene expression.*

are often reduced or absent in stickleback fish living in lakes that lack predatory fishes and that are also low in calcium. Spines may have been lost in such lakes because they are not advantageous in the absence of predators, and the limited calcium is needed for purposes other than constructing spines.

At the genetic level, the developmental gene *Pitx1* was known to influence whether stickleback fish have ventral spines. Was the reduction of spines in some lake populations due to changes in the *Pitx1* gene or to changes in how the gene is expressed (Figure 25.26)? The researchers' results indicate that the regulation of gene expression has changed, not the DNA sequence. Moreover, lake stickleback fish do express the *Pitx1* gene in tissues not related to the production of spines (for example, the mouth), illustrating how morphological change can be caused by altering the expression of a developmental gene in some parts of the body but not others. In a 2010 follow-up study, researchers showed that changes to the *Pel* enhancer, a noncoding DNA region that affects expression of the *Pitx1* gene, resulted in the reduction of ventral spines in lake sticklebacks.

CONCEPT CHECK 25.5

1. How can heterochrony cause the evolution of different body forms?

2. Why is it likely that *Hox* genes have played a major role in the evolution of novel morphological forms?

3. **MAKE CONNECTIONS** Given that changes in morphology are often caused by changes in the regulation of gene expression, predict whether noncoding DNA is likely to be affected by natural selection. See Concept 18.3 to review noncoding DNA and regulation of gene expression.

For suggested answers, see Appendix A.

CONCEPT 25.6

Evolution is not goal oriented

What does our study of macroevolution tell us about how evolution works? One lesson is that throughout the history of life, the origin of new species has been affected by both the small-scale factors described in Chapter 23 (such as natural selection operating in populations) and the large-scale factors described in this chapter (such as continental drift promoting bursts of speciation throughout the globe). Moreover, to paraphrase the Nobel Prize–winning geneticist François Jacob, evolution is like tinkering—a process in which new forms arise by the modification of existing structures or existing developmental genes. Over time, such tinkering has led to three key features of the natural world described in Chapter 22: the striking ways in which organisms are suited for life in their environments; the many shared characteristics of life; and the rich diversity of life.

Evolutionary Novelties

François Jacob's view of evolution harkens back to Darwin's concept of descent with modification. As new species form, novel and complex structures can arise as gradual modifications of ancestral structures. In many cases, complex structures have evolved in increments from simpler versions that performed the same basic function. For example, consider the human eye, an intricate organ constructed from numerous parts that work together in forming an image and transmitting it to the brain. How could the human eye have evolved in gradual increments? Some argue that if the eye needs all of its components to function, a partial eye could not have been of use to our ancestors.

The flaw in this argument, as Darwin himself noted, lies in the assumption that only complicated eyes are useful. In fact, many animals depend on eyes that are far less complex than our own. The simplest eyes that we know of are patches of light-sensitive photoreceptor cells. These simple eyes appear to have had a single evolutionary origin and are now found in a variety of animals, including small molluscs called limpets. Such eyes have no equipment for focusing images, but they do enable the animal to distinguish light from dark. Limpets cling more tightly to their rock when a shadow falls on them, a behavioral adaptation that reduces the risk of being eaten (Figure 25.27). Limpets have had a long evolutionary history, demonstrating that their "simple" eyes are quite adequate to support their survival and reproduction.

In the animal kingdom, complex eyes have evolved independently from such basic structures many times (Figure 25.28, on the next page). Some molluscs, such as squids and octopuses, have eyes as complex as those of humans and other vertebrates. Although complex mollusc eyes evolved independently of vertebrate eyes, both evolved from a simple cluster of photoreceptor cells present in a common ancestor. In each case, the complex eye evolved through a

▲ Figure 25.27 **Limpets (*Patella vulgata*), molluscs that can sense light and dark with a simple patch of photoreceptor cells.**

▼ Figure 25.28 A range of eye complexity among molluscs.

(a) Patch of pigmented cells

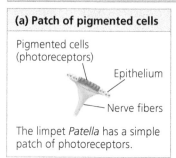

Pigmented cells (photoreceptors)

Epithelium

Nerve fibers

The limpet *Patella* has a simple patch of photoreceptors.

(b) Eyecup

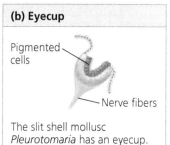

Pigmented cells

Nerve fibers

The slit shell mollusc *Pleurotomaria* has an eyecup.

(c) Pinhole camera-type eye

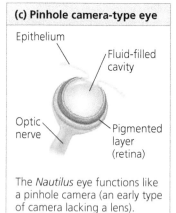

Epithelium

Fluid-filled cavity

Optic nerve

Pigmented layer (retina)

The *Nautilus* eye functions like a pinhole camera (an early type of camera lacking a lens).

(d) Eye with primitive lens

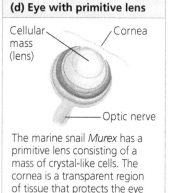

Cellular mass (lens)

Cornea

Optic nerve

The marine snail *Murex* has a primitive lens consisting of a mass of crystal-like cells. The cornea is a transparent region of tissue that protects the eye and helps focus light.

(e) Complex camera lens-type eye

Cornea

Lens

Retina

Optic nerve

The squid *Loligo* has a complex eye with features (cornea, lens, and retina) similar to those of vertebrate eyes. However, the squid eye evolved independently from vertebrate eyes.

series of steps that benefited the eyes' owners at every stage. Evidence of their independent evolution can be found in their structure: Vertebrate eyes detect light at the back layer of the retina and conduct nerve impulses toward the front, while complex mollusc eyes do the reverse.

Throughout their evolutionary history, eyes retained their basic function of vision. But evolutionary novelties can also arise when structures that originally played one role gradually acquire a different one. For example, as cynodonts gave rise to early mammals, bones that formerly comprised the jaw hinge (the articular and quadrate; see Figure 25.7) were incorporated into the ear region of mammals, where they eventually took on a new function: the transmission of sound (see Chapter 34). Structures that evolve in one context but become co-opted for another function are sometimes called *exaptations* to distinguish them from the adaptive origin of the original structure. Note that the concept of exaptation does not imply that a structure

somehow evolves in anticipation of future use. Natural selection cannot predict the future; it can only improve a structure in the context of its *current* utility. Novel features, such as the new jaw hinge and ear bones of early mammals, can arise gradually via a series of intermediate stages, each of which has some function in the organism's current context.

Evolutionary Trends

What else can we learn from patterns of macroevolution? Consider evolutionary "trends" observed in the fossil record. For instance, some evolutionary lineages exhibit a trend toward larger or smaller body size. An example is the evolution of the present-day horse (genus *Equus*), a descendant of the 55-million-year-old *Hyracotherium* **(Figure 25.29)**. About the size of a large dog, *Hyracotherium* had four toes on its front feet, three toes on its hind feet, and teeth adapted for browsing on bushes and trees. In comparison, present-day horses are larger, have only one toe on each foot, and possess teeth modified for grazing on grasses.

Extracting a single evolutionary progression from the fossil record can be misleading, however; it is like describing a bush as growing toward a single point by tracing only the branches that lead to that twig. For example, by selecting certain species from the available fossils, it is possible to arrange a succession of animals intermediate between *Hyracotherium* and living horses that shows a trend toward large, single-toed species (follow the yellow highlighting in Figure 25.29). However, if we consider *all* fossil horses known today, this apparent trend vanishes. The genus *Equus* did not evolve in a straight line; it is the only surviving twig of an evolutionary tree that is so branched that it is more like a bush. *Equus* actually descended through a series of speciation episodes that included several adaptive radiations, not all of which led to large, one-toed, grazing horses. In fact, phylogenetic analyses suggest that all lineages that include grazers are closely related to *Parahippus*; the many other horse lineages, all of which are now extinct, remained multi-toed browsers for 35 million years.

Branching evolution *can* result in a real evolutionary trend even if some species counter the trend. One model of long-term trends views species as analogous to individuals: Speciation is their birth, extinction is their death, and new species that diverge from them are their offspring. In this model, just as populations of individual organisms undergo natural selection, species undergo *species selection*. The species that endure the longest and generate the most new offspring species determine the direction of major evolutionary trends. The species selection model suggests that "differential speciation success" plays a role in macroevolution similar to the role of differential reproductive success in microevolution. Evolutionary trends can also result directly from natural selection. For example, when horse ancestors invaded the grasslands that spread during the mid-Cenozoic,

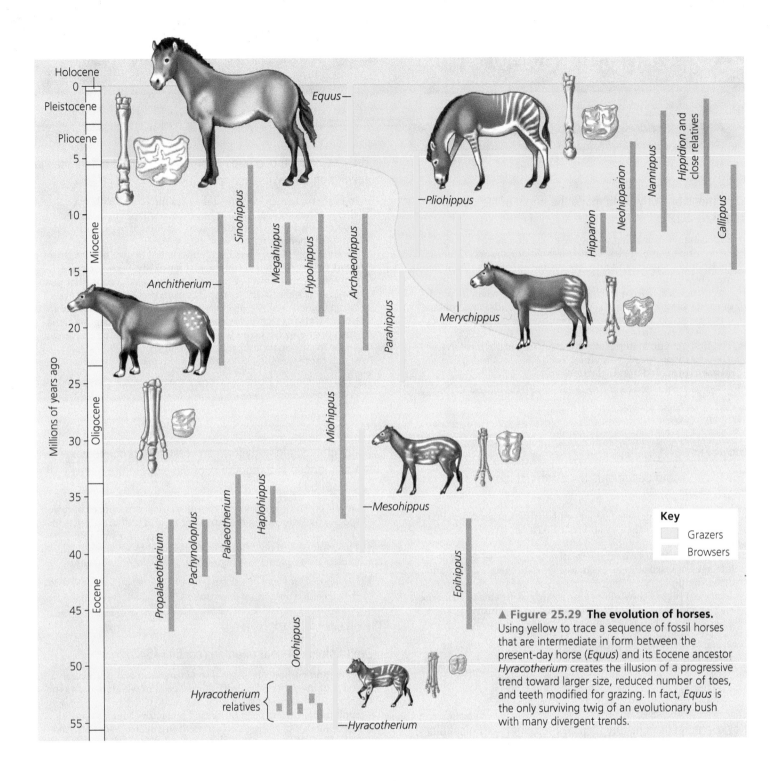

▲ **Figure 25.29 The evolution of horses.**
Using yellow to trace a sequence of fossil horses that are intermediate in form between the present-day horse (*Equus*) and its Eocene ancestor *Hyracotherium* creates the illusion of a progressive trend toward larger size, reduced number of toes, and teeth modified for grazing. In fact, *Equus* is the only surviving twig of an evolutionary bush with many divergent trends.

there was strong selection for grazers that could escape predators by running faster. This trend would not have occurred without open grasslands.

Whatever its cause, an evolutionary trend does not imply that there is some intrinsic drive toward a particular phenotype. Evolution is the result of the interactions between organisms and their current environments; if environmental conditions change, an evolutionary trend may cease or even reverse itself. The cumulative effect of these ongoing interactions between organisms and their environments is enormous: It is through them that the staggering diversity of life—Darwin's "endless forms most beautiful"—has arisen.

CONCEPT CHECK 25.6

1. How can the Darwinian concept of descent with modification explain the evolution of such complex structures as the vertebrate eye?

2. **WHAT IF?** The myxoma virus kills up to 99.8% of infected European rabbits in populations with no previous exposure to the virus. The virus is transmitted between living rabbits by mosquitoes. Describe an evolutionary trend (in either the rabbit or virus) that might occur after a rabbit population first encounters the virus.

For suggested answers, see Appendix A.

25 Chapter Review

SUMMARY OF KEY CONCEPTS

CONCEPT 25.1

Conditions on early Earth made the origin of life possible (pp. 520–522)

- Experiments simulating possible early atmospheres have produced organic molecules from inorganic precursors. Amino acids, lipids, sugars, and nitrogenous bases have also been found in meteorites.
- Amino acids and RNA nucleotides polymerize when dripped onto hot sand, clay, or rock. Organic compounds can spontaneously assemble into **protocells**, membrane-bounded droplets that have some properties of cells.
- The first genetic material may have self-replicating, catalytic RNA. Early protocells containing such RNA would have increased through natural selection.

? *Describe the roles that montmorillonite clay and vesicles may have played in the origin of life.*

CONCEPT 25.2

The fossil record documents the history of life (pp. 522–526)

- The **fossil record**, based largely on fossils found in sedimentary rocks, documents the rise and fall of different groups of organisms over time.
- Sedimentary strata reveal the relative ages of **fossils**. The absolute ages of fossils can be estimated by radiometric dating and other methods.
- The fossil record shows how new groups of organisms can arise via the gradual modification of preexisting organisms.

? *What are the challenges of estimating the absolute ages of old fossils? Explain how these challenges may be overcome in some circumstances.*

CONCEPT 25.3

Key events in life's history include the origins of unicellular and multicellular organisms and the colonization of land (pp. 526–531)

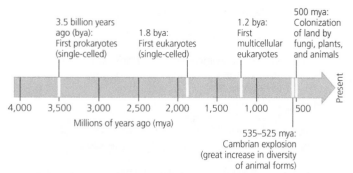

? *What is the "Cambrian explosion," and why is it significant?*

CONCEPT 25.4

The rise and fall of groups of organisms reflect differences in speciation and extinction rates (pp. 531–538)

- In **plate tectonics**, continental plates move gradually over time, altering the physical geography and climate of Earth. These changes lead to extinctions in some groups of organisms and bursts of speciation in others.
- Evolutionary history has been punctuated by five **mass extinctions** that radically altered the history of life. Some of these extinctions may have been caused by changes in continent positions, volcanic activity, or impacts from meteorites or comets.
- Large increases in the diversity of life have resulted from **adaptive radiations** that followed mass extinctions. Adaptive radiations have also occurred in groups of organisms that possessed major evolutionary innovations or that colonized new regions in which there was little competition from other organisms.

? *Explain how the broad evolutionary changes seen in the fossil record are the cumulative result of speciation and extinction events.*

CONCEPT 25.5

Major changes in body form can result from changes in the sequences and regulation of developmental genes (pp. 538–541)

- Developmental genes affect morphological differences between species by influencing the rate, timing, and spatial patterns of change in an organism's form as it develops into an adult.
- The evolution of new forms can be caused by changes in the nucleotide sequences or regulation of developmental genes.

? *How could changes in a single gene or DNA region ultimately lead to the origin of a new group of organisms?*

CONCEPT 25.6

Evolution is not goal oriented (pp. 541–543)

- Novel and complex biological structures can evolve through a series of incremental modifications, each of which benefits the organism that possesses it.
- Evolutionary trends can be caused by factors such as natural selection in a changing environment or species selection. Like all aspects of evolution, evolutionary trends result from interactions between organisms and their current environments.

? *Explain the reasoning behind the statement "Evolution is not goal oriented."*

TEST YOUR UNDERSTANDING

LEVEL 1: KNOWLEDGE/COMPREHENSION

1. Fossilized stromatolites
   a. formed around deep-sea vents.
   b. resemble structures formed by bacterial communities that are found today in some shallow marine bays.
   c. provide evidence that plants moved onto land in the company of fungi around 500 million years ago.
   d. contain the first undisputed fossils of eukaryotes and date from 1.8 billion years ago.

2. The oxygen revolution changed Earth's environment dramatically. Which of the following took advantage of the presence of free oxygen in the oceans and atmosphere?
   a. the evolution of cellular respiration, which used oxygen to help harvest energy from organic molecules
   b. the persistence of some animal groups in anaerobic habitats
   c. the evolution of photosynthetic pigments that protected early algae from the corrosive effects of oxygen
   d. the evolution of chloroplasts after early protists incorporated photosynthetic cyanobacteria

3. Which factor most likely caused animals and plants in India to differ greatly from species in nearby southeast Asia?
   a. The species became separated by convergent evolution.
   b. The climates of the two regions are similar.
   c. India is in the process of separating from the rest of Asia.
   d. India was a separate continent until 45 million years ago.

4. Adaptive radiations can be a direct consequence of three of the following four factors. Select the exception.
   a. vacant ecological niches
   b. genetic drift
   c. colonization of an isolated region that contains suitable habitat and few competitor species
   d. evolutionary innovation

5. Which of the following steps has *not* yet been accomplished by scientists studying the origin of life?
   a. synthesis of small RNA polymers by ribozymes
   b. formation of molecular aggregates with selectively permeable membranes
   c. formation of protocells that use DNA to direct the polymerization of amino acids
   d. abiotic synthesis of organic molecules

LEVEL 2: APPLICATION/ANALYSIS

6. A genetic change that caused a certain *Hox* gene to be expressed along the tip of a vertebrate limb bud instead of farther back helped make possible the evolution of the tetrapod limb. This type of change is illustrative of
   a. the influence of environment on development.
   b. paedomorphosis.
   c. a change in a developmental gene or in its regulation that altered the spatial organization of body parts.
   d. heterochrony.

7. A swim bladder is a gas-filled sac that helps fish maintain buoyancy. The evolution of the swim bladder from the air-breathing organ (a simple lung) of an ancestral fish is an example of
   a. exaptation.
   b. changes in *Hox* gene expression.
   c. paedomorphosis.
   d. adaptive radiation.

LEVEL 3: SYNTHESIS/EVALUATION

8. EVOLUTION CONNECTION
   Describe how gene flow, genetic drift, and natural selection all can influence macroevolution.

9. SCIENTIFIC INQUIRY
   Herbivory (plant eating) has evolved repeatedly in insects, typically from meat-eating or detritus-feeding ancestors (detritus is dead organic matter). Moths and butterflies, for example, eat plants, whereas their "sister group" (the insect group to which they are most closely related), the caddisflies, feed on animals, fungi, or detritus. As illustrated in the following phylogenetic tree, the combined moth/butterfly and caddisfly group shares a common ancestor with flies and fleas. Like caddisflies, flies and fleas are thought to have evolved from ancestors that did not eat plants.

There are 140,000 species of moths and butterflies and 7,000 species of caddisflies. State a hypothesis about the impact of herbivory on adaptive radiations in insects. How could this hypothesis be tested?

10. WRITE ABOUT A THEME: ORGANIZATION
    You have seen many examples of how form fits function at all levels of the biological hierarchy. However, we can imagine forms that would function better than some forms actually found in nature. For example, if the wings of a bird were not formed from its forelimbs, such a hypothetical bird could fly yet also hold objects with its forelimbs. In a short essay (100–150 words), use the concept of "evolution as tinkering" to explain why there are limits to the functionality of forms in nature.

11. SYNTHESIZE YOUR KNOWLEDGE

In 2010, the Soufriere Hills volcano on the Caribbean island of Montserrat erupted violently, spewing huge clouds of ash and gases into the sky. Explain how the volcanic eruptions at the end of the Permian period and the formation of Pangaea, both of which occurred about 251 million years ago, set in motion events that altered evolutionary history.

For suggested answers, see Appendix A.

MasteringBiology®

Students Go to **MasteringBiology** for assignments, the eText, and the Study Area with practice tests, animations, and activities.

Instructors Go to **MasteringBiology** for automatically graded tutorials and questions that you can assign to your students, plus Instructor Resources.

5 THE EVOLUTIONARY HISTORY OF BIOLOGICAL DIVERSITY

AN INTERVIEW WITH

Nicole King

Winner of a MacArthur Fellowship "genius" award, Nicole King is an Associate Professor of Genetics, Genomics, and Development at the University of California, Berkeley. Dr. King earned a B.S. in biology from Indiana University and a Ph.D. in biochemistry from Harvard University. Dr. King and her students are using an exciting mix of molecular genetic, developmental, and genomic approaches to reconstruct steps in a key event in the evolutionary history of life—how animals, which are multicellular, arose from their unicellular ancestors.

How did you first become interested in the history of life?

Growing up in Florida, my brother and I spent many hours exploring a creek near our home that was littered with fossilized sharks' teeth. We found tons of teeth, along with fossils of manta rays and other marine organisms. We could see that the land where we lived had once been covered by the ocean. Those fossils, combined with my love of being outdoors in nature, set the stage for my interest in the history of life. Also, my father is a historian. He took me on trips when he was working with Native American communities on reconstructing their oral histories. Just as you can learn about a human society today by studying its history, I became interested in what we can learn about animal biology by studying how animals first evolved.

> " **Just as you can learn about a human society today by studying its history, I became interested in what we can learn about animal biology by studying how animals first evolved.** "

You're studying choanoflagellates in your lab. What are these organisms?

Choanoflagellates are single-celled organisms, although some also form simple colonies. Each cell has a flagellum that is surrounded at its base by projections that form a "collar." To me, the collar looks like a sieve or filter. The collar traps bacteria, which the cell then eats. Sponges, which are very simple animals, have cells that are almost indistinguishable from choanoflagellate cells. Thus, based on shape alone, the early indication was that choanoflagellates were related to animals. And now, with the benefit of genomics and other methods, the jury is in—choanoflagellates and animals are each other's closest relatives.

What can you learn about the origin of animals by studying choanoflagellates?

A key step in the origin of animals was the evolution of true multicellularity. This occurs when an organism's cells can't survive on their own—they have to be associated with other cells. My students and I discovered that choanoflagellates possess some of the genes necessary for multicellularity in animals. Previously, these genes were thought to be unique to animals. We've also been studying a particular species of choanoflagellate that can form simple colonies. By studying this organism in detail, we are learning how it transitions from a single cell to a colony—a change that can help us to answer the evolutionary question, "How does multicellularity evolve from organisms that are unicellular?"

What is a typical work day like for you, and what advice do you have for students?

Each day is different, but I always try to talk with people in my lab about their research. Sometimes they share an exciting new result, or they describe an experiment that is failing and we brainstorm about what might be going wrong. A few times, it turned out that an experiment was done correctly, but the results were very different from what we expected. It can be hard to determine what causes such unexpected results, but doing so can reveal features of an organism's biology that you had no idea existed! I'm really lucky, because I love what I do, and I have a diverse and talented group of scientists in my lab. They all are learning from each other, and I'm learning from them. Overall, I think the key to a happy and successful career is to do what you love.

(MB) For an extended interview and video clip, go to the Study Area in MasteringBiology.

▲ Four choanoflagellate colonies.

26

Phylogeny and the Tree of Life

▲ Figure 26.1 **What kind of organism is this?**

Investigating the Tree of Life

Look closely at the organism in **Figure 26.1**. Although it resembles a snake, this animal is actually a legless lizard known as the eastern glass lizard (*Ophisaurus ventralis*). Why isn't this glass lizard considered a snake? More generally, how do biologists distinguish and categorize the millions of species on Earth?

An understanding of evolutionary relationships suggests one way to address these questions: We can decide in which category to place a species by comparing its traits with those of potential close relatives. For example, the eastern glass lizard does not have a highly mobile jaw, a large number of vertebrae, or a short tail located behind the anus, three traits shared by all snakes. These and other characteristics suggest that despite a superficial resemblance, the glass lizard is not a snake.

Snakes and lizards are part of the continuum of life extending from the earliest organisms to the great variety of species alive today. In this unit, we will survey this diversity and describe hypotheses regarding how it evolved. As we do so, our emphasis will shift from the *process* of evolution (the evolutionary mechanisms described in Unit Four) to its *pattern* (observations of evolution's products over time).

To set the stage for surveying life's diversity, in this chapter we consider how biologists trace **phylogeny**, the evolutionary history of a species or group of species. A phylogeny of lizards and snakes, for example, indicates that both the eastern glass lizard and snakes evolved from lizards with legs—but they evolved from

547

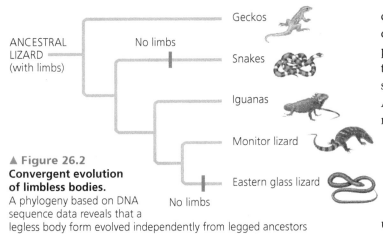

Geckos

Snakes

Iguanas

Monitor lizard

Eastern glass lizard

ANCESTRAL LIZARD (with limbs)

No limbs

No limbs

▲ **Figure 26.2**
Convergent evolution of limbless bodies.
A phylogeny based on DNA sequence data reveals that a legless body form evolved independently from legged ancestors in the lineages leading to the eastern glass lizard and to snakes.

different lineages of legged lizards **(Figure 26.2)**. Thus, it appears that their legless conditions evolved independently. As we'll see, biologists reconstruct and interpret phylogenies like that in Figure 26.2 using **systematics**, a discipline focused on classifying organisms and determining their evolutionary relationships.

CONCEPT 26.1

Phylogenies show evolutionary relationships

Organisms share many characteristics because of common ancestry (see Chapter 22). As a result, we can learn a great deal about a species if we know its evolutionary history. For example, an organism is likely to share many of its genes, metabolic pathways, and structural proteins with its close relatives. We'll consider practical applications of such information later in this section, but first we'll examine how organisms are named and classified, the scientific discipline of **taxonomy**. We'll also look at how we can interpret and use diagrams that represent evolutionary history.

Binomial Nomenclature

Common names for organisms—such as monkey, finch, and lilac—convey meaning in casual usage, but they can also cause confusion. Each of these names, for example, refers to more than one species. Moreover, some common names do not accurately reflect the kind of organism they signify. Consider these three "fishes": jellyfish (a cnidarian), crayfish (a small lobsterlike crustacean), and silverfish (an insect). And of course, a given organism has different names in different languages.

To avoid ambiguity when communicating about their research, biologists refer to organisms by Latin scientific names. The two-part format of the scientific name,

commonly called a **binomial**, was instituted in the 18th century by Carolus Linnaeus (see Chapter 22). The first part of a binomial is the name of the **genus** (plural, *genera*) to which the species belongs. The second part, called the specific epithet, is unique for each species within the genus. An example of a binomial is *Panthera pardus*, the scientific name for the large cat commonly called the leopard. Notice that the first letter of the genus is capitalized and the entire binomial is italicized. (Newly created scientific names are also "latinized": You can name an insect you discover after a friend, but you must add a Latin ending.) Many of the more than 11,000 binomials assigned by Linnaeus are still used today, including the optimistic name he gave our own species—*Homo sapiens*, meaning "wise man."

Hierarchical Classification

In addition to naming species, Linnaeus also grouped them into a hierarchy of increasingly inclusive categories. The first grouping is built into the binomial: Species that appear to be closely related are grouped into the same genus. For example, the leopard (*Panthera pardus*) belongs to a genus that also includes the African lion (*Panthera leo*), the tiger (*Panthera tigris*), and the jaguar (*Panthera onca*). Beyond genera, taxonomists employ progressively more comprehensive categories of classification. The taxonomic system named after Linnaeus, the Linnaean system, places related genera in the same **family**, families into **orders**, orders into **classes**, classes into **phyla** (singular, *phylum*), phyla into **kingdoms**, and, more recently, kingdoms into **domains** **(Figure 26.3)**. The resulting biological classification of a particular organism is somewhat like a postal address identifying a person in a particular apartment, in a building with many apartments, on a street with many apartment buildings, in a city with many streets, and so on.

The named taxonomic unit at any level of the hierarchy is called a **taxon** (plural, *taxa*). In the leopard example, *Panthera* is a taxon at the genus level, and Mammalia is a taxon at the class level that includes all the many orders of mammals. Note that in the Linnaean system, taxa broader than the genus are not italicized, though they are capitalized.

Classifying species is a way to structure our human view of the world. We lump together various species of trees to which we give the common name of pines and distinguish them from other trees that we call firs. Taxonomists have decided that pines and firs are different enough to be placed in separate genera, yet similar enough to be grouped into the same family, Pinaceae. As with pines and firs, higher levels of classification are usually defined by particular characters chosen by taxonomists. However, characters that are useful for classifying one group of organisms may not be appropriate for other organisms. For this reason, the larger categories often are not comparable between lineages; that is, an

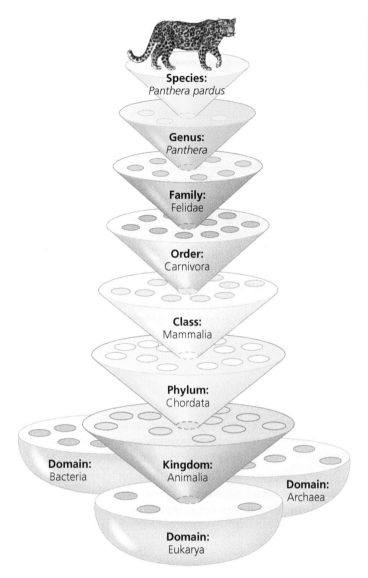

▲ **Figure 26.3 Linnaean classification.** At each level, or "rank," species are placed in groups within more inclusive groups.

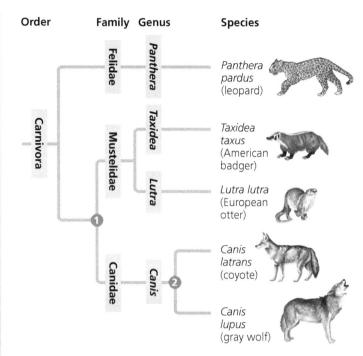

▲ **Figure 26.4 The connection between classification and phylogeny.** Hierarchical classification can reflect the branching patterns of phylogenetic trees. This tree traces possible evolutionary relationships between some of the taxa within order Carnivora, itself a branch of class Mammalia. The branch point ❶ represents the most recent common ancestor of all members of the weasel (Mustelidae) and dog (Canidae) families. The branch point ❷ represents the most recent common ancestor of coyotes and gray wolves.

> **?** *What does this phylogenetic tree indicate about the evolutionary relationships between the leopard, badger, and wolf?*

order of snails does not exhibit the same degree of morphological or genetic diversity as an order of mammals. Furthermore, as we'll see, the placement of species into orders, classes, and so on, does not necessarily reflect evolutionary history.

Linking Classification and Phylogeny

The evolutionary history of a group of organisms can be represented in a branching diagram called a **phylogenetic tree**. As in **Figure 26.4**, the branching pattern often matches how taxonomists have classified groups of organisms nested within more inclusive groups. Sometimes, however, taxonomists have placed a species within a genus (or other group) to which it is *not* most closely related. One reason for such a mistake might be that over the course of evolution, a species has lost a key feature shared by its close relatives. If

DNA or other new evidence indicates that an organism has been misclassified, the organism may be reclassified to accurately reflect its evolutionary history. Another issue is that while the Linnaean system may distinguish groups, such as amphibians, mammals, reptiles, and other classes of vertebrates, it tells us nothing about these groups' evolutionary relationships to one another.

Such difficulties in aligning Linnaean classification with phylogeny have led some systematists to propose that classification be based entirely on evolutionary relationships. In such systems, names are only assigned to groups that include a common ancestor and all of its descendants. As a consequence of this approach, some commonly recognized groups would become part of other groups previously at the same level of the Linnaean system. For example, because birds evolved from a group of reptiles, Aves (the Linnaean class to which birds are assigned) would be considered a subgroup of Reptilia (also a class in the Linnaean system).

Regardless of how groups are named, a phylogenetic tree represents a hypothesis about evolutionary relationships. These relationships often are depicted as a series of dichotomies, or two-way **branch points**. Each branch point

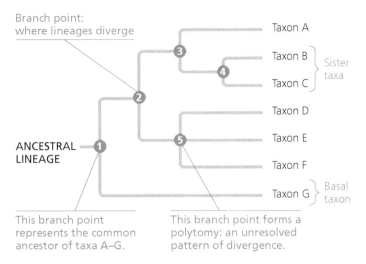

Branch point:
where lineages diverge

ANCESTRAL
LINEAGE

Taxon A

Taxon B

Taxon C } Sister taxa

Taxon D

Taxon E

Taxon F

Taxon G } Basal taxon

This branch point represents the common ancestor of taxa A–G.

This branch point forms a polytomy: an unresolved pattern of divergence.

▲ **Figure 26.5 How to read a phylogenetic tree.**

DRAW IT *Redraw this tree, rotating the branches around branch points ② and ④. Does your new version tell a different story about the evolutionary relationships between the taxa? Explain.*

represents the divergence of two evolutionary lineages from a common ancestor. In **Figure 26.5**, for example, branch point ③ represents the common ancestor of taxa A, B, and C. The position of branch point ④ to the right of ③ indicates that taxa B and C diverged after their shared lineage split from the lineage leading to taxon A. Note also that tree branches can be rotated around a branch point without changing their evolutionary relationships.

In Figure 26.5, taxa B and C are **sister taxa**, groups of organisms that share an immediate common ancestor (branch point ④) and hence are each other's closest relatives. In addition, this tree, like most of the phylogenetic trees in this book, is **rooted**, which means that a branch point within the tree (often drawn farthest to the left) represents the most recent common ancestor of all taxa in the tree. The term **basal taxon** refers to a lineage that diverges early in the history of a group and hence, like taxon G in Figure 26.5, lies on a branch that originates near the common ancestor of the group. Finally, the lineage leading to taxa D–F includes a **polytomy**, a branch point from which more than two descendant groups emerge. A polytomy signifies that evolutionary relationships among the taxa are not yet clear.

What We Can and Cannot Learn from Phylogenetic Trees

Let's summarize three key points about phylogenetic trees. First, they are intended to show patterns of descent, not phenotypic similarity. Although closely related organisms often resemble one another due to their common ancestry, they may not if their lineages have evolved at different rates or faced very different environmental conditions. For

example, even though crocodiles are more closely related to birds than to lizards (see Figure 22.17), they look more like lizards because morphology has changed dramatically in the bird lineage.

Second, the sequence of branching in a tree does not necessarily indicate the actual (absolute) ages of the particular species. For example, the tree in Figure 26.4 does not indicate that the wolf evolved more recently than the European otter; rather, the tree shows only that the most recent common ancestor of the wolf and otter (branch point ①) lived before the most recent common ancestor of the wolf and coyote (②). To indicate when wolves and otters evolved, the tree would need to include additional divergences in each evolutionary lineage, as well as the dates when those splits occurred. Generally, unless given specific information about what the branch lengths in a phylogenetic tree mean—for example, that they are proportional to time—we should interpret the diagram solely in terms of patterns of descent. No assumptions should be made about when particular species evolved or how much change occurred in each lineage.

Third, we should not assume that a taxon on a phylogenetic tree evolved from the taxon next to it. Figure 26.4 does not indicate that wolves evolved from coyotes or vice versa. We can infer only that the lineage leading to wolves and the lineage leading to coyotes both evolved from the common ancestor ②. That ancestor, which is now extinct, was neither a wolf nor a coyote. However, its descendants include the two *extant* (living) species shown here, wolves and coyotes.

Applying Phylogenies

Understanding phylogeny can have practical applications. Consider maize (corn), which originated in the Americas and is now an important food crop worldwide. From a phylogeny of maize based on DNA data, researchers have been able to identify two species of wild grasses that may be maize's closest living relatives. These two close relatives may be useful as "reservoirs" of beneficial alleles that can be transferred to cultivated maize by cross-breeding or genetic engineering (see Chapter 20).

A different use of phylogenetic trees is to infer species identities by analyzing the relatedness of DNA sequences from different organisms. Researchers have used this approach to investigate whether "whale meat" had been harvested illegally from whale species protected under international law rather than from species that can be harvested legally (**Figure 26.6**).

How do researchers construct trees like those we've considered here? In the next section, we'll begin to answer that question by examining the data used to determine phylogenies.

What is the species identity of food being sold as whale meat?

Experiment C. S. Baker and S. R. Palumbi purchased 13 samples of "whale meat" from Japanese fish markets. They sequenced part of the mitochondrial DNA (mtDNA) from each sample and compared their results with the comparable mtDNA sequence from known whale species. To infer the species identity of each sample, the team constructed a *gene tree*, a phylogenetic tree that shows patterns of relatedness among DNA sequences rather than among taxa.

Results Of the species in the resulting gene tree, only Minke whales caught in the Southern Hemisphere can be sold legally in Japan.

Minke
(Southern Hemisphere)
Unknowns #1a,
2, 3, 4, 5, 6, 7, 8

Minke
(North Atlantic)
Unknown #9

Humpback

Unknown #1b

Blue

Unknowns #10,
11, 12, 13

Fin

© 1994 AAAS

Conclusion This analysis indicated that mtDNA sequences of six of the unknown samples (in red) were most closely related to mtDNA sequences of whales that are not legal to harvest.

Source: C. S. Baker and S. R. Palumbi, Which whales are hunted? A molecular genetic approach to monitoring whaling, *Science* 265:1538–1539 (1994). Reprinted with permission from AAAS.

WHAT IF? *What different results would have indicated that the whale meat had* not *been harvested illegally?*

CONCEPT CHECK 26.1

1. Which levels of the classification in Figure 26.3 do humans share with leopards?

2. Which of the trees shown here depicts an evolutionary history different from the other two? Explain.

(a)   (b)   (c)

3. **WHAT IF?** Suppose new evidence indicates that taxon E in Figure 26.5 is the sister taxon of a group consisting of taxa D and F. Redraw the tree accordingly.

For suggested answers, see Appendix A.

Phylogenies are inferred from morphological and molecular data

To infer phylogeny, systematists must gather as much information as possible about the morphology, genes, and biochemistry of the relevant organisms. It is important to focus on features that result from common ancestry, because only such features reflect evolutionary relationships.

Morphological and Molecular Homologies

Recall that phenotypic and genetic similarities due to shared ancestry are called *homologies*. For example, the similarity in the number and arrangement of bones in the forelimbs of mammals is due to their descent from a common ancestor with the same bone structure; this is an example of a morphological homology (see Figure 22.15). In the same way, genes or other DNA sequences are homologous if they are descended from sequences carried by a common ancestor.

In general, organisms that share very similar morphologies or similar DNA sequences are likely to be more closely related than organisms with vastly different structures or sequences. In some cases, however, the morphological divergence between related species can be great and their genetic divergence small (or vice versa). Consider the Hawaiian silversword plants: some of these species are tall, twiggy trees, while others are dense, ground-hugging shrubs (see Figure 25.22). But despite these striking phenotypic differences, the silverswords' genes are very similar. Based on these small molecular divergences, scientists estimate that the silversword group began to diverge 5 million years ago. We'll discuss how scientists use molecular data to estimate such divergence times later in this chapter.

Sorting Homology from Analogy

A potential source of confusion in constructing a phylogeny is similarity between organisms that is due to convergent evolution—called **analogy**—rather than to shared ancestry (homology). Convergent evolution occurs when similar environmental pressures and natural selection produce similar (analogous) adaptations in organisms from different evolutionary lineages. For example, the two mole-like animals shown in **Figure 26.7**

Australian marsupial "mole"

North American eutherian mole

▲ **Figure 26.7 Convergent evolution in burrowers.** A long body, large front paws, small eyes, and a pad of thick skin that protects the nose all evolved independently in these species.

look very similar. However, their internal anatomy, physiology, and reproductive systems are very dissimilar. Indeed, genetic and fossil evidence indicate that the common ancestor of these moles lived 140 million years ago. This common ancestor and most of its descendents were not mole-like, but analogous characteristics evolved independently in these two mole lineages as they became adapted to similar lifestyles.

Distinguishing between homology and analogy is critical in reconstructing phylogenies. To see why, consider bats and birds, both of which have adaptations that enable flight. This superficial resemblance might imply that bats are more closely related to birds than they are to cats, which cannot fly. But a closer examination reveals that a bat's wing is more similar to the forelimbs of cats and other mammals than to a bird's wing. Bats and birds descended from a common tetrapod ancestor that lived about 320 million years ago. This common ancestor could not fly. Thus, although the underlying skeletal systems of bats and birds are homologous, their *wings* are not. Flight is enabled in different ways—stretched membranes in the bat wing versus feathers in the bird wing. Fossil evidence also documents that bat wings and bird wings arose independently from the forelimbs of different tetrapod ancestors. Thus, with respect to flight, a bat's wing is *analogous*, not homologous, to a bird's wing. Analogous structures that arose independently are also called **homoplasies** (from the Greek, meaning "to mold in the same way").

Besides corroborative similarities and fossil evidence, another clue to distinguishing between homology and analogy is the complexity of the characters being compared. The more elements that are similar in two complex structures, the more likely it is that they evolved from a common ancestor. For instance, the skulls of an adult human and an adult chimpanzee both consist of many bones fused together. The compositions of the skulls match almost perfectly, bone for bone. It is highly improbable that such complex structures, matching in so many details, have separate origins. More likely, the genes involved in the development of both skulls were inherited from a common ancestor. The same argument applies to comparisons at the gene level. Genes are sequences of thousands of nucleotides, each of which represents an inherited character in the form of one of the four DNA bases: A (adenine), G (guanine), C (cytosine), or T (thymine). If genes in two organisms share many portions of their nucleotide sequences, it is likely that the genes are homologous.

Evaluating Molecular Homologies

Comparing DNA molecules often poses technical challenges for researchers. The first step after sequencing the molecules is to align comparable sequences from the species being studied. If the species are very closely related, the sequences probably differ at only one or a few sites. In contrast, comparable nucleic acid sequences in distantly related

species usually have different bases at many sites and may have different lengths. This is because insertions and deletions accumulate over long periods of time.

Suppose, for example, that certain noncoding DNA sequences near a particular gene are very similar in two species, except that the first base of the sequence has been deleted in one of the species. The effect is that the remaining sequence shifts back one notch. A comparison of the two sequences that does not take this deletion into account would overlook what in fact is a very good match. To address such problems, researchers have developed computer programs that estimate the best way to align comparable DNA segments of differing lengths (Figure 26.8).

Such molecular comparisons reveal that many base substitutions and other differences have accumulated in the comparable genes of an Australian mole and a North American mole. The many differences indicate that their lineages have diverged greatly since their common ancestor; thus, we say that the living species are not closely related. In contrast, the high degree of gene sequence similarity among the silversword plants indicates that they are all very closely related, in spite of their considerable morphological differences.

Just as with morphological characters, it is necessary to distinguish homology from analogy in evaluating molecular similarities for evolutionary studies. Two sequences that

▲ **Figure 26.8 Aligning segments of DNA.** Systematists search for similar sequences along DNA segments from two species (only one DNA strand is shown for each species). In this example, 11 of the original 12 bases have not changed since the species diverged. Hence, those portions of the sequences still align once the length is adjusted.

ACGGATAGTCCACTAGGCACTA

TCACCGACAGGTCTTTGACTAG

▲ Figure 26.9 **A molecular homoplasy.**

resemble each other at many points along their length most likely are homologous (see Figure 26.8). But in organisms that do not appear to be closely related, the bases that their otherwise very different sequences happen to share may simply be coincidental matches, called molecular homoplasies. For example, if the two DNA sequences in **Figure 26.9** were from distantly related organisms, the fact that they share 23% of their bases would be coincidental. Statistical tools have been developed to determine whether DNA sequences that share more than 25% of their bases do so because they are homologous.

CONCEPT CHECK **26.2**

1. Decide whether each of the following pairs of structures more likely represents analogy or homology, and explain your reasoning: (a) a porcupine's quills and a cactus's spines; (b) a cat's paw and a human's hand; (c) an owl's wing and a hornet's wing.

2. **WHAT IF?** Suppose that two species, A and B, have similar appearances but very divergent gene sequences, while species B and C have very different appearances but similar gene sequences. Which pair of species is more likely to be closely related: A and B or B and C? Explain.

For suggested answers, see Appendix A.

Shared characters are used to construct phylogenetic trees

As we've discussed, a key step in reconstructing phylogenies is to distinguish homologous features from analogous ones (since only homology reflects evolutionary history). We must also choose a method of inferring phylogeny from these homologous characters. A widely used set of methods is known as cladistics.

Cladistics

In the approach to systematics called **cladistics**, common ancestry is the primary criterion used to classify organisms. Using this methodology, biologists attempt to place species into groups called **clades**, each of which includes an ancestral species and all of its descendants **(Figure 26.10a)**. Clades, like taxonomic categories of the Linnaean system, are nested within larger clades. In Figure 26.4, for example, the cat group (Felidae) represents a clade within a larger clade (Carnivora) that also includes the dog group (Canidae).

However, a taxon is equivalent to a clade only if it is **monophyletic** (from the Greek, meaning "single tribe"), signifying that it consists of an ancestral species and all of its descendants (see Figure 26.10a). Contrast this with a **paraphyletic** ("beside the tribe") group, which consists of an ancestral species and some, but not all, of its descendants **(Figure 26.10b)**, or a **polyphyletic** ("many tribes") group, which includes distantly related species but does not include their most recent common ancestor **(Figure 26.10c)**.

▼ Figure 26.10 **Monophyletic, paraphyletic, and polyphyletic groups.**

(a) Monophyletic group (clade)	**(b) Paraphyletic group**	**(c) Polyphyletic group**

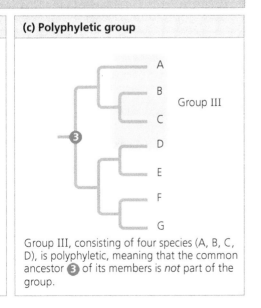

Group I, consisting of three species (A, B, C) and their common ancestor ❶, is a monophyletic group (clade), meaning that it consists of an ancestral species and *all* of its descendants.

Group II is paraphyletic, meaning that it consists of an ancestral species ❷ and some of its descendants (species D, E, F) but not all of them (missing species G).

Group III, consisting of four species (A, B, C, D), is polyphyletic, meaning that the common ancestor ❸ of its members is *not* part of the group.

This group is paraphyletic because it does not include all the descendants of the common ancestor (it excludes cetaceans).

Common ancestor of even-toed ungulates

Other even-toed ungulates

Hippopotamuses

Cetaceans

Seals

Bears

Other carnivores

This group is polyphyletic because it does not include the most recent common ancestor of its members.

▲ **Figure 26.11 Examples of a paraphyletic and a polyphyletic group.**

? *Circle the branch point that represents the most recent common ancestor of cetaceans and seals. Explain why that ancestor would not be part of a cetacean–seal group defined by their similar body forms.*

Note that in a paraphyletic group, the most recent common ancestor of all members of the group *is* part of the group, whereas in a polyphyletic group the most recent common ancestor *is not* part of the group. For example, a group consisting of even-toed ungulates (hippopotamuses, deer, and their relatives) and their common ancestor is paraphyletic because it includes the common ancestor but excludes cetaceans (whales, dolphins, and porpoises), which descended from that ancestor **(Figure 26.11)**. In contrast, a group consisting of seals and cetaceans (based on their similar body forms) would be polyphyletic because it does not include the common ancestor of seals and cetaceans. Biologists avoid defining such polyphyletic groups; if new evidence indicates that an existing group is polyphyletic, organisms in that group are reclassified.

Shared Ancestral and Shared Derived Characters

As a result of descent with modification, organisms have characteristics they share with their ancestors, and they also have characteristics that differ from those of their ancestors. For example, all mammals have backbones, but a backbone does not distinguish mammals from other vertebrates because *all* vertebrates have backbones. The backbone predates the branching of mammals from other vertebrates. Thus for mammals, the backbone is a **shared ancestral character**, a character that originated in an ancestor of the taxon. In contrast, hair is a character shared by all mammals but *not* found in their ancestors. Thus, in mammals, hair is considered a **shared derived character**, an evolutionary novelty unique to a clade.

	TAXA					
CHARACTERS	Lancelet (outgroup)	Lamprey	Bass	Frog	Turtle	Leopard
Vertebral column (backbone)	0	1	1	1	1	1
Hinged jaws	0	0	1	1	1	1
Four walking legs	0	0	0	1	1	1
Amnion	0	0	0	0	1	1
Hair	0	0	0	0	0	1

(a) Character table. A 0 indicates that a character is absent; a 1 indicates that a character is present.

(b) Phylogenetic tree. Analyzing the distribution of these derived characters can provide insight into vertebrate phylogeny.

▲ **Figure 26.12 Constructing a phylogenetic tree.** The characters used here include the amnion, a membrane that encloses the embryo inside a fluid-filled sac (see Figure 34.25).

DRAW IT *In (b), circle the most inclusive clade for which a hinged jaw is a shared ancestral character.*

Note that it is a relative matter whether a character is considered ancestral or derived. A backbone can also qualify as a shared derived character, but only at a deeper branch point that distinguishes all vertebrates from other animals.

Inferring Phylogenies Using Derived Characters

Shared derived characters are unique to particular clades. Because all features of organisms arose at some point in the history of life, it should be possible to determine the clade in which each shared derived character first appeared and to use that information to infer evolutionary relationships.

To see how this analysis is done, consider the set of characters shown in **Figure 26.12a** for each of five vertebrates—a leopard, turtle, frog, bass, and lamprey (a jawless aquatic vertebrate). As a basis of comparison, we need to select an outgroup. An **outgroup** is a species or group of species from an evolutionary lineage that is known to have diverged before the lineage that includes the species we are studying (the **ingroup**). A suitable outgroup can be determined based on evidence from morphology, paleontology, embryonic development, and gene sequences. An appropriate outgroup for our example is the lancelet, a small animal that lives in mudflats and (like vertebrates) is a member of the more inclusive group called the chordates. Unlike the vertebrates, however, the lancelet does not have a backbone.

By comparing members of the ingroup with each other and with the outgroup, we can determine which characters were derived at the various branch points of vertebrate evolution. For example, *all* of the vertebrates in the ingroup have backbones: This character was present in the ancestral vertebrate, but not in the outgroup. Now note that hinged jaws are a character absent in lampreys but present in other members of the ingroup; this character helps us to identify an early branch point in the vertebrate clade. Proceeding in this way, we can translate the data in our table of characters into a phylogenetic tree that groups all the ingroup taxa into a hierarchy based on their shared derived characters **(Figure 26.12b)**.

Phylogenetic Trees with Proportional Branch Lengths

In the phylogenetic trees we have presented so far, the lengths of the tree's branches do not indicate the degree of evolutionary change in each lineage. Furthermore, the chronology represented by the branching pattern of the tree is relative (earlier versus later) rather than absolute (how many millions of years ago). But in some tree diagrams, branch lengths are proportional to amount of evolutionary change or to the times at which particular events occurred.

In **Figure 26.13**, for example, the branch length of the phylogenetic tree reflects the number of changes that have taken place in a particular DNA sequence in that lineage. Note that the total length of the horizontal lines from the base of the tree to the mouse is less than that of the line leading to the outgroup species, the fruit fly *Drosophila*. This implies that in the time since the mouse and fly diverged from a common ancestor, more genetic changes have occurred in the *Drosophila* lineage than in the mouse lineage.

Even though the branches of a phylogenetic tree may have different lengths, among organisms alive today, all the different lineages that descend from a common ancestor have survived for the same number of years. To take an extreme example, humans and bacteria had a common ancestor that lived over 3 billion years ago. Fossils and genetic evidence indicate that this ancestor was a single-celled prokaryote. Even though bacteria have apparently changed

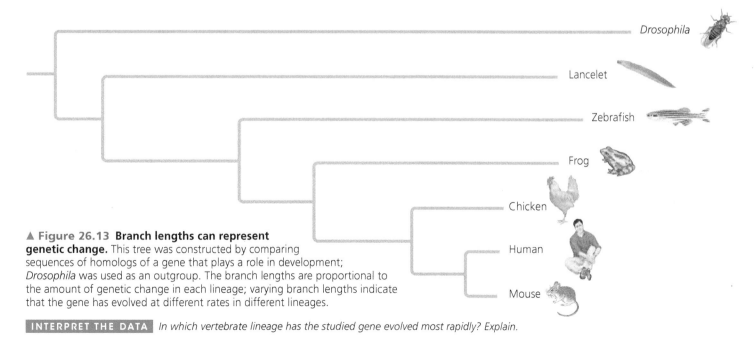

▲ **Figure 26.13 Branch lengths can represent genetic change.** This tree was constructed by comparing sequences of homologs of a gene that plays a role in development; *Drosophila* was used as an outgroup. The branch lengths are proportional to the amount of genetic change in each lineage; varying branch lengths indicate that the gene has evolved at different rates in different lineages.

INTERPRET THE DATA *In which vertebrate lineage has the studied gene evolved most rapidly? Explain.*

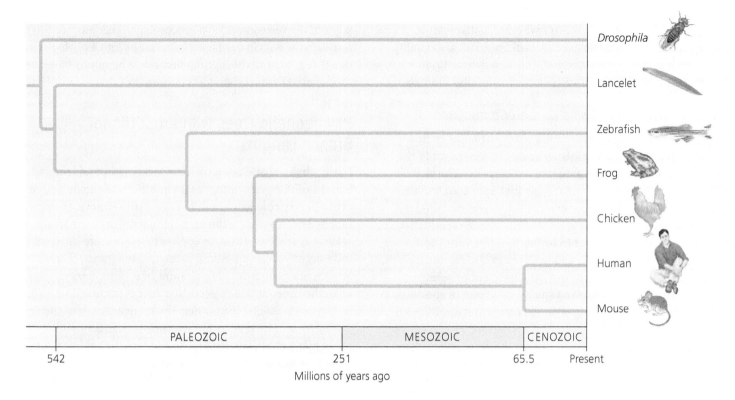

▲ **Figure 26.14 Branch lengths can indicate time.** This tree is based on the same molecular data as the tree in Figure 26.13, but here the branch points are mapped to dates based on fossil evidence. Thus, the branch lengths are proportional to time. Each lineage has the same total length from the base of the tree to the branch tip, indicating that all the lineages have diverged from the common ancestor for equal amounts of time.

little in their morphology since that common ancestor, there have nonetheless been 3 billion years of evolution in the bacterial lineage, just as there have been 3 billion years of evolution in the lineage that ultimately gave rise to humans.

These equal spans of chronological time can be represented in a phylogenetic tree whose branch lengths are proportional to time (**Figure 26.14**). Such a tree draws on fossil data to place branch points in the context of geologic time. Additionally, it is possible to combine these two types of trees by labeling branch points with information about rates of genetic change or dates of divergence.

Maximum Parsimony and Maximum Likelihood

As the database of DNA sequences that enables us to study more species grows, the difficulty of building the phylogenetic tree that best describes their evolutionary history also grows. What if you are analyzing data for 50 species? There are 3×10^{76} different ways to arrange 50 species into a tree! And which tree in this huge forest reflects the true phylogeny? Systematists can never be sure of finding the most accurate tree in such a large data set, but they can narrow the possibilities by applying the principles of maximum parsimony and maximum likelihood.

According to the principle of **maximum parsimony**, we should first investigate the simplest explanation that is consistent with the facts. (The parsimony principle is also called "Occam's razor" after William of Occam, a 14th-century English philosopher who advocated this minimalist problem-solving approach of "shaving away" unnecessary complications.) In the case of trees based on morphology, the most parsimonious tree requires the fewest evolutionary events, as measured by the origin of shared derived morphological characters. For phylogenies based on DNA, the most parsimonious tree requires the fewest base changes.

A **maximum likelihood** approach identifies the tree most likely to have produced a given set of DNA data, based on certain probability rules about how DNA sequences change over time. For example, the underlying probability rules could be based on the assumption that all nucleotide substitutions are equally likely. However, if evidence suggests that this assumption is not correct, more complex rules could be devised to account for different rates of change among different nucleotides or at different positions in a gene.

Scientists have developed many computer programs to search for trees that are parsimonious and likely. When a large amount of accurate data is available, the methods used in these programs usually yield similar trees. As an example of one method, **Figure 26.15** walks you through the process of identifying the most parsimonious molecular tree for a

Research Method

Applying Parsimony to a Problem in Molecular Systematics

Application In considering possible phylogenies for a group of species, systematists compare molecular data for the species. An efficient way to begin is by identifying the most parsimonious hypothesis—the one that requires the fewest evolutionary events (molecular changes) to have occurred.

Technique Follow the numbered steps as we apply the principle of parsimony to a hypothetical phylogenetic problem involving three closely related bird species.

Species I Species II Species III

1 First, draw the three possible phylogenies for the species. (Although only 3 trees are possible when ordering 3 species, the number of possible trees increases rapidly with the number of species: There are 15 trees for 4 species and 34,459,425 trees for 10 species.)

Three phylogenetic hypotheses:

2 Tabulate the molecular data for the species. In this simplified example, the data represent a DNA sequence consisting of just four nucleotide bases. Data from several outgroup species (not shown) were used to infer the ancestral DNA sequence.

	Site 1	2	3	4
Species I	C	T	A	T
Species II	C	T	T	C
Species III	A	G	A	C
Ancestral sequence	A	G	T	T

3 Now focus on site 1 in the DNA sequence. In the tree on the left, a single base-change event, represented by the purple hatchmark on the branch leading to species I and II (and labeled 1/C, indicating a change at site 1 to nucleotide C), is sufficient to account for the site 1 data. In the other two trees, two base-change events are necessary.

4 Continuing the comparison of bases at sites 2, 3, and 4 reveals that each of the three trees requires a total of five additional base-change events (purple hatchmarks).

Results To identify the most parsimonious tree, we total all of the base-change events noted in steps 3 and 4. We conclude that the first tree is the most parsimonious of the three possible phylogenies. (In a real example, many more sites would be analyzed. Hence, the trees would often differ by more than one base-change event.)

6 events   7 events   7 events

three-species problem. Computer programs use the principle of parsimony to estimate phylogenies in a similar way: They examine large numbers of possible trees and identify those that require the fewest evolutionary changes.

Phylogenetic Trees as Hypotheses

This is a good place to reiterate that any phylogenetic tree represents a hypothesis about how the organisms in the tree are related to one another. The best hypothesis is the one that best fits all the available data. A phylogenetic hypothesis may be modified when new evidence compels systematists to revise their trees. Indeed, while many older phylogenetic hypotheses have been supported by new morphological and molecular data, others have been changed or rejected.

Thinking of phylogenies as hypotheses also allows us to use them in a powerful way: We can make and test predictions based on the assumption that a particular phylogeny—our hypothesis—is correct. For example, in an approach known as *phylogenetic bracketing*, we can predict (by parsimony) that features shared by two groups of closely related organisms are present in their common ancestor and all of its descendants unless independent data indicate otherwise. (Note that "prediction" can refer to unknown past events as well as to evolutionary changes yet to occur.)

This approach has been used to make novel predictions about dinosaurs. For example, there is evidence that birds descended from the theropods, a group of bipedal saurischian dinosaurs. As seen in **Figure 26.16**, the closest living relatives of birds are crocodiles. Birds and crocodiles share numerous features: They have four-chambered hearts, they "sing" to defend territories and attract mates (although a crocodile's "song" is more like a bellow), and they build nests. Both birds and crocodiles also care for their eggs by *brooding*, a behavior in which a parent warms the eggs with its body. Birds brood by sitting on their eggs, whereas

crocodiles cover their eggs with their neck. Reasoning that any feature shared by birds and crocodiles is likely to have been present in their common ancestor (denoted by the blue dot in Figure 26.16) and *all* of its descendants, biologists predicted that dinosaurs had four-chambered hearts, sang, built nests, and exhibited brooding.

Internal organs, such as the heart, rarely fossilize, and it is, of course, difficult to test whether dinosaurs sang to defend territories and attract mates. However, fossilized dinosaur eggs and nests have provided evidence supporting the prediction of brooding in dinosaurs. First, a fossil embryo of an *Oviraptor* dinosaur was found, still inside its egg. This egg was identical to those found in another fossil, one that showed an *Oviraptor* crouching over a group of eggs in a posture similar to that seen in brooding birds today **(Figure 26.17)**. Researchers suggested that the *Oviraptor* dinosaur preserved in this second fossil died while incubating or protecting its eggs. The broader conclusion that emerged from this work—that dinosaurs built nests and exhibited brooding—has since been strengthened by additional fossil discoveries that show that other species of dinosaurs built nests and sat on their eggs. Finally, by supporting predictions based on the phylogenetic hypothesis shown in Figure 26.16, fossil discoveries of nests and brooding in dinosaurs provide independent data that suggest that the hypothesis is correct.

Front limb

Hind limb

Eggs

(a) Fossil remains of *Oviraptor* and eggs. The orientation of the bones, which surround and cover the eggs, suggests that the dinosaur died while incubating or protecting its eggs.

(b) Artist's reconstruction of the dinosaur's posture based on the fossil findings.

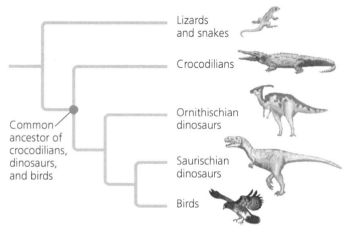

Lizards and snakes

Crocodilians

Ornithischian dinosaurs

Common ancestor of crocodilians, dinosaurs, and birds

Saurischian dinosaurs

Birds

▲ Figure 26.16 **A phylogenetic tree of birds and their close relatives.**

? *What is the most basal taxon represented in this tree?*

▲ Figure 26.17 **Fossil support for a phylogenetic prediction: Dinosaurs built nests and brooded their eggs.**

1. To distinguish a particular clade of mammals within the larger clade that corresponds to class Mammalia, would hair be a useful character? Why or why not?

2. The most parsimonious tree of evolutionary relationships can be inaccurate. How can this occur?

3. **WHAT IF?** Draw a phylogenetic tree that includes the relationships from Figure 25.7 and Figure 26.16. Traditionally, all the taxa shown besides birds and mammals were classified as reptiles. Would a cladistic approach support that classification? Explain.

For suggested answers, see Appendix A.

CONCEPT 26.4

An organism's evolutionary history is documented in its genome

As you have seen in this chapter, molecular systematics—using comparisons of nucleic acids or other molecules to deduce relatedness—can reveal phylogenetic relationships that cannot be determined by nonmolecular methods such as comparative anatomy. For example, molecular systematics helps us uncover evolutionary relationships between groups that have little common ground for morphological comparison, such as animals and fungi. And molecular methods allow us to reconstruct phylogenies among groups of present-day organisms for which the fossil record is poor or lacking entirely.

Different genes can evolve at different rates, even in the same evolutionary lineage. As a result, molecular trees can represent short or long periods of time, depending on which genes are used. For example, the DNA that codes for ribosomal RNA (rRNA) changes relatively slowly. Therefore, comparisons of DNA sequences in these genes are useful for investigating relationships between taxa that diverged hundreds of millions of years ago. Studies of rRNA sequences indicate, for instance, that fungi are more closely related to animals than to plants. In contrast, mitochondrial DNA (mtDNA) evolves relatively rapidly and can be used to explore recent evolutionary events. One research team has traced the relationships among Native American groups through their mtDNA sequences. The molecular findings corroborate other evidence that the Pima of Arizona, the Maya of Mexico, and the Yanomami of Venezuela are closely related, probably descending from the first of three waves of immigrants that crossed the Bering Land Bridge from Asia to the Americas about 15,000 years ago.

Gene Duplications and Gene Families

What do molecular data reveal about the evolutionary history of genome change? Consider gene duplication, which plays a particularly important role in evolution because it increases the number of genes in the genome, providing more opportunities for further evolutionary changes. Molecular techniques now allow us to trace the phylogenies of gene duplications. These molecular phylogenies must account for repeated duplications that have resulted in *gene families*, groups of related genes within an organism's genome (see Figure 21.11).

Accounting for such duplications leads us to distinguish two types of homologous genes **(Figure 26.18)**: orthologous genes and paralogous genes. In **orthologous genes** (from the Greek *orthos*, exact), the homology is the result of a

▼ **Figure 26.18 Two types of homologous genes.** Colored bands mark regions of the genes where differences in base sequences have accumulated.

(a) Formation of orthologous genes: a product of speciation

Ancestral gene

Ancestral species

Speciation with divergence of gene

Orthologous genes

Species A   **Species B**

(b) Formation of paralogous genes: within a species

Ancestral gene

Species C

Gene duplication and divergence

Paralogous genes

Species C after many generations

speciation event and hence occurs between genes found in different species (see Figure 26.18a). For example, the genes that code for cytochrome *c* (a protein that functions in electron transport chains) in humans and dogs are orthologous. In **paralogous genes** (from the Greek *para*, in parallel), the homology results from gene duplication; hence, multiple copies of these genes have diverged from one another within a species (see Figure 26.18b). In Chapter 23, you encountered the example of olfactory receptor genes, which have undergone many gene duplications in vertebrates; humans have 350 of these paralogous genes, while mice have 1,000.

Note that orthologous genes can only diverge after speciation has taken place, that is, after the genes are found in separate gene pools. For example, although the cytochrome *c* genes in humans and dogs serve the same function, the gene's sequence in humans has diverged from that in dogs in the time since these species last shared a common ancestor. Paralogous genes, on the other hand, can diverge within a species because they are present in more than one copy in the genome. The paralogous genes that make up the olfactory receptor gene family in humans have diverged from each other during our long evolutionary history. They now specify proteins that confer sensitivity to a wide variety of molecules, ranging from food odors to sex pheromones.

Genome Evolution

Now that we can compare the entire genomes of different organisms, including our own, two patterns have emerged. First, lineages that diverged long ago often share many orthologous genes. For example, though the human and mouse lineages diverged about 65 million years ago, 99% of the genes of humans and mice are orthologous. And 50% of human genes are orthologous with those of yeast, despite 1 billion years of divergent evolution. Such commonalities explain why disparate organisms nevertheless share many biochemical and developmental pathways. As a result of these shared pathways, the functioning of genes linked to diseases in humans can often be investigated by studying yeast and other organisms distantly related to humans.

Second, the number of genes a species has doesn't seem to increase through duplication at the same rate as perceived phenotypic complexity. Humans have only about four times as many genes as yeast, a single-celled eukaryote, even though—unlike yeast—we have a large, complex brain and a body with more than 200 different types of tissues. Evidence is emerging that many human genes are more versatile than those of yeast: A single human gene can encode multiple proteins that perform different tasks in various body tissues. Unraveling the mechanisms that cause this genomic versatility and phenotypic variation is an exciting challenge.

CONCEPT 26.5

Molecular clocks help track evolutionary time

One goal of evolutionary biology is to understand the relationships among all organisms, including those for which there is no fossil record. However, if we attempt to determine the timing of phylogenies that extend beyond the fossil record, we must rely on an important assumption about how change occurs at the molecular level.

Molecular Clocks

We stated earlier that researchers have estimated that the common ancestor of Hawaiian silversword plants lived about 5 million years ago. How did they make this estimate? They relied on the concept of a **molecular clock**, an approach for measuring the absolute time of evolutionary change based on the observation that some genes and other regions of genomes appear to evolve at constant rates. An assumption underlying the molecular clock is that the number of nucleotide substitutions in orthologous genes is proportional to the time that has elapsed since the genes branched from their common ancestor (divergence time). In the case of paralogous genes, the number of substitutions is proportional to the time since the ancestral gene was duplicated.

We can calibrate the molecular clock of a gene that has a reliable average rate of evolution by graphing the number of genetic differences—for example, nucleotide, codon, or amino acid differences—against the dates of evolutionary branch points that are known from the fossil record (**Figure 26.19**). The average rates of genetic change inferred from such graphs can then be used to estimate the dates of events that cannot be discerned from the fossil record, such as the origin of the silverswords discussed earlier.

Of course, no gene marks time with complete precision. In fact, some portions of the genome appear to have evolved

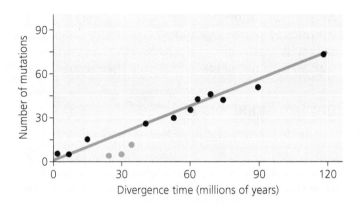

▲ **Figure 26.19 A molecular clock for mammals.** The number of accumulated mutations in seven proteins has increased over time in a consistent manner for most mammal species. The three green data points represent primate species, whose proteins appear to have evolved more slowly than those of other mammals. The divergence time for each data point was based on fossil evidence.

INTERPRET THE DATA *Use the graph to estimate the divergence time for a mammal with a total of 30 mutations in the seven proteins.*

in irregular bursts that are not at all clocklike. And even those genes that seem to act as reliable molecular clocks are accurate only in the statistical sense of showing a fairly smooth *average* rate of change. Over time, there may still be deviations from that average rate. Furthermore, the same gene may evolve at different rates in different groups of organisms. Finally, when comparing genes that are clocklike, the rate of the clock may vary greatly from one gene to another; some genes evolve a million times faster than others.

Differences in Clock Speed

What causes such differences in the speed at which clock-like genes evolve? The answer stems from the fact that some mutations are selectively neutral—neither beneficial nor detrimental. Of course, many new mutations are harmful and are removed quickly by selection. But if most of the rest are neutral and have little or no effect on fitness, then the rate of evolution of those neutral mutations should indeed be regular, like a clock. Differences in the clock rate for different genes are a function of how important a gene is. If the exact sequence of amino acids that a gene specifies is essential to survival, most of the mutational changes will be harmful and only a few will be neutral. As a result, such genes change only slowly. But if the exact sequence of amino acids is less critical, fewer of the new mutations will be harmful and more will be neutral. Such genes change more quickly.

Potential Problems with Molecular Clocks

In fact, molecular clocks do not run as smoothly as would be expected if the underlying mutations were selectively neutral. Many irregularities are likely to be the result of natural selection in which certain DNA changes are favored over

others. Indeed, evidence suggests that almost half the amino acid differences in proteins of two *Drosophila* species, *D. simulans* and *D. yakuba*, are not neutral but have resulted from natural selection. But because the direction of natural selection may change repeatedly over long periods of time (and hence may average out), some genes experiencing selection can nevertheless serve as approximate markers of elapsed time.

Another question arises when researchers attempt to extend molecular clocks beyond the time span documented by the fossil record. Although some fossils are more than 3 billion years old, these are very rare. An abundant fossil record extends back only about 550 million years, but molecular clocks have been used to date evolutionary divergences that occurred a billion or more years ago. These estimates assume that the clocks have been constant for all that time. Such estimates are highly uncertain.

In some cases, problems may be avoided by calibrating molecular clocks with data on the rates at which genes have evolved in different taxa. In other cases, problems may be avoided by using many genes rather than the common approach of using just one or a few genes. By using many genes, fluctuations in evolutionary rate due to natural selection or other factors that vary over time may average out. For example, one group of researchers constructed molecular clocks of vertebrate evolution from published sequence data for 658 nuclear genes. Despite the broad period of time covered (nearly 600 million years) and the fact that natural selection probably affected some of these genes, their estimates of divergence times agreed closely with fossil-based estimates. As this example suggests, if used with care, molecular clocks can aid our understanding of evolutionary relationships.

Applying a Molecular Clock: Dating the Origin of HIV

Researchers have used a molecular clock to date the origin of HIV infection in humans. Phylogenetic analysis shows that HIV, the virus that causes AIDS, is descended from viruses that infect chimpanzees and other primates. (Most of these viruses do not cause AIDS-like diseases in their native hosts.) When did HIV jump to humans? There is no simple answer, because the virus has spread to humans more than once. The multiple origins of HIV are reflected in the variety of strains (genetic types) of the virus. HIV's genetic material is made of RNA, and like other RNA viruses, it evolves quickly.

The most widespread strain in humans is HIV-1 M. To pinpoint the earliest HIV-1 M infection, researchers compared samples of the virus from various times during the epidemic, including a sample from 1959. A comparison of gene sequences showed that the virus has evolved in a clocklike

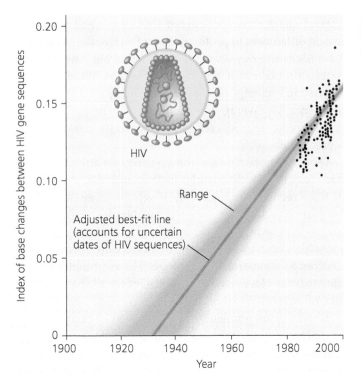

HIV

Range

Adjusted best-fit line
(accounts for uncertain
dates of HIV sequences)

Index of base changes between HIV gene sequences

Year

© 2000 AAAS

▲ **Figure 26.20 Dating the origin of HIV-1 M.** The black data points are based on DNA sequences of an HIV gene in patients' blood samples. (The dates when these individual HIV gene sequences arose are not certain because a person can harbor the virus for years before symptoms occur.) Projecting the gene's rate of change backward in time suggests that the virus originated in the 1930s.

fashion (**Figure 26.20**). Extrapolating backward in time using the molecular clock indicates that the HIV-1 M strain first spread to humans around 1930. A later study, which dated the origin of HIV using a more advanced molecular clock approach than that covered in this book, estimated that the HIV-1 M strain first spread to humans around 1910.

CONCEPT CHECK 26.5

1. What is a molecular clock? What assumption underlies the use of a molecular clock?

2. **MAKE CONNECTIONS** Review Concept 17.5. Then explain how numerous base changes could occur in an organism's DNA yet have no effect on its fitness.

3. **WHAT IF?** Suppose a molecular clock dates the divergence of two taxa at 80 million years ago, but new fossil evidence shows that the taxa diverged at least 120 million years ago. Explain how this could happen.

For suggested answers, see Appendix A.

CONCEPT 26.6

Our understanding of the tree of life continues to change based on new data

The discovery that the glass lizard in Figure 26.1 evolved from a different lineage of legless lizards than did snakes

is one example of how our understanding of life's diversity is informed by systematics. Indeed, in recent decades, systematists have gained insight into even the very deepest branches of the tree of life by analyzing DNA sequence data.

From Two Kingdoms to Three Domains

Taxonomists once classified all known species into two kingdoms: plants and animals. Classification schemes with more than two kingdoms gained broad acceptance in the late 1960s, when many biologists recognized five kingdoms: Monera (prokaryotes), Protista (a diverse kingdom consisting mostly of unicellular organisms), Plantae, Fungi, and Animalia. This system highlighted the two fundamentally different types of cells, prokaryotic and eukaryotic, and set the prokaryotes apart from all eukaryotes by placing them in their own kingdom, Monera.

However, phylogenies based on genetic data soon began to reveal a problem with this system: Some prokaryotes differ as much from each other as they do from eukaryotes. Such difficulties have led biologists to adopt a three-domain system. The three domains—Bacteria, Archaea, and Eukarya—are a taxonomic level higher than the kingdom level. The validity of these domains is supported by many studies, including a recent study that analyzed nearly 100 completely sequenced genomes.

The domain Bacteria contains most of the currently known prokaryotes, while the domain Archaea consists of a diverse group of prokaryotic organisms that inhabit a wide variety of environments. The domain Eukarya consists of all the organisms that have cells containing true nuclei. This domain includes many groups of single-celled organisms as well as multicellular plants, fungi, and animals. **Figure 26.21** represents one possible phylogenetic tree for the three domains and some of the many lineages they encompass.

The three-domain system highlights the fact that much of the history of life has been about single-celled organisms. The two prokaryotic domains consist entirely of single-celled organisms, and even in Eukarya, only the branches labeled in blue type (land plants, fungi, and animals) are dominated by multicellular organisms. Of the five kingdoms previously recognized by taxonomists, most biologists continue to recognize Plantae, Fungi, and Animalia, but not Monera and Protista. The kingdom Monera is obsolete because it would have members in two different domains. The kingdom Protista has also crumbled because it includes members that are more closely related to plants, fungi, or animals than to other protists (see Chapter 28).

The Important Role of Horizontal Gene Transfer

In the phylogeny shown in Figure 26.21, the first major split in the history of life occurred when bacteria diverged from

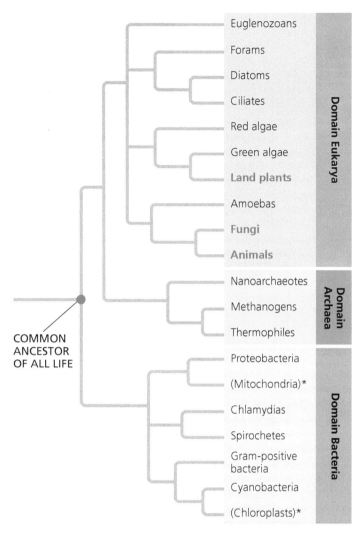

Euglenozoans
Forams
Diatoms
Ciliates
Red algae
Green algae
Land plants
Amoebas
Fungi
Animals

Domain Eukarya

Nanoarchaeotes
Methanogens
Thermophiles

Domain Archaea

COMMON
ANCESTOR
OF ALL LIFE

Proteobacteria
(Mitochondria)*
Chlamydias
Spirochetes
Gram-positive
bacteria
Cyanobacteria
(Chloroplasts)*

Domain Bacteria

▲ **Figure 26.21 The three domains of life.** This phylogenetic tree is based on sequence data for rRNA and other genes. For simplicity, only some of the major branches in each domain are shown. Lineages within Eukarya that are dominated by multicellular organisms (land plants, fungi, and animals) are in blue type, while the two lineages denoted by an asterisk are based on DNA from cellular organelles. All other lineages consist solely or mainly of single-celled organisms.

MAKE CONNECTIONS *After reviewing endosymbiont theory (see Figure 6.16), explain the specific positions of the mitochondrion and chloroplast lineages on this tree.*

other organisms. If this tree is correct, eukaryotes and archaea are more closely related to each other than either is to bacteria.

This reconstruction of the tree of life is based in part on sequence comparisons of rRNA genes, which code for the RNA components of ribosomes. However, some other genes reveal a different set of relationships. For example, researchers have found that many of the genes that influence metabolism in yeast (a unicellular eukaryote) are more similar to genes in the domain Bacteria than they are to genes in the domain Archaea—a finding that suggests that the eukaryotes may share a more recent common ancestor with bacteria than with archaea.

What causes trees based on data from different genes to yield such different results? Comparisons of complete genomes from the three domains show that there have been substantial movements of genes between organisms in the different domains. These took place through **horizontal gene transfer**, a process in which genes are transferred from one genome to another through mechanisms such as exchange of transposable elements and plasmids, viral infection (see Chapter 19), and perhaps fusions of organisms (as when a host and its endosymbiont become a single organism). Recent research reinforces the view that horizontal gene transfer is important. For example, a 2008 analysis indicated that, on average, 80% of the genes in 181 prokaryotic genomes had moved between species at some point during the course of evolution. Because phylogenetic trees are based on the assumption that genes are passed vertically from one generation to the next, the occurrence of such horizontal transfer events helps to explain why trees built using different genes can give inconsistent results.

Horizontal gene transfer can also occur between eukaryotes. For example, over 200 cases of the horizontal transfer of transposons have been reported in eukaryotes, including humans and other primates, plants, birds, and the gecko shown in **Figure 26.22**. Nuclear genes have also been transferred horizontally from one eukaryote to another. The Scientific Skills Exercise describes one such example, giving you the opportunity to interpret data on the transfer of a pigment gene to an aphid from another species.

Overall, horizontal gene transfer has played a key role throughout the evolutionary history of life and it continues to occur today. Some biologists have argued that horizontal gene transfer was so common that the early history of life should be represented not as a dichotomously branching tree like that in Figure 26.21, but rather as a tangled network

▼ **Figure 26.22 A recipient of transferred genes: the Mediterranean house gecko (*Hemidactylus turcicus*).** Recent genetic evidence indicates that this gecko is one of 17 reptile species that acquired the transposon *SPIN* as a result of horizontal gene transfer. The transposon may have been transferred from one species to another by the feeding activities of blood-sucking insects.

Using Protein Sequence Data to Test an Evolutionary Hypothesis

Did Aphids Acquire Their Ability to Make Carotenoids Through Horizontal Gene Transfer? Carotenoids are colored molecules that have diverse functions in many organisms, such as photosynthesis in plants and light detection in animals. Plants and many microorganisms can synthesize carotenoids from scratch, but animals generally cannot (they must obtain carotenoids from their diet). One exception is the pea aphid *Acyrthosiphon pisum*, a small plant-dwelling insect whose genome includes a full set of genes for the enzymes needed to make carotenoids. Because other animals lack these genes, it is unlikely that aphids inherited them from a single-celled common ancestor shared with microorganisms and plants. So where did they come from? Evolutionary biologists hypothesize that an aphid ancestor acquired these genes by horizontal gene transfer from distantly related organisms.

How the Experiment Was Done Scientists obtained the DNA sequences for the carotenoid-biosynthesis genes from several species, including aphids, fungi, bacteria, and plants. A computer "translated" these sequences into amino acid sequences of the encoded polypeptides and aligned the amino acid sequences. This allowed the team to compare the corresponding polypeptides in the different organisms.

Data from the Experiment The sequences below show the first 60 amino acids of one polypeptide of the carotenoid-biosynthesis enzymes in the plant *Arabidopsis thaliana* (bottom) and the corresponding amino acids in five nonplant species, using the one-letter abbreviations for the amino acids (see Figure 5.14). A hyphen (-) indicates that a species lacks

a particular amino acid found in the *Arabidopsis* sequence.

Interpret the Data

1. In the rows of data for the organisms being compared with the aphid, highlight the amino acids that are identical to the corresponding amino acids in the aphid.

2. Which organism has the most amino acids in common with the aphid? Rank the partial polypeptides from the other four organisms in degree of similarity to that of the aphid.

3. Do these data support the hypothesis that aphids acquired the gene for this polypeptide by horizontal gene transfer? Why or why not? If horizontal gene transfer did occur, what type of organism is likely to have been the source?

4. What additional sequence data would support your hypothesis?

5. How would you account for the similarities between the aphid sequence and the sequences for the bacteria and plant?

(MB) A version of this Scientific Skills Exercise can be assigned in MasteringBiology.

Data from Nancy A. Moran, Yale University. See N. A. Moran and T. Jarvik, Lateral transfer of genes from fungi underlies carotenoid production in aphids, *Science* 328:624–627 (2010).

Organism	Alignment of Amino Acid Sequences
Acyrthosiphon (aphid)	IKIIIIGSGV GGTAAAARLS KKGFQVEVYE KNSYNGGRCS IIR-HNGHRF DQGPSL--YL
Ustilago (fungus)	KKVVIIGAGA GGTALAARLG RRGYSVTVLE KNSFGGGRCS LIH-HDGHRW DQGPSL--YL
Gibberella (fungus)	KSVIVIGAGV GGVSTAARLA KAGFKVTILE KNDFTGGRCS LIH-NDGHRF DQGPSL--LL
Staphylococcus (bacterium)	MKIAVIGAGV TGLAAAARIA SQGHEVTIFE KNNNVGGRMN QLK-KDGFTF DMGPTI--VM
Pantoea (bacterium)	KRTFVIGAGF GGLALAIRLQ AAGIATTVLE QHDKPGGRAY VWQ-DQGFTF DAGPTV--IT
Arabidopsis (plant)	WDAVVIGGGH NGLTAAAYLA RGGLSVAVLE RRHVIGGAAV TEEIVPGFKF SRCSYLQGLL

▶ **Figure 26.23 A tangled web of life.** Horizontal gene transfer may have been so common in the early history of life that the base of a "tree of life" might be more accurately portrayed as a tangled web.

© 1999 AAAS

of connected branches **(Figure 26.23)**. Although scientists continue to debate whether early steps in the history of life are best represented as a tree or a tangled web, in recent decades there have been many exciting discoveries about evolutionary events that occurred over time. We'll explore such discoveries in the rest of this unit's chapters, beginning with Earth's earliest inhabitants, the prokaryotes.

CONCEPT CHECK 26.6

1. Why is the kingdom Monera no longer considered a valid taxon?

2. Explain why phylogenies based on different genes can yield different branching patterns for the tree of all life.

3. **WHAT IF?** Draw the three possible dichotomously branching trees showing evolutionary relationships for the domains Bacteria, Archaea, and Eukarya. Two of these trees have been supported by genetic data. Is it likely that the third tree might also receive such support? Explain your answer.

For suggested answers, see Appendix A.

26 Chapter Review

SUMMARY OF KEY CONCEPTS

CONCEPT 26.1

Phylogenies show evolutionary relationships (pp. 548–551)

- Linnaeus's **binomial** classification system gives organisms two-part names: a **genus** plus a specific epithet.
- In the Linnaean system, species are grouped in increasingly broad taxa: Related genera are placed in the same family, families in orders, orders in classes, classes in phyla, phyla in kingdoms, and (more recently) kingdoms in domains.
- Systematists depict evolutionary relationships as branching **phylogenetic trees**. Many systematists propose that classification be based entirely on evolutionary relationships.

- Unless branch lengths are proportional to time or genetic change, a phylogenetic tree indicates only patterns of descent.
- Much information can be learned about a species from its evolutionary history; hence, phylogenies are useful in a wide range of applications.

? *Humans and chimpanzees are sister species. Explain what that means.*

CONCEPT 26.2

Phylogenies are inferred from morphological and molecular data (pp. 551–553)

- Organisms with similar morphologies or DNA sequences are likely to be more closely related than organisms with very different structures and genetic sequences.
- To infer phylogeny, **homology** (similarity due to shared ancestry) must be distinguished from **analogy** (similarity due to convergent evolution).
- Computer programs are used to align comparable DNA sequences and to distinguish molecular homologies from coincidental matches between taxa that diverged long ago.

? *Why is it necessary to distinguish homology from analogy to infer phylogeny?*

CONCEPT 26.3

Shared characters are used to construct phylogenetic trees (pp. 553–559)

- A **clade** is a monophyletic grouping that includes an ancestral species and all of its descendants.

- Clades can be distinguished by their **shared derived characters**.

- Among phylogenies, the most parsimonious tree is the one that requires the fewest evolutionary changes. The most likely tree is the one based on the most likely pattern of changes.
- Well-supported phylogenetic hypotheses are consistent with a wide range of data.

? *Explain the logic of using shared derived characters to infer phylogeny.*

CONCEPT 26.4

An organism's evolutionary history is documented in its genome (pp. 559–560)

- **Orthologous genes** are homologous genes found in different species as a result of speciation. **Paralogous genes** are homologous genes within a species that result from gene duplication; such genes can diverge and potentially take on new functions.
- Distantly related species often have many orthologous genes. The small variation in gene number in organisms of varying complexity suggests that genes are versatile and may have multiple functions.

? *When reconstructing phylogenies, is it better to compare orthologous or paralogous genes? Explain.*

CONCEPT 26.5

Molecular clocks help track evolutionary time (pp. 560–562)

- Some regions of DNA change at a rate consistent enough to serve as a **molecular clock**, in which the amount of genetic change is used to estimate the date of past evolutionary events. Other DNA regions change in a less predictable way.
- Molecular clock analyses suggest that the most common strain of HIV jumped from primates to humans in the early 1900s.

? *Describe some assumptions and limitations of molecular clocks.*

CONCEPT 26.6

Our understanding of the tree of life continues to change based on new data (pp. 562–564)

- Past classification systems have given way to the current view of the tree of life, which consists of three great **domains**: Bacteria, Archaea, and Eukarya.

- Phylogenies based in part on rRNA genes suggest that eukaryotes are most closely related to archaea, while data from some other genes suggest a closer relationship to bacteria.
- Genetic analyses indicate that extensive horizontal gene transfer has occurred throughout the evolutionary history of life.

? *Why was the five-kingdom system abandoned for a three-domain system?*

TEST YOUR UNDERSTANDING

LEVEL 1: KNOWLEDGE/COMPREHENSION

1. In a comparison of birds and mammals, the condition of having four limbs is
   a. a shared ancestral character.
   b. a shared derived character.
   c. a character useful for distinguishing birds from mammals.
   d. an example of analogy rather than homology.

2. To apply parsimony to constructing a phylogenetic tree,
   a. choose the tree that assumes all evolutionary changes are equally probable.
   b. choose the tree in which the branch points are based on as many shared derived characters as possible.
   c. choose the tree that represents the fewest evolutionary changes, in either DNA sequences or morphology.
   d. choose the tree with the fewest branch points.

LEVEL 2: APPLICATION/ANALYSIS

3. In Figure 26.4, which similarly inclusive taxon descended from the same common ancestor as Canidae?
   a. Felidae   c. Carnivora
   b. Mustelidae   d. *Lutra*

4. Three living species X, Y, and Z share a common ancestor T, as do extinct species U and V. A grouping that consists of species T, X, Y, and Z (but not U or V) makes up
   a. a monophyletic taxon.
   b. an ingroup, with species U as the outgroup.
   c. a paraphyletic group.
   d. a polyphyletic group.

5. Based on the tree below, which statement is *not* correct?

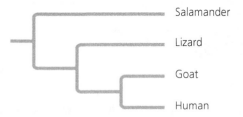

Salamander
Lizard
Goat
Human

   a. The salamander lineage is a basal taxon.
   b. Salamanders are a sister group to the group containing lizards, goats, and humans.
   c. Salamanders are as closely related to goats as to humans.
   d. Lizards are more closely related to salamanders than to humans.

6. If you were using cladistics to build a phylogenetic tree of cats, which of the following would be the best outgroup?
   a. wolf   c. lion
   b. domestic cat   d. leopard

7. The relative lengths of the frog and mouse branches in the phylogenetic tree in Figure 26.13 indicate that
   a. frogs evolved before mice.
   b. mice evolved before frogs.
   c. the homolog has evolved more rapidly in mice.
   d. the homolog has evolved more slowly in mice.

LEVEL 3: SYNTHESIS/EVALUATION

8. **EVOLUTION CONNECTION**
   Darwin suggested looking at a species' close relatives to learn what its ancestors may have been like. How does his suggestion anticipate recent methods, such as phylogenetic bracketing and the use of outgroups in cladistic analysis?

9. **SCIENTIFIC INQUIRY**
   DRAW IT (a) Draw a phylogenetic tree based on characters 1–5 in the table below. Place hatch marks on the tree to indicate the origin(s) of characters 1–6. (b) Assume that tuna and dolphins are sister species and redraw the phylogenetic tree accordingly. Use hatch marks to indicate the origin(s) of characters 1–6. (c) How many evolutionary changes are required in each tree? Which tree is most parsimonious?

Character	Lancelet (outgroup)	Lamprey	Tuna	Salamander	Turtle	Leopard	Dolphin
(1) Backbone	0	1	1	1	1	1	1
(2) Hinged jaw	0	0	1	1	1	1	1
(3) Four limbs	0	0	0	1	1	1	1*
(4) Amnion	0	0	0	0	1	1	1
(5) Milk	0	0	0	0	0	1	1
(6) Dorsal fin	0	0	1	0	0	0	1

*Although adult dolphins have only two obvious limbs (their flippers), as embryos they have two hind-limb buds, for a total of four limbs.

10. **WRITE ABOUT A THEME: INFORMATION**
    In a short essay (100–150 words), explain how genetic information—along with an understanding of the process of descent with modification—enables scientists to reconstruct phylogenies that extend hundreds of millions of years back in time.

11. **SYNTHESIZE YOUR KNOWLEDGE**

This West Indian manatee (*Trichechus manatus*) is an aquatic mammal. Like amphibians and reptiles, mammals are tetrapods (vertebrates with four limbs). Explain why manatees are considered tetrapods even though they lack hind limbs, and suggest traits that manatees likely share with leopards and other mammals (see Figure 26.12b). How might early members of the manatee lineage have differed from today's manatees?

For selected answers, see Appendix A.

MasteringBiology®

Students Go to **MasteringBiology** for assignments, the eText, and the Study Area with practice tests, animations, and activities.

Instructors Go to **MasteringBiology** for automatically graded tutorials and questions that you can assign to your students, plus Instructor Resources.

27

Bacteria and Archaea

▲ Figure 27.1 **Why is this lake's water pink?**

Masters of Adaptation

At certain times of year, the Laguna Salada de Torrevieja in Spain (the "Salty Lagoon") appears pink **(Figure 27.1)**, a sign of waters many times saltier than seawater. Yet despite these harsh conditions, the dramatic color is caused not by minerals or other nonliving sources, but by living things. What organisms can live in such an inhospitable environment, and how do they do it?

The pink color in the Laguna Salada de Torrevieja comes from trillions of prokaryotes in the domains Archaea and Bacteria, including archaea in the genus *Halobacterium*. These archaea have red membrane pigments, some of which capture light energy that is used to drive ATP synthesis. *Halobacterium* species are among the most salt-tolerant organisms on Earth; they thrive in salinities that dehydrate and kill other cells. A *Halobacterium* cell compensates for water lost through osmosis by pumping potassium ions (K^+) into the cell until the ionic concentration inside the cell matches the concentration outside.

Like *Halobacterium*, many other prokaryotes can tolerate extreme conditions. Examples include *Deinococcus radiodurans*, which can survive 3 million rads of radiation (3,000 times the dose fatal to humans), and *Picrophilus oshimae*, which can grow at a pH of 0.03 (acidic enough to dissolve metal). Other prokaryotes live in environments that are too cold or too hot for most other organisms, and some have even been found living in rocks 3.2 km (2 miles) below Earth's surface.

Prokaryotic species are also very well adapted to more "normal" habitats—the lands and waters in which most other species are found. Their ability to adapt to a broad range of habitats helps explain why prokaryotes are the most abundant organisms on Earth: Indeed, the number of prokaryotes in a handful of fertile soil is greater than the number of people who have ever lived. In this chapter, we'll examine the adaptations, diversity, and enormous ecological impact of these remarkable organisms.

CONCEPT 27.1

Structural and functional adaptations contribute to prokaryotic success

The first organisms to inhabit Earth were prokaryotes that lived 3.5 billion years ago (see Chapter 25). Throughout their long evolutionary history, prokaryotic populations have been (and continue to be) subjected to natural selection in all kinds of environments, resulting in their enormous diversity today.

We'll begin by describing prokaryotes. Most prokaryotes are unicellular, although the cells of some species remain attached to each other after cell division. Prokaryotic cells typically have diameters of 0.5–5 µm, much smaller than the 10–100 µm diameter of many eukaryotic cells. (One notable exception, *Thiomargarita namibiensis*, can be as large as 750 µm in diameter—bigger than the dot on this i.) Prokaryotic cells have a variety of shapes (Figure 27.2). Finally, although they are unicellular and small, prokaryotes are well organized, achieving all of an organism's life functions within a single cell.

Cell-Surface Structures

A key feature of nearly all prokaryotic cells is the cell wall, which maintains cell shape, protects the cell, and prevents it from bursting in a hypotonic environment (see Figure 7.12). In a hypertonic environment, most prokaryotes lose water and shrink away from their wall (plasmolyze). Such water losses can inhibit cell reproduction. Thus, salt can be used to preserve foods because it causes food-spoiling prokaryotes to lose water, preventing them from rapidly multiplying.

The cell walls of prokaryotes differ in structure from those of eukaryotes. In eukaryotes that have cell walls, such as plants and fungi, the walls are usually made of cellulose or chitin (see Concept 5.2). In contrast, most bacterial cell walls contain **peptidoglycan**, a polymer composed of modified sugars cross-linked by short polypeptides. This molecular fabric encloses the entire bacterium and anchors other

(a) Spherical   **(b) Rod-shaped**   **(c) Spiral**

▲ **Figure 27.2 The most common shapes of prokaryotes. (a)** Cocci (singular, *coccus*) are spherical prokaryotes. They occur singly, in pairs (diplococci), in chains of many cells (streptococci), and in clusters resembling bunches of grapes (staphylococci). **(b)** Bacilli (singular, *bacillus*) are rod-shaped prokaryotes. They are usually solitary, but in some forms the rods are arranged in chains (streptobacilli). **(c)** Spiral prokaryotes include spirilla, which range from comma-like shapes to loose coils, and spirochetes (shown here), which are corkscrew-shaped (colorized SEMs).

molecules that extend from its surface. Archaeal cell walls contain a variety of polysaccharides and proteins but lack peptidoglycan.

Using a technique called the **Gram stain**, developed by the 19th-century Danish physician Hans Christian Gram, scientists can categorize many bacterial species according to differences in cell wall composition. To do this, samples are first stained with crystal violet dye and iodine, then rinsed in alcohol, and finally stained with a red dye such as safranin. The structure of a bacterium's cell wall determines the staining response (Figure 27.3). **Gram-positive** bacteria have simpler walls with a relatively large amount of peptidoglycan. **Gram-negative** bacteria have less peptidoglycan and are structurally more complex, with an outer membrane that contains lipopolysaccharides (carbohydrates bonded to lipids).

Gram staining is a valuable tool in medicine for quickly determining if a patient's infection is due to gram-negative or to gram-positive bacteria. This information has treatment implications. The lipid portions of the lipopolysaccharides in the walls of many gram-negative bacteria are toxic, causing fever or shock. Furthermore, the outer membrane of a gram-negative bacterium helps protect it from the body's defenses. Gram-negative bacteria also tend to be more resistant than gram-positive species to antibiotics because the outer membrane impedes entry of the drugs. However, certain gram-positive species have virulent strains that are resistant to one or more antibiotics. (Figure 22.14 discusses

(a) Gram-positive bacteria

Gram-positive bacteria

Cell wall { Peptido-glycan layer

Plasma membrane

10 µm

Gram-positive bacteria have a thick wall made of peptidoglycan. The crystal violet enters the cell, where it forms a complex with the iodine in the stain. Too large to pass through the thick cell wall, this complex is not removed by the alcohol rinse. Result: The crystal violet masks the red safranin dye.

(b) Gram-negative bacteria

Gram-negative bacteria

Carbohydrate portion of lipopolysaccharide

Cell wall { Outer membrane } Peptido-glycan layer

Plasma membrane

Gram-negative bacteria have a thin layer of peptidoglycan, which is located between the plasma membrane and an outer membrane. The crystal violet–iodine complex can pass through this thin cell wall and hence is removed by the alcohol rinse. Result: The safranin dye stains the cell pink or red.

one example: methicillin-resistant *Staphylococcus aureus*, or MRSA, which can cause lethal skin infections.)

The effectiveness of certain antibiotics, such as penicillin, derives from their inhibition of peptidoglycan cross-linking. The resulting cell wall may not be functional, particularly in gram-positive bacteria. Such drugs destroy many species of pathogenic bacteria without adversely affecting human cells, which do not have peptidoglycan.

The cell wall of many prokaryotes is surrounded by a sticky layer of polysaccharide or protein. This layer is called a **capsule** if it is dense and well-defined **(Figure 27.4)** or a

slime layer if it is not as well organized. Both kinds of sticky outer layers enable prokaryotes to adhere to their substrate or to other individuals in a colony. Some capsules and slime layers protect against dehydration, and some shield pathogenic prokaryotes from attacks by their host's immune system.

In another way of withstanding harsh conditions, certain bacteria develop resistant cells called **endospores** when they lack an essential nutrient **(Figure 27.5)**. The original cell produces a copy of its chromosome and surrounds that copy with a tough multilayered structure, forming the endospore.

Bacterial cell wall

Bacterial capsule

Tonsil cell

200 nm

▲ **Figure 27.4 Capsule.** The polysaccharide capsule around this *Streptococcus* bacterium enables the prokaryote to attach to cells in the respiratory tract—in this colorized TEM, a tonsil cell.

Endospore

Coat

0.3 µm

▲ **Figure 27.5 An endospore.** *Bacillus anthracis*, the bacterium that causes the disease anthrax, produces endospores (TEM). An endospore's protective, multilayered coat helps it survive in the soil for years.

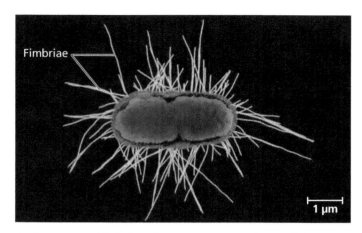

Fimbriae

▲ **Figure 27.6 Fimbriae.** These numerous protein-containing appendages enable some prokaryotes to attach to surfaces or to other cells (colorized TEM).

Water is removed from the endospore, and its metabolism halts. The original cell then lyses, releasing the endospore. Most endospores are so durable that they can survive in boiling water; killing them requires heating lab equipment to 121°C under high pressure. In less hostile environments, endospores can remain dormant but viable for centuries, able to rehydrate and resume metabolism when their environment improves.

Finally, some prokaryotes stick to their substrate or to one another by means of hairlike appendages called **fimbriae** (singular, *fimbria*) **(Figure 27.6)**. For example, the bacterium that causes gonorrhea, *Neisseria gonorrhoeae*, uses fimbriae to fasten itself to the mucous membranes of its host. Fimbriae are usually shorter and more numerous than **pili** (singular, *pilus*), appendages that pull two cells together prior to DNA transfer from one cell to the other (see Figure 27.12); pili are sometimes referred to as *sex pili*.

Motility

About half of all prokaryotes are capable of **taxis**, a directed movement toward or away from a stimulus (from the Greek *taxis*, to arrange). For example, prokaryotes that exhibit *chemotaxis* change their movement pattern in response to chemicals. They may move *toward* nutrients or oxygen (positive chemotaxis) or *away from* a toxic substance (negative chemotaxis). Some species can move at velocities exceeding 50 μm/sec—up to 50 times their body length per second. For perspective, consider that a person 1.7 m tall moving that fast would be running 306 km (190 miles) per hour!

Of the various structures that enable prokaryotes to move, the most common are flagella **(Figure 27.7)**. Flagella (singular, *flagellum*) may be scattered over the entire surface of the cell or concentrated at one or both ends. Prokaryotic flagella differ greatly from eukaryotic flagella: They are one-tenth the width and typically are not covered by an extension of the plasma membrane (see Figure 6.24). The flagella of prokaryotes and eukaryotes also differ in their molecular composition and their mechanism of propulsion. Among prokaryotes, bacterial and archaeal flagella are similar in size and propulsion mechanism, but they are composed of entirely different and unrelated proteins. Overall, these structural and molecular comparisons indicate that the flagella of bacteria, archaea, and eukaryotes arose independently. Since current evidence shows that the flagella of organisms in the three domains perform similar functions but are not related by common descent, they are described as analogous, not homologous, structures.

Evolutionary Origins of Bacterial Flagella

The bacterial flagellum shown in **Figure 27.7** has three main parts (the motor, hook, and filament) that are themselves composed of 42 different kinds of proteins. How could such a complex structure evolve? In fact, much evidence indicates that bacterial flagella originated as simpler structures that were modified in a stepwise fashion over time. As in the case of the human eye (see Concept 25.6), biologists asked whether a less complex version of the flagellum could still benefit its owner. Analyses of hundreds of bacterial genomes indicate that

Flagellum

Filament

20 nm

Hook

Motor

Cell wall

Plasma membrane

Rod

Peptidoglycan layer

▲ **Figure 27.7 A prokaryotic flagellum.** The motor of a prokaryotic flagellum consists of a system of rings embedded in the cell wall and plasma membrane (TEM). The electron transport chain pumps protons out of the cell. The diffusion of protons back into the cell provides the force that turns a curved hook and thereby causes the attached filament to rotate and propel the cell. (This diagram shows flagellar structures characteristic of gram-negative bacteria.)

only half of the flagellum's protein components appear to be necessary for it to function; the others are inessential or not encoded in the genomes of some species. Of the 21 proteins required by all species studied to date, 19 are modified versions of proteins that perform other tasks in bacteria. For example, a set of 10 proteins in the motor are homologous to 10 similar proteins in a secretory system found in bacteria. (A secretory system is a protein complex that enables a cell to secrete certain macromolecules.) Two other proteins in the motor are homologous to proteins that function in ion transport. The proteins that comprise the rod, hook, and filament are all related to each other and are descended from an ancestral protein that formed a pilus-like tube. These findings suggest that the bacterial flagellum evolved as other proteins were added to an ancestral secretory system. This is an example of *exaptation*, the process in which existing structures take on new functions through descent with modification.

Internal Organization and DNA

The cells of prokaryotes are simpler than those of eukaryotes in both their internal structure and the physical arrangement of their DNA (see Figure 6.5). Prokaryotic cells lack the complex compartmentalization associated with the membrane-enclosed organelles found in eukaryotic cells. However, some prokaryotic cells do have specialized membranes that perform metabolic functions **(Figure 27.8)**. These membranes are usually infoldings of the plasma membrane. Recent discoveries also indicate that some prokaryotes can store metabolic by-products in simple compartments that are made out of proteins; these compartments do not have a membrane.

The genome of a prokaryote is structurally different from a eukaryotic genome and in most cases has considerably less

(a) Aerobic prokaryote

(b) Photosynthetic prokaryote

▲ **Figure 27.8 Specialized membranes of prokaryotes.**
(a) Infoldings of the plasma membrane, reminiscent of the cristae of mitochondria, function in cellular respiration in some aerobic prokaryotes (TEM). **(b)** Photosynthetic prokaryotes called cyanobacteria have thylakoid membranes, much like those in chloroplasts (TEM).

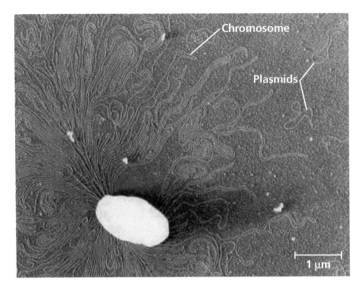

▲ **Figure 27.9 A prokaryotic chromosome and plasmids.** The thin, tangled loops surrounding this ruptured *E. coli* cell are parts of the cell's large, circular chromosome (colorized TEM). Three of the cell's plasmids, the much smaller rings of DNA, are also shown.

DNA. Prokaryotes generally have circular chromosomes **(Figure 27.9)**, whereas eukaryotes have linear chromosomes. In addition, in prokaryotes the chromosome is associated with many fewer proteins than are the chromosomes of eukaryotes. Also unlike eukaryotes, prokaryotes lack a nucleus; their chromosome is located in the **nucleoid**, a region of cytoplasm that is not enclosed by a membrane. In addition to its single chromosome, a typical prokaryotic cell may also have much smaller rings of independently replicating DNA molecules called **plasmids** (see Figure 27.9), most carrying only a few genes.

Although DNA replication, transcription, and translation are fundamentally similar processes in prokaryotes and eukaryotes, some of the details are different (see Chapter 17). For example, prokaryotic ribosomes are slightly smaller than eukaryotic ribosomes and differ in their protein and RNA content. These differences allow certain antibiotics, such as erythromycin and tetracycline, to bind to ribosomes and block protein synthesis in prokaryotes but not in eukaryotes. As a result, people can use these antibiotics to kill or inhibit the growth of bacteria without harming themselves.

Reproduction

Many prokaryotes can reproduce quickly in favorable environments. By *binary fission* (see Figure 12.12), a single prokaryotic cell divides into 2 cells, which then divide into 4, 8, 16, and so on. Under optimal conditions, many prokaryotes can divide every 1–3 hours; some species can produce a new generation in only 20 minutes. At this rate, a single prokaryotic cell could give rise to a colony outweighing Earth in only two days!

In reality, of course, this does not occur. The cells eventually exhaust their nutrient supply, poison themselves with metabolic wastes, face competition from other microorganisms, or are consumed by other organisms. Still, the fact that many prokaryotic species can divide after short periods of time draws attention to three key features of their biology: *They are small, they reproduce by binary fission, and they often have short generation times.* As a result, prokaryotic populations can consist of many trillions of individuals—far more than populations of multicellular eukaryotes, such as plants or animals.

CONCEPT CHECK 27.1

1. Identify and explain two adaptations that enable prokaryotes to survive in environments too harsh for other organisms.

2. Contrast the cellular and DNA structures of prokaryotes and eukaryotes.

3. **MAKE CONNECTIONS** Suggest a hypothesis to explain why the thylakoid membranes of chloroplasts resemble those of cyanobacteria. Refer to Figures 6.18 and 26.21.

For suggested answers, see Appendix A.

CONCEPT 27.2

Rapid reproduction, mutation, and genetic recombination promote genetic diversity in prokaryotes

As we discussed in Unit Four, evolution cannot occur without genetic variation. The diverse adaptations exhibited by prokaryotes suggest that their populations must have considerable genetic variation—and they do. In this section, we'll examine three factors that give rise to high levels of genetic diversity in prokaryotes: rapid reproduction, mutation, and genetic recombination.

Rapid Reproduction and Mutation

In sexually reproducing species, the generation of a novel allele by a new mutation is rare for any particular gene. Instead, most of the genetic variation in sexual populations results from the way existing alleles are arranged in new combinations during meiosis and fertilization (see Chapter 13). Prokaryotes do not reproduce sexually, so at first glance their extensive genetic variation may seem puzzling. But in many species, this variation can result from a combination of rapid reproduction and mutation.

Consider the bacterium *Escherichia coli* as it reproduces by binary fission in a human intestine, one of its natural environments. After repeated rounds of division, most of the

offspring cells are genetically identical to the original parent cell. However, if errors occur during DNA replication, some of the offspring cells may differ genetically. The probability of such a mutation occurring in a given *E. coli* gene is about one in 10 million (1×10^{-7}) per cell division. But among the 2×10^{10} new *E. coli* cells that arise each day in a person's intestine,

---

▼ Figure 27.10 | Inquiry

Can prokaryotes evolve rapidly in response to environmental change?

Experiment Vaughn Cooper and Richard Lenski tested the ability of *E. coli* populations to adapt to a new environment. They established 12 populations, each founded by a single cell from an *E. coli* strain, and followed these populations for 20,000 generations (3,000 days). To maintain a continual supply

Daily serial transfer

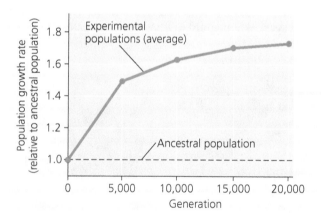

of resources, each day the researchers performed a *serial transfer*: They transferred 0.1 mL of each population to a new tube containing 9.9 mL of fresh growth medium. The growth medium used throughout the experiment provided a challenging environment that contained only low levels of glucose and other resources needed for growth.

Samples were periodically removed from the 12 populations and grown in competition with the common ancestral strain in the experimental (low-glucose) environment.

Results The fitness of the experimental populations, as measured by the growth rate of each population, increased rapidly for the first 5,000 generations (2 years) and more slowly for the next 15,000 generations. The graph shows the averages for the 12 populations.

Conclusion Populations of *E. coli* continued to accumulate beneficial mutations for 20,000 generations, allowing rapid evolution of increased population growth rates in their new environment.

Source: V. S. Cooper and R. E. Lenski, The population genetics of ecological specialization in evolving *Escherichia coli* populations, *Nature* 407:736–739 (2000).

WHAT IF? *Suggest possible functions of the genes whose sequence or expression was altered as the experimental populations evolved in the low-glucose environment.*

---

there will be approximately $(2 \times 10^{10}) \times (1 \times 10^{-7}) = 2{,}000$ bacteria that have a mutation in that gene. The total number of mutations when all 4,300 *E. coli* genes are considered is about $4{,}300 \times 2{,}000 = 9$ million per day per human host.

The key point is that new mutations, though rare on a per gene basis, can increase genetic diversity quickly in species with short generation times and large populations. This diversity, in turn, can lead to rapid evolution: Individuals that are genetically better equipped for their environment tend to survive and reproduce at higher rates than other individuals (Figure 27.10). The ability of prokaryotes to adapt rapidly to new conditions highlights the point that although the structure of their cells is simpler than that of eukaryotic cells, prokaryotes are not "primitive" or "inferior" in an evolutionary sense. They are, in fact, highly evolved: For 3.5 billion years, prokaryotic populations have responded successfully to many types of environmental challenges.

Genetic Recombination

Although new mutations are a major source of variation in prokaryotic populations, additional diversity arises from *genetic recombination*, the combining of DNA from two sources. In eukaryotes, the sexual processes of meiosis and fertilization combine DNA from two individuals in a single zygote. But meiosis and fertilization do not occur in prokaryotes. Instead, three other mechanisms—transformation, transduction, and conjugation—can bring together prokaryotic DNA from different individuals (that is, different cells). When the individuals are members of different species, this movement of genes from one organism to another is called *horizontal gene transfer*. Although scientists have found evidence that each of these mechanisms can transfer DNA within and between species in both domain Bacteria and domain Archaea, to date most of our knowledge comes from research on bacteria.

Transformation and Transduction

In **transformation**, the genotype and possibly phenotype of a prokaryotic cell are altered by the uptake of foreign DNA from its surroundings. For example, a harmless strain of *Streptococcus pneumoniae* can be transformed into pneumonia-causing cells if the cells are exposed to DNA from a pathogenic strain (see Concept 16.1). This transformation occurs when a nonpathogenic cell takes up a piece of DNA carrying the allele for pathogenicity and replaces its own allele with the foreign allele, an exchange of homologous DNA segments. The cell is now a recombinant: Its chromosome contains DNA derived from two different cells.

For many years after transformation was discovered in laboratory cultures, most biologists thought the process to be too rare and haphazard to play an important role in natural bacterial populations. But researchers have since learned that many bacteria have cell-surface proteins that recognize DNA from closely related species and transport it into the cell. Once inside the cell, the foreign DNA can be incorporated into the genome by homologous DNA exchange.

In **transduction**, phages (from "bacteriophages," the viruses that infect bacteria) carry prokaryotic genes from one host cell to another. In most cases, transduction results from accidents that occur during the phage replicative cycle (Figure 27.11). A virus that carries prokaryotic DNA may not be able to replicate because it lacks some or all of its own genetic material. However, the virus can attach to another prokaryotic cell (a recipient) and inject prokaryotic DNA acquired from the first cell (the donor). If some of this DNA is then incorporated into the recipient cell's chromosome by crossing over, a recombinant cell is formed.

1. A phage infects a bacterial cell that carries the A^+ and B^+ alleles on its chromosome (brown). This bacterium will be the "donor" cell.

Phage DNA

Donor cell

2. The phage DNA is replicated, and the cell makes many copies of the proteins encoded by its genes. Meanwhile, certain phage proteins halt the synthesis of proteins encoded by the host cell's DNA, and the host cell's DNA may be fragmented, as shown here.

3. As new phage particles assemble, a fragment of bacterial DNA carrying the A^+ allele happens to be packaged in a phage capsid.

A^+

Crossing over

4. The phage carrying the A^+ allele from the donor cell infects a recipient cell with alleles A^- and B^-. Crossing over at two sites (dotted lines) allows donor DNA (brown) to be incorporated into recipient DNA (green).

Recipient cell

Recombinant cell

5. The genotype of the resulting recombinant cell (A^+B^-) differs from the genotypes of both the donor (A^+B^+) and the recipient (A^-B^-).

▲ Figure 27.11 Transduction. Phages may carry pieces of a bacterial chromosome from one cell (the donor) to another (the recipient). If crossing over occurs after the transfer, genes from the donor may be incorporated into the recipient's genome.

❓ *Under what circumstances would a transduction event result in horizontal gene transfer?*

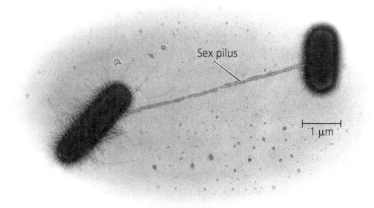

Sex pilus

1 µm

▲ **Figure 27.12 Bacterial conjugation.** The *E. coli* donor cell (left) extends a pilus that attaches to a recipient cell, a key first step in the transfer of DNA. The pilus is a flexible tube of protein subunits (TEM).

▼ **Figure 27.13 Conjugation and recombination in *E. coli*.** The DNA replication that accompanies transfer of an F plasmid or part of an Hfr bacterial chromosome is called *rolling circle replication*. In effect, the intact circular parental DNA strand "rolls" as its other strand peels off and a new complementary strand is synthesized.

Conjugation and Plasmids

In a process called **conjugation**, DNA is transferred between two prokaryotic cells (usually of the same species) that are temporarily joined. In bacteria, the DNA transfer is always one-way: One cell donates the DNA, and the other receives it. We'll focus here on the mechanism used by *E. coli*.

First, a pilus of the donor cell attaches to the recipient (**Figure 27.12**). The pilus then retracts, pulling the two cells together, like a grappling hook. The next step is thought to be the formation of a temporary "mating bridge" structure between the two cells, through which the donor may transfer DNA to the recipient. However, the mechanism by which DNA transfer occurs is unclear; indeed, recent evidence indicates that DNA may pass directly through the hollow pilus.

The ability to form pili and donate DNA during conjugation results from the presence of a particular piece of DNA called the **F factor** (F for *fertility*). The F factor of *E. coli* consists of about 25 genes, most required for the production of pili. As shown in **Figure 27.13**, the F factor can

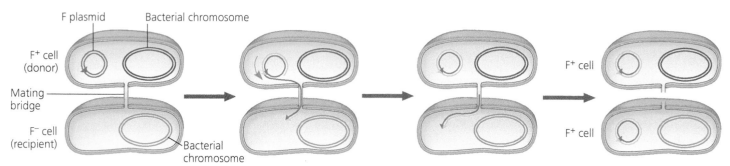

F plasmid Bacterial chromosome

F⁺ cell (donor)

Mating bridge

F⁻ cell (recipient) Bacterial chromosome

F⁺ cell

F⁺ cell

F⁺ cell

1 A cell carrying an F plasmid (an F⁺ cell) forms a mating bridge with an F⁻ cell. One strand of the plasmid's DNA breaks at the point marked by the arrowhead.

2 Using the unbroken strand as a template, the cell synthesizes a new strand (light blue). Meanwhile, the broken strand peels off (red arrow), and one end enters the F⁻ cell. There synthesis of its complementary strand begins.

3 DNA replication continues in both the donor and recipient cells, as the transferred plasmid strand moves farther into the recipient cell.

4 Once DNA transfer and synthesis are completed, the plasmid in the recipient cell circularizes. The recipient cell is now a recombinant F⁺ cell.

(a) Conjugation and transfer of an F plasmid

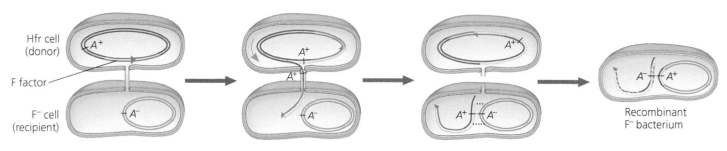

Hfr cell (donor) A^+

F factor

F⁻ cell (recipient) A^-

A^+ A^+

A^+ A^+

A^+ A^-

A^- A^+

Recombinant F⁻ bacterium

1 In an Hfr cell, the F factor (dark blue) is integrated into the bacterial chromosome. Since an Hfr cell has all of the F factor genes, it can form a mating bridge with an F⁻ cell and transfer DNA.

2 A single strand of the F factor breaks and begins to move through the bridge. DNA replication occurs in both donor and recipient cells, resulting in double-stranded DNA (daughter strands shown in lighter color).

3 The mating bridge usually breaks before the entire chromosome is transferred. Crossing over at two sites (dotted lines) can result in the exchange of homologous genes between the transferred DNA (brown) and the recipient's chromosome (green).

4 Cellular enzymes degrade any linear DNA not incorporated into the chromosome. The recipient cell, with a new combination of genes but no F factor, is now a recombinant F⁻ cell.

(b) Conjugation and transfer of part of an Hfr bacterial chromosome, resulting in recombination

exist either as a plasmid or as a segment of DNA within the bacterial chromosome.

The F Factor as a Plasmid The F factor in its plasmid form is called the **F plasmid**. Cells containing the F plasmid, designated F^+ cells, function as DNA donors during conjugation (**Figure 27.13a**). Cells lacking the F factor, designated F^-, function as DNA recipients during conjugation. The F^+ condition is transferable in the sense that an F^+ cell converts an F^- cell to F^+ if a copy of the entire F plasmid is transferred.

The F Factor in the Chromosome Chromosomal genes can be transferred during conjugation when the donor cell's F factor is integrated into the chromosome. A cell with the F factor built into its chromosome is called an *Hfr cell* (for *h*igh *f*requency of *r*ecombination). Like an F^+ cell, an Hfr cell functions as a donor during conjugation with an F^- cell (**Figure 27.13b**). When chromosomal DNA from an Hfr cell enters an F^- cell, homologous regions of the Hfr and F^- chromosomes may align, allowing segments of their DNA to be exchanged. As a result, the recipient cell becomes a recombinant bacterium that has genes derived from the chromosomes of two different cells—a new genetic variant on which evolution can act.

R Plasmids and Antibiotic Resistance During the 1950s in Japan, physicians started noticing that some hospital patients with bacterial dysentery, which produces severe diarrhea, did not respond to antibiotics that had been effective in the past. Apparently, resistance to these antibiotics had evolved in some strains of *Shigella*, the bacterium that causes the disease.

Eventually, researchers began to identify the specific genes that confer antibiotic resistance in *Shigella* and other pathogenic bacteria. Sometimes, mutation in a chromosomal gene of the pathogen can confer resistance. For example, a mutation in one gene may make it less likely that the pathogen will transport a particular antibiotic into its cell. Mutation in a different gene may alter the intracellular target protein for an antibiotic molecule, reducing its inhibitory effect. In other cases, bacteria have "resistance genes," which code for enzymes that specifically destroy or otherwise hinder the effectiveness of certain antibiotics, such as tetracycline or ampicillin. Such resistance genes are often carried by plasmids known as **R plasmids** (R for *r*esistance).

Exposing a bacterial population to a specific antibiotic will kill antibiotic-sensitive bacteria but not those that happen to have R plasmids with genes that counter the antibiotic. Under these circumstances, we would predict that natural selection would cause the fraction of the bacterial population carrying genes for antibiotic resistance to increase, and that is exactly what happens. The medical consequences are also predictable: Resistant strains of pathogens are becoming more common, making the treatment of certain bacterial infections more difficult. The problem is compounded by the fact that many R plasmids, like F plasmids, have genes that encode pili and enable DNA transfer from one bacterial cell to another by conjugation. Making the problem still worse, some R plasmids carry as many as ten genes for resistance to that many antibiotics.

CONCEPT CHECK 27.2

1. Although rare on a per gene basis, new mutations can add considerable genetic variation to prokaryotic populations in each generation. Explain how this occurs.
2. Distinguish between the three mechanisms of transferring DNA from one bacterial cell to another.
3. In a rapidly changing environment, which bacterial population would likely be more successful, one that includes individuals capable of conjugation or one that does not? Explain.
4. **WHAT IF?** If a nonpathogenic bacterium were to acquire resistance to antibiotics, could this strain pose a health risk to people? In general, how does DNA transfer among bacteria affect the spread of resistance genes?

For suggested answers, see Appendix A.

CONCEPT 27.3

Diverse nutritional and metabolic adaptations have evolved in prokaryotes

The extensive genetic variation found in prokaryotes is reflected in their diverse nutritional adaptations. Like all organisms, prokaryotes can be categorized by how they obtain energy and the carbon used in building the organic molecules that make up cells. Every type of nutrition observed in eukaryotes is represented among prokaryotes, along with some nutritional modes unique to prokaryotes. In fact, prokaryotes have an astounding range of metabolic adaptations, much broader than that found in eukaryotes.

Organisms that obtain energy from light are called *phototrophs*, and those that obtain energy from chemicals are called *chemotrophs*. Organisms that need only CO_2 or related compounds as a carbon source are called *autotrophs*. In contrast, *heterotrophs* require at least one organic nutrient, such as glucose, to make other organic compounds. Combining possible energy sources and carbon sources results in four major modes of nutrition, summarized in **Table 27.1** on the next page.

The Role of Oxygen in Metabolism

Prokaryotic metabolism also varies with respect to oxygen (O_2). **Obligate aerobes** must use O_2 for cellular respiration (see Chapter 9) and cannot grow without it. **Obligate anaerobes**, on the other hand, are poisoned by O_2. Some obligate anaerobes live exclusively by fermentation; others extract chemical energy by **anaerobic respiration**, in which substances other than O_2, such as nitrate ions (NO_3^-) or

Table 27.1 Major Nutritional Modes

Mode	Energy Source	Carbon Source	Types of Organisms
AUTOTROPH			
Photoautotroph	Light	CO_2, HCO_3^-, or related compound	Photosynthetic prokaryotes (for example, cyanobacteria); plants; certain protists (for example, algae)
Chemoautotroph	Inorganic chemicals (such as H_2S, NH_3, or Fe^{2+})	CO_2, HCO_3^-, or related compound	Unique to certain prokaryotes (for example, *Sulfolobus*)
HETEROTROPH			
Photoheterotroph	Light	Organic compounds	Unique to certain aquatic and salt-loving prokaryotes (for example, *Rhodobacter*, *Chloroflexus*)
Chemoheterotroph	Organic compounds	Organic compounds	Many prokaryotes (for example, *Clostridium*) and protists; fungi; animals; some plants

sulfate ions (SO_4^{2-}), accept electrons at the "downhill" end of electron transport chains. **Facultative anaerobes** use O_2 if it is present but can also carry out fermentation or anaerobic respiration in an anaerobic environment.

Nitrogen Metabolism

Nitrogen is essential for the production of amino acids and nucleic acids in all organisms. Whereas eukaryotes can obtain nitrogen from a limited group of nitrogen compounds, prokaryotes can metabolize nitrogen in many forms. For example, some cyanobacteria and some methanogens (a group of archaea) convert atmospheric nitrogen (N_2) to ammonia (NH_3), a process called **nitrogen fixation**. The cells can then incorporate this "fixed" nitrogen into amino acids and other organic molecules. In terms of nutrition, nitrogen-fixing cyanobacteria are some of the most self-sufficient organisms, since they need only light, CO_2, N_2, water, and some minerals to grow.

Nitrogen fixation has a large impact on other organisms. For example, nitrogen-fixing prokaryotes can increase the nitrogen available to plants, which cannot use atmospheric nitrogen but can use the nitrogen compounds that the prokaryotes produce from ammonia. Concept 55.4 discusses this and other essential roles that prokaryotes play in the nitrogen cycles of ecosystems.

Metabolic Cooperation

Cooperation between prokaryotic cells allows them to use environmental resources they could not use as individual cells. In some cases, this cooperation takes place between specialized cells of a filament. For instance, the cyanobacterium *Anabaena* has genes that encode proteins for photosynthesis and for nitrogen fixation, but a single cell cannot carry out both processes at the same time. The reason is that photosynthesis produces O_2, which inactivates the enzymes involved in nitrogen fixation. Instead of living as isolated cells, *Anabaena* forms filamentous chains (Figure 27.14). Most cells in a filament carry out only photosynthesis, while a few specialized cells called **heterocysts** (sometimes called *heterocytes*) carry out only nitrogen fixation. Each heterocyst is surrounded by a thickened cell wall that restricts entry of O_2 produced by neighboring photosynthetic cells. Intercellular connections allow heterocysts to transport fixed nitrogen to neighboring cells and to receive carbohydrates.

Metabolic cooperation between different prokaryotic species often occurs in surface-coating colonies known as **biofilms**. Cells in a biofilm secrete signaling molecules that recruit nearby cells, causing the colonies to grow. The cells also produce polysaccharides and proteins that stick the cells to the substrate and to one another; these polysaccharides and proteins form the capsule or slime layer mentioned earlier in the chapter. Channels in the biofilm allow nutrients to reach cells in the interior and wastes to be expelled. Biofilms are common in nature, but they can cause problems by contaminating industrial products and medical equipment and contributing to tooth decay and more serious health problems. Altogether, damage caused by biofilms costs billions of dollars annually.

In another example of cooperation between prokaryotes, sulfate-consuming bacteria coexist with methane-consuming archaea in ball-shaped aggregates on the ocean floor. The bacteria appear to use the archaea's waste products, such as organic compounds and hydrogen. In turn, the bacteria produce sulfur compounds that the archaea use as oxidizing agents when they consume methane in the absence of

▲ **Figure 27.14 Metabolic cooperation in a prokaryote.** In the filamentous freshwater cyanobacterium *Anabaena*, heterocysts fix nitrogen, while the other cells carry out photosynthesis (LM).

oxygen. This partnership has global ramifications: Each year, these archaea consume an estimated 300 billion kg of methane, a major greenhouse gas (see Concept 56.4).

CONCEPT CHECK 27.3

1. Distinguish between the four major modes of nutrition, noting which are unique to prokaryotes.
2. A bacterium requires only the amino acid methionine as an organic nutrient and lives in lightless caves. What mode of nutrition does it employ? Explain.
3. **WHAT IF?** Describe what you might eat for a typical meal if humans, like cyanobacteria, could fix nitrogen.

For suggested answers, see Appendix A.

CONCEPT 27.4

Prokaryotes have radiated into a diverse set of lineages

Since their origin 3.5 billion years ago, prokaryotic populations have radiated extensively as a wide range of structural and metabolic adaptations have evolved in them. Collectively, these adaptations have enabled prokaryotes to inhabit every environment known to support life—if there are organisms in a particular place, some of those organisms are prokaryotes. In recent decades, advances in genomics are beginning to reveal the extent of prokaryotic diversity.

An Overview of Prokaryotic Diversity

In the 1970s, microbiologists began using small-subunit ribosomal RNA as a marker for evolutionary relationships. Their results indicated that many prokaryotes once classified as bacteria are actually more closely related to eukaryotes and belong in a domain of their own: Archaea. Microbiologists have since analyzed larger amounts of genetic data—including more than 1,700 entire genomes—and have concluded that a few traditional taxonomic groups, such as cyanobacteria, are monophyletic. However, other traditional groups, such as gram-negative bacteria, are scattered throughout several lineages. **Figure 27.15** shows one phylogenetic hypothesis for some of the major taxa of prokaryotes based on molecular systematics.

One lesson from studying prokaryotic phylogeny is that the genetic diversity of prokaryotes is immense. When researchers began to sequence the genes of prokaryotes, they could investigate only the small fraction of species that could be cultured in the laboratory. In the 1980s, researchers began using the polymerase chain reaction (PCR; see Figure 20.8) to analyze the genes of prokaryotes collected from the environment (such as from soil or water samples). Such "genetic prospecting" is now widely used; in fact, today entire prokaryotic genomes can be obtained from environmental samples

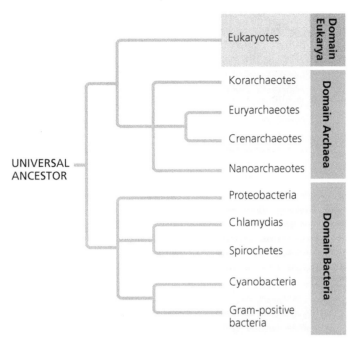

▲ **Figure 27.15 A simplified phylogeny of prokaryotes.** This phylogenetic tree based on molecular data shows one of several debated hypotheses of the relationships between the major prokaryotic groups discussed in this chapter. Within Archaea, the placement of the korarchaeotes and nanoarchaeotes remains unclear.

? *Which domain is the sister group of Archaea?*

using *metagenomics* (see Chapter 21). Each year these techniques add new branches to the tree of life. While only about 10,500 prokaryotic species worldwide have been assigned scientific names, a single handful of soil could contain 10,000 prokaryotic species by some estimates. Taking full stock of this diversity will require many years of research.

Another important lesson from molecular systematics is that horizontal gene transfer has played a key role in the evolution of prokaryotes. Over hundreds of millions of years, prokaryotes have acquired genes from even distantly related species, and they continue to do so today. As a result, significant portions of the genomes of many prokaryotes are actually mosaics of genes imported from other species. For example, a 2011 study of 329 sequenced bacterial genomes found that an average of 75% of the genes in each genome had been transferred horizontally at some point in their evolutionary history. As we saw in Chapter 26, such gene transfers can make it difficult to determine phylogenetic relationships. Still, it is clear that for billions of years, the prokaryotes have evolved in two separate lineages, the bacteria and the archaea (see Figure 27.15).

Bacteria

Eukarya
Archaea
Bacteria

As surveyed in **Figure 27.16**, bacteria include the vast majority of prokaryotic species familiar to most people, from the

Exploring Selected Major Groups of Bacteria

Proteobacteria

This large and diverse clade of gram-negative bacteria includes photo-autotrophs, chemoautotrophs, and heterotrophs. Some proteobacteria are anaerobic, while others are aerobic. Molecular systematists currently recognize five subgroups of proteobacteria; the phylogenetic tree at right shows their relationships based on molecular data.

Alpha
Beta
Gamma
Delta
Epsilon
} Proteobacteria

Subgroup: Alpha Proteobacteria

Many of the species in this subgroup are closely associated with eukaryotic hosts. For example, *Rhizobium* species live in nodules within the roots of legumes (plants of the pea/bean family), where the bacteria convert atmospheric N_2 to compounds the host plant can use to make proteins. Species in the genus *Agrobacterium* produce tumors in plants; genetic engineers use these bacteria to carry foreign DNA into the genomes of crop plants. Scientists hypothesize that mitochondria evolved from aerobic alpha proteobacteria through endosymbiosis.

Rhizobium (arrows) inside a root cell of a legume (TEM)

2.5 μm

Subgroup: Beta Proteobacteria

This nutritionally diverse subgroup includes *Nitrosomonas*, a genus of soil bacteria that play an important role in nitrogen recycling by oxidizing ammonium (NH_4^+), producing nitrite (NO_2^-) as a waste product. Other members of this subgroup include a wide range of aquatic species, such as the photoheterotroph *Rubrivivax*, along with pathogens such as the species that causes gonorrhea, *Neisseria gonorrhoeae*.

Nitrosomonas (colorized TEM)

1 μm

Subgroup: Gamma Proteobacteria

This subgroup's autotrophic members include sulfur bacteria such as *Thiomargarita namibiensis*, which obtain energy by oxidizing H_2S, producing sulfur as a waste product (the small globules in the photograph at right). Some heterotrophic gamma proteobacteria are pathogens; for example, *Legionella* causes Legionnaires' disease, *Salmonella* is responsible for some cases of food poisoning, and *Vibrio cholerae* causes cholera. *Escherichia coli*, a common resident of the intestines of humans and other mammals, normally is not pathogenic.

Thiomargarita namibiensis containing sulfur wastes (LM)

200 μm

Subgroup: Delta Proteobacteria

This subgroup includes the slime-secreting myxobacteria. When the soil dries out or food is scarce, the cells congregate into a fruiting body that releases resistant "myxospores." These cells found new colonies in favorable environments. Another group of delta proteobacteria, the bdellovibrios, attack other bacteria, charging at up to 100 μm/sec (comparable to a human running 240 km/hr). The attack begins when a bdellovibrio attaches to specific molecules found on the outer covering of some bacterial species. The bdellovibrio then drills into its prey by using digestive enzymes and spinning at 100 revolutions per second.

Fruiting bodies of *Chondromyces crocatus*, a myxobacterium (SEM)

300 μm

Subgroup: Epsilon Proteobacteria

Most species in this subgroup are pathogenic to humans or other animals. Epsilon proteobacteria include *Campylobacter*, which causes blood poisoning and intestinal inflammation, and *Helicobacter pylori*, which causes stomach ulcers.

Helicobacter pylori (colorized TEM)

2 μm

Chlamydias

These parasites can survive only within animal cells, depending on their hosts for resources as basic as ATP. The gram-negative walls of chlamydias are unusual in that they lack peptidoglycan. One species, *Chlamydia trachomatis*, is the most common cause of blindness in the world and also causes nongonococcal urethritis, the most common sexually transmitted disease in the United States.

Chlamydia (arrows) inside an animal cell (colorized TEM)

Spirochetes

These gram-negative heterotrophs spiral through their environment by means of rotating, internal, flagellum-like filaments. Many spirochetes are free-living, but others are notorious pathogenic parasites: *Treponema pallidum* causes syphilis, and *Borrelia burgdorferi* causes Lyme disease (see Figure 27.20).

Leptospira, a spirochete (colorized TEM)

Cyanobacteria

These gram-negative photoautotrophs are the only prokaryotes with plantlike, oxygen-generating photosynthesis. (In fact, chloroplasts likely evolved from an endosymbiotic cyanobacterium.) Both solitary and filamentous cyanobacteria are abundant components of freshwater and marine *phytoplankton*, the collection of photosynthetic organisms that drift near the water's surface. Some filaments have cells specialized for nitrogen fixation, the process that incorporates atmospheric N_2 into inorganic compounds that can be used in the synthesis of amino acids and other organic molecules (see Figure 27.14).

Oscillatoria, a filamentous cyanobacterium

Gram-Positive Bacteria

Gram-positive bacteria rival the proteobacteria in diversity. Species in one subgroup, the actinomycetes (from the Greek *mykes*, fungus, for which these bacteria were once mistaken), form colonies containing branched chains of cells. Two species of actinomycetes cause tuberculosis and leprosy. However, most actinomycetes are free-living species that help decompose the organic matter in soil; their secretions are partly responsible for the "earthy" odor of rich soil. Soil-dwelling species in the genus *Streptomyces* (top) are cultured by pharmaceutical companies as a source of many antibiotics, including streptomycin.

Gram-positive bacteria include many solitary species, such as *Bacillus anthracis* (see Figure 27.5), which causes anthrax, and *Clostridium botulinum*, which causes botulism. The various species of *Staphylococcus* and *Streptococcus* are also gram-positive bacteria.

Mycoplasmas (bottom) are the only bacteria known to lack cell walls. They are also the tiniest known cells, with diameters as small as 0.1 μm, only about five times as large as a ribosome. Mycoplasmas have small genomes—*Mycoplasma genitalium* has only 517 genes, for example. Many mycoplasmas are free-living soil bacteria, but others are pathogens.

Streptomyces, the source of many antibiotics (SEM)

Hundreds of mycoplasmas covering a human fibroblast cell (colorized SEM)

pathogenic species that cause strep throat and tuberculosis to the beneficial species used to make Swiss cheese and yogurt. Every major mode of nutrition and metabolism is represented among bacteria, and even a small taxonomic group of bacteria may contain species exhibiting many different nutritional modes. As we'll see, the diverse nutritional and metabolic capabilities of bacteria—and archaea—are behind the great impact these organisms have on Earth and its life.

Archaea

Archaea share certain traits with bacteria and other traits with eukaryotes **(Table 27.2).** However, archaea also have many unique characteristics, as we would expect in a taxon that has followed a separate evolutionary path for so long.

The first prokaryotes assigned to domain Archaea live in environments so extreme that few other organisms can survive there. Such organisms are called **extremophiles**, meaning "lovers" of extreme conditions (from the Greek *philos*, lover), and include extreme halophiles and extreme thermophiles.

Extreme halophiles (from the Greek *halo*, salt) live in highly saline environments, such as the Great Salt Lake in Utah, the Dead Sea in Israel, and the Spanish lake shown in

▲ **Figure 27.17 Extreme thermophiles.** Orange and yellow colonies of thermophilic prokaryotes grow in the hot water of Yellowstone National Park's Grand Prismatic Spring.

MAKE CONNECTIONS *How might the enzymes of thermophiles differ from those of other organisms? (Review enzymes in Concept 8.4.)*

Figure 27.1. Some species merely tolerate salinity, while others require an environment that is several times saltier than seawater (which has a salinity of 3.5%). For example, the proteins and cell wall of *Halobacterium* have unusual features that improve function in extremely salty environments but render these organisms incapable of survival if the salinity drops below 9%.

Extreme thermophiles (from the Greek *thermos*, hot) thrive in very hot environments **(Figure 27.17).** For example, archaea in the genus *Sulfolobus* live in sulfur-rich volcanic springs as hot as 90°C. At temperatures this high, the cells of most organisms die because their DNA does not remain in a double helix and many of their proteins denature. *Sulfolobus* and other extreme thermophiles avoid this fate because they have structural and biochemical adaptations that make their DNA and proteins stable at high temperatures. One extreme thermophile that lives near deep-sea hot springs called *hydrothermal vents* is informally known as "strain 121," since it can reproduce even at 121°C. Another extreme thermophile, *Pyrococcus furiosus*, is used in biotechnology as a source of DNA polymerase for the PCR technique (see Figure 20.8).

Many other archaea live in more moderate environments. Consider the **methanogens**, archaea that release methane as a by-product of their unique ways of obtaining energy. Many methanogens use CO_2 to oxidize H_2, a process that produces both energy and methane waste. Among the strictest of anaerobes, methanogens are poisoned by O_2. Although some methanogens live in extreme environments, such as under kilometers of ice in Greenland, others live in swamps and marshes where other microorganisms have consumed all the O_2. The "marsh gas" found in such environments is the

Table 27.2	A Comparison of the Three Domains of Life		
CHARACTERISTIC	DOMAIN		
	Bacteria	Archaea	Eukarya
Nuclear envelope	Absent	Absent	Present
Membrane-enclosed organelles	Absent	Absent	Present
Peptidoglycan in cell wall	Present	Absent	Absent
Membrane lipids	Unbranched hydrocarbons	Some branched hydrocarbons	Unbranched hydrocarbons
RNA polymerase	One kind	Several kinds	Several kinds
Initiator amino acid for protein synthesis	Formyl-methionine	Methionine	Methionine
Introns in genes	Very rare	Present in some genes	Present in many genes
Response to the antibiotics streptomycin and chloramphenicol	Growth usually inhibited	Growth not inhibited	Growth not inhibited
Histones associated with DNA	Absent	Present in some species	Present
Circular chromosome	Present	Present	Absent
Growth at temperatures > 100°C	No	Some species	No

methane released by these archaea. Other species inhabit the anaerobic guts of cattle, termites, and other herbivores, playing an essential role in the nutrition of these animals. Methanogens are also useful to humans as decomposers in sewage treatment facilities.

Many extreme halophiles and all known methanogens are archaea in the clade Euryarchaeota (from the Greek *eurys*, broad, a reference to their wide habitat range). The euryarchaeotes also include some extreme thermophiles, though most thermophilic species belong to a second clade, Crenarchaeota (*cren* means "spring," such as a hydrothermal spring). Recent metagenomic studies have identified many species of euryarchaeotes and crenarchaeotes that are not extremophiles. These archaea exist in habitats ranging from farm soils to lake sediments to the surface of the open ocean.

New findings continue to inform our understanding of archaeal phylogeny. In 1996, researchers sampling a hot spring in Yellowstone National Park discovered archaea that do not appear to belong to either Euryarchaeota or Crenarchaeota. They placed these archaea in a new clade, Korarchaeota (from the Greek *koron*, young man). In 2002, researchers exploring hydrothermal vents off the coast of Iceland discovered archaeal cells only 0.4 μm in diameter attached to a much larger crenarchaeote. The genome of the smaller archaean is one of the smallest known of any organism, containing only 500,000 base pairs. Genetic analysis indicates that this prokaryote belongs to a fourth archaeal clade, Nanoarchaeota (from the Greek *nanos*, dwarf). Within a year after this clade was named, three other DNA sequences from nanoarchaeote species were isolated: one from Yellowstone's hot springs, one from hot springs in Siberia, and one from a hydrothermal vent in the Pacific. As metagenomic prospecting continues, the tree in Figure 27.15 may well undergo further changes.

CONCEPT CHECK 27.4

1. Explain how molecular systematics and metagenomics have contributed to our understanding of the phylogeny and evolution of prokaryotes.

2. **WHAT IF?** What would the discovery of a bacterial species that is a methanogen imply about the evolution of the methane-producing pathway?

For suggested answers, see Appendix A.

CONCEPT 27.5

Prokaryotes play crucial roles in the biosphere

If people were to disappear from the planet tomorrow, life on Earth would change for many species, but few would be driven to extinction. In contrast, prokaryotes are so important to the biosphere that if they were to disappear, the prospects of survival for many other species would be dim.

Chemical Recycling

The atoms that make up the organic molecules in all living things were at one time part of inorganic substances in the soil, air, and water. Sooner or later, those atoms will return there. Ecosystems depend on the continual recycling of chemical elements between the living and nonliving components of the environment, and prokaryotes play a major role in this process. For example, chemoheterotrophic prokaryotes function as **decomposers**, breaking down dead organisms as well as waste products and thereby unlocking supplies of carbon, nitrogen, and other elements. Without the actions of prokaryotes and other decomposers such as fungi, life as we know it would cease. (See Concept 55.4 for a detailed discussion of chemical cycles.)

Prokaryotes also convert some molecules to forms that can be taken up by other organisms. Cyanobacteria and other autotrophic prokaryotes use CO_2 to make organic compounds such as sugars, which are then passed up through food chains. Cyanobacteria also produce atmospheric O_2, and a variety of prokaryotes fix atmospheric nitrogen (N_2) into forms that other organisms can use to make the building blocks of proteins and nucleic acids. Under some conditions, prokaryotes can increase the availability of nutrients that plants require for growth, such as nitrogen, phosphorus, and potassium **(Figure 27.18)**. Prokaryotes

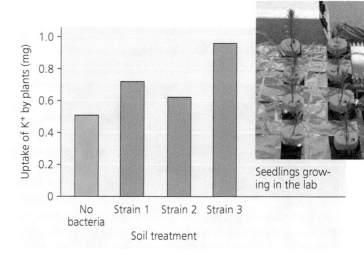

Seedlings growing in the lab

▲ **Figure 27.18 Impact of bacteria on soil nutrient availability.** Pine seedlings grown in sterile soils to which one of three strains of the bacterium *Burkholderia glathei* had been added absorbed more potassium (K^+) than did seedlings grown in soil without any bacteria. Other results (not shown) demonstrated that strain 3 increased the amount of K^+ released from mineral crystals to the soil.

WHAT IF? *Estimate the average uptake of K^+ for seedlings in soils with bacteria. What would you expect this average to be if bacteria had no effect on nutrient availability?*

can also *decrease* the availability of key plant nutrients; this occurs when prokaryotes "immobilize" nutrients by using them to synthesize molecules that remain within their cells. Thus, prokaryotes can have complex effects on soil nutrient concentrations. In marine environments, an archaean from the clade Crenarchaeota can perform nitrification, a key step in the nitrogen cycle (see Figure 55.14). Crenarchaeotes dominate the oceans by numbers, comprising an estimated 10^{28} cells. The sheer abundance of these organisms suggests that they may have a large impact on the global nitrogen cycle; scientists are investigating this possibility.

Ecological Interactions

Prokaryotes play a central role in many ecological interactions. Consider **symbiosis** (from a Greek word meaning "living together"), an ecological relationship in which two species live in close contact with each other. Prokaryotes often form symbiotic associations with much larger organisms. In general, the larger organism in a symbiotic relationship is known as the **host**, and the smaller is known as the **symbiont**. There are many cases in which a prokaryote and its host participate in **mutualism**, an ecological interaction between two species in which both benefit **(Figure 27.19)**. Other interactions take the form of **commensalism**, an ecological relationship in which one species benefits while the other is not harmed or helped in any significant way. For example, more than 150 bacterial species live on the surface of your body, covering portions of your skin with up to 10 million cells per square centimeter. Some of these species are commensalists: You provide them with food, such as the oils that exude from your pores, and a place to live, while they neither harm nor benefit you. Finally, some prokaryotes engage in **parasitism**, an ecological relationship in which a **parasite** eats the cell contents, tissues, or body fluids of its host. As a group, parasites harm

but usually do not kill their host, at least not immediately (unlike a predator). Parasites that cause disease are known as **pathogens**, many of which are prokaryotic. (We'll discuss mutualism, commensalism, and parasitism in greater detail in Chapter 54.)

The very existence of an ecosystem can depend on prokaryotes. For example, consider the diverse ecological communities found at hydrothermal vents. These communities are densely populated by many different kinds of animals, including worms, clams, crabs, and fishes. But since sunlight does not penetrate to the deep ocean floor, the community does not include photosynthetic organisms. Instead, the energy that supports the community is derived from the metabolic activities of chemoautotrophic bacteria. These bacteria harvest chemical energy from compounds such as hydrogen sulfide (H_2S) that are released from the vent. An active hydrothermal vent may support hundreds of eukaryotic species, but when the vent stops releasing chemicals, the chemoautotrophic bacteria cannot survive. As a result, the entire vent community collapses.

CONCEPT 27.6

Prokaryotes have both beneficial and harmful impacts on humans

Although the best-known prokaryotes tend to be the bacteria that cause human illness, these pathogens represent only a small fraction of prokaryotic species. Many other prokaryotes have positive interactions with people, and some play essential roles in agriculture and industry.

Mutualistic Bacteria

As is true for many other eukaryotes, human well-being can depend on mutualistic prokaryotes. For example, our intestines are home to an estimated 500–1,000 species of bacteria; their cells outnumber all human cells in the body by a factor of ten. Different species live in different portions of the intestines, and they vary in their ability to process different foods. Many of these species are mutualists, digesting food that our own intestines cannot break down. For example, the genome of one of these gut mutualists, *Bacteroides thetaiotaomicron*,

▲ **Figure 27.19 Mutualism: bacterial "headlights."** The glowing oval below the eye of the flashlight fish (*Photoblepharon palpebratus*) is an organ harboring bioluminescent bacteria. The fish uses the light to attract prey and to signal potential mates. The bacteria receive nutrients from the fish.

includes a large array of genes involved in synthesizing carbohydrates, vitamins, and other nutrients needed by humans. Signals from the bacterium activate human genes that build the network of intestinal blood vessels necessary to absorb nutrient molecules. Other signals induce human cells to produce antimicrobial compounds to which *B. thetaiotaomicron* is not susceptible. This action may reduce the population sizes of other, competing species, thus potentially benefiting both *B. thetaiotaomicron* and its human host.

Pathogenic Bacteria

All the pathogenic prokaryotes known to date are bacteria, and they deserve their negative reputation. Bacteria cause about half of all human diseases. For example, more than 1 million people die each year of the lung disease tuberculosis, caused by *Mycobacterium tuberculosis.* And another 2 million people die each year from diarrheal diseases caused by various bacteria.

Some bacterial diseases are transmitted by other species, such as fleas or ticks. In the United States, the most widespread pest-carried disease is Lyme disease, which infects 15,000 to 20,000 people each year (**Figure 27.20**). Caused by a bacterium carried by ticks that live on deer and field mice, Lyme disease can result in debilitating arthritis, heart disease, nervous disorders, and death if untreated.

Pathogenic prokaryotes usually cause illness by producing poisons, which are classified as exotoxins or endotoxins. **Exotoxins** are proteins secreted by certain bacteria and other organisms. Cholera, a dangerous diarrheal disease, is caused by an exotoxin secreted by the proteobacterium *Vibrio cholerae.* The exotoxin stimulates intestinal cells to release chloride ions into the gut, and water follows by osmosis. In another example, the potentially fatal disease botulism is caused by botulinum toxin, an exotoxin secreted by the gram-positive bacterium *Clostridium botulinum* as it

▲ **Figure 27.20 Lyme disease.** Ticks in the genus *Ixodes* spread the disease by transmitting the spirochete *Borrelia burgdorferi* (colorized SEM). A rash may develop at the site of the tick's bite; the rash may be large and ring-shaped (as shown) or much less distinctive.

ferments various foods, including improperly canned meat, seafood, and vegetables. Like other exotoxins, the botulinum toxin can produce disease even if the bacteria that manufacture it are no longer present when the food is eaten. Another species in the same genus, *C. difficile*, produces exotoxins that cause severe diarrhea, resulting in more than 12,000 deaths per year in the United States alone.

Endotoxins are lipopolysaccharide components of the outer membrane of gram-negative bacteria. In contrast to exotoxins, endotoxins are released only when the bacteria die and their cell walls break down. Endotoxin-producing bacteria include species in the genus *Salmonella*, such as *Salmonella typhi*, which causes typhoid fever. You might have heard of food poisoning caused by other *Salmonella* species that can be found in poultry and some fruits and vegetables.

Since the 19th century, improved sanitation systems in the industrialized world have greatly reduced the threat of pathogenic bacteria. Antibiotics have saved a great many lives and reduced the incidence of disease. However, resistance to antibiotics is currently evolving in many bacterial strains. As you read earlier, the rapid reproduction of bacteria enables cells carrying resistance genes to quickly give rise to large populations as a result of natural selection, and these genes can also spread to other species by horizontal gene transfer.

Horizontal gene transfer can also spread genes associated with virulence, turning normally harmless bacteria into potent pathogens. *E. coli*, for instance, is ordinarily a harmless symbiont in the human intestines, but pathogenic strains that cause bloody diarrhea have emerged. One of the most dangerous strains, O157:H7, is a global threat; in the United States alone, there are 75,000 cases of O157:H7 infection per year, often from contaminated beef or produce. In 2001, scientists sequenced the genome of O157:H7 and compared it with the genome of a harmless strain of *E. coli* called K-12. They discovered that 1,387 out of the 5,416 genes in O157:H7 have no counterpart in K-12. Many of these 1,387 genes are found in chromosomal regions that include phage DNA. This suggests that at least some of the 1,387 genes were incorporated into the genome of O157:H7 through phage-mediated horizontal gene transfer (transduction). Some of the genes found only in O157:H7 are associated with virulence, including genes that code for adhesive fimbriae that enable O157:H7 to attach itself to the intestinal wall and extract nutrients.

Prokaryotes in Research and Technology

On a positive note, we reap many benefits from the metabolic capabilities of both bacteria and archaea. For example, people have long used bacteria to convert milk to cheese and yogurt. In recent years, our greater understanding of prokaryotes has led to an explosion of new applications in biotechnology; two examples are the use of *E. coli* in gene cloning (see Figure 20.2) and the use of *Agrobacterium tumefaciens* in producing transgenic plants (see Figure 35.25). Naturally occurring soil bacteria may have potential for combating diseases that affect crop plants; in the Scientific Skills Exercise, you can interpret data from an experiment studying the effect of these bacteria.

Bacteria may soon figure prominently in another major industry: plastics. Globally, each year about 350 billion pounds of plastic are produced from petroleum and used to make toys, storage containers, soft drink bottles, and many other items. These products degrade slowly, creating environmental problems. Bacteria can now be used to make natural plastics (Figure 27.21). For example, some bacteria synthesize a type of polymer known as PHA

◀ **Figure 27.21 Bacteria synthesizing and storing PHA, a component of biodegradeable plastics.**

▶ **Figure 27.22 Bioremediation of an oil spill.** Spraying fertilizer stimulates the growth of native bacteria that metabolize oil, increasing the breakdown process up to fivefold.

(polyhydroxyalkanoate), which they use to store chemical energy. The PHA can be extracted, formed into pellets, and used to make durable, yet biodegradable, plastics.

Another way to harness prokaryotes is in **bioremediation**, the use of organisms to remove pollutants from soil, air, or water. For example, anaerobic bacteria and archaea decompose the organic matter in sewage, converting it to material that can be used as landfill or fertilizer after chemical sterilization. Other bioremediation applications include cleaning up oil spills (Figure 27.22) and precipitating radioactive material (such as uranium) out of groundwater.

Through genetic engineering, we can now modify bacteria to produce vitamins, antibiotics, hormones, and

SCIENTIFIC SKILLS EXERCISE

Making a Bar Graph and Interpreting Data

Do Soil Microorganisms Protect Against Crop Disease? The soil layer surrounding plant roots, called the *rhizosphere*, is a complex community in which archaea, bacteria, fungi, and plants interact with one another. When crop plants are attacked by fungal or bacterial pathogens, in some cases soil from the rhizosphere protects plants from future attacks. Such protective soil is called disease-suppressive soil. Plants grown in disease-suppressive soils appear to be less vulnerable to pathogen attack. In this exercise, you'll interpret data from an experiment studying whether microorganisms were responsible for the protective effects of disease-suppressive soils.

How the Experiment Was Done The researchers obtained disease-suppressive soil from 25 random sites in an agricultural field in the Netherlands in which sugar beet crops had previously been attacked by *Rhizoctonia solani*, a fungal pathogen that also afflicts potatoes and rice. The researchers collected other soil samples from the grassy margins of the field where sugar beets had not been grown. The researchers predicted that these soil samples from the margins would not offer protection against pathogens.

The researchers then planted and raised sugar beets in greenhouses, using five different soil treatments. Each soil treatment was applied to four pots, and each pot contained eight plants. The pots were inoculated with *R. solani*. After 20 days, the percentage of infected sugar beet seedlings was determined for each pot and then averaged for each soil treatment.

Data from the Experiment

Soil Treatment	Average Percentage of Seedlings Afflicted with Fungal Disease
Disease-suppressive soil	3.0
Soil from margin of field	62
Soil from margin of field + 10% disease-suppressive soil	39
Disease-suppressive soil heated to 50°C for 1 hour	31
Disease-suppressive soil heated to 80°C for 1 hour	70

Interpret the Data

1. What hypothesis were the researchers testing in this study? What is the independent variable in this study? What is the dependent variable?

2. What is the total number of pots used in this experiment, and how many plants received each soil treatment? Explain why multiple pots and plants were used for each treatment.

3. Use the data in the table to create a bar graph. Then, in words, describe and compare the results for the five soil treatments.

4. The researchers stated, "Collectively, these results indicated that disease suppressiveness [of soil] toward *Rhizoctonia solani* was microbiological in nature." Is this statement supported by the results shown in the graph? Explain.

(MB) A version of this Scientific Skills Exercise can be assigned in MasteringBiology.

Data from R. Mendes et al. Deciphering the rhizosphere for disease-suppressive bacteria, *Science* 332:1097–1100 (2011).

other products (see Chapter 20). Researchers are seeking to reduce fossil fuel use by engineering bacteria that can produce ethanol from various forms of biomass, including agricultural waste, switch-grass, municipal waste (such as paper products that are not recycled), and corn (Figure 27.23).

The usefulness of pro-karyotes largely derives from their diverse forms

▶ Figure 27.23 **Fuel produc-tion.** Researchers are developing bacteria that produce ethanol (E-85) fuel from renewable plant products.

of nutrition and metabolism. All this metabolic versatility evolved prior to the appearance of the structural novel-ties that heralded the evolution of eukaryotic organisms, to which we devote the remainder of this unit.

CONCEPT CHECK 27.6

1. Identify at least two ways that prokaryotes have affected you positively today.

2. A pathogenic bacterium's toxin causes symptoms that increase the bacterium's chance of spreading from host to host. Does this information indicate whether the poison is an exotoxin or endotoxin? Explain.

3. **WHAT IF?** How might a sudden and dramatic change in your diet affect the diversity of prokaryotic species that live in your digestive tract?

For suggested answers, see Appendix A.

27 Chapter Review

SUMMARY OF KEY CONCEPTS

CONCEPT 27.1

Structural and functional adaptations contribute to prokaryotic success (pp. 568–572)

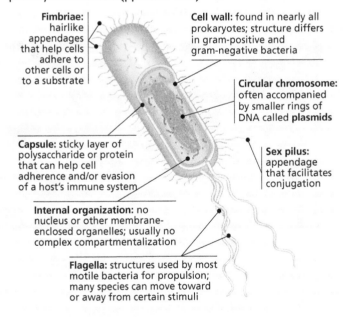

Fimbriae: hairlike appendages that help cells adhere to other cells or to a substrate

Cell wall: found in nearly all prokaryotes; structure differs in gram-positive and gram-negative bacteria

Circular chromosome: often accompanied by smaller rings of DNA called **plasmids**

Capsule: sticky layer of polysaccharide or protein that can help cell adherence and/or evasion of a host's immune system

Sex pilus: appendage that facilitates conjugation

Internal organization: no nucleus or other membrane-enclosed organelles; usually no complex compartmentalization

Flagella: structures used by most motile bacteria for propulsion; many species can move toward or away from certain stimuli

- Many prokaryotic species can reproduce quickly by binary fis-sion, leading to the formation of populations containing enor-mous numbers of individuals. Some form endospores, which can remain viable in harsh conditions for centuries.

? *Describe features of prokaryotes that enable them to thrive in a wide range of different environments.*

CONCEPT 27.2

Rapid reproduction, mutation, and genetic recombination promote genetic diversity in prokaryotes (pp. 572–575)

- Because prokaryotes can often proliferate rapidly, mutations can quickly increase a population's genetic variation. As a result, prokaryotic populations often can evolve in short periods of time in response to changing conditions.
- Genetic diversity in prokaryotes also can arise by recombination of the DNA from two different cells (via transformation, trans-duction, or conjugation). By transferring advantageous alleles, such as ones for antibiotic resistance, genetic recombination can promote adaptive evolution in prokaryotic populations.

? *Mutations are rare and prokaryotes reproduce asexually, yet their populations can have high genetic diversity. Explain how this can occur.*

CONCEPT 27.3

Diverse nutritional and metabolic adaptations have evolved in prokaryotes (pp. 575–577)

- Nutritional diversity is much greater in prokaryotes than in eu-karyotes. As a group, prokaryotes perform all four modes of nu-trition: photoautotrophy, chemoautotrophy, photoheterotrophy, and chemoheterotrophy.
- Among prokaryotes, **obligate aerobes** require O_2, **obligate anaerobes** are poisoned by O_2, and **facultative anaerobes** can survive with or without O_2.
- Unlike eukaryotes, prokaryotes can metabolize nitrogen in many different forms. Some can convert atmospheric nitrogen to am-monia, a process called **nitrogen fixation**.
- Prokaryotic cells and even species may cooperate metabolically. In *Anabaena*, photosynthetic cells and nitrogen-fixing cells ex-change metabolic products. Metabolic cooperation also occurs in surface-coating **biofilms** that include different species.

? *Describe the range of prokaryotic metabolic adaptations.*

CONCEPT 27.4

Prokaryotes have radiated into a diverse set of lineages (pp. 577–581)

- Molecular systematics is helping biologists classify prokaryotes and identify new clades.
- Diverse nutritional types are scattered among the major groups of bacteria. The two largest groups are the proteobacteria and gram-positive bacteria.
- Some archaea, such as extreme thermophiles and extreme halophiles, live in extreme environments. Other archaea live in moderate environments such as soils and lakes.

? *How have molecular data informed prokaryotic phylogeny?*

CONCEPT 27.5

Prokaryotes play crucial roles in the biosphere (pp. 581–582)

- Decomposition by heterotrophic prokaryotes and the synthetic activities of autotrophic and nitrogen-fixing prokaryotes contribute to the recycling of elements in ecosystems.
- Many prokaryotes have a symbiotic relationship with a host; the relationships between prokaryotes and their hosts range from mutualism to commensalism to parasitism.

? *In what ways are prokaryotes key to the survival of many species?*

CONCEPT 27.6

Prokaryotes have both beneficial and harmful impacts on humans (pp. 582–585)

- People depend on mutualistic prokaryotes, including hundreds of species that live in our intestines and help digest food.
- Pathogenic bacteria typically cause disease by releasing **exotoxins** or **endotoxins**. Horizontal gene transfer can spread genes associated with virulence to harmless species or strains.
- Prokaryotes can be used in bioremediation, production of biodegradable plastics, and the synthesis of vitamins, antibiotics, and other products.

? *Describe beneficial and harmful impacts of prokaryotes on humans.*

TEST YOUR UNDERSTANDING

LEVEL 1: KNOWLEDGE/COMPREHENSION

1. Genetic variation in bacterial populations cannot result from
   a. transduction.
   c. mutation.
   b. conjugation.
   d. meiosis.

2. Photoautotrophs use
   a. light as an energy source and CO_2 as a carbon source.
   b. light as an energy source and methane as a carbon source.
   c. N_2 as an energy source and CO_2 as a carbon source.
   d. CO_2 as both an energy source and a carbon source.

3. Which of the following statements is *not* true?
   a. Archaea and bacteria have different membrane lipids.
   b. The cell walls of archaea lack peptidoglycan.
   c. Only bacteria have histones associated with DNA.
   d. Only some archaea use CO_2 to oxidize H_2, releasing methane.

4. Which of the following involves metabolic cooperation among prokaryotic cells?
   a. binary fission
   c. biofilms
   b. endospore formation
   d. photoautotrophy

5. Bacteria perform the following ecological roles. Which role typically does *not* involve symbiosis?
   a. skin commensalist
   c. gut mutualist
   b. decomposer
   d. pathogen

6. Plantlike photosynthesis that releases O_2 occurs in
   a. cyanobacteria.
   c. archaea.
   b. gram-positive bacteria.
   d. chemoautotrophic bacteria.

LEVEL 2: APPLICATION/ANALYSIS

7. **EVOLUTION CONNECTION**
   In patients with nonresistant strains of the tuberculosis bacterium, antibiotics can relieve symptoms in a few weeks. However, it takes much longer to halt the infection, and patients may discontinue treatment while bacteria are still present. How might this result in the evolution of drug-resistant pathogens?

LEVEL 3: SYNTHESIS/EVALUATION

8. **SCIENTIFIC INQUIRY**
   INTERPRET THE DATA The nitrogen-fixing bacterium *Rhizobium* infects the roots of some plant species, forming a mutualism in which the bacterium provides nitrogen, and the plant provides carbohydrates. Scientists measured the 12-week growth of one such plant species (*Acacia irrorata*) when infected by six different *Rhizobium* strains. (a) Graph the data. (b) Interpret your graph.

Rhizobium strain	1	2	3	4	5	6
Plant mass (g)	0.91	0.06	1.56	1.72	0.14	1.03

Source: J. J. Burdon et al., Variation in the effectiveness of symbiotic associations between native rhizobia and temperate Australian *Acacia*: within species interactions, *Journal of Applied Ecology* 36:398–408 (1999).

Note: Without *Rhizobium*, after 12 weeks, *Acacia* plants have a mass of about 0.1 g.

9. **WRITE ABOUT A THEME: ENERGY**
   In a short essay (about 100–150 words), discuss how prokaryotes and other members of hydrothermal vent communities transfer and transform energy.

10. **SYNTHESIZE YOUR KNOWLEDGE**

Explain how the small size and rapid reproduction rate of bacteria (such as the population shown here on the tip of a pin) contribute to their large population sizes and high genetic variation.

For selected answers, see Appendix A.

MasteringBiology®

28

Protists

KEY CONCEPTS

28.1 Most eukaryotes are single-celled organisms

28.2 Excavates include protists with modified mitochondria and protists with unique flagella

28.3 The "SAR" clade is a highly diverse group of protists defined by DNA similarities

28.4 Red algae and green algae are the closest relatives of land plants

28.5 Unikonts include protists that are closely related to fungi and animals

28.6 Protists play key roles in ecological communities

▲ Figure 28.1 **Which of these organisms are prokaryotes and which are eukaryotes?**

Living Small

Knowing that most prokaryotes are extremely small organisms, you might assume that **Figure 28.1** depicts six prokaryotes and one much larger eukaryote. But in fact, the only prokaryote is the organism immediately above the scale bar. The other six organisms are members of diverse, mostly unicellular groups of eukaryotes informally known as **protists**. These very small eukaryotes have intrigued biologists for more than 300 years, ever since the Dutch scientist Antoni van Leeuwenhoek first laid eyes on them under a light microscope. Some protists change their forms as they creep along using blob-like appendages, while others resemble tiny trumpets or miniature jewelry. Recalling his observations, van Leeuwenhoek wrote, "No more pleasant sight has met my eye than this, of so many thousands of living creatures in one small drop of water."

The protists that fascinated van Leeuwenhoek continue to surprise us today. Metagenomic studies have revealed a treasure trove of previously unknown protists within the world of microscopic life. Many of these newly discovered organisms are just 0.5–2 μm in diameter—as small as many prokaryotes. Genetic and morphological studies have also shown that some protists are more closely related to plants, fungi, or animals than they are to other protists. As

◀ **Trumpet-shaped protists (*Stentor coeruleus*)**

587

a result, the kingdom in which all protists once were classified, Protista, has been abandoned, and various protist lineages are now recognized as kingdoms in their own right. Most biologists still use the term *protist*, but only as a convenient way to refer to eukaryotes that are not plants, animals, or fungi.

In this chapter, you will become acquainted with some of the most significant groups of protists. You will learn about their structural and biochemical adaptations as well as their enormous impact on ecosystems, agriculture, industry, and human health.

CONCEPT 28.1

Most eukaryotes are single-celled organisms

Protists, along with plants, animals, and fungi, are classified as eukaryotes; they are in domain Eukarya, one of the three domains of life. Unlike the cells of prokaryotes, eukaryotic cells have a nucleus and other membrane-enclosed organelles, such as mitochondria and the Golgi apparatus. Such organelles provide specific locations where particular cellular functions are accomplished, making the structure and organization of eukaryotic cells more complex than those of prokaryotic cells.

Eukaryotic cells also have a well-developed cytoskeleton that extends throughout the cell (see Figure 6.20). The cytoskeleton provides the structural support that enables eukaryotic cells to have asymmetric (irregular) forms, as well as to change in shape as they feed, move, or grow. In contrast, prokaryotic cells lack a well-developed cytoskeleton, thus limiting the extent to which they can maintain asymmetric forms or change shape over time.

We'll survey the diversity of eukaryotes throughout the rest of this unit, beginning in this chapter with the protists. As you explore this material, bear in mind that

- the organisms in most eukaryotic lineages are protists, and
- most protists are unicellular.

Thus, life differs greatly from how most of us commonly think of it. The large, multicellular organisms that we know best (plants, animals, and fungi) are the tips of just a few branches on the great tree of life (see Figure 26.21).

Structural and Functional Diversity in Protists

Given that they are classified in a number of different kingdoms, it isn't surprising that few general characteristics of protists can be cited without exceptions. In fact, protists exhibit more structural and functional diversity than the eukaryotes with which we are most familiar—plants, animals, and fungi.

For example, most protists are unicellular, although there are some colonial and multicellular species. Single-celled protists are justifiably considered the simplest eukaryotes,

but at the cellular level, many protists are very complex—the most elaborate of all cells. In multicellular organisms, essential biological functions are carried out by organs. Unicellular protists carry out the same essential functions, but they do so using subcellular organelles, not multicellular organs. The organelles that protists use are mostly those discussed in Chapter 6, including the nucleus, endoplasmic reticulum, Golgi apparatus, and lysosomes. Certain protists also rely on organelles not found in most other eukaryotic cells, such as contractile vacuoles that pump excess water from the protistan cell (see Figure 7.13).

Protists are also very diverse in their nutrition. Some protists are photoautotrophs and contain chloroplasts. Some are heterotrophs, absorbing organic molecules or ingesting larger food particles. Still other protists, called **mixotrophs**, combine photosynthesis and heterotrophic nutrition. Photoautotrophy, heterotrophy, and mixotrophy have all arisen independently in many different protist lineages.

Reproduction and life cycles also are highly varied among protists. Some protists are only known to reproduce asexually; others can also reproduce sexually or at least employ the sexual processes of meiosis and fertilization. All three basic types of sexual life cycles (see Figure 13.6) are represented among protists, along with some variations that do not quite fit any of these types. We will examine the life cycles of several protist groups later in this chapter.

Four Supergroups of Eukaryotes

Our understanding of the evolutionary history of eukaryotic diversity has been in flux in recent years. Not only has kingdom Protista been abandoned, but other hypotheses have been discarded as well. For example, many biologists once thought that the oldest lineage of living eukaryotes was the *amitochondriate protists*, organisms without conventional mitochondria and with fewer membrane-enclosed organelles than other protist groups. But recent structural and DNA data have undermined this hypothesis. Many of the so-called amitochondriate protists have been shown to have mitochondria—though reduced ones—and some of these organisms are now classified in entirely different groups.

The ongoing changes in our understanding of the phylogeny of protists pose challenges to students and instructors alike. Hypotheses about these relationships are a focus of scientific activity, changing rapidly as new data cause previous ideas to be modified or discarded. We'll focus here on one current hypothesis: the four supergroups of eukaryotes shown in **Figure 28.2**, on the page after next. Because the root of the eukaryotic tree is not known, all four supergroups are shown as diverging simultaneously from a common ancestor. We know that this is not correct, but we do not know which organisms were the first to diverge from the others. In addition, while some of the groups in Figure 28.2 are well supported by morphological and DNA data, others are more controversial. As you read this chapter, it may be helpful to focus less on the specific names of groups of organisms and more on why the organisms are important and how ongoing research is elucidating their evolutionary relationships.

Endosymbiosis in Eukaryotic Evolution

What gave rise to the enormous diversity of protists that exist today? There is abundant evidence that much of protistan diversity has its origins in **endosymbiosis**, a relationship between two species in which one organism lives inside the cell or cells of another organism (the host). In particular, as we discussed in Concept 25.3, structural, biochemical, and DNA sequence data indicate that mitochondria and plastids are derived from prokaryotes that were engulfed by the ancestors of early eukaryotic cells. The evidence also suggests that mitochondria evolved before plastids. Thus, a defining moment in the origin of eukaryotes occurred when a host cell engulfed a bacterium that would later become an organelle found in all eukaryotes—the mitochondrion.

To determine which prokaryotic lineage gave rise to mitochondria, researchers have compared the DNA sequences of mitochondrial genes (mtDNA) to those found in major clades of bacteria and archaea. In the Scientific Skills Exercise, you will interpret one such set of DNA sequence

---

SCIENTIFIC SKILLS EXERCISE

Interpreting Comparisons of Genetic Sequences

Which Prokaryotes Are Most Closely Related to Mitochondria?
Early eukaryotes acquired mitochondria by endosymbiosis: A host cell engulfed an aerobic prokaryote that persisted within the cytoplasm to the mutual benefit of both cells. In studying which living prokaryotes might be most closely related to mitochondria, researchers compared ribosomal RNA (rRNA) sequences. Because most cells contain thousands of ribosomes, rRNA is the most abundant form of RNA in living cells and is suitable for comparing even distantly related species. In this exercise, you'll interpret some of the research data to draw conclusions about the phylogeny of mitochondria.

◀ Wheat, used as the source of mitochondrial RNA

How the Research Was Done Researchers isolated and cloned nucleotide sequences from the gene that codes for the small-subunit rRNA molecule for wheat (a eukaryote) and five bacterial species:

- Wheat, used as the source of mitochondrial rRNA genes
- *Agrobacterium tumefaciens*, an alpha proteobacterium that lives within plant tissue and produces tumors in the host
- *Comamonas testosteroni*, a beta proteobacterium
- *Escherichia coli*, a well-studied gamma proteobacterium that inhabits human intestines
- *Mycoplasma capricolum*, a gram-positive mycoplasma, which is the only group of bacteria lacking cell walls
- *Anacystis nidulans*, a cyanobacterium

Data from the Research Cloned rRNA gene sequences for the six organisms were aligned and compared. The data table below, called a *comparison matrix*, summarizes the comparison of 617 nucleotide positions from the gene sequences. Each value in the table is the percentage of the 617 nucleotide positions for which the pair of organisms have the same composition. Any positions that were identical across the rRNA genes of all six organisms were omitted from this comparison matrix.

Interpret the Data
1. First, make sure you understand how to read the comparison matrix. Find the cell that represents the comparison of *C. testosteroni* and *E. coli*. What value is given in this cell? What does that value signify about the comparable rRNA gene sequences in those two organisms? Explain why some cells have a dash rather than a value. Why are some cells shaded gray, with no value?

2. Why did the researchers choose one plant mitochondrion and five bacterial species to include in the comparison matrix?

3. Which species of bacteria has an rRNA gene that is most similar to that of the wheat mitochondrion? What is the significance of this similarity?

(MB) A version of this Scientific Skills Exercise can be assigned in MasteringBiology.

Data from D. Yang et al., Mitochondrial origins, *Proceedings of the National Academy of Sciences USA* 82:4443–4447 (1985).

	Wheat mitochondrion	A. tumefaciens	C. testosteroni	E. coli	M. capricolum	A. nidulans
Wheat mitochondrion	–	48	38	35	34	34
A. tumefaciens		–	55	57	52	53
C. testosteroni			–	61	52	52
E. coli				–	48	52
M. capricolum					–	50
A. nidulans						–

The tree below represents a phylogenetic hypothesis for the relationships among all the eukaryotes on Earth today. The eukaryotic groups at the branch tips are related in larger "supergroups," labeled vertically at the far right of the tree. Groups that were formerly classified in the kingdom Protista are highlighted in yellow. Dotted lines indicate evolutionary relationships that are uncertain and proposed clades that are under active debate. For clarity, this tree only includes representative clades from each supergroup. In addition, the recent discoveries of many new groups of eukaryotes indicate that eukaryotic diversity is much greater than shown here.

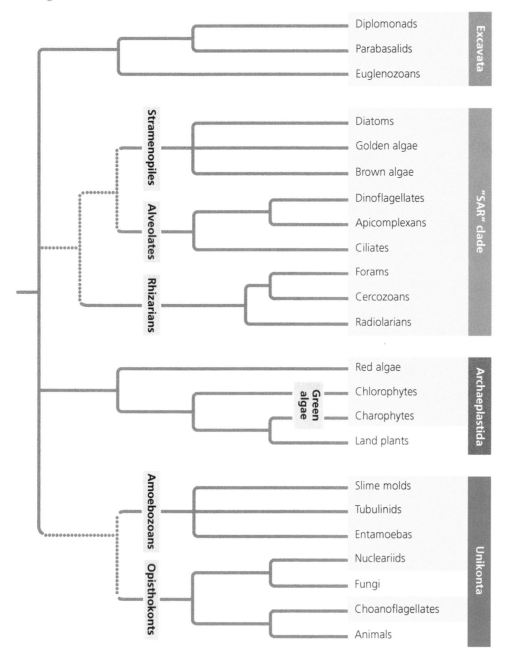

■ Excavata

Some members of this supergroup have an "excavated" groove on one side of the cell body. Two major clades (the parabasalids and diplomonads) have modified mitochondria; others (the euglenozoans) have flagella that differ in structure from those of other organisms. Excavates include parasites such as *Giardia*, as well as many predatory and photosynthetic species.

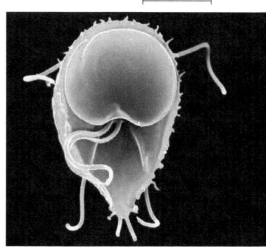

Giardia intestinalis, **a diplomonad parasite.** This diplomonad (colorized SEM), which lacks the characteristic surface groove of the Excavata, inhabits the intestines of mammals. It can infect people when they drink water contaminated with feces containing *Giardia* cysts. Drinking such water—even from a seemingly pristine stream—can cause severe diarrhea. Boiling the water kills the parasite.

■ "SAR" Clade

This supergroup contains (and is named after) three large and very diverse clades: Stramenopila, Alveolata, and Rhizaria. Stramenopiles include some of the most important photosynthetic organisms on Earth, such as the diatoms shown here. Alveolates also include many photosynthetic species as well as important pathogens, such as *Plasmodium*, which causes malaria. Many of the key groups of photosynthetic stramenopiles and alveolates are thought to have arisen by secondary endosymbiosis.

50 μm

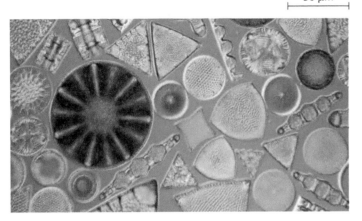

Diatom diversity. These beautiful single-celled protists are important photosynthetic organisms in aquatic communities (LM).

The rhizarian subgroup of the SAR clade includes many species of amoebas, most of which have pseudopodia that are threadlike in shape. Pseudopodia are extensions that can bulge from any portion of the cell; they are used in movement and in the capture of prey.

100 μm

Globigerina, a rhizarian in the SAR clade. This species is a foram, a group whose members have threadlike pseudopodia that extend through pores in the shell, or *test* (LM). The inset SEM shows a foram test, which is hardened by calcium carbonate.

■ Archaeplastida

This group of eukaryotes includes red algae and green algae, along with land plants (kingdom Plantae). Red algae and green algae include unicellular species, colonial species (such as the green alga *Volvox*), and multicellular species. Many of the large algae known informally as "seaweeds" are multicellular red or green algae. Protists in Archaeplastida include key photosynthetic species that form the base of the food web in some aquatic communities.

20 μm

50 μm

***Volvox*, a colonial freshwater green alga.** The colony is a hollow ball whose wall is composed of hundreds of biflagellated cells (see inset LM) embedded in a gelatinous matrix. The cells are usually connected by cytoplasmic strands; if isolated, these cells cannot reproduce. The large colonies seen here will eventually release the small "daughter" colonies within them (LM).

■ Unikonta

This group of eukaryotes includes amoebas that have lobe- or tube-shaped pseudopodia, as well as animals, fungi, and non-amoeba protists that are closely related to animals or fungi. According to one current hypothesis, the unikonts may have been the first group of eukaryotes to diverge from other eukaryotes; however, this hypothesis has yet to be widely accepted.

100 μm

A unikont amoeba. This amoeba (*Amoeba proteus*) is using its pseudopodia to move.

comparisons. Collectively, such studies indicate that mitochondria arose from an alpha proteobacterium (see Figure 27.16). Results from mtDNA sequence analyses also indicate that the mitochondria of protists, animals, fungi and plants descended from a single common ancestor, thus suggesting that mitochondria arose only once over the course of evolution. Similar analyses show that plastids arose once from an engulfed cyanobacterium.

While the lineages that gave rise to mitochondria and plastids have been identified, questions remain about the identity of the host cell that engulfed an alpha proteobacterium—and in so doing, set the stage for the origin of eukaryotes. According to recent genomic studies, the host came from an archaeal lineage, but which lineage remains undetermined. In addition, while the host may have been an archaean, it is also possible that the host was a member of a lineage that was related to, but had diverged from its archaeal ancestors. In the latter case, the host may have been a "protoeukaryote" in which certain features of eukaryotic cells had evolved, such as a cytoskeleton that enabled it to change shape (and thereby engulf the alpha proteobacterium).

Plastid Evolution: A Closer Look

As you've seen, current evidence indicates that mitochondria are descended from a bacterium that was engulfed by a cell from an archaeal lineage. This event gave rise to the eukaryotes. There is also much evidence that later in eukaryotic history, a lineage of heterotrophic eukaryotes acquired an additional endosymbiont—a photosynthetic cyanobacterium—that then evolved into plastids. According to the hypothesis illustrated in **Figure 28.3**, this plastid-bearing lineage gave rise to two lineages of photosynthetic protists, or **algae**: red algae and green algae.

Let's examine some of the steps in Figure 28.3 more closely. First, recall that cyanobacteria are gram-negative and that gram-negative bacteria have two cell membranes, an inner plasma membrane and an outer membrane that is part of the cell wall (see Figure 27.3). Plastids in red algae and green algae are also surrounded by two membranes. Transport proteins in these membranes are homologous to proteins in the inner and outer membranes of cyanobacteria, providing further support for the hypothesis that plastids originated from a cyanobacterial endosymbiont.

▼ **Figure 28.3 Diversity of plastids produced by endosymbiosis.** Studies of plastid-bearing eukaryotes suggest that plastids evolved from a cyanobacterium that was engulfed by an ancestral heterotrophic eukaryote (primary endosymbiosis). That ancestor then diversified into red algae and green algae, some of which were subsequently engulfed by other eukaryotes (secondary endosymbiosis).

MAKE CONNECTIONS *How many distinct genomes does a chlorarachniophyte cell contain? Explain. (See Figures 6.17 and 6.18).*

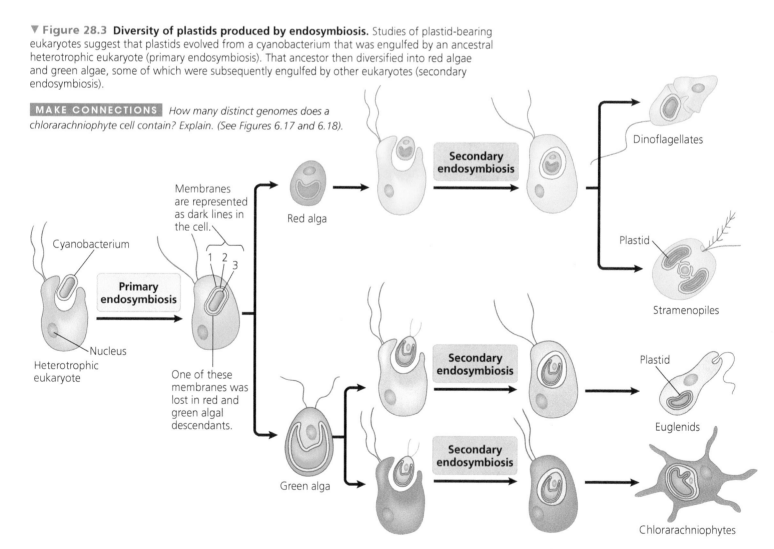

On several occasions during eukaryotic evolution, red algae and green algae underwent **secondary endosymbiosis**, meaning they were ingested in the food vacuoles of heterotrophic eukaryotes and became endosymbionts themselves. For example, protists known as chlorarachniophytes likely evolved when a heterotrophic eukaryote engulfed a green alga. Evidence for this process can be found within the engulfed cell, which contains a tiny vestigial nucleus, called a *nucleomorph* (**Figure 28.4**). Genes from the nucleomorph are still transcribed, and their DNA sequences indicate that the engulfed cell was a green alga.

▲ **Figure 28.4 Nucleomorph within a plastid of a chlorarachniophyte.**

Inner plastid membrane

Nucleomorph

Outer plastid membrane

Nuclear pore-like gap

CONCEPT CHECK 28.1

1. Cite at least four examples of structural and functional diversity among protists.

2. Summarize the role of endosymbiosis in eukaryotic evolution.

3. **WHAT IF?** After studying Figure 28.2, draw a simplified version of the phylogenetic tree that shows only the four supergroups of eukaryotes. Now sketch how the tree would look if the unikonts were the first group of eukaryotes to diverge from other eukaryotes.

For suggested answers, see Appendix A.

CONCEPT 28.2

Excavates include protists with modified mitochondria and protists with unique flagella

Now that we have examined some of the broad patterns in eukaryotic evolution, we will look more closely at the four main groups of protists shown in Figure 28.2.

We begin with **Excavata** (the excavates), a clade that was originally proposed based on morphological studies of the cytoskeleton. Some members of this diverse group also have an "excavated" feeding groove on one side of the cell body. The excavates include the diplomonads, parabasalids, and euglenozoans. Molecular data indicate that each of these three groups is monophyletic, and recent genomic studies support the monophyly of the excavate supergroup.

Diplomonads and Parabasalids

The protists in these two groups lack plastids and have highly modified mitochondria (until recently, they were thought to lack mitochondria altogether). Most diplomonads and parabasalids are found in anaerobic environments.

Diplomonads have reduced mitochondria called *mitosomes*. These organelles lack functional electron transport chains and hence cannot use oxygen to help extract energy from carbohydrates and other organic molecules. Instead, diplomonads get the energy they need from anaerobic biochemical pathways. Many diplomonads are parasites, including the infamous *Giardia intestinalis* (see Figure 28.2), which inhabits the intestines of mammals.

Structurally, diplomonads have two equal-sized nuclei and multiple flagella. Recall that eukaryotic flagella are extensions of the cytoplasm, consisting of bundles of microtubules covered by the cell's plasma membrane (see Figure 6.24). They are quite different from prokaryotic flagella, which are filaments composed of globular proteins attached to the cell surface (see Figure 27.7).

Parabasalids also have reduced mitochondria; called *hydrogenosomes*, these organelles generate some energy anaerobically, releasing hydrogen gas as a by-product. The best-known parabasalid is *Trichomonas vaginalis*, a sexually transmitted parasite that infects some 5 million people each year. *T. vaginalis* travels along the mucus-coated lining of the human reproductive and urinary tracts by moving its flagella and by undulating part of its plasma membrane (**Figure 28.5**). In females, if the vagina's normal acidity is disturbed, *T. vaginalis* can outcompete beneficial microorganisms there and infect the vagina. (*Trichomonas* infections also can occur in the urethra of males, though often without symptoms.) *T. vaginalis* has a gene that allows it to feed on the vaginal lining, promoting infection. Studies suggest that the protist acquired this gene by horizontal gene transfer from bacterial parasites in the vagina.

Flagella

Undulating membrane

5 µm

▲ **Figure 28.5 The parabasalid parasite, *Trichomonas vaginalis* (colorized SEM).**

Flagella

0.2 μm

8 μm

Crystalline rod
(cross section)

Ring of microtubules
(cross section)

▲ **Figure 28.6 Euglenozoan flagellum.** Most euglenozoans have a crystalline rod inside one of their flagella (the TEM is a flagellum shown in cross section). The rod lies alongside the 9 + 2 ring of microtubules found in all eukaryotic flagella (compare with Figure 6.24).

9 μm

▲ **Figure 28.7** *Trypanosoma*, **the kinetoplastid that causes sleeping sickness.** The purple, ribbon-shaped cells among these red blood cells are the trypanosomes (colorized SEM).

Euglenozoans

Protists called **euglenozoans** belong to a diverse clade that includes predatory heterotrophs, photosynthetic autotrophs, mixotrophs, and parasites. The main morphological feature that distinguishes protists in this clade is the presence of a rod with either a spiral or a crystalline structure inside each of their flagella **(Figure 28.6)**. The two best-studied groups of euglenozoans are the kinetoplastids and the euglenids.

Kinetoplastids

Protists called **kinetoplastids** have a single, large mitochondrion that contains an organized mass of DNA called a *kinetoplast*. These protists include species that feed on prokaryotes in freshwater, marine, and moist terrestrial ecosystems, as well as species that parasitize animals, plants, and other protists. For example, kinetoplastids in the genus *Trypanosoma* infect humans and cause sleeping sickness, a neurological disease that is invariably fatal if not treated. The infection occurs via the bite of a vector (carrier) organism, the African tsetse fly **(Figure 28.7)**. Trypanosomes also cause Chagas' disease, which is transmitted by bloodsucking insects and can lead to congestive heart failure.

Trypanosomes evade immune responses with an effective "bait-and-switch" defense. The surface of a trypanosome is coated with millions of copies of a single protein. However, before the host's immune system can recognize the protein and mount an attack, new generations of the parasite switch to another surface protein with a different molecular structure. Frequent changes in the surface protein prevent the host from developing immunity. (See the Scientific Skills Exercise in Chapter 43 to explore this topic further.) About a third of *Trypanosoma*'s genome is dedicated to producing these surface proteins.

Euglenids

A **euglenid** has a pocket at one end of the cell from which one or two flagella emerge **(Figure 28.8)**. Some euglenids are

Long flagellum

Eyespot: pigmented organelle that functions as a light shield, allowing light from only a certain direction to strike the light detector

Short flagellum

Contractile vacuole

Nucleus

Chloroplast

Plasma membrane

5 μm

Euglena (LM)

▼ **Figure 28.8**
Euglena, **a euglenid commonly found in pond water.**

Light detector: swelling near the base of the long flagellum; detects light that is not blocked by the eyespot. As a result, *Euglena* moves toward light of appropriate intensity, an important adaptation that enhances photosynthesis.

Pellice: protein bands beneath the plasma membrane that provide strength and flexibility (*Euglena* lacks a cell wall.)

mixotrophs: They perform photosynthesis when sunlight is available, but when it is not, they can become heterotrophic, absorbing organic nutrients from their environment. Many other euglenids engulf prey by phagocytosis.

CONCEPT CHECK 28.2

1. Why do some biologists describe the mitochondria of diplomonads and parabasalids as "highly reduced"?

2. **WHAT IF?** DNA sequence data for a diplomonad, a euglenid, a plant, and an unidentified protist suggest that the unidentified species is most closely related to the diplomonad. Further studies reveal that the unknown species has fully functional mitochondria. Based on these data, at what point on the phylogenetic tree in Figure 28.2 did the mystery protist's lineage probably diverge from other eukaryote lineages? Explain.

For suggested answers, see Appendix A.

CONCEPT 28.3

The "SAR" clade is a highly diverse group of protists defined by DNA similarities

Our second supergroup, the so-called **"SAR" clade**, was proposed recently based on whole-genome DNA sequence analyses. These studies have found that three major clades of protists—the stramenopiles, alveolates, and rhizarians—form a monophyletic supergroup. This supergroup contains a large, extremely diverse collection of protists. To date, this supergroup has not received a formal name but is instead known by the first letters of its major clades: the SAR clade.

Some morphological and DNA sequence data suggest that two of these groups, the stramenopiles and alveolates, originated more than a billion years ago, when a common ancestor of these two clades engulfed a single-celled, photosynthetic red alga. Because red algae are thought to have originated by primary endosymbiosis (see Figure 28.3), such an origin for the stramenopiles and alveolates is referred to as secondary endosymbiosis. Others question this idea, noting that some species in these groups lack plastids or their remnants (including any trace of plastid genes in their nuclear DNA).

Hairy flagellum

Smooth flagellum

5 μm

▲ Figure 28.9 **Stramenopile flagella.** Most stramenopiles, such as *Synura petersenii*, have two flagella: one covered with fine, stiff hairs and a shorter one that is smooth.

As its lack of a formal name suggests, the SAR clade is one of the most controversial of the four supergroups we describe in this chapter. Even so, for many scientists, this supergroup represents the best current hypothesis for the phylogeny of the three large protist clades to which we now turn.

Stramenopiles

One major subgroup of the SAR clade, the **stramenopiles**, includes some of the most important photosynthetic organisms on the planet. Their name (from the Latin *stramen*, straw, and *pilos*, hair) refers to their characteristic flagellum, which has numerous fine, hairlike projections. In most stramenopiles, this "hairy" flagellum is paired with a shorter "smooth" (nonhairy) flagellum (Figure 28.9). Here we'll focus on three groups of stramenopiles: diatoms, golden algae, and brown algae.

Diatoms

A key group of photosynthetic protists, **diatoms** are unicellular algae that have a unique glass-like wall made of silicon dioxide embedded in an organic matrix (Figure 28.10). The wall consists of two parts that overlap like a shoe box and its lid. These walls provide effective protection from the crushing jaws of predators: Live diatoms can withstand pressures as great as 1.4 million kg/m^2, equal to the pressure under each leg of a table supporting an elephant!

▶ Figure 28.10 **The diatom** *Triceratium morlandii* (color-ized SEM).

40 μm

With an estimated 100,000 living species, diatoms are a highly diverse group of protists (see Figure 28.2). They are among the most abundant photosynthetic organisms both in the ocean and in lakes: One bucket of water scooped from the surface of the sea may contain millions of these microscopic algae. The abundance of diatoms in the past is also evident in the fossil record, where massive accumulations of fossilized diatom walls are major constituents of sediments known as *diatomaceous earth.* These sediments are mined for their quality as a filtering medium and for many other uses.

Diatoms are so widespread and abundant that their photosynthetic activity affects global carbon dioxide levels. Diatoms have this effect in part because of events that occur during episodes of rapid population growth, or *blooms*, when ample nutrients are available. Typically, diatoms are eaten by a variety of protists and invertebrates, but during a bloom, many escape this fate. When these uneaten diatoms die, their bodies sink to the ocean floor. It takes decades to centuries for diatoms that sink to the ocean floor to be broken down by bacteria and other decomposers. As a result, the carbon in their bodies remains there for some time, rather than being released immediately as carbon dioxide as the decomposers respire. The overall effect of these events is that carbon dioxide absorbed by diatoms during photosynthesis is transported, or "pumped," to the ocean floor.

With an eye toward reducing global warming by lowering atmospheric carbon dioxide levels, some scientists advocate promoting diatom blooms by fertilizing the ocean with essential nutrients such as iron. In a 2012 study, researchers found that carbon dioxide was indeed pumped to the ocean floor after iron was added to a small region of the ocean. Further tests are planned to examine whether iron fertilization has undesirable side effects (such as oxygen depletion or the production of nitrous oxide, a more potent greenhouse gas than carbon dioxide).

Golden Algae

The characteristic color of **golden algae** results from their yellow and brown carotenoids. The cells of golden algae are typically biflagellated, with both flagella attached near one end of the cell.

Many golden algae are components of freshwater and marine *plankton*, communities of mostly microscopic organisms that drift in currents near the water's surface. While all golden algae are photosynthetic, some species are mixotrophic. These mixotrophs can absorb dissolved organic compounds or ingest food particles, including living cells, by phagocytosis. Most species are unicellular, but some, such as those in the freshwater genus *Dinobryon*, are colonial **(Figure 28.11)**. If environmental conditions deteriorate, many species form protective cysts that can survive for decades.

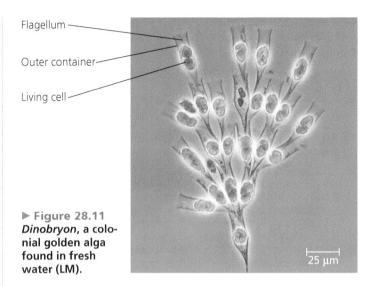

Flagellum
Outer container
Living cell

25 μm

▶ **Figure 28.11** ***Dinobryon*, a colonial golden alga found in fresh water (LM).**

Brown Algae

The largest and most complex algae are **brown algae**. All are multicellular, and most are marine. Brown algae are especially common along temperate coasts that have cold-water currents. They owe their characteristic brown or olive color to the carotenoids in their plastids.

Many of the species commonly called "seaweeds" are brown algae. Some brown algal seaweeds have specialized tissues and organs that resemble those in plants, such as a rootlike **holdfast**, which anchors the alga, and a stemlike **stipe**, which supports the leaflike **blades (Figure 28.12)**. However, morphological and DNA evidence show that these

Blade
Stipe
Holdfast

▲ **Figure 28.12 Seaweeds: adapted to life at the ocean's margins.** The sea palm (*Postelsia*) lives on rocks along the coast of the northwestern United States and western Canada. The body of this brown alga is well adapted to maintaining a firm foothold despite the crashing surf.

similarities evolved independently in the algal and plant lineages and are thus analogous, not homologous. In addition, while plants have adaptations (such as rigid stems) that provide support against gravity, brown algae have adaptations that enable their main photosynthetic surfaces (the leaflike blades) to be near the water surface. Some brown algae accomplish this task with gas-filled, bubble-shaped floats. Giant brown algae known as kelps that live in deep waters use a different means: Their blades are attached to stipes that can rise as much as 60 m from the seafloor, more than half the length of a football field.

Brown algae are important commodities for humans. Some species are eaten, such as *Laminaria* (Japanese "kombu"), which is used in soups. In addition, the cell walls of brown algae contain a gel-forming substance, called algin, which is used to thicken many processed foods, including pudding and salad dressing.

Alternation of Generations

A variety of life cycles have evolved among the multicellular algae. The most complex life cycles include an **alternation of generations**, the alternation of multicellular haploid and diploid forms. Although haploid and diploid conditions alternate in *all* sexual life cycles—human gametes, for example, are haploid—the term *alternation of generations* applies only to life cycles in which both haploid and diploid stages are multicellular. As you will read in Chapter 29, alternation of generations also evolved in plants.

The complex life cycle of the brown alga *Laminaria* provides an example of alternation of generations (Figure 28.13).

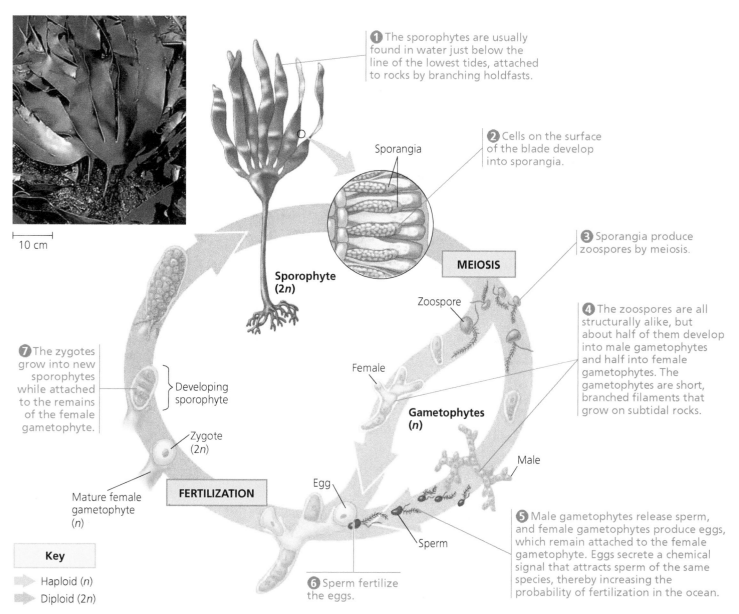

1 The sporophytes are usually found in water just below the line of the lowest tides, attached to rocks by branching holdfasts.

2 Cells on the surface of the blade develop into sporangia.

3 Sporangia produce zoospores by meiosis.

4 The zoospores are all structurally alike, but about half of them develop into male gametophytes and half into female gametophytes. The gametophytes are short, branched filaments that grow on subtidal rocks.

5 Male gametophytes release sperm, and female gametophytes produce eggs, which remain attached to the female gametophyte. Eggs secrete a chemical signal that attracts sperm of the same species, thereby increasing the probability of fertilization in the ocean.

6 Sperm fertilize the eggs.

7 The zygotes grow into new sporophytes while attached to the remains of the female gametophyte.

Sporangia

MEIOSIS

Zoospore

Female

Gametophytes (n)

Male

Sperm

Egg

FERTILIZATION

Mature female gametophyte (n)

Zygote (2n)

Developing sporophyte

Sporophyte (2n)

10 cm

Key

Haploid (n)

Diploid (2n)

▲ Figure 28.13 The life cycle of the brown alga *Laminaria*: an example of alternation of generations.

? *Are the sperm shown in* **5** *genetically identical to one another? Explain.*

The diploid individual is called the *sporophyte* because it produces spores. The spores are haploid and move by means of flagella; they are called zoospores. The zoospores develop into haploid, multicellular male and female *gametophytes*, which produce gametes. The union of two gametes (fertilization) results in a diploid zygote, which matures and gives rise to a new multicellular sporophyte.

In *Laminaria*, the two generations are **heteromorphic**, meaning that the sporophytes and gametophytes are structurally different. Other algal life cycles have an alternation of **isomorphic** generations, in which the sporophytes and gametophytes look similar to each other, although they differ in chromosome number.

Alveolates

Members of the next subgroup of the SAR clade, the **alveolates**, have membrane-enclosed sacs (alveoli) just under the plasma membrane (Figure 28.14). Alveolates are abundant in many habitats and include a wide range of photosynthetic and heterotrophic protists. We'll discuss three alveolate clades here: a group of flagellates (the dinoflagellates), a group of parasites (the apicomplexans), and a group of protists that move using cilia (the ciliates).

▲ Figure 28.14 **Alveoli.** These sacs under the plasma membrane are a characteristic that distinguishes alveolates from other eukaryotes (TEM).

Dinoflagellates

The cells of many **dinoflagellates** are reinforced by cellulose plates. Two flagella located in grooves in this "armor" make dinoflagellates (from the Greek *dinos*, whirling) spin as they move through the waters of their marine and freshwater communities (Figure 28.15a). Although the group is thought to have originated by secondary endosymbiosis (see Figure 28.3), roughly half of all dinoflagellates are now

(a) **Dinoflagellate flagella.** Beating of the spiral flagellum, which lies in a groove that encircles the cell, makes this specimen of *Pfiesteria shumwayae* spin (colorized SEM).

(b) **Red tide in the Gulf of Carpentaria in northern Australia.** The red color is due to high concentrations of a carotenoid-containing dinoflagellate.

▲ Figure 28.15 **Dinoflagellates.**

purely heterotrophic. Others are important species of *phytoplankton* (photosynthetic plankton, which include photosynthetic bacteria as well as algae); many photosynthetic dinoflagellates are mixotrophic.

Periods of explosive population growth (blooms) in dinoflagellates sometimes cause a phenomenon called "red tide" (Figure 28.15b). The blooms make coastal waters appear brownish red or pink because of the presence of carotenoids, the most common pigments in dinoflagellate plastids. Toxins produced by certain dinoflagellates have caused massive kills of invertebrates and fishes. Humans who eat molluscs that have accumulated the toxins are affected as well, sometimes fatally.

Apicomplexans

Nearly all **apicomplexans** are parasites of animals—and virtually all animal species examined so far are attacked by these parasites. The parasites spread through their host as tiny infectious cells called *sporozoites*. Apicomplexans are so named because one end (the *apex*) of the sporozoite cell contains a *complex* of organelles specialized for penetrating

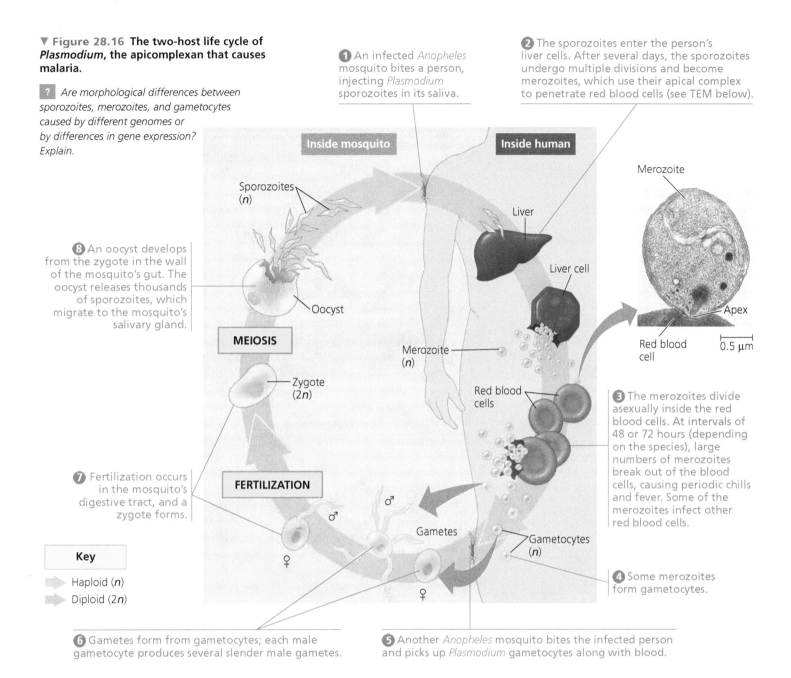

▼ **Figure 28.16 The two-host life cycle of _Plasmodium_, the apicomplexan that causes malaria.**

❓ _Are morphological differences between sporozoites, merozoites, and gametocytes caused by different genomes or by differences in gene expression? Explain._

❶ An infected _Anopheles_ mosquito bites a person, injecting _Plasmodium_ sporozoites in its saliva.

❷ The sporozoites enter the person's liver cells. After several days, the sporozoites undergo multiple divisions and become merozoites, which use their apical complex to penetrate red blood cells (see TEM below).

❸ An oocyst develops from the zygote in the wall of the mosquito's gut. The oocyst releases thousands of sporozoites, which migrate to the mosquito's salivary gland.

❼ Fertilization occurs in the mosquito's digestive tract, and a zygote forms.

Inside mosquito

Inside human

Sporozoites (n)

Oocyst

MEIOSIS

Zygote (2n)

FERTILIZATION

♂

♂

♀

Gametes

♀

Liver

Liver cell

Merozoite (n)

Red blood cells

Merozoite

Apex

Red blood cell

0.5 µm

❸ The merozoites divide asexually inside the red blood cells. At intervals of 48 or 72 hours (depending on the species), large numbers of merozoites break out of the blood cells, causing periodic chills and fever. Some of the merozoites infect other red blood cells.

Gametocytes (n)

❹ Some merozoites form gametocytes.

Key

➡ Haploid (n)
➡ Diploid (2n)

❻ Gametes form from gametocytes; each male gametocyte produces several slender male gametes.

❺ Another _Anopheles_ mosquito bites the infected person and picks up _Plasmodium_ gametocytes along with blood.

host cells and tissues. Although apicomplexans are not photosynthetic, recent data show that they retain a modified plastid (apicoplast), most likely of red algal origin.

Most apicomplexans have intricate life cycles with both sexual and asexual stages. Those life cycles often require two or more host species for completion. For example, _Plasmodium_, the parasite that causes malaria, lives in both mosquitoes and humans (**Figure 28.16**).

Historically, malaria has rivaled tuberculosis as the leading cause of human death by infectious disease. The incidence of malaria was diminished in the 1960s by insecticides that reduced carrier populations of _Anopheles_ mosquitoes and by drugs that killed _Plasmodium_ in humans. But the emergence of resistant varieties of both _Anopheles_ and _Plasmodium_ has led to a resurgence of malaria. About 250 million people in the tropics are currently infected, and 900,000

die each year. In regions where malaria is common, the lethal effects of this disease have resulted in the evolution of high frequencies of the sickle-cell allele; for an explanation of this connection, see Figure 23.17.

The search for malarial vaccines has been hampered by the fact that _Plasmodium_ lives mainly inside cells, hidden from the host's immune system. And, like trypanosomes, _Plasmodium_ continually changes its surface proteins. The urgent need for treatments has led researchers to track the expression of most of the parasite's genes at numerous points in its life cycle. This research could help identify vaccine targets. Drugs that target the apicoplast are also in development. This approach may be effective because the apicoplast, derived by secondary endosymbiosis from a prokaryote, has metabolic pathways different from those in humans.

Ciliates

The **ciliates** are a large and varied group of protists named for their use of cilia to move and feed **(Figure 28.17a)**. Most ciliates are predators, typically of bacteria or small protists. Their cilia may completely cover the cell surface or may be clustered in a few rows or tufts. In certain species, rows of tightly packed cilia function collectively in locomotion.

Other ciliates scurry about on leg-like structures constructed from many cilia bonded together.

A distinctive feature of ciliates is the presence of two types of nuclei: tiny micronuclei and large macronuclei. A cell has one or more nuclei of each type. Genetic variation results from **conjugation**, a sexual process in which two individuals exchange haploid micronuclei but do not

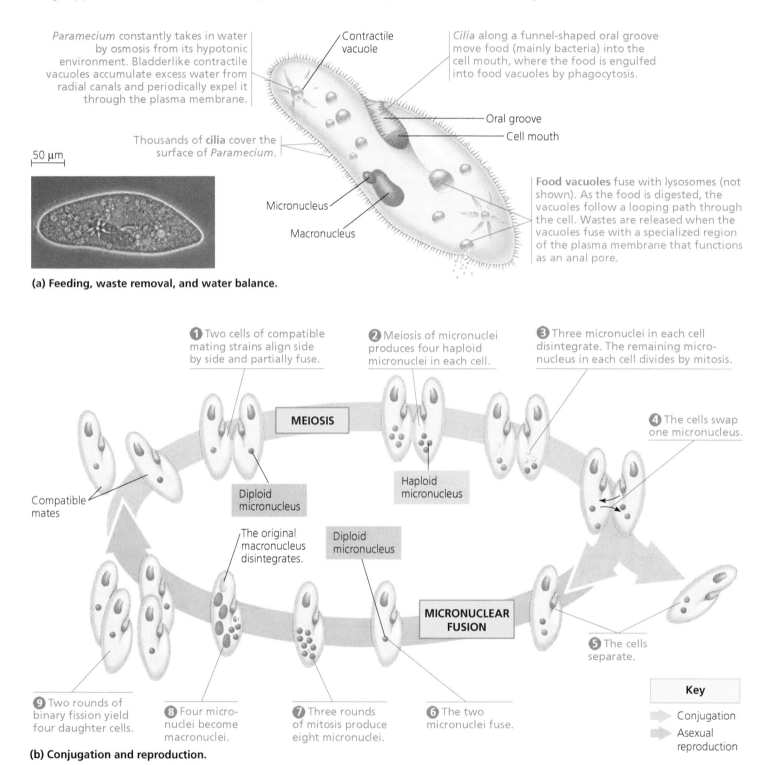

Paramecium constantly takes in water by osmosis from its hypotonic environment. Bladderlike contractile vacuoles accumulate excess water from radial canals and periodically expel it through the plasma membrane.

Contractile vacuole

Cilia along a funnel-shaped oral groove move food (mainly bacteria) into the cell mouth, where the food is engulfed into food vacuoles by phagocytosis.

Oral groove

Cell mouth

50 μm

Thousands of **cilia** cover the surface of *Paramecium*.

Micronucleus

Macronucleus

Food vacuoles fuse with lysosomes (not shown). As the food is digested, the vacuoles follow a looping path through the cell. Wastes are released when the vacuoles fuse with a specialized region of the plasma membrane that functions as an anal pore.

(a) Feeding, waste removal, and water balance.

❶ Two cells of compatible mating strains align side by side and partially fuse.

❷ Meiosis of micronuclei produces four haploid micronuclei in each cell.

❸ Three micronuclei in each cell disintegrate. The remaining micronucleus in each cell divides by mitosis.

MEIOSIS

❹ The cells swap one micronucleus.

Compatible mates

Diploid micronucleus

Haploid micronucleus

The original macronucleus disintegrates.

Diploid micronucleus

Diploid micronucleus

MICRONUCLEAR FUSION

❺ The cells separate.

❾ Two rounds of binary fission yield four daughter cells.

❽ Four micronuclei become macronuclei.

❼ Three rounds of mitosis produce eight micronuclei.

❻ The two micronuclei fuse.

Key

➡ Conjugation

➡ Asexual reproduction

(b) Conjugation and reproduction.

▲ Figure 28.17 Structure and function in the ciliate *Paramecium caudatum.*

reproduce (Figure 28.17b). Ciliates generally reproduce asexually by binary fission, during which the existing macronucleus disintegrates and a new one is formed from the cell's micronuclei. Each macronucleus typically contains multiple copies of the ciliate's genome. Genes in the macronucleus control the everyday functions of the cell, such as feeding, waste removal, and maintaining water balance.

Rhizarians

Our next subgroup of the SAR clade is the **rhizarians**. Many species in this group are **amoebas**, protists that move and feed by means of **pseudopodia**, extensions that may bulge from almost anywhere on the cell surface. As it moves, an amoeba extends a pseudopodium and anchors the tip; more cytoplasm then streams into the pseudopodium. Amoebas do not constitute a monophyletic group; instead, they are dispersed across many distantly related eukaryotic taxa. Most amoebas that are rhizarians differ morphologically from other amoebas by having threadlike pseudopodia. Rhizarians also include flagellated (non-amoeboid) protists that feed using threadlike pseudopodia.

We'll examine three groups of rhizarians here: radiolarians, forams, and cercozoans.

Radiolarians

The protists called **radiolarians** have delicate, intricately symmetrical internal skeletons that are generally made of silica. The pseudopodia of these mostly marine protists radiate from the central body (Figure 28.18) and are reinforced by bundles of microtubules. The microtubules are covered by a thin layer of cytoplasm, which engulfs smaller microorganisms that become attached to the pseudopodia. Cytoplasmic streaming then carries the captured prey into the main part of the cell. After radiolarians die, their skeletons

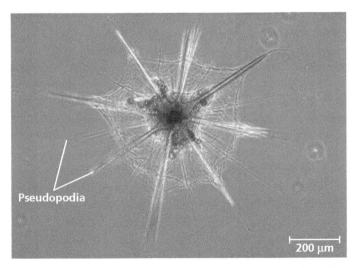

Pseudopodia

200 μm

▲ **Figure 28.18 A radiolarian.** Numerous threadlike pseudopodia radiate from the central body of this radiolarian (LM).

▲ **Figure 28.19 Fossil forams.** By measuring the magnesium content in fossilized forams like these, researchers seek to learn how ocean temperatures have changed over time. Forams take up more magnesium in warmer water than in colder water.

settle to the seafloor, where they have accumulated as an ooze that is hundreds of meters thick in some locations.

Forams

The protists called **foraminiferans** (from the Latin *foramen*, little hole, and *ferre*, to bear), or **forams**, are named for their porous shells, called **tests** (see Figure 28.2). Foram tests consist of a single piece of organic material hardened with calcium carbonate. The pseudopodia that extend through the pores function in swimming, test formation, and feeding. Many forams also derive nourishment from the photosynthesis of symbiotic algae that live within the tests.

Forams are found in both the ocean and fresh water. Most species live in sand or attach themselves to rocks or algae, but some are abundant in plankton. The largest forams, though single-celled, have tests measuring several centimeters in diameter.

Ninety percent of all identified species of forams are known from fossils. Along with the calcium-containing remains of other protists, the fossilized tests of forams are part of marine sediments, including sedimentary rocks that are now land formations. Foram fossils are excellent markers for correlating the ages of sedimentary rocks in different parts of the world. Researchers are also studying these fossils to obtain information about climate change and its effects on the oceans and their life (Figure 28.19).

Cercozoans

First identified in molecular phylogenies, the **cercozoans** are a large group of amoeboid and flagellated protists that feed using threadlike pseudopodia. Cercozoan protists are common inhabitants of marine, freshwater, and soil ecosystems.

Chromatophore

▲ Figure 28.20 **A second case of primary endosymbiosis?** The cercozoan *Paulinella* conducts photosynthesis in a unique sausage-shaped structure called a chromatophore (LM). Chromatophores are surrounded by a membrane with a peptidoglycan layer, suggesting that they are derived from a bacterium. DNA evidence indicates that chromatophores are derived from a different cyanobacterium than that from which plastids are derived.

Most cercozoans are heterotrophs. Many are parasites of plants, animals, or other protists; many others are predators. The predators include the most important consumers of bacteria in aquatic and soil ecosystems, along with species that eat other protists, fungi, and even small animals. One small group of cercozoans, the chlorarachniophytes (mentioned earlier in the discussion of secondary endosymbiosis), are mixotrophic: These organisms ingest smaller protists and bacteria as well as perform photosynthesis. At least one other cercozoan, *Paulinella chromatophora*, is an autotroph, deriving its energy from light and its carbon from carbon dioxide. As described in **Figure 28.20**, *Paulinella* appears to represent an intriguing additional evolutionary example of a eukaryotic lineage that obtained its photosynthetic apparatus directly from a cyanobacterium.

CONCEPT CHECK 28.3

1. Explain why forams have such a well-preserved fossil record.

2. **WHAT IF?** Would you expect the plastid DNA of photosynthetic dinoflagellates, diatoms, and golden algae to be more similar to the nuclear DNA of plants (domain Eukarya) or to the chromosomal DNA of cyanobacteria (domain Bacteria)? Explain.

3. **MAKE CONNECTIONS** Which of the three life cycles in Figure 13.6 exhibits alternation of generations? How does it differ from the other two?

4. **MAKE CONNECTIONS** Review Figures 9.2 and 10.6, and then summarize how CO_2 and O_2 are both used and produced by chlorarachniophytes and other aerobic algae.

For suggested answers, see Appendix A.

Red algae and green algae are the closest relatives of land plants

As described earlier, morphological and molecular evidence indicates that plastids arose when a heterotrophic protist acquired a cyanobacterial endosymbiont. Later, photosynthetic descendants of this ancient protist evolved into red algae and green algae (see Figure 28.3), and the lineage that produced green algae then gave rise to land plants. Together, red algae, green algae, and land plants make up our third eukaryotic supergroup, which is called **Archaeplastida**. Archaeplastida is a monophyletic group that descended from the ancient protist that engulfed a cyanobacterium. We will examine land plants in Chapters 29 and 30; here we will look at the diversity of their closest algal relatives, red algae and green algae.

Red Algae

Many of the 6,000 known species of **red algae** (rhodophytes, from the Greek *rhodos*, red) are reddish, owing to a photosynthetic pigment called phycoerythrin, which masks the green of chlorophyll **(Figure 28.21)**. However, other species (those adapted to more shallow water) have less phycoerythrin. As a result, red algal species may be greenish red in very shallow water, bright red at moderate depths, and almost black in deep water. Some species lack pigmentation altogether and function heterotrophically as parasites on other red algae.

Red algae are the most abundant large algae in the warm coastal waters of tropical oceans. Some of their photosynthetic pigments, including phycoerythrin, allow them to absorb blue and green light, which penetrate relatively far into the water. A species of red alga has been discovered near the Bahamas at a depth of more than 260 m. There are also a small number of freshwater and terrestrial species.

Most red algae are multicellular. Although none are as big as the giant brown kelps, the largest multicellular red algae are included in the informal designation "seaweeds." You may have eaten one of these multicellular red algae, *Porphyra* (Japanese "nori"), as crispy sheets or as a wrap for sushi (see Figure 28.21). Red algae reproduce sexually and have diverse life cycles in which alternation of generations is common. However, unlike other algae, red algae do not have

► **Bonnemaisonia hamifera.** This red alga has a filamentous form.

20 cm

8 mm

◄ **Dulse (*Palmaria palmata*).** This edible species has a "leafy" form.

▼ **Nori.** The red alga *Porphyra* is the source of a traditional Japanese food.

The seaweed is grown on nets in shallow coastal waters.

Paper-thin, glossy sheets of dried nori make a mineral-rich wrap for rice, seafood, and vegetables in sushi.

▲ **Figure 28.21 Red algae.**

flagellated gametes, so they depend on water currents to bring gametes together for fertilization.

Green Algae

The grass-green chloroplasts of **green algae** have a structure and pigment composition much like the chloroplasts of land plants. Molecular systematics and cellular morphology leave little doubt that green algae and land plants are closely related. In fact, some systematists now advocate including green algae in an expanded "plant" kingdom, Viridiplantae (from the Latin *viridis*, green). Phylogenetically, this change makes sense, since otherwise the green algae are a paraphyletic group.

Green algae are divided into two main groups, the charophytes and the chlorophytes. The charophytes are the algae most closely related to land plants, and we will discuss them along with plants in Chapter 29.

The second group, the chlorophytes (from the Greek *chloros*, green), includes more than 7,000 species. Most live in fresh water, but there are also many marine and some terrestrial species. The simplest chlorophytes are unicellular organisms such as *Chlamydomonas*, which resemble gametes of more complex chlorophytes. Various species of unicellular chlorophytes live independently in aquatic habitats as phytoplankton or inhabit damp soil. Some live symbiotically within other eukaryotes, contributing part of their photosynthetic output to the food supply of their hosts. Still other chlorophytes live in environments exposed to intense visible and ultraviolet radiation; these species are protected by radiation-blocking compounds in their cytoplasm, cell wall, or zygote coat.

Larger size and greater complexity evolved in chlorophytes by three different mechanisms:

1. The formation of colonies of individual cells, as seen in *Volvox* (see Figure 28.2) and in filamentous forms that contribute to the stringy masses known as pond scum
2. The formation of true multicellular bodies by cell division and differentiation, as in *Ulva* (Figure 28.22a)
3. The repeated division of nuclei with no cytoplasmic division, as in *Caulerpa* (Figure 28.22b)

2 cm

(a) *Ulva*, or sea lettuce. This multicellular, edible chlorophyte has differentiated structures, such as its leaflike blades and a rootlike holdfast that anchors the alga.

(b) *Caulerpa*, an intertidal chlorophyte. The branched filaments lack cross-walls and thus are multinucleate. In effect, the body of this alga is one huge "supercell."

▲ **Figure 28.22 Multicellular chlorophytes.**

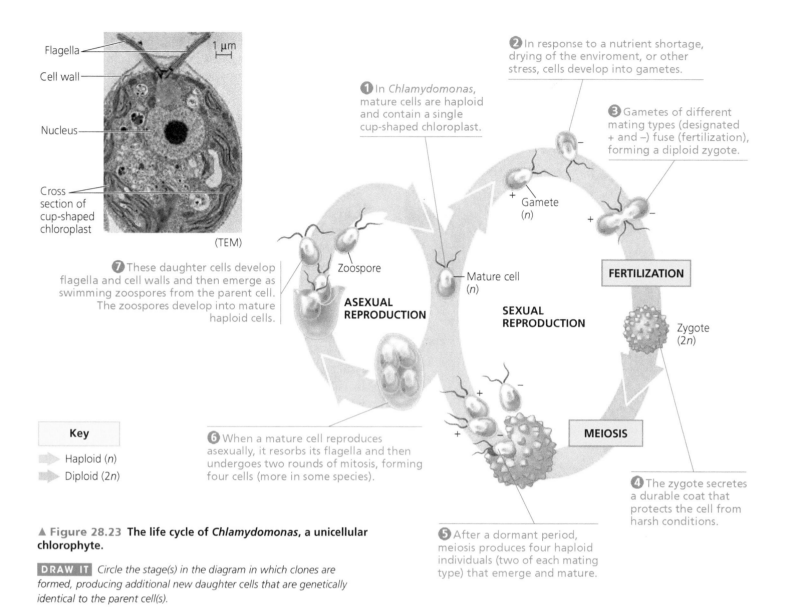

Flagella

Cell wall

Nucleus

Cross section of cup-shaped chloroplast

1 μm

(TEM)

❶ In *Chlamydomonas*, mature cells are haploid and contain a single cup-shaped chloroplast.

❷ In response to a nutrient shortage, drying of the enviroment, or other stress, cells develop into gametes.

❸ Gametes of different mating types (designated + and –) fuse (fertilization), forming a diploid zygote.

Gamete (*n*)

Mature cell (*n*)

FERTILIZATION

Zygote (2*n*)

❼ These daughter cells develop flagella and cell walls and then emerge as swimming zoospores from the parent cell. The zoospores develop into mature haploid cells.

Zoospore

ASEXUAL REPRODUCTION

SEXUAL REPRODUCTION

Key

⟹ Haploid (*n*)
⟹ Diploid (2*n*)

❻ When a mature cell reproduces asexually, it resorbs its flagella and then undergoes two rounds of mitosis, forming four cells (more in some species).

MEIOSIS

❹ The zygote secretes a durable coat that protects the cell from harsh conditions.

❺ After a dormant period, meiosis produces four haploid individuals (two of each mating type) that emerge and mature.

▲ **Figure 28.23 The life cycle of *Chlamydomonas*, a unicellular chlorophyte.**

DRAW IT *Circle the stage(s) in the diagram in which clones are formed, producing additional new daughter cells that are genetically identical to the parent cell(s).*

Most chlorophytes have complex life cycles, with both sexual and asexual reproductive stages. Nearly all species of chlorophytes reproduce sexually by means of biflagellated gametes that have cup-shaped chloroplasts (**Figure 28.23**). Alternation of generations has evolved in some chlorophytes, including *Ulva*.

CONCEPT CHECK 28.4

1. Contrast red algae and brown algae.
2. Why is it accurate to say that *Ulva* is truly multicellular but *Caulerpa* is not?
3. **WHAT IF?** Suggest a possible reason why species in the green algal lineage may have been more likely to colonize land than species in the red algal lineage.

For suggested answers, see Appendix A.

CONCEPT 28.5

Unikonts include protists that are closely related to fungi and animals

Excavata
SAR clade
Archaeplastida
Slime molds
Tubulinids
Entamoebas
Nucleariids
Fungi
Choanoflagellates
Animals

Unikonta

Unikonta is an extremely diverse supergroup of eukaryotes that includes animals, fungi, and some protists. There are two major clades of unikonts, the amoebozoans and the opisthokonts (animals, fungi, and closely related protist groups). Each of these two major clades is strongly supported by molecular systematics. The close relationship between amoebozoans and opisthokonts is more controversial. Support for this close relationship is provided by comparisons of myosin proteins and by some (but not all) studies based on multiple genes or whole genomes.

Another controversy involving the unikonts concerns the root of the eukaryotic tree. Recall that the root of a phylogenetic tree anchors the tree in time: Branch points close to the root are the oldest. At present, the root of the eukaryotic tree is uncertain; hence, we do not know which group of eukaryotes was the first to diverge from other eukaryotes. Some hypotheses, such as the amitochondriate hypothesis described earlier, have been abandoned, but researchers have yet to agree on an alternative. If the root of the eukaryotic tree were known, scientists could infer characteristics of the common ancestor of all eukaryotes.

In trying to determine the root of the eukaryotic tree, researchers have based their phylogenies on different sets of genes, some of which have produced conflicting results. Researchers have also tried a different approach, based on tracing the occurrence of a rare evolutionary event **(Figure 28.24)**. Results from this "rare event" approach suggest that the unikonts were the first eukaryotes to diverge from other eukaryotes. If this hypothesis is correct, animals and fungi belong to an early-diverging group of eukaryotes, while protists that lack typical mitochondria (such as the diplomonads and parabasalids) diverged later in the history of life. This idea remains controversial and will require more supporting evidence to be widely accepted.

Amoebozoans

The **amoebozoan** clade includes many species of amoebas that have lobe- or tube-shaped pseudopodia, rather than the threadlike pseudopodia found in rhizarians. Amoebozoans include slime molds, tubulinids, and entamoebas.

Slime Molds

Slime molds, or mycetozoans (from the Latin, meaning "fungus animals"), were once thought to be fungi because, like fungi, they produce fruiting bodies that aid in spore dispersal. However, DNA sequence analyses indicate that the resemblance between slime molds and fungi is a case of evolutionary convergence. DNA sequence analyses also show that slime molds descended from unicellular ancestors—an example of the independent origin of multicellularity in eukaryotes.

Slime molds have diverged into two main branches, plasmodial slime molds and cellular slime molds. We'll compare their characteristics and life cycles.

▼ Figure 28.24 | Inquiry

What is the root of the eukaryotic tree?

Experiment Responding to the difficulty in determining the root of the eukaryotic phylogenetic tree, Alexandra Stechmann and Thomas Cavalier-Smith proposed a new approach. They studied two genes, one coding for the enzyme dihydrofolate reductase (DHFR), the other for the enzyme thymidylate synthase (TS). Their approach took advantage of a rare evolutionary event: In some organisms, the genes for DHFR and TS have fused, leading to the production of a single protein with both enzyme activities. Stechmann and Cavalier-Smith amplified (using PCR; see Figure 20.8) and sequenced the genes for DHFR and TS in nine species (one choanoflagellate, two amoebozoans, one euglenozoan, one stramenopile, one alveolate, and three rhizarians). They combined their data with previously published data for species of bacteria, animals, plants, and fungi.

Results The bacteria studied all have separate genes coding for DHFR and TS, suggesting that this is the ancestral condition (red dot on the tree below). Other taxa with separate genes are denoted by red type. Fused genes are a derived character, found in certain members (blue type) of the supergroups Excavata, SAR clade, and Archaeplastida:

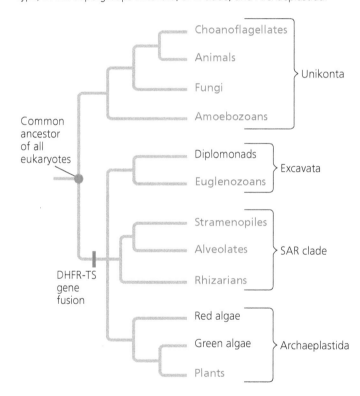

Conclusion These results support the hypothesis that the root of the tree is located between the unikonts and all other eukaryotes, suggesting that the unikonts were the first group of eukaryotes to diverge. Because support for this hypothesis is based on only one trait—the fusion of the genes for DHFR and TS—more data are needed to evaluate its validity.

Source: A. Stechmann and T. Cavalier-Smith, Rooting the eukaryote tree by using a derived gene fusion, *Science* 297:89–91 (2002).

WHAT IF? *Stechmann and Cavalier-Smith wrote that their conclusions are "valid only if the genes fused just once and were never secondarily split." Why is this assumption critical to their approach?*

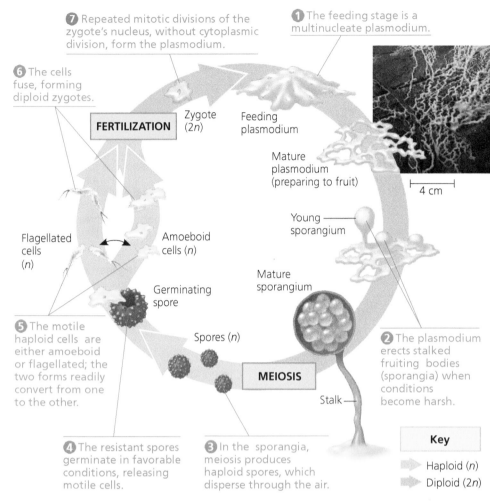

7 Repeated mitotic divisions of the zygote's nucleus, without cytoplasmic division, form the plasmodium.

1 The feeding stage is a multinucleate plasmodium.

6 The cells fuse, forming diploid zygotes.

Zygote (2n)

FERTILIZATION

Feeding plasmodium

Mature plasmodium (preparing to fruit)

4 cm

Flagellated cells (n)

Amoeboid cells (n)

Young sporangium

Germinating spore

Mature sporangium

5 The motile haploid cells are either amoeboid or flagellated; the two forms readily convert from one to the other.

Spores (n)

MEIOSIS

Stalk

2 The plasmodium erects stalked fruiting bodies (sporangia) when conditions become harsh.

4 The resistant spores germinate in favorable conditions, releasing motile cells.

3 In the sporangia, meiosis produces haploid spores, which disperse through the air.

Key

Haploid (n)

Diploid (2n)

▲ **Figure 28.25 A plasmodial slime mold.** This photograph shows a mature plasmodium, the feeding stage in the life cycle of a plasmodial slime mold. When food becomes scarce, the plasmodium forms stalked fruiting bodies that produce haploid spores that function in sexual reproduction.

Plasmodial Slime Molds Many plasmodial slime molds are brightly colored, often yellow or orange **(Figure 28.25)**. As they grow, they form a mass called a plasmodium, which can be many centimeters in diameter. (Don't confuse a slime mold's plasmodium with the genus *Plasmodium*, which includes the parasitic apicomplexan that causes malaria.) Despite its size, the plasmodium is not multicellular; it is a single mass of cytoplasm that is undivided by plasma membranes and that contains many nuclei. This "supercell" is the product of mitotic nuclear divisions that are not followed by cytokinesis. The plasmodium extends pseudopodia through moist soil, leaf mulch, or rotting logs, engulfing food particles by phagocytosis as it grows. If the habitat begins to dry up or there is no food left, the plasmodium stops growing and differentiates into fruiting bodies which function in sexual reproduction.

Cellular Slime Molds The life cycle of the protists called cellular slime molds can prompt us to question what it means to be an individual organism. The feeding stage of these

organisms consists of solitary cells that function individually, but when food is depleted, the cells form a sluglike aggregate that functions as a unit **(Figure 28.26)**. Unlike the feeding stage (plasmodium) of a plasmodial slime mold, these aggregated cells remain separated by their individual plasma membranes. Ultimately, the aggregated cells form an asexual fruiting body.

Dictyostelium discoideum, a cellular slime mold commonly found on forest floors, has become a model organism for studying the evolution of multicellularity. One line of research has focused on the slime mold's fruiting body stage. During this stage, the cells that form the stalk die as they dry out, while the spore cells at the top survive and have the potential to reproduce (see Figure 28.26). Scientists have found that mutations in a single gene can turn individual *Dictyostelium* cells into "cheaters" that never become part of the stalk. Because these mutants gain a strong reproductive advantage over noncheaters, why don't all *Dictyostelium* cells cheat?

Recent discoveries suggest an answer to this question. Cheating cells lack a specific surface protein and noncheating cells can recognize this difference. Noncheaters preferentially aggregate with other noncheaters, thus depriving cheaters of the chance to exploit them. Such a recognition system may have been important in the evolution of other multicellular eukaryotes, such as animals and plants.

Tubulinids

Tubulinids constitute a large and varied group of amoebozoans that have lobe- or tube-shaped pseudopodia. These unicellular protists are ubiquitous in soil as well as freshwater and marine environments. Most are heterotrophs that actively seek and consume bacteria and other protists; one such tubulinid species, *Amoeba proteus*, is shown in

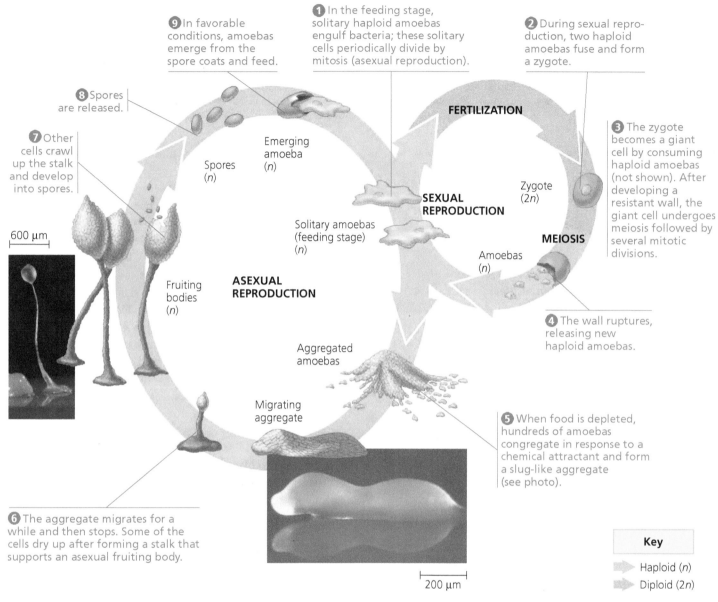

9 In favorable conditions, amoebas emerge from the spore coats and feed.

1 In the feeding stage, solitary haploid amoebas engulf bacteria; these solitary cells periodically divide by mitosis (asexual reproduction).

2 During sexual reproduction, two haploid amoebas fuse and form a zygote.

8 Spores are released.

7 Other cells crawl up the stalk and develop into spores.

FERTILIZATION

3 The zygote becomes a giant cell by consuming haploid amoebas (not shown). After developing a resistant wall, the giant cell undergoes meiosis followed by several mitotic divisions.

Emerging amoeba (n)

Spores (n)

Zygote (2n)

SEXUAL REPRODUCTION

600 μm

Solitary amoebas (feeding stage) (n)

MEIOSIS

Amoebas (n)

Fruiting bodies (n)

ASEXUAL REPRODUCTION

4 The wall ruptures, releasing new haploid amoebas.

Aggregated amoebas

Migrating aggregate

5 When food is depleted, hundreds of amoebas congregate in response to a chemical attractant and form a slug-like aggregate (see photo).

6 The aggregate migrates for a while and then stops. Some of the cells dry up after forming a stalk that supports an asexual fruiting body.

200 μm

Key

Haploid (n)
Diploid (2n)

▲ **Figure 28.26 The life cycle of *Dictyostelium*, a cellular slime mold.**

Figure 28.2. Some tubulinids also feed on detritus (nonliving organic matter).

Entamoebas

Whereas most amoebozoans are free-living, those that belong to the genus *Entamoeba* are parasites. They infect all classes of vertebrate animals as well as some invertebrates. Humans are host to at least six species of *Entamoeba*, but only one, *E. histolytica*, is known to be pathogenic. *E. histolytica* causes amebic dysentery and is spread via contaminated drinking water, food, or eating utensils. Responsible for up to 100,000 deaths worldwide every year, the disease is the third-leading cause of death due to eukaryotic parasites, after malaria (see Figure 28.16) and schistosomiasis (see Figure 33.11).

Opisthokonts

Opisthokonts are an extremely diverse group of eukaryotes that includes animals, fungi, and several groups of protists. We will discuss the evolutionary history of fungi and animals in Chapters 31–34. Of the opisthokont protists, we will discuss the nucleariids in Chapter 31 because they are more closely related to fungi than they are to other protists. Similarly, we will discuss choanoflagellates in Chapter 32, since they are more closely related to animals than they are to other protists. The nucleariids and choanoflagellates illustrate why scientists have abandoned the former kingdom Protista: A monophyletic group that includes these single-celled eukaryotes would also have to include the multicellular animals and fungi that are closely related to them.

1. Contrast the pseudopodia of amoebozoans and forams.

2. In what sense is "fungus animal" a fitting description of a slime mold? In what sense is it not fitting?

3. **WHAT IF?** If further evidence indicates that the root of the eukaryotic tree is as shown in Figure 28.24, would this evidence support, contradict, or have no bearing on the hypothesis that Excavata is monophyletic?

For suggested answers, see Appendix A.

CONCEPT 28.6

Protists play key roles in ecological communities

Most protists are aquatic, and they are found almost anywhere there is water, including moist terrestrial habitats such as damp soil and leaf litter. In oceans, ponds, and lakes, many protists are bottom-dwellers that attach to rocks and other substrates or creep through the sand and silt. As we've seen, other protists are important constituents of plankton. We'll focus here on two key roles that protists play in the varied habitats in which they live: that of symbiont and that of producer.

Symbiotic Protists

Many protists form symbiotic associations with other species. For example, photosynthetic dinoflagellates are food-providing symbiotic partners of the animals (coral polyps) that build coral reefs. Coral reefs are highly diverse ecological communities. That diversity ultimately depends on corals—and on the mutualistic protists that nourish them. Corals support reef diversity by providing food to some species and habitat to many others.

Another example is the wood-digesting protists that inhabit the gut of many termite species (**Figure 28.27**). Unaided, termites cannot digest wood, and they rely on

▶ **Figure 28.27**
A symbiotic protist. This organism is a hypermastigote, a member of a group of parabasalids that live in the gut of termites and certain cockroaches and enable the hosts to digest wood (SEM).

10 μm

▶ **Figure 28.28**
Sudden oak death. Many dead oak trees are visible in this Monterey County, California landscape. Infected trees lose their ability to adjust to cycles of wet and dry weather.

protistan or prokaryotic symbionts to do so. Termites cause over $3.5 billion in damage annually to wooden homes in the United States.

Symbiotic protists also include parasites that have compromised the economies of entire countries. Consider the malaria-causing protist *Plasmodium*: Income levels in countries hard hit by malaria are 33% lower than in similar countries free of the disease. Protists can have devastating effects on other species too. Massive fish kills have been attributed to *Pfiesteria shumwayae* (see Figure 28.15), a dinoflagellate parasite that attaches to its victims and eats their skin. Among species that parasitize plants, the stramenopile *Phytophthora ramorum* has emerged as a major new forest pathogen. This species causes sudden oak death (SOD), a disease that has killed millions of oaks and other trees in the United States and Great Britain (**Figure 28.28**; also see Chapter 54). A closely related species, *P. infestans*, causes potato late blight, which turns the stalks and stems of potato plants into black slime. Late blight contributed to the devastating Irish famine of the 19th century, in which a million people died and at least that many were forced to leave Ireland. The disease continues to be a major problem today, causing crop losses as high as 70% in some regions.

Photosynthetic Protists

Many protists are important **producers**, organisms that use energy from light (or inorganic chemicals) to convert carbon dioxide to organic compounds. Producers form the base of ecological food webs. In aquatic communities, the main producers are photosynthetic protists and prokaryotes **Figure 28.29**). All other organisms in the community depend on them for food, either directly (by eating them) or indirectly (by eating an organism that ate a producer). Scientists estimate that roughly 30% of the world's photosynthesis is performed by diatoms, dinoflagellates, multicellular algae, and other aquatic protists. Photosynthetic prokaryotes contribute another 20%, and land plants are responsible for the remaining 50%.

Because producers form the foundation of food webs, factors that affect producers can dramatically affect their entire community. In aquatic environments, photosynthetic protists are often held in check by low concentrations of nitrogen, phosphorus, or iron. Various human actions can increase the concentrations of these elements in aquatic

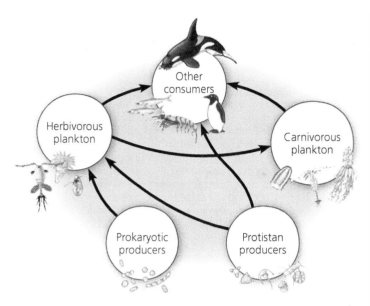

▲ **Figure 28.29 Protists: key producers in aquatic communities.** Arrows in this simplified food web lead from food sources to the organisms that eat them.

communities. For example, when fertilizer is applied to a field, some of the fertilizer may be washed by rainfall into a river that drains into a lake or ocean. When people add nutrients to aquatic communities in this or other ways, the abundance of photosynthetic protists can increase spectacularly. Such increases can alter the abundance of other species in the community, as we'll see in Chapter 55.

A pressing question is how global warming will affect photosynthetic protists and other producers. As shown in **Figure 28.30**, the growth and biomass of photosynthetic protists and prokaryotes have declined in many ocean

regions as sea surface temperatures have increased. By what mechanism do rising sea surface temperatures reduce the growth of marine producers? One hypothesis relates to the rise or upwelling of cold, nutrient-rich waters from below. Many marine producers rely on nutrients brought to the surface in this way. However, rising sea surface temperatures can cause the formation of a layer of light, warm water that acts as a barrier to nutrient upwelling—thus reducing the growth of marine producers. If sustained, the changes shown in Figure 28.29 would likely have far-reaching effects on marine ecosystems, fishery yields, and the global carbon cycle (see Chapter 55). Global warming can also affect producers on land, but there the base of food webs is occupied not by protists but by land plants, which we will discuss in Chapters 29 and 30.

CONCEPT CHECK 28.6

1. Justify the claim that photosynthetic protists are among the biosphere's most important organisms.

2. Describe three symbioses that include protists.

3. **WHAT IF?** High water temperatures and pollution can cause corals to expel their dinoflagellate symbionts. How might such "coral bleaching" affect corals and other species?

4. **MAKE CONNECTIONS** The bacterium *Wolbachia* is a symbiont that lives in mosquito cells and spreads rapidly through mosquito populations. *Wolbachia* can make mosquitoes resistant to infection by *Plasmodium*; researchers are seeking a strain that confers resistance and does not harm mosquitoes. Compare evolutionary changes that could occur if malaria control is attempted using such a *Wolbachia* strain versus using insecticides to kill mosquitoes. (Review Figure 28.16 and Concept 23.4.)

For suggested answers, see Appendix A.

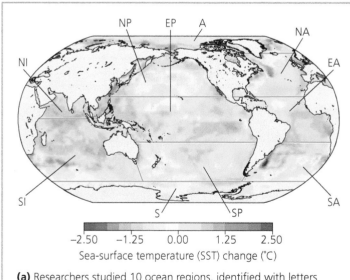

(a) Researchers studied 10 ocean regions, identified with letters on the map (see (b) for the corresponding names). SSTs have increased since 1950 in most areas of these regions.

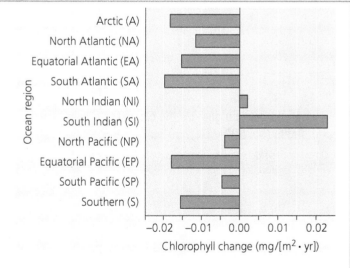

(b) The concentration of chlorophyll, an index for the biomass and growth of marine producers, has decreased over the same time period in most ocean regions.

▲ **Figure 28.30 Effects of climate change on marine producers.**

CONCEPT 28.1

Most eukaryotes are single-celled organisms (pp. 588–593)

- Domain Eukarya includes many groups of **protists**, along with plants, animals, and fungi. Unlike prokaryotes, protists and other eukaryotes have a nucleus and other membrane-enclosed organelles, as well as a cytoskeleton that enables them to have asymmetric forms and to change shape as they feed, move, or grow.
- Protists are structurally and functionally diverse and have a wide variety of life cycles. Most are unicellular. Protists include photoautotrophs, heterotrophs, and mixotrophs.

- Current evidence indicates that eukaryotes originated by **endosymbiosis** when an archaeal host (or a host with archaeal ancestors) engulfed an alpha proteobacterium that would evolve into an organelle found in all eukaryotes, the mitochondrion.
- Plastids are thought to be descendants of cyanobacteria that were engulfed by early eukaryotic cells. The plastid-bearing lineage eventually evolved into red algae and green algae. Other protist groups evolved from **secondary endosymbiosis** events in which red algae or green algae were themselves engulfed.
- In one hypothesis, eukaryotes are grouped into four supergroups, each a monophyletic clade: Excavata, "SAR" clade, Archaeplastida, and Unikonta.

? *Describe similarities and differences between protists and other eukaryotes.*

Key Concept/Eukaryote Supergroup	Major Groups	Key Morphological Characteristics	Specific Examples
CONCEPT 28.2 **Excavates include protists with modified mitochondria and protists with unique flagella (pp. 593–595)** ? *What evidence indicates that the excavates form a clade?*	**Diplomonads and parabasalids** **Euglenozoans** Kinetoplastids Euglenids	Modified mitochondria Spiral or crystalline rod inside flagella	*Giardia, Trichomonas* *Trypanosoma, Euglena*
CONCEPT 28.3 **The "SAR" clade is a highly diverse group of protists defined by DNA similarities (pp. 595–602)** ? *Although they are not photosynthetic, apicomplexan parasites such as* Plasmodium *have modified plastids. Describe a current hypothesis that explains this observation.*	**Stramenopiles** Diatoms Golden algae Brown algae **Alveolates** Dinoflagellates Apicomplexans Ciliates **Rhizarians** Radiolarians Forams Cercozoans	Hairy and smooth flagella Membrane-enclosed sacs (alveoli) beneath plasma membrane Amoebas with threadlike pseudopodia	*Phytophthora, Laminaria* *Pfiesteria, Plasmodium, Paramecium* *Globigerina*
CONCEPT 28.4 **Red algae and green algae are the closest relatives of land plants (pp. 602–604)** ? *On what basis do some systematists place land plants in the same supergroup (Archaeplastida) as red and green algae?*	**Red algae** **Green algae** **Land plants**	Phycoerythrin (photosynthetic pigment) Plant-type chloroplasts (See Chapters 29 and 30.)	*Porphyra* *Chlamydomonas, Ulva* Mosses, ferns, conifers, flowering plants
CONCEPT 28.5 **Unikonts include protists that are closely related to fungi and animals (pp. 604–608)** ? *Describe a key feature for each of the main protist subgroups of Unikonta.*	**Amoebozoans** Slime molds Tubulinids Entamoebas **Opisthokonts**	Amoebas with lobe-shaped or tube-shaped pseudopodia (Highly variable; see Chapters 31–34.)	*Amoeba, Dictyostelium* Choanoflagellates, nucleariids, animals, fungi

CONCEPT 28.6

Protists play key roles in ecological communities (pp. 608–609)

- Protists form a wide range of mutualistic and parasitic relationships that affect their symbiotic partners and many other members of the community.
- Photosynthetic protists are among the most important producers in aquatic communities. Because they are at the base of the food web, factors that affect photosynthetic protists affect many other species in the community.

? *Describe several protists that are ecologically important.*

TEST YOUR UNDERSTANDING

LEVEL 1: KNOWLEDGE/COMPREHENSION

1. Plastids that are surrounded by more than two membranes are evidence of
   a. evolution from mitochondria.
   b. fusion of plastids.
   c. origin of the plastids from archaea.
   d. secondary endosymbiosis.

2. Biologists think that endosymbiosis gave rise to mitochondria before plastids partly because
   a. the products of photosynthesis could not be metabolized without mitochondrial enzymes.
   b. all eukaryotes have mitochondria (or their remnants), whereas many eukaryotes do not have plastids.
   c. mitochondrial DNA is less similar to prokaryotic DNA than is plastid DNA.
   d. without mitochondrial CO_2 production, photosynthesis could not occur.

3. Which group is *incorrectly* paired with its description?
   a. diatoms—important producers in aquatic communities
   b. red algae—eukaryotes that acquired plastids by secondary endosymbiosis
   c. apicomplexans—unicellular parasites with intricate life cycles
   d. diplomonads—unicellular eukaryotes with modified mitochondria

4. According to the phylogeny presented in this chapter, which protists are in the same eukaryotic supergroup as land plants?
   a. green algae
   b. dinoflagellates
   c. red algae
   d. both a and c

5. In a life cycle with alternation of generations, multicellular haploid forms alternate with
   a. unicellular haploid forms.
   b. unicellular diploid forms.
   c. multicellular haploid forms.
   d. multicellular diploid forms.

LEVEL 2: APPLICATION/ANALYSIS

6. Based on the phylogenetic tree in Figure 28.2, which of the following statements is correct?
   a. The most recent common ancestor of Excavata is older than that of the SAR clade.
   b. The most recent common ancestor of the SAR clade is older than that of Unikonta.
   c. The most basal (first to diverge) eukaryotic supergroup cannot be determined.
   d. Excavata is the most basal eukaryotic supergroup.

7. **EVOLUTION CONNECTION**
   DRAW IT Medical researchers seek to develop drugs that can kill or restrict the growth of human pathogens yet have few harmful effects on patients. These drugs often work by disrupting the metabolism of the pathogen or by targeting its structural features.
   Draw and label a phylogenetic tree that includes an ancestral prokaryote and the following groups of organisms: Excavata, SAR clade, Archaeplastida, Unikonta, and, within Unikonta, amoebozoans, animals, choanoflagellates, fungi, and nucleariids. Based on this tree, hypothesize whether it would be most difficult to develop drugs to combat human pathogens that are prokaryotes, protists, animals, or fungi. (You do not need to consider the evolution of drug resistance by the pathogen.)

LEVEL 3: SYNTHESIS/EVALUATION

8. **SCIENTIFIC INQUIRY**
   Applying the "If . . . then" logic of science (see Chapter 1), what are a few of the predictions that arise from the hypothesis that plants evolved from green algae? Put another way, how could you test this hypothesis?

9. **WRITE ABOUT A THEME: INTERACTIONS**
   Organisms interact with each other and the physical environment. In a short essay (100–150 words), explain how the response of diatom populations to a drop in nutrient availability can affect both other organisms and aspects of the physical environment (such as carbon dioxide concentrations).

10. **SYNTHESIZE YOUR KNOWLEDGE**

This micrograph shows a single-celled eukaryote, the ciliate *Didinium* (left), about to engulf its *Paramecium* prey, which is also a ciliate. Identify the eukaryotic supergroup to which ciliates belong and describe the role of endosymbiosis in the evolutionary history of that supergroup. Are these ciliates more closely related to all other protists than they are to plants, fungi, or animals? Explain.

For selected answers, see Appendix A.

MasteringBiology®

Students Go to **MasteringBiology** for assignments, the eText, and the Study Area with practice tests, animations, and activities.

Instructors Go to **MasteringBiology** for automatically graded tutorials and questions that you can assign to your students, plus Instructor Resources.

29

Plant Diversity I: How Plants Colonized Land

▲ Figure 29.1 **How did plants change the world?**

The Greening of Earth

Looking at a lush landscape, such as that shown in **Figure 29.1**, it is hard to imagine the land without plants or other organisms. Yet for much of Earth's history, the land was largely lifeless. Geochemical analysis and fossil evidence suggest that thin coatings of cyanobacteria and protists existed on land by 1.2 billion years ago. But it was only within the last 500 million years that small plants, fungi, and animals joined them ashore. Finally, by about 385 million years ago, tall plants appeared, leading to the first forests (but with very different species than those in Figure 29.1).

Today, there are more than 290,000 known plant species. Plants inhabit all but the harshest environments, such as some mountaintop and desert areas and the polar ice sheets. A few plant species, such as sea grasses, returned to aquatic habitats during their evolution. In this chapter, we'll refer to all plants as *land* plants, even those that are now aquatic, to distinguish them from algae, which are photosynthetic protists.

Land plants enabled other life-forms to survive on land. Plants supply oxygen and ultimately most of the food eaten by terrestrial animals. Also, plant roots create habitats for other organisms by stabilizing the soil. This chapter traces the first 100 million years of plant evolution, including the emergence of seedless plants such as mosses and ferns. Chapter 30 examines the later evolution of seed plants.

Land plants evolved from green algae

As you read in Chapter 28, green algae called charophytes are the closest relatives of land plants. We'll begin with a closer look at the evidence for this relationship.

Morphological and Molecular Evidence

Many key traits of land plants also appear in some algae. For example, plants are multicellular, eukaryotic, photosynthetic autotrophs, as are brown, red, and certain green algae. Plants have cell walls made of cellulose, and so do green algae, dinoflagellates, and brown algae. And chloroplasts with chlorophylls *a* and *b* are present in green algae, euglenids, and a few dinoflagellates, as well as in plants.

However, the charophytes are the only present-day algae that share the following distinctive traits with land plants, suggesting that they are the closest living relatives of plants:

30 nm

- **Rings of cellulose-synthesizing proteins.** The cells of both land plants and charophytes have distinctive circular rings of proteins (right) in the plasma membrane. These protein rings synthesize the cellulose microfibrils of the cell wall. In contrast, noncharophyte algae have linear sets of proteins that synthesize cellulose.
- **Structure of flagellated sperm.** In species of land plants that have flagellated sperm, the structure of the sperm closely resembles that of charophyte sperm.
- **Formation of a phragmoplast.** Particular details of cell division occur only in land plants and certain charophytes, including the genera *Chara* and *Coleochaete*. For example, a group of microtubules known as the phragmoplast forms between the daughter nuclei of a dividing cell. A cell plate then develops in the middle of the phragmoplast, across the midline of the dividing cell (see Figure 12.10). The cell plate, in turn, gives rise to a new cross wall that separates the daughter cells.

Studies of nuclear and chloroplast genes from a wide range of plants and algae also indicate that certain groups of charophytes—including *Chara* and *Coleochaete*—are the closest living relatives of land plants. Although this evidence suggests that land plants arose from within the charophyte lineage, it does not mean that plants are descended from these living algae. But present-day charophytes may tell us something about the algal ancestors of plants.

Adaptations Enabling the Move to Land

Many species of charophyte algae inhabit shallow waters around the edges of ponds and lakes, where they are subject to occasional drying. In such environments, natural selection favors individual algae that can survive periods when they are not submerged. In charophytes, a layer of a durable polymer called **sporopollenin** prevents exposed zygotes from drying out. A similar chemical adaptation is found in the tough sporopollenin walls that encase plant spores.

The accumulation of such traits by at least one population of charophyte ancestors probably enabled their descendants—the first land plants—to live permanently above the waterline. This ability opened a new frontier: a terrestrial habitat that offered enormous benefits. The bright sunlight was unfiltered by water and plankton; the atmosphere offered more plentiful carbon dioxide than did water; and the soil by the water's edge was rich in some mineral nutrients. But these benefits were accompanied by challenges: a relative scarcity of water and a lack of structural support against gravity. (To appreciate why such support is important, picture how the soft body of a jellyfish sags when taken out of water.) Land plants diversified as adaptations evolved that enabled plants to thrive despite these challenges.

Today, what adaptations are unique to plants? The answer depends on where you draw the boundary dividing land plants from algae (**Figure 29.2**). Since the placement of this boundary is the subject of ongoing debate, this text uses a traditional definition that equates the kingdom Plantae with embryophytes (plants with embryos). In this context, let's now examine the derived traits that separate land plants from their closest algal relatives.

Derived Traits of Plants

A series of adaptations that facilitate survival and reproduction on dry land emerged after land plants diverged from their algal relatives. **Figure 29.3** depicts five such traits that are found in land plants but not in charophyte algae.

▲ **Figure 29.2 Three possible "plant" kingdoms.**

❓ *A branch with three parallel lines leading to a group indicates that the group is paraphyletic. Explain why charophyte algae are represented as a paraphyletic group.*

Exploring Derived Traits of Land Plants

Charophyte algae lack the key traits of land plants described in this figure: alternation of generations; multicellular, dependent embryos; walled spores produced in sporangia; multicellular gametangia; and apical meristems. This suggests that these traits were absent in the ancestor common to land plants and charophytes but instead evolved as derived traits of land plants. Not every land plant exhibits all of these traits; certain lineages of plants have lost some traits over time.

Alternation of Generations

The life cycles of all land plants alternate between two generations of distinct multicellular organisms: gametophytes and sporophytes. As shown in the diagram below (using a fern as an example), each generation gives rise to the other, a process that is called **alternation of generations**. This type of reproductive cycle evolved in various groups of algae but does not occur in the charophytes, the algae most closely related to land plants. Take care not to confuse the alternation of generations in plants with the haploid and diploid stages in the life cycles of other sexually reproducing organisms (see Figure 13.6). Alternation of generations is distinguished by the fact that the life cycle

includes both multicellular haploid organisms and multicellular diploid organisms. The multicellular haploid **gametophyte** ("gamete-producing plant") is named for its production by mitosis of haploid gametes—eggs and sperm—that fuse during fertilization, forming diploid zygotes. Mitotic division of the zygote produces a multicellular diploid **sporophyte** ("spore-producing plant"). Meiosis in a mature sporophyte produces haploid **spores**, reproductive cells that can develop into a new haploid organism without fusing with another cell. Mitotic division of the spore cell produces a new multicellular gametophyte, and the cycle begins again.

Alternation of generations: five generalized steps

① The gametophyte produces haploid gametes by mitosis.

Gametophyte (n)

Gamete from another plant

Mitosis

Mitosis

n

n

n — Spore

Gamete

n

② Two gametes unite (fertilization) and form a diploid zygote.

⑤ The spores develop into multicellular haploid gametophytes.

MEIOSIS

FERTILIZATION

④ The sporophyte produces unicellar haploid spores by meiosis.

Zygote

2n

③ The zygote develops into a multicellular diploid sporophyte.

Sporophyte (2n)

Mitosis

Key
⇒ Haploid (n)
⇒ Diploid (2n)

Multicellular, Dependent Embryos

As part of a life cycle with alternation of generations, multicellular plant embryos develop from zygotes that are retained within the tissues of the female parent (a gametophyte). The parental tissues protect the developing embryo from harsh environmental conditions and provide nutrients such as sugars and amino acids. The embryo has specialized *placental transfer cells* that enhance the transfer of nutrients to the embryo through elaborate ingrowths of the wall surface (plasma membrane and cell wall). The multicellular, dependent embryo of land plants is such a significant derived trait that land plants are also known as **embryophytes**.

Embryo (LM) and placental transfer cell (TEM) of *Marchantia* (a liverwort)

Embryo

Maternal tissue

10 μm

2 μm

Wall ingrowths

Placental transfer cell (blue outline)

MAKE CONNECTIONS *Review sexual life cycles in Figure 13.6. Identify which type of sexual life cycle has alternation of generations, and summarize how it differs from other life cycles.*

Walled Spores Produced in Sporangia

Plant spores are haploid reproductive cells that can grow into multicellular haploid gametophytes by mitosis. The polymer sporopollenin makes the walls of plant spores tough and resistant to harsh environments. This chemical adaptation enables spores to be dispersed through dry air without harm.

The sporophyte has multicellular organs called **sporangia** (singular, *sporangium*) that produce the spores. Within a sporangium, diploid cells called **sporocytes**, or spore mother cells, undergo meiosis and generate the haploid spores. The outer tissues of the sporangium protect the developing spores until they are released into the air. Multicellular sporangia that produce spores with sporopollenin-enriched walls are key terrestrial adaptations of land plants. Although charophytes also produce spores, these algae lack multicellular sporangia, and their flagellated, water-dispersed spores lack sporopollenin.

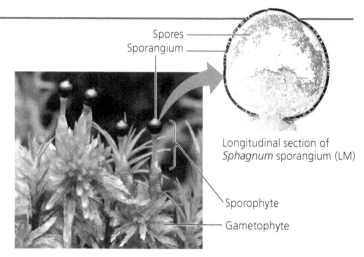

Spores
Sporangium

Longitudinal section of
Sphagnum sporangium (LM)

Sporophyte

Gametophyte

Sporophytes and sporangia of *Sphagnum* (a moss)

Multicellular Gametangia

Another feature distinguishing early land plants from their algal ancestors was the production of gametes within multicellular organs called **gametangia**. The female gametangia are called **archegonia** (singular, archegonium). Each archegonium is a pear-shaped organ that produces a single nonmotile egg retained within the bulbous part of the organ (the top for the species shown here). The male gametangia, called **antheridia** (singular, antheridium), produce sperm and release them into the environment. In many groups of present-day plants, the sperm have flagella and swim to the eggs through water droplets or a film of water. Each egg is fertilized within an archegonium, where the zygote develops into an embryo. As you will see in Chapter 30, the gametophytes of seed plants are so reduced in size that the archegonia and antheridia have been lost in many lineages.

Female
gametophyte

Archegonia,
each with an
egg (yellow)

Antheridia
(brown),
containing
sperm

Male
gametophyte

Archegonia and antheridia of *Marchantia* (a liverwort)

Apical Meristems

In terrestrial habitats, a photosynthetic organism finds essential resources in two very different places. Light and CO_2 are mainly available above ground; water and mineral nutrients are found mainly in the soil. Though plants cannot move from place to place, their roots and shoots can elongate, increasing exposure to environmental resources. This growth in length is sustained throughout the plant's life by the activity of **apical meristems**, localized regions of cell division at the tips of roots and shoots. Cells produced by apical meristems differentiate into the outer epidermis, which protects the body, and various types of internal tissues. Shoot apical meristems also generate leaves in most plants. Thus, the complex bodies of plants have specialized below- and aboveground organs.

Apical meristems of plant roots and shoots. The LMs are longitudinal sections at the tips of a root and shoot.

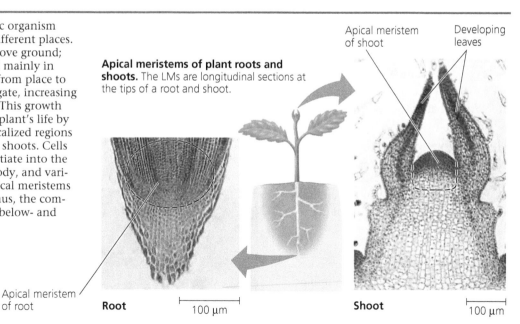

Apical meristem
of shoot

Developing
leaves

Apical meristem
of root

Root

100 μm

Shoot

100 μm

Additional derived traits that relate to terrestrial life have evolved in many plant species. For example, the epidermis in many species has a covering, the **cuticle**, that consists of wax and other polymers. Permanently exposed to the air, land plants run a far greater risk of desiccation (drying out) than their algal ancestors. The cuticle acts as waterproofing, helping prevent excessive water loss from the aboveground plant organs, while also providing some protection from microbial attack. Most plants also have specialized pores called **stomata** (singular, *stoma*), which support photosynthesis by allowing the exchange of CO_2 and O_2 between the outside air and the plant (see Figure 10.4). Stomata are also the main avenues by which water evaporates from the plant; in hot, dry conditions, the stomata close, minimizing water loss.

The earliest land plants lacked true roots and leaves. Without roots, how did these plants absorb nutrients from the soil? Fossils dating from 420 million years ago reveal an adaptation that may have aided early plants in nutrient uptake: They formed symbiotic associations with fungi. We'll describe these associations, called *mycorrhizae*, and their benefits to both plants and fungi in more detail in Chapter 31. For now, the main point is that mycorrhizal fungi form extensive networks of filaments through the soil and transfer nutrients to their symbiotic plant partner. This benefit may have helped plants without roots to colonize land.

The Origin and Diversification of Plants

The algae from which land plants evolved include many unicellular species and small colonial species. Since these ancestors were small, the search for the earliest fossils of land plants has focused on the microscopic world. As mentioned earlier, microorganisms colonized land as early as 1.2 billion years ago. But the microscopic fossils documenting life on land changed dramatically 470 million years ago with the appearance of spores from early land plants.

What distinguishes these spores from those of algae or fungi? One clue comes from their chemical composition, which matches the composition of plant spores today but differs from that of the spores of other organisms. In addition, the structure of the walls of these ancient spores shows features found only in the spores of certain land plants (liverworts). And in rocks dating to 450 million years ago, researchers have discovered similar spores embedded in plant cuticle material that resembles spore-bearing tissue in living plants (Figure 29.4).

Fossils of larger plant structures, such as the *Cooksonia* sporangium shown here, date to 425 million years ago—45 million years after the appearance of plant spores in the fossil record. While the precise age (and form) of the first land plants has yet to be discovered, those ancestral species gave rise

(a) Fossilized spores. The chemical composition and wall structure of these 450-million-year-old spores match those found in land plants.

(b) Fossilized sporophyte tissue. The spores were embedded in tissue that appears to be from plants.

▲ **Figure 29.4 Ancient plant spores and tissue** (colorized SEMs).

to the vast diversity of living plants. **Table 29.1** summarizes the ten extant phyla in the taxonomic scheme used in this text. (Extant lineages are those that have surviving members.) As you read the rest of this section, look at Table 29.1 together with **Figure 29.5**, which reflects a view of plant phylogeny that is based on plant morphology, biochemistry, and genetics.

One way to distinguish groups of plants is whether or not they have an extensive system of **vascular tissue**, cells joined into tubes that transport water and nutrients throughout the plant body. Most present-day plants have a complex vascular tissue system and are therefore called **vascular plants**. Plants that do not have an extensive transport system—liverworts, mosses, and hornworts—are described as "nonvascular" plants, even though some mosses do have simple vascular tissue. Nonvascular plants are often informally called **bryophytes** (from the Greek *bryon*, moss, and *phyton*, plant). Although the term *bryophyte* is commonly used to refer to all nonvascular plants, molecular studies and morphological analyses of sperm structure have concluded that bryophytes do not form a monophyletic group (a clade).

Vascular plants, which form a clade that comprises about 93% of all extant plant species, can be categorized further into smaller clades. Two of these clades are the **lycophytes** (the club mosses and their relatives) and the **monilophytes** (ferns and their relatives). The plants in each of these clades lack seeds, which is why collectively the two clades are often informally called **seedless vascular plants**. However, notice in Figure 29.5 that, like bryophytes, seedless vascular plants do not form a clade.

0.3 mm

▲ *Cooksonia* **sporangium fossil**

Table 29.1	Ten Phyla of Extant Plants	
	Common Name	Number of Known Species
Nonvascular Plants (Bryophytes)		
Phylum Hepatophyta	Liverworts	9,000
Phylum Bryophyta	Mosses	15,000
Phylum Anthocerophyta	Hornworts	100
Vascular Plants		
Seedless Vascular Plants		
Phylum Lycophyta	Lycophytes	1,200
Phylum Monilophyta	Monilophytes	12,000
Seed Plants		
Gymnosperms		
Phylum Ginkgophyta	Ginkgo	1
Phylum Cycadophyta	Cycads	130
Phylum Gnetophyta	Gnetophytes	75
Phylum Coniferophyta	Conifers	600
Angiosperms		
Phylum Anthophyta	Flowering plants	250,000

A group such as the bryophytes or the seedless vascular plants is sometimes referred to as a *grade*, a collection of organisms that share key biological features. Grades can be informative by grouping organisms according to their features, such as having a vascular system but lacking seeds. But members of a grade, unlike members of a clade, do not necessarily share the same ancestry. For example, even though monilophytes and lycophytes are all seedless vascular plants, monilophytes share a more recent common ancestor with seed plants. As a result, we would expect monilophytes and seed plants to share key traits not found in lycophytes—and they do, as you'll read in Concept 29.3.

A third clade of vascular plants consists of seed plants, which represent the vast majority of living plant species. A **seed** is an embryo packaged with a supply of nutrients inside a protective coat. Seed plants can be divided into two groups, gymnosperms and angiosperms, based on the absence or presence of enclosed chambers in which seeds mature. **Gymnosperms** (from the Greek *gymnos*, naked, and *sperm*, seed) are grouped together as "naked seed" plants because their seeds are not enclosed in chambers. Living gymnosperm species, the most familiar of which are the conifers, probably form a clade. **Angiosperms** (from the Greek *angion*, container) are a huge clade consisting of all flowering plants; their seeds develop inside chambers that originate within flowers. Nearly 90% of living plant species are angiosperms.

Note that the phylogeny depicted in Figure 29.5 focuses only on the relationships between extant plant lineages. Paleobotanists have also discovered fossils belonging to extinct plant lineages. As you'll read later in the chapter, these fossils can reveal intermediate steps in the emergence of plant groups found on Earth today.

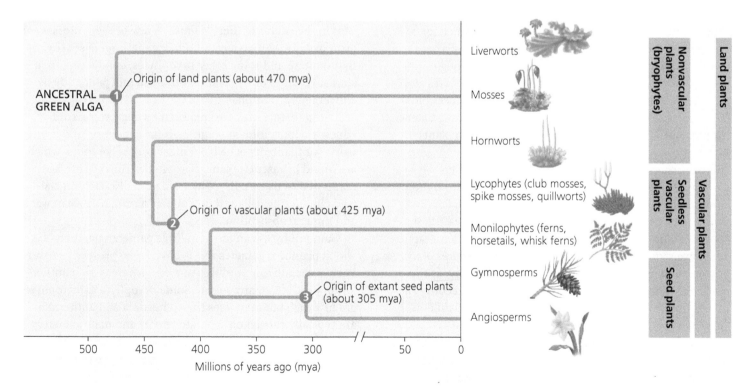

▲ **Figure 29.5 Highlights of plant evolution.** The phylogeny shown here illustrates a leading hypothesis about the relationships between plant groups.

1. Why do researchers identify the charophytes rather than another group of algae as the closest living relatives of land plants?

2. Identify four derived traits that distinguish plants from charophyte green algae *and* that facilitate life on land. Explain.

3. **WHAT IF?** What would the human life cycle be like if we had alternation of generations? Assume that the multicellular diploid stage would be similar in form to an adult human.

4. **MAKE CONNECTIONS** Figure 29.5 identifies which lineages are land plants, nonvascular plants, vascular plants, seedless vascular plants, and seed plants. Which of these categories are monophyletic, and which are paraphyletic? Explain. See Figure 26.10.

For suggested answers, see Appendix A.

CONCEPT 29.2

Mosses and other nonvascular plants have life cycles dominated by gametophytes

Nonvascular plants (bryophytes)
Seedless vascular plants
Gymnosperms
Angiosperms

The nonvascular plants (bryophytes) are represented today by three phyla of small herbaceous (nonwoody) plants: **liverworts** (phylum Hepatophyta), **mosses** (phylum Bryophyta), and **hornworts** (phylum Anthocerophyta). Liverworts and hornworts are named for their shapes, plus the suffix *wort* (from the Anglo-Saxon for "herb"). Mosses are familiar to many people, although some plants commonly called "mosses" are not really mosses at all. These include Irish moss (a red seaweed), reindeer moss (a lichen), club mosses (seedless vascular plants), and Spanish mosses (lichens in some regions and flowering plants in others).

Researchers think that liverworts, mosses, and hornworts were the earliest lineages to have diverged from the common ancestor of land plants (see Figure 29.5). Fossil evidence provides some support for this idea: The earliest spores of land plants (dating from 470 to 450 million years ago) have structural features found only in the spores of liverworts, and by 430 million years ago spores similar to those of mosses and hornworts also occur in the fossil record. The earliest fossils of vascular plants date to about 425 million years ago.

Over the long course of their evolution, liverworts, mosses, and hornworts have acquired many unique adaptations. Next, we'll examine some of those features.

Bryophyte Gametophytes

Unlike vascular plants, in all three bryophyte phyla the haploid gametophytes are the dominant stage of the life cycle: They are usually larger and longer-living than the sporophytes, as shown in the moss life cycle in **Figure 29.6**. The sporophytes are typically present only part of the time.

When bryophyte spores are dispersed to a favorable habitat, such as moist soil or tree bark, they may germinate and grow into gametophytes. Germinating moss spores, for example, characteristically produce a mass of green, branched, one-cell-thick filaments known as a **protonema** (plural, *protonemata*). A protonema has a large surface area that enhances absorption of water and minerals. In favorable conditions, a protonema produces one or more "buds." (Note that when referring to nonvascular plants, we often use quotation marks for structures similar to the buds, stems, and leaves of vascular plants because the definitions of these terms are based on vascular plant organs.) Each of these bud-like growths has an apical meristem that generates a gamete-producing structure known as a **gametophore**. Together, a protonema and one or more gametophores make up the body of a moss gametophyte.

Bryophyte gametophytes generally form ground-hugging carpets, partly because their body parts are too thin to support a tall plant. A second constraint on the height of many bryophytes is the absence of vascular tissue, which would enable long-distance transport of water and nutrients. (The thin structure of bryophyte organs makes it possible to distribute materials for short distances without specialized vascular tissue.) However, some mosses have conducting tissues in the center of their "stems." A few of these mosses can grow as tall as 2 m as a result. Phylogenetic analyses suggest that in these and some other bryophytes, conducting tissues similar to those of vascular plants arose independently by convergent evolution.

The gametophytes are anchored by delicate **rhizoids**, which are long, tubular single cells (in liverworts and hornworts) or filaments of cells (in mosses). Unlike roots, which are found in vascular plant sporophytes, rhizoids are not composed of tissues. Bryophyte rhizoids also lack specialized conducting cells and do not play a primary role in water and mineral absorption.

Gametophytes can form multiple gametangia, each of which produces gametes and is covered by protective tissue. Each archegonium produces one egg, whereas each antheridium produces many sperm. Some bryophyte gametophytes are bisexual, but in mosses the archegonia and antheridia are typically carried on separate female and male gametophytes. Flagellated sperm swim through a film of water toward eggs, entering the archegonia in response to chemical attractants. Eggs are not released but instead remain within

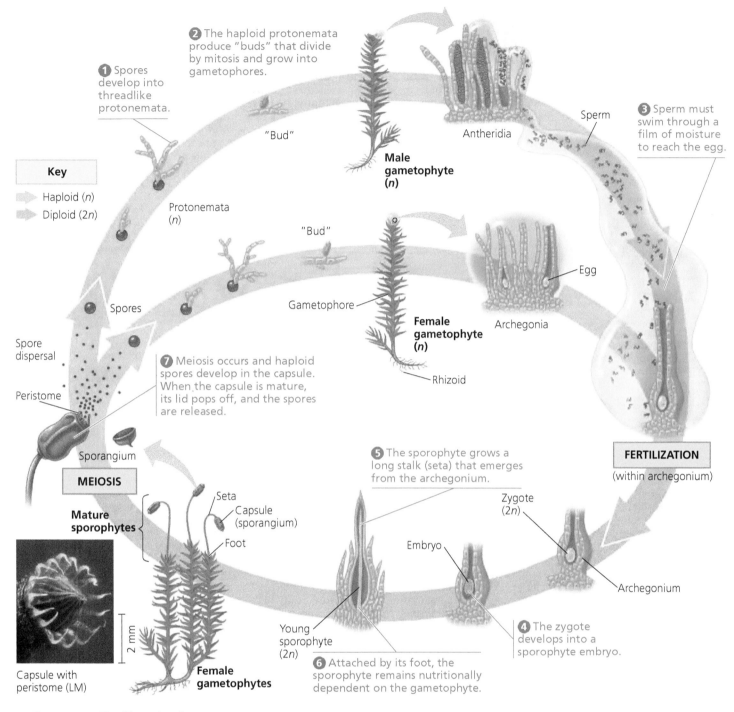

1 Spores develop into threadlike protonemata.

2 The haploid protonemata produce "buds" that divide by mitosis and grow into gametophores.

"Bud"

Male gametophyte (*n*)

Antheridia

Sperm

3 Sperm must swim through a film of moisture to reach the egg.

Key

⇨ Haploid (*n*)
⇨ Diploid (2*n*)

Protonemata (*n*)

"Bud"

Gametophore

Female gametophyte (*n*)

Archegonia

Egg

Spores

Rhizoid

Spore dispersal

Peristome

7 Meiosis occurs and haploid spores develop in the capsule. When the capsule is mature, its lid pops off, and the spores are released.

Sporangium

MEIOSIS

Mature sporophytes

Seta

Capsule (sporangium)

Foot

5 The sporophyte grows a long stalk (seta) that emerges from the archegonium.

FERTILIZATION

(within archegonium)

Zygote (2*n*)

Embryo

Archegonium

2 mm

Capsule with peristome (LM)

Female gametophytes

Young sporophyte (2*n*)

6 Attached by its foot, the sporophyte remains nutritionally dependent on the gametophyte.

4 The zygote develops into a sporophyte embryo.

▲ **Figure 29.6 The life cycle of a moss.**

? *In this diagram, does the sperm cell that fertilizes the egg cell differ genetically from the egg? Explain.*

the bases of archegonia. After fertilization, embryos are retained within the archegonia. Layers of placental transfer cells help transport nutrients to the embryos as they develop into sporophytes.

Bryophyte sperm typically require a film of water to reach the eggs. Given this requirement, it is not surprising that many bryophyte species are found in moist habitats. The fact that sperm swim through water to reach the egg also means that in species with separate male and female gametophytes (most species of mosses), sexual reproduction is likely to be more successful when individuals are located close to one another.

Liverworts (Phylum Hepatophyta)

This phylum's common and scientific names (from the Latin hepaticus, liver) refer to the liver-shaped gametophytes of its members, such as Marchantia, shown below. In medieval times, their shape was thought to be a sign that the plants could help treat liver diseases. Some liverworts, including *Marchantia*, are described as "thalloid" because of the flattened shape of their gametophytes. *Marchantia* gametangia are elevated on gametophores that look like miniature trees. You would need a magnifying glass to see the sporophytes, which have a short seta (stalk) with an oval or round capsule. Other liverworts, such as *Plagiochila*, below, are called "leafy" because their stemlike gametophytes have many leaflike appendages. There are many more species of leafy liverworts than thalloid liverworts.

Thallus
Gametophore of female gametophyte
Sporophyte

Foot
Seta
Capsule (sporangium)

**Marchantia polymorpha,
a "thalloid" liverwort**

Marchantia sporophyte (LM)

500 μm

*Plagiochila
deltoidea,
a "leafy"
liverwort*

Hornworts (Phylum Anthocerophyta)

This phylum's common and scientific names (from the Greek *keras*, horn) refer to the long, tapered shape of the sporophyte. A typical sporophyte can grow to about 5 cm high. Unlike a liverwort or moss sporophyte, a hornwort sporophyte lacks a seta and consists only of a sporangium. The sporangium releases mature spores by splitting open, starting at the tip of the horn. The gametophytes, which are usually 1–2 cm in diameter, grow mostly horizontally and often have multiple sporophytes attached. Hornworts are frequently among the first species to colonize open areas with moist soils; a symbiotic relationship with nitrogen-fixing cyanobacteria contributes to their ability to do this (nitrogen is often in short supply in such areas).

Mosses (Phylum Bryophyta)

Moss gametophytes, which range in height from less than 1 mm to up to 2 m, are less than 15 cm tall in most species. The familiar carpet of moss you observe consists mainly of gametophytes. The blades of their "leaves" are usually only one cell thick, but more complex "leaves" that have ridges coated with cuticle can be found on the common hairy-cap moss (*Polytrichum*, below) and its close relatives. Moss sporophytes are typically elongated and visible to the naked eye, with heights ranging up to about 20 cm. Though green and photosynthetic when young, they turn tan or brownish red when ready to release spores.

**An *Anthoceros*
hornwort species**

Sporophyte

Gametophyte

Polytrichum commune,
hairy-cap moss

Capsule
Sporophyte (a sturdy plant that takes months to grow)
Seta

Gametophyte

Many bryophyte species can increase the number of individuals in a local area through various methods of asexual reproduction. For example, some mosses reproduce asexually by forming *brood bodies*, small plantlets (as shown at left) that detach from the parent plant and grow into new, genetically identical copies of their parent.

Bryophyte Sporophytes

The cells of bryophyte sporophytes contain plastids that are usually green and photosynthetic when the sporophytes are young. Even so, bryophyte sporophytes cannot live independently. A bryophyte sporophyte remains attached to its parental gametophyte throughout the sporophyte's lifetime, dependent on the gametophyte for supplies of sugars, amino acids, minerals, and water.

Bryophytes have the smallest sporophytes of all extant plant groups, consistent with the hypothesis that larger sporophytes evolved only later, in the vascular plants. A typical bryophyte sporophyte consists of a foot, a seta, and a sporangium. Embedded in the archegonium, the **foot** absorbs nutrients from the gametophyte. The **seta** (plural, *setae*), or stalk, conducts these materials to the sporangium, also called a **capsule**, which uses them to produce spores by meiosis.

Bryophyte sporophytes can produce enormous numbers of spores. A single moss capsule, for example, can generate up to 50 million spores. In most mosses, the seta becomes elongated, enhancing spore dispersal by elevating the capsule. Typically, the upper part of the capsule features a ring of interlocking, tooth-like structures known as the **peristome** (see Figure 29.6). These "teeth" open under dry conditions and close again when it is moist. This allows moss spores to be discharged gradually, via periodic gusts of wind that can carry them long distances.

Moss and hornwort sporophytes are often larger and more complex than those of liverworts. For example, hornwort sporophytes, which superficially resemble grass blades, have a cuticle. Moss and hornwort sporophytes also have stomata, as do all vascular plants (but not liverworts).

Figure 29.7 shows some examples of gametophytes and sporophytes in the bryophyte phyla.

The Ecological and Economic Importance of Mosses

Wind dispersal of lightweight spores has distributed mosses throughout the world. These plants are particularly common and diverse in moist forests and wetlands. Some mosses colonize bare, sandy soil, where, researchers have found, they help retain nitrogen in the soil **(Figure 29.8)**. In northern coniferous forests, species such as the feather moss *Pleurozium* harbor nitrogen-fixing cyanobacteria that increase the availability of nitrogen in the ecosystem. Other mosses inhabit such extreme environments as mountaintops, tundra, and deserts. Many mosses are able to live in very cold or dry habitats because they can survive the loss of most of their body water, then rehydrate when moisture is available. Few vascular plants can survive the same degree of desiccation. Moreover, phenolic compounds in moss cell walls absorb damaging levels of UV radiation present in deserts or at high altitudes.

▼ Figure 29.8 | Inquiry

Can bryophytes reduce the rate at which key nutrients are lost from soils?

Experiment Soils in terrestrial ecosystems are often low in nitrogen, a nutrient required for normal plant growth. Richard Bowden, of Allegheny College, measured annual inputs (gains) and outputs (losses) of nitrogen in a sandy-soil ecosystem dominated by the moss *Polytrichum*. Nitrogen inputs were measured from rainfall (dissolved ions, such as nitrate, NO_3^-), biological N_2 fixation, and wind deposition. Nitrogen losses were measured in leached water (dissolved ions, such as NO_3^-) and gaseous emissions (such as N_2O emitted by bacteria). Bowden measured losses for soils with *Polytrichum* and for soils where the moss was removed two months before the experiment began.

Results A total of 10.5 kg of nitrogen per hectare (kg/ha) entered the ecosystem each year. Little nitrogen was lost by gaseous emissions (0.10 kg/ha · yr). The results of comparing nitrogen losses by leaching are shown below.

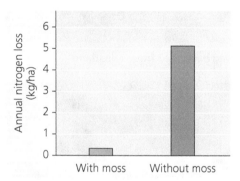

Conclusion The moss *Polytrichum* greatly reduced the loss of nitrogen by leaching in this ecosystem. Each year, the moss ecosystem retained over 95% of the 10.5 kg/ha of total nitrogen inputs (only 0.1 kg/ha and 0.3 kg/ha were lost to gaseous emissions and leaching, respectively).

Source: R. D. Bowden, Inputs, outputs, and accumulation of nitrogen in an early successional moss (*Polytrichum*) ecosystem, *Ecological Monographs* 61:207–223 (1991).

WHAT IF? *How might the presence of* Polytrichum *affect plant species that typically colonize the sandy soils after the moss?*

One wetland moss genus, *Sphagnum*, or "peat moss," is often a major component of deposits of partially decayed organic material known as **peat (Figure 29.9a)**. Boggy regions with thick layers of peat are called peatlands. *Sphagnum* does not decay readily, in part because of phenolic compounds embedded in its cell walls. The low temperature, pH, and oxygen level of peatlands also inhibit decay of moss and other organisms in these boggy wetlands. As a result, some peatlands have preserved corpses for thousands of years **(Figure 29.9b)**.

Peat has long been a fuel source in Europe and Asia, and it is still harvested for fuel today, notably in Ireland and Canada. Peat moss is also useful as a soil conditioner and for packing plant roots during shipment because it has large dead cells that can absorb roughly 20 times the moss's weight in water.

Peatlands cover 3% of Earth's land surface and contain roughly 30% of the world's soil carbon: Globally, an estimated 450 billion tons of organic carbon is stored as peat. These carbon reservoirs have helped to stabilize atmospheric CO_2 concentrations (see Chapter 55). Current overharvesting of *Sphagnum*—primarily for use in peat-fired power stations—may reduce peat's beneficial ecological effects and contribute to global warming by releasing stored CO_2. In addition, if global temperatures continue to rise, the water levels of some peatlands are expected to drop. Such a change would expose peat to air and cause it to decompose, thereby releasing additional stored CO_2 and contributing further to global warming. The historical and expected future effects of *Sphagnum* on the global climate underscore the importance of preserving and managing peatlands.

Mosses may have a long history of affecting climate change. In the Scientific Skills Exercise, you will explore the question of whether they did so during the Ordovician period by contributing to the weathering of rocks.

(a) Peat being harvested from a peatland

(b) "Tollund Man," a bog mummy dating from 405–100 B.C.E.
The acidic, oxygen-poor conditions produced by *Sphagnum* can preserve human or other animal bodies for thousands of years.

▲ Figure 29.9 *Sphagnum*, or peat moss: a bryophyte with economic, ecological, and archaeological significance.

CONCEPT CHECK 29.2

1. How do bryophytes differ from other plants?

2. Give three examples of how structure fits function in bryophytes.

3. **MAKE CONNECTIONS** Review the discussion of feedback regulation in Concept 1.1. Could effects of global warming on peatlands alter CO_2 concentrations in ways that result in negative or positive feedback? Explain.

For suggested answers, see Appendix A.

CONCEPT 29.3

Ferns and other seedless vascular plants were the first plants to grow tall

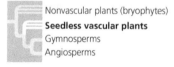

Nonvascular plants (bryophytes)
Seedless vascular plants
Gymnosperms
Angiosperms

During the first 100 million years of plant evolution, bryophytes were prominent types of vegetation. But it is vascular plants that dominate most landscapes today. The earliest fossils of vascular plants date to 425 million years ago. These plants lacked seeds but had well-developed vascular systems, an evolutionary novelty that set the stage for vascular plants to grow taller than their bryophyte counterparts. As in bryophytes, however, the sperm of ferns and all other seedless vascular plants are flagellated and swim through a film of water to reach eggs. In part because of these swimming sperm, seedless vascular plants today are most common in damp environments.

Origins and Traits of Vascular Plants

Unlike the nonvascular plants, early vascular plants had branched sporophytes that were not dependent on gametophytes for nutrition **(Figure 29.10)**. Although these ancient

Making Bar Graphs and Interpreting Data

Could Nonvascular Plants Have Caused Weathering of Rocks and Contributed to Climate Change During the Ordovician Period? The oldest traces of terrestrial plants are fossilized spores formed 470 million years ago. Between that time and the end of the Ordovician period 444 million years ago, the atmospheric CO_2 level dropped by half, and the climate cooled dramatically.

One possible cause of the drop in CO_2 during the Ordovician period is the breakdown, or weathering, of rock. As rock weathers, calcium silicate (Ca_2SiCO_3) is released and combines with CO_2 from the air, producing calcium carbonate ($CaCO_3$). In later periods of time, the roots of vascular plants increased rock weathering and mineral release by producing acids that break down rock and soil. Although nonvascular plants lack roots, they require the same mineral nutrients as vascular plants. Could nonvascular plants also increase chemical weathering of rock? If so, they could have contributed to the decline in atmospheric CO_2 during the Ordovician. In this exercise, you will interpret data from a study of the effects of moss on releasing minerals from two types of rock.

How the Experiment Was Done The researchers set up experimental and control microcosms, or small artificial ecosystems, to measure mineral release from rocks. First, they placed rock fragments of volcanic origin, either granite or andesite, into small glass containers. Then they mixed water and macerated (chopped and crushed) moss of the species *Physcomitrella patens*. They added this mixture to the experimental microcosms (72 granite and 41 andesite). For the control microcosms (77 granite and 37 andesite), they filtered out the moss and just added the water. After 130 days, they measured the amounts of various minerals found in the water in the control microcosms and in the water and moss in the experimental microcosms.

Data from the Experiment The moss grew (increased its biomass) in the experimental microcosms. The table shows the mean amounts in micromoles (μmol) of several minerals measured in the water and the moss in the microcosms.

Interpret the Data

1. Why did the researchers add filtrate from which macerated moss had been removed to the control microcosms?

2. Make two bar graphs (for granite and andesite) comparing the mean amounts of each element weathered from rocks in the control and experimental microcosms. (Hint: For an experimental microcosm, what sum represents the total amount weathered from rocks?)

3. Overall, what is the effect of moss on chemical weathering of rock? Are the results similar or different for granite and andesite?

4. Based on their experimental results, the researchers added weathering of rock by nonvascular plants to simulation models of the Ordovician climate. The new models predicted decreased CO_2 levels and global cooling sufficient to produce the glaciations in the late Ordovician period. What assumptions did the researchers make in using results from their experiments in climate simulation models?

5. "Life has profoundly changed the Earth." Explain whether or not these experimental results support this statement.

(MB) A version of this Scientific Skills Exercise can be assigned in MasteringBiology.

Data from T.M. Lenton, et al, First plants cooled the Ordovician. *Nature Geoscience* 5:86-89 (2012).

	Ca²⁺ (μmol)		Mg²⁺ (μmol)		K⁺ (μmol)	
	Granite	Andesite	Granite	Andesite	Granite	Andesite
Mean weathered amount released in water in the control microcosms	1.68	1.54	0.42	0.13	0.68	0.60
Mean weathered amount released in water in the experimental microcosms	1.27	1.84	0.34	0.13	0.65	0.64
Mean weathered amount taken up by moss in the experimental microcosms	1.09	3.62	0.31	0.56	1.07	0.28

Sporangia

2 cm

Rhizoids

25 μm

▲ **Figure 29.10 Sporophytes of *Aglaophyton major*, an ancient relative of living vascular plants.** This reconstruction from 405-million-year-old fossils exhibits dichotomous (Y-shaped) branching with sporangia at the ends of branches. Sporophyte branching characterizes living vascular plants but is lacking in living nonvascular plants (bryophytes). *Aglaophyton* had rhizoids that anchored it to the ground. The inset shows a fossilized stoma of *A. major* (colorized LM).

vascular plants were less than 20 cm tall, their branching enabled their bodies to become more complex and to have multiple sporangia. As plant bodies became increasingly complex, competition for space and sunlight probably increased. As we'll see, that competition may have stimulated still more evolution in vascular plants, eventually leading to the formation of the first forests.

The ancestors of vascular plants had some derived traits of today's vascular plants, but they lacked roots and some other adaptations that evolved later. The main traits that characterize living vascular plants are life cycles with dominant sporophytes, transport in vascular tissues called xylem and phloem, and well-developed roots and leaves, including spore-bearing leaves called sporophylls.

Life Cycles with Dominant Sporophytes

As mentioned earlier, mosses and other bryophytes have life cycles dominated by gametophytes (see Figure 29.6). Fossils suggest that a change began to develop in the ancestors of vascular plants, whose gametophytes and sporophytes were about equal in size. Further reductions in gametophyte size occurred among extant vascular plants; in these groups, the sporophyte generation is the larger and more complex form in the alternation of generations (Figure 29.11). In ferns, for example, the familiar leafy plants are the sporophytes. You would have to get down on your hands and knees and search the ground carefully to find fern gametophytes, which are tiny structures that often grow on or just below the soil surface.

Transport in Xylem and Phloem

Vascular plants have two types of vascular tissue: xylem and phloem. **Xylem** conducts most of the water and minerals. The xylem of most vascular plants includes **tracheids**, tube-shaped cells that carry water and minerals up from the roots (see Figure 35.10). (Tracheids have been lost in some highly specialized species, such as *Wolffia*, a tiny aquatic angiosperm.) The water-conducting cells in vascular plants are *lignified*; that is, their cell walls are strengthened by the polymer **lignin**. The tissue called **phloem** has cells arranged into tubes that distribute sugars, amino acids, and other organic products (see Figure 35.10).

Lignified vascular tissue helped enable vascular plants to grow tall. Their stems became strong enough to provide support against gravity, and they could transport water and mineral nutrients high above the ground. Tall plants could also outcompete short plants for access to the sunlight needed for photosynthesis. In addition, the spores of tall plants could disperse farther than those of short plants, enabling tall species to colonize new environments rapidly. Overall, the ability to grow tall gave vascular plants a competitive edge over nonvascular plants, which rarely grow above 20 cm in height. Competition among vascular plants also increased, and taller growth forms were favored by natural selection—such as the trees that formed the first forests about 385 million years ago.

▼ **Figure 29.11 The life cycle of a fern.**

WHAT IF? *If the ability to disperse sperm by wind evolved in a fern, how might its life cycle be affected?*

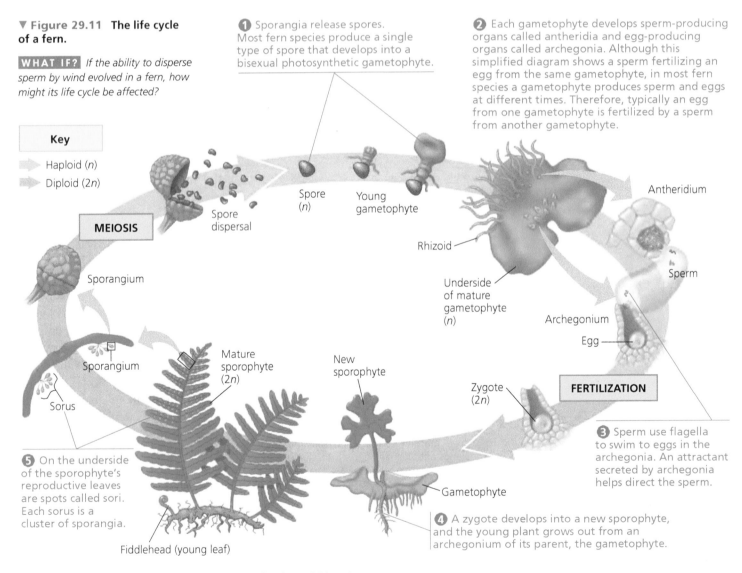

Key
- Haploid (*n*)
- Diploid (*2n*)

MEIOSIS

Sporangium

Spore dispersal

Sporangium

Sorus

❺ On the underside of the sporophyte's reproductive leaves are spots called sori. Each sorus is a cluster of sporangia.

Fiddlehead (young leaf)

Mature sporophyte (*2n*)

New sporophyte

❶ Sporangia release spores. Most fern species produce a single type of spore that develops into a bisexual photosynthetic gametophyte.

Spore (*n*)

Young gametophyte

Rhizoid

Underside of mature gametophyte (*n*)

❷ Each gametophyte develops sperm-producing organs called antheridia and egg-producing organs called archegonia. Although this simplified diagram shows a sperm fertilizing an egg from the same gametophyte, in most fern species a gametophyte produces sperm and eggs at different times. Therefore, typically an egg from one gametophyte is fertilized by a sperm from another gametophyte.

Antheridium

Sperm

Archegonium

Egg

Zygote (*2n*)

FERTILIZATION

❸ Sperm use flagella to swim to eggs in the archegonia. An attractant secreted by archegonia helps direct the sperm.

Gametophyte

❹ A zygote develops into a new sporophyte, and the young plant grows out from an archegonium of its parent, the gametophyte.

Evolution of Roots

Vascular tissue also provides benefits below ground. Instead of the rhizoids seen in bryophytes, roots evolved in the sporophytes of almost all vascular plants. **Roots** are organs that absorb water and nutrients from the soil. Roots also anchor vascular plants, hence allowing the shoot system to grow taller.

Root tissues of living plants closely resemble stem tissues of early vascular plants preserved in fossils. This suggests that roots may have evolved from the lowest belowground portions of stems in ancient vascular plants. It is unclear whether roots evolved only once in the common ancestor of all vascular plants or independently in different lineages. Although the roots of living members of these lineages of vascular plants share many similarities, fossil evidence hints at convergent evolution. The oldest fossils of lycophytes, for example, already displayed simple roots 400 million years ago, when the ancestors of ferns and seed plants still had none. Studying genes that control root development in different vascular plant species may help resolve this question.

Evolution of Leaves

Leaves increase the surface area of the plant body and serve as the primary photosynthetic organ of vascular plants. In terms of size and complexity, leaves can be classified as either microphylls or megaphylls **(Figure 29.12)**. All of the lycophytes (the oldest lineage of extant vascular plants)—and only the lycophytes—have **microphylls**, small, often spine-shaped leaves supported by a single strand of vascular tissue. Almost all other vascular plants have **megaphylls**, leaves with a highly branched vascular system; a few species have reduced leaves that appear to have evolved from megaphylls. Megaphylls are typically larger than microphylls and therefore support greater photosynthetic productivity than microphylls. Microphylls first appear in the fossil record 410 million years ago, but megaphylls do not emerge until about 370 million years ago, toward the end of the Devonian period.

Sporophylls and Spore Variations

One milestone in the evolution of plants was the emergence of **sporophylls**, modified leaves that bear sporangia. Sporophylls vary greatly in structure. For example, fern sporophylls produce clusters of sporangia known as **sori** (singular, *sorus*), usually on the undersides of the sporophylls (see Figure 29.11). In many lycophytes and in most gymnosperms, groups of sporophylls form cone-like structures called **strobili** (singular, *strobilus*; from the Greek *strobilos*, cone).

Most seedless vascular plant species are **homosporous**: They have one type of sporangium that produces one type of spore, which typically develops into a bisexual gametophyte, as in most ferns. In contrast, a **heterosporous** species has two types of sporangia and produces two kinds of spores:

▼ **Figure 29.12 Microphyll and megaphyll leaves.**

Microphyll leaves

Microphylls

Unbranched vascular tissue

Selaginella kraussiana (Krauss's spike moss)

Megaphyll leaves

Megaphylls

Branched vascular tissue

Hymenophyllum tunbrigense (Tunbridge filmy fern)

Megasporangia on megasporophylls produce **megaspores**, which develop into female gametophytes; microsporangia on microsporophylls produce the comparatively smaller **microspores**, which develop into male gametophytes. All seed plants and a few seedless vascular plants are heterosporous. The following diagram compares the two conditions:

Homosporous spore production

Sporangium on sporophyll → Single type of spore → Typically a bisexual gametophyte → Eggs, Sperm

Heterosporous spore production

Megasporangium on megasporophyll → Megaspore → Female gametophyte → Eggs

Microsporangium on microsporophyll → Microspore → Male gametophyte → Sperm

Classification of Seedless Vascular Plants

As we noted earlier, biologists recognize two clades of living seedless vascular plants: the lycophytes (phylum Lycophyta) and the monilophytes (phylum Monilophyta). The lycophytes include the club mosses, the spike mosses, and the quillworts. The monilophytes include the ferns, the horsetails, and the whisk ferns and their relatives. Although ferns,

Exploring Seedless Vascular Plant Diversity

Lycophytes (Phylum Lycophyta)

Many lycophytes grow on tropical trees as *epiphytes*, plants that use other plants as a substrate but are not parasites. Other species grow on temperate forest floors. In some species, the tiny gametophytes live above ground and are photosynthetic. Others live below ground, nurtured by symbiotic fungi.

Sporophytes have upright stems with many small leaves, as well as ground-hugging stems that produce dichotomously branching roots. Spike mosses are usually relatively small and often grow horizontally. In many club mosses and spike mosses, sporophylls are clustered into club-shaped cones (strobili). Quillworts, named for their leaf shape, form a single genus whose members live in marshy areas or as submerged aquatic plants. Club mosses are all homosporous, whereas spike mosses and quillworts are all heterosporous. The spores of club mosses are released in clouds and are so rich in oil that magicians and photographers once ignited them to create smoke or flashes of light.

Selaginella moellendorffii, a spike moss

Isoetes gunnii, a quillwort

Strobili (clusters of sporophylls)

2.5 cm

1 cm

Diphasiastrum tristachyum, a club moss

Monilophytes (Phylum Monilophyta)

Athyrium filix-femina, lady fern

25 cm

Equisetum telmateia, giant horsetail

Strobilus on fertile stem

Vegetative stem

3 cm

Psilotum nudum, a whisk fern

4 cm

Ferns

Unlike the lycophytes, ferns have mega-phylls (see Figure 29.12). The sporophytes typically have horizontal stems that give rise to large leaves called fronds, often divided into leaflets. A frond grows as its coiled tip, the fiddlehead, unfurls.

Almost all species are homosporous. The gametophyte in some species shrivels and dies after the young sporophyte detaches itself. In most species, sporophytes have stalked sporangia with springlike devices that catapult spores several meters. Air-borne spores can be carried far from their origin. Some species produce more than a trillion spores in a plant's lifetime.

Horsetails

The group's name refers to the brushy appearance of the stems, which have a gritty texture that made them historically useful as "scouring rushes" for pots and pans. Some species have separate fertile (cone-bearing) and vegetative stems. Horsetails are homosporous, with cones releasing spores that typically give rise to bisexual gametophytes.

Horsetails are also called arthrophytes ("jointed plants") because their stems have joints. Rings of small leaves or branches emerge from each joint, but the stem is the main photosynthetic organ. Large air canals carry oxygen to the roots, which often grow in waterlogged soil.

Whisk Ferns and Relatives

Like primitive vascular plant fossils, the sporophytes of whisk ferns (genus *Psilotum*) have dichotomously branching stems but no roots. Stems have scalelike outgrowths that lack vascular tissue and may have resulted from the evolutionary reduction of leaves. Each yellow knob on a stem consists of three fused sporangia. Species of the genus *Tmesipteris*, closely related to whisk ferns and found only in the South Pacific, also lack roots but have small, leaflike outgrowths in their stems, giving them a vine-like appearance. Both genera are homo-sporous, with spores giving rise to bisexual gametophytes that grow underground and are only about a centimeter long.

horsetails, and whisk ferns differ greatly in appearance, recent anatomical and molecular comparisons provide convincing evidence that these three groups make up a clade. Accordingly, many systematists now classify them together as the phylum Monilophyta, as we do in this chapter. Others refer to these groups as three separate phyla within a clade. **Figure 29.13** describes the two main groups of seedless vascular plants.

Phylum Lycophyta:
Club Mosses, Spike Mosses, and Quillworts

Present-day species of lycophytes, the most ancient group of vascular plants, are relics of a far more impressive past. By the Carboniferous period (359–299 million years ago), the lycophyte evolutionary lineage included small herbaceous plants and giant trees with diameters of more than 2 m and heights of more than 40 m. The giant lycophyte trees thrived for millions of years in moist swamps, but they became extinct when Earth's climate became drier at the end of the Carboniferous period. The small lycophytes survived, represented today by about 1,200 species. Though some are commonly called club mosses and spike mosses, they are not true mosses (which, as discussed earlier, are nonvascular plants).

Phylum Monilophyta:
Ferns, Horsetails, and Whisk Ferns and Relatives

Ferns radiated extensively from their Devonian origins and grew alongside lycophyte trees and horsetails in the great Carboniferous swamp forests. Today, ferns are by far the most widespread seedless vascular plants, numbering more than 12,000 species. Though most diverse in the tropics, many ferns thrive in temperate forests, and some species are even adapted to arid habitats.

As mentioned earlier, ferns and other monilophytes are more closely related to seed plants than to lycophytes. As a result, monilophytes and seed plants share traits that are not found in lycophytes, including megaphyll leaves and roots that can branch at various points along the length of an existing root. In lycophytes, by contrast, roots branch only at the growing tip of the root, forming a Y-shaped structure.

The monilophytes called horsetails were very diverse during the Carboniferous period, some growing as tall as 15 m. Today, only 15 species survive as a single, widely distributed genus, *Equisetum*, found in marshy places and along streams.

Psilotum (whisk ferns) and a closely related genus, *Tmesipteris*, form a clade consisting mainly of tropical epiphytes. Plants in these two genera, the only vascular plants lacking true roots, are called "living fossils" because of their resemblance to fossils of ancient relatives of living vascular plants (see Figure 29.10 and 29.13). However, much evidence, including analyses of DNA sequences and sperm structure,

▲ **Figure 29.14 Artist's conception of a Carboniferous forest based on fossil evidence.** Lycophyte trees, with trunks covered with small leaves, thrived in the "coal forests" of the Carboniferous, along with giant ferns and horsetails.

indicates that the genera *Psilotum* and *Tmesipteris* are closely related to ferns. This hypothesis suggests that their ancestor's true roots were lost during evolution. Today, plants in these two genera absorb water and nutrients through numerous absorptive rhizoids.

The Significance of Seedless Vascular Plants

The ancestors of living lycophytes, horsetails, and ferns, along with their extinct seedless vascular relatives, grew to great heights during the Devonian and early Carboniferous, forming the first forests **(Figure 29.14)**. How did their dramatic growth affect Earth and its other life?

One major effect was that early forests contributed to a large drop in CO_2 levels during the Carboniferous period, causing global cooling that resulted in widespread glacier formation. Plants enhance the rate at which chemicals such as calcium and magnesium are released from rocks into the soil. These chemicals react with carbon dioxide dissolved in rain water, forming compounds that ultimately wash into the oceans, where they are incorporated into rocks (calcium or magnesium carbonates). The net effect of these processes—which were set in motion by plants—is that CO_2 removed from the air is stored in marine rocks. Although carbon stored in these rocks can be returned to the atmosphere, this process occurs over millions of years (as when geological uplift brings the rocks to the surface, exposing them to erosion).

Another major effect is that the seedless vascular plants that formed the first forests eventually became coal, again removing CO_2 from the atmosphere for long periods of time. In the stagnant waters of Carboniferous swamps, dead plants did not completely decay. This organic material turned to thick layers of peat, later covered by the sea. Marine sediments piled on top, and over millions of years, heat and pressure converted the peat to coal. In fact, Carboniferous coal deposits are the most extensive ever formed. Coal was crucial to the Industrial Revolution, and people worldwide still burn 6 billion tons a year. It is ironic that coal, formed from plants that contributed to a global cooling, now contributes to global warming by returning carbon to the atmosphere (see Figure 55.14).

Growing along with the seedless plants in Carboniferous swamps were primitive seed plants. Though seed plants were not dominant at that time, they rose to prominence after the swamps began to dry up at the end of the Carboniferous period. The next chapter traces the origin and diversification of seed plants, continuing our story of adaptation to life on land.

29 Chapter Review

SUMMARY OF KEY CONCEPTS

CONCEPT 29.1

Land plants evolved from green algae (pp. 613–618)

- Morphological and biochemical traits, as well as similarities in nuclear and chloroplast genes, indicate that certain groups of charophytes are the closest living relatives of land plants.
- A protective layer of **sporopollenin** and other traits allow charophytes to tolerate occasional drying along the edges of ponds and lakes. Such traits may have enabled the algal ancestors of plants to survive in terrestrial conditions, opening the way to the colonization of dry land.
- Derived traits that distinguish the clade of land plants from charophytes, their closest algal relatives, include **cuticles**, **stomata**, multicellular dependent embryos, and the four shown here:

❶ Alternation of generations ❷ Apical meristems

❸ Multicellular gametangia ❹ Walled spores in sporangia

- Fossils show that land plants arose more than 470 million years ago. Subsequently, plants diverged into several major groups, including nonvascular plants (bryophytes); seedless vascular plants, such as lycophytes and ferns; and the two groups of seed plants: gymnosperms and angiosperms.

? *Draw a phylogenetic tree illustrating our current understanding of land plant phylogeny; label the common ancestor of land plants and the origins of multicellular gametangia, vascular tissue, and seeds.*

CONCEPT 29.2

Mosses and other nonvascular plants have life cycles dominated by gametophytes (pp. 618–622)

- The three extant clades of nonvascular plants or **bryophytes**—liverworts, mosses, and hornworts—are the earliest-diverging plant lineages.
- In bryophytes, the dominant generation consists of haploid **gametophytes**, such as those that make up a carpet of moss. **Rhizoids** anchor gametophytes to the substrate on which they grow. The flagellated sperm produced by **antheridia** require a film of water to travel to the eggs in the **archegonia**.
- The diploid stage of the life cycle—the **sporophytes**—grow out of archegonia and are attached to the gametophytes and dependent on them for nourishment. Smaller and simpler than vascular plant sporophytes, they typically consist of a **foot**, **seta** (stalk), and **sporangium**.
- *Sphagnum*, or peat moss, is common in large regions known as peatlands and has many practical uses, including as a fuel.

? *Summarize the ecological importance of mosses.*

CONCEPT 29.3

Ferns and other seedless vascular plants were the first plants to grow tall (pp. 622–628)

- Fossils of the forerunners of today's vascular plants date back about 425 million years and show that these small plants had independent, branching sporophytes and a vascular system.
- Over time, other derived traits of living vascular plants arose, such as a life cycle with dominant sporophytes, lignified vascular tissue, well-developed roots and leaves, and sporophylls.
- Seedless vascular plants include the **lycophytes** (phylum Lycophyta: club mosses, spike mosses, and quillworts) and the

monilophytes (phylum Monilophyta: ferns, horsetails, and whisk ferns and relatives). Current evidence indicates that seedless vascular plants, like bryophytes, do not form a clade.

- Ancient lineages of lycophytes included both small herbaceous plants and large trees. Present-day lycophytes are small herbaceous plants.
- Seedless vascular plants formed the earliest forests about 385 million years ago. Their growth may have contributed to a major global cooling that took place during the Carboniferous period. The decaying remnants of the first forests eventually became coal.

? *What trait(s) allowed vascular plants to grow tall, and why might increased height have been advantageous?*

TEST YOUR UNDERSTANDING

LEVEL 1: KNOWLEDGE/COMPREHENSION

1. Three of the following are evidence that charophytes are the closest algal relatives of plants. Select the exception.
   a. similar sperm structure
   b. the presence of chloroplasts
   c. similarities in cell wall formation during cell division
   d. genetic similarities in chloroplasts

2. Which of the following characteristics of plants is absent in their closest relatives, the charophyte algae?
   a. chlorophyll *b*
   b. cellulose in cell walls
   c. sexual reproduction
   d. alternation of multicellular generations

3. In plants, which of the following are produced by meiosis?
   a. haploid gametes
   b. diploid gametes
   c. haploid spores
   d. diploid spores

4. Microphylls are found in which plant group?
   a. lycophytes
   b. liverworts
   c. ferns
   d. hornworts

LEVEL 2: APPLICATION/ANALYSIS

5. Suppose an efficient conducting system evolved in a moss that could transport water and other materials as high as a tall tree. Which of the following statements about "trees" of such a species would *not* be true?
   a. Spore dispersal distances would probably increase.
   b. Females could produce only one archegonium.
   c. Unless its body parts were strengthened, such a "tree" would probably flop over.
   d. Individuals would probably compete more effectively for access to light.

6. Identify each of the following structures as haploid or diploid.
   (a) sporophyte
   (b) spore
   (c) gametophyte
   (d) zygote

7. **EVOLUTION CONNECTION**
   DRAW IT Draw a phylogenetic tree that represents our current understanding of evolutionary relationships between a moss, a gymnosperm, a lycophyte, and a fern. Use a charophyte alga as the outgroup. (See Chapter 26 to review phylogenetic trees.) Label each branch point of the phylogeny with at least one derived character unique to the clade descended from the common ancestor represented by the branch point.

LEVEL 3: SYNTHESIS/EVALUATION

8. **SCIENTIFIC INQUIRY**
   INTERPRET THE DATA The feather moss *Pleurozium schreberi* harbors species of symbiotic nitrogen-fixing bacteria. Scientists studying this moss in northern forests found that the percentage of the ground surface "covered" by the moss increased from about 5% in forests that burned 35 to 41 years ago to about 70% in forests that burned 170 or more years ago. From mosses growing in these forests, they also obtained the following data on nitrogen fixation:

Age (years after fire)	N fixation rate (kg N per ha per yr)
35	0.001
41	0.005
78	0.08
101	0.3
124	0.9
170	2.0
220	1.3
244	2.1
270	1.6
300	3.0
355	2.3

Source: Data from O. Zackrisson et al., Nitrogen fixation increases with successional age in boreal forests, *Ecology* 85:3327–3334 (2006).

   (a) Use the data to draw a line graph, with age on the *x*-axis and the nitrogen fixation rate on the *y*-axis.
   (b) Along with the nitrogen added by nitrogen fixation, about 1 kg of nitrogen per hectare per year is deposited into northern forests from the atmosphere as rain and small particles. Evaluate the extent to which *Pleurozium* affects nitrogen availability in northern forests of different ages.

9. **WRITE ABOUT A THEME: INTERACTIONS**
   Giant lycophyte trees had microphylls, whereas ferns and seed plants have megaphylls. Write a short essay (100–150 words) describing how a forest of lycophyte trees may have differed from a forest of large ferns or seed plants. In your answer, consider how the type of forest may have affected interactions among small plants growing beneath the tall ones.

10. **SYNTHESIZE YOUR KNOWLEDGE**

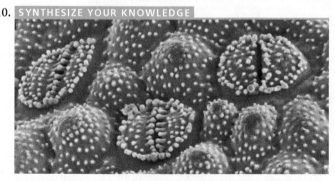

These stomata are from the leaf of a common horsetail. Describe how stomata and other adaptations facilitated life on land and ultimately led to the formation of the first forests.

For selected answers, see Appendix A.

MasteringBiology®

Students Go to **MasteringBiology** for assignments, the eText, and the Study Area with practice tests, animations, and activities.

Instructors Go to **MasteringBiology** for automatically graded tutorials and questions that you can assign to your students, plus Instructor Resources.

30

Plant Diversity II: The Evolution of Seed Plants

KEY CONCEPTS

30.1 Seeds and pollen grains are key adaptations for life on land

30.2 Gymnosperms bear "naked" seeds, typically on cones

30.3 The reproductive adaptations of angiosperms include flowers and fruits

30.4 Human welfare depends on seed plants

▶ Fireweed seed

▲ **Figure 30.1 How could these plants have reached this remote location?**

Transforming the World

On May 18, 1980, Mount St. Helens erupted with a force 500 times that of the Hiroshima atomic bomb. Traveling at over 300 miles per hour, the blast destroyed hundreds of hectares of forest, leaving the region covered in ash and devoid of visible life. Within a few years, however, plants such as fireweed (*Chamerion angustifolium*) had colonized the barren landscape (**Figure 30.1**).

Fireweed and other early arrivals reached the blast zone as seeds. A **seed** consists of an embryo and its food supply, surrounded by a protective coat. When mature, seeds are dispersed from their parent by wind or other means, enabling them to colonize distant locations.

Plants not only have affected the recovery of regions such as Mount St. Helens but also have transformed Earth. Continuing the saga of how this occurred, this chapter follows the emergence and diversification of the group to which fireweed belongs, the seed plants. Fossils and comparative studies of living plants offer clues about the origin of seed plants some 360 million years ago. As this new group became established, they dramatically altered the course of plant evolution. Indeed, seed plants have become the dominant producers on land, and they make up the vast majority of plant biodiversity today.

In this chapter, we will first examine the general features of seed plants. Then we will look at their evolutionary history and enormous impact on human society.

Seeds and pollen grains are key adaptations for life on land

We begin with an overview of terrestrial adaptations that seed plants added to those already present in nonvascular plants (bryophytes) and seedless vascular plants (see Chapter 29). In addition to seeds, all seed plants have reduced gametophytes, heterospory, ovules, and pollen. As we'll see, these adaptations helped seed plants cope with conditions such as drought and exposure to ultraviolet (UV) radiation in sunlight. They also freed seed plants from requiring water for fertilization, enabling reproduction under a broader range of conditions than in seedless plants.

Advantages of Reduced Gametophytes

Mosses and other bryophytes have life cycles dominated by gametophytes, whereas ferns and other seedless vascular plants have sporophyte-dominated life cycles. The evolutionary trend of gametophyte reduction continued further in the vascular plant lineage that led to seed plants. While the gametophytes of seedless vascular plants are visible to the naked eye, the gametophytes of most seed plants are microscopic.

This miniaturization allowed for an important evolutionary innovation in seed plants: Their tiny gametophytes can develop from spores retained within the sporangia of the parental sporophyte. This arrangement can protect the gametophytes from environmental stresses. For example, the moist reproductive tissues of the sporophyte shield the gametophytes from UV radiation and protect them from drying out. This relationship also enables the developing gametophytes to obtain nutrients from the parental sporophyte. In contrast, the free-living gametophytes of seedless vascular plants must fend for themselves. Figure 30.2 provides an overview of the gametophyte-sporophyte relationships in nonvascular plants, seedless vascular plants, and seed plants.

	PLANT GROUP		
	Mosses and other nonvascular plants	**Ferns and other seedless vascular plants**	**Seed plants (gymnosperms and angiosperms)**
Gametophyte	Dominant	Reduced, independent (photosynthetic and free-living)	Reduced (usually microscopic), dependent on surrounding sporophyte tissue for nutrition
Sporophyte	Reduced, dependent on gametophyte for nutrition	Dominant	Dominant
Example			

▲ Figure 30.2 **Gametophyte-sporophyte relationships in different plant groups.**

MAKE CONNECTIONS *In seed plants, how does retaining the gametophyte within the sporophyte likely affect embryo fitness?(See Concepts 17.5, 23.1, and 23.4 to review mutagens, mutations, and fitness.)*

Heterospory: The Rule Among Seed Plants

You read in Chapter 29 that most seedless plants are *homosporous*—they produce one kind of spore, which usually gives rise to a bisexual gametophyte. Ferns and other close relatives of seed plants are homosporous, suggesting that seed plants had homosporous ancestors. At some point, seed plants or their ancestors became *heterosporous*, producing two kinds of spores: Megasporangia produce *megaspores* that give rise to female gametophytes, and microsporangia produce *microspores* that give rise to male gametophytes. Each megasporangium has one megaspore, whereas each microsporangium has many microspores.

As noted previously, the miniaturization of seed plant gametophytes probably contributed to the great success of this clade. Next, we'll look at the development of the female gametophyte within an ovule and the development of the male gametophyte in a pollen grain. Then we'll follow the transformation of a fertilized ovule into a seed.

Ovules and Production of Eggs

Although a few species of seedless plants are heterosporous, seed plants are unique in retaining the megasporangium within the parent sporophyte. A layer of sporophyte tissue called **integument** envelops and protects the megasporangium. Gymnosperm megasporangia are surrounded by one integument, whereas those in angiosperms usually have two integuments. The whole structure—megasporangium, megaspore, and their integument(s)—is called an **ovule** (**Figure 30.3a**). Inside each ovule (from the Latin *ovulum*, little egg), a female gametophyte develops from a megaspore and produces one or more eggs.

Pollen and Production of Sperm

A microspore develops into a **pollen grain** that consists of a male gametophyte enclosed within the pollen wall. (The wall's outer layer is made of molecules secreted by sporophyte cells, so we refer to the male gametophyte as being *in* the pollen grain, not *equivalent to* the pollen grain.) Sporopollenin in the pollen wall protects the pollen grain as it is transported by wind or by hitchhiking on an animal. The transfer of pollen to the part of a seed plant that contains the ovules is called **pollination**. If a pollen grain germinates (begins growing), it gives rise to a pollen tube that discharges sperm into the female gametophyte within the ovule, as shown in **Figure 30.3b**.

In nonvascular plants and seedless vascular plants such as ferns, free-living gametophytes release flagellated sperm that swim through a film of water to reach eggs. So it is not surprising that many of these species live in moist habitats. But a pollen grain can be carried by wind or animals, eliminating the dependence on water for sperm transport. The ability of seed plants to transfer sperm without water likely contributed to their colonization of dry habitats. The sperm of seed plants also do not require motility because they are carried to the eggs by pollen tubes. The sperm of some gymnosperm species (such as cycads and ginkgos, shown in Figure 30.7) retain the ancient flagellated condition, but flagella have been lost in the sperm of most gymnosperms and all angiosperms.

The Evolutionary Advantage of Seeds

If a sperm fertilizes an egg of a seed plant, the zygote grows into a sporophyte embryo. As shown in **Figure 30.3c**, the

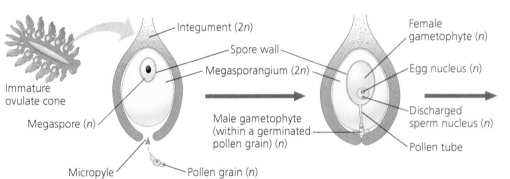

(a) Unfertilized ovule. In this longitudinal section through the ovule of a pine (a gymnosperm), a fleshy megasporangium is surrounded by a protective layer of tissue called an integument. The micropyle, the only opening through the integument, allows entry of a pollen grain.

(b) Fertilized ovule. A megaspore develops into a female gametophyte, which produces an egg. The pollen grain, which had entered through the micropyle, contains a male gametophyte. The male gametophyte develops a pollen tube that discharges sperm, thereby fertilizing the egg.

(c) Gymnosperm seed. Fertilization initiates the transformation of the ovule into a seed, which consists of a sporophyte embryo, a food supply, and a protective seed coat derived from the integument. The megasporangium dries out and collapses.

▲ **Figure 30.3 From ovule to seed in a gymnosperm.**

? *A gymnosperm seed contains cells from how many different plant generations? Identify the cells and whether each is haploid or diploid.*

SCIENTIFIC SKILLS EXERCISE

Using Natural Logarithms to Interpret Data

How Long Can Seeds Remain Viable in Dormancy? Environmental conditions can vary greatly over time, and they may not be favorable for germination when seeds are produced. One way that plants cope with such variation is through seed dormancy. Under favorable conditions, seeds of some species can germinate after many years of dormancy.

One unusual opportunity to test how long seeds can remain viable occurred when seeds from date palm trees (*Phoenix dactylifera*) were discovered under the rubble of a 2,000-year-old fortress near the Dead Sea. As you saw in the Chapter 2 Scientific Skills Exercise and Concept 25.2, scientists use radiometric dating to estimate the ages of fossils and other old objects. In this exercise, you will estimate the ages of three of these ancient seeds by using natural logarithms.

How the Experiment Was Done Scientists measured the fraction of carbon-14 that remained in three ancient date palm seeds: two that were not planted and one that was planted and germinated. For the germinated seed, the scientists used a seed-coat fragment found clinging to a root of the seedling. (The seedling grew into the plant in the photo.)

Data from the Experiment This table shows the fraction of carbon-14 remaining from the three ancient date palm seeds.

	Fraction of Carbon-14 Remaining
Seed 1 (not planted)	0.7656
Seed 2 (not planted)	0.7752
Seed 3 (germinated)	0.7977

Interpret the Data A logarithm is the power to which a base is raised to produce a given number x. For example, if the base is 10 and $x = 100$, the logarithm of 100 equals 2 (because $10^2 = 100$). A natural logarithm (ln) is the logarithm of a number x to the base e, where e is about 2.718. Natural logarithms are useful in calculating rates of some natural processes, such as radioactive decay.

1. The equation $F = e^{-kt}$ describes the fraction F of an original isotope remaining after a period of t years; the exponent is negative because it refers to a *decrease* over time. The constant k provides a measure of how rapidly the original isotope decays. For the decay of carbon-14 to nitrogen-14, $k = 0.00012097$. To find t, rearrange the equation by following these steps: (a) Take the natural logarithm of both sides of the equation: $\ln(F) = \ln(e^{-kt})$. Rewrite the right side of this equation by applying the following rule: $\ln(e^x) = x \ln(e)$. (b) Since $\ln(e) = 1$, simplify the equation. (c) Now solve for t and write the equation in the form "$t = \_\_\_\_$."

2. Using the equation you developed, the data from the table, and a calculator, estimate the ages of Seed 1, Seed 2, and Seed 3.

3. Why do you think there was more carbon-14 in the germinated seed?

(MB) A version of this Scientific Skills Exercise can be assigned in MasteringBiology.

Data from S. Sallon, et al, Germination, genetics, and growth of an ancient date seed. *Science* 320:1464 (2008).

---

ovule develops into a seed: the embryo, with a food supply, packaged in a protective coat derived from the integument(s).

Until the advent of seeds, the spore was the only protective stage in any plant life cycle. Moss spores, for example, may survive even if the local environment becomes too cold, too hot, or too dry for the mosses themselves to live. Their tiny size enables the spores to be dispersed in a dormant state to a new area, where they can germinate and give rise to new moss gametophytes if and when conditions are favorable enough for them to break dormancy. Spores were the main way that mosses, ferns, and other seedless plants spread over Earth for the first 100 million years of plant life on land.

Although mosses and other seedless plants continue to be very successful today, seeds represent a major evolutionary innovation that contributed to the opening of new ways of life for seed plants. What advantages do seeds provide over spores? Spores are usually single-celled, whereas seeds are multicellular, consisting of an embryo protected by a layer of tissue, the seed coat. A seed can remain dormant for days, months, or even years after being released from the parent plant, whereas most spores have shorter lifetimes. Also, unlike spores, seeds have a supply of stored food. Most seeds land close to their parent sporophyte plant, but some are carried long distances (up to hundreds of kilometers) by wind or animals. If conditions are favorable where it lands, the seed can emerge from dormancy and germinate, with its stored food providing critical support for growth as the sporophyte embryo emerges as a

seedling. As we explore in the Scientific Skills Exercise, some seeds have germinated after more than 1,000 years.

CONCEPT CHECK 30.1

1. Contrast how sperm reach the eggs of seedless plants with how sperm reach the eggs of seed plants.

2. What features not present in seedless plants have contributed to the success of seed plants on land?

3. **WHAT IF?** If a seed could not enter dormancy, how might that affect the embryo's transport or survival?

For suggested answers, see Appendix A.

CONCEPT 30.2

Gymnosperms bear "naked" seeds, typically on cones

Nonvascular plants (bryophytes)
Seedless vascular plants
Gymnosperms
Angiosperms

Extant seed plants form two sister clades: gymnosperms and angiosperms. Recall from Chapter 29 that gymnosperms have "naked" seeds exposed on modified leaves (sporophylls) that usually form cones (strobili). (Angiosperm seeds are enclosed in chambers that mature into fruits.) Most gymnosperms are cone-bearing plants called **conifers**, such as pines, firs, and redwoods.

CHAPTER 30 Plant Diversity II: The Evolution of Seed Plants **633**

The Life Cycle of a Pine

As you read earlier, seed plant evolution has included three key reproductive adaptations: the miniaturization of their gametophytes; the advent of the seed as a resistant, dispersible stage in the life cycle; and the appearance of pollen as an airborne agent that brings gametes together. **Figure 30.4** shows how these adaptations come into play during the life cycle of a pine, a familiar conifer.

The pine tree is the sporophyte; its sporangia are located on scalelike structures packed densely in cones. Like all seed plants, conifers are heterosporous. In conifers, the two types of spores are produced by separate cones: small pollen cones and large ovulate cones. In most pine species, each tree has both types of cones. In pollen cones, cells called microsporocytes undergo meiosis, producing haploid microspores. Each microspore develops into a pollen grain containing a male

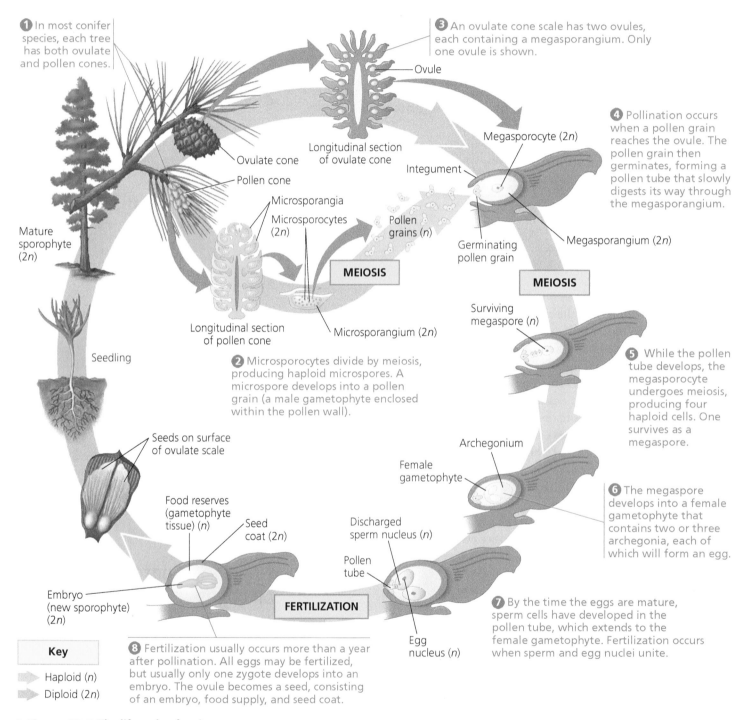

1 In most conifer species, each tree has both ovulate and pollen cones.

3 An ovulate cone scale has two ovules, each containing a megasporangium. Only one ovule is shown.

Ovule

Longitudinal section of ovulate cone

Ovulate cone

Pollen cone

Microsporangia

Microsporocytes (2n)

Pollen grains (n)

Mature sporophyte (2n)

MEIOSIS

Longitudinal section of pollen cone

Microsporangium (2n)

Seedling

2 Microsporocytes divide by meiosis, producing haploid microspores. A microspore develops into a pollen grain (a male gametophyte enclosed within the pollen wall).

Megasporocyte (2n)

Integument

Germinating pollen grain

Megasporangium (2n)

4 Pollination occurs when a pollen grain reaches the ovule. The pollen grain then germinates, forming a pollen tube that slowly digests its way through the megasporangium.

MEIOSIS

Surviving megaspore (n)

5 While the pollen tube develops, the megasporocyte undergoes meiosis, producing four haploid cells. One survives as a megaspore.

Archegonium

Female gametophyte

6 The megaspore develops into a female gametophyte that contains two or three archegonia, each of which will form an egg.

Seeds on surface of ovulate scale

Food reserves (gametophyte tissue) (n)

Seed coat (2n)

Discharged sperm nucleus (n)

Pollen tube

Embryo (new sporophyte) (2n)

FERTILIZATION

7 By the time the eggs are mature, sperm cells have developed in the pollen tube, which extends to the female gametophyte. Fertilization occurs when sperm and egg nuclei unite.

Egg nucleus (n)

8 Fertilization usually occurs more than a year after pollination. All eggs may be fertilized, but usually only one zygote develops into an embryo. The ovule becomes a seed, consisting of an embryo, food supply, and seed coat.

Key

Haploid (n)

Diploid (2n)

▲ **Figure 30.4 The life cycle of a pine.**

MAKE CONNECTIONS *What type of cell division occurs as a megaspore develops into a female gametophyte? (See Figure 13.10.)*

gametophyte. In conifers, the yellow pollen is released in large amounts and carried by the wind, dusting everything in its path. Meanwhile, in ovulate cones, megasporocytes undergo meiosis and produce haploid megaspores inside the ovule. Surviving megaspores develop into female gametophytes, which are retained within the sporangia.

From the time pollen and ovulate cones appear on the tree, it takes nearly three years for the male and female gametophytes to be produced and brought together and for mature seeds to form from fertilized ovules. The scales of each ovulate cone then separate, and seeds are dispersed by the wind. A seed that lands in a suitable environment germinates, its embryo emerging as a pine seedling.

Early Seed Plants and the Rise of Gymnosperms

The origins of characteristics found in pines and other living seed plants date back to the late Devonian period (about 380 million years ago). Fossils from that time reveal that some plants had acquired features that are also present in seed plants, such as megaspores and microspores. For example, *Archaeopteris* was a heterosporous tree with a woody stem (Figure 30.5). But it did not bear seeds and therefore is not classified as a seed plant. Growing up to 20 m tall, it had fernlike leaves.

The first seed plants to appear in the fossil record date from around 360 million years ago, 55 million years before the first fossils of extant gymnosperms and more than 200 million years before the first fossils of extant angiosperms. These early seed plants became extinct, and we don't know which extinct lineage gave rise to the gymnosperms.

The earliest fossils of extant gymnosperms are about 305 million years old. These early gymnosperms lived in moist Carboniferous ecosystems still dominated by lycophytes, horsetails, ferns, and other seedless vascular plants. As the Carboniferous period gave way to the Permian (299 to 251 million years ago), the climate became much drier. As a result, the lycophytes, horsetails, and ferns that dominated Carboniferous swamps were largely replaced by gymnosperms, which were better suited to the drier climate.

Gymnosperms thrived as the climate dried, in part because they have the key terrestrial adaptations found in all seed plants, such as seeds and pollen. In addition, some gymnosperms were particularly well suited to arid conditions because of the thick cuticles and relatively small surface areas of their needle-shaped leaves.

▲ Figure 30.5 **A tree with transitional features.**

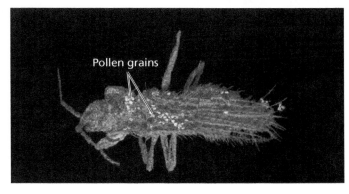

Pollen grains

▲ Figure 30.6 **An ancient pollinator.** This 110-million-year-old fossil shows pollen on an insect, the thrip *Gymnopollisthrips minor*. Structural features of the pollen suggest that it was produced by gymnosperms (most likely by species related to extant ginkos or cycads). Although most gymnosperms today are wind-pollinated, many cycads are insect-pollinated.

Gymnosperms dominated terrestrial ecosystems throughout much of the Mesozoic era, which lasted from 251 to 65.5 million years ago. These gymnosperms served as the food supply for giant herbivorous dinosaurs, and they also interacted with animals in other ways. Recent fossil discoveries, for example, show that some gymnosperms were pollinated by insects more than 100 million years ago—the earliest evidence of insect pollination in any plant group (Figure 30.6). Late in the Mesozoic, angiosperms began to replace gymnosperms in some ecosystems.

Gymnosperm Diversity

Although angiosperms now dominate most terrestrial ecosystems, gymnosperms remain an important part of Earth's flora. For example, vast regions in northern latitudes are covered by forests of conifers (see Figure 52.11).

Of the ten plant phyla (see Table 29.1), four are gymnosperms: Cycadophyta, Ginkgophyta, Gnetophyta, and Coniferophyta. It is uncertain how the four phyla of gymnosperms are related to each other. Figure 30.7 surveys the diversity of extant gymnosperms.

CONCEPT CHECK 30.2

1. Use examples from Figure 30.7 to describe how various gymnosperms are similar yet distinctive.

2. Explain how the pine life cycle in Figure 30.4 reflects the five adaptations common to all seed plants.

3. **MAKE CONNECTIONS** Does the hypothesis that extant gymnosperms and angiosperms are sister clades imply they arose at the same time? See Figure 26.5.

For suggested answers, see Appendix A.

Exploring Gymnosperm Diversity

Phylum Cycadophyta

The 300 species of living cycads have large cones and palmlike leaves (true palm species are angiosperms). Unlike most seed plants, cycads have flagellated sperm, indicating their descent from seedless vascular plants that had motile sperm. Cycads thrived during the Mesozoic era, known as the age of cycads as well as the age of dinosaurs. Today, however, cycads are the most endangered of all plant groups: 75% of their species are threatened by habitat destruction and other human actions.

Phylum Ginkgophyta

Cycas revoluta

Ginkgo biloba is the only surviving species of this phylum; like cycads, ginkos have flagellated sperm. Also known as the maidenhair tree, Ginkgo biloba has deciduous fanlike leaves that turn gold in autumn. It is a popular ornamental tree in cities because it tolerates air pollution well. Landscapers often plant only pollen-producing trees because the fleshy seeds smell rancid as they decay.

Phylum Gnetophyta

Phylum Gnetophyta includes plants in three genera: Gnetum, Ephedra, and Welwitschia. Some species are tropical, whereas others live in deserts. Although very different in appearance, the genera are grouped together based on molecular data.

▶ **Welwitschia.** This genus consists of one species, *Welwitschia mirabilis*, a plant that can live for thousands of years and is found only in the deserts of southwestern Africa. Its straplike leaves are among the largest leaves known.

◀ **Gnetum.** This genus includes about 35 species of tropical trees, shrubs, and vines, mainly native to Africa and Asia. Their leaves look similar to those of flowering plants, and their seeds look somewhat like fruits.

Ovulate cones

▶ **Ephedra.** This genus includes about 40 species that inhabit arid regions worldwide. These desert shrubs, commonly called "Mormon tea", produce the compound ephedrine, which is used medicinally as a decongestant.

Phylum Coniferophyta

Phylum Coniferophyta, the largest gymnosperm phyla, consists of about 600 species of conifers (from the Latin *conus*, cone, and *ferre*, to carry), including many large trees. Most species have woody cones, but a few have fleshy cones. Some, such as pines, have needle-like leaves. Others, such as redwoods, have scale-like leaves. Some species dominate vast northern forests, whereas others are native to the Southern Hemisphere.

Most conifers are evergreens; they retain their leaves throughout the year. Even during winter, a limited amount of photosynthesis occurs on sunny days. When spring comes, conifers already have fully developed leaves that can take advantage of the sunnier, warmer days. Some conifers, such as the dawn redwood, tamarack, and larch, are deciduous trees that lose leaves each autumn.

► **Douglas fir.** This evergreen tree (*Pseudotduga menziesii*) provides more timber than any other North American tree species. Some uses include house framing, plywood, pulpwood for paper, railroad ties, and boxes and crates.

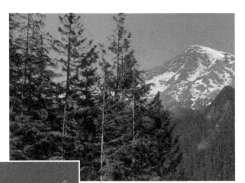

► **Common juniper.** The "berries" of the common juniper (*Juniperus communis*) are actually ovule-producing cones consisting of fleshy sporophylls.

◄ **European larch.** The needle-like leaves of this deciduous conifer (*Larix decidua*) turn yellow before they are shed in autumn. Native to the mountains of central Europe, including Switzerland's Matterhorn, depicted here, this species is extremely cold-tolerant, able to survive winter temperatures that plunge to –50°C.

◄ **Wollemi pine.** Survivors of a conifer group once known only from fossils, living Wollemi pines (*Wollemia nobilis*) were discovered in 1994 in a national park only 150 km from Sydney, Australia. The species consists of just 40 known individuals in two small groves. The inset photo compares the leaves of this "living fossil" with actual fossils.

► **Sequoia.** This giant sequoia (*Sequoiadendron giganteum*) in California's Sequoia National Park weighs about 2,500 metric tons, equivalent to about 24 blue whales (the largest animals) or 40,000 people. The giant sequoia is one of the largest living organisms and also among the most ancient, with some individuals estimated to be between 1,800 and 2,700 years old. Their cousins, the coast redwoods (*Sequoia sempervirens*), grow to heights of more than 110 m (taller than the Statue of Liberty) and are found only in a narrow coastal strip of northern California and southern Oregon.

► **Bristlecone pine.** This species (*Pinus longaeva*), which is found in the White Mountains of California, includes some of the oldest living organisms, reaching ages of more than 4,600 years. One tree (not shown here) is called Methuselah because it may be the word's oldest living tree. To protect the tree, scientists keep its location a secret.

CONCEPT 30.3

The reproductive adaptations of angiosperms include flowers and fruits

Nonvascular plants (bryophytes)
Seedless vascular plants
Gymnosperms
Angiosperms

Commonly known as flowering plants, angiosperms are seed plants with the reproductive structures called flowers and fruits. The name *angiosperm* (from the Greek *angion*, container) refers to seeds contained in fruits. Angiosperms are the most diverse and widespread of all plants, with more than 250,000 species (about 90% of all plant species).

Characteristics of Angiosperms

All angiosperms are classified in a single phylum, Anthophyta. Before considering the evolution of angiosperms, we will examine two of their key adaptations—flowers and fruits—and the roles of these structures in the angiosperm life cycle.

Flowers

The **flower** is a unique angiosperm structure specialized for sexual reproduction. In many angiosperm species, insects or other animals transfer pollen from one flower to the sex organs on another flower, which makes pollination more directed than the wind-dependent pollination of most gymnosperms. However, some angiosperms *are* wind-pollinated, particularly those species that occur in dense populations, such as grasses and tree species in temperate forests.

A flower is a specialized shoot that can have up to four types of modified leaves (sporophylls) called floral organs: sepals, petals, stamens, and carpels **(Figure 30.8)**. Starting at the base of the flower are the **sepals**, which are usually green

and enclose the flower before it opens (think of a rosebud). Interior to the sepals are the **petals**, which are brightly colored in most flowers and aid in attracting pollinators. Flowers that are wind-pollinated, such as grasses, generally lack brightly colored parts. In all angiosperms, the sepals and petals are sterile floral organs, meaning that they do not produce sperm or eggs. Within the petals are two types of fertile floral organs that produce spores, the stamens and carpels. **Stamens** produce microspores that develop into pollen grains containing male gametophytes. A stamen consists of a stalk called the **filament** and a terminal sac, the **anther**, where pollen is produced. **Carpels** make megaspores and their products, female gametophytes. The carpel is the "container" mentioned earlier in which seeds are enclosed; as such, it is a key structure that distinguishes angiosperms from gymnosperms. Some flowers have a single carpel, whereas others have multiple carpels. At the tip of the carpel is a sticky **stigma** that receives pollen. A **style** leads from the stigma to a structure at the base of the carpel, the **ovary**; the ovary contains one or more ovules. If fertilized, an ovule develops into a seed.

Flowers that have all four organs are called **complete flowers**. Those that lack one or more of these organs are known as **incomplete flowers**. For example, some lack functional stamens, and others lack functional carpels. Flowers also vary in structure **(Figure 30.9)**, as well as size, color, and odor (see Figure 38.3). Much of this diversity results from adaptation to specific pollinators (see Figures 38.5 and 38.6).

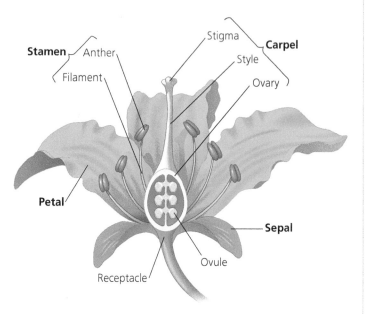

▲ **Figure 30.8 The structure of an idealized flower.**

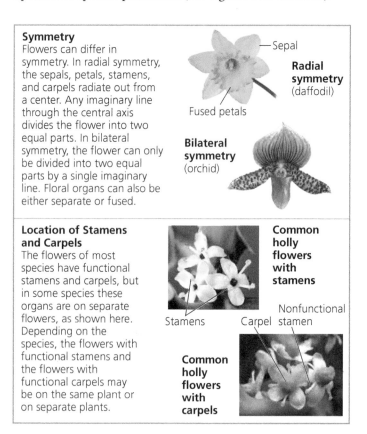

Symmetry
Flowers can differ in symmetry. In radial symmetry, the sepals, petals, stamens, and carpels radiate out from a center. Any imaginary line through the central axis divides the flower into two equal parts. In bilateral symmetry, the flower can only be divided into two equal parts by a single imaginary line. Floral organs can also be either separate or fused.

Sepal
Radial symmetry (daffodil)
Fused petals
Bilateral symmetry (orchid)

Location of Stamens and Carpels
The flowers of most species have functional stamens and carpels, but in some species these organs are on separate flowers, as shown here. Depending on the species, the flowers with functional stamens and the flowers with functional carpels may be on the same plant or on separate plants.

Common holly flowers with stamens
Stamens
Carpel
Nonfunctional stamen
Common holly flowers with carpels

▲ **Figure 30.9 Some variations in flower structure.**

Fruits

As seeds develop from ovules after fertilization, the ovary wall thickens and the ovary matures into a **fruit**. A pea pod is an example of a fruit, with seeds (mature ovules, the peas) encased in the ripened ovary (the pod).

Fruits protect seeds and aid in their dispersal. Mature fruits can be either fleshy or dry (**Figure 30.10**). Tomatoes, plums, and grapes are examples of fleshy fruits, in which the wall (pericarp) of the ovary becomes soft during ripening. Dry fruits include beans, nuts, and grains. Some dry fruits split open at maturity to release seeds, whereas others remain closed. The dry, wind-dispersed fruits of grasses, harvested while on the plant, are major staple foods for humans. The cereal grains of maize, rice, wheat, and other grasses, though easily mistaken for seeds, are each actually a fruit with a dry outer covering (the former wall of the ovary) that adheres to the seed coat of the seed within.

As shown in **Figure 30.11**, various adaptations of fruits and seeds help to disperse seeds (see also Figure 38.12). The seeds of some flowering plants, such as dandelions and maples, are contained within fruits that function like parachutes or propellers, adaptations that enhance dispersal by wind. Some fruits, such as coconuts, are adapted to dispersal by water. And the seeds of many angiosperms are carried by animals. Some angiosperms have fruits modified as burrs that cling to animal fur (or the clothes of humans). Others produce edible fruits, which are usually nutritious, sweet tasting, and vividly colored, advertising their ripeness. When an animal eats the fruit, it digests the fruit's fleshy part, but the tough seeds usually pass unharmed through the animal's digestive tract. When the animal defecates, it may deposit the seeds, along with a supply of natural fertilizer, many kilometers from where the fruit was eaten.

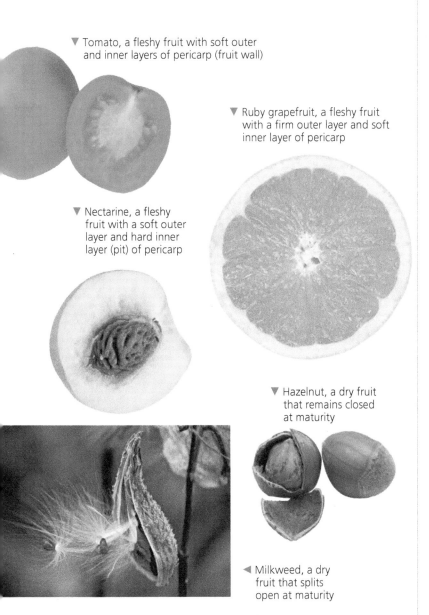

▼ Tomato, a fleshy fruit with soft outer and inner layers of pericarp (fruit wall)

▼ Ruby grapefruit, a fleshy fruit with a firm outer layer and soft inner layer of pericarp

▼ Nectarine, a fleshy fruit with a soft outer layer and hard inner layer (pit) of pericarp

▼ Hazelnut, a dry fruit that remains closed at maturity

◄ Milkweed, a dry fruit that splits open at maturity

▲ Figure 30.10 **Some variations in fruit structure.**

◄ Some plants have mechanisms that disperse seeds by explosive action.

► Wings enable maple fruits to be carried by the wind.

◄ Seeds within berries and other edible fruits are often dispersed in animal feces.

► The barbs of cockleburs facilitate seed dispersal by allowing the fruits to "hitchhike" on animals.

▲ Figure 30.11 **Fruit adaptations that enhance seed dispersal.**

The Angiosperm Life Cycle

You can follow a typical angiosperm life cycle in **Figure 30.12**. The flower of the sporophyte produces microspores that form male gametophytes and megaspores that form female gametophytes. The male gametophytes are in the pollen grains, which develop within microsporangia in the anthers. Each male gametophyte has two haploid cells: a *generative cell* that divides, forming two sperm, and a *tube cell* that produces a pollen tube. Each ovule, which develops in the ovary, contains a female gametophyte, also known as an **embryo sac**. The embryo sac consists of only a few cells, one of which is the egg. (We will discuss gametophyte development in more detail in Chapter 38.)

After its release from the anther, the pollen is carried to the sticky stigma at the tip of a carpel. Although some flowers self-pollinate, most have mechanisms that ensure **cross-pollination**, which in angiosperms is the transfer of pollen from an anther of a flower on one plant to the stigma of a flower on another plant of the same species. Cross-pollination enhances genetic variability. In some species, stamens and

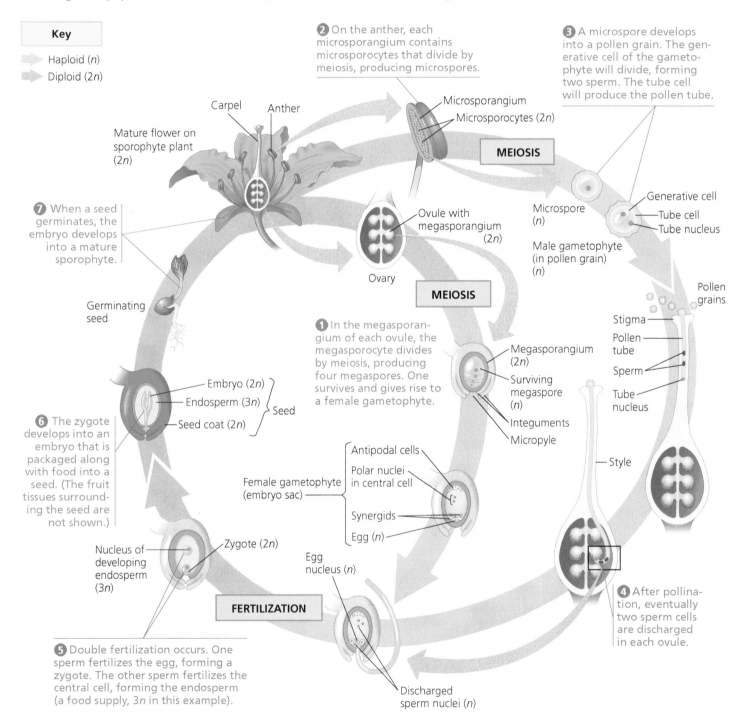

▲ **Figure 30.12** **The life cycle of an angiosperm.**

carpels of a single flower may mature at different times, or they may be so arranged that self-pollination is unlikely.

The pollen grain absorbs water and germinates after it adheres to the stigma of a carpel. The tube cell produces a pollen tube that grows down within the style of the carpel. After reaching the ovary, the pollen tube penetrates through the **micropyle**, a pore in the integuments of the ovule, and discharges two sperm cells into the female gametophyte (embryo sac). One sperm fertilizes the egg, forming a diploid zygote. The other sperm fuses with the two nuclei in the large central cell of the female gametophyte, producing a triploid cell. This type of **double fertilization**, in which one fertilization event produces a zygote and the other produces a triploid cell, is unique to angiosperms.

After double fertilization, the ovule matures into a seed. The zygote develops into a sporophyte embryo with a rudimentary root and one or two seed leaves called **cotyledons**. The triploid central cell of the female gametophyte develops into **endosperm**, tissue rich in starch and other food reserves that nourish the developing embryo.

What is the function of double fertilization in angiosperms? One hypothesis is that double fertilization synchronizes the development of food storage in the seed with the development of the embryo. If a particular flower is not pollinated or sperm cells are not discharged into the embryo sac, fertilization does not occur, and neither endosperm nor embryo forms. So perhaps double fertilization is an adaptation that prevents flowering plants from squandering nutrients on infertile ovules.

Another type of double fertilization occurs in some gymnosperm species belonging to the phylum Gnetophyta. However, double fertilization in these species gives rise to two embryos rather than to an embryo and endosperm.

As you read earlier, the seed consists of the embryo, the endosperm, and a seed coat derived from the integuments. An ovary develops into a fruit as its ovules become seeds. After being dispersed, a seed may germinate if environmental conditions are favorable. The coat ruptures and the embryo emerges as a seedling, using food stored in the endosperm and cotyledons until it can produce its own food by photosynthesis.

Angiosperm Evolution

Charles Darwin once referred to the origin of angiosperms as an "abominable mystery." He was particularly troubled by the relatively sudden and geographically widespread appearance of angiosperms in the fossil record (about 100 million years ago, based on fossils known to Darwin). Fossil evidence and phylogenetic analyses have led to progress in solving Darwin's mystery, but we still do not fully understand how angiosperms arose from earlier seed plants.

Fossil Angiosperms

Angiosperms are now thought to have originated in the early Cretaceous period, about 140 million years ago. By the mid-Cretaceous (100 million years ago), angiosperms began to dominate some terrestrial ecosystems. Landscapes changed dramatically as conifers and other gymnosperms gave way to flowering plants in many parts of the world. The Cretaceous ended about 65 million years ago with mass extinctions of dinosaurs and many other animal groups and further increases in the diversity and importance of angiosperms.

What evidence suggests that angiosperms arose 140 million years ago? First, although pollen grains are common in rocks from the Jurassic period (200 to 145 million years ago), none of these pollen fossils have features characteristic of angiosperms, suggesting that angiosperms may have originated after the Jurassic. Indeed, the earliest fossils with distinctive angiosperm features are of 130-million-year-old pollen grains discovered in China, Israel, and England. Early fossils of larger flowering plant structures include those of *Archaefructus* **(Figure 30.13)** and *Leefructus*, both of which

(a) *Archaefructus sinensis***, a 125-million-year-old fossil.** This herbaceous species had simple flowers and bulbous structures that may have served as floats, suggesting it was aquatic. Recent phylogenetic analyses indicate that *Archaefructus* may belong to the water lily group.

(b) Artist's reconstruction of *Archaefructus sinensis*

▲ **Figure 30.13 An early flowering plant.**

were discovered in China in rocks that are about 125 million years old. Overall, early angiosperm fossils indicate that the group arose and began to diversify over a 20- to 30-million-year period—a less sudden event than was suggested by the fossils known during Darwin's lifetime.

Can we infer traits of the angiosperm common ancestor from traits found in early fossil angiosperms? *Archaefructus*, for example, was herbaceous and had bulbous structures that may have served as floats, suggesting it was aquatic. But investigating whether the angiosperm common ancestor was herbaceous and aquatic also requires examining fossils of other seed plants thought to have been closely related to angiosperms. All of those plants were woody, indicating that the common ancestor was probably woody and probably not aquatic. As we'll see, this conclusion has been supported by recent phylogenetic analyses.

Angiosperm Phylogeny

To shed light on the body plan of early angiosperms, scientists have long sought to identify which seed plants, including fossil species, are most closely related to angiosperms. Molecular and morphological evidence suggests that living gymnosperm lineages diverged from the ancestors of angiosperms about 305 million years ago. Note that this does not imply that angiosperms originated 305 million years ago, but that the most recent common ancestor of extant gymnosperms and angiosperms lived at that time. Indeed, extant angiosperms may be more closely related to several extinct lineages of woody seed plants than they are to extant gymnosperms. One such lineage is the Bennettitales, a group with flowerlike structures that may have been pollinated by insects (**Figure 30.14a**).

Making sense of the origin of angiosperms also depends on working out the order in which angiosperm clades diverged from one another. Here, dramatic progress has been made in recent years. Molecular and morphological evidence suggests that a shrub called *Amborella trichopoda* and water lilies are living representatives of two of the most ancient lineages of extant angiosperms (**Figure 30.14b**). *Amborella* is woody, supporting the conclusion mentioned earlier that the angiosperm common ancestor was probably woody. Like the Bennettitales, *Amborella* and other basal angiosperms lacked *vessel elements*, efficient water-conducting cells that are found in angiosperms from later-diverging lineages. Overall, based on the features of ancestral species and basal angiosperms such as *Amborella*, some researchers have hypothesized that early angiosperms were shrubs that had small flowers and relatively simple water-conducting cells.

Evolutionary Links with Animals

Plants and animals have interacted for hundreds of millions of years, and those interactions have led to evolutionary

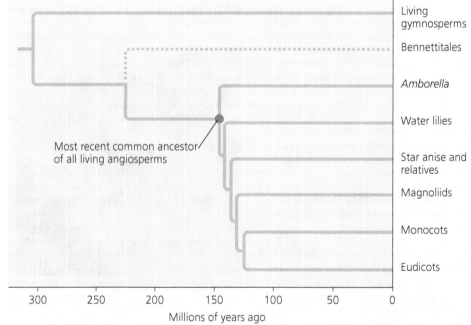

Most recent common ancestor of all living angiosperms

Millions of years ago

(a) A close relative of the angiosperms? This reconstruction shows a longitudinal section through the flowerlike structures found in the Bennettitales, an extinct group of seed plants hypothesized to be more closely related to extant angiosperms than to extant gymnosperms.

(b) Angiosperm phylogeny. This tree represents a current hypothesis of angiosperm evolutionary relationships, based on morphological and molecular evidence. Angiosperms originated about 140 million years ago. The dotted line indicates the uncertain position of the Bennettitales, a possible sister group to extant angiosperms.

▲ **Figure 30.14 Angiosperm evolutionary history.**

? *Would the branching order of the phylogeny in (b) necessarily have to be redrawn if a 150-million-year-old fossil monocot were discovered? Explain.*

Stamens

◄ **Figure 30.15 A bee pollinating a bilaterally symmetrical flower.** To harvest nectar (a sugary solution secreted by flower glands) from this Scottish broom flower, a honeybee must land as shown. This releases a tripping mechanism that arches the flower's stamens over the bee and dusts it with pollen. Later, some of this pollen may rub off onto the stigma of the next flower of this species that the bee visits.

change. For example, herbivores can reduce a plant's reproductive success by eating its roots, leaves, or seeds. As a result, if an effective defense against herbivores originates in a group of plants, those plants may be favored by natural selection—as will herbivores that overcome this new defense. Plant-pollinator and other mutually beneficial interactions also can have such reciprocal evolutionary effects.

Plant-pollinator interactions also may have affected the rates at which new species form. Consider the impact of a flower's symmetry (see Figure 30.9). On a flower with bilateral symmetry, an insect pollinator can obtain nectar only when approaching from a certain direction (Figure 30.15). This constraint makes it more likely that pollen is placed on a part of the insect's body that will come into contact with the stigma of a flower of the same species. Such specificity of pollen transfer reduces gene flow between diverging populations and could lead to increased rates of speciation in plants with bilateral symmetry. This hypothesis can be tested using the approach illustrated in this diagram:

A key step in this approach is to identify cases in which a clade with bilaterally symmetric flowers shares an immediate common ancestor with a clade whose members have radially symmetric flowers. One recent study identified 19 pairs of closely related "bilateral" and "radial" clades. On average, the clade with bilaterally symmetric flowers had nearly 2,400 more species than did the related clade with radial symmetry. This result suggests that flower shape can affect the rate at which new species form, perhaps by affecting the behavior of insect pollinators. Overall, plant-pollinator interactions may have contributed to the increasing dominance of flowering plants in the Cretaceous period, helping to make angiosperms of central importance in ecological communities.

Angiosperm Diversity

From their humble beginnings in the Cretaceous period, angiosperms have diversified into more than 250,000 living species. Until the late 1990s, most systematists divided flowering plants into two groups, based partly on the number of cotyledons, or seed leaves, in the embryo. Species with one cotyledon were called **monocots**, and those with two were called **dicots**. Other features, such as flower and leaf structure, were also used to define the two groups. Recent DNA studies, however, indicate that the species traditionally called dicots are paraphyletic. The vast majority of species once categorized as dicots form a large clade, now known as **eudicots** ("true" dicots). **Figure 30.16** compares the main characteristics of monocots and eudicots. The rest of the former dicots are now grouped into four small lineages. Three of these are informally called **basal angiosperms** because they appear to include the flowering plants belonging to the oldest lineages (see Figure 30.14b). A fourth lineage, the **magnoliids**, evolved later. **Figure 30.17** provides an overview of angiosperm diversity.

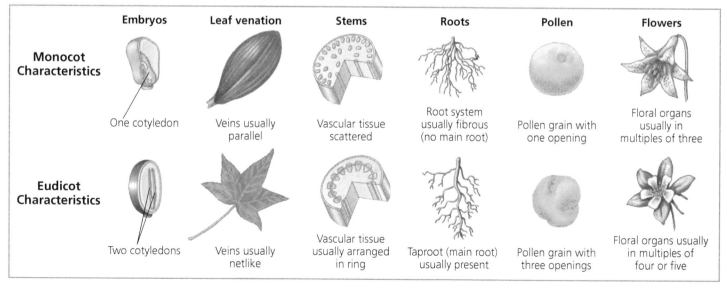

▲ **Figure 30.16 Characteristics of monocots and eudicots.**

Exploring Angiosperm Diversity

Basal Angiosperms

Surviving basal angiosperms are currently thought to consist of three lineages comprising only about 100 species. The oldest lineage seems to be represented by a single species, *Amborella trichopoda* (far right). The other surviving lineages diverged later: a clade that includes water lilies and a clade consisting of the star anise and its relatives.

Amborella trichopoda. ▶ This small shrub, found only on the South Pacific island of New Caledonia, may be the sole survivor of a branch at the base of the angiosperm tree.

◀ **Water lily (*Nymphaea "Rene Gerard"*).** Species of water lilies are found in aquatic habitats throughout the world. Water lilies are living members of a clade that may be predated only by the *Amborella* lineage.

◀ **Star anise (*Illicium*).** This genus belongs to a third surviving lineage of basal angiosperms.

Magnoliids

Magnoliids consist of about 8,000 species, most notably magnolias, laurels, and black pepper plants. They include both woody and herbaceous species. Although they share some traits with basal angiosperms, such as a typically spiral rather than whorled arrangement of floral organs, magnoliids are more closely related to eudicots and monocots.

◀ **Southern magnolia (*Magnolia grandiflora*).** This member of the magnolia family is a large tree. The variety of southern magnolia shown here, called "Goliath," has flowers that measure up to about a foot across.

Monocots

About one-quarter of angiosperm species are monocots—about 70,000 species. Some of the largest groups are the orchids, grasses, and palms. Grasses include some of the most important crops, such as maize, rice, and wheat.

◀ **Orchid (*Lemboglossum rossii*)**

Pygmy ▶ **date palm (*Phoenix roebelenii*)**

▲ **Barley (*Hordeum vulgare*), a grass**

Eudicots

More than two-thirds of angiosperm species are eudicots—roughly 170,000 species. The largest group is the legume family, which includes such crops as peas and beans. Also important economically is the rose family, which includes many plants with ornamental flowers as well as some species with edible fruits, such as strawberry plants and apple and pear trees. Most of the familiar flowering trees are eudicots, such as oak, walnut, maple, willow, and birch.

◀ **Pyrenean oak (*Quercus pyrenaica*)**

◀ **Snow pea (*Pisum sativum*), a legume**

Dog rose ▶ **(*Rosa canina*), a wild rose**

1. It is said that an oak is an acorn's way of making more acorns. Write an explanation that includes these terms: sporophyte, gametophyte, ovule, seed, ovary, and fruit.

2. Compare and contrast a pine cone and a flower in terms of structure and function.

3. **WHAT IF?** Do speciation rates in closely related clades of flowering plants show that flower shape is *correlated with* the rate at which new species form or that flower shape is *responsible for* this rate? Explain.

For suggested answers, see Appendix A.

CONCEPT 30.4

Human welfare depends on seed plants

In forests and on farms, seed plants are key sources of food, fuel, wood products, and medicine. Our reliance on them makes the preservation of plant diversity critical.

Products from Seed Plants

Most of our food comes from angiosperms. Just six crops—maize, rice, wheat, potatoes, cassava, and sweet potatoes—yield 80% of all the calories consumed by humans. We also depend on angiosperms to feed livestock: It takes 5–7 kg of grain to produce 1 kg of grain-fed beef.

Today's crops are the products of artificial selection—the result of plant domestication that began about 12,000 years ago. To appreciate the scale of this transformation, note how the number and size of seeds in domesticated plants are greater than those of their wild relatives, as in the case of maize and the grass teosinte (see Figure 38.16). Scientists can glean information about domestication by comparing the genes of crops with those of wild relatives. With maize, dramatic changes such as increased cob size and loss of the hard coating around teosinte kernels may have been initiated by as few as five mutations.

Flowering plants also provide other edible products. Two popular beverages come from tea leaves and coffee beans, and you can thank the cacao tree for cocoa and chocolate. Spices are derived from various plant parts, such as flowers (cloves, saffron), fruits and seeds (vanilla, black pepper, mustard), leaves (basil, mint, sage), and even bark (cinnamon).

Many seed plants are sources of wood, which is absent in all living seedless plants. Wood consists of tough-walled xylem cells (see Figure 35.22). It is the primary source of fuel for much of the world, and wood pulp, typically derived from conifers such as fir and pine, is used to make paper. Wood remains the most widely used construction material.

For centuries, humans have also depended on seed plants for medicines. Many cultures use herbal remedies, and scientists have extracted and identified medicinally active compounds from many of these plants, and later synthesized

Table 30.1 Examples of Plant-Derived Medicines

Compound	Source	Use
Atropine	Belladonna plant	Eye pupil dilator
Digitalin	Foxglove	Heart medication
Menthol	Eucalyptus tree	Throat soother
Quinine	Cinchona tree	Malaria preventive
Taxol	Pacific yew	Ovarian cancer drug
Tubocurarine	Curare tree	Muscle relaxant
Vinblastine	Periwinkle	Leukemia drug

them. Willow leaves and bark have long been used in pain-relieving remedies, including prescriptions by the Greek physician Hippocrates. In the 1800s, scientists traced the willow's medicinal property to the chemical salicin. A synthesized derivative, acetylsalicylic acid, is what we call aspirin. Plants are also a direct source of medicinal compounds (Table 30.1). In the United States, about 25% of prescription drugs contain an active ingredient from plants, usually seed plants.

Threats to Plant Diversity

Although plants may be a renewable resource, plant diversity is not. The exploding human population and its demand for space and resources are threatening plant species across the globe. The problem is especially severe in the tropics, where more than two-thirds of the human population live and where population growth is fastest. About 55,000 km^2 (14 million acres) of tropical rain forest are cleared each year (Figure 30.18), a rate that would completely eliminate the remaining 11 million km^2 of tropical forests in 200 years. The loss of forests reduces the absorption of atmospheric carbon dioxide (CO_2) that occurs during photosynthesis, potentially contributing to global warming. Also, as forests disappear, so do large numbers of plant species. Of course, once a species becomes extinct, it can never return.

The loss of plant species is often accompanied by the loss of insects and other rain forest animals. Scientists estimate that if current rates of loss in the tropics and elsewhere continue, 50% or more of Earth's species will become extinct

▲ **Figure 30.18 Clear-cutting of tropical forests.** Over the past several hundred years, nearly half of Earth's tropical forests have been cut down and converted to farmland and other uses. A satellite image from 1975 (left) shows a dense forest in Brazil. By 2012, much of this forest had been cut down. Deforested and urban areas are shown as light purple.

within the next few centuries. Such losses would constitute a global mass extinction, rivaling the Permian and Cretaceous mass extinctions and forever changing the evolutionary history of land plants (and many other organisms).

Many people have ethical concerns about contributing to the extinction of species. In addition, there are practical reasons to be concerned about the loss of plant diversity. So far, we have explored the potential uses of only a tiny fraction of the more than 290,000 known plant species. For example, almost all our food is based on the cultivation of only about two dozen species of seed plants. And fewer than 5,000 plant species have been studied as potential sources of medicines. The tropical rain forest may be a medicine chest of healing

plants that could be extinct before we even know they exist. If we begin to view rain forests and other ecosystems as living treasures that can regenerate only slowly, we may learn to harvest their products at sustainable rates.

CONCEPT CHECK 30.4

1. Explain why plant diversity can be considered a nonrenewable resource.
2. **WHAT IF?** How could phylogenies be used to help researchers search more efficiently for novel medicines derived from seed plants?

For suggested answers, see Appendix A.

30 Chapter Review

SUMMARY OF KEY CONCEPTS

CONCEPT 30.1

Seeds and pollen grains are key adaptations for life on land (pp. 631–633)

Five Derived Traits of Seed Plants		
Reduced gametophytes	Microscopic male and female gametophytes (n) are nourished and protected by the sporophyte (2n)	Male gametophyte — Female gametophyte
Heterospory	Microspore (gives rise to a male gametophyte)	
	Megaspore (gives rise to a female gametophyte)	
Ovules	Ovule (gymnosperm) { Integument (2n) — Megaspore (n) — Megasporangium (2n) }	
Pollen	Pollen grains make water unnecessary for fertilization	
Seeds	Seeds: survive better than unprotected spores, can be transported long distances	Seed coat — Food supply — Embryo

? Describe how the parts of an ovule (integument, megaspore, megasporangium) correspond to the parts of a seed.

CONCEPT 30.2

Gymnosperms bear "naked" seeds, typically on cones (pp. 633–637)

- Dominance of the sporophyte generation, the development of seeds from fertilized ovules, and the role of pollen in transferring sperm to ovules are key features of a typical gymnosperm life cycle.
- Gymnosperms appear early in the plant fossil record and dominated many Mesozoic terrestrial ecosystems. Living seed plants can be divided into two monophyletic groups: gymnosperms and angiosperms. Extant gymnosperms include cycads, *Ginkgo biloba*, gnetophytes, and conifers.

? Although there are fewer than 1,000 species of gymnosperms, the group is still very successful in terms of its evolutionary longevity, adaptations, and geographic distribution. Explain.

CONCEPT 30.3

The reproductive adaptations of angiosperms include flowers and fruits (pp. 638–645)

- Flowers generally consist of four types of modified leaves: sepals, petals, stamens (which produce pollen), and carpels (which produce ovules). Ovaries ripen into fruits, which often carry seeds by wind, water, or animals to new locations.
- Flowering plants originated about 140 million years ago, and by the mid-Cretaceous (100 mya) had begun to dominate some terrestrial ecosystems. Fossils and phylogenetic analyses offer insights into the origin of flowers.
- Several groups of basal angiosperms have been identified. Other major clades of angiosperms include magnoliids, monocots, and eudicots.
- Pollination and other interactions between angiosperms and animals may have contributed to the success of flowering plants during the last 100 million years.

? Explain why Darwin called the origin of angiosperms an "abominable mystery," and describe what has been learned from fossil evidence and phylogenetic analyses.

Human welfare depends on seed plants (pp. 645–646)

- Humans depend on seed plants for products such as food, wood, and many medicines.
- Destruction of habitat threatens the extinction of many plant species and the animal species they support.

? *Explain why destroying the remaining tropical forests might harm humans and lead to a mass extinction.*

TEST YOUR UNDERSTANDING

LEVEL 1: KNOWLEDGE/COMPREHENSION

1. Where in an angiosperm would you find a megasporangium?
   a. in the style of a flower
   b. enclosed in the stigma of a flower
   c. within an ovule contained within an ovary of a flower
   d. packed into pollen sacs within the anthers found on a stamen

2. A fruit is usually
   a. a mature ovary.
   b. a thickened style.
   c. an enlarged ovule.
   d. a mature female gametophyte.

3. With respect to angiosperms, which of the following is *incorrectly* paired with its chromosome count?
   a. egg—n
   b. megaspore—$2n$
   c. microspore—n
   d. zygote—$2n$

4. Which of the following is *not* a characteristic that distinguishes gymnosperms and angiosperms from other plants?
   a. dependent gametophytes
   b. ovules
   c. pollen
   d. alternation of generations

5. Gymnosperms and angiosperms have the following in common *except*
   a. seeds.
   b. pollen.
   c. ovaries.
   d. ovules.

LEVEL 2: APPLICATION/ANALYSIS

6. **DRAW IT** Use the letters a–d to label where on the phylogenetic tree each of the following derived characters appears.
   a. flowers
   b. embryos
   c. seeds
   d. vascular tissue

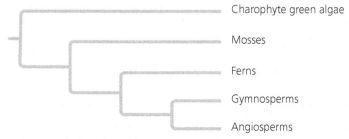

Charophyte green algae

Mosses

Ferns

Gymnosperms

Angiosperms

7. **EVOLUTION CONNECTION**
   The history of life has been punctuated by several mass extinctions. For example, the impact of a meteorite may have wiped out most of the dinosaurs and many forms of marine life at the end of the Cretaceous period (see Chapter 25). Fossils indicate that plants were less severely affected by this mass extinction. What adaptations may have enabled plants to withstand this disaster better than animals?

LEVEL 3: SYNTHESIS/EVALUATION

8. **SCIENTIFIC INQUIRY**
   DRAW IT As will be described in detail in Chapter 38, the female gametophyte of angiosperms typically has seven cells, one of which, the central cell, contains two haploid nuclei. After double fertilization, the central cell develops into endosperm, which is triploid. Because magnoliids, monocots, and eudicots typically have female gametophytes with seven cells and triploid endosperm, scientists assumed that this was the ancestral state for angiosperms. Consider, however, the following recent discoveries:
   - Our understanding of angiosperm phylogeny has changed to that shown in Figure 30.14b.
   - *Amborella trichopoda* has eight-celled female gametophytes and triploid endosperm.
   - Water lilies and star anise have four-celled female gametophytes and diploid endosperm.
   a. Draw a phylogeny of the angiosperms (see Figure 30.14b), incorporating the data given above about the number of cells in female gametophytes and the ploidy of the endosperm. Assume that all of the star anise relatives have four-celled female gametophytes and diploid endosperm.
   b. What does your labeled phylogeny suggest about the evolution of the female gametophyte and endosperm in angiosperms?

9. **WRITE ABOUT A THEME: ORGANIZATION**
   Cells are the basic units of structure and function in all organisms. A key feature in the life cycle of plants is the alternation of multicellular haploid and diploid generations. Imagine a lineage of flowering plants in which mitotic cell division did not occur between the events of meiosis and fertilization (see Figure 30.12). In a short essay (100–150 words), describe how this change in the timing of cell division would affect the structure and life cycle of plants in this lineage.

10. **SYNTHESIZE YOUR KNOWLEDGE**

This colorized scanning electron micrograph shows pollen grains from six seed plant species. Describe how pollen and other adaptations in seed plants contributed to the rise of seed plants and their dominant role in plant communities today.

For selected answers, see Appendix A.

MasteringBiology®

Students Go to **MasteringBiology** for assignments, the eText, and the Study Area with practice tests, animations, and activities.

Instructors Go to **MasteringBiology** for automatically graded tutorials and questions that you can assign to your students, plus Instructor Resources.

31

Fungi

▲ Figure 31.1 **What is the largest organism in this forest?**

Mighty Mushrooms

Hiking through the Malheur National Forest in eastern Oregon, you might notice a few clusters of honey mushrooms (*Armillaria ostoyae*) scattered here and there beneath the towering trees (**Figure 31.1**). Although you might think that the surrounding conifers dwarf the mushrooms, the reverse is actually true. All these mushrooms are just the aboveground portion of a single enormous fungus. Its subterranean network of filaments spreads through 965 hectares of the forest—more than the area of 1,800 football fields. Based on its current growth rate, scientists estimate that this fungus, which weighs hundreds of tons, has been growing for more than 1,900 years.

The inconspicuous honey mushrooms on the forest floor are a fitting symbol of the neglected grandeur of the kingdom Fungi. Most of us are barely aware of these eukaryotes beyond the mushrooms we eat or the occasional brush with athlete's foot. Yet fungi are a huge and important component of the biosphere. While about 100,000 species have been described, there may be as many as 1.5 million species of fungi. Some fungi are exclusively single-celled, though most have complex multicellular bodies. These diverse organisms are found in just about every imaginable terrestrial and aquatic habitat.

Fungi are not only diverse and widespread but also essential for the well-being of most ecosystems. They break down organic material and recycle nutrients, allowing other organisms to assimilate essential chemical elements. Humans make use of fungi as a food source, for applications in agriculture and forestry, and in manufacturing products ranging from bread to antibiotics. But it is also true that some fungi cause disease in plants and animals.

In this chapter, we will investigate the structure and evolutionary history of fungi, survey the major groups of fungi, and discuss their ecological and commercial significance.

CONCEPT 31.1

Fungi are heterotrophs that feed by absorption

Despite their vast diversity, all fungi share some key traits, most importantly the way they derive nutrition. In addition, many fungi grow by forming multicellular filaments, a body structure that plays an important role in how they obtain food.

Nutrition and Ecology

Like animals, fungi are heterotrophs: They cannot make their own food as plants and algae can. But unlike animals, fungi do not ingest (eat) their food. Instead, a fungus absorbs nutrients from the environment outside of its body. Many fungi do this by secreting hydrolytic enzymes into their surroundings. These enzymes break down complex molecules to smaller organic compounds that the fungi can absorb into their bodies and use. Other fungi use enzymes to penetrate the walls of cells, enabling the fungi to absorb nutrients from the cells. Collectively, the different enzymes found in various fungal species can digest compounds from a wide range of sources, living or dead.

This diversity of food sources corresponds to the varied roles of fungi in ecological communities: Different species live as decomposers, parasites, or mutualists. Fungi that are decomposers break down and absorb nutrients from nonliving organic material, such as fallen logs, animal corpses, and the wastes of living organisms. Parasitic fungi absorb nutrients from the cells of living hosts. Some parasitic fungi are pathogenic, including many species that cause diseases in plants. Mutualistic fungi also absorb nutrients from a host organism, but they reciprocate with actions that benefit the host. For example, mutualistic fungi that live inside certain termite species use their enzymes to break down

wood, as do mutualistic protists in other termite species (see Figure 28.27).

The versatile enzymes that enable fungi to digest a wide range of food sources are not the only reason for their ecological success. Another important factor is how their body structure increases the efficiency of nutrient absorption.

Body Structure

The most common fungal body structures are multicellular filaments and single cells (**yeasts**). Many fungal species can grow as both filaments and yeasts, but even more grow only as filaments; relatively few species grow only as yeasts. Yeasts often inhabit moist environments, including plant sap and animal tissues, where there is a ready supply of soluble nutrients, such as sugars and amino acids.

The morphology of multicellular fungi enhances their ability to grow into and absorb nutrients from their surroundings (**Figure 31.2**). The bodies of these fungi typically form a network of tiny filaments called **hyphae** (singular, *hypha*). Hyphae consist of tubular cell walls surrounding the plasma membrane and cytoplasm of the cells. The cell walls are strengthened by **chitin**, a strong but flexible polysaccharide. Chitin-rich walls can enhance feeding by absorption. As a fungus absorbs nutrients from its environment, the concentrations of those nutrients in its cells increases, causing water

Reproductive structure. Tiny haploid cells called spores are produced inside the mushroom.

Hyphae. The mushroom and its subterranean mycelium are a continuous network of hyphae.

Spore-producing structures

60 µm

Mycelium (a mass of hyphae)

▲ **Figure 31.2 Structure of a multicellular fungus.** The top photograph shows the sexual structures, in this case called mushrooms, of the penny bun fungus (*Boletus edulis*). The bottom photograph shows a mycelium growing on fallen conifer needles. The inset SEM shows hyphae.

? *Although the mushrooms in the top photograph appear to be different individuals, could their DNA be identical? Explain.*

(a) Septate hypha   (b) Coenocytic hypha

▲ Figure 31.3 **Two forms of hyphae.**

to move into the cells by osmosis. The movement of water into fungal cells creates pressure that could cause them to burst if they were not surrounded by a rigid cell wall.

Another important structural feature of most fungi is that their hyphae are divided into cells by cross-walls, or **septa** (singular, *septum*) **(Figure 31.3a)**. Septa generally have pores large enough to allow ribosomes, mitochondria, and even nuclei to flow from cell to cell. Some fungi lack septa **(Figure 31.3b)**. Known as **coenocytic fungi**, these organisms consist of a continuous cytoplasmic mass having hundreds or thousands of nuclei. As we'll describe later, the coenocytic condition results from the repeated division of nuclei without cytokinesis.

Fungal hyphae form an interwoven mass called a **mycelium** (plural, *mycelia*) that infiltrates the material on which the fungus feeds (see Figure 31.2). The structure of a mycelium maximizes its surface-to-volume ratio, making feeding very efficient. Just 1 cm^3 of rich soil may contain as much as 1 km of hyphae with a total surface area of 300 cm^2 in contact with the soil. A fungal mycelium grows rapidly, as proteins and other materials synthesized by the fungus move through cytoplasmic streaming to the tips of the extending hyphae. The fungus concentrates its energy and resources on adding hyphal length and thus overall absorptive surface area, rather than on increasing hyphal girth. Fungi are not motile in the typical sense—they cannot run, swim, or fly in search of food or mates. However, as they grow, fungi can move into new territory, swiftly extending the tips of their hyphae.

Specialized Hyphae in Mycorrhizal Fungi

Some fungi have specialized hyphae that allow them to feed on living animals **(Figure 31.4a)**. Other fungal species have specialized hyphae called **haustoria** (singular, *haustorium*), which the fungi use to extract nutrients from, or exchange nutrients with, their plant hosts **(Figure 31.4b)**. Mutually beneficial relationships between such fungi and plant roots are called **mycorrhizae** (the term means "fungus roots").

Mycorrhizal fungi (fungi that form mycorrhizae) can improve delivery of phosphate ions and other minerals to plants because the vast mycelial networks of the fungi are more efficient than the plants' roots at acquiring these minerals from the soil. In exchange, the plants supply the fungi with organic nutrients such as carbohydrates.

(a) **Hyphae adapted for trapping and killing prey.** In *Arthrobotrys*, a soil fungus, portions of the hyphae are modified as hoops that can constrict around a nematode (roundworm) in less than a second. The growing hyphae then penetrate the worm's body, and the fungus digests its prey's inner tissues (SEM).

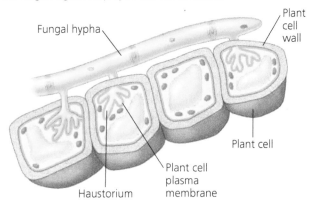

(b) **Haustoria.** Some mutualistic and parasitic fungi grow specialized hyphae called haustoria that can extract nutrients from living plant cells. Haustoria remain separated from a plant cell's cytoplasm by the plasma membrane of the plant cell (orange).

▲ Figure 31.4 **Specialized hyphae.**

There are two main types of mycorrhizal fungi. **Ectomycorrhizal fungi** (from the Greek *ektos*, out) form sheaths of hyphae over the surface of a root and typically grow into the extracellular spaces of the root cortex (see Figure 37.13a). **Arbuscular mycorrhizal fungi** (from the Latin *arbor*, tree) extend branching hyphae through the root cell wall and into tubes formed by invagination (pushing inward, as in Figure 31.4b) of the root cell plasma membrane (see Figure 37.13b). In the Scientific Skills Exercise, you'll compare genomic data from fungi that form mycorrhizae and fungi that do not.

Mycorrhizae are enormously important both in natural ecosystems and in agriculture. Almost all vascular plants have mycorrhizae and rely on their fungal partners for essential nutrients. Many studies have shown the significance of mycorrhizae by comparing the growth of plants with and without them. Foresters commonly inoculate pine seedlings with mycorrhizal fungi to promote growth. In the absence of human intervention, mycorrhizal fungi colonize soils by

Interpreting Genomic Data and Generating Hypotheses

What Can Genomic Analysis of a Mycorrhizal Fungus Reveal About Mycorrhizal Interactions? The first genome of a mycorrhizal fungus to be sequenced was that of the basidiomycete *Laccaria bicolor* (see photo). In nature, *L. bicolor* is a common ectomycorrhizal fungus of trees such as poplar and fir, as well as a free-living soil organism. In forest nurseries, it is used in large-scale inoculation programs to enhance seedling growth. The fungus can easily be grown alone in culture and can establish mycorrhizae with tree roots in the laboratory. Researchers hope that studying the genome of *Laccaria* will yield clues to the processes by which it interacts with its mycorrhizal partners—and by extension, to mycorrhizal interactions involving other fungi.

How the Study Was Done Using the whole-genome shotgun method (see Figure 21.2) and bioinformatics, researchers sequenced the genome of *L. bicolor* and compared it with the genomes of some nonmycorrhizal basidiomycete fungi. By analyzing gene expression using microarrays, the researchers were able to compare gene expression levels for different protein-coding genes and for the same genes in a mycorrhizal mycelium and a free-living mycelium. They could thus identify the genes for fungal proteins that are made specifically in mycorrhizae.

Data from the Study

Table 1. Numbers of Genes in *L. bicolor* and Four Nonmycorrhizal Fungal Species

	L. bicolor	1	2	3	4
Protein-coding genes	20,614	13,544	10,048	7,302	6,522
Genes for membrane transporters	505	412	471	457	386
Genes for small secreted proteins (SSPs)	2,191	838	163	313	58

Table 2. *L. bicolor* Genes Most Highly Upregulated in Ectomycorrhizal Mycelium (ECM) of Douglas Fir or Poplar vs. Free-Living Mycelium (FLM)

Protein ID	Protein Feature or Function	Douglas Fir ECM/FLM Ratio	Poplar ECM/FLM Ratio
298599	Small secreted protein	22,877	12,913
293826	Enzyme inhibitor	14,750	17,069
333839	Small secreted protein	7,844	1,931
316764	Enzyme	2,760	1,478

Interpret the Data

1. (a) From the data in Table 1, which fungal species has the most genes encoding membrane transporters (membrane transport proteins; see Chapter 7)? (b) Why might these genes be of particular importance to *L. bicolor*?

2. The researchers used the phrase "small secreted proteins" (SSPs) to refer to proteins less than 100 amino acids in length that the fungi secrete; their function is not yet known. (a) What is most striking about the Table 1 data on SSPs? (b) The researchers found that the SSP genes shared a common feature that indicated the encoded proteins were destined for secretion. Based on Figure 17.21 and the text discussion of this figure, predict what this common characteristic of the SSP genes was. (c) Suggest a hypothesis for the roles of SSPs in mycorrhizae.

3. Table 2 shows data from gene expression studies for the four *L. bicolor* genes whose transcription was most increased ("upregulated") in mycorrhizae. (a) For the gene encoding the first protein listed, what does the number 22,877 indicate? (b) Do the data in Table 2 support your hypothesis in 2(c)? Explain.

4. (a) In Table 2, how do the data for poplar mycorrhizae compare with those for Douglas fir mycorrhizae? (b) Suggest a general hypothesis for this difference.

(MB) A version of this Scientific Skills Exercise can be assigned in MasteringBiology.

Data from F. Martin et al., The genome of *Laccaria bicolor* provides insights into mycorrhizal symbiosis, *Nature* 452: 88–93 (2008).

---

dispersing haploid cells called **spores** that form new mycelia after germinating. Spore dispersal is a key component of how fungi reproduce and spread to new areas, as we discuss next.

CONCEPT CHECK 31.1

1. Compare and contrast the nutritional mode of a fungus with your own nutritional mode.

2. **WHAT IF?** Suppose a certain fungus is a mutualist that lives within an insect host, yet its ancestors were parasites that grew in and on the insect's body. What derived traits might you find in this mutualistic fungus?

3. **MAKE CONNECTIONS** Review Figure 10.4 and Figure 10.6. If a plant has mycorrhizae, where might carbon that enters the plant's stomata as CO_2 eventually be deposited: in the plant, in the fungus, or both? Explain.

For suggested answers, see Appendix A.

CONCEPT 31.2

Fungi produce spores through sexual or asexual life cycles

Most fungi propagate themselves by producing vast numbers of spores, either sexually or asexually. For example, puffballs, the reproductive structures of certain fungal species, may release trillions of spores (see Figure 31.17). Spores can be carried long distances by wind or water. If they land in a moist place where there is food, they germinate, producing a new mycelium. To appreciate how effective spores are at dispersing, leave a slice of melon exposed to the air. Even without a visible source of spores nearby, within a week, you will likely observe fuzzy mycelia growing from microscopic spores that have fallen onto the melon.

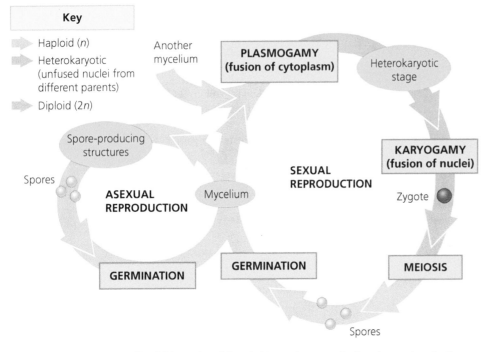

Key

→ Haploid (*n*)
→ Heterokaryotic (unfused nuclei from different parents)
→ Diploid (2*n*)

PLASMOGAMY (fusion of cytoplasm)

Another mycelium

Heterokaryotic stage

Spore-producing structures

Spores

ASEXUAL REPRODUCTION

Mycelium

SEXUAL REPRODUCTION

KARYOGAMY (fusion of nuclei)

Zygote

GERMINATION

GERMINATION

MEIOSIS

Spores

▲ **Figure 31.5 Generalized life cycle of fungi.** Many—but not all—fungi reproduce both sexually and asexually. Some reproduce only sexually, others only asexually.

? *Compare the genetic variation found in spores produced in the sexual and asexual portions of the life cycle and explain why these differences occur.*

Figure 31.5 generalizes the many different life cycles that can produce fungal spores. In this section, we will survey the main aspects of sexual and asexual reproduction in fungi.

Sexual Reproduction

The nuclei of fungal hyphae and the spores of most fungi are haploid, although many species have transient diploid stages that form during sexual life cycles. Sexual reproduction often begins when hyphae from two mycelia release sexual signaling molecules called **pheromones**. If the mycelia are of different mating types, the pheromones from each partner bind to receptors on the other, and the hyphae extend toward the source of the pheromones. When the hyphae meet, they fuse. In species with such a "compatibility test," this process contributes to genetic variation by preventing hyphae from fusing with other hyphae from the same mycelium or another genetically identical mycelium.

The union of the cytoplasms of two parent mycelia is known as **plasmogamy** (see Figure 31.5). In most fungi, the haploid nuclei contributed by each parent do not fuse right away. Instead, parts of the fused mycelium contain coexisting, genetically different nuclei. Such a mycelium is said to be a **heterokaryon** (meaning "different nuclei"). In some species, the haploid nuclei pair off two to a cell, one from each parent. Such a mycelium is **dikaryotic** (meaning "two nuclei"). As a dikaryotic mycelium grows, the two nuclei in each cell divide in tandem without fusing. Because these cells retain two separate haploid nuclei, they differ from diploid

cells, which have pairs of homologous chromosomes within a single nucleus.

Hours, days, or (in some fungi) even centuries may pass between plasmogamy and the next stage in the sexual cycle, **karyogamy**. During karyogamy, the haploid nuclei contributed by the two parents fuse, producing diploid cells. Zygotes and other transient structures form during karyogamy, the only diploid stage in most fungi. Meiosis then restores the haploid condition, ultimately leading to the formation of genetically diverse spores. Meiosis is a key step in sexual reproduction, so spores produced in this way are sometimes referred to as "sexual spores."

The sexual processes of karyogamy and meiosis generate extensive genetic variation, a prerequisite for natural selection. (See Chapters 13 and 23 to review how sex can increase genetic diversity.) The heterokaryotic condition also offers some of the advantages of diploidy in that one haploid genome may compensate for harmful mutations in the other.

Asexual Reproduction

Although many fungi can reproduce both sexually and asexually, some 20,000 species are only known to reproduce asexually. As with sexual reproduction, the processes of asexual reproduction vary widely among fungi.

Many fungi reproduce asexually by growing as filamentous fungi that produce (haploid) spores by mitosis; such species are informally referred to as **molds** if they form visible mycelia. Depending on your housekeeping habits, you may have observed molds in your kitchen, forming furry carpets on bread or fruit (Figure 31.6).

1.5 μm

▲ **Figure 31.6 *Penicillium*, a mold commonly encountered as a decomposer of food.** The bead-like clusters in the colorized SEM are conidia, structures involved in asexual reproduction.

Molds typically grow rapidly and produce many spores asexually, enabling the fungi to colonize new sources of food. Many species that produce such spores can also reproduce sexually if they happen to contact a member of their species of a different mating type.

Other fungi reproduce asexually by growing as single-celled yeasts. Instead of producing spores, asexual reproduction in yeasts occurs by ordinary cell division or by the pinching of small "bud cells" off a parent cell (Figure 31.7). As already mentioned, some fungi that grow as yeasts can also grow as filamentous mycelia.

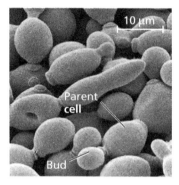

▲ Figure 31.7 **The yeast** *Sac-charomyces cerevisiae* **in several stages of budding (SEM).**

Many yeasts and filamentous fungi have no known sexual stage in their life cycle. Since early mycologists (biologists who study fungi) classified fungi based mainly on their type of sexual structure, this posed a problem. Mycologists have traditionally lumped all fungi lacking sexual reproduction into a group called **deuteromycetes** (from the Greek *deutero*, second, and *mycete*, fungus). Whenever a sexual stage is discovered for a so-called deuteromycete, the species is reclassified in a particular phylum, depending on the type of sexual structures it forms. In addition to searching for sexual stages of such unassigned fungi, mycologists can now use genomic techniques to classify them.

CONCEPT CHECK 31.2

1. **MAKE CONNECTIONS** Compare Figure 31.5 with Figure 13.6. In terms of haploidy versus diploidy, how do the life cycles of fungi and humans differ?

2. **WHAT IF?** Suppose that you sample the DNA of two mushrooms on opposite sides of your yard and find that they are identical. Propose two hypotheses that could reasonably account for this result.

For suggested answers, see Appendix A.

CONCEPT 31.3

The ancestor of fungi was an aquatic, single-celled, flagellated protist

Data from both paleontology and molecular systematics offer insights into the early evolution of fungi. As a result, systematists now recognize that fungi and animals are more closely related to each other than either group is to plants or most other eukaryotes.

▲ Figure 31.8 **Fungi and their close relatives.** Molecular evidence indicates that the nucleariids, a group of single-celled protists, are the closest living relatives of fungi. The three parallel lines leading to the chytrids indicate that this group is paraphyletic.

The Origin of Fungi

Phylogenetic analyses suggest that fungi evolved from a flagellated ancestor. While the majority of fungi lack flagella, some of the earliest-diverging lineages of fungi (the chytrids, as we'll discuss shortly) do have flagella. Moreover, most of the protists that share a close common ancestor with animals and fungi also have flagella. DNA sequence data indicate that these three groups of eukaryotes—the fungi, the animals, and their protistan relatives—form a clade (Figure 31.8). As discussed in Chapter 28, members of this clade are called **opisthokonts**, a name that refers to the posterior (*opistho-*) location of the flagellum in these organisms.

DNA sequence data also indicate that fungi are more closely related to several groups of single-celled protists than they are to animals, suggesting that the ancestor of fungi was unicellular. One such group of unicellular protists, the **nucleariids**, consists of amoebas that feed on algae and bacteria. DNA evidence further indicates that animals are more closely related to a *different* group of protists (the choanoflagellates) than they are to either fungi or nucleariids. Together, these results suggest that multicellularity must have evolved in animals and fungi independently, from different single-celled ancestors.

Using molecular clock analyses, scientists have estimated that the ancestors of animals and fungi diverged into separate lineages 1–1.5 billion years ago. Fossils of certain unicellular, marine eukaryotes that lived as early as 1.5 billion years ago have been interpreted as fungi, but those claims remain controversial. Furthermore, although most scientists think that fungi originated in aquatic environments, the oldest fossils that are widely accepted as fungi are of terrestrial species that lived about 460 million years ago (Figure 31.9). Overall, more

▲ Figure 31.9 **Fossil fungal hyphae and spores from the Ordovician period (about 460 million years ago) (LM).**

fossils will be needed to help clarify when fungi originated and what features were present in their earliest lineages.

Early-Diverging Fungal Groups

Insights into the nature of early-diverging fungal groups have begun to emerge from recent genomic studies. For example, several studies have identified chytrids in the genus *Rozella* as one of the first lineages to have diverged from the fungal common ancestor. Furthermore, results in a 2011 study placed *Rozella* within a large, previously unknown clade of unicellular fungi, tentatively called "cryptomycota." Like *Rozella* (and chytrids in general), fungi in the cryptomycota clade have flagellated spores. Current evidence indicates that *Rozella* and other members of the cryptomycota are unique among fungi in that they do not synthesize a chitin-rich cell wall during any of their life cycle stages. This suggests that a cell wall strengthened by chitin—a key structural feature of the fungi—may have arisen after the cryptomycota diverged from other fungi.

The Move to Land

Plants colonized land about 470 million years ago (see Chapter 29), and fungi may well have colonized land before plants. Indeed, some researchers have described life on land before the arrival of plants as a "green slime" that consisted of cyanobacteria, algae, and a variety of small, heterotrophic species, including fungi. With their capacity for extracellular digestion, fungi would have been well suited for feeding on other early terrestrial organisms (or their remains).

Once on land, some fungi formed symbiotic associations with early land plants. For example, 405-million-year-old fossils of the early land plant *Aglaophyton* contain evidence of mycorrhizal relationships between plants and fungi (see Figure 25.12). This evidence includes fossils of hyphae that have penetrated within plant cells and formed structures that resemble the haustoria of arbuscular mycorrhizae. Similar structures have been found in a variety of other early land plants, suggesting that plants probably existed in beneficial relationships with fungi from the earliest periods of colonization of land. The earliest land plants lacked roots, limiting their ability to extract nutrients from the soil. As occurs in mycorrhizal associations today, it is likely that soil nutrients were transferred to early land plants via the extensive mycelia formed by their symbiotic fungal partners.

Support for the antiquity of mycorrhizal associations has also come from recent molecular studies. For a mycorrhizal fungus and its plant partner to establish a symbiotic relationship, certain genes must be expressed by the fungus and other genes must be expressed by the plant. Researchers focused on three plant genes (called "*sym*" genes) whose expression is required for the formation of mycorrhizae in flowering plants. They found that these genes were present in all major plant lineages, including basal lineages such as liverworts (see Figure 29.7). Furthermore, after they transferred a liverwort *sym* gene to a flowering plant mutant that could not form mycorrhizae, the mutant recovered its ability to form mycorrhizae. These results suggest that mycorrhizal *sym* genes were present in the common ancestor of land plants—and that the function of these genes has been conserved for hundreds of millions of years as plants continued to adapt to life on land.

CONCEPT CHECK 31.3

1. Why are fungi classified as opisthokonts despite the fact that most fungi lack flagella?
2. Describe the importance of mycorrhizae, both today and in the colonization of land. What evidence supports the antiquity of mycorrhizal associations?
3. **WHAT IF?** If fungi colonized land before plants, where might the fungi have lived? How would their food sources have differed from what they feed on today?

For suggested answers, see Appendix A.

CONCEPT 31.4

Fungi have radiated into a diverse set of lineages

In the past decade, molecular analyses have helped clarify the evolutionary relationships between fungal groups, although there are still areas of uncertainty. **Figure 31.10** presents a simplified version of one current hypothesis. In this section, we will survey each of the major fungal groups identified in this phylogenetic tree.

The fungal groups shown in Figure 31.10 may represent only a small fraction of the diversity of extant fungi. While there are roughly 100,000 known species of fungi, scientists have estimated that the actual diversity may be closer to 1.5 million species. Two metagenomic studies published in 2011 support such higher estimates: the cryptomycota (see Concept 31.3) and other entirely new groups of unicellular fungi were discovered, and the genetic variation found in some of these groups is as large as that found across all of the groups shown in Figure 31.10.

Chytrids

Chytrids
Zygomycetes
Glomeromycetes
Ascomycetes
Basidiomycetes

The fungi classified in the phylum Chytridiomycota, called **chytrids**, are ubiquitous in lakes and soil, and as described in several recent metagenomic studies, more than 20 new clades of chytrids have been found in hydrothermal vent and other marine communities. Some of the approximately 1,000 chytrid species are decomposers, while others are parasites of protists, other fungi, plants, or animals; as

Exploring Fungal Diversity

Many mycologists currently recognize five major groups of fungi, although recent genomic evidence indicates that the chytrids and zygomycetes are paraphyletic (as indicated by the parallel lines).

Chytrids (1,000 species)

In chytrids such as *Chytridium*, the globular fruiting body forms multicellular, branched hyphae (LM); other species are single-celled. Ubiquitous in lakes and soil, chytrids have flagellated spores and are thought to include some of the earliest fungal groups to diverge from other fungi.

Hyphae   25 μm

Zygomycetes (1,000 species)

The hyphae of some zygomycetes, including this mold in the genus *Mucor* (LM), grow rapidly on foods such as fruits and bread. As such, the fungi may act as decomposers (if the food is not alive) or parasites; other species live as neutral (commensal) symbionts.

Glomeromycetes (160 species)

The glomeromycetes form arbuscular mycorrhizae with plant roots, supplying minerals and other nutrients to the roots; more than 80% of all plant species have such mutualistic partnerships with glomeromycetes. This LM shows glomeromycete hyphae (filaments stained dark blue) within a plant root.

Fungal hypha   25 μm

Ascomycetes (65,000 species)

Also called sac fungi, members of this diverse group are common to many marine, freshwater, and terrestrial habitats. The cup-shaped ascocarp (fruiting body) of the ascomycete shown here (*Aleuria aurantia*) gives this species its common name: orange peel fungus.

Basidiomycetes (30,000 species)

Widely important as decomposers and ectomycorrhizal fungi, basidiomycetes, or club fungi, are unusual in having a long-lived, heterokaryotic stage in which each cell has two nuclei (one from each parent). The fruiting bodies—commonly called mushrooms—of this fly agaric (*Amanita muscaria*) are a familiar sight in coniferous forests of the Northern Hemisphere.

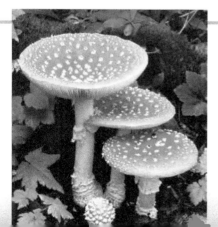

we'll see later in the chapter, one such chytrid parasite has likely contributed to the global decline of amphibian populations. Still other chytrids are important mutualists. For example, anaerobic chytrids that live in the digestive tracts of sheep and cattle help to break down plant matter, thereby contributing significantly to the animal's growth.

▲ Figure 31.11 Flagellated chytrid zoospore (TEM).

As discussed earlier, molecular evidence indicates that some chytrid lineages diverged early in fungal evolution. The fact that chytrids are unique among fungi in having flagellated spores, called **zoospores** (Figure 31.11), agrees with this hypothesis. Like other fungi, chytrids (other than those in the recently discovered cryptomycota clade) have cell walls made of chitin, and they also share certain key enzymes and metabolic pathways with other fungal groups. Some chytrids form colonies with hyphae, while others exist as single spherical cells.

Zygomycetes

Chytrids
Zygomycetes
Glomeromycetes
Ascomycetes
Basidiomycetes

There are approximately 1,000 known species of **zygomycetes**, fungi in the phylum Zygomycota. This diverse phylum includes species of fast-growing molds responsible for causing foods such as bread, peaches, strawberries, and sweet potatoes to rot during storage. Other zygomycetes live as parasites or as commensal (neutral) symbionts of animals.

The life cycle of *Rhizopus stolonifer* (black bread mold) is fairly typical of zygomycete species (Figure 31.12). Its

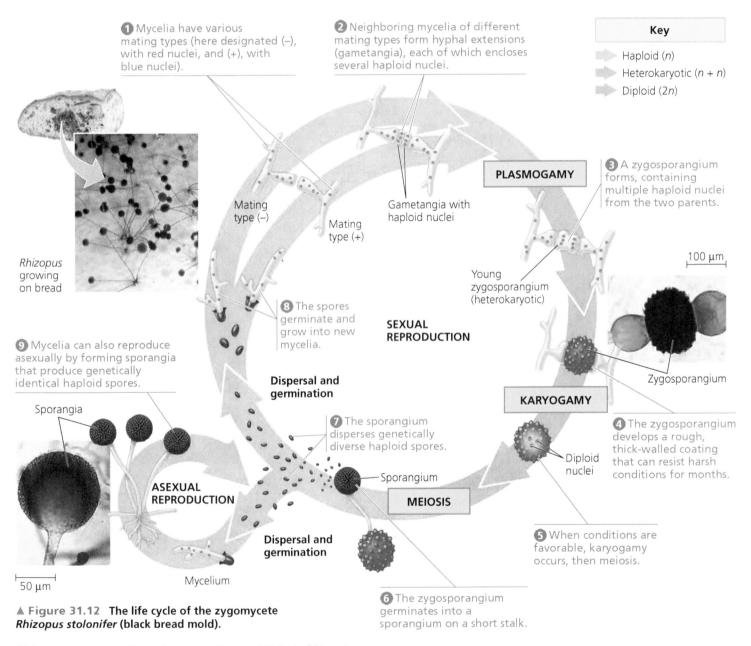

❶ Mycelia have various mating types (here designated (–), with red nuclei, and (+), with blue nuclei).

❷ Neighboring mycelia of different mating types form hyphal extensions (gametangia), each of which encloses several haploid nuclei.

Key

Haploid (*n*)
Heterokaryotic (*n* + *n*)
Diploid (2*n*)

Rhizopus growing on bread

Mating type (–)

Mating type (+)

Gametangia with haploid nuclei

PLASMOGAMY

❸ A zygosporangium forms, containing multiple haploid nuclei from the two parents.

Young zygosporangium (heterokaryotic)

100 μm

Zygosporangium

❽ The spores germinate and grow into new mycelia.

SEXUAL REPRODUCTION

KARYOGAMY

❹ The zygosporangium develops a rough, thick-walled coating that can resist harsh conditions for months.

❾ Mycelia can also reproduce asexually by forming sporangia that produce genetically identical haploid spores.

Sporangia

Dispersal and germination

❼ The sporangium disperses genetically diverse haploid spores.

Diploid nuclei

Sporangium

MEIOSIS

❺ When conditions are favorable, karyogamy occurs, then meiosis.

ASEXUAL REPRODUCTION

Dispersal and germination

50 μm

Mycelium

❻ The zygosporangium germinates into a sporangium on a short stalk.

▲ Figure 31.12 **The life cycle of the zygomycete** *Rhizopus stolonifer* **(black bread mold).**

◀ **Figure 31.13** *Pilobolus* aiming its sporangia. This zygomycete decomposes animal dung. Its spore-bearing hyphae bend toward light, where there are likely to be openings in the vegetation through which spores may reach fresh grass. The fungus then launches its sporangia in a jet of water that can travel up to 2.5 m. Grazing animals ingest the fungi with the grass and then scatter the spores in feces, thereby enabling the next generation of fungi to grow.

hyphae spread out over the food surface, penetrate it, and absorb nutrients. The hyphae are coenocytic, with septa found only where reproductive cells are formed. In the asexual phase, bulbous black sporangia develop at the tips of upright hyphae. Within each sporangium, hundreds of genetically identical haploid spores develop and are dispersed through the air. Spores that happen to land on moist food germinate, growing into new mycelia.

If environmental conditions deteriorate—for instance, if the mold consumes all its food—*Rhizopus* may reproduce sexually. The parents in a sexual union are mycelia of different mating types, which possess different chemical markers but may appear identical. Plasmogamy produces a sturdy structure called a **zygosporangium** (plural, *zygosporangia*), in which karyogamy and then meiosis occur. Note that while a zygosporangium represents the zygote (2*n*) stage in the life cycle, it is not a zygote in the usual sense (that is, a cell with one diploid nucleus). Rather, a zygosporangium is a multinucleate structure, first heterokaryotic with many haploid nuclei from the two parents, then with many diploid nuclei after karyogamy.

Zygosporangia are resistant to freezing and drying and are metabolically inactive. When conditions improve, the nuclei of the zygosporangium undergo meiosis, the zygosporangium germinates into a sporangium, and the sporangium releases genetically diverse haploid spores that may colonize a new substrate. Some zygomycetes, such as *Pilobolus*, can actually "aim" and then shoot their sporangia toward bright light (**Figure 31.13**).

Glomeromycetes

Chytrids
Zygomycetes
Glomeromycetes
Ascomycetes
Basidiomycetes

The **glomeromycetes**, fungi assigned to the phylum Glomeromycota, were formerly thought to be zygomycetes. But recent molecular studies, including a phylogenetic analysis of DNA sequence data from hundreds of fungal species, indicate that glomeromycetes form a separate clade (monophyletic group). Although only 160 species have been identified to date, the glomeromycetes are an ecologically

▲ **Figure 31.14** **Arbuscular mycorrhizae.** Most glomeromycetes form arbuscular mycorrhizae with plant roots, supplying minerals and other nutrients to the roots. This SEM depicts the branched hyphae—an arbuscule—of *Glomus mosseae* bulging into a root cell by pushing in the membrane (the root has been treated to remove the cytoplasm).

significant group in that nearly all of them form arbuscular mycorrhizae (**Figure 31.14**). The tips of the hyphae that push into plant root cells branch into tiny treelike arbuscules. More than 80% of all plant species have such mutualistic partnerships with glomeromycetes.

Ascomycetes

Chytrids
Zygomycetes
Glomeromycetes
Ascomycetes
Basidiomycetes

Mycologists have described 65,000 species of **ascomycetes**, fungi in the phylum Ascomycota, from a wide variety of marine, freshwater, and terrestrial habitats. The defining feature of ascomycetes is the production of spores (called ascospores) in saclike **asci** (singular, *ascus*); thus, they are commonly called *sac fungi*. During their sexual stage, most ascomycetes develop fruiting bodies, called **ascocarps**, which range in size from microscopic to macroscopic (**Figure 31.15**). The ascocarps contain the spore-forming asci.

▶ *Tuber melanosporum* is a truffle species that forms ectomycorrhizae with trees. The ascocarp grows underground and emits a strong odor. These ascocarps have been dug up and the middle one sliced open.

◀ The edible ascocarp of *Morchella esculenta*, the tasty morel, is often found under trees in orchards.

▲ **Figure 31.15** **Ascomycetes (sac fungi).**

? *Ascomycetes vary greatly in morphology (see also Figure 31.10). How could you confirm that a fungus is an ascomycete?*

Ascomycetes vary in size and complexity from unicellular yeasts to elaborate cup fungi and morels (see Figure 31.15). They include some of the most devastating plant pathogens, which we will discuss later. However, many ascomycetes are important decomposers, particularly of plant material. More than 25% of all ascomycete species live with green algae or cyanobacteria in beneficial symbiotic associations called lichens. Some ascomycetes form mycorrhizae with plants. Many others live between mesophyll cells in leaves; some of these species release toxic compounds that help protect the plant from insects.

Although the life cycles of various ascomycete groups differ in the details of their reproductive structures and processes, we'll illustrate some common elements using the bread mold *Neurospora crassa* (Figure 31.16). Ascomycetes reproduce asexually by producing enormous numbers of asexual spores called **conidia** (singular, *conidium*). Unlike the asexual spores of most zygomycetes, conidia are not formed inside sporangia. Rather, they are produced externally at the tips of specialized hyphae called conidiophores, often in clusters or long chains, from which they may be dispersed by the wind.

Conidia may also be involved in sexual reproduction, fusing with hyphae from a mycelium of a different mating type, as occurs in *Neurospora*. Fusion of two different mating types is followed by plasmogamy, resulting in the

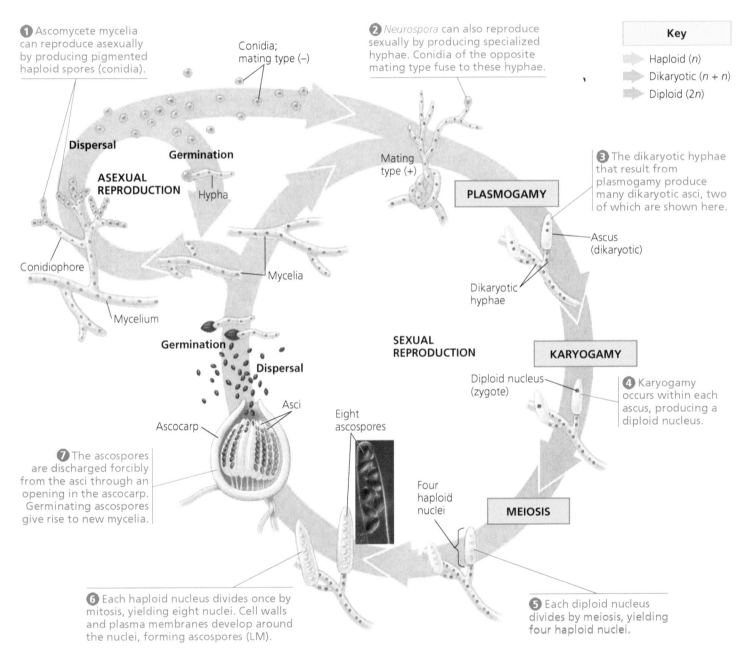

❶ Ascomycete mycelia can reproduce asexually by producing pigmented haploid spores (conidia).

Conidia; mating type (−)

❷ *Neurospora* can also reproduce sexually by producing specialized hyphae. Conidia of the opposite mating type fuse to these hyphae.

Key

Haploid (*n*)
Dikaryotic (*n* + *n*)
Diploid (2*n*)

Dispersal

Germination

ASEXUAL REPRODUCTION

Hypha

Conidiophore

Mycelium

Mycelia

Mating type (+)

PLASMOGAMY

❸ The dikaryotic hyphae that result from plasmogamy produce many dikaryotic asci, two of which are shown here.

Ascus (dikaryotic)

Dikaryotic hyphae

SEXUAL REPRODUCTION

KARYOGAMY

Diploid nucleus (zygote)

❹ Karyogamy occurs within each ascus, producing a diploid nucleus.

Germination

Dispersal

Asci

Eight ascospores

Ascocarp

❼ The ascospores are discharged forcibly from the asci through an opening in the ascocarp. Germinating ascospores give rise to new mycelia.

Four haploid nuclei

MEIOSIS

❻ Each haploid nucleus divides once by mitosis, yielding eight nuclei. Cell walls and plasma membranes develop around the nuclei, forming ascospores (LM).

❺ Each diploid nucleus divides by meiosis, yielding four haploid nuclei.

▲ Figure 31.16 **The life cycle of *Neurospora crassa*, an ascomycete.** *Neurospora* is a bread mold and research organism that also grows in the wild on burned vegetation.

formation of dikaryotic cells, each with two haploid nuclei representing the two parents. The cells at the tips of these dikaryotic hyphae develop into many asci. Within each ascus, karyogamy combines the two parental genomes, and then meiosis forms four genetically different nuclei. This is usually followed by a mitotic division, forming eight ascospores. The ascospores develop in and are eventually discharged from the ascocarp.

Compared to the life cycle of zygomycetes, the extended dikaryotic stage of ascomycetes (and also basidiomycetes) provides additional opportunities for genetic recombination. In *Neurospora*, for example, many dikaryotic cells can develop into asci. The haploid nuclei in these asci fuse, and their genomes then recombine during meiosis, resulting in a multitude of genetically different offspring from one mating event (see steps 3–5 in Figure 31.16).

As we discussed in Chapter 17, biologists in the 1930s used *Neurospora* in research that led to the one gene–one enzyme hypothesis. Today, this ascomycete continues to serve as a model research organism. In 2003, its entire genome was published. This tiny fungus has about three-fourths as many genes as the fruit fly *Drosophila* and about half as many as a human (Table 31.1). The *Neurospora* genome is relatively compact, having few of the stretches of noncoding DNA that occupy so much space in the genomes of humans and many other eukaryotes. In fact, there is evidence that *Neurospora* has a genomic defense system that prevents noncoding DNA such as transposons from accumulating.

Table 31.1	Comparison of Gene Density in *Neurospora*, *Drosophila*, and *Homo sapiens*		
	Genome Size (million base pairs)	Number of Genes	Gene Density (genes per million base pairs)
Neurospora crassa (ascomycete fungus)	41	9,700	236
Drosophila melanogaster (fruit fly)	165	14,000	85
Homo sapiens (human)	3,000	<21,000	7

Basidiomycetes

Chytrids
Zygomycetes
Glomeromycetes
Ascomycetes
Basidiomycetes

About 30,000 species, including mushrooms, puffballs, and shelf fungi, are called **basidiomycetes** and are classified in the phylum Basidiomycota **(Figure 31.17)**. This

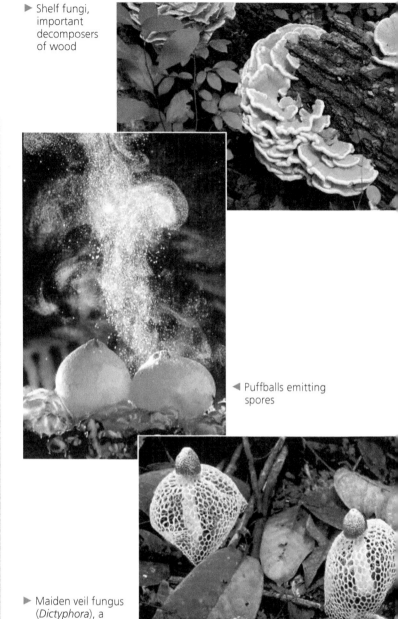

▶ Shelf fungi, important decomposers of wood

◀ Puffballs emitting spores

▶ Maiden veil fungus (*Dictyphora*), a fungus with an odor like rotting meat

▲ Figure 31.17 Basidiomycetes (club fungi).

phylum also includes mutualists that form mycorrhizae and two groups of destructive plant parasites: rusts and smuts. The name of the phylum derives from the **basidium** (plural, *basidia*; Latin for "little pedestals"), a cell in which karyogamy occurs, followed immediately by meiosis. The club-like shape of the basidium also gives rise to the common name *club fungus*.

Basidiomycetes are important decomposers of wood and other plant material. Of all the fungi, certain basidiomycetes are the best at decomposing the complex polymer lignin, an abundant component of wood. Many shelf fungi break down the wood of weak or damaged trees and continue to decompose the wood after the tree dies.

The life cycle of a basidiomycete usually includes a long-lived dikaryotic mycelium (**Figure 31.18**). As in ascomycetes, this extended dikaryotic stage provides many opportunities for genetic recombination events, in effect multiplying the result of a single mating. Periodically, in response to environmental stimuli, the mycelium reproduces sexually by producing elaborate fruiting bodies called **basidiocarps**. The common white mushrooms in the supermarket are familiar examples of a basidiocarp.

By concentrating growth in the hyphae of mushrooms, a basidiomycete mycelium can erect its fruiting structures in just a few hours; a mushroom pops up as it absorbs water and as cytoplasm streams in from the dikaryotic mycelium. By this process, a ring of mushrooms, popularly called a "fairy ring," may appear literally overnight (**Figure 31.19**). The mycelium below the fairy ring expands outward at a rate of about 30 cm per year, decomposing organic matter in the soil as it grows. Some giant fairy rings are produced by mycelia that are centuries old.

After a mushroom forms, its cap supports and protects a large surface area of dikaryotic basidia on gills. During karyogamy, the two nuclei in each basidium fuse, producing a diploid nucleus (see Figure 31.18). This nucleus then undergoes meiosis, yielding four haploid nuclei, each of which ultimately develops into a basidiospore. Large numbers of basidiospores are produced: The gills of a common white mushroom have a surface area of about 200 cm² and may drop a billion basidiospores, which blow away.

▼ **Figure 31.18 The life cycle of a mushroom-forming basidiomycete.**

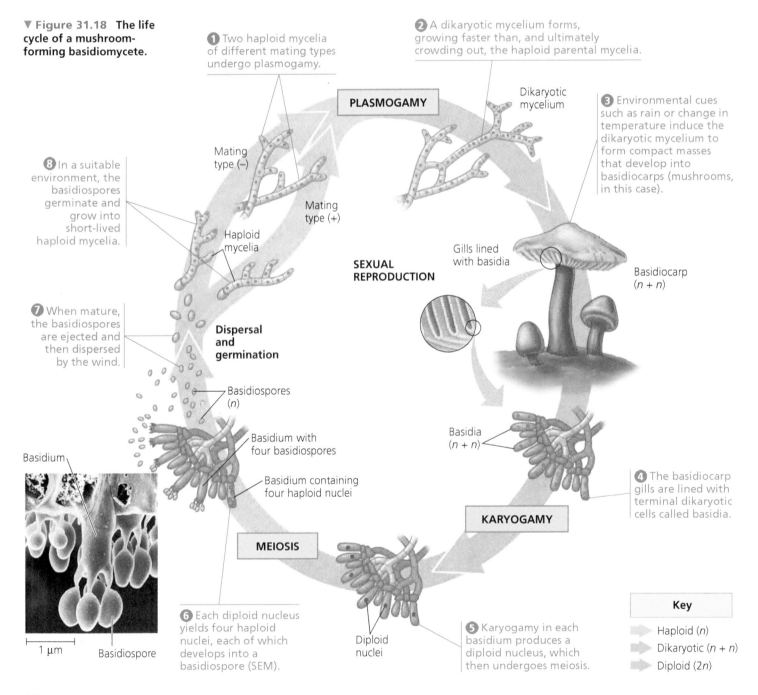

① Two haploid mycelia of different mating types undergo plasmogamy.

PLASMOGAMY

② A dikaryotic mycelium forms, growing faster than, and ultimately crowding out, the haploid parental mycelia.

Dikaryotic mycelium

③ Environmental cues such as rain or change in temperature induce the dikaryotic mycelium to form compact masses that develop into basidiocarps (mushrooms, in this case).

Mating type (–)

Mating type (+)

⑧ In a suitable environment, the basidiospores germinate and grow into short-lived haploid mycelia.

Haploid mycelia

SEXUAL REPRODUCTION

Gills lined with basidia

Basidiocarp (n + n)

⑦ When mature, the basidiospores are ejected and then dispersed by the wind.

Dispersal and germination

Basidiospores (n)

Basidium with four basidiospores

Basidium containing four haploid nuclei

Basidium

Basidia (n + n)

④ The basidiocarp gills are lined with terminal dikaryotic cells called basidia.

KARYOGAMY

MEIOSIS

⑥ Each diploid nucleus yields four haploid nuclei, each of which develops into a basidiospore (SEM).

Diploid nuclei

⑤ Karyogamy in each basidium produces a diploid nucleus, which then undergoes meiosis.

1 μm

Basidiospore

Key

Haploid (n)

Dikaryotic (n + n)

Diploid (2n)

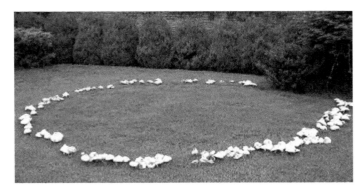

▲ **Figure 31.19** **A fairy ring.** According to legend, mushroom rings spring up where fairies have danced on a moonlit night. The text provides a biological explanation of how these rings form.

CONCEPT CHECK 31.4

1. What feature of chytrids supports the hypothesis that they include members of early-diverging fungal lineages?

2. Give examples of how form fits function in zygomycetes, glomeromycetes, ascomycetes, and basidiomycetes.

3. **WHAT IF?** Suppose that the mutation of an ascomycete changed its life cycle so that plasmogamy, karyogamy, and meiosis occurred in quick succession. How might this affect the ascospores and ascocarps?

For suggested answers, see Appendix A.

CONCEPT 31.5

Fungi play key roles in nutrient cycling, ecological interactions, and human welfare

In our survey of fungal classification, we've touched on some of the ways fungi influence other organisms. We will now look more closely at these impacts, focusing on how fungi act as decomposers, mutualists, and pathogens.

Fungi as Decomposers

Fungi are well adapted as decomposers of organic material, including the cellulose and lignin of plant cell walls. In fact, almost any carbon-containing substrate—even jet fuel and house paint—can be consumed by at least some fungi. The same is true of bacteria. As a result, fungi and bacteria are primarily responsible for keeping ecosystems stocked with the inorganic nutrients essential for plant growth. Without these decomposers, carbon, nitrogen, and other elements would remain tied up in organic matter. If that were to happen, plants and the animals that eat them could not exist because elements taken from the soil would not be returned (see Chapter 55). Without decomposers, life as we know it would cease.

Fungi as Mutualists

Fungi may form mutualistic relationships with plants, algae, cyanobacteria, and animals. Mutualistic fungi absorb nutrients from a host organism, but they reciprocate with actions that benefit the host—as we already saw for the key mycorrhizal associations that fungi form with most vascular plants.

Fungus-Plant Mutualisms

Along with mycorrhizal fungi, all plant species studied to date appear to harbor symbiotic **endophytes**, fungi (or bacteria) that live inside leaves or other plant parts without causing harm. Most fungal endophytes identified to date are ascomycetes. Fungal endophytes benefit certain grasses and other nonwoody plants by making toxins that deter herbivores or by increasing host plant tolerance of heat, drought, or heavy metals. As described in **Figure 31.20**, researchers

▼ **Figure 31.20** **Inquiry**

Do fungal endophytes benefit a woody plant?

Experiment Fungal endophytes are symbiotic fungi found within the bodies of all plants examined to date. A. Elizabeth Arnold, at the University of Arizona, Tucson, and colleagues tested whether fungal endophytes benefit the cacao tree (*Theobroma cacao*). This tree, whose name means "food of the gods" in Greek, is the source of the beans used to make chocolate, and it is cultivated throughout the tropics. A particular mixture of fungal endophytes was added to the leaves of some cacao seedlings, but not others. (In cacao, fungal endophytes colonize leaves after the seedling germinates.) The seedlings were then inoculated with a virulent pathogen, the protist *Phytophthora*.

Results Fewer leaves were killed by the pathogen in seedlings with fungal endophytes than in seedlings without endophytes. Among leaves that survived, pathogens damaged less of the leaf surface area in seedlings with endophytes than in seedlings without endophytes.

Endophyte not present; pathogen present (E−P+)

Both endophyte and pathogen present (E+P+)

Conclusion The presence of endophytes appears to benefit cacao trees by reducing the leaf mortality and damage caused by *Phytophthora*.

Source: A. E. Arnold et al., Fungal endophytes limit pathogen damage in a tropical tree, *Proceedings of the National Academy of Sciences* 100:15649–15654 (2003).

WHAT IF? *Arnold and colleagues also performed control treatments. Suggest two controls they might have used, and explain how each would be helpful in interpreting the results described here.*

▲ **Figure 31.21 Fungus-gardening insects.** These leaf-cutting ants depend on fungi to convert plant material to a form the insects can digest. The fungi, in turn, depend on the nutrients from the leaves the ants feed them.

studying how fungal endophytes affect a woody plant tested whether leaf endophytes benefit seedlings of the cacao tree, *Theobroma cacao*. Their findings show that the fungal endophytes of woody flowering plants can play an important role in defending against pathogens.

Fungus-Animal Mutualisms

As mentioned earlier, some fungi share their digestive services with animals, helping break down plant material in the guts of cattle and other grazing mammals. Many species of ants take advantage of the digestive power of fungi by raising them in "farms." Leaf-cutter ants, for example, scour tropical forests in search of leaves, which they cannot digest on their own but carry back to their nests and feed to the fungi (Figure 31.21). As the fungi grow, their hyphae develop specialized swollen tips that are rich in proteins and carbohydrates. The ants feed primarily on these nutrient-rich tips. Not only do the fungi break down plant leaves into substances the insects can digest, but they also detoxify plant defensive compounds that would otherwise kill or harm the ants. In some tropical forests, the fungi have helped these insects become the major consumers of leaves.

The evolution of such farmer ants and that of their fungal "crops" have been tightly linked for over 50 million years. The fungi have become so dependent on their caretakers that in many cases they can no longer survive without the ants, and vice versa.

Lichens

A **lichen** is a symbiotic association between a photosynthetic microorganism and a fungus in which millions of photosynthetic cells are held in a mass of fungal hyphae. Lichens grow on the surfaces of rocks, rotting logs, trees, and roofs in various forms (Figure 31.22). The photosynthetic partners

are unicellular or filamentous green algae or cyanobacteria. The fungal component is most often an ascomycete, but one glomeromycete and 75 basidiomycete lichens are known. The fungus usually gives a lichen its overall shape and structure, and tissues formed by hyphae account for most of the lichen's mass. The cells of the alga or cyanobacterium generally occupy an inner layer below the lichen surface (Figure 31.23).

The merger of fungus and alga or cyanobacterium is so complete that lichens are given scientific names as though they were single organisms; to date, 17,000 lichen species have been described. As might be expected of such "dual organisms," asexual reproduction as a symbiotic unit is common. This can occur either by fragmentation of the parental lichen or by the formation of **soredia** (singular, *soredium*), small clusters of hyphae with embedded algae (see Figure 31.23). The fungi of many lichens also reproduce sexually.

◀ A fruticose (shrublike) lichen

▶ A foliose (leaflike) lichen

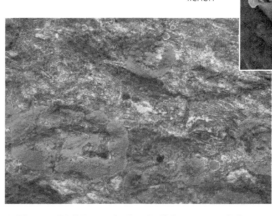

◀ Crustose (encrusting) lichens

▲ **Figure 31.22 Variation in lichen growth forms.**

Ascocarp of fungus

Fungal hyphae

Algal layer

Soredia

50 μm

Fungal hyphae

Algal cell

▲ **Figure 31.23 Anatomy of an ascomycete lichen** (colorized SEM).

In most lichens, each partner provides something the other could not obtain on its own. The alga or cyanobacterium provides carbon compounds; a cyanobacterium also fixes nitrogen (see Chapter 27) and provides organic nitrogen compounds. The fungus provides its photosynthetic partner with a suitable environment for growth. The physical arrangement of hyphae allows for gas exchange, protects the photosynthetic partner, and retains water and minerals, most of which are absorbed from airborne dust or from rain. The fungus also secretes acids, which aid in the uptake of minerals.

Lichens are important pioneers on cleared rock and soil surfaces, such as volcanic flows and burned forests. They break down the surface by physically penetrating and chemically attacking it, and they trap windblown soil. Nitrogen-fixing lichens also add organic nitrogen to some ecosystems. These processes make it possible for a succession of plants to grow (see Chapter 54). Fossils show that lichens were on land 420 million years ago. These early lichens may have modified rocks and soil much as they do today, helping pave the way for plants.

Fungi as Parasites

Like mutualistic fungi, parasitic fungi absorb nutrients from the cells of living hosts, but they provide no benefits in return. About 30% of the 100,000 known species of fungi make a living as parasites or pathogens, mostly of plants (**Figure 31.24**). An example of a plant pathogen is *Cryphonectria parasitica*, the ascomycete fungus that causes chestnut blight, which dramatically changed the landscape of the northeastern United States. Accidentally introduced on trees imported from Asia in the early 1900s, spores of the fungus entered cracks in the bark of American chestnut trees and produced hyphae, killing many trees. The once-common chestnuts now survive mainly as sprouts from the stumps of former trees. Another ascomycete, *Fusarium circinatum*, causes pine pitch canker, a disease that threatens pines throughout the world. Between 10% and 50% of the world's fruit harvest is lost annually due to fungi, and grain crops also suffer major losses each year.

Some fungi that attack food crops produce compounds that are toxic to humans. One example is the ascomycete *Claviceps purpurea*, which grows on rye plants, forming purple structures called ergots (see Figure 31.24c). If infected rye is milled into flour, toxins from the ergots can cause ergotism, characterized by gangrene, nervous spasms, burning sensations, hallucinations, and temporary insanity. An epidemic of ergotism around 944 CE killed up to 40,000 people in France. One compound that has been isolated from ergots is lysergic acid, the raw material from which the hallucinogen LSD is made.

Although animals are less susceptible to parasitic fungi than are plants, about 500 fungi are known to parasitize animals. One such parasite, the chytrid *Batrachochytrium dendrobatidis*, has been implicated in the recent decline or extinction of about 200 species of frogs and other

(a) Corn smut on corn

(b) Tar spot fungus on maple leaves

(c) Ergots on rye

▲ **Figure 31.24 Examples of fungal diseases of plants.**

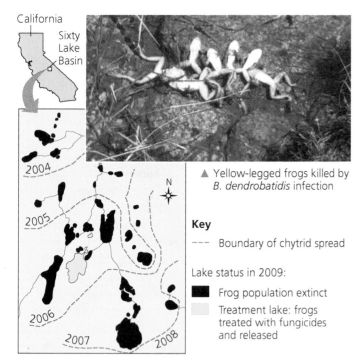

California

Sixty Lake Basin

2004
2005
2006
2007
2008

▲ Yellow-legged frogs killed by
B. dendrobatidis infection

Key

--- Boundary of chytrid spread

Lake status in 2009:

■ Frog population extinct

▫ Treatment lake: frogs treated with fungicides and released

▲ **Figure 31.25 Amphibians under attack.** Could a fungal parasite have caused some of the many amphibian population declines and extinctions in recent decades? One study found that the number of yellow-legged frogs (*Rana muscosa*) plummeted after the chytrid *Batrachochytrium dendrobatidis* reached the Sixty Lake Basin area of California. In the years leading up to the chytrid's 2004 arrival, there were more than 2,300 frogs in these lakes. By 2009, only 38 frogs remained; all the survivors were in two lakes (yellow) where frogs had been treated with a fungicide to reduce the chytrid's impact.

INTERPRET THE DATA *Do the data depicted indicate that the chytrid caused or is correlated to the drop in frog numbers? Explain.*

amphibians (**Figure 31.25**). This chytrid can cause severe skin infections, leading to massive die-offs. Field observations and studies of museum specimens indicate that *B. dendrobatidis* first appeared in frog populations shortly before their declines in Australia, Costa Rica, the United States, and other countries. In addition, in regions where it infects frogs, this chytrid has very low levels of genetic diversity. These findings are consistent with the hypothesis that *B. dendrobatidis* has emerged recently and spread rapidly across the globe, decimating many amphibian populations.

The general term for an infection in an animal by a fungal parasite is **mycosis**. In humans, skin mycoses include the disease ringworm, so named because it appears as circular red areas on the skin. Most commonly, the ascomycetes that cause ringworm grow on the feet, causing the intense itching and blisters known as athlete's foot. Though highly contagious, athlete's foot and other ringworm infections can be treated with fungicidal lotions and powders.

Systemic mycoses, by contrast, spread through the body and usually cause very serious illnesses. They are typically caused by inhaled spores. For example, coccidioidomycosis is a systemic mycosis that produces tuberculosis-like symptoms in the lungs. Each year, hundreds of cases in North America require treatment with antifungal drugs, without which the disease could be fatal.

Some mycoses are opportunistic, occurring only when a change in the body's microorganisms, chemical environment, or immune system allows fungi to grow unchecked. *Candida albicans*, for example, is one of the normal inhabitants of moist epithelia, such as the vaginal lining. Under certain circumstances, *Candida* can grow too rapidly and become pathogenic, leading to so-called "yeast infections." Many other opportunistic mycoses in humans have become more common in recent decades, due in part to AIDS, which compromises the immune system.

Practical Uses of Fungi

The dangers posed by fungi should not overshadow their immense benefits. We depend on their ecological services as decomposers and recyclers of organic matter. And without mycorrhizae, farming would be far less productive.

Mushrooms are not the only fungi of interest for human consumption. Fungi are used to ripen Roquefort and other blue cheeses. Morels and truffles, the edible fruiting bodies of various ascomycetes, are highly prized for their complex flavors (see Figure 31.15). These fungi can sell for hundreds to thousands of dollars a pound. Truffles release strong odors that attract mammals and insects, which in nature feed on them and disperse their spores. In some cases, the odors mimic the pheromones (sex attractants) of certain mammals. For example, the odors of several European truffles mimic the pheromones released by male pigs, which explains why truffle hunters use female pigs to help find these delicacies.

Humans have used yeasts to produce alcoholic beverages and bread for thousands of years. Under anaerobic conditions, yeasts ferment sugars to alcohol and CO_2, which causes dough to rise. Only relatively recently have the yeasts involved been separated into pure cultures for more controlled use. The yeast *Saccharomyces cerevisiae* is the most important of all cultured fungi (see Figure 31.7). It is available as many strains of baker's yeast and brewer's yeast.

Many fungi have great medical value as well. For example, a compound extracted from ergots is used to reduce high blood pressure and to stop maternal bleeding after childbirth. Some fungi produce antibiotics that are effective in treating bacterial infections. In fact, the first antibiotic discovered was penicillin, made by the ascomycete mold *Penicillium*. Other examples of pharmaceuticals derived from fungi include cholesterol-lowering drugs and cyclosporine, a drug used to suppress the immune system after organ transplants.

Fungi also figure prominently in basic research. For example, the yeast *Saccharomyces cerevisiae* is used to study the molecular genetics of eukaryotes because its cells are easy to culture and manipulate. Scientists are gaining insight into the genes involved in Parkinson's disease by examining the functions of homologous genes in *S. cerevisiae*.

Genetically modified fungi also hold much promise. For example, scientists have succeeded in engineering a strain of *S. cerevisiae* that produces human glycoproteins, including insulin-like growth factor. Such fungus-produced glycoproteins have the potential to treat people with medical conditions that prevent them from producing these compounds. Meanwhile, other researchers are sequencing the genome of *Gliocladium roseum*, an ascomycete that can grow on wood or agricultural waste and that naturally produces hydrocarbons similar to those in diesel fuel (Figure 31.26). They hope to decipher the metabolic pathways by which *G. roseum* synthesizes hydrocarbons, with the goal of harnessing those pathways to produce biofuels without reducing land area for growing food crops (as occurs when ethanol is produced from corn).

Having now completed our survey of the kingdom Fungi, we will turn in the rest of this unit to the closely related kingdom Animalia, to which we humans belong.

▶ **Figure 31.26 Can this fungus be used to produce biofuels?** The ascomycete *Gliocladium roseum* can produce hydrocarbons similar to those in diesel fuel (colorized SEM).

CONCEPT CHECK 31.5

1. What are some of the benefits that lichen algae can derive from their relationship with fungi?

2. What characteristics of pathogenic fungi result in their being efficiently transmitted?

3. **WHAT IF?** How might life on Earth differ from what we know today if no mutualistic relationships between fungi and other organisms had ever evolved?

For suggested answers, see Appendix A.

31 Chapter Review

SUMMARY OF KEY CONCEPTS

CONCEPT 31.1

Fungi are heterotrophs that feed by absorption (pp. 649–651)

- All **fungi** (including decomposers and symbionts) are heterotrophs that acquire nutrients by absorption. Many fungi secrete enzymes that break down complex molecules.
- Most fungi grow as thin, multicellular filaments called **hyphae**; relatively few species grow only as single-celled **yeasts**. In their multicellular form, fungi consist of **mycelia**, networks of branched hyphae adapted for absorption. Mycorrhizal fungi have specialized hyphae that enable them to form a mutually beneficial relationship with plants.

? *How does the morphology of multicellular fungi affect the efficiency of nutrient absorption?*

CONCEPT 31.2

Fungi produce spores through sexual or asexual life cycles (pp. 651–653)

- In fungi, the sexual life cycle involves cytoplasmic fusion (**plasmogamy**) and nuclear fusion (**karyogamy**), with an intervening heterokaryotic stage in which cells have haploid nuclei from two parents. The diploid cells resulting from karyogamy are short-lived and undergo meiosis, producing genetically diverse haploid **spores**.

- Many fungi can reproduce asexually as filamentous fungi or yeasts.

DRAW IT *Draw a generalized fungal life cycle, labeling asexual and sexual reproduction, meiosis, plasmogamy, karyogamy, and the points in the cycle when spores and the zygote are produced.*

CONCEPT 31.3

The ancestor of fungi was an aquatic, single-celled, flagellated protist (pp. 653–654)

- Molecular evidence indicates that fungi and animals diverged 1–1.5 billion years ago from a common unicellular ancestor that had a flagellum. However, the oldest fossils that are widely accepted as fungi are 460 million years old.
- Chytrids, a group of fungi with flagellated spores, include some basal lineages.
- Fungi were among the earliest colonizers of land; fossil evidence indicates that these included species that were symbionts with early land plants.

? *Did multicellularity originate independently in fungi and animals? Explain.*

CONCEPT 31.4

Fungi have radiated into a diverse set of lineages (pp. 654–661)

Fungal Phylum	Distinguishing Features	
Chytridiomycota (chytrids)	Flagellated spores	
Zygomycota (zygomycetes)	Resistant zygosporangium as sexual stage	
Glomeromycota (arbuscular mycorrhizal fungi)	Arbuscular mycorrhizae formed with plants	
Ascomycota (ascomycetes)	Sexual spores (ascospores) borne internally in sacs called asci; vast numbers of asexual spores (conidia) produced	
Basidiomycota (basidiomycetes)	Elaborate fruiting body (basidiocarp) containing many basidia that produce sexual spores (basidiospores)	

DRAW IT *Draw a phylogenetic tree of the major groups of fungi.*

CONCEPT 31.5

Fungi play key roles in nutrient cycling, ecological interactions, and human welfare (pp. 661–665)

- Fungi perform essential recycling of chemical elements between the living and nonliving world.
- **Lichens** are highly integrated symbiotic associations of fungi and algae or cyanobacteria.
- Many fungi are parasites, mostly of plants.
- Humans use fungi for food and to make antibiotics.

? *How are fungi important as decomposers, mutualists, and pathogens?*

TEST YOUR UNDERSTANDING

LEVEL 1: KNOWLEDGE/COMPREHENSION

1. *All* fungi are
   a. symbiotic.
   b. heterotrophic.
   c. flagellated.
   d. decomposers.

2. Which of the following cells or structures are associated with *asexual* reproduction in fungi?
   a. ascospores
   b. basidiospores
   c. zygosporangia
   d. conidiophores

3. The closest relatives of fungi are thought to be the
   a. animals
   b. vascular plants
   c. mosses
   d. slime molds

LEVEL 2: APPLICATION/ANALYSIS

4. The most important adaptive advantage associated with the filamentous nature of fungal mycelia is
   a. the ability to form haustoria and parasitize other organisms.
   b. the potential to inhabit almost all terrestrial habitats.
   c. the increased chance of contact between mating types.
   d. an extensive surface area well suited for invasive growth and absorptive nutrition.

5. **SCIENTIFIC INQUIRY**
   INTERPRET THE DATA The grass *Dichanthelium languinosum* lives in hot soils and houses fungi of the genus *Curvularia* as endophytes. Researchers tested the impact of *Curvularia* on the heat tolerance of this grass. They grew plants without (E−) and with (E+) *Curvularia* endophytes at different temperatures and measured plant mass and the number of new shoots the plants produced. Draw a bar graph for plant mass versus temperature and interpret it.

Soil Temp.	*Curvularia* + or −	Plant Mass (g)	No. of New Shoots
30°C	E−	16.2	32
	E+	22.8	60
35°C	E−	21.7	43
	E+	28.4	60
40°C	E−	8.8	10
	E+	22.2	37
45°C	E−	0	0
	E+	15.1	24

Source: R. S. Redman et al., Thermotolerance generated by plant/fungal symbiosis, *Science* 298:1581 (2002).

LEVEL 3: SYNTHESIS/EVALUATION

6. **EVOLUTION CONNECTION**
   The fungus-alga symbiosis that makes up a lichen is thought to have evolved multiple times independently in different fungal groups. However, lichens fall into three well-defined growth forms (see Figure 31.22). How could you test the following hypotheses: **Hypothesis 1:** Crustose, foliose, and fruticose lichens each represent a monophyletic group; and **Hypothesis 2:** Each lichen growth form represents convergent evolution by taxonomically diverse fungi.

7. **WRITE ABOUT A THEME: ORGANIZATION**
   As you read in this chapter, fungi have long formed symbiotic associations with plants and with algae. In a short essay (100–150 words), describe how these two types of associations may lead to emergent properties in biological communities.

8. **SYNTHESIZE YOUR KNOWLEDGE**

This wasp is the unfortunate victim of an entamopathogenic fungus (a parasitic fungus of insects). Write a paragraph describing what this image illustrates about the nutritional mode, body structure, and ecological role of the fungus.

For selected answers, see Appendix A.

MasteringBiology®

Students Go to **MasteringBiology** for assignments, the eText, and the Study Area with practice tests, animations, and activities.

Instructors Go to **MasteringBiology** for automatically graded tutorials and questions that you can assign to your students, plus Instructor Resources.

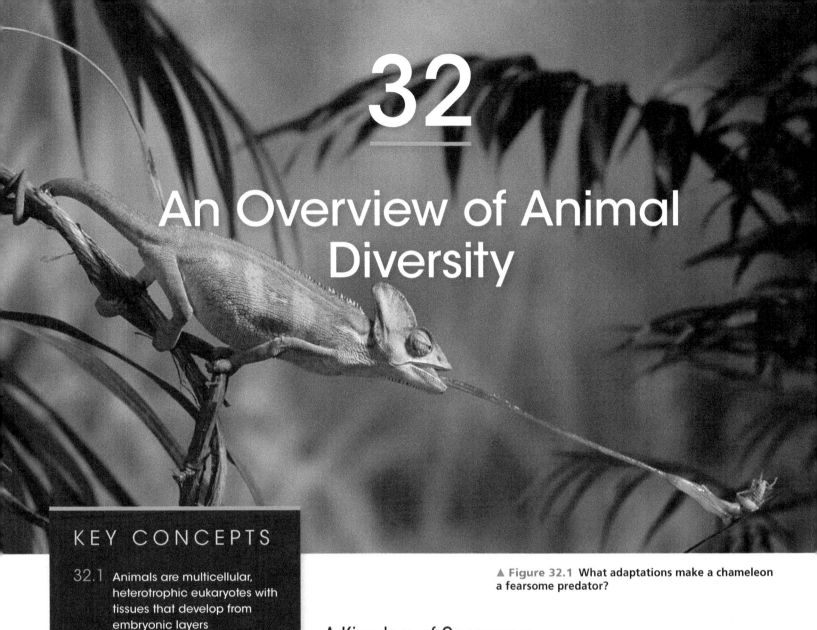

32

An Overview of Animal Diversity

▲ Figure 32.1 **What adaptations make a chameleon a fearsome predator?**

A Kingdom of Consumers

Although slow-moving on its feet, the chameleon in **Figure 32.1** can wield its long, sticky tongue with blinding speed to capture its unsuspecting prey. Many species of chameleons can also change their color and thereby blend into their surroundings—making them hard to detect, both by their prey and by the animals that would eat them.

The chameleon is just one example of an animal that is an efficient consumer of other organisms. Other predatory animals overwhelm their prey using their strength, speed, or toxins, while still others capture the unwary by building concealed traps such as webs. Likewise, herbivorous animals can strip the plants they eat bare of leaves or seeds, while parasitic animals weaken their hosts by consuming their tissues or body fluids. These and other animals are effective eating machines in part because they have specialized muscle and nerve cells that enable them to detect, capture, and eat other organisms—including those that can flee from attack. Animals are also very good at processing the food they have eaten; most animals do this using an efficient digestive system that has a mouth at one end and an anus at the other.

In this chapter, we embark on a tour of the animal kingdom that will continue in the next two chapters. Here we will consider the characteristics that all animals share, as well as the evolutionary history of this kingdom of consumers.

Animals are multicellular, heterotrophic eukaryotes with tissues that develop from embryonic layers

Listing features shared by all animals is challenging, as there are exceptions to nearly every criterion we might select. When taken together, however, several characteristics of animals sufficiently describe the group for our discussion.

Nutritional Mode

Animals differ from both plants and fungi in their mode of nutrition. Plants are autotrophic eukaryotes capable of generating organic molecules through photosynthesis. Fungi are heterotrophs that grow on or near their food and that feed by absorption (often after they have released enzymes that digest the food outside their bodies). Unlike plants, animals cannot construct all of their own organic molecules, and so, in most cases, they ingest them—either by eating other living organisms or by eating nonliving organic material. But unlike fungi, most animals feed by ingesting their food and then using enzymes to digest it within their bodies.

Cell Structure and Specialization

Animals are eukaryotes, and like plants and most fungi, animals are multicellular. In contrast to plants and fungi, however, animals lack the structural support of cell walls. Instead, proteins external to the cell membrane provide structural support to animal cells and connect them to one another (see Figure 6.28). The most abundant of these proteins is collagen, which is not found in plants or fungi.

The cells of most animals are organized into **tissues**, groups of similar cells that act as a functional unit. For example, muscle tissue and nervous tissue are responsible for moving the body and conducting nerve impulses, respectively. The ability to move and conduct nerve impulses underlies many of the adaptations that differentiate animals from plants and fungi (which lack muscle and nerve cells). For this reason, muscle and nerve cells are central to the animal lifestyle.

Reproduction and Development

Most animals reproduce sexually, and the diploid stage usually dominates the life cycle. In the haploid stage, sperm and egg cells are produced directly by meiotic division, unlike what occurs in plants and fungi (see Figure 13.6). In most animal species, a small, flagellated sperm fertilizes a larger, nonmotile egg, forming a diploid zygote. The zygote then undergoes **cleavage**, a succession of mitotic cell divisions without cell growth between the divisions. During the development of most animals, cleavage leads to the formation of a multicellular stage called a **blastula**, which in many animals takes the form of a hollow

ball (**Figure 32.2**). Following the blastula stage is the process of **gastrulation**, during which the layers of embryonic tissues that will develop into adult body parts are produced. The resulting developmental stage is called a **gastrula**.

Although some animals, including humans, develop directly into adults, the life cycles of most animals include at least one larval stage. A **larva** is a sexually immature form of an animal that is morphologically distinct from the adult, usually eats different food, and may even have a different habitat than the adult, as in the case of the aquatic larva of a mosquito or dragonfly. Animal larvae eventually undergo **metamorphosis**, a developmental transformation that turns the animal into a juvenile that resembles an adult but is not yet sexually mature.

Though adult animals vary widely in morphology, the genes that control animal development are similar across a broad range of taxa. All animals have developmental genes that regulate the expression of other genes,

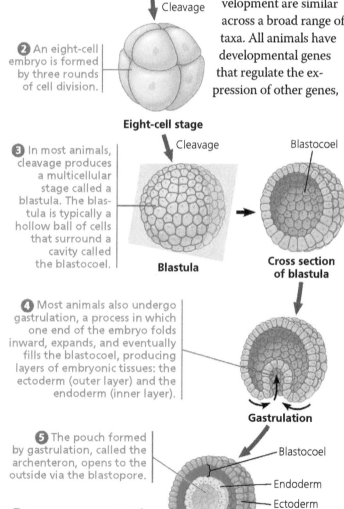

① The zygote of an animal undergoes a series of mitotic cell divisions called cleavage.

Zygote

Cleavage

② An eight-cell embryo is formed by three rounds of cell division.

Eight-cell stage

Cleavage

③ In most animals, cleavage produces a multicellular stage called a blastula. The blastula is typically a hollow ball of cells that surround a cavity called the blastocoel.

Blastula

Blastocoel

Cross section of blastula

④ Most animals also undergo gastrulation, a process in which one end of the embryo folds inward, expands, and eventually fills the blastocoel, producing layers of embryonic tissues: the ectoderm (outer layer) and the endoderm (inner layer).

Gastrulation

⑤ The pouch formed by gastrulation, called the archenteron, opens to the outside via the blastopore.

⑥ The endoderm of the archenteron develops into the tissue lining the animal's digestive tract.

Blastocoel

Endoderm

Ectoderm

Archenteron

Cross section of gastrula

Blastopore

▲ **Figure 32.2 Early embryonic development in animals.**

and many of these regulatory genes contain sets of DNA sequences called *homeoboxes* (see Chapter 21). In particular, most animals share a unique homeobox-containing family of genes, known as *Hox* genes. *Hox* genes play important roles in the development of animal embryos, controlling the expression of many other genes that influence morphology.

Sponges, which are among the simplest extant (living) animals, lack *Hox* genes. However, they have other homeobox genes that influence their shape, such as those that regulate the formation of water channels in the body wall, a key feature of sponge morphology (see Figure 33.4). In the ancestors of more complex animals, the *Hox* gene family arose via the duplication of earlier homeobox genes. Over time, the *Hox* gene family underwent a series of duplications, yielding a versatile "toolkit" for regulating development. In most animals, *Hox* genes regulate the formation of the anterior-posterior (front-to-back) axis, as well as other aspects of development. Similar sets of conserved genes govern the development of both flies and humans, despite their obvious differences and hundreds of millions of years of divergent evolution.

CONCEPT CHECK **32.1**

1. Summarize the main stages of animal development. What family of control genes plays a major role?
2. **WHAT IF?** What animal characteristics would be needed by an imaginary plant that could chase, capture, and digest its prey—yet could also extract nutrients from soil and conduct photosynthesis?

For suggested answers, see Appendix A.

The history of animals spans more than half a billion years

To date, biologists have identified 1.3 million extant species of animals, and estimates of the actual number run far higher. This vast diversity encompasses a spectacular range of morphological variation, from corals to cockroaches to crocodiles. Various studies suggest that this great diversity originated during the last billion years. For example, researchers have unearthed 710-million-year-old sediments containing the fossilized remains of steroids that today are primarily produced by a particular group of sponges. Hence, these fossil steroids suggest that animals had arisen by 710 million years ago.

DNA analyses generally agree with this fossil biochemical evidence; for example, one recent molecular clock study estimated that sponges originated about 700 million years ago. These findings are also consistent with molecular analyses suggesting that the common ancestor of all extant animal species lived about 770 million years ago. What was this common ancestor like, and how did animals arise from their single-celled ancestors?

Steps in the Origin of Multicellular Animals

One way to gather information about the origin of animals is to identify protist groups that are closely related to animals. As shown in **Figure 32.3**, a combination of morphological

▼ **Figure 32.3 Three lines of evidence that choanoflagellates are closely related to animals.**

Are the data described in ❸ consistent with predictions that could be made from the evidence in ❶ and ❷? Explain.

❶ Morphologically, choanoflagellate cells and the collar cells (or *choanocytes*) of sponges are almost indistinguishable.

Individual choanoflagellate

Choanoflagellates

OTHER EUKARYOTES

Animals

Sponges

Collar cell (choanocyte)

Other animals

❸ DNA sequence data indicate that choanoflagellates and animals are sister groups. In addition, genes for signaling and adhesion proteins previously known only from animals have been discovered in choanoflagellates.

❷ Similar collar cells have been identified in other animals, including cnidarians, flatworms, and echinoderms—but they have never been observed in non-choanoflagellate protists or in plants or fungi.

▶ Figure 32.4 **Cadherin proteins in choanoflagellates and animals.** The ancestral cadherin-like protein of choanoflagellates has seven kinds of domains (regions), each represented here by a particular symbol. With the exception of the "CCD" domain, which is found only in animals, the domains of animal cadherin proteins are present in the choanoflagellate cadherin-like protein. The cadherin protein domains shown here were identified from whole-genome sequence data; evolutionary relationships are based on morphological and DNA sequence data.

and molecular evidence points to choanoflagellates as the closest living relatives of animals. Based on such evidence, researchers have hypothesized that the common ancestor of choanoflagellates and living animals may have been a suspension feeder similar to present-day choanoflagellates.

Scientists exploring *how* animals may have arisen from their single-celled ancestors have noted that the origin of multicellularity requires the evolution of new ways for cells to adhere (attach) and signal (communicate) to each other. In an effort to learn more about such mechanisms, Dr. Nicole King (featured in the interview before Chapter 26) and colleagues compared the genome of the unicellular choanoflagellate *Monosiga brevicollis* with those of representative animals. This analysis uncovered 78 protein domains in *M. brevicollis* that were otherwise only known to occur in animals. (A *domain* is a key structural or functional region of a protein.) For example, *M. brevicollis* has genes that encode domains of certain proteins (known as cadherins) that play key roles in how animal cells attach to one another, as well as genes that encode protein domains that animals (and only animals) use in cell-signaling pathways.

Let's take a closer look at the cadherin attachment proteins we just mentioned. DNA sequence analyses show that animal cadherin proteins are composed primarily of domains that are also found in a cadherin-like protein of choanoflagellates (Figure 32.4). However, animal cadherin proteins also contain a highly conserved region not found in the choanoflagellate protein (the "CCD" domain labeled in Figure 32.4). These data suggest that the cadherin attachment protein originated by the rearrangement of protein domains found in choanoflagellates plus the incorporation of a novel domain, the conserved CCD region. Overall, comparisons of choanoflagellate and animal genomes suggest that key steps in the transition to multicellularity in animals involved new ways of using proteins or parts of proteins that were encoded by genes found in choanoflagellates.

Next, we'll survey the fossil evidence for how animals evolved from their distant common ancestor over four geologic eras (see Table 25.1 to review the geologic time scale).

Neoproterozoic Era (1 Billion–542 Million Years Ago)

Although data from fossil steroids and molecular clocks indicate an earlier origin, the first generally accepted macroscopic fossils of animals date from about 560 million years ago. These fossils are members of an early group of soft-bodied multicellular eukaryotes, known collectively as the **Ediacaran biota**. The name comes from the Ediacara Hills of Australia, where fossils of these organisms were first discovered (Figure 32.5). Similar fossils have since been found on other continents. Among the oldest Ediacaran fossils that resemble animals, some are thought to be molluscs (snails and their relatives), while others may be related to sponges and cnidarians (sea anemones and their relatives). Still others have proved

(a) *Mawsonites spriggi*   (b) *Spriggina floundersi*

▲ Figure 32.5 **Ediacaran fossil animals.** Fossils dating to about 560 million years ago include those resembling animals **(a)** with simple, radial forms and **(b)** with many body segments.

▲ Figure 32.6 **Early evidence of predation.** This 550-million-year-old fossil of the animal *Cloudina* shows evidence of having been attacked by a predator that bored through its shell.

difficult to classify, as they do not seem to be closely related to any living animal or algal groups. In addition to these macroscopic fossils, Neoproterozoic rocks have also yielded what may be microscopic fossils of early animal embryos. Although these microfossils appear to exhibit the basic structural organization of present-day animal embryos, debate continues about whether these fossils are indeed of animals.

The fossil record from the Ediacaran period (635–542 million years ago) also provides early evidence of predation. Consider *Cloudina*, a small animal whose body was protected by a shell resembling a series of nested cones (Figure 32.6). Some *Cloudina* fossils show signs of attack: round "bore holes" that resemble those formed today by predators that drill through the shells of their prey to gain access to the soft-bodied organisms lying within. Like *Cloudina*, some other small Ediacaran animals had shells or other defensive structures that may have been selected for by predators. Overall, the fossil evidence indicates that the Ediacaran was a time of increasing animal diversity—a trend that continued in the Paleozoic.

Paleozoic Era (542–251 Million Years Ago)

Another wave of animal diversification occurred 535–525 million years ago, during the Cambrian period of the Paleozoic era—a phenomenon referred to as the **Cambrian explosion** (see Chapter 25). In strata formed before the Cambrian explosion, only a few animal phyla have been observed. But in strata that are 535–525 million years old, paleontologists have found the oldest fossils of about half of all extant animal phyla, including the first arthropods, chordates, and echinoderms. Many of these fossils, which include the first large animals

Hallucigenia fossil (530 mya)

with hard, mineralized skeletons, look very different from most living animals (Figure 32.7). Even so, paleontologists have established that these Cambrian fossils are members of extant animal phyla, or at least are close relatives. In particular, most of the fossils from the Cambrian explosion are of **bilaterians**, an enormous clade whose members (unlike sponges and cnidarians) have a two-sided or bilaterally symmetric form and a complete digestive tract, an efficient digestive system that has a mouth at one end and an anus at the other. As we'll discuss later in the chapter, bilaterians include molluscs, arthropods, chordates, and most other living animal phyla.

As the diversity of animal phyla increased during the Cambrian, the diversity of Ediacaran life-forms declined. What caused these trends? Fossil evidence suggests that during the Cambrian period, predators acquired novel adaptations, such as forms of locomotion that helped them catch prey, while prey species acquired new defenses, such as protective shells. As new predator-prey relationships emerged, natural selection may have led to the decline of the soft-bodied Ediacaran species and the rise of various bilaterian phyla. Another hypothesis focuses on an increase in atmospheric oxygen that preceded the Cambrian explosion. More plentiful oxygen would have enabled animals with higher metabolic rates and larger body sizes to thrive, while potentially harming other species. A third hypothesis proposes that genetic changes affecting development, such as the origin of *Hox* genes and the addition of new microRNAs (small RNAs involved in gene regulation), facilitated the evolution of new

▲ Figure 32.7 **A Cambrian seascape.** This artist's reconstruction depicts a diverse array of organisms found in fossils from the Burgess Shale site in British Columbia, Canada. The animals include *Pikaia* (eel-like chordate at top left), *Marella* (small arthropod swimming at left), *Anomalocaris* (large animal with grasping limbs and a circular mouth), and *Hallucigenia* (animals with toothpick-like spikes on the seafloor and in inset).

Calculating and Interpreting Correlation Coefficients

Is Animal Complexity Correlated with miRNA Diversity? Animal phyla vary greatly in morphology, from simple sponges that lack tissues and symmetry to complex vertebrates. Members of different animal phyla have similar developmental genes, but the number of miRNAs varies considerably. In this exercise, you will explore whether miRNA diversity is correlated to morphological complexity.

How the Study Was Done In the analysis, miRNA diversity is represented by the average number of miRNAs in a phylum (x), while morphological complexity is represented by the average number of cell types

Data from the Study

Animal Phylum	i	No. of miRNAs (x_i)	$(x_i - \bar{x})$	$(x_i - \bar{x})^2$	No. of Cell Types (y_i)	$(y_i - \bar{y})$	$(y_i - \bar{y})^2$	$(x_i - \bar{x})(y_i - \bar{y})$
Porifera	1	5.8			25			
Platyhelminthes	2	35			30			
Cnidaria	3	2.5			34			
Nematoda	4	26			38			
Echinodermata	5	38.6			45			
Cephalochordata	6	33			68			
Arthropoda	7	59.1			73			
Urochordata	8	25			77			
Mollusca	9	50.8			83			
Annelida	10	58			94			
Vertebrata	11	147.5			172.5			
		$\bar{x} =$		$\Sigma =$	$\bar{y} =$		$\Sigma =$	$\Sigma =$
		$s_x =$			$s_y =$			

(y). The researchers examined the relationship between these two variables by calculating the correlation coefficient (r). The correlation coefficient indicates the extent and direction of a linear relationship between two variables (x and y) and ranges in value between -1 and 1. When $r < 0$, y and x are negatively correlated, meaning that values of y become smaller as values of x become larger. When $r > 0$, y and x are positively correlated (y becomes larger as x becomes larger). When $r = 0$, the variables are not correlated.

The formula for the correlation coefficient r is:

$$r = \frac{\frac{1}{n-1}\sum(x_i - \bar{x})(y_i - \bar{y})}{s_x s_y}$$

In this formula, n is the number of observations, x_i is the value of the ith observation of variable x, and y_i is the value of the ith observation of variable y. $\bar{x}$ and $\bar{y}$ are the means of variables x and y, and s_x and s_y are the standard deviations of variables x and y. The "Σ" symbol indicates that the n values of the product ($x_i - \bar{x}$) ($y_i - \bar{y}$) are to be added together.

Interpret the Data

1. First, practice reading the data table. For the eighth observation ($i = 8$), what are x_i and y_i? For which phylum are these data?
2. Next, we'll calculate the mean and standard deviation for each variable. (a) The **mean** ($\bar{x}$) is the sum of the data values divided by n, the number of observations: $\bar{x} = \frac{\sum x_i}{n}$. Calculate the mean number of miRNAs ($\bar{x}$) and the mean number of cell types ($\bar{y}$) and enter them in the data table (for $\bar{y}$, replace each x in the formula with a y). (b) Next, calculate ($x_i - \bar{x}$) and ($y_i - \bar{y}$) for each observation, recording your results in the appropriate column. Square each of those results to complete the ($x_i - \bar{x}$)^2 and ($y_i - \bar{y}$)^2 columns; sum the results for those columns. (c) The **standard deviation**, s_x, which describes the variation found in the data, is calculated using the following formula:

$$s_x = \sqrt{\frac{1}{n-1}\sum(x_i - \bar{x})^2}$$

   (d) Calculate s_x and s_y by substituting the results in (b) into the formula for the standard deviation.
3. Next, calculate the correlation coefficient r for the variables x and y. (a) First, use the results in 3(b) to complete the ($x_i - \bar{x}$)($y_i - \bar{y}$) column; sum the results in that column. (b) Now use the values for s_x and s_y from 3(c) along with the results from 4(a) in the formula for r.
4. Do these data indicate that miRNA diversity and animal complexity are negatively correlated, positively correlated, or uncorrelated? Explain.
5. What does your analysis suggest about the role of miRNA diversity in the evolution of animal complexity?

(MB) A version of this Scientific Skills Exercise can be assigned in MasteringBiology.

Data from Bradley Deline, University of West Georgia, and Kevin Peterson, Dartmouth College, 2013.

body forms. In the Scientific Skills Exercise, you can investigate whether there is a correlation between microRNAs (miRNAs; see Figure 18.14) and body complexity in various animal phyla. These various hypotheses are not mutually exclusive; predator-prey relationships, atmospheric changes, and changes in development may each have played a role.

The Cambrian period was followed by the Ordovician, Silurian, and Devonian periods, when animal diversity continued to increase, although punctuated by episodes of mass extinction (see Figure 25.17). Vertebrates (fishes) emerged as the top predators of the marine food web. By 450 million years ago, groups that diversified during the Cambrian period began to make an impact on land. Arthropods were the first animals to adapt to terrestrial habitats, as indicated

by fragments of arthropod remains and by well-preserved fossils from several continents of millipedes, centipedes, and spiders. Another clue is seen in fossilized fern galls—enlarged cavities that fern plants form in response to stimulation by resident insects, which then use the galls for protection. Fossils indicate that fern galls date back at least 302 million years, suggesting that insects and plants were influencing each other's evolution by that time.

Vertebrates colonized land around 365 million years ago and diversified into numerous terrestrial groups. Two of these survive today: the amphibians (such as frogs and salamanders) and the amniotes (reptiles, including birds, and mammals). We will explore these groups, known collectively as the tetrapods, in more detail in Chapter 34.

Mesozoic Era (251–65.5 Million Years Ago)

The animal phyla that had evolved during the Paleozoic now began to spread into new habitats. In the oceans, the first coral reefs formed, providing other marine animals with new places to live. Some reptiles returned to the water, leaving plesiosaurs (see Figure 25.5) and other large aquatic predators as their descendants. On land, descent with modification in some tetrapods led to the origin of wings and other flight equipment in pterosaurs and birds. Large and small dinosaurs emerged, both as predators and herbivores. At the same time, the first mammals—tiny nocturnal insect-eaters—appeared on the scene. In addition, as you read in Chapter 30, flowering plants (angiosperms) and insects both underwent dramatic diversifications during the late Mesozoic.

Cenozoic Era (65.5 Million Years Ago to the Present)

Mass extinctions of both terrestrial and marine animals ushered in a new era, the Cenozoic. Among the groups of species that disappeared were the large, nonflying dinosaurs and the marine reptiles. The fossil record of the early Cenozoic documents the rise of large mammalian herbivores and predators as mammals began to exploit the vacated ecological niches. The global climate gradually cooled throughout the Cenozoic, triggering significant shifts in many animal lineages. Among primates, for example, some species in Africa adapted to the open woodlands and savannas that replaced many of the former dense forests. The ancestors of our own species were among those grassland apes.

CONCEPT CHECK 32.2

1. Put the following milestones in animal evolution in order from oldest to most recent: (a) origin of mammals, (b) earliest evidence of terrestrial arthropods, (c) Ediacaran fauna, (d) extinction of large, nonflying dinosaurs.

2. **WHAT IF?** Suppose the most recent common ancestor of extant fungi and animals lived 1 billion years ago. If the first fungi lived 990 million years ago, would extant animals also have been alive at that time? Explain.

3. **MAKE CONNECTIONS** Evaluate whether the origin of cell-to-cell attachment proteins in animals illustrates descent with modification. (See Concept 22.2.)

For suggested answers, see Appendix A.

CONCEPT 32.3

Animals can be characterized by "body plans"

Animal species vary tremendously in morphology, but their great diversity in form can be described by a relatively small number of major "body plans." A **body plan** is a particular set of morphological and developmental traits,

integrated into a functional whole—the living animal. The term *plan* here does not imply that animal forms are the result of conscious planning or invention. But body plans do provide a succinct way to compare and contrast key animal features. They also are of interest in the study of *evo-devo*, the interface between evolution and development.

Like all features of organisms, animal body plans have evolved over time. In some cases, including key stages in gastrulation, novel body plans emerged early in the history of animal life and have not changed since. As we'll discuss, however, other aspects of animal body plans have changed multiple times over the course of evolution. As we explore the major features of animal body plans, bear in mind that similar body forms may have evolved independently in different lineages. In addition, body features can be lost over the course of evolution, causing some closely related species to look very different from one another.

Symmetry

A basic feature of animal bodies is their type of symmetry—or absence of symmetry. (Many sponges, for example, lack symmetry altogether.) Some animals exhibit **radial symmetry**, the type of symmetry found in a flowerpot (Figure 32.8a). Sea anemones, for example, have a top side (where the mouth is located) and a bottom side. But they have no front and back ends and no left and right sides.

The two-sided symmetry of a shovel is an example of **bilateral symmetry** (Figure 32.8b). A bilateral animal has two axes of orientation: front to back and top to bottom. Such animals have a **dorsal** (top) side and a **ventral** (bottom) side, a left side and a right side, and an **anterior** (front) end

(a) Radial symmetry.
A radial animal, such as a sea anemone (phylum Cnidaria), does not have a left side and a right side. Any imaginary slice through the central axis divides the animal into mirror images.

(b) Bilateral symmetry.
A bilateral animal, such as a lobster (phylum Arthropoda), has a left side and a right side. Only one imaginary cut divides the animal into mirror-image halves.

▲ **Figure 32.8 Body symmetry.** The flowerpot and shovel are included to help you remember the radial-bilateral distinction.

and a **posterior** (back) end. Many animals with a bilaterally symmetrical body plan (such as arthropods and mammals) have sensory equipment concentrated at their anterior end, including a central nervous system ("brain") in the head.

The symmetry of an animal generally fits its lifestyle. Many radial animals are sessile (living attached to a substrate) or planktonic (drifting or weakly swimming, such as jellies, commonly called jellyfishes). Their symmetry equips them to meet the environment equally well from all sides. In contrast, bilateral animals typically move actively from place to place. Most bilateral animals have a central nervous system that enables them to coordinate the complex movements involved in crawling, burrowing, flying, or swimming. Fossil evidence indicates that these two fundamentally different kinds of symmetry have existed for at least 550 million years.

Tissues

Animal body plans also vary with regard to tissue organization. Recall that tissues are collections of specialized cells that act as a functional unit; in animals, true tissues are isolated from other tissues by membranous layers. Sponges and a few other groups lack true tissues. In all other animals, the embryo becomes layered during gastrulation. As development progresses, these layers, called *germ layers*, form the various tissues and organs of the body. **Ectoderm**, the germ layer covering the surface of the embryo, gives rise to the outer covering of the animal and, in some phyla, to the central nervous system. **Endoderm**, the innermost germ layer, lines the pouch that forms during gastrulation (the archenteron) and gives rise to the lining of the digestive tract (or cavity) and organs such as the liver and lungs of vertebrates.

Cnidarians and a few other animal groups that have only these two germ layers are said to be **diploblastic**. All bilaterally symmetrical animals have a third germ layer, called the **mesoderm**, which fills much of the space between the ectoderm and endoderm. Thus, animals with bilateral symmetry are also said to be **triploblastic** (having three germ layers). In triploblasts, the mesoderm forms the muscles and most other organs between the digestive tract and the outer covering of the animal. Triploblasts include a broad range of animals, from flatworms to arthropods to vertebrates. (Although some diploblasts actually do have a third germ layer, it is not nearly as well developed as the mesoderm of animals considered to be triploblastic.)

Body Cavities

Most triploblastic animals have a **body cavity**, a fluid- or air-filled space located between the digestive tract and the outer body wall. This body cavity is also called a **coelom** (from the Greek *koilos*, hollow). A so-called "true" coelom forms from tissue derived from mesoderm. The inner and outer layers of tissue that surround the cavity connect and

form structures that suspend the internal organs. Animals with a true coelom are known as **coelomates** (Figure 32.9a).

Some triploblastic animals have a body cavity that is formed from mesoderm and endoderm (Figure 32.9b). Such a cavity is called a "pseudocoelom" (from the Greek *pseudo*, false), and the animals that have one are called **pseudocoelomates**. Despite its name, however, a pseudocoelom is not false; it is a fully functional body cavity. Finally, some triploblastic animals lack a body cavity altogether (Figure 32.9c). They are known collectively as **acoelomates** (from the Greek *a-*, without).

▼ **Figure 32.9 Body cavities of triploblastic animals.** The organ systems develop from the three embryonic germ layers.

(a) Coelomate

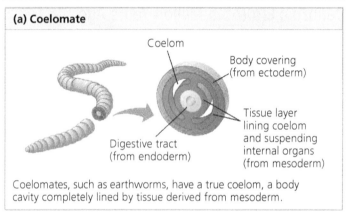

Coelomates, such as earthworms, have a true coelom, a body cavity completely lined by tissue derived from mesoderm.

(b) Pseudocoelomate

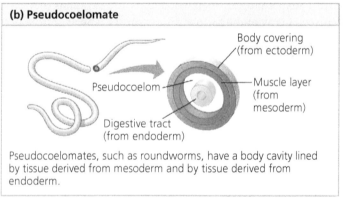

Pseudocoelomates, such as roundworms, have a body cavity lined by tissue derived from mesoderm and by tissue derived from endoderm.

(c) Acoelomate

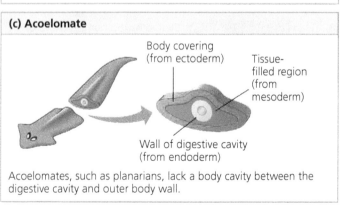

Acoelomates, such as planarians, lack a body cavity between the digestive cavity and outer body wall.

Key

■ Ectoderm   ■ Mesoderm   ■ Endoderm

A body cavity has many functions. Its fluid cushions the suspended organs, helping to prevent internal injury. In soft-bodied coelomates, such as earthworms, the coelom contains noncompressible fluid that acts like a skeleton against which muscles can work. The cavity also enables the internal organs to grow and move independently of the outer body wall. If it were not for your coelom, for example, every beat of your heart or ripple of your intestine would warp your body's surface.

Terms such as *coelomates* and *pseudocoelomates* refer to organisms that have a similar body plan and hence belong to the same *grade* (a group whose members share key biological features). However, phylogenetic studies show that true coeloms and pseudocoeloms have been independently gained or lost multiple times in the course of animal evolution. As shown by this example, a grade is not necessarily equivalent to a *clade* (a group that includes an ancestral species and all of its descendants). Thus, while terms such as coelomate or pseudocoelomate can be helpful in describing an organism's features, these terms must be interpreted with caution when seeking to understand evolutionary history.

Protostome and Deuterostome Development

Based on certain aspects of early development, many animals can be described as having one of two developmental modes: **protostome development** or **deuterostome development**. These modes can generally be distinguished by differences in cleavage, coelom formation, and fate of the blastopore.

Cleavage

Many animals with protostome development undergo **spiral cleavage**, in which the planes of cell division are diagonal to the vertical axis of the embryo; as seen in the eight-cell stage of the embryo, smaller cells are centered over the grooves between larger, underlying cells (**Figure 32.10a**, left). Furthermore, the so-called **determinate cleavage** of some animals with protostome development rigidly casts ("determines") the developmental fate of each embryonic cell very early. A cell isolated from a snail at the four-cell stage, for example, cannot develop into a whole animal. Instead, after repeated divisions, such a cell will form an inviable embryo that lacks many parts.

In contrast to the spiral cleavage pattern, deuterostome development is predominantly characterized by **radial cleavage**. The cleavage planes are either parallel or perpendicular to the vertical axis of the embryo; as seen at the eight-cell stage, the tiers of cells are aligned, one directly above the other (see Figure 32.10a, right). Most animals with deuterostome development also have **indeterminate cleavage**, meaning that each cell produced by early

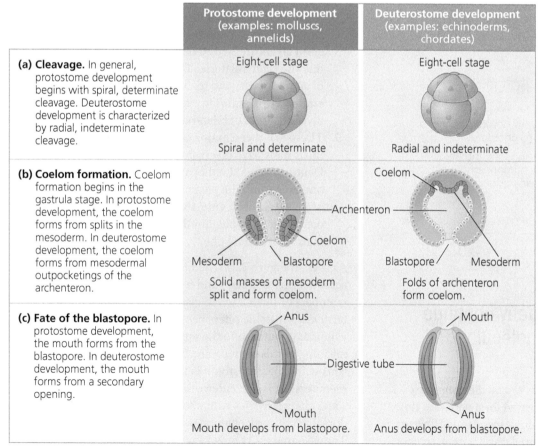

	Protostome development (examples: molluscs, annelids)	Deuterostome development (examples: echinoderms, chordates)
(a) Cleavage. In general, protostome development begins with spiral, determinate cleavage. Deuterostome development is characterized by radial, indeterminate cleavage.	Eight-cell stage Spiral and determinate	Eight-cell stage Radial and indeterminate
(b) Coelom formation. Coelom formation begins in the gastrula stage. In protostome development, the coelom forms from splits in the mesoderm. In deuterostome development, the coelom forms from mesodermal outpocketings of the archenteron.	Archenteron — Coelom — Mesoderm — Blastopore Solid masses of mesoderm split and form coelom.	Coelom — Blastopore — Mesoderm Folds of archenteron form coelom.
(c) Fate of the blastopore. In protostome development, the mouth forms from the blastopore. In deuterostome development, the mouth forms from a secondary opening.	Anus — Digestive tube — Mouth Mouth develops from blastopore.	Mouth — Digestive tube — Anus Anus develops from blastopore.

◀ **Figure 32.10 A comparison of protostome and deuterostome development.** These are useful general distinctions, though there are many variations and exceptions to these patterns.

MAKE CONNECTIONS *Review Figure 20.21. As an early embryo, which would more likely have stem cells capable of giving rise to cells of any type: an animal with protostome development or one with deuterostome development? Explain.*

Key
- Ectoderm
- Mesoderm
- Endoderm

cleavage divisions retains the capacity to develop into a complete embryo. For example, if the cells of a sea urchin embryo are separated at the four-cell stage, each can form a complete larva. Similarly, it is the indeterminate cleavage of the human zygote that makes identical twins possible.

Coelom Formation

During gastrulation, an embryo's developing digestive tube initially forms as a blind pouch, the **archenteron**, which becomes the gut (Figure 32.10b). As the archenteron forms in protostome development, initially solid masses of mesoderm split and form the coelom. In contrast, in deuterostome development, the mesoderm buds from the wall of the archenteron, and its cavity becomes the coelom.

Fate of the Blastopore

Protostome and deuterostome development often differ in the fate of the **blastopore**, the indentation that during gastrulation leads to the formation of the archenteron (Figure 32.10c). After the archenteron develops, in most animals a second opening forms at the opposite end of the gastrula. In many species, the blastopore and this second opening become the two openings of the digestive tube: the mouth and the anus. In protostome development, the mouth generally develops from the first opening, the blastopore, and it is for this characteristic that the term *protostome* derives (from the Greek *protos*, first, and *stoma*, mouth). In deuterostome development (from the Greek *deuteros*, second), the mouth is derived from the secondary opening, and the blastopore usually forms the anus.

CONCEPT CHECK 32.3

1. Distinguish the terms *grade* and *clade*.
2. Compare three aspects of the early development of a snail (a mollusc) and a human (a chordate).
3. **WHAT IF?** Evaluate this claim: Ignoring the details of their specific anatomy, worms, humans, and most other triploblasts have a shape analogous to that of a doughnut.

For suggested answers, see Appendix A.

CONCEPT 32.4

Views of animal phylogeny continue to be shaped by new molecular and morphological data

As animals with diverse body plans radiated during the early Cambrian, some lineages arose, thrived for a period of time, and then became extinct, leaving no descendants. However, by 500 million years ago, most animal phyla with members alive today were established. Next, we'll examine relationships among these taxa along with some remaining questions that are currently being addressed using genomic data.

The Diversification of Animals

Zoologists currently recognize about three dozen phyla of extant animals, 15 of which are shown in **Figure 32.11**. Researchers infer evolutionary relationships among these phyla by analyzing whole genomes, as well as morphological traits, ribosomal RNA (rRNA) genes, *Hox* genes, protein-coding nuclear genes, and mitochondrial genes. Notice how the following points are reflected in Figure 32.11.

1. **All animals share a common ancestor.** Current evidence indicates that animals are monophyletic, forming a clade called Metazoa. All extant and extinct animal lineages have descended from a common ancestor.
2. **Sponges are basal animals.** Among the extant taxa, sponges (phylum Porifera) branch from the base of the animal tree. Recent morphological and molecular analyses indicate that sponges are monophyletic, as shown here.
3. **Eumetazoa is a clade of animals with true tissues.** All animals except for sponges and a few others belong to a clade of **eumetazoans** ("true animals"). True tissues evolved in the common ancestor of living eumetazoans. Basal eumetazoans, which include the phyla Ctenophora (comb jellies) and Cnidaria, are diploblastic and generally have radial symmetry.
4. **Most animal phyla belong to the clade Bilateria.** Bilateral symmetry and the presence of three prominent germ layers are shared derived characters that help define the clade Bilateria. This clade contains the majority of animal phyla, and its members are known as *bilaterians*. The Cambrian explosion was primarily a rapid diversification of bilaterians.
5. **There are three major clades of bilaterian animals.** Bilaterians have diversified into three main lineages, Deuterostomia, Lophotrochozoa, and Ecdysozoa. With one exception, the phyla in these clades consist entirely of **invertebrates**, animals that lack a backbone; Chordata is the only phylum that includes **vertebrates**, animals with a backbone.

As seen in Figure 32.11, hemichordates (acorn worms), echinoderms (sea stars and relatives), and chordates are members of the bilaterian clade **Deuterostomia**; thus, the term *deuterostome* refers not only to a mode of animal development, but also to the members of this clade. (The dual meaning of this term can be confusing since some organisms with a deuterostome developmental pattern are *not* members of clade Deuterostomia.) Hemichordates share some characteristics with chordates, such as gill slits and a dorsal nerve cord; echinoderms lack these characteristics. These shared traits may have been present in the common

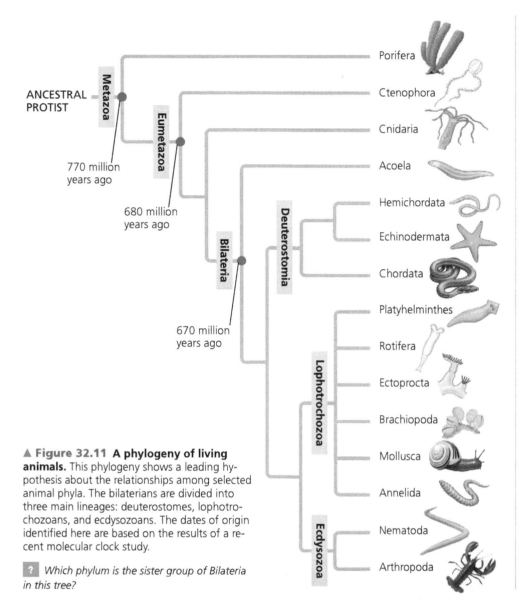

▲ **Figure 32.11 A phylogeny of living animals.** This phylogeny shows a leading hypothesis about the relationships among selected animal phyla. The bilaterians are divided into three main lineages: deuterostomes, lophotrochozoans, and ecdysozoans. The dates of origin identified here are based on the results of a recent molecular clock study.

❓ *Which phylum is the sister group of Bilateria in this tree?*

(a) Lophophore feeding structures of an ectoproct

(b) Structure of a trochophore larva

▲ **Figure 32.12 Morphological characteristics of lophotrochozoans.**

ancestor of the deuterostome clade (and lost in the echinoderm lineage). As mentioned above, phylum Chordata, the only phylum with vertebrate members, also includes invertebrates.

Bilaterians also diversified in two major clades that are composed entirely of invertebrates: the *ecdysozoans* and the *lophotrochozoans*. The clade name **Ecdysozoa** refers to a characteristic shared by nematodes, arthropods, and some of the other ecdysozoan phyla that are not included in our survey. These animals secrete external skeletons (exoskeletons); the stiff covering of a cricket and the flexible cuticle of a nematode are examples. As the animal grows, it molts, squirming out of its old exoskeleton and secreting a larger one. The process of shedding the old exoskeleton is called *ecdysis*. Though named for this characteristic, the clade was proposed mainly on the basis of molecular data that support the common ancestry of its members. Furthermore, some taxa excluded from this clade by their molecular data, such as certain species of leeches, do in fact molt.

The name **Lophotrochozoa** refers to two different features observed in some animals belonging to this clade. Some lophotrochozoans, such as ectoprocts, develop a unique structure called a **lophophore** (from the Greek *lophos*, crest, and *pherein*, to carry), a crown of ciliated tentacles that function in feeding (**Figure 32.12a**). Individuals in other phyla, including molluscs and annelids, go through a distinctive developmental stage called the **trochophore larva** (**Figure 32.12b**)—hence the name lophotrochozoan.

Future Directions in Animal Systematics

While many scientists think that current evidence supports the evolutionary relationships shown in Figure 32.11, aspects of this phylogeny continue to be debated. Although it can be frustrating that the phylogenies in textbooks cannot be memorized as set-in-stone truths, the uncertainty inherent in these diagrams is a healthy reminder that science is an ongoing, dynamic process of inquiry. We'll conclude with three questions that are the focus of ongoing research.

1. **Are sponges monophyletic?** Traditionally, sponges were placed in a single phylum, Porifera. This view began to change in the 1990s, when molecular studies indicated that sponges were paraphyletic; as a result, sponges were placed into several different phyla that branched near the base of the animal tree. Since 2009, however, several morphological and molecular studies have concluded that sponges are a monophyletic group after all, as traditionally thought and as shown in Figure 32.11. Researchers are currently sequencing the entire genomes of various sponges to investigate whether sponges are indeed monophyletic.

2. **Are ctenophores basal metazoans?** Many researchers have concluded that sponges are basal metazoans (see Figure 32.11). However, several recent studies have placed the comb jellies (phylum Ctenophora) at the base of the animal tree. Data that are consistent with placing sponges at the base of the animal tree include fossil steroid evidence, molecular clock analyses, the morphological similarity of sponge collar cells to the cells of choanoflagellates (see Figure 32.3), and the fact that sponges are one of the few animal groups that lack true tissues (as might be expected for basal animals). Ctenophores, on the other hand, have true tissues and their cells do not resemble the cells of choanoflagellates. At present, the idea that ctenophores are basal metazoans remains an intriguing but controversial hypothesis.

3. **Are acoelomate flatworms basal bilaterians?** A series of recent molecular papers have indicated that acoelomate flatworms (phylum Acoela) are basal bilaterians, as shown in Figure 32.11. A different conclusion was supported by a 2011 analysis, which placed acoelomates within Deuterostomia. Researchers are currently sequencing the genomes of several acoelomates and species from closely related groups to provide a more definitive test of the hypothesis that acoelomate flatworms are basal bilaterians. If further evidence supports this hypothesis, this would suggest that the bilaterians may have descended from a common ancestor that resembled living acoelomate flatworms—that is, from an ancestor that had a simple nervous system, a saclike gut with a single opening (the "mouth"), and no excretory system.

CONCEPT CHECK 32.4

1. Describe the evidence that cnidarians share a more recent common ancestor with other animals than with sponges.
2. **WHAT IF?** Suppose ctenophores are basal metazoans and sponges are the sister group of all remaining animals. Under this hypothesis, redraw Figure 32.11 and discuss whether animals with true tissues would form a clade.
3. **MAKE CONNECTIONS** Based on the phylogeny in Figure 32.11 and the information in Figure 25.11, evaluate this statement: "The Cambrian explosion actually consists of three explosions, not one."

For suggested answers, see Appendix A.

32 Chapter Review

SUMMARY OF KEY CONCEPTS

CONCEPT 32.1

Animals are multicellular, heterotrophic eukaryotes with tissues that develop from embryonic layers (pp. 668–669)

- Animals are heterotrophs that ingest their food.
- Animals are multicellular eukaryotes. Their cells are supported and connected to one another by collagen and other structural proteins located outside the cell membrane. Nervous tissue and muscle tissue are key animal features.
- In most animals, **gastrulation** follows the formation of the **blastula** and leads to the formation of embryonic tissue layers. Most animals have *Hox* genes that regulate the development of body form. Although *Hox* genes have been highly conserved over the course of evolution, they can produce a wide diversity of animal morphology.

? Describe key ways that animals differ from plants and fungi.

CONCEPT 32.2

The history of animals spans more than half a billion years (pp. 669–673)

- Fossil biochemical evidence and molecular clock analyses indicate that animals arose over 700 million years ago.
- Genomic analyses suggest that key steps in the origin of animals involved new ways of using proteins that were encoded by genes found in choanoflagellates.

? What caused the Cambrian explosion? Describe current hypotheses.

CONCEPT 32.3

Animals can be characterized by "body plans" (pp. 673–676)

- Animals may lack symmetry or may have radial or bilateral symmetry. Bilaterally symmetrical animals have dorsal and ventral sides, as well as anterior and posterior ends.
- Eumetazoan embryos may be **diploblastic** (two germ layers) or **triploblastic** (three germ layers). Triploblastic animals with a body cavity may have a **pseudocoelom** or a true **coelom**.
- **Protostome** and **deuterostome** development often differ in patterns of cleavage, coelom formation, and blastopore fate.

? *Describe how body plans provide useful information yet should be interpreted cautiously as evidence of evolutionary relationships.*

CONCEPT 32.4

Views of animal phylogeny continue to be shaped by new molecular and morphological data (pp. 676–678)

This phylogenetic tree shows key steps in animal evolution:

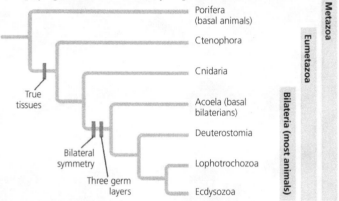

? *Consider clades Bilateria, Lophotrochozoa, Metazoa, Chordata, Ecdysozoa, Eumetazoa, and Deuterostomia. List the clades to which humans belong in order from the most to the least inclusive clade.*

TEST YOUR UNDERSTANDING

LEVEL 1: KNOWLEDGE/COMPREHENSION

1. Among the characteristics unique to animals is
   - a. gastrulation.
   - b. multicellularity.
   - c. sexual reproduction.
   - d. flagellated sperm.

2. The distinction between sponges and other animal phyla is based mainly on the absence versus the presence of
   - a. a body cavity.
   - b. a complete digestive tract.
   - c. mesoderm.
   - d. true tissues.

3. Which of the following was probably the *least* important factor in bringing about the Cambrian explosion?
   - a. the emergence of predator-prey relationships
   - b. an increase in the concentration of atmospheric oxygen
   - c. the movement of animals onto land
   - d. the origin of *Hox* genes

LEVEL 2: APPLICATION/ANALYSIS

4. Based on the tree in Figure 32.11, which statement is false?
   - a. The animal kingdom is monophyletic.
   - b. Acoelomate flatworms are more closely related to echinoderms than to annelids.
   - c. Sponges are basal animals.
   - d. Bilaterians form a clade.

LEVEL 3: SYNTHESIS/EVALUATION

5. **EVOLUTION CONNECTION**
   A professor begins a lecture on animal phylogeny (as shown in Figure 32.11) by saying, "We are all worms." In this context, what did she mean?

6. **SCIENTIFIC INQUIRY**
   INTERPRET THE DATA Redraw the bilaterian portion of Figure 32.11 for the nine phyla in the table below. Consider these blastopore fates: protostomy (mouth develops from the blastopore), deuterostomy (anus develops from the blastopore), or neither (the blastopore closes and the mouth develops elsewhere). Depending on the blastopore fate of its members, label each branch that leads to a phylum with P, D, N, or a combination of these letters. What is the ancestral blastopore fate? How many times has blastopore fate changed over the course of evolution? Explain.

Blastopore Fate	Phyla
Protostomy (P)	Platyhelminthes, Rotifera, Nematoda; most Mollusca, most Annelida; few Arthropoda
Deuterostomy (D)	Echinodermata, Chordata; most Arthropoda; few Mollusca, few Annelida
Neither (N)	Acoela

Source: A. Hejnol and M. Martindale, The mouth, the anus, and the blastopore—open questions about questionable openings. In *Animal Evolution: Genomes, Fossils and Trees,* eds. D. T. J. Littlewood and M. J. Telford, Oxford University Press, pp. 33–40 (2009).

7. **WRITE ABOUT A THEME: INTERACTIONS**
   Animal life changed greatly during the Cambrian explosion, with some groups expanding in diversity and others declining. Write a short essay (100–150 words) interpreting these events as feedback regulation at the level of the biological community.

8. **SYNTHESIZE YOUR KNOWLEDGE**

This organism is an animal. What can you infer about its body structure and lifestyle (that might not be obvious from its appearance)? This animal has a deuterostome developmental pattern and a lophophore. To which major clades does this animal belong? Explain your selection, and describe when these clades originated and how they are related to one another.

For selected answers, see Appendix A.

MasteringBiology®

Students Go to **MasteringBiology** for assignments, the eText, and the Study Area with practice tests, animations, and activities.

Instructors Go to **MasteringBiology** for automatically graded tutorials and questions that you can assign to your students, plus Instructor Resources.

33

An Introduction to Invertebrates

▲ Figure 33.1 **Which of these organisms are invertebrate animals?**

Life Without a Backbone

At first glance, you might think that fishes were the only animals shown in Figure 33.1. But the diverse organisms visible here are all animals, including those that appear to resemble lacy branches, thick stems, and curly leaves. Most of these animals are **invertebrates**—animals that lack a backbone.

Invertebrates account for over 95% of known animal species. They occupy almost every habitat on Earth, from the scalding water released by deep-sea "black smoker" hydrothermal vents to the frozen ground of Antarctica. Evolution in these varied environments has produced an immense diversity of forms, ranging from a species consisting of a flat bilayer of cells to other species with features such as silk-spinning glands, pivoting spines, and tentacles covered with suction cups. Invertebrates also show enormous variation in size, from microscopic organisms to organisms that can grow to 18 m long (1.5 times the length of a school bus).

In this chapter, we'll take a tour of the invertebrate world, using the phylogenetic tree in **Figure 33.2** as a guide. **Figure 33.3**, on the next three pages, surveys 23 invertebrate phyla as representatives of invertebrate diversity. Many of those phyla are explored in more detail in the rest of this chapter.

◀ **Figure 33.2 Review of animal phylogeny.** Except for sponges (phylum Porifera) and a few other groups, all animals have tissues and are in the clade Eumetazoa. Most animals are in the diverse clade Bilateria (for a more complete view of animal relationships, see Figure 32.11).

Exploring Invertebrate Diversity

Kingdom Animalia encompasses 1.3 million known species, and estimates of total species range as high as 10–20 million species. Of the 23 phyla surveyed here, 12 are discussed more fully in this chapter, Chapter 32, or Chapter 34; cross-references are given at the end of their descriptions.

Porifera (5,500 species)

Animals in this phylum are informally called sponges. Sponges are sessile animals that lack true tissues. They live as filter feeders, trapping particles that pass through the internal channels of their body (see Concept 33.1).

A sponge

Cnidaria (10,000 species)

Cnidarians include corals, jellies, and hydras. These animals have a diploblastic, radially symmetrical body plan that includes a gastrovascular cavity with a single opening that serves as both mouth and anus (see Concept 33.2).

A jelly

Acoela (400 species)

Acoel flatworms have a simple nervous system and a saclike gut, and thus were once placed in phylum Platyhelminthes. Some molecular analyses, however, indicate that Acoela is a separate lineage that diverged before the three main bilaterian clades (see Concept 32.4).

Acoel flatworms (LM)

Placozoa (1 species)

The single known species in this phylum, *Trichoplax adhaerens*, doesn't even look like an animal. It consists of a simple bilayer of a few thousand cells. Placozoans are thought to be basal animals, but it is not yet known how they are related to other early-diverging animal groups such as Porifera and Cnidaria. *Trichoplax* can reproduce by dividing into two individuals or by budding off many multicellular individuals.

A placozoan (LM)

Ctenophora (100 species)

Ctenophores (comb jellies) are diploblastic and radially symmetrical like cnidarians, suggesting that both phyla diverged from other animals very early (see Figure 32.11). Comb jellies make up much of the ocean's plankton. They have many distinctive traits, including eight "combs" of cilia that propel the animals through the water. When a small animal contacts the tentacles of some comb jellies, specialized cells burst open, covering the prey with sticky threads.

A ctenophore, or comb jelly

Lophotrochozoa

Platyhelminthes (20,000 species)

Flatworms (including tapeworms, planarians, and flukes) have bilateral symmetry and a central nervous system that processes information from sensory structures. They have no body cavity or specialized organs for circulation (see Concept 33.3).

A marine flatworm

Ectoprocta (4,500 species)

Ectoprocts (also known as bryozoans) live as sessile colonies and are covered by a tough exoskeleton (see Concept 33.3).

Ectoprocts

Rotifera (1,800 species)

Despite their microscopic size, rotifers have specialized organ systems, including an *alimentary canal* (a digestive tract with both a mouth and an anus). They feed on microorganisms suspended in water (see Concept 33.3).

A rotifer (LM)

Brachiopoda (335 species)

Brachiopods, or lamp shells, may be easily mistaken for clams or other molluscs. However, most brachiopods have a unique stalk that anchors them to their substrate, as well as a crown of cilia called a lophophore (see Concept 33.3).

A brachiopod

Continued on next page

Exploring Invertebrate Diversity

Lophotrochozoa (continued)

Acanthocephala (1,100 species)

Acanthocephalans are called spiny-headed worms because of the curved hooks on the proboscis at the anterior end of their body. All species are parasites. Some acantho-cephalans manipulate the behavior of their inter-mediate hosts (generally arthropods) in ways that increase their chances of reaching their final

Curved hooks

An acanthocephalan (LM)

hosts (generally vertebrates). For example, acanthocephalans that infect New Zealand mud crabs force their hosts to move to more visible areas on the beach, where the crabs are more likely to be eaten by birds, the worms' final hosts. Some phylogenetic analyses place the acanthocephalans within Rotifera.

Nemertea (900 species)

A ribbon worm

Also called proboscis worms or ribbon worms, nemerte-ans swim through water or burrow in sand, extending a unique proboscis to capture prey. Like flatworms, they lack a true coelom. However, unlike flatworms, nemerteans have an alimentary canal and a closed circulatory system in which the blood is contained in vessels and hence is distinct from fluid in the body cavity.

Cycliophora (1 species)

100 μm

A cycliophoran (colorized SEM)

The only known cycliopho-ran species, *Symbion pandora*, was discovered in 1995 on the mouthparts of a lobster. This tiny, vase-shaped crea-ture has a unique body plan and a particularly bizarre life cycle. Males impregnate females that are still develop-ing in their mothers' bodies. The fertilized females then escape, settle elsewhere on the lobster, and release their offspring. The offspring apparently leave that lobster and search for another one to which they attach.

Annelida (16,500 species)

Annelids, or segmented worms, are distinguished from other worms by their body segmen-tation. Earthworms are the most familiar annelids, but the phylum consists primarily of marine and freshwater species (see Concept 33.3).

A marine annelid

Mollusca (100,000 species)

Molluscs (including snails, clams, squids, and octopus-es) have a soft body that in many species is protected by a hard shell (see Concept 33.3).

An octopus

Ecdysozoa

Loricifera (10 species)

Loriciferans (from the Latin *lorica*, corset, and *ferre*, to bear) are tiny animals that inhabit sediments on the sea floor. A loriciferan can telescope its head, neck, and thorax in and out of the lorica, a pocket formed by six plates surrounding the abdomen. Though the natural history of loricifer-ans is mostly a mystery, at least some species likely eat bacteria.

50 μm

A loriciferan (LM)

Priapula (16 species)

A priapulan

Priapulans are worms with a large, rounded proboscis at the anterior end. (They are named after Priapos, the Greek god of fertility, who was symbolized by a giant penis.) Ranging from 0.5 mm to 20 cm in length, most species burrow through seafloor sediments. Fossil evidence suggests that priapulans were among the major predators during the Cambrian period.

Onychophora (110 species)

An onychophoran

Onychophorans, also called velvet worms, originated during the Cambrian explosion (see Chapter 32). Originally, they thrived in the ocean, but at some point they succeeded in colonizing land. Today they live only in humid forests. Onychophorans have fleshy antennae and several dozen pairs of saclike legs.

Tardigrada (800 species)

Tardigrades (from the Latin *tardus*, slow, and *gradus*, step) are sometimes called water bears for their rounded shape, stubby appendages, and lumbering, bearlike gait. Most tardigrades are less than 0.5 mm in length. Some live in oceans or fresh water, while others live on plants or animals. As many as 2 million tardigrades can be found on a square meter of moss. Harsh conditions may cause tardigrades to enter a state of dormancy; while dormant, they can survive for days at temperatures as low as −200°C!

100 μm

Tardigrades (colorized SEM)

Nematoda (25,000 species)

A roundworm

Also called roundworms, nematodes are enormously abundant and diverse in the soil and in aquatic habitats; many species parasitize plants and animals. Their most distinctive feature is a tough cuticle that coats the body (see Concept 33.4).

Arthropoda (1,000,000 species)

The vast majority of known animal species, including insects, crustaceans, and arachnids, are arthropods. All arthropods have a segmented exoskeleton and jointed appendages (see Concept 33.4).

A scorpion (an arachnid)

Deuterostomia

Hemichordata (85 species)

An acorn worm

Like echinoderms and chordates, hemichordates are members of the deuterostome clade (see Chapter 32). Hemichordates share some traits with chordates, such as gill slits and a dorsal nerve cord. The largest group of hemichordates is the enteropneusts, or acorn worms. Acorn worms are marine and generally live buried in mud or under rocks; they may grow to more than 2 m in length.

Chordata (56,000 species)

More than 90% of all known chordate species have backbones (and thus are vertebrates). However, the phylum Chordata also includes three groups of invertebrates: lancelets, tunicates, and hagfishes. See Chapter 34 for a full discussion of this phylum.

A tunicate

Echinodermata (7,000 species)

A sea urchin

Echinoderms, such as sand dollars, sea stars, and sea urchins, are marine animals in the deuterostome clade that are bilaterally symmetrical as larvae but not as adults. They move and feed by using a network of internal canals to pump water to different parts of their body (see Concept 33.5).

Sponges are basal animals that lack true tissues

Porifera
Cnidaria
Lophotrochozoa
Ecdysozoa
Deuterostomia

Animals in the phylum Porifera are known informally as sponges. (Recent molecular studies indicate that sponges are monophyletic, and that is the phylogeny we present here; this remains under debate, however, as some studies suggest that sponges are paraphyletic.) Among the simplest of animals, sponges are sedentary and were mistaken for plants by the ancient Greeks. Most species are marine, and they range in size from a few millimeters to a few meters. Sponges are **filter feeders**: They filter out food particles suspended in the surrounding water as they draw it through their body, which in some species resembles a sac perforated with pores. Water is drawn through the pores into a central cavity, the **spongocoel**, and then flows out of the sponge through a larger opening called the **osculum** (Figure 33.4). More complex sponges have folded body walls, and many contain branched water canals and several oscula.

Sponges represent a lineage that originates near the root of the phylogenetic tree of animals; thus, they are said to be *basal animals*. Unlike nearly all other animals, sponges lack true tissues, groups of similar cells that act as a functional unit and (in animals) are isolated from other tissues by membranous layers. However, the sponge body does contain several different cell types. For example, lining the interior of the spongocoel are flagellated **choanocytes**, or collar cells (named for the finger-like projections that form a "collar" around the flagellum). These cells engulf bacteria and other food particles by phagocytosis. The similarity between choanocytes and the cells of choanoflagellates supports molecular evidence suggesting that animals evolved from a choanoflagellate-like ancestor (see Figure 32.3).

The body of a sponge consists of two layers of cells separated by a gelatinous region called the **mesohyl**. Because both cell layers are in contact with water, processes such as gas exchange and waste removal can occur by diffusion across the membranes of these cells. Other tasks are performed by cells called **amoebocytes**, named for their use of pseudopodia. These cells move through the mesohyl and have many functions. For example, they take up food from the surrounding water and from choanocytes, digest it, and carry nutrients to other cells. Amoebocytes also

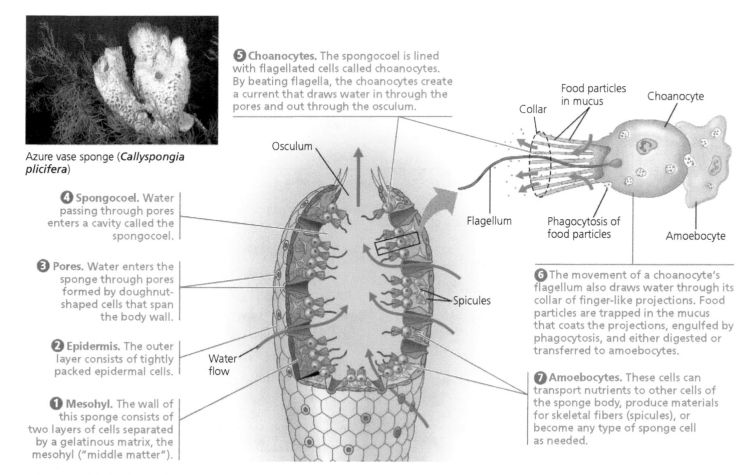

Azure vase sponge (*Callyspongia plicifera*)

5 Choanocytes. The spongocoel is lined with flagellated cells called choanocytes. By beating flagella, the choanocytes create a current that draws water in through the pores and out through the osculum.

4 Spongocoel. Water passing through pores enters a cavity called the spongocoel.

3 Pores. Water enters the sponge through pores formed by doughnut-shaped cells that span the body wall.

2 Epidermis. The outer layer consists of tightly packed epidermal cells.

1 Mesohyl. The wall of this sponge consists of two layers of cells separated by a gelatinous matrix, the mesohyl ("middle matter").

Osculum

Water flow

Spicules

Food particles in mucus

Collar

Choanocyte

Flagellum

Phagocytosis of food particles

Amoebocyte

6 The movement of a choanocyte's flagellum also draws water through its collar of finger-like projections. Food particles are trapped in the mucus that coats the projections, engulfed by phagocytosis, and either digested or transferred to amoebocytes.

7 Amoebocytes. These cells can transport nutrients to other cells of the sponge body, produce materials for skeletal fibers (spicules), or become any type of sponge cell as needed.

▲ Figure 33.4 Anatomy of a sponge.

manufacture tough skeletal fibers within the mesohyl. In some sponges, these fibers are sharp spicules made from calcium carbonate or silica. Other sponges produce more flexible fibers composed of a protein called spongin; you may have seen these pliant skeletons being sold as brown bath sponges. Finally, and perhaps most importantly, amoebocytes are *totipotent* (capable of becoming other types of sponge cells). This gives the sponge body remarkable flexibility, enabling it to adjust its shape in response to changes in its physical environment (such as the direction of water currents).

Most sponges are **hermaphrodites**, meaning that each individual functions as both male and female in sexual reproduction by producing sperm *and* eggs. Almost all sponges exhibit sequential hermaphroditism: They function first as one sex and then as the other. Cross-fertilization can result when sperm released into the water current by an individual functioning as a male is drawn into a neighboring individual that is functioning as a female. The resulting zygotes develop into flagellated, swimming larvae that disperse from the parent sponge. After settling on a suitable substrate, a larva develops into a sessile adult.

Sponges produce a variety of antibiotics and other defensive compounds, which hold promise for fighting human diseases. For example, a compound called cribrostatin isolated from marine sponges can kill both cancer cells and penicillin-resistant strains of the bacterium *Streptococcus*. Other sponge-derived compounds are also being tested as possible anticancer agents.

CONCEPT CHECK 33.1

1. Describe how sponges feed.

2. **WHAT IF?** Some molecular evidence suggests that the sister group of animals is not the choanoflagellates, but rather a group of parasitic protists, Mesomycetozoa. Given that these parasites lack collar cells, can this hypothesis be correct? Explain.

For suggested answers, see Appendix A.

CONCEPT 33.2

Cnidarians are an ancient phylum of eumetazoans

All animals except sponges and a few other groups are *eumetazoans* ("true animals"), members of a clade of animals with tissues. One of the oldest lineages in this clade is the phylum Cnidaria, which originated about 680 million years ago according to DNA analyses. Cnidarians

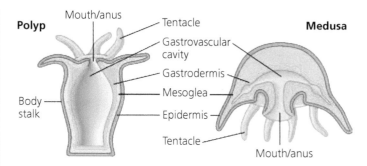

▲ Figure 33.5 **Polyp and medusa forms of cnidarians.** The body wall of a cnidarian has two layers of cells: an outer layer of epidermis (darker blue; derived from ectoderm) and an inner layer of gastrodermis (yellow; derived from endoderm). Digestion begins in the gastrovascular cavity and is completed inside food vacuoles in the gastrodermal cells. Sandwiched between the epidermis and gastrodermis is a gelatinous layer, the mesoglea.

have diversified into a wide range of sessile and motile forms, including hydras, corals, and jellies (commonly called "jellyfish"). Yet most cnidarians still exhibit the relatively simple, diploblastic, radial body plan that existed in early members of the group some 560 million years ago.

The basic body plan of a cnidarian is a sac with a central digestive compartment, the **gastrovascular cavity**. A single opening to this cavity functions as both mouth and anus. There are two variations on this body plan: the largely sessile polyp and the more motile medusa (**Figure 33.5**). **Polyps** are cylindrical forms that adhere to the substrate by the aboral end of their body (the end opposite the mouth) and extend their tentacles, waiting for prey. Examples of the polyp form include hydras and sea anemones. Although they are primarily sedentary, many polyps can move slowly across their substrate using muscles at the aboral end of their body. When threatened by a predator, some sea anemones can detach from the substrate and "swim" by bending their body column back and forth, or thrashing their tentacles. A **medusa** (plural, *medusae*) resembles a flattened, mouth-down version of the polyp. It moves freely in the water by a combination of passive drifting and contractions of its bell-shaped body. Medusae include free-swimming jellies. The tentacles of a jelly dangle from the oral surface, which points downward. Some cnidarians exist only as polyps or only as medusae; others have both a polyp stage and a medusa stage in their life cycle.

Cnidarians are predators that often use tentacles arranged in a ring around their mouth to capture prey and push the food into their gastrovascular cavity, where digestion begins. Enzymes are secreted into the cavity, thus breaking down the prey into a nutrient-rich broth. Cells lining the cavity then absorb these nutrients and complete the digestive process; any undigested remains are expelled through the cnidarian's mouth/anus. The tentacles are armed with batteries of **cnidocytes**, cells unique to cnidarians that function in defense and prey capture

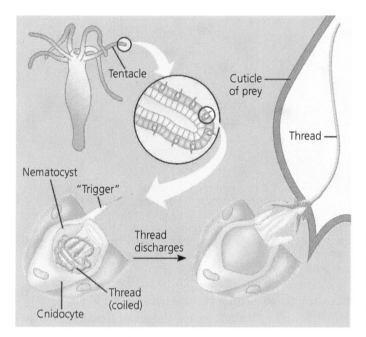

▲ **Figure 33.6 A cnidocyte of a hydra.** This type of cnidocyte contains a stinging capsule, the nematocyst, which contains a coiled thread. When a "trigger" is stimulated by touch or by certain chemicals, the thread shoots out, puncturing and injecting poison into prey.

(Figure 33.6). Cnidocytes contain *cnidae* (from the Greek *cnide*, nettle), capsule-like organelles that are capable of exploding outward and that give phylum Cnidaria its name. Specialized cnidae called **nematocysts** contain a stinging thread that can penetrate the body wall of the cnidarian's prey. Other kinds of cnidae have long threads that stick to or entangle small prey that bump into the cnidarian's tentacles.

Contractile tissues and nerves occur in their simplest forms in cnidarians. Cells of the epidermis (outer layer) and gastrodermis (inner layer) have bundles of microfilaments arranged into contractile fibers. The gastrovascular cavity acts as a hydrostatic skeleton (see Concept 50.6) against which the contractile cells can work. When a cnidarian closes its mouth, the volume of the cavity is fixed, and contraction of selected cells causes the animal to change shape. Movements are coordinated by a nerve net. Cnidarians have no brain, and the noncentralized nerve net is associated with sensory structures distributed around the body. Thus, the animal can detect and respond to stimuli from all directions.

Fossil and molecular evidence suggests that early in its evolutionary history, the phylum Cnidaria diverged into two major clades, Medusozoa and Anthozoa **(Figure 33.7).**

Medusozoans

All cnidarians that produce a medusa are members of clade Medusozoa, a group that includes the *scyphozoans* (jellies) and *cubozoans* (box jellies) shown in Figure 33.7a, along with the *hydrozoans*. Most hydrozoans alternate between

▼ **Figure 33.7 Cnidarians.**

(a) Medusozoans

Many jellies are bioluminescent. Food captured by nematocyst-bearing tentacles is transferred to specialized oral arms (that lack nematocysts) for transport to the mouth.

This sea wasp produces a poison that can subdue fish (as seen here) and other large prey. The poison is more potent than cobra venom.

(b) Anthozoans

Sea anemones and other anthozoans exist only as polyps. Many anthozoans form symbiotic relationships with photosynthetic algae.

These star corals live as colonies of polyps. Their soft bodies are enclosed at the base by a hard exoskeleton.

the polyp and medusa forms, as seen in the life cycle of *Obelia* **(Figure 33.8).** The polyp stage, a colony of interconnected polyps in the case of *Obelia*, is more conspicuous than the medusa. Hydras, among the few cnidarians found in fresh water, are also unusual hydrozoans in that they exist only in polyp form.

Unlike hydrozoans, most scyphozoans and cubozoans spend the majority of their life cycles in the medusa stage. Coastal scyphozoans, for example, often have a brief polyp stage during their life cycle, whereas those that live in the open ocean generally lack the polyp stage altogether. As their name (which means "cube animals") suggests, cubozoans have a box-shaped medusa stage. Most cubozoans live in tropical oceans and are equipped with highly toxic cnidocytes. The sea wasp (*Chironex fleckeri*), a cubozoan that lives off the coast of northern Australia, is one of the deadliest organisms known: Its sting causes intense pain

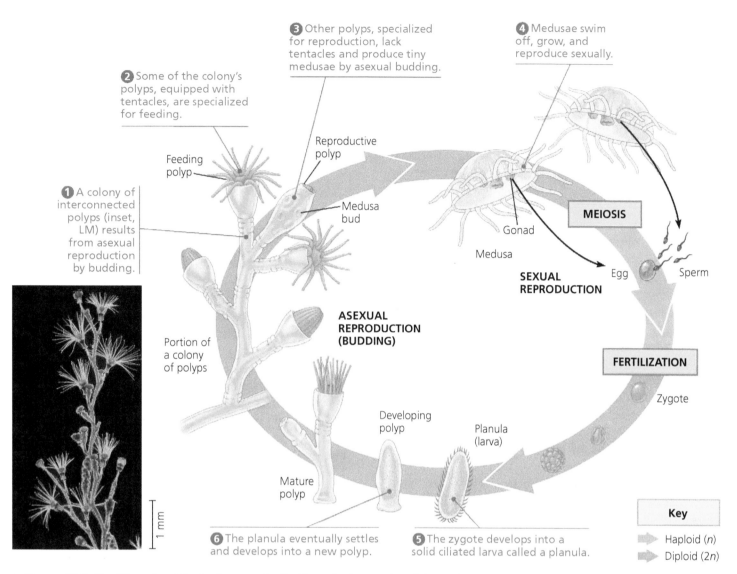

1 A colony of interconnected polyps (inset, LM) results from asexual reproduction by budding.

2 Some of the colony's polyps, equipped with tentacles, are specialized for feeding.

3 Other polyps, specialized for reproduction, lack tentacles and produce tiny medusae by asexual budding.

4 Medusae swim off, grow, and reproduce sexually.

Feeding polyp

Reproductive polyp

Medusa bud

MEIOSIS

Gonad

Medusa

SEXUAL REPRODUCTION

Egg

Sperm

ASEXUAL REPRODUCTION (BUDDING)

Portion of a colony of polyps

FERTILIZATION

Zygote

Developing polyp

Planula (larva)

Mature polyp

1 mm

6 The planula eventually settles and develops into a new polyp.

5 The zygote develops into a solid ciliated larva called a planula.

Key

Haploid (*n*)

Diploid (2*n*)

▲ **Figure 33.8 The life cycle of the hydrozoan *Obelia*.** The polyp is asexual, and the medusa is sexual, releasing eggs and sperm. These two stages alternate, one producing the other.

MAKE CONNECTIONS *Compare and contrast the* Obelia *life cycle to the life cycles in Figure 13.6. Which life cycle in that figure is most similar to that of Obelia? Explain. (See also Figure 29.3.)*

and can lead to respiratory failure, cardiac arrest, and death within minutes.

Anthozoans

Sea anemones and corals belong to the clade Anthozoa (see Figure 33.7). These cnidarians occur only as polyps. Corals live as solitary or colonial forms, often forming symbioses with algae. Many species secrete a hard **exoskeleton** (external skeleton) of calcium carbonate. Each polyp generation builds on the skeletal remains of earlier generations, constructing "rocks" with shapes characteristic of their species. These skeletons are what we usually think of as coral.

Coral reefs are to tropical seas what rain forests are to tropical land areas: They provide habitat for many other species. Unfortunately, these reefs are being destroyed at an alarming rate. Pollution, overharvesting, and ocean acidification (see Figure 3.11) are major threats; global warming may also be contributing to their demise by raising seawater temperatures above the range in which corals thrive.

CONCEPT CHECK **33.2**

1. Compare and contrast the polyp and medusa forms of cnidarians.

2. Describe the structure and function of the stinging cells for which cnidarians are named.

3. **MAKE CONNECTIONS** Many new animal body plans emerged during and after the Cambrian explosion. In contrast, cnidarians today retain the same diploblastic, radial body plan found in cnidarians 560 million years ago. Are cnidarians therefore less successful or less "highly evolved" than other animal groups? Explain. (See Concepts 25.3 and 25.6.)

For suggested answers, see Appendix A.

CONCEPT 33.3

Lophotrochozoans, a clade identified by molecular data, have the widest range of animal body forms

Porifera
Cnidaria
Lophotrochozoa
Ecdysozoa
Deuterostomia

Bilateria

The vast majority of animal species belong to the clade Bilateria, whose members exhibit bilateral symmetry and triploblastic development (see Chapter 32). Most bilaterians also have a digestive tract with two openings (a mouth and an anus) and a coelom. Recent DNA analyses suggest that the common ancestor of living bilaterians lived about 670 million years ago. To date, however, the oldest fossil that is widely accepted as a bilaterian is of the mollusc *Kimberella*, which lived 560 million years ago. Many other bilaterian groups first appeared in the fossil record during the Cambrian explosion (535 to 525 million years ago).

As you read in Chapter 32, molecular evidence suggests that there are three major clades of bilaterally symmetrical animals: Lophotrochozoa, Ecdysozoa, and Deuterostomia. This section will focus on the first of these clades, the lophotrochozoans. Concepts 33.4 and 33.5 will explore the other two clades.

Although the clade Lophotrochozoa was identified by molecular data, its name comes from features found in some of its members. Some lophotrochozoans develop a structure called a *lophophore*, a crown of ciliated tentacles that functions in feeding, while others go through a distinctive stage called the *trochophore larva* (see Figure 32.12). Other members of the group have neither of these features. Few other unique morphological features are widely shared within the group—in fact, the lophotrochozoans are the most diverse bilaterian clade in terms of body plan. This diversity in form is reflected in the number of phyla classified in the group: Lophotrochozoa includes 18 phyla, more than twice the number in any other clade of bilaterians.

We'll now introduce six of the diverse lophotrochozoan phyla: the flatworms, rotifers, ectoprocts, brachiopods, molluscs, and annelids.

Flatworms

Flatworms (phylum Platyhelminthes) live in marine, freshwater, and damp terrestrial habitats. In addition to free-living species, flatworms include many parasitic species, such as flukes and tapeworms. Flatworms are so named because they have thin bodies that are flattened dorsoventrally (between the dorsal and ventral surfaces); the word *platyhelminth* means "flat worm." (Note that *worm* is not a formal taxonomic name but rather refers to a grade of animals with long, thin bodies.) The smallest flatworms are nearly microscopic free-living species, while some tapeworms are more than 20 m long.

Although flatworms undergo triploblastic development, they are acoelomates (animals that lack a body cavity). Their flat shape increases their surface area, placing all their cells close to water in the surrounding environment or in their gut. Because of this proximity to water, gas exchange and the elimination of nitrogenous waste (ammonia) can occur by diffusion across the body surface. As seen in **Figure 33.9**, a flat shape is one of several structural features that maximize surface area and have arisen (by convergent evolution) in different groups of animals and other organisms.

As you might expect since all their cells are close to water, flatworms have no organs specialized for gas exchange, and their relatively simple excretory apparatus functions mainly to maintain osmotic balance with their surroundings. This apparatus consists of **protonephridia**, networks of tubules with ciliated structures called *flame bulbs* that pull fluid through branched ducts opening to the outside (see Figure 44.9). Most flatworms have a gastrovascular cavity with only one opening. Though flatworms lack a circulatory system, the fine branches of the gastrovascular cavity distribute food directly to the animal's cells.

Early in their evolutionary history, flatworms separated into two lineages, Catenulida and Rhabditophora. Catenulida is a small clade of about 100 flatworm species, most of which live in freshwater habitats. Catenulids typically reproduce asexually by budding at their posterior end. The offspring often produce their own buds before detaching from the parent, thereby forming a chain of two to four genetically identical individuals—hence their informal name, "chain worms."

The other ancient flatworm lineage, Rhabditophora, is a diverse clade of about 20,000 freshwater and marine species, one example of which is shown in Figure 33.9. We'll explore the rhabditophorans in more detail, focusing on free-living and parasitic members of this clade.

Free-Living Species

Free-living rhabditophorans are important as predators and scavengers in a wide range of freshwater and marine habitats. The best-known members of this group are freshwater species in the genus *Dugesia*, commonly called **planarians**. Abundant in unpolluted ponds and streams, planarians prey on smaller animals or feed on dead animals. They move by using cilia on their ventral surface, gliding along a film of mucus they secrete. Some other rhabditophorans also use their muscles to swim through water with an undulating motion.

A planarian's head features a pair of light-sensitive eyespots as well as lateral flaps that function mainly to detect specific chemicals. The planarian nervous system is more complex and centralized than the nerve nets of cnidarians

MAKE CONNECTIONS

Maximizing Surface Area

In general, the amount of metabolic or chemical activity an organism can carry out is proportional to its mass or volume. Maximizing metabolic rate, however, requires the efficient uptake of energy and raw materials, such as nutrients and oxygen, as well as the effective disposal of waste products. For large cells, plants, and animals, these exchange processes have the potential to be limiting due to simple geometry. When a cell or organism grows without changing shape, its volume increases more rapidly than its surface area (see Figure 6.7). As a result, there is proportionately less surface area available to support chemical activity. The challenge posed by the relationship of surface area and volume occurs in diverse contexts and organisms, but the evolutionary adaptations that meet this challenge are similar. Structures that maximize surface area through flattening, folding, branching, and projections have an essential role in biological systems.

These diagrams compare surface area (SA) for two different shapes with the same volume (V). Note which shape has the greater surface area.

SA: $6\,(3\text{ cm}\times 3\text{ cm}) = 54\text{ cm}^2$
V: $3\text{ cm}\times 3\text{ cm}\times 3\text{ cm} = 27\text{ cm}^3$

SA: $2\,(3\text{ cm}\times 1\text{ cm}) + 2\,(9\text{ cm}\times 1\text{ cm}) + 2\,(3\text{ cm}\times 9\text{ cm}) = 78\text{ cm}^2$
V: $1\text{ cm}\times 3\text{ cm}\times 9\text{ cm} = 27\text{ cm}^3$

Flattening

By having a body that is only a few cells thick, an organism such as this flatworm can use its entire body surface for exchange. *See Figure 40.3.*

Folding

This TEM shows portions of two chloroplasts in a plant leaf. Photosynthesis occurs in chloroplasts, which have a flattened and interconnected set of internal membranes called thylakoid membranes. The foldings of the thylakoid membranes increase their surface area, enhancing the exposure to light and thus increasing the rate of photosynthesis. *See Figure 10.4.*

1 µm   Thylakoid

Branching

Water uptake relies on passive diffusion. The highly branched filaments of a fungal mycelium increase the surface area across which water and minerals can be absorbed from the environment. *See Figure 31.2.*

Projections

In vertebrates, the small intestine is lined with finger-like projections called villi that absorb nutrients released by the digestion of food. Each of the villi shown here is covered with large numbers of microscopic projections called microvilli, resulting in a total surface area of about 300 m^2 in humans, as large as a tennis court. *See Figure 41.13.*

MAKE CONNECTIONS *Find other examples of flattening, folding, branching, and projections (see Chapters 6, 9, 35, and 42). How is maximizing surface area important to the structure's function in each example?*

Digestion is completed within the cells lining the gastrovascular cavity, which has many fine subbranches that provide an extensive surface area.

Pharynx. A muscular pharynx can be extended through the mouth. Digestive juices are spilled onto prey, and the pharynx sucks small pieces of food into the gastrovascular cavity, where digestion continues.

Undigested wastes are egested through an opening at the tip of the pharynx.

Gastrovascular cavity

Mouth

Eyespots

Ventral nerve cords. From the ganglia, a pair of ventral nerve cords runs the length of the body.

Ganglia. At the anterior end of the worm, near the main sources of sensory input, is a pair of ganglia, dense clusters of nerve cells.

▲ Figure 33.10 **Anatomy of a planarian.**

(Figure 33.10). Experiments have shown that planarians can learn to modify their responses to stimuli.

Some planarians can reproduce asexually through fission. The parent constricts roughly in the middle of its body, separating into a head end and a tail end; each end then regenerates the missing parts. Sexual reproduction also occurs. Planarians are hermaphrodites, and copulating mates typically cross-fertilize each other.

Parasitic Species

More than half of the known species of rhabditophorans live as parasites in or on other animals. Many have suckers that attach to the internal organs or outer surfaces of the host animal. In most species, a tough covering helps protect the parasites within their hosts. We'll discuss two ecologically and economically important subgroups of parasitic rhabditophorans, the trematodes and the tapeworms.

Trematodes As a group, trematodes parasitize a wide range of hosts, and most species have complex life cycles with alternating sexual and asexual stages. Many trematodes require an intermediate host in which larvae develop before infecting the final host (usually a vertebrate), where the adult worms live. For example, various trematodes that parasitize humans spend part of their lives in snail hosts (Figure 33.11). Around the world, about 200 million people are infected with trematodes called blood flukes (*Schistosoma*) and suffer from schistosomiasis, a disease whose symptoms include pain, anemia, and diarrhea.

Living within more than one kind of host puts demands on trematodes that free-living animals don't face. A blood

fluke, for instance, must evade the immune systems of both snails and humans. By mimicking the surface proteins of its hosts, the blood fluke creates a partial immunological camouflage for itself. It also releases molecules that manipulate the hosts' immune systems into tolerating the parasite's existence. These defenses are so effective that individual blood flukes can survive in humans for more than 40 years.

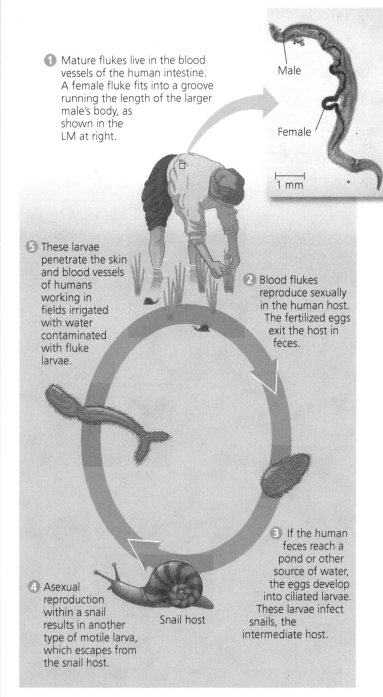

1 Mature flukes live in the blood vessels of the human intestine. A female fluke fits into a groove running the length of the larger male's body, as shown in the LM at right.

Male

Female

1 mm

5 These larvae penetrate the skin and blood vessels of humans working in fields irrigated with water contaminated with fluke larvae.

2 Blood flukes reproduce sexually in the human host. The fertilized eggs exit the host in feces.

3 If the human feces reach a pond or other source of water, the eggs develop into ciliated larvae. These larvae infect snails, the intermediate host.

4 Asexual reproduction within a snail results in another type of motile larva, which escapes from the snail host.

Snail host

▲ Figure 33.11 **The life cycle of a blood fluke (*Schistosoma mansoni*), a trematode.**

WHAT IF? *Snails eat algae, whose growth is stimulated by nutrients found in fertilizer. How would the contamination of irrigation water with fertilizer likely affect the occurrence of schistosomiasis? Explain.*

Tapeworms The tapeworms are a second large and diverse group of parasitic rhabditophorans (**Figure 33.12**). The adults live mostly inside vertebrates, including humans. In many tapeworms, the anterior end, or scolex, is armed with suckers and often hooks that the worm uses to attach itself to the intestinal lining of its host. Tapeworms lack a mouth and gastrovascular cavity; they simply absorb nutrients released by digestion in the host's intestine. Absorption occurs across the tapeworm's body surface.

Posterior to the scolex is a long ribbon of units called proglottids, which are little more than sacs of sex organs. After sexual reproduction, proglottids loaded with thousands of fertilized eggs are released from the posterior end of a tapeworm and leave the host's body in feces. In one type of life cycle, feces carrying the eggs contaminate the food or water of intermediate hosts, such as pigs or cattle, and the tapeworm eggs develop into larvae that encyst in muscles of these animals. A human acquires the larvae by eating undercooked meat containing the cysts, and the worms develop into mature adults within the human. Large tapeworms can block the intestines and rob enough nutrients from the human host to cause nutritional deficiencies. Several different oral medications can kill the adult worms.

Rotifers

Rotifers (phylum Rotifera) are tiny animals that inhabit freshwater, marine, and damp soil habitats. Ranging in size from about 50 μm to 2 mm, rotifers are smaller than many protists but nevertheless are multicellular and have specialized organ systems (**Figure 33.13**). In contrast to cnidarians and flatworms, which have a gastrovascular cavity, rotifers have an **alimentary canal**, a digestive tube with two openings, a mouth and an anus. Internal organs lie within the pseudocoelom, a body cavity that is not completely lined by mesoderm (see Figure 32.9b). Fluid in the pseudocoelom serves as a hydrostatic skeleton. Movement of a rotifer's body distributes the fluid throughout the body, circulating nutrients.

The word *rotifer* is derived from the Latin meaning "wheel-bearer," a reference to the crown of cilia that draws a vortex of water into the mouth. Posterior to the mouth, rotifers have jaws called trophi that grind up food, mostly microorganisms suspended in the water. Digestion is then completed farther along the alimentary canal. Most other bilaterians also have an alimentary canal, which enables the stepwise digestion of a wide range of food particles.

Rotifers exhibit some unusual forms of reproduction. Some species consist only of females that produce more females from unfertilized eggs, a type of asexual reproduction called **parthenogenesis**. Some other invertebrates (for example, aphids and some bees) and even some vertebrates (for example, some lizards and some fishes) can also reproduce in this way. In addition to being able to produce females by parthenogenesis, some rotifers can also reproduce sexually under certain conditions, such as high levels of crowding. The resulting embryos can remain dormant for years. Once they break dormancy, the embryos develop into another generation of females that reproduce asexually.

It is puzzling that many rotifer species persist without males. The vast majority of animals and plants reproduce sexually at least some of the time, and sexual reproduction has certain advantages over asexual reproduction (see Concept 46.1). For example, species that reproduce

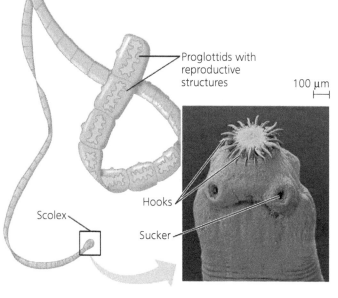

▲ **Figure 33.12 Anatomy of a tapeworm.** The inset shows a close-up of the scolex (colorized SEM).

Proglottids with reproductive structures

100 μm

Hooks

Scolex

Sucker

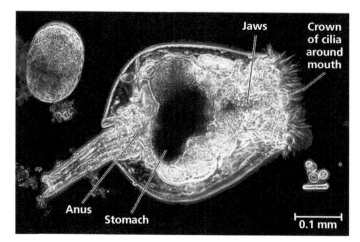

Jaws

Crown of cilia around mouth

Anus

Stomach

0.1 mm

▲ **Figure 33.13 A rotifer.** These pseudocoelomates, smaller than many protists, are generally more anatomically complex than flatworms (LM).

asexually tend to accumulate harmful mutations in their genomes faster than sexually reproducing species. As a result, asexual species should experience higher rates of extinction and lower rates of speciation.

Seeking to understand this unusual group, researchers have been studying a clade of asexual rotifers named Bdelloidea. Some 360 species of bdelloid rotifers are known, and all of them reproduce by parthenogenesis without any males. Paleontologists have discovered bdelloid rotifers preserved in 35-million-year-old amber, and the morphology of these fossils resembles only the female form, with no evidence of males. By comparing the DNA of bdelloids with that of their closest sexually reproducing rotifer relatives, scientists have concluded that bdelloids have likely been asexual for 100 million years. How these animals manage to flout the general rule against long-lasting asexuality remains a puzzle.

Lophophorates: Ectoprocts and Brachiopods

Bilaterians in the phyla Ectoprocta and Brachiopoda are among those known as lophophorates. These animals have a *lophophore*, a crown of ciliated tentacles around their mouth (see Figure 32.12a). As the cilia draw water toward the mouth, the tentacles trap suspended food particles. Other similarities, such as a U-shaped alimentary canal and the absence of a distinct head, reflect these organisms' sessile existence. In contrast to flatworms, which lack a body cavity, and rotifers, which have a pseudocoelom, lophophorates have a true coelom that is completely lined by mesoderm (see Figure 32.9a).

Ectoprocts (from the Greek *ecto*, outside, and *procta*, anus) are colonial animals that superficially resemble clumps of moss. (In fact, their common name, bryozoans, means "moss animals.") In most species, the colony is encased in a hard exoskeleton studded with pores through which the lophophores extend (Figure 33.14a). Most ectoproct species live in the sea, where they are among the most widespread and numerous sessile animals. Several species are important reef builders. Ectoprocts also live in lakes and rivers. Colonies of the freshwater ectoproct *Pectinatella magnifica* grow on submerged sticks or rocks and can grow into a gelatinous, ball-shaped mass more than 10 cm across.

Brachiopods, or lamp shells, superficially resemble clams and other hinge-shelled molluscs, but the two halves of the brachiopod shell are dorsal and ventral rather than lateral, as in clams (Figure 33.14b). All brachiopods are marine. Most live attached to the seafloor by a stalk, opening their shell slightly to allow water to flow through the lophophore. The living brachiopods are remnants of a much richer past that included 30,000 species in the Paleozoic and Mesozoic eras. Some living brachiopods, such as those in the genus *Lingula*, appear nearly identical to fossils of species that lived 400 million years ago.

(a) Ectoprocts, such as this creeping bryozoan (*Plumatella repens*), are colonial lophophorates.

(b) Brachiopods, such as this lampshell (*Terebratulina retusa*), have a hinged shell. The two parts of the shell are dorsal and ventral.

▲ **Figure 33.14 Lophophorates.**

Molluscs

Snails and slugs, oysters and clams, and octopuses and squids are all molluscs (phylum Mollusca). There are over 100,000 known species, making them the second most diverse phylum of animals (after the arthropods, discussed later). Although the majority of molluscs are marine, roughly 8,000 species inhabit fresh water, and 28,000 species of snails and slugs live on land. All molluscs are soft-bodied, and most secrete a hard protective shell made of calcium carbonate. Slugs, squids, and octopuses have a reduced internal shell or have lost their shell completely during their evolution.

Despite their apparent differences, all molluscs have a similar body plan (Figure 33.15). Molluscs are coelomates, and their bodies have three main parts: a muscular **foot**, usually used for movement; a **visceral mass** containing most of the internal organs; and a **mantle**, a fold of tissue that drapes over the visceral mass and secretes a shell (if one is present). In many molluscs, the mantle extends beyond the visceral mass, producing a water-filled chamber, the **mantle cavity**, which houses the gills, anus, and excretory pores. Many molluscs feed by using a straplike organ called a **radula** to scrape up food.

Most molluscs have separate sexes, and their gonads (ovaries or testes) are located in the visceral mass. Many snails, however, are hermaphrodites. The life cycle of many marine molluscs includes a ciliated larval stage, the trochophore (see Figure 32.12b), which is also characteristic of marine annelids (segmented worms) and some other lophotrochozoans.

The basic body plan of molluscs has evolved in various ways in the phylum's eight major clades. We'll examine four of those clades here: Polyplacophora (chitons), Gastropoda (snails and slugs), Bivalvia (clams, oysters, and other bivalves), and Cephalopoda (squids, octopuses, cuttlefishes, and chambered nautiluses). We will then focus on threats facing some groups of molluscs.

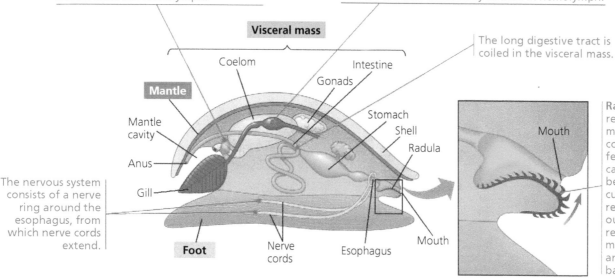

Metanephridium. Excretory organs called metanephridia remove metabolic wastes from the hemolymph.

Heart. Most molluscs have an open circulatory system. The dorsally located heart pumps circulatory fluid called hemolymph through arteries into sinuses (body spaces). The organs of the mollusc are thus continually bathed in hemolymph.

Visceral mass

Coelom

Intestine

Gonads

The long digestive tract is coiled in the visceral mass.

Mantle

Mantle cavity

Stomach

Shell

Radula

Anus

Mouth

The nervous system consists of a nerve ring around the esophagus, from which nerve cords extend.

Gill

Foot

Nerve cords

Esophagus

Mouth

Radula. The mouth region in many mollusc species contains a rasp-like feeding organ called a radula. This belt of backward-curved teeth repeatedly thrusts outward and then retracts into the mouth, scraping and scooping like a backhoe.

▲ **Figure 33.15 The basic body plan of a mollusc.**

Chitons

Chitons have an oval-shaped body and a shell composed of eight dorsal plates **(Figure 33.16)**. The chiton's body itself, however, is unsegmented. You can find these marine animals clinging to rocks along the shore during low tide. If you try to dislodge a chiton by hand, you will be surprised at how well its foot, acting as a suction cup, grips the rock. A chiton can also use its foot to creep slowly over the rock surface. Chitons use their radula to scrape algae off the rock surface.

Gastropods

About three-quarters of all living species of molluscs are gastropods **(Figure 33.17)**. Most gastropods are marine, but there are also freshwater species. Still other gastropods have adapted to life on land, where snails and slugs thrive in habitats ranging from deserts to rain forests.

Gastropods move literally at a snail's pace by a rippling motion of their foot or by means of cilia—a slow process that can leave them vulnerable to attack. Most gastropods have a single, spiraled shell into which the animal can retreat when threatened. The shell, which is secreted by glands at the edge of the mantle, has several functions, including protecting the animal's soft body from injury and dehydration. One of its most important roles is as a defense against predators, as is demonstrated by comparing populations with different histories of predation (see the Scientific Skills Exercise). As they move slowly about, most gastropods use their radula to graze on algae

▲ **Figure 33.16 A chiton.** Note the eight-plate shell characteristic of molluscs in the clade Polyplacophora.

(a) A land snail

▲ **Figure 33.17 Gastropods.** The many species of gastropods have colonized terretrial as well as aquatic environments.

(b) A sea slug. Nudibranchs, or sea slugs, lost their shell during their evolution.

Understanding Experimental Design and Interpreting Data

Is There Evidence of Selection for Defensive Adaptations in Mollusc Populations Exposed to Predators? The fossil record shows that historically, increased risk to prey species from predators is often accompanied by increased incidence and expression of prey defenses. Researchers tested whether populations of the predatory European green crab (*Carcinus maenas*) have exerted similar selective pressures on its gastropod prey, the flat periwinkle (*Littorina obtusata*). Periwinkles from southern sites in the Gulf of Maine have experienced predation by European green crabs for over 100 generations, at about one generation per year. Periwinkles from northern sites in the Gulf have been interacting with the invasive green crabs for relatively few generations, as the invasive crabs spread to the northern Gulf comparatively recently.

▲ A periwinkle

Previous research shows that (1) flat periwinkle shells recently collected from the Gulf are thicker than those collected in the late 1800s, and (2) periwinkle populations from southern sites in the Gulf have thicker shells than periwinkle populations from northern sites. In this exercise, you'll interpret the design and results of the researchers' experiment studying the rates of predation by European green crabs on periwinkles from northern and southern populations.

How the Experiment Was Done The researchers collected periwinkles and crabs from sites in the northern and southern Gulf of Maine, separated by 450 km of coastline. A single crab was placed in a cage with eight periwinkles of different sizes. After three days, researchers assessed the fate of the eight periwinkles. Four different treatments were set up, with crabs from northern or southern populations offered periwinkles from northern and southern populations. All crabs were of similar size and included equal numbers of males and females. Each experimental treatment was tested 12 to 14 times.

In a second part of the experiment, the bodies of periwinkles from northern and southern populations were removed from their shells and presented to crabs from northern and southern populations.

Data from the Experiment

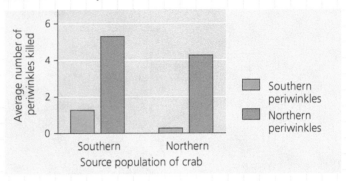

When the researchers presented the crabs with unshelled periwinkles, all the unshelled periwinkles were consumed in less than an hour.

Interpret the Data

1. What hypotheses were the researchers testing in this study? What are the independent variables in this study? What are the dependent variables in this study?

2. Why did the research team set up four different treatments?

3. Why did researchers present unshelled periwinkles to the crabs? Explain what the results of this part of the experiment indicate.

4. Summarize the results of the experiment in words. Do these results support the hypothesis you identified in question 1? Explain.

5. Suggest how natural selection may have affected populations of flat periwinkles in the southern Gulf of Maine over the last 100 years.

(MB) A version of this Scientific Skills Exercise can be assigned in MasteringBiology.

Data from R. Rochette et al., Interaction between an invasive decapod and a native gastropod: Predator foraging tactics and prey architectural defenses, *Marine Ecology Progress Series* 330:179–188 (2007).

---

or plants. Several groups, however, are predators, and their radula has become modified for boring holes in the shells of other molluscs or for tearing apart prey. In the cone snails, the teeth of the radula act as poison darts that are used to subdue prey.

Many gastropods have a head with eyes at the tips of tentacles. Terrestrial snails lack the gills typical of most aquatic gastropods. Instead, the lining of their mantle cavity functions as a lung, exchanging respiratory gases with the air.

Bivalves

The molluscs of the clade Bivalvia are all aquatic and include many species of clams, oysters, mussels, and scallops. Bivalves have a shell divided into two halves (**Figure 33.18**). The halves are hinged, and powerful adductor muscles draw them tightly together to protect the animal's soft body. Bivalves have no distinct head, and the radula has been lost.

▲ **Figure 33.18 A bivalve.** This scallop has many eyes (dark blue spots) lining each half of its hinged shell.

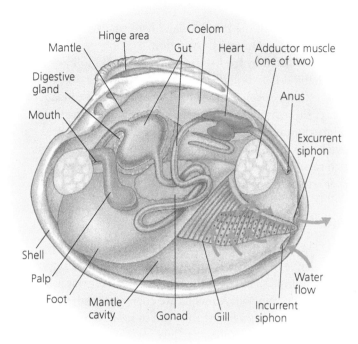

Coelom
Hinge area
Mantle
Gut   Heart   Adductor muscle
(one of two)
Digestive
gland
Anus
Mouth
Excurrent
siphon
Shell
Palp
Water
flow
Foot
Mantle
cavity
Gonad   Gill
Incurrent
siphon

▲ **Figure 33.19 Anatomy of a clam.** Food particles suspended in water that enters through the incurrent siphon are collected by the gills and passed via cilia and the palps to the mouth.

Some bivalves have eyes and sensory tentacles along the outer edge of their mantle.

The mantle cavity of a bivalve contains gills that are used for feeding as well as gas exchange in most species **(Figure 33.19)**. Most bivalves are suspension feeders. They trap small food particles in mucus that coats their gills, and cilia then convey those particles to the mouth. Water enters the mantle cavity through an incurrent siphon, passes over the gills, and then exits the mantle cavity through an excurrent siphon.

Most bivalves lead sedentary lives, a characteristic suited to suspension feeding. Mussels secrete strong threads that tether them to rocks, docks, boats, and the shells of other animals. However, clams can pull themselves into the sand or mud, using their muscular foot for an anchor, and scallops can skitter along the seafloor by flapping their shells, rather like the mechanical false teeth sold in novelty shops.

Cephalopods

Cephalopods are active marine predators **(Figure 33.20)**. They use their tentacles to grasp prey, which they then bite with beak-like jaws and immobilize with a poison present in their saliva. The foot of a cephalopod has become modified into a muscular excurrent siphon and part of the tentacles. Squids dart about by drawing water into their mantle cavity and then firing a jet of water through the excurrent siphon; they steer by pointing the siphon in different directions. Octopuses use a similar mechanism to escape predators.

The mantle covers the visceral mass of cephalopods, but the shell is generally reduced and internal (in most species)

or missing altogether (in some cuttlefishes and some octopuses). One small group of cephalopods with external shells, the chambered nautiluses, survives today.

Cephalopods are the only molluscs with a *closed circulatory system*, in which the blood remains separate from fluid in the body cavity. They also have well-developed sense organs and a complex brain. The ability to learn and behave in a complex manner is probably more critical to fast-moving predators than to sedentary animals such as clams.

The ancestors of octopuses and squids were probably shelled molluscs that took up a predatory lifestyle; the shell was lost in later evolution. Shelled cephalopods called **ammonites**, some of them as large as truck tires, were the dominant invertebrate predators of the seas for hundreds of millions of years until their disappearance during the mass extinction at the end of the Cretaceous period, 65.5 million years ago.

Most species of squid are less than 75 cm long, but some are much larger. The giant squid (*Architeuthis dux*), for example, has an estimated maximum length of 13 m for females and 10 m for males. The colossal squid (*Mesonychoteuthis hamiltoni*), is even larger, with an estimated maximum length of 14 m. Unlike *A. dux*, which has large suckers and small teeth on its tentacles, *M. hamiltoni* has two rows of sharp hooks at the ends of its tentacles that can inflict deadly lacerations.

▶ Squids are speedy carnivores with beak-like jaws and well-developed eyes.

◀ Octopuses are considered among the most intelligent invertebrates.

▶ Chambered nautiluses are the only living cephalopods with an external shell.

▲ **Figure 33.20 Cephalopods.**

It is likely that *A. dux* and *M. hamiltoni* spend most of their time in the deep ocean, where they may feed on large fishes. Remains of both giant squid species have been found in the stomachs of sperm whales, which are probably their only natural predator. Scientists first photographed *A. dux* in the wild in 2005 while it was attacking baited hooks at a depth of 900 m. *M. hamiltoni* has yet to be observed in nature. Overall, these marine giants remain among the great mysteries of invertebrate life.

Protecting Freshwater and Terrestrial Molluscs

Species extinction rates have increased dramatically in the last 400 years, raising concern that a sixth, human-caused mass extinction may be under way (see Concept 25.4). Among the many taxa under threat, molluscs have the dubious distinction of being the animal group with the largest number of documented extinctions (Figure 33.21).

Threats to molluscs are especially severe in two groups, freshwater bivalves and terrestrial gastropods. The pearl mussels, a group of freshwater bivalves that can make natural pearls (gems that form when a mussel or oyster secretes layers of a lustrous coating around a grain of sand or other small irritant), are among the world's most endangered animals. Roughly 10% of the 300 pearl mussel species that once lived in North America have become extinct in the last 100 years, and over two-thirds of those that remain are threatened by extinction. Terrestrial gastropods, such as the snail in Figure 33.21, are faring no better. Hundreds of Pacific island land snails have disappeared since 1800. Overall, more than 50% of the Pacific island land snails are extinct or under imminent threat of extinction.

Threats faced by freshwater and terrestrial molluscs include habitat loss, pollution, and competition or predation by non-native species introduced by people. Is it too late to protect these molluscs? In some locations, reducing water pollution and changing how water is released from dams have led to dramatic rebounds in pearl mussel populations. Such results provide hope that with corrective measures, other endangered mollusc species can be revived.

Annelids

Annelida means "little rings," referring to the annelid body's resemblance to a series of fused rings. Annelids are segmented worms that live in the sea, in most freshwater habitats, and in damp soil. Annelids are coelomates, and they range in length from less than 1 mm to more than 3 m, the length of a giant Australian earthworm.

Traditionally, the phylum Annelida was divided into three main groups, Polychaeta (the polychaetes), Oligochaeta (the oligochaetes), and Hirudinea (the leeches). The names of the first two of these groups reflected the relative number of chaetae, bristles made of chitin, on their bodies: polychaetes (from the Greek *poly*, many, and *chaitē*, long hair) have many more chaetae per segment than do oligochaetes.

However, a 2011 phylogenomic study and other recent molecular analyses have indicated that the oligochaetes are a subgroup of the polychaetes, making the polychaetes (as

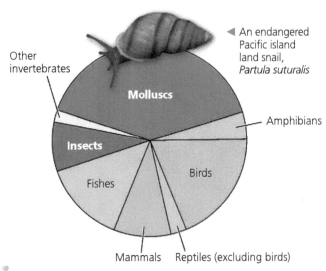

▲ Recorded extinctions of animal species
© 2004 American Institute of Biology Sciences

◀ An endangered Pacific island land snail, *Partula suturalis*

▲ Workers on a mound of pearl mussels killed to make buttons (ca. 1919)

▲ **Figure 33.21 The silent extinction.** Molluscs account for a largely unheralded but sobering 40% of all documented extinctions of animal species. These extinctions have resulted from habitat loss, pollution, introduced species, overharvesting, and other human actions. Many pearl mussel populations, for example, were driven to extinction by overharvesting for their shells, which were used to make buttons and other goods. Land snails are highly vulnerable to the same threats; like pearl mussels, they are among the world's most imperiled animal groups.

MAKE CONNECTIONS *Freshwater bivalves feed on and can reduce the abundance of photosynthetic protists and bacteria. As such, would the extinction of freshwater bivalves likely have weak or strong effects on aquatic communities (see Concept 28.6)? Explain.*

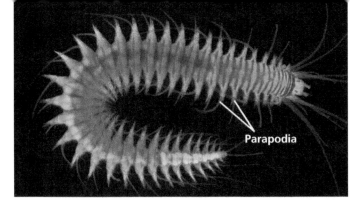

▲ **Figure 33.22 An errantian, the predator *Nereimyra punctata*.** This marine annelid ambushes prey from burrows it has constructed on the seafloor. *N. punctata* hunts by touch, detecting its prey with long sensory organs called cirri that extend from the burrow.

Parapodia

defined morphologically) a paraphyletic group. Likewise, the leeches have been shown to be a subgroup of the oligochaetes. As a result, these traditional names are no longer used to describe the evolutionary history of the annelids. Instead, current evidence indicates that the annelids can be divided into two major clades, Errantia and Sedentaria—a grouping that reflects broad differences in lifestyle.

Errantians

Clade Errantia (from the Old French *errant*, traveling) is a large and diverse group, most of whose members are marine. As their name suggests, many errantians are mobile; some swim among the plankton (small, drifting organisms), while many others crawl on or burrow in the seafloor. Many are predators, while others are grazers that feed on large, multicellular algae. The group also includes some relatively immobile species, such as the tube-dwelling *Platynereis*, a marine species that recently has become a model organism for studying neurobiology and development.

In many errantians, each body segment has a pair of prominent paddle-like or ridge-like structures called parapodia ("beside feet") that function in locomotion **(Figure 33.22)**. Each parapodium has numerous chaetae. (Possession of parapodia with numerous chaetae is not unique to Errantia, however, as some members of the other major clade of annelids, Sedentaria, also have these features.) In many species, the parapodia are richly supplied with blood vessels and also function as gills. Errantians also tend to have well-developed jaws and sensory organs, as might be expected of predators or grazers that move about in search of food.

Sedentarians

Species in the other major clade of annelids, Sedentaria (from the Latin *sedere*, sit), tend to be less mobile than those in Errantia. Some species burrow slowly through marine sediments or soil, while others live within tubes that protect and support their soft bodies. Tube-dwelling sedentarians often have elaborate gills or tentacles used for filter feeding **(Figure 33.23)**.

▲ **Figure 33.23 The Christmas tree worm, *Spirobranchus giganteus*.** The two tree-shaped whorls of this sedentarian are tentacles, which the worm uses for gas exchange and for removing small food particles from the surrounding water. The tentacles emerge from a tube of calcium carbonate secreted by the worm that protects and supports its soft body.

Although the Christmas tree worm shown in Figure 33.23 once was classified as a "polychaete," current evidence indicates it is a sedentarian. The clade Sedentaria also contains former "oligochaetes," including the two groups we turn to next, the leeches and the earthworms.

Leeches Most leeches inhabit fresh water, but there are also marine species and terrestrial leeches, which live in moist vegetation. Leeches range in length from 1 to 30 cm. Many are predators that feed on other invertebrates, but some are parasites that suck blood by attaching temporarily to other animals, including humans **(Figure 33.24)**. Some parasitic species use bladelike jaws to slit the skin of their host. The host is usually oblivious to this attack because the leech secretes an anesthetic. After making the incision, the leech secretes a chemical, hirudin, which keeps the blood of the host from coagulating near the incision. The parasite then sucks as much blood as it can hold, often more than ten times its own weight. After this gorging, a leech can last for months without another meal.

Until the 20th century, leeches were frequently used for bloodletting. Today they are used to drain blood that accumulates in tissues following certain injuries or surgeries. In addition, forms of hirudin produced with recombinant DNA

▶ **Figure 33.24 A leech.** A nurse applied this medicinal leech (*Hirudo medicinalis*) to a patient's sore thumb to drain blood from a hematoma (an abnormal accumulation of blood around an internal injury).

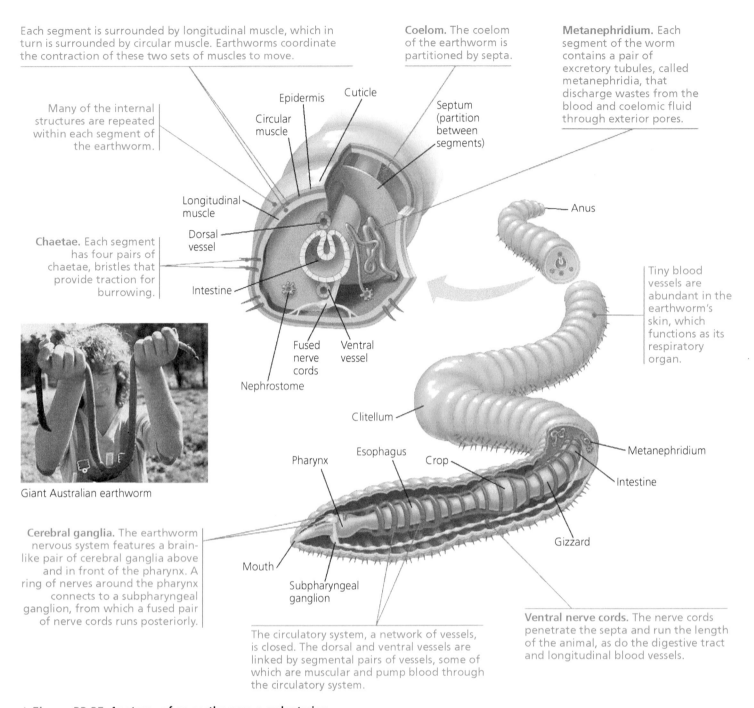

Each segment is surrounded by longitudinal muscle, which in turn is surrounded by circular muscle. Earthworms coordinate the contraction of these two sets of muscles to move.

Coelom. The coelom of the earthworm is partitioned by septa.

Metanephridium. Each segment of the worm contains a pair of excretory tubules, called metanephridia, that discharge wastes from the blood and coelomic fluid through exterior pores.

Many of the internal structures are repeated within each segment of the earthworm.

Epidermis

Cuticle

Circular muscle

Septum (partition between segments)

Longitudinal muscle

Dorsal vessel

Chaetae. Each segment has four pairs of chaetae, bristles that provide traction for burrowing.

Intestine

Fused nerve cords

Ventral vessel

Nephrostome

Anus

Tiny blood vessels are abundant in the earthworm's skin, which functions as its respiratory organ.

Giant Australian earthworm

Clitellum

Metanephridium

Intestine

Pharynx

Esophagus

Crop

Cerebral ganglia. The earthworm nervous system features a brain-like pair of cerebral ganglia above and in front of the pharynx. A ring of nerves around the pharynx connects to a subpharyngeal ganglion, from which a fused pair of nerve cords runs posteriorly.

Mouth

Subpharyngeal ganglion

Gizzard

The circulatory system, a network of vessels, is closed. The dorsal and ventral vessels are linked by segmental pairs of vessels, some of which are muscular and pump blood through the circulatory system.

Ventral nerve cords. The nerve cords penetrate the septa and run the length of the animal, as do the digestive tract and longitudinal blood vessels.

▲ Figure 33.25 **Anatomy of an earthworm, a sedentarian.**

techniques can be used to dissolve unwanted blood clots that form during surgery or as a result of heart disease.

Earthworms Earthworms eat their way through the soil, extracting nutrients as the soil passes through the alimentary canal. Undigested material, mixed with mucus secreted into the canal, is eliminated as fecal castings through the anus. Farmers value earthworms because the animals till and aerate the earth, and their castings improve the texture of the soil. (Charles Darwin estimated that one acre of farmland contains about 50,000 earthworms, producing 18 tons of castings per year.)

A guided tour of the anatomy of an earthworm, which is representative of annelids, is shown in **Figure 33.25**. Earthworms are hermaphrodites, but they do cross-fertilize. Two earthworms mate by aligning themselves in opposite directions in such a way that they exchange sperm, and then they separate. Some earthworms can also reproduce asexually by fragmentation followed by regeneration.

As a group, Lophotrochozoa encompasses a remarkable range of body plans, as illustrated by members of such phyla as Rotifera, Ectoprocta, Mollusca, and Annelida. Next we'll explore the diversity of Ecdysozoa, a dominant presence on Earth in terms of sheer number of species.

1. Explain how tapeworms can survive without a coelom, a mouth, a digestive system, or an excretory system.

2. Annelid anatomy can be described as "a tube within a tube." Explain.

3. **MAKE CONNECTIONS** Explain how the molluscan foot in gastropods and the excurrent siphon in cephalopods represent examples of descent with modification (see Concept 22.2).

For suggested answers, see Appendix A.

CONCEPT 33.4

Ecdysozoans are the most species-rich animal group

Porifera
Cnidaria
Lophotrochozoa
Ecdysozoa
Deuterostomia

Although defined primarily by molecular evidence, the clade Ecdysozoa includes animals that shed a tough external coat (**cuticle**) as they grow; in fact, the group derives its name from this process, which is called *ecdysis*, or **molting**. Ecdysozoa includes about eight animal phyla and contains more known species than all other animal, protist, fungus, and plant groups combined. Here we'll focus on the two largest ecdysozoan phyla, the nematodes and arthropods, which are among the most successful and abundant of all animal groups.

Nematodes

Among the most ubiquitous of animals, nematodes (phylum Nematoda), or roundworms, are found in most aquatic habitats, in the soil, in the moist tissues of plants, and in the body fluids and tissues of animals. The cylindrical bodies of nematodes range from less than 1 mm to more than 1 m long, often tapering to a fine tip at the posterior end and to a blunter tip at the anterior end (**Figure 33.26**). A nematode's body is covered by a tough cuticle (a type of exoskeleton); as the worm grows, it periodically sheds its old cuticle and

secretes a new, larger one. Nematodes have an alimentary canal, though they lack a circulatory system. Nutrients are transported throughout the body via fluid in the pseudocoelom. The body wall muscles are all longitudinal, and their contraction produces a thrashing motion.

Multitudes of nematodes live in moist soil and in decomposing organic matter on the bottoms of lakes and oceans. While 25,000 species are known, perhaps 20 times that number actually exist. It has been said that if nothing of Earth or its organisms remained but nematodes, they would still preserve the outline of the planet and many of its features. These free-living worms play an important role in decomposition and nutrient cycling, but little is known about most species. One species of soil nematode, *Caenorhabditis elegans*, however, is very well studied and has become a model research organism in biology (see Chapter 47). Ongoing studies of *C. elegans* are providing insight into mechanisms involved in aging in humans, as well as many other topics.

Phylum Nematoda includes many species that parasitize plants, and some are major agricultural pests that attack the roots of crops. Other nematodes parasitize animals. Some of these species benefit humans by attacking insects such as cutworms that feed on the roots of crop plants. On the other hand, humans are hosts to at least 50 nematode species, including various pinworms and hookworms. One notorious nematode is *Trichinella spiralis*, the worm that causes trichinosis (**Figure 33.27**). Humans acquire this nematode by eating raw or undercooked pork or other meat (including wild game such as bear or walrus) that has juvenile worms encysted in the muscle tissue. Within the human intestines, the juveniles develop into sexually mature adults. Females burrow into the intestinal muscles and produce more juveniles, which bore through the body or travel in lymphatic vessels to other organs, including skeletal muscles, where they encyst.

▶ **Figure 33.26 A free-living nematode** (colorized SEM).

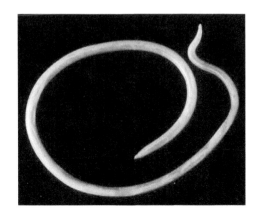

Encysted juveniles   Muscle tissue   50 µm

▲ **Figure 33.27 Juveniles of the parasitic nematode *Trichinella spiralis* encysted in human muscle tissue** (LM).

Parasitic nematodes have an extraordinary molecular toolkit that enables them to redirect some of the cellular functions of their hosts. Some species inject their plant hosts with molecules that induce the development of root cells, which then supply nutrients to the parasites. When *Trichinella* parasitizes animals, it regulates the expression of specific muscle cell genes encoding proteins that make the cell elastic enough to house the nematode. Additionally, the infected muscle cell releases signals that promote the growth of new blood vessels, which then supply the nematode with nutrients.

Arthropods

Zoologists estimate that there are about a billion billion (10^{18}) arthropods living on Earth. More than 1 million arthropod species have been described, most of which are insects. In fact, two out of every three known species are arthropods, and members of the phylum Arthropoda can be found in nearly all habitats of the biosphere. By the criteria of species diversity, distribution, and sheer numbers, arthropods must be regarded as the most successful of all animal phyla.

Arthropod Origins

Biologists hypothesize that the diversity and success of **arthropods** are related to their body plan—their segmented body, hard exoskeleton, and jointed appendages. The earliest fossils with this body plan are from the Cambrian explosion (535–525 million years ago), indicating that the arthropods are at least that old.

Along with arthropods, the fossil record of the Cambrian explosion contains many species of *lobopods*, a group from which arthropods may have evolved. Lobopods such as *Hallucigenia* (see Figure 32.7) had segmented bodies, but most of their body segments were identical to one another. Early arthropods, such as the trilobites, also showed little variation from segment to segment (Figure 33.28). As arthropods continued to evolve, the segments tended to fuse and become fewer, and the appendages became specialized for a variety of functions. These evolutionary changes resulted not only in great diversification but also in efficient body plans that permit the division of labor among different body regions.

▶ **Figure 33.28 A trilobite fossil.** Trilobites were common denizens of the shallow seas throughout the Paleozoic era but disappeared with the great Permian extinctions about 250 million years ago. Paleontologists have described about 4,000 trilobite species.

What genetic changes led to the increasing complexity of the arthropod body plan? Arthropods today have two unusual *Hox* genes, both of which influence segmentation. To test whether these genes could have driven the evolution of increased body segment diversity in arthropods, researchers studied *Hox* genes in onychophorans (see Figure 33.3), close relatives of arthropods **(Figure 33.29)**. Their results indicate

▼ **Figure 33.29** | Inquiry

Did the arthropod body plan result from new *Hox* genes?

Experiment One hypothesis suggests that the arthropod body plan resulted from the origin (by gene duplication followed by mutation) of two unusual *Hox* genes found in arthropods: *Ultrabithorax* (*Ubx*) and *abdominal-A* (*abd-A*). To test this hypothesis, Sean Carroll, of the University of Wisconsin, Madison, and colleagues turned to the onychophorans, a group of invertebrates closely related to arthropods. Unlike many living arthropods, onychophorans have a body plan in which most body segments are identical to one another. If the origin of the *Ubx* and *abd-A Hox* genes drove the evolution of body segment diversity in arthropods, these genes probably arose on the arthropod branch of the evolutionary tree:

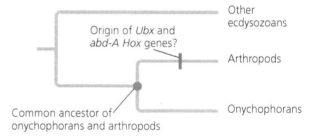

According to this hypothesis, *Ubx* and *abd-A* would not have been present in the common ancestor of arthropods and onychophorans; hence, onychophorans should not have these genes. The researchers examined the *Hox* genes of the onychophoran *Acanthokara kaputensis*.

Results The onychophoran *A. kaputensis* has all arthropod *Hox* genes, including *Ubx* and *abd-A*.

Red indicates the body regions of this onychophoran embryo in which *Ubx* or *abd-A* genes were expressed. (The inset shows this area enlarged.)

Ant = antenna
J = jaws
L1–L15 = body segments

Conclusion The evolution of increased body segment diversity in arthropods was not related to the origin of new *Hox* genes.

Source: J. K. Grenier et al., Evolution of the entire arthropod Hox gene set predated the origin and radiation of the onychophoran/arthropod clade, Current Biology 7:547–553 (1997).

WHAT IF? *Suppose A. kaputensis did not have the Ubx and abd-A Hox genes. How would the conclusions of this study have been affected? Explain.*

that the diversity of arthropod body plans did *not* arise from the acquisition of new *Hox* genes. Instead, the evolution of body segment diversity in arthropods was probably driven by changes in the sequence or regulation of existing *Hox* genes (see Concept 25.5).

General Characteristics of Arthropods

Over the course of evolution, the appendages of some arthropods have become modified, specializing in functions such as walking, feeding, sensory reception, reproduction, and defense. Like the appendages from which they were derived, these modified structures are jointed and come in pairs. **Figure 33.30** illustrates the diverse appendages and other arthropod characteristics of a lobster.

The body of an arthropod is completely covered by the cuticle, an exoskeleton constructed from layers of protein and the polysaccharide chitin. As you know if you've ever eaten a crab or lobster, the cuticle can be thick and hard over some parts of the body and thin and flexible over others, such as the joints. The rigid exoskeleton protects the animal and provides points of attachment for the muscles that move the appendages. But it also prevents the arthropod from growing, unless it occasionally sheds its exoskeleton and produces a larger one. This molting process is energetically expensive, and it leaves the arthropod vulnerable to predation and other dangers until its new, soft exoskeleton hardens.

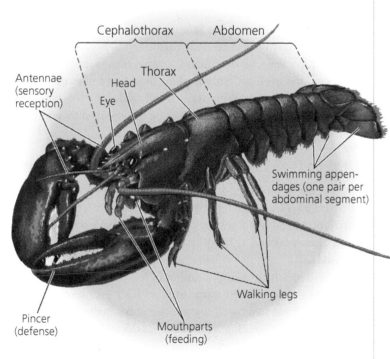

▲ **Figure 33.30 External anatomy of an arthropod.** Many of the distinctive features of arthropods are apparent in this dorsal view of a lobster. The body is segmented, but this characteristic is obvious only in the abdomen. The appendages (including antennae, pincers, mouthparts, walking legs, and swimming appendages) are jointed. The head bears a pair of compound (multilens) eyes. The whole body, including appendages, is covered by an exoskeleton.

When the arthropod exoskeleton first evolved in the sea, its main functions were probably protection and anchorage for muscles, but it later enabled certain arthropods to live on land. The exoskeleton's relative impermeability to water helped prevent desiccation, and its strength provided support when arthropods left the buoyancy of water. Fossil evidence suggests that arthropods were among the first animals to colonize land, roughly 450 million years ago. These fossils include fragments of arthropod remains, as well as possible millipede burrows. Arthropod fossils from several continents indicate that by 410 million years ago, millipedes, centipedes, spiders, and a variety of wingless insects all had colonized land.

Arthropods have well-developed sensory organs, including eyes, olfactory (smell) receptors, and antennae that function in both touch and smell. Most sensory organs are concentrated at the anterior end of the animal, although there are interesting exceptions. Female butterflies, for example, "taste" plants using sensory organs on their feet.

Like many molluscs, arthropods have an **open circulatory system**, in which fluid called *hemolymph* is propelled by a heart through short arteries and then into spaces called sinuses surrounding the tissues and organs. (The term *blood* is generally reserved for fluid in a closed circulatory system.) Hemolymph reenters the arthropod heart through pores that are usually equipped with valves. The hemolymph-filled body sinuses are collectively called the *hemocoel*, which is not part of the coelom. Although arthropods are coelomates, in most species the coelom that forms in the embryo becomes much reduced as development progresses, and the hemocoel becomes the main body cavity in adults.

A variety of specialized gas exchange organs have evolved in arthropods. These organs allow the diffusion of respiratory gases in spite of the exoskeleton. Most aquatic species have gills with thin, feathery extensions that place an extensive surface area in contact with the surrounding water. Terrestrial arthropods generally have internal surfaces specialized for gas exchange. Most insects, for instance, have tracheal systems, branched air ducts leading into the interior of the body from pores in the cuticle.

Morphological and molecular evidence suggests that living arthropods consist of three major lineages that diverged early in the evolution of the phylum: **chelicerates** (sea spiders, horseshoe crabs, scorpions, ticks, mites, and spiders); **myriapods** (centipedes and millipedes); and **pancrustaceans** (a recently defined, diverse group that includes insects as well as lobsters, shrimp, barnacles, and other crustaceans).

Chelicerates

Chelicerates (clade Chelicerata) are named for clawlike feeding appendages called **chelicerae**, which serve as pincers or fangs. Chelicerates have an anterior cephalothorax and a posterior abdomen. They lack antennae, and most have simple eyes (eyes with a single lens).

▲ **Figure 33.31 Horseshoe crabs (*Limulus polyphemus*).** Common on the Atlantic and Gulf coasts of the United States, these "living fossils" have changed little in hundreds of millions of years. They are surviving members of a rich diversity of chelicerates that once filled the seas.

The earliest chelicerates were **eurypterids**, or water scorpions. These marine and freshwater predators grew up to 3 m long; it is thought that some species could have walked on land, much as land crabs do today. Most of the marine chelicerates, including all of the eurypterids, are extinct. Among the marine chelicerates that survive today are the sea spiders (pycnogonids) and horseshoe crabs (**Figure 33.31**).

The bulk of modern chelicerates are **arachnids**, a group that includes scorpions, spiders, ticks, and mites (**Figure 33.32**). Ticks and many mites are among a large group of parasitic arthropods. Nearly all ticks are bloodsucking parasites that live on the body surfaces of reptiles or mammals. Parasitic mites live on or in a wide variety of vertebrates, invertebrates, and plants.

Arachnids have six pairs of appendages: the chelicerae; a pair of appendages called *pedipalps* that function in sensing, feeding, defense, or reproduction; and four pairs of walking legs. Spiders use their fang-like chelicerae, which are equipped with poison glands, to attack prey. As the chelicerae pierce the prey, the spider secretes digestive juices onto the prey's torn tissues. The food softens, and the spider sucks up the liquid meal. In most spiders, gas exchange is carried out by **book lungs**, stacked platelike structures contained in an internal chamber. The extensive surface area of these respiratory organs is a structural adaptation that enhances the exchange of O_2 and CO_2 between the hemolymph and air.

Heart

Book lungs   Chelicera   Pedipalp

A unique adaptation of many spiders is the ability to catch insects by constructing webs of silk, a liquid protein produced by specialized abdominal glands. The silk is spun by organs called spinnerets into fibers that then solidify. Each spider engineers a web characteristic of its species and builds it perfectly on the first try, indicating that this

▲ Scorpions have pedipalps that are pincers specialized for defense and the capture of food. The tip of the tail bears a poisonous stinger.

50 µm

▲ Dust mites are ubiquitous scavengers in human dwellings but are harmless except to those people who are allergic to them (colorized SEM).

◄ Web-building spiders are generally most active during the daytime.

▲ **Figure 33.32 Arachnids.**

complex behavior is inherited. Various spiders also use silk in other ways: as droplines for rapid escape, as a cover for eggs, and even as "gift wrap" for food that males offer females during courtship. Many small spiders also extrude silk into the air and let themselves be transported by wind, a behavior known as "ballooning."

Myriapods

Millipedes and centipedes belong to the clade Myriapoda (**Figure 33.33**). All living myriapods are terrestrial. The myriapod head has a pair of antennae and three pairs of appendages modified as mouthparts, including the jaw-like mandibles.

Millipedes have a large number of legs, though fewer than the thousand their name implies. Each trunk segment is formed from two fused segments and bears two pairs of legs (see Figure 33.33a). Millipedes eat decaying leaves and other plant matter. They may have been among the earliest animals on land, living on mosses and early vascular plants.

Unlike millipedes, centipedes are carnivores. Each segment of a centipede's trunk region has one pair of legs (see Figure 33.33b). Centipedes have poison claws on their foremost trunk segment that paralyze prey and aid in defense.

(a) Millipede

(b) Centipede

▲ Figure 33.33 Myriapods.

Pancrustaceans

A series of recent papers, including a 2010 phylogenomic study, present evidence that terrestrial insects are more closely related to lobsters and other crustaceans than they are to the terrestrial group we just discussed, the myriapods (millipedes and centipedes). These studies also suggest that the diverse group of organisms referred to as crustaceans are paraphyletic: Some lineages of crustaceans are more closely related to insects than they are to other crustaceans (Figure 33.34). However, together the insects and crustaceans form a clade, which systematists have named Pancrustacea (from the Greek *pan*, all). We turn next to a description of the members of Pancrustacea, focusing first on crustaceans and then on the insects.

Crustaceans Crustaceans (crabs, lobsters, shrimps, barnacles, and many others) thrive in a broad range of marine, freshwater, and terrestrial environments. Many crustaceans have highly specialized appendages. Lobsters and crayfishes, for instance, have a toolkit of 19 pairs of appendages (see Figure 33.30). The anterior-most appendages are antennae; crustaceans are the only arthropods with two pairs. Three or more pairs of appendages are modified as mouthparts, including the hard mandibles. Walking legs are present on the thorax, and, unlike their terrestrial relatives, the insects, crustaceans also have appendages on their abdomen.

Small crustaceans exchange gases across thin areas of the cuticle; larger species have gills. Nitrogenous wastes also diffuse through thin areas of the cuticle, but a pair of glands regulates the salt balance of the hemolymph.

Sexes are separate in most crustaceans. In the case of lobsters and crayfishes, the male uses a specialized pair of abdominal appendages to transfer sperm to the reproductive pore of the female during copulation. Most aquatic crustaceans go through one or more swimming larval stages.

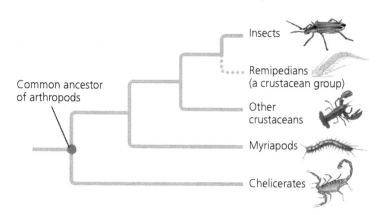

▲ Figure 33.34 **The phylogenetic position of the insects.** Recent results have shown that the insects are nested within lineages of aquatic crustaceans. The remipedians are one of several groups of aquatic crustaceans that may be the sister group to the insects.

? *Circle the portions of this tree that comprise the clade Pancrustacea.*

One of the largest groups of crustaceans (numbering over 11,000 species) is the *isopods*, which include terrestrial, freshwater, and marine species. Some isopod species are abundant in habitats at the bottom of the deep ocean. Among the terrestrial isopods are the pill bugs, or wood lice, common on the undersides of moist logs and leaves.

Lobsters, crayfishes, crabs, and shrimps are all relatively large crustaceans called *decapods* (Figure 33.35). The cuticle of decapods is hardened by calcium carbonate; the portion that covers the dorsal side of the cephalothorax forms a shield called the carapace. Most decapod species are marine. Crayfishes, however, live in fresh water, and some tropical crabs live on land.

Many small crustaceans are important members of marine and freshwater plankton communities. Planktonic crustaceans include many species of *copepods*, which are among the most numerous of all animals. Some copepods are grazers that feed upon algae, while others are predators that eat small animals (including smaller copepods!). Copepods are

▲ Figure 33.35 **A ghost crab, an example of a decapod.** Ghost crabs live on sandy ocean beaches worldwide. Primarily nocturnal, they take shelter in burrows during the day.

▲ Figure 33.36 **Krill.** These planktonic crustaceans are consumed in vast quantities by some whales.

▲ Figure 33.37 **Barnacles.** The jointed appendages projecting from the barnacles' shells capture organisms and organic particles suspended in the water.

rivaled in abundance by the shrimplike krill, which grow to about 5 cm long (Figure 33.36). A major food source for baleen whales (including blue whales, humpbacks, and right whales), krill are now being harvested in great numbers by humans for food and agricultural fertilizer. The larvae of many larger-bodied crustaceans are also planktonic.

With the exception of a few parasitic species, barnacles are a group of sessile crustaceans whose cuticle is hardened into a shell containing calcium carbonate (Figure 33.37). Most barnacles anchor themselves to rocks, boat hulls,

pilings, and other submerged surfaces. Their natural adhesive is as strong as synthetic glues. These barnacles feed by extending appendages from their shell to strain food from the water. Barnacles were not recognized as crustaceans until the 1800s, when naturalists discovered that barnacle larvae resemble the larvae of other crustaceans. The remarkable mix of unique traits and crustacean homologies found in barnacles was a major inspiration to Charles Darwin as he developed his theory of evolution.

We turn now to a group nested within the paraphyletic crustaceans, the insects.

Insects Insects and their six-legged terrestrial relatives form an enormous clade, Hexapoda; we'll focus here on the insects, since as a group they are more species-rich than all other forms of life combined. Insects live in almost every terrestrial habitat and in fresh water, and flying insects fill the air. Insects are rare, though not absent, in marine habitats. The internal anatomy of an insect includes several complex organ systems, which are highlighted in Figure 33.38.

The oldest insect fossils date to about 415 million years ago. Later, an explosion in insect diversity took place when insect flight evolved during the Carboniferous and Permian periods (359–251 million years ago). An animal that can fly can escape predators, find food and mates, and disperse to new habitats more effectively than an animal that must crawl about on the ground. Many insects have one or two pairs of wings that emerge from the dorsal side of the thorax.

▼ Figure 33.38 **Anatomy of a grasshopper, an insect.** The insect body has three regions: head, thorax, and abdomen. The segmentation of the thorax and abdomen is obvious, but the segments that form the head are fused.

Heart. The insect heart drives hemolymph through an open circulatory system.

Cerebral ganglion. The two nerve cords meet in the head, where the ganglia of several anterior segments are fused into a cerebral ganglion (brain, colored white below). The antennae, eyes, and other sense organs are concentrated on the head.

Abdomen   Thorax   Head

Compound eye

Antennae

Dorsal artery   Crop

Anus

Malpighian tubules. Metabolic wastes are removed from the hemolymph by excretory organs called Malpighian tubules, which are outpocketings of the digestive tract.

Vagina

Ovary

Tracheal tubes. Gas exchange in insects is accomplished by a tracheal system of branched, chitin-lined tubes that infiltrate the body and carry oxygen directly to cells. The tracheal system opens to the outside of the body through spiracles, pores that can control air flow and water loss by opening or closing.

Nerve cords. The insect nervous system consists of a pair of ventral nerve cords with several segmental ganglia.

Insect mouthparts are formed from several pairs of modified appendages. The mouthparts include mandibles, which grasshoppers use for chewing. In other insects, mouthparts are specialized for lapping, piercing, or sucking.

Because the wings are extensions of the cuticle, insects can fly without sacrificing any walking legs (Figure 33.39). By contrast, the flying vertebrates—birds and bats—have one of their two pairs of walking legs modified into wings, making some of these species clumsy on the ground.

▲ Figure 33.39 Ladybird beetle in flight.

Insects also radiated in response to the origin of new plant species, which provided new sources of food. By the speciation mechanisms described in Chapter 24, an insect population feeding on a new plant species can diverge from other populations, eventually forming a new species of insect. A fossil record of diverse insect mouthparts, for example, suggests that specialized modes of feeding on gymnosperms and other Carboniferous plants contributed to early adaptive radiations of insects. Later, a major increase in insect diversity appears to have been stimulated by the evolutionary expansion of flowering plants during the mid-Cretaceous period (about 90 million years ago). Although insect and plant diversity decreased during the Cretaceous mass extinction, both groups have rebounded over the past 65 million years. Increases in the diversity of particular insect groups have often been associated with radiations of the flowering plants on which they fed.

Many insects undergo metamorphosis during their development. In the **incomplete metamorphosis** of grasshoppers and some other insect groups, the young (called nymphs) resemble adults but are smaller, have different body proportions, and lack wings. The nymph undergoes a series of molts, each time looking more like an adult. With the final molt, the insect reaches full size, acquires wings, and becomes sexually mature. Insects with **complete metamorphosis** have larval stages specialized for eating and growing that are known by such names as caterpillar, maggot, or grub. The larval stage looks entirely different from the adult stage, which is specialized for dispersal and reproduction. Metamorphosis from the larval stage to the adult occurs during a pupal stage (Figure 33.40).

Reproduction in insects is usually sexual, with separate male and female individuals. Adults come together and recognize each other as members of the same species by advertising with bright colors (as in butterflies), sounds (as in crickets), or odors (as in moths). Fertilization is generally internal. In most species, sperm are deposited directly into the female's vagina at the time of copulation, though in some species the male deposits a sperm packet outside the female, and the female picks it up. An internal structure in the female called the spermatheca stores the sperm, usually enough to fertilize more than one batch of eggs. Many insects mate only once in a lifetime. After mating, a female often lays her eggs on an appropriate food source where the next generation can begin eating as soon as it hatches.

Insects are classified in more than 30 orders, 8 of which are introduced in Figure 33.41.

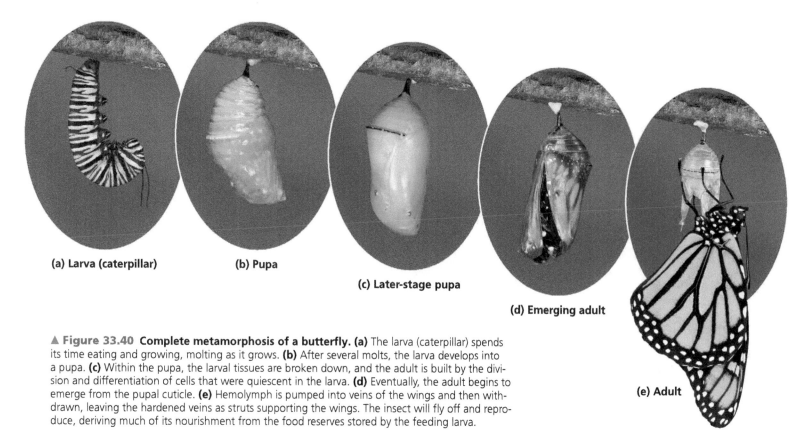

(a) Larva (caterpillar)

(b) Pupa

(c) Later-stage pupa

(d) Emerging adult

(e) Adult

▲ Figure 33.40 **Complete metamorphosis of a butterfly. (a)** The larva (caterpillar) spends its time eating and growing, molting as it grows. **(b)** After several molts, the larva develops into a pupa. **(c)** Within the pupa, the larval tissues are broken down, and the adult is built by the division and differentiation of cells that were quiescent in the larva. **(d)** Eventually, the adult begins to emerge from the pupal cuticle. **(e)** Hemolymph is pumped into veins of the wings and then withdrawn, leaving the hardened veins as struts supporting the wings. The insect will fly off and reproduce, deriving much of its nourishment from the food reserves stored by the feeding larva.

Exploring Insect Diversity

Although there are more than 30 orders of insects, we'll focus on just 8 here. Two early-diverging groups of wingless insects are the bristletails (Archaeognatha) and silverfish (Zygentoma). Evolutionary relationships among the other groups discussed here are under debate and so are not depicted on the tree.

Archaeognatha (bristletails; 350 species)

These wingless insects are found under bark and in other moist, dark habitats such as leaf litter, compost piles, and rock crevices. They feed on algae, plant debris, and lichens.

Zygentoma (silverfish; 450 species)

These small, wingless insects have a flattened body and reduced eyes. They live in leaf litter or under bark. They can also infest buildings, where they can become pests.

Winged insects (many orders; six are shown below)

Complete metamorphosis

Coleoptera (beetles; 350,000 species)

Beetles, such as this male snout weevil (*Rhiastus lasternus*), constitute the most species-rich order of insects. They have two pairs of wings, one of which is thick and stiff, the other membranous. They have an armored exoskeleton and mouthparts adapted for biting and chewing.

Diptera (151,000 species)

Dipterans have one pair of wings; the second pair has become modified into balancing organs called halteres. Their mouthparts are adapted for sucking, piercing, or lapping. Flies and mosquitoes are among the best-known dipterans, which live as scavengers, predators, and parasites. Like many other insects, flies such as this red tachinid (*Adejeania vexatrix*) have well-developed compound eyes that provide a wide-angle view and excel at detecting fast movements.

Hymenoptera (125,000 species)

Most hymenopterans, which include ants, bees, and wasps, are highly social insects. They have two pairs of membranous wings, a mobile head, and chewing or sucking mouthparts. The females of many species have a posterior stinging organ. Many species, such as this European paper wasp (*Polistes dominulus*), build elaborate nests.

Proboscis

Lepidoptera (120,000 species)

Butterflies and moths have two pairs of wings covered with tiny scales. To feed, they uncoil a long proboscis, visible in this photograph of a hummingbird hawkmoth (*Macroglossum stellatarum*). This moth's name refers to its ability to hover in the air while feeding from a flower. Most lepidopterans feed on nectar, but some species feed on other substances, including animal blood or tears.

Incomplete metamorphosis

Hemiptera (85,000 species)

Hemipterans include so-called "true bugs," such as stink bugs, bed bugs, and assassin bugs. (Insects in other orders are sometimes erroneously called bugs.) Hemipterans have two pairs of wings, one pair partly leathery, the other pair membranous. They have piercing or sucking mouthparts and undergo incomplete metamorphosis, as shown in this image of an adult stink bug guarding its offspring (nymphs).

Orthoptera (13,000 species)

Grasshoppers, crickets, and their relatives are mostly herbivorous. They have large hind legs adapted for jumping, two pairs of wings (one leathery, one membranous), and biting or chewing mouthparts. This aptly named spear-bearer katydid (*Cophiphora* sp.) has a face and legs specialized for making a threatening display. Male orthopterans commonly make courtship sounds by rubbing together body parts, such as ridges on their hind legs.

Animals as numerous, diverse, and widespread as insects are bound to affect the lives of most other terrestrial organisms, including humans. Insects consume enormous quantities of plant matter; play key roles as predators, parasites, and decomposers; and are an essential source of food for larger animals such as lizards, rodents, and birds. Humans depend on bees, flies, and many other insects to pollinate crops and orchards. In addition, people in many parts of the world eat insects as an important source of protein. On the other hand, insects are carriers for many diseases, including African sleeping sickness (spread by tsetse flies that carry the protist *Trypanosoma*; see Figure 28.7) and malaria (spread by mosquitoes that carry the protist *Plasmodium*; see Figure 23.17 and Figure 28.16).

Insects also compete with humans for food. In parts of Africa, for instance, insects claim about 75% of the crops. In the United States, billions of dollars are spent each year on pesticides, spraying crops with massive doses of some of the deadliest poisons ever invented. Try as they may, not even humans have challenged the preeminence of insects and their arthropod kin. As one prominent entomologist put it: "Bugs are not going to inherit the Earth. They own it now. So we might as well make peace with the landlord."

CONCEPT CHECK 33.4

1. How do nematode and annelid body plans differ?
2. Describe two adaptations that have enabled insects to thrive on land.
3. **MAKE CONNECTIONS** Historically, annelids and arthropods were viewed as closely related because both have body segmentation. Yet DNA sequence data indicate that annelids belong to one clade (Lophotrochozoa) and arthropods to another (Ecdysozoa). Could traditional and molecular hypotheses be tested by studying the *Hox* genes that control body segmentation (see Concept 21.6)? Explain.

For suggested answers, see Appendix A.

CONCEPT 33.5

Echinoderms and chordates are deuterostomes

Porifera
Cnidaria
Lophotrochozoa
Ecdysozoa
Deuterostomia

Sea stars, sea urchins, and other echinoderms (phylum Echinodermata) may seem to have little in common with vertebrates (animals that have a backbone) and other members of phylum Chordata. Nevertheless, DNA evidence indicates that echinoderms and chordates are closely related, with both phyla belonging to the Deuterostomia clade of bilaterian animals.

Echinoderms and chordates also share features characteristic of a deuterostome mode of development, such as radial cleavage and formation of the anus from the blastopore (see Figure 32.10). As discussed in Concept 32.4, however, some animal phyla with members that have deuterostome developmental features, including ectoprocts and brachiopods, are not in the deuterostome clade. Hence, despite its name, the clade Deuterostomia is defined primarily by DNA similarities, not developmental similarities.

Echinoderms

Sea stars (commonly called starfish) and most other groups of **echinoderms** (from the Greek *echin*, spiny, and *derma*, skin) are slow-moving or sessile marine animals. A thin epidermis covers an endoskeleton of hard calcareous plates. Most echinoderms are prickly from skeletal bumps and spines. Unique to echinoderms is the **water vascular system**, a network of hydraulic canals branching into extensions called **tube feet** that function in locomotion and feeding (**Figure 33.42**, on the next page). Sexual reproduction of echinoderms usually involves separate male and female individuals that release their gametes into the water.

Echinoderms descended from bilaterally symmetrical ancestors, yet on first inspection most species seem to have a radially symmetrical form. The internal and external parts of most adult echinoderms radiate from the center, often as five spokes. However, echinoderm larvae have bilateral symmetry. Furthermore, the symmetry of adult echinoderms is not truly radial. For example, the opening (madreporite) of a sea star's water vascular system is not central but shifted to one side.

Living echinoderms are divided into five clades.

Asteroidea: Sea Stars and Sea Daisies

Sea stars have arms radiating from a central disk; the undersurfaces of the arms bear tube feet. By a combination of muscular and chemical actions, the tube feet can attach to or detach from a substrate. The sea star adheres firmly to rocks or creeps along slowly as its tube feet extend, grip, release, extend, and grip again. Although the base of the tube foot has a flattened disk that resembles a suction cup, the gripping action results from adhesive chemicals, not suction (see Figure 33.42).

Sea stars also use their tube feet to grasp prey, such as clams and oysters. The arms of the sea star embrace the closed bivalve, clinging tightly with their tube feet. The sea star then turns part of its stomach inside out, everting it through its mouth and into the narrow opening between the halves of the bivalve's shell. Next, the digestive system of the sea star secretes juices that begin digesting the mollusc within its own shell. The sea star then brings its stomach back inside its body, where digestion of the mollusc's (now

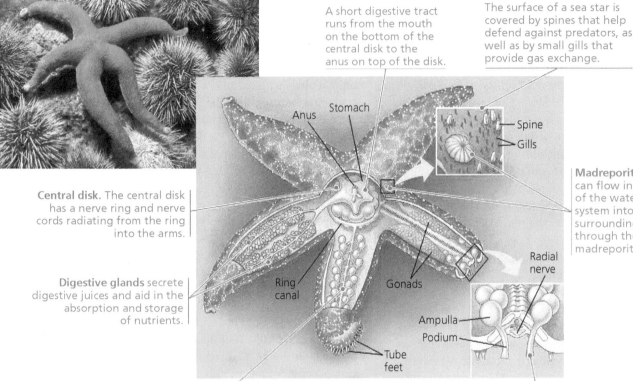

A short digestive tract runs from the mouth on the bottom of the central disk to the anus on top of the disk.

The surface of a sea star is covered by spines that help defend against predators, as well as by small gills that provide gas exchange.

Stomach

Anus

Spine

Gills

Central disk. The central disk has a nerve ring and nerve cords radiating from the ring into the arms.

Madreporite. Water can flow in or out of the water vascular system into the surrounding water through the madreporite.

Radial nerve

Digestive glands secrete digestive juices and aid in the absorption and storage of nutrients.

Ring canal

Gonads

Ampulla

Podium

Tube feet

Radial canal. The water vascular system consists of a ring canal in the central disk and five radial canals, each running in a groove down the entire length of an arm. Branching from each radial canal are hundreds of hollow, muscular tube feet filled with fluid.

Each tube foot consists of a bulb-like ampulla and a podium (foot portion). When the ampulla squeezes, water is forced into the podium, which expands and contacts the substrate. Adhesive chemicals are then secreted from the base of the podium, attaching it to the substrate. To detach the tube foot, de-adhesive chemicals are secreted and muscles in the podium contract, forcing water back into the ampulla and shortening the podium. As it moves, a sea star leaves an observable "footprint" of adhesive material on the substrate.

▲ Figure 33.42 **Anatomy of a sea star, an echinoderm (top view).** The photograph shows a sea star surrounded by sea urchins, which are members of the echinoderm clade Echinoidea.

liquefied) body is completed. The ability to begin the digestive process outside of its body allows a sea star to consume bivalves and other prey species that are much larger than its mouth.

Sea stars and some other echinoderms have considerable powers of regeneration. Sea stars can regrow lost arms, and members of one genus can even regrow an entire body from a single arm if part of the central disk remains attached.

The clade Asteroidea, to which sea stars belong, also includes a small group of armless species, the *sea daisies*. Only three species of sea daisies are known, all of which live on submerged wood. A sea daisy's body is typically disk-shaped; it has a five-sided organization and measures less than a centimeter in diameter **(Figure 33.43)**. The edge of the body is ringed with small spines. Sea daisies absorb nutrients through a membrane that surrounds their body.

Ophiuroidea: Brittle Stars

Brittle stars have a distinct central disk and long, flexible arms **(Figure 33.44)**. They move primarily by lashing their arms in serpentine movements. The base of a brittle star tube foot lacks the flattened disk found in sea stars but does

▶ Figure 33.43 **A sea daisy (clade Asteroidea).**

▲ Figure 33.44 **A brittle star (clade Ophiuroidea).**

▲ **Figure 33.45 A sea urchin (clade Echinoidea).**

▲ **Figure 33.47 A sea cucumber (clade Holothuroidea).**

secrete adhesive chemicals. Hence, like sea stars and other echinoderms, brittle stars can use their tube feet to grip substrates. Some species are suspension feeders; others are predators or scavengers.

Echinoidea: Sea Urchins and Sand Dollars

Sea urchins and sand dollars have no arms, but they do have five rows of tube feet that function in slow movement. Sea urchins also have muscles that pivot their long spines, which aid in locomotion as well as protection (Figure 33.45). A sea urchin's mouth, located on its underside, is ringed by highly complex, jaw-like structures that are well adapted to eating seaweed. Sea urchins are roughly spherical, whereas sand dollars are flat disks.

Crinoidea: Sea Lilies and Feather Stars

Sea lilies live attached to the substrate by a stalk; feather stars crawl about by using their long, flexible arms. Both use their arms in suspension feeding. The arms encircle the mouth, which is directed upward, away from the substrate (Figure 33.46). Crinoidea is an ancient group whose

morphology has changed little over the course of evolution; fossilized sea lilies some 500 million years old are extremely similar to present-day members of the clade.

Holothuroidea: Sea Cucumbers

On casual inspection, sea cucumbers do not look much like other echinoderms. They lack spines, and their endoskeleton is much reduced. They are also elongated in their oral-aboral axis, giving them the shape for which they are named and further disguising their relationship to sea stars and sea urchins (Figure 33.47). Closer examination, however, reveals that sea cucumbers have five rows of tube feet. Some of the tube feet around the mouth are developed as feeding tentacles.

Chordates

Phylum Chordata consists of two basal groups of invertebrates, the lancelets and the tunicates, as well as the vertebrates. Chordates are bilaterally symmetrical coelomates with segmented bodies. The close relationship between echinoderms and chordates does not mean that one phylum evolved from the other. In fact, echinoderms and chordates have evolved independently of one another for over 500 million years. We will trace the phylogeny of chordates in Chapter 34, focusing on the history of vertebrates.

▲ **Figure 33.46 A feather star (clade Crinoidea).**

CONCEPT CHECK **33.5**

1. How do sea star tube feet attach to substrates?

2. **WHAT IF?** The insect *Drosophila melanogaster* and the nematode *Caenorhabditis elegans* are prominent model organisms. Are these species the most appropriate invertebrates for making inferences about humans and other vertebrates? Explain.

3. **MAKE CONNECTIONS** Describe how the features and diversity of echinoderms illustrate the unity of life, the diversity of life, and the match between organisms and their environments (see Concept 22. 2).

For suggested answers, see Appendix A.

This table recaps the animal groups surveyed in this chapter.

Key Concept			Phylum		Description
CONCEPT 33.1 **Sponges are basal animals that lack true tissues (pp. 684–685)** ? *Lacking tissues and organs, how do sponges accomplish tasks such as gas exchange, nutrient transport, and waste disposal?*			Porifera (sponges)		Lack true tissues; have choanocytes (collar cells—flagellated cells that ingest bacteria and tiny food particles)
CONCEPT 33.2 **Cnidarians are an ancient phylum of eumetazoans (pp. 685–687)** ? *Describe the cnidarian body plan and its two major variations.*			Cnidaria (hydras, jellies, sea anemones, corals)		Unique stinging structures (nematocysts) housed in specialized cells (cnidocytes); diploblastic; radially symmetrical; gastrovascular cavity (digestive compartment with a single opening)
CONCEPT 33.3 **Lophotrochozoans, a clade identified by molecular data, have the widest range of animal body forms (pp. 688–699)** ? *Is the lophotrochozoan clade united by unique morphological features shared by all of its members? Explain.*		Lophotrochozoa	Platyhelminthes (flatworms)		Dorsoventrally flattened acoelomates; gastrovascular cavity or no digestive tract
			Rotifera (rotifers)		Pseudocoelomates with alimentary canal (digestive tube with mouth and anus); jaws (trophi); head with ciliated crown
			Lophophorates: Ectoprocta, Brachiopoda		Coelomates with lophophores (feeding structures bearing ciliated tentacles)
			Mollusca (clams, snails, squids)		Coelomates with three main body parts (muscular foot, visceral mass, mantle); coelom reduced; most have hard shell made of calcium carbonate
			Annelida (segmented worms)		Coelomates with segmented body wall and internal organs (except digestive tract, which is unsegmented)
CONCEPT 33.4 **Ecdysozoans are the most species-rich animal group (pp. 699–707)** ? *Describe some ecological roles of nematodes and arthropods.*		Ecdysozoa	Nematoda (roundworms)		Cylindrical pseudocoelomates with tapered ends; no circulatory system; undergo ecdysis
			Arthropoda (spiders, centipedes, crustaceans, and insects)		Coelomates with segmented body, jointed appendages, and exoskeleton made of protein and chitin
CONCEPT 33.5 **Echinoderms and chordates are deuterostomes (pp. 707–709)** ? *You've read that echinoderms and chordates are closely related and have evolved independently for over 500 million years. Explain how both of these statements can be correct.*		Deuterostomia	Echinodermata (sea stars, sea urchins)		Coelomates with bilaterally symmetrical larvae and five-part body organization as adults; unique water vascular system; endoskeleton
			Chordata (lancelets, tunicates, vertebrates)		Coelomates with notochord; dorsal, hollow nerve cord; pharyngeal slits; post-anal tail (see Chapter 34)

Vertical bracket labels: Metazoa, Eumetazoa, Bilateria span the appropriate rows.

LEVEL 1: KNOWLEDGE/COMPREHENSION

1. A land snail, a clam, and an octopus all share
   a. a mantle.
   b. a radula.
   c. gills.
   d. distinct cephalization.

2. Which phylum is characterized by animals that have a segmented body?
   a. Cnidaria
   b. Platyhelminthes
   c. Arthropoda
   d. Mollusca

3. The water vascular system of echinoderms
   a. functions as a circulatory system that distributes nutrients to body cells.
   b. functions in locomotion and feeding.
   c. is bilateral in organization, even though the adult animal is not bilaterally symmetrical.
   d. moves water through the animal's body during filter feeding.

4. Which of the following combinations of phylum and description is *incorrect?*
   a. Echinodermata—bilateral symmetry as a larva, coelomate
   b. Nematoda—roundworms, pseudocoelomate
   c. Platyhelminthes—flatworms, gastrovascular cavity, acoelomate
   d. Porifera—gastrovascular cavity, coelomate

LEVEL 2: APPLICATION/ANALYSIS

5. In Figure 33.2, which two main clades branch from the most recent common ancestor of the eumetazoans?
   a. Porifera and Cnidaria
   b. Lophotrochozoa and Ecdysozoa
   c. Cnidaria and Bilateria
   d. Deuterostomia and Bilateria

6. **MAKE CONNECTIONS** In Figure 33.8, assume that the two medusae shown at step 4 were produced by one polyp colony. Review Concept 12.1 and Concept 13.3, and then use your understanding of mitosis and meiosis to evaluate whether the following sentence is true or false. If false, select the answer that provides the correct reason. *Although the two medusae are genetically identical, a sperm produced by one will differ genetically from an egg produced by the other.*
   a. F (both the medusae and the gametes are genetically identical)
   b. F (neither the medusae nor the gametes are genetically identical)
   c. F (the medusae are not identical but the gametes are)
   d. T

LEVEL 3: SYNTHESIS/EVALUATION

7. EVOLUTION CONNECTION
   INTERPRET THE DATA Draw a phylogenetic tree of Bilateria that includes the ten phyla of bilaterians discussed in detail in this chapter. Label each branch that leads to a phylum with a C, P, or A, depending on whether members of the phylum are coelomates (C), pseudocoelomates (P), or acoelomates (A). Use your labeled tree to answer the following questions:
   (a) For each of the three major clades of bilaterians, what (if anything) can be inferred about whether the common ancestor of the clade had a true coelom?
   (b) To what extent has the presence of a true coelom in animals changed over the course of evolution?

8. SCIENTIFIC INQUIRY
   Bats emit ultrasonic sounds and then use the returning echoes of those sounds to locate and capture flying insects, such as moths, in the dark. In response to bat attacks, some tiger moths make ultrasonic clicks of their own. Researchers hypothesize that tiger moth clicks likely either (1) jam the bat's sonar or (2) warn the bat about the moth's toxic chemical defenses. The graph below shows two patterns observed in studies of moth capture rates over time.

Bats in these experiments were "naive," meaning that prior to the study the bats had not previously hunted tiger moths. Do the results support hypothesis (1), hypothesis (2), or both? Explain why the researchers used naive bats in this study.

9. WRITE ABOUT A THEME: ORGANIZATION
   Write a short essay (100–150 words) that explains how the structure of the digestive tract in different invertebrate groups affects the size of the organisms that they can eat.

10. **SYNTHESIZE YOUR KNOWLEDGE**

Collectively, do these beetles and all other invertebrate species combined form a monophyletic group? Explain your answer and provide an overview of the evolutionary history of invertebrate life.

For selected answers, see Appendix A.

MasteringBiology®

Students Go to **MasteringBiology** for assignments, the eText, and the Study Area with practice tests, animations, and activities.

Instructors Go to **MasteringBiology** for automatically graded tutorials and questions that you can assign to your students, plus Instructor Resources.

34

The Origin and Evolution of Vertebrates

▲ **Figure 34.1 What is the relationship between this ancient organism and humans?**

Half a Billion Years of Backbones

Early in the Cambrian period, some 530 million years ago, an immense variety of invertebrate animals inhabited Earth's oceans. Predators used sharp claws and mandibles to capture and break apart their prey. Many animals had protective spikes or armor as well as modified mouthparts that enabled their bearers to filter food from the water.

Amidst this bustle, it would have been easy to overlook certain slender, 3-cm-long creatures gliding through the water: members of the species *Myllokunmingia fengjiaoa* (Figure 34.1). Although lacking armor and appendages, this ancient species was closely related to one of the most successful groups of animals ever to swim, walk, slither, or fly: the **vertebrates**, which derive their name from vertebrae, the series of bones that make up the vertebral column, or backbone.

For more than 150 million years, vertebrates were restricted to the oceans, but about 365 million years ago, the evolution of limbs in one lineage of vertebrates set the stage for these vertebrates to colonize land. Over time, as the descendants of these early colonists adapted to life on land, they gave rise to the three groups of terrestrial vertebrates alive today: amphibians, reptiles (including birds), and mammals.

There are more than 57,000 species of vertebrates, a relatively small number compared to, say, the 1 million insect species on Earth. But what vertebrates may lack in number of species, they make up for in *disparity*, varying enormously in characteristics such as body mass. Vertebrates include the heaviest animals ever to walk on land, plant-eating dinosaurs that were as massive as 40,000 kg (more than 13 pickup trucks). The biggest animal ever to exist on Earth is also a vertebrate—the blue whale, which can exceed 100,000 kg. On the other end of the spectrum, the fish *Schindleria brevipinguis*, discovered in 2004, is just 8.4 mm long and has a mass roughly 100 billion times smaller than that of a blue whale.

In this chapter, you will learn about current hypotheses regarding the origins of vertebrates from invertebrate ancestors. We will track the evolution of the vertebrate body plan, from a notochord to a head to a mineralized skeleton. We'll also explore the major groups of vertebrates (both living and extinct), as well as the evolutionary history of our own species—*Homo sapiens*.

Chordates have a notochord and a dorsal, hollow nerve cord

Vertebrates are members of the phylum Chordata, the chordates. **Chordates** are bilaterian (bilaterally symmetrical) animals, and within Bilateria, they belong to the clade of animals known as Deuterostomia (see Figure 32.11). As shown in **Figure 34.2**, there are two groups of invertebrate deuterostomes that are more closely related to vertebrates than they are to other invertebrates: the cephalochordates and the urochordates. Thus, along with the vertebrates, these two invertebrate groups are classified within the chordates.

Derived Characters of Chordates

All chordates share a set of derived characters, though many species possess some of these traits only during embryonic

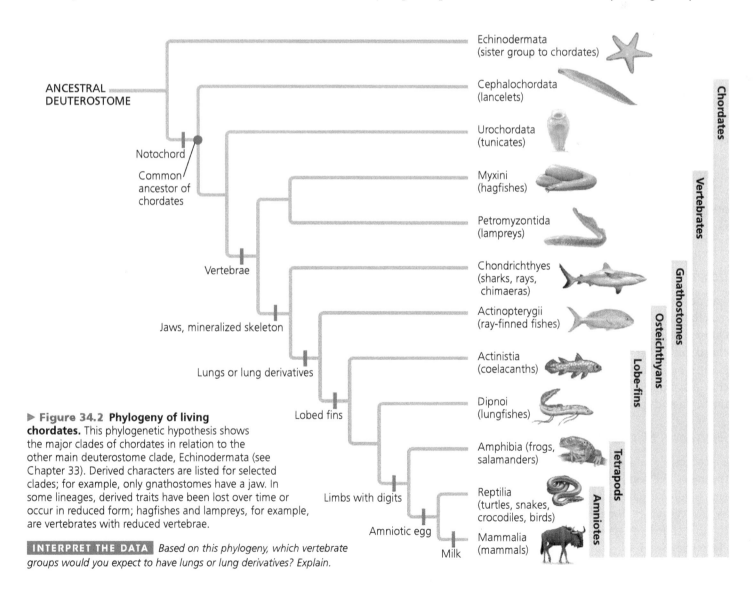

▶ **Figure 34.2 Phylogeny of living chordates.** This phylogenetic hypothesis shows the major clades of chordates in relation to the other main deuterostome clade, Echinodermata (see Chapter 33). Derived characters are listed for selected clades; for example, only gnathostomes have a jaw. In some lineages, derived traits have been lost over time or occur in reduced form; hagfishes and lampreys, for example, are vertebrates with reduced vertebrae.

INTERPRET THE DATA *Based on this phylogeny, which vertebrate groups would you expect to have lungs or lung derivatives? Explain.*

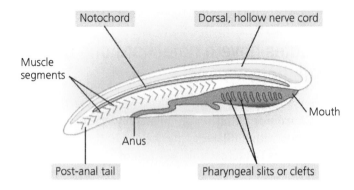

▲ Figure 34.3 Chordate characteristics. All chordates possess the four highlighted structural trademarks at some point during their development.

development. **Figure 34.3** illustrates four key characters of chordates: a notochord; a dorsal, hollow nerve cord; pharyngeal slits or clefts; and a muscular, post-anal tail.

Notochord

Chordates are named for a skeletal structure, the notochord, present in all chordate embryos as well as in some adult chordates. The **notochord** is a longitudinal, flexible rod located between the digestive tube and the nerve cord. It is composed of large, fluid-filled cells encased in fairly stiff, fibrous tissue. The notochord provides skeletal support throughout most of the length of a chordate, and in larvae or adults that retain it, it also provides a firm but flexible structure against which muscles can work during swimming. In most vertebrates, a more complex, jointed skeleton develops around the ancestral notochord, and the adult retains only remnants of the embryonic notochord. In humans, the notochord is reduced and forms part of the gelatinous disks sandwiched between the vertebrae.

Dorsal, Hollow Nerve Cord

The nerve cord of a chordate embryo develops from a plate of ectoderm that rolls into a tube located dorsal to the notochord. The resulting dorsal, hollow nerve cord is unique to chordates. Other animal phyla have solid nerve cords, and in most cases they are ventrally located. The nerve cord of a chordate embryo develops into the central nervous system: the brain and spinal cord.

Pharyngeal Slits or Clefts

The digestive tube of chordates extends from the mouth to the anus. The region just posterior to the mouth is the pharynx. In all chordate embryos, a series of arches separated by grooves forms along the outer surface of the pharynx. In most chordates, these grooves (known as **pharyngeal clefts**) develop into slits that open into the pharynx. These **pharyngeal slits** allow water entering the mouth to exit the body without passing through the entire digestive tract.

Pharyngeal slits function as suspension-feeding devices in many invertebrate chordates. In vertebrates (with the exception of vertebrates with limbs, the tetrapods), these slits and the pharyngeal arches that support them have been modified for gas exchange and are called gills. In tetrapods, the pharyngeal clefts do not develop into slits. Instead, the pharyngeal arches that surround the clefts develop into parts of the ear and other structures in the head and neck.

Muscular, Post-Anal Tail

Chordates have a tail that extends posterior to the anus, although in many species it is greatly reduced during embryonic development. In contrast, most nonchordates have a digestive tract that extends nearly the whole length of the body. The chordate tail contains skeletal elements and muscles, and it helps propel many aquatic species in the water.

Lancelets

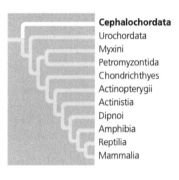

The most basal (earliest-diverging) group of living chordates are animals called **lancelets** (Cephalochordata), which get their name from their bladelike shape **(Figure 34.4)**. As larvae, lancelets develop a notochord, a dorsal, hollow nerve cord, numerous pharyngeal slits, and a post-anal tail. The larvae feed on plankton in the water column, alternating between upward swimming and passive sinking. As the larvae sink, they trap plankton and other suspended particles in their pharynx.

Adult lancelets can reach 6 cm in length. They retain key chordate traits, closely resembling the idealized chordate shown in Figure 34.3. Following metamorphosis, an adult lancelet swims down to the seafloor and wriggles backward into the sand, leaving only its anterior end exposed. Cilia draw seawater into the lancelet's mouth. A net of mucus secreted across the pharyngeal slits removes tiny food particles as the water passes through the slits, and the trapped food enters the intestine. The pharynx and pharyngeal slits play a minor role in gas exchange, which occurs mainly across the external body surface.

A lancelet frequently leaves its burrow to swim to a new location. Though feeble swimmers, these invertebrate chordates display, in a simple form, the swimming mechanism of fishes. Coordinated contraction of muscles arranged like rows of chevrons (>>>>) along the sides of the notochord flexes the notochord, producing side-to-side undulations that thrust the body forward. This serial arrangement of muscles is evidence of the lancelet's segmentation. The muscle segments develop from blocks of mesoderm called

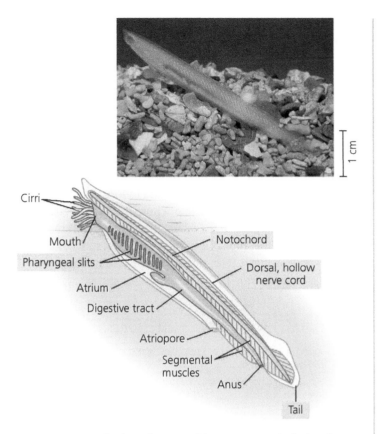

▲ **Figure 34.4 The lancelet *Branchiostoma*, a cephalochordate.** This small invertebrate displays all four main chordate characters. Water enters the mouth and passes through the pharyngeal slits into the atrium, a chamber that vents to the outside via the atriopore; large particles are blocked from entering the mouth by tentacle-like cirri. The serially arranged segmental muscles produce the lancelet's wavelike swimming movements.

somites, which are found along each side of the notochord in all chordate embryos.

Globally, lancelets are rare, but in a few areas (such as Tampa Bay, on the Florida coast), they may reach densities of more than 5,000 individuals per square meter.

Tunicates

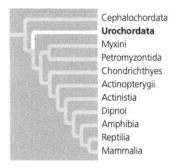

Recent molecular studies indicate that the **tunicates** (Urochordata) are more closely related to other chordates than are lancelets. The chordate characters of tunicates are most apparent during their larval stage, which may be as brief as a few minutes (**Figure 34.5a**). In many species, the larva uses its tail muscles and notochord to swim through water in search of a suitable substrate on which it can settle, guided by cues it receives from light- and gravity-sensitive cells.

Once a tunicate has settled on a substrate, it undergoes a radical metamorphosis in which many of its chordate characters disappear. Its tail and notochord are resorbed; its nervous system degenerates; and its remaining organs rotate 90°. As an adult, a tunicate draws in water through an incurrent siphon; the water then passes through the pharyngeal slits into a chamber called the atrium and exits through an excurrent siphon (**Figure 34.5b** and **c**). Food particles are

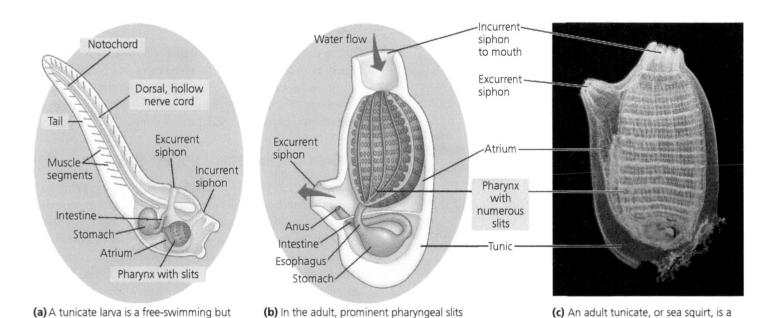

(a) A tunicate larva is a free-swimming but nonfeeding "tadpole" in which all four main characters of chordates are evident.

(b) In the adult, prominent pharyngeal slits function in suspension feeding, but other chordate characters are not obvious.

(c) An adult tunicate, or sea squirt, is a sessile animal (photo is approximately life-sized).

▲ **Figure 34.5 A tunicate, a urochordate.**

filtered from the water by a mucous net and transported by cilia to the esophagus. The anus empties into the excurrent siphon. Some tunicate species shoot a jet of water through their excurrent siphon when attacked, earning them the informal name of "sea squirts."

The loss of chordate characters in the adult stage of tunicates appears to have occurred after the tunicate lineage branched off from other chordates. Even the tunicate larva appears to be highly derived. For example, tunicates have 9 *Hox* genes, whereas all other chordates studied to date—including the early-diverging lancelets—share a set of 13 *Hox* genes. The apparent loss of four *Hox* genes indicates that the chordate body plan of a tunicate larva is built using a different set of genetic controls than other chordates.

Early Chordate Evolution

Although lancelets and tunicates are relatively obscure animals, they occupy key positions in the history of life and can provide clues about the evolutionary origin of vertebrates. As you have read, for example, lancelets display key chordate characters as adults, and their lineage branches from the base of the chordate phylogenetic tree. These findings suggest that the ancestral chordate may have looked something like a lancelet—that is, it had an anterior end with a mouth; a notochord; a dorsal, hollow nerve cord; pharyngeal slits; and a post-anal tail.

Research on lancelets has also revealed important clues about the evolution of the chordate brain. Rather than a full-fledged brain, lancelets have only a slightly swollen tip on the anterior end of their dorsal nerve cord (**Figure 34.6**). But the same *Hox* genes that organize major regions of the

▲ Figure 34.6 Expression of developmental genes in lancelets and vertebrates. *Hox* genes (including *BF1*, *Otx*, and *Hox3*) control the development of major regions of the vertebrate brain. These genes are expressed in the same anterior-to-posterior order in lancelets and vertebrates. Each colored bar is positioned above the portion of the brain whose development that gene controls.

MAKE CONNECTIONS *What do these expression patterns and those in Figure 21.19 indicate about* Hox *genes and their evolution?*

forebrain, midbrain, and hindbrain of vertebrates express themselves in a corresponding pattern in this small cluster of cells in the lancelet's nerve cord. This suggests that the vertebrate brain is an elaboration of an ancestral structure similar to the lancelet's simple nerve cord tip.

As for tunicates, several of their genomes have been completely sequenced and can be used to identify genes likely to have been present in early chordates. Researchers taking this approach have suggested that ancestral chordates had genes associated with vertebrate organs such as the heart and thyroid gland. These genes are found in tunicates and vertebrates but are absent from nonchordate invertebrates. In contrast, tunicates lack many genes that in vertebrates are associated with the long-range transmission of nerve impulses. This result suggests that such genes arose in an early vertebrate and are unique to the vertebrate evolutionary lineage.

CONCEPT CHECK 34.1

1. Identify four derived characters that all chordates have at some point during their life.

2. You are a chordate, yet you lack most of the main derived characters of chordates. Explain.

3. **WHAT IF?** Suppose lancelets lacked a gene found in tunicates and vertebrates. Would this imply that the chordates' most recent common ancestor also lacked this gene? Explain.

For suggested answers, see Appendix A.

CONCEPT 34.2

Vertebrates are chordates that have a backbone

During the Cambrian period, half a billion years ago, a lineage of chordates gave rise to vertebrates. With a skeletal system and a more complex nervous system than that of their ancestors, vertebrates became more efficient at two essential tasks: capturing food and avoiding being eaten.

Derived Characters of Vertebrates

Living vertebrates share a set of derived characters that distinguish them from other chordates. As a result of gene duplication, vertebrates possess two or more sets of *Hox* genes (lancelets and tunicates have only one). Other important families of genes that produce transcription factors and signaling molecules are also duplicated in vertebrates. The resulting additional genetic complexity may be associated with innovations in the vertebrate nervous system and skeleton, including the development of a skull and a backbone composed of vertebrae. In some vertebrates, the vertebrae are little more than small prongs of cartilage arrayed dorsally along the notochord. In the majority of vertebrates, however, the vertebrae enclose the spinal cord and have taken over the mechanical roles of the notochord. Over time, dorsal, ventral, and anal fins stiffened by bony structures called fin rays also evolved in aquatic vertebrates. Fin rays provide thrust and steering control when aquatic vertebrates swim after prey or away from predators. Faster swimming was supported by other adaptations, including a more efficient gas exchange system in the gills.

Hagfishes and Lampreys

Cephalochordata
Urochordata
Myxini
Petromyzontida
Chondrichthyes
Actinopterygii
Actinistia
Dipnoi
Amphibia
Reptilia
Mammalia

The **hagfishes** (Myxini) and the **lampreys** (Petromyzontida) are the only lineages of living vertebrates whose members lack jaws. Unlike most vertebrates, lampreys and hagfishes also do not have a backbone. Nevertheless, lampreys were traditionally classified as vertebrates because they have rudimentary vertebrae (composed of cartilage, not bone). The hagfishes, in contrast, were thought to lack vertebrae altogether; hence, they were classified as invertebrate chordates closely related to vertebrates.

In the past few years, however, this interpretation has changed. Recent research has shown that hagfishes, like lampreys, have rudimentary vertebrae. In addition, a series of molecular phylogenetic studies have supported the hypothesis that hagfishes are vertebrates.

Molecular analyses also have indicated that hagfishes and lampreys are sister groups, as shown in the phylogenetic tree at the beginning of this section. Together, the hagfishes and lampreys form a clade of living jawless vertebrates, the **cyclostomes**. (Vertebrates with jaws make up a much larger clade, the gnathostomes, which we will discuss in Concept 34.3.)

Hagfishes

The hagfishes are jawless vertebrates that have highly reduced vertebrae and a skull that is made of cartilage. They swim in a snakelike fashion by using their segmental muscles to exert force against their notochord, which they retain in adulthood as a strong, flexible rod of cartilage. Hagfishes have a small brain, eyes, ears, and a nasal opening that connects with the pharynx. Their mouths contain tooth-like formations made of the protein keratin.

All of the 30 living species of hagfishes are marine. Measuring up to 60 cm in length, most are bottom-dwelling

Slime glands

▲ Figure 34.7 **A hagfish.**

scavengers **(Figure 34.7)** that feed on worms and sick or dead fish. Rows of slime glands on a hagfish's flanks secrete a substance that absorbs water, forming a slime that may repel other scavengers when a hagfish is feeding. When attacked by a predator, a hagfish can produce several liters of slime in less than a minute. The slime coats the gills of the attacking fish, sending it into retreat or even suffocating it. Biologists and engineers are investigating the properties of hagfish slime as a model for developing a space-filling gel that could be used, for instance, to stop bleeding during surgery.

Lampreys

The second group of living jawless vertebrates, the lampreys, consists of about 35 species inhabiting various marine and freshwater environments **(Figure 34.8)**. Most are parasites that feed by clamping their round, jawless mouth onto the flank of a live fish, their "host." Lampreys use their rasping mouth and tongue to penetrate the skin of the fish and ingest the fish's blood and other tissues.

▲ Figure 34.8 **A sea lamprey.** Most lampreys use their mouth (inset) and tongue to bore a hole in the side of a fish. The lamprey then ingests the blood and other tissues of its host.

As larvae, lampreys live in freshwater streams. The larva is a suspension feeder that resembles a lancelet and spends much of its time partially buried in sediment. Some species of lampreys feed only as larvae; following several years in streams, they mature sexually, reproduce, and die within a few days. Most lampreys, however, migrate to the sea or lakes as they mature into adults. Sea lampreys (*Petromyzon marinus*) have invaded the Great Lakes over the past 170 years and have devastated a number of fisheries there.

The skeleton of lampreys is made of cartilage. Unlike the cartilage found in most vertebrates, lamprey cartilage contains no collagen. Instead, it is a stiff matrix of other proteins. The notochord of lampreys persists as the main axial skeleton in the adult, as it does in hagfishes. However, lampreys also have a flexible sheath around their rodlike notochord. Along the length of this sheath, pairs of cartilaginous projections related to vertebrae extend dorsally, partially enclosing the nerve cord.

Early Vertebrate Evolution

In the late 1990s, paleontologists working in China discovered a vast collection of fossils of early chordates that appear to straddle the transition to vertebrates. The fossils were formed during the Cambrian explosion 530 million years ago, when many animal groups were undergoing rapid diversification (see Concept 32.2).

The most primitive of the fossils are the 3-cm-long *Haikouella* (Figure 34.9). In many ways, *Haikouella* resembled a lancelet. Its mouth structure indicates that, like lancelets, it probably was a suspension feeder. However, *Haikouella* also had some of the characters of vertebrates. For example, it had a well-formed brain, small eyes, and muscle segments along the body, as do the vertebrate fishes. Unlike the vertebrates, however, *Haikouella* did not have a skull or ear organs, suggesting that these characters emerged with further innovations to the chordate nervous system. (The earliest "ears" were organs for maintaining balance, a function still performed by the ears of humans and other living vertebrates.)

Early signs of a skull can be seen in *Myllokunmingia* (see Figure 34.1). About the same size as *Haikouella*, *Myllokunmingia* had ear capsules and eye capsules, parts of the skull that surround these organs. Based on these and other characters, *Myllokunmingia* is considered the first chordate to have a head. The origin of a head—consisting of a brain at the anterior end of the dorsal nerve cord, eyes and other sensory organs, and a skull—enabled chordates to coordinate more complex movement and feeding behaviors. Although it had a head, *Myllokunmingia* lacked vertebrae and hence is not classified as a vertebrate.

The earliest fossils of vertebrates date to 500 million years ago and include those of **conodonts**, a group of slender, soft-bodied vertebrates that lacked jaws and whose internal

▲ **Figure 34.9 Fossil of an early chordate.** Discovered in 1999 in southern China, *Haikouella* had eyes and a brain but lacked a skull, a trait found in vertebrates. The organism's color in the drawing is fanciful.

skeleton was composed of cartilage. Conodonts had large eyes, which they may have used in locating prey that were then impaled on a set of barbed hooks at the anterior end of their mouth. These hooks were made of dental tissues that were *mineralized*—hardened by the incorporation of minerals such as calcium (Figure 34.10). The food was then passed back to the pharynx, where a different set of dental elements sliced and crushed the food.

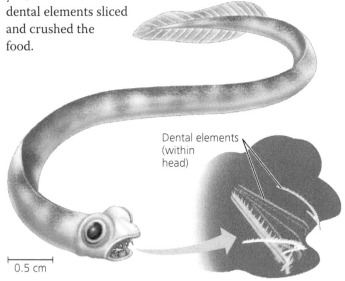

▲ **Figure 34.10 A conodont.** Conodonts were early jawless vertebrates that lived from 500 million to 200 million years ago. Unlike hagfishes and lampreys, conodonts had mineralized mouthparts, which they used for either predation or scavenging.

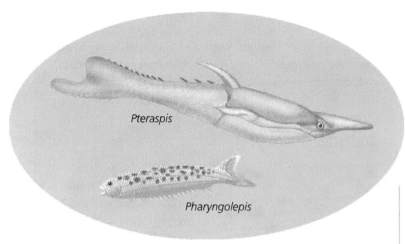

© 2002 The McGraw-Hill Companies, Inc.

▲ **Figure 34.11 Jawless armored vertebrates.** *Pteraspis* and *Pharyngolepis* were two of many genera of jawless vertebrates that emerged during the Ordovician, Silurian, and Devonian periods.

Conodonts were extremely abundant for 300 million years. Their fossilized dental elements are so plentiful that they have been used for decades by petroleum geologists as guides to the age of rock layers in which they search for oil.

Vertebrates with additional innovations emerged during the Ordovician, Silurian, and Devonian periods (488–359 million years ago). These vertebrates had paired fins and, as in lampreys, an inner ear with two semicircular canals that provided a sense of balance. Like conodonts, these vertebrates lacked jaws, but they had a muscular pharynx, which they may have used to suck in bottom-dwelling organisms or detritus. They were also armored with mineralized bone, which covered varying amounts of their body and may have offered protection from predators **(Figure 34.11)**. There were many species of these jawless, armored swimming vertebrates, but they all became extinct by the end of the Devonian.

Origins of Bone and Teeth

The human skeleton is heavily mineralized bone, whereas cartilage plays a fairly minor role. But a bony skeleton was a relatively late development in the history of vertebrates. Instead, the vertebrate skeleton evolved initially as a structure made of unmineralized cartilage.

What initiated the process of mineralization in vertebrates? One hypothesis is that mineralization was associated with a transition in feeding mechanisms. Early chordates probably were suspension feeders, like lancelets, but over time they became larger and were able to ingest larger particles, including some small animals. The earliest known mineralized structures in vertebrates—conodont dental elements—were an adaptation that may have allowed these animals to become scavengers and predators. In addition, when the bony armor of later jawless vertebrates was examined under the microscope, scientists found that it was composed of small tooth-like structures. These findings suggest that mineralization of the vertebrate body may have begun

in the mouth and later was incorporated into protective armor. Only in more derived vertebrates did the endoskeleton begin to mineralize, starting with the skull. As you'll read in Concept 34.3, more recent lineages of vertebrates underwent even more mineralization.

CONCEPT CHECK **34.2**

1. How are differences in the anatomy of lampreys and conodonts reflected in each animal's feeding method?

2. **WHAT IF?** In several different animal lineages, organisms with a head first appeared around 530 million years ago. Does this finding constitute proof that having a head is favored by natural selection? Explain.

3. **WHAT IF?** Suggest key roles that mineralized bone might have played in early vertebrates.

For suggested answers, see Appendix A.

CONCEPT 34.3

Gnathostomes are vertebrates that have jaws

Hagfishes and lampreys are survivors from the early Paleozoic era, when jawless vertebrates were common. Since then, jawless vertebrates have been far outnumbered by the jawed vertebrates, the **gnathostomes**. Living gnathostomes are a diverse group that includes sharks and their relatives, ray-finned fishes, lobe-finned fishes, amphibians, reptiles (including birds), and mammals.

Derived Characters of Gnathostomes

Gnathostomes ("jaw mouth") are named for their jaws, hinged structures that, especially with the help of teeth, enable gnathostomes to grip food items firmly and slice them. According to one hypothesis, gnathostome jaws evolved by modification of the skeletal rods that had previously supported the anterior pharyngeal (gill) slits. **Figure 34.12** shows a stage in this evolutionary process in which several of these skeletal rods have been modified into precursors of jaws (green) and their structural supports (red). The remaining gill slits, no longer

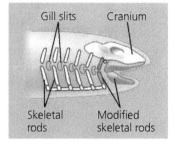

▲ **Figure 34.12 Possible step in the evolution of jawbones.**

required for suspension feeding, remained as the major sites of respiratory gas exchange with the external environment.

Gnathostomes share other derived characters besides jaws. The common ancestors of all gnathostomes underwent an additional duplication of *Hox* genes, such that the single set present in early chordates became four. In fact, the entire genome appears to have duplicated, and together these genetic changes likely enabled the origin of jaws and other novel features in gnathostomes. The gnathostome forebrain is enlarged compared to that of other vertebrates, and it is associated with enhanced senses of smell and vision. Another characteristic of aquatic gnathostomes is the **lateral line system**, organs that form a row along each side of the body and are sensitive to vibrations in the surrounding water. Precursors of these organs were present in the head shields of some jawless vertebrates.

Fossil Gnathostomes

Gnathostomes appeared in the fossil record about 440 million years ago and steadily became more diverse. Their success probably resulted from a combination of anatomical features: Their paired fins and tail (which were also found in jawless vertebrates) allowed them to swim efficiently after prey, and their jaws enabled them to grab prey or simply bite off chunks of flesh.

The earliest gnathostomes include extinct lineages of armored vertebrates known collectively as **placoderms**, which means "plate-skinned." Most placoderms were less than a meter long, though some giants measured more than 10 m (**Figure 34.13**). Other jawed vertebrates, called **acanthodians**, emerged at roughly the same time and radiated during the Silurian and Devonian periods (444–359 million years ago). Placoderms had disappeared by 359 million years ago, and acanthodians became extinct about 70 million years later.

Overall, a series of recent fossil discoveries have revealed that 440–420 million years ago was a period of tumultuous evolutionary change. Gnathostomes that lived during this period had highly variable

0.5 m

▲ **Figure 34.13 Fossil of an early gnathostome.** A formidable predator, the placoderm *Dunkleosteus* grew up to 10 m in length. Its jaw structure indicates that *Dunkleosteus* could exert a force of 560 kg/cm² (8,000 pounds per square inch) at the tip of its jaws.

forms, and by 420 million years ago, they had diverged into the three lineages of jawed vertebrates that survive today: chondrichthyans, ray-finned fishes, and lobe-fins.

Chondrichthyans (Sharks, Rays, and Their Relatives)

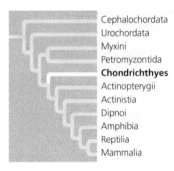

Cephalochordata
Urochordata
Myxini
Petromyzontida
Chondrichthyes
Actinopterygii
Actinistia
Dipnoi
Amphibia
Reptilia
Mammalia

Sharks, rays, and their relatives include some of the biggest and most successful vertebrate predators in the oceans. They belong to the clade Chondrichthyes, which means "cartilage fish." As their name indicates, the **chondrichthyans** have a skeleton composed predominantly of cartilage, though often impregnated with calcium.

When the name Chondrichthyes was first coined in the 1800s, scientists thought that chondrichthyans represented an early stage in the evolution of the vertebrate skeleton and that mineralization had evolved only in more derived lineages (such as "bony fishes"). However, as conodonts and armored jawless vertebrates demonstrate, the mineralization of the vertebrate skeleton had already begun before the chondrichthyan lineage branched off from other vertebrates. Moreover, bone-like tissues have been found in early chondrichthyans, such as the fin skeleton of a shark that lived in the Carboniferous period. Traces of bone can also be found in living chondrichthyans—in their scales, at the base of their teeth, and, in some sharks, in a thin layer on the surface of their vertebrae. Such findings strongly suggest that the restricted distribution of bone in the chondrichthyan body is a derived condition, emerging after chondrichthyans diverged from other gnathostomes.

There are about 1,000 species of living chondrichthyans. The largest and most diverse group consists of the sharks, rays, and skates (**Figure 34.14a** and **b**). A second group is composed of a few dozen species of ratfishes, also called chimaeras (**Figure 34.14c**).

Most sharks have a streamlined body and are swift swimmers, but they do not maneuver very well. Powerful movements of the trunk and the tail fin propel them forward. The dorsal fins function mainly as stabilizers, and the paired pectoral (fore) and pelvic (hind) fins are important for maneuvering. Although a shark gains buoyancy by storing a large amount of oil in its huge liver, the animal is still more dense than water, and if it stops swimming it sinks. Continual swimming also ensures that water flows into the shark's mouth and out through the gills, where gas exchange occurs. However, some sharks and many skates and rays spend a good deal of time resting on the seafloor. When resting, they use muscles of their jaws and pharynx to pump water over the gills.

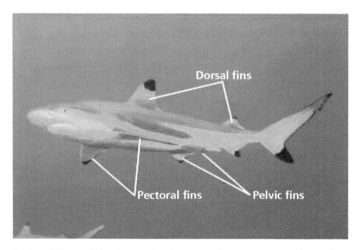

(a) Blacktip reef shark (*Carcharhinus melanopterus*). Sharks are fast swimmers with acute senses. Like all gnathostomes, they have paired pectoral and pelvic fins.

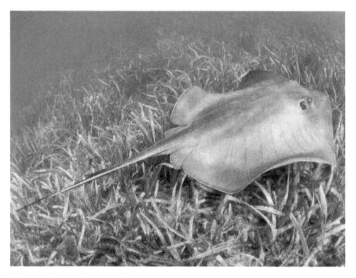

(b) Southern stingray (*Dasyatis americana*). Most rays are bottom-dwellers that feed on molluscs and crustaceans. Some rays cruise in open water and scoop food into their gaping mouths.

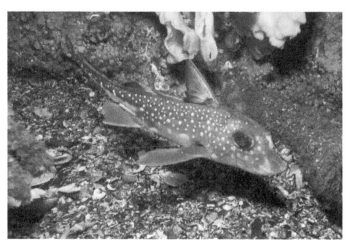

(c) Spotted ratfish (*Hydrolagus colliei*). Ratfishes, or chimaeras, typically live at depths greater than 80 m and feed on shrimp, molluscs, and sea urchins. Some species have a venomous spine at the front of their first dorsal fin.

▲ **Figure 34.14 Chondrichthyans.**

The largest sharks and rays are suspension feeders that consume plankton. Most sharks, however, are carnivores that swallow their prey whole or use their powerful jaws and sharp teeth to tear flesh from animals too large to swallow in one piece. Sharks have several rows of teeth that gradually move to the front of the mouth as old teeth are lost. The digestive tract of many sharks is proportionately shorter than that of many other vertebrates. Within the shark intestine is a *spiral valve*, a corkscrew-shaped ridge that increases surface area and prolongs the passage of food through the digestive tract.

Acute senses are adaptations that go along with the active, carnivorous lifestyle of sharks. Sharks have sharp vision but cannot distinguish colors. The nostrils of sharks, like those of most aquatic vertebrates, open into dead-end cups. They function only for olfaction (smelling), not for breathing. Like some other vertebrates, sharks have a pair of regions in the skin of their head that can detect electric fields generated by the muscle contractions of nearby animals. Like all nonmammalian aquatic vertebrates, sharks have no eardrums, structures that terrestrial vertebrates use to transmit sound waves in air to the auditory organs. Sound reaches a shark through water, and the animal's entire body transmits the sound to the hearing organs of the inner ear.

Shark eggs are fertilized internally. The male has a pair of claspers on its pelvic fins that transfer sperm into the female's reproductive tract. Some species of sharks are **oviparous**; they lay eggs that hatch outside the mother's body. These sharks release their fertilized eggs after encasing them in protective coats. Other species are **ovoviviparous**; they retain the fertilized eggs in the oviduct. Nourished by the egg yolk, the embryos develop into young that are born after hatching within the uterus. A few species are **viviparous**; the young develop within the uterus and obtain nourishment prior to birth by receiving nutrients from the mother's blood through a yolk sac placenta, by absorbing a nutritious fluid produced by the uterus, or by eating other eggs. The reproductive tract of the shark empties along with the excretory system and digestive tract into the **cloaca**, a common chamber that has a single opening to the outside.

Although rays are closely related to sharks, they have adopted a very different lifestyle. Most rays are bottom-dwellers that feed by using their jaws to crush molluscs and crustaceans. They have a flattened shape and use their greatly enlarged pectoral fins like water wings to propel themselves through the water. The tail of many rays is whip-like and, in some species, bears venomous barbs that function in defense.

Chondrichthyans have thrived for over 400 million years. Today, however, they are severely threatened by overfishing. A 2012 report, for example, indicated that shark populations in the Pacific have plummeted by up to 95%, and shark populations that live closest to people have declined the most.

Ray-Finned Fishes and Lobe-Fins

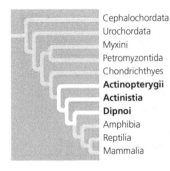

Cephalochordata
Urochordata
Myxini
Petromyzontida
Chondrichthyes
Actinopterygii
Actinistia
Dipnoi
Amphibia
Reptilia
Mammalia

The vast majority of vertebrates belong to the clade of gnathostomes called Osteichthyes. Unlike chondrichthyans, nearly all living **osteichthyans** have an ossified (bony) endoskeleton with a hard matrix of calcium phosphate. Like many other taxonomic names, the name Osteichthyes ("bony fish") was coined long before the advent of phylogenetic systematics. When it was originally defined, the group excluded tetrapods, but we now know that such a taxon would be paraphyletic (see Figure 34.2). Therefore, systematists today include tetrapods along with bony fishes in the clade Osteichthyes. Clearly, the name of the group does not accurately describe all of its members.

This section discusses the aquatic osteichthyans known informally as fishes. Most fishes breathe by drawing water over four or five pairs of gills located in chambers covered by a protective bony flap called the **operculum** (Figure 34.15). Water is drawn into the mouth, through the pharynx, and out between the gills by movement of the operculum and contraction of muscles surrounding the gill chambers.

Most fishes can maintain a buoyancy equal to the surrounding water by filling an air sac known as a swim bladder. (If a fish swims to greater depths or towards the surface, where water pressure differs, the fish shuttles gas between its blood and swim bladder, keeping the volume of gas in the bladder constant.) Charles Darwin proposed that the lungs of tetrapods evolved from swim bladders, but strange as it may sound, the opposite seems to be true. Osteichthyans in many early-branching lineages have lungs, which they use to breathe air as a supplement to gas exchange in their gills.

This suggests that lungs arose in early osteichthyans; later, swim bladders evolved from lungs in some lineages.

In nearly all fishes, the skin is covered by flattened, bony scales that differ in structure from the tooth-like scales of sharks. Glands in the skin secrete a slimy mucus over the skin, an adaptation that reduces drag during swimming. Like the ancient aquatic gnathostomes mentioned earlier, fishes have a lateral line system, which is evident as a row of tiny pits in the skin on either side of the body.

The details of fish reproduction vary extensively. Most species are oviparous, reproducing by external fertilization after the female sheds large numbers of small eggs. However, internal fertilization and birthing characterize other species.

Ray-Finned Fishes

Nearly all the aquatic osteichthyans familiar to us are among the over 27,000 species of **ray-finned fishes** (Actinopterygii) (Figure 34.16). Named for the bony rays that support their fins, the ray-finned fishes originated during the Silurian period (444–416 million years ago). The group has diversified greatly since that time, resulting in numerous species and many modifications in body form and fin structure that affect maneuvering, defense, and other functions (see Figure 34.16).

Ray-finned fishes serve as a major source of protein for humans, who have harvested them for thousands of years. However, industrial-scale fishing operations appear to have driven some of the world's biggest fisheries to collapse. For example, after decades of abundant harvests, in the 1990s the catch of cod (*Gadus morhua*) in the northwest Atlantic plummeted to just 5% of its historic maximum, bringing cod fishing there to a near halt. Despite ongoing restrictions on the fishery, cod populations have yet to recover to sustainable levels. Ray-finned fishes also face other pressures from humans, such as the diversion of rivers by dams. Changing water flow patterns can hamper the fishes' ability to obtain food and interferes with migratory pathways and spawning grounds.

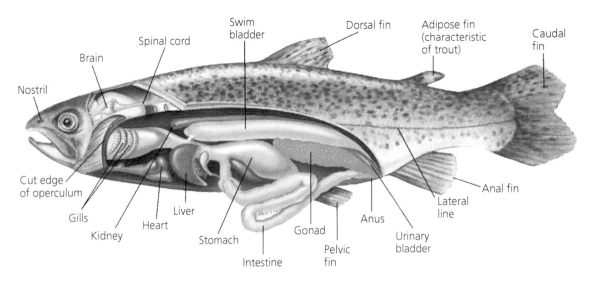

▲ Figure 34.15 Anatomy of a trout, a ray-finned fish.

▲ Yellowfin tuna (*Thunnus albacares*) is a fast-swimming, schooling fish that is commercially important worldwide.

▶ Native to coral reefs of the Pacific Ocean, the brightly colored red lionfish (*Pterois volitans*) can inject venom through its spines, causing a severe and painful reaction in humans.

▲ The sea horse has a highly modified body form, as exemplified by *Hippocampus ramulosus,* shown above. Sea horses are unusual among animals in that the male carries the young during their embryonic development.

▲ The fine-spotted moray eel (*Gymnothorax dovii*) is a predator that ambushes prey from crevices in its coral reef habitat.

▲ **Figure 34.16 Ray-finned fishes (Actinopterygii).**

Lobe-Fins

Like the ray-finned fishes, the other major lineage of osteichthyans, the **lobe-fins** (Sarcopterygii), also originated during the Silurian period (**Figure 34.17**). The key derived character of lobe-fins is the presence of rod-shaped bones surrounded by a thick layer of muscle in their pectoral and pelvic fins. During the Devonian (416–359 million years ago), many lobe-fins lived in brackish waters, such as in coastal wetlands. There they may have used their lobed fins to swim and "walk" underwater across the substrate (as do some living lobe-fins). Some Devonian lobe-fins were gigantic predators. It is not uncommon to find spike-shaped fossils of Devonian lobe-fin teeth as big as your thumb.

▲ **Figure 34.17 A reconstruction of an ancient lobe-fin.** Discovered in 2009, *Guiyu oneiros* is the earliest known lobe-fin, dating to 420 million years ago. The fossil of this species was nearly complete, allowing for an accurate reconstruction; regions shown in gray were missing from the fossil.

By the end of the Devonian period, lobe-fin diversity was dwindling, and today only three lineages survive. One lineage, the coelacanths (Actinistia), was thought to have become extinct 75 million years ago. However, in 1938, fishermen caught a living coelacanth off the east coast of South Africa (**Figure 34.18**). Until the 1990s, all subsequent discoveries were near the Comoros Islands in the western Indian Ocean. Since 1999, coelacanths have also been found at various places along the eastern coast of Africa and in the eastern Indian Ocean, near Indonesia. The Indonesian population may represent a second species.

The second lineage of living lobe-fins, the lungfishes (Dipnoi), is represented today by six species in three genera, all of which are found in the Southern Hemisphere. Lungfishes arose in the ocean but today are found only in fresh water, generally in stagnant ponds and swamps. They surface to gulp air into lungs connected to their pharynx. Lungfishes also have gills, which are the main organs for gas exchange in Australian lungfishes. When ponds shrink during the dry

▲ **Figure 34.18 A coelacanth (*Latimeria*).** These lobe-fins were found living off the coasts of southern Africa and Indonesia.

season, some lungfishes can burrow into the mud and estivate (wait in a state of torpor; see Concept 40.4).

The third lineage of lobe-fins that survives today is far more diverse than the coelacanths or the lungfishes. During the mid-Devonian, these organisms adapted to life on land and gave rise to vertebrates with limbs and feet, called tetrapods—a lineage that includes humans.

CONCEPT CHECK 34.3

1. What derived characters do sharks and tuna share? What features distinguish tuna from sharks?
2. Describe key adaptations of aquatic gnathostomes.
3. DRAW IT Redraw Figure 34.2 to show four lineages: cyclostomes, lancelets, gnathostomes, and tunicates. Label the vertebrate common ancestor and circle the lineage that includes humans.
4. WHAT IF? Imagine that we could replay the history of life. Is it possible that a group of vertebrates that colonized land could have arisen from aquatic gnathostomes other than the lobe-fins? Explain.

For suggested answers, see Appendix A.

Tetrapods are gnathostomes that have limbs

One of the most significant events in vertebrate history took place 365 million years ago, when the fins of a lineage of lobe-fins gradually evolved into the limbs and feet of tetrapods. Until then, all vertebrates had shared the same basic fishlike anatomy. After the colonization of land, early tetrapods gave rise to many new forms, from leaping frogs to flying eagles to bipedal humans.

Derived Characters of Tetrapods

The most significant character of **tetrapods** gives the group its name, which means "four feet" in Greek. In place of pectoral and pelvic fins, tetrapods have limbs with digits. Limbs support a tetrapod's weight on land, while feet with digits efficiently transmit muscle-generated forces to the ground when it walks.

Fish Characters	Tetrapod Characters
Scales	Neck
Fins	Ribs
Gills and lungs	Fin skeleton
	Flat skull
	Eyes on top of skull

▲ **Figure 34.19 Discovery of a "fishapod": *Tiktaalik*.** Paleontologists were on the hunt for fossils that could shed light on the evolutionary origin of tetrapods. Based on the ages of previously discovered fossils, researchers were looking for a dig site with rocks about 365–385 million years old. Ellesmere Island, in the Canadian Arctic, was one of the few such sites that was also likely to contain fossils, because it was once a river. The search at this site was rewarded by the discovery of fossils of a 375-million-year-old lobe-fin, named *Tiktaalik*. As shown in the chart and photographs, *Tiktaalik* exhibits both fish and tetrapod characters.

MAKE CONNECTIONS *Describe how* Tiktaalik's *features illustrate Darwin's concept of descent with modification (see Concept 22.2).*

Life on land selected for numerous other changes to the tetrapod body plan. In tetrapods, the head is separated from the body by a neck that originally had one vertebra on which the skull could move up and down. Later, with the origin of a second vertebra in the neck, the head could also swing from side to side. The bones of the pelvic girdle, to which the hind legs are attached, are fused to the backbone, permitting forces generated by the hind legs against the ground to be transferred to the rest of the body. Except for some fully aquatic species (such as the axolotl discussed below), the adults of living tetrapods do not have gills; during embryonic development, the pharyngeal clefts instead give rise to parts of the ears, certain glands, and other structures.

We'll discuss later how some of these characters were dramatically altered or lost in various lineages of tetrapods. In birds, for example, the pectoral limbs became wings, and in whales, the entire body converged toward a fishlike shape.

The Origin of Tetrapods

As you have read, the Devonian coastal wetlands were home to a wide range of lobe-fins. Those that entered shallow, oxygen-poor water could use their lungs to breathe air. Some species probably used their stout fins to help them move across logs or the muddy bottom. Thus, the tetrapod body plan did not evolve "out of nowhere" but was simply a modification of a preexisting body plan.

The discovery in 2006 of a fossil called *Tiktaalik* has provided new details on how this process occurred. Like a fish, this species had fins, gills, and lungs, and its body was covered in scales. But unlike a fish, *Tiktaalik* had a full set of ribs that would have helped it breathe air and support its body (Figure 34.19). Also unlike a fish, *Tiktaalik* had a neck and shoulders, allowing it to move its head about. Finally, the bones of *Tiktaalik*'s front fin have the same basic pattern found in all limbed animals: one bone (the humerus), followed by two bones (the radius and ulna), followed by a group of small bones that comprise the wrist. Although it is unlikely that *Tiktaalik* could walk on land, its front fin skeleton suggests that it could prop itself up in water on its fins. Since *Tiktaalik* predates the oldest known tetrapod,

its features suggest that key "tetrapod" traits, such as a wrist, ribs, and a neck, were in fact ancestral to the tetrapod lineage.

Tiktaalik and other extraordinary fossil discoveries have allowed paleontologists to reconstruct how fins became progressively more limb-like over time, culminating in the appearance in the fossil record of the first tetrapods 365 million years ago (Figure 34.20). Over the next 60 million years, a great diversity of tetrapods arose. Some of these species retained functional gills and had weak limbs, while others had lost their gills and had stronger limbs that facilitated walking on land. Overall, judging from the morphology and locations of their fossils, most of these early tetrapods probably remained tied to water, a characteristic they share with some members of the most basal group of living tetrapods, the amphibians.

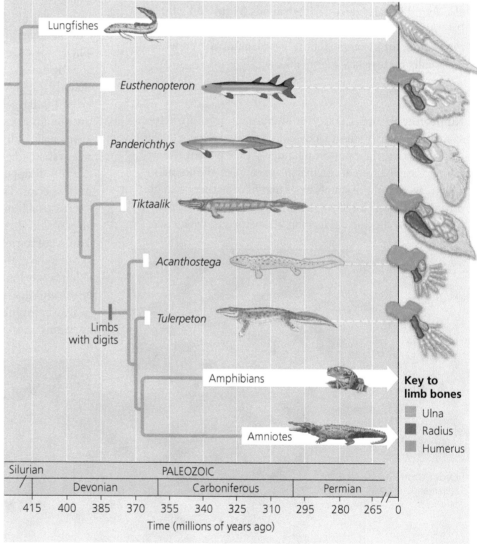

▲ Figure 34.20 **Steps in the origin of limbs with digits.** The white bars on the branches of this diagram place known fossils in time; arrowheads indicate lineages that extend to today. The drawings of extinct organisms are based on fossilized skeletons, but the colors are fanciful.

WHAT IF? *If the most recent common ancestor of* Tulerpeton *and living tetrapods originated 370 million years ago, what range of dates would include the origin of amphibians?*

Amphibians

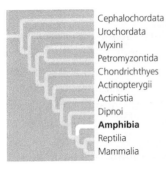

Cephalochordata
Urochordata
Myxini
Petromyzontida
Chondrichthyes
Actinopterygii
Actinistia
Dipnoi
Amphibia
Reptilia
Mammalia

The **amphibians** are represented today by about 6,150 species in three clades: salamanders (clade Urodela, "tailed ones"), frogs (clade Anura, "tailless ones"), and caecilians (clade Apoda, "legless ones").

Salamanders

There are about 550 known species of urodeles, or salamanders. Some are entirely aquatic, but others live on land as adults or throughout life. Most salamanders that live on land walk with a side-to-side bending of the body, a trait also found in early terrestrial tetrapods (**Figure 34.21a**). Paedomorphosis is common among aquatic salamanders; the axolotl, for instance, retains larval features even when it is sexually mature (see Figure 25.24).

Frogs

Numbering about 5,420 species, anurans, or frogs, are better suited than salamanders to locomotion on land (**Figure 34.21b**). Adult frogs use their powerful hind legs to hop along the terrain. Although often distinctive in appearance, the animals known as "toads" are simply frogs that have leathery skin or other adaptations for life on land. A frog nabs insects and other prey by flicking out its long, sticky tongue, which is attached to the front of the mouth. Frogs display a great variety of adaptations that help them avoid being eaten by larger predators. Their skin glands secrete distasteful or even poisonous mucus. Many poisonous species have color patterns that camouflage them or have bright coloration, which predators appear to associate with danger (see Figure 54.5).

Caecilians

The approximately 170 species of apodans, or caecilians, are legless and nearly blind, and superficially they resemble earthworms (**Figure 34.21c**). Their absence of legs is a secondary adaptation, as they evolved from a legged ancestor. Caecilians inhabit tropical areas, where most species burrow in moist forest soil.

Lifestyle and Ecology of Amphibians

The term *amphibian* (derived from *amphibious*, meaning "both ways of life") refers to the life stages of many frog species that live first in water and then on land (**Figure 34.22**). The larval stage of a frog, called a tadpole, is usually an aquatic herbivore with gills, a lateral line system resembling that of aquatic vertebrates, and a long, finned tail. The tadpole initially lacks legs; it swims by undulating its tail. During the metamorphosis that leads to the "second life," the tadpole develops legs, lungs, a pair of external eardrums, and a digestive system adapted to a carnivorous diet. At the same time, the gills disappear; the lateral line system also disappears in most species. The young frog crawls onto shore and becomes a terrestrial hunter. In spite of their name, however, many amphibians do not live a dual—aquatic and terrestrial—life. There are some strictly aquatic or strictly terrestrial frogs, salamanders, and caecilians. Moreover, salamander and caecilian larvae look much like the adults, and typically both the larvae and the adults are carnivorous.

Most amphibians are found in damp habitats such as swamps and rain forests. Even those adapted to drier

(a) Order Urodela. Urodeles (salamanders) retain their tail as adults.

(b) Order Anura. Anurans, such as this variable harlequin toad, lack a tail as adults.

(c) Order Apoda. Apodans, or caecilians, are legless, mainly burrowing amphibians.

▲ Figure 34.21 **Amphibians.**

(a) The tadpole is an aquatic herbivore with a fishlike tail and internal gills.

(b) During metamorphosis, the gills and tail are resorbed, and walking legs develop. The adult frog will live on land.

(c) The adults return to water to mate. The male grasps the female, stimulating her to release eggs. The eggs are laid and fertilized in water. They have a jelly coat but lack a shell and would desiccate in air.

▲ **Figure 34.22 The "dual life" of a frog** (*Rana temporaria*).

habitats spend much of their time in burrows or under moist leaves, where humidity is high. Amphibians generally rely heavily on their moist skin for gas exchange with the environment. Some terrestrial species lack lungs and breathe exclusively through their skin and oral cavity.

Fertilization is external in most amphibians; the male grasps the female and spills his sperm over the eggs as the female sheds them (see Figure 34.22c). Amphibians typically lay their eggs in water or in moist environments on land; the eggs lack a shell and dehydrate quickly in dry air. Some amphibian species lay vast numbers of eggs in temporary pools, and egg mortality is high. In contrast, other species lay relatively few eggs and display various types of parental care. Depending on the species, either males or females may house eggs on their back **(Figure 34.23)**, in their mouth, or even in their stomach. Certain tropical tree frogs stir their egg masses into moist, foamy nests that resist drying. There are also some species that retain the eggs in the female reproductive tract, where embryos can develop without drying out.

▲ **Figure 34.23 A mobile nursery.** A female pygmy marsupial frog, *Flectonotus pygmaeus,* incubates her eggs in a pouch of skin on her back, helping to protect the eggs from predators. When the eggs hatch, the female deposits the tadpoles in water where they begin life on their own.

Many amphibians exhibit complex and diverse behaviors, especially during their breeding seasons. Frogs are usually quiet, but the males of many species vocalize to defend their breeding territory or to attract females. In some species, migrations to specific breeding sites may involve vocal communication, celestial navigation, or chemical signaling.

Over the past 30 years, zoologists have documented a rapid and alarming decline in amphibian populations in locations throughout the world. There appear to be several causes, including the spread of a disease-causing chytrid fungus (see Figure 31.25), habitat loss, climate change, and pollution. In some cases, declines have become extinctions. A recent study indicates that at least 9 amphibian species have become extinct since 1980; more than 100 other species have not been seen since that time and are considered possibly extinct.

CONCEPT CHECK 34.4

1. Describe the origin of tetrapods and identify some of their key derived traits.
2. Some amphibians never leave the water, whereas others can survive in relatively dry terrestrial environments. Contrast the adaptations that facilitate these two lifestyles.
3. **WHAT IF?** Scientists think that amphibian populations may provide an early warning system of environmental problems. What features of amphibians might make them particularly sensitive to environmental problems?

For suggested answers, see Appendix A.

CONCEPT 34.5

Amniotes are tetrapods that have a terrestrially adapted egg

The **amniotes** are a group of tetrapods whose extant members are the reptiles (including birds, as we'll discuss in this section) and mammals **(Figure 34.24)**. During their evolution, amniotes acquired a number of new adaptations to life on land.

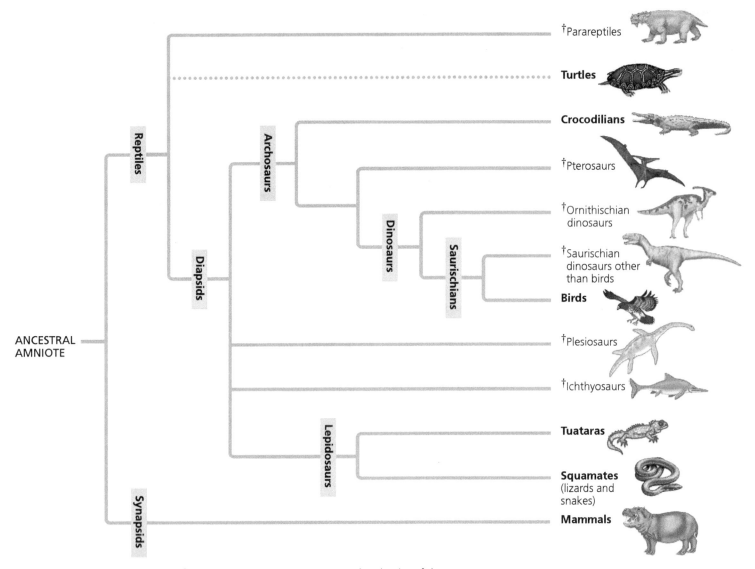

▲ **Figure 34.24 A phylogeny of amniotes.** Extant groups are named at the tips of the branches in boldface type. The dagger symbols (†) indicate extinct groups. The dotted line indicates the uncertain relationship of turtles to other reptiles.

? *Based on this phylogeny, are pterosaurs dinosaurs? Are birds? Explain.*

Derived Characters of Amniotes

Amniotes are named for the major derived character of the clade, the **amniotic egg**, which contains four specialized membranes: the amnion, the chorion, the yolk sac, and the allantois **(Figure 34.25)**. Called *extraembryonic membranes* because they are not part of the body of the embryo itself, these membranes develop from tissue layers that grow out from the embryo. The amniotic egg is named for the amnion, which encloses a compartment of fluid that bathes the embryo and acts as a hydraulic shock absorber. The other membranes in the egg function in gas exchange, the transfer of stored nutrients to the embryo, and waste storage. The amniotic egg was a key evolutionary innovation for terrestrial life: It allowed the embryo to develop on land in its own private "pond," hence reducing the dependence of tetrapods on an aqueous environment for reproduction.

In contrast to the shell-less eggs of amphibians, the amniotic eggs of most reptiles and some mammals have a shell. A shell slows dehydration of the egg in air, an adaptation that helped amniotes to occupy a wider range of terrestrial habitats than amphibians, their closest living relatives. (Seeds played a similar role in the evolution of land plants, as discussed in Concept 30.1.) Most mammals have dispensed with the eggshell over the course of their evolution, and the embryo avoids desiccation by developing within the amnion inside the mother's body.

Amniotes have acquired other key adaptations to life on land. For example, amniotes use their rib cage to ventilate their lungs. This method is more efficient than throat-based

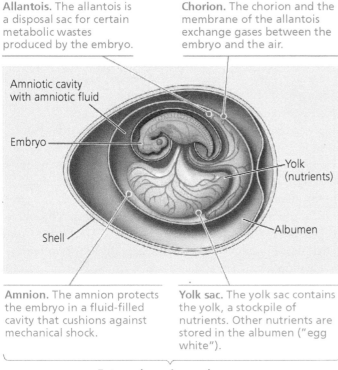

Extraembryonic membranes

Allantois. The allantois is a disposal sac for certain metabolic wastes produced by the embryo.

Chorion. The chorion and the membrane of the allantois exchange gases between the embryo and the air.

Amniotic cavity with amniotic fluid

Embryo

Yolk (nutrients)

Shell

Albumen

Amnion. The amnion protects the embryo in a fluid-filled cavity that cushions against mechanical shock.

Yolk sac. The yolk sac contains the yolk, a stockpile of nutrients. Other nutrients are stored in the albumen ("egg white").

Extraembryonic membranes

▲ **Figure 34.25 The amniotic egg.** The embryos of reptiles and mammals form four extraembryonic membranes: the allantois, chorion, amnion, and yolk sac. This diagram shows these membranes in the shelled egg of a reptile.

ventilation, which amphibians use as a supplement to breathing through their skin. The increased efficiency of rib cage ventilation may have allowed amniotes to abandon breathing through their skin and develop less permeable skin, thereby conserving water.

Early Amniotes

The most recent common ancestor of living amphibians and amniotes lived about 350 million years ago. No fossils of amniotic eggs have been found from that time, which is not surprising given how delicate they are. Thus, it is not yet possible to say when the amniotic egg evolved, although it must have existed in the last common ancestor of living amniotes, which all have amniotic eggs.

Based on where their fossils have been found, the earliest amniotes lived in warm, moist environments, as did the first tetrapods. Over time, however, early amniotes expanded into a wide range of new environments, including dry and high-latitude regions. The earliest amniotes resembled small lizards with sharp teeth, a sign that they were predators **(Figure 34.26)**. Later groups of amniotes also included herbivores, as evidenced by their grinding teeth and other features.

▲ **Figure 34.26** Artist's reconstruction of *Hylonomus*, an early amniote. About 25 cm long, this species lived 310 million years ago and probably ate insects and other small invertebrates.

Reptiles

Cephalochordata
Urochordata
Myxini
Petromyzontida
Chondrichthyes
Actinopterygii
Actinistia
Dipnoi
Amphibia
Reptilia
Mammalia

The **reptile** clade includes tuataras, lizards, snakes, turtles, crocodilians, and birds, along with a number of extinct groups, such as plesiosaurs and ichthyosaurs (see Figure 34.24).

As a group, the reptiles share several derived characters that distinguish them from other tetrapods. For example, unlike amphibians, reptiles have scales that contain the protein keratin (as does a human nail). Scales help protect the animal's skin from desiccation and abrasion. In addition, most reptiles lay their shelled eggs on land **(Figure 34.27)**. Fertilization occurs internally, before the eggshell is secreted.

Reptiles such as lizards and snakes are sometimes described as "cold-blooded" because they do not use their metabolism extensively to control their body temperature. However, they do regulate their body temperature by using behavioral adaptations. For example, many lizards bask in

▲ **Figure 34.27 Hatching reptiles.** These bushmaster snakes (*Lachesis muta*) are breaking out of their parchment-like shells, a common type of shell among living reptiles other than birds.

the sun when the air is cool and seek shade when the air is too warm. A more accurate description of these reptiles is to say that they are **ectothermic**, which means that they absorb external heat as their main source of body heat. By warming themselves directly with solar energy rather than through the metabolic breakdown of food, an ectothermic reptile can survive on less than 10% of the food energy required by a mammal of the same size. But the reptile clade is not entirely ectothermic; birds are **endothermic**, capable of maintaining body temperature through metabolic activity.

The Origin and Evolutionary Radiation of Reptiles

Fossil evidence indicates that the earliest reptiles lived about 310 million years ago and resembled lizards. As reptiles diverged from their lizard-like ancestors, one of the first major groups to emerge were the **parareptiles**, which were mostly large, stocky, quadrupedal herbivores. Some parareptiles had plates on their skin that may have provided them with defense against predators. Parareptiles died out by about 200 million years ago, at the end of the Triassic period.

As parareptiles were dwindling, another ancient clade of reptiles, the **diapsids**, was diversifying. One of the most obvious derived characters of diapsids is a pair of holes on each side of the skull, behind the eye sockets; muscles pass through these holes and attach to the jaw, controlling jaw movement. The diapsids are composed of two main lineages. One lineage gave rise to the **lepidosaurs**, which include tuataras, lizards, and snakes. This lineage also produced some marine reptiles, including the giant mososaurs. Some of these marine species rivaled today's whales in length; all of them are extinct. The other main diapsid lineage, the **archosaurs**, produced the crocodilians, pterosaurs, and dinosaurs. Our focus here will be on extinct lineages of lepidosaurs and archosaurs; we'll discuss living reptiles shortly.

Pterosaurs, which originated in the late Triassic, were the first tetrapods to exhibit flapping flight. The pterosaur wing was completely different from the wings of birds and bats. It consisted of a collagen-strengthened membrane that stretched between the trunk or hind leg and a very long digit on the foreleg. The smallest pterosaurs were no bigger than a sparrow, and the largest had a wingspan of nearly 11 m. They appear to have converged on many of the ecological roles later played by birds; some were insect-eaters, others grabbed fish out of the ocean, and still others filtered small animals through thousands of fine needlelike teeth. But by 65.5 million years ago, pterosaurs had become extinct.

On land, the **dinosaurs** diversified into a vast range of shapes and sizes, from bipeds the size of a pigeon to 45-m-long quadrupeds with necks long enough to let them browse the tops of trees. One lineage of dinosaurs, the ornithischians, were herbivores; they included many species with elaborate defenses against predators, such as tail clubs and

horned crests. The other main lineage of dinosaurs, the saurischians, included the long-necked giants and a group called the **theropods**, which were bipedal carnivores. Theropods included the famous *Tyrannosaurus rex* as well as the ancestors of birds.

Traditionally, dinosaurs were considered slow, sluggish creatures. Since the early 1970s, however, fossil discoveries and research have led to the conclusion that many dinosaurs were agile and fast moving. Dinosaurs had a limb structure that enabled them to walk and run more efficiently than could earlier tetrapods, which had a sprawling gait. Fossilized footprints and other evidence suggest that some species were social—they lived and traveled in groups, much as many mammals do today. Paleontologists have also discovered evidence that some dinosaurs built nests and brooded their eggs, as birds do today (see Figure 26.17). Finally, some anatomical evidence supports the hypothesis that at least some dinosaurs were endotherms.

All dinosaurs except birds became extinct by the end of the Cretaceous period (65.5 million years ago). Their extinction may have been caused at least in part by the asteroid or comet impact described in Chapter 25. Some analyses of the fossil record are consistent with this idea in that they show a sudden decline in dinosaur diversity at the end of the Cretaceous. However, other analyses indicate that the number of dinosaur species had begun to decline several million years before the Cretaceous ended. Further fossil discoveries and new analyses will be needed to resolve this debate.

Next, we'll discuss extant lineages of reptiles, including turtles, lepidosaurs, and two groups of archosaurs— crocodilians and birds.

Turtles

Turtles are one of the most distinctive groups of reptiles alive today. To date, their phylogenetic position remains uncertain (see Figure 34.24). Turtles may be a sister group to parareptiles, as indicated by some morphological data. However, it is also possible that turtles may be diapsids more closely related to lepidosaurs (as indicated by other morphological analyses and by a 2012 miRNA study) or to archosaurs (as indicated by many molecular studies).

All turtles have a boxlike shell made of upper and lower shields that are fused to the vertebrae, clavicles (collarbones), and ribs **(Figure 34.28a)**. Most of the 307 known

▼ **Figure 34.28** Extant reptiles (other than birds).

(a) Eastern box turtle (*Terrapene carolina carolina*)

species of turtles have a hard shell, providing excellent defense against predators. A 2008 study reported the discovery of the oldest known fossil of the turtle lineage, dating to 220 million years ago. This fossil has a complete lower shell but an incomplete upper shell, suggesting that turtles may have acquired full shells in stages. Scientists continue to hunt for fossils that could shed light on the origin of the turtle shell.

The earliest turtles could not retract their head into their shell, but mechanisms for doing so evolved independently in two separate branches of turtles. The side-necked turtles fold their neck horizontally, while the vertical-necked turtles fold their neck vertically.

Some turtles have adapted to deserts, and others live almost entirely in ponds and rivers. Still others live in the sea. Sea turtles have a reduced shell and enlarged forelimbs that function as flippers. They include the largest living turtles, the deep-diving leatherbacks, which can exceed a mass of 1,500 kg and feed on jellies. Leatherbacks and other sea turtles are endangered by being caught in fishing nets, as well as by the residential and commercial development of the beaches where the turtles lay their eggs.

Lepidosaurs

One surviving lineage of lepidosaurs is represented by two species of lizard-like reptiles called tuataras (Figure 34.28b). Fossil evidence indicates that tuatara ancestors lived at least 220 million years ago. These organisms thrived on many continents well into the Cretaceous period and reached up to a meter in length. Today, however, tuataras are found only on 30 islands off the coast of New Zealand. When humans arrived in New Zealand 750 years ago, the rats that accompanied them devoured tuatara eggs, eventually eliminating the reptiles on the main islands. The tuataras that remain on the outlying islands are about 50 cm long and feed on insects, small lizards, and bird eggs and chicks. They can live to be over 100 years old. Their future survival depends on whether their remaining habitats are kept rat-free.

The other major living lineage of lepidosaurs consists of the lizards and snakes, or squamates, which number about 7,900 species (Figure 34.28c and d). Many squamates are small; the Jaragua lizard, discovered in the Dominican Republic in 2001, is only 16 mm long—small enough to fit comfortably on a dime. In contrast, the Komodo dragon of Indonesia is a lizard that can reach a length of 3 m. It hunts deer and other large prey, delivering venom with its bite.

Snakes descended from lizards with legs—hence they are classified as legless lizards (see the opening paragraphs of Chapter 26). Today, some species of snakes retain vestigial pelvic and limb bones, providing evidence of their ancestry. Despite their lack of legs, snakes are quite proficient at moving on land, most often by producing waves of lateral bending that pass from head to tail. Force exerted by the bends against solid objects pushes the snake

(d) Wagler's pit viper (*Tropidolaemus wagleri*)

(b) Tuatara (*Sphenodon punctatus*)

(c) Australian thorny devil lizard (*Moloch horridus*)

(e) American alligator (*Alligator mississippiensis*)

forward. Snakes can also move by gripping the ground with their belly scales at several points along the body while the scales at intervening points are lifted slightly off the ground and pulled forward.

Snakes are carnivorous, and a number of adaptations aid them in hunting and eating prey. They have acute chemical sensors, and though they lack eardrums, they are sensitive to ground vibrations, which helps them detect the movements of prey. Heat-detecting organs between the eyes and nostrils of pit vipers, including rattlesnakes, are sensitive to minute temperature changes, enabling these night hunters to locate warm animals. Venomous snakes inject their toxin through a pair of sharp teeth that may be hollow or grooved. The flicking tongue is not venomous but helps fan odors toward olfactory (smell) organs on the roof of the mouth. Loosely articulated jawbones and elastic skin enable most snakes to swallow prey larger than the diameter of the snake's head (see Figure 23.14).

We'll conclude our survey of the reptiles by discussing the two clades of archosaurs with living members, the crocodilians and the birds.

Crocodilians

Alligators and crocodiles (collectively called crocodilians) belong to a lineage that reaches back to the late Triassic. The earliest members of this lineage were small terrestrial quadrupeds with long, slender legs. Later species became larger and adapted to aquatic habitats, breathing air through their upturned nostrils. Some Mesozoic crocodilians grew as long as 12 m and may have attacked dinosaurs and other prey at the water's edge.

The 23 known species of living crocodilians are confined to warm regions of the globe. In the southeastern United States, the American alligator (Figure 34.28e) has made a comeback after spending years on the endangered species list.

Birds

There are about 10,000 species of birds in the world. Like crocodilians, birds are archosaurs, but almost every feature of their anatomy has been modified in their adaptation to flight.

Derived Characters of Birds Many of the characters of birds are adaptations that facilitate flight, including weight-saving modifications that make flying more efficient. For example, birds lack a urinary bladder, and the females of most species have only one ovary. The gonads of both females and males are usually small, except during the breeding season, when they increase in size. Living birds are also toothless, an adaptation that trims the weight of the head.

A bird's most obvious adaptations for flight are its wings and feathers (Figure 34.29). Feathers are made of the protein β-keratin, which is also found in the scales of other reptiles. The shape and arrangement of the feathers form the wings into airfoils, and they illustrate some of the same principles of aerodynamics as the wings of an airplane. Power for flapping the wings comes from contractions of large pectoral (breast) muscles anchored to a keel on the

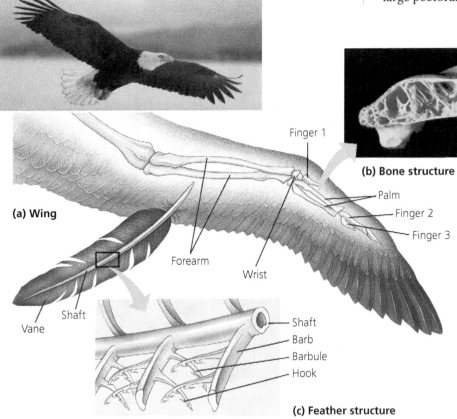

(a) Wing

Finger 1
Palm
Finger 2
Finger 3
Forearm
Wrist
Shaft
Vane

(b) Bone structure

Shaft
Barb
Barbule
Hook

(c) Feather structure

◀ **Figure 34.29 Form fits function: the avian wing and feather. (a)** A wing is a remodeled version of the tetrapod forelimb. **(b)** The bones of many birds have a honeycombed internal structure and are filled with air. **(c)** A feather consists of a central air-filled shaft, from which radiate the vanes. The vanes are made up of barbs, which bear small branches called barbules. Birds have contour feathers and downy feathers. Contour feathers are stiff and contribute to the aerodynamic shapes of the wings and body. Their barbules have hooks that cling to barbules on neighboring barbs. When a bird preens, it runs the length of each contour feather through its beak, engaging the hooks and uniting the barbs into a precise shape. Downy feathers lack hooks, and the free-form arrangement of their barbs produces a fluffiness that provides insulation by trapping air.

sternum (breastbone). Some birds, such as eagles and hawks, have wings adapted for soaring on air currents and flap their wings only occasionally; other birds, including humming-birds, must flap continuously to stay aloft (see Figure 34.33). Among the fastest birds are the appropriately named swifts, which can fly up to 170 km/hr.

Flight provides numerous benefits. It enhances scaveng-ing and hunting, including enabling many birds to feed on flying insects, an abundant, nutritious food resource. Flight also provides ready escape from earthbound predators and enables some birds to migrate great distances to exploit dif-ferent food resources and seasonal breeding areas.

Flying requires a great expenditure of energy from an active metabolism. Birds are endothermic; they use their own metabolic heat to maintain a high, constant body tem-perature. Feathers and in some species a layer of fat provide insulation that enables birds to retain body heat. The lungs have tiny tubes leading to and from elastic air sacs that im-prove airflow and oxygen uptake. This efficient respiratory system and a circulatory system with a four-chambered heart keep tissues well supplied with oxygen and nutrients, supporting a high rate of metabolism.

Flight also requires both acute vision and fine muscle control. Birds have color vision and excellent eyesight. The visual and motor areas of the brain are well developed, and the brain is proportionately larger than those of amphibians and nonbird reptiles.

Birds generally display very complex behaviors, particu-larly during breeding season, when they engage in elaborate courtship rituals. Because eggs have shells by the time they are laid, fertilization must be internal. Copulation usually involves contact between the openings to the birds' cloacas. After eggs are laid, the avian embryo must be kept warm through brooding by the mother, the father, or both, de-pending on the species.

The Origin of Birds Cladistic analyses of birds and reptilian fossils indicate that birds belong to the group of bipedal saurischian dinosaurs called theropods. Since the late 1990s, Chinese paleontologists have unearthed a spectacular trove of feathered theropod fossils that are shedding light on the origin of birds. Several species of dinosaurs closely related to birds had feathers with vanes, and a wider range of species had filamentous feathers. Such findings imply that feath-ers evolved long before powered flight. Among the possible functions of these early feathers were insulation, camou-flage, and courtship display.

By about 160 million years ago, feathered theropods had evolved into birds. Many researchers consider *Archaeop-teryx*, which was discovered in a German limestone quarry in 1861, to be the earliest known bird **(Figure 34.30)**. It had feathered wings but retained ancestral characters such as teeth, clawed digits in its wings, and a long tail. *Archaeop-teryx* flew well at high speeds, but unlike a present-day bird,

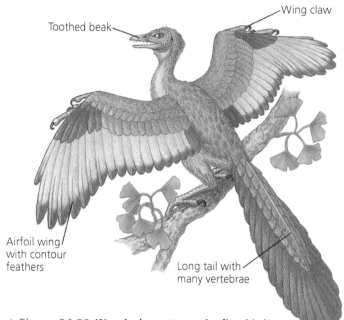

▲ **Figure 34.30 Was *Archaeopteryx* the first bird?** Fossil evidence indicates that *Archaeopteryx* was capable of powered flight but retained many characters of nonbird dinosaurs. Although it has long been considered the first bird, recent fossil discov-eries have sparked debate. Some analyses indicate that *Archaeopteryx* was a nonbird dinosaur closely related to the birds. Others indicate that Archaeopteryx was a bird—as traditionally thought—but that it was not the first bird.

it could not take off from a standing position. Fossils of later birds from the Cretaceous show a gradual loss of certain ancestral dinosaur features, such as teeth and clawed fore-limbs, as well as the acquisition of innovations found in ex-tant birds, including a short tail covered by a fan of feathers.

Living Birds Clear evidence of Neornithes, the clade that in-cludes the 28 orders of living birds, can be found before the Cretaceous-Paleogene boundary 65.5 million years ago. Sev-eral groups of living and extinct birds include one or more flightless species. The **ratites** (order Struthioniformes), which consist of the ostrich, rhea, kiwi, cassowary, and emu, are all flightless **(Figure 34.31)**. In ratites, the sternal keel is

▲ **Figure 34.31 An emu (*Dromaius novaehollandiae*), a flight-less bird native to Australia.**

▲ **Figure 34.32 A king penguin (*Aptenodytes patagonicus*) "flying" underwater.** With their streamlined shape and powerful pectoral muscles, penguins are fast and agile swimmers.

absent, and the pectoral muscles are small relative to those of birds that can fly.

Penguins make up the flightless order Sphenisciformes, but, like flying birds, they have powerful pectoral muscles. They use these muscles to "fly" in the water: As they swim, they flap their flipper-like wings in a manner that resembles the flight stroke of a more typical bird (**Figure 34.32**). Certain species of rails, ducks, and pigeons are also flightless.

Although the demands of flight have rendered the general body forms of many flying birds similar to one another, experienced bird-watchers can distinguish species by their profile, colors, flying style, behavior, and beak shape. The skeleton of a hummingbird's wing is unique, making it the only bird that can hover and fly backward (**Figure 34.33**). Adult birds lack teeth, but during the course of avian evolution their beaks have taken on a variety of shapes suited to different diets. Some birds, such as parrots, have crushing

▲ **Figure 34.33 Hummingbird feeding while hovering.** A hummingbird can rotate its wings in all directions, enabling it to hover and fly backward.

▲ **Figure 34.34 A specialized beak.** This greater flamingo (*Phoenicopterus ruber*) dips its beak into the water and strains out the food.

▲ **Figure 34.35 Feet adapted to perching.** This great tit (*Parus major*) is a member of the Passeriformes, the perching birds. The toes of these birds can lock around a branch or wire, enabling the bird to rest for long periods.

beaks with which they can crack open hard nuts and seeds. Other birds, such as flamingoes, are filter feeders. Their beaks have "strainers" that enable them to capture food particles from the water (**Figure 34.34**). Foot structure, too, shows considerable variation. Various birds use their feet for perching on branches (**Figure 34.35**), grasping food, defense, swimming or walking, and even courtship (see Figure 24.3e).

CONCEPT CHECK 34.5

1. Describe three key amniote adaptations for life on land.
2. Are snakes tetrapods? Explain.
3. Identify four avian adaptations for flight.
4. **WHAT IF?** Suppose turtles are more closely related to lepidosaurs than to other reptiles. Redraw Figure 34.24 to show this relationship, and mark the node that represents the most recent common ancestor shared by all living reptiles. Defining the reptile clade as consisting of all descendants of that ancestor, list the reptiles.

For suggested answers, see Appendix A.

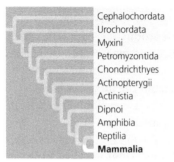

CONCEPT 34.6

Mammals are amniotes that have hair and produce milk

Cephalochordata
Urochordata
Myxini
Petromyzontida
Chondrichthyes
Actinopterygii
Actinistia
Dipnoi
Amphibia
Reptilia
Mammalia

The reptiles we have been discussing represent one of the two living lineages of amniotes. The other amniote lineage is our own, the **mammals**. Today, there are more than 5,300 known species of mammals on Earth.

Derived Characters of Mammals

Mammals are named for their distinctive mammary glands, which produce milk for offspring. All mammalian mothers nourish their young with milk, a balanced diet rich in fats, sugars, proteins, minerals, and vitamins. Hair, another mammalian characteristic, and a fat layer under the skin help the body retain heat. Like birds, mammals are endothermic, and most have a high metabolic rate. Efficient respiratory and circulatory systems (including a four-chambered heart) support a mammal's metabolism. A sheet of muscle called the diaphragm helps ventilate the lungs.

Like birds, mammals generally have a larger brain than other vertebrates of equivalent size, and many species are capable learners. And as in birds, the relatively long duration of parental care extends the time for offspring to learn important survival skills by observing their parents.

Differentiated teeth are another important mammalian trait. Whereas the teeth of reptiles are generally uniform in size and shape, the jaws of mammals bear a variety of teeth with sizes and shapes adapted for chewing many kinds of foods. Humans, like most mammals, have teeth modified for shearing (incisors and canine teeth) and for crushing and grinding (premolars and molars).

Early Evolution of Mammals

Mammals belong to a group of amniotes known as **synapsids**. Early nonmammalian synapsids lacked hair, had a sprawling gait, and laid eggs. A distinctive characteristic of

synapsids is the single temporal fenestra, a hole behind the eye socket on each side of the skull. Humans retain this feature; your jaw muscles pass through the temporal fenestra and anchor on your temple. Fossil evidence shows that the jaw was remodeled as mammalian features arose gradually in successive lineages of earlier synapsids (see Figure 25.7); in all, these changes took more than 100 million years. In addition, two of the bones that formerly made up the jaw joint (the quadrate and the articular) were incorporated into the mammalian middle ear (**Figure 34.36**). This evolutionary change is reflected in changes that occur during development. For example, as a mammalian embryo grows, the posterior region of its jaw—which in a reptile forms the articular bone—can be observed to detach from the jaw and migrate to the ear, where it forms the malleus.

Synapsids evolved into large herbivores and carnivores during the Permian period (299–251 million years ago), and for a time they were the dominant tetrapods. However, the Permian-Triassic extinctions took a heavy toll on them, and their diversity fell during the Triassic (251–200 million years ago). Increasingly mammal-like synapsids emerged by the end of the Triassic. While not true mammals, these

(a) In *Biarmosuchus*, the meeting of the articular and quadrate bones formed the jaw joint.

(b) During the evolutionary remodeling of the mammalian skull, a new jaw joint formed between the dentary and squamosal bones (see Figure 25.7). No longer used in the jaw, the quadrate and articular bones became incorporated into the middle ear as two of the three bones that transmit sound from the eardrum to the inner ear.

▲ **Figure 34.36 The evolution of the mammalian ear bones.** *Biarmosuchus* was a synapsid, a lineage that eventually gave rise to the mammals. Bones that transmit sound in the ear of mammals arose from the modification of bones in the jaw of nonmammalian synapsids.

MAKE CONNECTIONS *Review the definition of exaptation in Concept 25.6. Summarize the process by which exaptation occurs and explain how the incorporation of the articular and quadrate bones into the mammalian inner ear is an example.*

synapsids had acquired a number of the derived characters that distinguish mammals from other amniotes. They were small and probably hairy, and they likely fed on insects at night. Their bones show that they grew faster than other synapsids, suggesting that they probably had a relatively high metabolic rate; however, they still laid eggs.

During the Jurassic (200–145 million years ago), the first true mammals arose and diversified into many short-lived lineages. A diverse set of mammal species coexisted with dinosaurs in the Jurassic and Cretaceous periods, but these species were not abundant or dominant members of their communities, and most measured less than 1 m in length. One factor that may have contributed to their small size is that dinosaurs already occupied ecological niches of large-bodied animals.

By the early Cretaceous (140 million years ago), the three major lineages of mammals had emerged: those leading to monotremes (egg-laying mammals), marsupials (mammals with a pouch), and eutherians (placental mammals). After the extinction of large dinosaurs, pterosaurs, and marine reptiles during the late Cretaceous period, mammals underwent an adaptive radiation, giving rise to large predators and herbivores as well as flying and aquatic species.

Monotremes

Monotremes are found only in Australia and New Guinea and are represented by one species of platypus and four species of echidnas (spiny anteaters; **Figure 34.37**). Monotremes lay eggs, a character that is ancestral for amniotes and retained in most reptiles. Like all mammals, monotremes have hair and produce milk, but they lack nipples. Milk is secreted by glands on the belly of the mother. After hatching, the baby sucks the milk from the mother's fur.

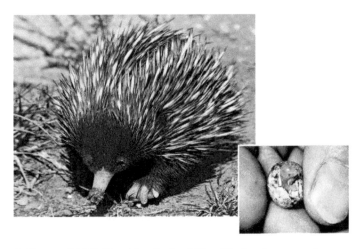

▲ **Figure 34.37 Short-beaked echidna (*Tachyglossus aculeatus*), an Australian monotreme.** Monotremes have hair and produce milk, but they lack nipples. Monotremes are the only mammals that lay eggs (inset).

Marsupials

Opossums, kangaroos, and koalas are examples of the group called **marsupials**. Both marsupials and eutherians share derived characters not found among monotremes. They have higher metabolic rates and nipples that provide milk, and they give birth to live young. The embryo develops inside the uterus of the female's reproductive tract. The lining of the uterus and the extraembryonic membranes that arise from the embryo form a **placenta**, a structure in which nutrients diffuse into the embryo from the mother's blood.

A marsupial is born very early in its development and completes its embryonic development while nursing **(Figure 34.38a)**. In most species, the nursing young are held within a maternal pouch called a *marsupium*. A red kangaroo, for instance, is about the size of a honeybee at its birth, just 33 days after fertilization. Its back legs are merely buds,

(a) A young brushtail possum. The offspring of marsupials are born very early in their development. They finish their growth while nursing from a nipple (in their mother's pouch in most species).

(b) A greater bilby. The greater bilby is a digger and burrower that eats termites and other insects, along with the seeds, roots, and bulbs of various plants. The female's rear-opening pouch helps protect the young from dirt as the mother digs. Other marsupials, such as kangaroos, have a pouch that opens to the front.

▲ **Figure 34.38 Australian marsupials.**

but its front legs are strong enough for it to crawl from the exit of its mother's reproductive tract to a pouch that opens to the front of her body, a journey that lasts a few minutes. In other species, the marsupium opens to the rear of the mother's body; in greater bilbies, this protects the young as their mother burrows in the dirt (Figure 34.38b).

Marsupials existed worldwide during the Mesozoic era, but today they are found only in the Australian region and in North and South America. The biogeography of marsupials illustrates the interplay between biological and geologic evolution (see Concept 25.4). After the breakup of the supercontinent Pangaea, South America and Australia became island continents, and their marsupials diversified in isolation from the eutherians that began an adaptive radiation on the northern continents. Australia has not been in contact with another continent since early in the Cenozoic era, about 65 million years ago. In Australia, convergent evolution has resulted in a diversity of marsupials that resemble eutherians in similar ecological roles in other parts of the world (Figure 34.39). In contrast, although South America had a diverse marsupial fauna throughout the Paleogene, it has experienced several immigrations of eutherians. One of the most important occurred about 3 million years ago, when North and South America joined at the Panamanian isthmus and extensive two-way traffic of animals took place over the land bridge. Today, only three families of marsupials live outside the Australian region, and the only marsupials found in the wild in North America are a few species of opossum.

Eutherians (Placental Mammals)

Eutherians are commonly called placental mammals because their placentas are more complex than those of marsupials. Eutherians have a longer pregnancy than marsupials. Young eutherians complete their embryonic development within the uterus, joined to their mother by the placenta. The eutherian placenta provides an intimate and long-lasting association between the mother and her developing young.

The major groups of living eutherians are thought to have diverged from one another in a burst of evolutionary change. The timing of this burst is uncertain: Molecular data suggest it occurred about 100 million years ago, while morphological data suggest it was about 60 million years ago. Figure 34.40 explores several major eutherian orders and their phylogenetic relationships with each other as well as with the monotremes and marsupials.

Primates

The mammalian order Primates includes the lemurs, tarsiers, monkeys, and apes. Humans are members of the ape group.

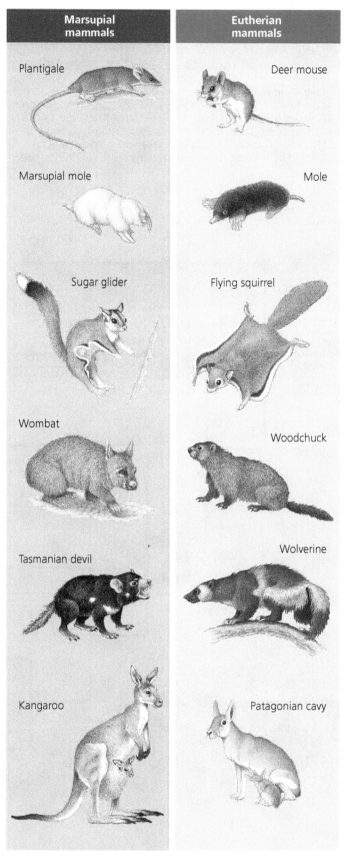

▲ Figure 34.39 **Convergent evolution of marsupials and eutherians (placental mammals).** (Note that the drawings are not to scale.)

Exploring Mammalian Diversity

Phylogenetic Relationships of Mammals

Evidence from numerous fossils and molecular analyses indicates that monotremes diverged from other mammals about 180 million years ago and that marsupials diverged from eutherians (placental mammals) about 140 million years ago. Molecular systematics has helped to clarify the evolutionary relationships between the eutherian orders, though there is still no broad consensus on a phylogenetic tree. One current hypothesis, represented by the tree shown below, clusters the eutherian orders into four main clades.

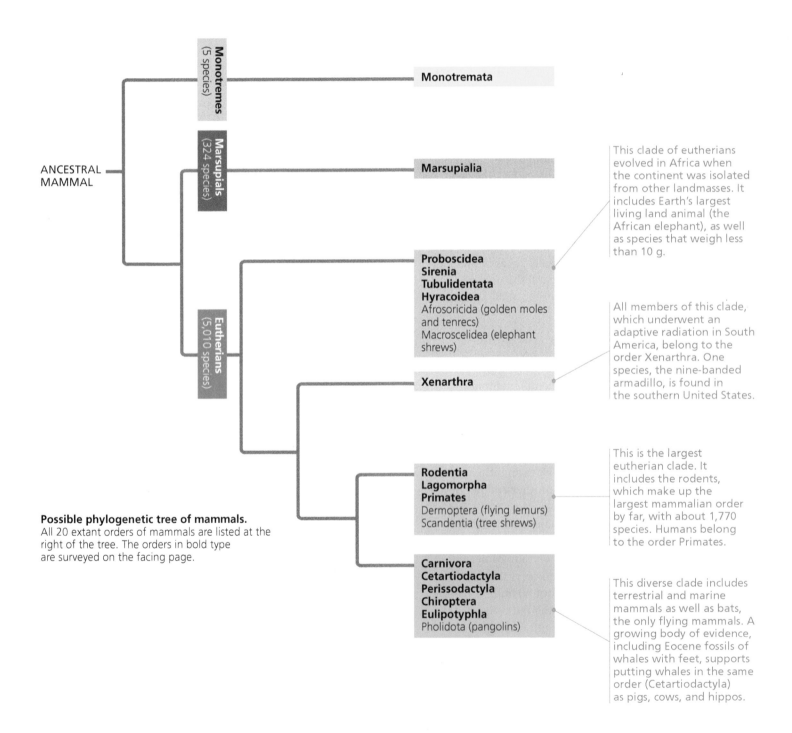

Possible phylogenetic tree of mammals.
All 20 extant orders of mammals are listed at the right of the tree. The orders in bold type are surveyed on the facing page.

This clade of eutherians evolved in Africa when the continent was isolated from other landmasses. It includes Earth's largest living land animal (the African elephant), as well as species that weigh less than 10 g.

All members of this clade, which underwent an adaptive radiation in South America, belong to the order Xenarthra. One species, the nine-banded armadillo, is found in the southern United States.

This is the largest eutherian clade. It includes the rodents, which make up the largest mammalian order by far, with about 1,770 species. Humans belong to the order Primates.

This diverse clade includes terrestrial and marine mammals as well as bats, the only flying mammals. A growing body of evidence, including Eocene fossils of whales with feet, supports putting whales in the same order (Cetartiodactyla) as pigs, cows, and hippos.

Orders and Examples	Main Characteristics	Orders and Examples	Main Characteristics
Monotremata Platypuses, echidnas Echidna	Lay eggs; no nipples; young suck milk from fur of mother	**Marsupialia** Kangaroos, opossums, koalas Koala	Completes embryonic development in pouch on mother's body
Proboscidea Elephants African elephant	Long, muscular trunk; thick, loose skin; upper incisors elongated as tusks	**Tubulidentata** Aardvarks Aardvark	Teeth consisting of many thin tubes cemented together; eats ants and termites
Sirenia Manatees, dugongs Manatee	Aquatic; finlike fore-limbs and no hind limbs; herbivorous	**Hyracoidea** Hyraxes Rock hyrax	Short legs; stumpy tail; herbivorous; complex, multi-chambered stomach
Xenarthra Sloths, anteaters, armadillos Tamandua	Reduced teeth or no teeth; herbivorous (sloths) or carnivorous (anteaters, armadillos)	**Rodentia** Squirrels, beavers, rats, porcupines, mice Red squirrel	Chisel-like, continuously growing incisors worn down by gnawing; herbivorous
Lagomorpha Rabbits, hares, picas Jackrabbit	Chisel-like incisors; hind legs longer than forelegs and adapted for running and jump-ing; herbivorous	**Primates** Lemurs, monkeys, chimpanzees, gorillas, humans 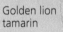 Golden lion tamarin	Opposable thumbs; forward-facing eyes; well-developed cerebral cortex; omnivorous
Carnivora Dogs, wolves, bears, cats, weasels, otters, seals, walruses Coyote	Sharp, pointed canine teeth and molars for shearing; carnivorous	**Perissodactyla** Horses, zebras, tapirs, rhinoceroses Indian rhinoceros	Hooves with an odd number of toes on each foot; herbivorous
Cetartiodactyla Artiodactyls: sheep, pigs, cattle, deer, giraffes Bighorn sheep	Hooves with an even number of toes on each foot; herbivorous	**Chiroptera** Bats Frog-eating bat	Adapted for flight; broad skinfold that extends from elongated fingers to body and legs; carnivorous or herbivorous
Cetaceans: whales, dolphins, porpoises Pacific white-sided porpoise	Aquatic; streamlined body; paddle-like forelimbs and no hind limbs; thick layer of insulating blubber; carnivorous	**Eulipotyphla** "Core insectivores": some moles, some shrews Star-nosed mole	Eat mainly insects and other small invertebrates

Derived Characters of Primates Most primates have hands and feet adapted for grasping, and their digits have flat nails instead of the narrow claws of other mammals. There are other characteristic features of the hands and feet, too, such as skin ridges on the fingers (which account for human fingerprints). Relative to other mammals, primates have a large brain and short jaws, giving them a flat face. Their forward-looking eyes are close together on the front of the face. Primates also exhibit relatively well-developed parental care and complex social behavior.

The earliest known primates were tree-dwellers, and many of the characteristics of primates are adaptations to the demands of living in the trees. Grasping hands and feet allow primates to hang onto tree branches. All living primates except humans have a big toe that is widely separated from the other toes, enabling them to grasp branches with their feet. All primates also have a thumb that is relatively movable and separate from the fingers, but monkeys and apes have a fully **opposable thumb**; that is, they can touch the ventral surface (fingerprint side) of the tip of all four fingers with the ventral surface of the thumb of the same hand. In monkeys and apes other than humans, the opposable thumb functions in a grasping "power grip." In humans, a distinctive bone structure at the base of the thumb allows it to be used for more precise manipulation. The unique dexterity of humans represents descent with modification from our tree-dwelling ancestors. Arboreal maneuvering also requires excellent eye-hand coordination. The overlapping visual fields of the two forward-facing eyes enhance depth perception, an obvious advantage when brachiating (traveling by swinging from branch to branch in trees).

Living Primates There are three main groups of living primates: (1) the lemurs of Madagascar **(Figure 34.41)** and the lorises and bush babies of tropical Africa and southern Asia; (2) the tarsiers, which live in southeastern Asia; and (3) the **anthropoids**, which include monkeys and apes and are found worldwide. The first group—lemurs, lorises, and bush babies—probably resemble early arboreal primates. The oldest known tarsier fossils date to 55 million years ago, while the oldest anthropoid fossils date to 45 million years ago; along with DNA evidence, these fossils

▶ **Figure 34.41**
Verreaux's sifakas (*Propithecus verreauxi*), a type of lemur.

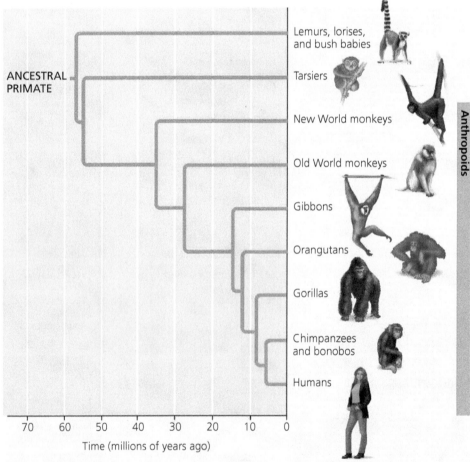

▲ **Figure 34.42 A phylogenetic tree of primates.** The fossil record indicates that anthropoids began diverging from other primates about 55 million years ago. New World monkeys, Old World monkeys, and apes (the clade that includes gibbons, orangutans, gorillas, chimpanzees, and humans) have been evolving as separate lineages for more than 25 million years. The lineages leading to humans branched off from other apes sometime between 6 and 7 million years ago.

? *Is the phylogeny shown here consistent with the idea that humans evolved from chimpanzees? Explain.*

indicate that tarsiers are more closely related to anthropoids than to the lemur group **(Figure 34.42)**.

You can see in Figure 34.42 that monkeys do not form a clade but rather consist of two groups, the New and Old World monkeys. Both of these groups are thought to have originated in Africa or Asia. The fossil record indicates that New World monkeys first colonized South America roughly 25 million years ago. By that time, South America and Africa had drifted apart, and monkeys may have reached South America from Africa by rafting on logs or other debris. What is certain is that New World monkeys and Old World monkeys underwent separate adaptive radiations during their many millions of years of separation **(Figure 34.43)**. All species of New World monkeys are arboreal, whereas Old World monkeys include ground-dwelling as well as arboreal species. Most monkeys in both groups are diurnal (active during the day) and usually live in bands held together by social behavior.

The other group of anthropoids consists of primates informally called apes **(Figure 34.44)**. The ape group includes the genera *Hylobates* (gibbons), *Pongo* (orangutans), *Gorilla* (gorillas), *Pan* (chimpanzees and bonobos), and *Homo*

(a) New World monkeys, such as spider monkeys (shown here), squirrel monkeys, and capuchins, have a prehensile tail (one adapted for grasping) and nostrils that open to the sides.

(b) Old World monkeys lack a prehensile tail, and their nostrils open downward. This group includes macaques (shown here), mandrils, baboons, and rhesus monkeys.

▲ **Figure 34.43 New World monkeys and Old World monkeys.**

(a) Gibbons, such as this Muller's gibbon, are found only in southeastern Asia. Their very long arms and fingers are adaptations for brachiating (swinging by the arms from branch to branch).

(b) Orangutans are shy apes that live in the rain forests of Sumatra and Borneo. They spend most of their time in trees; note the foot adapted for grasping andthe opposable thumb.

(c) Gorillas are the largest apes; some males are almost 2 m tall and weigh about 200 kg. Found only in Africa, these herbivores usually live in groups of up to about 20 individuals.

(d) Chimpanzees live in tropical Africa. They feed and sleep in trees but also spend a great deal of time on the ground. Chimpanzees are intelligent, communicative, and social.

(e) Bonobos are in the same genus (*Pan*) as chimpanzees but are smaller. They survive today only in the African nation of Congo.

▲ **Figure 34.44 Nonhuman apes.**

(humans). The apes diverged from Old World monkeys about 25–30 million years ago. Today, nonhuman apes are found exclusively in tropical regions of the Old World. With the exception of gibbons, living apes are larger than either New or Old World monkeys. All living apes have relatively long arms, short legs, and no tail. Although all nonhuman apes spend time in trees, only gibbons and orangutans are primarily arboreal. Social organization varies among the apes; gorillas and chimpanzees are highly social. Finally, compared to other primates, apes have a larger brain in proportion to their body size, and their behavior is more flexible. These two characteristics are especially prominent in the next group we'll consider, the hominins.

CONCEPT CHECK 34.6

1. Contrast monotremes, marsupials, and eutherians in terms of how they bear young.

2. Identify at least five derived traits of primates.

3. **MAKE CONNECTIONS** Develop a hypothesis to explain why the diversity of mammals increased in the Cenozoic. Your explanation should consider mammalian adaptations as well as factors such as mass extinctions and continental drift (review these factors in Concept 25.4).

For suggested answers, see Appendix A.

CONCEPT 34.7

Humans are mammals that have a large brain and bipedal locomotion

In our tour of Earth's biodiversity, we come at last to our own species, *Homo sapiens*, which is about 200,000 years old. When you consider that life has existed on Earth for at least 3.5 billion years, we are clearly evolutionary newcomers.

Derived Characters of Humans

Many characters distinguish humans from other apes. Most obviously, humans stand upright and are bipedal (walk on two legs). Humans have a much larger brain and are capable of language, symbolic thought, artistic expression, and the manufacture and use of complex tools. Humans also have reduced jawbones and jaw muscles, along with a shorter digestive tract.

At the molecular level, the list of derived characters of humans is growing as scientists compare the genomes of humans and chimpanzees. Although the two genomes are 99% identical, a difference of 1% can translate into a large number of changes in a genome that contains 3 billion base pairs. Furthermore, changes in a small number of genes can have large effects. This point was highlighted by recent results showing that humans and chimpanzees differ in the expression of 19 regulatory genes. These genes turn other genes on and off and hence may account for many differences between humans and chimpanzees.

Bear in mind that such genomic differences—and whatever derived phenotypic traits they encode—separate humans from other *living* apes. But many of these new characters first emerged in our ancestors, long before our own species appeared. We will consider some of these ancestors to see how these characters originated.

The Earliest Hominins

The study of human origins is known as **paleoanthropology**. Paleoanthropologists have unearthed fossils of approximately 20 extinct species that are more closely related to humans than to chimpanzees. These species are known as **hominins** (Figure 34.45). (Although most anthropologists now use the term *hominin*, its older synonym, *hominid*, continues to be used by some.) Since 1994, fossils of four hominin species dating to more than 4 million years ago have been discovered. The oldest of these hominins, *Sahelanthropus tchadensis*, lived about 6.5 million years ago.

Sahelanthropus and other early hominins shared some of the derived characters of humans. For example, they had reduced canine teeth, and some fossils suggest that they had relatively flat faces. They also show signs of having been more upright and bipedal than other apes. One clue to their upright stance can be found in the foramen magnum, the hole at the base of the skull through which the spinal cord passes. In chimpanzees, the foramen magnum is relatively far back on the skull, while in early hominins (and in humans), it is located underneath the skull. This position allows us to hold our head directly over our body, as early hominins apparently did as well. The pelvis, leg bones, and feet of the 4.4-million-year-old *Ardipithecus ramidus* also suggest that early hominins were increasingly bipedal (Figure 34.46). (We will return to the subject of bipedalism later in the chapter.)

▲ Figure 34.46 The skeleton of "Ardi," a 4.4-million-year-old hominin, *Ardipithecus ramidus*.

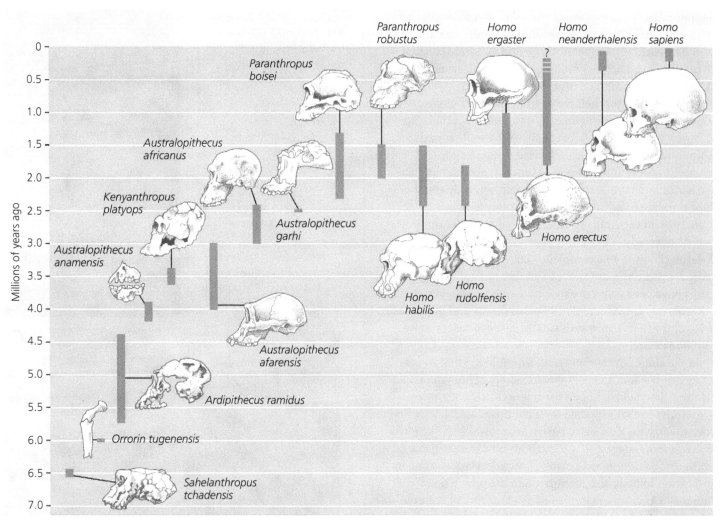

▲ Figure 34.45 A timeline for selected hominin species. Most of the fossils illustrated here come from sites in eastern and southern Africa. Note that at most times in hominin history, two or more hominin species were contemporaries. Some of the species are controversial, reflecting phylogenetic debates about the interpretation of skeletal details and biogeography.

Note that the characters that distinguish humans from other living apes did not all evolve in tight unison. While early hominins were showing signs of bipedalism, their brains remained small—about 300–450 cm³ in volume, compared with an average of 1,300 cm³ for *Homo sapiens*. The earliest hominins were also small overall. *A. ramidus*, for example, is estimated to have been about 1.2 m tall, with relatively large teeth and a jaw that projected beyond the upper part of the face. Humans, in contrast, average about 1.7 m in height and have a relatively flat face; compare your own face with that of the chimpanzees in Figure 34.44d.

It's important to avoid two common misconceptions about early hominins. One is to think of them either as chimpanzees or as having evolved from chimpanzees. Chimpanzees represent the tip of a separate branch of evolution, and they acquired derived characters of their own after they diverged from their common ancestor with humans.

Another misconception is to think of human evolution as a ladder leading directly from an ancestral ape to *Homo sapiens*. This error is often illustrated as a parade of fossil species that become progressively more like ourselves as they march across the page. If human evolution is a parade, it is a very disorderly one, with many groups breaking away to wander other evolutionary paths. At times, several hominin species coexisted. These species often differed in skull shape, body size, and diet (as inferred from their teeth). Ultimately, all but one lineage—the one that gave rise to *Homo sapiens*—ended in extinction. But when the characteristics of all hominins that lived over the past 6.5 million years are considered, *H. sapiens* appears not as the end result of a straight evolutionary path, but rather as the only surviving member of a highly branched evolutionary tree.

Australopiths

The fossil record indicates that hominin diversity increased dramatically between 4 and 2 million years ago. Many of the hominins from this period are collectively called australopiths. Their phylogeny remains unresolved on many points, but as a group, they are almost certainly paraphyletic. The earliest member of the group, *Australopithecus anamensis*, lived 4.2–3.9 million years ago, close in time to older hominins such as *Ardipithecus ramidus*.

Australopiths got their name from the 1924 discovery in South Africa of *Australopithecus africanus* ("southern ape of Africa"), which lived between 3 and 2.4 million years ago. With the discovery of more fossils, it became clear that *A. africanus* walked fully erect (was bipedal) and had human-like hands and teeth. However, its brain was only about one-third the size of the brain of a present-day human.

In 1974, in the Afar region of Ethiopia, paleoanthropologists discovered a 3.2-million-year-old *Australopithecus* skeleton that was 40% complete. "Lucy," as the fossil was named, was short—only about 1 m tall. Lucy and similar fossils have been given the species name *Australopithecus afarensis* (for the Afar region). Fossils discovered in the early 1990s show that *A. afarensis* existed as a species for at least 1 million years.

At the risk of oversimplifying, we could say that *A. afarensis* had fewer of the derived characters of humans above the neck than below. Lucy's brain was the size of a softball, a size similar to that expected for a chimpanzee of Lucy's body size. *A. afarensis* skulls also have a long lower jaw. Skeletons of *A. afarensis* suggest that these hominins were capable of arboreal locomotion, with arms that were relatively long in proportion to body size (compared to the proportions in humans). However, fragments of pelvic and skull bones indicate that *A. afarensis* walked on two legs. Fossilized footprints in Laetoli, Tanzania, corroborate the skeletal evidence that hominins living at the time of *A. afarensis* were bipedal (Figure 34.47).

Another lineage of australopiths consisted of the "robust" australopiths. These hominins, which included species such as *Paranthropus boisei*, had sturdy skulls with powerful jaws and large teeth, adapted for grinding and chewing hard, tough foods. They contrast with the "gracile" (slender) australopiths, including *A. afarensis* and *A. africanus*, which had lighter feeding equipment adapted for softer foods.

Combining evidence from the earliest hominins with the much richer fossil record of later australopiths makes it possible to formulate hypotheses about significant trends in hominin evolution. In the Scientific Skills Exercise, you'll examine one such trend: how hominin brain volume has changed over time. Here we'll consider two other trends: the emergence of bipedalism and tool use.

Bipedalism

Our anthropoid ancestors of 35–30 million years ago were still tree-dwellers. But by about 10 million years ago, the Himalayan mountain range had formed, thrust up in the aftermath of the Indian plate's collision with the Eurasian plate

▶ **Figure 34.47** Evidence that hominins walked upright 3.5 million years ago.

(a) The Laetoli footprints, more than 3.5 million years old, confirm that upright posture evolved quite early in hominin history.

(b) An artist's reconstruction of *A. afarensis*, a hominin alive at the time of the Laetoli footprints.

(see Figure 25.16). The climate became drier, and the forests of what are now Africa and Asia contracted. The result was an increased area of savanna (grassland) habitat, with fewer trees. Researchers have hypothesized that as the habitat changed, natural selection may have favored adaptations that made moving over open ground more efficient. Underlying this idea is the fact that while nonhuman apes are superbly adapted for climbing trees, they are less well suited for ground travel. For example, as a chimpanzee walks, it uses four times the amount of energy used by a human.

Although elements of this hypothesis survive, the picture now appears somewhat more complex. Although all recently discovered fossils of early hominins show indications of bipedalism, none of these hominins lived in savannas. Instead, they lived in mixed habitats ranging from forests to open woodlands. Furthermore, whatever the selective pressure that led to bipedalism, hominins did not become more bipedal in a simple, linear fashion. *Ardipithecus* had skeletal elements indicating that it could switch to upright walking but also was well suited for climbing trees. Australopiths seem to have had various locomotor styles, and some species spent more time on the ground than others. Only about 1.9 million years ago did hominins begin to walk long distances on two legs. These

Determining the Equation of a Regression Line

How Has Brain Volume Changed Over Time in the Hominin Lineage?

The hominin taxon includes *Homo sapiens* and about 20 extinct species that are thought to represent early relatives of humans. Researchers have found that the brain volume of the earliest hominins ranged between 300 and 450 cm³, similar to the brain volume of chimpanzees. The brain volumes of modern humans range between 1,200 and 1,800 cm³. In this exercise, you'll examine how mean brain volume changed over time and across various hominin species.

How the Study Was Done In this table, *x* is the mean age of each hominin species, and *y* is the mean brain volume (cm³). Ages with negative values represent millions of years before the present (which has an age of 0.0).

Hominin Species	Mean age (millions of years; x)	$x_i - \bar{x}$	Mean Brain Volume (cm³; y)	$y_i - \bar{y}$	$(x_i - \bar{x})$ × $(y_i - \bar{y})$
Ardipithecus ramidus	−4.4		325		
Australopithecus afarensis	−3.4		375		
Homo habilis	−1.9		550		
Homo ergaster	−1.6		850		
Homo erectus	−1.2		1,000		
Homo heidelbergensis	−0.5		1,200		
Homo neanderthalensis	−0.1		1,400		
Homo sapiens	0.0		1,350		

Interpret the Data

How did the brain volume of hominin species change over time? In particular, is there a linear (straight-line) relationship between brain volume and time?

To find out, we'll perform a linear regression, a technique for determining the equation for the straight line that provides a "best fit" to a set of data. Recall that the equation for a straight line between two variables, *x* and *y*, is:

$$y = mx + b$$

In this equation, *m* represents the slope of the line, while *b* represents the *y*-intercept (the point at which the straight line crosses the *y*-axis). When $m < 0$, the line has a negative slope, indicating that the values of *y* become *smaller* as values of *x* become *larger*. When $m > 0$, the line has a positive slope, meaning that the values of *y* become larger as values of *x* become larger. When $m = 0$, *y* has a constant value (*b*).

The correlation coefficient, *r*, can be used to calculate the values of *m* and *b* in a linear regression:

$$m = r\frac{s_y}{s_x} \quad \text{and} \quad b = \bar{y} - m\bar{x}.$$

In these equations, s_x and s_y are the standard deviations of variables *x* and *y*, respectively, while $\bar{x}$ and $\bar{y}$ are the means of those two variables. (See the Scientific Skills Exercise for Chapter 32 for more information about the correlation coefficient, mean, and standard deviation.)

1. Calculate the means ($\bar{x}$ and $\bar{y}$) from data in the table. Next, fill in the ($x_i - \bar{x}$) and ($y_i - \bar{y}$) columns in the data table, and use those results to calculate the standard deviations s_x and s_y.

2. As described in the Scientific Skills Exercise for Chapter 32, the formula for a correlation coefficient is

$$r = \frac{\frac{1}{n-1}\sum(x_i - \bar{x})(y_i - \bar{y})}{s_x s_y}$$

   Fill in the column in the data table for the product $(x_i - \bar{x}) \times (y_i - \bar{y})$. Use these values and the standard deviations calculated in Question 1 to calculate the correlation coefficient *r* between the brain volume of hominin species (*y*) and the ages of those species (*x*).

3. Based on the value of *r* that you calculated in Question 2, describe in words the correlation between mean brain volume of hominin species and the mean age of the species.

4. (a) Use your calculated value of *r* to calculate the slope (*m*) and the *y*-intercept (*b*) of a regression line for this data set. (b) Graph the regression line for the mean brain volume of hominin species versus the mean age of the species. Be careful to select and label your axes correctly. (c) Plot the data from the table on the same graph that shows the regression line. Does the regression line appear to provide a reasonable fit to the data?

5. The equation for a regression line can be used to calculate the value of *y* expected for any particular value of *x*. For example, suppose that a linear regression indicated that $m = 2$ and $b = 4$. In this case, when $x = 5$, we expect that $y = 2x + 4 = (2 \times 5) + 4 = 14$. Based on the values of *m* and *b* that you determined in Question 4, use this approach to determine the expected mean brain volume for a hominin that lived 4 million years ago (that is, $x = -4$).

6. The slope of a line can be defined as $m = \dfrac{y_2 - y_1}{x_2 - x_1}$, where (x_1, y_1) and (x_2, y_2) are the coordinates of two points on the line. As such, the slope represents the ratio of the rise of a line (how much the line rises vertically) to the run of the line (how much the line changes horizontally). Use the definition of the slope to estimate how long it took for mean brain volume to increase by 100 cm³ over the course of hominin evolution.

(MB) A version of this Scientific Skills Exercise can be assigned in MasteringBiology.

Data from Dean Falk, Florida State University, 2013.

hominins lived in more arid environments, where bipedal walking requires less energy than walking on all fours.

Tool Use

As you read earlier, the manufacture and use of complex tools are derived behavioral characters of humans. Determining the origin of tool use in hominin evolution is one of paleoanthropology's great challenges. Other apes are capable of surprisingly sophisticated tool use. Orangutans, for example, can fashion sticks into probes for retrieving insects from their nests. Chimpanzees are even more adept, using rocks to smash open food and putting leaves on their feet to walk over thorns. It's likely that early hominins were capable of this sort of simple tool use, but finding fossils of modified sticks or leaves that were used as shoes is practically impossible.

The oldest generally accepted evidence of tool use by hominins is 2.5-million-year-old cut marks on animal bones found in Ethiopia. These marks suggest that hominins cut flesh from the bones of animals using stone tools. Interestingly, the hominins whose fossils were found near the site where the bones were discovered had a relatively small brain. If these hominins, which have been named *Australopithecus garhi*, were in fact the creators of the stone tools used on the bones, that would suggest that stone tool use originated before the evolution of large brains in hominins.

Early *Homo*

The earliest fossils that paleoanthropologists place in our genus, *Homo*, include those of the species *Homo habilis.* These fossils, ranging in age from about 2.4 to 1.6 million years, show clear signs of certain derived hominin characters above the neck. Compared to the australopiths, *H. habilis* had a shorter jaw and a larger brain volume, about 600–750 cm^3. Sharp stone tools have also been found with some fossils of *H. habilis* (the name means "handy man").

Fossils from 1.9 to 1.5 million years ago mark a new stage in hominin evolution. A number of paleoanthropologists recognize these fossils as those of a distinct species, *Homo ergaster. Homo ergaster* had a substantially larger brain than *H. habilis* (over 900 cm^3), as well as long, slender legs with hip joints well adapted for long-distance walking **(Figure 34.48)**. The fingers were relatively short and straight, suggesting that *H. ergaster* did not climb trees like earlier hominins. *Homo ergaster* fossils have been discovered in far more arid environments than earlier hominins and have been associated with more sophisticated stone tools. Its smaller teeth also suggest that *H. ergaster* either ate different foods than australopiths (more meat and less plant material) or prepared some of its food before chewing, perhaps by cooking or mashing the food. Consistent with the possible importance of cooking, a 2012 study described 1-million-year-old fragments of burnt bone that were found in a cave; the researchers concluded that human ancestors were using fire by that time.

Homo ergaster marks an important shift in the relative sizes of the sexes. In primates, a size difference between males and females is a major component of sexual dimorphism (see Chapter 23). On average, male gorillas and orangutans weigh about twice as much as females of their species. In *Australopithecus afarensis*, males were 1.5 times as heavy as females.

▲ **Figure 34.48 Fossil of *Homo ergaster.*** This 1.7-million-year-old fossil from Kenya belongs to a young *Homo ergaster* male. This individual was tall, slender, and fully bipedal, and he had a relatively large brain.

The extent of sexual dimorphism decreased further in early *Homo*, a trend that continues through our own species: Human males weigh only about 1.2 times as much as females.

The reduced sexual dimorphism may offer some clues to the social systems of extinct hominins. In extant primates, extreme sexual dimorphism is associated with intense male-male competition for multiple females. In species that undergo more pair-bonding (including our own), sexual dimorphism is less dramatic. In *H. ergaster*, therefore, males and females may have engaged in more pair-bonding than earlier hominins did. This shift may have been associated with long-term care of the young by both parents. Human babies depend on their parents for food and protection much longer than do the young of other apes.

Fossils now generally recognized as *H. ergaster* were originally considered early members of another species, *Homo erectus*, and some paleoanthropologists still hold this position. *Homo erectus* originated in Africa and was the first hominin to migrate out of Africa. The oldest fossils of hominins outside Africa, dating back 1.8 million years, were discovered in 2000 in the country of Georgia. *Homo erectus* eventually migrated as far as the Indonesian archipelago. Fossil evidence indicates that *H. erectus* became extinct sometime after 200,000 years ago, although one group may have persisted on Java until roughly 50,000 years ago.

Neanderthals

In 1856, miners discovered some mysterious human fossils in a cave in the Neander Valley in Germany. The 40,000-year-old fossils belonged to a thick-boned hominin with a prominent brow. The hominin was named *Homo neanderthalensis* and is commonly called a Neanderthal. Neanderthals were living in Europe by 350,000 years ago and later spread to the Near East, central Asia, and southern Siberia. They had a brain larger than that of present-day humans, buried their dead, and made hunting tools from stone and wood. But despite their adaptations and culture, Neanderthals became extinct about 28,000 years ago.

What is the evolutionary relationship of Neanderthals to *Homo sapiens*? Genetic data indicate that the lineages leading to *H. sapiens* and to Neanderthals diverged about 400,000 years ago. This indicates that while Neanderthals and humans share a recent common ancestor, humans did not descend directly from Neanderthals (as was once thought).

Another long-standing question is whether mating occurred between the two species. Some researchers have argued that evidence of gene flow can be found in fossils that show a mixture of human and Neanderthal characteristics. Other researchers have disputed this conclusion. Until recently, results from genetic analyses have also been unclear. In 2010, however, an analysis of the DNA sequence of the Neanderthal genome indicated that limited gene flow did occur between the two species (**Figure 34.49**). This study also showed that the Neanderthal and human genomes were identical at 99.7% of the nucleotide sites. Results from a second genome study, also published in 2010, indicate that gene flow also occurred between Neanderthals and the "Denisovans," an as-yet unidentified hominin whose DNA was isolated from 40,000-year-old bone fragments discovered in a Siberian cave.

Homo sapiens

Evidence from fossils, archaeology, and DNA studies has improved our understanding about how our own species, *Homo sapiens*, emerged and spread around the world.

Fossil evidence indicates that the ancestors of humans originated in Africa. Older species (perhaps *H. ergaster* or *H. erectus*) gave rise to later species, ultimately including *H. sapiens*. Furthermore, the oldest known fossils of our own species have been found at two different sites in Ethiopia and include specimens that are 195,000 and 160,000 years old. These early humans had less pronounced browridges than those found in *H. erectus* and Neanderthals, and they were more slender than other recent hominins.

The Ethiopian fossils support inferences about the origin of humans from molecular evidence. DNA analyses indicate that all living humans are more closely related to one another than to Neanderthals. Other studies on human DNA show that Europeans and Asians share a relatively recent common ancestor and that many African lineages branched off more basal positions on the human family tree. These findings strongly suggest that all living humans have ancestors that originated as *H. sapiens* in Africa.

The oldest fossils of *H. sapiens* outside Africa are from the Middle East and date back about 115,000 years. Fossil evidence and genetic analyses suggest that humans spread beyond Africa in one or more waves, first into Asia and then to Europe and Australia. The date of the first arrival of humans in the New World is uncertain, although the oldest generally accepted evidence puts that date at about 15,000 years ago.

New findings continually update our understanding of the human evolutionary lineage. For example, in 2004, researchers reported an

▲ A 160,000-year-old fossil of *Homo sapiens.*

▼ **Figure 34.49** | Inquiry

Did gene flow occur between Neanderthals and humans?

Experiment Fossils discovered in Europe have been interpreted by some researchers as showing a mixture of Neanderthal and human features, suggesting that humans may have bred with Neanderthals. To assess this idea, Richard Green, Svante Paabo, and their colleagues extracted DNA from several Neanderthal fossils and used this DNA to construct a draft sequence of the Neanderthal genome. Under the hypothesis that little or no gene flow occurred between Neanderthals and *H. sapiens* after their evolutionary lineages diverged, the Neanderthal genome should be equally similar to all human genomes, regardless of the geographic region from which the human genomes were obtained.

To test this hypothesis, the researchers compared the Neanderthal genome to the genomes of five living humans: one from southern Africa, one from western Africa, and three from regions outside of Africa (France, China, and Papua New Guinea). They used a genetic similarity index, D, equal to the percentage of Neanderthal DNA that matched one human population minus the percentage of Neanderthal DNA that matched a second human population. If little or no gene flow occurred between Neanderthals and humans, D should be close to zero for each such comparison. Values of D that are substantially greater than zero indicate that Neanderthals are more similar genetically to the first of the two comparison populations—providing evidence of gene flow between Neanderthals and members of that population.

Results Neanderthals consistently shared more genetic variants with non-Africans than with Africans. In contrast, the Neanderthal genome was equally close to the genomes of humans from each of the three different regions outside of Africa.

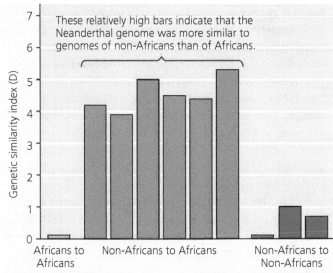

Conclusion Genomic analyses indicate that gene flow occurred between Neanderthals and human populations outside of Africa (where the ranges of the two species overlapped).

Source: R. E. Green et al., A draft sequence of the Neanderthal genome, *Science* 328:710 -722 (2010).

WHAT IF? *Neanderthal fossils have been found only in Europe and the Middle East. Explain how Neanderthals could be more similar genetically to non-Africans than to Africans, and yet be equally close to humans from France, China, and Papua New Guinea.*

astonishing find: skeletal remains of adult hominins dating from just 18,000 years ago and representing a previously unknown species, which they named *Homo floresiensis*. Discovered in a limestone cave on the Indonesian island of Flores, the individuals were much shorter and had a much smaller brain volume than *H. sapiens*—more similar, in fact, to an australopith. The researchers who discovered these fossils argue that certain features of the skeletons, such as the shape of the teeth and the thickness and proportions of the skull, suggest that *H. floresiensis* descended from the larger *H. erectus*. Not convinced, some researchers have argued that the fossils represent small *H. sapiens* individuals with deformed, miniature brains, a condition called microcephaly.

However, a 2007 study found that the wrist bones of the Flores fossils are similar in shape to those of nonhuman apes and early hominins, but different from those of Neanderthals and *H. sapiens*. These researchers concluded that the Flores fossils represent a species whose lineage branched off before the origin of the clade that includes Neanderthals and humans. A later study comparing the foot bones of the Flores fossils with those of other hominins also indicated that *H. floresiensis* arose before *H. sapiens*; in fact, these researchers suggested that *H. floresiensis* may have descended from an as-yet-unidentified hominin that lived even earlier than *H. erectus*.

If further evidence continues to support the designation of *H. floresiensis* as a new hominin, one intriguing explanation for this species' apparent "shrinkage" is that isolation on the island may have resulted in selection for greatly reduced size. Such dramatic size reduction is well studied in other dwarf mammalian species that are endemic to islands. One such study found that on islands, the brains of dwarf fossil hippos were proportionally even smaller than their bodies. One possible explanation for this finding is that smaller brains resulted from selection for reduced energy consumption (the mammalian brain uses large amounts of energy). Applying their results to the Flores fossils, the researchers concluded that the brain size of *H. floresiensis* closely matches that predicted for a dwarf hominin of its body size. Compelling questions that may yet be answered from the cache of anthropological and archaeological finds on Flores include how *H. floresiensis* originated and whether it encountered *H. sapiens*, which also was living in Indonesia 18,000 years ago.

The rapid expansion of our species may have been spurred by changes in human cognition as *H. sapiens* evolved in Africa. Evidence of sophisticated thought in *H. sapiens* includes a 2002 discovery in South Africa of 77,000-year-old art—geometric markings made on pieces of ochre (**Figure 34.50**). And in 2004, archaeologists working in southern and eastern Africa found 75,000-year-old ostrich eggs and snail shells with holes neatly drilled through them. By 30,000 years ago, humans were producing spectacular cave paintings.

While these developments can help us understand the spread of *H. sapiens*, it is not clear whether they played a

▲ **Figure 34.50 Art, a human hallmark.** The engravings on this 77,000-year-old piece of ochre, discovered in South Africa's Blombos Cave, are among the earliest signs of symbolic thought in humans.

role in the extinction of other hominins. Neanderthals, for example, also made complex tools and showed a capacity for symbolic thought. As a result, the earlier suggestion that Neanderthals were driven to extinction by competition with *H. sapiens* is now being questioned by some scientists.

Our discussion of humans brings this unit on biological diversity to an end. But keep in mind that our sequence of topics isn't meant to imply that life consists of a ladder leading from lowly microorganisms to lofty humanity. Biological diversity is the product of branching phylogeny, not ladderlike "progress." The fact that there are almost as many species of ray-finned fishes alive today as in all other vertebrate groups combined shows that our finned relatives are not outmoded underachievers that failed to leave the water. The tetrapods—amphibians, reptiles, and mammals—are derived from one lineage of lobe-finned vertebrates. As tetrapods diversified on land, fishes continued their branching evolution in the greatest portion of the biosphere's volume. Similarly, the ubiquity of diverse prokaryotes throughout the biosphere today is a reminder of the enduring ability of these relatively simple organisms to keep up with the times through adaptive evolution. Biology exalts life's diversity, past and present.

CONCEPT CHECK 34.7

1. Identify some characters that distinguish hominins from other apes.

2. Provide an example in which different features of organisms in the hominin evolutionary lineage evolved at different rates.

3. **WHAT IF?** Some genetic studies suggest that the most recent common ancestor of *Homo sapiens* that lived outside of Africa left Africa about 50,000 years ago. Compare this date with the dates of fossils given in the text. Can both the genetic results and the dates ascribed to the fossils be correct? Explain.

For suggested answers, see Appendix A.

Key Concept		Clade	Description
CONCEPT 34.1 **Chordates have a notochord and a dorsal, hollow nerve cord (pp. 713–716)** ? *Describe likely features of the chordate common ancestor and explain your reasoning.*	**Chordates:** notochord; dorsal, hollow nerve cord; pharyngeal slits; post-anal tail	Cephalochordata (lancelets)	Basal chordates; marine suspension feeders that exhibit four key derived characters of chordates
		Urochordata (tunicates)	Marine suspension feeders; larvae display the derived traits of chordates
		Myxini (hagfishes)	Jawless marine vertebrates with reduced vertebrae; have head that includes a skull and brain, eyes, and other sensory organs
CONCEPT 34.2 **Vertebrates are chordates that have a backbone (pp. 716–719)** ? *Identify the shared features of early fossil vertebrates.*	**Vertebrates:** *Hox* genes duplication, backbone of vertebrae	Petromyzontida (lampreys)	Jawless aquatic vertebrates with reduced vertebrae; typically feed by attaching to a live fish and ingesting its blood
CONCEPT 34.3 **Gnathostomes are vertebrates that have jaws (pp. 719–724)** ? *How would the appearance of organisms with jaws have altered ecological interactions? Provide supporting evidence.*	**Gnathostomes:** hinged jaws, four sets of *Hox* genes	Chondrichthyes (sharks, rays, skates, ratfishes)	Aquatic gnathostomes; have cartilaginous skeleton, a derived trait formed by the reduction of an ancestral mineralized skeleton
	Osteichthyans: bony skeleton	Actinopterygii (ray-finned fishes)	Aquatic gnathostomes; have bony skeleton and maneuverable fins supported by rays
	Lobe-fins: muscular fins or limbs	Actinistia (coelacanths)	Ancient lineage of aquatic lobe-fins still surviving in Indian Ocean
		Dipnoi (lungfishes)	Freshwater lobe-fins with both lungs and gills; sister group of tetrapods
CONCEPT 34.4 **Tetrapods are gnathostomes that have limbs (pp. 724–727)** ? *Which features of amphibians restrict most species to living in aquatic or moist terrestrial habitats?*	**Tetrapods:** four limbs, neck, fused pelvic girdle	Amphibia (salamanders, frogs, caecilians)	Have four limbs descended from modified fins; most have moist skin that functions in gas exchange; many live both in water (as larvae) and on land (as adults)
CONCEPT 34.5 **Amniotes are tetrapods that have a terrestrially adapted egg (pp. 727–734)** ? *Explain why birds are considered reptiles.*	**Amniotes:** amniotic egg, rib cage ventilation	Reptilia (tuataras, lizards and snakes, turtles, crocodilians, birds)	One of two groups of living amniotes; have amniotic eggs and rib cage ventilation, key adaptations for life on land
CONCEPT 34.6 **Mammals are amniotes that have hair and produce milk (pp. 735–742)** ? *Describe the origin and early evolution of mammals.*		Mammalia (monotremes, marsupials, eutherians)	Evolved from synapsid ancestors; include egg-laying monotremes (echidnas, platypus); pouched marsupials (such as kangaroos, opossums); and eutherians (placental mammals, such as rodents, primates)

Humans are mammals that have a large brain and bipedal locomotion (pp. 742–748)

- Derived characters of humans include bipedalism and a larger brain and reduced jaw compared with other apes.
- Hominins—humans and species that are more closely related to humans than to chimpanzees—originated in Africa about 6 million years ago. Early hominins had a small brain but probably walked upright.
- The oldest evidence of tool use is 2.5 million years old.
- *Homo ergaster* was the first fully bipedal, large-brained hominin. *Homo erectus* was the first hominin to leave Africa.
- Neanderthals lived in Europe and the Near East from about 350,000 to 28,000 years ago.
- *Homo sapiens* originated in Africa about 195,000 years ago and began to spread to other continents about 115,000 years ago.

? *Explain why it is misleading to portray human evolution as a "ladder" leading to* Homo sapiens.

TEST YOUR UNDERSTANDING

LEVEL 1: KNOWLEDGE/COMPREHENSION

1. Vertebrates and tunicates share
   a. jaws adapted for feeding.
   b. a high degree of cephalization.
   c. an endoskeleton that includes a skull.
   d. a notochord and a dorsal, hollow nerve cord.

2. Living vertebrates can be divided into two major clades. Select the appropriate pair.
   a. the chordates and the tetrapods
   b. the urochordates and the cephalochordates
   c. the cyclostomes and the gnathostomes
   d. the marsupials and the eutherians

3. Unlike eutherians, *both* monotremes and marsupials
   a. lack nipples.
   b. have some embryonic development outside the uterus.
   c. lay eggs.
   d. are found in Australia and Africa.

4. Which clade does *not* include humans?
   a. synapsids   c. diapsids
   b. lobe-fins   d. osteichthyans

5. As hominins diverged from other primates, which of the following appeared first?
   a. reduced jawbones   c. the making of stone tools
   b. an enlarged brain   d. bipedal locomotion

LEVEL 2: APPLICATION/ANALYSIS

6. Which of the following could be considered the most recent common ancestor of living tetrapods?
   a. a sturdy-finned, shallow-water lobe-fin whose appendages had skeletal supports similar to those of terrestrial vertebrates
   b. an armored, jawed placoderm with two pairs of appendages
   c. an early ray-finned fish that developed bony skeletal supports in its paired fins
   d. a salamander that had legs supported by a bony skeleton but moved with the side-to-side bending typical of fishes

7. **EVOLUTION CONNECTION**
   Living members of a vertebrate lineage can be very different from early members of the lineage, and evolutionary reversals (character losses) are common. Give examples that illustrate these observations, and explain their evolutionary causes.

LEVEL 3: SYNTHESIS/EVALUATION

8. **SCIENTIFIC INQUIRY**
   INTERPRET THE DATA As a consequence of size alone, larger organisms tend to have larger brains than smaller organisms. However, some organisms have brains that are considerably larger than expected for their size. There are high energetic costs associated with the development and maintenance of brains that are large relative to body size.
   (a) The fossil record documents trends in which brains that are large relative to body size evolved in certain lineages, including hominins. In such lineages, what can you infer about the costs and benefits of large brains?
   (b) Hypothesize how natural selection might favor the evolution of large brains despite their high maintenance costs.
   (c) Data for 14 bird species are listed below. Graph the data, placing deviation from expected brain size on the *x*-axis and mortality rate on the *y*-axis. What can you conclude about the relationship between brain size and mortality?

Deviation from Expected Brain Size*	-2.4	-2.1	2.0	-1.8	-1.0	0.0	0.3	0.7	1.2	1.3	2.0	2.3	3.0	3.2
Mortality Rate	0.9	0.7	0.5	0.9	0.4	0.7	0.8	0.4	0.8	0.3	0.6	0.6	0.3	0.6

D. Sol et al., Big-brained birds survive better in nature, *Proceedings of the Royal Society B* 274:763–769 (2007).

* Values < 0 indicate brain sizes smaller than expected; values > 0 indicate sizes larger than expected.

9. **WRITE ABOUT A THEME: ORGANIZATION**
   Early tetrapods had a sprawling gait (like that of a lizard): As the right front foot moved forward, the body twisted to the left and the left rib cage and lung were compressed; the reverse occurred with the next step. Normal breathing, in which both lungs expand equally with each breath, was hindered during walking and prevented during running. In a short essay (100–150 words), explain how the origin of organisms such as dinosaurs, whose gait allowed them to move without compressing their lungs, could have led to emergent properties.

10. **SYNTHESIZE YOUR KNOWLEDGE**

This animal is a vertebrate with hair. What can you infer about its phylogeny? Use the information in the chapter to identify as many key derived characters as you can.

For selected answers, see Appendix A.

MasteringBiology®

Students Go to **MasteringBiology** for assignments, the eText, and the Study Area with practice tests, animations, and activities.

Instructors Go to **MasteringBiology** for automatically graded tutorials and questions that you can assign to your students, plus Instructor Resources.

UNIT 6 PLANT FORM AND FUNCTION

AN INTERVIEW WITH

Jeffery Dangl

Jeffery Dangl is an HHMI-GBMF Plant Science Investigator and the John N. Couch Distinguished Professor of Biology at the University of North Carolina, Chapel Hill. He is also a member of the National Academy of Sciences. After double majoring in English and biological sciences at Stanford University, Dr. Dangl continued at Stanford and earned a Ph.D. in genetics and immunology. His background in animal immunology prepared the way for his interest in, and thinking about, whether plants also have an immune system.

What sparked your interest in biology?

After I was diagnosed as having fascioscapulohumeral (FSH) muscular dystrophy when I was 12, I spent time at various neuromuscular clinics. The researchers let me look at muscle cells from the biopsies through a microscope. They said, "This is what muscle cells should look like. Here's what yours look like. We don't know why that is, but that's it. That's the cellular cause of your disease." I was amazed.

> " **Why do plants have an immune system? Because they can't run away and hide.** "

What led you to be an immunologist?

Like many college students, I decided after a boring summer job at home that that was never going to happen again. I went around the Stanford Medical School stuffing my resume into faculty mailboxes. As a result, I received a call from one of the founding fathers of molecular genetics, who wanted somebody to help him edit manuscripts. Later, I got a job in a lab studying antibodies in mice. I didn't leave there until I finished my Ph.D.

Immunology is usually considered an "animal" subject. How did you wind up studying plants?

In grad school, my future wife said, "I want to be a plant scientist, and one of the world's best plant biology institutes is the Max Planck Institute in Cologne, Germany." My initial plan was to accompany her there and work at a leading immunology lab, but then serendipity struck. I had gone to the library to look for a particular paper, and as I was thumbing through the journal it fell open to a completely unrelated paper on how plants respond to fragments of fungal pathogens by gene activation and biochemical reprogramming. I was fascinated by this "plant defense response," and when we arrived at Max Planck and saw this gorgeous plant biology institute, I thought, "I have to give plant biology a whirl."

Your proposal that plants have an immune system is a bit shocking at first. Plants don't even have circulating cells.

Leaves get bombarded with the spores of fungi every day. Viruses blow in the wind and are delivered by insects. Bacteria splash up from the soil and get carried in rainwater. So plants get bombarded with organisms, some of which have evolved in ways that enable them to use plants as carbon sources. Why do plants have an immune system? Because they can't run away and hide. Twenty years ago, people thought about plant defense responses, but they didn't think about an immune system. The cloning of the first plant disease-resistance genes showed that they encode proteins that have very similar structures. Plant disease-resistance proteins recognize every class of pathogen, from viruses that move from cell to cell, to fungi that grow between cells, to aphids that stick a feeding stylet into cells. Plant disease-resistance proteins have no functions other than the recognition of pathogens. That's an immune system.

Do you have any parting wisdom for students?

Always try to look at a problem from a different angle, unencumbered by the baggage of the discipline.

MB For an extended interview and video clip, go to the Study Area in MasteringBiology.

◄ An uninfected *Arabidopsis* leaf (far left) and four leaves infected with various pathogens.

35

Plant Structure, Growth, and Development

▲ Figure 35.1 Computer art?

Are Plants Computers?

The object in **Figure 35.1** is not the creation of a computer genius with a flair for the artistic. It is a head of romanesco, an edible relative of broccoli. Romanesco's mesmerizing beauty is attributable to the fact that each of its smaller buds resembles in miniature the entire vegetable (shown below). (Mathematicians refer to such repetitive patterns as *fractals*.) If romanesco looks as if it were generated by a computer, it's because its growth pattern follows a repetitive sequence of instructions. As in most plants, the growing shoot tips lay down a pattern of stem . . . leaf . . . bud, over and over again. These repetitive developmental patterns are genetically determined and subject to natural selection. For example, a mutation that shortens the stem segments between leaves will generate a bushier plant. If this altered architecture enhances the plant's ability to access resources such as light and, by doing so, to produce more offspring, then this trait will occur more frequently in later generations—the population will have evolved.

Romanesco is unusual in adhering so rigidly to its basic body organization. Most plants show much greater diversity in their individual forms because the growth of most plants, much more than in animals, is affected by local environmental conditions. All adult lions, for example, have four legs and are of roughly the same size, but oak trees vary in the number and arrangement of their branches. This is because plants respond to challenges and opportunities in their local environment by altering their growth. (In contrast, animals typically respond by movement.) Illumination of a plant from the side, for example, creates asymmetries in its basic body plan. Branches grow more quickly from the illuminated side of a shoot than from the shaded side, an architectural change of obvious benefit for photosynthesis. The highly adaptive development of plants is critical in facilitating their acquisition of resources from their local environments.

Chapters 29 and 30 described the evolution of nonvascular and vascular plants. In Unit Six, we focus on vascular plants, particularly angiosperms (flowering plants) because they are the primary producers in many terrestrial ecosystems and are of great agricultural importance. This chapter explores the structure, growth, and development of vascular plants, noting key differences between the two main groups of flowering plants, eudicots and monocots (see Figure 30.16).

CONCEPT 35.1

Plants have a hierarchical organization consisting of organs, tissues, and cells

Plants, like most animals, are composed of organs, tissues, and cells. An **organ** consists of several types of tissues that together carry out particular functions. A **tissue** is a group of cells, consisting of one or more cell types that together perform a specialized function.

In looking at the hierarchy of plant organs, tissues, and cells, we begin with plant organs because they are the most familiar plant structures. As you learn about the hierarchy of plant structure, keep in mind how natural selection has produced plant forms that fit plant function at all levels of organization. Note also that vegetative growth—production of leaves, stems, and roots—is only one stage in a plant's life. Most plants also undergo growth relating to sexual reproduction. In angiosperms, reproductive growth is associated with the production of flowers. Later in this chapter, we'll discuss the transition from vegetative shoot formation to reproductive shoot formation.

The Three Basic Plant Organs: Roots, Stems, and Leaves

The basic morphology of vascular plants reflects their evolutionary history as terrestrial organisms that inhabit and draw resources from two very different environments— below the ground and above the ground. They must absorb water and minerals from below the ground surface and CO_2 and light from above the ground surface. The ability to acquire these resources efficiently is traceable to the evolution

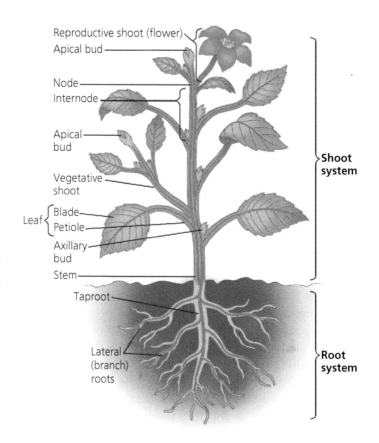

▲ **Figure 35.2 An overview of a flowering plant.** The plant body is divided into a root system and a shoot system, connected by vascular tissue (purple strands in this diagram) that is continuous throughout the plant. The plant shown is an idealized eudicot.

of roots, stems, and leaves as the three basic organs. These organs form a **root system** and a **shoot system**, the latter consisting of stems and leaves (**Figure 35.2**). Vascular plants, with few exceptions, rely on both systems for survival. Roots are almost never photosynthetic; they starve unless *photosynthates*, the sugars and the other carbohydrates produced during photosynthesis, are imported from the shoot system. Conversely, the shoot system depends on the water and minerals that roots absorb from the soil.

Roots

A **root** is an organ that anchors a vascular plant in the soil, absorbs minerals and water, and often stores carbohydrates and other reserves. The *primary root*, originating in the seed embryo, is the first root (and the first organ) to emerge from a germinating seed. It soon branches to form **lateral roots** (see Figure 35.2) that greatly enhance the ability of the root system to anchor the plant and to acquire resources such as water and minerals from the soil.

Tall, erect plants with large shoot masses generally have a *taproot system*, consisting of one main vertical root, the **taproot**, which usually develops form the primary root and which helps prevent the plant from toppling. In taproot

◀ Figure 35.3 Root hairs of a radish seedling. Root hairs grow by the thousands just behind the tip of each root. By increasing the root's surface area, they greatly enhance the absorption of water and minerals from the soil.

systems, the role of absorption is restricted largely to lateral roots. A taproot, although energetically expensive to make, allows the plant to be taller, thereby giving it access to more favorable light conditions and, in some cases, providing an advantage for pollen and seed dispersal. Taproots can also be specialized for food storage.

Small plants or those that have a trailing growth habit are particularly susceptible to grazing animals that can potentially uproot the plant and kill it. Such plants are most efficiently anchored by a *fibrous root system*, a thick mat of slender roots spreading out below the soil surface (see Figure 30.16). In plants that have fibrous root systems, including most monocots, the primary root dies early on and does not form a taproot. Instead, many small roots emerge from the stem. Such roots are said to be *adventitious* (from the Latin *adventicus*, extraneous), a term describing a plant organ that grows from an unusual source, such as roots arising from stems or leaves. Each root forms its own lateral roots, which in turn form their own lateral roots. Because this mat of roots holds the topsoil in place, plants such as grasses that have dense fibrous root systems are especially good at preventing soil erosion.

In most plants, the absorption of water and minerals occurs primarily near the tips of elongating roots, where vast numbers of **root hairs**, thin, finger-like extensions of root epidermal cells, emerge and increase the surface area of the root enormously **(Figure 35.3)**. Most terrestrial plant root systems also form *mycorrhizal associations*, symbiotic interactions with soil fungi that increase a plant's ability to absorb minerals (see Figure 31.15). The roots of many plants are adapted for specialized functions **(Figure 35.4)**.

◀ **Buttress roots.** Because of moist conditions in the tropics, root systems of many of the tallest trees are surprisingly shallow. Aerial roots that look like buttresses, such as seen in *Gyranthera caribensis* in Venezuela, give architectural support to the trunks of trees.

▼ Figure 35.4 Evolutionary adaptations of roots.

▲ **Prop roots.** The aerial, adventitious roots of maize (corn) are prop roots, so named because they support tall, top-heavy plants. All roots of a mature maize plant are adventitious whether they emerge above or below ground.

▲ **Pneumatophores.** Also known as air roots, pneumatophores are produced by trees such as mangroves that inhabit tidal swamps. By projecting above the water's surface at low tide, they enable the root system to obtain oxygen, which is lacking in the thick, waterlogged mud.

▲ **Storage roots.** Many plants, such as the common beet, store food and water in their roots.

▶ **"Strangling" aerial roots.** Strangler fig seeds germinate in the crevices of tall trees. Aerial roots grow to the ground, wrapping around the host tree and objects such as this Cambodian temple. Shoots grow upward and shade out the host tree, killing it.

Stems

A **stem** is a plant organ bearing leaves and buds. Its chief function is to elongate and orient the shoot in a way that maximizes photosynthesis by the leaves. Another function of stems is to elevate reproductive structures, thereby facilitating the dispersal of pollen and fruit. Green stems may also perform a limited amount of photosynthesis. Each stem consists of an alternating system of **nodes**, the points at which leaves are attached, and **internodes**, the stem segments between nodes (see Figure 35.2). Most of the growth of a young shoot is concentrated near the growing shoot tip or **apical bud**. Apical buds are not the only types of buds found in shoots. In the upper angle (axil) formed by each leaf and the stem is an **axillary bud**, which can potentially form a lateral branch or, in some cases, a thorn or flower.

Some plants have stems with alternative functions, such as food storage or asexual reproduction. Many of these modified stems, including rhizomes, stolons, and tubers, are often mistaken for roots **(Figure 35.5)**.

◀ **Rhizomes.** The base of this iris plant is an example of a rhizome, a horizontal shoot that grows just below the surface. Vertical shoots emerge from axillary buds on the rhizome.

▶ **Stolons.** Shown here on a strawberry plant, stolons are horizontal shoots that grow along the surface. These "runners" enable a plant to reproduce asexually, as plantlets form at nodes along each runner.

◀ **Tubers.** Tubers, such as these potatoes, are enlarged ends of rhizomes or stolons specialized for storing food. The "eyes" of a potato are clusters of axillary buds that mark the nodes.

▲ **Figure 35.5 Evolutionary adaptations of stems.**

Leaves

In most vascular plants, the **leaf** is the main photosynthetic organ. In addition to intercepting light, leaves exchange gases with the atmosphere, dissipate heat, and defend themselves from herbivores and pathogens. These functions may have conflicting physiological, anatomical, or morphological requirements. For example, a dense covering of hairs may help repel herbivorous insects but may also trap air near the leaf surface, thereby reducing gas exchange and, consequently, photosynthesis. Because of these conflicting demands and trade-offs, leaves vary extensively in form. In general, however, a leaf consists of a flattened **blade** and a stalk, the **petiole**, which joins the leaf to the stem at a node (see Figure 35.2). Grasses and many other monocots lack petioles; instead, the base of the leaf forms a sheath that envelops the stem.

Monocots and eudicots differ in the arrangement of **veins**, the vascular tissue of leaves. Most monocots have parallel major veins of equal diameter that run the length of the blade. Eudicots generally have a branched network of veins arising from a major vein (the *midrib*) that runs down the center of the blade (see Figure 30.16).

In identifying angiosperms according to structure, taxonomists rely mainly on floral morphology, but they also use variations in leaf morphology, such as leaf shape, the branching pattern of veins, and the spatial arrangement of leaves. **Figure 35.6** illustrates a difference in leaf shape: simple versus compound. Compound leaves may withstand strong wind with less tearing. They may also confine some pathogens that invade the leaf to a single leaflet, rather than allowing them to spread to the entire leaf.

▼ **Figure 35.6 Simple versus compound leaves.**

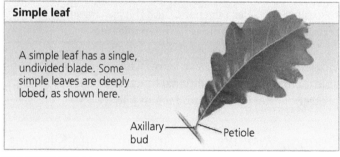

Simple leaf

A simple leaf has a single, undivided blade. Some simple leaves are deeply lobed, as shown here.

Axillary bud — Petiole

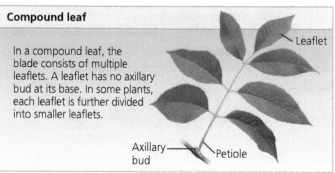

Compound leaf

In a compound leaf, the blade consists of multiple leaflets. A leaflet has no axillary bud at its base. In some plants, each leaflet is further divided into smaller leaflets.

Leaflet

Axillary bud — Petiole

▶ **Tendrils.** The tendrils by which this pea plant clings to a support are modified leaves. After it has "lassoed" a support, a tendril forms a coil that brings the plant closer to the support. Tendrils are typically modified leaves, but some tendrils are modified stems, as in grapevines.

◀ **Spines.** The spines of cacti, such as this prickly pear, are actually leaves; photosynthesis is carried out by the fleshy green stems.

◀ **Storage leaves.** Bulbs, such as this cut onion, have a short underground stem and modified leaves that store food.

Storage leaves

Stem

◀ **Reproductive leaves.** The leaves of some succulents, such as *Kalanchoë daigremontiana*, produce adventitious plantlets, which fall off the leaf and take root in the soil.

▲ **Figure 35.7 Evolutionary adaptations of leaves.**

The morphological features of leaves are often products of genetic programs that are tweaked by environmental influences. Interpret the data in the Scientific Skills Exercise to explore the roles of genetics and the environment in determining leaf morphology in red maple trees.

Almost all leaves are specialized for photosynthesis. However, some species have leaves with adaptations that enable them to perform additional functions, such as support, protection, storage, or reproduction (**Figure 35.7**).

Dermal, Vascular, and Ground Tissue Systems

All three basic plant organs—roots, stems, and leaves—are composed of dermal, vascular, and ground tissues. Each tissue type forms a **tissue system** that connects all of the plant's organs. Tissue systems are continuous throughout the plant, but their specific characteristics and spatial relationships to one another vary in different organs (**Figure 35.8**).

The **dermal tissue system** is the plant's outer protective covering. Like our skin, it forms the first line of defense against physical damage and pathogens. In nonwoody plants, it is usually a single tissue called the **epidermis**, a

Using Bar Graphs to Interpret Data

Nature Versus Nurture: Why Are Leaves from Northern Red Maples "Toothier" Than Leaves from Southern Red Maples? Not all leaves of the red maple (*Acer rubrum*) are the same. The "teeth" along the margins of leaves growing in northern locations differ in size and number compared with their southern counterparts. (The leaf seen here has an intermediate appearance.) Are these morphological differences due to genetic differences between northern and southern *Acer rubrum* populations, or do they arise from environmental differences between northern and southern locations, such as average temperature, that affect gene expression?

How the Experiment Was Done Seeds of *Acer rubrum* were collected from four latitudinally distinct sites: Ontario (Canada), Pennsylvania, South Carolina, and Florida. The seeds from the four sites were then grown in a northern location (Rhode Island) and a southern location (Florida). After a few years of growth, leaves were harvested from the four sets of plants growing in the two locations. The average area of single teeth and the average number of teeth per leaf area were determined.

Data from the Experiment

Seed Collection Site	Average Area of a Single Tooth (cm²)		Number of Teeth per cm² of Leaf Area	
	Grown in Rhode Island	Grown in Florida	Grown in Rhode Island	Grown in Florida
Ontario (43.32°N)	0.017	0.017	3.9	3.2
Pennsylvania (42.12°N)	0.020	0.014	3.0	3.5
South Carolina (33.45°N)	0.024	0.028	2.3	1.9
Florida (30.65°N)	0.027	0.047	2.1	0.9

Interpret the Data

1. Make a bar graph for tooth size and a bar graph for number of teeth. (For information on bar graphs, see the Scientific Skills Review in Appendix F and the Study Area in MasteringBiology.) From north to south, what is the general trend in tooth size and number of teeth in leaves of *Acer rubrum*?

2. Based on the data, would you conclude that leaf tooth traits in the red maple are largely determined by genetic heritage (genotype), by the capacity for responding to environmental change within a single genotype (phenotypic plasticity), or by both? Make specific reference to the data in answering the question.

3. The "toothiness" of leaf fossils of known age has been used by paleoclimatologists to estimate past temperatures in a region. If a 10,000-year-old fossilized red maple leaf from South Carolina had an average of 4.2 teeth per square centimeter of leaf area, what could you infer about the temperature of South Carolina 10,000 years ago compared with the temperature today? Explain your reasoning.

(MB) A version of this Scientific Skills Exercise can be assigned in MasteringBiology.

Data from D. L. Royer et al., Phenotypic plasticity of leaf shape along a temperature gradient in *Acer rubrum*, *PLoS ONE* 4(10):e7653 (2009).

300 μm

▲ **Figure 35.9 Trichome diversity on the surface of a leaf.** Three types of trichomes are found on the surface of marjoram (*Origanum majorana*). Spear-like trichomes help hinder the movement of crawling insects, while the other two types of trichomes secrete oils and other chemicals involved in defense (colorized SEM).

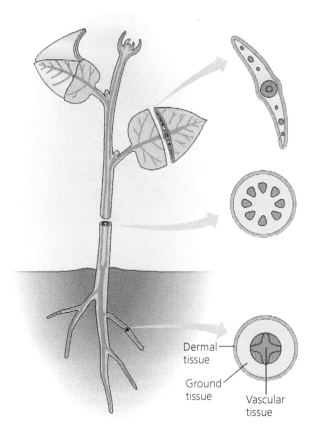

Dermal tissue

Ground tissue

Vascular tissue

▲ **Figure 35.8 The three tissue systems.** The dermal tissue system (blue) provides a protective cover for the entire body of a plant. The vascular tissue system (purple), which transports materials between the root and shoot systems, is also continuous throughout the plant but is arranged differently in each organ. The ground tissue system (yellow), which is responsible for most of the metabolic functions, is located between the dermal tissue and the vascular tissue in each organ.

layer of tightly packed cells. In leaves and most stems, the **cuticle**, a waxy epidermal coating, helps prevent water loss. In woody plants, protective tissues called **periderm** replace the epidermis in older regions of stems and roots. In addition to protecting the plant from water loss and disease, the epidermis has specialized characteristics in each organ. In roots, water and minerals absorbed from the soil enter through the epidermis, especially in root hairs. In shoots, specialized epidermal cells called guard cells are involved in gaseous exchange. Trichomes are another class of highly specialized epidermal cells found in shoots. In some desert species, hairlike trichomes reduce water loss and reflect excess light. Some trichomes defend against insects through shapes that hinder movement or glands that secrete sticky fluids or toxic compounds **(Figure 35.9)**.

The chief functions of the **vascular tissue system** are to facilitate the transport of materials through the plant and to provide mechanical support. The two types of vascular tissues are xylem and phloem. **Xylem** conducts water and dissolved minerals upward from roots into the shoots. **Phloem** transports sugars, the products of photosynthesis, from where they are made (usually the leaves) to where they are

needed—usually roots and sites of growth, such as developing leaves and fruits. The vascular tissue of a root or stem is collectively called the **stele** (the Greek word for "pillar"). The arrangement of the stele varies, depending on the species and organ. In angiosperms, for example, the root stele is a solid central *vascular cylinder* of xylem and phloem, whereas the stele of stems and leaves consists of *vascular bundles*, separate strands containing xylem and phloem (see Figure 35.8). Both xylem and phloem are composed of a variety of cell types, including cells that are highly specialized for transport or support.

Tissues that are neither dermal nor vascular are part of the **ground tissue system**. Ground tissue that is internal to the vascular tissue is known as **pith**, and ground tissue that is external to the vascular tissue is called **cortex**. The ground tissue system is not just filler: It includes cells specialized for functions such as storage, photosynthesis, support, and short-distance transport.

Common Types of Plant Cells

In a plant, as in any multicellular organism, cells undergo cell *differentiation*; that is, they become specialized in structure and function during the course of development. Cell differentiation may involve changes both in the cytoplasm and its organelles and in the cell wall. **Figure 35.10**, on the next two pages, focuses on the major types of plant cells. Notice the structural adaptations that make specific functions possible. You may also wish to review basic plant cell structure (see Figures 6.8 and 6.28).

CONCEPT CHECK **35.1**

1. How does the vascular tissue system enable leaves and roots to function together in supporting growth and development of the whole plant?

2. **WHAT IF?** If humans were photoautotrophs, making food by capturing light energy for photosynthesis, how might our anatomy be different?

3. **MAKE CONNECTIONS** Explain how central vacuoles and cellulose cell walls contribute to plant growth (see Concepts 6.4 and 6.7).

For suggested answers, see Appendix A.

Exploring Examples of Differentiated Plant Cells

Parenchyma Cells

Parenchyma cells in a privet
(*Ligustrum*) leaf (LM)

25 μm

Mature **parenchyma cells** have primary walls that are relatively thin and flexible, and most lack secondary walls. When mature, parenchyma cells generally have a large central vacuole. Parenchyma cells perform most of the metabolic functions of the plant, synthesizing and storing various organic products. For example, photosynthesis occurs within the chloroplasts of parenchyma cells in the leaf. Some parenchyma cells in stems and roots have colorless plastids that store starch. The fleshy tissue of many fruits is composed mainly of parenchyma cells. Most parenchyma cells retain the ability to divide and differentiate into other types of plant cells under particular conditions—during wound repair, for example. It is even possible to grow an entire plant from a single parenchyma cell.

Collenchyma Cells

Collenchyma cells
(in *Helianthus* stem) (LM)

5 μm

Grouped in strands, **collenchyma cells** (seen here in cross section) help support young parts of the plant shoot. Collenchyma cells are generally elongated cells that have thicker primary walls than parenchyma cells, though the walls are unevenly thickened. Young stems and petioles often have strands of collenchyma cells just below their epidermis. Collenchyma cells provide flexible support without restraining growth. At maturity, these cells are living and flexible, elongating with the stems and leaves they support.

Sclerenchyma Cells

5 μm

Sclereid cells in pear (LM)

25 μm

Cell wall

Fiber cells (cross section from ash tree) (LM)

Sclerenchyma cells also function as supporting elements in the plant, but they are much more rigid than collenchyma cells. In sclerenchyma cells, the secondary cell wall, produced after cell elongation has ceased, is thick and contains large amounts of **lignin**, a relatively indigestible strengthening polymer that accounts for more than a quarter of the dry mass of wood. Lignin is present in all vascular plants but not in bryophytes. Unlike collenchyma cells, mature sclerenchyma cells cannot elongate, and they occur in regions of the plant that have stopped growing in length. Sclerenchyma cells are so specialized for support that many are dead at functional maturity, but they produce secondary walls before the protoplast (the living part of the cell) dies. The rigid walls remain as a "skeleton" that supports the plant, in some cases for hundreds of years.

Two types of sclerenchyma cells, known as **sclereids** and **fibers**, are specialized entirely for support and strengthening. Sclereids, which are boxier than fibers and irregular in shape, have very thick, lignified secondary walls. Sclereids impart the hardness to nutshells and seed coats and the gritty texture to pear fruits. Fibers, which are usually grouped in strands, are long, slender, and tapered. Some are used commercially, such as hemp fibers for making rope and flax fibers for weaving into linen.

Water-Conducting Cells of the Xylem

The two types of water-conducting cells, **tracheids** and **vessel elements**, are tubular, elongated cells that are dead at functional maturity. Tracheids occur in the xylem of all vascular plants. In addition to tracheids, most angiosperms, as well as a few gymnosperms and a few seedless vascular plants, have vessel elements. When the living cellular contents of a tracheid or vessel element disintegrate, the cell's thickened walls remain behind, forming a nonliving conduit through which water can flow. The secondary walls of tracheids and vessel elements are often interrupted by pits, thinner regions where only primary walls are present. Water can migrate laterally between neighboring cells through pits.

Tracheids are long, thin cells with tapered ends. Water moves from cell to cell mainly through the pits, where it does not have to cross thick secondary walls.

Vessel elements are generally wider, shorter, thinner walled, and less tapered than tracheids. They are aligned end to end, forming long pipes known as **vessels** that in some cases are visible with the naked eye. The end walls of vessel elements have perforation plates that enable water to flow freely through the vessels.

The secondary walls of tracheids and vessel elements are hardened with lignin. This hardening provides support and prevents collapse under the tension of water transport.

100 µm

Vessel   Tracheids

Tracheids and vessels
(colorized SEM)

Perforation plate

Vessel element

Pits

Vessel elements, with perforated end walls

Tracheids

Sugar-Conducting Cells of the Phloem

Unlike the water-conducting cells of the xylem, the sugar-conducting cells of the phloem are alive at functional maturity. In seedless vascular plants and gymnosperms, sugars and other organic nutrients are transported through long, narrow cells called sieve cells. In the phloem of angiosperms, these nutrients are transported through sieve tubes, which consist of chains of cells that are called **sieve-tube elements**, or sieve-tube members.

Though alive, sieve-tube elements lack a nucleus, ribosomes, a distinct vacuole, and cytoskeletal elements. This reduction in cell contents enables nutrients to pass more easily through the cell. The end walls between sieve-tube elements, called **sieve plates**, have pores that facilitate the flow of fluid from cell to cell along the sieve tube. Alongside each sieve-tube element is a nonconducting cell called a **companion cell**, which is connected to the sieve-tube element by numerous plasmodesmata. The nucleus and ribosomes of the companion cell serve not only that cell itself but also the adjacent sieve-tube element. In some plants, the companion cells in leaves also help load sugars into the sieve-tube elements, which then transport the sugars to other parts of the plant.

ANIMATION

BioFlix Visit the Study Area in **MasteringBiology** for the BioFlix® 3-D Animation Tour of a Plant Cell.

3 µm

Sieve-tube element (left) and companion cell: cross section (TEM)

Sieve plate

Plasmodesma

Sieve plate

Nucleus of companion cell

Sieve-tube elements: longitudinal view

Sieve-tube elements: longitudinal view (LM)

Companion cells

Sieve-tube elements

30 µm

15 µm

Sieve plate with pores (LM)

CONCEPT 35.2

Different meristems generate new cells for primary and secondary growth

How do plant organs develop? A major difference between plants and most animals is that plant growth is not limited to an embryonic or juvenile period. Instead, growth occurs throughout the plant's life, a process that is known as **indeterminate growth**. Plants can keep growing because they have perpetually dividing, unspecialized tissues called **meristems** that divide when conditions permit, leading to new cells that elongate and become specialized. Except for dormant periods, most plants grow continuously. In contrast, most animals and some plant organs—such as leaves, thorns, and flowers—undergo **determinate growth**; they stop growing after reaching a certain size.

There are two main types of meristems: apical meristems and lateral meristems **(Figure 35.11)**. **Apical meristems**, located at the tips of roots and shoots, provide additional cells that enable growth in length, a process known as **primary growth**. Primary growth allows roots to extend throughout the soil and shoots to increase their exposure to light. In herbaceous (nonwoody) plants, primary growth produces all, or almost all, of the plant body. Woody plants, however, also grow in circumference in the parts of stems and roots that no longer grow in length. This growth in thickness, known as **secondary growth**, is caused by **lateral meristems** called the vascular cambium and cork cambium.

These cylinders of dividing cells extend along the length of roots and stems. The **vascular cambium** adds layers of vascular tissue called secondary xylem (wood) and secondary phloem. The **cork cambium** replaces the epidermis with the thicker, tougher periderm.

The cells within meristems divide relatively frequently, generating additional cells. Some new cells remain in the meristem and produce more cells, while others differentiate and are incorporated into tissues and organs of the growing plant. Cells that remain as sources of new cells have traditionally been called *initials* but are increasingly being called *stem cells* to correspond to animal stem cells that also perpetually divide and remain functionally unspecialized. The new cells displaced from the meristem, which are known as *derivatives*, divide until the cells they produce become specialized in mature tissues.

The relationship between primary and secondary growth is seen in the winter twig of a deciduous tree. At the shoot tip is the dormant apical bud, enclosed by scales that protect its apical meristem **(Figure 35.12)**. In spring, the bud sheds its scales and begins a new spurt of primary growth, producing a series of nodes and internodes. On each growth segment, nodes are marked by scars that were left when leaves fell. Above each leaf scar is an axillary bud or a branch formed by an axillary bud. Farther down are bud scars from whorls of scales that enclosed the apical bud during the previous winter. During each growing season, primary growth extends shoots, and secondary growth increases the diameter of the parts that formed in previous years.

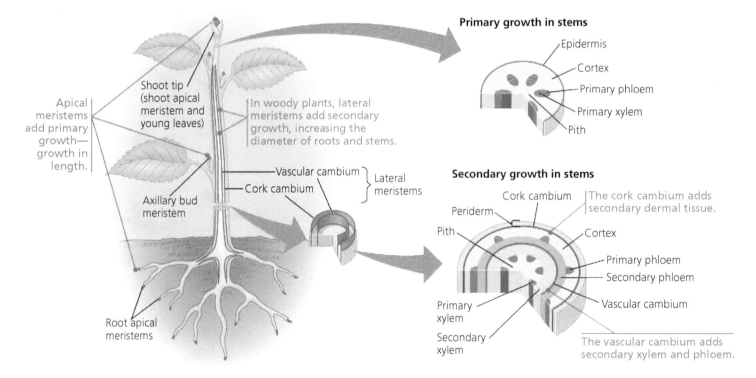

▲ **Figure 35.11 An overview of primary and secondary growth.**

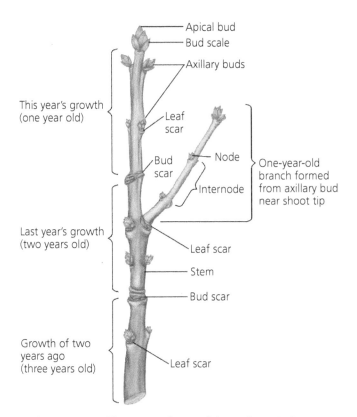

▲ **Figure 35.12 Three years' growth in a winter twig.**

Labels on figure:
- Apical bud
- Bud scale
- Axillary buds
- This year's growth (one year old)
- Leaf scar
- Bud scar
- Node
- Internode
- One-year-old branch formed from axillary bud near shoot tip
- Last year's growth (two years old)
- Leaf scar
- Stem
- Bud scar
- Growth of two years ago (three years old)
- Leaf scar

Although plants grow throughout their lives, they do die, of course. Based on the length of their life cycle, flowering plants can be categorized as annuals, biennials, or perennials. *Annuals* complete their life cycle—from germination to flowering to seed production to death—in a single year or less. Many wildflowers are annuals, as are most staple food crops, including legumes and cereal grains such as wheat and rice. *Biennials*, such as turnips, generally require two growing seasons to complete their life cycle, flowering and fruiting only in their second year. *Perennials* live many years and include trees, shrubs, and some grasses. Some buffalo grass of the North American plains is thought to have been growing for 10,000 years from seeds that sprouted at the close of the last ice age.

CONCEPT CHECK 35.2

1. Would primary and secondary growth ever occur simultaneously in the same plant?

2. Roots and stems grow indeterminately, but leaves do not. How might this benefit the plant?

3. **WHAT IF?** Suppose a gardener uproots some carrots after one season and sees they are too small. Knowing that carrots are biennials, the gardener leaves the remaining plants in the ground, thinking their roots will grow larger during their second year. Is this a good idea? Explain.

For suggested answers, see Appendix A.

Primary growth lengthens roots and shoots

As you have learned, primary growth arises directly from cells produced by apical meristems. In herbaceous plants, almost the entire plant consists of primary growth, whereas in woody plants, only the nonwoody, more recently formed parts of the plant represent primary growth. Although the elongation of both roots and shoots arises from cells derived from apical meristems, the primary growth of roots and primary growth of shoots differ in many ways.

Primary Growth of Roots

The tip of a root is covered by a thimble-like **root cap**, which protects the delicate apical meristem as the root pushes through the abrasive soil. The root cap also secretes a polysaccharide slime that lubricates the soil around the tip of the root. Growth occurs just behind the tip in three overlapping zones of cells at successive stages of primary growth. These are the zones of cell division, elongation, and differentiation **(Figure 35.13)**.

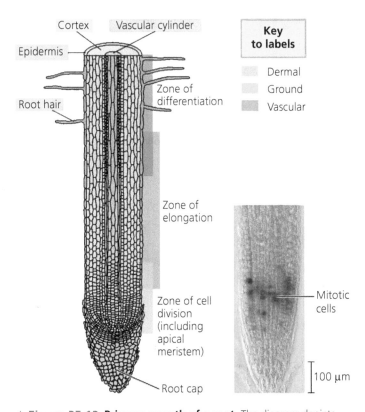

Labels on figure:
- Cortex
- Vascular cylinder
- Epidermis
- Root hair
- Zone of differentiation
- Key to labels
  - Dermal
  - Ground
  - Vascular
- Zone of elongation
- Zone of cell division (including apical meristem)
- Root cap
- Mitotic cells
- 100 μm

▲ **Figure 35.13 Primary growth of a root.** The diagram depicts the anatomical features of the tip of a typical eudicot root. The apical meristem produces all the cells of the root. Most lengthening of the root occurs in the zone of elongation. In the micrograph, cells undergoing mitosis in the apical meristem are revealed by staining for cyclin, a protein that plays an important role in cell division (LM).

The *zone of cell division* includes the root apical meristem and its derivatives. New root cells are produced in this region, including cells of the root cap. Typically, a few millimeters behind the tip of the root is the *zone of elongation*, where most of the growth occurs as root cells elongate—sometimes to more than ten times their original length. Cell elongation in this zone pushes the tip farther into the soil. Meanwhile, the root apical meristem keeps adding cells to the younger end of the zone of elongation. Even before the root cells finish lengthening, many begin specializing in structure and function. In the *zone of differentiation*, or zone of maturation, cells complete their differentiation and become distinct cell types.

The primary growth of a root produces its epidermis, ground tissue, and vascular tissue. In angiosperm roots,

the stele is a vascular cylinder, consisting of a solid core of xylem and phloem tissues. In most eudicot roots, the xylem has a starlike appearance in cross section, and the phloem occupies the indentations between the arms of the xylem "star" **(Figure 35.14a)**. In many monocot roots, the vascular tissue consists of a central core of unspecialized parenchyma cells surrounded by a ring of alternating xylem and phloem tissues **(Figure 35.14b)**.

The ground tissue of roots, consisting mostly of parenchyma cells, is found in the cortex, the region between the vascular cylinder and epidermis. In addition to storing carbohydrates, cortical cells transport water and salts from the root hairs to the center of the root. The cortex, because of its large intercellular spaces, also allows for the *extracellular* diffusion of water, minerals, and oxygen from the root

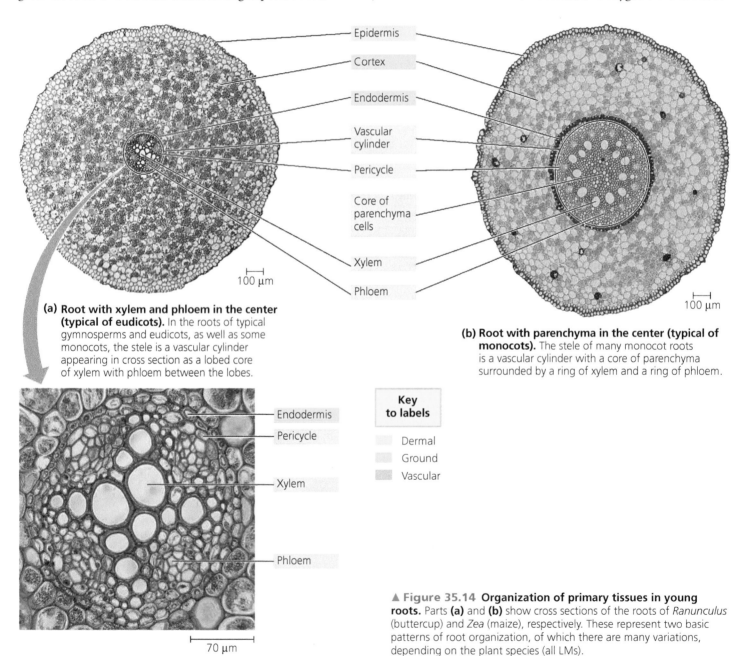

(a) Root with xylem and phloem in the center (typical of eudicots). In the roots of typical gymnosperms and eudicots, as well as some monocots, the stele is a vascular cylinder appearing in cross section as a lobed core of xylem with phloem between the lobes.

(b) Root with parenchyma in the center (typical of monocots). The stele of many monocot roots is a vascular cylinder with a core of parenchyma surrounded by a ring of xylem and a ring of phloem.

Epidermis
Cortex
Endodermis
Vascular cylinder
Pericycle
Core of parenchyma cells
Xylem
Phloem

100 μm

100 μm

70 μm

Endodermis
Pericycle
Xylem
Phloem

Key to labels

Dermal
Ground
Vascular

▲ Figure 35.14 **Organization of primary tissues in young roots.** Parts **(a)** and **(b)** show cross sections of the roots of *Ranunculus* (buttercup) and *Zea* (maize), respectively. These represent two basic patterns of root organization, of which there are many variations, depending on the plant species (all LMs).

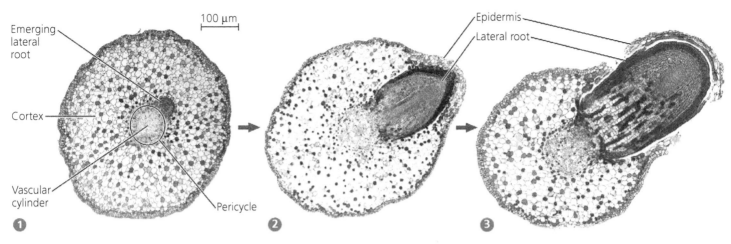

▲ **Figure 35.15 The formation of a lateral root.** A lateral root originates in the pericycle, the outermost layer of the vascular cylinder of a root, and grows out through the cortex and epidermis. In this series of light micrographs, the view of the original root is a cross section, while the view of the lateral root is a longitudinal section.

hairs inward. The innermost layer of the cortex is called the **endodermis**, a cylinder one cell thick that forms the boundary with the vascular cylinder. The endodermis is a selective barrier that regulates passage of substances from the soil into the vascular cylinder (see Figure 36.8).

Lateral roots arise from meristematically active regions of the **pericycle**, the outermost cell layer in the vascular cylinder, which is adjacent to and just inside the endodermis (see Figure 35.14). The emerging lateral roots destructively push through the cortex and epidermis **(Figure 35.15)**.

Primary Growth of Shoots

A shoot apical meristem is a dome-shaped mass of dividing cells at the shoot tip **(Figure 35.16)**. Leaves develop from **leaf primordia** (singular, *primordium*), projections shaped like a

▲ **Figure 35.16 The shoot tip.** Leaf primordia arise from the flanks of the dome of the apical meristem. This is a longitudinal section of the shoot tip of *Coleus* (LM).

cow's horns that emerge along the sides of the apical meristem. Within a bud, young leaves are spaced close together because the internodes are very short. Shoot elongation is due to the lengthening of internode cells below the shoot tip.

Branching, which is also part of primary growth, arises from the activation of axillary buds, each of which has its own shoot apical meristem. Because of chemical communication by plant hormones, the closer an axillary bud is to an active apical bud, the more inhibited it is, a phenomenon called **apical dominance**. (The specific hormonal changes underlying apical dominance are discussed in Chapter 39.) If an animal eats the end of the shoot or if shading results in the light being more intense on the side of the shoot, the chemical communication underlying apical dominance is disrupted. As a result, the axillary buds break dormancy and start to grow. Released from dormancy, an axillary bud eventually gives rise to a lateral shoot, complete with its own apical bud, leaves, and axillary buds. When gardeners prune shrubs and pinch back houseplants, they are reducing the number of apical buds a plant has, thereby allowing branches to elongate and giving the plants a fuller, bushier appearance.

In some monocots, particularly grasses, meristematic activity occurs at the bases of stems and leaves. These areas, called *intercalary meristems*, allow damaged leaves to rapidly regrow, which accounts for the ability of lawns to grow following mowing. The ability of grasses to regrow leaves by intercalary meristems enables the plant to recover more effectively from damage incurred from grazing herbivores.

Tissue Organization of Stems

The epidermis covers stems as part of the continuous dermal tissue system. Vascular tissue runs the length of a stem in vascular bundles. Unlike lateral roots, which arise from vascular tissue deep within a root and disrupt the vascular cylinder, cortex, and epidermis as they emerge (see Figure 35.15), lateral shoots develop from axillary bud

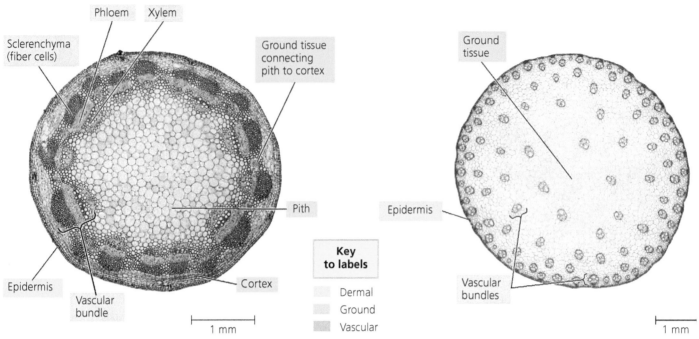

Phloem   Xylem

Sclerenchyma
(fiber cells)

Ground tissue
connecting
pith to cortex

Ground
tissue

Pith

Epidermis

Epidermis

Cortex

Vascular
bundle

Vascular
bundles

**Key
to labels**

Dermal

Ground

Vascular

1 mm

1 mm

**(a) Cross section of stem with vascular bundles forming a
ring (typical of eudicots).** Ground tissue toward the
inside is called pith, and ground tissue toward the outside is
called cortex (LM).

**(b) Cross section of stem with scattered vascular bundles
(typical of monocots).** In such an arrangement, ground tissue is
not partitioned into pith and cortex (LM).

▲ **Figure 35.17** **Organization of primary tissues in young stems.**

? Why aren't the terms *pith* and *cortex* used to describe the ground tissue of monocot stems?

meristems on the stem's surface and disrupt no other tissues
(see Figure 35.16). Near the soil surface, in the transition
zone between shoot and root, the bundled vascular arrangement of the stem converges with the solid vascular cylinder
of the root.

In most eudicot species, the vascular tissue of stems consists of vascular bundles arranged in a ring **(Figure 35.17a)**.
The xylem in each vascular bundle is adjacent to the pith,
and the phloem in each bundle is adjacent to the cortex.
In most monocot stems, the vascular bundles are scattered
throughout the ground tissue rather than forming a ring
(Figure 35.17b). In the stems of both monocots and eudicots, the ground tissue consists mostly of parenchyma cells.
However, collenchyma cells just beneath the epidermis
strengthen many stems during primary growth. Sclerenchyma cells, especially fiber cells, also provide support in
those parts of the stems that are no longer elongating.

Tissue Organization of Leaves

Figure 35.18 provides an overview of leaf structure. The
epidermis is interrupted by pores called **stomata** (singular,
stoma), which allow exchange of CO_2 and O_2 between the
surrounding air and the photosynthetic cells inside the leaf.
In addition to regulating CO_2 uptake for photosynthesis,
stomata are major avenues for the evaporative loss of water.
The term *stoma* can refer to the stomatal pore or to the

entire stomatal complex consisting of a pore flanked by two
specialized epidermal cells called **guard cells**, which regulate the opening and closing of the pore. We will discuss
stomata in detail in Chapter 36.

The leaf's ground tissue, called the **mesophyll** (from the
Greek *mesos*, middle, and *phyll*, leaf), is sandwiched between
the upper and lower epidermal layers. Mesophyll consists
mainly of parenchyma cells specialized for photosynthesis.
The mesophyll in many eudicot leaves has two distinct layers: palisade and spongy. *Palisade mesophyll* consists of one
or more layers of elongated parenchyma cells on the upper
part of the leaf. *Spongy mesophyll* is below the palisade mesophyll. These parenchyma cells are more loosely arranged,
with a labyrinth of air spaces through which CO_2 and O_2 circulate around the cells and up to the palisade region. The air
spaces are particularly large in the vicinity of stomata, where
CO_2 is taken up from the outside air and O_2 is released.

The vascular tissue of each leaf is continuous with the
vascular tissue of the stem. Veins subdivide repeatedly and
branch throughout the mesophyll. This network brings
xylem and phloem into close contact with the photosynthetic tissue, which obtains water and minerals from the
xylem and loads its sugars and other organic products into
the phloem for transport to other parts of the plant. The
vascular structure also functions as a framework that reinforces the shape of the leaf. Each vein is enclosed by a

Key to labels

- Dermal
- Ground
- Vascular

Cuticle

Sclerenchyma fibers

Stoma

Bundle-sheath cell

Xylem

Phloem

Vein

Guard cells

(a) Cutaway drawing of leaf tissues

Guard cells

Stomatal pore

Epidermal cell

50 μm

(b) Surface view of a spiderwort (*Tradescantia*) leaf (LM)

Upper epidermis

Palisade mesophyll

Spongy mesophyll

Lower epidermis

Cuticle

100 μm

Vein   Air spaces   Guard cells

(c) Cross section of a lilac (*Syringa*) leaf (LM)

protective *bundle sheath*, a layer of cells that regulates the movement of substances between the vascular tissue and the mesophyll. Bundle-sheath cells are very prominent in leaves of species that carry out C_4 photosynthesis (see Chapter 10).

CONCEPT CHECK 35.3

1. Contrast primary growth in roots and shoots.
2. **WHAT IF?** If a plant species has vertically oriented leaves, would you expect its mesophyll to be divided into spongy and palisade layers? Explain.
3. **MAKE CONNECTIONS** How are root hairs and microvilli analogous structures? (See Figure 6.8 and the discussion of analogy in Concept 26.2.)

For suggested answers, see Appendix A.

CONCEPT 35.4

Secondary growth increases the diameter of stems and roots in woody plants

Many land plants display secondary growth, the growth in thickness produced by lateral meristems. The advent of secondary growth during plant evolution allowed the production of novel plant forms ranging from massive forest trees to woody vines. All gymnosperm species and many

eudicot species undergo secondary growth, but it is unusual in monocots. It occurs in stems and roots of woody plants, but rarely in leaves. Secondary growth consists of the tissues produced by the vascular cambium and cork cambium. The vascular cambium adds secondary xylem (wood) and secondary phloem, thereby increasing vascular flow and support for the shoots. The cork cambium produces a tough, thick covering of waxy cells that protect the stem from water loss and from invasion by insects, bacteria, and fungi.

In woody plants, primary growth and secondary growth occur simultaneously. As primary growth adds leaves and lengthens stems and roots in the younger regions of a plant, secondary growth increases the diameter of stems and roots in older regions where primary growth has ceased. The process is similar in shoots and roots. **Figure 35.19**, on the next page, provides an overview of growth in a woody stem.

The Vascular Cambium and Secondary Vascular Tissue

The vascular cambium, a cylinder of meristematic cells only one cell thick, is wholly responsible for the production of secondary vascular tissue. In a typical woody stem, the vascular cambium is located outside the pith and primary xylem and to the inside of the primary phloem and the cortex. In a typical woody root, the vascular cambium forms exterior to the primary xylem and interior to the primary phloem and pericycle.

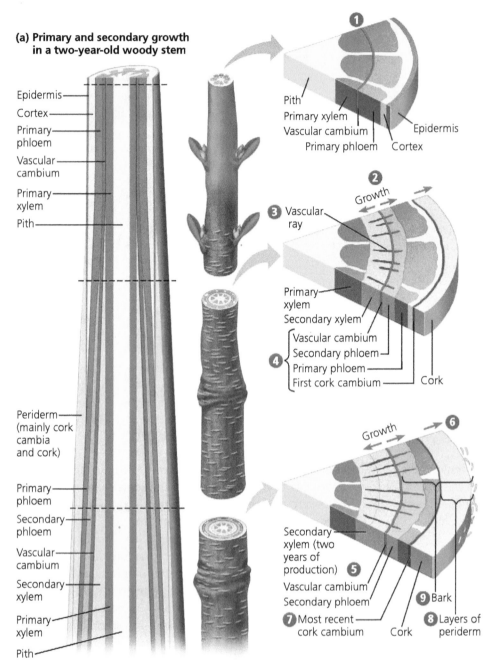

(a) Primary and secondary growth in a two-year-old woody stem

Epidermis
Cortex
Primary phloem
Vascular cambium
Primary xylem
Pith

Periderm (mainly cork cambia and cork)
Primary phloem
Secondary phloem
Vascular cambium
Secondary xylem
Primary xylem
Pith

Pith
Primary xylem
Vascular cambium
Primary phloem
Epidermis
Cortex

1

2

Growth

3 Vascular ray

Primary xylem
Secondary xylem
Vascular cambium
Secondary phloem
Primary phloem
First cork cambium
4
Cork

Growth
6

Secondary xylem (two years of production) **5**
Vascular cambium
Secondary phloem
7 Most recent cork cambium
Cork
9 Bark
8 Layers of periderm

1 Primary growth from the activity of the apical meristem is nearing completion. The vascular cambium has just formed.

2 Although primary growth continues in the apical bud, only secondary growth occurs in this region. The stem thickens as the vascular cambium forms secondary xylem to the inside and secondary phloem to the outside.

3 Some initials of the vascular cambium give rise to vascular rays.

4 As the vascular cambium's diameter increases, the secondary phloem and other tissues external to the cambium can't keep pace because their cells no longer divide. As a result, these tissues, including the epidermis, will eventually rupture. A second lateral meristem, the cork cambium, develops from parenchyma cells in the cortex. The cork cambium produces cork cells, which replace the epidermis.

5 In year 2 of secondary growth, the vascular cambium produces more secondary xylem and phloem, and the cork cambium produces more cork.

6 As the stem's diameter increases, the outermost tissues exterior to the cork cambium rupture and are sloughed off.

7 In many cases, the cork cambium re-forms deeper in the cortex. When none of the cortex is left, the cambium develops from phloem parenchyma cells.

8 Each cork cambium and the tissues it produces form a layer of periderm.

9 Bark consists of all tissues exterior to the vascular cambium.

▲ **Figure 35.19 Primary and secondary growth of a woody stem.** The progress of secondary growth can be tracked by examining the sections through sequentially older parts of the stem.

? *How does the vascular cambium cause some tissues to rupture?*

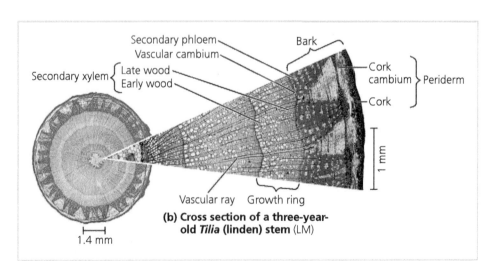

Secondary phloem
Vascular cambium
Secondary xylem { Late wood / Early wood
Bark
Cork cambium } Periderm
Cork
1 mm

Vascular ray   Growth ring

(b) Cross section of a three-year-old *Tilia* (linden) stem (LM)

1.4 mm

In cross section, the vascular cambium appears as a ring of meristematic cells (see Figure 35.19). As these cells divide, they increase the cambium's circumference and add secondary xylem to the inside and secondary phloem to the outside (Figure 35.20). Each ring is larger than the previous ring, increasing the diameter of roots and stems.

Some of the initials produced by the vascular cambium are elongated and oriented with their long axis parallel to the axis of the stem or root. They produce cells such as the tracheids, vessel elements, and fibers of the xylem, as well as the sieve-tube elements, companion cells, axially oriented parenchyma, and fibers of the phloem. The other initials are shorter and are oriented perpendicular to the axis of the stem or root. They produce *vascular rays*—radial files of mostly parenchyma cells that connect the secondary xylem and phloem (see Figure 35.19b). These cells move water and nutrients between the secondary xylem and phloem, store carbohydrates and other reserves, and aid in wound repair.

As secondary growth continues, layers of secondary xylem (wood) accumulate, consisting mainly of tracheids, vessel elements, and fibers (see Figure 35.10). In most gymnosperms, tracheids are the only water-conducting cells. Most angiosperms also have vessel elements. The walls of secondary xylem cells are heavily lignified, giving wood its hardness and strength.

In temperate regions, wood that develops early in the spring, known as early (or spring) wood, usually has secondary xylem cells with large diameters and thin cell walls (see Figure 35.19b). This structure maximizes delivery of water to leaves. Wood produced later in the growing season is called late (or summer) wood. It has thick-walled cells that do not transport as much water but provide more support. Because there is a marked contrast between the large cells of the new early wood and the smaller cells of the late wood of the previous growing season, a year's growth appears as a distinct *growth ring* in cross sections of most tree trunks and roots. Therefore, researchers can estimate a tree's age by counting growth rings. *Dendrochronology* is the science of analyzing tree growth ring patterns. Growth rings vary in thickness, depending on seasonal growth. Trees grow well in wet and warm years but may grow hardly at all in cold or dry years. Since a thick ring indicates a warm year and a thin ring indicates a cold or dry one, scientists use ring patterns to study climate changes (Figure 35.21).

▼ Figure 35.21 **Research Method**

Using Dendrochronology to Study Climate

Application Dendrochronology, the science of analyzing growth rings, is useful in studying climate change. Most scientists attribute recent global warming to the burning of fossil fuels and release of CO_2 and other greenhouse gases, whereas a small minority think it is a natural variation. Studying climate patterns requires comparing past and present temperatures, but instrumental climate records span only the last two centuries and apply only to some regions. By examining growth rings of Mongolian conifers dating back to the mid-1500s, Gordon C. Jacoby and Rosanne D'Arrigo, of the Lamont-Doherty Earth Observatory, and colleagues sought to learn whether Mongolia has experienced similar warm periods in the past.

Technique Researchers can analyze patterns of rings in living and dead trees. They can even study wood used for building long ago by matching samples with those from naturally situated specimens of overlapping age. Core samples, each about the diameter of a pencil, are taken from the bark to the center of the trunk. Each sample is dried and sanded to reveal the rings. By comparing, aligning, and averaging many samples from the conifers, the researchers compiled a chronology. The trees became a chronicle of environmental change.

Results This graph summarizes a composite record of the ring-width indexes for the Mongolian conifers from 1550 to 1993. The higher indexes indicate wider rings and higher temperatures.

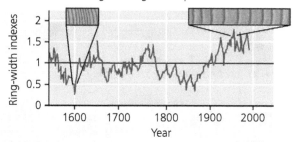

Source: Figure adapted from "Mongolian Tree Rings and 20th-Century Warming" by Gordon C. Jacoby, et al., from *Science*, August 9, 1996, Volume 273(5276): 771–773. Reprinted with permission from AAAS.

INTERPRET THE DATA *What does the graph indicate about environmental change during the period 1550–1993?*

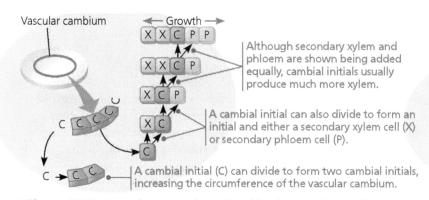

Although secondary xylem and phloem are shown being added equally, cambial initials usually produce much more xylem.

A cambial initial can also divide to form an initial and either a secondary xylem cell (X) or secondary phloem cell (P).

A cambial initial (C) can divide to form two cambial initials, increasing the circumference of the vascular cambium.

▲ Figure 35.20 **Secondary growth produced by the vascular cambium.**

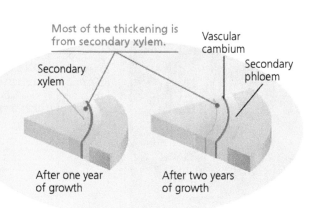

Most of the thickening is from secondary xylem.

Vascular cambium

Secondary xylem

Secondary phloem

After one year of growth

After two years of growth

As a tree or woody shrub ages, older layers of secondary xylem no longer transport water and minerals (a solution called xylem sap). These layers are called *heartwood* because they are closer to the center of a stem or root (Figure 35.22). The newest, outer layers of secondary xylem still transport xylem sap and are therefore known as *sapwood*. Sapwood allows a large tree to survive even if the center of its trunk is hollow (Figure 35.23). Because each new layer of secondary xylem has a larger circumference, secondary growth enables the xylem to transport more sap each year, supplying an increasing number of leaves. Heartwood is generally darker than sapwood because of resins and other compounds that

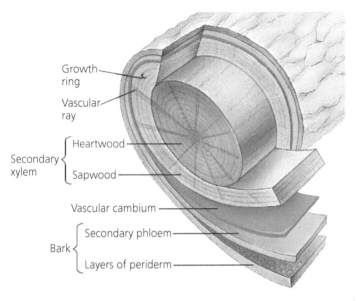

▲ Figure 35.22 **Anatomy of a tree trunk.**

▲ Figure 35.23 **Is this tree living or dead?** The Wawona Sequoia tunnel in Yosemite National Park in California was cut in 1881 as a tourist attraction. This giant sequoia (*Sequoiadendron giganteum*) lived for another 88 years before falling during a severe winter. It was 71.3 m tall and estimated to be 2,100 years old. Though conservation policies today would forbid the mutilation of such an important specimen, the Wawona Sequoia did teach a valuable botanical lesson: Trees can survive the excision of large portions of their heartwood.

permeate the cell cavities and help protect the core of the tree from fungi and wood-boring insects.

Only the youngest secondary phloem, closest to the vascular cambium, functions in sugar transport. As a stem or root increases in circumference, the older secondary phloem is sloughed off, which is one reason secondary phloem does not accumulate as extensively as secondary xylem.

The Cork Cambium and the Production of Periderm

During the early stages of secondary growth, the epidermis is pushed outward, causing it to split, dry, and fall off the stem or root. It is replaced by tissues produced by the first cork cambium, a cylinder of dividing cells that arises in the outer cortex of stems (see Figure 35.19a) and in the pericycle in roots. The cork cambium gives rise to *cork cells* that accumulate to the exterior of the cork cambium. As cork cells mature, they deposit a waxy, hydrophobic material called *suberin* in their walls and then die. This waxy cork layer thus functions as a barrier that helps protect the stem or root from water loss, physical damage, and pathogens. The cork cambium and the tissues it produces comprise a layer of periderm.

How can living cells in the interior tissues of woody organs absorb oxygen and respire if they are surrounded by a waxy periderm? Dotting the periderm are small, raised areas called **lenticels**, in which there is more space between cork cells, enabling living cells within a woody stem or root to exchange gases with the outside air. Lenticels often appear as horizontal slits, as shown on the stem in Figure 35.19a.

The thickening of a stem or root often splits the first cork cambium, which loses its meristematic activity and differentiates into cork cells. A new cork cambium forms to the inside, resulting in another layer of periderm. As this process continues, older layers of periderm are sloughed off, as evident in the cracked, peeling exteriors of many tree trunks. It should be noted that cork is commonly and incorrectly referred to as "bark." In botany, **bark** includes all tissues external to the vascular cambium. Its main components are the secondary phloem (produced by the vascular cambium) and, external to that, the most recent periderm and all the older layers of periderm (see Figure 35.22).

Evolution of Secondary Growth

EVOLUTION Surprisingly, some insights into the evolution of secondary growth have been achieved by studying the herbaceous plant *Arabidopsis thaliana*. Researchers have found that they can stimulate some secondary growth in *Arabidopsis* stems by adding weights to the plant. These findings suggest that weight carried by the stem activates a developmental program leading to wood formation.

Moreover, several developmental genes that regulate shoot apical meristems in *Arabidopsis* have been found to regulate vascular cambium activity in poplar (*Populus*) trees. This suggests that the processes of primary and secondary growth are evolutionarily more closely related than was previously thought.

CONCEPT CHECK 35.4

1. A sign is hammered into a tree 2 m from the tree's base. If the tree is 10 m tall and elongates 1 m each year, how high will the sign be after 10 years?

2. Stomata and lenticels are both involved in exchange of CO_2 and O_2. Why do stomata need to be able to close, but lenticels do not?

3. Would you expect a tropical tree to have distinct growth rings? Why or why not?

4. **WHAT IF?** If a complete ring of bark is removed from around a tree trunk (a process called girdling), would the tree die slowly (in weeks) or quickly (in days)? Explain why.

For suggested answers, see Appendix A.

▲ **Figure 35.24 Developmental plasticity in the aquatic plant *Cabomba caroliniana*.** The underwater leaves of *Cabomba* are feathery, an adaptation that protects them from damage by lessening their resistance to moving water. In contrast, the surface leaves are pads that aid in flotation. Both leaf types have genetically identical cells, but their different environments result in the turning on or off of different genes during leaf development.

CONCEPT 35.5

Growth, morphogenesis, and cell differentiation produce the plant body

The specific series of changes by which cells form tissues, organs, and organisms is called **development**. Development unfolds according to the genetic information that an organism inherits from its parents but is also influenced by the external environment. A single genotype can produce different phenotypes in different environments. For example, the aquatic plant called the fanwort (*Cabomba caroliniana*) forms two very different types of leaves, depending on whether the shoot apical meristem is submerged (**Figure 35.24**). This ability to alter form in response to local environmental conditions is called *developmental plasticity*. Dramatic examples of plasticity, as in *Cabomba,* are much more common in plants than in animals and may help compensate for plants' inability to escape adverse conditions by moving.

The three overlapping processes involved in the development of a multicellular organism are growth, morphogenesis, and cell differentiation. *Growth* is an irreversible increase in size. *Morphogenesis* (from the Greek *morphê*, shape, and *genesis*, creation) is the process that gives a tissue, organ, or organism its shape and determines the positions of cell types. *Cell differentiation* is the process by which cells with the same genes become different from one another. We'll examine these three processes in turn, but first we'll discuss how applying techniques of modern molecular biology to model organisms, particularly *Arabidopsis thaliana,* has revolutionized the study of plant development.

Model Organisms: Revolutionizing the Study of Plants

As in other branches of biology, molecular biological techniques and a focus on model organisms such as *Arabidopsis thaliana* have catalyzed a research explosion in the last few decades. *Arabidopsis*, a tiny weed in the mustard family, has no inherent agricultural value but is a favored model organism of plant geneticists and molecular biologists for many reasons. It is so small that thousands of plants can be cultivated in a few square meters of lab space. It also has a short generation time, taking about six weeks for a seed to grow into a mature plant that produces more seeds. This rapid maturation enables biologists to conduct genetic cross experiments in a relatively short time. One plant can produce over 5,000 seeds, another property that makes *Arabidopsis* useful for genetic analysis.

Beyond these basic traits, the plant's genome makes it particularly well suited for analysis by molecular genetic methods. The *Arabidopsis* genome, which includes about 27,000 protein-encoding genes, is among the smallest known in plants. Furthermore, the plant has only five pairs of chromosomes, making it easier for geneticists to locate specific genes. Because *Arabidopsis* has such a small genome, it was the first plant to have its entire genome sequenced—a six-year, multinational effort.

Another property that makes *Arabidopsis* attractive to molecular biologists is that its cells can be easily transformed with transgenes, genes from different organisms. Biologists usually transform plant cells by infecting them with genetically altered varieties of the bacterium *Agrobacterium tumefaciens* (see Figure 35.25). *Arabidopsis* researchers also use a variation of this technique to produce a plant with a particular mutation. Studying the effect of a mutation in a gene often yields important information about the gene's normal function. Because *Agrobacterium* inserts its transforming DNA randomly into the genome, the DNA may be inserted in the middle of a gene. Such an insertion usually destroys the function of the disrupted gene, resulting in a "knock-out mutant."

Large-scale projects using this technique are under way to determine the function of every gene in *Arabidopsis*. By identifying each gene's function and tracking every biochemical pathway, researchers aim to determine the blueprints for plant development, a major goal of systems biology. It may one day be possible to make a computer-generated "virtual plant" that enables researchers to visualize which genes are activated in different parts of the plant as the plant develops.

Basic research involving model organisms such as *Arabidopsis* has accelerated the pace of discovery in the plant sciences, including the identification of the complex genetic pathways underlying plant structure. As you read more about this, you'll be able to appreciate not just the power of studying model organisms but also the rich history of investigation that underpins all modern plant research.

Growth: Cell Division and Cell Expansion

Cell division enhances the potential for growth by increasing the number of cells, but plant growth itself is brought about by cell enlargement. The process of plant cell division is described more fully in Chapter 12 (see Figure 12.10), and Chapter 39 discusses the process of cell elongation (see Figure 39.7). Here we are concerned with how cell division and enlargement contribute to plant form.

The Plane and Symmetry of Cell Division

The new cell walls that bisect plant cells during cytokinesis develop from the cell plate (see Figure 12.10). The precise plane of cell division, determined during late interphase, usually corresponds to the shortest path that will halve the volume of the parent cell. The first sign of this spatial orientation is rearrangement of the cytoskeleton. Microtubules in the cytoplasm become concentrated into a ring called the *preprophase band* (Figure 35.26). The band disappears before metaphase but predicts the future plane of cell division.

It had long been thought that the plane of cell division provides the foundation for the forms of plant organs, but

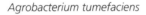

▼ Figure 35.25   Research Method

Using the Ti Plasmid to Produce Transgenic Plants

Application Genes conferring useful traits, such as pest resistance, herbicide resistance, delayed ripening, and increased nutritional value, can be transferred from one plant variety or species to another using the Ti plasmid as a vector.

Technique

① The Ti plasmid is isolated from the bacterium *Agrobacterium tumefaciens*. The segment of the plasmid that integrates into the genome of host cells is called T DNA.

Agrobacterium tumefaciens

Ti plasmid

Site where restriction enzyme cuts

T DNA

② The foreign gene of interest is inserted into the middle of the T DNA.

DNA with the gene of interest

Recombinant Ti plasmid

③ Recombinant plasmids can be introduced into cultured plant cells by electroporation. Or plasmids can be returned to *Agrobacterium*, which is then applied as a liquid suspension to the leaves of susceptible plants, infecting them. Once a plasmid is taken into a plant cell, its T DNA integrates into the cell's chromosomal DNA.

Plant with new trait

Results Transformed cells carrying the transgene of interest can regenerate complete plants that exhibit the new trait conferred by the transgene.

◀ **Figure 35.26 The preprophase band and the plane of cell division.** The location of the preprophase band predicts the plane of cell division. In this light micrograph, the preprophase band has been stained with green fluorescent protein bound to a microtubule-associated protein.

7 μm

studies of an internally disorganized maize mutant called *tangled-1* now indicate that this is not the case. In wild-type maize plants, leaf cells divide either transversely (crosswise) or longitudinally relative to the axis of the parent cell. Transverse divisions precede leaf elongation, and longitudinal divisions precede leaf broadening. In *tangled-1* leaves, transverse divisions are normal, but most longitudinal divisions are oriented abnormally, leading to cells that are crooked or curved **(Figure 35.27)**. However, these abnormal cell divisions do not affect leaf shape. Mutant leaves grow more slowly than wild-type leaves, but their overall shapes remain normal, indicating that leaf shape does not depend solely on precise spatial control of cell division. In addition, recent evidence suggests that the shape of the shoot apex in *Arabidopsis* depends not on the plane of cell division but on microtubule-dependent mechanical stresses stemming from the "crowding" associated with cell proliferation and growth.

An important feature of cell division that does affect plant development is the *symmetry* of cell division—the distribution of cytoplasm between daughter cells. Although chromosomes are allocated to daughter cells equally during mitosis, the cytoplasm may sometimes divide asymmetrically. *Asymmetrical cell division*, in which one daughter cell receives more cytoplasm than the other during mitosis, usually signals a key event in development. For example, the formation of guard cells typically involves both an asymmetrical cell division and a change in the plane of cell division. An epidermal cell divides asymmetrically, forming a large cell that remains an unspecialized epidermal cell and a small cell that becomes the guard cell "mother cell." Guard cells form when this small mother cell divides in a plane perpendicular to the first cell division **(Figure 35.28)**. Thus, asymmetrical cell division generates cells with different fates—that is, cells that mature into different types.

Asymmetrical cell divisions also play a role in the establishment of **polarity**, the condition of having structural or chemical differences at opposite ends of an organism. Plants typically have an axis, with a root end and a shoot end. Such polarity is most obvious in morphological differences, but it is also apparent in physiological properties, including the movement of the hormone auxin in a single direction and the emergence of adventitious roots and shoots from "cuttings." In a stem cutting, adventitious roots emerge from the end that was nearest the root; in a root cutting, adventitious shoots arise from the end that was nearest the shoot.

The first division of a plant zygote is normally asymmetrical, initiating polarization of the plant body into shoot and root. This polarity is difficult to reverse experimentally, indicating that the proper establishment of axial polarity is a critical step in a plant's morphogenesis. In the *gnom* (from the German for a dwarf and misshapen creature) mutant of *Arabidopsis*, the establishment of polarity is defective.

Leaf epidermal cells of wild-type maize

Leaf epidermal cells of *tangled-1* maize mutant

30 μm

▲ **Figure 35.27 Cell division patterns in wild-type and mutant maize plants.** Compared with the epidermal cells of wild-type maize plants (left), the epidermal cells of the *tangled-1* mutant of maize (right) are highly disordered (SEMs). Nevertheless, *tangled-1* maize plants produce normal-looking leaves.

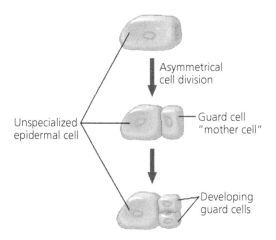

Asymmetrical cell division

Unspecialized epidermal cell

Guard cell "mother cell"

Developing guard cells

▲ **Figure 35.28 Asymmetrical cell division and stomatal development.** An asymmetrical cell division precedes the development of epidermal guard cells, the cells that border stomata (see Figure 35.18).

◄ **Figure 35.29 Establishment of axial polarity.** The normal *Arabidopsis* seedling (left) has a shoot end and a root end. In the *gnom* mutant (right), the first division of the zygote was not asymmetrical; as a result, the plant is ball-shaped and lacks leaves and roots. The defect in *gnom* mutants has been traced to an inability to transport the hormone auxin in a polar manner.

▲ **Figure 35.30 The orientation of plant cell expansion.** Growing plant cells expand mainly through water uptake. In a growing cell, enzymes weaken cross-links in the cell wall, allowing it to expand as water diffuses into the vacuole by osmosis; at the same time, more microfibrils are made. The orientation of the cell expansion is mainly perpendicular to the orientation of cellulose microfibrils in the wall. The orientation of microtubules in the cell's outermost cytoplasm determines the orientation of cellulose microfibrils (fluorescent LM). The microfibrils are embedded in a matrix of other (noncellulose) polysaccharides, some of which form the cross-links visible in the TEM.

The first cell division of the zygote is abnormal because it is symmetrical, and the resulting ball-shaped plant has neither roots nor leaves (**Figure 35.29**).

Orientation of Cell Expansion

Before discussing how cell expansion contributes to plant form, it is useful to consider the difference in cell expansion between plants and animals. Animal cells grow mainly by synthesizing protein-rich cytoplasm, a metabolically expensive process. Growing plant cells also produce additional protein-rich material in their cytoplasm, but water uptake typically accounts for about 90% of expansion. Most of this water is stored in the large central vacuole. The vacuolar solution or *vacuolar sap* is very dilute and nearly devoid of the energetically expensive macromolecules that are found in great abundance in the rest of the cytoplasm. Large vacuoles are therefore a "cheap" way of filling space, enabling a plant to grow rapidly and economically. Bamboo shoots, for instance, can elongate more than 2 m per week. Rapid and efficient extensibility of shoots and roots was an important evolutionary adaptation that increased their exposure to light and soil.

Plant cells rarely expand equally in all directions. Their greatest expansion is usually oriented along the plant's main axis. For example, cells near the tip of the root may elongate up to 20 times their original length, with relatively little increase in width. The orientation of cellulose microfibrils in the innermost layers of the cell wall causes this differential growth. The microfibrils do not stretch, so the cell expands mainly perpendicular to the main orientation of the microfibrils, as shown in **Figure 35.30**. A leading hypothesis proposes that microtubules positioned just beneath the plasma membrane organize the cellulose-synthesizing enzyme complexes and guide their movement through the plasma membrane as they create the microfibrils that form much of the cell wall.

Morphogenesis and Pattern Formation

A plant's body is more than a collection of dividing and expanding cells. During morphogenesis, cells acquire different identities in an ordered spatial arrangement. For example, dermal tissue forms on the exterior, and vascular tissue in the interior—never the other way around. The development of specific structures in specific locations is called **pattern formation**.

Two types of hypotheses have been put forward to explain how the fate of plant cells is determined during pattern formation. Hypotheses based on *lineage-based mechanisms* propose that cell fate is determined early in development and that cells pass on this destiny to their progeny. In this view, the basic pattern of cell differentiation is mapped out according to the directions in which meristematic cells divide and expand. On the other hand, hypotheses based on *position-based mechanisms* propose that the cell's final position in an emerging organ determines what kind of cell it will become. In support of this view, experiments in which neighboring cells have been destroyed with lasers have demonstrated that a plant cell's fate is established late in the cell's development and largely depends on signaling from its neighbors.

In contrast, cell fate in animals is largely determined by lineage-dependent mechanisms involving transcription

▲ **Figure 35.31 Overexpression of a *Hox*-like gene in leaf formation.** *KNOTTED-1* is a gene that is involved in leaf and leaflet formation. An increase in its expression in tomato plants results in leaves that are "super-compound" (right) compared with normal leaves (left).

When an epidermal cell borders a single cortical cell, the homeotic gene *GLABRA-2* is expressed, and the cell remains hairless. (The blue color indicates cells in which *GLABRA-2* is expressed.)

Cortical cells

Here an epidermal cell borders two cortical cells. *GLABRA-2* is not expressed, and the cell will develop a root hair.

20 μm

The root cap cells external to the epidermal layer will be sloughed off before root hairs emerge.

▲ **Figure 35.32 Control of root hair differentiation by a homeotic gene (LM).**

WHAT IF? *What would the roots look like if* GLABRA-2 *were rendered dysfunctional by a mutation?*

factors. The homeotic (*Hox*) genes that encode such transcription factors are critical for the proper number and placement of embryonic structures, such as legs and antennae, in the fruit fly *Drosophila* (see Figure 18.19). Interestingly, maize has a homolog of *Hox* genes called *KNOTTED-1*, but unlike its counterparts in the animal world, *KNOTTED-1* does not affect the number or placement of plant organs. As you will see, an unrelated class of transcription factors called *MADS-box* proteins plays that role in plants. *KNOTTED-1* is, however, important in the development of leaf morphology, including the production of compound leaves. If the *KNOTTED-1* gene is expressed in greater quantity than normal in the genome of tomato plants, the normally compound leaves will then become "super-compound" **(Figure 35.31)**.

Gene Expression and the Control of Cell Differentiation

The cells of a developing organism can synthesize different proteins and diverge in structure and function even though they share a common genome. If a mature cell removed from a root or leaf can dedifferentiate in tissue culture and give rise to the diverse cell types of a plant, then it must possess all the genes necessary to make any kind of cell in the plant (see Figure 20.15). Therefore, cell differentiation depends, to a large degree, on the control of gene expression—the regulation of transcription and translation, resulting in the production of specific proteins.

Evidence suggests that the activation or inactivation of specific genes involved in cell differentiation results largely from cell-to-cell communication. Cells receive information about how they should specialize from neighboring cells. For example, two cell types arise in the root epidermis of *Arabidopsis*: root hair cells and hairless epidermal cells. Cell fate is associated with the position of the epidermal cells.

The immature epidermal cells that are in contact with two underlying cells of the root cortex differentiate into root hair cells, whereas the immature epidermal cells in contact with only one cortical cell differentiate into mature hairless cells. The differential expression of a homeotic gene called *GLABRA-2* (from the Latin *glaber*, bald) is needed for proper distribution of root hairs **(Figure 35.32)**. Researchers have demonstrated this requirement by coupling the *GLABRA-2* gene to a "reporter gene" that causes every cell expressing *GLABRA-2* in the root to turn pale blue following a certain treatment. The *GLABRA-2* gene is normally expressed only in epidermal cells that will not develop root hairs.

Shifts in Development: Phase Changes

Multicellular organisms generally pass through developmental stages. In humans, these are infancy, childhood, adolescence, and adulthood, with puberty as the dividing line between the nonreproductive and reproductive stages. Plants also pass through stages, developing from a juvenile stage to an adult vegetative stage to an adult reproductive stage. In animals, the developmental changes take place throughout the entire organism, such as when a larva develops into an adult animal. In contrast, plant developmental stages, called *phases*, occur within a single region, the shoot apical meristem. The morphological changes that arise from these transitions in shoot apical meristem activity are called **phase changes**. In the transition from a juvenile phase to an adult phase, some species exhibit some striking

Leaves produced by adult phase of apical meristem

Leaves produced by juvenile phase of apical meristem

▲ **Figure 35.33 Phase change in the shoot system of *Acacia koa*.** This native of Hawaii has compound juvenile leaves, consisting of many small leaflets, and simple mature leaves. This dual foliage reflects a phase change in the development of the apical meristem of each shoot. Once a node forms, the developmental phase—juvenile or adult—is fixed; compound leaves do not mature into simple leaves.

changes in leaf morphology (Figure 35.33). Juvenile nodes and internodes retain their juvenile status even after the shoot continues to elongate and the shoot apical meristem has changed to the adult phase. Therefore, any *new* leaves that develop on branches that emerge from axillary buds at juvenile nodes will also be juvenile, even though the apical meristem of the stem's main axis may have been producing mature nodes for years.

If environmental conditions permit, an adult plant is induced to flower. Biologists have made great progress in explaining the genetic control of floral development—the topic of the next section.

Genetic Control of Flowering

Flower formation involves a phase change from vegetative growth to reproductive growth. This transition is triggered by a combination of environmental cues, such as day length, and internal signals, such as hormones. (You will learn more about the roles of these signals in flowering in Chapter 39.) Unlike vegetative growth, which is indeterminate, floral growth is usually determinate: The production of a flower by a shoot apical meristem generally stops the primary growth of that shoot. The transition from vegetative growth to flowering is associated with the switching on of floral **meristem identity genes**. The protein products of these genes are transcription factors that regulate the genes required for the conversion of the indeterminate vegetative meristems to determinate floral meristems.

When a shoot apical meristem is induced to flower, the order of each primordium's emergence determines its development into a specific type of floral organ—a sepal, petal, stamen, or carpel (see Figure 30.8 to review basic flower structure). These floral organs form four whorls that can be described roughly as concentric "circles" when viewed from above. Sepals form the first (outermost) whorl; petals form the second; stamens form the third; and carpels form the fourth (innermost) whorl. Plant biologists have identified several **organ identity genes** belonging to the *MADS-box* family that encode transcription factors that regulate the development of this characteristic floral pattern. Positional information determines which organ identity genes are expressed in a particular floral organ primordium. The result is the development of an emerging floral primordium into a specific floral organ. A mutation in a plant organ identity gene can cause abnormal floral development, such as petals growing in place of stamens (Figure 35.34). Some homeotic mutants with increased petal numbers produce showier flowers that are prized by gardeners.

By studying mutants with abnormal flowers, researchers have identified and cloned three classes of floral organ identity genes, and their studies are beginning to reveal

▲ **Normal *Arabidopsis* flower.** *Arabidopsis* normally has four whorls of flower parts: sepals (Se), petals (Pe), stamens (St), and carpels (Ca).

▶ **Abnormal *Arabidopsis* flower.** Researchers have identified several mutations of organ identity genes that cause abnormal flowers to develop. This flower has an extra set of petals in place of stamens and an internal flower where normal plants have carpels.

▲ **Figure 35.34 Organ identity genes and pattern formation in flower development.**

MAKE CONNECTIONS *Provide another example of a homeotic gene mutation that leads to organs being produced in the wrong place (see Concept 18.4).*

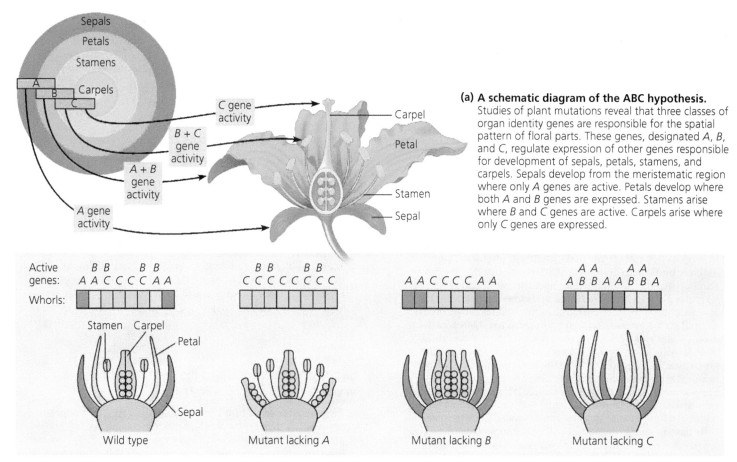

(a) **A schematic diagram of the ABC hypothesis.** Studies of plant mutations reveal that three classes of organ identity genes are responsible for the spatial pattern of floral parts. These genes, designated A, B, and C, regulate expression of other genes responsible for development of sepals, petals, stamens, and carpels. Sepals develop from the meristematic region where only A genes are active. Petals develop where both A and B genes are expressed. Stamens arise where B and C genes are active. Carpels arise where only C genes are expressed.

(b) **Side view of flowers with organ identity mutations.** The phenotype of mutants lacking a functional A, B, or C organ identity gene can be explained by combining the model in part (a) with the rule that if A or C activity is missing, the other activity occurs through all four whorls.

▲ **Figure 35.35** The ABC hypothesis for the functioning of organ identity genes in flower development.

WHAT IF? *What would a flower look like if the A genes and B genes were inactivated?*

how these genes function. **Figure 35.35a** shows a simplified version of the **ABC hypothesis** of flower formation, which proposes that three classes of genes direct the formation of the four types of floral organs. According to the ABC hypothesis, each class of organ identity genes is switched on in two specific whorls of the floral meristem. Normally, A genes are switched on in the two outer whorls (sepals and petals); B genes are switched on in the two middle whorls (petals and stamens); and C genes are switched on in the two inner whorls (stamens and carpels). Sepals arise from those parts of floral meristems in which only A genes are active; petals arise where A and B genes are active; stamens where B and C genes are active; and carpels where only C genes are active. The ABC hypothesis can account for the phenotypes of mutants lacking A, B, or C gene activity, with one addition: Where A gene activity is present, it inhibits C, and vice versa. If either A or C is missing, the other gene takes its place. **Figure 35.35b** shows the floral patterns of mutants lacking each of the three classes of organ identity genes and depicts how the hypothesis accounts for the floral

phenotypes. By constructing such hypotheses and designing experiments to test them, researchers are tracing the genetic basis of plant development.

In dissecting the plant to examine its parts, as we have done in this chapter, we must remember that the whole plant functions as an integrated organism. Plant structures largely reflect evolutionary adaptations to the challenges of a photoautotrophic existence on land.

CONCEPT CHECK **35.5**

1. How can two cells in a plant have vastly different structures even though they have the same genome?

2. What are three differences between animal development and plant development?

3. **WHAT IF?** In some species, sepals look like petals, and both are collectively called "tepals." Suggest an extension to the ABC hypothesis that could account for tepals.

For suggested answers, see Appendix A.

SUMMARY OF KEY CONCEPTS

CONCEPT 35.1

Plants have a hierarchical organization consisting of organs, tissues, and cells (pp. 753–759)

- Vascular plants have shoots consisting of **stems**, **leaves**, and, in angiosperms, flowers. **Roots** anchor the plant, absorb and conduct water and minerals, and store food. Leaves are attached to stem **nodes** and are the main **organs** of photosynthesis. The **axillary buds**, in axils of leaves and stems, give rise to branches. Plant organs may be adapted for specialized functions.
- Vascular plants have three **tissue systems**—dermal, vascular, and ground—which are continuous throughout the plant. The **dermal tissue** protects against pathogens, herbivores, and drought and aids in absorption of water, minerals, and carbon dioxide. **Vascular tissues** (**xylem** and **phloem**) facilitate the long-distance transport of substances. **Ground tissues** function in storage, metabolism, and regeneration.
- **Parenchyma cells** are relatively unspecialized and thin-walled cells that retain the ability to divide; they perform most of the metabolic functions of synthesis and storage. **Collenchyma cells** have unevenly thickened walls; they support young, growing parts of the plant. **Sclerenchyma cells**—**sclereids** and **fibers**—have thick, lignified walls that help support mature, nongrowing parts of the plant. **Tracheids** and **vessel elements**, the water-conducting cells of xylem, have thick walls and are dead at functional maturity. **Sieve-tube elements** are living but highly modified cells that are largely devoid of internal organelles; they function in the transport of sugars through the phloem of angiosperms.

? *Describe at least three specializations in plant organs and plant cells that are adaptations to life on land.*

CONCEPT 35.2

Different meristems generate new cells for primary and secondary growth (pp. 760–761)

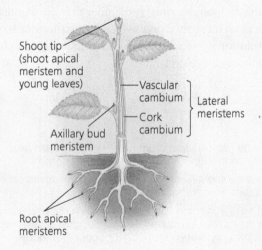

Shoot tip (shoot apical meristem and young leaves)

Axillary bud meristem

Vascular cambium

Cork cambium

Lateral meristems

Root apical meristems

? *What is the difference between primary and secondary growth?*

CONCEPT 35.3

Primary growth lengthens roots and shoots (pp. 761–765)

- The root **apical meristem** is located near the tip of the root, where it generates cells for the growing root axis and the **root cap**.
- The apical meristem of a shoot is located in the **apical bud**, where it gives rise to alternating **internodes** and leaf-bearing nodes.
- Eudicot stems have vascular bundles in a ring, whereas monocot stems have scattered vascular bundles.
- **Mesophyll** cells are adapted for photosynthesis. **Stomata**, epidermal pores formed by pairs of **guard cells**, allow for gaseous exchange and are major avenues for water loss.

? *How does branching differ in roots versus stems?*

CONCEPT 35.4

Secondary growth increases the diameter of stems and roots in woody plants (pp. 765–769)

- The **vascular cambium** is a meristematic cylinder that produces secondary xylem and secondary phloem during **secondary growth**. Older layers of secondary xylem (heartwood) become inactive, whereas younger layers (sapwood) still conduct water.
- The **cork cambium** gives rise to a thick protective covering called the periderm, which consists of the cork cambium plus the layers of cork cells it produces.

? *What advantages did plants gain from the evolution of secondary growth?*

CONCEPT 35.5

Growth, morphogenesis, and cell differentiation produce the plant body (pp. 769–775)

- Cell division and cell expansion are the primary determinants of growth. A preprophase band of microtubules determines where a cell plate will form in a dividing cell. Microtubule orientation also affects the direction of cell elongation by controlling the orientation of cellulose microfibrils in the cell wall.
- Morphogenesis, the development of body shape and organization, depends on cells responding to positional information from their neighbors.
- Cell differentiation, arising from differential gene activation, enables cells within the plant to assume different functions despite having identical genomes. The way in which a plant cell differentiates is determined largely by the cell's position in the developing plant.
- Internal or environmental cues may cause a plant to switch from one developmental stage to another—for example, from developing juvenile leaves to developing mature leaves. Such morphological changes are called **phase changes**.
- Research on **organ identity genes** in developing flowers provides a model system for studying **pattern formation**. The **ABC hypothesis** identifies how three classes of organ identity genes control formation of sepals, petals, stamens, and carpels.

? *By what mechanism do plant cells tend to elongate along one axis instead of expanding in all directions?*

LEVEL 1: KNOWLEDGE/COMPREHENSION

1. Most of the growth of a plant body is the result of
   a. cell differentiation.
   b. morphogenesis.
   c. cell division.
   d. cell elongation.

2. The innermost layer of the root cortex is the
   a. core.
   b. pericycle.
   c. endodermis.
   d. pith.

3. Heartwood and sapwood consist of
   a. bark.
   b. periderm.
   c. secondary xylem.
   d. secondary phloem.

4. The phase change of an apical meristem from the juvenile to the mature vegetative phase is often revealed by
   a. a change in the morphology of the leaves produced.
   b. the initiation of secondary growth.
   c. the formation of lateral roots.
   d. the activation of floral meristem identity genes.

LEVEL 2: APPLICATION/ANALYSIS

5. Suppose a flower had normal expression of genes *A* and *C* and expression of gene *B* in all four whorls. Based on the ABC hypothesis, what would be the structure of that flower, starting at the outermost whorl?
   a. carpel-petal-petal-carpel
   b. petal-petal-stamen-stamen
   c. sepal-carpel-carpel-sepal
   d. sepal-sepal-carpel-carpel

6. Which of the following arise, directly or indirectly, from meristematic activity?
   a. secondary xylem
   b. leaves
   c. dermal tissue
   d. all of the above

7. Which of the following would not be seen in a cross section through the woody part of a root?
   a. sclerenchyma cells
   b. parenchyma cells
   c. sieve-tube elements
   d. root hairs

8. **DRAW IT** On this cross section from a woody eudicot, label a growth ring, late wood, early wood, and a vessel element. Then draw an arrow in the pith-to-cork direction.

LEVEL 3: SYNTHESIS/EVALUATION

9. **EVOLUTION CONNECTION**
   Evolutionary biologists have coined the term *exaptation* to describe a common occurrence in the evolution of life: A limb or organ evolves in a particular context but over time takes on a new function (see Concept 23.4). What are some examples of exaptations in plant organs?

10. **SCIENTIFIC INQUIRY**
    Grasslands typically do not flourish when large herbivores are removed. Instead, grasslands are replaced by broad-leaved herbaceous eudicots, shrubs, and trees. Based on your knowledge of the structure and growth habits of monocots versus eudicots, suggest a reason why.

11. **SCIENCE, TECHNOLOGY, AND SOCIETY**
    Hunger and malnutrition are urgent problems for many poor countries, yet plant biologists in wealthy nations have focused most of their research efforts on *Arabidopsis thaliana*. Some people have argued that if plant biologists are truly concerned about fighting world hunger, they should study cassava and plantain because these two crops are staples for many of the world's poor. If you were an *Arabidopsis* researcher, how might you respond to this argument?

12. **WRITE ABOUT A THEME: ORGANIZATION**
    In a short essay (100–150 words), explain how the evolution of lignin affected vascular plant structure and function.

13. **SYNTHESIZE YOUR KNOWLEDGE**

This is a light micrograph of a cross section through a plant organ from an angiosperm with an unusual morphology. Is the organ a stem, leaf, or root? Explain your reasoning.

For selected answers, see Appendix A.

MasteringBiology®

Students Go to **MasteringBiology** for assignments, the eText, and the Study Area with practice tests, animations, and activities.

Instructors Go to **MasteringBiology** for automatically graded tutorials and questions that you can assign to your students, plus Instructor Resources.

36

Resource Acquisition and Transport in Vascular Plants

▲ Figure 36.1 **Why do aspens quake?**

A Whole Lot of Shaking Going On

If you walk amidst an aspen (*Populus tremuloides*) forest on a clear day, you will be treated to a fantastic light display **(Figure 36.1)**. Even on a day with little wind, the trembling of leaves causes shafts of brilliant sunlight to dapple the forest floor with ever-changing flecks of radiance. The mechanism underlying these passive leaf movements is not difficult to discern: The petiole of each leaf is flattened along its sides, permitting the leaf to flop only in the horizontal plane. Perhaps more curious is why this peculiar adaptation has evolved in *Populus*.

Many hypotheses have been put forward to explain how leaf quaking benefits *Populus*. Old ideas that leaf trembling helps replace the CO_2-depleted air near the leaf surface, or deters herbivores, have not been supported by experiments. The leading hypothesis is that leaf trembling increases the photosynthetic productivity of the whole plant by allowing more light to reach the lower leaves of the tree. If not for the shafts of transient sunlight provided by leaf trembling, the lower leaves would be too shaded to photosynthesize sufficiently.

In this chapter, we'll examine various adaptations, such as the flattened petioles of *Populus*, that help plants acquire water, minerals, carbon dioxide, and light more efficiently. The acquisition of these resources, however, is just the beginning of the story. Resources must be transported to where they are needed. Thus, we will also examine how water, minerals, and sugars are transported through the plant.

Adaptations for acquiring resources were key steps in the evolution of vascular plants

EVOLUTION Land plants typically inhabit two worlds—above ground, where shoots acquire sunlight and CO_2, and below ground, where roots acquire water and minerals. Without adaptations that allow acquisition of these resources, plants could not have colonized land.

The algal ancestors of land plants absorbed water, minerals, and CO_2 directly from the water in which they lived. Transport in these algae was relatively simple because every cell was close to the source of these substances. The earliest land plants were nonvascular plants that grew photosynthetic shoots above the shallow fresh water in which they lived. These leafless shoots typically had waxy cuticles and few stomata, which allowed them to avoid excessive water loss while still permitting some exchange of CO_2 and O_2 for photosynthesis. The anchoring and absorbing functions of early land plants were assumed by the base of the stem or by threadlike rhizoids (see Figure 29.6).

As land plants evolved and increased in number, competition for light, water, and nutrients intensified. Taller plants with broad, flat appendages had an advantage in absorbing light. This increase in surface area, however, resulted in more evaporation and therefore a greater need for water. Larger shoots also required stronger anchorage. These needs favored the production of multicellular, branching roots. Meanwhile, as greater shoot heights further separated the top of the photosynthetic shoot from the nonphotosynthetic parts below ground, natural selection favored plants capable of efficient long-distance transport of water, minerals, and products of photosynthesis.

The evolution of vascular tissue consisting of xylem and phloem made possible the development of extensive root and shoot systems that carry out long-distance transport (see Figure 35.10). The **xylem** transports water and minerals from roots to shoots. The **phloem** transports products of photosynthesis from where they are made or stored to where they are needed. **Figure 36.2** provides an overview of resource acquisition and transport in a vascular plant.

Because plant success is generally related to photosynthesis, evolution has resulted in many structural adaptations for efficiently acquiring light from the sun and CO_2 from the air. The broad surface of most leaves, for example, favors light capture, while open stomatal pores allow for the diffusion of CO_2 into the photosynthetic tissues. Open stomatal pores, however, also promote evaporation of water from the plant. Consequently, the adaptations of plants represent compromises between enhancing photosynthesis and minimizing water loss, particularly in environments where water is scarce.

▼ **Figure 36.2** **An overview of resource acquisition and transport in a vascular plant.**

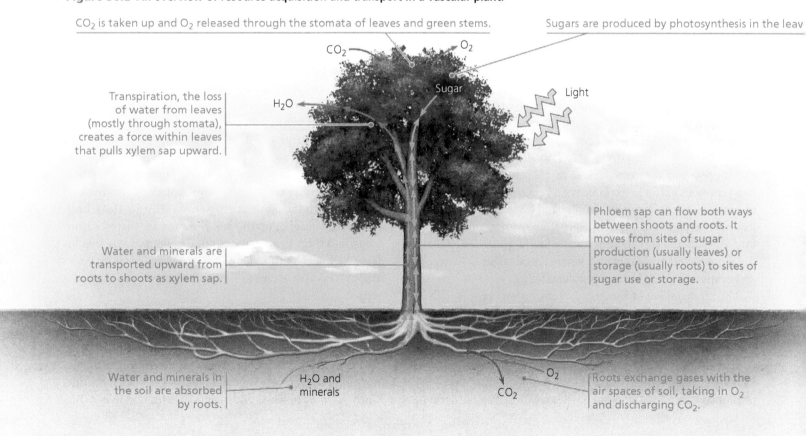

CO_2 is taken up and O_2 released through the stomata of leaves and green stems.

Sugars are produced by photosynthesis in the leav

Transpiration, the loss of water from leaves (mostly through stomata), creates a force within leaves that pulls xylem sap upward.

Water and minerals are transported upward from roots to shoots as xylem sap.

Phloem sap can flow both ways between shoots and roots. It moves from sites of sugar production (usually leaves) or storage (usually roots) to sites of sugar use or storage.

Water and minerals in the soil are absorbed by roots.

H_2O and minerals

Roots exchange gases with the air spaces of soil, taking in O_2 and discharging CO_2.

Later in the chapter, we'll discuss the mechanisms by which plants enhance CO_2 uptake and minimize water loss by regulating the opening of stomatal pores. Here, we examine how the basic architecture of shoots and roots helps plants acquire resources such as water, minerals, and sunlight.

Shoot Architecture and Light Capture

Much of the diversity we see in plants is a reflection of differences in the branching patterns, dimensions, shapes, and orientations of the shoot's two components— stems and leaves. Shoot architecture typically facilitates light capture for photosynthesis.

Stems serve as supporting structures for leaves and as conduits for the transport of water and nutrients. The length of stems and their branching patterns are two architectural features affecting light capture. Plants that grow tall avoid shading from neighboring plants. Most tall plants require thick stems, which enable greater vascular flow to and from the leaves and stronger mechanical support for them. Vines are an exception, relying on other objects (usually other plants) to support their stems. In woody plants, stems become thicker through secondary growth (see Figure 35.11).

Branching generally enables plants to harvest sunlight for photosynthesis more effectively. However, some species, such as the coconut palm, do not branch at all. Why is there so much variation in branching patterns? Plants have only a finite amount of energy to devote to shoot growth. If most of that energy goes into branching, there is less available for growing tall, and the risk of being shaded by taller plants increases. Conversely, if most of the energy goes into growing tall, the plants are not optimally harvesting sunlight. Natural selection has produced a variety of shoot architectures among species, fine-tuning the ability to absorb light in the ecological niche each species occupies.

Leaf size and structure account for much of the outward diversity in plant form. Leaves range in length from 1.3 mm in the pygmy weed (*Crassula erecta*), a native of dry, sandy regions in the western United States, to 20 m in the palm *Raphia regalis*, a native of African rain forests. These species represent extreme examples of a general correlation observed between water availability and leaf size. The largest leaves are typically found in species from tropical rain forests, whereas the smallest are usually found in species from dry or very cold environments, where liquid water is scarce and evaporative loss is more problematic.

The arrangement of leaves on a stem, known as **phyllotaxy**, is an architectural feature important in light capture. Phyllotaxy is determined by the shoot apical meristem (see Figure 35.16) and is specific to each species **(Figure 36.3)**. A species may have one leaf per node (alternate, or spiral, phyllotaxy), two leaves per node (opposite phyllotaxy), or more (whorled phyllotaxy). Most angiosperms

▲ **Figure 36.3 Emerging phyllotaxy of Norway spruce.** This SEM, taken from above a shoot tip, shows the pattern of emergence of leaves. The leaves are numbered, with 1 being the youngest. (Some numbered leaves are not visible in the close-up.)

? *With your finger, trace the progression of leaf emergence, moving from leaf number 29 to 28 and so on. What is the pattern?*

have alternate phyllotaxy, with leaves arranged in an ascending spiral around the stem, each successive leaf emerging 137.5° from the site of the previous one. Why 137.5°? One hypothesis is that this angle minimizes shading of the lower leaves by those above. In environments where intense sunlight can harm leaves, the greater shading provided by oppositely arranged leaves may be advantageous.

The total area of the leafy portions of all the plants in a community, from the top layer of vegetation to the bottom layer, affects the productivity of each plant. When there are many layers of vegetation, the shading of the lower leaves is so great that they photosynthesize less than they respire. When this happens, the nonproductive leaves or branches undergo programmed cell death and are eventually shed, a process called *self-pruning*.

Plant features that reduce self-shading increase light capture. A useful measurement in this regard is the *leaf area index*, the ratio of the total upper leaf surface of a single plant or an entire crop divided by the surface area of the land on which the plant or crop grows **(Figure 36.4)**. Leaf area index values of up to 7 are common for many mature crops, and there is little agricultural benefit to leaf area indexes higher than this value. Adding more leaves increases shading of lower leaves to the point that self-pruning occurs.

Another factor affecting light capture is leaf orientation. Some plants have horizontally oriented leaves; others, such as grasses, have leaves that are vertically oriented. In low-light conditions, horizontal leaves capture sunlight much more effectively than vertical leaves. In grasslands or other sunny regions, however, horizontal orientation may expose

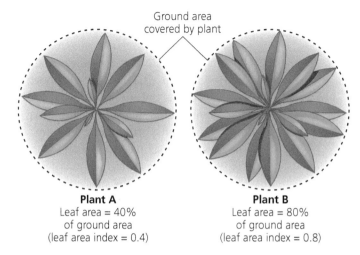

Ground area
covered by plant

Plant A
Leaf area = 40%
of ground area
(leaf area index = 0.4)

Plant B
Leaf area = 80%
of ground area
(leaf area index = 0.8)

▲ **Figure 36.4 Leaf area index.** The leaf area index of a single plant is the ratio of the total area of the top surfaces of the leaves to the area of ground covered by the plant, as shown in this illustration of two plants viewed from the top. With many layers of leaves, a leaf area index value can easily exceed 1.

? *Would a higher leaf area index always increase the amount of photosynthesis? Explain.*

upper leaves to overly intense light, injuring leaves and reducing photosynthesis. But if a plant's leaves are nearly vertical, light rays are essentially parallel to the leaf surfaces, so no leaf receives too much light, and light penetrates more deeply to the lower leaves.

Root Architecture and Acquisition of Water and Minerals

Just as carbon dioxide and sunlight are resources exploited by the shoot system, soil contains resources mined by the root system. Plants rapidly adjust the architecture and physiology of their roots to exploit patches of available nutrients in the soil. The roots of many plants, for example, respond to pockets of low nitrate availability in soils by extending straight through the pockets instead of branching within them. Conversely, when encountering a pocket rich in nitrate, a root will often branch extensively there. Root cells also respond to high soil nitrate levels by synthesizing more proteins involved in nitrate transport and assimilation. Thus, not only does the plant devote more of its mass to exploiting a nitrate-rich patch; the cells also absorb nitrate more efficiently.

Efficient absorption of limited nutrients is also enhanced by reduced competition within the root system of a plant. For example, cuttings taken from stolons of buffalo grass (*Buchloe dactyloides*) develop fewer and shorter roots in the presence of cuttings from the same plant than they do in the presence of cuttings from another buffalo grass plant. Researchers are trying to uncover the mechanism underlying this ability to distinguish self from nonself.

The evolution of **mycorrhizae**, mutualistic associations between roots and fungi, was a critical step in the successful colonization of land by plants. Mycorrhizal hyphae indirectly endow the root systems of many plants with an enormous surface area for absorbing water and minerals, particularly phosphate. The role of mycorrhizal associations in plant nutrition will be examined more fully in Chapter 37.

Once acquired, resources must be transported to other parts of the plant that need them. In the next section, we examine the processes and pathways that enable resources such as water, minerals, and sugars to be transported throughout the plant.

CONCEPT CHECK 36.1

1. Why is long-distance transport important for vascular plants?

2. What architectural features influence self-shading?

3. Some plants can detect increased levels of light reflected from leaves of encroaching neighbors. This detection elicits stem elongation, production of erect leaves, and reduced lateral branching. How do these responses help the plant compete?

4. **WHAT IF?** If you prune a plant's shoot tips, what will be the short-term effect on the plant's branching and leaf area index?

5. **MAKE CONNECTIONS** Explain how fungal hyphae provide more surface area for nutrient absorption (see Concept 31.1).

For suggested answers, see Appendix A.

CONCEPT 36.2

Different mechanisms transport substances over short or long distances

Given the diversity of substances that move through plants and the great range of distances and barriers over which such substances must be transported, it is not surprising that plants employ a variety of transport processes. Before examining these processes, however, we'll look at the two major pathways of transport: the apoplast and the symplast.

The Apoplast and Symplast: Transport Continuums

Plant tissues may be viewed as having two major compartments—the apoplast and the symplast. The **apoplast** consists of everything external to the plasma membranes of living cells and includes cell walls, extracellular spaces, and the interior of dead cells such as vessel elements and tracheids (see Figure 35.10). The **symplast** consists of the entire mass of cytosol of all the living cells in a plant, as well

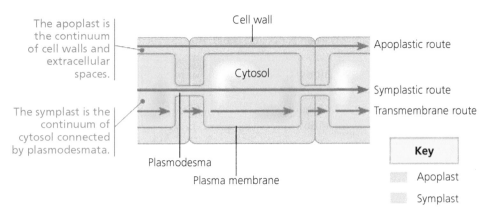

The apoplast is the continuum of cell walls and extracellular spaces.

The symplast is the continuum of cytosol connected by plasmodesmata.

Cell wall

Cytosol

Apoplastic route

Symplastic route
Transmembrane route

Plasmodesma

Plasma membrane

Key

Apoplast

Symplast

▲ **Figure 36.5 Cell compartments and routes for short-distance transport.** Some substances may use more than one transport route.

as the plasmodesmata, the cytoplasmic channels that interconnect them.

The compartmental structure of plants provides three routes for transport within a plant tissue or organ: the apoplastic, symplastic, and transmembrane routes (**Figure 36.5**). In the *apoplastic route*, water and solutes (dissolved chemicals) move along the continuum of cell walls and extracellular spaces. In the *symplastic route*, water and solutes move along the continuum of cytosol. This route requires substances to cross a plasma membrane once, when they first enter the plant. After entering one cell, substances can move from cell to cell via plasmodesmata. In the *transmembrane route*, water and solutes move out of one cell, across the cell wall, and into the neighboring cell, which may pass them to the next cell in the same way. The transmembrane route requires repeated crossings of plasma membranes as substances exit one cell and enter the next. These three routes are not mutually exclusive, and some substances may use more than one route to varying degrees.

Short-Distance Transport of Solutes Across Plasma Membranes

In plants, as in any organism, the selective permeability of the plasma membrane controls the short-distance movement of substances into and out of cells (see Chapter 7). Both active and passive transport mechanisms occur in plants, and plant cell membranes are equipped with the same general types of pumps and transport proteins (channel proteins, carrier proteins, and cotransporters) that function in other cells. In this section, we focus on some ways that plants differ from animals in solute transport across plasma membranes.

Unlike in animal cells, hydrogen ions (H^+) rather than sodium ions (Na^+) play the primary role in basic transport processes in plant cells. For example, in plant cells the membrane potential (the voltage across the membrane) is established mainly through the pumping of H^+ by proton pumps

(**Figure 36.6a**), rather than the pumping of Na^+ by sodium-potassium pumps. Also, H^+ is most often cotransported in plants, whereas Na^+ is typically cotransported in animals. During cotransport, plant cells use the energy in the H^+ gradient and membrane potential to drive the active transport of many different solutes. For instance, cotransport with H^+ is responsible for absorption of neutral solutes, such as the sugar sucrose, by phloem cells and other plant cells. An H^+/sucrose cotransporter couples movement of sucrose against its concentration gradient with movement of H^+ down its electrochemical gradient (**Figure 36.6b**). Cotransport with H^+ also facilitates movement of ions, as in the uptake of nitrate (NO_3^-) by root cells (**Figure 36.6c**).

The membranes of plant cells also have ion channels that allow only certain ions to pass (**Figure 36.6d**). As in animal cells, most channels are gated, opening or closing in response to stimuli such as chemicals, pressure, or voltage. Later in this chapter, we'll discuss how K^+ ion channels in guard cells function in opening and closing stomata. Ion channels are also involved in producing electrical signals analogous to the action potentials of animals (see Chapter 48). However, these signals are 1,000 times slower and employ Ca^{2+}-activated anion channels rather than the Na^+ ion channels used by animal cells.

Short-Distance Transport of Water Across Plasma Membranes

The absorption or loss of water by a cell occurs by **osmosis**, the diffusion of free water—water that is not bound to solutes or surfaces—across a membrane (see Figure 7.12). The physical property that predicts the direction in which water will flow is called **water potential**, a quantity that includes the effects of solute concentration and physical pressure. Free water moves from regions of higher water potential to regions of lower water potential if there is no barrier to its flow. The word *potential* in the term *water potential* refers to water's potential energy—water's capacity to perform work when it moves from a region of higher water potential to a region of lower water potential. For example, if a plant cell or seed is immersed in a solution that has a higher water potential, water will move into the cell or seed, causing it to expand. The expansion of plant cells and seeds can be a powerful force: The expansion of cells in tree roots can break concrete sidewalks, and the swelling of wet grain seeds within the holds of damaged ships can produce catastrophic hull failure and sink the ships. Given the strong forces generated by swelling seeds, it is interesting to consider what causes water uptake by seeds. You can explore this question

CYTOPLASM   EXTRACELLULAR FLUID

Proton pump

(a) H⁺ and membrane potential. The plasma membranes of plant cells use ATP-dependent proton pumps to pump H⁺ out of the cell. These pumps contribute to the membrane potential and the establishment of a pH gradient across the membrane. These two forms of potential energy can drive the transport of solutes.

H⁺/sucrose cotransporter   Sucrose (neutral solute)

(b) H⁺ and cotransport of neutral solutes. Neutral solutes such as sugars can be loaded into plant cells by cotransport with H⁺ ions. H⁺/sucrose cotransporters, for example, play a key role in loading sugar into the phloem prior to sugar transport throughout the plant.

Nitrate

H⁺/NO₃⁻ cotransporter

(c) H⁺ and cotransport of ions. Cotransport mechanisms involving H⁺ also participate in regulating ion fluxes into and out of cells. For example, H⁺/NO₃⁻ cotransporters in the plasma membranes of root cells are important for the uptake of NO_3^- by plant roots.

Potassium ion

Ion channel

(d) Ion channels. Plant ion channels open and close in response to voltage, stretching of the membrane, and chemical factors. When open, ion channels allow specific ions to diffuse across membranes. For example, a K⁺ ion channel is involved in the release of K⁺ from guard cells when stomata close.

▲ **Figure 36.6 Solute transport across plant cell plasma membranes.**

? *Assume that a plant cell has all four of the plasma membrane transport proteins shown above and that you have a specific inhibitor for each protein. Predict the effect of each inhibitor on the cell's membrane potential.*

in the Scientific Skills Exercise (on the next page) by examining the effect of temperature.

Water potential is abbreviated by the Greek letter ψ (psi, pronounced "sigh"). Plant biologists measure ψ in a unit of pressure called a **megapascal** (abbreviated MPa). By definition, the ψ of pure water in a container open to the atmosphere under standard conditions (at sea level and at room temperature) is 0 MPa. One MPa is equal to about 10 times atmospheric pressure at sea level. The internal pressure of a living plant cell due to the osmotic uptake of water is approximately 0.5 MPa, about twice the air pressure inside an inflated car tire.

How Solutes and Pressure Affect Water Potential

Both solute concentration and physical pressure can affect water potential, as expressed in the *water potential equation*:

$$\psi = \psi_S + \psi_P$$

where ψ is the water potential, ψ_S is the solute potential (osmotic potential), and ψ_P is the pressure potential. The **solute potential** (ψ_S) of a solution is directly proportional to its molarity. Solute potential is also called *osmotic potential* because solutes affect the direction of osmosis. The solutes in plants are typically mineral ions and sugars. By definition, the ψ_S of pure water is 0. When solutes are added, they bind water molecules. As a result, there are fewer free water molecules, reducing the capacity of the water to move and do work. In this way, an increase in solute concentration has a negative effect on water potential, which is why the ψ_S of a solution is always expressed as a negative number. For example, a 0.1 *M* solution of a sugar has a ψ_S of −0.23 MPa. As the solute concentration increases, ψ_S will become more negative.

Pressure potential (ψ_P) is the physical pressure on a solution. Unlike ψ_S, ψ_P can be positive or negative relative to atmospheric pressure. For example, when a solution is being withdrawn by a syringe, it is under negative pressure; when it is being expelled from a syringe, it is under positive pressure. The water in living cells is usually under positive pressure due to the osmotic uptake of water. Specifically, the **protoplast** (the living part of the cell, which also includes the plasma membrane) presses against the cell wall, creating what is known as **turgor pressure**. This pushing effect of internal pressure, much like the air in an inflated tire, is critical for plant function because it helps maintain the stiffness of plant tissues and also serves as the driving force for cell elongation. Conversely, the water in the hollow nonliving xylem cells (tracheids and vessel elements) of a plant is often under a negative pressure potential (tension) of less than −2 MPa.

Calculating and Interpreting Temperature Coefficients

Does the Initial Uptake of Water by Seeds Depend on Temperature? One way to answer this question is to soak seeds in water at different temperatures and measure the rate of water uptake at each temperature. The data can be used to calculate the temperature coefficient, Q_{10}, the factor by which a physiological reaction (or process) rate increases when the temperature is raised by 10°C:

$$Q_{10} = \left(\frac{k_2}{k_1}\right)^{\frac{10}{t_2 - t_1}}$$

where t_2 is the higher temperature (°C), t_1 is the lower temperature, k_2 is the reaction (or process) rate at t_2, and k_1 is the reaction (or process) rate at t_1. (If $t_2 - t_1 = 10$, as here, the math is simplified.)

Q_{10} values may be used to make inferences about the physiological process under investigation. Chemical (metabolic) processes involving large-scale protein shape changes are highly dependent on temperature and have higher Q_{10} values, closer to 2 or 3. In contrast, many, but not all, physical parameters are relatively independent of temperature and have Q_{10} values closer to 1. For example, the Q_{10} of the change in the viscosity of water is 1.2–1.3. In this exercise, you will calculate Q_{10} using data from radish seeds (*Raphanus sativum*) to assess whether the initial uptake of water by seeds is more likely to be a physical or a chemical process.

How the Experiment Was Done Samples of radish seeds were weighed and placed in water at four different temperatures. After 30 minutes, the seeds were removed, blotted dry, and reweighed. The researchers then calculated the percent increase in mass due to water uptake for each sample.

Data from the Experiment

Temperature	% Increase in Mass Due to Water Uptake after 30 Minutes
5°C	18.5
15°C	26.0
25°C	31.0
35°C	36.2

Interpret the Data

1. Based on the data, does the initial uptake of water by radish seeds vary with temperature? What is the relationship between temperature and water uptake?

2. (a) Using the data for 35°C and 25°C, calculate Q_{10} for water uptake by radish seeds. Repeat the calculation using the data for 25°C and 15°C and the data for 15°C and 5°C. (b) What is the average Q_{10}? (c) Do your results imply that the uptake of water by radish seeds is mainly a physical process or a chemical (metabolic) process? (d) Given that the Q_{10} for the change in the viscosity of water is 1.2–1.3, could the slight temperature dependence of water uptake by seeds be a reflection of the slight temperature dependence of the viscosity of water?

3. Besides temperature, what other independent variables could you alter to test whether radish seed swelling is essentially a physical process or a chemical process?

4. Would you expect plant growth to have a Q_{10} closer to 1 or 3? Why?

(MB) A version of this Scientific Skills Exercise can be assigned in MasteringBiology.

Data from J. D. Murphy and D. L. Noland, Temperature effects on seed imbibition and leakage mediated by viscosity and membranes, *Plant Physiology* 69:428–431 (1982).

As you learn to apply the water potential equation, keep in mind the key point: *Water moves from regions of higher water potential to regions of lower water potential.*

Water Movement Across Plant Cell Membranes

Now let's consider how water potential affects absorption and loss of water by a living plant cell. First, imagine a cell that is **flaccid** (limp) as a result of losing water. The cell has a ψ_P of 0 MPa. Suppose this flaccid cell is bathed in a solution of higher solute concentration (more negative solute potential) than the cell itself **(Figure 36.7a)**. Since the external solution has the lower (more negative) water potential, water diffuses out of the cell. The cell's protoplast undergoes **plasmolysis**—that is, it shrinks and pulls away from the cell wall. If we place the same flaccid cell in pure water ($\psi = 0$ MPa) **(Figure 36.7b)**, the cell, because it contains solutes, has a lower water potential than the water, and water enters the cell by osmosis. The contents of the cell begin to swell and press the plasma membrane against the cell wall. The partially elastic wall, exerting turgor pressure, confines the pressurized protoplast. When this pressure is enough to offset the tendency for water to enter because of the solutes in the cell, then ψ_P and ψ_S are equal, and $\psi = 0$. This matches the water potential of the extracellular environment—in this example, 0 MPa. A dynamic equilibrium has been reached, and there is no further *net* movement of water.

Turgid

Wilted

In contrast to a flaccid cell, a walled cell with a greater solute concentration than its surroundings is **turgid**, or very firm. When turgid cells in a nonwoody tissue push against each other, the tissue is stiffened. The effects of turgor loss are seen during **wilting**, when leaves and stems droop as a result of cells losing water.

Aquaporins: Facilitating Diffusion of Water

A difference in water potential determines the *direction* of water movement across membranes, but how do water molecules actually cross the membranes? Water molecules are small enough to diffuse across the phospholipid bilayer, even though the bilayer's interior is hydrophobic. However, their movement across biological membranes is too rapid to

Initial flaccid cell:
$\psi_P = 0$
$\psi_S = -0.7$
$\overline{\psi = -0.7 \text{ MPa}}$

Environment
0.4 *M* sucrose solution:
$\psi_P = 0$
$\psi_S = -0.9$
$\overline{\psi = -0.9 \text{ MPa}}$

Final plasmolyzed cell
at osmotic equilibrium
with its surroundings:
$\psi_P = 0$
$\psi_S = -0.9$
$\overline{\psi = -0.9 \text{ MPa}}$

(a) Initial conditions: cellular ψ > environmental ψ. The protoplast loses water, and the cell plasmolyzes. After plasmolysis is complete, the water potentials of the cell and its surroundings are the same.

Initial flaccid cell:
$\psi_P = 0$
$\psi_S = -0.7$
$\overline{\psi = -0.7 \text{ MPa}}$

Environment
Pure water:
$\psi_P = 0$
$\psi_S = 0$
$\overline{\psi = 0 \text{ MPa}}$

Final turgid cell
at osmotic equilibrium
with its surroundings:
$\psi_P = 0.7$
$\psi_S = -0.7$
$\overline{\psi = 0 \text{ MPa}}$

(b) Initial conditions: cellular ψ < environmental ψ. There is a net uptake of water by osmosis, causing the cell to become turgid. When this tendency for water to enter is offset by the back pressure of the elastic wall, water potentials are equal for the cell and its surroundings. (The volume change of the cell is exaggerated in this diagram.)

▲ **Figure 36.7 Water relations in plant cells.** In these experiments, flaccid cells (cells in which the protoplast contacts the cell wall but lacks turgor pressure) are placed in two environments. The blue arrows indicate initial net water movement.

be explained by unaided diffusion. Transport proteins called **aquaporins** (see Chapter 7) facilitate the transport of water molecules across plant cell plasma membranes. Aquaporin channels, which have the ability to open and close, affect the *rate* at which water moves osmotically across the membrane. Their permeability is decreased by increases in cytosolic Ca^{2+} or decreases in cytosolic pH.

Long-Distance Transport: The Role of Bulk Flow

Diffusion is an effective transport mechanism over the spatial scales typically found at the cellular level. However, diffusion is much too slow to function in long-distance transport within a plant. Although diffusion from one end of a cell to the other takes just seconds, diffusion from the roots to the top of a giant redwood would take several centuries. Instead, long-distance transport occurs through **bulk flow**, the movement of liquid in response to a pressure gradient. The bulk flow of material always occurs from higher to lower pressure. Unlike osmosis, bulk flow is independent of solute concentration.

Long-distance bulk flow occurs within the tracheids and vessel elements of the xylem and within the sieve-tube elements of the phloem. The structures of these conducting cells facilitate bulk flow. Mature tracheids and vessel elements are dead cells and therefore have no cytoplasm, and the cytoplasm of sieve-tube elements is almost devoid of internal organelles (see Figure 35.10). If you have ever dealt with a partially clogged drain, you know that the volume of flow depends on the pipe's diameter. Clogs reduce the effective diameter of the drainpipe. Such experiences help us

understand how the structures of plant cells specialized for bulk flow fit their function. Like the unclogging of a kitchen drain, the absence or reduction of cytoplasm in a plant's "plumbing" facilitates bulk flow through the xylem and phloem. Bulk flow is also enhanced by the perforation plates at the ends of vessel elements and the porous sieve plates connecting sieve-tube elements.

Diffusion, active transport, and bulk flow act in concert to transport resources throughout the whole plant. For example, bulk flow due to a pressure difference is the mechanism of long-distance transport of sugars in the phloem, but active transport of sugar at the cellular level maintains this pressure difference. In the next three sections, we'll examine in more detail the transport of water and minerals from roots to shoots, the control of evaporation, and the transport of sugars.

CONCEPT CHECK **36.2**

1. If a plant cell immersed in distilled water has a ψ_S of −0.7 MPa and a ψ of 0 MPa, what is the cell's ψ_P? If you put it in an open beaker of solution that has a ψ of −0.4 MPa, what would be its ψ_P at equilibrium?

2. How would a reduction in the number of aquaporin channels affect a plant cell's ability to adjust to new osmotic conditions?

3. How would the long-distance transport of water be affected if tracheids and vessel elements were alive at maturity? Explain.

4. **WHAT IF?** What would happen if you put plant protoplasts in pure water? Explain.

For suggested answers, see Appendix A.

CONCEPT 36.3

Transpiration drives the transport of water and minerals from roots to shoots via the xylem

Picture yourself struggling to carry a 19-liter (5-gallon) container of water weighing 19 kilograms (42 pounds) up several flights of stairs. Imagine doing this 40 times a day. Then consider the fact that an average-sized tree, despite having neither heart nor muscle, transports a similar volume of water effortlessly on a daily basis. How do trees accomplish this feat? To answer this question, we'll follow each step in the journey of water and minerals from roots to leaves.

Absorption of Water and Minerals by Root Cells

Although all living plant cells absorb nutrients across their plasma membranes, the cells near the tips of roots are particularly important because most of the absorption of water and minerals occurs there. In this region, the epidermal cells are permeable to water, and many are differentiated into root hairs, modified cells that account for much of the absorption of water by roots (see Figure 35.3). The root hairs absorb the soil solution, which consists of water molecules and dissolved mineral ions that are not bound tightly to soil particles. The soil solution is drawn into the hydrophilic walls of epidermal cells and passes freely along the cell walls and the extracellular spaces into the root cortex. This flow enhances the exposure of the cells of the cortex to the soil solution, providing a much greater membrane surface area for absorption than the surface area of the epidermis alone. Although the soil solution usually has a low mineral concentration, active transport enables roots to accumulate essential minerals, such as K^+, to concentrations hundreds of times greater than in the soil.

Transport of Water and Minerals into the Xylem

Water and minerals that pass from the soil into the root cortex cannot be transported to the rest of the plant until they enter the xylem of the vascular cylinder, or stele. The **endodermis**, the innermost layer of cells in the root cortex, functions as a last checkpoint for the selective passage of minerals from the cortex into the vascular cylinder (**Figure 36.8**). Minerals already in the symplast when they reach the endodermis continue through the plasmodesmata of endodermal cells and pass into the vascular cylinder. These minerals were already screened by the plasma membrane they had to cross to enter the symplast in the epidermis or cortex.

Minerals that reach the endodermis via the apoplast encounter a dead end that blocks their passage into the vascular cylinder. This barrier, located in the transverse and radial walls of each endodermal cell, is the **Casparian strip**, a belt made of suberin, a waxy material impervious to water and dissolved minerals (see Figure 36.8). Because of the Casparian strip, water and minerals cannot cross the endodermis and enter the vascular cylinder via the apoplast. Instead, water and minerals that are passively moving through the apoplast must cross the *selectively permeable* plasma membrane of an endodermal cell before they can enter the vascular cylinder. In this way, the endodermis transports needed minerals from the soil into the xylem and keeps many unneeded or toxic substances out. The endodermis also prevents solutes that have accumulated in the xylem from leaking back into the soil solution.

The last segment in the soil-to-xylem pathway is the passage of water and minerals into the tracheids and vessel elements of the xylem. These water-conducting cells lack protoplasts when mature and are therefore parts of the apoplast. Endodermal cells, as well as living cells within the vascular cylinder, discharge minerals from their protoplasts into their own cell walls. Both diffusion and active transport are involved in this transfer of solutes from the symplast to the apoplast, and the water and minerals can now enter the tracheids and vessel elements, where they are transported to the shoot system by bulk flow.

Bulk Flow Transport via the Xylem

Water and minerals from the soil enter the plant through the epidermis of roots, cross the root cortex, and pass into the vascular cylinder. From there the **xylem sap**, the water and dissolved minerals in the xylem, is transported long distances by bulk flow to the veins that branch throughout each leaf. As noted earlier, bulk flow is much faster than diffusion or active transport. Peak velocities in the transport of xylem sap can range from 15 to 45 m/hr for trees with wide vessel elements. The stems and leaves depend on this rapid delivery system for their supply of water and minerals.

The process of transporting xylem sap involves the loss of an astonishing amount of water by **transpiration**, the loss of water vapor from leaves and other aerial parts of the plant. A single maize plant, for example, transpires 60 L of water (the equivalent of 170 12-ounce bottles) during a growing season. A maize crop growing at a typical density of 60,000 plants per hectare transpires almost 4 million L of water per hectare (about 400,000 gallons of water per acre) every growing season. If the transpired water is not replaced by water transported up from the roots, the leaves will wilt, and the plants will eventually die.

Xylem sap rises to heights of more than 120 m in the tallest trees. Is the sap mainly *pushed* upward from the roots, or is it mainly *pulled* upward? Let's evaluate the relative contributions of these two mechanisms.

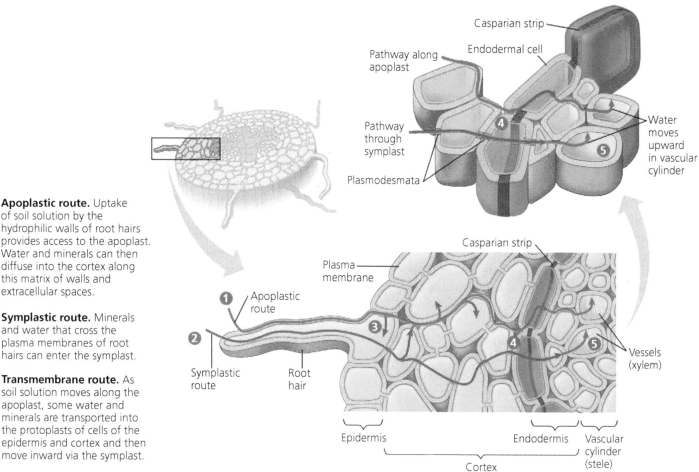

1 Apoplastic route. Uptake of soil solution by the hydrophilic walls of root hairs provides access to the apoplast. Water and minerals can then diffuse into the cortex along this matrix of walls and extracellular spaces.

2 Symplastic route. Minerals and water that cross the plasma membranes of root hairs can enter the symplast.

3 Transmembrane route. As soil solution moves along the apoplast, some water and minerals are transported into the protoplasts of cells of the epidermis and cortex and then move inward via the symplast.

4 The endodermis: controlled entry to the vascular cylinder (stele). Within the transverse and radial walls of each endodermal cell is the Casparian strip, a belt of waxy material (purple band) that blocks the passage of water and dissolved minerals. Only minerals already in the symplast or entering that pathway by crossing the plasma membrane of an endodermal cell can detour around the Casparian strip and pass into the vascular cylinder (stele).

5 Transport in the xylem. Endodermal cells and also living cells within the vascular cylinder discharge water and minerals into their walls (apoplast). The xylem vessels then transport the water and minerals by bulk flow upward into the shoot system.

▲ **Figure 36.8 Transport of water and minerals from root hairs to the xylem.**

? *How does the Casparian strip force water and minerals to pass through the plasma membranes of endodermal cells?*

Pushing Xylem Sap: Root Pressure

At night, when there is almost no transpiration, root cells continue actively pumping mineral ions into the xylem of the vascular cylinder. Meanwhile, the Casparian strip of the endodermis prevents the ions from leaking back out into the cortex and soil. The resulting accumulation of minerals lowers the water potential within the vascular cylinder. Water flows in from the root cortex, generating **root pressure**, a push of xylem sap. The root pressure sometimes causes more water to enter the leaves than is transpired, resulting in **guttation**, the exudation of water droplets that can be seen in the morning on the tips or edges of some plant leaves **(Figure 36.9)**. Guttation fluid should not be confused with dew, which is condensed atmospheric moisture.

In most plants, root pressure is a minor mechanism driving the ascent of xylem sap, pushing water only a few

▲ **Figure 36.9 Guttation.** Root pressure is forcing excess water from this strawberry leaf.

meters at most. The positive pressures produced are simply too weak to overcome the gravitational force of the water column in the xylem, particularly in tall plants. Many plants do not generate any root pressure or do so only during part of the growing season. Even in plants that display guttation, root pressure cannot keep pace with transpiration after sunrise. For the most part, xylem sap is not pushed from below by root pressure but is pulled up.

Pulling Xylem Sap: The Cohesion-Tension Hypothesis

As we have seen, root pressure, which depends on the active transport of solutes by plants, is only a minor force in the ascent of xylem sap. Far from depending on the metabolic activity of cells, most of the xylem sap that rises through a tree does not even require living cells to do so. As demonstrated by Eduard Strasburger in 1891, leafy stems with their lower end immersed in toxic solutions of copper sulfate or acid will readily draw these poisons up if the stem is cut below the surface of the liquid. As the toxic solutions ascend, they kill all living cells in their path, eventually arriving in the transpiring leaves and killing the leaf cells as well. Nevertheless, as Strasburger noted, the uptake of the toxic solutions and the loss of water from the dead leaves can continue for weeks.

In 1894, a few years after Strasburger's findings, two Irish scientists, John Joly and Henry Dixon, put forward a hypothesis that remains the leading explanation of the ascent of xylem sap. According to their **cohesion-tension hypothesis**, transpiration provides the pull for the ascent of xylem sap, and the cohesion of water molecules transmits

this pull along the entire length of the xylem from shoots to roots. Hence, xylem sap is normally under negative pressure, or tension. Since transpiration is a "pulling" process, our exploration of the rise of xylem sap by the cohesion-tension mechanism begins not with the roots but with the leaves, where the driving force for transpirational pull begins.

Transpirational Pull Stomata on a leaf's surface lead to a maze of internal air spaces that expose the mesophyll cells to the CO_2 they need for photosynthesis. The air in these spaces is saturated with water vapor because it is in contact with the moist walls of the cells. On most days, the air outside the leaf is drier; that is, it has lower water potential than the air inside the leaf. Therefore, water vapor in the air spaces of a leaf diffuses down its water potential gradient and exits the leaf via the stomata. It is this loss of water vapor by diffusion and evaporation that we call transpiration.

But how does loss of water vapor from the leaf translate into a pulling force for upward movement of water through a plant? The negative pressure potential that causes water to move up through the xylem develops at the surface of mesophyll cell walls in the leaf (Figure 36.10). The cell wall acts like a very thin capillary network. Water adheres to the cellulose microfibrils and other hydrophilic components of the cell wall. As water evaporates from the water film that covers the cell walls of mesophyll cells, the air-water interface retreats farther into the cell wall. Because of the high surface tension of water, the curvature of the interface

5 Water from the xylem is pulled into the surrounding cells and air spaces to replace the water that was lost.

4 The increased surface tension shown in step 3 pulls water from surrounding cells and air spaces.

3 The evaporation of the water film causes the air-water interface to retreat farther into the cell wall and to become more curved. This curvature increases the surface tension and the rate of transpiration.

2 At first, the water vapor lost by transpiration is replaced by evaporation from the water film that coats mesophyll cells.

Cuticle
Upper epidermis
Xylem
Mesophyll
Microfibrils in cell wall of mesophyll cell
Air space
Lower epidermis
Cuticle
Stoma
Microfibril (cross section) Water film Air-water interface

1 In transpiration, water vapor (shown as blue dots) diffuses from the moist air spaces of the leaf to the drier air outside via stomata.

▲ **Figure 36.10 Generation of transpirational pull.** Negative pressure (tension) at the air-water interface in the leaf is the basis of transpirational pull, which draws water out of the xylem.

induces a tension, or negative pressure potential, in the water. As more water evaporates from the cell wall, the curvature of the air-water interface increases and the pressure of the water becomes more negative. Water molecules from the more hydrated parts of the leaf are then pulled toward this area, reducing the tension. These pulling forces are transferred to the xylem because each water molecule is cohesively bound to the next by hydrogen bonds. Thus, transpirational pull depends on several of the properties of water discussed in Chapter 3: adhesion, cohesion, and surface tension.

The role of negative pressure potential in transpiration is consistent with the water potential equation because negative pressure potential (tension) *lowers* water potential. Because water moves from areas of higher water potential to areas of lower water potential, the more negative pressure potential at the air-water interface causes water in xylem cells to be "pulled" into mesophyll cells, which lose water to the air spaces, the water diffusing out through stomata. In this way, the negative water potential of leaves provides the "pull" in transpirational pull. The transpirational pull on xylem sap is transmitted all the way from the leaves to the young roots and even into the soil solution **(Figure 36.11)**.

Adhesion and Cohesion in the Ascent of Xylem Sap

Adhesion and cohesion facilitate the transport of water by bulk flow. Adhesion is the attractive force between water molecules and other polar substances. Because both water and cellulose are polar molecules, there is a strong attraction between water molecules and the cellulose molecules in the xylem cell walls. Cohesion is the attractive force between molecules of the same substance. Water has an unusually high cohesive force due to the hydrogen bonds each water molecule can potentially make with other water molecules. It is estimated that water's cohesive force within the xylem gives it a tensile strength equivalent to that of a steel wire of similar diameter. The cohesion of water makes it possible to pull a column of

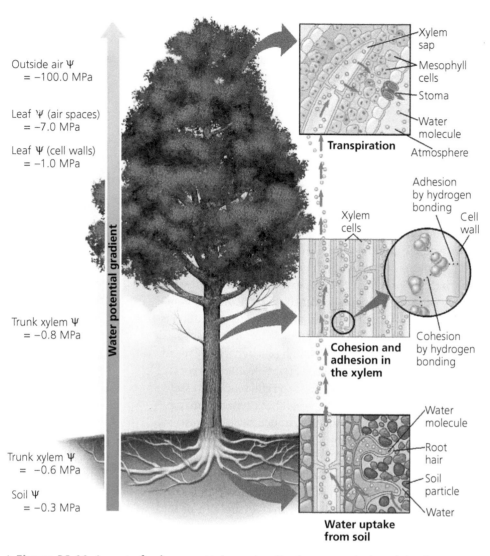

Outside air Ψ = −100.0 MPa

Leaf Ψ (air spaces) = −7.0 MPa

Leaf Ψ (cell walls) = −1.0 MPa

Trunk xylem Ψ = −0.8 MPa

Trunk xylem Ψ = −0.6 MPa

Soil Ψ = −0.3 MPa

Water potential gradient

Xylem sap
Mesophyll cells
Stoma
Water molecule
Transpiration
Atmosphere

Adhesion by hydrogen bonding
Xylem cells
Cell wall
Cohesion and adhesion in the xylem
Cohesion by hydrogen bonding

Water molecule
Root hair
Soil particle
Water
Water uptake from soil

▲ **Figure 36.11 Ascent of xylem sap.** Hydrogen bonding forms an unbroken chain of water molecules extending from leaves to the soil. The force driving the ascent of xylem sap is a gradient of water potential (ψ). For bulk flow over long distance, the ψ gradient is due mainly to a gradient of the pressure potential (ψ_P). Transpiration results in the ψ_P at the leaf end of the xylem being lower than the ψ_P at the root end. The ψ values shown at the left are a "snapshot." They may vary during daylight, but the direction of the ψ gradient remains the same.

 BioFlix Visit the Study Area in MasteringBiology for the BioFlix® 3-D Animation on Water Transport in Plants. BioFlix Tutorials can also be assigned in MasteringBiology.

xylem sap from above without the water molecules separating. Water molecules exiting the xylem in the leaf tug on adjacent water molecules, and this pull is relayed, molecule by molecule, down the entire column of water in the xylem. Meanwhile, the strong adhesion of water molecules (again by hydrogen bonds) to the hydrophilic walls of xylem cells helps offset the downward force of gravity.

The upward pull on the sap creates tension within the vessel elements and tracheids, which are like elastic pipes. Positive pressure causes an elastic pipe to swell, whereas tension pulls the walls of the pipe inward. On a warm day, a decrease in the diameter of a tree trunk can even be measured. As transpirational pull puts the vessel elements and tracheids under tension, their thick secondary walls prevent them from collapsing, much as wire rings maintain the shape of a vacuum-cleaner hose. The tension produced by transpirational pull lowers water potential in the root xylem to such an extent that water flows passively from the soil, across the root cortex, and into the vascular cylinder.

Transpirational pull can extend down to the roots only through an unbroken chain of water molecules. Cavitation, the formation of a water vapor pocket, breaks the chain. It is more common in wide vessel elements than in tracheids and can occur during drought stress or when xylem sap freezes in winter. The air bubbles resulting from cavitation expand and block water channels of the xylem. The rapid expansion of air bubbles produces clicking noises that can be heard by placing sensitive microphones at the surface of the stem.

The interruption of xylem sap transport by cavitation is not always permanent. The chain of water molecules can detour around the air bubbles through pits between adjacent tracheids or vessel elements (see Figure 35.10). Moreover, root pressure enables small plants to refill blocked vessel elements. Recent evidence suggests that cavitation may even be repaired when the xylem sap is under negative pressure, although the mechanism by which this occurs is uncertain. In addition, secondary growth adds a layer of new xylem each year. Only the youngest, outermost secondary xylem layers transport water. Although the older secondary xylem no longer transports water, it does provide support for the tree (see Figure 35.22).

Xylem Sap Ascent by Bulk Flow: *A Review*

The cohesion-tension mechanism that transports xylem sap against gravity is an excellent example of how physical principles apply to biological processes. In the long-distance transport of water from roots to leaves by bulk flow, the movement of fluid is driven by a water potential difference at opposite ends of xylem tissue. The water potential difference is created at the leaf end of the xylem by the evaporation of water from leaf cells. Evaporation lowers the water potential at the air-water interface, thereby generating the negative pressure (tension) that pulls water through the xylem.

Bulk flow in the xylem differs from diffusion in some key ways. First, it is driven by differences in pressure potential (ψ_P); solute potential (ψ_S) is not a factor. Therefore, the water potential gradient within the xylem is essentially a pressure gradient. Also, the flow does not occur across plasma membranes of living cells, but instead within hollow, dead cells. Furthermore, it moves the entire solution together—not just water or solutes—and at much greater speed than diffusion.

The plant expends no energy to lift xylem sap by bulk flow. Instead, the absorption of sunlight drives most of transpiration by causing water to evaporate from the moist walls of mesophyll cells and by lowering the water potential in the air spaces within a leaf. Thus, the ascent of xylem sap, like the process of photosynthesis, is ultimately solar powered.

CONCEPT 36.4

The rate of transpiration is regulated by stomata

Leaves generally have large surface areas and high surface-to-volume ratios. The large surface area enhances light absorption for photosynthesis. The high surface-to-volume ratio aids in CO_2 absorption during photosynthesis as well as in the release of O_2, a by-product of photosynthesis. Upon diffusing through the stomata, CO_2 enters a honeycomb of air spaces formed by the spongy mesophyll cells (see Figure 35.18). Because of the irregular shapes of these cells, the leaf's internal surface area may be 10 to 30 times greater than the external surface area.

Although large surface areas and high surface-to-volume ratios increase the rate of photosynthesis, they also increase water loss by way of the stomata. Thus, a plant's tremendous requirement for water is largely a consequence of the shoot system's need for ample exchange of CO_2 and O_2 for photosynthesis. By opening and closing the stomata, guard cells help balance the plant's requirement to conserve water with its requirement for photosynthesis (**Figure 36.12**).

Stomata: Major Pathways for Water Loss

About 95% of the water a plant loses escapes through stomata, although these pores account for only 1–2% of the external leaf surface. The waxy cuticle limits water loss

▲ **Figure 36.12** An open stoma (left) and closed stoma (LMs).

through the remaining surface of the leaf. Each stoma is flanked by a pair of guard cells. Guard cells control the diameter of the stoma by changing shape, thereby widening or narrowing the gap between the guard cell pair. Under the same environmental conditions, the amount of water lost by a leaf depends largely on the number of stomata and the average size of their pores.

The stomatal density of a leaf, which may be as high as 20,000 per square centimeter, is under both genetic and environmental control. For example, as a result of evolution by natural selection, desert plants are genetically programmed to have lower stomatal densities than do marsh plants. Stomatal density, however, is a developmentally plastic feature of many plants. High light exposures and low CO_2 levels during leaf development lead to increased density in many species. By measuring the stomatal density of leaf fossils, scientists have gained insight into the levels of atmospheric CO_2 in past climates. A recent British survey found that stomatal density of many woodland species has decreased since 1927, when a similar survey was made. This observation is consistent with other findings that atmospheric CO_2 levels increased dramatically during the late 20th century.

Mechanisms of Stomatal Opening and Closing

When guard cells take in water from neighboring cells by osmosis, they become more turgid. In most angiosperm species, the cell walls of guard cells are uneven in thickness, and the cellulose microfibrils are oriented in a direction that causes the guard cells to bow outward when turgid (Figure 36.13a). This bowing outward increases the size of the pore between the guard cells. When the cells lose water and become flaccid, they become less bowed, and the pore closes.

The changes in turgor pressure in guard cells result primarily from the reversible absorption and loss of K^+.

Stomata open when guard cells actively accumulate K^+ from neighboring epidermal cells (Figure 36.13b). The flow of K^+ across the plasma membrane of the guard cell is coupled to the generation of a membrane potential by proton pumps (see Figure 36.6a). Stomatal opening correlates with active transport of H^+ out of the guard cell. The resulting voltage (membrane potential) drives K^+ into the cell through specific membrane channels. The absorption of K^+ causes the water potential to become more negative within the guard cells, and the cells become more turgid as water enters by osmosis. Because most of the K^+ and water are stored in the vacuole, the vacuolar membrane also plays a role in regulating guard cell dynamics. Stomatal closing results from a loss of K^+ from guard cells to neighboring cells, which leads to an osmotic loss of water. Aquaporins also help regulate the osmotic swelling and shrinking of guard cells.

Guard cells turgid/Stoma open   **Guard cells flaccid/Stoma closed**

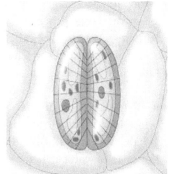

(a) Changes in guard cell shape and stomatal opening and closing (surface view). Guard cells of a typical angiosperm are illustrated in their turgid (stoma open) and flaccid (stoma closed) states. The radial orientation of cellulose microfibrils in the cell walls causes the guard cells to increase more in length than width when turgor increases. Since the two guard cells are tightly joined at their tips, they bow outward when turgid, causing the stomatal pore to open.

(b) Role of potassium ions (K^+) in stomatal opening and closing. The transport of K^+ (symbolized here as red dots) across the plasma membrane and vacuolar membrane causes the turgor changes of guard cells. The uptake of anions, such as malate and chloride ions (not shown), also contributes to guard cell swelling.

▲ **Figure 36.13** Mechanisms of stomatal opening and closing.

Stimuli for Stomatal Opening and Closing

In general, stomata are open during the day and mostly closed at night, preventing the plant from losing water under conditions when photosynthesis cannot occur. At least three cues contribute to stomatal opening at dawn: light, CO_2 depletion, and an internal "clock" in guard cells.

Light stimulates guard cells to accumulate K^+ and become turgid. This response is triggered by illumination of blue-light receptors in the plasma membrane of guard cells. Activation of these receptors stimulates the activity of proton pumps in the plasma membrane of the guard cells, in turn promoting absorption of K^+.

Stomata also open in response to depletion of CO_2 within the leaf's air spaces as a result of photosynthesis. As CO_2 concentrations decrease during the day, the stomata progressively open if sufficient water is supplied to the leaf.

A third cue, the internal "clock" in the guard cells, ensures that stomata continue their daily rhythm of opening and closing. This rhythm occurs even if a plant is kept in a dark location. All eukaryotic organisms have internal clocks that regulate cyclic processes. Cycles with intervals of approximately 24 hours are called **circadian rhythms** (which you'll learn more about in Chapter 39).

Environmental stresses, such as drought, high temperature, and wind, can cause stomata to close during the daytime. When the plant has a water deficiency, guard cells may lose turgor and close stomata. In addition, a hormone called **abscisic acid (ABA)**, produced in roots and leaves in response to water deficiency, signals guard cells to close stomata. This response reduces wilting but also restricts CO_2 absorption, thereby slowing photosynthesis. Since turgor is necessary for cell elongation, growth ceases throughout the plant. These are some reasons why droughts reduce crop yields.

Guard cells control the photosynthesis-transpiration compromise on a moment-to-moment basis by integrating a variety of internal and external stimuli. Even the passage of a cloud or a transient shaft of sunlight through a forest can affect the rate of transpiration.

Effects of Transpiration on Wilting and Leaf Temperature

As long as most stomata remain open, transpiration is greatest on a day that is sunny, warm, dry, and windy because these environmental factors increase evaporation. If transpiration cannot pull sufficient water to the leaves, the shoot becomes slightly wilted as cells lose turgor pressure. Although plants respond to such mild drought stress by rapidly closing stomata, some evaporative water loss still occurs through the cuticle. Under prolonged drought conditions, leaves can become severely wilted and irreversibly injured.

Transpiration also results in evaporative cooling, which can lower a leaf's temperature by as much as 10°C compared with the surrounding air. This cooling prevents the leaf from reaching temperatures that could denature enzymes involved in photosynthesis and other metabolic processes.

Adaptations That Reduce Evaporative Water Loss

Water availability is a major determinant of plant productivity. The main reason water availability is tied to plant productivity is not related to photosynthesis's direct need for water as a substrate but rather because freely available water allows plants to keep stomata open and take up more CO_2. The problem of reducing water loss is especially acute for desert plants. Plants adapted to arid environments are called **xerophytes** (from the Greek *xero*, dry).

Many species of desert plants avoid drying out by completing their short life cycles during the brief rainy seasons. Rain comes infrequently in deserts, but when it arrives, the vegetation is transformed as dormant seeds of annual species quickly germinate and bloom, completing their life cycle before dry conditions return.

Other xerophytes have unusual physiological or morphological adaptations that enable them to withstand harsh desert conditions. The stems of many xerophytes are fleshy because they store water for use during long dry periods. Cacti have highly reduced leaves that resist excessive water loss; photosynthesis is carried out mainly in their stems. Another adaptation common in arid habitats is crassulacean acid metabolism (CAM), a specialized form of photosynthesis found in succulents of the family Crassulaceae and several other families (see Figure 10.21). Because the leaves of CAM plants take in CO_2 at night, the stomata can remain closed during the day, when evaporative stresses are greatest. Other examples of xerophytic adaptations are discussed in **Figure 36.14**.

CONCEPT CHECK 36.4

1. What are the stimuli that control the opening and closing of stomata?
2. The pathogenic fungus *Fusicoccum amygdali* secretes a toxin called fusicoccin that activates the plasma membrane proton pumps of plant cells and leads to uncontrolled water loss. Suggest a mechanism by which the activation of proton pumps could lead to severe wilting.
3. **WHAT IF?** If you buy cut flowers, why might the florist recommend cutting the stems underwater and then transferring the flowers to a vase while the cut ends are still wet?
4. **MAKE CONNECTIONS** Explain why the evaporation of water from leaves lowers their temperature (see Concept 3.2).

For suggested answers, see Appendix A.

▶ Ocotillo (*Fouquieria splendens*) is common in the southwestern region of the United States and northern Mexico. It is leafless during most of the year, thereby avoiding excessive water loss (right). Immediately after a heavy rainfall, it produces small leaves (below and inset). As the soil dries, the leaves quickly shrivel and die.

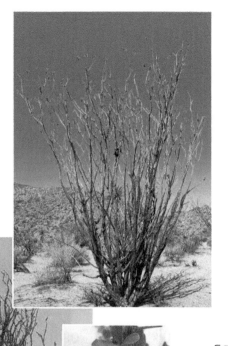

▼ Oleander (*Nerium oleander*), shown in the inset, is commonly found in arid climates. Its leaves have a thick cuticle and multiple-layered epidermal tissue that reduce water loss. Stomata are recessed in cavities called "crypts," an adaptation that reduces the rate of transpiration by protecting the stomata from hot, dry wind. Trichomes help minimize transpiration by breaking up the flow of air, allowing the chamber of the crypt to have a higher humidity than the surrounding atmosphere (LM).

Thick cuticle   Upper epidermal tissue

100 µm

Trichomes ("hairs")   Crypt   Stoma   Lower epidermal tissue

▶ The long, white hairlike bristles along the stem of the old man cactus (*Cephalocereus senilis*) help reflect the intense sunlight of the Mexican desert.

▲ **Figure 36.14 Some xerophytic adaptations.**

CONCEPT 36.5

Sugars are transported from sources to sinks via the phloem

You have read how water and minerals are absorbed by root cells, transported through the endodermis, released into the vessel elements and tracheids of the xylem, and carried to the tops of plants by the bulk flow driven by transpiration. However, transpiration cannot meet all the long-distance transport needs of the plant. The flow of water and minerals from soil to roots to leaves is largely in a direction opposite to the direction necessary for transporting sugars from mature leaves to lower parts of the plant, such as root tips that require large amounts of sugars for energy and growth. The transport of the products of photosynthesis, known as **translocation**, is carried out by another tissue, the phloem.

Movement from Sugar Sources to Sugar Sinks

In angiosperms, the specialized cells that are conduits for translocation are the sieve-tube elements. Arranged end to end, they form long sieve tubes (see Figure 35.10). Between these cells are sieve plates, structures that allow the flow of sap along the sieve tube.

Phloem sap, the aqueous solution that flows through sieve tubes, differs markedly from the xylem sap that is transported by tracheids and vessel elements. By far the most prevalent solute in phloem sap is sugar, typically sucrose in most species. The sucrose concentration may be as high as 30% by weight, giving the sap a syrupy thickness. Phloem sap may also contain amino acids, hormones, and minerals.

In contrast to the unidirectional transport of xylem sap from roots to leaves, phloem sap moves from sites of sugar production to sites of sugar use or storage (see Figure 36.2). A **sugar source** is a plant organ that is a net producer of sugar, by photosynthesis or by breakdown of starch. A **sugar sink** is an organ that is a net consumer or depository of sugar. Growing roots, buds, stems, and fruits are sugar sinks. Although expanding leaves are sugar sinks, mature leaves, if well illuminated, are sugar sources. A storage organ, such as a tuber or a bulb, may be a source or a sink, depending on the season. When stockpiling carbohydrates in the summer, it is a sugar sink. After breaking dormancy in the spring, it is a sugar source because its starch is broken down to sugar, which is carried to the growing shoot tips.

Sinks usually receive sugar from the nearest sugar sources. The upper leaves on a branch, for example, may export sugar to the growing shoot tip, whereas the lower leaves may export sugar to the roots. A growing fruit may monopolize the sugar sources that surround it. For each sieve tube, the direction of transport depends on the locations of the sugar source and sugar sink that are connected by that tube. Therefore, neighboring sieve tubes may carry sap in opposite directions if they originate and end in different locations.

Sugar must be transported, or loaded, into sieve-tube elements before being exported to sugar sinks. In some species, it moves from mesophyll cells to sieve-tube elements via the symplast, passing through plasmodesmata. In other species, it moves by symplastic and apoplastic pathways. In maize leaves, for example, sucrose diffuses through the symplast from photosynthetic mesophyll cells into small veins. Much of it then moves into the apoplast and is accumulated by nearby sieve-tube elements, either directly or through companion cells **(Figure 36.15a)**. In some plants, the walls of the companion cells feature many ingrowths, enhancing solute transfer between apoplast and symplast.

In many plants, sugar movement into the phloem requires active transport because sucrose is more concentrated in sieve-tube elements and companion cells than in mesophyll. Proton pumping and H^+/sucrose cotransport enable sucrose to move from mesophyll cells to sieve-tube elements or companion cells **(Figure 36.15b)**.

Sucrose is unloaded at the sink end of a sieve tube. The process varies by species and organ. However, the concentration of free sugar in the sink is always lower than in the sieve tube because the unloaded sugar is consumed during growth and metabolism of the cells of the sink or converted to insoluble polymers such as starch. As a result of this sugar concentration gradient, sugar molecules diffuse from the phloem into the sink tissues, and water follows by osmosis.

Bulk Flow by Positive Pressure: The Mechanism of Translocation in Angiosperms

Phloem sap flows from source to sink at rates as great as 1 m/hr, much faster than diffusion or cytoplasmic streaming. Researchers have concluded that phloem sap moves through the sieve tubes of angiosperms by bulk flow driven by positive pressure, known as *pressure flow* **(Figure 36.16)**. The building of pressure at the source and reduction of that pressure at the sink cause sap to flow from source to sink.

The pressure-flow hypothesis explains why phloem sap flows from source to sink, and experiments build a strong case for pressure flow as the mechanism of translocation in angiosperms **(Figure 36.17)**. However, studies using electron microscopes suggest that in nonflowering vascular

Key

▨ Apoplast

▨ Symplast

(a) Sucrose manufactured in mesophyll cells can travel via the symplast (blue arrows) to sieve-tube elements. In some species, sucrose exits the symplast near sieve tubes and travels through the apoplast (red arrow). It is then actively accumulated from the apoplast by sieve-tube elements and their companion cells.

(b) A chemiosmotic mechanism is responsible for the active transport of sucrose into companion cells and sieve-tube elements. Proton pumps generate an H^+ gradient, which drives sucrose accumulation with the help of a cotransport protein that couples sucrose transport to the diffusion of H^+ back into the cell.

▲ Figure 36.15 **Loading of sucrose into phloem.**

Vessel (xylem)   Sieve tube (phloem)   **Source cell** (leaf)

1 Loading of sugar (green dots) into the sieve tube at the source reduces water potential inside the sieve-tube elements. This causes the tube to take up water by osmosis.

2 This uptake of water generates a positive pressure that forces the sap to flow along the tube.

3 The pressure is relieved by the unloading of sugar and the consequent loss of water at the sink.

4 In leaf-to-root translocation, xylem recycles water from sink to source.

H_2O

Bulk flow by negative pressure

Bulk flow by positive pressure

Sink cell (storage root)

Sucrose

H_2O

▲ Figure 36.16 **Bulk flow by positive pressure (pressure flow) in a sieve tube.**

plants, the pores between phloem cells may be too small or obstructed to permit pressure flow.

Sinks vary in energy demands and capacity to unload sugars. Sometimes there are more sinks than can be supported by sources. In such cases, a plant might abort some flowers, seeds, or fruits—a phenomenon called *self-thinning*. Removing sinks can also be a horticulturally useful practice. For example, since large apples command a much better price than small ones, growers sometimes remove flowers or young fruits so that their trees produce fewer but larger apples.

CONCEPT CHECK 36.5

1. Compare and contrast the forces that move phloem sap and xylem sap over long distances.

2. Identify plant organs that are sugar sources, organs that are sugar sinks, and organs that might be either. Explain.

3. Why can xylem transport water and minerals using dead cells, whereas phloem requires living cells?

4. **WHAT IF?** Apple growers in Japan sometimes make a nonlethal spiral slash around the bark of trees that are destined for removal after the growing season. This practice makes the apples sweeter. Why?

For suggested answers, see Appendix A.

▼ Figure 36.17 | **Inquiry**

Does phloem sap contain more sugar near sources than near sinks?

Experiment The pressure-flow hypothesis predicts that phloem sap near sources should have a higher sugar content than phloem sap near sinks. To test this idea, researchers used aphids that feed on phloem sap. An aphid probes with a hypodermic-like mouthpart called a stylet that penetrates a sieve-tube element. As sieve-tube pressure forced out phloem sap into the stylets, the researchers separated the aphids from the stylets, which then acted as taps exuding sap for hours. Researchers measured the sugar concentration of sap from stylets at different points between a source and sink.

25 μm

Sieve-tube element

Sap droplet

Stylet

Sap droplet

Aphid feeding   Stylet in sieve-tube element   Separated stylet exuding sap

Results The closer the stylet was to a sugar source, the higher its sugar concentration was.

Conclusion The results of such experiments support the pressure-flow hypothesis, which predicts that sugar concentrations should be higher in sieve tubes closer to sugar sources.

*Source: S. Rogers and A. J. Peel, Some evidence for the existence of turgor pressure in the sieve tubes of willow (*Salix*), Planta 126:259–267 (1975).*

WHAT IF? *Spittlebugs (Clasirptora sp.) are xylem sap feeders that use strong muscles to pump xylem sap through their guts. Could you isolate xylem sap from the excised stylets of spittlebugs?*

CONCEPT 36.6

The symplast is highly dynamic

Although we have been discussing transport in mostly physical terms, almost like the flow of solutions through pipes, plant transport is a dynamic and finely tuned process that changes during development. A leaf, for example, may begin as a sugar sink but spend most of its life as a sugar source. Also, environmental changes may trigger responses in plant transport processes. Water stress may activate signal transduction pathways that greatly alter the membrane transport proteins governing the overall transport of water and minerals. Because the symplast is living tissue, it is largely responsible for the dynamic changes in plant transport processes. We'll look now at some other examples: changes in plasmodesmata, chemical signaling, and electrical signaling.

Changes in Plasmodesmatal Number and Pore Size

Based mostly on the static images provided by electron microscopy, biologists formerly considered plasmodesmata to be unchanging, pore-like structures. More recent studies, however, have revealed that plasmodesmata are highly dynamic. They can open or close rapidly in response to changes in turgor pressure, cytosolic Ca^{2+} levels, or cytosolic pH. Although some plasmodesmata form during cytokinesis, they can also form much later. Moreover, loss of function is common during differentiation. For example, as a leaf matures from a sink to a source, its plasmodesmata either close or are eliminated, causing phloem unloading to cease.

Early studies by plant physiologists and pathologists came to differing conclusions regarding pore sizes of plasmodesmata. Physiologists injected fluorescent probes of different molecular sizes into cells and recorded whether the molecules passed into adjacent cells. Based on these observations, they concluded that the pore sizes were approximately 2.5 nm—too small for macromolecules such as proteins to pass. In contrast, pathologists provided electron micrographs showing evidence of the passage of virus particles with diameters of 10 nm or greater (**Figure 36.18**).

Subsequently, it was learned that plant viruses produce *viral movement proteins* that cause the plasmodesmata to dilate, enabling the viral RNA to pass between cells. More recent evidence shows that plant cells themselves regulate plasmodesmata as part of a communication network. The viruses can subvert this network by mimicking the cell's regulators of plasmodesmata.

A high degree of cytosolic interconnectedness exists only within certain groups of cells and tissues, which are known as *symplastic domains*. Informational molecules, such as proteins and RNAs, coordinate development between cells within each symplastic domain. If symplastic communication is disrupted, development can be grossly affected.

Phloem: An Information Superhighway

In addition to transporting sugars, the phloem is a "superhighway" for the transport of macromolecules and viruses. This transport is systemic (throughout the body), affecting many or all of the plant's systems or organs. Macromolecules translocated through the phloem include proteins and various types of RNA that enter the sieve tubes through plasmodesmata. Although they are often likened to the gap junctions between animal cells, plasmodesmata are unique in their ability to traffic proteins and RNA.

Systemic communication through the phloem helps integrate the functions of the whole plant. One classic example is the delivery of a flower-inducing chemical signal from leaves to vegetative meristems. Another is a defensive response to localized infection, in which chemical signals traveling through the phloem activate defense genes in non-infected tissues.

Electrical Signaling in the Phloem

Rapid, long-distance electrical signaling through the phloem is another dynamic feature of the symplast. Electrical signaling has been studied extensively in plants that have rapid leaf movements, such as the sensitive plant (*Mimosa pudica*) and Venus flytrap (*Dionaea muscipula*). However, its role in other species is less clear. Some studies have revealed that a stimulus in one part of a plant can trigger an electrical signal in the phloem that affects another part, where it may elicit a change in gene transcription, respiration, photosynthesis, phloem unloading, or hormonal levels. Thus, the phloem can serve a nerve-like function, allowing for swift electrical communication between widely separated organs.

The coordinated transport of materials and information is central to plant survival. Plants can acquire only so many resources in the course of their lifetimes. Ultimately, the successful acquisition of these resources and their optimal distribution are the most critical determinants of whether the plant will compete successfully.

▲ **Figure 36.18** **Virus particles moving cell to cell through plasmodesma connecting turnip leaf cells (TEM).**

CONCEPT CHECK 36.6

1. How do plasmodesmata differ from gap junctions?

2. Nerve-like signals in animals are thousands of times faster than their plant counterparts. Suggest a behavioral reason for the difference.

3. **WHAT IF?** Suppose plants were genetically modified to be unresponsive to viral movement proteins. Would this be a good way to prevent the spread of infection? Explain.

For suggested answers, see Appendix A.

SUMMARY OF KEY CONCEPTS

CONCEPT 36.1

Adaptations for acquiring resources were key steps in the evolution of vascular plants (pp. 779–781)

- Leaves typically function in gathering sunlight and CO_2. Stems serve as supporting structures for leaves and as conduits for the long-distance transport of water and nutrients. Roots mine the soil for water and minerals and anchor the whole plant.
- Natural selection has produced plant architectures that optimize resource acquisition in the ecological niche in which the plant species naturally exists.

? *How did the evolution of xylem and phloem contribute to the successful colonization of land by vascular plants?*

CONCEPT 36.2

Different mechanisms transport substances over short or long distances (pp. 781–785)

- The selective permeability of the plasma membrane controls the movement of substances into and out of cells. Both active and passive transport mechanisms occur in plants.
- Plant tissues have two major compartments: the **apoplast** (everything outside the cells' plasma membranes) and the **symplast** (the cytosol and connecting plasmodesmata).
- Direction of water movement depends on the **water potential**, a quantity that incorporates solute concentration and physical pressure. The osmotic uptake of water by plant cells and the resulting internal pressure that builds up make plant cells **turgid**.
- Long-distance transport occurs through **bulk flow**, the movement of liquid in response to a pressure gradient. Bulk flow occurs within the tracheids and vessel elements of the **xylem** and within the sieve-tube elements of the **phloem**.

? *Is xylem sap usually pulled or pushed up the plant?*

CONCEPT 36.3

Transpiration drives the transport of water and minerals from roots to shoots via the xylem (pp. 786–790)

- Water and minerals from the soil enter the plant through the epidermis of roots, cross the root cortex, and then pass into the vascular cylinder by way of the selectively permeable cells of the **endodermis**. From the vascular cylinder, the **xylem sap** is transported long distances by bulk flow to the veins that branch throughout each leaf.
- The **cohesion-tension hypothesis** proposes that the movement of xylem sap is driven by a water potential difference created at the leaf end of the xylem by the evaporation of water from leaf cells. Evaporation lowers the water potential at the air-water interface, thereby generating the negative pressure that pulls water through the xylem.

? *Why is the ability of water molecules to form hydrogen bonds important for the movement of xylem sap?*

CONCEPT 36.4

The rate of transpiration is regulated by stomata (pp. 790–792)

- **Transpiration** is the loss of water vapor from plants. **Wilting** occurs when the water lost by transpiration is not replaced by absorption from roots. Plants respond to water deficits by closing their stomata. Under prolonged drought conditions, plants can become irreversibly injured.
- Stomata are the major pathway for water loss from plants. A stoma opens when guard cells bordering the stomatal pore take up K^+. The opening and closing of stomata are controlled by light, CO_2, the drought hormone **abscisic acid**, and a **circadian rhythm**.
- **Xerophytes** are plants that are adapted to arid environments. Reduced leaves and CAM photosynthesis are examples of adaptations to arid environments.

? *Why are stomata necessary?*

CONCEPT 36.5

Sugars are transported from sources to sinks via the phloem (pp. 793–795)

- Mature leaves are the main **sugar sources**, although storage organs can be seasonal sources. Growing organs such as roots, stems, and fruits are the main **sugar sinks**. The direction of phloem transport is always from sugar source to sugar sink.
- Phloem loading depends on the active transport of sucrose. Sucrose is cotransported with H^+, which diffuses down a gradient generated by proton pumps. Loading of sugar at the source and unloading at the sink maintain a pressure difference that keeps sap flowing through a sieve tube.

? *Why is phloem transport considered an active process?*

CONCEPT 36.6

The symplast is highly dynamic (pp. 795–796)

- Plasmodesmata can change in permeability and number. When dilated, they provide a passageway for the symplastic transport of proteins, RNAs, and other macromolecules over long distances. The phloem also conducts nerve-like electrical signals that help integrate whole-plant function.

? *By what mechanisms is symplastic communication regulated?*

LEVEL 1: KNOWLEDGE/COMPREHENSION

1. Which of the following is an adaptation that enhances the uptake of water and minerals by roots?
   a. mycorrhizae
   b. pumping through plasmodesmata
   c. active uptake by vessel elements
   d. rhythmic contractions by cortical cells

2. Which structure or compartment is part of the symplast?
   a. the interior of a vessel element
   b. the interior of a sieve tube
   c. the cell wall of a mesophyll cell
   d. an extracellular air space

3. Movement of phloem sap from a source to a sink
   a. occurs through the apoplast of sieve-tube elements.
   b. depends ultimately on the activity of proton pumps.
   c. depends on tension, or negative pressure potential.
   d. results mainly from diffusion.

LEVEL 2: APPLICATION/ANALYSIS

4. Photosynthesis ceases when leaves wilt, mainly because
   a. the chlorophyll in wilting leaves is degraded.
   b. accumulation of CO_2 in the leaf inhibits enzymes.
   c. stomata close, preventing CO_2 from entering the leaf.
   d. photolysis, the water-splitting step of photosynthesis, cannot occur when there is a water deficiency.

5. What would enhance water uptake by a plant cell?
   a. decreasing the ψ of the surrounding solution
   b. positive pressure on the surrounding solution
   c. the loss of solutes from the cell
   d. increasing the ψ of the cytoplasm

6. A plant cell with a ψ_S of -0.65 MPa maintains a constant volume when bathed in a solution that has a ψ_S of -0.30 MPa and is in an open container. The cell has a
   a. ψ_P of $+0.65$ MPa.
   b. ψ of -0.65 MPa.
   c. ψ_P of $+0.35$ MPa.
   d. ψ_P of 0 MPa.

7. Compared with a cell with few aquaporin proteins in its membrane, a cell containing many aquaporin proteins will
   a. have a faster rate of osmosis.
   b. have a lower water potential.
   c. have a higher water potential.
   d. accumulate water by active transport.

8. Which of the following would tend to increase transpiration?
   a. spiny leaves
   b. sunken stomata
   c. a thicker cuticle
   d. higher stomatal density

LEVEL 3: SYNTHESIS/EVALUATION

9. EVOLUTION CONNECTION
   Large brown algae called kelps can grow as tall as 25 m. Kelps consist of a holdfast anchored to the ocean floor, blades that float at the surface and collect light, and a long stalk connecting the blades to the holdfast (see Figure 28.12). Specialized cells in the stalk, although nonvascular, can transport sugar. Suggest a reason why these structures analogous to sieve-tube elements might have evolved in kelps.

10. SCIENTIFIC INQUIRY
    INTERPRET THE DATA A Minnesota gardener notes that the plants immediately bordering a walkway are stunted compared with those farther away. Suspecting that the soil near the walkway may be contaminated from salt added to the walkway in winter, the gardener tests the soil. The composition of the soil near the walkway is identical to that farther away except that it contains an additional 50 mM NaCl. Assuming that the NaCl is completely ionized, calculate how much it will lower the solute potential of the soil at 20°C using the *solute potential equation*:

    $$\psi_S = -iCRT$$

    where i is the ionization constant (2 for NaCl), C is the molar concentration (in mol/L), R is the pressure constant [$R = 0.00831$ L · MPa/(mol · K)], and T is the temperature in Kelvin (273 + °C).
    How would this change in the solute potential of the soil affect the water potential of the soil? In what way would the change in the water potential of the soil affect the movement of water in or out of the roots?

11. SCIENTIFIC INQUIRY
    Cotton plants wilt within a few hours of flooding of their roots. The flooding leads to low-oxygen conditions, increases in cytosolic Ca^{2+} concentration, and decreases in cytosolic pH. Suggest a hypothesis to explain how flooding leads to wilting.

12. WRITE ABOUT A THEME: ORGANIZATION
    Natural selection has led to changes in the architecture of plants that enable them to photosynthesize more efficiently in the ecological niches they occupy. In a short essay (100–150 words), explain how shoot architecture enhances photosynthesis.

13. SYNTHESIZE YOUR KNOWLEDGE

Imagine yourself as a water molecule in the soil solution of a forest. In a short essay (100–150 words), explain what pathways and what forces would be necessary to carry you to the leaves of these trees.

For suggested answers, see Appendix A.

MasteringBiology®

Students Go to **MasteringBiology** for assignments, the eText, and the Study Area with practice tests, animations, and activities.

Instructors Go to **MasteringBiology** for automatically graded tutorials and questions that you can assign to your students, plus Instructor Resources.

37

Soil and Plant Nutrition

▲ Figure 37.1 **Does this plant have roots?**

The Corkscrew Carnivore

The pale, rootlike appendages of *Genlisea*, the wetland herb seen in **Figure 37.1**, are actually highly modified underground leaves adapted for trapping and digesting a variety of small soil inhabitants, including bacteria, algae, protozoa, nematodes, and copepods. But how do these trap-leaves work? Imagine twisting a narrow strip of paper to make a drinking straw. This is essentially the mechanism by which these corkscrew-shaped tubular leaves form. A narrow spiral slit runs along most of the trap-leaf's length; it is lined with curved hairs that allow microorganisms to enter the leaf tube but not exit. Once inside, prey find themselves traveling inexorably upward toward a small chamber lined with digestive glands that seal their fate. The inability of prey to backtrack is ensured by another set of curved hairs that allow only one-way passage (see micrograph at left). *Genlisea*'s carnivorous habit is a marvelous adaptation that enables the plant to supplement the meager mineral rations available from the boggy, nutrient-poor soils in which it grows with minerals released from its digested prey.

As discussed in Chapter 36, plants obtain nutrients from both the atmosphere and the soil. Using sunlight as an energy source, they produce organic nutrients by reducing carbon dioxide to sugars through the process of photosynthesis. They also take up water and various inorganic nutrients from the soil through their root systems. This chapter focuses on plant nutrition, the study of the minerals necessary for plant growth. After discussing the physical properties of soils and factors that govern soil quality, we'll explore why certain mineral nutrients are essential for plant function. Finally, we examine some nutritional adaptations that have evolved, often in relationships with other organisms.

CONCEPT 37.1

Soil contains a living, complex ecosystem

The upper layers of the soil, from which plants absorb nearly all of the water and minerals they require, contain a wide range of living organisms that interact with each other and with the physical environment. This complex ecosystem may take centuries to form but can be destroyed by human mismanagement in just a few years. To understand why soil must be conserved and why particular plants grow where they do, it is necessary to first consider the basic physical properties of soil: its texture and composition.

Soil Texture

The texture of soil depends on the sizes of its particles. Soil particles can range from coarse sand (0.02–2 mm in diameter) to silt (0.002–0.02 mm) to microscopic clay particles (less than 0.002 mm). These different-sized particles arise ultimately from the weathering of rock. Water freezing in crevices of rocks causes mechanical fracturing, and weak acids in the soil break rocks down chemically. When organisms penetrate the rock, they accelerate breakdown by chemical and mechanical means. Roots, for example, secrete acids that dissolve the rock, and their growth in fissures leads to mechanical fracturing. Mineral particles released by weathering become mixed with living organisms and **humus**, the remains of dead organisms and other organic matter, forming **topsoil**. The topsoil and other soil layers are called **soil horizons (Figure 37.2)**. The topsoil, or A horizon, can range in depth from millimeters to meters. We focus mostly on properties of topsoil because it is generally the most important soil layer for plant growth.

In the topsoil, plants are nourished by the soil solution, the water and dissolved minerals in the pores between soil particles. The pores also contain air pockets. After a heavy rain, water drains from the larger spaces in the soil, but smaller spaces retain water because water molecules are attracted to the negatively charged surfaces of clay and other particles.

The topsoils that are the most fertile—supporting the most abundant growth—are **loams**, which are composed of roughly equal amounts of sand, silt, and clay. Loamy soils have enough small silt and clay particles to provide ample surface area for the adhesion and retention of minerals and water. Meanwhile, the large spaces between sand particles enable efficient diffusion of oxygen to the roots. Sandy soils

The A horizon is the topsoil, a mixture of broken-down rock of various textures, living organisms, and decaying organic matter.

The B horizon contains much less organic matter than the A horizon and is less weathered.

The C horizon is composed mainly of partially broken-down rock. Some of the rock served as "parent" material for minerals that later helped form the upper horizons.

▲ **Figure 37.2 Soil horizons.**

generally don't retain enough water to support vigorous plant growth, and clayey soils tend to retain too much water. When soil does not drain adequately, the air is replaced by water, and the roots suffocate from lack of oxygen. Typically, the most fertile topsoils have pores that are about half water and half air, providing a good balance between aeration, drainage, and water storage capacity. The physical properties of soils can be adjusted by adding soil amendments, such as peat moss, compost, manure, or sand.

Topsoil Composition

A soil's composition encompasses its inorganic (mineral) and organic chemical components. The organic components include the many life-forms that inhabit the soil.

Inorganic Components

The surface charges of soil particles determine their ability to bind many nutrients. Most soil particles are negatively charged. Positively charged ions (cations)—such as potassium (K^+), calcium (Ca^{2+}), and magnesium (Mg^{2+})—adhere to these particles and are less easily lost by *leaching*, the percolation of water through the soil.

Roots, however, do not absorb mineral cations directly from soil particles; they absorb them from the soil solution. Mineral cations enter the soil solution by **cation exchange**, a process in which cations are displaced from soil particles by other cations, particularly H^+ **(Figure 37.3)**. Therefore, a soil's capacity to exchange cations is determined by the number of cation adhesion sites and by the soil's pH. In general, the more clay and organic matter in the soil, the higher the cation exchange capacity. The clay content is important

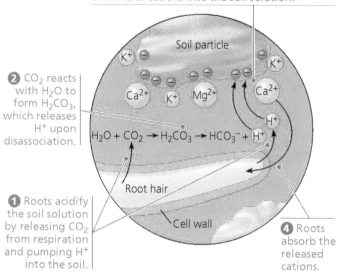

❸ H+ ions in the soil solution neutralize the negative charge of soil particles, causing release of mineral cations into the soil solution.

Soil particle

❷ CO₂ reacts with H₂O to form H₂CO₃, which releases H⁺ upon disassociation.

K^+ K^+ Ca^{2+} K^+ Mg^{2+} Ca^{2+}

H^+

$H_2O + CO_2 \rightarrow H_2CO_3 \rightarrow HCO_3^- + H^+$

Root hair

❶ Roots acidify the soil solution by releasing CO₂ from respiration and pumping H⁺ into the soil.

Cell wall

❹ Roots absorb the released cations.

▲ Figure 37.3 **Cation exchange in soil.**

? *Which are more likely to be leached from the soil by heavy rains— cations or anions? Explain.*

because these small particles have a high ratio of surface area to volume. Negatively charged ions (anions)—such as the plant nutrients nitrate (NO_3^-), phosphate ($H_2PO_4^-$), and sulfate (SO_4^{2-})—do not bind to the negatively charged soil particles typically found in the most productive soils and are therefore more easily lost by leaching.

Organic Components

The major organic component of topsoil is humus, which consists of organic material produced by the decomposition of fallen leaves, dead organisms, feces, and other organic matter by bacteria and fungi. Humus prevents clay particles from packing together and forms a crumbly soil that retains water but is still porous enough to aerate roots. Humus also increases the soil's capacity to exchange cations and is a reservoir of mineral nutrients that return gradually to the soil as microorganisms decompose the organic matter.

Topsoil is home to an astonishing number and variety of organisms. A teaspoon of topsoil has about 5 billion bacteria, which cohabit with fungi, algae and other protists, insects, earthworms, nematodes, and plant roots. The activities of all these organisms affect the soil's physical and chemical properties. Earthworms, for example, consume organic matter and derive their nutrition from the bacteria and fungi growing on this material. They excrete wastes and move large amounts of material to the soil surface. In addition, they move organic matter into deeper layers. Earthworms mix and clump the soil particles, allowing for better gaseous diffusion and water retention. Roots also affect soil texture and composition. For example, by binding the soil, they reduce erosion, and by excreting acids, they lower soil pH.

Soil Conservation and Sustainable Agriculture

Ancient farmers recognized that yields on a particular plot of land decreased over the years. Moving to uncultivated areas, they observed the same pattern of reduced yields over time. Eventually, they realized that fertilization could make soil a renewable resource that enabled crops to be cultivated season after season at a fixed location. This sedentary agriculture facilitated a new way of life. Humans began to build permanent dwellings—the first villages. They also stored food for use between harvests, and food surpluses enabled some people to specialize in nonfarming occupations. In short, soil management, by fertilization and other practices, helped prepare the way for modern societies.

Unfortunately, soil mismanagement has been a recurrent problem throughout human history, as exemplified by the American Dust Bowl, an ecological and human disaster that ravaged the southwestern Great Plains of the United States in the 1930s. This region suffered through devastating dust storms that resulted from a prolonged drought and decades of inappropriate farming techniques. Before the arrival of farmers, the Great Plains had been covered by hardy grasses that held the soil in place in spite of recurring droughts and torrential rains. But in the late 1800s and early 1900s, many homesteaders settled in the region, planting wheat and raising cattle. These land uses left the soil exposed to erosion by winds. A few years of drought made the problem worse. During the 1930s, huge quantities of fertile soil were blown away in "black blizzards," rendering millions of hectares of farmland useless (Figure 37.4). In one of the worst dust storms, clouds of dust blew eastward to Chicago, where soil fell like snow, and even reached the Atlantic coast. Hundreds of thousands of people in the Dust Bowl region were forced to abandon their homes and land, a plight immortalized in John Steinbeck's novel *The Grapes of Wrath*.

Soil mismanagement continues to be a major problem to this day. More than 30% of the world's farmland has reduced productivity stemming from poor soil conditions, such as chemical contamination, mineral deficiencies, acidity,

▲ Figure 37.4 **A massive dust storm in the American Dust Bowl during the 1930s.**

▲ Figure 37.5 **Sudden land subsidence.** Overuse of groundwater for irrigation triggered formation of this sinkhole in Florida.

salinity, and poor drainage. As the world's population grows, the demand for food increases. Because soil quality greatly affects crop yield, soil resources must be managed prudently.

We'll now discuss how farmers irrigate and modify soil in order to maintain good crop yields. The goal is **sustainable agriculture**, a commitment embracing a variety of farming methods that are conservation minded, environmentally safe, and profitable. We will also examine problems and solutions relating to soil degradation.

Irrigation

Because water is often the limiting factor in plant growth, perhaps no technology has increased crop yield as much as irrigation. However, irrigation is a huge drain on freshwater resources. Globally, about 75% of all freshwater use is devoted to agriculture. Many rivers in arid regions have been reduced to trickles by the diversion of water for irrigation. The primary source of irrigation water, however, is not surface waters, such as rivers and lakes, but underground water reserves called *aquifers*. In some parts of the world, the rate of water removal is exceeding the natural refilling of the aquifers. The result is *land subsidence*, a gradual settling or sudden sinking of Earth's surface (**Figure 37.5**). Land subsidence alters drainage patterns, causes damage to human-made structures, contributes to loss of underground springs, and increases the risk of flooding.

Irrigation, particularly from groundwater, can also lead to soil *salinization*—the addition of salts to the soil that make it too salty for cultivating plants. Salts dissolved in irrigation water accumulate in the soil as the water evaporates, making the water potential of the soil solution more negative. The water potential gradient from soil to roots is reduced, diminishing water uptake (see Chapter 36).

Many forms of irrigation, such as the flooding of fields, are wasteful because much of the water evaporates. To use water efficiently, farmers must understand the water-holding capacity of their soil, the water needs of their crops, and the

appropriate irrigation technology. One popular technology is *drip irrigation*, the slow release of water to soil and plants from perforated plastic tubing placed directly at the root zone. Because drip irrigation requires less water and reduces salinization, it is used in many arid agricultural regions.

Fertilization

In natural ecosystems, mineral nutrients are usually recycled by the excretion of animal wastes and the decomposition of humus. Agriculture, however, is unnatural. The lettuce you eat, for example, contains minerals extracted from a farmer's field. As you excrete wastes, these minerals are deposited far from their original source. Over many harvests, the farmer's field will eventually become depleted of nutrients. Nutrient depletion is a major cause of global soil degradation. Farmers must reverse nutrient depletion by means of **fertilization**, the addition of mineral nutrients to the soil.

Today, most farmers in industrialized nations use fertilizers containing minerals that are either mined or prepared by energy-intensive processes. These fertilizers are usually enriched in nitrogen (N), phosphorus (P), and potassium (K)—the nutrients most commonly deficient in depleted soils. You may have seen fertilizers labeled with a three-number code, called the N–P–K ratio. A fertilizer marked "15–10–5," for instance, is 15% N (as ammonium or nitrate), 10% P (as phosphate), and 5% K (as the mineral potash).

Manure, fishmeal, and compost are called "organic" fertilizers because they are of biological origin and contain decomposing organic material. Before plants can use organic material, however, it must be decomposed into the inorganic nutrients that roots can absorb. Whether from organic fertilizer or a chemical factory, the minerals a plant extracts are in the same form. However, organic fertilizers release them gradually, whereas minerals in commercial fertilizers are immediately available but may not be retained by the soil for long. Minerals not absorbed by roots are often leached from the soil by rainwater or irrigation. To make matters worse, mineral runoff into lakes may lead to explosions in algal populations that can deplete oxygen levels and decimate fish populations.

Adjusting Soil pH

Soil pH is an important factor that influences mineral availability by its effect on cation exchange and the chemical form of minerals. Depending on the soil pH, a particular mineral may be bound too tightly to clay particles or may be in a chemical form that the plant cannot absorb. Most plants prefer slightly acidic soil because the high H^+ concentrations can displace positively charged minerals from soil particles, making them more available for absorption. Adjusting soil pH is tricky because a change in H^+ concentration may make one mineral more available but another less available. At pH 8, for instance, plants can absorb calcium, but iron is almost unavailable. The soil pH should be matched to a crop's mineral needs. If the soil is too alkaline, adding sulfate will lower the pH. Soil that is too acidic can be adjusted by adding lime (calcium carbonate or calcium hydroxide).

When the soil pH dips to 5 or lower, toxic aluminum ions (Al^{3+}) become more soluble and are absorbed by roots, stunting root growth and preventing the uptake of calcium, a needed plant nutrient. Some plants can cope with high Al^{3+} levels by secreting organic anions that bind Al^{3+} and render it harmless. However, low soil pH and Al^{3+} toxicity continue to pose serious problems, especially in tropical regions, where the pressure of producing food for a growing population is often most acute.

Controlling Erosion

As happened most dramatically in the Dust Bowl, water and wind erosion can remove large amounts of topsoil. Erosion is a major cause of soil degradation because nutrients are carried away by wind and streams. To limit erosion, farmers plant rows of trees as windbreaks, terrace hillside crops, and cultivate crops in a contour pattern (Figure 37.6). Crops such as alfalfa and wheat provide good ground cover and protect the soil better than maize and other crops that are usually planted in more widely spaced rows.

Erosion can also be reduced by a plowing technique called **no-till agriculture**. In traditional plowing, the entire field is tilled, or turned over. This practice helps control weeds but disrupts the meshwork of roots that holds the soil in place, leading to increased surface runoff and erosion. In no-till agriculture, a special plow creates narrow furrows for seeds and fertilizer. In this way, the field is seeded with minimal disturbance to the soil, while also using less fertilizer.

Phytoremediation

Some land areas are unfit for cultivation because toxic metals or organic pollutants have contaminated the soil or groundwater. Traditionally, soil remediation, the detoxification of contaminated soils, has focused on nonbiological technologies, such as removing and storing contaminated soil in landfills, but these techniques are costly and often disrupt the landscape. **Phytoremediation** is a nondestructive biotechnology that harnesses the ability of some plants to extract soil pollutants and concentrate them in portions of the plant that can be easily removed for safe disposal. For example, alpine pennycress (*Thlaspi caerulescens*) can accumulate zinc in its shoots at concentrations 300 times higher than most plants can tolerate. The shoots can be harvested and the zinc removed. Such plants show promise for cleaning up areas contaminated by smelters, mines, or nuclear tests. Phytoremediation is a type of bioremediation, which also uses prokaryotes and protists to detoxify polluted sites (see Chapters 27 and 55).

▲ **Figure 37.6 Contour tillage.** These crops are planted in rows that go around, rather than up and down, the hills. Contour tillage helps slow water runoff and topsoil erosion after heavy rains.

We have discussed the importance of soil conservation for sustainable agriculture. Mineral nutrients contribute greatly to soil fertility, but which minerals are most important, and why do plants need them? These are the topics of the next section.

CONCEPT CHECK 37.1

1. Explain how the phrase "too much of a good thing" can apply to watering and fertilizing plants.
2. Some lawn mowers collect clippings. What is a drawback of this practice with respect to plant nutrition?
3. **WHAT IF?** How would adding clay to loamy soil affect capacity to exchange cations and retain water? Explain.
4. **MAKE CONNECTIONS** Note three ways the properties of water contribute to soil formation. See Concept 3.2.

For suggested answers, see Appendix A.

CONCEPT 37.2

Plants require essential elements to complete their life cycle

Water, air, and soil minerals all contribute to plant growth. A plant's water content can be measured by comparing the mass before and after drying. Typically, 80–90% of a plant's fresh mass is water. Some 96% of the remaining dry mass consists of carbohydrates such as cellulose and starch that are produced by photosynthesis. Thus, the components of carbohydrates—carbon, oxygen, and hydrogen—are the most abundant elements in dried plant residue. Inorganic substances from the soil, although essential for plant survival, account for only about 4% of a plant's dry mass.

Essential Elements

The inorganic substances in plants contain more than 50 chemical elements. In studying the chemical composition of plants, we must distinguish elements that are essential from those that are merely present in the plant. A chemical element is considered an **essential element** only if it is required for a plant to complete its life cycle and produce another generation.

To determine which chemical elements are essential, researchers use **hydroponic culture**, in which plants are grown in mineral solutions instead of soil (**Figure 37.7**). Such studies have helped identify 17 essential elements needed by all plants (**Table 37.1**). Hydroponic culture is also used on a small scale to grow some greenhouse crops.

Nine of the essential elements are called **macronutrients** because plants require them in relatively large amounts. Six of these are the major components of organic compounds forming a plant's structure: carbon, oxygen, hydrogen, nitrogen, phosphorus, and sulfur. The other three macronutrients are potassium, calcium, and magnesium. Of all the mineral nutrients, nitrogen contributes the most to plant growth and crop yields.

The other essential elements are called **micronutrients** because plants need them in only tiny quantities. They are chlorine, iron, manganese, boron, zinc, copper, nickel, and molybdenum. In some cases, sodium may be a ninth essential micronutrient: Plants that use the C_4 and CAM pathways of photosynthesis (see Chapter 10) require sodium ions to regenerate phosphophenolpyruvate, which is the CO_2 acceptor in these two types of carbon fixation.

Micronutrients function in plants mainly as cofactors, nonprotein helpers in enzymatic reactions (see Chapter 8). Iron, for example, is a metallic component of cytochromes, the proteins in the electron transport chains of chloroplasts

and mitochondria. It is because micronutrients generally play catalytic roles that plants need only tiny quantities. The requirement for molybdenum, for instance, is so modest that there is only one atom of this rare element for every 60 million atoms of hydrogen in dried plant material. Yet a deficiency of molybdenum or any other micronutrient can weaken or kill a plant.

Symptoms of Mineral Deficiency

The symptoms of a deficiency depend partly on the mineral's function as a nutrient. For example, a deficiency of magnesium, a component of chlorophyll, causes *chlorosis*, yellowing of leaves. In some cases, the relationship between a deficiency and its symptoms is less direct. For instance, iron deficiency can cause chlorosis even though chlorophyll contains no iron, because iron ions are required as a cofactor in an enzymatic step of chlorophyll synthesis.

Mineral deficiency symptoms depend not only on the role of the nutrient but also on its mobility within the plant. If a nutrient moves about freely, symptoms appear first in older organs because young, growing tissues are a greater sink for nutrients that are in short supply. For example, magnesium is relatively mobile and is shunted preferentially to young leaves. Therefore, a plant deficient in magnesium first shows signs of chlorosis in its older leaves. The mechanism for preferential routing is the source-to-sink translocation in phloem, as minerals move along with sugars to the growing tissues (see Figure 36.16). In contrast, a deficiency of a mineral that is relatively immobile affects young parts of the plant first. Older tissues may have adequate amounts that they retain during periods of short supply. For example, iron does not move freely within a plant, and an iron deficiency causes yellowing of young leaves before any effect on older leaves is visible. The mineral requirements of a plant may also change with the time of the year and the age of the plant. Young seedlings, for example, rarely show mineral deficiency symptoms because their mineral requirements are met largely by minerals released from stored reserves in the seed itself.

Deficiencies of phosphorus, potassium, and especially nitrogen are most common. Micronutrient shortages are less common and tend to occur in certain geographic regions because of differences in soil composition. Symptoms of a deficiency may vary between species but are often distinctive enough for a plant physiologist or farmer to diagnose (see the Scientific Skills Exercise). One way to confirm a diagnosis is to analyze the mineral content of the plant or soil. The amount of a micronutrient needed to correct a deficiency is usually small. For example, a zinc deficiency in fruit trees can usually be cured by hammering a few zinc nails into each tree trunk. Moderation is important because overdoses can be detrimental or toxic. Too much nitrogen, for example, can lead to excessive vine growth in tomato plants at the expense of good fruit production.

▼ Figure 37.7 | **Research Method**

Hydroponic Culture

Application In hydroponic culture, plants are grown in mineral solutions without soil. One use of hydroponic culture is to identify essential elements in plants.

Technique Plant roots are bathed in aerated solutions of known mineral composition. Aerating the water provides the roots with oxygen for cellular respiration. (Note: The flasks would normally be opaque to prevent algal growth.) A mineral, such as potassium, can be omitted to test whether it is essential.

Control: Solution containing all minerals

Experimental: Solution without potassium

Results If the omitted mineral is essential, mineral deficiency symptoms occur, such as stunted growth and discolored leaves. By definition, the plant would not be able to complete its life cycle. Deficiencies of different elements may have different symptoms, which can aid in diagnosing mineral deficiencies in soil.

Table 37.1 Essential Elements in Plants

Element (Form Primarily Absorbed by Plants)	% Mass in Dry Tissue	Major Functions	Early Visual Symptoms of Nutrient Deficiencies
Macronutrients			
Carbon (CO_2)	45%	Major component of plant's organic compounds	Poor growth
Oxygen (CO_2)	45%	Major component of plant's organic compounds	Poor growth
Hydrogen (H_2O)	6%	Major component of plant's organic compounds	Wilting, poor growth
Nitrogen (NO_3^-, NH_4^+)	1.5%	Component of nucleic acids, proteins, and chlorophyll	Chlorosis at tips of older leaves (common in heavily cultivated soils or soils low in organic material)
Potassium (K^+)	1.0%	Cofactor of many enzymes; major solute functioning in water balance; operation of stomata	Mottling of older leaves, with drying of leaf edges; weak stems; roots poorly developed (common in acidic or sandy soils)
Calcium (Ca^{2+})	0.5%	Important component of middle lamella and cell walls; maintains membrane function; signal transduction	Crinkling of young leaves; death of terminal buds (common in acidic or sandy soils)
Magnesium (Mg^{2+})	0.2%	Component of chlorophyll; cofactor of many enzymes	Chlorosis between veins, found in older leaves (common in acidic or sandy soils)
Phosphorus ($H_2PO_4^-$, HPO_4^{2-})	0.2%	Component of nucleic acids, phospholipids, ATP	Healthy appearance but very slow development; thin stems; purpling of veins; poor flowering and fruiting (common in acidic, wet, or cold soils)
Sulfur (SO_4^{2-})	0.1%	Component of proteins	General chlorosis in young leaves (common in sandy or very wet soils)
Micronutrients			
Chlorine (Cl^-)	0.01%	Photosynthesis (water-splitting); functions in water balance	Wilting; stubby roots; leaf mottling (uncommon)
Iron (Fe^{3+}, Fe^{2+})	0.01%	Respiration; photosynthesis: chlorophyll synthesis; N_2 fixation	Chlorosis between veins, found in young leaves (common in basic soils)
Manganese (Mn^{2+})	0.005%	Active in formation of amino acids; activates some enzymes; required for water-splitting step of photosynthesis	Chlorosis between veins, found in young leaves (common in basic soils rich in humus)
Boron ($H_2BO_3^-$)	0.002%	Cofactor in chlorophyll synthesis; role in cell wall function; pollen tube growth	Death of meristems; thick, leathery, and discolored leaves (occurs in any soil; most common micronutrient deficiency)
Zinc (Zn^{2+})	0.002%	Active in formation of chlorophyll; cofactor of some enzymes; needed for DNA transcription	Reduced internode length; crinkled leaves (common in some geographic regions)
Copper (Cu^+, Cu^{2+})	0.001%	Component of many redox and lignin-biosynthetic enzymes	Light green color throughout young leaves, with drying of leaf tips; roots stunted and excessively branched (common in some geographic regions)
Nickel (Ni^{2+})	0.001%	Nitrogen metabolism	General chlorosis in all leaves; death of leaf tips (common in acidic or sandy soils)
Molybdenum (MoO_4^{2-})	0.0001%	Nitrogen metabolism	Death of root and shoot tips; chlorosis in older leaves (common in acidic soils in some geographic areas)

MAKE CONNECTIONS *Explain why CO_2, rather than O_2, is the source of much of the dry mass oxygen in plants. See Concept 10.1.*

Improving Plant Nutrition by Genetic Modification

In exploring plant nutrition so far, we have discussed how farmers use irrigation, fertilization, and other means to tailor soil conditions for a crop. An opposite approach is tailoring the plant by genetic engineering to better fit the soil. Here we highlight two examples of how genetic engineering improves plant nutrition and fertilizer usage.

Resistance to Aluminum Toxicity

Aluminum in acidic soils damages roots and reduces crop yields. The major mechanism of aluminum resistance is secretion of organic acids (such as malic acid and citric acid) by roots. These acids bind to free aluminum ions and lower the levels of aluminum in the soil. Scientists have altered tobacco and papaya plants by introducing a citrate synthase gene from a bacterium into the plants' genomes. The resulting overproduction of citric acid increased aluminum resistance.

Making Observations

What Mineral Deficiency Is This Plant Exhibiting? Plant growers often diagnose deficiencies in their crops by examining changes to the foliage, such as chlorosis (yellowing), death of some leaves, discoloring, mottling, scorching, or changes in size or texture. In this exercise, you will diagnose a mineral deficiency by observing a plant's leaves and applying what you have learned about symptoms from the text and Table 37.1.

Data The data for this exercise come from the photograph below of leaves on an orange tree exhibiting a mineral deficiency.

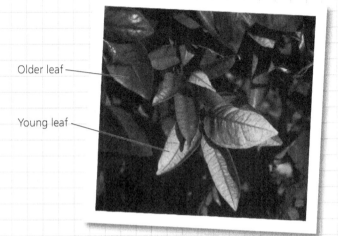

Older leaf

Young leaf

Interpret the Data

1. How do the young leaves differ in appearance from the older leaves?

2. In three words, what is the most prominent mineral deficiency symptom seen in this photo? List the three nutrients whose deficiencies give rise to this symptom. Based on the symptom's location, which one of these three nutrients can be ruled out, and why? What does the location suggest about the other two nutrients?

3. How would your hypothesis about the cause of this deficiency be influenced if tests showed that the soil was low in humus?

(MB) A version of this Scientific Skills Exercise can be assigned in MasteringBiology.

Smart Plants

Agricultural researchers are developing ways to maintain crop yields while reducing fertilizer use. One approach is to genetically engineer "smart" plants that signal when a nutrient deficiency is imminent—but *before* damage has occurred. One type of smart plant takes advantage of a promoter (a DNA sequence indicating where the transcription of a gene starts) that more readily binds RNA polymerase (the transcription enzyme) when the phosphorus content of the plant's tissues begins to decline. This promoter is linked to a "reporter" gene that leads to production of a light blue pigment in the leaf cells **(Figure 37.8)**. When leaves of these smart plants develop a blue tinge, the farmer knows it is time to add phosphate-containing fertilizer.

No phosphorus deficiency

Beginning phosphorus deficiency

Well-developed phosphorus deficiency

▲ **Figure 37.8 Deficiency warnings from "smart" plants.** Some plants have been genetically modified to signal an impending nutrient deficiency before irreparable damage occurs. For example, after laboratory treatments, the research plant *Arabidopsis* develops a blue color in response to an imminent phosphate deficiency.

So far, you have learned that soil, to support vigorous plant growth, must have an adequate supply of mineral nutrients, sufficient aeration, good water-holding capacity, low salinity, and a pH near neutrality. It must also be free of toxic concentrations of minerals and other chemicals. These physical and chemical features of soil, however, are just part of the story: We must also consider the living components of soil.

CONCEPT CHECK 37.2

1. Are some essential elements more important than others? Explain.

2. **WHAT IF?** If an element increases the growth rate of a plant, can it be defined as an essential element?

3. **MAKE CONNECTIONS** Based on the information on fermentation in Figure 9.17, explain why hydroponically grown plants would grow much more slowly if they were not sufficiently aerated.

For suggested answers, see Appendix A.

CONCEPT 37.3

Plant nutrition often involves relationships with other organisms

To this point, we have portrayed plants as exploiters of soil resources. However, plants and soil actually have a two-way relationship. Dead plants provide much of the energy that is needed by soil-dwelling microorganisms, while the secretions produced by living roots support a wide variety of microbes. Here we'll focus on some of the *mutualistic*—mutually beneficial—relationships between plants and bacteria or fungi. Then we'll look at some unusual plants that form nonmutualistic relationships with other plants or, in a few cases, with animals.

Bacteria and Plant Nutrition

A variety of mutualistic bacteria play roles in plant nutrition. **Rhizobacteria** live in the **rhizosphere**, the soil closely surrounding the plant's roots. **Endophytes** are nonpathogenic bacteria (or fungi)that live between cells within the plant itself but do not form deep, intimate associations with the cells or alter their morphology. Both endophytic bacteria and rhizobacteria depend on nutrients such as sugars, amino acids, and organic acids that are secreted by plant cells. In the case of the rhizosphere, up to 20% of a plant's photosynthetic production fuels the organisms in this miniature ecosystem. In turn, endophytic bacteria and rhizobacteria enhance plant growth by a variety of mechanisms. Some produce chemicals that stimulate plant growth. Others produce antibiotics that protect roots from disease. Still others absorb toxic metals or make nutrients more available to roots. Inoculation of seeds with plant-growth-promoting rhizobacteria can increase crop yield and reduce the need for fertilizers and pesticides.

Both the intercellular spaces occupied by endophytic bacteria and the rhizosphere associated with each plant root system contain a unique and complex cocktail of root secretions and microbial products that differ from those of the surrounding soil. A recent metagenomics study by Jeff Dangl (see the Unit 6 interview before Chapter 35) and his colleagues has revealed that the compositions of bacterial communities living endophytically and in the rhizosphere are not identical **(Figure 37.9)**. A better understanding of the bacteria within and around roots could have profound agricultural benefits.

▼ **Figure 37.9** | **Inquiry**

How variable are the compositions of bacterial communities inside and outside of roots?

Experiment The bacterial communities found within and immediately outside of root systems are known to improve plant growth. In order to devise agricultural strategies to increase the benefits of these bacterial communities, it is necessary to determine how complex they are and what factors affect their composition. A problem inherent in studying these bacterial communities is that a handful of soil contains as many as 10,000 types of bacteria, more than all the bacterial species that have been described. One cannot

▲ Bacteria (green) on surface of root (fluorescent LM)

simply culture each species and use a taxonomic key to identify them; a molecular approach is needed.

Jeffery Dangl (see the Unit 6 interview before Chapter 35) and his colleagues estimated the number of bacterial "species" in various samples using a technique called *metagenomics* (see Concept 21.1). The bacterial community samples they studied differed in location (endophytic, rhizospheric, or outside the rhizosphere), soil type (clayey or porous), and the developmental stage of the root system with which they were associated (old or young). The DNA from each sample was purified, and the polymerase chain reaction (PCR) was used to amplify the DNA that codes for the 16S ribosomal RNA subunits. Many thousands of DNA sequence variations were found in each sample. The researchers then lumped the sequences that were more than 97% identical into "taxonomic units" or "species." (The word *species* is in quotation marks because "two organisms having a single gene that is more than 97% identical" is not explicit in any definition of species.) Having established the types of "species" in each community, the researchers constructed a tree diagram showing the percent of bacterial "species" that were found in common in each community.

Results This tree diagram breaks down the relatedness of bacterial communities into finer and finer levels of detail. The two explanatory labels give examples of how to interpret the diagram.

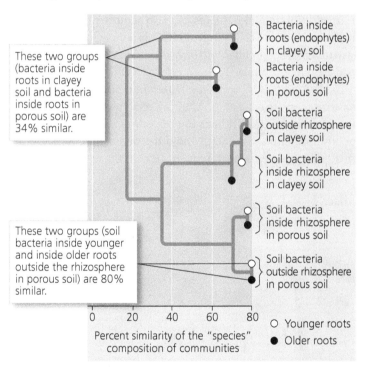

These two groups (bacteria inside roots in clayey soil and bacteria inside roots in porous soil) are 34% similar.

Bacteria inside roots (endophytes) in clayey soil

Bacteria inside roots (endophytes) in porous soil

Soil bacteria outside rhizosphere in clayey soil

Soil bacteria inside rhizosphere in clayey soil

Soil bacteria inside rhizosphere in porous soil

Soil bacteria outside rhizosphere in porous soil

These two groups (soil bacteria inside younger and inside older roots outside the rhizosphere in porous soil) are 80% similar.

Percent similarity of the "species" composition of communities

○ Younger roots
● Older roots

Conclusion The "species" composition of the bacterial communities varied markedly according to the location inside the root versus outside the root and according to soil type.

INTERPRET THE DATA **(a)** *Which of the three community locations was least like the other two?* **(b)** *Rank the three variables (community location, developmental stage of roots, and soil type) in terms of how strongly they affect the "species" composition of the bacterial communities.*

Data from D.S. Lundberg et al., Defining the core *Arabidopsis thaliana* root microbiome, *Nature* 488:86–94 (2012).

Bacteria in the Nitrogen Cycle

Plants have mutualistic relationships with several groups of bacteria that help make nitrogen more available. From a global perspective, no mineral nutrient is more limiting to plant growth than nitrogen, which is required in large amounts for synthesizing proteins and nucleic acids. Here we focus on processes leading directly to nitrogen assimilation by plants.

Unlike other soil minerals, ammonium ions (NH_4^+) and nitrate ions (NO_3^-)—the forms of nitrogen that plants can use—are not derived from the weathering of rocks. Although lightning produces small amounts of NO_3^- that get carried to the soil in rain, most soil nitrogen comes from the activity of bacteria (**Figure 37.10**).

The **nitrogen cycle**, also discussed in Figure 55.14, describes transformations of nitrogen and nitrogenous compounds in nature. When a plant or animal dies, or an animal expels waste, the initial form of nitrogen is organic. Decomposers convert the organic nitrogen within the remains back into ammonium (NH_4^+), a process called ammonification. Other sources of soil NH_4^+ are *nitrogen-fixing bacteria* that convert gaseous nitrogen (N_2) to NH_3, which then picks up another H^+ in the soil solution, forming NH_4^+.

In addition to NH_4^+, plants can also acquire nitrogen in the form of nitrate (NO_3^-). Soil NO_3^- is largely formed by a two-step process called *nitrification*, which consists of the oxidation of ammonia (NH_3) to nitrite (NO_2^-), followed by oxidation of NO_2^- to NO_3^-. Different types of *nitrifying bacteria* mediate each step. After the roots absorb NO_3^-, a plant enzyme reduces it back to NH_4^+, which other enzymes incorporate into amino acids and other organic compounds. Most plant species export nitrogen from roots to shoots via the xylem as NO_3^- or organic compounds synthesized in the roots. Some soil nitrogen is lost, particularly in anaerobic soils, when denitrifying bacteria convert NO_3^- to N_2, which diffuses into the atmosphere.

Nitrogen-Fixing Bacteria: *A Closer Look*

Although Earth's atmosphere is 79% nitrogen, plants cannot use free gaseous nitrogen (N_2) because there is a triple bond between the two nitrogen atoms, making the molecule almost inert. For atmospheric N_2 to be of use to plants, it must be reduced to NH_3 by a process known as **nitrogen fixation**. All nitrogen-fixing organisms are bacteria. Some nitrogen-fixing bacteria are free-living in the soil (see Figure 37.10), whereas others are endophytic. Still others, particularly members of the genus *Rhizobium*, form efficient and intimate associations with the roots of legumes (such as peas, soybeans, alfalfa, and peanuts), altering the structure of the hosts' roots markedly, as will be discussed shortly.

The multistep conversion of N_2 to NH_3 by nitrogen fixation can be summarized as follows:

$$N_2 + 8e^- + 8\,H^+ + 16\,ATP \rightarrow 2\,NH_3 + H_2 + 16\,ADP + 16\,\circled{P}_i$$

The reaction is driven by the enzyme complex *nitrogenase*. Because the process of nitrogen fixation requires 16 ATP molecules for every 2 NH_3 molecules synthesized, nitrogen-fixing bacteria require a rich supply of carbohydrates from decaying material, root secretions, or (in the case of the *Rhizobium* bacteria) the vascular tissue of roots.

The specialized mutualism between *Rhizobium* bacteria and legume roots involves dramatic changes in root structure. Along a legume's roots are swellings called **nodules**,

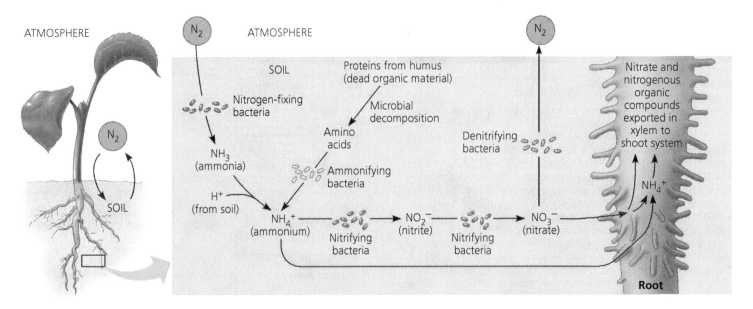

▲ **Figure 37.10 The roles of soil bacteria in the nitrogen nutrition of plants.** Ammonium is made available to plants by two types of soil bacteria: those that fix atmospheric N_2 (nitrogen-fixing bacteria) and those that decompose organic material (ammonifying bacteria). Although plants absorb some ammonium from the soil, they absorb mainly nitrate, which is produced from ammonium by nitrifying bacteria. Plants reduce nitrate back to ammonium before incorporating the nitrogen into organic compounds.

composed of plant cells "infected" by *Rhizobium* ("root living") bacteria **(Figure 37.11)**. Inside each nodule, *Rhizobium* bacteria assume a form called **bacteroids**, which are contained within vesicles formed in the root cells. Legume-*Rhizobium* relationships generate more usable nitrogen for plants than all industrial fertilizers used today, and the mutualism provides the right amount of nitrogen at the right time at virtually no cost to the farmer.

The location of the bacteroids inside living, nonphotosynthetic cells is conducive to nitrogen fixation, which requires an anaerobic environment. Lignified external layers of root nodules also limit gas exchange. Some root nodules appear reddish because of a molecule called leghemoglobin (*leg-* for "legume"), an iron-containing protein that binds reversibly to oxygen (similar to the hemoglobin in human red blood cells). This protein is an oxygen "buffer," reducing the concentration of free oxygen and thereby providing an anaerobic environment for nitrogen fixation while regulating the oxygen supply for the intense cellular respiration required to produce ATP for nitrogen fixation.

Each legume species is associated with a particular strain of *Rhizobium*. **Figure 37.12** describes how a root nodule develops after bacteria enter through an "infection thread."

▲ **Figure 37.11 Root nodules on a legume.** The spherical structures along this soybean root system are nodules containing *Rhizobium* bacteria. The bacteria fix nitrogen and obtain photosynthetic products supplied by the plant.

? *How is the relationship between legume plants and* Rhizobium *bacteria mutualistic?*

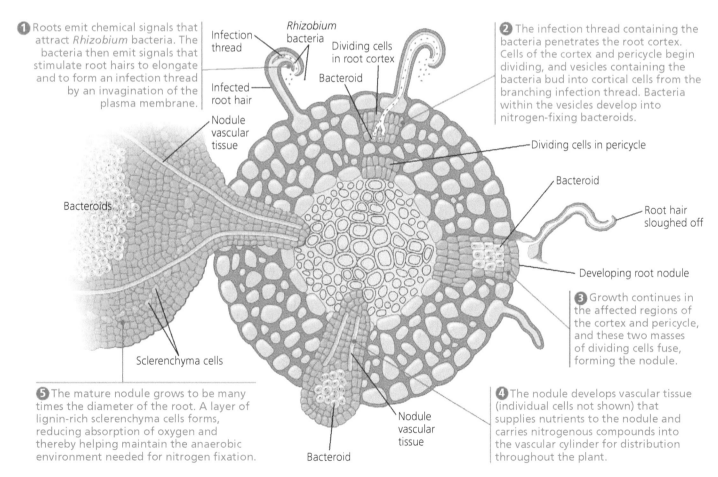

❶ Roots emit chemical signals that attract *Rhizobium* bacteria. The bacteria then emit signals that stimulate root hairs to elongate and to form an infection thread by an invagination of the plasma membrane.

❷ The infection thread containing the bacteria penetrates the root cortex. Cells of the cortex and pericycle begin dividing, and vesicles containing the bacteria bud into cortical cells from the branching infection thread. Bacteria within the vesicles develop into nitrogen-fixing bacteroids.

❸ Growth continues in the affected regions of the cortex and pericycle, and these two masses of dividing cells fuse, forming the nodule.

❹ The nodule develops vascular tissue (individual cells not shown) that supplies nutrients to the nodule and carries nitrogenous compounds into the vascular cylinder for distribution throughout the plant.

❺ The mature nodule grows to be many times the diameter of the root. A layer of lignin-rich sclerenchyma cells forms, reducing absorption of oxygen and thereby helping maintain the anaerobic environment needed for nitrogen fixation.

Labels: Infection thread · *Rhizobium* bacteria · Dividing cells in root cortex · Bacteroid · Infected root hair · Nodule vascular tissue · Bacteroids · Sclerenchyma cells · Dividing cells in pericycle · Bacteroid · Root hair sloughed off · Developing root nodule · Nodule vascular tissue · Bacteroid

▲ **Figure 37.12 Development of a soybean root nodule.**

? *What plant tissue systems are modified by root nodule formation?*

The symbiotic relationship between a legume and nitrogen-fixing bacteria is mutualistic in that the bacteria supply the host plant with fixed nitrogen while the plant provides the bacteria with carbohydrates and other organic compounds. The root nodules use most of the ammonium produced to make amino acids, which are then transported up to the shoot through the xylem.

How does a legume species recognize a certain strain of *Rhizobium* among the many bacterial strains in the soil? And how does an encounter with that specific *Rhizobium* strain lead to development of a nodule? These two questions have led researchers to uncover a chemical dialogue between the bacteria and the root. Each partner responds to chemical signals from the other by expressing certain genes whose products contribute to nodule formation. By understanding the molecular biology underlying the formation of root nodules, researchers hope to learn how to induce *Rhizobium* uptake and nodule formation in crop plants that do not normally form such nitrogen-fixing mutualistic relationships.

Nitrogen Fixation and Agriculture

The agricultural benefits of mutualistic nitrogen fixation underlie most types of **crop rotation**. In this practice, a non-legume such as maize is planted one year, and the following year alfalfa or some other legume is planted to restore the concentration of fixed nitrogen in the soil. To ensure that the legume encounters its specific *Rhizobium* strain, the seeds are exposed to bacteria before sowing. Instead of being harvested, the legume crop is often plowed under so that it will decompose as "green manure," reducing the need for manufactured fertilizers.

Many plant families besides legumes include species that benefit from mutualistic nitrogen fixation. For example, alder trees and certain tropical grasses host nitrogen-fixing actinomycete bacteria (see the gram-positive bacteria in Figure 27.16). Rice, a crop of great commercial importance, benefits indirectly from mutualistic nitrogen fixation. Rice farmers culture a free-floating aquatic fern, *Azolla*, which has mutualistic cyanobacteria that fix N_2. The growing rice eventually shades and kills the *Azolla*, and decomposition of this nitrogen-rich organic material increases the paddy's fertility.

Fungi and Plant Nutrition

Certain species of soil fungi also form mutualistic relationships with roots and play a major role in plant nutrition. Some of these fungi are endophytic, but the most important relationships are **mycorrhizae** ("fungus roots"), the intimate mutualistic associations of roots and fungi (see Figure 31.14). The host plant provides the fungus with a steady supply of sugar. Meanwhile, the fungus increases the surface area for

water uptake and also supplies the plant with phosphate and other minerals absorbed from the soil. The fungi of mycorrhizae also secrete growth factors that stimulate roots to grow and branch, as well as antibiotics that help protect the plant from soil pathogens.

Mycorrhizae and Plant Evolution

EVOLUTION Mycorrhizae are not oddities; they are formed by most plant species. In fact, this plant-fungus mutualism might have been one of the evolutionary adaptations that helped plants initially colonize land (see Chapter 29). When the earliest plants, which evolved from green algae, began to invade the land 400 to 500 million years ago, they encountered a harsh environment. Although the soil contained mineral nutrients, it lacked organic matter. Therefore, rain probably quickly leached away many of the soluble mineral nutrients. The barren land, however, was also a place of opportunities because there was very little competition, and light and carbon dioxide were readily available. Neither the early land plants nor early land fungi, which evolved from an aquatic protist, were fully equipped to exploit the terrestrial environment. The early plants lacked the ability to extract essential nutrients from the soil, while the fungi were unable to manufacture carbohydrates. Instead of the fungi becoming parasitic on the rhizoids of the evolving plants (roots or root hairs had not yet evolved), the two organisms formed mycorrhizal associations, a mutualistic symbiosis that allowed both of them to exploit the terrestrial environment. Fossil evidence supports the idea that mycorrhizal associations occurred in the earliest land plants. The small minority of extant angiosperms that are nonmycorrhizal probably lost this ability through gene loss.

The Two Main Types of Mycorrhizae

One type of mycorrhizae—the **ectomycorrhizae**—form a dense sheath, or mantle of mycelia (mass of branching hyphae; see Chapter 31), over the *surface* of the root **(Figure 37.13a)**. Fungal hyphae extend from the mantle into the soil, greatly increasing the surface area for water and mineral absorption. Hyphae also grow into the root cortex. These hyphae do not penetrate the root cells but form a network in the apoplast, or extracellular space, that facilitates nutrient exchange between the fungus and the plant. Compared with "uninfected" roots, ectomycorrhizae are generally thicker, shorter, and more branched. They typically do not form root hairs, which would be superfluous given the extensive surface area of the fungal mycelium. About 10% of plant families have species that form ectomycorrhizae, and the vast majority of these species are woody, including members of the pine, oak, birch, and eucalyptus families.

Unlike ectomycorrhizae, **arbuscular mycorrhizae** do not form a dense mantle ensheathing the root **(Figure 37.13b)**.

Arbuscular mycorrhizae are much more common than ectomycorrhizae and are found in over 85% of plant species. Among those species are most crop plants, including grains and legumes.

To the unaided eye, arbuscular mycorrhizae look like "normal" roots with root hairs, but a microscope reveals the enormous extent of the mutualistic relationship. Arbuscular mycorrhizal associations start when microscopic soil hyphae respond to the presence of a root by growing toward it, establishing contact, and growing along its surface. The hyphae penetrate between epidermal cells and then enter the root cortex. These hyphae digest small patches of the cortical cell walls, but they do not actually pierce the plasma membrane and enter the cytoplasm. Instead, a hypha grows into a tube formed by invagination of the root cell's membrane. The process of invagination is analogous to poking a finger gently into a balloon without popping it; your finger is like the fungal hypha, and the balloon skin is like the root cell's membrane. After the fungal hyphae have penetrated in this way, some of them branch densely, forming structures called arbuscules ("little trees"), which are important sites of nutrient transfer between the fungus and the plant. Within the hyphae themselves, oval vesicles may form, possibly serving as food storage sites for the fungus.

Agricultural and Ecological Importance of Mycorrhizae

Roots can form mycorrhizal symbioses only if exposed to the appropriate species of fungus. In most ecosystems, these fungi are present in the soil, and seedlings develop mycorrhizae. But if seeds are collected in one environment and planted in foreign soil, the plants may show signs of malnutrition (particularly phosphorus deficiency), resulting from the absence of fungal partners. Treating seeds with spores of mycorrhizal fungi can sometimes help seedlings to form mycorrhizae and improve crop yield.

Mycorrhizal associations are also important in understanding ecological relationships. Arbuscular mycorrhizae fungi exhibit little host specificity; a single fungus may form a shared mycorrhizal network with several plants, even plants of different species. Mycorrhizal networks in a plant community may benefit one plant species more than another. Another example of how mycorrhizae may affect the structures of plant communities comes from studies of exotic invasive plant species. Garlic mustard (*Alliaria petiolata*), an exotic European species that has invaded woodlands throughout the eastern United States, does not form mycorrhizae but hinders the growth of other plant species by preventing the growth of arbuscular mycorrhizal fungi.

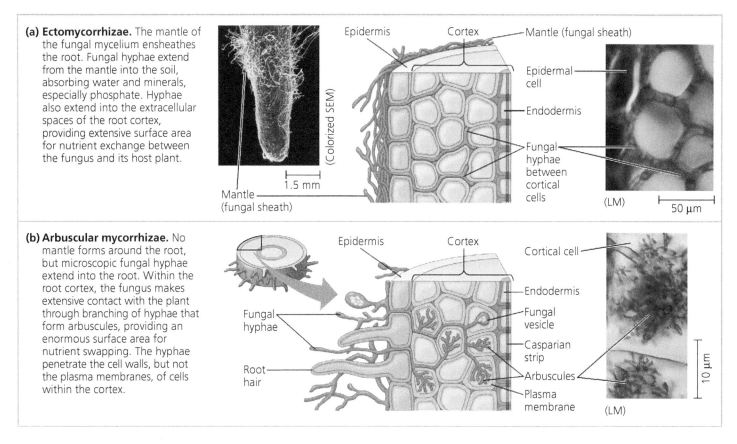

(a) **Ectomycorrhizae.** The mantle of the fungal mycelium ensheathes the root. Fungal hyphae extend from the mantle into the soil, absorbing water and minerals, especially phosphate. Hyphae also extend into the extracellular spaces of the root cortex, providing extensive surface area for nutrient exchange between the fungus and its host plant.

Mantle (fungal sheath)
1.5 mm
(Colorized SEM)

Epidermis   Cortex   Mantle (fungal sheath)
Epidermal cell
Endodermis
Fungal hyphae between cortical cells
(LM)   50 µm

(b) **Arbuscular mycorrhizae.** No mantle forms around the root, but microscopic fungal hyphae extend into the root. Within the root cortex, the fungus makes extensive contact with the plant through branching of hyphae that form arbuscules, providing an enormous surface area for nutrient swapping. The hyphae penetrate the cell walls, but not the plasma membranes, of cells within the cortex.

Fungal hyphae
Root hair

Epidermis   Cortex
Cortical cell
Endodermis
Fungal vesicle
Casparian strip
Arbuscules
Plasma membrane
(LM)   10 µm

▲ Figure 37.13 **Mycorrhizae.**

Exploring Unusual Nutritional Adaptations in Plants

Epiphytes

An **epiphyte** (from the Greek *epi*, upon, and *phyton*, plant) is a plant that grows on another plant. Epiphytes produce and gather their own nutrients; they do not tap into their hosts for sustenance. Usually anchored to the branches or trunks of living trees, epiphytes absorb water and minerals from rain, mostly through leaves rather than roots. Some examples are staghorn ferns, bromeliads, and many orchids, including the vanilla plant.

▶ **Staghorn fern**, an epiphyte

Parasitic Plants

Unlike epiphytes, parasitic plants absorb water, minerals, and sometimes products of photosynthesis from their living hosts. Many species have roots that function as haustoria, nutrient-absorbing projections that tap into the host plant. Some parasitic species, such as *Rafflesia arnoldii*, lack chlorophyll entirely, whereas others, such as mistletoe (genus *Phoradendron*), are photosynthetic. Still others, such as Indian pipe (*Monotropa uniflora*), absorb nutrients from the hyphae of mycorrhizae associated with other plants.

◀ **Mistletoe**, a photosynthetic parasite

▲ ***Rafflesia***, a nonphotosynthetic parasite

▲ **Indian pipe**, a nonphotosynthetic parasite of mycorrhizae

Carnivorous Plants

Carnivorous plants are photosynthetic but supplement their mineral diet by capturing insects and other small animals. They live in acid bogs and other habitats where soils are poor in nitrogen and other minerals. Pitcher plants such as *Nepenthes* and *Sarracenia* have water-filled funnels into which prey slip and drown, eventually to be digested by enzymes. Sundews (genus *Drosera*) exude a sticky fluid from tentacle-like glands on highly modified leaves. Stalked glands secrete sweet mucilage that attracts and ensnares insects, and they also release digestive enzymes. Other glands then absorb the nutrient "soup." The highly modified leaves of Venus flytrap (*Dionaea muscipula*) close quickly but partially when a prey hits two trigger hairs in rapid enough succession. Smaller insects can escape, but larger ones are trapped by the teeth lining the margins of the lobes. Excitation by the prey causes the trap to narrow more and digestive enzymes to be released.

▲ **Sundew**

◀ **Pitcher plants**

◀ **Venus flytraps**

Epiphytes, Parasitic Plants, and Carnivorous Plants

Almost all plant species have mutualistic relationships with soil fungi, bacteria, or both. Some plant species, including epiphytes, parasites, and carnivores, have unusual adaptations that facilitate exploiting other organisms (Figure 37.14). A recent study suggests that such behaviors may be the norm. Chanyarat Paungfoo-Lonhienne and her colleagues at the University of Queensland in Australia have provided evidence that *Arabidopsis* and tomato can take up bacteria and yeast into their roots and digest them. This pioneering research suggests that carnivory by plants may not be an adaptation limited to only a handful of odd species such as *Genlisea* (see Figure 37.1), but that many plant species might engage in a limited amount of heterotrophy.

CONCEPT CHECK 37.3

1. Why is the study of the rhizosphere critical to understanding plant nutrition?

2. How do soil bacteria and mycorrhizae contribute to plant nutrition?

3. **MAKE CONNECTIONS** What is a general term used to describe the strategy of using photosynthesis *and* heterotrophy for nutrition (see Chapter 28)? What is a well-known example of a class of protists that uses this strategy?

4. **WHAT IF?** A peanut farmer finds that the older leaves of his plants are turning yellow following a long period of wet weather. Suggest a reason why.

For suggested answers, see Appendix A.

37 Chapter Review

SUMMARY OF KEY CONCEPTS

CONCEPT 37.1

Soil contains a living, complex ecosystem (pp. 800–803)

- Soil particles of various sizes derived from the breakdown of rock are found in soil. Soil particle size affects the availability of water, oxygen, and minerals in the soil.
- A soil's composition refers to its inorganic and organic components. **Topsoil** is a complex ecosystem teeming with bacteria, fungi, protists, animals, and the roots of plants.
- Some agricultural practices can deplete the mineral content of soil, tax water reserves, and promote erosion. The goal of soil conservation is to minimize this damage.

? How is soil a complex ecosystem?

CONCEPT 37.2

Plants require essential elements to complete their life cycle (pp. 803–806)

- **Macronutrients**, elements required in relatively large amounts, include carbon, oxygen, hydrogen, nitrogen, and other major ingredients of organic compounds. **Micronutrients**, elements required in very small amounts, typically have catalytic functions as cofactors of enzymes.
- Deficiency of a mobile nutrient usually affects older organs more than younger ones; the reverse is true for nutrients that are less mobile within a plant. Macronutrient deficiencies are most common, particularly deficiencies of nitrogen, phosphorus, and potassium.
- Rather than tailoring the soil to match the plant, genetic engineers are tailoring the plant to match the soil.

? Do plants need soil to grow? Explain.

CONCEPT 37.3

Plant nutrition often involves relationships with other organisms (pp. 806–813)

- **Rhizobacteria** derive their energy from the **rhizosphere**, a microbe-enriched ecosystem intimately associated with roots. Plant secretions support the energy needs of the rhizosphere. Some rhizobacteria produce antibiotics, whereas others make nutrients more available for plants. Most are free-living, but some live inside plants. Plants satisfy most of their huge needs for nitrogen from the bacterial decomposition of **humus** and the fixation of gaseous nitrogen.

Nitrogen-fixing bacteria convert atmospheric N_2 to nitrogenous minerals that plants can absorb as a nitrogen source for organic synthesis. The most efficient mutualism between plants and nitrogen-fixing bacteria occurs in the **nodules** that are formed by *Rhizobium* bacteria growing in the roots of legumes. These bacteria obtain sugar from the plant and supply the plant with fixed nitrogen. In agriculture, legume crops are rotated with other crops to restore nitrogen to the soil.

- **Mycorrhizae** are mutualistic associations of fungi and roots. The fungal hyphae of mycorrhizae absorb water and minerals, which they supply to their plant hosts.
- **Epiphytes** grow on the surfaces of other plants but acquire water and minerals from rain. Parasitic plants absorb nutrients from host plants. Carnivorous plants supplement their mineral nutrition by digesting animals.

? *Do all plants gain energy directly from photosynthesis? Explain.*

TEST YOUR UNDERSTANDING

LEVEL 1: KNOWLEDGE/COMPREHENSION

1. The inorganic nutrient most often lacking in crops is
   a. carbon.
   b. nitrogen.
   c. phosphorus.
   d. potassium.

2. Micronutrients are needed in very small amounts because
   a. most of them are mobile in the plant.
   b. most serve mainly as cofactors of enzymes.
   c. most are supplied in large enough quantities in seeds.
   d. they play only a minor role in the growth and health of the plant.

3. Mycorrhizae enhance plant nutrition mainly by
   a. absorbing water and minerals through the fungal hyphae.
   b. providing sugar to root cells, which have no chloroplasts.
   c. converting atmospheric nitrogen to ammonia.
   d. enabling the roots to parasitize neighboring plants.

4. Epiphytes are
   a. fungi that attack plants.
   b. fungi that form mutualistic associations with roots.
   c. nonphotosynthetic parasitic plants.
   d. plants that grow on other plants.

5. Some of the problems associated with intensive irrigation include all of the following except
   a. soil salinization.
   b. overfertilization.
   c. land subsidence.
   d. aquifer depletion.

LEVEL 2: APPLICATION/ANALYSIS

6. A mineral deficiency is likely to affect older leaves more than younger leaves if
   a. the mineral is a micronutrient.
   b. the mineral is very mobile within the plant.
   c. the mineral is required for chlorophyll synthesis.
   d. the mineral is a macronutrient.

7. The greatest difference in health between two groups of plants of the same species, one group with mycorrhizae and one group without mycorrhizae, would be in an environment
   a. where nitrogen-fixing bacteria are abundant.
   b. that has soil with poor drainage.
   c. that has hot summers and cold winters.
   d. in which the soil is relatively deficient in mineral nutrients.

8. Two groups of tomatoes were grown under laboratory conditions, one with humus added to the soil and one a control without humus. The leaves of the plants grown without humus were yellowish (less green) compared with those of the plants grown in humus-enriched soil. The best explanation is that
   a. the healthy plants used the food in the decomposing leaves of the humus for energy to make chlorophyll.
   b. the humus made the soil more loosely packed, so water penetrated more easily to the roots.
   c. the humus contained minerals such as magnesium and iron needed for the synthesis of chlorophyll.
   d. the heat released by the decomposing leaves of the humus caused more rapid growth and chlorophyll synthesis.

9. The specific relationship between a legume and its mutualistic *Rhizobium* strain probably depends on
   a. each legume having a chemical dialogue with a fungus.
   b. each *Rhizobium* strain having a form of nitrogenase that works only in the appropriate legume host.
   c. each legume being found where the soil has only the *Rhizobium* specific to that legume.
   d. specific recognition between chemical signals and signal receptors of the *Rhizobium* strain and legume species.

10. **DRAW IT** Draw a simple sketch of cation exchange, showing a root hair, a soil particle with anions, and a hydrogen ion displacing a mineral cation.

LEVEL 3: SYNTHESIS/EVALUATION

11. **EVOLUTION CONNECTION**
    Imagine taking the plant out of the picture in Figure 37.10. Write a paragraph explaining how soil bacteria could sustain the recycling of nitrogen *before* land plants evolved.

12. **SCIENTIFIC INQUIRY**
    Acid precipitation has an abnormally high concentration of hydrogen ions (H^+). One effect of acid precipitation is to deplete the soil of nutrients such as calcium (Ca^{2+}), potassium (K^+), and magnesium (Mg^{2+}). Suggest a hypothesis to explain how acid precipitation washes these nutrients from the soil. How might you test your hypothesis?

13. **SCIENCE, TECHNOLOGY, AND SOCIETY**
    In many countries, irrigation is depleting aquifers to such an extent that land is subsiding, harvests are decreasing, and it is becoming necessary to drill wells deeper. In many cases, the withdrawal of groundwater has now greatly surpassed the aquifers' rates of natural recharge. Discuss the possible consequences of this trend. What can society and science do to help alleviate this growing problem?

14. **WRITE ABOUT A THEME: INTERACTIONS**
    The soil in which plants grow teems with organisms from every taxonomic kingdom. In a short essay (100–150 words), discuss examples of how the mutualistic interactions of plants with bacteria, fungi, and animals improve plant nutrition.

15. **SYNTHESIZE YOUR KNOWLEDGE**

Making a footprint in the soil seems like an insignificant event. In a short essay (100–150 words), explain how a footprint would affect the properties of the soil and how these changes would affect soil organisms and the emergence of seedlings.

For suggested answers, see Appendix A.

MasteringBiology®

Students Go to **MasteringBiology** for assignments, the eText, and the Study Area with practice tests, animations, and activities.

Instructors Go to **MasteringBiology** for automatically graded tutorials and questions that you can assign to your students, plus Instructor Resources.

38

Angiosperm Reproduction and Biotechnology

▲ **Figure 38.1 Why is this bee trying to mate with this flower?**

Flowers of Deceit

Male long-horned bees (*Eucera longicornis*) often attempt to copulate with flowers of the European orchid *Ophrys scolopax* **(Figure 38.1)**. During this encounter, a sac of pollen becomes glued to the insect's body. Eventually frustrated, the bee flies off and deposits the pollen onto another *Ophrys* flower that has become the object of his misplaced ardor. *Ophrys* flowers offer no reward such as nectar to the male bees, only sexual frustration. So what makes the male bees so enamored of this orchid? The traditional answer has been that the flower's shape and partial frill of yellow bristles vaguely resemble the female bee. These visual cues, however, are only part of the deception: *Ophrys* orchids also emit chemicals with a scent similar to that produced by sexually receptive female bees.

This is just one example of the amazing ways in which angiosperms (flowering plants) reproduce sexually with spatially distant members of their own species. But sex is not the only means of angiosperm reproduction. Many species also reproduce asexually, creating offspring that are genetically identical to the parent.

An unusual aspect of the orchid and bee example is that the insect does not profit from interacting with the flower. In fact, by wasting time and energy, the bee is probably rendered less fit. More typically, a plant lures an animal pollinator to its flowers not with offers of sex but with rewards of energy-rich nectar or pollen. Thus, both plant and pollinator benefit. Participating in such mutually beneficial relationships with other organisms is common in the plant kingdom. In fact, in recent evolutionary times, some flowering plants have formed relationships with an animal that not only disperses their seeds but also provides the plants with water and mineral nutrients and vigorously protects them from encroaching competitors, pathogens, and predators. In return for these favors, the animal typically gets to eat a fraction of some part of the plants, such as their seeds or fruits. These plants are called crops; the animals are humans.

For over 10,000 years, plant breeders have genetically manipulated traits of a few hundred wild angiosperm species by artificial selection, transforming them into the crops we grow today. Genetic engineering has dramatically increased the variety of ways and the speed with which we can modify plants.

In Chapters 29 and 30, we approached plant reproduction from an evolutionary perspective, tracing the descent of land plants from algal ancestors. Because angiosperms are the most important group of plants in agricultural as well as most other terrestrial ecosystems, we'll explore their reproductive biology in detail in this chapter. After discussing the sexual and asexual reproduction of angiosperms, we'll examine the role of humans in genetically altering crop species, as well as the controversies surrounding modern plant biotechnology.

CONCEPT 38.1

Flowers, double fertilization, and fruits are key features of the angiosperm life cycle

The life cycles of all plants are characterized by an alternation of generations, in which sporophytes (spore-producing plants) and gametophytes (gamete-producing plants) alternate producing each other. In the angiosperms, the sporophytes are the plants we see; they are much larger, more conspicuous, and longer-lived than the gametophytes. In exploring the life cycle of angiosperms, we'll pay especially close attention to three key derived traits of angiosperm reproduction that can be remembered as the "three Fs": *f*lowers, double *f*ertilization, and *f*ruits.

Flower Structure and Function

Flowers, the reproductive shoots of angiosperm sporophytes, are typically composed of four types of floral organs: **carpels**, **stamens**, **petals**, and **sepals** (Figure 38.2). When viewed from above, these organs take the form of concentric whorls. Carpels form the first (innermost) whorl, stamens the second, petals the third, and sepals the fourth (outermost) whorl. All are attached to a part of the stem called the **receptacle**. Unlike vegetative shoots, flowers are determinate shoots; they cease growing after the flower and fruit are formed.

Carpels and stamens are reproductive organs; sepals and petals are sterile. A carpel has an **ovary** at its base and a long, slender neck called the **style**. At the top of the style is a sticky structure called the **stigma** that captures pollen. Within the ovary are one or more **ovules**, which become seeds if fertilized; the number of ovules depends on the species. The flower shown in Figure 38.2 has a single carpel, but many species have multiple carpels. In most species, two or more carpels are fused into a single structure; the result is an ovary with two or more chambers, each containing one or more ovules. The term **pistil** is sometimes used to refer to a single carpel or two or more fused carpels. A stamen consists of a stalk called the filament and a terminal structure called the **anther**; within the anther are chambers called microsporangia (pollen sacs) that produce pollen. Petals are typically more brightly colored than sepals and advertise the flower to insects and other animal pollinators. Sepals, which enclose and protect unopened floral buds, usually resemble leaves more than the other floral organs do.

Complete flowers have all four basic floral organs (see Figure 38.2). Some species have **incomplete flowers**, lacking sepals, petals, stamens, or carpels. For example, most grass flowers lack petals. Some incomplete flowers are sterile, lacking functional stamens and carpels; others are *unisexual*, lacking either stamens or carpels. Flowers also vary in size, shape, color, odor, organ arrangement, and time of opening. Some are borne singly, while others are arranged in showy clusters called **inflorescences**. For example, a sunflower is actually an inflorescence consisting of a central disk composed of hundreds of tiny incomplete flowers, surrounded by sterile, incomplete flowers that look like yellow petals (see Figure 40.22). Much of floral diversity represents adaptation to specific pollinators. **Figure 38.3** shows some examples of variations in floral structures that have evolved.

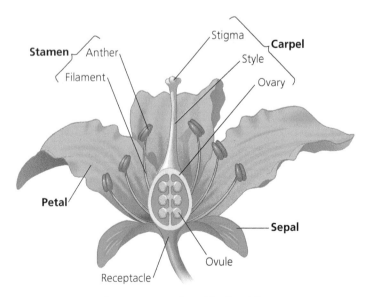

▲ Figure 38.2 **The structure of an idealized flower.**

Exploring Trends in the Evolution of Flowers

EVOLUTION Charles Darwin described the origin of flowering plants as an "abominable mystery." He was puzzled by their relatively sudden appearance and rapid diversification in the fossil record. Scientists now estimate that angiosperms arose about 140 million years ago. Much of their diversity has evolved through selective pressures that made flower-pollinator interactions more specific. However, there can be negative consequences associated with floral overspecialization if, for example, a pollinator goes extinct. Also, there are selective pressures associated with preventing the plunder of nectar and floral parts by "robbers," animals that feed on a flower without transferring its pollen to other plants of the same species. Despite these varied and sometimes opposing selective pressures, four general trends can be seen in the evolution of flowers: bilateral symmetry, reduction in the number of floral parts, fusion of floral parts, and the location of ovaries inside receptacles.

Bilateral Symmetry

The flowers of musk mallow (*Malva moschata*) exhibit radial symmetry. That is, any imaginary line through the central axis divides the flower into two equal parts. In contrast, the "Bramley" orchid (*Disa watsonii*) is bilaterally symmetrical. That is, only a single imaginary line can divide the flower into equal halves. Flowers with bilateral symmetry orient insects such as bees in their approach to the flower, enabling the insects to find their way to the nectar and enhancing pollen transfer between insect and flower.

▲ Musk mallow
(radial symmetry)

▼ "Bramley" orchid
(bilateral symmetry)

Reduction in Number of Floral Parts

The flower of bloodroot (*Sanguinaria canadensis*) has many petals and stamens, with the exact number varying among individual flowers. In contrast, the flowers of drooping trillium (*Trillium flexipes*) have fewer floral parts and have a fixed number of them. Although a greater number of floral parts may attract pollinators, such a large display may also entice unwanted visitors, such as pollen or nectar "robbers."

▲ Bloodroot

▼ Drooping trillium

Fusion of Floral Parts

The petals of Star of Bethlehem (*Ornithogalum arabicum*) are unfused, whereas the petals of hedge bindweed (*Calystegia septium*) are fused together. The fusion of floral parts often increases the specificity of animal pollinators that visit the flower. For example, a long "floral tube" made from fused petals may allow only certain animal pollinators to reach the nectar.

▲ Star of Bethlehem

▼ Hedge bindweed

Ovaries Located Inside Receptacles

In the flowers of the stone plant (*Lithops* sp.), the ovary is situated above the receptacle. In contrast, the ovary of Japanese quince (*Chaenomeles japonica*) is embedded in the receptacle, providing the seeds with even greater protection during their development and later enhancing the dispersal of seeds by animals.

▲ Stone plant
(longitudinal section)

Ovary

▼ Japanese quince
(longitudinal section)

Ovary

The Angiosperm Life Cycle: An Overview

Figure 38.4 shows the angiosperm life cycle, including gametophyte development, pollination, double fertilization, and seed development. We'll begin by examining the development of gametophytes.

Gametophyte Development

Over the course of seed plant evolution, gametophytes became reduced in size and wholly dependent on the sporophyte for nutrients (see Figure 30.2). The gametophytes of angiosperms are the most reduced of all plants, consisting of only a few cells: they are microscopic, and their development is obscured by protective tissues.

Development of Female Gametophytes (Embryo Sacs) As a carpel develops, one or more ovules form deep within its ovary, its swollen base. A female gametophyte, also known as an **embryo sac**, develops inside each ovule. The process of embryo sac formation occurs in a tissue called the megasporangium ❶ within each ovule. Two *integuments* (layers of protective sporophytic tissue that will develop into the seed coat) surround each megasporangium, except at a gap called the *micropyle*. Female gametophyte development begins when one cell in the megasporangium of each ovule, the *megasporocyte* (or megaspore mother cell), enlarges and undergoes meiosis, producing four haploid **megaspores**. Only one megaspore survives; the others degenerate.

The nucleus of the surviving megaspore divides by mitosis three times without cytokinesis, resulting in one large cell with eight haploid nuclei. The multinucleate mass is then divided by membranes to form the embryo sac. The cell fates of the nuclei are determined by a gradient of the hormone auxin originating near the micropyle. At the micropylar end of the embryo sac, two cells called synergids flank the egg and help attract and guide the pollen tube to the embryo sac. At the opposite end of the embryo sac are three antipodal cells of unknown function. The other two nuclei, called polar nuclei, are not partitioned into separate cells but share the cytoplasm of the large central cell of the embryo sac. The mature embryo sac thus consists of eight nuclei contained within seven cells. The ovule, which will become a seed if fertilized, now consists of the embryo sac, enclosed by the megasporangium (which eventually withers) and two surrounding integuments.

Development of Male Gametophytes in Pollen Grains As the stamens are produced, each anther ❷ develops four microsporangia, also called pollen sacs. Within the microsporangia are many diploid cells called *microsporocytes,* or microspore mother cells. Each microsporocyte undergoes meiosis, forming four haploid **microspores**, ❸ each of which eventually gives rise to a haploid male gametophyte. Each microspore then undergoes mitosis, producing a

haploid male gametophyte consisting of only two cells: the *generative cell* and the *tube cell*. Together, these two cells *and* the spore wall constitute a **pollen grain**. The spore wall, which consists of material produced by both the microspore and the anther, usually exhibits an elaborate pattern unique to the species. During maturation of the male gametophyte, the generative cell passes into the tube cell: The tube cell now has a completely free-standing cell inside it.

Pollination

After the microsporangium breaks open and releases the pollen, a pollen grain may be transferred to a receptive surface of a stigma—the act of **pollination**. Here we'll focus on how a pollen grain delivers sperm after pollination. Later we'll look at the various ways that a pollen grain can be transported from an anther to a stigma.

At the time of pollination, the pollen grain typically consists of only the tube cell and the generative cell. It then absorbs water and germinates by producing a **pollen tube**, a long cellular protuberance that delivers sperm to the female gametophyte. A pollen tube can grow very quickly, at a rate of 1 cm/hr or more. As the pollen tube elongates through the style, the nucleus of the generative cell divides by mitosis and produces two sperm, which remain inside the tube cell. The tube nucleus then leads the two sperm as the tip of the pollen tube grows toward the micropyle in response to chemical attractants produced by the synergids. The arrival of the pollen tube initiates the death of one of the two synergids, thereby providing a passageway into the embryo sac. The tube nucleus and the two sperm are then discharged from the pollen tube ❹ in the vicinity of the female gametophyte.

Double Fertilization

Fertilization, the fusion of gametes, occurs after the two sperm reach the female gametophyte. One sperm fertilizes the egg, forming the zygote. The other sperm combines with the two polar nuclei, forming a triploid ($3n$) nucleus in the center of the large central cell of the female gametophyte. This cell will give rise to the **endosperm**, a food-storing tissue of the seed. ❺ The union of the two sperm cells with different nuclei of the female gametophyte is called **double fertilization**. Double fertilization ensures that endosperm develops only in ovules where the egg has been fertilized, thereby preventing angiosperms from squandering nutrients on infertile ovules. Near the time of double fertilization, the tube nucleus, the other synergid, and the antipodal cells degenerate.

Seed Development

❻ After double fertilization, each ovule develops into a seed. Meanwhile, the ovary develops into a fruit, which encloses the seeds and aids in their dispersal by wind or animals. As the sporophyte embryo develops from the zygote, the seed stockpiles proteins, oils, and starch to varying degrees, depending on the species. This is why seeds are such a major nutrient drain. Initially, carbohydrates and other nutrients are stored in the seed's endosperm, but later, depending on the species, the swelling cotyledons (seed leaves) of the embryo may take over this function. When a seed germinates, ⑦ the embryo develops into a new sporophyte. The mature sporophyte produces its own flowers and fruits.

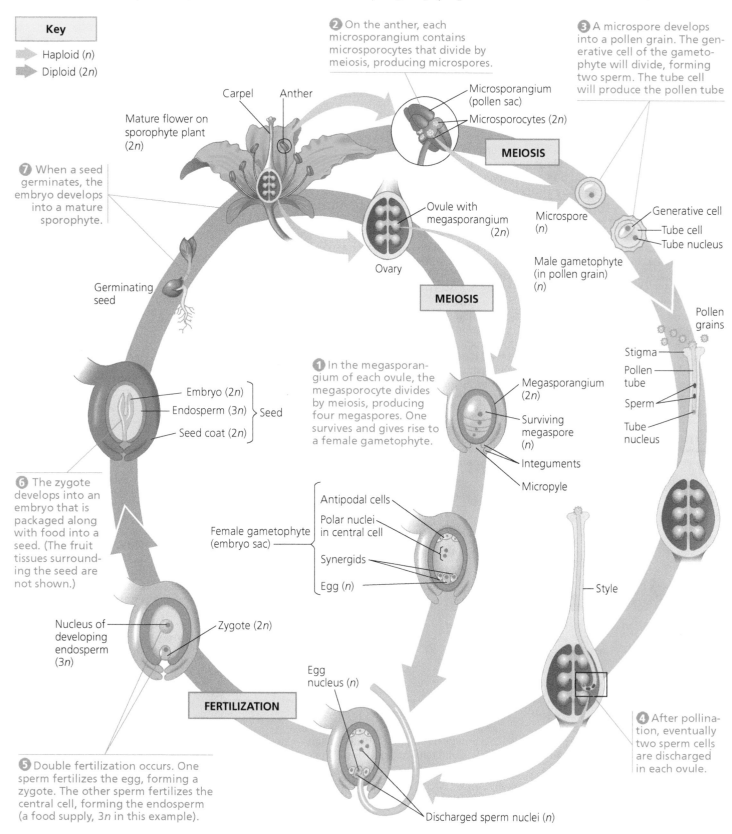

Key

Haploid (*n*)
Diploid (2*n*)

❷ On the anther, each microsporangium contains microsporocytes that divide by meiosis, producing microspores.

❸ A microspore develops into a pollen grain. The generative cell of the gametophyte will divide, forming two sperm. The tube cell will produce the pollen tube

Carpel   Anther

Mature flower on sporophyte plant (2*n*)

Microsporangium (pollen sac)

Microsporocytes (2*n*)

MEIOSIS

❼ When a seed germinates, the embryo develops into a mature sporophyte.

Ovule with megasporangium (2*n*)

Ovary

Microspore (*n*)

Generative cell
Tube cell
Tube nucleus

Male gametophyte (in pollen grain) (*n*)

MEIOSIS

Germinating seed

Pollen grains

❶ In the megasporangium of each ovule, the megasporocyte divides by meiosis, producing four megaspores. One survives and gives rise to a female gametophyte.

Megasporangium (2*n*)

Surviving megaspore (*n*)

Integuments

Micropyle

Stigma
Pollen tube
Sperm
Tube nucleus

Embryo (2*n*)
Endosperm (3*n*)   } Seed
Seed coat (2*n*)

Antipodal cells

Polar nuclei in central cell

Female gametophyte (embryo sac)

Synergids

Egg (*n*)

❻ The zygote develops into an embryo that is packaged along with food into a seed. (The fruit tissues surrounding the seed are not shown.)

Style

Nucleus of developing endosperm (3*n*)

Zygote (2*n*)

Egg nucleus (*n*)

FERTILIZATION

❹ After pollination, eventually two sperm cells are discharged in each ovule.

❺ Double fertilization occurs. One sperm fertilizes the egg, forming a zygote. The other sperm fertilizes the central cell, forming the endosperm (a food supply, 3*n* in this example).

Discharged sperm nuclei (*n*)

▲ Figure 38.4 **The life cycle of angiosperms.**

Methods of Pollination

Now that we've examined the angiosperm life cycle in general, we'll explore the methods of pollination. The transfer of pollen from an anther to a stigma is accomplished by wind, water, or animals (Figure 38.5). In wind-pollinated species, including grasses and many trees, the release of enormous quantities of smaller-sized pollen compensates for the randomness of dispersal by the wind. At certain times of the year, the air is loaded with pollen grains, as

---

▼ Figure 38.5

Exploring Flower Pollination

Most angiosperm species rely on a living (biotic) or nonliving (abiotic) pollinating agent that can move pollen from the anther of a flower on one plant to the stigma of a flower on another plant. Approximately 80% of all angiosperm pollination is biotic, employing animal go-betweens. Among abiotically pollinated species, 98% rely on wind and 2% on water. (Some angiosperm species can self-pollinate, but such species are limited to inbreeding in nature.)

Abiotic Pollination by Wind

About 20% of all angiosperm species are wind-pollinated. Since their reproductive success does not depend on attracting pollinators, there has been no selective pressure favoring colorful or scented flowers. Accordingly, the flowers of wind-pollinated species are often small, green, and inconspicuous, and they produce neither scent nor the sugary solution called nectar. Most temperate trees and grasses are wind-pollinated. The flowers of hazel (*Corylus avellana*) and many other temperate, wind-pollinated trees appear in the early spring, when there are no leaves to interfere with pollen movement. The relative inefficiency of wind pollination is compensated for by production of copious amounts of pollen grains. Wind tunnel studies reveal that wind pollination is often more efficient than it appears because floral structures can create eddy currents that aid in pollen capture.

▲ Hazel carpellate flower (carpels only)

▲ Hazel staminate flowers (stamens only) releasing clouds of pollen

Pollination by Bees

▲ Common dandelion under normal light

▲ Common dandelion under ultraviolet light

About 65% of all flowering plants require insects for pollination; the percentage is even greater for major crops. Bees are the most important insect pollinators, and there is great concern in Europe and North America that honeybee populations have shrunk. Pollinating bees depend on nectar and pollen for food. Typically, bee-pollinated flowers have a delicate, sweet fragrance. Bees are attracted to bright colors, primarily yellow and blue. Red appears dull to them, but they can see ultraviolet radiation. Many bee-pollinated flowers, such as the common dandelion (*Taraxacum vulgare*), have ultraviolet markings called "nectar guides" that help insects locate the nectaries (nectar-producing glands) but are only visible to human eyes under ultraviolet light.

Pollination by Moths and Butterflies

Moths and butterflies detect odors, and the flowers they pollinate are often sweetly fragrant. Butterflies perceive many bright colors, but moth-pollinated flowers are usually white or yellow, which stand out at night when moths are active. A yucca plant (shown here) is typically pollinated by a single species of moth with appendages that pack pollen onto the stigma. The moth then deposits eggs directly into the ovary. The larvae eat some developing seeds, but this cost is outweighed by the benefit of an efficient and reliable pollinator. If a moth deposits too many eggs, the flower aborts and drops off, selecting against individuals that overexploit the plant.

[?] *What are the benefits and dangers to a plant of having a highly specific animal pollinator?*

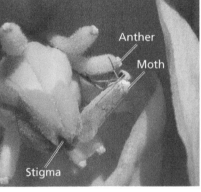

▲ Moth on yucca flower

Anther
Moth
Stigma

anyone who is plagued with pollen allergies can attest. Some species of aquatic plants rely on water to disperse pollen. Most angiosperm species, however, depend on insects, birds, or other animal pollinators to transfer pollen directly from one flower to another.

Pollination by Bats

Bat-pollinated flowers, like moth-pollinated flowers, are light-colored and aromatic, attracting their nocturnal pollinators. The lesser long-nosed bat (*Leptonycteris curasoae yerbabuenae*) feeds on the nectar and pollen of agave and cactus flowers in the southwestern United States and Mexico. In feeding, the bats transfer pollen from plant to plant. Long-nosed bats are an endangered species.

▲ Long-nosed bat feeding on cactus flower at night

Pollination by Flies

▲ Blowfly on carrion flower

Many fly-pollinated flowers are reddish and fleshy, with an odor like rotten meat. Blowflies visiting carrion flowers (*Stapelia* species) mistake the flower for a rotting corpse and lay their eggs on it. In the process, the blowflies become dusted with pollen that they carry to other flowers. When the eggs hatch, the larvae find no carrion to eat and die.

Pollination by Birds

Bird-pollinated flowers, such as columbine flowers, are usually large and bright red or yellow, but they have little odor. Since birds often do not have a well-developed sense of smell, there has been no selective pressure favoring scent production. However, the flowers produce the sugary nectar that helps meet the high energy demands of the pollinating birds. The primary function of nectar, which is produced by nectaries at the base of many flowers, is to "reward" the pollinator. The petals of such flowers are often fused, forming a bent floral tube that fits the curved beak of the bird.

▶ Hummingbird drinking nectar of columbine flower

EVOLUTION Many species of flowering plants have evolved with specific pollinators. The joint evolution of two interacting species, each in response to selection imposed by the other, is called **coevolution**. Natural selection favors individual plants or insects having slight deviations of structure that enhance the flower-pollinator mutualism. For example, some species have flower petals fused together, forming long, tubelike structures bearing nectaries tucked deep inside. Charles Darwin suggested that a race between flower and insect might lead to correspondences between the length of a floral tube and the length of an insect's proboscis, a straw-like mouthpart. Imagine an insect with a tongue long enough to drink the nectar of flowers without picking up pollen on its body. The resulting failure of these plants to fertilize others would render them less evolutionarily fit. Natural selection would then favor flowers with longer tubes. At the same time, an insect with a tongue that was too short for the tube wouldn't be able to use the nectar as a food source and therefore would be at a selective disadvantage compared with long-tongued rivals. As a result, the shapes and sizes of flowers often show a close correspondence to the pollen-adhering parts of their animal pollinators. In fact, based on the length of a long, tubular flower that grows in Madagascar, Darwin predicted the existence of a pollinating moth with a 28-cm-long proboscis. Such a moth was discovered two decades after Darwin's death **(Figure 38.6)**.

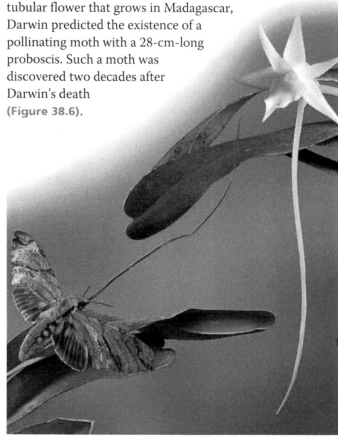

▲ **Figure 38.6 Coevolution of a flower and an insect pollinator.** The long floral tube of the Madagascar orchid *Angraecum sesquipedale* has coevolved with the 28-cm-long proboscis of its pollinator, the hawk moth *Xanthopan morganii praedicta*. The moth is named in honor of Darwin's prediction of its existence.

From Seed to Flowering Plant: *A Closer Look*

Let's look at how a seed develops into a flowering plant after pollination and fertilization. This process includes endosperm development, embryo development, seed dormancy, seed germination, seedling development, and flowering.

Endosperm Development

Endosperm usually develops before the embryo does. After double fertilization, the triploid nucleus of the ovule's central cell divides, forming a multinucleate "supercell" that has a milky consistency. This liquid mass, the endosperm, becomes multicellular when cytokinesis partitions the cytoplasm by forming membranes between the nuclei. Eventually, these "naked" cells produce cell walls, and the endosperm becomes solid. Coconut "milk" and "meat" are examples of liquid and solid endosperm, respectively. The white fluffy part of popcorn is also endosperm.

In grains and most other species of monocots, as well as many eudicots, the endosperm stores nutrients that can be used by the seedling after germination. In other eudicot seeds, the food reserves of the endosperm are completely exported to the cotyledons before the seed completes its development; consequently, the mature seed lacks endosperm.

Embryo Development

The first mitotic division of the zygote splits the fertilized egg into a basal cell and a terminal cell (**Figure 38.7**). The terminal cell eventually gives rise to most of the embryo. The basal cell continues to divide, producing a thread of cells called the suspensor, which anchors the embryo to the parent plant. The suspensor helps in transferring nutrients to the embryo from the parent plant and, in some species, from the endosperm. As the suspensor elongates, it pushes the embryo deeper into the nutritive and protective tissues. Meanwhile, the terminal cell divides several times and forms a spherical proembryo (early embryo) attached to the suspensor. The cotyledons begin to form as bumps on the proembryo. A eudicot, with its two cotyledons, is heart-shaped at this stage. Only one cotyledon develops in monocots.

Soon after the rudimentary cotyledons appear, the embryo elongates. Cradled between the two cotyledons is the embryonic shoot apex. At the opposite end of the embryo's axis, where the suspensor attaches, an embryonic root apex forms. After the seed germinates—indeed, for the rest of the plant's life—the apical meristems at the apices of shoots and roots sustain primary growth (see Figure 35.11).

Structure of the Mature Seed

During the last stages of its maturation, the seed dehydrates until its water content is only about 5–15% of its weight. The embryo, which is surrounded by a food supply (cotyledons, endosperm, or both), enters **dormancy**; that is, it stops growing and its metabolism nearly ceases. The embryo

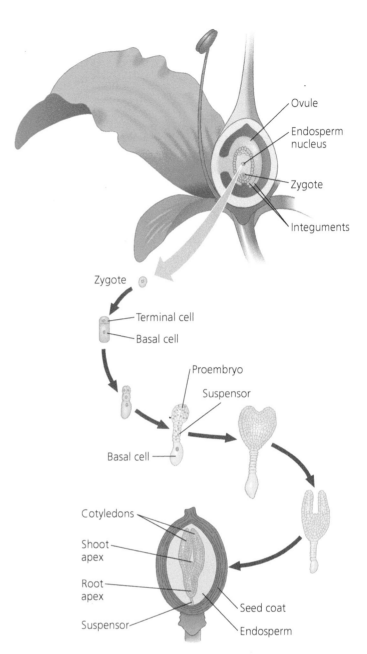

▲ **Figure 38.7 The development of a eudicot plant embryo.** By the time the ovule becomes a mature seed and the integuments harden and thicken into the seed coat, the zygote has given rise to an embryonic plant with rudimentary organs.

and its food supply are enclosed by a hard, protective **seed coat** formed from the integuments of the ovule. In some species, dormancy is imposed by the presence of an intact seed coat rather than by the embryo itself.

You can look closely at one type of eudicot seed by splitting open the seed of a common garden bean. The embryo consists of an elongate structure, the embryonic axis, attached to fleshy cotyledons (**Figure 38.8a**). Below where the two cotyledons are attached, the embryonic axis is called the **hypocotyl** (from the Greek *hypo*, under). The hypocotyl terminates in the **radicle**, or embryonic root. The portion of the embryonic axis above where the cotyledons are attached and below the first pair of miniature leaves is the **epicotyl** (from the Greek *epi*, on, over). The epicotyl, young leaves, and shoot apical meristem are collectively called the *plumule*.

The cotyledons of the common garden bean are packed with starch before the seed germinates because they absorbed carbohydrates from the endosperm when the seed was developing. However, the seeds of some eudicot species, such as castor beans (*Ricinus communis*), retain their food supply in the endosperm and have very thin cotyledons (Figure 38.8b). The cotyledons absorb nutrients from the endosperm and transfer them to the rest of the embryo when the seed germinates.

The embryos of monocots possess only a single cotyledon (Figure 38.8c). Grasses, including maize and wheat, have a specialized cotyledon called a *scutellum* (from the Latin *scutella*, small shield, a reference to its shape). The scutellum, which has a large surface area, is pressed against the endosperm, from which it absorbs nutrients during germination. The embryo of a grass seed is enclosed within two protective sheaths: a **coleoptile**, which covers the young shoot, and a **coleorhiza**, which covers the young root. Both structures aid in soil penetration after germination.

Seed weights range from less than 1 µg for some orchids to 20 kg for coco-de-mer palms. Orchid seeds have almost no food reserves and must bond symbiotically with mycorrhizae prior to germination. Large, endosperm-rich palm seeds are an adaptation for seedling establishment on nutrient-poor beaches.

Seed Dormancy: An Adaptation for Tough Times

Environmental conditions required to break seed dormancy vary among species. Seeds of some species germinate as soon as they are in a suitable environment. Others remain dormant, even if sown in a favorable place, until a specific environmental cue causes them to break dormancy.

The requirement for specific cues to break seed dormancy increases the chances that germination will occur at a time and place most advantageous to the seedling. Seeds of many desert plants, for instance, germinate only after a substantial rainfall. If they were to germinate after a mild drizzle, the soil might soon become too dry to support the seedlings. Where natural fires are common, many seeds require intense heat or smoke to break dormancy; seedlings are therefore most abundant after fire has cleared away competing vegetation. Where winters are harsh, seeds may require extended exposure to cold before they germinate; seeds sown during summer or fall will therefore not germinate until the following spring, ensuring a long growth season before the next winter. Certain small seeds, such as those of some lettuce varieties, require light for germination and will break dormancy only if buried shallow enough for the seedlings to poke through the soil surface. Some seeds have coats that must be weakened by chemical attack as they pass through an animal's digestive tract and thus are usually carried a long distance before germinating from feces.

The length of time a dormant seed remains viable and capable of germinating varies from a few days to decades or

(a) Common garden bean, a eudicot with thick cotyledons. The fleshy cotyledons store food absorbed from the endosperm before the seed germinates.

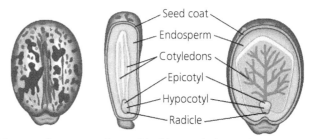

(b) Castor bean, a eudicot with thin cotyledons. The narrow, membranous cotyledons (shown in edge and flat views) absorb food from the endosperm when the seed germinates.

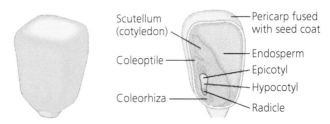

(c) Maize, a monocot. Like all monocots, maize has only one cotyledon. Maize and other grasses have a large cotyledon called a scutellum. The rudimentary shoot is sheathed in a structure called the coleoptile, and the coleorhiza covers the young root.

▲ **Figure 38.8 Seed structure.**

MAKE CONNECTIONS *In addition to cotyledon number, how do the structures of monocots and eudicots differ? (See Figure 30.16.)*

even longer, depending on the plant species and environmental conditions. The oldest carbon-14–dated seed that has grown into a viable plant was a 2,000-year-old date palm seed recovered from excavations of Herod's palace in Israel. Most seeds are durable enough to last a year or two until conditions are favorable for germinating. Thus, the soil has a bank of ungerminated seeds that may have accumulated for several years. This is one reason vegetation reappears so rapidly after an environmental disruption such as fire.

Seed Germination and Seedling Development

Germination depends on **imbibition**, the uptake of water due to the low water potential of the dry seed. Imbibition causes the seed to expand and rupture its coat and triggers changes in the embryo that enable it to resume growth. Following hydration, enzymes digest the storage materials of the endosperm or cotyledons, and the nutrients are transferred to the growing regions of the embryo.

The first organ to emerge from the germinating seed is the radicle, the embryonic root. The development of a root system anchors the seedling in the soil and supplies it with water necessary for cell expansion. A ready supply of water is a prerequisite for the next step, the emergence of the shoot tip into the drier conditions encountered above ground. In garden beans and many other eudicots, a hook forms in the hypocotyl, and growth pushes the hook above ground (Figure 38.9a). In response to light, the hypocotyl straightens, the cotyledons separate, and the delicate epicotyl, now exposed, spreads its first true leaves (as distinct from the cotyledons, or seed leaves). These leaves expand, become green, and begin making food by photosynthesis. The cotyledons shrivel and fall away, their food reserves having been exhausted by the germinating embryo.

Some monocots, such as maize and other grasses, use a different method for breaking ground when they germinate (Figure 38.9b). The coleoptile pushes up through the soil and into the air. The shoot tip grows through the tunnel provided by the coleoptile and breaks through the coleoptile's tip.

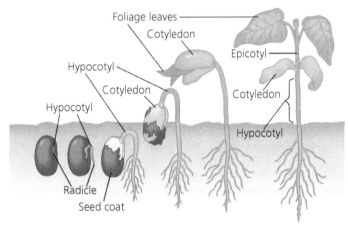

(a) **Common garden bean.** In common garden beans, straightening of a hook in the hypocotyl pulls the cotyledons from the soil.

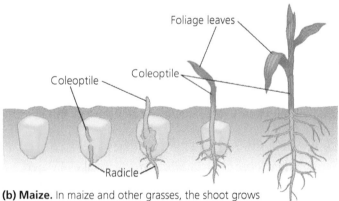

(b) **Maize.** In maize and other grasses, the shoot grows straight up through the tube of the coleoptile.

▲ Figure 38.9 **Two common types of seed germination.**

? *How do bean and maize seedlings protect their shoot systems as they push through the soil?*

Once a seed has germinated and started to photosynthesize, most of the plant's resources are devoted to vegetative growth. Vegetative growth, including both primary and secondary growth, arises from the activity of meristematic cells (see Concept 35.2). During this stage, usually the best strategy is to photosynthesize and grow as much as possible before the reproductive phase (flowering). Vegetative growth is the period of growth between germination and the beginning of sexual maturity characterized by flowering.

Flowering

The flowers of a given plant species typically appear suddenly and simultaneously at a specific time of year. Such synchrony promotes outbreeding, the main advantage of sexual reproduction. Flower formation involves a developmental switch in the shoot apical meristem from a vegetative to a reproductive growth mode. This transition into a *floral meristem* is triggered by a combination of environmental cues (such as day length) and internal signals, as you'll learn in Chapter 39. Once the transition to flowering has begun, the order of each organ's emergence from the floral meristem determines whether it will develop into a sepal, petal, stamen, or carpel (see Figure 35.35).

Fruit Structure and Function

Before a seed can germinate and develop into a mature plant, it must be deposited in suitable soil. Fruits play a key role in this process. A **fruit** is the mature ovary of a flower. While the seeds are developing from ovules, the flower develops into a fruit (Figure 38.10). The fruit protects the enclosed seeds and, when mature, aids in their dispersal by wind or animals. Fertilization triggers hormonal changes that cause the ovary to begin its transformation into a fruit. If a flower has not been pollinated, fruit typically does not develop, and the flower usually withers and falls away.

During fruit development, the ovary wall becomes the *pericarp*, the thickened wall of the fruit. In some fruits, such as soybean pods, the ovary wall dries out completely at maturity, whereas in other fruits, such as grapes, it remains

▲ Figure 38.10 **The flower-to-fruit transition** After flowers, such as those of the American pokeweed, are fertilized, stamens and petals fall off, stigmas and styles wither, and the ovary walls that house the developing seeds swell to form fruits. Developing seeds and fruits are major sinks for sugars and other carbohydrates.

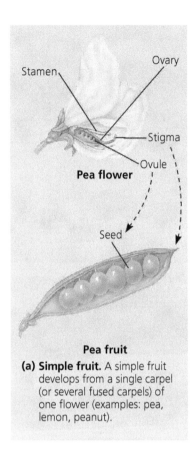

Pea flower

Stamen
Ovary
Stigma
Ovule
Seed

Pea fruit

(a) Simple fruit. A simple fruit develops from a single carpel (or several fused carpels) of one flower (examples: pea, lemon, peanut).

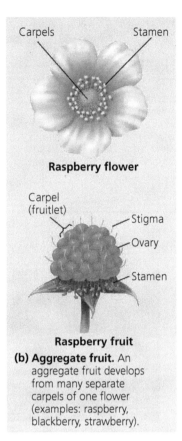

Carpels
Stamen

Raspberry flower

Carpel (fruitlet)
Stigma
Ovary
Stamen

Raspberry fruit

(b) Aggregate fruit. An aggregate fruit develops from many separate carpels of one flower (examples: raspberry, blackberry, strawberry).

Flowers

Pineapple inflorescence

Each segment develops from the carpel of one flower

Pineapple fruit

(c) Multiple fruit. A multiple fruit develops from many carpels of the many flowers that form an inflorescence (examples: pineapple, fig).

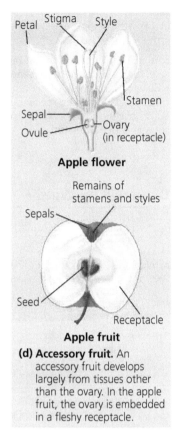

Petal
Stigma
Style
Stamen
Sepal
Ovule
Ovary (in receptacle)

Apple flower

Remains of stamens and styles
Sepals
Seed
Receptacle

Apple fruit

(d) Accessory fruit. An accessory fruit develops largely from tissues other than the ovary. In the apple fruit, the ovary is embedded in a fleshy receptacle.

▲ **Figure 38.11 Developmental origin of different classes of fruits.**

fleshy. In still others, such as peaches, the inner part of the ovary becomes stony (the pit) while the outer parts stay fleshy. As the ovary grows, the other parts of the flower usually wither and are shed.

Fruits are classified into several types, depending on their developmental origin. Most fruits are derived from a single carpel or several fused carpels and are called **simple fruits** (Figure 38.11a). An **aggregate fruit** results from a single flower that has more than one separate carpel, each forming a small fruit (Figure 38.11b). These "fruitlets" are clustered together on a single receptacle, as in a raspberry. A **multiple fruit** develops from an inflorescence, a group of flowers tightly clustered together. When the walls of the many ovaries start to thicken, they fuse together and become incorporated into one fruit, as in a pineapple (Figure 38.11c).

In some angiosperms, other floral parts contribute to what we commonly call the fruit. Such fruits are called **accessory fruits**. In apple flowers, the ovary is embedded in the receptacle, and the fleshy part of this simple fruit is derived mainly from the enlarged receptacle; only the apple core develops from the ovary (Figure 38.11d). Another example is the strawberry, an aggregate fruit consisting of an enlarged receptacle studded with tiny, partially embedded fruits, each bearing a single seed.

A fruit usually ripens about the same time that its seeds complete their development. Whereas the ripening of a dry fruit, such as a soybean pod, involves the aging and drying

out of fruit tissues, the process in a fleshy fruit is more elaborate. Complex interactions of hormones result in an edible fruit that entices animals that disperse the seeds. The fruit's "pulp" becomes softer as enzymes digest components of cell walls. The color usually changes from green to a more overt color, such as red, orange, or yellow. The fruit becomes sweeter as organic acids or starch molecules are converted to sugar, which may reach a concentration of 20% in a ripe fruit. Figure 38.12 examines some mechanisms of seed and fruit dispersal in more detail.

In this section, you have learned about the key features of sexual reproduction in angiosperms—flowers, double fertilization, and fruits. Next, we'll examine asexual reproduction.

CONCEPT CHECK 38.1

1. Distinguish between pollination and fertilization.
2. What is the benefit of seed dormancy?
3. **WHAT IF?** If flowers had shorter styles, pollen tubes would more easily reach the embryo sac. Suggest an explanation for why very long styles have evolved in most flowering plants.
4. **MAKE CONNECTIONS** Does the life cycle of animals have any structures analogous to plant gametophytes? Explain your answer. (See Figure 13.6.)

For suggested answers, see Appendix A.

Exploring Fruit and Seed Dispersal

A plant's life depends on finding fertile ground. But a seed that falls and sprouts beneath the parent plant will stand little chance of competing successfully for nutrients. To prosper, seeds must be widely dispersed. Plants use biotic dispersal agents as well as abiotic agents such as water and wind.

Dispersal by Water

► Some buoyant seeds and fruits can survive months or years at sea. In coconut, the seed embryo and fleshy white "meat" (endosperm) are within a hard layer (endocarp) surrounded by a thick and buoyant fibrous husk.

Dispersal by Wind

► With a wingspan of 12 cm, the giant seed of the tropical Asian climbing gourd *Alsomitra macrocarpa* glides through the air of the rain forest in wide circles when released.

▼ The winged fruit of a maple spins like a helicopter blade, slowing descent and increasing the chance of being carried farther by horizontal winds.

Dandelion fruit

► Tumbleweeds break off at the ground and tumble across the terrain, scattering their seeds.

▲ Some seeds and fruits are attached to umbrella-like "parachutes" that are made of intricately branched hairs and often produced in puffy clusters. These dandelion "seeds" (actually one-seeded fruits) are carried aloft by the slightest gust of wind.

Dispersal by Animals

◄ The sharp, tack-like spines on the fruits of puncture vine (*Tribulus terrestris*) can pierce bicycle tires and injure animals, including humans. When these painful "tacks" are removed and discarded, the seeds are dispersed.

◄ Some animals, such as squirrels, hoard seeds or fruits in underground caches. If the animal dies or forgets the cache's location, the buried seeds are well positioned to germinate.

► Seeds in edible fruits are often dispersed in feces, such as the black bear feces shown here. Such dispersal may carry seeds far from the parent plant.

► Ants are chemically attracted to seeds with "food bodies" rich in fatty acids, amino acids, and sugars. The ants carry the seed to their underground nest, where the food body (the lighter-colored portion shown here) is removed and fed to larvae. Due to the seed's size, unwieldy shape, or hard coating, the remainder is usually left intact in the nest, where it germinates.

Flowering plants reproduce sexually, asexually, or both

Imagine chopping off your finger and watching it develop into an exact copy of you. If this could actually occur, it would be an example of **asexual reproduction**, in which offspring are derived from a single parent without fusion of egg and sperm. The result would be a clone, an asexually produced, genetically identical organism. Asexual reproduction is common in angiosperms, as well as in other plants, and for some species it is the main mode of reproduction.

Mechanisms of Asexual Reproduction

Asexual reproduction in plants is typically an extension of the capacity for indeterminate growth. Plant growth can be sustained or renewed indefinitely by meristems, regions of undifferentiated, dividing cells (see Concept 35.2). In addition, parenchyma cells throughout the plant can divide and differentiate into more specialized types of cells, enabling plants to regenerate lost parts. Detached vegetative fragments of some plants can develop into whole offspring; for example, pieces of a potato with an "eye" (vegetative bud) can each regenerate a whole plant. Such **fragmentation**, the separation of a parent plant into parts that develop into whole plants, is one of the most common modes of asexual reproduction. The adventitious plantlets on *Kalanchoë* leaves exemplify an unusual type of fragmentation (see Figure 35.7). In other cases, the root system of a single parent, such as an aspen tree, can give rise to many adventitious shoots that become separate shoot systems **(Figure 38.13)**. One aspen clone in Utah has been estimated to be composed of 47,000 stems of genetically identical trees. Although it is likely that some of the root system connections have been severed, making some of the trees isolated from the rest of the clone, each tree still shares a common genome.

A different mechanism of asexual reproduction has evolved in dandelions and some other plants. These plants

▲ **Figure 38.13 Asexual reproduction in aspen trees.** Some aspen groves, such as those shown here, consist of thousands of trees descended by asexual reproduction. Each grove of trees derives from the root system of one parent. Thus, the grove is a clone. Notice that genetic differences between groves descended from different parents result in different timing for the development of fall color.

can sometimes produce seeds without pollination or fertilization. This asexual production of seeds is called **apomixis** (from the Greek words meaning "away from the act of mixing") because there is no joining or, indeed, production of sperm and egg. Instead, a diploid cell in the ovule gives rise to the embryo, and the ovules mature into seeds, which in the dandelion are dispersed by windblown fruits. Thus, these plants clone themselves by an asexual process but have the advantage of seed dispersal, usually associated with sexual reproduction. Plant breeders are interested in introducing apomixis into hybrid crops because it would allow hybrid plants to pass desirable genomes intact to offspring.

Advantages and Disadvantages of Asexual and Sexual Reproduction

EVOLUTION An advantage of asexual reproduction is that there is no need for a pollinator. This may be beneficial in situations where plants of the same species are sparsely distributed and unlikely to be visited by the same pollinator. Asexual reproduction also allows the plant to pass on all of its genetic legacy intact to its progeny. In contrast, when reproducing sexually, a plant passes on only half of its alleles. If a plant is superbly suited to its environment, asexual reproduction can be advantageous. A vigorous plant can potentially clone many copies of itself, and if the environmental circumstances remain stable, these offspring will also be genetically well adapted to the same environmental conditions under which the parent flourished.

Generally, the progeny produced by asexual reproduction are stronger than seedlings produced by sexual reproduction. The offspring usually arise from mature vegetative fragments from the parent plant, which is why asexual reproduction in plants is also known as **vegetative reproduction**. In contrast, seed germination is a precarious stage in a plant's life. The tough seed gives rise to a fragile seedling that may face exposure to predators, parasites, wind, and other hazards. In the wild, few seedlings survive to become parents themselves. Production of enormous numbers of seeds compensates for the odds against individual survival and gives natural selection ample genetic variations to screen. However, this is an expensive means of reproduction in terms of the resources consumed in flowering and fruiting.

Because sexual reproduction generates variation in offspring and populations, it can be advantageous in unstable environments where evolving pathogens and other fluctuating conditions affect survival and reproductive success. In contrast, the genotypic uniformity of asexually produced plants puts them at great risk of local extinction if there is a catastrophic environmental change, such as a new strain of disease. Moreover, seeds (which are almost always produced sexually) facilitate the dispersal of offspring to more distant locations. Finally, seed dormancy allows growth to be suspended until environmental conditions become more

Using Positive and Negative Correlations to Interpret Data

Do Monkey Flower Species Differ in Allocating Their Energy to Sexual Versus Asexual Reproduction? Over the course of its lifespan, a plant captures only a finite amount of resources and energy, which must be allocated to best meet the plant's individual requirements for maintenance, growth, defense, and reproduction. Researchers examined how five species of monkey flower (genus *Mimulus*) use their resources for sexual and asexual reproduction.

How the Experiment Was Done
After growing specimens of each species in separate pots in the open, the researchers determined averages for nectar volume, nectar concentration, seeds produced per flower, and the number of times the plants were visited by broad-tailed hummingbirds (*Selasphorus platycercus*, shown on

right). Using greenhouse-grown specimens, they determined the average number of rooted branches per gram fresh shoot weight for each of the species. The phrase *rooted branches* refers to asexual reproduction through horizontal shoots that develop roots.

Interpret the Data

1. A correlation is a way to describe the relationship between two variables. In a positive correlation, as the values of one of the variables increase, the values of the second variable also increase. In a negative correlation, as the values of one of the variables increase, the values of the second variable decrease. Or there may be no correlation between two variables. If researchers know how two variables are correlated, they can make a prediction about one variable based on what they know about the other variable. (a) Which variable(s) is/are positively correlated with the volume of nectar production in this genus? (b) Which is/are negatively correlated? (c) Which show(s) no clear relationship?

2. (a) Which *Mimulus* species would you categorize as mainly asexual reproducers? Why? (b) Which species would you categorize as mainly sexual reproducers? Why?

3. (a) Which species would probably fare better in response to a pathogen that infects all *Mimulus* species? (b) Which species would fare better if a pathogen caused hummingbird populations to dwindle?

Data from S. Sutherland and R. K. Vickery, Jr. Trade-offs between sexual and asexual reproduction in the genus *Mimulus*. *Oecologia* 76:330–335 (1998).

(MB) A version of this Scientific Skills Exercise can be assigned in MasteringBiology.

Data from the Experiment

Species	Nectar Volume (μL)	Nectar Concentration (% wt of sucrose/ total wt)	Seeds per Flower	Visits per Flower	Rooted Branches per Gram Shoot Weight
M. rupestris	4.93	16.6	2.2	0.22	0.673
M. eastwoodiae	4.94	19.8	25	0.74	0.488
M. nelson	20.25	17.1	102.5	1.08	0.139
M. verbenaceus	38.96	16.9	155.1	1.26	0.091
M. cardinalis	50.00	19.9	283.7	1.75	0.069

favorable. In the Scientific Skills Exercise, you can use data to determine which species of monkey flower are mainly asexual reproducers and which are mainly sexual reproducers.

Although sexual reproduction involving two genetically different plants produces the most genetically diverse offspring, some plants, such as garden peas, usually self-fertilize. This process, called "selfing," is a desirable attribute in some crop plants because it ensures that every ovule will develop into a seed. In many angiosperm species, however, mechanisms have evolved that make it difficult or impossible for a flower to fertilize itself, as we'll discuss next.

Mechanisms That Prevent Self-Fertilization

The various mechanisms that prevent self-fertilization contribute to genetic variety by ensuring that the sperm and egg come from different parents. In the case of **dioecious** species, plants cannot self-fertilize because different individuals have either staminate flowers (lacking carpels) or carpellate flowers (lacking stamens) **(Figure 38.14a)**. Other plants

have flowers with functional stamens and carpels that mature at different times or are structurally arranged in such a way that it is unlikely that an animal pollinator could transfer pollen from an anther to a stigma of the same flower **(Figure 38.14b)**. However, the most common anti-selfing mechanism in flowering plants is **self-incompatibility**, the ability of a plant to reject its own pollen and the pollen of closely related individuals. If a pollen grain lands on a stigma of a flower of the same plant or a closely related plant, a biochemical block prevents the pollen from completing its development and fertilizing an egg. This plant response is analogous to the immune response of animals because both are based on the ability to distinguish the cells of "self" from those of "nonself." The key difference is that the animal immune system rejects nonself, as when the immune system mounts a defense against a pathogen or rejects a transplanted organ (see Chapter 43). In contrast, self-incompatibility in plants is a rejection of self.

Researchers are unraveling the molecular mechanisms of self-incompatibility. Recognition of "self" pollen is based on

(a) Some species, such as *Sagittaria latifolia* (common arrowhead), are dioecious, having plants that produce only staminate flowers (left) or carpellate flowers (right).

Thrum flower   Pin flower

(b) Some species, such as *Oxalis alpina* (alpine woodsorrel), produce two types of flowers on different individuals: "thrums," which have short styles and long stamens, and "pins," which have long styles and short stamens. An insect foraging for nectar would collect pollen on different parts of its body; thrum pollen would be deposited on pin stigmas, and vice versa.

▲ **Figure 38.14 Some floral adaptations that prevent self-fertilization.**

genes called *S*-genes. In the gene pool of a population, there can be dozens of alleles of an *S*-gene. If a pollen grain has an allele that matches an allele of the stigma on which it lands, the pollen tube either fails to germinate or its tube fails to grow through the style to the ovary. There are two types of self-incompatibility: gametophytic and sporophytic.

In gametophytic self-incompatibility, the *S*-allele in the pollen genome governs the blocking of fertilization. For example, an S_1 pollen grain from an S_1S_2 parental sporophyte cannot fertilize eggs of an S_1S_2 flower but can fertilize an S_2S_3 flower. An S_2 pollen grain cannot fertilize either flower. In some plants, this self-recognition involves the enzymatic destruction of RNA within a pollen tube. RNA-hydrolyzing enzymes are produced by the style and enter the pollen tube. If the pollen tube is a "self" type, they destroy its RNA.

In sporophytic self-incompatibility, fertilization is blocked by *S*-allele gene products in tissues of the parental sporophyte. For example, neither an S_1 nor an S_2 pollen grain from an S_1S_2 parental sporophyte can fertilize eggs of an S_1S_2 flower or an S_2S_3 flower, due to the S_1S_2 parental tissue attached to the pollen wall. Sporophytic incompatibility involves a signal transduction pathway in epidermal cells of the stigma that prevents germination of the pollen grain.

Research on self-incompatibility may have agricultural applications. Breeders often hybridize different genetic strains

of a crop to combine the best traits of the two strains and to counter the loss of vigor that can often result from excessive inbreeding. To prevent self-fertilization within the two strains, breeders must either laboriously remove the anthers from the parent plants that provide the seeds (as Mendel did) or use male-sterile strains of the crop plant, if they exist. If self-compatibility can be genetically engineered back into domesticated plant varieties, these limitations to commercial hybridization of crop seeds could be overcome.

Totipotency, Vegetative Reproduction, and Tissue Culture

In a multicellular organism, any cell that can divide and asexually generate a clone of the original organism is said to be **totipotent**. Totipotency is found to a high degree in many plants and is usually associated with meristematic tissues. In some plants, however, some cells can dedifferentiate and become meristematic. With the objective of improving crops and ornamental plants, humans have devised methods for asexual propagation of angiosperms. Most of these methods are based on the ability of plants to form adventitious roots or shoots.

Vegetative Propagation and Grafting

Vegetative reproduction occurs naturally in many plants, but it can often be facilitated or induced by humans, in which case it is called **vegetative propagation**. Most houseplants, woody ornamentals, and orchard trees are asexually reproduced from plant fragments called cuttings. In some cases, shoot cuttings are used. At the cut end of the shoot, a mass of dividing, undifferentiated totipotent cells called a **callus** forms, and adventitious roots develop from the callus. If the shoot fragment includes a node, then adventitious roots form without a callus stage. Some plants, including African violets, can be propagated from single leaves rather than stems. For other plants, cuttings are taken from specialized storage stems, such as potato tubers. The Bartlett pear and Red Delicious apple are examples of varieties that have been propagated asexually for over 150 years.

In a modification of vegetative reproduction from cuttings, a twig or bud from one plant can be grafted onto a plant of a closely related species or a different variety of the same species. This process can combine the best qualities of different species or varieties into one plant. The plant that provides the roots is called the **stock**; the twig grafted onto the stock is known as the **scion**. For example, scions from varieties of vines that produce superior wine grapes are grafted onto rootstocks of varieties that produce inferior grapes but are more resistant to certain soil pathogens. The genes of the scion determine the quality of the fruit. During grafting, a callus first forms between the adjoining cut ends of the scion and stock; cell differentiation then completes the functional unification of the grafted individuals.

Test-Tube Cloning and Related Techniques

Plant biologists have adopted *in vitro* methods to clone plants for research or horticulture. Whole plants can be obtained by culturing small pieces of tissue from the parent plant on an artificial medium containing nutrients and hormones. The cells or tissues can come from any part of a plant, but growth may vary depending on the plant part, species, and artificial medium. In some media, the cultured cells divide and form a callus of undifferentiated totipotent cells **(Figure 38.15a)**. When the concentrations of hormones and nutrients are manipulated appropriately, a callus can sprout shoots and roots with fully differentiated cells **(Figure 38.15b and c)**. If desired, the plantlets can then be transferred to soil, where they continue their growth. A single plant can be cloned into thousands of copies by dividing calluses as they grow.

Plant tissue culture is important in eliminating weakly pathogenic viruses from vegetatively propagated varieties. Although the presence of weak viruses may not be obvious, yield or quality may be substantially reduced as a result of infection. Strawberry plants, for example, are susceptible to more than 60 viruses, and typically the plants must be replaced each year because of viral infection. However, the distribution of viruses in a plant is not uniform, and the apical meristems are sometimes virus-free. Therefore, apical meristems can be excised and used to produce virus-free material for tissue culture.

Plant tissue culture also facilitates genetic engineering. Most techniques for the introduction of foreign genes into plants require small pieces of plant tissue or single plant cells as the starting material. Test-tube culture makes it possible to regenerate genetically modified (GM) plants from a single plant cell into which the foreign DNA has been incorporated. The techniques of genetic engineering are discussed in more detail in Chapter 20. In the next section, we take a closer look at some of the promises and challenges surrounding the use of GM plants in agriculture.

CONCEPT CHECK 38.2

1. What are three ways that flowering plants avoid self-fertilization?
2. The seedless banana, the world's most popular fruit, is losing the battle against two fungal epidemics. Why do such epidemics generally pose a greater risk to asexually propagated crops?
3. Self-fertilization, or selfing, seems to have obvious disadvantages as a reproductive "strategy" in nature, and it has even been called an "evolutionary dead end." So it is surprising that about 20% of angiosperm species primarily rely on selfing. Suggest a reason why selfing might be advantageous and yet still be an evolutionary dead end.

For suggested answers, see Appendix A.

CONCEPT 38.3

People modify crops by breeding and genetic engineering

People have intervened in the reproduction and genetic makeup of plants since the dawn of agriculture. Maize, for example, owes its existence to humans. Left on its own in nature, maize would soon become extinct for the simple reason that it cannot spread its seeds. Maize kernels are not only permanently attached to the central axis (the "cob") but also permanently protected by tough, overlapping leaf sheaths (the "husk") **(Figure 38.16)**. These attributes arose

(a) **(b)** **(c) Developing root**

▲ **Figure 38.15 Cloning a garlic plant. (a)** A root from a garlic clove gave rise to this callus culture, a mass of undifferentiated totipotent cells. **(b and c)** The differentiation of a callus into a plantlet depends on the nutrient levels and hormone concentrations in the artificial medium, as can be seen in these cultures grown for different lengths of time.

▲ **Figure 38.16 Maize: a product of artificial selection.** Modern maize (bottom) was derived from teosinte (top). Teosinte kernels are tiny, and each row has a husk that must be removed to get at the kernel. The seeds are loose at maturity, allowing dispersal, which probably made harvesting difficult for early farmers. Neolithic farmers selected seeds from plants with larger cob and kernel size as well as the permanent attachment of seeds to the cob and the encasing of the entire cob by a tough husk.

by artificial selection by humans. (See Chapter 22 to review the basic concept of artificial selection.) Despite having no understanding of the scientific principles underlying plant breeding, early farmers domesticated most of our crop species over a relatively short period about 10,000 years ago. But genetic modification began long before humans started altering crops by artificial selection. For example, the wheat species we rely on for much of our food evolved by the natural hybridization between different species of grasses. Such hybridization is common in plants and has long been exploited by breeders to introduce genetic variation for artificial selection and crop improvement.

Plant Breeding

The art of recognizing valuable traits is important in plant breeding. Breeders scrutinize their fields carefully and travel far and wide searching for domesticated varieties or wild relatives with desirable traits. Such traits occasionally arise spontaneously through mutation, but the natural rate of mutation is too slow and unreliable to produce all the mutations that breeders would like to study. Breeders sometimes hasten mutations by treating large batches of seeds or seedlings with radiation or chemicals.

When a desirable trait is identified in a wild species, the wild species is crossed with a domesticated variety. Generally, those progeny that have inherited the desirable trait from the wild parent have also inherited many traits that are not desirable for agriculture, such as small fruits or low yields. The progeny that express the desired trait are again crossed with members of the domesticated species and their progeny examined for the desired trait. This process is continued until the progeny with the desired wild trait resemble the original domesticated parent in their other agricultural attributes.

While most breeders cross-pollinate plants of a single species, some breeding methods rely on hybridization between two distant species of the same genus. Such crosses sometimes result in the abortion of the hybrid seed during development. Often in these cases the embryo begins to develop, but the endosperm does not. Hybrid embryos are sometimes rescued by surgically removing them from the ovule and culturing them *in vitro*.

Plant Biotechnology and Genetic Engineering

Plant biotechnology has two meanings. In the general sense, it refers to innovations in the use of plants (or substances obtained from plants) to make products of use to humans—an endeavor that began in prehistory. In a more specific sense, biotechnology refers to the use of GM organisms in agriculture and industry. Indeed, in the last two decades,

genetic engineering has become such a powerful force that the terms *genetic engineering* and *biotechnology* have become synonymous in the media.

Unlike traditional plant breeders, modern plant biotechnologists, using techniques of genetic engineering, are not limited to the transfer of genes between closely related species or genera. For example, traditional breeding techniques could not be used to insert a desired gene from daffodil into rice because the many intermediate species between rice and daffodil and their common ancestor are extinct. In theory, if breeders had the intermediate species, over the course of several centuries they could probably introduce a daffodil gene into rice by traditional hybridization and breeding methods. With genetic engineering, however, such gene transfers can be done more quickly, more specifically, and without the need for intermediate species. The term **transgenic** is used to describe organisms that have been engineered to express a gene from another species (see Chapter 20 for a discussion of the methods underlying genetic engineering).

In the remainder of this chapter, we explore the prospects and controversies surrounding the use of GM crops. Advocates for plant biotechnology believe that the genetic engineering of crop plants is the key to overcoming some of the most pressing problems of the 21st century, including world hunger and fossil fuel dependency.

Reducing World Hunger and Malnutrition

Currently, 800 million people suffer from nutritional deficiencies, with 40,000 dying each day of malnutrition, half of them children. There is much disagreement about the causes of such hunger. Some argue that food shortages arise from inequities in distribution and that the dire poor simply cannot afford food. Others regard food shortages as evidence that the world is overpopulated—that the human species has exceeded the carrying capacity of the planet (see Chapter 53). Whatever the social and demographic causes of malnutrition, increasing food production is a humane objective. Because land and water are the most limiting resources, the best option is to increase yields on already existing farmland. Indeed, there is very little "extra" land that can be farmed, especially if the few remaining pockets of wilderness are to be preserved. Based on conservative estimates of population growth, farmers will have to produce 40% more grain per hectare to feed the human population in 2030. Plant biotechnology can help make these crop yields possible.

The commercial use of transgenic crops has been one of the most dramatic examples of rapid technology adoption in the history of agriculture. These crops include varieties and hybrids of cotton, maize, and potatoes that contain genes from the bacterium *Bacillus thuringiensis*. These "transgenes" encode a protein (*Bt* toxin) that is toxic to insect

Non-*Bt* maize   *Bt* maize

▲ **Figure 38.17 Non-*Bt* versus *Bt* maize.** Field trials reveal that non-*Bt* maize (left) is heavily damaged by insect feeding and *Fusarium* mold infection, whereas *Bt* maize (right) suffers little or no damage.

pests **(Figure 38.17)**. The use of such plant varieties greatly reduces the need for chemical insecticides. The *Bt* toxin used in crops is produced in the plant as a harmless protoxin that only becomes toxic if activated by alkaline conditions, such as occur in the guts of insects. Because vertebrates have highly acidic stomachs, protoxin consumed by humans or livestock is rendered harmless by denaturation.

Considerable progress has also been made in developing transgenic crops that tolerate certain herbicides. The cultivation of these plants may reduce production costs by enabling farmers to "weed" crops with herbicides that do not damage the transgenic crop plants, instead of using heavy tillage, which can cause soil erosion. Researchers are also engineering plants with enhanced resistance to disease. In one case, a transgenic papaya that is resistant to a ring spot virus was introduced into Hawaii, thereby saving its papaya industry.

The nutritional quality of plants is also being improved. For example, some 250,000 to 500,000 children go blind each year because of vitamin A deficiencies. More than half of these children die within a year of becoming blind. In response to this crisis, genetic engineers have created

▶ **Figure 38.18 Fighting world hunger with transgenic cassava (*Manihot esculenta*).** This starchy root crop is the primary food for 800 million of the world's poor, but it does not provide a balanced diet. Moreover, it must be processed to remove chemicals that release cyanide, a toxin. Transgenic cassava plants have been developed with greatly increased levels of iron and beta-carotene (a vitamin A precursor). Researchers have also created cassava plants with root masses twice the normal size that contain almost no cyanide-producing chemicals.

MAKE CONNECTIONS *Genetic transformation using Agrobacterium tumefaciens, which causes crown gall disease, is the preferred method for transporting new genes into cassava cells. Review Concept 20.4, and explain why the use of this pathogen in genetic engineering does not produce crown gall disease in transgenic plants.*

"Golden Rice," a transgenic variety supplemented with transgenes that enable it to produce grain with increased levels of beta-carotene, a precursor of vitamin A. Golden Rice is close to commercial production in the Philippines. Another target for improvement by genetic engineering is cassava, a staple for 800 million of the poorest people on our planet **(Figure 38.18)**.

Reducing Fossil Fuel Dependency

Global sources of inexpensive fossil fuels, particularly oil, are rapidly being depleted. Moreover, most climatologists attribute global warming mainly to the rampant burning of fossil fuels, such as coal and oil, and the resulting release of the greenhouse gas CO_2. How can the world meet its energy demands in the 21st century in an economical and nonpolluting way? In certain localities, wind or solar power may become economically viable, but such alternative energy sources are unlikely to fill the global energy demands completely. Many scientists predict that **biofuels**—fuels derived from living biomass—could produce a sizable fraction of the world's energy needs in the not-too-distant future. **Biomass** is the total mass of organic matter in a group of organisms in a particular habitat. The use of biofuels from plant biomass would reduce the net emission of CO_2. Whereas burning fossil fuels increases atmospheric CO_2 concentrations, biofuel crops reabsorb by photosynthesis the CO_2 emitted when biofuels are burned, creating a cycle that is carbon neutral.

In working to create biofuel crops from wild precursors, scientists are focusing their domestication efforts on fast-growing plants, such as switchgrass (*Panicum virgatum*) and poplar (*Populus trichocarpa*), that can grow on soil that is too poor for food production. Scientists do not envisage the plant biomass being burned directly. Instead, the polymers in cell walls, such as cellulose and hemicellulose, which constitute the most abundant organic compounds on Earth, would be broken down into sugars by enzymatic reactions. These sugars, in turn, would be fermented into alcohol and distilled to yield biofuels. Currently, the enzymes and pretreatment processes involved in converting cellulosic biomass to ethanol are very expensive. In addition to increasing plant polysaccharide content and overall biomass, researchers are trying to genetically engineer plants with cell wall properties, such as reduced lignin content, that will lower the costs of biofuel production.

The Debate over Plant Biotechnology

Much of the debate about GM organisms (GMOs) in agriculture is political, social, economic, or ethical and therefore outside the scope of this book. But we *should* consider the biological concerns about GM crops. Some biologists, particularly ecologists, are concerned about the unknown risks associated with the release of GMOs into the environment.

The debate centers on the extent to which GMOs could harm the environment or human health. Those who want to proceed more slowly with agricultural biotechnology (or end it) are concerned about the unstoppable nature of the "experiment." If a drug trial produces unanticipated harmful results, the trial is stopped. But we may not be able to stop the "trial" of introducing novel organisms into the biosphere. Here we examine some criticisms that have been leveled by opponents of GMOs, including the alleged effects on human health and non-target organisms and the potential for transgene escape.

Issues of Human Health

Many GMO opponents worry that genetic engineering may inadvertently transfer allergens, molecules to which some people are allergic, from a species that produces an allergen to a plant used for food. However, biotechnologists are already engaged in removing genes that encode allergenic proteins from soybeans and other crops. So far, there is no credible evidence that GM plants specifically designed for human consumption have adverse effects on human health. In fact, some GM foods are potentially healthier than non-GM foods. For example, *Bt* maize (the transgenic variety with the *Bt* toxin) contains 90% less of a fungal toxin that causes cancer and birth defects than non-*Bt* maize. Called fumonisin, this toxin is highly resistant to degradation and has been found in alarmingly high concentrations in some batches of processed maize products, ranging from cornflakes to beer. Fumonisin is produced by a fungus (*Fusarium*) that infects insect-damaged maize. Because *Bt* maize generally suffers less insect damage than non-GM maize, it contains much less fumonisin.

Assessing the impact of GMOs on human health also involves considering the health of farmworkers, many of whom were commonly exposed to high levels of chemical insecticides prior to the adoption of *Bt* crops. In India, for example, the widespread adoption of *Bt* cotton has led to a 41% decrease in insecticide use and a 80% reduction in the number of acute poisoning cases involving farmers.

Possible Effects on Nontarget Organisms

Many ecologists are concerned that the growing of GM crops might have unforeseen effects on nontarget organisms. One laboratory study indicated that the larvae (caterpillars) of monarch butterflies responded adversely and even died after eating milkweed leaves (their preferred food) heavily dusted with pollen from transgenic *Bt* maize. This study has since been discredited, affording a good example of the self-correcting nature of science. As it turns out, when the original researcher shook the male maize inflorescences onto the milkweed leaves in the laboratory, the filaments of stamens, opened microsporangia, and other floral parts also rained onto the leaves. Subsequent research found that it was these other floral parts, *not* the pollen, that contained *Bt* toxin in high concentrations. Unlike pollen, these floral parts would not be carried by the wind to neighboring milkweed plants when shed under natural field conditions. Only one *Bt* maize line, accounting for less than 2% of commercial *Bt* maize production (and now discontinued), produced pollen with high *Bt* toxin concentrations.

In considering the negative effects of *Bt* pollen on monarch butterflies, one must also weigh the effects of an alternative to the cultivation of *Bt* maize—the spraying of non-*Bt* maize with chemical pesticides. Subsequent studies have shown that such spraying is much more harmful to nearby monarch populations than is *Bt* maize production. Although the effects of *Bt* maize pollen on monarch butterfly larvae appear to be minor, the controversy has emphasized the need for accurate field testing of all GM crops and the importance of targeting gene expression to specific tissues to improve safety.

Addressing the Problem of Transgene Escape

Perhaps the most serious concern raised about GM crops is the possibility of the introduced genes escaping from a transgenic crop into related weeds through crop-to-weed hybridization. The fear is that the spontaneous hybridization between a crop engineered for herbicide resistance and a wild relative might give rise to a "superweed" that would have a selective advantage over other weeds in the wild and would be much more difficult to control in the field. GMO advocates point out that the likelihood of transgene escape depends on the ability of the crop and weed to hybridize and on how the transgenes affect the overall fitness of the hybrids. A desirable crop trait—a dwarf phenotype, for example—might be disadvantageous to a weed growing in the wild. In other instances, there are no weedy relatives nearby with which to hybridize; soybean, for example, has no wild relatives in the United States. However, canola, sorghum, and many other crops do hybridize readily with weeds, and crop-to-weed transgene escape in a turfgrass has occurred. In 2003 a transgenic variety of creeping bentgrass (*Agrostis stolonifera*) genetically engineered to resist the herbicide glyphosate escaped from an experimental plot in Oregon following a windstorm. Despite efforts to eradicate the escapee, 62% of the *Agrostis* plants found in the vicinity three years later were glyphosate resistant. So far, the ecological impact of this event appears to be minor, but that may not be the case with future transgenic escapes.

Many different strategies are being pursued with the goal of preventing transgene escape. For example, if male sterility could be engineered into plants, these plants would still produce seeds and fruit if pollinated by nearby nontransgenic plants, but they would produce no viable pollen. A second approach involves genetically engineering apomixis into transgenic crops. When a seed is produced by apomixis, the embryo and endosperm develop without fertilization.

The transfer of this trait to transgenic crops would therefore minimize the possibility of transgene escape via pollen because plants could be male-sterile without compromising seed or fruit production. A third approach is to engineer the transgene into the chloroplast DNA of the crop. Chloroplast DNA in many plant species is inherited strictly from the egg, so transgenes in the chloroplast cannot be transferred by pollen (see Chapter 15 to review maternal inheritance). A fourth approach for preventing transgene escape is to genetically engineer flowers that develop normally but fail to open. Consequently, self-pollination would occur, but pollen would be unlikely to escape from the flower. This solution would require modifications to flower design. Several floral genes have been identified that could be manipulated to this end.

The continuing debate about GMOs in agriculture exemplifies one of this textbook's recurring ideas: the relationship of science and technology to society. Technological advances almost always involve some risk of unintended outcomes. In the case of genetically engineered crops, zero risk is probably unattainable. Therefore, scientists and the public must assess on a case-by-case basis the possible benefits of transgenic products versus the risks that society is willing to take. The best scenario is for these discussions and decisions to be based on sound scientific information and rigorous testing rather than on reflexive fear or blind optimism.

CONCEPT CHECK 38.3

1. Compare traditional plant-breeding methods with genetic engineering.
2. Why does *Bt* maize have less fumonisin than non-GM maize?
3. **WHAT IF?** In a few species, chloroplast genes are inherited only from sperm. How might this influence efforts to prevent transgene escape?

For suggested answers, see Appendix A.

38 Chapter Review

SUMMARY OF KEY CONCEPTS

CONCEPT 38.1

Flowers, double fertilization, and fruits are key features of the angiosperm life cycle (pp. 816–826)

- Angiosperm reproduction involves an alternation of generations between a multicellular diploid sporophyte generation and a multicellular haploid gametophyte generation. Flowers, produced by the sporophyte, function in sexual reproduction.
- The four floral organs are sepals, petals, stamens, and carpels. **Sepals** protect the floral bud. **Petals** help attract pollinators. **Stamens** bear anthers in which haploid **microspores** develop into **pollen grains** containing a male gametophyte. **Carpels** contain ovules (immature seeds) in their swollen bases. Within the ovules, **embryo sacs** (female gametophytes) develop from megaspores.
- **Pollination**, which precedes fertilization, is the placing of pollen on the stigma of a carpel. After pollination, the pollen tube discharges two sperm into the female gametophyte. Two sperm are needed for **double fertilization**, a process in which one sperm fertilizes the egg, forming a zygote and eventually an embryo, while the other

Tube nucleus

One sperm will fuse with the egg, forming a zygote (2*n*).

One sperm cell will fuse with the 2 polar nuclei, forming an endosperm nucleus (3*n*).

sperm combines with the polar nuclei, giving rise to the food-storing endosperm.
- The **seed coat** encloses the embryo along with a food supply stocked in either the **endosperm** or the **cotyledons**. Seed **dormancy** ensures that seeds germinate only when conditions for seedling survival are optimal. The breaking of dormancy often requires environmental cues, such as temperature or lighting changes.
- The **fruit** protects the enclosed seeds and aids in wind dispersal or in the attraction of seed-dispersing animals.

? *What changes occur to the four types of floral parts as a flower changes into a fruit?*

CONCEPT 38.2

Flowering plants reproduce sexually, asexually, or both (pp. 827–830)

- **Asexual reproduction**, also known as **vegetative reproduction**, enables successful plants to proliferate quickly. Sexual reproduction generates most of the genetic variation that makes evolutionary adaptation possible.
- Plants have evolved many mechanisms to avoid self-fertilization, including having male and female flowers on different individuals, nonsynchronous production of male and female parts within a single flower, and **self-incompatibility** reactions in which pollen grains that bear an allele identical to one in the female are rejected.
- Plants can be cloned from single cells, which can be genetically manipulated before being allowed to develop into a plant.

? *What are the advantages and disadvantages of asexual reproduction?*

CONCEPT 38.3

People modify crops by breeding and genetic engineering (pp. 830–834)

- Hybridization of different varieties and even species of plants is common in nature and has been used by breeders, ancient and modern, to introduce new genes into crops. After two plants are successfully hybridized, plant breeders select those progeny that have the desired traits.
- In genetic engineering, genes from unrelated organisms are incorporated into plants. Genetically modified (GM) plants can increase the quality and quantity of food worldwide and may also become increasingly important as biofuels.
- Two important GM crops are Golden Rice, which provides more vitamin A, and *Bt* maize, which is insect resistant.
- There are concerns about the unknown risks of releasing GM organisms into the environment, but the potential benefits of transgenic crops need to be considered.

? *Give three examples of how genetic engineering has improved food quality or agricultural productivity.*

TEST YOUR UNDERSTANDING

LEVEL 1: KNOWLEDGE/COMPREHENSION

1. A fruit is
   a. a mature ovary.
   b. a mature ovule.
   c. a seed plus its integuments.
   d. an enlarged embryo sac.

2. Double fertilization means that
   a. flowers must be pollinated twice to yield fruits and seeds.
   b. every egg must receive two sperm to produce an embryo.
   c. one sperm is needed to fertilize the egg, and a second sperm is needed to fertilize the polar nuclei.
   d. every sperm has two nuclei.

3. "Golden Rice"
   a. is resistant to various herbicides, making it practical to weed rice fields with those herbicides.
   b. contains transgenes that increase vitamin A content.
   c. includes bacterial genes that produce a toxin that reduces damage from insect pests.
   d. produces larger, golden grains that increase crop yields.

4. Which statement concerning grafting is correct?
   a. Stocks and scions refer to twigs of different species.
   b. Stocks and scions must come from unrelated species.
   c. Stocks provide root systems for grafting.
   d. Grafting creates new species.

LEVEL 2: APPLICATION/ANALYSIS

5. Some dioecious species have the XY genotype for male and XX for female. After double fertilization, what would be the genotypes of the embryos and endosperm nuclei?
   a. embryo XY/endosperm XXX or embryo XX/endosperm XXY
   b. embryo XX/endosperm XX or embryo XY/endosperm XY
   c. embryo XX/endosperm XXX or embryo XY/endosperm XYY
   d. embryo XX/endosperm XXX or embryo XY/endosperm XXY

6. A small flower with green petals is most likely
   a. bee-pollinated.
   b. bird-pollinated.
   c. bat-pollinated.
   d. wind-pollinated.

7. The black dots that cover strawberries are actually fruits formed from the separate carpels of a single flower. The fleshy and tasty portion of a strawberry derives from the receptacle of a flower with many separate carpels. Therefore, a strawberry is
   a. a simple fruit with many seeds.
   b. both a multiple fruit and an accessory fruit.
   c. both a simple fruit and an aggregate fruit.
   d. both an aggregate fruit and an accessory fruit.

8. **DRAW IT** Draw and label the parts of a flower.

LEVEL 3: SYNTHESIS/EVALUATION

9. **EVOLUTION CONNECTION**
   With respect to sexual reproduction, some plant species are fully self-fertile, others are fully self-incompatible, and some exhibit a "mixed strategy" with partial self-incompatibility. These reproductive strategies differ in their implications for evolutionary potential. How, for example, might a self-incompatible species fare as a small founder population or remnant population in a severe population bottleneck (see Chapter 23), as compared with a self-fertile species?

10. **SCIENTIFIC INQUIRY**
    Critics of GM foods have argued that transgenes may disturb cellular functioning, causing unexpected and potentially harmful substances to appear inside cells. Toxic intermediary substances that normally occur in very small amounts may arise in larger amounts, or new substances may appear. The disruption may also lead to loss of substances that help maintain normal metabolism. If you were your nation's chief scientific advisor, how would you respond to these criticisms?

11. **SCIENCE, TECHNOLOGY, AND SOCIETY**
    Humans have engaged in genetic manipulation for millennia, producing plant and animal varieties through selective breeding and hybridization that significantly modify genomes of organisms. Why do you think modern genetic engineering, which often entails introducing or modifying only one or a few genes, has met with so much opposition? Should some forms of genetic engineering be of greater concern than others? Explain.

12. **WRITE ABOUT A THEME: ORGANIZATION**
    In a short essay (100–150 words), discuss how a flower's ability to reproduce with other flowers of the same species is an emergent property arising from floral parts and their organization.

13. **SYNTHESIZE YOUR KNOWLEDGE**

(a) What is a pollen grain? (b) How does it form? (c) What is its function, and how does it accomplish this function? (d) In an evolutionary context, why was pollen an important step in allowing seed plants to become the dominant plants?

For selected answers, see Appendix A.

MasteringBiology®

Students Go to **MasteringBiology** for assignments, the eText, and the Study Area with practice tests, animations, and activities.

Instructors Go to **MasteringBiology** for automatically graded tutorials and questions that you can assign to your students, plus Instructor Resources.

39

Plant Responses to Internal and External Signals

▲ Figure 39.1 A "vampire" plant?

Stimuli and a Stationary Life

Slowly, the hunter slinks through the brush toward the shade, where its prey can best be found. It began its hunt with only a week of provisions. If it does not find food soon, it will perish. At long last, it detects a promising scent and steers toward the source. When it's within reach, it lassoes its quarry. Then it senses even better prey! It sets course for this new target, lassoes it, and taps into the vital juices of its nutritious victim.

The hunter is a parasitic, nonphotosynthetic flowering plant called dodder (*Cuscuta*). Upon germination, a dodder seedling, fueled by nutrients stored during embryo development, searches for a host plant (Figure 39.1). If a host is not found within a week or so, the seedling dies. Dodder attacks by sending out tendrils that coil around the host, as seen in photo at the lower left. Within an hour, it either exploits the host or moves on. If it stays, it takes several days to tap into the host's phloem by means of feeding appendages called haustoria. Depending on how nutritious its host is, dodder grows more or fewer coils.

How does dodder locate its victims? Biologists have long known that it grows toward the shade (where better to find a stem?) but thought it just bumped into its victims. However, new studies reveal that chemicals released by a potential host plant attract dodder, causing it to rapidly set course in that direction.

Dodder's behavior is unusual, but photosynthetic plants also sense their environment, taking advantage of available sunlight and nutrient-rich patches in the soil. These behaviors involve signal transduction pathways not far removed from some pathways by which you interact with your environment. At the levels of signal reception and signal transduction, your cells are not that different from those of plants—the similarities far outweigh the differences. As an animal, however, your responses to environmental stimuli are generally quite different from those of plants. Animals commonly respond by movement; plants do so by altering growth and development.

Plants must also adjust to changes in time, such as the passage of seasons, to compete successfully. In addition, they interact with a wide range of organisms. All of these physical and chemical interactions involve complex signal transduction pathways. In this chapter, we focus on understanding the internal chemicals (hormones) that regulate plant growth and development and how plants perceive and respond to their environments.

Signal transduction pathways link signal reception to response

Dodder plants receive specific signals from their environment and respond to them in ways that enhance survival and reproductive success, but dodder is not unique in this regard. Consider a more mundane example, a forgotten potato in the back corner of a kitchen cupboard. This modified underground stem, or tuber, has sprouted shoots from its "eyes" (axillary buds). These shoots, however, scarcely resemble those of a typical plant. Instead of sturdy stems and broad green leaves, this plant has ghostly pale stems and unexpanded leaves, as well as short, stubby roots (**Figure 39.2a**). These morphological adaptations for growing in darkness, collectively referred to as **etiolation**, make sense if we consider that a young potato plant in nature usually encounters continuous darkness when sprouting underground. Under these circumstances, expanded leaves would be a hindrance to soil penetration and would be damaged as the shoots pushed through the soil. Because the leaves are unexpanded and underground, there is little evaporative loss of water and little requirement for an extensive root system to replace the water lost by transpiration. Moreover, the energy expended in producing green chlorophyll would be wasted because there is no light for photosynthesis. Instead, a potato plant growing in the dark allocates as much energy as possible to elongating its stems. This adaptation enables the shoots to break ground before the nutrient reserves in the tuber are exhausted. The etiolation response is one example of how a plant's morphology and physiology are tuned to its surroundings by complex interactions between environmental and internal signals.

(a) **Before exposure to light.** A dark-grown potato has tall, spindly stems and nonexpanded leaves—morphological adaptations that enable the shoots to penetrate the soil. The roots are short, but there is little need for water absorption because little water is lost by the shoots.

(b) **After a week's exposure to natural daylight.** The potato plant begins to resemble a typical plant with broad green leaves, short sturdy stems, and long roots. This transformation begins with the reception of light by a specific pigment, phytochrome.

▲ Figure 39.2 **Light-induced de-etiolation (greening) of dark-grown potatoes.**

When a shoot reaches light, the plant undergoes profound changes, collectively called **de-etiolation** (informally known as greening). Stem elongation slows; leaves expand; roots elongate; and the shoot produces chlorophyll. In short, it begins to resemble a typical plant (**Figure 39.2b**). In this section, we will use this de-etiolation response as an example of how a plant cell's reception of a signal—in this case, light—is transduced into a response (greening). Along the way, we will explore how studies of mutants provide insights into the molecular details of the stages of cell signal processing: reception, transduction, and response (**Figure 39.3**).

▲ Figure 39.3 **Review of a general model for signal transduction pathways.** As discussed in Chapter 11, a hormone or other kind of stimulus interacting with a specific receptor protein can trigger the sequential activation of relay proteins and also the production of second messengers that participate in the pathway. The signal is passed along, ultimately bringing about cellular responses. In this diagram, the receptor is on the surface of the target cell; in other cases, the stimulus interacts with receptors inside the cell.

Reception

Signals are first detected by receptors, proteins that undergo changes in shape in response to a specific stimulus. The receptor involved in de-etiolation is a type of *phytochrome*, a member of a class of photoreceptors that we'll discuss more fully later in the chapter. Unlike most receptors, which are built into the plasma membrane, the type of phytochrome that functions in de-etiolation is located in the cytoplasm. Researchers demonstrated the requirement for phytochrome in de-etiolation through studies of the tomato, a close relative of the potato. The *aurea* mutant of tomato, which has reduced levels of phytochrome, greens less than wild-type tomatoes when exposed to light. (*Aurea* is Latin for "gold." In the absence of chlorophyll, the yellow and orange accessory pigments called carotenoids are more obvious.) Researchers produced a normal de-etiolation response in individual *aurea* leaf cells by injecting phytochrome from other plants and then exposing the cells to light. Such experiments indicated that phytochrome functions in light detection during de-etiolation.

Transduction

Receptors can be sensitive to very weak environmental or chemical signals. Some de-etiolation responses are triggered by extremely low levels of light, in certain cases as little as the equivalent of a few seconds of moonlight. The transduction of these extremely weak signals involves **second messengers**—small molecules and ions in the cell that amplify the signal and transfer it from the receptor to other proteins that carry out the response (**Figure 39.4**). In Chapter 11, we discussed several kinds of second messengers (see Figures 11.12 and 11.14). Here, we examine the particular roles of two types of second messengers in de-etiolation: calcium ions (Ca^{2+}) and cyclic GMP (cGMP).

Changes in cytosolic Ca^{2+} levels play an important role in phytochrome signal transduction. The concentration of cytosolic Ca^{2+} is generally very low (about 10^{-7} M), but phytochrome activation leads to the opening of Ca^{2+} channels and a transient 100-fold increase in cytosolic Ca^{2+} levels. In response to light, phytochrome undergoes a change in shape

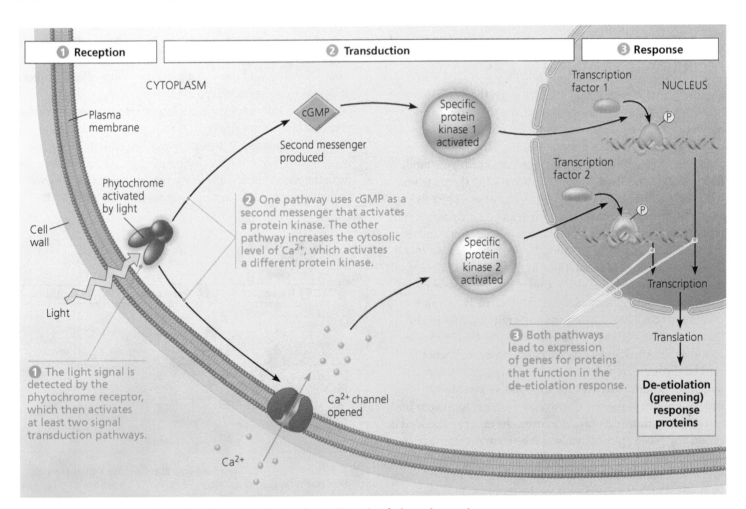

▲ **Figure 39.4 An example of signal transduction in plants: the role of phytochrome in the de-etiolation (greening) response.**

MAKE CONNECTIONS *Which panel in Figure 11.17 best exemplifies the phytochrome-dependent signal transduction pathway during de-etiolation? Explain.*

that leads to the activation of guanylyl cyclase, an enzyme that produces the second messenger cyclic GMP. Both Ca^{2+} and cGMP must be produced for a complete de-etiolation response. The injection of cGMP into *aurea* tomato leaf cells, for example, induces only a partial de-etiolation response.

Response

Ultimately, second messengers regulate one or more cellular activities. In most cases, these responses involve the increased activity of particular enzymes. There are two main mechanisms by which a signaling pathway can enhance an enzymatic step in a biochemical pathway: post-translational modification and transcriptional regulation. Post-translational modification activates preexisting enzymes. Transcriptional regulation increases or decreases the synthesis of mRNA encoding a specific enzyme.

Post-Translational Modification of Preexisting Proteins

In most signal transduction pathways, preexisting proteins are modified by the phosphorylation of specific amino acids, which alters the protein's hydrophobicity and activity. Many second messengers, including cGMP and Ca^{2+}, activate protein kinases directly. Often, one protein kinase will phosphorylate another protein kinase, which then phosphorylates another, and so on (see Figure 11.10). Such kinase cascades may link initial stimuli to responses at the level of gene expression, usually via the phosphorylation of transcription factors. As we'll discuss soon, many signal transduction pathways ultimately regulate the synthesis of new proteins by turning specific genes on or off.

Signal transduction pathways must also have a means for turning off when the initial signal is no longer present, such as when a sprouting potato is put back into the cupboard. Protein phosphatases, which are enzymes that dephosphorylate specific proteins, are important in these "switch-off" processes. At any particular moment, a cell's functioning depends on the balance of activity of many types of protein kinases and protein phosphatases.

Transcriptional Regulation

As discussed in Chapter 18, the proteins we call *specific transcription factors* bind to specific regions of DNA and control the transcription of specific genes (see Figure 18.10). In the case of phytochrome-induced de-etiolation, several such transcription factors are activated by phosphorylation in response to the appropriate light conditions. The activation of some of these transcription factors depends on their phosphorylation by protein kinases activated by cGMP or Ca^{2+}.

The mechanism by which a signal promotes developmental changes may depend on transcription factors that are activators (which *increase* transcription of specific genes) or repressors (which *decrease* transcription) or both. For example, some *Arabidopsis* mutants, except for their pale color, have a light-grown morphology when grown in the dark; they have expanded leaves and short, sturdy stems but are not green because the final step in chlorophyll production requires light directly. These mutants have defects in a repressor that normally inhibits the expression of other genes that are activated by light. When the repressor is eliminated by mutation, the pathway that is normally blocked proceeds. Thus, these mutants appear to have been grown in the light, except for their pale color.

De-Etiolation ("Greening") Proteins

What types of proteins are either activated by phosphorylation or newly transcribed during the de-etiolation process? Many are enzymes that function in photosynthesis directly; others are enzymes involved in supplying the chemical precursors necessary for chlorophyll production; still others affect the levels of plant hormones that regulate growth. For example, the levels of auxin and brassinosteroids, hormones that enhance stem elongation, decrease following the activation of phytochrome. That decrease explains the slowing of stem elongation that accompanies de-etiolation.

We have discussed the signal transduction involved in the de-etiolation response of a potato plant in some detail to give you a sense of the complexity of biochemical changes that underlie this one process. Every plant hormone and environmental stimulus will trigger one or more signal transduction pathways of comparable complexity. As in the studies on the *aurea* mutant tomato, the isolation of mutants (a genetic approach) and techniques of molecular biology are helping researchers identify these various pathways. But this recent research builds on a long history of careful physiological and biochemical investigations into how plants work. As you will read in the next section, classic experiments provided the first clues that transported signaling molecules called hormones are internal regulators of plant growth.

CONCEPT CHECK 39.1

1. What are the morphological differences between dark- and light-grown plants? Explain how etiolation helps a seedling compete successfully.

2. Cycloheximide is a drug that inhibits protein synthesis. Predict what effect cycloheximide would have on de-etiolation.

3. **WHAT IF?** The sexual dysfunction drug Viagra inhibits an enzyme that breaks down cyclic GMP. If tomato leaf cells have a similar enzyme, would applying Viagra to these cells cause a normal de-etiolation of *aurea* mutant tomato leaves?

For suggested answers, see Appendix A.

CONCEPT 39.2

Plant hormones help coordinate growth, development, and responses to stimuli

A **hormone**, in the original meaning of the term, is a signaling molecule that is produced in tiny amounts by one part of an organism's body and transported to other parts, where it binds to a specific receptor and triggers responses in target cells and tissues. In animals, hormones are usually transported through the circulatory system, a criterion often included in definitions of the term. Many modern plant biologists, however, argue that the hormone concept, which originated from studies of animals, is too limiting to describe plant physiological processes. For example, plants don't have circulating blood to transport hormone-like signaling molecules. Moreover, some signaling molecules that are considered plant hormones act only locally. Finally, there are some signaling molecules in plants, such as glucose, that typically occur in plants at concentrations that are thousands of times greater than a typical hormone. Nevertheless, they activate signal transduction pathways that greatly alter the functioning of plants in a manner similar to a hormone. Thus, many plant biologists prefer the broader term *plant growth regulator* to describe organic compounds, either natural or synthetic, that modify or control one or more specific physiological processes within a plant. At this point in time, the terms *plant hormone* and *plant growth regulator* are used about equally, but for historical continuity we will use the term *plant hormone* and adhere to the criterion that plant hormones are active at very low concentrations.

Plant hormones are produced in very low concentrations, but a tiny amount of hormone can have a profound effect on plant growth and development. Virtually every

Table 39.1	Overview of Plant Hormones	
Hormone	**Where Produced or Found in Plant**	**Major Functions**
Auxin (IAA)	Shoot apical meristems and young leaves are the primary sites of auxin synthesis. Root apical meristems also produce auxin, although the root depends on the shoot for much of its auxin. Developing seeds and fruits contain high levels of auxin, but it is unclear whether it is newly synthesized or transported from maternal tissues.	Stimulates stem elongation (low concentration only); promotes the formation of lateral and adventitious roots; regulates development of fruit; enhances apical dominance; functions in phototropism and gravitropism; promotes vascular differentiation; retards leaf abscission
Cytokinins	These are synthesized primarily in roots and transported to other organs, although there are many minor sites of production as well.	Regulate cell division in shoots and roots; modify apical dominance and promote lateral bud growth; promote movement of nutrients into sink tissues; stimulate seed germination; delay leaf senescence
Gibberellins (GA)	Meristems of apical buds and roots, young leaves, and developing seeds are the primary sites of production.	Stimulate stem elongation, pollen development, pollen tube growth, fruit growth, and seed development and germination; regulate sex determination and the transition from juvenile to adult phases
Abscisic acid (ABA)	Almost all plant cells have the ability to synthesize abscisic acid, and its presence has been detected in every major organ and living tissue; it may be transported in the phloem or xylem.	Inhibits growth; promotes stomatal closure during drought stress; promotes seed dormancy and inhibits early germination; promotes leaf senescence; promotes desiccation tolerance
Ethylene	This gaseous hormone can be produced by most parts of the plant. It is produced in high concentrations during senescence, leaf abscission, and the ripening of some types of fruits. Synthesis is also stimulated by wounding and stress.	Promotes ripening of many types of fruit, leaf abscission, and the triple response in seedlings (inhibition of stem elongation, promotion of lateral expansion, and horizontal growth); enhances the rate of senescence; promotes root and root hair formation; promotes flowering in the pineapple family
Brassinosteroids	These compounds are present in all plant tissues, although different intermediates predominate in different organs. Internally produced brassinosteroids act near the site of synthesis.	Promote cell expansion and cell division in shoots; promote root growth at low concentrations; inhibit root growth at high concentrations; promote xylem differentiation and inhibit phloem differentiation; promote seed germination and pollen tube elongation
Jasmonates	These are a small group of related molecules derived from the fatty acid linolenic acid. They are produced in several parts of the plant and travel in the phloem to other parts of the plant.	Regulate a wide variety of functions, including fruit ripening, floral development, pollen production, tendril coiling, root growth, seed germination, and nectar secretion; also produced in response to herbivory and pathogen invasion
Strigolactones	These carotenoid-derived hormones and extracellular signals are produced in roots in response to low phosphate conditions or high auxin flow from the shoot.	Promote seed germination, control of apical dominance, and the attraction of mycorrhizal fungi to the root

aspect of plant growth and development is under hormonal control to some degree. Each hormone has multiple effects, depending on its site of action, its concentration, and the developmental stage of the plant. Conversely, multiple hormones can influence a single process. Plant hormone responses commonly depend on both the amounts of the hormones involved and their relative concentrations. It is often the interactions between different hormones, rather than hormones acting in isolation, that control growth and development. These interactions will become apparent in the following survey of hormone function.

A Survey of Plant Hormones

Table 39.1 previews the major types and actions of plant hormones, including auxin, cytokinins, gibberellins, abscisic acid, ethylene, brassinosteroids, jasmonates, and strigolactones.

Auxin

The idea that chemical messengers exist in plants emerged from a series of classic experiments on how stems respond to light. As you know, the shoot of a houseplant on a windowsill grows toward light. Any growth response that results in plant organs curving toward or away from stimuli is called a **tropism** (from the Greek *tropos*, turn). The growth of a shoot toward light or away from it is called **phototropism**; the former is positive phototropism, and the latter is negative phototropism.

In natural ecosystems, where plants may be crowded, phototropism directs shoot growth toward the sunlight that powers photosynthesis. This response results from a differential growth of cells on opposite sides of the shoot; the cells on the darker side elongate faster than the cells on the brighter side.

Charles Darwin and his son Francis conducted some of the earliest experiments on phototropism in the late 1800s (Figure 39.5). They observed that a grass seedling ensheathed in its coleoptile (see Figure 38.9b) could bend toward light only if the tip of the coleoptile was present. If the tip was removed, the coleoptile did not curve. The seedling also failed to grow toward light if the tip was covered with an opaque cap, but neither a transparent cap over the tip nor an opaque shield placed below the coleoptile tip prevented the phototropic response. It was the tip of the coleoptile, the Darwins concluded, that was responsible for sensing light. However, they noted that the differential growth response that led to curvature of the coleoptile occurred some distance below the tip. The Darwins postulated that some signal was transmitted downward from the tip to the elongating region of the coleoptile. A few decades later, the Danish scientist Peter Boysen-Jensen demonstrated that the signal was a mobile chemical substance. He separated

▼ Figure 39.5   Inquiry

What part of a grass coleoptile senses light, and how is the signal transmitted?

Experiment In 1880, Charles and Francis Darwin removed and covered parts of grass coleoptiles to determine what part senses light. In 1913, Peter Boysen-Jensen separated coleoptiles with different materials to determine how the signal for phototropism is transmitted.

Results

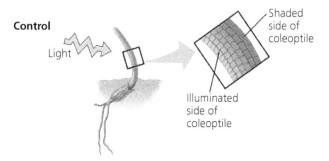

Control

Light

Shaded side of coleoptile

Illuminated side of coleoptile

Darwin and Darwin: Phototropism occurs only when the tip is illuminated.

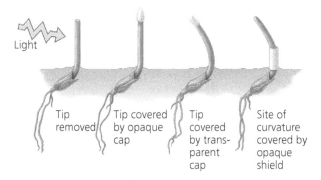

Light

Tip removed

Tip covered by opaque cap

Tip covered by transparent cap

Site of curvature covered by opaque shield

Boysen-Jensen: Phototropism occurs when the tip is separated by a permeable barrier but not an impermeable barrier.

Light

Tip separated by gelatin (permeable)

Tip separated by mica (impermeable)

Conclusion The Darwins' experiment suggested that only the tip of the coleoptile senses light. The phototropic bending, however, occurred at a distance from the site of light perception (the tip). Boysen-Jensen's results suggested that the signal for the bending is a light-activated mobile chemical.

Source: C. R. Darwin, The power of movement in plants, John Murray, London (1880). P. Boysen-Jensen, Concerning the performance of phototropic stimuli on the Avenacoleoptile, *Berichte der Deutschen Botanischen Gesellschaft* (*Reports of the German Botanical Society*) 31:559–566 (1913).

WHAT IF? *How could you experimentally determine which colors of light cause the most phototropic bending?*

the tip from the remainder of the coleoptile by a cube of gelatin, which prevented cellular contact but allowed chemicals to pass through. These seedlings responded normally, bending toward light. However, if the tip was experimentally separated from the lower coleoptile by an impermeable barrier, such as the mineral mica, no phototropic response occurred.

Subsequent research showed that a chemical was released from coleoptile tips and could be collected by means of diffusion into agar blocks. Little cubes of agar containing this chemical could induce "phototropic-like" curvatures even in complete darkness if the agar cubes were placed off-center atop the cut surface of decapitated coleoptiles. Coleoptiles curve toward light because of a higher concentration of this growth-promoting chemical on the darker side of the coleoptile. Since this chemical stimulated growth as it passed down the coleoptile, it was dubbed "auxin"(from the Greek *auxein*, to increase). Auxin was later purified, and its chemical structure determined to be indoleacetic acid (IAA). The term **auxin** is used for any chemical substance that promotes elongation of coleoptiles, although auxins have multiple functions in flowering plants. The major natural auxin in plants is IAA, although several other compounds, including some synthetic ones, have auxin activity.

Auxin is produced predominantly in shoot tips and is transported from cell to cell down the stem at a rate of about 1 cm/hr. It moves only from tip to base, not in the reverse direction. This unidirectional transport of auxin is called *polar transport.* Polar transport is unrelated to gravity; experiments have shown that auxin travels upward when a stem or coleoptile segment is placed upside down. Rather, the polarity of auxin movement is attributable to the polar distribution of auxin transport protein in the cells. Concentrated at the basal end of a cell, the auxin transporters move the hormone out of the cell. The auxin can then enter the apical end of the neighboring cell (**Figure 39.6**). Auxin has a variety of effects, including stimulating cell elongation and regulating plant architecture.

The Role of Auxin in Cell Elongation One of auxin's chief functions is to stimulate elongation of cells within young developing shoots. As auxin from the shoot apex moves down to the region of cell elongation (see Figure 35.16), the hormone stimulates cell growth, probably by binding to a receptor in the plasma membrane. Auxin stimulates growth only over a certain concentration range, from about 10^{-8} to 10^{-4} M. At higher concentrations, auxin may inhibit cell elongation, by inducing production of ethylene, a hormone that generally hinders growth. We will return to this hormonal interaction when we discuss ethylene.

According to a model called the *acid growth hypothesis*, proton pumps play a major role in the growth response of cells to auxin. In a shoot's region of elongation, auxin

▼ Figure 39.6   Inquiry

What causes polar movement of auxin from shoot tip to base?

Experiment To investigate how auxin is transported unidirectionally, Leo Gälweiler and colleagues designed an experiment to identify the location of the auxin transport protein. They used a greenish yellow fluorescent molecule to label antibodies that bind to the auxin transport protein. Then they applied the antibodies to longitudinally sectioned *Arabidopsis* stems.

Results The light micrograph on the left shows that auxin transport proteins are not found in all stem tissues, but only in the xylem parenchyma. In the light micrograph on the right, a higher magnification reveals that these proteins are primarily localized at the basal ends of the cells.

Conclusion The results support the hypothesis that concentration of the auxin transport protein at the basal ends of cells mediates the polar transport of auxin.

Source: L. Gälweiler et al., Regulation of polar auxin transport by AtPIN1 in *Arabidopsis* vascular tissue, *Science* 282:2226–2230 (1998).

WHAT IF? *If auxin transport proteins were equally distributed at both ends of the cells, would polar auxin transport still be possible? Explain.*

stimulates the plasma membrane's proton (H^+) pumps. This pumping of H^+ increases the voltage across the membrane (membrane potential) and lowers the pH in the cell wall within minutes (**Figure 39.7**). Acidification of the wall activates proteins called **expansins** that break the cross-links (hydrogen bonds) between cellulose microfibrils and other cell wall constituents, loosening the wall's fabric. Increasing the membrane potential enhances ion uptake into the cell, which causes osmotic uptake of water and increased turgor. Increased turgor and increased cell wall plasticity enable the cell to elongate.

Auxin also rapidly alters gene expression, causing cells in the region of elongation to produce new proteins within minutes. Some of these proteins are short-lived transcription factors that repress or activate the expression of other genes. For sustained growth after this initial spurt, cells

③ Wedge-shaped expansins (red), activated by low pH, separate cellulose microfibrils (brown) from cross-linking polysaccharides (green). The exposed cross-linking polysaccharides are now more accessible to cell wall–loosening enzymes (purple).

CELL WALL

④ Cell wall-loosening enzymes (purple) cleave cross-linking polysaccharides (green), allowing cellulose microfibrils to slide. The extensibility of the cell wall is increased. Turgor causes the cell to expand.

② The cell wall becomes more acidic.

① Auxin increases the activity of proton pumps.

ATP

Plasma membrane

CYTOPLASM

H_2O

Plasma membrane

Cell wall

Nucleus

Cytoplasm

Vacuole

⑤ With the cellulose loosened, the cell can elongate.

▲ Figure 39.7 Cell elongation in response to auxin: the acid growth hypothesis.

must make more cytoplasm and wall material. In addition, auxin stimulates this sustained growth response.

Auxin's Role in Plant Development The polar transport of auxin is a central element controlling the spatial organization, or *pattern formation*, of the developing plant. Auxin is synthesized in shoot tips, and it carries integrated information about the development, size, and environment of individual branches. This flow of information controls branching patterns. A reduced flow of auxin from a branch, for example, indicates that the branch is not being sufficiently productive: New branches are needed elsewhere. Thus, lateral buds below the branch are released from dormancy and begin to grow.

Transport of auxin also plays a key role in establishing *phyllotaxy* (see Figure 36.3), the arrangement of leaves on a stem. A leading model proposes that polar auxin transport in the shoot tip generates local peaks in auxin concentration that determine the site of leaf primordium formation and thereby the different phyllotaxies found in nature.

The polar transport of auxin from the leaf margin also directs the patterns of leaf veins. Inhibitors of polar auxin transport result in leaves that lack vascular continuity through the petiole and have broad, loosely organized main veins, an increased number of secondary veins, and a dense band of irregularly shaped vascular cells adjacent to the leaf margin.

The activity of the vascular cambium, the meristem that produces woody tissues, is also under the control of auxin transport. When a plant becomes dormant at the end of a growing season, there is a reduction in auxin transport capacity and the expression of genes encoding auxin transporters.

Auxin's effects on plant development are not limited to the familiar sporophyte plant that we see. Recent evidence suggests that the organization of the microscopic angiosperm female gametophytes is regulated by an auxin gradient.

Practical Uses for Auxins Auxins, both natural and synthetic, have many commercial applications. For example, the natural auxin indolebutyric acid (IBA) is used in the vegetative propagation of plants by cuttings. Treating a detached leaf or stem with powder containing IBA often causes adventitious roots to form near the cut surface.

Certain synthetic auxins are widely used as herbicides, including 2,4-dichlorophenoxyacetic acid (2,4-D). Monocots, such as maize and turfgrass, can rapidly inactivate such synthetic auxins. However, eudicots cannot and therefore die from hormonal overdose. Spraying cereal fields or turf with 2,4-D eliminates eudicot (broadleaf) weeds.

Developing seeds produce auxin, which promotes fruit growth. In tomato plants grown in greenhouses, often fewer seeds are produced, resulting in poorly developed tomato fruits. However, spraying synthetic auxins on greenhouse-grown tomato vines induces normal fruit development, making the greenhouse-cultivated tomatoes commercially viable.

Cytokinins

Trial-and-error attempts to find chemical additives that would enhance the growth and development of plant cells in tissue culture led to the discovery of **cytokinins**. In the 1940s, researchers stimulated the growth of plant embryos in culture by adding coconut milk, the liquid endosperm of a coconut's giant seed. Subsequent researchers found that they could induce cultured tobacco cells to divide by adding degraded DNA samples. The active ingredients of both experimental additives turned out to be modified forms of adenine, a component of nucleic acids. These growth regulators were named cytokinins because they stimulate cytokinesis, or cell division. The most common natural cytokinin is zeatin, so named because it was discovered first in maize (*Zea mays*). The effects of cytokinins on cell division and differentiation, apical dominance, and aging are well documented.

Control of Cell Division and Differentiation Cytokinins are produced in actively growing tissues, particularly in roots, embryos, and fruits. Cytokinins produced in roots reach their target tissues by moving up the plant in the xylem sap. Acting in concert with auxin, cytokinins stimulate cell division and influence the pathway of differentiation. The effects of cytokinins on cells growing in tissue culture provide clues about how this class of hormones may function in an intact plant. When a piece of parenchyma tissue from a stem is cultured in the absence of cytokinins, the cells grow very large but do not divide. But if cytokinins are added along with auxin, the cells divide. Cytokinins alone have no effect. The ratio of cytokinins to auxin controls cell differentiation. When the concentrations of these two hormones are at certain levels, the mass of cells continues to grow, but it remains a cluster of undifferentiated cells called a callus (see Figure 38.15). If cytokinin levels increase, shoot buds develop from the callus. If auxin levels increase, roots form.

Control of Apical Dominance Cytokinins, auxin, and newly discovered plant hormones called strigolactones interact in the control of apical dominance, the ability of the apical bud to suppress the development of axillary buds (Figure 39.8a). Until recently, the leading hypothesis to explain the hormonal regulation of apical dominance—the direct inhibition hypothesis—proposed that auxin and cytokinins act antagonistically in regulating axillary bud growth. According to this view, auxin transported down the shoot from the apical bud directly inhibits axillary buds from growing, causing a shoot to lengthen at the expense of lateral branching. Meanwhile, cytokinins entering the shoot system from roots counter the action of auxin by signaling axillary buds to begin growing. Thus, the ratio of auxin and cytokinins was viewed as the critical factor in controlling axillary bud inhibition.

Many observations are consistent with the direct inhibition hypothesis. If the apical bud, the primary source of auxin, is removed, the inhibition of axillary buds is removed and the plant becomes bushier (Figure 39.8b). Applying auxin to the cut surface of the decapitated shoot resuppresses the growth of the lateral buds (Figure 39.8c). Mutants that overproduce cytokinins or plants treated with cytokinins also tend to be bushier than normal. It now appears, however, that auxin's effects are partially indirect. The polar flow of auxin down the shoot triggers the synthesis of strigolactones, which repress bud growth. Moreover, another signal, perhaps an electrical one, appears to cause buds to begin growing much earlier than can be explained by disrupted auxin flow. Thus, the control of apical dominance is much more complicated than previously thought.

Anti-Aging Effects Cytokinins slow the aging of certain plant organs by inhibiting protein breakdown, stimulating RNA and protein synthesis, and mobilizing nutrients from surrounding tissues. If leaves removed from a plant are dipped in a cytokinin solution, they stay green much longer than otherwise.

Gibberellins

In the early 1900s, farmers in Asia noticed that some rice seedlings in their paddies grew so tall and spindly that they toppled over before they could mature. In 1926, it was

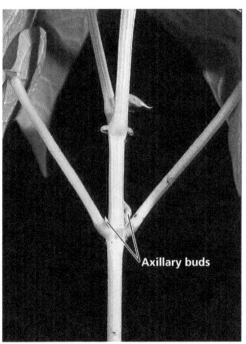

(a) Apical bud intact (not shown in photo)

(b) Apical bud removed

(c) Auxin added to decapitated stem

▲ Figure 39.8 **Apical dominance.** (a) The inhibition of growth of axillary buds, possibly influenced by auxin from the apical bud, favors elongation of the shoot's main axis. (b) Removal of the apical bud from the same plant enables lateral branches to grow. (c) Applying a gelatin capsule containing auxin to the stump prevents the lateral branches from growing.

discovered that a fungus of the genus *Gibberella* causes this "foolish seedling disease." By the 1930s, it was determined that the fungus causes hyperelongation of rice stems by secreting a chemical, which was given the name **gibberellin**. In the 1950s, researchers discovered that plants also produce gibberellins (GAs). Since that time, scientists have identified more than 100 different gibberellins that occur naturally in plants, although a much smaller number occur in each plant species. "Foolish rice" seedlings, it seems, suffer from too much gibberellin. Gibberellins have a variety of effects, such as stem elongation, fruit growth, and seed germination.

Stem Elongation The major sites of gibberellin production are young roots and leaves. Gibberellins are best known for stimulating stem and leaf growth by enhancing cell elongation *and* cell division. One hypothesis proposes that they activate enzymes that loosen cell walls, facilitating entry of expansin proteins. Thus, gibberellins act in concert with auxin to promote stem elongation.

The effects of gibberellins in enhancing stem elongation are evident when certain dwarf (mutant) varieties of plants are treated with gibberellins. For instance, some dwarf pea plants (including the variety Mendel studied; see Chapter 14) grow tall if treated with gibberellins. But there is often no response if the gibberellins are applied to wild-type plants. Apparently, these plants already produce an optimal dose of the hormone. The most dramatic example of gibberellin-induced stem elongation is *bolting*, rapid growth of the floral stalk **(Figure 39.9a)**.

Fruit Growth In many plants, both auxin and gibberellins must be present for fruit to develop. The most important commercial application of gibberellins is in the spraying of Thompson seedless grapes **(Figure 39.9b)**. The hormone makes the individual grapes grow larger, a trait valued by the consumer. The gibberellin sprays also make the internodes of the grape bunch elongate, allowing more space for the individual grapes. By enhancing air circulation between the grapes, this increase in space also makes it harder for yeasts and other microorganisms to infect the fruit.

Germination The embryo of a seed is a rich source of gibberellins. After water is imbibed, the release of gibberellins from the embryo signals the seed to break dormancy and germinate. Some seeds that normally require particular

(a) Some plants develop in a rosette form, low to the ground with very short internodes, as in the *Arabidopsis* plant shown at the left. As the plant switches to reproductive growth, a surge of gibberellins induces bolting: Internodes elongate rapidly, elevating floral buds that develop at stem tips (right).

(b) The Thompson seedless grape bunch on the left is from an untreated control vine. The bunch on the right is growing from a vine that was sprayed with gibberellin during fruit development.

◀ **Figure 39.9 Effects of gibberellins on stem elongation and fruit growth.**

environmental conditions to germinate, such as exposure to light or low temperatures, break dormancy if they are treated with gibberellins. Gibberellins support the growth of cereal seedlings by stimulating the synthesis of digestive enzymes such as α-amylase that mobilize stored nutrients **(Figure 39.10)**.

❶ After a seed imbibes water, the embryo releases gibberellin (GA), which sends a signal to the aleurone, the thin outer layer of the endosperm.

❷ The aleurone responds to GA by synthesizing and secreting digestive enzymes that hydrolyze nutrients stored in the endosperm. One example is α-amylase, which hydrolyzes starch.

❸ Sugars and other nutrients absorbed from the endosperm by the scutellum (cotyledon) are consumed during growth of the embryo into a seedling.

Aleurone
Endosperm
α-amylase
GA
Sugar
GA
Water
Scutellum (cotyledon)
Radicle

▲ **Figure 39.10 Mobilization of nutrients by gibberellins during the germination of grain seeds such as barley.**

Abscisic Acid

In the 1960s, one research group studying the chemical changes that precede bud dormancy and leaf abscission in deciduous trees and another team investigating chemical changes preceding abscission of cotton fruits isolated the same compound, **abscisic acid (ABA)**. Ironically, ABA is no longer thought to play a primary role in bud dormancy or leaf abscission, but it is very important in other functions. Unlike the growth-stimulating hormones we have discussed so far—auxin, cytokinins, gibberellins, and brassinosteroids—ABA *slows* growth. ABA often antagonizes the actions of growth hormones, and the ratio of ABA to one or more growth hormones determines the final physiological outcome. We will consider here two of ABA's many effects: seed dormancy and drought tolerance.

Seed Dormancy Seed dormancy increases the likelihood that seeds will germinate only when there are sufficient amounts of light, temperature, and moisture for the seedlings to survive (see Chapter 38). What prevents seeds dispersed in autumn from germinating immediately, only to die in the winter? What mechanisms ensure that such seeds do not germinate until spring? For that matter, what prevents seeds from germinating in the dark, moist interior of the fruit? The answer to these questions is ABA. The levels of ABA may increase 100-fold during seed maturation. The high levels of ABA in maturing seeds inhibit germination and induce the production of proteins that help the seeds withstand the extreme dehydration that accompanies maturation.

Many types of dormant seeds germinate when ABA is removed or inactivated. The seeds of some desert plants break dormancy only when heavy rains wash ABA out of them. Other seeds require light or prolonged exposure to cold to inactivate ABA. Often, the ratio of ABA to gibberellins determines whether seeds remain dormant or germinate, and adding ABA to seeds that are primed to germinate makes them dormant again. Inactivated ABA or low levels of ABA can lead to precocious (early) germination (Figure 39.11). For example, a maize mutant with grains that germinate while still on the cob lacks a functional transcription factor required for ABA to induce expression of certain genes. Precocious germination of red mangrove seeds, due to low ABA levels, is actually an adaptation that helps the young seedlings to plant themselves like darts in the soft mud below the parent tree.

Drought Tolerance ABA plays a major role in drought signaling. When a plant begins to wilt, ABA accumulates in the leaves and causes stomata to close rapidly, reducing transpiration and preventing further water loss. By affecting second messengers such as calcium, ABA causes potassium channels in the plasma membrane of guard cells to open, leading

◀ Red mangrove (*Rhizophora mangle*) seeds produce only low levels of ABA, and their seeds germinate while still on the tree. In this case, early germination is a useful adaptation. When released, the radicle of the dart-like seedling deeply penetrates the soft mudflats in which the mangroves grow.

Coleoptile

▲ Precocious germination in this maize mutant is caused by lack of a functional transcription factor required for ABA action.

▲ **Figure 39.11 Precocious germination of wild-type mangrove and mutant maize seeds.**

to a massive loss of potassium ions from the cells. The accompanying osmotic loss of water reduces guard cell turgor and leads to closing of the stomatal pores (see Figure 36.13). In some cases, water shortage stresses the root system before the shoot system, and ABA transported from roots to leaves may function as an "early warning system." Many mutants that are especially prone to wilting are deficient in ABA production.

Ethylene

During the 1800s, when coal gas was used as fuel for streetlights, leakage from gas pipes caused nearby trees to drop leaves prematurely. In 1901, the gas **ethylene** was demonstrated to be the active factor in coal gas. But the idea that it is a plant hormone was not widely accepted until the advent of a technique called gas chromatography simplified its identification.

Plants produce ethylene in response to stresses such as drought, flooding, mechanical pressure, injury, and infection. Ethylene is also produced during fruit ripening and programmed cell death and in response to high concentrations of externally applied auxin. Indeed, many effects previously ascribed to auxin, such as inhibition of root elongation, may be due to auxin-induced ethylene production. We will focus here on four of ethylene's many effects: response to mechanical stress, senescence, leaf abscission, and fruit ripening.

The Triple Response to Mechanical Stress Imagine a pea seedling pushing upward through the soil, only to come up against a stone. As it pushes against the obstacle, the stress in its delicate tip induces the seedling to produce ethylene. The hormone then instigates a growth maneuver known as the **triple response** that enables the shoot to avoid the obstacle. The three parts of this response are a slowing of stem elongation, a thickening of the stem (which makes it stronger), and a curvature that causes the stem to start growing horizontally. As the effects of the initial ethylene pulse lessen, the stem resumes vertical growth. If it again contacts a barrier, another burst of ethylene is released, and horizontal growth resumes. However, if the upward touch detects no solid object, then ethylene production decreases, and the stem, now clear of the obstacle, resumes its normal upward growth. It is ethylene that induces the stem to grow horizontally rather than the physical obstruction itself; when ethylene is applied to normal seedlings growing free of physical impediments, they still undergo the triple response (**Figure 39.12**).

Studies of *Arabidopsis* mutants with abnormal triple responses are an example of how biologists identify a signal transduction pathway. Scientists isolated ethylene-insensitive (*ein*) mutants, which fail to undergo the triple

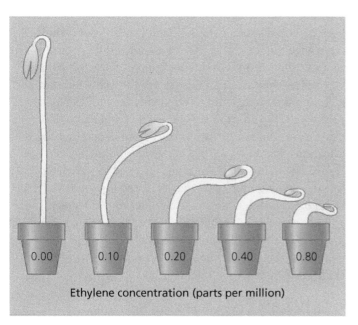

▲ **Figure 39.12 The ethylene-induced triple response.** In response to ethylene, a gaseous plant hormone, germinating pea seedlings grown in the dark undergo the triple response—slowing of stem elongation, stem thickening, and horizontal stem growth. The response is greater with increased ethylene concentration.

Ethylene concentration (parts per million)

0.00 0.10 0.20 0.40 0.80

(a) *ein* mutant. An ethylene-insensitive (*ein*) mutant fails to undergo the triple response in the presence of ethylene.

(b) *ctr* mutant. A constitutive triple-response (*ctr*) mutant undergoes the triple response even in the absence of ethylene.

▲ **Figure 39.13 Ethylene triple-response *Arabidopsis* mutants.**

response after exposure to ethylene (**Figure 39.13a**). Some types of *ein* mutants are insensitive to ethylene because they lack a functional ethylene receptor. Mutants of a different sort undergo the triple response even out of soil, in the air, where there are no physical obstacles. Some of these mutants have a regulatory defect that causes them to produce ethylene at rates 20 times normal. The phenotype of such ethylene-overproducing (*eto*) mutants can be restored to wild-type by treating the seedlings with inhibitors of ethylene synthesis. Other mutants, called constitutive triple-response (*ctr*) mutants, undergo the triple response in air but do not respond to inhibitors of ethylene synthesis (**Figure 39.13b**). (Constitutive genes are genes that are continually expressed in all cells of an organism.) In *ctr* mutants, ethylene signal transduction is permanently turned on, even though ethylene is not present.

The affected gene in *ctr* mutants codes for a protein kinase. The fact that this mutation *activates* the ethylene response suggests that the normal kinase product of the wild-type allele is a *negative* regulator of ethylene signal transduction. Thus, binding of the hormone ethylene to the ethylene receptor normally leads to inactivation of the kinase, and the inactivation of this negative regulator allows synthesis of the proteins required for the triple response.

Senescence Consider the shedding of a leaf in autumn or the death of an annual after flowering. Or think about the final step in differentiation of a vessel element, when its living contents are destroyed, leaving a hollow tube behind. Such events involve **senescence**—the programmed death of certain cells or organs or the entire plant. Cells, organs, and plants genetically programmed to die on a schedule do not simply shut down cellular machinery and await death. Instead, at the molecular level, the onset of the programmed cell death called apoptosis is a very busy time in a cell's life, requiring new gene expression. During apoptosis, newly formed enzymes break down many chemical components, including chlorophyll, DNA, RNA, proteins, and membrane lipids. The plant salvages many of the breakdown products. A burst of ethylene is almost always associated with the apoptosis of cells during senescence.

Leaf Abscission The loss of leaves from deciduous trees helps prevent desiccation during seasonal periods when the availability of water to the roots is severely limited. Before dying leaves abscise, many essential elements are salvaged from them and stored in stem parenchyma cells. These nutrients are recycled back to developing leaves the following spring. Autumn leaf color is due to newly made red pigments as well as yellow and orange carotenoids (see Chapter 10) that were already present in the leaf and are rendered visible by the breakdown of the dark green chlorophyll in autumn.

When an autumn leaf falls, it detaches from the stem at an abscission layer that develops near the base of the petiole **(Figure 39.14)**. The small parenchyma cells of this layer have very thin walls, and there are no fiber cells around the vascular tissue. The abscission layer is further weakened when enzymes hydrolyze polysaccharides in the cell walls. Finally, the weight of the leaf, with the help of the wind, causes a separation within the abscission layer. Even before

the leaf falls, a layer of cork forms a protective scar on the twig side of the abscission layer, preventing pathogens from invading the plant.

A change in the ratio of ethylene to auxin controls abscission. An aging leaf produces less and less auxin, rendering the cells of the abscission layer more sensitive to ethylene. As the influence of ethylene on the abscission layer prevails, the cells produce enzymes that digest the cellulose and other components of cell walls.

Fruit Ripening Immature fleshy fruits are generally tart, hard, and green—features that help protect the developing seeds from herbivores. After ripening, the mature fruits help *attract* animals that disperse the seeds (see Figures 30.10 and 30.11). In many cases, a burst of ethylene production in the fruit triggers the ripening process. The enzymatic breakdown of cell wall components softens the fruit, and the conversion of starches and acids to sugars makes the fruit sweet. The production of new scents and colors helps advertise ripeness to animals, which eat the fruits and disperse the seeds.

A chain reaction occurs during ripening: Ethylene triggers ripening, and ripening triggers more ethylene production. The result is a huge burst in ethylene production. Because ethylene is a gas, the signal to ripen spreads from fruit to fruit. If you pick or buy green fruit, you may be able to speed ripening by storing the fruit in a paper bag, allowing ethylene to accumulate. On a commercial scale, many kinds of fruits are ripened in huge storage containers in which ethylene levels are enhanced. In other cases, fruit producers take measures to slow ripening caused by natural ethylene. Apples, for instance, are stored in bins flushed with carbon dioxide. Circulating the air prevents ethylene from accumulating, and carbon dioxide inhibits synthesis of new ethylene. Stored in this way, apples picked in autumn can still be shipped to grocery stores the following summer.

Given the importance of ethylene in the postharvest physiology of fruits, the genetic engineering of ethylene signal transduction pathways has potential commercial applications. For example, by engineering a way to block the transcription of one of the genes required for ethylene synthesis, molecular biologists have created tomato fruits that ripen on demand. These fruits are picked while green and will not ripen unless ethylene gas is added. As such methods are refined, they will reduce spoilage of fruits and vegetables, a problem that ruins almost half the produce harvested in the United States.

More Recently Discovered Plant Hormones

Auxin, gibberellins, cytokinins, abscisic acid, and ethylene are often considered the five "classic" plant hormones. However, more recently discovered hormones have swelled the list of important plant growth regulators.

0.5 mm

Protective layer   Abscission layer

Stem   Petiole

▲ **Figure 39.14 Abscission of a maple leaf.** Abscission is controlled by a change in the ratio of ethylene to auxin. The abscission layer is seen in this longitudinal section as a vertical band at the base of the petiole. After the leaf falls, a protective layer of cork becomes the leaf scar that helps prevent pathogens from invading the plant (LM).

Brassinosteroids are steroids similar to cholesterol and the sex hormones of animals. They induce cell elongation and division in stem segments and seedlings at concentrations as low as 10^{-12} M. They also slow leaf abscission (leaf drop) and promote xylem differentiation. These effects are so qualitatively similar to those of auxin that it took years for plant physiologists to determine that brassinosteroids were not types of auxins.

The identification of brassinosteroids as plant hormones arose from studies of an *Arabidopsis* mutant that even when grown in the dark exhibited morphological features similar to plants grown in the light. The researchers discovered that the mutation affects a gene that normally codes for an enzyme similar to one involved in steroid synthesis in mammals. They also found that this brassinosteroid-deficient mutant could be restored to the wild-type phenotype by applying brassinosteroids.

Jasmonates, including *jasmonate* (JA) and *methyl jasmonate* (MeJA), are fatty acid–derived molecules that play important roles both in plant defense (see Concept 39.5) and, as discussed here, in plant development. Chemists first isolated MeJA as a key ingredient producing the enchanting fragrance of jasmine (*Jasminum grandiflorum*) flowers. Interest in jasmonates exploded when it was realized that jasmonates are produced by wounded plants and play a key role in controlling plant defenses against herbivores and pathogens. In studying jasmonate signal transduction mutants as well as the effects of applying jasmonates to plants, it soon became apparent that jasmonates and their derivatives regulate a wide variety of physiological processes in plants, including nectar secretion, fruit ripening, pollen production, flowering time, seed germination, root growth, tuber formation, mycorrhizal symbioses, and tendril coiling. In controlling plant processes, jasmonates also engage in cross-talk with phytochrome and various hormones, including GA, IAA, and ethylene.

Strigolactones are xylem-mobile chemicals that stimulate seed germination, suppress adventitious root formation, help establish mycorrhizal associations, and (as noted earlier) help control apical dominance. Their recent discovery relates back to studies of their namesake, *Striga*, a colorfully named genus of rootless parasitic plants that penetrate the roots of other plants, diverting essential nutrients from them and stunting their growth. (In Romanian legend, Striga is a vampire-like creature that lives for thousands of years, only needing to feed every 25 years or so.) Also known as witchweed, *Striga* may be the greatest obstacle to food production in Africa, infesting about two-thirds of the area devoted to cereal crops. Each *Striga* plant produces tens of thousands of tiny seeds that can remain dormant in the soil for many years until a suitable host begins to grow. Thus, *Striga* cannot be eradicated by growing non-grain crops for several years. Strigolactones, exuded by the host roots, were first identified as the chemical signals that stimulate the germination of *Striga* seeds.

CONCEPT CHECK 39.2

1. Fusicoccin is a fungal toxin that stimulates the plasma membrane H⁺ pumps of plant cells. How may it affect the growth of isolated stem sections?

2. **WHAT IF?** If a plant has the double mutation *ctr* and *ein*, what is its triple-response phenotype? Explain your answer.

3. **MAKE CONNECTIONS** What type of feedback process is exemplified by the production of ethylene during fruit ripening? Explain. (See Figure 1.11.)

For suggested answers, see Appendix A.

CONCEPT 39.3

Responses to light are critical for plant success

Light is an especially important environmental factor in the lives of plants. In addition to being required for photosynthesis, light triggers many key events in plant growth and development, collectively known as **photomorphogenesis**. Light reception also allows plants to measure the passage of days and seasons.

Plants detect not only the presence of light signals but also their direction, intensity, and wavelength (color). A graph called an **action spectrum** depicts the relative effectiveness of different wavelengths of radiation in driving a particular process, such as photosynthesis (see Figure 10.10b). Action spectra are useful in studying *any* process that depends on light. By comparing action spectra of various plant responses, researchers determine which responses are mediated by the same photoreceptor (pigment). They also compare action spectra with absorption spectra of pigments; a close correspondence for a given pigment suggests that the pigment is the photoreceptor mediating the response. Action spectra reveal that red and blue light are the most important colors in regulating a plant's photomorphogenesis. These observations led researchers to two major classes of light receptors: **blue-light photoreceptors** and **phytochromes**, photoreceptors that absorb mostly red light.

Blue-Light Photoreceptors

Blue light initiates a variety of responses in plants, including phototropism, the light-induced opening of stomata (see Figure 36.12), and the light-induced slowing of hypocotyl elongation that occurs when a seedling breaks ground. The biochemical identity of the blue-light photoreceptor was so elusive that in the 1970s, plant physiologists began to call this receptor "cryptochrome" (from the Greek *kryptos*, hidden, and *chrom*, pigment). In the 1990s, molecular biologists analyzing *Arabidopsis* mutants found that plants use different types of pigments to detect blue light. *Cryptochromes*, molecular relatives of DNA repair enzymes, are involved in the blue-light-induced inhibition of stem elongation that occurs, for example, when a seedling first emerges from the soil. *Phototropin* is a protein kinase involved in mediating blue-light-mediated stomatal opening, chloroplast movements in response to light, and phototropic curvatures (Figure 39.15), such as those studied by the Darwins.

(a) This action spectrum illustrates that only light wavelengths below 500 nm (blue and violet light) induce curvature.

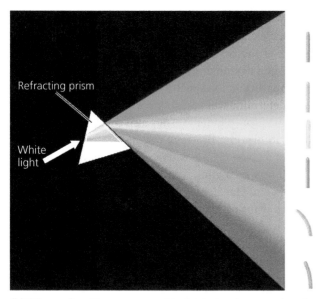

(b) When coleoptiles are exposed to light of various wavelengths as shown here, violet light induces slight curvature toward the light and blue light induces the most curvature. The other colors do not induce any curvature.

▲ **Figure 39.15 Action spectrum for blue-light-stimulated phototropism in maize coleoptiles.** Phototropic bending toward light is controlled by phototropin, a photoreceptor sensitive to blue and violet light, particularly blue light.

Phytochrome Photoreceptors

When introducing signal transduction in plants earlier in the chapter, we discussed the role of the plant pigments called phytochromes in the de-etiolation process. Phytochromes are another class of photoreceptors that regulate many plant responses to light, including seed germination and shade avoidance.

Phytochromes and Seed Germination

Studies of seed germination led to the discovery of phytochromes. Because of limited nutrient reserves, many types of seeds, especially small ones, germinate only when the light environment and other conditions are near optimal. Such seeds often remain dormant for years until light conditions change. For example, the death of a shading tree or the plowing of a field may create a favorable light environment for germination.

In the 1930s, scientists determined the action spectrum for light-induced germination of lettuce seeds. They exposed water-swollen seeds to a few minutes of single-colored light of various wavelengths and then stored the seeds in the dark. After two days, the researchers counted the number of seeds that had germinated under each light regimen. They found that red light of wavelength 660 nm increased the germination percentage of lettuce seeds maximally, whereas far-red light—that is, light of wavelengths near the upper edge of human visibility (730 nm)—*inhibited* germination compared with dark controls (Figure 39.16). What happens when the lettuce seeds are subjected to a flash of red light followed by a flash of far-red light or, conversely, to far-red light followed by red light? The *last* flash of light determines the seeds' response: The effects of red and far-red light are reversible.

The photoreceptors responsible for the opposing effects of red and far-red light are phytochromes. So far, researchers have identified five phytochromes in *Arabidopsis*, each with a slightly different polypeptide component. In most phytochromes, the light-absorbing portion is photoreversible, converting back and forth between two forms, depending on the color of light to which it is exposed. In its red-absorbing form (P_r), a phytochrome absorbs red (R) light maximally and is converted to its far-red-absorbing form (P_{fr}); in its P_{fr} form, it absorbs far-red (FR) light and is converted to its P_r form (Figure 39.17). This $P_r \leftrightarrow P_{fr}$ interconversion is a switching mechanism that controls various light-induced events in the life of the plant. P_{fr} is the form of phytochrome that triggers many of a plant's developmental responses to light. For example, P_r in lettuce seeds exposed to red light is converted to P_{fr}, stimulating the cellular responses that lead to germination. When red-illuminated seeds are then exposed to far-red light, the P_{fr} is converted back to P_r, inhibiting the germination response.

How does the order of red and far-red illumination affect seed germination?

Experiment Scientists at the U.S. Department of Agriculture briefly exposed batches of lettuce seeds to red light or far-red light to test the effects on germination. After the light exposure, the seeds were placed in the dark, and the results were compared with control seeds that were not exposed to light.

Results The bar below each photo indicates the sequence of red light exposure, far-red light exposure, and darkness. The germination rate increased greatly in groups of seeds that were last exposed to red light (left). Germination was inhibited in groups of seeds that were last exposed to far-red light (right).

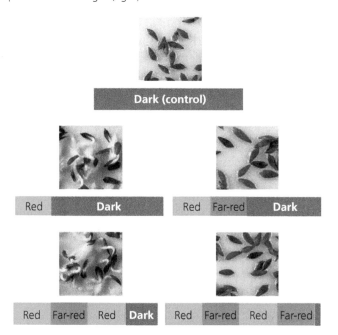

Conclusion Red light stimulates germination, and far-red light inhibits germination. The final light exposure is the determining factor. The effects of red and far-red light are reversible.

Source: H. Borthwick et al., A reversible photoreaction controlling seed germination, *Proceedings of the National Academy of Sciences, USA* 38:662–666 (1952).

WHAT IF? *Phytochrome responds faster to red light than to far-red light. If the seeds had been placed in white light instead of the dark after their red light and far-red light treatments, would the results have been different?*

How does phytochrome switching explain light-induced germination in nature? Plants synthesize phytochrome as P_r, and if seeds are kept in the dark, the pigment remains almost entirely in the P_r form (see Figure 39.17). Sunlight contains both red light and far-red light, but the conversion to P_{fr} is faster than the conversion to P_r. Therefore, the ratio of P_{fr} to P_r increases in the sunlight. When seeds are exposed to adequate sunlight, the production and accumulation of P_{fr} triggers their germination.

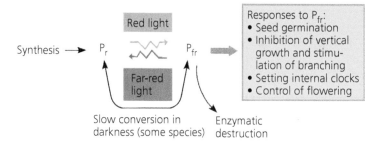

▲ **Figure 39.17 Phytochrome: a molecular switching mechanism.** The absorption of red light causes P_r to change to P_{fr}. Far-red light reverses this conversion. In most cases, it is the P_{fr} form of the pigment that switches on physiological and developmental responses in the plant.

Phytochromes and Shade Avoidance

The phytochrome system also provides the plant with information about the *quality* of light. Because sunlight includes both red and far-red radiation, during the day the $P_r \leftrightarrow P_{fr}$ interconversion reaches a dynamic equilibrium, with the ratio of the two phytochrome forms indicating the relative amounts of red and far-red light. This sensing mechanism enables plants to adapt to changes in light conditions. Consider, for example, the "shade avoidance" response of a tree that requires relatively high light intensity. If other trees in a forest shade this tree, the phytochrome ratio shifts in favor of P_r because the forest canopy screens out more red light than far-red light. This is because the chlorophyll pigments in the leaves of the canopy absorb red light and allow far-red light to pass. The shift in the ratio of red to far-red light induces the tree to allocate more of its resources to growing taller. In contrast, direct sunlight increases the proportion of P_{fr}, which stimulates branching and inhibits vertical growth.

In addition to helping plants detect light, phytochrome helps a plant keep track of the passage of days and seasons. To understand phytochrome's role in these timekeeping processes, we must first examine the nature of the plant's internal clock.

Biological Clocks and Circadian Rhythms

Many plant processes, such as transpiration and the synthesis of certain enzymes, undergo a daily oscillation. Some of these cyclic variations are responses to the changes in light levels and temperature that accompany the 24-hour cycle of day and night. We can control these external factors by growing plants in growth chambers under rigidly maintained conditions of light and temperature. But even under artificially constant conditions, many physiological processes in plants, such as the opening and closing of stomata and the production of photosynthetic enzymes, continue to oscillate with a frequency of about 24 hours. For example, many legumes lower their leaves in the evening and raise

Noon   10:00 PM

▲ Figure 39.18 **Sleep movements of a bean plant (*Phaseolus vulgaris*).** The movements are caused by reversible changes in the turgor pressure of cells on opposing sides of the pulvini, motor organs of the leaf.

them in the morning (**Figure 39.18**). A bean plant continues these "sleep movements" even if kept in constant light or constant darkness; the leaves are not simply responding to sunrise and sunset. Such cycles, with a frequency of about 24 hours and not directly controlled by any known environmental variable, are called **circadian rhythms** (from the Latin *circa*, approximately, and *dies*, day).

Recent research supports the idea that the molecular "gears" of the circadian clock really are internal and not a daily response to some subtle but pervasive environmental cycle, such as geomagnetism or cosmic radiation. Organisms, including plants and humans, continue their rhythms even after being placed in deep mine shafts or when orbited in satellites, conditions that alter these subtle geophysical periodicities. However, daily signals from the environment can entrain (set) the circadian clock to a period of precisely 24 hours.

If an organism is kept in a constant environment, its circadian rhythms deviate from a 24-hour period (a period is the duration of one cycle). These free-running periods, as they are called, vary from about 21 to 27 hours, depending on the particular rhythmic response. The sleep movements of bean plants, for instance, have a period of 26 hours when the plants are kept in the free-running condition of constant darkness. Deviation of the free-running period from exactly 24 hours does not mean that biological clocks drift erratically. Free-running clocks are still keeping perfect time, but they are not synchronized with the outside world. To understand the mechanisms underlying circadian rhythms, we must distinguish between the clock and the rhythmic processes it controls. For example, the leaves of the bean plant in Figure 39.18 are the clock's "hands" but are not the essence of the clock itself. If bean leaves are restrained for several hours and then released, they will reestablish the position appropriate for the time of day. We can interfere with a biological rhythm, but the underlying clockwork continues to tick.

At the heart of the molecular mechanisms underlying circadian rhythms are oscillations in the transcription of certain genes. Mathematical models propose that the 24-hour period arises from negative-feedback loops involving the transcription of a few central "clock genes." Some clock genes may encode transcription factors that inhibit, after a time delay, the transcription of the gene that encodes the transcription factor itself. Such negative-feedback loops, together with a time delay, are enough to produce oscillations.

Researchers have recently used a novel technique to identify clock mutants of *Arabidopsis*. One prominent circadian rhythm in plants is the daily production of certain photosynthesis-related proteins. Molecular biologists traced the source of this rhythm to the promoter that initiates the transcription of the genes for these photosynthesis proteins. To identify clock mutants, scientists spliced the gene for an enzyme responsible for the bioluminescence of fireflies, called luciferase, to the promoter. When the biological clock turned on the promoter in the *Arabidopsis* genome, it also turned on the production of luciferase. The plants began to glow with a circadian periodicity. Clock mutants were then isolated by selecting specimens that glowed for a longer or shorter time than normal. The genes altered in some of these mutants affect proteins that normally bind photoreceptors. Perhaps these particular mutations disrupt a light-dependent mechanism that sets the biological clock.

The Effect of Light on the Biological Clock

As we have discussed, the free-running period of the circadian rhythm of bean leaf movements is 26 hours. Consider a bean plant placed at dawn in a dark cabinet for 72 hours: Its leaves would not rise again until 2 hours after natural dawn on the second day, 4 hours after natural dawn on the third day, and so on. Shut off from environmental cues, the plant becomes desynchronized. Desynchronization happens to humans when we fly across several time zones; when we reach our destination, the clocks on the wall are not synchronized with our internal clocks. Most organisms are probably prone to jet lag.

The factor that entrains the biological clock to precisely 24 hours every day is light. Both phytochromes and blue-light photoreceptors can entrain circadian rhythms in plants, but our understanding of how phytochromes do this is more complete. The mechanism involves turning cellular responses on and off by means of the $P_r \leftrightarrow P_{fr}$ switch.

Consider again the photoreversible system in Figure 39.17. In darkness, the phytochrome ratio shifts gradually in favor of the P_r form, partly as a result of turnover in the overall phytochrome pool. The pigment is synthesized in the P_r form, and enzymes destroy more P_{fr} than

P_r. In some plant species, P_{fr} present at sundown slowly converts to P_r. In darkness, there is no means for the P_r to be reconverted to P_{fr}, but upon illumination, the P_{fr} level suddenly increases again as P_r is rapidly converted. This increase in P_{fr} each day at dawn resets the biological clock: Bean leaves reach their most extreme night position 16 hours after dawn.

In nature, interactions between phytochrome and the biological clock enable plants to measure the passage of night and day. The relative lengths of night and day, however, change over the course of the year (except at the equator). Plants use this change to adjust activities in synchrony with the seasons.

Photoperiodism and Responses to Seasons

Imagine the consequences if a plant produced flowers when pollinators were not present or if a deciduous tree produced leaves in the middle of winter. Seasonal events are of critical importance in the life cycles of most plants. Seed germination, flowering, and the onset and breaking of bud dormancy are all stages that usually occur at specific times of the year. The environmental stimulus that plants use most often to detect the time of year is the photoperiod, the interval in a 24-hour period during which an organism is exposed to light. A physiological response to photoperiod, such as flowering, is called **photoperiodism**.

Photoperiodism and Control of Flowering

An early clue to how plants detect seasons came from a mutant variety of tobacco, Maryland Mammoth, that grew tall but failed to flower during summer. It finally bloomed in a greenhouse in December. After trying to induce earlier flowering by varying temperature, moisture, and mineral nutrition, researchers learned that the shortening days of winter stimulated this variety to flower. Experiments revealed that flowering occurred only if the photoperiod was 14 hours or shorter. This variety did not flower during summer because at Maryland's latitude the photoperiods were too long.

The researchers called Maryland Mammoth a **short-day plant** because it apparently required a light period *shorter* than a critical length to flower. Chrysanthemums, poinsettias, and some soybean varieties are also short-day plants, which generally flower in late summer, fall, or winter. Another group of plants flower only when the light period is *longer* than a certain number of hours. These **long-day plants** generally flower in late spring or early summer. Spinach, for example, flowers when days are 14 hours or longer. Radishes, lettuce, irises, and many cereal varieties are also long-day plants. **Day-neutral plants**, such as tomatoes, rice, and dandelions, are unaffected by photoperiod and flower when they reach a certain stage of maturity, regardless of photoperiod.

Critical Night Length In the 1940s, researchers learned that flowering and other responses to photoperiod are actually controlled by night length, not day length. Many of these scientists worked with cocklebur (*Xanthium strumarium*), a short-day plant that flowers only when days are 16 hours or shorter (and nights are at least 8 hours long). These researchers found that if the light portion of the photoperiod is broken by a brief exposure to darkness, flowering proceeds. However, if the dark part of the photoperiod is interrupted by even a few minutes of dim light, cocklebur will not flower, and this turned out to be true for other short-day plants as well (**Figure 39.19a**). Cocklebur is unresponsive to day length, but it requires at least 8 hours of continuous darkness to flower. Short-day plants are really long-night plants, but the older term is embedded firmly in the lexicon of plant physiology. Similarly, long-day plants are actually short-night plants. A long-day plant grown under long-night conditions that would not normally induce flowering will flower if the period of continuous darkness is interrupted by a few minutes of light (**Figure 39.19b**). Notice that we distinguish long-day from short-day plants *not* by an absolute night length but by whether the critical night length sets a maximum (long-day plants) or minimum (short-day plants) number of hours of darkness required for flowering. In both cases, the actual number of hours in the critical night length is specific to each species of plant.

Red light is the most effective color in interrupting the nighttime portion of the photoperiod. Action spectra and

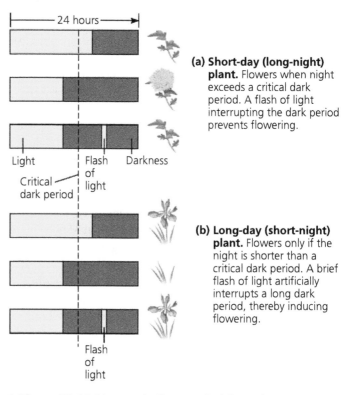

(a) **Short-day (long-night) plant.** Flowers when night exceeds a critical dark period. A flash of light interrupting the dark period prevents flowering.

(b) **Long-day (short-night) plant.** Flowers only if the night is shorter than a critical dark period. A brief flash of light artificially interrupts a long dark period, thereby inducing flowering.

▲ Figure 39.19 **Photoperiodic control of flowering.**

▲ **Figure 39.20 Reversible effects of red and far-red light on photoperiodic response.** A flash of red (R) light shortens the dark period. A subsequent flash of far-red (FR) light cancels the red flash's effect.

? *How would a single flash of full-spectrum light affect each plant?*

photoreversibility experiments show that phytochrome is the pigment that detects the red light **(Figure 39.20)**. For example, if a flash of red (R) light during the dark period is followed by a flash of far-red (FR) light, then the plant detects no interruption of night length. As in the case of phytochrome-mediated seed germination, red/far-red photoreversibility occurs.

Plants detect night length very precisely; some short-day plants will not flower if night is even 1 minute shorter than the critical length. Some plant species always flower on the same day each year. It appears that plants use their biological clock, entrained by night length with the help of phytochrome, to tell the season of the year. The floriculture (flower-growing) industry applies this knowledge to produce flowers out of season. Chrysanthemums, for instance, are short-day plants that normally bloom in fall, but their blooming can be stalled until Mother's Day in May by punctuating each long night with a flash of light, thus turning one long night into two short nights.

Some plants bloom after a single exposure to the photoperiod required for flowering. Other species need several successive days of the appropriate photoperiod. Still others respond to a photoperiod only if they have been previously exposed to some other environmental stimulus, such as a period of cold. Winter wheat, for example, will not flower unless it has been exposed to several weeks of temperatures below 10°C. The use of pretreatment with cold to

induce flowering is called **vernalization** (from the Latin for "spring"). Several weeks after winter wheat is vernalized, a photoperiod with long days (short nights) induces flowering.

A Flowering Hormone?

Although flowers form from apical or axillary bud meristems, it is leaves that detect changes in photoperiod and produce signaling molecules that cue buds to develop as flowers. In many short-day and long-day plants, exposing just one leaf to the appropriate photoperiod is enough to induce flowering. Indeed, as long as one leaf is left on the plant, photoperiod is detected and floral buds are induced. If all leaves are removed, the plant is insensitive to photoperiod.

Classic experiments revealed that the floral stimulus could move across a graft from an induced plant to a noninduced plant and trigger flowering in the latter. Moreover, the flowering stimulus appears to be the same for short-day and long-day plants, despite the different photoperiodic conditions required for leaves to send this signal **(Figure 39.21)**. The hypothetical signaling molecule for flowering, called **florigen**, remained unidentified for over 70 years as scientists focused on small hormone-like molecules. However, large macromolecules, such as mRNA and proteins, can move by the symplastic route via plasmodesmata and regulate plant development. It now appears that florigen is a protein. A gene called *FLOWERING LOCUS T* (*FT*) is activated in leaf cells during conditions favoring flowering, and the FT protein travels through the symplasm to the shoot apical

▲ **Figure 39.21 Experimental evidence for a flowering hormone.** If grown individually under short-day conditions, a short-day plant will flower and a long-day plant will not. However, both will flower if grafted together and exposed to short days. This result indicates that a flower-inducing substance (florigen) is transmitted across grafts and induces flowering in both short-day and long-day plants.

WHAT IF? *If flowering were inhibited in both parts of the grafted plants, what would you conclude?*

meristem, initiating the transition of a bud's meristem from a vegetative to a flowering state.

CONCEPT CHECK 39.3

1. If an enzyme in field-grown soybean leaves is most active at noon and least active at midnight, is its activity under circadian regulation?
2. **WHAT IF?** If a plant flowers in a controlled chamber with a daily cycle of 10 hours of light and 14 hours of darkness, is it a short-day plant? Explain.
3. **MAKE CONNECTIONS** Plants detect the quality of their light environment by using blue-light photoreceptors and red-light-absorbing phytochromes. After reviewing Figure 10.10, suggest a reason why plants are so sensitive to these colors of light.

For suggested answers, see Appendix A.

CONCEPT 39.4

Plants respond to a wide variety of stimuli other than light

Plants are immobile, but mechanisms have evolved by natural selection that enable them to adjust to a wide range of environmental circumstances by developmental or physiological means. Light is so important in the life of a plant that we devoted the entire previous section to a plant's reception of and response to this one environmental factor. In this section, we examine responses to some of the other environmental stimuli that a plant commonly encounters.

Gravity

Because plants are photoautotrophs, it is not surprising that mechanisms for growing toward light have evolved. But what environmental cue does the shoot of a young seedling use to grow upward when it is completely underground and there is no light for it to detect? Similarly, what environmental factor prompts the young root to grow downward? The answer to both questions is gravity.

Place a plant on its side, and it adjusts its growth so that the shoot bends upward and the root curves downward. In their responses to gravity, or **gravitropism**, roots display positive gravitropism (Figure 39.22a) and shoots exhibit negative gravitropism. Gravitropism occurs as soon as a seed germinates, ensuring that the root grows into the soil and the shoot grows toward sunlight, regardless of how the seed is oriented when it lands.

Plants may detect gravity by the settling of **statoliths**, dense cytoplasmic components that settle under the influence of gravity to the lower portions of the cell. The statoliths of vascular plants are specialized plastids containing dense starch grains (Figure 39.22b). In roots, statoliths are

Statoliths
20 μm

(a) Over the course of hours, a horizontally oriented primary root of maize bends gravitropically until its growing tip becomes vertically oriented (LMs).

(b) Within minutes after the root is placed horizontally, plastids called statoliths begin settling to the lowest sides of root cap cells. This settling may be the gravity-sensing mechanism that leads to redistribution of auxin and differing rates of elongation by cells on opposite sides of the root (LMs).

▲ Figure 39.22 **Positive gravitropism in roots: the statolith hypothesis.**

located in certain cells of the root cap. According to one hypothesis, the aggregation of statoliths at the low points of these cells triggers a redistribution of calcium, which causes lateral transport of auxin within the root. The calcium and auxin accumulate on the lower side of the root's zone of elongation. At high concentration, auxin inhibits cell elongation, an effect that slows growth on the root's lower side. The more rapid elongation of cells on the upper side causes the root to grow straight downward.

Falling statoliths, however, may not be necessary for gravitropism. For example, there are mutants of *Arabidopsis* and tobacco that lack statoliths but are still capable of gravitropism, though the response is slower than in wild-type plants. It could be that the entire cell helps the root sense gravity by mechanically pulling on proteins that tether the protoplast to the cell wall, stretching the proteins on the "up" side and compressing the proteins on the "down" side of the root cells. Dense organelles, in addition to starch granules, may also contribute by distorting the cytoskeleton as they are pulled by gravity. Statoliths, because of their density, may enhance gravitational sensing by a mechanism that simply works more slowly in their absence.

Mechanical Stimuli

Trees in windy environments usually have shorter, stockier trunks than a tree of the same species growing in more

▲ **Figure 39.23 Thigmorphogenesis in *Arabidopsis*.** The shorter plant on the left was rubbed twice a day. The untouched plant (right) grew much taller.

sheltered locations. The advantage of this stunted morphology is that it enables the plant to hold its ground against strong gusts of wind. The term **thigmomorphogenesis** (from the Greek *thigma*, touch) refers to the changes in form that result from mechanical perturbation. Plants are very sensitive to mechanical stress: Even the act of measuring the length of a leaf with a ruler alters its subsequent growth. Rubbing the stems of a young plant a couple of times daily results in plants that are shorter than controls **(Figure 39.23)**.

Some plant species have become, over the course of their evolution, "touch specialists." Acute responsiveness to mechanical stimuli is an integral part of these plants' "life strategies." Most vines and other climbing plants have tendrils that coil rapidly around supports (see Figure 35.7). These grasping organs usually grow straight until they touch something; the contact stimulates a coiling response caused by differential growth of cells on opposite sides of the tendril. This directional growth in response to touch is called **thigmotropism**, and it allows the vine to take advantage of whatever mechanical supports it comes across as it climbs upward toward a forest canopy.

Other examples of touch specialists are plants that undergo rapid leaf movements in response to mechanical stimulation. For example, when the compound leaf of the sensitive plant *Mimosa pudica* is touched, it collapses and its leaflets fold together **(Figure 39.24)**. This response, which takes only a second or

two, results from a rapid loss of turgor in cells within pulvini, specialized motor organs located at the joints of the leaf. The motor cells suddenly become flaccid after stimulation because they lose potassium ions, causing water to leave the cells by osmosis. It takes about 10 minutes for the cells to regain their turgor and restore the "unstimulated" form of the leaf. The function of the sensitive plant's behavior invites speculation. Perhaps the plant appears less leafy and appetizing to herbivores by folding its leaves and reducing its surface area when jostled.

A remarkable feature of rapid leaf movements is the mode of transmission of the stimulus through the plant. If one leaflet on a sensitive plant is touched, first that leaflet responds, then the adjacent leaflet responds, and so on, until all the leaflet pairs have folded together. From the point of stimulation, the signal that produces this response travels at a speed of about 1 cm/sec. An electrical impulse traveling at the same rate can be detected when electrodes are attached to the leaf. These impulses, called **action potentials**, resemble nerve impulses in animals, though the action potentials of plants are thousands of times slower. Action potentials have been discovered in many species of algae and plants and may be used as a form of internal communication. For example, in the Venus flytrap (*Dionaea muscipula*), action potentials are transmitted from sensory hairs in the trap to the cells that respond by closing the trap (see Figure 37.14). In the case of *Mimosa pudica*, more violent stimuli, such as touching a leaf with a hot needle, causes *all* the leaves and leaflets on a plant to droop, but this whole-plant response involves the spread of signaling molecules released from the injured area to other parts of the shoot.

Environmental Stresses

Certain factors in the environment may change severely enough to have a potentially adverse effect on a plant's survival, growth, and reproduction. Environmental stresses, such as flooding, drought, or extreme temperatures, can

(a) Unstimulated state (leaflets spread apart)   **(b) Stimulated state (leaflets folded)**

▲ **Figure 39.24 Rapid turgor movements by the sensitive plant (*Mimosa pudica*).**

have a devastating impact on crop yields in agriculture. In natural ecosystems, plants that cannot tolerate an environmental stress will either succumb or be outcompeted by other plants. Thus, environmental stresses are an important factor in determining the geographic ranges of plants. Here we will consider some of the more common **abiotic** (nonliving) stresses that plants encounter. In the last section of this chapter, we will examine the defensive responses of plants to common **biotic** (living) stresses, such as herbivores and pathogens.

(a) Control root (aerated)　　　(b) Experimental root (nonaerated)

▲ **Figure 39.25 A developmental response of maize roots to flooding and oxygen deprivation. (a)** A cross section of a control root grown in an aerated hydroponic medium. **(b)** A root grown in a nonaerated hydroponic medium. Ethylene-stimulated apoptosis (programmed cell death) creates the air tubes (SEMs).

Drought

On a sunny, dry day, a plant may wilt because its water loss by transpiration exceeds water absorption from the soil. Prolonged drought, of course, will kill a plant, but plants have control systems that enable them to cope with less extreme water deficits.

Many of a plant's responses to water deficit help the plant conserve water by reducing the rate of transpiration. Water deficit in a leaf causes stomata to close, thereby slowing transpiration dramatically (see Figure 36.13). Water deficit stimulates increased synthesis and release of abscisic acid in the leaves; this hormone helps keep stomata closed by acting on guard cell membranes. Leaves respond to water deficit in several other ways. For example, when the leaves of grasses wilt, they roll into a tubelike shape that reduces transpiration by exposing less leaf surface to dry air and wind. Other plants, such as ocotillo (see Figure 36.14), shed their leaves in response to seasonal drought. Although these leaf responses conserve water, they also reduce photosynthesis, which is one reason why a drought diminishes crop yield. Plants can even take advantage of early warnings in the form of chemical signals from wilting neighbors and prime themselves to respond more readily and intensely to impending drought stress (see the Scientific Skills Exercise).

Flooding

Too much water is also a problem for a plant. An overwatered houseplant may suffocate because the soil lacks the air spaces that provide oxygen for cellular respiration in the roots. Some plants are structurally adapted to very wet habitats. For example, the submerged roots of mangroves, which inhabit coastal marshes, are continuous with aerial roots exposed to oxygen (see Figure 35.4). But how do less specialized plants cope with oxygen deprivation in waterlogged soils? Oxygen deprivation stimulates the production of ethylene, which causes some cells in the root cortex to die. The destruction of these cells creates air tubes that function as "snorkels," providing oxygen to the submerged roots (Figure 39.25).

Salt Stress

An excess of sodium chloride or other salts in the soil threatens plants for two reasons. First, by lowering the water potential of the soil solution, salt can cause a water deficit in plants even though the soil has plenty of water. As the water potential of the soil solution becomes more negative, the water potential gradient from soil to roots is lowered, thereby reducing water uptake (see Chapter 36). Another problem with saline soil is that sodium and certain other ions are toxic to plants when their concentrations are too high. Many plants can respond to moderate soil salinity by producing solutes that are well tolerated at high concentrations: These mostly organic compounds keep the water potential of cells more negative than that of the soil solution without admitting toxic quantities of salt. However, most plants cannot survive salt stress for long. The exceptions are halophytes, salt-tolerant plants with adaptations such as salt glands that pump salts out across the leaf epidermis.

Heat Stress

Excessive heat may harm and even kill a plant by denaturing its enzymes. Transpiration helps cool leaves by evaporative cooling. On a warm day, for example, the temperature of a leaf may be 3–10°C below the ambient air temperature. Hot, dry weather also tends to dehydrate many plants; the closing of stomata in response to this stress conserves water but

Interpreting Experimental Results from a Bar Graph

Do Drought-Stressed Plants Communicate Their Condition to Their Neighbors? Researchers wanted to learn if plants can communicate drought-induced stress to neighboring plants and, if so, whether they use above-ground or below-ground signals. In this exercise, you will interpret a bar graph concerning widths of stomatal openings to investigate whether drought-induced stress can be communicated from plant to plant.

How the Experiment Was Done Eleven potted pea plants (*Pisum sativum*) were placed equidistantly in a row. The root systems of plants 6–11 were connected to those of their immediate neighbors by tubes, which allowed chemicals to move from the roots of one plant to the roots of the next plant without moving through the soil. The root systems of plants 1–6 were not connected. Osmotic shock was inflicted on plant 6 using a highly concentrated solution of mannitol, a natural sugar commonly used to mimic drought stress in vascular plants.

Fifteen minutes following the osmotic shock to plant 6, researchers measured the width of stomatal openings in leaves from all the plants. A control experiment was also done in which water was added to plant 6 instead of mannitol.

Data from the Experiment

▶ Pea plant (*Pisum sativum*)

Interpret the Data

1. How do the widths of the stomatal openings of plants 6–8 and plants 9 and 10 compare with those of the other plants in the experiment? What does this indicate about the state of plants 6–8 and 9 and 10? (For information about reading graphs, see the Scientific Skills Review in Appendix F and in the Study Area at www.masteringbiology.com.)

2. Do the data support the idea that plants can communicate their drought-stressed condition to their neighbors? If so, do the data indicate that the communication is via the shoot system or the root system? Make specific reference to the data in answering both questions.

3. Why was it necessary to make sure that chemicals could not move through the soil from one plant to the next?

4. When the experiment was run for 1 hour rather than 15 minutes, the results were about the same except that the stomatal openings of plants 9–11 were comparable to those of plants 6–8. Suggest a reason why.

5. Why was water added to plant 6 instead of mannitol in the control experiment? What do the results of the control experiment indicate?

(MB) A version of this Scientific Skills Exercise can be assigned in MasteringBiology.

Data from O. Falik et al., Rumor has it . . . : Relay communication of stress cues in plants, *PLoS ONE* 6(11):e23625 (2011).

then sacrifices evaporative cooling. This dilemma is one reason why very hot, dry days take a toll on most plants.

Most plants have a backup response that enables them to survive heat stress. Above a certain temperature—about 40°C for most plants in temperate regions—plant cells begin synthesizing **heat-shock proteins**, which help protect other proteins from heat stress. This response also occurs in heat-stressed animals and microorganisms. Some heat-shock proteins are chaperone proteins (chaperonins), which function in unstressed cells as temporary scaffolds that help other proteins fold into their functional shapes (see Chapter 5). In their roles as heat-shock proteins, perhaps these molecules bind to other proteins and help prevent their denaturation.

Cold Stress

One problem plants face when the temperature of the environment falls is a change in the fluidity of cell membranes. When a membrane cools below a critical point, membranes lose their fluidity as the lipids become locked into crystalline structures. This alters solute transport across the membrane and also adversely affects the functions of membrane proteins. Plants respond to cold stress by altering the lipid composition of their membranes. For example, membrane lipids increase in their proportion of unsaturated fatty acids, which have shapes that help keep membranes more fluid at low temperatures. Such membrane modification requires from several hours to days, which is one reason why unseasonably cold temperatures are generally more stressful to plants than the more gradual seasonal drop in air temperature.

Freezing is another type of cold stress. At subfreezing temperatures, ice forms in the cell walls and intercellular spaces of most plants. The cytosol generally does not freeze at the cooling rates encountered in nature because it contains more solutes than the very dilute solution found in the cell wall, and solutes lower the freezing point of a solution. The reduction in liquid water in the cell wall caused by ice formation lowers the extracellular water potential, causing water to leave the cytoplasm. The resulting increase in the concentration of ions in the cytoplasm is harmful and can lead to cell death. Whether the cell survives depends largely on how well it resists dehydration. In regions with cold winters, native plants are adapted to cope with freezing stress. For example, before the onset of winter, the cells of many frost-tolerant species increase cytoplasmic levels of specific solutes, such as sugars, that are well tolerated at high concentrations and that help reduce the loss of water from the cell during extracellular freezing. The unsaturation of membrane lipids also increases, thereby maintaining proper levels of membrane fluidity.

EVOLUTION Many organisms, including certain vertebrates, fungi, bacteria, and many species of plants, have special proteins that hinder ice crystals from growing, helping the organism escape freezing damage. First described in Arctic fish in the 1950s, these *antifreeze proteins* permit survival at temperatures below 0°C. Antifreeze proteins bind to small ice crystals and inhibit their growth or, in the case of plants, prevent the crystallization of ice. The five major classes of antifreeze proteins differ markedly in their amino acid sequences but have a similar three-dimensional structure, suggesting convergent evolution. Surprisingly, antifreeze proteins from winter rye are homologous to antifungal defense proteins, but they are produced in response to cold temperatures and shorter days, not fungal pathogens. Progress is being made in increasing the freezing tolerance of crop plants by genetically engineering antifreeze protein genes into their genomes.

CONCEPT CHECK 39.4

1. Thermal images are photographs of the heat emitted by an object. Researchers have used thermal imaging of plants to isolate mutants that overproduce abscisic acid. Suggest a reason why these mutants are warmer than wild-type plants under conditions that are normally nonstressful.

2. A greenhouse worker finds that potted chrysanthemums nearest to the aisles are often shorter than those in the middle of the bench. Explain this "edge effect," a common problem in horticulture.

3. **WHAT IF?** If you removed the root cap from a root, would the root still respond to gravity? Explain.

For suggested answers, see Appendix A.

CONCEPT 39.5

Plants respond to attacks by pathogens and herbivores

Through natural selection, plants have evolved many types of interactions with other species in their communities. Some interspecific interactions are mutually beneficial, such as the associations of plants with mycorrhizal fungi (see Figure 37.13) or with pollinators (see Figure 38.5). Many plant interactions with other organisms, however, do not benefit the plant. As primary producers, plants are at the base of most food webs and are subject to attack by a wide range of plant-eating (herbivorous) animals. A plant is also subject to infection by diverse viruses, bacteria, and fungi that can damage tissues or even kill the plant. Plants counter these threats with defense systems that deter animals and prevent infection or combat pathogens that infect the plant.

Defenses Against Pathogens

A plant's first line of defense against infection is the physical barrier presented by the epidermis and periderm of the plant body (see Figure 35.19). This line of defense, however, is not impenetrable. The mechanical wounding of leaves by herbivores, for example, opens up portals for invasion by pathogens. Even when plant tissues are intact, viruses, bacteria, and the spores and hyphae of fungi can still enter the plant through natural openings in the epidermis, such as stomata. Once the physical lines of defense are breached, a plant's next lines of defense are two types of immune responses.

Immune Responses of Plants

When a pathogen succeeds in invading a host plant, the plant mounts the first of two lines of immune defense, which ultimately results in a chemical attack that isolates the pathogen and prevents its spread from the site of infection. This first line of immune defense, called *PAMP-triggered immunity*, depends on the plant's ability to recognize **pathogen-associated molecular patterns** (**PAMPs**; formerly called *elicitors*), molecular sequences that are specific to certain pathogens. For example, bacterial *flagellin*, a major protein found in bacterial flagella, is a PAMP. Many soil bacteria, including some pathogenic varieties, get splashed onto the shoots of plants by raindrops. If these bacteria penetrate the plant, a specific amino-acid sequence within flagellin is perceived by a Toll-like receptor, a type of receptor that is also found in invertebrates and vertebrates and that plays a key role in the innate immune system (see Concept 43.1). The innate immune system is an evolutionarily old defense strategy and is the dominant immune system in plants, fungi, insects, and primitive multicellular organisms. Unlike vertebrates, plants do not have an adaptive immune system: Plants neither generate antibody or T cell responses nor possess mobile cells that detect and attack pathogens.

PAMP recognition in plants leads to a chain of signaling events that lead ultimately to the local production of broad spectrum, antimicrobial chemicals called *phytoalexins,* which are compounds having fungicidal and bactericidal properties. The plant cell wall is also toughened to hinder further progress of the pathogen during PAMP-triggered immunity. Similar but even stronger defenses are initiated by a second plant immune system, as discussed in the next section.

EVOLUTION Over the course of evolution, plants and pathogens have engaged in an arms race. PAMP-triggered immunity can be overcome by the evolution of pathogens that can evade detection by the plant. The key to these pathogens' success is their ability to deliver **effectors**, pathogen-encoded proteins that cripple the host's innate immune system, directly into the plant cell. For example, several bacterial pathogens deliver effectors inside the plant cell that actively block the perception of flagellin. Thus, these effectors suppress PAMP-mediated immunity and allow the pathogen to redirect the host's metabolism to the pathogen's advantage.

The suppression of PAMP-triggered immunity by pathogen effectors led to the evolution of a second level of the plant immune defense system. Because there are thousands of effectors, this branch of the plant immune system is typically made up of hundreds of disease resistance (R) genes in a plant's genome. Each R protein can be activated by its specific effector, resulting in a suite of strong defense responses called *effector-triggered immunity*. This second type of immune defense involves signal transduction pathways that lead to the activation of an arsenal of defense responses, including a local defense called the *hypersensitive response* and a general defense called *systemic acquired resistance*. Local

and systemic responses to pathogens require extensive genetic reprogramming and commitment of cellular resources. Therefore, a plant activates these defenses only after detecting an invading pathogen.

The Hypersensitive Response

The **hypersensitive response** refers to the local cell and tissue death that occurs at and near the infection site. In some cases, the hypersensitive response restricts the spread of a pathogen, but in other cases it appears to be merely a consequence of the overall defense response. As indicated in Figure 39.26, the hypersensitive response is initiated as part of effector-triggered immunity. The hypersensitive response is part of a complex defense response that involves transcriptional activation of over 10% of the plant's genes that can encode enzymes that hydrolyze components in the cell walls of pathogens. Effector-triggered immunity also stimulates the formation of lignin and the cross-linking of molecules within the plant cell wall, responses that hinder the spread of the pathogen to other parts of the plant. We can see the result of a hypersensitive response as lesions on a leaf, as shown at the upper right in the figure. As "sick" as such a leaf appears, it will still survive, and its defensive response will help protect the rest of the plant.

Systemic Acquired Resistance

The hypersensitive response is localized and specific. However, as noted previously, pathogen invasions can also produce signaling molecules that "sound the alarm" of infection to the whole plant. The resulting **systemic acquired resistance** arises from the plant-wide expression of defense genes. It is nonspecific, providing protection against a diversity of pathogens that can last for days. The search for a signaling molecule that moves from the infection site to elicit systemic acquired resistance led to the identification of *methylsalicylic acid* as the most likely candidate. Methylsalicylic acid is produced around the infection site and carried by the phloem throughout the plant, where it is converted to **salicylic acid** in areas remote from the sites of infection. Salicylic acid activates a signal transduction pathway that poises the defense system to respond rapidly to another infection (see Figure 39.27).

Plant disease epidemics, such as the potato blight (see Concept 28.6) that caused the Irish potato famine of the 1840s, can lead to incalculable human misery. Other diseases, such as chestnut blight (see Concept 31.5) and sudden oak death (see Concept 54.5), can dramatically alter community structures. Plant epidemics are often the result of infected plants or timber being inadvertently transported around the world. As global commerce increases, such epidemics will become increasingly more common. To prepare for such outbreaks, plant biologists are stockpiling the seeds

❹ Before they die, infected cells release the signaling molecule methylsalicylic acid.

❸ In a hypersensitive response, plant cells produce antimicrobial molecules, seal off infected areas by modifying their walls, and then destroy themselves. This localized response produces lesions and protects other parts of an infected leaf.

❷ The identification in step ① triggers a signal transduction pathway.

❶ Effector-mediated immunity is based on the binding of pathogen effector molecules to specific plant resistance (R) proteins.

❹ Signal

❸ Hypersensitive response

❷ Signal transduction pathway

① R protein

Pathogen

Effector protein

Hypersensitive response

Infected tobacco leaf with lesions

❺ The signaling molecule is distributed to the rest of the plant.

❻ In cells remote from the infection site, methylsalicylic acid is converted to salicylic acid, which initiates a signal transduction pathway.

❼ Systemic acquired resistance is activated: the production of molecules that help protect the cell against a diversity of pathogens for several days.

❺

❻ Signal transduction pathway

❼ Acquired resistance

Systemic acquired resistance

▲ **Figure 39.26 Defense responses against pathogens.** Plants can often prevent the systemic spread of infection by instigating a hypersensitive response. This response helps isolate the pathogen by producing lesions that form "rings of death" around the sites of infection.

of wild relatives of crop plants in special storage facilities. Scientists hope that undomesticated relatives may have genes that will be able to curb the next plant epidemic.

Defenses Against Herbivores

Herbivory, animals eating plants, is a stress that plants face in any ecosystem. The mechanical damage caused by herbivores reduces the size of plants, hindering their ability to acquire resources. It can also restrict growth because many species divert some of their energy to defend against herbivores. Furthermore, it opens up portals for infection by viruses, bacteria, and fungi. Plants prevent excessive herbivory through methods that span all levels of biological organization (**Figure 39.27**, preceding the Chapter Review), including physical defenses, such as thorns and trichomes (see Figure 35.9), and chemical defenses, such as the production of distasteful or toxic compounds.

CONCEPT CHECK 39.5

1. What are some drawbacks of spraying fields with general-purpose insecticides?

2. Chewing insects mechanically damage plants and lessen the surface area of leaves for photosynthesis. In addition, these insects make plants more vulnerable to pathogen attack. Suggest a reason why.

3. Many fungal pathogens get their food by causing plant cells to become leaky, thereby releasing nutrients into the intercellular spaces. Would it benefit the fungus to kill the host plant in a way that results in all the nutrients leaking out?

4. **WHAT IF?** Suppose a scientist finds that a population of plants growing in a breezy location is more prone to herbivory by insects than a population of the same species growing in a sheltered area. Suggest a hypothesis to account for this observation.

For suggested answers, see Appendix A.

MAKE CONNECTIONS

Levels of Plant Defenses Against Herbivores

Herbivory, animals eating plants, is ubiquitous in nature. Plant defenses against herbivores are examples of how biological processes can be observed at multiple levels of biological organization: molecular, cellular, tissue, organ, organism, population, and community (*see Figure 1.3*).

Cellular-Level Defenses

Some plant cells are specialized for deterring herbivores. Trichomes on leaves and stems hinder the access of chewing insects. Laticifers and, more generally, the central vacuoles of plant cells may serve as storage depots for chemicals that deter herbivores. *Idioblasts* are specialized cells found in the leaves and stems of many species, including taro (*Colocasia esculenta*). Some idioblasts contain needle-shaped crystals of calcium oxalate called *raphides*. They penetrate the soft tissues of the tongue and palate, making it easier for an irritant produced by the plant, possibly a protease, to enter animal tissues and cause temporary swelling of the lips, mouth, and throat. The crystals act as a carrier for the irritant, enabling it to seep deeper into the herbivore's tissues. The irritant is destroyed by cooking.

Raphide crystals from taro plant

Molecular-Level Defenses

At the molecular level, plants produce chemical compounds that deter attackers. These compounds are typically terpenoids, phenolics, and alkaloids. Some terpenoids mimic insect hormones and cause insects to molt prematurely and die. Some examples of phenolics are tannins, which have an unpleasant taste and hinder the digestion of proteins. Their synthesis is often enhanced following attack. The opium poppy (*Papaver somniferum*) is the source of the narcotic alkaloids morphine, heroin, and codeine. These drugs accumulate in secretory cells called laticifers, which exude a milky-white latex (opium) when the plant is damaged.

Opium poppy fruit

Tissue-Level Defenses

Some leaves deter herbivores by being especially tough to chew as a result of extensive growth of thick, hardened sclerenchyma tissue. The bright red cells with thick cell walls seen in this cross section through the major vein of an olive leaf (*Olea europaea*) are tough sclerenchyma fibers.

Organ-Level Defenses

The shapes of plant organs may deter herbivores by causing pain or making the plant appear unappealing. Spines (modified leaves) and thorns (modified stems) provide mechanical defenses against herbivores. Bristles on the spines of some cacti have fearsome barbs that tear flesh during removal. The leaf of the snowflake plant (*Trevesia palmata*) looks as if it has been partially eaten, perhaps making it less attractive. Some plants mimic the presence of insect eggs on their leaves, dissuading insects from laying eggs there. For example, the leaf glands of some species of *Passiflora* (passion flowers) closely imitate the bright yellow eggs of *Heliconius* butterflies.

Bristles on cactus spines

Leaf of snowflake plant

Egg mimicry on leaf of passion flower plant

Organismal-Level Defenses

Mechanical damage by herbivores can greatly alter a plant's entire physiology, deterring further attack. For example, a species of wild tobacco called *Nicotiana attenuata* changes the timing of its flowering as a result of herbivory. It normally flowers at night, emitting the chemical benzyl acetone, which attracts hawk-moths as pollinators. Unfortunately for the plant, the moths often lay eggs on the leaves as they pollinate, and the larvae are herbivores. When the plants become too larvae-infested, they stop producing the chemical and instead open their flowers at dawn, when the moths are gone. They are then pollinated by hummingbirds. Research has shown that oral secretions from the munching larvae trigger the dramatic shift in the timing of flower opening.

Hummingbird pollinating wild tobacco plant

Population-Level Defenses

In some species, a coordinated behavior at the population level helps defend against herbivores. Some plants can communicate their distress from attack by releasing molecules that warn nearby plants of the same species. For example, lima bean (*Phaseolus lunatus*) plants infested with spider mites release a cocktail of chemicals that signal "news" of the attack to noninfested lima bean plants. In response, these neighbors instigate biochemical changes that make them less susceptible to attack. Another type of population-level defense is a phenomenon in some species called masting, in which a population synchronously produces a massive amount of seeds after a long interval. Regardless of environmental conditions, an internal clock signals each plant in the population that it is time to flower. Bamboo populations, for example, grow vegetatively for decades and suddenly flower en masse, set seed, and die. As much as 80,000 kg of bamboo seeds are released per hectare, much more than the local herbivores, mostly rodents, can eat. As a result, some seeds escape the herbivores' attention, germinate, and grow.

Flowering bamboo plants

Community-Level Defenses

Some plant species "recruit" predatory animals that help defend the plant against specific herbivores. Parasitoid wasps, for example, inject their eggs into caterpillars feeding on plants. The eggs hatch within the caterpillars, and the larvae eat through their organic containers from the inside out. The larvae then form cocoons on the surface of the host before emerging as adult wasps. The plant has an active role in this drama. A leaf damaged by caterpillars releases compounds that attract parasitoid wasps. The stimulus for this response is a combination of physical damage to the leaf caused by the munching caterpillar and a specific compound in the caterpillar's saliva.

Parasitoid wasp cocoons on caterpillar host

Adult wasp emerging from a cocoon

MAKE CONNECTIONS *As with plant adaptations against herbivores, other biological processes can involve multiple levels of biological organization (Figure 1.3). Discuss examples of specialized photosynthetic adaptations that involve modifications at the molecular (Concept 10.4), tissue (Concept 36.4), and organismal (Concept 36.1) levels.*

SUMMARY OF KEY CONCEPTS

CONCEPT 39.1

Signal transduction pathways link signal reception to response (pp. 837–839)

? What are two common ways by which signal transduction pathways enhance the activity of specific enzymes?

CONCEPT 39.2

Plant hormones help coordinate growth, development, and responses to stimuli (pp. 840–849)

* Hormones control plant growth and development by affecting the division, elongation, and differentiation of cells. Some also mediate the responses of plants to environmental stimuli.

Plant Hormone	Major Responses
Auxin	Stimulates cell elongation; regulates branching and organ bending
Cytokinins	Stimulate plant cell division; promote later bud growth; slow organ death
Gibberellins	Promote stem elongation; help seeds break dormancy and use stored reserves
Abscisic acid	Promotes stomatal closure in response to drought; promotes seed dormancy
Ethylene	Mediates fruit ripening and the triple response
Brassinosteroids	Chemically similar to the sex hormones of animals; induce cell elongation and division
Jasmonates	Mediate plant defenses against insect herbivores; regulate a wide range of physiological processes
Strigolactones	Regulate apical dominance, seed germination, and mycorrhizal associations

? Is there any truth to the old adage, "One bad apple spoils the whole bunch?" Explain.

CONCEPT 39.3

Responses to light are critical for plant success (pp. 849–855)

* **Blue-light photoreceptors** control hypocotyl elongation, stomatal opening, and phototropism.
* **Phytochromes** act like molecular "on-off" switches that regulate shade avoidance and germination of many seed

* **Phytochrome conversion** also provides information about the relative lengths of day and night (photoperiod) and hence the time of year. Photoperiodism regulates the time of flowering in many species. **Short-day plants** require a night longer than a critical length to flower. **Long-day plants** need a night length shorter than a critical period to flower.
* Many daily rhythms in plant behavior are controlled by an internal circadian clock. Free-running circadian cycles are approximately 24 hours long but are entrained to exactly 24 hours by dawn and dusk effects on phytochrome form.

? Why did plant physiologists propose the existence of a mobile molecule (florigen) that triggers flowering?

CONCEPT 39.4

Plants respond to a wide variety of stimuli other than light (pp. 855–859)

* **Gravitropism** is bending in response to gravity. Roots show positive gravitropism, and stems show negative gravitropism. **Statoliths**, starch-filled plastids, enable roots to detect gravity.
* **Thigmotropism** is a growth response to touch. Rapid leaf movements involve transmission of electrical impulses.
* Plants are sensitive to environmental stresses, including drought, flooding, high salinity, and extremes of temperature.

Environmental Stress	Major Response
Drought	ABA production, reducing water loss by closing stomata
Flooding	Formation of air tubes that help roots survive oxygen deprivation
Salt	Avoiding osmotic water loss by producing solutes tolerated at high concentrations
Heat	Synthesis of heat-shock proteins, which reduce protein denaturation at high temperatures
Cold	Adjusting membrane fluidity; avoiding osmotic water loss; producing antifreeze proteins

? Plants that have acclimated to drought stress are often more resistant to freezing stress as well. Suggest a reason why.

CONCEPT 39.5

Plants respond to attacks by pathogens and herbivores (pp. 859–861)

* The **hypersensitive response** seals off an infection and destroys both pathogen and host cells in the region. **Systemic acquired resistance** is a generalized defense response in organs distant from the infection site.
* In addition to physical defenses such as thorns and trichomes, plants produce distasteful or toxic chemicals, as well as attractants that recruit animals that destroy herbivores.

? How can insects make plants more susceptible to pathogens?

TEST YOUR UNDERSTANDING

LEVEL 1: KNOWLEDGE/COMPREHENSION

1. The hormone that helps plants respond to drought is
   a. auxin.
   b. abscisic acid.
   c. cytokinin.
   d. ethylene.

2. Auxin enhances cell elongation in all of these ways *except*
   a. increased uptake of solutes.
   b. gene activation.
   c. acid-induced denaturation of cell wall proteins.
   d. cell wall loosening.

3. Charles and Francis Darwin discovered that
   a. auxin is responsible for phototropic curvature.
   b. red light is most effective in shoot phototropism.
   c. light destroys auxin.
   d. light is perceived by the tips of coleoptiles.

4. How may a plant respond to *severe* heat stress?
   a. by reorienting leaves to increase evaporative cooling
   b. by creating air tubes for ventilation
   c. by producing heat-shock proteins, which may protect the plant's proteins from denaturing
   d. by increasing the proportion of unsaturated fatty acids in cell membranes, reducing their fluidity

LEVEL 2: APPLICATION/ANALYSIS

5. The signaling molecule for flowering might be released earlier than usual in a long-day plant exposed to flashes of
   a. far-red light during the night.
   b. red light during the night.
   c. red light followed by far-red light during the night.
   d. far-red light during the day.

6. If a long-day plant has a critical night length of 9 hours, which 24-hour cycle would prevent flowering?
   a. 16 hours light/8 hours dark
   b. 14 hours light/10 hours dark
   c. 4 hours light/8 hours dark/4 hours light/8 hours dark
   d. 8 hours light/8 hours dark/light flash/8 hours dark

7. A plant mutant that shows normal gravitropic bending but does not store starch in its plastids would require a reevaluation of the role of _____ in gravitropism.
   a. auxin
   b. calcium
   c. statoliths
   d. differential growth

8. **DRAW IT** Indicate the response to each condition by drawing a straight seedling or one with the triple response.

	Control	Ethylene added	Ethylene synthesis inhibitor
Wild-type			
Ethylene insensitive (*ein*)			
Ethylene overproducing (*eto*)			
Constitutive triple response (*ctr*)			

LEVEL 3: SYNTHESIS/EVALUATION

9. **EVOLUTION CONNECTION**
   In general, light-sensitive germination is more pronounced in small seeds compared with germination of large seeds. Suggest a reason why.

10. **SCIENTIFIC INQUIRY**
    A plant biologist observed a peculiar pattern when a tropical shrub was attacked by caterpillars. After a caterpillar ate a leaf, it would skip over nearby leaves and attack a leaf some distance away. Simply removing a leaf did not deter caterpillars from eating nearby leaves. The biologist suspected that an insect-damaged leaf sent out a chemical that signaled nearby leaves. How could the researcher test this hypothesis?

11. **SCIENCE, TECHNOLOGY, AND SOCIETY**
    Describe how our knowledge about the control systems of plants is being applied to agriculture or horticulture.

12. **WRITE ABOUT A THEME: INTERACTIONS**
    In a short essay (100–150 words), summarize phytochrome's role in altering shoot growth for the enhancement of light capture.

13. **SYNTHESIZE YOUR KNOWLEDGE**

This mule deer is grazing on the shoot tips of a shrub. Describe how this event will alter the physiology, biochemistry, structure, and health of the plant, and identify which hormones are involved in making these changes.

For selected answers, see Appendix A.

MasteringBiology®

Students Go to **MasteringBiology** for assignments, the eText, and the Study Area with practice tests, animations, and activities.

Instructors Go to **MasteringBiology** for automatically graded tutorials and questions that you can assign to your students, plus Instructor Resources.

ANIMAL FORM AND FUNCTION

AN INTERVIEW WITH

Ulrike Heberlein

Born in Chile, Ulrike Heberlein received her B.S. and M.S. degrees from the University of Concepción. At the University of California, Berkeley, she completed a Ph.D. in biochemistry as well as postdoctoral work in genetics. In 1993, she set up her own laboratory at the University of California, San Francisco, to study alcohol tolerance and addiction. Since 2012, Dr. Heberlein has been the Scientific Program Director at the Janelia Farm Research Campus of the Howard Hughes Medical Institute. She was elected in 2010 to the U.S. National Academy of Sciences as a foreign member.

What path led you to your current research?

In Chile, at the time I finished my studies, it wasn't clear that science was something a woman should be doing in a serious way. Instead, I came to the United States where I did a lot of river rafting, earning money part of the year as a lab technician. I was just about to move overseas to coordinate trips on the Zambesi River in Africa when I realized that rafting wasn't really going to be it for me in the long run. My lab supervisors told me, "You know, you really should go to grad school." I did, and I'm very grateful to them. In grad school I did biochemistry, then learned fly genetics as a postdoctoral fellow. Afterwards, I wrote a proposal to use flies as a model for studying alcohol use and addiction, which I've been doing ever since.

> **"That's the idea of the inebriometer—it really is chromatography of drunk flies."**

◄ Inebriometer setups in Dr. Heberlein's lab.

How does one study the effects of alcohol on flies?

We use an "inebriometer," which is a column containing a set of partial separations called baffles. If you put flies in the column and put a light at the top, the flies have a natural tendency to walk up the sides against gravity toward the light. Then, if you circulate alcohol vapor through the column, the flies inhale the alcohol and start falling from one baffle to the next. They right themselves and then resume falling. The idea of the baffles is that you don't want them to fall once and go all the way to the bottom. You want it to be like chromatography in a biochemistry lab, where molecules bind and unbind, over and over, separating according to their properties. Once the flies are really drunk, they come out the bottom. So we measure the time it takes for them to reach the bottom. Instead of getting a peak of protein, you get a peak of drunk flies with a mean time to exit the column. That's the idea of the inebriometer—it really is chromatography of drunk flies.

Tell us about some of the things you've discovered.

Our goal is to identify mutations that cause altered responses to alcohol. For example, we can identify flies that are more sensitive to alcohol because they come out of the inebriometer at, say, 15 minutes instead of 20, or flies that are more resistant, because they come out at, for example, 30 minutes. The first two or three mutants that we isolated and analyzed turned out to be learning and memory mutants. That was a satisfying result, because addiction involves learning and remembering the association between a certain feeling (such as intoxication) and the environment (for example, a bar). We have also identified mutations that affect tolerance, the decrease in response to a given level of alcohol over time. What was really cool is that we were able to identify a mutation in the corresponding gene in mice and found that the mice with this mutation also have a defect in alcohol tolerance.

What do you most want to know about addiction?

The goal is to understand the biological mechanism that changes the way neurons talk to each other in addiction. If we can get at that core, we might be able to develop effective medications. Currently there are no good drugs that work for most alcohol addicts.

 For an extended interview and video clip, go to the Study Area in MasteringBiology.

40

Basic Principles of Animal Form and Function

▲ Figure 40.1 How do long legs help this scavenger survive in the scorching desert heat?

Diverse Forms, Common Challenges

The desert ant (genus *Cataglyphis*) in **Figure 40.1** is a scavenger, devouring insects that have succumbed to the daytime heat of the Sahara Desert. To gather corpses for feeding, the ant forages when surface temperatures on the sunbaked sand exceed 60°C (140°F), well above the thermal limit for virtually all animals. How, then, does the desert ant survive in these conditions? To answer this question, we need to look closely at the ant's **anatomy**, or biological form.

In studying the desert ant, researchers noted that its stilt-like legs are disproportionately long. Elevated 4 mm above the sand by these legs, the ant's body is exposed to a temperature 6°C lower than that at ground level. Researchers have also found that a desert ant can use its long legs to run as fast as 1 m/sec, close to the top speed recorded for any running arthropod. Speedy sprinting minimizes the time that the ant is out of its nest and exposed to the sun. Thus, having long legs allows the desert ant to be active during the heat of the day, when competition for food and the risk of predation are lowest.

Over the course of its life, an ant faces the same fundamental challenges as any other animal, whether hydra, hawk, or human. All animals must obtain nutrients and oxygen, fight off infection, and produce offspring. Given that they share these and other basic requirements, why do species vary so enormously in organization and appearance? The answer lies in natural selection and adaptation. Natural selection favors those variations in a population that increase relative fitness (see Chapter 23). The evolutionary adaptations that enable survival vary among environments and species but frequently result in a close match of form to function, as shown by the legs of the desert ant.

Because form and function are correlated, examining anatomy often provides clues to **physiology**—biological function. In this chapter, we'll begin our study of animal form and function by examining the levels of organization in the animal body and the systems for coordinating the activities of different body parts. Next, we'll use the example of body temperature regulation to illustrate how animals control their internal environment. Finally, we'll explore how anatomy and physiology relate to an animal's interactions with the environment and its management of energy use.

CONCEPT 40.1

Animal form and function are correlated at all levels of organization

An animal's size and shape are fundamental aspects of form that significantly affect the way the animal interacts with its environment. Although we may refer to size and shape as elements of a "body plan" or "design," this does not imply a process of conscious invention. The body plan of an animal is the result of a pattern of development programmed by the genome, itself the product of millions of years of evolution.

Evolution of Animal Size and Shape

EVOLUTION Many different body plans have arisen during the course of evolution, but these variations fall within certain bounds. Physical laws that govern strength, diffusion, movement, and heat exchange limit the range of animal forms.

As an example of how physical laws constrain evolution, let's consider how some properties of water limit the possible shapes for animals that are fast swimmers. Water is about a thousand times denser than air and also far more viscous. Therefore, any bump on an animal's body surface that causes drag impedes a swimmer more than it would a runner or flyer. Tuna and other fast ray-finned fishes can swim at speeds up to 80 km/hr (50 miles/ hour). Sharks, penguins, dolphins, and seals are also relatively fast swimmers. As illustrated by the three examples in **Figure 40.2**, these animals all have a shape that is fusiform, meaning tapered on both ends. The similar streamlined shape found in these speedy

Seal

Penguin

Tuna

▲ **Figure 40.2 Convergent evolution in fast swimmers.**

vertebrates is an example of convergent evolution (see Chapter 22). Natural selection often results in similar adaptations when diverse organisms face the same environmental challenge, such as overcoming drag during swimming.

Physical laws also influence animal body plans with regard to maximum size. As body dimensions increase, thicker skeletons are required to maintain adequate support. This limitation affects internal skeletons, such as those of vertebrates, as well as external skeletons, such as those of insects and other arthropods. In addition, as bodies increase in size, the muscles required for locomotion must represent an ever-larger fraction of the total body mass. At some point, mobility becomes limited. By considering the fraction of body mass in leg muscles and the effective force such muscles generate, scientists can estimate maximum running speed for a wide range of body plans. Such calculations indicate that the dinosaur *Tyrannosaurus rex*, which stood more than 6 m tall, probably could run at 30 km/hr (19 miles/hour), about as fast as the fastest humans today can run.

Exchange with the Environment

Animals must exchange nutrients, waste products, and gases with their environment, and this requirement imposes an additional limitation on body plans. Exchange occurs as substances dissolved in an aqueous solution move across the plasma membrane of each cell. A single-celled organism, such as the amoeba in **Figure 40.3a**, has a sufficient membrane surface area in contact with its environment to carry out all necessary exchange. In contrast, an animal is composed of many cells, each with its own plasma membrane across which exchange must occur. The rate of exchange is proportional to membrane surface area involved in exchange, whereas the amount of material that must be exchanged is proportional to the body volume. A multicellular organization therefore works only if every cell has access to a suitable aqueous environment, either inside or outside the animal's body.

Many animals with a simple internal organization have body plans that enable direct exchange between almost all their cells and the external environment. For example, a pond-dwelling hydra, which has a saclike body plan, has a body wall only two cell layers thick **(Figure 40.3b)**. Because its gastrovascular cavity opens to the external environment, both the outer and inner layers of cells are constantly bathed by pond water. Another common body plan that maximizes exposure to the surrounding medium is a flat shape. Consider, for instance, a parasitic tapeworm,

▼ Figure 40.3 Direct exchange with the environment.

Exchange

0.1 mm

(a) An amoeba, a single-celled organism

Mouth

Gastrovascular cavity

Exchange

Exchange

1 mm

(b) A hydra, an animal with two layers of cells

which can reach several meters in length (see Figure 33.12). A thin, flat shape places most cells of the worm in direct contact with its particular environment—the nutrient-rich intestinal fluid of a vertebrate host.

Our bodies and those of most other animals are composed of compact masses of cells, with an internal organization much more complex than that of a hydra or a tapeworm. For such a body plan, increasing the number of cells decreases the ratio of outer surface area to total volume. As an extreme comparison, the ratio of outer surface area to volume for a whale is hundreds of thousands of times smaller than that for a water flea. Nevertheless, every cell in the whale must be bathed in fluid and have access to oxygen, nutrients, and other resources. How is this accomplished?

In whales and most other animals, the evolutionary adaptations that enable sufficient exchange with the environment are specialized surfaces that are extensively branched or folded (**Figure 40.4**). In almost all cases, these exchange surfaces lie within the body, an arrangement that protects their delicate tissues from abrasion or dehydration and allows for streamlined body contours. The branching or folding greatly increases surface area: In humans, the internal exchange surfaces for digestion, respiration, and circulation each have an area more than 25 times that of the skin.

Internal body fluids link exchange surfaces to body cells. The spaces between cells are filled with fluid, in many animals called **interstitial fluid** (from the Latin for "stand between"). Complex body plans also include a circulatory fluid, such as blood. Exchange between the interstitial fluid and the circulatory fluid enables cells throughout the body to obtain nutrients and get rid of wastes (see Figure 40.4).

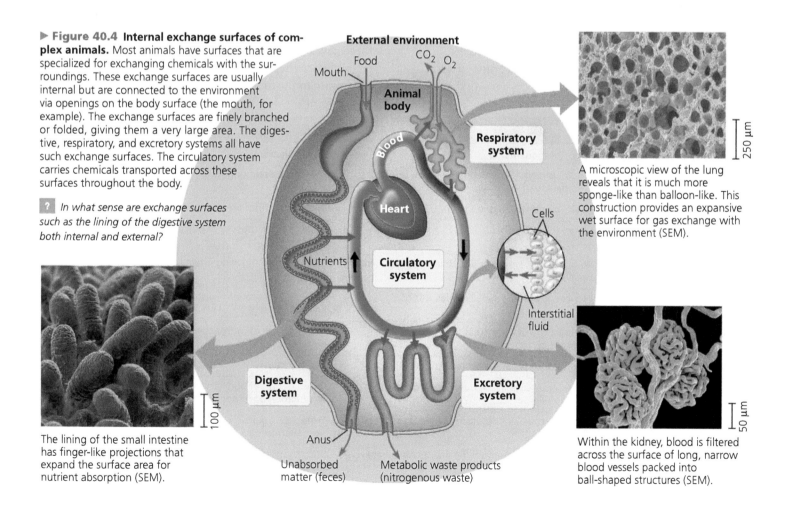

▶ Figure 40.4 Internal exchange surfaces of complex animals. Most animals have surfaces that are specialized for exchanging chemicals with the surroundings. These exchange surfaces are usually internal but are connected to the environment via openings on the body surface (the mouth, for example). The exchange surfaces are finely branched or folded, giving them a very large area. The digestive, respiratory, and excretory systems all have such exchange surfaces. The circulatory system carries chemicals transported across these surfaces throughout the body.

? *In what sense are exchange surfaces such as the lining of the digestive system both internal and external?*

External environment

Food   CO$_2$ O$_2$

Mouth

Animal body

Blood

Respiratory system

Heart

Cells

Nutrients

Circulatory system

Interstitial fluid

Digestive system

Excretory system

Anus

Unabsorbed matter (feces)

Metabolic waste products (nitrogenous waste)

A microscopic view of the lung reveals that it is much more sponge-like than balloon-like. This construction provides an expansive wet surface for gas exchange with the environment (SEM).

250 μm

The lining of the small intestine has finger-like projections that expand the surface area for nutrient absorption (SEM).

100 μm

Within the kidney, blood is filtered across the surface of long, narrow blood vessels packed into ball-shaped structures (SEM).

50 μm

Despite the greater challenges of exchange with the environment, complex body plans have distinct benefits over simple ones. For example, an external skeleton can protect against predators, and sensory organs can provide detailed information on the animal's surroundings. Internal digestive organs can break down food gradually, controlling the release of stored energy. In addition, specialized filtration systems can adjust the composition of the internal fluid that bathes the animal's body cells. In this way, an animal can maintain a relatively stable internal environment while living in a changeable external environment. A complex body plan is especially advantageous for animals living on land, where the external environment may be highly variable.

Hierarchical Organization of Body Plans

Cells form a working animal body through their emergent properties, which arise from successive levels of structural and functional organization (see Chapter 1). Cells are organized into **tissues**, groups of cells with a similar appearance and a common function. Different types of tissues are further organized into functional units called **organs**. (The simplest animals, such as sponges, lack organs or even true tissues.) Groups of organs that work together, providing an additional level of organization and coordination, make up an **organ system** (Table 40.1). Thus, for example, the skin is an organ of the integumentary system, which protects against infection and helps regulate body temperature.

Many organs contain tissues with distinct physiological roles. In some cases, the roles are different enough that we consider the organ to belong to more than one organ system. The pancreas, for instance, produces enzymes critical to the function of the digestive system and also regulates the level of sugar in the blood as a vital part of the endocrine system.

Just as viewing the body's organization from the "bottom up" (from cells to organ systems) reveals emergent properties, a "top-down" view of the hierarchy reveals the multilayered basis of specialization. Consider the human digestive system: the mouth, pharynx, esophagus, stomach, small and large intestines, accessory organs, and anus. Each organ has specific roles in digestion. One role of the stomach, for example, is to initiate the breakdown of proteins. This process requires a churning motion powered by stomach muscles, as well as digestive juices secreted by the stomach lining. Producing digestive juices, in turn, requires highly specialized cell types: One cell type secretes a protein-digesting enzyme, a second generates concentrated hydrochloric acid, and a third produces mucus, which protects the stomach lining.

The specialized and complex organ systems of animals are built from a limited set of cell and tissue types. For example, lungs and blood vessels have different functions but are lined by tissues that are of the same basic type and that therefore share many properties.

There are four main types of animal tissues: epithelial, connective, muscle, and nervous. Figure 40.5, on the next three pages, explores the structure and function of each type. In later chapters, we'll discuss how these tissue types contribute to the functions of particular organ systems.

Table 40.1	Organ Systems in Mammals	
Organ System	**Main Components**	**Main Functions**
Digestive	Mouth, pharynx, esophagus, stomach, intestines, liver, pancreas, anus	Food processing (ingestion, digestion, absorption, elimination)
Circulatory	Heart, blood vessels, blood	Internal distribution of materials
Respiratory	Lungs, trachea, other breathing tubes	Gas exchange (uptake of oxygen; disposal of carbon dioxide)
Immune and lymphatic	Bone marrow, lymph nodes, thymus, spleen, lymph vessels	Body defense (fighting infections and cancer)
Excretory	Kidneys, ureters, urinary bladder, urethra	Disposal of metabolic wastes; regulation of osmotic balance of blood
Endocrine	Pituitary, thyroid, pancreas, adrenal, and other hormone-secreting glands	Coordination of body activities (such as digestion and metabolism)
Reproductive	Ovaries or testes and associated organs	Reproduction
Nervous	Brain, spinal cord, nerves, sensory organs	Coordination of body activities; detection of stimuli and formulation of responses to them
Integumentary	Skin and its derivatives (such as hair, claws, skin glands)	Protection against mechanical injury, infection, dehydration; thermoregulation
Skeletal	Skeleton (bones, tendons, ligaments, cartilage)	Body support, protection of internal organs, movement
Muscular	Skeletal muscles	Locomotion and other movement

Exploring Structure and Function in Animal Tissues

Epithelial Tissue

Occurring as sheets of cells, **epithelial tissues**, or **epithelia** (singular, *epithelium*), cover the outside of the body and line organs and cavities within the body. Because epithelial cells are closely packed, often with tight junctions, they function as a barrier against mechanical injury, pathogens, and fluid loss. Epithelia also form active interfaces with the environment. For example, the epithelium that lines the nasal passages is crucial for olfaction, the sense of smell. Note how different cell shapes and arrangements correlate with distinct functions.

Stratified squamous epithelium

Apical surface

Basal surface

A stratified squamous epithelium is multilayered and regenerates rapidly. New cells formed by division near the basal surface (see micrograph below) push outward, replacing cells that are sloughed off. This epithelium is commonly found on surfaces subject to abrasion, such as the outer skin and the linings of the mouth, anus, and vagina.

Cuboidal epithelium

A cuboidal epithelium, with dice-shaped cells specialized for secretion, makes up the epithelium of kidney tubules and many glands, including the thyroid gland and salivary glands.

Simple columnar epithelium

The large, brick-shaped cells of simple columnar epithelia are often found where secretion or active absorption is important. For example, a simple columnar epithelium lines the intestines, secreting digestive juices and absorbing nutrients.

Simple squamous epithelium

The single layer of platelike cells that form a simple squamous epithelium functions in the exchange of material by diffusion. This type of epithelium, which is thin and leaky, lines blood vessels and the air sacs of the lungs, where diffusion of nutrients and gases is critical.

Pseudostratified columnar epithelium

A pseudostratified epithelium consists of a single layer of cells varying in height and the position of their nuclei. In many vertebrates, a pseudostratified epithelium of ciliated cells forms a mucous membrane that lines portions of the respiratory tract. The beating cilia sweep the film of mucus along the surface.

Lumen

Apical surface

Basal surface

10 μm

Polarity of epithelia

All epithelia are polarized, meaning that they have two different sides. The *apical* surface faces the lumen (cavity) or outside of the organ and is therefore exposed to fluid or air. Specialized projections often cover this surface. For example, the apical surface of the epithelium lining the small intestine is covered with microvilli, projections that increase the surface area available for absorbing nutrients. The opposite side of each epithelium is the *basal* surface.

Continued on next page

Exploring Structure and Function in Animal Tissues

Connective Tissue

Connective tissue, consisting of a sparse population of cells scattered through an extracellular matrix, holds many tissues and organs together and in place. The matrix generally consists of a web of fibers embedded in a liquid, jellylike, or solid foundation. Within the matrix are numerous cells called **fibroblasts**, which secrete fiber proteins, and **macrophages**, which engulf foreign particles and any cell debris by phagocytosis.

Connective tissue fibers are of three kinds: *Collagenous fibers* provide strength and flexibility,

reticular fibers join connective tissue to adjacent tissues, and *elastic fibers* make tissues elastic. If you pinch a fold of tissue on the back of your hand, the collagenous and reticular fibers prevent the skin from being pulled far from the bone, whereas the elastic fibers restore the skin to its original shape when you release your grip. Different mixtures of fibers and foundation form the major types of connective tissue shown below.

Loose connective tissue

The most widespread connective tissue in the vertebrate body is *loose connective tissue,* which binds epithelia to underlying tissues and holds organs in place. Loose connective tissue gets its name from the loose weave of its fibers, which include all three types. It is found in the skin and throughout the body.

Collagenous fiber

120 µm

Elastic fiber

Fibrous connective tissue

Fibrous connective tissue is dense with collagenous fibers. It is found in **tendons**, which attach muscles to bones, and in **ligaments**, which connect bones at joints.

30 µm

Nuclei

Bone

The skeleton of most vertebrates is made of **bone**, a mineralized connective tissue. Bone-forming cells called *osteoblasts* deposit a matrix of collagen. Calcium, magnesium, and phosphate ions combine into a hard mineral within the matrix. The microscopic structure of hard mammalian bone consists of repeating units called *osteons*. Each osteon has concentric layers of the mineralized matrix, which are deposited around a central canal containing blood vessels and nerves.

Central canal

700 µm

Osteon

Adipose tissue

Adipose tissue is a specialized loose connective tissue that stores fat in adipose cells distributed throughout its matrix. Adipose tissue pads and insulates the body and stores fuel as fat molecules. Each adipose cell contains a large fat droplet that swells when fat is stored and shrinks when the body uses that fat as fuel.

Fat droplets

150 µm

Blood

Blood has a liquid extracellular matrix called plasma, which consists of water, salts, and dissolved proteins. Suspended in plasma are erythrocytes (red blood cells), leukocytes (white blood cells), and cell fragments called platelets. Red cells carry oxygen, white cells function in defense, and platelets aid in blood clotting.

Plasma

White blood cells

55 µm

Red blood cells

Cartilage

Cartilage contains collagenous fibers embedded in a rubbery protein-carbohydrate complex called chondroitin sulfate. Cells called *chondrocytes* secrete the collagen and chondroitin sulfate, which together make cartilage a strong yet flexible support material. The skeletons of many vertebrate embryos contain cartilage that is replaced by bone as the embryo matures. Cartilage remains in some locations, such as the disks that act as cushions between vertebrae.

Chondrocytes

100 µm

Chondroitin sulfate

Muscle Tissue

The tissue responsible for nearly all types of body movement is **muscle tissue**. All muscle cells consist of filaments containing the proteins actin and myosin, which together enable muscles to contract. There are three types of muscle tissue in the vertebrate body: skeletal, smooth, and cardiac.

Skeletal muscle

Attached to bones by tendons, **skeletal muscle**, or *striated muscle*, is responsible for voluntary movements. Skeletal muscle consists of bundles of long cells called muscle fibers. During development, skeletal muscle fibers form by the fusion of many cells, resulting in multiple nuclei in each muscle fiber. The arrangement of contractile units, or sarcomeres, along the fibers gives the cells a striped (striated) appearance. In adult mammals, building muscle increases the size but not the number of muscle fibers.

Smooth muscle

Smooth muscle, which lacks striations, is found in the walls of the digestive tract, urinary bladder, arteries, and other internal organs. The cells are spindle-shaped. Smooth muscles are responsible for involuntary body activities, such as churning of the stomach and constriction of arteries.

Cardiac muscle

Cardiac muscle forms the contractile wall of the heart. It is striated like skeletal muscle and has similar contractile properties. Unlike skeletal muscle, however, cardiac muscle has fibers that interconnect via intercalated disks, which relay signals from cell to cell and help synchronize heart contraction.

Nuclei
Muscle fiber
Sarcomere
100 μm

Nucleus   Muscle fibers   25 μm

Nucleus   Intercalated disk   25 μm

Nervous Tissue

Nervous tissue functions in the receipt, processing, and transmission of information. Nervous tissue contains **neurons**, or nerve cells, which transmit nerve impulses, as well as support cells called **glial cells**, or simply **glia.** In many animals, a concentration of nervous tissue forms a brain, an information-processing center.

Neurons

Neurons are the basic units of the nervous system. A neuron receives nerve impulses from other neurons via its cell body and multiple extensions called dendrites. Neurons transmit impulses to neurons, muscles, or other cells via extensions called axons, which are often bundled together into nerves.

Neuron:
Dendrites
Cell body
Axon
40 μm
(Fluorescent LM)

Glia

The various types of glia help nourish, insulate, and replenish neurons, and in some cases, modulate neuron function.

Glia
15 μm
Axons of neurons
Blood vessel
(Confocal LM)

Coordination and Control

An animal's tissues, organs, and organ systems must act in concert with one another. For example, during long dives, the seal shown in Figure 40.2 slows its heart rate, collapses its lungs, and lowers its body temperature while propelling itself forward with its hind flippers. Coordinating activity across an animal's body in this way requires communication between different locations in the body. What signals are used to coordinate activity? How do the signals move within the body? There are two sets of answers to these questions, reflecting the two major systems for coordinating and controlling responses to stimuli: the endocrine and nervous systems (Figure 40.6).

In the **endocrine system**, signaling molecules released into the bloodstream by endocrine cells are carried to all locations in the body. In the **nervous system**, neurons transmit signals along dedicated routes connecting specific locations in the body. In each system, the type of pathway used is the same regardless of whether the signal's ultimate target is at the other end of the body or just a few cell diameters away.

The signaling molecules broadcast throughout the body by the endocrine system are called **hormones**. Different hormones cause distinct effects, and only cells that have receptors for a particular hormone respond (Figure 40.6a). Depending on which cells have receptors for that hormone, the hormone may have an effect in just a single location or in sites throughout the body. For example, thyroid-stimulating hormone (TSH), which acts solely on thyroid cells, stimulates release of thyroid hormone, which acts on nearly every body tissue to increase oxygen consumption and heat production. It takes seconds for hormones to be released into the bloodstream and carried throughout the body. The effects are often long-lasting, however, because hormones can remain in the bloodstream for minutes or even hours.

In the nervous system, signals called nerve impulses travel to specific target cells along communication lines consisting mainly of axons (Figure 40.6b). Nerve impulses can act on other neurons, on muscle cells, and on cells and glands that produce secretions. Unlike the endocrine system, the nervous system conveys information by the particular *pathway* the signal takes. For example, a person can distinguish different musical notes because within the ear, each note's frequency activates neurons that connect to slightly different regions of the brain.

Communication in the nervous system usually involves more than one type of signal. Nerve impulses travel along axons, sometimes over long distances, as changes in voltage. In contrast, passing information from one neuron to another often involves very short-range chemical signals. Overall, transmission in the nervous system is extremely fast; nerve impulses take only a fraction of a second to reach the target and last only a fraction of a second.

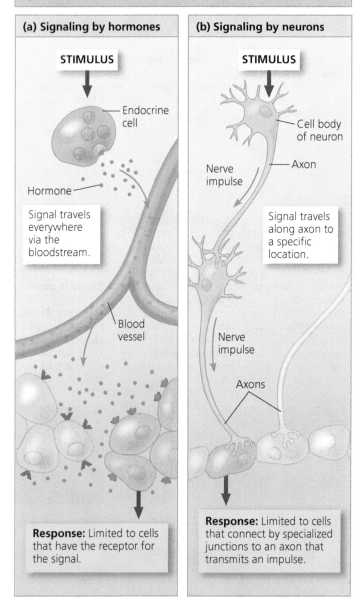

▼ Figure 40.6 **Signaling in the endocrine and nervous systems.**

(a) Signaling by hormones

STIMULUS

Endocrine cell

Hormone

Signal travels everywhere via the bloodstream.

Blood vessel

Response: Limited to cells that have the receptor for the signal.

(b) Signaling by neurons

STIMULUS

Cell body of neuron

Axon

Nerve impulse

Signal travels along axon to a specific location.

Nerve impulse

Axons

Response: Limited to cells that connect by specialized junctions to an axon that transmits an impulse.

Because the two major communication systems of the body differ in signal type, transmission, speed, and duration, it is not surprising that they are adapted to different functions. The endocrine system is especially well adapted for coordinating gradual changes that affect the entire body, such as growth, development, reproduction, metabolic processes, and digestion. The nervous system is well suited for directing immediate and rapid responses to the environment, such as reflexes and other rapid movements.

Although the functions of the endocrine and nervous systems are distinct, the two systems often work in close coordination. Both contribute to maintaining a stable internal environment, our next topic of discussion.

1. What properties do all types of epithelia share?

2. Consider the idealized animal in Figure 40.4. At which sites must oxygen cross a plasma membrane in traveling from the external environment to the cytoplasm of a body cell?

3. **WHAT IF?** Suppose you are standing at the edge of a cliff and suddenly slip—you barely manage to keep your balance and avoid falling. As your heart races, you feel a burst of energy, due in part to a surge of blood into dilated (widened) vessels in your muscles and an upward spike in the level of glucose in your blood. Why might you expect that this "fight-or-flight" response requires both the nervous and endocrine systems?

For suggested answers, see Appendix A.

CONCEPT 40.2

Feedback control maintains the internal environment in many animals

Many organ systems play a role in managing an animal's internal environment, a task that can present a major challenge. Imagine if your body temperature soared every time you took a hot shower or drank a freshly brewed cup of coffee. Faced with environmental fluctuations, animals manage their internal environment by either regulating or conforming.

Regulating and Conforming

An animal is a **regulator** for an environmental variable if it uses internal mechanisms to control internal change in the face of external fluctuation. The otter in **Figure 40.7** is a regulator for temperature, keeping its body at a temperature that is largely independent of that of the water in which it swims. In contrast, an animal is a **conformer** for a particular variable if it allows its internal condition to change in accordance with external changes in the variable. The bass in Figure 40.7 conforms to the temperature of the lake it inhabits. As the water warms or cools, so does the bass's body. Some animals conform to more constant environments. For example, many marine invertebrates, such as spider crabs of the genus *Libinia*, let their internal solute concentration conform to the relatively stable solute concentration (salinity) of their ocean environment.

Regulating and conforming represent extremes on a continuum. An animal may regulate some internal conditions while allowing others to conform to the environment. For instance, even though the bass conforms to the temperature of the surrounding water, it regulates the solute concentration in its blood and interstitial fluid. You'll learn more about the mechanisms of this regulation in Chapter 44.

Homeostasis

The steady body temperature of a river otter and the stable concentration of solutes in a freshwater bass are examples of **homeostasis**, which means "steady state," referring to the maintenance of internal balance. In achieving homeostasis, animals maintain a relatively constant internal environment even when the external environment changes significantly.

Many animals exhibit homeostasis for a range of physical and chemical properties. For example, humans maintain a fairly constant body temperature of about 37°C (98.6°F), a blood pH within 0.1 pH unit of 7.4, and a blood glucose concentration that is predominantly in the range of 70–110 mg of glucose per 100 mL of blood.

▶ **Figure 40.7 The relationship between body and environmental temperatures in an aquatic temperature regulator and an aquatic temperature conformer.** The river otter regulates its body temperature, keeping it stable across a wide range of environmental temperatures. The largemouth bass, meanwhile, allows its internal environment to conform to the water temperature.

River otter (temperature regulator)

Largemouth bass (temperature conformer)

Body temperature (°C) — vertical axis, 0 to 40
Ambient (environmental) temperature (°C) — horizontal axis, 0 to 40

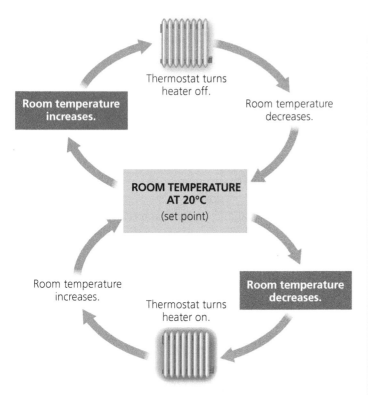

Room temperature increases.

Thermostat turns heater off.

Room temperature decreases.

ROOM TEMPERATURE AT 20°C
(set point)

Room temperature increases.

Thermostat turns heater on.

Room temperature decreases.

▲ **Figure 40.8 A nonliving example of temperature regulation: control of room temperature.** Regulating room temperature depends on a control center (a thermostat) that detects temperature change and activates mechanisms that reverse that change.

WHAT IF? *Label at least one stimulus, response, and sensor/control center in the above figure. How would adding an air conditioner to the system contribute to homeostasis?*

Mechanisms of Homeostasis

Before exploring homeostasis in animals, let's first consider a nonliving example: the regulation of room temperature **(Figure 40.8)**. Let's assume you want to keep a room at 20°C (68°F), a comfortable temperature for normal activity. You set a control device—the thermostat—to 20°C. A thermometer in the thermostat monitors the room temperature. If the temperature falls below 20°C, the thermostat responds by turning on a radiator, furnace, or other heater. Once the room temperature reaches 20°C, the thermostat switches off the heater. If the temperature then drifts below 20°C, the thermostat activates another heating cycle.

Like a home heating system, an animal achieves homeostasis by maintaining a variable, such as body temperature or solute concentration, at or near a particular value, or **set point**. A fluctuation in the variable above or below the set point serves as the **stimulus** detected by a **sensor**. Upon receiving a signal from the sensor, a *control center* generates output that triggers a **response**, a physiological activity that helps return the variable to the set point. In the home heating example, a drop in temperature below the set point acts as a stimulus, the thermostat serves as the sensor and control center, and the heater produces the response.

Feedback Control in Homeostasis

Just as in the circuit shown in Figure 40.8, homeostasis in animals relies largely on **negative feedback**, a control mechanism that reduces, or "damps," the stimulus. For example, when you exercise vigorously, you produce heat, which increases your body temperature. Your nervous system detects this increase and triggers sweating. As you sweat, the evaporation of moisture from your skin cools your body, helping return your body temperature to its set point and eliminating the stimulus.

Homeostasis is a dynamic equilibrium, an interplay between external factors that tend to change the internal environment and internal control mechanisms that oppose such changes. Note that physiological responses to stimuli are not instantaneous, just as switching on a furnace does not immediately warm a room. As a result, homeostasis moderates but doesn't eliminate changes in the internal environment. Additional fluctuation occurs if a variable has a *normal range*—an upper and lower limit—rather than a set point. This is equivalent to a thermostat that turns on a heater when the room temperature drops to 19°C (66°F) and turns off the heater when the temperature reaches 21°C (70°F). Regardless of whether there is a set point or a normal range, homeostasis is enhanced by adaptations that reduce fluctuations, such as insulation in the case of temperature and physiological buffers in the case of pH.

Unlike negative feedback, **positive feedback** is a control mechanism that amplifies rather than reduces the stimulus (see Figure 1.11). In animals, positive-feedback loops do not play a major role in homeostasis, but instead help drive processes to completion. During childbirth, for instance, the pressure of the baby's head against sensors near the opening of the mother's uterus stimulates the uterus to contract. These contractions result in greater pressure against the opening of the uterus, heightening the contractions and thereby causing even greater pressure, until the baby is born.

Alterations in Homeostasis

The set points and normal ranges for homeostasis can change under various circumstances. In fact, *regulated changes* in the internal environment are essential to normal body functions. Some regulated changes occur during a particular stage in life, such as the radical shift in hormone balance that occurs during puberty. Other regulated changes are cyclic, such as the variation in hormone levels responsible for a woman's menstrual cycle (see Figure 46.14).

In all animals (and plants, too), certain cyclic alterations in metabolism reflect a **circadian rhythm**, a set of physiological changes that occur roughly every 24 hours. One way to observe this rhythm is to monitor body temperature, which in humans typically undergoes a cyclic rise and fall

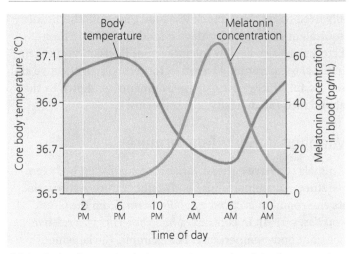

(a) **Variation in core body temperature and melatonin concentration in blood.** Researchers measured these two variables in resting but awake volunteers in an isolation chamber with constant temperature and low light. (Melatonin is a hormone that appears to be involved in sleep/wake cycles.)

(b) **The human circadian clock.** Metabolic activities undergo daily cycles in response to the circadian clock. As illustrated for a typical individual who rises early in the morning, eats lunch around noon, and sleeps at night, these cyclic changes occur throughout a 24-hour day.

▲ **Figure 40.9 Human circadian rhythm.**

of more than 0.6°C (1°F) in every 24-hour period. Remarkably, a biological clock maintains this rhythm even when variations in human activity, room temperature, and light levels are minimized **(Figure 40.9a)**. A circadian rhythm is thus intrinsic to the body, although the biological clock is normally coordinated with the cycle of light and darkness in the environment **(Figure 40.9b)**. For example, the hormone melatonin is secreted at night, and more is released during the longer nights of winter. External stimuli can reset the biological clock, but the effect is not immediate. That is why flying across several time zones results in jet lag, a mismatch between the circadian rhythm and local environment that persists until the clock fully resets.

▲ **Figure 40.10 Acclimitization by mountain climbers in the Himalayas.** To lessen the risk of altitude sickness when ascending a high peak, climbers acclimatize by camping partway up the mountain. Spending time at an intermediate altitude allows the circulatory and respiratory systems to become more efficient in capturing and distributing oxygen at a lower concentration.

One way in which homeostasis may be altered is through **acclimatization**, the gradual process by which an animal adjusts to changes in its external environment. For instance, when an elk moves up into the mountains from sea level, the lower oxygen concentration in the high mountain air stimulates the animal to breathe more rapidly and deeply. As a result, more CO_2 is lost through exhalation, raising blood pH above its normal range. As the animal acclimatizes over several days, changes in kidney function cause it to excrete more alkaline urine, returning blood pH to its normal range. Other mammals, including humans, are also capable of acclimitizing to dramatic altitude changes **(Figure 40.10)**.

Note that acclimatization, a temporary change during an animal's lifetime, should not be confused with adaptation, a process of change in a population brought about by natural selection acting over many generations.

CONCEPT CHECK **40.2**

1. **MAKE CONNECTIONS** How does negative feedback in thermoregulation differ from feedback inhibition in an enzyme-catalyzed biosynthetic process (see Figure 8.21)?

2. If you were deciding where to put the thermostat in a house, what factors would govern your decision? How do these factors relate to the fact that many homeostatic control sensors in humans are located in the brain?

3. **MAKE CONNECTIONS** Like animals, cyanobacteria have a circadian rhythm. By analyzing the genes that maintain biological clocks, scientists concluded that the 24-hour rhythms of humans and cyanobacteria reflect convergent evolution (see Concept 26.2). What evidence would have supported this conclusion? Explain.

For suggested answers, see Appendix A.

CONCEPT 40.3

Homeostatic processes for thermoregulation involve form, function, and behavior

In this section, we'll examine the regulation of body temperature as an example of how form and function work together in regulating an animal's internal environment. Later chapters in this unit will discuss other physiological systems involved in maintaining homeostasis.

Thermoregulation is the process by which animals maintain their body temperature within a normal range. Body temperatures outside the normal range can reduce the efficiency of enzymatic reactions, alter the fluidity of cellular membranes, and affect other temperature-sensitive biochemical processes, potentially with fatal results.

Endothermy and Ectothermy

Heat for thermoregulation can come from either internal metabolism or the external environment. Humans and other mammals, as well as birds, are **endothermic**, meaning that they are warmed mostly by heat generated by metabolism. A few nonavian reptiles, some fishes, and many insect species are also mainly endothermic. In contrast, many nonavian reptiles and fishes, amphibians, and most invertebrates are **ectothermic**, meaning that they gain most of their heat from external sources. Endothermy and ectothermy are not mutually exclusive, however. For example, a bird is mainly endothermic, but it may warm itself in the sun on a cold morning, much as an ectothermic lizard does.

Endotherms can maintain a stable body temperature even in the face of large fluctuations in the environmental temperature. In a cold environment, an endotherm generates enough heat to keep its body substantially warmer than its surroundings **(Figure 40.11a)**. In a hot environment, endothermic vertebrates have mechanisms for cooling their bodies, enabling them to withstand heat loads that are intolerable for most ectotherms.

Although ectotherms do not generate enough heat for thermoregulation, many adjust their body temperature by behavioral means, such as seeking out shade or basking in the sun **(Figure 40.11b)**. Because their

heat source is largely environmental, ectotherms generally need to consume much less food than endotherms of equivalent size—an advantage if food supplies are limited. Ectotherms also usually tolerate larger fluctuations in their internal temperature. Overall, ectothermy is an effective and successful strategy in most environments, as shown by the abundance and diversity of ectotherms.

Variation in Body Temperature

Animals can have either a variable or a constant body temperature. An animal whose body temperature varies with its environment is called a *poikilotherm* (from the Greek *poikilos*, varied). In contrast, a *homeotherm* has a relatively constant body temperature. For example, the largemouth bass is a poikilotherm, and the river otter is a homeotherm (see Figure 40.7).

From the descriptions of ectotherms and endotherms, it might seem that all ectotherms are poikilothermic and all endotherms are homeothermic. In fact, there is no fixed relationship between the source of heat and the stability of body temperature. Many ectothermic marine fishes and invertebrates inhabit waters with such stable temperatures that their body temperature varies less than that of mammals and other endotherms. Conversely, the body temperature of a few endotherms varies considerably. For example, bats and hummingbirds may periodically enter an inactive state in which they maintain a lower body temperature.

It is a common misconception that ectotherms are "cold-blooded" and endotherms are "warm-blooded." Ectotherms do not necessarily have low body temperatures. On the contrary, when sitting in the sun, many ectothermic lizards have higher body temperatures than mammals. Thus, the terms *cold-blooded* and *warm-blooded* are misleading and are avoided in scientific communication.

(a) A walrus, an endotherm

▲ **Figure 40.11 Thermoregulation by internal or external sources of heat.** Endotherms obtain heat from their internal metabolism, whereas ectotherms rely on heat from their external environment.

(b) A lizard, an ectotherm

Balancing Heat Loss and Gain

Thermoregulation depends on an animal's ability to control the exchange of heat with its environment. An organism, like any object, exchanges heat by radiation, evaporation, convection, and conduction **(Figure 40.12)**. Note that heat is always transferred from an object of higher temperature to one of lower temperature.

The essence of thermoregulation is maintaining a rate of heat gain that equals the rate of heat loss. Animals do this through mechanisms that either reduce heat exchange overall or favor heat exchange in a particular direction. In mammals, several of these mechanisms involve the **integumentary system**, the outer covering of the body, consisting of the skin, hair, and nails (claws or hooves in some species).

Insulation

A major thermoregulatory adaptation in mammals and birds is insulation, which reduces the flow of heat between an animal's body and its environment. Such insulation may include hair or feathers as well as layers of fat formed by adipose tissue.

Many animals that rely on insulation to reduce overall heat exchange also adjust their insulating layers to help thermoregulate. Most land mammals and birds, for example, react to cold by raising their fur or feathers. This action traps a thicker layer of air, thereby increasing the effectiveness of the insulation. To repel water that would reduce the insulating capacity of feathers or fur, some animals secrete oily substances, such as the oils that birds apply to their feathers during preening. Lacking feathers or fur, humans must rely primarily on fat for insulation. We do, however, get "goose bumps," a vestige of hair raising inherited from our furry ancestors.

Insulation is particularly important for marine mammals, such as whales and walruses. These animals swim in water colder than their body core, and many species spend at least part of the year in nearly freezing polar seas. The problem of thermoregulation is made worse by the fact that the transfer of heat to water occurs 50 to 100 times more rapidly than heat transfer to air. Just under their skin, marine mammals have a very thick layer of insulating fat called blubber. The insulation that blubber provides is so effective that marine mammals can maintain body core temperatures of about 36–38°C (97–100°F) without

Radiation is the emission of electromagnetic waves by all objects warmer than absolute zero. Here, a lizard absorbs heat radiating from the distant sun and radiates a smaller amount of energy to the surrounding air.

Evaporation is the removal of heat from the surface of a liquid that is losing some of its molecules as gas. Evaporation of water from a lizard's moist surfaces that are exposed to the environment has a strong cooling effect.

Convection is the transfer of heat by the movement of air or liquid past a surface, as when a breeze contributes to heat loss from a lizard's dry skin or when blood moves heat from the body core to the extremities.

Conduction is the direct transfer of thermal motion (heat) between molecules of objects in contact with each other, as when a lizard sits on a hot rock.

▲ **Figure 40.12 Heat exchange between an organism and its environment.**

? *Which type or types of heat exchange occur when you fan yourself on a hot day?*

requiring much more energy from food than land mammals of similar size.

Circulatory Adaptations

Circulatory systems provide a major route for heat flow between the interior and exterior of the body. Adaptations that regulate the extent of blood flow near the body surface or that trap heat within the body core play a significant role in thermoregulation.

In response to changes in the temperature of their surroundings, many animals alter the amount of blood (and hence heat) flowing between their body core and their skin. Nerve signals that relax the muscles of the vessel walls result in *vasodilation*, a widening of superficial blood vessels (those near the body surface). As a consequence of the increase in vessel diameter, blood flow in the skin increases. In endotherms, vasodilation usually warms the skin and increases the transfer of body heat to the environment by radiation, conduction, and convection (see Figure 40.12). The reverse process, *vasoconstriction*, reduces blood flow and heat transfer by decreasing the diameter of superficial vessels.

Like endotherms, some ectotherms control heat exchange by regulating blood flow. For example, when the marine iguana of the Galápagos Islands swims in the cold ocean, its superficial blood vessels undergo vasoconstriction.

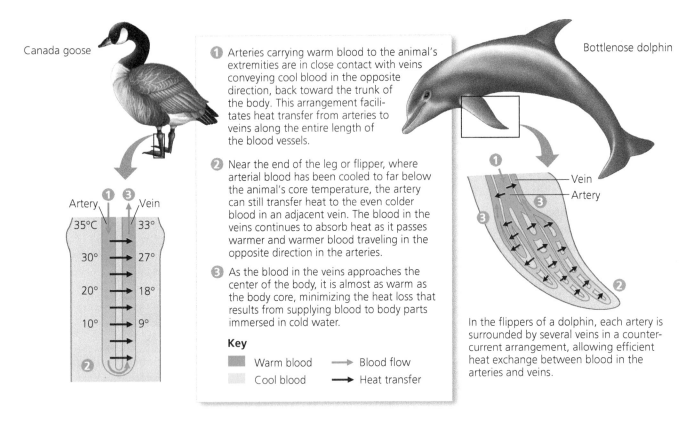

Canada goose

1. Arteries carrying warm blood to the animal's extremities are in close contact with veins conveying cool blood in the opposite direction, back toward the trunk of the body. This arrangement facilitates heat transfer from arteries to veins along the entire length of the blood vessels.

2. Near the end of the leg or flipper, where arterial blood has been cooled to far below the animal's core temperature, the artery can still transfer heat to the even colder blood in an adjacent vein. The blood in the veins continues to absorb heat as it passes warmer and warmer blood traveling in the opposite direction in the arteries.

3. As the blood in the veins approaches the center of the body, it is almost as warm as the body core, minimizing the heat loss that results from supplying blood to body parts immersed in cold water.

Bottlenose dolphin

Artery ① ③ Vein

35°C   33°
30° → 27°
20° → 18°
10° → 9°

In the flippers of a dolphin, each artery is surrounded by several veins in a countercurrent arrangement, allowing efficient heat exchange between blood in the arteries and veins.

Key

▨ Warm blood	→	Blood flow
▨ Cool blood	➡	Heat transfer

▲ **Figure 40.13 Countercurrent heat exchangers.** A countercurrent exchange system traps heat in the body core, thus reducing heat loss from the extremities, particularly when they are immersed in cold water or in contact with ice or snow. In essence, heat in the arterial blood emerging from the body core is transferred directly to the returning venous blood instead of being lost to the environment.

This process routes more blood to the core of the iguana's body, conserving body heat.

In many birds and mammals, reducing heat loss from the body relies on **countercurrent exchange**, the transfer of heat (or solutes) between fluids that are flowing in opposite directions. In a countercurrent heat exchanger, arteries and veins are located adjacent to each other (**Figure 40.13**). Because blood flows through the arteries and veins in opposite directions, this arrangement allows heat exchange to be remarkably efficient. As warm blood moves from the body core in the arteries, it transfers heat to the colder blood returning from the extremities in the veins. Most importantly, heat is transferred along the entire length of the exchanger, maximizing the rate of heat exchange.

Certain sharks, fishes, and insects also use countercurrent heat exchange. Although most sharks and fishes are temperature conformers, countercurrent heat exchangers are found in some large, powerful swimmers, including great white sharks, bluefin tuna, and swordfish. By keeping the main swimming muscles several degrees warmer than tissues near the animal's surface, this adaptation enables the vigorous, sustained activity that is characteristic of these animals. Similarly, many endothermic insects (bumblebees, honeybees, and some moths) have a countercurrent exchanger that helps maintain a high temperature in their thorax, where flight muscles are located.

Cooling by Evaporative Heat Loss

Many mammals and birds live in places where thermoregulation requires cooling as well as warming. If the environmental temperature is above their body temperature, animals gain heat from the environment as well as from metabolism. In this situation, evaporation is the only way to keep body temperature from rising. Terrestrial animals lose water by evaporation from their skin and respiratory surfaces. Water absorbs considerable heat when it evaporates (see Chapter 3); this heat is carried away from the body surface with the water vapor.

Some animals exhibit adaptations that greatly facilitate evaporative cooling. Bathing or sweating moistens the skin; many terrestrial mammals have sweat glands controlled by the nervous system. Panting is also important in many mammals and in birds. Some birds have a pouch richly supplied with blood vessels in the floor of the mouth; fluttering the pouch increases evaporation. Pigeons, for example, can use this adaptation to keep their body temperature close to 40°C (104°F) in air temperatures as high as 60°C (140°F), as long as they have sufficient water.

Behavioral Responses

Both endotherms and ectotherms control body temperature through behavioral responses to changes in the environment. Many ectotherms maintain a nearly constant body temperature by engaging in relatively simple behaviors. When cold, they seek warm places, orienting themselves toward heat sources and expanding the portion of their body surface exposed to the heat source (see Figure 40.11b). When hot, they bathe, move to cool areas, or turn in another direction, minimizing their absorption of heat from the sun. For example, a dragonfly's "obelisk" posture is an adaptation that minimizes the amount of body surface exposed to the sun and thus to heating (Figure 40.14).

Honeybees use a thermo-regulatory mechanism that depends on social behavior. In cold weather, they increase heat production and huddle

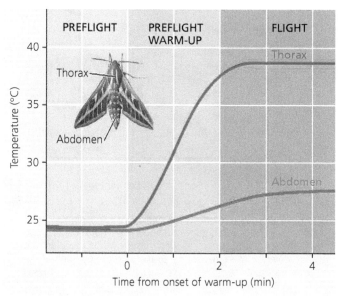

▲ Figure 40.14 **Thermoregulatory behavior in a dragonfly.** By orienting its body so that the narrow tip of its abdomen faces the sun, the dragonfly minimizes heating by solar radiation.

together, thereby retaining heat. Individuals move between the cooler outer edges of the huddle and the warmer center, thus circulating and distributing the heat. Even when huddling, honeybees must expend considerable energy to keep warm during long periods of cold weather. (This is the main function of storing large quantities of fuel in the hive in the form of honey.) In hot weather, honeybees cool the hive by transporting water to the hive and fanning with their wings, promoting evaporation and convection. Thus, a honeybee colony uses many of the mechanisms of thermoregulation seen in individual animals.

Adjusting Metabolic Heat Production

Because endotherms generally maintain a body temperature considerably higher than that of the environment, they must counteract continual heat loss. Endotherms can vary heat production—*thermogenesis*—to match changing rates of heat loss. Thermogenesis is increased by such muscle activity as moving or shivering. For example, shivering helps chickadees, birds with a body mass of only 20 g, remain active and hold their body temperature nearly constant at 40°C (104°F) in environmental temperatures as low as −40°C (−40°F), as long as they have adequate food.

The smallest endotherms—flying insects such as bees and moths—are also capable of varying heat production. Their capacity to elevate body temperature depends on powerful flight muscles, which generate large amounts of heat when contracting. Many endothermic insects warm up by shivering before taking off. As they contract their flight muscles in synchrony, only slight wing movements occur, but considerable heat is produced. Chemical reactions, and hence cellular respiration, accelerate in the warmed-up flight "motors," enabling these insects to fly even when the air is cold (Figure 40.15).

In some mammals, certain hormones can cause mitochondria to increase their metabolic activity and produce heat instead of ATP. This process, called *nonshivering thermogenesis,* takes place throughout the body. Some mammals also have a tissue called *brown fat* in their neck and between their shoulders that is specialized for rapid heat production. (The presence of many more mitochondria than in white adipose tissue is what gives brown fat its characteristic color.) Brown fat is found in the infants of many mammals, as well as in adult mammals that hibernate. In human infants, brown fat represents about 5% of total body weight. Brown fat has recently been detected in human adults; adults were observed to have larger amounts of brown fat in cooler conditions than in warmer ones. Together, nonshivering and shivering thermogenesis enable mammals and birds to increase their metabolic heat production by as much as five to ten times.

© 1974 AAAS

▲ Figure 40.15 **Preflight warm-up in the hawkmoth.** The hawkmoth (*Manduca sexta*) is one of many insect species that use a shivering-like mechanism for preflight warm-up of thoracic flight muscles. Warming up helps these muscles produce enough power to let the animal take off. Once the moth is airborne, flight muscle activity maintains a high thoracic temperature.

A few large reptiles become endothermic in particular circumstances. Researchers found that a female Burmese python (*Python molurus bivittatus*) maintained a body temperature roughly 6°C (11°F) above that of the surrounding air during the month when she was incubating eggs. Where did the heat come from? Further studies showed that some pythons, like mammals and birds, can raise their body temperature through shivering (**Figure 40.16**). These findings contributed to the idea, still under debate, that certain groups of Mesozoic dinosaurs were endothermic (see Chapter 34).

▼ **Figure 40.16** **Inquiry**

How does a Burmese python generate heat while incubating eggs?

Experiment Herndon Dowling and colleagues at the Bronx Zoo in New York observed that when a female Burmese python incubated eggs by wrapping her body around them, she raised her body temperature and frequently contracted the muscles in her coils. To learn if the contractions were elevating her body temperature, they placed the python and her eggs in a chamber. As they varied the chamber's temperature, they monitored the python's muscle contractions as well as her oxygen uptake, a measure of her rate of cellular respiration.

Results The python's oxygen consumption increased when the temperature in the chamber decreased. Her oxygen consumption also increased with the rate of muscle contraction.

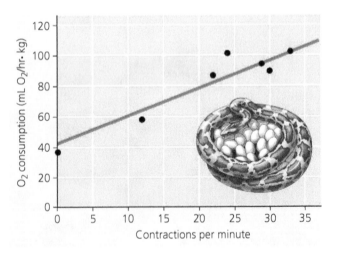

Conclusion Because oxygen consumption, which generates heat through cellular respiration, increased linearly with the rate of muscle contraction, the researchers concluded that the muscle contractions, a form of shivering, were the source of the Burmese python's elevated body temperature.

Source: V. H. Hutchison, H. G. Dowling, and A. Vinegar, Thermoregulation in a brooding female Indian python, *Python molurus bivittatus, Science* 151:694–696 (1966). Reprinted with permission of AAAS.

WHAT IF? *Suppose you varied air temperature and measured oxygen consumption for a female Burmese python without a clutch of eggs. Since she would not show shivering behavior, how would you expect the snake's oxygen consumption to vary with environmental temperature?*

Acclimatization in Thermoregulation

Acclimatization contributes to thermoregulation in many animal species. In birds and mammals, acclimatization to seasonal temperature changes often includes adjusting insulation—growing a thicker coat of fur in the winter and shedding it in the summer, for example. These changes help endotherms keep a constant body temperature year-round.

Acclimatization in ectotherms often includes adjustments at the cellular level. Cells may produce variants of enzymes that have the same function but different optimal temperatures. Also, the proportions of saturated and unsaturated lipids in membranes may change; unsaturated lipids help keep membranes fluid at lower temperatures (see Figure 7.5). Some ectotherms that experience subzero body temperatures protect themselves by producing "antifreeze" proteins that prevent ice formation in their cells. In the Arctic and Southern (Antarctic) Oceans, these proteins enable certain fishes to survive in water as cold as −2°C (28°F), below the freezing point of unprotected body fluids (about −1°C, or 30°F).

Physiological Thermostats and Fever

The regulation of body temperature in humans and other mammals is brought about by a complex system based on feedback mechanisms. The sensors for thermoregulation are concentrated in the **hypothalamus**, the brain region that also controls the circadian clock. Within the hypothalamus, a group of nerve cells functions as a thermostat, responding to body temperatures outside the normal range by activating mechanisms that promote heat loss or gain (**Figure 40.17**).

Warm sensors signal the hypothalamic thermostat when the temperature of the blood increases; cold sensors signal when it decreases. (Because the same blood vessel supplies the hypothalamus and ears, an ear thermometer records the temperature detected by the hypothalamic thermostat.) At body temperatures below the normal range, the thermostat inhibits heat loss mechanisms while activating mechanisms that either save heat, including constriction of vessels in the skin, or generate heat, such as shivering. In response to elevated body temperature, the thermostat shuts down heat retention mechanisms and promotes cooling of the body by dilation of vessels in the skin, sweating, or panting.

In the course of certain bacterial and viral infections, mammals and birds develop *fever*, an elevated body temperature. A variety of experiments have shown that fever reflects an increase in the normal range for the biological thermostat. For example, artificially raising the temperature of the hypothalamus in an infected animal reduces fever in the rest of the body!

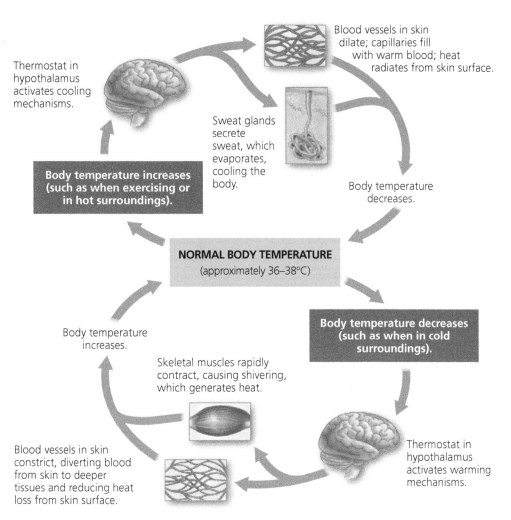

◀ **Figure 40.17** **The thermostatic function of the hypothalamus in human thermoregulation.**

WHAT IF? *Suppose at the end of a hard run on a hot day you find that there are no drinks left in the cooler. If, out of desperation, you dunk your head into the cooler, how might the ice-cold water affect the rate at which your body temperature returns to normal?*

Blood vessels in skin dilate; capillaries fill with warm blood; heat radiates from skin surface.

Thermostat in hypothalamus activates cooling mechanisms.

Sweat glands secrete sweat, which evaporates, cooling the body.

Body temperature increases (such as when exercising or in hot surroundings).

Body temperature decreases.

NORMAL BODY TEMPERATURE (approximately 36–38°C)

Body temperature increases.

Body temperature decreases (such as when in cold surroundings).

Skeletal muscles rapidly contract, causing shivering, which generates heat.

Blood vessels in skin constrict, diverting blood from skin to deeper tissues and reducing heat loss from skin surface.

Thermostat in hypothalamus activates warming mechanisms.

Although only endotherms develop fever, lizards exhibit a related response. When infected with certain bacteria, the desert iguana (*Dipsosaurus dorsalis*) seeks a warmer environment and then maintains a body temperature that is elevated by 2–4°C (4–7°F). Similar observations in fishes, amphibians, and even cockroaches indicate that this response to certain infections is a common feature of many animal species.

Having explored thermoregulation in depth, we'll conclude our introduction to animal form and function by considering the different ways that animals allocate, use, and conserve energy.

CONCEPT CHECK 40.3

1. What mode of heat exchange is involved in "wind chill," when moving air feels colder than still air at the same temperature? Explain.

2. Flowers differ in how much sunlight they absorb. Why might this matter to a hummingbird seeking nectar on a cool morning?

3. **WHAT IF?** Why is shivering likely during the onset of a fever?

For suggested answers, see Appendix A.

CONCEPT 40.4

Energy requirements are related to animal size, activity, and environment

One of the unifying themes of biology introduced in Chapter 1 is that life requires energy transfer and transformation. Like other organisms, animals use chemical energy for growth, repair, activity, and reproduction. The overall flow and transformation of energy in an animal—its **bioenergetics**—determines nutritional needs and is related to the animal's size, activity, and environment.

Energy Allocation and Use

Organisms can be classified by how they obtain chemical energy. Most autotrophs, such as plants, harness light energy to build energy-rich organic molecules and then use those molecules for fuel. Most heterotrophs, such as animals, obtain their chemical energy from food, which contains organic molecules synthesized by other organisms.

Animals use chemical energy harvested from the food they eat to fuel metabolism and activity. Food is digested

External environment

Organic molecules in food

Animal body

Digestion and absorption → Heat

Energy lost in feces

Nutrient molecules in body cells → Energy lost in nitrogenous waste

Carbon skeletons

Cellular respiration → Heat

ATP

Biosynthesis: growth, storage, and reproduction

Cellular work → Heat

Heat

▲ Figure 40.18 **Bioenergetics of an animal: an overview.**

MAKE CONNECTIONS *Use the idea of energy coupling to explain why heat is produced in the absorption of nutrients, in cellular respiration, and in the synthesis of biopolymers (see Concept 8.3).*

by enzymatic hydrolysis (see Figure 5.2b), and nutrients are absorbed by body cells **(Figure 40.18)**. Most nutrient molecules are used to generate ATP. The ATP produced by cellular respiration and fermentation powers cellular work, enabling cells, organs, and organ systems to perform the functions that keep an animal alive. Energy in the form of ATP is also used in biosynthesis, which is needed for body growth and repair, synthesis of storage material such as fat, and production of gametes. The production and use of ATP generate heat, which the animal eventually gives off to its surroundings.

Quantifying Energy Use

How much of the total energy an animal obtains from food does it need just to stay alive? How much energy must be expended to walk, run, swim, or fly from one place to another? What fraction of the energy intake is used for

reproduction? Physiologists answer such questions by measuring the rate at which an animal uses chemical energy and how this rate changes in different circumstances.

The sum of all the energy an animal uses in a given time interval is called its **metabolic rate**. Energy is measured in joules (J) or in calories (cal) and kilocalories (kcal). (A kilocalorie equals 1,000 calories, or 4,184 joules. The unit Calorie, with a capital C, as used by many nutritionists, is actually a kilocalorie.)

Metabolic rate can be determined in several ways. Because nearly all of the chemical energy used in cellular respiration eventually appears as heat, metabolic rate can be measured by monitoring an animal's rate of heat loss. For this approach, researchers use a calorimeter, which is a closed, insulated chamber equipped with a device that records an animal's heat loss. Metabolic rate can also be determined from the amount of oxygen consumed or carbon dioxide produced by an animal's cellular respiration **(Figure 40.19)**. To calculate metabolic rate over longer periods, researchers record the rate of food consumption, the energy content of the food (about 4.5–5 kcal per gram of protein or carbohydrate and about 9 kcal per gram of fat), and the chemical energy lost in waste products (feces and urine or other nitrogenous wastes).

Minimum Metabolic Rate and Thermoregulation

Animals must maintain a minimum metabolic rate for basic functions such as cell maintenance, breathing, and heartbeat. Researchers measure this minimum metabolic rate differently for endotherms and ectotherms. The minimum metabolic rate of a nongrowing endotherm that is at rest, has an empty stomach, and is not experiencing stress is called the **basal metabolic rate (BMR)**. BMR is measured under a "comfortable" temperature range—a range

▲ Figure 40.19 **Measuring the rate of oxygen consumption by a swimming shark.** A researcher monitors the decrease in oxygen level over time in the recirculating water of a juvenile hammerhead's tank.

that requires no generation or shedding of heat above the minimum. The minimum metabolic rate of ectotherms is determined at a specific temperature because changes in the environmental temperature alter body temperature and therefore metabolic rate. The metabolic rate of a fasting, nonstressed ectotherm at rest at a particular temperature is called its **standard metabolic rate (SMR)**.

Comparisons of minimum metabolic rates reveal that endothermy and ectothermy have different energy costs. The BMR for humans averages 1,600–1,800 kcal per day for adult males and 1,300–1,500 kcal per day for adult females. These BMRs are about equivalent to the rate of energy use by a 75-watt lightbulb. In contrast, the SMR of an American alligator is only about 60 kcal per day at 20°C (68°F). Since this represents less than $\frac{1}{20}$ the energy used by a comparably sized adult human, the lower energetic requirement of ectothermy is readily apparent.

Influences on Metabolic Rate

Metabolic rate is affected by many factors besides whether the animal is an endotherm or an ectotherm. Some key factors are age, sex, size, activity, temperature, and nutrition. Here we'll examine the effects of size and activity.

Size and Metabolic Rate

Larger animals have more body mass and therefore require more chemical energy. Remarkably, the relationship between overall metabolic rate and body mass is constant across a wide range of sizes and forms, as illustrated for various mammals in **Figure 40.20a**. In fact, for even more varied organisms ranging in size from bacteria to blue whales, metabolic rate remains roughly proportional to body mass to the three-quarter power ($m^{3/4}$). Scientists are still researching the basis of this relationship, which applies to ectotherms as well as endotherms.

The relationship of metabolic rate to size profoundly affects energy consumption by body cells and tissues. As shown in **Figure 40.20b**, the energy it takes to maintain each gram of body mass is inversely related to body size. Each gram of a mouse, for instance, requires about 20 times as many calories as a gram of an elephant, even though the whole elephant uses far more calories than the whole mouse. The smaller animal's higher metabolic rate per gram demands a higher rate of oxygen delivery. To meet this demand, the smaller animal must have a higher breathing rate, blood volume (relative to its size), and heart rate.

Thinking about body size in bioenergetic terms reveals how trade-offs shape the evolution of body plans. As body size decreases, each gram of tissue increases in energy cost. As body size increases, energy costs per gram of tissue decrease, but an ever-larger fraction of body tissue is required for exchange, support, and locomotion.

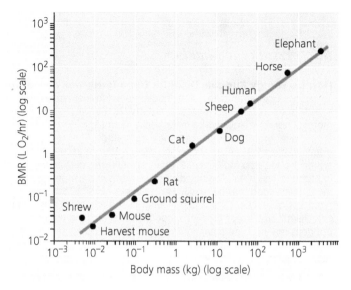

(a) Relationship of basal metabolic rate (BMR) to body size for various mammals. From shrew to elephant, size increases 1 millionfold.

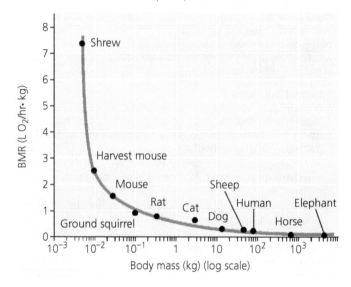

(b) Relationship of BMR per kilogram of body mass to body size for the same mammals as in (a).

▲ **Figure 40.20 The relationship of metabolic rate to body size.**

INTERPRET THE DATA *Based on the graph in (a), one observer suggests that a group of 100 ground squirrels has the same basal metabolic rate as 1 dog. A second observer looking at the same graph disagrees. Who is correct?*

Activity and Metabolic Rate

For both ectotherms and endotherms, activity greatly affects metabolic rate. Even a person reading quietly at a desk or an insect twitching its wings consumes energy beyond the BMR or SMR. Maximum metabolic rates (the highest rates of ATP use) occur during peak activity, such as lifting heavy weights, sprinting, or high-speed swimming. In general, the maximum metabolic rate an animal can sustain is inversely related to the duration of activity.

Interpreting Pie Charts

How Do Energy Budgets Differ for Three Terrestrial Vertebrates?
To explore bioenergetics in animal bodies, let's consider typical annual energy budgets for three terrestrial vertebrates that vary in size and thermoregulatory strategy: a 4-kg male Adélie penguin, a 25-g (0.025-kg) female deer mouse, and a 4-kg female ball python. The penguin is well-insulated against his Antarctic environment but must expend energy in swimming to catch food, incubating eggs laid by his partner, and bringing food to his chicks. The tiny deer mouse lives in a temperate environment where food may be readily available, but her small size causes rapid loss of body heat. Unlike the penguin and mouse, the python is ectothermic and keeps growing throughout her life. She produces eggs but does not incubate them. In this exercise, we'll compare the energy expenditures of these animals for five important functions: basal (standard) metabolism, reproduction, thermoregulation, activity, and growth.

How the Data Were Obtained Energy budgets were calculated for each of the animals based on measurements from field and laboratory studies.

Data from the Experiments Pie charts are a good way to compare *relative* differences in a set of variables. In the pie charts here, the sizes of the wedges represent the relative annual energy expenditures for the functions shown in the key. The total annual expenditure for each animal is given below its pie chart.

Interpret the Data
1. You can estimate the contribution of each wedge in a pie chart by remembering that the entire circle represents 100%, half is 50%, and so on. What percent of the mouse's energy budget goes to basal metabolism? What percent of the penguin's budget is for activity?
2. Without considering the sizes of the wedges, how do the three pie charts differ in which functions they include? Explain these differences.
3. Does the penguin or the mouse expend a greater proportion of its energy budget on thermoregulation? Why?
4. Now look at the *total* annual energy expenditures for each animal. How much more energy does the penguin expend each year compared to the similarly sized python?
5. Which animal expends the most kilocalories per year on thermoregulation?

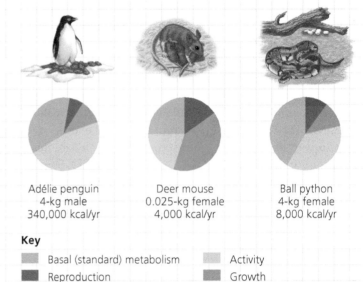

Adélie penguin	Deer mouse	Ball python
4-kg male	0.025-kg female	4-kg female
340,000 kcal/yr	4,000 kcal/yr	8,000 kcal/yr

Key

- ▧ Basal (standard) metabolism
- ▧ Reproduction
- ▧ Thermoregulation
- ▧ Activity
- ▧ Growth

6. If you monitored energy allocation in the penguin for just a few months instead of an entire year, you might find the growth category to be a significant part of the pie chart. Given that adult penguins don't grow from year to year, how would you explain this finding?

(MB) A version of this Scientific Skills Exercise can be assigned in MasteringBiology.

Data from M. A. Chappell et al., Energetics of foraging in breeding Adélie penguins, *Ecology* 74:2450–2461 (1993); M. A. Chappell et al., Voluntary running in deer mice: speed, distance, energy costs, and temperature effects, *Journal of Experimental Biology* 207:3839–3854 (2004); T. M. Ellis and M. A. Chappell, Metabolism, temperature relations, maternal behavior, and reproductive energetics in the ball python (*Python regius*), *Journal of Comparative Physiology B* 157:393–402 (1987).

For most terrestrial animals, the average daily rate of energy consumption is two to four times BMR (for endotherms) or SMR (for ectotherms). Humans in most developed countries have an unusually low average daily metabolic rate of about 1.5 times BMR—an indication of a relatively sedentary lifestyle.

The fraction of an animal's energy "budget" that is devoted to activity depends on many factors, including its environment, behavior, size, and thermoregulation. In the Scientific Skills Exercise, you'll interpret data on the annual energy budgets of three terrestrial vertebrates.

Torpor and Energy Conservation

Despite their many adaptations for homeostasis, animals may encounter conditions that severely challenge their abilities to balance their heat, energy, and materials budgets. For example, at certain times of the day or year, their surroundings may be extremely hot or cold, or food may be unavailable. **Torpor**, a physiological state of decreased activity and metabolism, is an adaptation that enables animals to save energy while avoiding difficult and dangerous conditions.

Many small mammals and birds exhibit a daily torpor that seems to be adapted to feeding patterns. For instance, some bats feed at night and go into torpor in daylight. Chickadees and hummingbirds feed during the day and often go into torpor on cold nights; the body temperature of chickadees drops as much as 10°C (18°F) at night, and the temperature of hummingbirds can fall 25°C (45°F) or more. All endotherms that exhibit daily torpor are relatively small; when active, they have high metabolic rates and thus very high rates of energy consumption.

Hibernation is long-term torpor that is an adaptation to winter cold and food scarcity. When a mammal enters hibernation, its body temperature declines as its body's thermostat is turned down. The temperature reduction may be dramatic: Some hibernating mammals cool to as low as 1–2°C (34–36°F), and at least one, the Arctic ground squirrel (*Spermophilus parryii*), can enter a supercooled (unfrozen) state in which its body temperature dips below 0°C (32°F). Periodically, perhaps every two weeks or so, hibernating animals undergo arousal, raising their body temperature and becoming active briefly before resuming hibernation.

▲ **Hibernating dormouse**
(*Muscardinus avellanarius*)

The energy savings from hibernation are huge: Metabolic rates during hibernation can be 20 times lower than if the animal attempted to maintain normal body temperatures of 36–38°C (97–100°F). As a result, hibernators such as the ground squirrel can survive through the winter on limited supplies of energy stored in the body tissues or as food cached in a burrow. Similarly, the slow metabolism and inactivity of *estivation*, or summer torpor, enables animals to survive long periods of high temperatures and scarce water.

What happens to the circadian rhythm in hibernating animals? In the past, researchers reported detecting daily biological rhythms in hibernating animals. However, in some cases the animals were probably in a state of torpor from which they could readily arouse, rather than "deep" hibernation. More recently, a group of researchers in France addressed this question in a different way, examining the machinery of the biological clock rather than the rhythms it controls (**Figure 40.21**). Working with the European hamster, they found that molecular components of the clock stopped oscillating during hibernation. These findings support the hypothesis that the circadian clock ceases operation during hibernation, at least in this species.

From tissue types to homeostasis, this chapter has focused on the whole animal. We also investigated how animals exchange materials with the environment and how size and activity affect metabolic rate. For much of the rest of this unit, we'll explore how specialized organs and organ systems enable animals to meet the basic challenges of life. In Unit 6, we investigated how plants meet the same challenges. **Figure 40.22**, on the next two pages, highlights some fundamental similarities and differences in the evolutionary adaptations of plants and animals. This figure is thus a review of Unit 6, an introduction to Unit 7, and, most importantly, an illustration of the connections that unify the myriad forms of life.

▼ **Figure 40.21** | Inquiry

What happens to the circadian clock during hibernation?

Experiment To determine whether the 24-hour biological clock continues to run during hibernation, Paul Pévet and colleagues at the University of Louis Pasteur in Strasbourg, France, studied molecular components of the circadian clock in the European hamster (*Cricetus cricetus*). The researchers measured RNA levels for two clock genes—*Per2* and *Bmal1*—during normal activity (euthermia) and during hibernation in constant darkness. The RNA samples were obtained from the suprachiasmatic nuclei (SCN), a pair of structures in the mammalian brain that control circadian rhythms.

Results

Conclusion Hibernation disrupted circadian variation in the hamster's clock gene RNA levels. Further experiments demonstrated that this disruption was not simply due to the dark environment during hibernation, since for nonhibernating animals RNA levels during a darkened daytime were the same as in daylight. The researchers concluded that the biological clock stops running in hibernating European hamsters and, perhaps, in other hibernators as well.

Source: F. G. Revel et al., The circadian clock stops ticking during deep hibernation in the European hamster, *Proceedings of the National Academy of Sciences USA* 104:13816–13820 (2007).

WHAT IF? *Suppose you discovered a new hamster gene and found that the levels of RNA for this gene were constant during hibernation. What could you conclude about the day and night RNA levels for this gene during euthermia?*

CONCEPT CHECK 40.4

1. If a mouse and a small lizard of the same mass (both at rest) were placed in experimental chambers under identical environmental conditions, which animal would consume oxygen at a higher rate? Explain.

2. Which animal must eat a larger proportion of its weight in food each day: a house cat or an African lion caged in a zoo? Explain.

3. **WHAT IF?** Suppose the animals at a zoo were resting comfortably and remained at rest while the nighttime air temperature dropped. If the temperature change were sufficient to cause a change in metabolic rate, what changes would you expect for an alligator and a lion?

For suggested answers, see Appendix A.

Life Challenges and Solutions in Plants and Animals

Multicellular organisms face a common set of challenges. Comparing the solutions that have evolved in plants and animals reveals both unity (shared elements) and diversity (distinct features) across these two lineages.

Nutritional Mode

All living things must obtain energy and carbon from the environment to grow, survive, and reproduce. Plants are autotrophs, obtaining their energy through photosynthesis and their carbon from inorganic sources, whereas animals are heterotrophs, obtaining their energy and carbon from food. Evolutionary adaptations in plants and animals support these different nutritional modes. The broad surface of many leaves (left) enhances light capture for photosynthesis. When hunting, a bobcat relies on stealth, speed, and sharp claws (right). *See Concepts 36.1 and 41.1.*

Growth and Regulation

The growth and development of both plants and animals are controlled by hormones. In plants, hormones may act in a local area or be transported in the body. They control growth patterns, flowering, fruit development, and more (left). In animals, hormones circulate throughout the body and act in specific target tissues, controlling homeostatic processes and developmental events such as molting (below). *See Concepts 39.2 and 45.3.*

Environmental Response

All forms of life must detect and respond appropriately to conditions in their environment. Specialized organs sense environmental signals. For example, the floral head of a sunflower (left) and an insect's eyes (right) both contain photoreceptors that detect light. Environmental signals activate specific receptor proteins, triggering signal transduction pathways that initiate cellular responses coordinated by chemical and electrical communication.
See Concepts 39.1 and 50.1.

Transport

All but the simplest
multicellular organisms
must transport nutrients and
waste products between locations
in the body. A system of tubelike vessels is the common evolutionary solution, while the mechanism of circulation varies.
Plants harness solar energy to transport water, minerals, and
sugars through specialized tubes (left). In animals, a pump
(heart) moves circulatory fluid through vessels (right).
See Concepts 35.1 and 42.3.

Reproduction

In sexual reproduction,
specialized tissues and structures produce and exchange
gametes. Offspring are generally supplied with nutritional
stores that facilitate rapid
growth and development. For
example, seeds (left) have stored food reserves that supply energy
to the young seedling, while milk provides sustenance for
juvenile mammals (right).
See Concepts 38.1 and 46.5.

Absorption

Organisms need to absorb nutrients. The root hairs of
plants (left) and the villi (projections) that line the
intestines of vertebrates (right) increase the surface area
available for absorption. *See Concepts 36.3 and 41.3.*

Gas Exchange

The exchange of certain
gases with the environ-
ment is essential for life.
Respiration by plants
and animals requires
taking up oxygen (O_2) and releasing carbon dioxide (CO_2). In
photosynthesis, net exchange occurs in the opposite direction:
CO_2 uptake and O_2 release. In both plants and animals, highly
convoluted surfaces that increase the area available for gas
exchange have evolved, such as the spongy mesophyll of leaves
(left) and the alveoli of lungs (right). *See Concepts 35.3 and 42.5.*

MAKE CONNECTIONS *Compare the adaptations that enable
plants and animals to respond to the challenges of living in hot
and cold environments. See Concepts 39.4 and 40.3.*

ANIMATION Visit the Study Area in **MasteringBiology**
for related BioFlix® 3-D Animations
in Chapters 36, 42, and 45.

SUMMARY OF KEY CONCEPTS

CONCEPT 40.1

Animal form and function are correlated at all levels of organization (pp. 868–875)

- Physical laws constrain the evolution of an animal's size and shape. These constraints contribute to convergent evolution in animal body forms.
- Each animal cell must have access to an aqueous environment. Simple two-layered sacs and flat shapes maximize exposure to the surrounding medium. More complex body plans have highly folded internal surfaces specialized for exchanging materials.
- Animal bodies are based on a hierarchy of cells, **tissues**, **organs**, and **organ systems**. **Epithelial tissue** forms active interfaces on external and internal surfaces; **connective tissue** binds and supports other tissues; **muscle tissue** contracts, moving body parts; and **nervous tissue** transmits nerve impulses throughout the body.
- The endocrine and nervous systems are the two means of communication between different locations in the body. The endocrine system broadcasts signaling molecules called **hormones** everywhere via the bloodstream, but only certain cells are responsive to each hormone. The nervous system uses dedicated cellular circuits involving electrical and chemical signals to send information to specific locations.

? *For a large animal, what challenges would a spherical shape pose for carrying out exchange with the environment?*

CONCEPT 40.2

Feedback control maintains the internal environment in many animals (pp. 875–877)

- Animals *regulate* (control) certain internal variables while allowing other internal variables to *conform* to external changes. **Homeostasis** is the maintenance of a steady state despite internal and external changes.
- Homeostatic mechanisms are usually based on **negative feedback**, in which the **response** reduces the **stimulus**. In contrast, **positive feedback** involves amplification of a stimulus by the response and often brings about a change in state, such as the transition from pregnancy to childbirth.

- Regulated change in the internal environment is essential to normal function. **Circadian rhythms** are daily fluctuations in metabolism and behavior tuned to the cycles of light and dark in the environment. Other environmental changes may trigger **acclimatization**, a temporary shift in the steady state.

? *Is it accurate to define homeostasis as a constant internal environment? Explain.*

CONCEPT 40.3

Homeostatic processes for thermoregulation involve form, function, and behavior (pp. 878–883)

- An animal maintains its internal temperature within a tolerable range by **thermoregulation**. **Endotherms** are warmed mostly by heat generated by metabolism. **Ectotherms** get most of their heat from external sources. Endothermy requires a greater expenditure of energy. Body temperature may vary with environmental temperature, as in *poikilotherms*, or be relatively constant, as in *homeotherms*.
- In thermoregulation, physiological and behavioral adjustments balance heat gain and loss, which occur through **radiation**, **evaporation**, **convection**, and **conduction**. Insulation and **countercurrent exchange** reduce heat loss, whereas panting, sweating, and bathing increase evaporation, cooling the body. Many ectotherms and endotherms adjust their rate of heat exchange with their surroundings by vasodilation or vasoconstriction and by behavioral responses.
- Many mammals and birds adjust their amount of body insulation in response to changes in environmental temperature. Ectotherms undergo a variety of changes at the cellular level to acclimatize to shifts in temperature.
- The **hypothalamus** acts as the thermostat in mammalian regulation of body temperature. Fever reflects a resetting of this thermostat to a higher normal range in response to infection.

? *Given that humans thermoregulate, explain why your skin is cooler than your body core.*

CONCEPT 40.4

Energy requirements are related to animal size, activity, and environment (pp. 883–889)

- Animals obtain chemical energy from food, storing it for short-term use in ATP. The total amount of energy used in a unit of time defines an animal's **metabolic rate**.
- Under similar conditions and for animals of the same size, the **basal metabolic rate** of endotherms is substantially higher than the **standard metabolic rate** of ectotherms. Minimum metabolic rate per gram is inversely related to body size among similar animals. Animals allocate energy for basal (or standard) metabolism, activity, homeostasis, growth, and reproduction.
- **Torpor**, a state of decreased activity and metabolism, conserves energy during environmental extremes. Animals may enter torpor during sleep periods (daily torpor), in winter (**hibernation**), or in summer (estivation).

? *Why do small animals breathe more rapidly than large animals?*

TEST YOUR UNDERSTANDING

LEVEL 1: KNOWLEDGE/COMPREHENSION

1. The body tissue that consists largely of material located outside of cells is
   a. epithelial tissue.
   b. connective tissue.
   c. muscle tissue.
   d. nervous tissue.

2. Which of the following would increase the rate of heat exchange between an animal and its environment?
   a. feathers or fur
   b. vasoconstriction
   c. wind blowing across the body surface
   d. countercurrent heat exchanger

3. Consider the energy budgets for a human, an elephant, a penguin, a mouse, and a snake. The _____ would have the highest total annual energy expenditure, and the _____ would have the highest energy expenditure per unit mass.
   a. elephant; mouse
   b. elephant; human
   c. mouse; snake
   d. penguin; mouse

LEVEL 2: APPLICATION/ANALYSIS

4. Compared with a smaller cell, a larger cell of the same shape has
   a. less surface area.
   b. less surface area per unit of volume.
   c. the same surface area-to-volume ratio.
   d. a smaller cytoplasm-to-nucleus ratio.

5. An animal's inputs of energy and materials would exceed its outputs
   a. if the animal is an endotherm, which must always take in more energy because of its high metabolic rate.
   b. if it is actively foraging for food.
   c. if it is growing and increasing its mass.
   d. never; homeostasis makes these energy and material budgets always balance.

6. You are studying a large tropical reptile that has a high and relatively stable body temperature. How would you determine whether this animal is an endotherm or an ectotherm?
   a. You know from its high and stable body temperature that it must be an endotherm.
   b. You subject this reptile to various temperatures in the lab and find that its body temperature and metabolic rate change with the ambient temperature. You conclude that it is an ectotherm.
   c. You note that its environment has a high and stable temperature. Because its body temperature matches the environmental temperature, you conclude that it is an ectotherm.
   d. You measure the metabolic rate of the reptile, and because it is higher than that of a related species that lives in temperate forests, you conclude that this reptile is an endotherm and its relative is an ectotherm.

7. Which of the following animals uses the largest percentage of its energy budget for homeostatic regulation?
   a. a marine jelly (an invertebrate)
   b. a snake in a temperate forest
   c. a desert insect
   d. a desert bird

8. **DRAW IT** Draw a model of the control circuit(s) required for driving an automobile at a fairly constant speed over a hilly road. Indicate each feature that represents a sensor, stimulus, or response.

LEVEL 3: SYNTHESIS/EVALUATION

9. EVOLUTION CONNECTION
   In 1847, the German biologist Christian Bergmann noted that mammals and birds living at higher latitudes (farther from the equator) are on average larger and bulkier than related species found at lower latitudes. Suggest an evolutionary hypothesis to explain this observation.

10. SCIENTIFIC INQUIRY
    Eastern tent caterpillars (*Malacosoma americanum*) live in large groups in silk nests, resembling tents, which they build in trees. They are among the first insects to be active in early spring, when daily temperature fluctuates from freezing to very hot. Over the course of a day, they display striking differences in behavior: Early in the morning, they rest in a tightly packed group on the tent's east-facing surface. In midafternoon, they are on its undersurface, each caterpillar hanging by a few of its legs. Propose a hypothesis to explain this behavior. How could you test it?

11. SCIENCE, TECHNOLOGY, AND SOCIETY
    Medical researchers are investigating artificial substitutes for various human tissues. Why might artificial blood or skin be useful? What characteristics would these substitutes need in order to function well in the body? Why do real tissues work better? Why not use the real tissues if they work better? What other artificial tissues might be useful? What problems do you anticipate in developing and applying them?

12. WRITE ABOUT A THEME: ENERGY AND MATTER
    In a short essay (about 100–150 words) focusing on energy transfer and transformation, discuss the advantages and disadvantages of hibernation.

13. **SYNTHESIZE YOUR KNOWLEDGE**

These macaques (*Macaca fuscata*) are partially immersed in a hot spring in a snowy region of Japan. What are some ways that form, function, and behavior contribute to homeostasis for these animals?

For selected answers, see Appendix A.

MasteringBiology®

Students Go to **MasteringBiology** for assignments, the eText, and the Study Area with practice tests, animations, and activities.

Instructors Go to **MasteringBiology** for automatically graded tutorials and questions that you can assign to your students, plus Instructor Resources.

41

Animal Nutrition

▲ Figure 41.1 **How does a crab help an otter make fur?**

The Need to Feed

Dinnertime has arrived for the sea otter in **Figure 41.1** (and for the crab, though in quite a different sense). The muscles and other organs of the crab will be chewed into pieces, broken down by acid and enzymes in the otter's digestive system, and finally absorbed as small molecules into the body of the otter. Such a process is what is meant by animal **nutrition**: food being taken in, taken apart, and taken up.

Although dining on fish, crabs, urchins, and abalone is the sea otter's specialty, all animals eat other organisms—dead or alive, piecemeal or whole. Unlike plants, animals must consume food for both energy and the organic molecules used to assemble new molecules, cells, and tissues. Despite this shared need, animals have diverse diets. **Herbivores**, such as cattle, sea slugs, and caterpillars, dine mainly on plants or algae. **Carnivores**, such as sea otters, hawks, and spiders, mostly eat other animals. Rats and other **omnivores** (from the Latin *omnis*, all) don't in fact eat everything, but they do regularly consume animals as well as plants or algae. We humans are typically omnivores, as are cockroaches and crows.

The terms *herbivore*, *carnivore*, and *omnivore* represent the kinds of food an animal usually eats. Keep in mind, however, that most animals are opportunistic feeders, eating foods outside their standard diet when their usual foods aren't available.

For example, deer are herbivores, but in addition to feeding on grass and other plants, they occasionally eat insects, worms, or bird eggs. Note as well that microorganisms are an unavoidable "supplement" in every animal's diet.

Animals must eat. But to survive and reproduce, they must also balance their consumption, storage, and use of food. Sea otters, for example, support a high rate of metabolism by eating up to 25% of their body mass each day. Eating too little food, too much food, or the wrong mixture of foods can endanger an animal's health. In this chapter, we'll survey the nutritional requirements of animals, explore diverse evolutionary adaptations for obtaining and processing food, and investigate the regulation of energy intake and expenditure.

CONCEPT 41.1

An animal's diet must supply chemical energy, organic molecules, and essential nutrients

Overall, an adequate diet must satisfy three nutritional needs: chemical energy for cellular processes, organic building blocks for macromolecules, and essential nutrients.

The activities of cells, tissues, organs, and whole animals depend on sources of chemical energy in the diet. This energy is used to produce ATP, which powers processes ranging from DNA replication and cell division to vision and flight. To meet the continuous requirement for ATP, animals ingest and digest nutrients, including carbohydrates, proteins, and lipids, for use in cellular respiration and energy storage.

In addition to providing fuel for ATP production, an animal's diet must supply the raw materials needed for biosynthesis. To build the complex molecules it needs to grow, maintain itself, and reproduce, an animal must obtain two types of organic precursors from its food. Animals need a source of organic carbon (such as sugar) and a source of organic nitrogen (such as protein). Starting with these materials, animals can construct a great variety of organic molecules.

Essential Nutrients

Some cellular processes require materials that an animal cannot assemble from simpler organic precursors. These materials—preassembled organic molecules and minerals—are called **essential nutrients**. Obtained from an animal's diet, essential nutrients include essential amino acids and fatty acids, vitamins, and minerals. Essential nutrients have key functions in cells, including serving as substrates of enzymes, as coenzymes, and as cofactors in biosynthetic reactions **(Figure 41.2)**. Needs for particular nutrients vary among species. For instance, ascorbic acid (vitamin C) is an essential nutrient for humans and other primates, as well as guinea pigs, but not for many other animals.

Essential Amino Acids

Animals require 20 amino acids to make proteins (see Figure 5.14). Most animal species have the enzymes to synthesize about half of these amino acids, as long as their diet includes sulfur and organic nitrogen. The remaining amino acids must be obtained from food in prefabricated form and are therefore called **essential amino acids**. Many animals, including adult humans, require eight amino acids in their diet: isoleucine, leucine, lysine, methionine, phenylalanine, threonine, tryptophan, and valine. (Human infants also need a ninth, histidine.)

The proteins in animal products such as meat, eggs, and cheese are "complete," which means that they provide all the essential amino acids in their proper proportions. In contrast, most plant proteins are "incomplete," being deficient in one or more essential amino acids. Corn (maize), for example, is deficient in tryptophan and lysine, whereas beans are lacking in methionine. However, vegetarians can easily obtain all of the essential amino acids by eating a varied diet of plant proteins.

▲ **Figure 41.2 Roles of essential nutrients.** Linoleic acid is converted by the enzyme fatty acid desaturase to γ-linoleic acid, a precursor for phospholipids and prostaglandins. This biosynthetic reaction illustrates common functions of the four classes of essential nutrients, labeled in blue. Note that nearly every enzyme or other protein in animal bodies contains some essential amino acids, as indicated in the partial sequence shown for fatty acid desaturase.

Essential Fatty Acids

Animals require fatty acids to synthesize a variety of cellular components, including membrane phospholipids, signaling molecules, and storage fats. Although animals can synthesize many fatty acids, they lack the enzymes to form the double bonds found in certain required fatty acids. Instead, these molecules must be obtained from the diet and are considered **essential fatty acids**. In mammals, they include linoleic acid (see Figure 41.2). Because seeds, grains, and vegetables generally furnish ample quantities of essential fatty acids, deficiencies in this class of nutrients are rare.

Vitamins

As Albert Szent-Györgyi, the discoverer of vitamin C, once quipped, "A vitamin is a substance that makes you ill if you *don't* eat it." **Vitamins** are organic molecules that are required in the diet in very small amounts. They have diverse functions. Vitamin B_2, for example, is converted in the body to FAD, a coenzyme used in many metabolic processes, including cellular respiration (see Figure 9.12). For humans, 13 vitamins have been identified. Depending on the vitamin, the required amount ranges from 0.01 to 100 mg per day.

Vitamins are classified as water-soluble or fat-soluble (Table 41.1). B vitamins, which generally act as coenzymes, are water-soluble. So is vitamin C, which is required for the production of connective tissue. Fat-soluble vitamins include vitamin A, which is incorporated into visual pigments of the eye, and vitamin D, which aids in calcium absorption and bone formation. The dietary requirement for vitamin D is variable in humans because we can synthesize it from other molecules when our skin is exposed to sunlight.

For people with imbalanced diets, taking vitamin supplements that provide recommended daily levels is certainly reasonable. It is far less clear that massive doses of vitamins confer any health benefits or are even safe. Moderate overdoses of water-soluble vitamins are probably harmless because excesses are excreted in urine. However, excesses of fat-soluble vitamins are deposited in body fat, so overconsumption may cause them to accumulate to toxic levels.

Minerals

Dietary **minerals** are inorganic nutrients, such as iron and sulfur, that are usually required in small amounts—from less than 1 mg to about 2,500 mg per day. As shown in Table 41.2,

---

Table 41.1 Vitamin Requirements of Humans

Vitamin	Major Dietary Sources	Major Functions in the Body	Symptoms of Deficiency
Water-Soluble Vitamins			
B_1 (thiamine)	Pork, legumes, peanuts, whole grains	Coenzyme used in removing CO_2 from organic compounds	Beriberi (tingling, poor coordination, reduced heart function)
B_2 (riboflavin)	Dairy products, meats, enriched grains, vegetables	Component of coenzymes FAD and FMN	Skin lesions, such as cracks at corners of mouth
B_3 (niacin)	Nuts, meats, grains	Component of coenzymes NAD^+ and $NADP^+$	Skin and gastrointestinal lesions, delusions, confusion
B_5 (pantothenic acid)	Meats, dairy products, whole grains, fruits, vegetables	Component of coenzyme A	Fatigue, numbness, tingling of hands and feet
B_6 (pyridoxine)	Meats, vegetables, whole grains	Coenzyme used in amino acid metabolism	Irritability, convulsions, muscular twitching, anemia
B_7 (biotin)	Legumes, other vegetables, meats	Coenzyme in synthesis of fat, glycogen, and amino acids	Scaly skin inflammation, neuromuscular disorders
B_9 (folic acid)	Green vegetables, oranges, nuts, legumes, whole grains	Coenzyme in nucleic acid and amino acid metabolism	Anemia, birth defects
B_{12} (cobalamin)	Meats, eggs, dairy products	Production of nucleic acids and red blood cells	Anemia, numbness, loss of balance
C (ascorbic acid)	Citrus fruits, broccoli, tomatoes	Used in collagen synthesis; antioxidant	Scurvy (degeneration of skin and teeth), delayed wound healing
Fat-Soluble Vitamins			
A (retinol)	Dark green and orange vegetables and fruits, dairy products	Component of visual pigments; maintenance of epithelial tissues	Blindness, skin disorders, impaired immunity
D	Dairy products, egg yolk	Aids in absorption and use of calcium and phosphorus	Rickets (bone deformities) in children, bone softening in adults
E (tocopherol)	Vegetable oils, nuts, seeds	Antioxidant; helps prevent damage to cell membranes	Nervous system degeneration
K (phylloquinone)	Green vegetables, tea; also made by colon bacteria	Important in blood clotting	Defective blood clotting

---

minerals have diverse functions in animal physiology. Some are assembled into the structure of proteins; iron, for example, is incorporated into the oxygen carrier hemoglobin as well as some enzymes (see Figure 41.2). In contrast, sodium, potassium, and chloride are important in the functioning of nerves and muscles and in maintaining osmotic balance between cells and the surrounding body fluid. In vertebrates, the mineral iodine is incorporated into thyroid hormone, which regulates metabolic rate. Vertebrates also require relatively large quantities of calcium and phosphorus for building and maintaining bone.

Ingesting large amounts of some minerals can upset homeostatic balance and impair health. For example, excess salt (sodium chloride) can contribute to high blood pressure. This is a particular problem in the United States, where the typical person consumes enough salt to provide about 20 times the required amount of sodium. Packaged (prepared) foods often contain large amounts of sodium chloride, even if they do not taste very salty.

Dietary Deficiencies

A diet that lacks one or more essential nutrients or consistently supplies less chemical energy than the body requires results in *malnutrition*, a failure to obtain adequate nutrition. Malnutrition resulting from either type of dietary deficiency can have negative impacts on health and survival and affects one out of four children worldwide.

Deficiencies in Essential Nutrients

Insufficient intake of essential nutrients can cause deformities, disease, and even death. For example, cattle, deer, and other herbivores may develop dangerously fragile bones if they graze on plants growing in soil that lacks phosphorus. In such environments, some grazing animals obtain missing nutrients by consuming concentrated sources of salt or other minerals (Figure 41.3). Similarly, some birds supplement their diet with snail shells, and certain tortoises ingest stones.

▲ Figure 41.3 **Obtaining essential nutrients from an unusual source.** A juvenile chamois (*Rupicapra rupicapra*), an herbivore, licks salts from exposed rocks in its alpine habitat. This behavior is common among herbivores that live where soils and plants provide insufficient amounts of minerals, such as sodium, calcium, phosphorus, and iron.

Table 41.2 Mineral Requirements of Humans*			
Mineral	**Major Dietary Sources**	**Major Functions in the Body**	**Symptoms of Deficiency**
Calcium (Ca)	Dairy products, dark green vegetables, legumes	Bone and tooth formation, blood clotting, nerve and muscle function	Impaired growth, loss of bone mass
Phosphorus (P)	Dairy products, meats, grains	Bone and tooth formation, acid-base balance, nucleotide synthesis	Weakness, loss of minerals from bone, calcium loss
Sulfur (S)	Proteins from many sources	Component of certain amino acids	Impaired growth, fatigue, swelling
Potassium (K)	Meats, dairy products, many fruits and vegetables, grains	Acid-base balance, water balance, nerve function	Muscular weakness, paralysis, nausea, heart failure
Chlorine (Cl)	Table salt	Acid-base balance, formation of gastric juice, nerve function, osmotic balance	Muscle cramps, reduced appetite
Sodium (Na)	Table salt	Acid-base balance, water balance, nerve function	Muscle cramps, reduced appetite
Magnesium (Mg)	Whole grains, green leafy vegetables	Enzyme cofactor; ATP bioenergetics	Nervous system disturbances
Iron (Fe)	Meats, eggs, legumes, whole grains, green leafy vegetables	Component of hemoglobin and of electron carriers; enzyme cofactor	Iron-deficiency anemia, weakness, impaired immunity
Fluorine (F)	Drinking water, tea, seafood	Maintenance of tooth structure	Higher frequency of tooth decay
Iodine (I)	Seafood, iodized salt	Component of thyroid hormones	Goiter (enlarged thyroid gland)

(Bracket at left of first seven rows labeled: More than 200 mg per day required)

*Additional minerals required in trace amounts include cobalt (Co), copper (Cu), manganese (Mn), molybdenum (Mo), selenium (Se), and zinc (Zn). All of these minerals, as well as those in the table, can be harmful in excess.

Like other animals, humans sometimes suffer from diets lacking in essential nutrients. A diet that provides insufficient amounts of one or more essential amino acids causes protein deficiency, the most common type of malnutrition among humans. In children, protein deficiency may arise if their diet shifts from breast milk to foods that contain relatively little protein, such as rice. Such children, if they survive infancy, often have impaired physical and mental development.

In populations subsisting on simple rice diets, individuals are often deficient in vitamin A, which can result in blindness or death. To overcome this problem, scientists have engineered "Golden Rice," a strain of rice that synthesizes the orange-colored pigment beta-carotene, which the body converts to vitamin A (see Concept 38.3).

Undernutrition

A diet that fails to provide adequate sources of chemical energy results in *undernutrition*. When an animal is undernourished, a series of events unfold: The body uses up stored carbohydrates and fat and then begins breaking down its own proteins for fuel; muscles begin to decrease in size; and the brain may become protein-deficient. If energy intake remains less than energy expenditures, the animal will eventually die. Even if a seriously undernourished animal survives, some of the damage may be irreversible.

Human undernutrition is most common when drought, war, or another crisis severely disrupts the food supply. In sub-Saharan Africa, where the AIDS epidemic has crippled both rural and urban communities, approximately 200 million children and adults cannot obtain enough food.

Sometimes undernutrition occurs within well-fed human populations as a result of eating disorders. For example, anorexia nervosa leads individuals, usually female, to starve themselves compulsively.

Assessing Nutritional Needs

Determining the ideal diet for the human population is an important but difficult problem for scientists. As objects of study, people present many challenges. Unlike laboratory animals, humans are genetically diverse. They also live in settings far more varied than the stable and uniform environment that scientists use to facilitate comparisons in laboratory experiments. Ethical concerns present an additional barrier. For example, it is not acceptable to investigate the nutritional needs of children in a way that might harm a child's growth or development.

Many insights into human nutrition have come from *epidemiology*, the study of human health and disease at the population level. In the 1970s, for instance, researchers discovered that children born to women of low socioeconomic status were more likely to have neural tube defects, which occur when tissue fails to enclose the developing brain and

▼ Figure 41.4 Inquiry

Can diet influence the frequency of birth defects?

Experiment Richard Smithells, of the University of Leeds, in England, examined the effect of vitamin supplementation on the risk of neural tube defects. Women who had had one or more babies with such a defect were put into two study groups. The experimental group consisted of those who were planning a pregnancy and began taking a multivitamin at least four weeks before attempting conception. The control group, who were not given vitamins, included women who declined them and women who were already pregnant. The numbers of neural tube defects resulting from the pregnancies were recorded for each group.

Results

Group	Number of Infants/Fetuses Studied	Infants/Fetuses with a Neural Tube Defect
Vitamin supplements (experimental group)	141	1
No vitamin supplements (control group)	204	12

Conclusion This controlled study provided evidence that vitamin supplementation protects against neural tube defects, at least after the first pregnancy. Follow-up trials demonstrated that folic acid alone provided an equivalent protective effect.

Source: R. W. Smithells et al., Possible prevention of neural-tube defects by periconceptional vitamin supplementation, *Lancet* 315:339–340 (1980).

Inquiry in Action Read and analyze the original paper in *Inquiry in Action: Interpreting Scientific Papers.*

INTERPRET THE DATA *After folic acid supplementation became standard in the U.S., the frequency of neural tube defects dropped to an average of just 1 in 5,000 live births. Propose two explanations why the observed frequency was much higher in the experimental group of the Smithells study.*

WHAT IF? *Subsequent studies were designed to learn if folic acid supplements prevent neural tube defects during first-time pregnancies. To determine the required number of subjects, what type of additional information did the researchers need?*

spinal cord (see Concept 47.2). The English scientist Richard Smithells thought that malnutrition among these women might be responsible. As described in **Figure 41.4**, he found that vitamin supplementation greatly reduced the risk of neural tube defects. In other studies, he obtained evidence that folic acid (vitamin B_9) was the specific vitamin responsible, a finding confirmed by other researchers. Based on this evidence, the United States in 1998 began to require that folic acid be added to enriched grain products used to make bread, cereals, and other foods. Follow-up studies have documented the effectiveness of this program in reducing the frequency of neural tube defects. Thus, at a time when microsurgery and sophisticated diagnostic imaging dominate the headlines, a simple dietary change such as folic acid supplementation may be among the greatest contributors to human health.

CONCEPT CHECK 41.1

1. All 20 amino acids are needed to make animal proteins. Why aren't they all essential to animal diets?

2. **MAKE CONNECTIONS** Considering the role of enzymes in metabolic reactions (see Concept 8.4), explain why vitamins are required in very small amounts in the diet.

3. **WHAT IF?** If a zoo animal eating ample food shows signs of malnutrition, how might a researcher determine which nutrient is lacking in its diet?

For suggested answers, see Appendix A.

CONCEPT 41.2

The main stages of food processing are ingestion, digestion, absorption, and elimination

In this section, we turn from nutritional requirements to the mechanisms by which animals process food. Food processing can be divided into four distinct stages: ingestion, digestion, absorption, and elimination (**Figure 41.5**).

The first stage, **ingestion**, is the act of eating or feeding. Given the variation in food sources among animal species, it is not surprising that strategies for extracting resources from food also differ widely. **Figure 41.6**, on the next page, surveys and classifies the principal feeding mechanisms

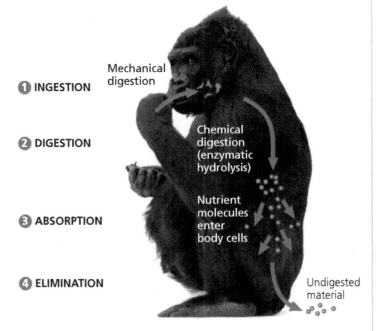

1 INGESTION — Mechanical digestion

2 DIGESTION — Chemical digestion (enzymatic hydrolysis)

Nutrient molecules enter body cells

3 ABSORPTION

4 ELIMINATION — Undigested material

▲ **Figure 41.5 The stages of food processing.**

that have evolved in animals. We will focus in this chapter on the shared aspects of food processing, pausing periodically to consider some adaptations to particular diets or environments.

During **digestion**, the second stage of food processing, food is broken down into molecules small enough for the body to absorb. Mechanical digestion, such as chewing, typically precedes chemical digestion. Mechanical digestion breaks food into smaller pieces, increasing the surface area available for chemical processes. Chemical digestion is necessary because animals cannot directly use the proteins, carbohydrates, nucleic acids, fats, and phospholipids in food. One problem is that these molecules are too large to pass through membranes and enter the cells of the animal. In addition, the large molecules in food are not all identical to those the animal needs for its particular tissues and functions. When large molecules in food are broken down into their components, however, the animal can use these smaller molecules to assemble the large molecules it needs. For example, although fruit flies and humans have very different diets, both convert proteins in their food to the same 20 amino acids from which they assemble all of the specific proteins in their bodies.

A cell makes a macromolecule or fat by linking together smaller components; it does so by removing a molecule of water for each new covalent bond formed. Chemical digestion by enzymes reverses this process by breaking bonds through the addition of water (see Figure 5.2). This splitting process is called *enzymatic hydrolysis*. A variety of enzymes catalyze the digestion of large molecules in food. Polysaccharides and disaccharides are split into simple sugars; proteins are broken down into amino acids; and nucleic acids are cleaved into nucleotides and their components. Enzymatic hydrolysis also releases fatty acids and other components from fats and phospholipids. In many animals, such as the gorilla in Figure 41.5, digestion of some materials is accomplished by bacteria living in the digestive system.

The last two stages of food processing occur after the food is digested. In the third stage, **absorption**, the animal's cells take up (absorb) small molecules such as amino acids and simple sugars. **Elimination** completes the process as undigested material passes out of the digestive system.

Digestive Compartments

In our overview of food processing, we have seen that digestive enzymes hydrolyze the same biological materials (such as proteins, fats, and carbohydrates) that make up the bodies of the animals themselves. How, then, are animals able to digest food without digesting their own cells and tissues? The evolutionary adaptation that allows animals to avoid self-digestion is the processing of food within specialized intracellular or extracellular compartments.

Exploring Four Main Feeding Mechanisms of Animals

Filter Feeding

Baleen

Many aquatic animals are **filter feeders**, which strain small organisms or food particles from the surrounding medium. The humpback whale, shown above, is one example. Attached to the whale's upper jaw are comblike plates called baleen, which remove small invertebrates and fish from enormous volumes of water and sometimes mud. Filter feeding in water is a type of suspension feeding, which also includes removing suspended food particles from the surrounding medium by capture or trapping mechanisms.

Substrate Feeding

Substrate feeders are animals that live in or on their food source. This leaf miner caterpillar, the larva of a moth, is eating through the soft tissue of an oak leaf, leaving a dark trail of feces in its wake. Other substrate feeders include maggots (fly larvae), which burrow into animal carcasses.

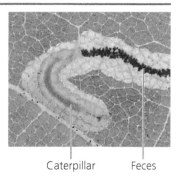

Caterpillar   Feces

Fluid Feeding

Fluid feeders suck nutrient-rich fluid from a living host. This mosquito has pierced the skin of its human host with hollow, needlelike mouthparts and is consuming a blood meal (colorized SEM). Similarly, aphids are fluid feeders that tap the phloem sap of plants. In contrast to such parasites, some fluid feeders actually benefit their hosts. For example, hummingbirds and bees move pollen between flowers as they fluid-feed on nectar.

Bulk Feeding

Most animals, including humans, are **bulk feeders**, which eat relatively large pieces of food. Their adaptations include tentacles, pincers, claws, venomous fangs, jaws, and teeth that kill their prey or tear off pieces of meat or vegetation. In this amazing scene, a rock python is beginning to ingest a gazelle it has captured and killed. Snakes cannot chew their food into pieces and must swallow it whole—even if the prey is much bigger than the diameter of the snake. They can do so because the lower jaw is loosely hinged to the skull by an elastic ligament that permits the mouth and throat to open very wide. After swallowing its prey, which may take more than an hour, the python will spend two weeks or longer digesting its meal.

Intracellular Digestion

Food vacuoles—cellular organelles in which hydrolytic enzymes break down food—are the simplest digestive compartments. The hydrolysis of food inside vacuoles, called intracellular digestion, begins after a cell engulfs solid food by phagocytosis or liquid food by pinocytosis (see Figure 7.19). Newly formed food vacuoles fuse with lysosomes, organelles containing hydrolytic enzymes. This fusion of organelles brings food in contact with the enzymes, allowing digestion to occur safely within a compartment enclosed by a protective membrane. A few animals, such as sponges, digest their food entirely by this intracellular mechanism (see Figure 33.4).

Extracellular Digestion

In most animal species, hydrolysis occurs largely by extracellular digestion, the breakdown of food in compartments that are continuous with the outside of the animal's body. Having one or more extracellular compartments for digestion enables an animal to devour much larger pieces of food than can be ingested by phagocytosis.

Many animals with relatively simple body plans have a digestive compartment with a single opening (Figure 41.7). This pouch, called a **gastrovascular cavity**, functions in digestion as well as in the distribution of nutrients throughout the body (hence the *vascular* part of the term). The cnidarians called hydras provide a good example of how a gastrovascular cavity works. A carnivore, the hydra uses its tentacles to stuff captured prey through its mouth into its gastrovascular cavity. Specialized gland cells of the hydra's gastrodermis, the tissue layer that lines the cavity, then secrete digestive enzymes that break the soft tissues of the prey into tiny pieces. Other cells of the gastrodermis engulf these

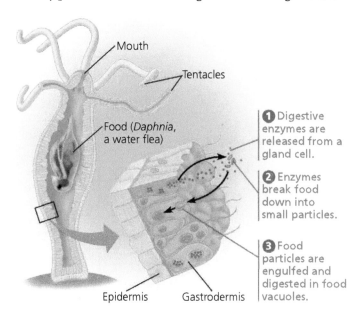

1 Digestive enzymes are released from a gland cell.

2 Enzymes break food down into small particles.

3 Food particles are engulfed and digested in food vacuoles.

▲ **Figure 41.7 Digestion in a hydra.** Digestion begins in the gastrovascular cavity and is completed intracellularly after small food particles are engulfed by specialized cells of the gastrodermis.

food particles, and most of the hydrolysis of macromolecules occurs intracellularly, as in sponges. After the hydra has digested its meal, undigested materials that remain in its gastrovascular cavity, such as exoskeletons of small crustaceans, are eliminated through its mouth. Many flatworms also have a gastrovascular cavity (see Figure 33.10).

In contrast with cnidarians and flatworms, most animals have a digestive tube extending between two openings, a mouth and an anus (Figure 41.8). Such a tube is called a *complete digestive tract* or, more commonly, an **alimentary canal**. Because food moves along the alimentary canal in a

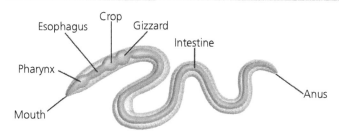

(a) Earthworm. The alimentary canal of an earthworm includes a muscular pharynx that sucks food in through the mouth. Food passes through the esophagus and is stored and moistened in the crop. Mechanical digestion occurs in the muscular gizzard, which pulverizes food with the aid of small bits of sand and gravel. Further digestion and absorption occur in the intestine.

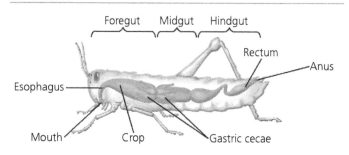

(b) Grasshopper. A grasshopper has several digestive chambers grouped into three main regions: a foregut, with an esophagus and crop; a midgut; and a hindgut. Food is moistened and stored in the crop, but most digestion occurs in the midgut. Pouches called gastric cecae (singular, *ceca*) extend from the beginning of the midgut and function in digestion and absorption.

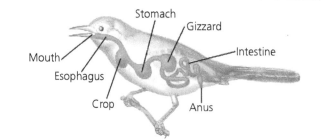

(c) Bird. Many birds have a crop for storing food and a stomach and gizzard for mechanically digesting it. Chemical digestion and absorption of nutrients occur in the intestine.

▲ **Figure 41.8 Alimentary canals.** These examples illustrate variation in the organization and structure of compartments that carry out stepwise digestion, storage, and absorption in different animals.

single direction, the tube can be organized into specialized compartments that carry out digestion and nutrient absorption in a stepwise fashion. An animal with an alimentary canal can ingest food while earlier meals are still being digested, a feat that is likely to be difficult or inefficient for an animal with a gastrovascular cavity. In the next section, we'll explore the organization of a mammalian alimentary canal.

For suggested answers, see Appendix A.

CONCEPT CHECK 41.2

1. Distinguish the overall structure of a gastrovascular cavity from that of an alimentary canal.
2. In what sense are nutrients from a recently ingested meal not really "inside" your body prior to the absorption stage of food processing?
3. **WHAT IF?** Thinking in broad terms, what similarities can you identify between digestion in an animal body and the breakdown of gasoline in an automobile? (You don't have to know about auto mechanics.)

CONCEPT 41.3

Organs specialized for sequential stages of food processing form the mammalian digestive system

Because most animals, including mammals, have an alimentary canal, the mammalian digestive system can serve to illustrate the general principles of food processing. In mammals, the digestive system consists of the alimentary canal and various accessory glands that secrete digestive juices through ducts into the canal (Figure 41.9). The accessory glands of the mammalian digestive system are three pairs of salivary glands, the pancreas, the liver, and the gallbladder.

Food is pushed along the alimentary canal by **peristalsis**, alternating waves of contraction and relaxation in the smooth muscles lining the canal. At some of the junctions between specialized compartments, the muscular layer forms ringlike valves called **sphincters**. Acting like drawstrings to close off the alimentary canal, sphincters regulate the passage of material between compartments.

Using the human digestive system as a model, let's now follow a meal through the alimentary canal. As we do so, we'll examine in more detail what happens to the food in each digestive compartment along the way.

The Oral Cavity, Pharynx, and Esophagus

Ingestion and the initial steps of digestion occur in the mouth, or **oral cavity**. Mechanical digestion begins as teeth of various shapes cut, mash, and grind food, making the food easier to swallow and increasing its surface area. Meanwhile, the **salivary glands** deliver saliva through ducts to the oral cavity. The release of saliva when food enters the mouth is a reflex, an automatic reaction mediated by the nervous system. Saliva may also be released before food enters the mouth, triggered by a learned association between eating and the time of day, a cooking odor, or another stimulus.

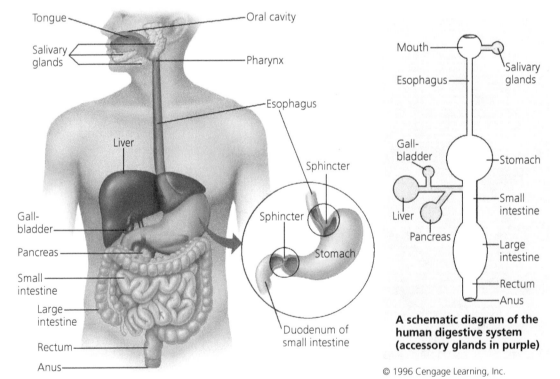

▶ Figure 41.9 The human digestive system. After food is chewed and swallowed, it takes 5–10 seconds for it to pass down the esophagus and into the stomach, where it spends 2–6 hours being partially digested. Final digestion and nutrient absorption occur in the small intestine over a period of 5–6 hours. Within 12–24 hours, any undigested material passes through the large intestine, and feces are expelled through the anus.

A schematic diagram of the human digestive system (accessory glands in purple)

© 1996 Cengage Learning, Inc.

© Pearson Education, Inc.

Saliva initiates chemical digestion while also protecting the oral cavity. The enzyme **amylase**, found in saliva, hydrolyzes starch (a glucose polymer from plants) and glycogen (a glucose polymer from animals) into smaller polysaccharides and the disaccharide maltose. Much of the protective effect of saliva is provided by **mucus**, a viscous mixture of water, salts, cells, and slippery glycoproteins (carbohydrate-protein complexes) called mucins. Mucus in saliva protects the lining of the mouth from abrasion and lubricates food for easier swallowing. Additional components of saliva include buffers, which help prevent tooth decay by neutralizing acid, and antimicrobial agents (such as lysozyme; see Figure 5.16), which protect against bacteria that enter the mouth with food.

Much as a doorman screens and assists people entering a fancy hotel, the tongue aids digestive processes by evaluating ingested material and then enabling its further passage. When food arrives at the oral cavity, the tongue plays a critical role in distinguishing which foods should be processed further. (See Chapter 50 for a discussion of the sense of taste.) After food is deemed acceptable and chewing commences, tongue movements manipulate the mixture of saliva and food, helping shape it into a ball called a **bolus**. During swallowing, the tongue provides further help, pushing the bolus to the back of the oral cavity and into the pharynx.

The **pharynx**, or throat region, opens to two passageways: the trachea (windpipe) and the esophagus **(Figure 41.10)**. The trachea leads to the lungs (see Figure 42.23), whereas the **esophagus** connects to the stomach. Once food enters the esophagus, peristaltic contractions of smooth muscle move each bolus to the stomach.

Swallowing must be carefully choreographed to keep food and liquids from entering the trachea and causing choking, a blockage of the trachea. The resulting lack of airflow into the lungs can be fatal if the material is not dislodged by vigorous coughing, a series of back slaps, or a forced upward thrust of the diaphragm (the Heimlich maneuver).

Digestion in the Stomach

The **stomach**, which is located just below the diaphragm, stores food and begins digestion of proteins. With accordion-like folds and a very elastic wall, this organ can stretch to accommodate about 2 L of food and fluid. The stomach secretes a digestive fluid called **gastric juice** and mixes it with the food through a churning action. This mixture of ingested food and gastric juice is called **chyme**.

Chemical Digestion in the Stomach

Two components of gastric juice carry out chemical digestion. One is hydrochloric acid (HCl), which disrupts the extracellular matrix that binds cells together in meat and plant material. The concentration of HCl is so high that the pH of gastric juice is about 2, acidic enough to dissolve iron nails (and to kill most bacteria). This low pH denatures (unfolds) proteins in food, increasing exposure of their peptide bonds. The exposed bonds are attacked by the second component of gastric juice—a **protease**, or protein-digesting enzyme, called **pepsin**. Unlike most enzymes, pepsin works best in a very acidic environment. By breaking peptide bonds, it cleaves proteins into smaller polypeptides. Further digestion to individual amino acids occurs in the small intestine.

Why doesn't gastric juice destroy the stomach cells that make it? The answer is that the ingredients of gastric juice are kept inactive until they are released into the lumen (cavity) of the stomach.

The components of gastric juice are produced by two types of cells in the gastric glands of the stomach. *Parietal cells* use an ATP-driven pump to expel hydrogen ions into the lumen. At the same time, chloride ions diffuse into the

▶ **Figure 41.10 Intersection of the human airway and digestive tract.** In humans, the pharynx connects to the trachea and the esophagus. **(a)** At most times, a contracted sphincter seals off the esophagus while the trachea remains open. **(b)** When a food bolus arrives at the pharynx, the swallowing reflex is triggered. Movement of the larynx, the upper part of the airway, tips a flap of tissue called the epiglottis down, preventing food from entering the trachea. At the same time, the esophageal sphincter relaxes, allowing the bolus to pass into the esophagus. The trachea then reopens, and peristaltic contractions of the esophagus move the bolus to the stomach.

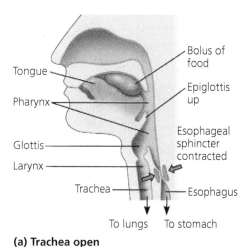

(a) Trachea open

(b) Esophagus open

lumen through specific membrane channels of the parietal cells. It is therefore only within the lumen that hydrogen and chloride ions combine to form HCl (Figure 41.11). Meanwhile, *chief cells* release pepsin into the lumen in an inactive form called **pepsinogen**. HCl converts pepsinogen to active pepsin by clipping off a small portion of the molecule and exposing its active site. Through these processes, both HCl and pepsin form in the lumen of the stomach, not within the cells of the gastric glands.

Interior surface of stomach. The interior surface of the stomach wall is highly folded and dotted with pits leading into tubular gastric glands.

Gastric gland. The gastric glands have three types of cells that secrete different components of the gastric juice: mucous cells, chief cells, and parietal cells.

Mucous cells secrete mucus, which lubricates and protects the cells lining the stomach.

Chief cells secrete pepsinogen, an inactive form of the digestive enzyme pepsin.

Parietal cells produce the components of hydrochloric acid (HCl).

The production of gastric juice

1. Pepsinogen and HCl are introduced into the lumen of the stomach.

2. HCl converts pepsinogen to pepsin.

3. Pepsin then activates more pepsinogen, starting a chain reaction. Pepsin begins the chemical digestion of proteins.

▲ **Figure 41.11** **The stomach and its secretions.**

After hydrochloric acid converts a small amount of pepsinogen to pepsin, pepsin itself helps activate the remaining pepsinogen. Pepsin, like HCl, can clip pepsinogen to expose the enzyme's active site. This generates more pepsin, which activates more pepsinogen. This series of events is an example of positive feedback (see Concept 40.2).

Why don't HCl and pepsin eat through the lining of the stomach? For one thing, mucus secreted by cells in gastric glands protects against self-digestion (see Figure 41.11). In addition, cell division adds a new epithelial layer every three days, replacing cells before they are fully eroded by digestive juices. Under certain circumstances, however, damaged areas of the stomach lining called gastric ulcers can appear. It had been thought that they were caused by psychological stress and resulting excess acid secretion. However, Australian researchers Barry Marshall and Robin Warren discovered that infection by the acid-tolerant bacterium *Helicobacter pylori* causes ulcers. They also demonstrated that an antibiotic could cure most gastric ulcers. For these findings, they were awarded the Nobel Prize in 2005.

Stomach Dynamics

Chemical digestion by gastric juice is facilitated by the churning action of the stomach. This coordinated series of muscle contractions and relaxations mixes the stomach contents about every 20 seconds. As a result of mixing and enzyme action, what begins as a recently swallowed meal becomes the acidic, nutrient-rich broth known as chyme. Most of the time, sphincters close off the stomach at both ends (see Figure 41.9). The sphincter between the esophagus and the stomach normally opens only when a bolus arrives. Occasionally, however, a person experiences acid reflux, a backflow of chyme from the stomach into the lower end of the esophagus. The resulting irritation of the esophagus is commonly called "heartburn."

Peristaltic contractions typically empty the contents of the stomach into the small intestine within 2–6 hours after a meal. The sphincter located where the stomach opens to the small intestine helps regulate passage into the small intestine, allowing only one squirt of chyme at a time.

Digestion in the Small Intestine

Although chemical digestion of some nutrients begins in the oral cavity or stomach, most enzymatic hydrolysis of the macromolecules from food occurs in the small intestine (Figure 41.12). The **small intestine** is the alimentary canal's longest compartment—over 6 m (20 feet) long in humans! Its name refers to its small diameter, compared with that of the large intestine. The first 25 cm (10 inches) or so of the small intestine forms the **duodenum**. It is here that chyme from the stomach mixes with digestive juices from the pancreas, liver, and gallbladder, as well as from gland cells of the intestinal wall itself. As you will see in Concept 41.5, hormones released by the stomach and duodenum control the digestive secretions into the alimentary canal.

Pancreatic Secretions

The **pancreas** aids chemical digestion by producing an alkaline solution rich in bicarbonate as well as several enzymes (see Figure 41.12). The bicarbonate neutralizes the acidity of chyme and acts as a buffer. Among the pancreatic enzymes are trypsin and chymotrypsin, proteases secreted into the duodenum in inactive forms. In a chain reaction similar to the activation of pepsin, they are activated when safely located in the lumen of the duodenum.

Bile Production by the Liver

Digestion of fats and other lipids begins in the small intestine and relies on the production of **bile**, a mixture of substances that is made in the **liver**. Bile contains bile salts, which act as emulsifiers (detergents) that aid in digestion and absorption of lipids. Bile is stored and concentrated in the **gallbladder**.

Bile production is integral to one of the other vital functions of the liver: the destruction of red blood cells that are no longer fully functional. In producing bile, the liver incorporates some pigments that are by-products of red blood cell disassembly. These bile pigments are then eliminated from the body with the feces. In some liver or blood disorders, bile pigments accumulate in the skin, resulting in a characteristic yellowing called jaundice.

Secretions of the Small Intestine

The epithelial lining of the duodenum is the source of several digestive enzymes (see Figure 41.12). Some are secreted into the lumen of the duodenum, whereas others are bound to the surface of epithelial cells.

▼ **Figure 41.12 Chemical digestion in the human digestive system.** The timing and location of chemical breakdown are specific to each class of nutrients.

? *Pepsin is resistant to the denaturing effect of the low pH environment of the stomach. Thinking about the different digestive processes that occur in the small intestine, describe an adaptation shared by the digestive enzymes in that compartment.*

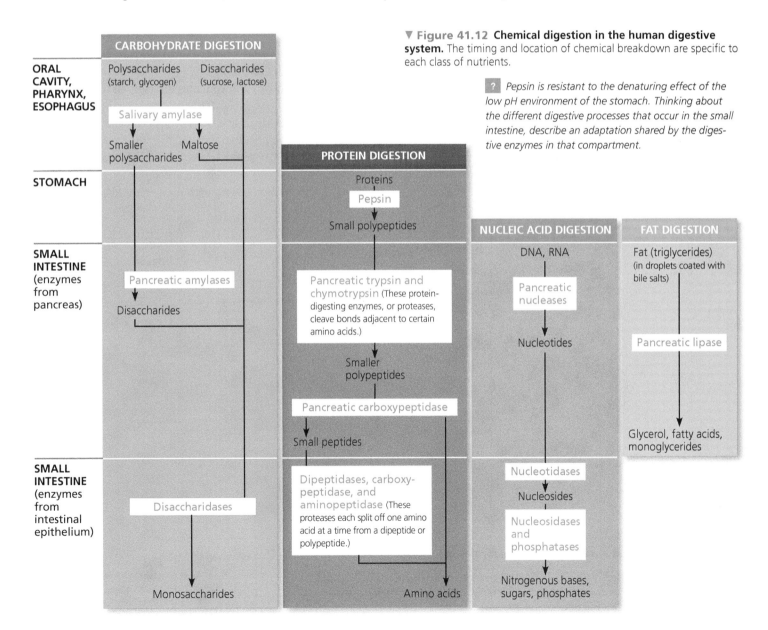

While enzymatic hydrolysis proceeds, peristalsis moves the mixture of chyme and digestive juices along the small intestine. Most digestion is completed in the duodenum. The remaining regions of the small intestine, called the *jejunum* and *ileum*, are the major sites for absorption of nutrients, as discussed next.

Absorption in the Small Intestine

To reach body tissues, nutrients in the lumen must first be absorbed across the lining of the alimentary canal. Most of this absorption occurs at the highly folded surface of the small intestine, as illustrated in Figure 41.13. Large folds in the lining encircle the intestine and are studded with finger-like projections called **villi**. In turn, each epithelial cell of a villus has on its apical surface many microscopic projections, or **microvilli**, that are exposed to the intestinal lumen. The many side-by-side microvilli give cells of the intestinal epithelium a brush-like appearance that is reflected in the name *brush border*. Together, the folds, villi, and microvilli of the small intestine have a surface area of 200–300 m^2, roughly the size of a tennis court. This enormous surface area is an evolutionary adaptation that greatly increases the rate of nutrient absorption (see Figure 33.9 for more discussion and examples of maximizing surface area in diverse organisms).

Depending on the nutrient, transport across the epithelial cells can be passive or active (see Chapter 7). The sugar fructose, for example, moves by facilitated diffusion down its concentration gradient from the lumen of the small intestine into the epithelial cells. From there, fructose exits the basal surface and is absorbed into microscopic blood vessels, or capillaries, at the core of each villus. Other nutrients, including amino acids, small peptides, vitamins, and most glucose molecules, are pumped against concentration gradients into the epithelial cells of the villus. This active transport allows much more absorption of those nutrients than would be possible with passive diffusion alone.

The capillaries and veins that carry nutrient-rich blood away from the villi converge into the **hepatic portal vein**, a blood vessel that leads directly to the liver. From the liver, blood travels to the heart and then to other tissues and organs. This arrangement serves two major functions. First, it allows the liver to regulate the distribution of nutrients to the rest of the body. Because the liver can interconvert many organic molecules, blood that leaves the liver may have a very different nutrient balance than the blood that entered. Second, the arrangement allows the liver to remove toxic substances before the blood circulates broadly. The liver is the primary site for the detoxification of many organic molecules, including drugs, that are foreign to the body.

Although many nutrients leave the small intestine through the bloodstream, some products of fat (triglyceride, also known as triacylglycerol) digestion take a different path (Figure 41.14). Hydrolysis of fats by lipases in the small intestine generates fatty acids and monoglycerides. (A monoglyceride is a single fatty acid joined to glycerol.) These products are absorbed by epithelial cells and recombined into triglycerides. They are then coated with phospholipids, cholesterol,

▲ Figure 41.13 **Nutrient absorption in the small intestine.**

? *Tapeworms sometimes infect the human alimentary canal, anchoring themselves to the wall of the small intestine. Based on how digestion is compartmentalized along the mammalian alimentary canal, what digestive functions would you expect these parasites to have?*

ANIMATION ***BioFlix*** Visit the Study Area in **MasteringBiology** for the BioFlix® 3-D Animation on Membrane Transport.

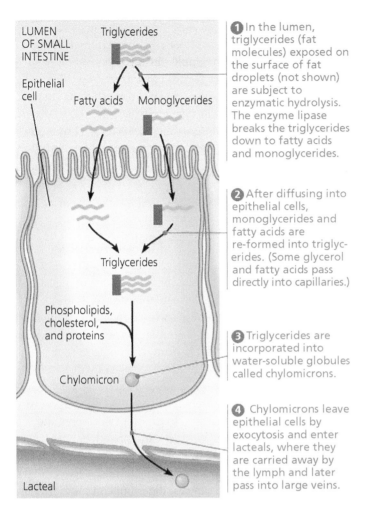

① In the lumen, triglycerides (fat molecules) exposed on the surface of fat droplets (not shown) are subject to enzymatic hydrolysis. The enzyme lipase breaks the triglycerides down to fatty acids and monoglycerides.

② After diffusing into epithelial cells, monoglycerides and fatty acids are re-formed into triglycerides. (Some glycerol and fatty acids pass directly into capillaries.)

③ Triglycerides are incorporated into water-soluble globules called chylomicrons.

④ Chylomicrons leave epithelial cells by exocytosis and enter lacteals, where they are carried away by the lymph and later pass into large veins.

▲ Figure 41.14 **Absorption of fats.** Because fats are insoluble in water, adaptations are needed to digest and absorb them. Bile salts (not shown) break up large fat droplets and maintain a small droplet size in the intestinal lumen, exposing more of the fat at the surface to enzymatic hydrolysis. The fatty acids and monoglycerides released by hydrolysis can diffuse into epithelial cells, where fats are reassembled and incorporated into water-soluble chylomicrons that enter the lymphatic system.

and proteins, forming globules called **chylomicrons**. Being water soluble, chylomicrons can dissolve in the blood and travel via the circulatory system.

Before reaching the bloodstream, chylomicrons are first transported from an epithelial cell in the intestine into a **lacteal**, a vessel at the core of each villus (see Figures 41.13 and 41.14). Lacteals are part of the vertebrate lymphatic system, which is a network of vessels filled with a clear fluid called lymph. Starting at the lacteals, lymph containing the chylomicrons passes into the larger vessels of the lymphatic system and eventually into large veins that return the blood to the heart.

In addition to absorbing nutrients, the small intestine has an important function in the recovery of water and ions. Each day we consume about 2 L of water and secrete another 7 L in digestive juices. Typically all but 0.1 L of the water is reabsorbed in the intestines, with most of the

recovery occurring in the small intestine. There is no mechanism for active transport of water. Instead, water is reabsorbed by osmosis when sodium and other ions are pumped out of the lumen of the intestine.

Processing in the Large Intestine

The alimentary canal ends with the **large intestine**, which includes the colon, cecum, and rectum. The small intestine connects to the large intestine at a T-shaped junction (**Figure 41.15**). One arm of the T is the 1.5-m-long **colon**, which leads to the rectum and anus. The other arm is a pouch called the **cecum**. The cecum is important for fermenting ingested material, especially in animals that eat large amounts of plant material.

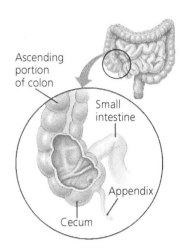

▲ Figure 41.15 **Junction of the small and large intestines.**

Compared with many other mammals, humans have a small cecum. The **appendix**, a finger-like extension of the human cecum, has a minor and dispensable role in immunity.

The colon completes the reabsorption of water that began in the small intestine. What remain are the **feces**, the wastes of the digestive system, which become increasingly solid as they are moved along the colon by peristalsis. It takes approximately 12–24 hours for material to travel the length of the colon. If the lining of the colon is irritated—by a viral or bacterial infection, for instance—less water than normal may be reabsorbed, resulting in diarrhea. The opposite problem, constipation, occurs when the feces move along the colon too slowly. Too much water is reabsorbed, and the feces become compacted.

The undigested material in feces includes cellulose fiber. Although it provides no caloric value (energy) to humans, fiber helps move food along the alimentary canal.

A rich community of mostly harmless bacteria lives on the unabsorbed organic material in the human colon, contributing approximately one-third of the dry weight of feces. As by-products of their metabolism, many colon bacteria generate gases, including methane and hydrogen sulfide, the latter of which has an offensive odor. These gases and ingested air are expelled through the anus.

The terminal portion of the large intestine is the **rectum**, where the feces are stored until they can be eliminated. Between the rectum and the anus are two sphincters, the inner one being involuntary and the outer one being voluntary. Periodically, strong contractions of the colon create an urge to defecate. Because filling of the stomach triggers a reflex that increases the rate of contractions in the colon, the urge to defecate often follows a meal.

We have followed a meal from one opening (the mouth) of the alimentary canal to the other (the anus). Next we'll look at some adaptations of this general digestive plan in different animals.

CONCEPT CHECK 41.3

1. Explain why a proton pump inhibitor, such as the drug Prilosec, relieves the symptoms of acid reflux.
2. Thinking about our nutritional needs and feeding behavior, propose an evolutionary explanation for why amylase, unlike other digestive enzymes, is secreted into the mouth.
3. **WHAT IF?** If you mixed gastric juice with crushed food in a test tube, what would happen?

For suggested answers, see Appendix A.

CONCEPT 41.4

Evolutionary adaptations of vertebrate digestive systems correlate with diet

EVOLUTION The digestive systems of mammals and other vertebrates are variations on a common plan, but there are many intriguing adaptations, often associated with the animal's diet. To highlight how form fits function, we'll examine a few of them.

Dental Adaptations

Dentition, an animal's assortment of teeth, is one example of structural variation reflecting diet (Figure 41.16). The evolutionary adaptation of teeth for processing different kinds of food is one of the major reasons mammals have been so successful. For example, the sea otter in Figure 41.1 uses its sharp canine teeth to tear apart prey such as crabs and its slightly rounded molars to crush their shells. Nonmammalian vertebrates generally have less specialized dentition, but there are interesting exceptions. Venomous snakes, such as rattlesnakes, have fangs, modified teeth that inject venom into prey. Some fangs are hollow, like syringes, whereas others drip the toxin along grooves on the surfaces of the teeth.

Stomach and Intestinal Adaptations

Evolutionary adaptations to differences in diet are sometimes apparent as variations in the dimensions of digestive organs. For example, large, expandable stomachs are common in carnivorous vertebrates, which may wait a long time between meals and must eat as much as they can when they do catch prey. An expandable stomach enables a rock python to ingest a whole gazelle (see Figure 41.6) and a 200-kg African lion to consume 40 kg of meat in one meal!

Adaptation is also apparent in the length of the digestive system in different vertebrates. In general, herbivores and omnivores have longer alimentary canals relative to their body size than do carnivores. Plant matter is more difficult to digest than meat because it contains cell walls. A longer digestive tract furnishes more time for digestion and more surface area for the absorption of nutrients. As an example, consider the coyote and koala in **Figure 41.17**. Although these two mammals are about the same size, the koala's intestines are much longer, enhancing the processing of fibrous, protein-poor eucalyptus leaves from which the koala obtains nearly all of its nutrients and water.

▼ Figure 41.16 **Dentition and diet.**

Carnivore

Carnivores, such as members of the dog and cat families, generally have large, pointed incisors and canines that can be used to kill prey and rip or cut away pieces of flesh. The jagged premolars and molars crush and shred food.

Herbivore

Herbivores, such as horses and deer, usually have premolars and molars with broad, ridged surfaces that grind tough plant material. The incisors and canines are generally modified for biting off pieces of vegetation. In some herbivores, canines are absent.

Omnivore

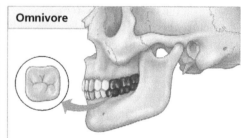

As omnivores, humans are adapted to eating both plants and meat. Adults have 32 teeth. From front to back along either side of the mouth are four bladelike incisors for biting, a pair of pointed canines for tearing, four premolars for grinding, and six molars for crushing (see inset, top view).

Key   Incisors   Canines   Premolars   Molars

▲ Figure 41.17 The alimentary canals of a carnivore (coyote) and herbivore (koala). The relatively short digestive tract of the coyote is sufficient for digesting meat and absorbing its nutrients. In contrast, the koala's long alimentary canal is specialized for digesting eucalyptus leaves. Extensive chewing chops the leaves into tiny pieces, increasing exposure to digestive juices. In the long cecum and the upper portion of the colon, symbiotic bacteria further digest the shredded leaves, releasing nutrients that the koala can absorb.

Mutualistic Adaptations

An estimated 10–100 trillion bacteria live in the human digestive system. One bacterial inhabitant, *Escherichia coli*, is so common in the digestive system that its presence in lakes and streams is a useful indicator of contamination by untreated sewage.

The coexistence of humans and many of these bacteria involves mutualistic symbiosis, a mutually beneficial interaction between two species (see Concept 54.1). For example, some intestinal bacteria produce vitamins, such as vitamin K, biotin, and folic acid, that supplement our dietary intake when absorbed into the blood. Intestinal bacteria also regulate the development of the intestinal epithelium and the function of the innate immune system.

Recently, we have greatly expanded our knowledge of the collection of bacteria, called the *microbiome,* in the human digestive system. To identify these bacteria, both beneficial and harmful, scientists are using a DNA sequencing approach based on the polymerase chain reaction (see Figure 20.8). They have found more than 400 bacterial species in the human digestive tract, a far greater number than had been identified through approaches relying on laboratory culture and characterization.

▲ Figure 41.18 The stomach microbiome. By copying and sequencing bacterial DNA in samples obtained from human stomachs, researchers characterized the bacterial community that makes up the stomach microbiome. In samples from individuals infected with *Helicobacter pylori*, more than 95% of the sequences were from that species, which belongs to the phylum Proteobacteria. The stomach microbiome in uninfected individuals was much more diverse.

One recent microbiome study provided an important clue as to why the bacterium *H. pylori* disrupts stomach health, leading to ulcers. After collecting stomach tissue from uninfected and *H. pylori*-infected adults, researchers identified all the bacterial species in each sample. What they found was remarkable: *H. pylori* infection led to a near complete elimination from the stomach of all other bacterial species **(Figure 41.18)**. Such studies on differences in the microbiome as a result of particular diseases holds promise for the development of new and more effective therapies.

Mutualistic Adaptations in Herbivores

Mutualistic symbiosis is particularly important in herbivores. Much of the chemical energy in herbivore diets comes from the cellulose of plant cell walls, but animals do not produce enzymes that hydrolyze cellulose. Instead, many vertebrates (as well as termites, whose wooden diets consist largely of cellulose) host large populations of mutualistic bacteria and protists in fermentation chambers in their alimentary canals. These microorganisms have enzymes that can digest cellulose to simple sugars and other compounds that the animal can absorb. In many cases, the microorganisms also use the sugars from digested cellulose in the production of a variety of nutrients essential to the animal, such as vitamins and amino acids.

In horses, koalas, and elephants, mutualistic microorganisms are housed in a large cecum. In contrast, the hoatzin, an herbivorous bird found in South American rain forests,

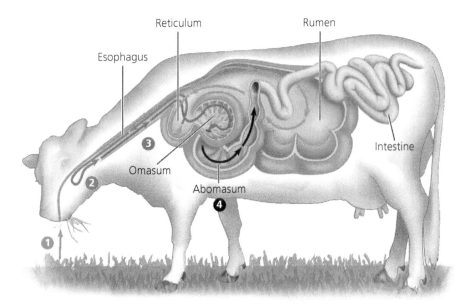

Reticulum

Rumen

Esophagus

Intestine

Omasum

Abomasum

◀ **Figure 41.19 Ruminant digestion.** The stomach of a cow, a ruminant, has four chambers. ❶ Chewed food first enters the rumen and reticulum, where mutualistic microorganisms digest cellulose in the plant material. ❷ Periodically, the cow regurgitates and rechews "cud" from the reticulum, further breaking down fibers and thereby enhancing microbial action. ❸ The reswallowed cud passes to the omasum, where some water is removed. ❹ It then passes to the abomasum, for digestion by the cow's enzymes. In this way, the cow obtains significant nutrients from both the grass and the mutualistic microorganisms, which maintain a stable population in the rumen.

hosts microorganisms in a large, muscular crop (an esophageal pouch; see Figure 41.8). Hard ridges in the wall of the crop grind plant leaves into small fragments, and the microorganisms break down cellulose.

In rabbits and some rodents, mutualistic bacteria live in the large intestine as well as in the cecum. Since most nutrients are absorbed in the small intestine, nourishing byproducts of fermentation by bacteria in the large intestine are initially lost with the feces. Rabbits and rodents recover these nutrients by *coprophagy* (from the Greek, meaning "dung eating"), feeding on some of their feces and then passing the food through the alimentary canal a second time. The familiar rabbit "pellets," which are not reingested, are the feces eliminated after food has passed through the digestive tract twice.

The most elaborate adaptations for an herbivorous diet have evolved in the animals called *ruminants*, the cud-chewing animals that include deer, sheep, and cattle (**Figure 41.19**).

Although we have focused our discussion on vertebrates, adaptations related to digestion are also widespread among other animals. Some of the most remarkable examples are the giant tubeworms (over 3 m long) that live at pressures as high as 260 atmospheres around deep-sea hydrothermal vents (see Figure 52.14). These worms have no mouth or digestive system. Instead, they obtain all of their energy and nutrients from mutualistic bacteria that live within their bodies. The bacteria carry out chemoautotrophy (see

▲ **Giant tubeworm**

Concept 27.3) using the carbon dioxide, oxygen, hydrogen sulfide, and nitrate available at the vents. Thus, for invertebrates and vertebrates alike, mutualistic symbiosis has evolved as an adaptation that expands the sources of nutrition available to animals. Having examined how animals optimize their extraction of nutrients from food, we'll next turn to the challenge of balancing the use of these nutrients.

CONCEPT CHECK 41.4

1. What are two advantages of a longer alimentary canal for processing plant material that is difficult to digest?

2. What features of a mammal's digestive system make it an attractive habitat for mutualistic microorganisms?

3. **WHAT IF?** "Lactose-intolerant" people have a shortage of lactase, the enzyme that breaks down lactose in milk. As a result, they sometimes develop cramps, bloating, or diarrhea after consuming dairy products. Suppose such a person ate yogurt containing bacteria that produce lactase. Why would eating yogurt likely provide at best only temporary relief of the symptoms?

For suggested answers, see Appendix A.

CONCEPT 41.5

Feedback circuits regulate digestion, energy storage, and appetite

The processes that enable an animal to obtain nutrients are matched to the organism's circumstances and need for energy—an example of evolutionary adaptation.

Regulation of Digestion

Many animals have long intervals between meals and do not need their digestive systems to be active continuously.

Instead, each step in processing is activated as food reaches a new compartment in the alimentary canal. The arrival of food triggers the secretion of substances that promote the next stage of chemical digestion, as well as muscular contractions that propel food farther along the canal. For example, you learned earlier that nervous reflexes stimulate the release of saliva when food enters the oral cavity and orchestrate swallowing when a bolus of food reaches the pharynx. Similarly, the arrival of food in the stomach triggers churning and the release of gastric juices. A branch of the nervous system called the *enteric division*, which is dedicated to the digestive organs, regulates these events as well as peristalsis in the small and large intestines.

The endocrine system also plays a critical role in controlling digestion. As described in **Figure 41.20**, a series of hormones released by the stomach and duodenum help ensure that digestive secretions are present only when needed. Like all hormones, they are transported through the bloodstream. This is true even for the hormone gastrin, whose target (the stomach) is the same organ that secretes it.

Regulation of Energy Storage

When an animal takes in more energy-rich molecules than it needs for metabolism and activity, it stores the excess energy (see Concept 40.4). In concluding our overview of nutrition, we'll examine some ways in which animals manage their energy allocation.

In humans, the first sites used for energy storage are liver and muscle cells. In these cells, excess energy from the diet is stored in glycogen, a polymer made up of many glucose units (see Figure 5.6b). Once glycogen depots are full, any additional excess energy is usually stored in fat in adipose cells.

When fewer calories are taken in than are expended—perhaps because of sustained heavy exercise or lack of food—the human body generally expends liver glycogen first and then draws on muscle glycogen and fat. Fats are especially rich in energy; oxidizing a gram of fat liberates about twice the energy liberated from a gram of carbohydrate or protein. For this reason, adipose tissue provides the most space-efficient way for the body to store large amounts of energy. Most healthy people have enough stored fat to sustain them through several weeks without food.

Glucose Homeostasis

The synthesis and breakdown of glycogen are central not only to energy storage, but also to maintaining metabolic balance through glucose homeostasis. In humans, the normal range for the concentration of glucose in the blood is 70–110 mg/100 mL. Because glucose is a major fuel for cellular respiration and a key source of carbon skeletons for biosynthesis, maintaining blood glucose concentrations near this normal range is critical.

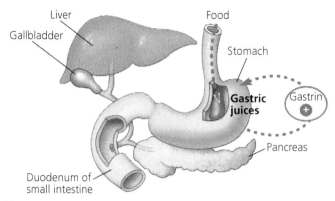

1 As food arrives at the stomach, it stretches the stomach walls, triggering release of the hormone *gastrin*. Gastrin circulates via the bloodstream back to the stomach, where it stimulates production of gastric juices.

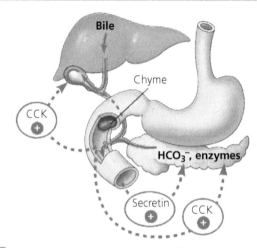

2 Chyme—an acidic mixture of partially digested food—eventually passes from the stomach to the duodenum. The duodenum responds to amino acids or fatty acids in the chyme by releasing the digestive hormones cholecystokinin and secretin. *Cholecystokinin (CCK)* stimulates the release of digestive enzymes from the pancreas and of bile from the gallbladder. *Secretin* stimulates the pancreas to release bicarbonate (HCO_3^-), which neutralizes chyme.

3 If the chyme is rich in fats, the high levels of secretin and CCK released act on the stomach to inhibit peristalsis and secretion of gastric juices, thereby slowing digestion.

Key Stimulation ⊖ Inhibition

▲ **Figure 41.20 Hormonal control of digestion.**

Glucose homeostasis relies predominantly on the antagonistic (opposing) effects of two hormones, insulin and glucagon (Figure 41.21). When the blood glucose level rises above the normal range, the secretion of **insulin** triggers the uptake of glucose from the blood into body cells, decreasing the blood glucose concentration. When the blood glucose level drops below the normal range, the secretion of **glucagon** promotes the release of glucose into the blood from energy stores, such as liver glycogen, increasing the blood glucose concentration.

The liver is a key site for insulin and glucagon action. After a carbohydrate-rich meal, for example, rising levels of insulin promote biosynthesis of glycogen from glucose entering the liver in the hepatic portal vein. Between meals, when blood in the hepatic portal vein has a much lower glucose concentration, glucagon stimulates the liver to break down glycogen, convert amino acids and glycerol to glucose, and release glucose into the blood.

Insulin also acts on nearly all body cells to stimulate glucose uptake from blood. A major exception is brain cells, which can take up glucose whether or not insulin is present. This evolutionary adaptation ensures that the brain almost always has access to circulating fuel, even if supplies are low.

Glucagon and insulin are both produced in the pancreas. Scattered throughout this organ are cell clusters called pancreatic islets. Each pancreatic islet has *alpha cells*, which make glucagon, and *beta cells*, which make insulin. Like all hormones, insulin and glucagon are secreted into the interstitial fluid and enter the circulatory system.

Overall, hormone-secreting cells make up only 1–2% of the mass of the pancreas. Other cells in the pancreas produce and secrete bicarbonate ions and the digestive enzymes active in the small intestine (see Figure 41.12). These secretions are released into small ducts that empty into the pancreatic duct, which leads to the small intestine. Thus, the pancreas has functions in both the endocrine and digestive systems.

Diabetes Mellitus

In discussing the role of insulin and glucagon in glucose homeostasis, we have focused exclusively on a healthy metabolic state. However, a number of disorders can disrupt glucose homeostasis with potentially serious consequences, especially for the heart, blood vessels, eyes, and kidneys. The best known and most prevalent of these disorders is diabetes mellitus.

The disease **diabetes mellitus** is caused by a deficiency of insulin or a decreased response to insulin in target tissues. Blood glucose levels rise, but cells are unable to take up enough glucose to meet metabolic needs. Instead, fat becomes the main substrate for cellular respiration. In severe

▶ **Figure 41.21 Homeostatic regulation of cellular fuel.** After a meal is digested, glucose and other monomers are absorbed into the blood from the digestive tract. The human body regulates the use and storage of glucose, a major cellular fuel.

MAKE CONNECTIONS *What form of feedback control does each of these regulatory circuits reflect (see Concept 40.2)?*

ANIMATION **BioFlix** Visit the Study Area in **MasteringBiology** for the BioFlix® 3-D Animation on Homeostasis: Regulating Blood Sugar.

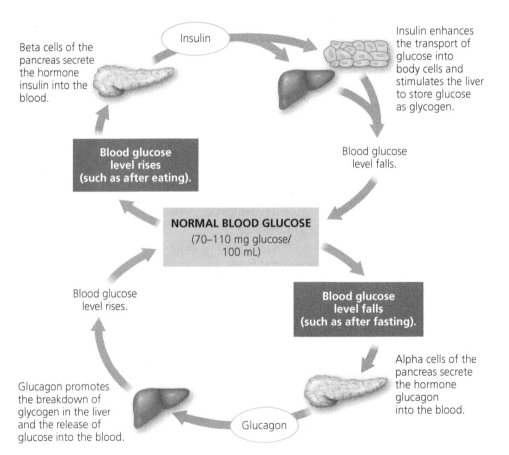

Insulin

Beta cells of the pancreas secrete the hormone insulin into the blood.

Insulin enhances the transport of glucose into body cells and stimulates the liver to store glucose as glycogen.

Blood glucose level rises (such as after eating).

Blood glucose level falls.

NORMAL BLOOD GLUCOSE
(70–110 mg glucose/ 100 mL)

Blood glucose level rises.

Blood glucose level falls (such as after fasting).

Alpha cells of the pancreas secrete the hormone glucagon into the blood.

Glucagon promotes the breakdown of glycogen in the liver and the release of glucose into the blood.

Glucagon

cases, acidic metabolites formed during fat breakdown accumulate in the blood, threatening life by lowering blood pH and depleting sodium and potassium ions from the body.

In people with diabetes mellitus, the level of glucose in the blood may exceed the capacity of the kidneys to reabsorb this nutrient. Glucose that remains in the kidney filtrate is excreted. For this reason, the presence of sugar in urine is one test for this disorder. As glucose is concentrated in the urine, more water is excreted along with it, resulting in excessive volumes of urine. *Diabetes* (from the Greek *diabainein*, to pass through) refers to this copious urination, and *mellitus* (from the Greek *meli*, honey) refers to the presence of sugar in urine.

Type 1 Diabetes There are two main types of diabetes mellitus. Each is marked by high blood glucose levels, but with very different causes. *Type 1 diabetes*, or insulin-dependent diabetes, is an autoimmune disorder in which the immune system destroys the beta cells of the pancreas. Type 1 diabetes, which usually appears during childhood, destroys the person's ability to produce insulin. Treatment consists of insulin injections, typically given several times daily. In the past, insulin was extracted from animal pancreases, but now human insulin can be obtained from genetically engineered bacteria, a relatively inexpensive source (see Figure 20.2). Stem cell research may someday provide a cure for type 1 diabetes by generating replacement beta cells that restore insulin production by the pancreas.

Type 2 Diabetes Non-insulin-dependent diabetes, or *type 2 diabetes*, is characterized by a failure of target cells to respond normally to insulin. Insulin is produced, but target cells fail to take up glucose from the blood, and blood glucose levels remain elevated. Although heredity can play a role in type 2 diabetes, excess body weight and lack of exercise significantly increase the risk. This form of diabetes generally appears after age 40, but even children can develop the disease, particularly if they are overweight and sedentary. More than 90% of people with diabetes have type 2. Many can control their blood glucose levels with regular exercise and a healthy diet; some require medications. Nevertheless, type 2 diabetes is the seventh most common cause of death in the United States and a growing public health problem worldwide.

The resistance to insulin signaling in type 2 diabetes is sometimes due to a genetic defect in the insulin receptor or the insulin response pathway. In many cases, however, events in target cells suppress activity of an otherwise functional response pathway. One source of this suppression appears to be inflammatory signals generated by the innate immune system (see Chapter 43). How obesity and inactivity relate to this suppression is being studied in both humans and laboratory animals.

Regulation of Appetite and Consumption

Consuming more calories than the body needs for normal metabolism, or *overnourishment*, can lead to obesity, the excessive accumulation of fat. Obesity, in turn, contributes to a number of health problems, including type 2 diabetes, cancer of the colon and breast, and cardiovascular disease that can result in heart attacks and strokes. It is estimated that obesity is a factor in about 300,000 deaths per year in the United States alone.

Researchers have discovered several homeostatic mechanisms that operate as feedback circuits controlling the storage and metabolism of fat. A network of neurons relays and integrates information from the digestive system to regulate secretion of hormones that regulate long-term and short-term appetite. The target for these hormones is a "satiety center" in the brain **(Figure 41.22)**. For example, *ghrelin*, a hormone secreted by the stomach wall, triggers feelings of hunger before meals. In contrast, both insulin and *PYY*, a hormone secreted by the small intestine after meals,

Satiety center

Ghrelin +

Insulin −

Leptin −

PYY −

Secreted by the stomach wall, **ghrelin** is one of the signals that triggers feelings of hunger as mealtimes approach. In dieters who lose weight, ghrelin levels increase, which may be one reason it's so hard to stay on a diet.

A rise in blood sugar level after a meal stimulates the pancreas to secrete **insulin**. In addition to its other functions, insulin suppresses appetite by acting on the brain.

Produced by adipose (fat) tissue, **leptin** suppresses appetite. When the amount of body fat decreases, leptin levels fall, and appetite increases.

The hormone **PYY**, secreted by the small intestine after meals, acts as an appetite suppressant that counters the appetite stimulant ghrelin.

© 2003 AAAS

▲ **Figure 41.22 A few of the appetite-regulating hormones.** Secreted by various organs and tissues, the hormones reach the brain via the bloodstream. These signals act on a region of the brain that in turn controls the "satiety center," which generates the nervous impulses that make us feel either hungry or satiated ("full"). The hormone ghrelin is an appetite stimulant; the other three hormones shown here are appetite suppressants.

Interpreting Data from Experiments with Genetic Mutants

What Are the Roles of the *ob* and *db* Genes in Appetite Regulation? A mutation that disrupts a physiological process is often used to study the normal function of the mutated gene. Ideally, researchers use a standard set of conditions and compare animals that differ genetically only in whether a particular gene is mutant (nonfunctional) or wild-type (normal). In this way, a difference in phenotype, the physiological property being measured, can be attributed to a difference in genotype, the presence or absence of the mutation. To study the role of specific genes in regulating appetite, researchers used laboratory animals with known mutations in those genes.

Mice in which recessive mutations inactivate both copies of either the *ob* gene or the *db* gene eat voraciously and grow much more massive than wild-type mice. In the photograph below, the mouse on the right is wild-type, whereas the obese mouse on the left has an inactivating mutation in both copies of the *ob* gene.

One hypothesis for the normal role of the *ob* and *db* genes is that they participate in a hormone pathway that suppresses appetite when caloric intake is sufficient. Before setting out to isolate the potential hormone, researchers explored this hypothesis genetically.

How the Experiment Was Done The researchers measured the mass of young subject mice of various genotypes and surgically linked the circulatory system of each one to that of another mouse. This procedure ensured that any factor circulating in the bloodstream of either mouse would be transferred to the other in the pair. After eight weeks, they again measured the mass of each subject mouse.

Data from the Experiment

	Genotype Pairing (red type indicates mutant genes)		Average Change in Body Mass of Subject (g)
	Subject	**Paired with**	
(a)	$ob^+/ob^+, db^+/db^+$	$ob^+/ob^+, db^+/db^+$	8.3
(b)	*ob/ob, db⁺/db⁺*	*ob/ob, db⁺/db⁺*	38.7
(c)	*ob/ob, db⁺/db⁺*	$ob^+/ob^+, db^+/db^+$	8.2
(d)	*ob/ob, db⁺/db⁺*	ob^+/ob^+, *db/db*	−14.9*

*Due to pronounced weight loss and weakening, subjects in this pairing were remeasured after less than eight weeks.

Interpret the Data

1. First, practice reading the genotype information given in the data table. For example, pairing (a) joined two mice that each had the wild-type version of both genes. Describe the two mice in pairing (b), pairing (c), and pairing (d). Explain how each pairing contributed to the experimental design.

2. Compare the results observed for pairing (a) and pairing (b) in terms of phenotype. If the results had been identical for these two pairings, what would that outcome have implied about the experimental design?

3. Compare the results observed for pairing (c) to those observed for pairing (b). Based on these results, does the ob^+ gene product appear to promote or suppress appetite? Explain your answer.

4. Describe the results observed for pairing (d). Note how these results differ from those for pairing (b). Suggest a hypothesis to explain this difference. How could you test your hypothesis using the kinds of mice in this study?

(MB) A version of this Scientific Skills Exercise can be assigned in MasteringBiology.

Data from D. L. Coleman, Effects of parabiosis of obese mice with diabetes and normal mice, *Diabetologia* 9:294–298 (1973).

---

suppress appetite. *Leptin*, a hormone produced by adipose (fat) tissue, also suppresses appetite and appears to play a major role in regulating body fat levels. In the Scientific Skills Exercise, you'll interpret data from an experiment studying genes that affect leptin production and function in mice.

Obtaining food, digesting it, and absorbing nutrients are part of the larger story of how animals fuel their activities. Provisioning the body also involves distributing nutrients (circulation), and using nutrients for metabolism requires exchanging respiratory gases with the environment. These processes and the adaptations that facilitate them are the focus of Chapter 42.

CONCEPT CHECK 41.5

1. Explain how people can become obese even if their intake of dietary fat is relatively low compared with carbohydrate intake.

2. **WHAT IF?** Suppose you were studying two groups of obese people with genetic abnormalities in the leptin pathway. In one group, the leptin levels are abnormally high; in the other group, they are abnormally low. How would each group's leptin levels change if they ate a low-calorie diet for an extended period? Explain.

3. **WHAT IF?** An insulinoma is a cancerous mass of pancreatic beta cells that secrete insulin but do not respond to feedback mechanisms. How you would expect an insulinoma to affect blood glucose levels and liver activity?

For suggested answers, see Appendix A.

SUMMARY OF KEY CONCEPTS

- Animals have diverse diets. **Herbivores** mainly eat plants; **carnivores** mainly eat other animals; and **omnivores** eat both. In meeting their nutritional needs, animals must balance consumption, storage, and use of food.

CONCEPT 41.1

An animal's diet must supply chemical energy, organic molecules, and essential nutrients (pp. 893–897)

- Food provides animals with energy for ATP production, carbon skeletons for biosynthesis, and **essential nutrients**—nutrients that must be supplied in preassembled form. Essential nutrients include certain amino acids and fatty acids that animals cannot synthesize; **vitamins**, which are organic molecules; and **minerals**, which are inorganic substances.
- Animals can suffer from two types of malnutrition: an inadequate intake of essential nutrients and a deficiency in sources of chemical energy. Studies of disease at the population level help researchers determine human dietary requirements.

? *How can an enzyme cofactor needed for a process that is vital to all animals be an essential nutrient (vitamin) for only some?*

CONCEPT 41.2

The main stages of food processing are ingestion, digestion, absorption, and elimination (pp. 897–900)

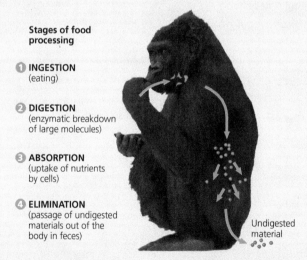

Stages of food processing

1. **INGESTION** (eating)
2. **DIGESTION** (enzymatic breakdown of large molecules)
3. **ABSORPTION** (uptake of nutrients by cells)
4. **ELIMINATION** (passage of undigested materials out of the body in feces)

Undigested material

- Animals differ in the ways they obtain and ingest food. Many animals are **bulk feeders**, eating large pieces of food. Other strategies include filter feeding, suspension feeding, and fluid feeding.
- Compartmentalization is necessary to avoid self-digestion. In intracellular digestion, food particles are engulfed by endocytosis and digested within food vacuoles that have fused with lysosomes. In extracellular digestion, which is used by most animals, enzymatic hydrolysis occurs outside cells in a **gastrovascular cavity** or **alimentary canal**.

? *Propose an artificial diet that would eliminate the need for one of the first three steps in food processing.*

CONCEPT 41.3

Organs specialized for sequential stages of food processing form the mammalian digestive system (pp. 900–906)

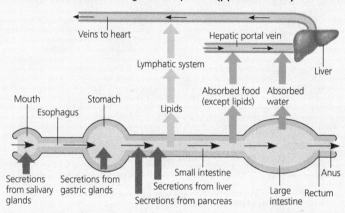

Veins to heart | Hepatic portal vein | Liver
Lymphatic system
Mouth | Stomach | Lipids | Absorbed food (except lipids) | Absorbed water
Esophagus
Secretions from salivary glands | Secretions from gastric glands | Secretions from liver | Small intestine | Secretions from pancreas | Large intestine | Rectum | Anus

? *What structural feature of the small intestine makes it better suited for absorption of nutrients than the stomach?*

CONCEPT 41.4

Evolutionary adaptations of vertebrate digestive systems correlate with diet (pp. 906–908)

- Vertebrate digestive systems display many evolutionary adaptations associated with diet. For example, dentition, which is the assortment of teeth, generally correlates with diet. In a form of mutualism, many herbivores, including cows, have fermentation chambers where microorganisms digest cellulose. Herbivores also usually have longer alimentary canals than carnivores, reflecting the longer time needed to digest vegetation.

? *How does human anatomy indicate that our primate ancestors were not strict vegetarians?*

CONCEPT 41.5

Feedback circuits regulate digestion, energy storage, and appetite (pp. 908–912)

- **Nutrition** is regulated at multiple levels. Food in the alimentary canal triggers nervous and hormonal responses that control the secretion of digestive juices and that promote the movement of ingested material through the canal. The availability of glucose for energy production is regulated by the hormones **insulin** and **glucagon**, which control the synthesis and breakdown of glycogen.
- Vertebrates store excess calories in glycogen (in liver and muscle cells) and in fat (in adipose cells). These energy stores can be tapped when an animal expends more calories than it consumes. If, however, an animal consumes more calories than it needs for normal metabolism, the resulting overnourishment can lead to the serious health problem of obesity.
- Several hormones, including leptin and insulin, regulate appetite by affecting the brain's satiety center.

? *Explain why your stomach might make growling noises when you skip a meal.*

TEST YOUR UNDERSTANDING

LEVEL 1: KNOWLEDGE/COMPREHENSION

1. Fat digestion yields fatty acids and glycerol, whereas protein digestion yields amino acids. Both digestive processes
   a. occur inside cells in most animals.
   b. add a water molecule to break bonds.
   c. require a low pH resulting from HCl production.
   d. consume ATP.

2. The mammalian trachea and esophagus both connect to the
   a. pharynx.
   b. stomach.
   c. large intestine.
   d. rectum.

3. Which of the following organs is *incorrectly* paired with its function?
   a. stomach—protein digestion
   b. large intestine—bile production
   c. small intestine—nutrient absorption
   d. pancreas—enzyme production

4. Which of the following is *not* a major activity of the stomach?
   a. mechanical digestion
   b. HCl production
   c. nutrient absorption
   d. enzyme secretion

LEVEL 2: APPLICATION/ANALYSIS

5. After surgical removal of an infected gallbladder, a person must be especially careful to restrict dietary intake of
   a. starch.
   b. protein.
   c. sugar.
   d. fat.

6. If you were to jog 1 km a few hours after lunch, which stored fuel would you probably tap?
   a. muscle proteins
   b. muscle and liver glycogen
   c. fat in the liver
   d. fat in adipose tissue

LEVEL 3: SYNTHESIS/EVALUATION

7. **DRAW IT** Make a flowchart of the events that occur after partially digested food leaves the stomach. Use the following terms: bicarbonate secretion, circulation, decrease in acidity, increase in acidity, secretin secretion, signal detection. Next to each term, indicate the compartment(s) involved. You may use terms more than once.

8. EVOLUTION CONNECTION
   The human esophagus and trachea share a passage leading from the mouth and nasal passages, which can cause problems. After reviewing vertebrate evolution (see Chapter 34), explain how the evolutionary concept of descent with modification explains this "imperfect" anatomy.

9. SCIENTIFIC INQUIRY
   In human populations of northern European origin, the disorder called hemochromatosis causes excess iron uptake from food and affects one in 200 adults. Among adults, men are ten times as likely as women to suffer from iron overload. Taking into account the existence of a menstrual cycle in humans, devise a hypothesis that explains this difference.

10. WRITE ABOUT A THEME: ORGANIZATION
    Hair is largely made up of the protein keratin. In a short essay (100–150 words), explain why a shampoo containing protein is not effective in replacing the protein in damaged hair.

11. SYNTHESIZE YOUR KNOWLEDGE

Hummingbirds are well adapted to obtain sugary nectar from flowers, but they use some of the energy obtained from nectar when they forage for insects and spiders. Explain why this foraging is necessary.

For selected answers, see Appendix A.

MasteringBiology®

Students Go to **MasteringBiology** for assignments, the eText, and the Study Area with practice tests, animations, and activities.

Instructors Go to **MasteringBiology** for automatically graded tutorials and questions that you can assign to your students, plus Instructor Resources.

42

Circulation and Gas Exchange

▲ Figure 42.1 **How does a feathery fringe help this animal survive?**

Trading Places

The animal in **Figure 42.1** may look like a creature from a science fiction film, but it's actually an axolotl, a salamander native to shallow ponds in central Mexico. The feathery red appendages jutting out from the head of this albino adult are gills. Although external gills are uncommon in adult animals, they help the axolotl carry out a process common to all organisms—the exchange of substances between body cells and the environment.

The exchange of substances between an axolotl or any other animal and its surroundings ultimately occurs at the cellular level. The resources that an animal cell requires, such as nutrients and oxygen (O_2), enter the cytoplasm by crossing the plasma membrane. Metabolic by-products, such as carbon dioxide (CO_2), exit the cell by crossing the same membrane. In unicellular organisms, exchange occurs directly with the external environment. For most multicellular organisms, however, direct transfer of materials between every cell and the environment is not possible. Instead, these organisms rely on specialized systems that carry out exchange with the environment and that transport materials between sites of exchange and the rest of the body.

The reddish color and the branching structure of the axolotl's gills reflect the intimate association between exchange and transport. Tiny blood vessels lie close

915

to the surface of each filament in the gills. Across this surface, there is a net diffusion of O_2 from the surrounding water into the blood and of CO_2 from the blood into the water. The short distances involved allow diffusion to be rapid. Pumping of the axolotl's heart propels the oxygen-rich blood from the gill filaments to all other tissues of the body. There, more short-range exchange occurs, involving nutrients and O_2 as well as CO_2 and other wastes.

Because internal transport and gas exchange are functionally related in most animals, not just axolotls, we'll discuss circulatory and respiratory systems together in this chapter. By considering examples of these systems from a range of species, we'll explore the common elements as well as the remarkable variation in form and organization. We'll also highlight the roles of circulatory and respiratory systems in maintaining homeostasis.

CONCEPT 42.1

Circulatory systems link exchange surfaces with cells throughout the body

The molecular trade that an animal carries out with its environment—gaining O_2 and nutrients while shedding CO_2 and other waste products—must ultimately involve every cell in the body. Small molecules, including O_2 and CO_2, can move between cells and their immediate surroundings by diffusion (see Chapter 7). When there is a difference in concentration, diffusion can result in net movement. But such movement is very slow for distances of more than a few millimeters. That's because the time it takes for a substance to diffuse from one place to another is proportional to the *square* of the distance. For example, a quantity of glucose that takes 1 second to diffuse 100 μm will take 100 seconds to diffuse 1 mm and almost 3 hours to diffuse 1 cm! This relationship between diffusion time and distance places a substantial constraint on the body plan of any animal.

Given that net movement by diffusion is rapid only over very small distances, how does each cell of an animal participate in exchange? Natural selection has resulted in two basic adaptations that permit effective exchange for all of an animal's cells. One adaptation is a body plan that places many or all cells in direct contact with the environment. Each cell can thus exchange materials directly with the surrounding medium. This type of body plan is found only in certain invertebrates, including cnidarians and flatworms. The other adaptation, found in all other animals, is a circulatory system. Such systems move fluid between each cell's immediate surroundings and the body tissues where exchange with the environment occurs.

Gastrovascular Cavities

Let's begin by looking at some animals whose body shapes put many of their cells into contact with their environment, enabling them to live without a distinct circulatory system. In hydras, jellies, and other cnidarians, a central **gastrovascular cavity** functions in the distribution of substances throughout the body, as well as in digestion (see Figure 41.7). An opening at one end connects the cavity to the surrounding water. In a hydra, thin branches of the gastrovascular cavity extend into the animal's tentacles. In jellies and some other cnidarians, the gastrovascular cavity has a much more elaborate branching pattern **(Figure 42.2a)**.

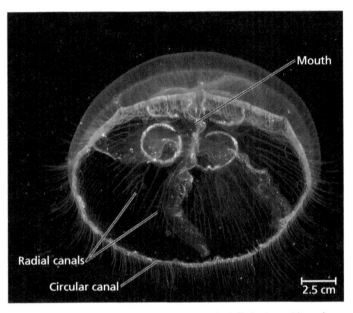

(a) The moon jelly *Aurelia*, a cnidarian. The jelly is viewed here from its underside (oral surface). The mouth leads to an elaborate gastrovascular cavity that consists of radial canals leading to and from a circular canal. Ciliated cells lining the canals circulate fluid within the cavity.

(b) The planarian *Dugesia*, a flatworm. The mouth and pharynx on the ventral side lead to the highly branched gastrovascular cavity, stained dark red in this specimen (LM).

▲ **Figure 42.2 Internal transport in gastrovascular cavities.**

WHAT IF? *Suppose a gastrovascular cavity were open at two ends, with fluid entering one end and leaving the other. How would this affect the cavity's functions in gas exchange and digestion?*

In animals with a gastrovascular cavity, fluid bathes both the inner and outer tissue layers, facilitating exchange of gases and cellular waste. Only the cells lining the cavity have direct access to nutrients released by digestion. However, because the body wall is a mere two cells thick, nutrients need diffuse only a short distance to reach the cells of the outer tissue layer.

Planarians and most other flatworms also survive without a circulatory system. Their combination of a gastrovascular cavity and a flat body is well suited for exchange with the environment (Figure 42.2b). A flat body optimizes exchange by increasing surface area and minimizing diffusion distances.

Open and Closed Circulatory Systems

A circulatory system has three basic components: a circulatory fluid, a set of interconnecting vessels, and a muscular pump, the **heart**. The heart powers circulation by using metabolic energy to elevate the circulatory fluid's hydrostatic pressure, the pressure the fluid exerts on surrounding vessels. The fluid then flows through the vessels and back to the heart.

By transporting fluid throughout the body, the circulatory system functionally connects the aqueous environment of the body cells to the organs that exchange gases, absorb nutrients, and dispose of wastes. In mammals, for example, O_2 from inhaled air diffuses across only two layers of cells in the lungs before reaching the blood. The circulatory system then carries the oxygen-rich blood to all parts of the body. As the blood courses throughout the body tissues in tiny blood vessels, O_2 in the blood diffuses only a short distance before entering the fluid that directly bathes the cells.

Circulatory systems are either open or closed. In an **open circulatory system**, the circulatory fluid, called **hemolymph**, is also the *interstitial fluid* that bathes body cells. Arthropods, such as grasshoppers, and some molluscs, including clams, have open circulatory systems. Heart contraction pumps the hemolymph through the circulatory vessels into interconnected sinuses, spaces surrounding the organs (Figure 42.3a). Within the sinuses, chemical exchange occurs between the hemolymph and body cells. Relaxation of the heart draws hemolymph back in through pores, which are equipped with valves that close when the heart contracts. Body movements periodically squeeze the sinuses, helping circulate the hemolymph. The open circulatory system of larger crustaceans, such as lobsters and crabs, includes a more extensive system of vessels as well as an accessory pump.

In a **closed circulatory system**, a circulatory fluid called **blood** is confined to vessels and is distinct from the interstitial fluid (Figure 42.3b). One or more hearts pump blood into large vessels that branch into smaller ones that infiltrate the organs. Chemical exchange occurs between the blood

▼ Figure 42.3 **Open and closed circulatory systems.**

(a) An open circulatory system

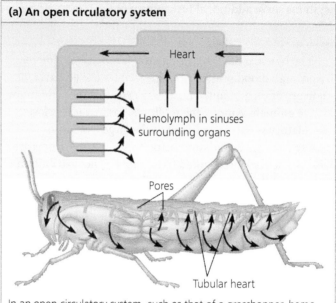

In an open circulatory system, such as that of a grasshopper, hemolymph surrounding body tissues also acts as the circulatory fluid.

(b) A closed circulatory system

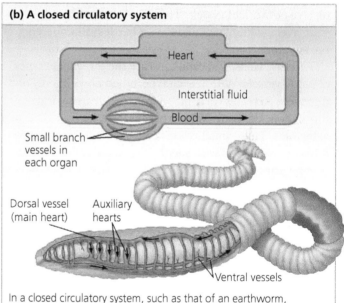

In a closed circulatory system, such as that of an earthworm, interstitial fluid surrounding body tissues is distinct from blood acting as the circulatory fluid.

and the interstitial fluid, as well as between the interstitial fluid and body cells. Annelids (including earthworms), cephalopods (including squids and octopuses), and all vertebrates have closed circulatory systems.

The fact that both open and closed circulatory systems are widespread among animals suggests that each system offers evolutionary advantages. The lower hydrostatic pressures typically associated with open circulatory systems make them less costly than closed systems in terms of energy expenditure. In some invertebrates, open circulatory systems serve additional functions. For example, spiders use the hydrostatic pressure generated by their open circulatory system to extend their legs.

The benefits of closed circulatory systems include relatively high blood pressure, which enables the effective delivery of O_2 and nutrients to the cells of larger and more active animals. Among the molluscs, for instance, closed circulatory systems are found in the largest and most active species, the squids and octopuses. Closed systems are also particularly well suited to regulating the distribution of blood to different organs, as you'll learn later in this chapter. In examining closed circulatory systems in more detail, we'll focus on vertebrates.

Organization of Vertebrate Circulatory Systems

The closed circulatory system of humans and other vertebrates is often called the **cardiovascular system**. Blood circulates to and from the heart through an amazingly extensive network of vessels: The total length of blood vessels in an average human adult is twice Earth's circumference at the equator!

Arteries, veins, and capillaries are the three main types of blood vessels. Within each type, blood flows in only one direction. **Arteries** carry blood from the heart to organs throughout the body. Within organs, arteries branch into **arterioles**. These small vessels convey blood to **capillaries**, microscopic vessels with very thin, porous walls. Networks of capillaries, called **capillary beds**, infiltrate tissues, passing within a few cell diameters of every cell in the body. Across the thin walls of capillaries, chemicals, including dissolved gases, are exchanged by diffusion between the blood and the interstitial fluid around the tissue cells. At their "downstream" end, capillaries converge into **venules**, and venules converge into **veins**, the vessels that carry blood back to the heart.

Note that arteries and veins are distinguished by the *direction* in which they carry blood, not by the O_2 content or other characteristics of the blood they contain. Arteries carry blood *away* from the heart toward capillaries, and veins return blood *toward* the heart from capillaries. The only exceptions are the portal veins, which carry blood between pairs of capillary beds. The hepatic portal vein, for example, carries blood from capillary beds in the digestive system to capillary beds in the liver (see Chapter 41).

The hearts of all vertebrates contain two or more muscular chambers. The chambers that receive blood entering the heart are called **atria** (singular, *atrium*). The chambers responsible for pumping blood out of the heart are called **ventricles**. The number of chambers and the extent to which they are separated from one another differ substantially among groups of vertebrates, as we'll discuss next. These important differences reflect the close fit of form to function that arises from natural selection.

Single Circulation

In bony fishes, rays, and sharks, the heart consists of two chambers: an atrium and a ventricle **(Figure 42.4a)**. The blood passes through the heart once in each complete circuit through the body, an arrangement called **single circulation**. Blood entering the heart collects in the atrium before transfer to the ventricle. Contraction of the ventricle pumps blood to a capillary bed in the gills, where there is a net diffusion of O_2 into the blood and of CO_2 out of the blood. As blood leaves the gills, the capillaries converge into a vessel that carries oxygen-rich blood to capillary beds throughout the body. Blood then returns to the heart.

In single circulation, blood that leaves the heart passes through two capillary beds before returning to the heart. When blood flows through a capillary bed, blood pressure drops substantially, for reasons we'll explain shortly. The drop in blood pressure in the gills limits the rate of blood flow in the rest of the animal's body. As the animal swims, however, the contraction and relaxation of its muscles help accelerate the relatively sluggish pace of circulation.

Double Circulation

The circulatory systems of amphibians, reptiles, and mammals have two circuits, an arrangement called **double circulation (Figure 42.4b and c)**. In animals with double circulation, the pumps for the two circuits are combined into a single organ, the heart. Having both pumps within a single heart simplifies coordination of the pumping cycles. One pump, the right side of the heart, delivers oxygen-poor blood to the capillary beds of the gas exchange tissues, where there is a net movement of O_2 into the blood and of CO_2 out of the blood. This part of the circulation is called a *pulmonary circuit* if the capillary beds involved are all in the lungs, as in reptiles and mammals. It is called a *pulmocutaneous circuit* if it includes capillaries in both the lungs and the skin, as in many amphibians.

After the oxygen-enriched blood leaves the gas exchange tissues, it enters the other pump, the left side of the heart. Contraction of the heart propels this blood to capillary beds in organs and tissues throughout the body. Following the exchange of O_2 and CO_2, as well as nutrients and waste products, the now oxygen-poor blood returns to the heart, completing the **systemic circuit**.

Double circulation provides a vigorous flow of blood to the brain, muscles, and other organs because the heart repressurizes the blood destined for these tissues after it passes through the capillary beds of the lungs or skin.

▼ **Figure 42.4 Examples of vertebrate circulatory schemes.**

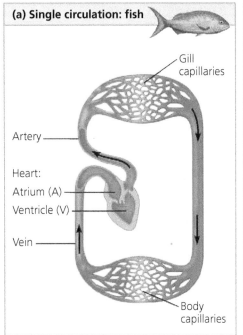

(a) Single circulation: fish

Gill capillaries

Artery

Heart:
Atrium (A)
Ventricle (V)

Vein

Body capillaries

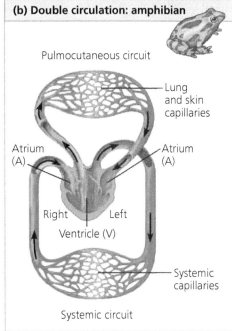

(b) Double circulation: amphibian

Pulmocutaneous circuit

Lung and skin capillaries

Atrium (A)

Atrium (A)

Right   Left

Ventricle (V)

Systemic capillaries

Systemic circuit

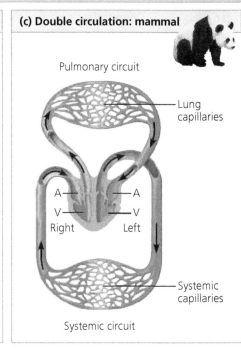

(c) Double circulation: mammal

Pulmonary circuit

Lung capillaries

A   A
V   V
Right   Left

Systemic capillaries

Systemic circuit

Key
■ Oxygen-rich blood
■ Oxygen-poor blood

(Note that circulatory systems are shown as if the body were facing you: The right side of the heart is shown on the left, and vice versa.)

Indeed, blood pressure is often much higher in the systemic circuit than in the gas exchange circuit. In contrast, with single circulation blood flows under reduced pressure directly from the gas exchange organs to other organs.

Evolutionary Variation in Double Circulation

EVOLUTION Some vertebrates with double circulation are intermittent breathers. For example, amphibians and many reptiles fill their lungs with air periodically, passing long periods without gas exchange or relying on another gas exchange tissue, typically the skin. These animals have adaptations that enable the circulatory system to temporarily bypass the lungs in part or in whole:

- Frogs and other amphibians have a heart with three chambers—two atria and one ventricle (see Figure 42.4b). A ridge within the ventricle diverts most (about 90%) of the oxygen-rich blood from the left atrium into the systemic circuit and most of the oxygen-poor blood from the right atrium into the pulmocutaneous circuit. When a frog is underwater, the incomplete division of the ventricle allows the frog to adjust its circulation, shutting off most blood flow to its temporarily ineffective lungs. Blood flow continues to the skin, which acts as the sole site of gas exchange while the frog is submerged.

- In the three-chambered heart of turtles, snakes, and lizards, an incomplete septum partially divides the single

ventricle into separate right and left chambers. Two major arteries, called aortas, lead to the systemic circulation. As with amphibians, the circulatory system enables control of the relative amount of blood flowing to the lungs and the rest of the body.

- In alligators, caimans, and other crocodilians, the ventricles are divided by a complete septum, but the pulmonary and systemic circuits connect where the arteries exit the heart. This connection allows arterial valves to shunt blood flow away from the lungs temporarily, such as when the animal is underwater.

Double circulation in birds and mammals is quite different from that in other vertebrates. As shown for a panda in Figure 42.4c, the heart has two atria and two completely divided ventricles. The left side of the heart receives and pumps only oxygen-rich blood, while the right side receives and pumps only oxygen-poor blood. Unlike amphibians and many reptiles, birds and mammals cannot vary blood flow to the lungs without varying blood flow throughout the body in parallel.

How has natural selection shaped the double circulation of birds and mammals? As endotherms, birds and mammals use about ten times as much energy as equal-sized ectotherms. Their circulatory systems therefore need to deliver about ten times as much fuel and O_2 to their tissues and remove ten times as much CO_2 and other wastes. This large traffic of substances is made possible by the separate and independently powered systemic and pulmonary circuits and by large hearts that pump the necessary volume of blood. A powerful four-chambered heart arose independently in the distinct ancestors of birds and mammals and thus reflects convergent evolution (see Chapter 34).

In the next section, we'll restrict our focus to circulation in mammals and to the anatomy and physiology of the key circulatory organ—the heart.

CONCEPT CHECK 42.1

1. How is the flow of hemolymph through an open circulatory system similar to the flow of water through an outdoor fountain?

2. Three-chambered hearts with incomplete septa were once viewed as being less adapted to circulatory function than mammalian hearts. What advantage of such hearts did this viewpoint overlook?

3. **WHAT IF?** The heart of a normally developing human fetus has a hole between the left and right atria. In some cases, this hole does not close completely before birth. If the hole weren't surgically corrected, how would it affect the O_2 content of the blood entering the systemic circuit?

For suggested answers, see Appendix A.

CONCEPT 42.2

Coordinated cycles of heart contraction drive double circulation in mammals

The timely delivery of O_2 to the body's organs is critical: Some brain cells, for example, die if their O_2 supply is interrupted for as little as a few minutes. How does the mammalian cardiovascular system meet the body's continuous (although variable) demand for O_2? To answer this question, we must consider how the parts of the system are arranged and how each part functions.

Mammalian Circulation

Let's first examine the overall organization of the mammalian cardiovascular system, beginning with the pulmonary circuit. (The circled numbers refer to corresponding locations in **Figure 42.5**.) Contraction of ❶ the right ventricle pumps blood to the lungs via ❷ the pulmonary arteries. As the blood flows through ❸ capillary beds in the left and right lungs, it loads O_2 and unloads CO_2. Oxygen-rich blood returns from the lungs via the pulmonary veins to ❹ the left atrium of the heart. Next, the oxygen-rich blood flows into ❺ the heart's left ventricle, which pumps the oxygen-rich blood out to body tissues through the systemic circuit. Blood leaves the left ventricle via ❻ the aorta, which conveys blood to arteries leading throughout the body. The first

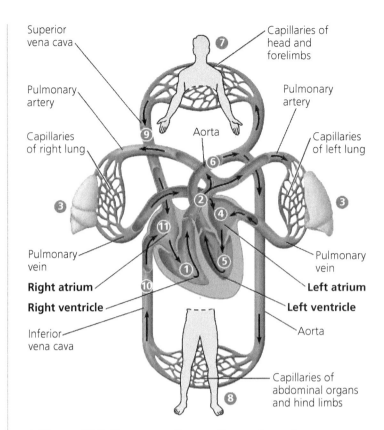

Superior vena cava

Capillaries of head and forelimbs

Pulmonary artery

Pulmonary artery

Aorta

Capillaries of right lung

Capillaries of left lung

Pulmonary vein

Pulmonary vein

Right atrium

Left atrium

Right ventricle

Left ventricle

Inferior vena cava

Aorta

Capillaries of abdominal organs and hind limbs

▲ **Figure 42.5 The mammalian cardiovascular system: an overview.** Note that the dual circuits operate simultaneously, not in the serial fashion that the numbering in the diagram suggests. The two ventricles pump in unison; while some blood is traveling in the pulmonary circuit, the rest of the blood is flowing in the systemic circuit.

branches leading from the aorta are the coronary arteries (not shown), which supply blood to the heart muscle itself. Then branches lead to ❼ capillary beds in the head and arms (forelimbs). The aorta then descends into the abdomen, supplying oxygen-rich blood to arteries leading to ❽ capillary beds in the abdominal organs and legs (hind limbs). Within the capillaries, there is a net diffusion of O_2 from the blood to the tissues and of CO_2 (produced by cellular respiration) into the blood. Capillaries rejoin, forming venules, which convey blood to veins. Oxygen-poor blood from the head, neck, and forelimbs is channeled into a large vein, ❾ the superior vena cava. Another large vein, ❿ the inferior vena cava, drains blood from the trunk and hind limbs. The two venae cavae empty their blood into ⓫ the right atrium, from which the oxygen-poor blood flows into the right ventricle.

The Mammalian Heart: *A Closer Look*

Using the human heart as an example, let's now take a closer look at how the mammalian heart works (**Figure 42.6**). Located behind the sternum (breastbone), the human heart is about the size of a clenched fist and consists mostly of cardiac muscle (see Figure 40.5). The two atria have relatively

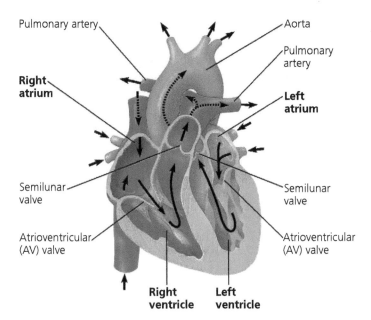

Pulmonary artery

Aorta

Pulmonary artery

Right atrium

Left atrium

Semilunar valve

Semilunar valve

Atrioventricular (AV) valve

Atrioventricular (AV) valve

Right ventricle

Left ventricle

▲ **Figure 42.6 The mammalian heart: a closer look.** Notice the locations of the valves, which prevent backflow of blood within the heart. Also notice how the atria and left and right ventricles differ in the thickness of their muscular walls.

❶ Atrial and ventricular diastole. During a relaxation phase, blood returning from the large veins flows into the atria and then into the ventricles through the AV valves.

❷ Atrial systole and ventricular diastole. A brief period of atrial contraction then forces all blood remaining in the atria into the ventricles.

0.1 sec

0.3 sec

0.4 sec

❸ Ventricular systole and atrial diastole. During the remainder of the cycle, ventricular contraction pumps blood into the large arteries through the semilunar valves.

▲ **Figure 42.7 The cardiac cycle.** For an adult human at rest with a heart rate of about 72 beats per minute, one complete cardiac cycle takes about 0.8 second. Note that during all but 0.1 second of the cardiac cycle, the atria are relaxed and are filling with blood returning via the veins.

thin walls and serve as collection chambers for blood returning to the heart from the lungs or other body tissues. Much of the blood that enters the atria flows into the ventricles while all heart chambers are relaxed. The remainder is transferred by contraction of the atria before the ventricles begin to contract. Compared to the atria, the ventricles have thicker walls and contract much more forcefully—especially the left ventricle, which pumps blood throughout the body via the systemic circuit. Although the left ventricle contracts with greater force than the right ventricle, it pumps the same volume of blood as the right ventricle during each contraction.

The heart contracts and relaxes in a rhythmic cycle. When it contracts, it pumps blood; when it relaxes, its chambers fill with blood. One complete sequence of pumping and filling is referred to as the **cardiac cycle**. The contraction phase of the cycle is called **systole**, and the relaxation phase is called **diastole** (Figure 42.7).

The volume of blood each ventricle pumps per minute is the **cardiac output**. Two factors determine cardiac output: the rate of contraction, or **heart rate** (number of beats per minute), and the **stroke volume**, the amount of blood pumped by a ventricle in a single contraction. The average stroke volume in humans is about 70 mL. Multiplying this stroke volume by a resting heart rate of 72 beats per minute yields a cardiac output of 5 L/min—about equal to the total volume of blood in the human body. During heavy exercise, cardiac output increases as much as fivefold.

Four valves in the heart prevent backflow and keep blood moving in the correct direction (see Figures 42.6 and 42.7).

Made of flaps of connective tissue, the valves open when pushed from one side and close when pushed from the other. An **atrioventricular (AV) valve** lies between each atrium and ventricle. The AV valves are anchored by strong fibers that prevent them from turning inside out. Pressure generated by the powerful contraction of the ventricles closes the AV valves, keeping blood from flowing back into the atria. **Semilunar valves** are located at the two exits of the heart: where the aorta leaves the left ventricle and where the pulmonary artery leaves the right ventricle. These valves are pushed open by the pressure generated during contraction of the ventricles. When the ventricles relax, blood pressure built up in the aorta and pulmonary artery closes the semilunar valves and prevents significant backflow.

You can follow the closing of the two sets of heart valves either with a stethoscope or by pressing your ear tightly against the chest of a friend (or a friendly dog). The sound pattern is "lub-dup, lub-dup, lub-dup." The first heart sound ("lub") is created by the recoil of blood against the closed AV valves. The second sound ("dup") is due to the vibrations caused by closing of the semilunar valves.

If blood squirts backward through a defective valve, it may produce an abnormal sound called a **heart murmur**. Some people are born with heart murmurs; in others, the valves may be damaged by infection (from rheumatic fever, for instance). When a valve defect is severe enough to endanger health, surgeons may implant a mechanical replacement valve. However, not all heart murmurs are caused by a defect, and most valve defects do not reduce the efficiency of blood flow enough to warrant surgery.

Maintaining the Heart's Rhythmic Beat

In vertebrates, the heartbeat originates in the heart itself. Some cardiac muscle cells are autorhythmic, meaning they can contract and relax repeatedly without any signal from the nervous system. You can see these rhythmic contractions in tissue that has been removed from the heart and placed in a dish in the laboratory! Because each of these cells has its own intrinsic contraction rhythm, how are their contractions coordinated in the intact heart? The answer lies in a group of autorhythmic cells located in the wall of the right atrium, near where the superior vena cava enters the heart. This cluster of cells is called the **sinoatrial (SA) node**, or *pacemaker*, and it sets the rate and timing at which all cardiac muscle cells contract. (In contrast, some arthropods have pacemakers located in the nervous system, outside the heart.)

The SA node produces electrical impulses much like those produced by nerve cells. Because cardiac muscle cells are electrically coupled through gap junctions (see Figure 6.30), impulses from the SA node spread rapidly within heart tissue. In addition, these impulses generate currents that are conducted to the skin via body fluids. In an **electrocardiogram** (**ECG** or, often, **EKG**, from the German spelling), these currents are recorded by electrodes placed on the skin. The resulting graph of current against time has a characteristic shape that represents the stages in the cardiac cycle (**Figure 42.8**).

Impulses from the SA node first spread rapidly through the walls of the atria, causing both atria to contract in unison. During atrial contraction, the impulses originating at the SA node reach other autorhythmic cells located

in the wall between the left and right atria. These cells form a relay point called the **atrioventricular (AV) node**. Here the impulses are delayed for about 0.1 second before spreading to the heart apex. This delay allows the atria to empty completely before the ventricles contract. Then the signals from the AV node are conducted to the heart apex and throughout the ventricular walls by specialized structures called bundle branches and Purkinje fibers.

Physiological cues alter heart tempo by regulating the pacemaker function of the SA node. Two portions of the nervous system, the sympathetic and parasympathetic divisions, are largely responsible for this regulation. They function like the accelerator and brake in a car: For example, when you stand up and start walking, the sympathetic division speeds up your pacemaker. The resulting increase in heart rate provides the additional O_2 needed by the muscles that are powering your activity. If you then sit down and relax, the parasympathetic division slows down your pacemaker, decreasing your heart rate and thus conserving energy. Hormones secreted into the blood also influence the pacemaker. For instance, epinephrine, the "fight-or-flight" hormone secreted by the adrenal glands, speeds up the pacemaker. A third type of input that affects the pacemaker is body temperature. An increase of only 1°C raises the heart rate by about 10 beats per minute. This is the reason your heart beats faster when you have a fever.

Having examined the operation of the circulatory pump, we turn in the next section to the forces and structures that influence blood flow in the vessels of each circuit.

❶ Signals (yellow) from SA node spread through atria.

❷ Signals are delayed at AV node.

❸ Bundle branches pass signals to heart apex.

❹ Signals spread throughout ventricles.

SA node (pacemaker)

AV node

Bundle branches   Heart apex

Purkinje fibers

ECG

▲ **Figure 42.8 The control of heart rhythm.** Electrical signals follow a set path through the heart in establishing the heart rhythm. The diagrams at the top trace the movement of these signals (yellow) during the cardiac cycle; specialized muscle cells involved in controlling of the rhythm are indicated in orange. Under each step, the corresponding portion of an electrocardiogram (ECG) is highlighted (yellow). In step 4, the portion of the ECG to the right of the "spike" represents electrical activity that reprimes the ventricles for the next round of contraction.

WHAT IF? *If your doctor gave you a copy of your ECG recording, how could you determine what your heart rate had been during the test?*

CONCEPT CHECK 42.2

1. Explain why blood has a higher O_2 concentration in the pulmonary veins than in the venae cavae, which are also veins.

2. Why is it important that the AV node delay the electrical impulse moving from the SA node and the atria to the ventricles?

3. **WHAT IF?** After you exercise regularly for several months, your resting heart rate decreases, but your cardiac output at rest is unchanged. What other change in the function of your heart at rest could explain these findings?

For suggested answers, see Appendix A.

CONCEPT 42.3

Patterns of blood pressure and flow reflect the structure and arrangement of blood vessels

The vertebrate circulatory system enables blood to deliver oxygen and nutrients and remove wastes throughout the body. In doing so, the circulatory system relies on a branching network of vessels much like the plumbing system that delivers fresh water to a city and removes its wastes. In fact, the same physical principles that govern the operation of plumbing systems apply to the functioning of blood vessels.

Blood Vessel Structure and Function

Blood vessels contain a central lumen (cavity) lined with an **endothelium**, a single layer of flattened epithelial cells. The smooth surface of the endothelium minimizes resistance to the flow of blood. Surrounding the endothelium are layers of tissue that differ in capillaries, arteries, and veins, reflecting the specialized functions of these vessels.

Capillaries are the smallest blood vessels, having a diameter only slightly greater than that of a red blood cell (Figure 42.9). Capillaries also have very thin walls, which consist of just an endothelium and a surrounding extracellular layer called the *basal lamina*. The exchange of substances between the blood and interstitial fluid occurs only in capillaries because only there are blood vessel walls thin enough to permit this exchange.

The walls of arteries and veins have a more complex organization than those of capillaries. Both arteries and veins have two layers of tissue surrounding the endothelium. The outer layer is formed by connective tissue that contains elastic fibers, which allow the vessel to stretch and recoil, and collagen, which provides strength. The layer next to the endothelium contains smooth muscle and more elastic fibers.

While similar in organization, the walls of arteries and veins differ, reflecting distinct adaptations to the particular functions of these vessels in circulation. The walls of arteries are thick and strong, accommodating blood pumped at high pressure by the heart. They are also elastic. When the heart relaxes between contractions, the arterial walls recoil, helping maintain blood pressure and flow to capillaries. Signals from the nervous system and hormones circulating in the blood act on the smooth muscle in arteries and arterioles, dilating or constricting these vessels and thus controlling blood flow to different parts of the body.

▲ Figure 42.9 **The structure of blood vessels.**

Because veins convey blood back to the heart at a lower pressure, they do not require thick walls. For a given blood vessel diameter, a vein has a wall only about a third as thick as that of an artery. Unlike arteries, veins contain valves, which maintain a unidirectional flow of blood despite the low blood pressure in these vessels.

We consider next how blood vessel diameter, vessel number, and blood pressure influence the speed at which blood flows in different locations within the body.

Blood Flow Velocity

To understand how blood vessel diameter influences blood flow, consider how water flows through a thick hose connected to a faucet. When the faucet is turned on, water flows at the same velocity at each point along the hose. However, if a narrow nozzle is attached to the end of the hose, the water will exit the nozzle at a much greater velocity. Because water doesn't compress under pressure, the volume of water moving through the nozzle in a given time must be the same as the volume moving through the rest of the hose. The cross-sectional area of the nozzle is smaller than that of the hose, so the water speeds up in the nozzle.

An analogous situation exists in the circulatory system, but blood *slows* as it moves from arteries to arterioles to the much narrower capillaries. Why? The reason is that the number of capillaries is enormous, roughly 7 billion in a human body. Each artery conveys blood to so many capillaries that the *total* cross-sectional area is much greater in capillary beds than in the arteries or any other part of the circulatory system (Figure 42.10). The result is a dramatic decrease in velocity from the arteries to the capillaries: Blood travels 500 times more slowly in the capillaries (about 0.1 cm/sec) than in the aorta (about 48 cm/sec). After passing through the capillaries, the blood speeds up as it enters the venules and veins, which have smaller *total* cross-sectional areas than the capillaries.

Blood Pressure

Blood, like all fluids, flows from areas of higher pressure to areas of lower pressure. Contraction of a heart ventricle generates blood pressure, which exerts a force in all directions. The part of the force directed lengthwise in an artery causes the blood to flow away from the heart, the site of highest pressure. The part of the force exerted sideways stretches the wall of the artery. Following ventricular contraction, the recoil of the elastic arterial walls plays a critical role in maintaining blood pressure, and hence blood flow, throughout the cardiac cycle. Once the blood enters the millions of tiny arterioles and capillaries, the narrow diameter of these vessels generates substantial resistance to flow. By the time the blood enters the veins, this resistance has dissipated much of the pressure generated by the pumping heart.

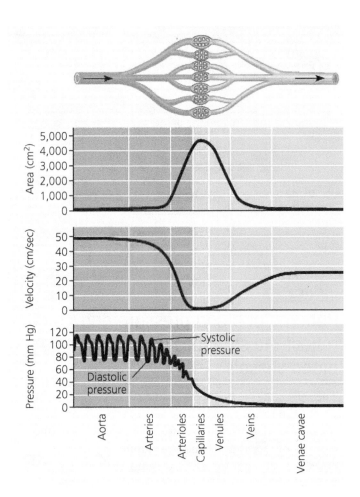

▲ **Figure 42.10 The interrelationship of cross-sectional area of blood vessels, blood flow velocity, and blood pressure.** As a result of an increase in total cross-sectional area, blood flow velocity decreases markedly in the arterioles and is lowest in the capillaries. Blood pressure, the main force driving blood from the heart to the capillaries, is highest in the aorta and other arteries.

Changes in Blood Pressure During the Cardiac Cycle

Arterial blood pressure is highest when the heart contracts during ventricular systole. The pressure at this time is called **systolic pressure** (see Figure 42.10). Each spike in blood pressure caused by ventricular contraction stretches the arteries. By placing your fingers on the inside of your wrist, you can feel a **pulse**—the rhythmic bulging of the artery walls with each heartbeat. The pressure surge is partly due to the narrow openings of arterioles impeding the exit of blood from the arteries. When the heart contracts, blood enters the arteries faster than it can leave, and the vessels stretch from the rise in pressure.

During diastole, the elastic walls of the arteries snap back. As a consequence, there is a lower but still substantial blood pressure when the ventricles are relaxed (**diastolic pressure**). Before enough blood has flowed into the arterioles to completely relieve pressure in the arteries, the heart contracts again. Because the arteries remain pressurized throughout the cardiac cycle (see Figure 42.10), blood continuously flows into arterioles and capillaries.

Regulation of Blood Pressure

Homeostatic mechanisms regulate arterial blood pressure by altering the diameter of arterioles. As the smooth muscles in arteriole walls contract, the arterioles narrow, a process called **vasoconstriction**. Narrowing of the arterioles increases blood pressure upstream in the arteries. When the smooth muscles relax, the arterioles undergo **vasodilation**, an increase in diameter that causes blood pressure in the arteries to fall.

Researchers have identified nitric oxide (NO), a gas, as a major inducer of vasodilation and endothelin, a peptide, as the most potent inducer of vasoconstriction. Cues from the nervous and endocrine systems regulate production of NO and endothelin in blood vessels, where their activities regulate blood pressure.

Vasoconstriction and vasodilation are often coupled to changes in cardiac output that also affect blood pressure. This coordination of regulatory mechanisms maintains adequate blood flow as the body's demands on the circulatory system change. During heavy exercise, for example, the arterioles in working muscles dilate, causing a greater flow of oxygen-rich blood to the muscles. By itself, this increased flow to the muscles would cause a drop in blood pressure (and therefore blood flow) in the body as a whole. However, cardiac output increases at the same time, maintaining blood pressure and supporting the necessary increase in blood flow.

Blood Pressure and Gravity

Blood pressure is generally measured for an artery in the arm at the same height as the heart (Figure 42.11). For a healthy 20-year-old human at rest, arterial blood pressure in the systemic circuit is typically about 120 millimeters of mercury (mm Hg) at systole and 70 mm Hg at diastole, expressed as 120/70. (Arterial blood pressure in the pulmonary circuit is six to ten times lower.)

Gravity has a significant effect on blood pressure. When you are standing, for example, your head is roughly 0.35 m higher than your chest, and the arterial blood pressure in your brain is about 27 mm Hg less than that near your heart. If the blood pressure in your brain is too low to provide adequate

blood flow, you will likely faint. By causing your body to collapse to the ground, fainting effectively places your head at the level of your heart, quickly increasing blood flow to your brain.

For animals with very long necks, the blood pressure required to overcome gravity is particularly high. A giraffe, for example, requires a systolic pressure of more than 250 mm Hg near the heart to get blood to its head. When a giraffe lowers its head to drink, one-way valves and sinuses, along with feedback mechanisms that reduce cardiac output, prevent this high pressure from damaging its brain. We can calculate that a dinosaur with a neck nearly 10 m long would have required even greater systolic pressure—nearly 760 mm Hg—to pump blood to its brain when its head was fully raised. However, calculations based on anatomy and inferred metabolic rate suggest that dinosaurs did not have a heart powerful enough to generate such high pressure. Based on this evidence as well as studies of neck bone structure, some biologists have concluded that the long-necked dinosaurs fed close to the ground rather than on high foliage.

Gravity is also a consideration for blood flow in veins, especially those in the legs. When you stand or sit, gravity draws blood downward to your legs and feet and impedes its upward return to the heart. Although blood pressure in veins is relatively low, valves inside the veins help maintain

Pressure in cuff greater than 120 mm Hg

Pressure in cuff drops below 120 mm Hg

Pressure in cuff below 70 mm Hg

Cuff inflated with air

Artery closed

Sounds audible in stethoscope

Sounds stop

❶ A sphygmomanometer, an inflatable cuff attached to a pressure gauge, measures blood pressure in an artery. The cuff is inflated until the pressure closes the artery, so that no blood flows past the cuff. When this occurs, the pressure exerted by the cuff exceeds the pressure in the artery.

❷ The cuff is allowed to deflate gradually. When the pressure exerted by the cuff falls just below that in the artery, blood pulses into the forearm, generating sounds that can be heard with the stethoscope. The pressure measured at this point is the systolic pressure (120 mm Hg in this example).

❸ The cuff is allowed to deflate further, just until the blood flows freely through the artery and the sounds below the cuff disappear. The pressure at this point is the diastolic pressure (70 mm Hg in this example).

▲ Figure 42.11 **Measurement of blood pressure.** Blood pressure is recorded as two numbers separated by a slash. The first number is the systolic pressure; the second is the diastolic pressure.

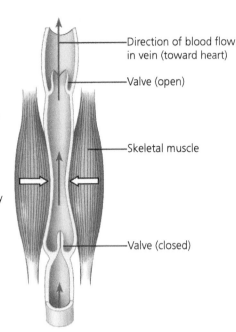

▶ **Figure 42.12 Blood flow in veins.** Skeletal muscle contraction squeezes and constricts veins. Flaps of tissue within the veins act as one-way valves that keep blood moving only toward the heart. If you sit or stand too long, the lack of muscular activity may cause your feet to swell as blood pools in your veins.

Direction of blood flow in vein (toward heart)

Valve (open)

Skeletal muscle

Valve (closed)

the unidirectional flow of blood within these vessels. The return of blood to the heart is further enhanced by rhythmic contractions of smooth muscles in the walls of venules and veins and by the contraction of skeletal muscles during exercise (Figure 42.12).

In rare instances, runners and other athletes can suffer heart failure if they stop vigorous exercise abruptly. When the leg muscles suddenly cease contracting and relaxing, less blood returns to the heart, which continues to beat rapidly. If the heart is weak or damaged, this inadequate blood flow may cause the heart to malfunction. To reduce the risk of stressing the heart excessively, athletes are encouraged to follow hard exercise with moderate activity, such as walking, to "cool down" until their heart rate approaches its resting level.

Capillary Function

At any given time, only about 5–10% of the body's capillaries have blood flowing through them. However, each tissue has many capillaries, so every part of the body is supplied with blood at all times. Capillaries in the brain, heart, kidneys, and liver are usually filled to capacity, but at many other sites the blood supply varies over time as blood is diverted from one destination to another. For example, blood flow to the skin is regulated to help control body temperature, and blood supply to the digestive tract increases after a meal. In contrast, blood is diverted from the digestive tract and supplied more generously to skeletal muscles and skin during strenuous exercise.

Given that capillaries lack smooth muscle, how is blood flow in capillary beds altered? One mechanism is constriction or dilation of the arterioles that supply capillary beds. A second mechanism involves *precapillary sphincters*, rings of smooth muscle located at the entrance to capillary beds (Figure 42.13). Opening and closing these muscular rings

regulate and redirect the passage of blood into particular sets of capillaries. The signals regulating blood flow by these mechanisms include nerve impulses, hormones traveling throughout the bloodstream, and chemicals produced locally. For example, the chemical histamine released by cells at a wound site causes vasodilation. The result is increased blood flow and increased access of disease-fighting white blood cells to invading microorganisms.

As you have read, the critical exchange of substances between the blood and interstitial fluid takes place across the thin endothelial walls of the capillaries. Some substances are carried across the endothelium in vesicles that form on one side by endocytosis and release their contents on the opposite side by exocytosis. Small molecules, such as O_2 and CO_2, simply diffuse across the endothelial cells or, in some tissues, through microscopic pores in the capillary wall. These openings also provide the route for transport of small solutes such as sugars, salts, and urea, as well as for bulk flow of fluid into tissues driven by blood pressure within the capillary.

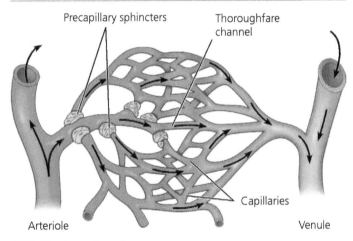

Precapillary sphincters

Thoroughfare channel

Capillaries

Arteriole

Venule

(a) Sphincters relaxed

Arteriole

Venule

(b) Sphincters contracted

▲ **Figure 42.13 Blood flow in capillary beds.** Precapillary sphincters regulate the passage of blood into capillary beds. Some blood flows directly from arterioles to venules through capillaries called thoroughfare channels, which are always open.

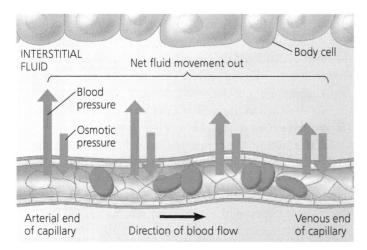

INTERSTITIAL FLUID

Net fluid movement out

Body cell

Blood pressure

Osmotic pressure

Arterial end of capillary

Direction of blood flow

Venous end of capillary

▲ **Figure 42.14 Fluid exchange between capillaries and the interstitial fluid.** This diagram shows a hypothetical capillary in which blood pressure exceeds osmotic pressure throughout the entire length of the capillary. In other capillaries, blood pressure may be lower than osmotic pressure along all or part of the capillary.

Two opposing forces control the movement of fluid between the capillaries and the surrounding tissues: Blood pressure tends to drive fluid out of the capillaries, and the presence of blood proteins tends to pull fluid back (**Figure 42.14**). Many blood proteins (and all blood cells) are too large to pass readily through the endothelium, and they remain in the capillaries. These dissolved proteins are responsible for much of the blood's *osmotic pressure* (the pressure produced by the difference in solute concentration across a membrane). The difference in osmotic pressure between the blood and the interstitial fluid opposes fluid movement out of the capillaries. On average, blood pressure is greater than the opposing forces, leading to a net loss of fluid from capillaries. The net loss is generally greatest at the arterial end of these vessels, where blood pressure is highest.

Fluid Return by the Lymphatic System

The adult human body each day loses approximately 4–8 L of fluid from capillaries to the surrounding tissues. There is also some leakage of blood proteins, even though the capillary wall is not very permeable to large molecules. The lost fluid and proteins return to the blood via the **lymphatic system**, which includes a network of tiny vessels intermingled among capillaries of the cardiovascular system, as well as larger vessels into which small vessels empty.

After entering the lymphatic system by diffusion, the fluid lost by capillaries is called **lymph**; its composition is about the same as that of interstitial fluid. The lymphatic system drains into large veins of the cardiovascular system at the base of the neck (see Figure 43.7). This joining of the lymphatic and cardiovascular systems enables lipids to be transferred from the small intestine to the blood (see Chapter 41).

The movement of lymph from peripheral tissues to the heart relies on much the same mechanisms that assist blood

▶ **Figure 42.15 Human lymph nodes and vessels.** In this colorized X-ray image of the groin, lymph nodes and vessels are visible next to the upper thigh bone (femur).

Lymph nodes

flow in veins. Lymph vessels, like veins, have valves that prevent the backflow of fluid. Rhythmic contractions of the vessel walls help draw fluid into the small lymphatic vessels. In addition, skeletal muscle contractions play a role in moving lymph.

Disruptions in lymph flow often result in fluid accumulation, or edema, in affected tissues. In some circumstances, the consequence is more severe. For example, certain species of parasitic worms that lodge in lymph vessels and thereby block lymph movement cause elephantiasis, a condition marked by extreme swelling in limbs or other body parts.

Along a lymph vessel are small, lymph-filtering organs called **lymph nodes**, which play an important role in the body's defense (**Figure 42.15**). Inside each lymph node is a honeycomb of connective tissue with spaces filled by white blood cells, which function in defense. When the body is fighting an infection, the white blood cells multiply rapidly, and the lymph nodes become swollen and tender. This is why your doctor may check for swollen lymph nodes in your neck, armpits, or groin when you feel sick. Because lymph nodes also trap circulating cancer cells, doctors may examine the lymph nodes of cancer patients to detect the spread of the disease.

In recent years, evidence has surfaced demonstrating that the lymphatic system also plays a role in harmful immune responses, such as those responsible for asthma. Because of these and other findings, the lymphatic system, largely ignored until the 1990s, has become a very active and promising area of biomedical research.

CONCEPT CHECK **42.3**

1. What is the primary cause of the low velocity of blood flow in capillaries?

2. What short-term changes in cardiovascular function might best enable skeletal muscles to help an animal escape from a dangerous situation?

3. **WHAT IF?** If you had additional hearts distributed throughout your body, what would be one likely advantage and one likely disadvantage?

For suggested answers, see Appendix A.

Blood components function in exchange, transport, and defense

As you read in Concept 42.1, the fluid transported by an open circulatory system is continuous with the fluid that surrounds all of the body cells and therefore has the same composition. In contrast, the fluid in a closed circulatory system can be much more highly specialized, as is the case for the blood of vertebrates.

Blood Composition and Function

Vertebrate blood is a connective tissue consisting of cells suspended in a liquid matrix called **plasma**. Separating the components of blood using a centrifuge reveals that cellular elements (cells and cell fragments) occupy about 45% of the volume of blood **(Figure 42.16)**. The remainder is plasma. Dissolved in the plasma are ions and proteins that, together with the blood cells, function in osmotic regulation, transport, and defense.

Plasma

Among the many solutes in plasma are inorganic salts in the form of dissolved ions, sometimes referred to as blood electrolytes (see Figure 42.16). The dissolved ions are an essential component of the blood. Some of these ions buffer the blood, which in humans normally has a pH of 7.4. Ions are also important in maintaining the osmotic balance of the blood. In addition, the concentration of ions in plasma directly affects the composition of the interstitial fluid, where many of these ions have a vital role in muscle and nerve activity. Serving all of these functions necessitates keeping plasma electrolytes within narrow concentration ranges (a homeostatic function we'll explore in Chapter 44).

Plasma proteins, including albumins, act as buffers against pH changes and help maintain the osmotic balance between blood and interstitial fluid. Certain plasma proteins have additional functions. Immunoglobulins, or antibodies, combat viruses and other foreign agents that invade the body (see Figure 43.10). Apolipoproteins escort lipids, which are insoluble in water and can travel in blood only when bound to proteins. Plasma also contains fibrinogens, which are clotting factors that help plug leaks when blood vessels are injured. (The term *serum* refers to blood plasma from which these clotting factors have been removed.)

Plasma also contains a wide variety of other substances in transit from one part of the body to another, including

Plasma 55%	
Constituent	**Major functions**
Water	Solvent
Ions (blood electrolytes) Sodium Potassium Calcium Magnesium Chloride Bicarbonate	Osmotic balance, pH buffering, and regulation of membrane permeability
Plasma proteins Albumin	Osmotic balance, pH buffering
Immunoglobulins (antibodies)	Defense
Apolipoproteins	Lipid transport
Fibrinogen	Clotting
Substances transported by blood	
Nutrients (such as glucose, fatty acids, vitamins) Waste products of metabolism Respiratory gases (O_2 and CO_2) Hormones	

Separated blood elements

Cellular elements 45%		
Cell type	**Number per μL (mm^3) of blood**	**Functions**
Leukocytes (white blood cells) Basophils Lymphocytes Eosinophils Neutrophils Monocytes	5,000–10,000	Defense and immunity
Platelets	250,000–400,000	Blood clotting
Erythrocytes (red blood cells)	5,000,000–6,000,000	Transport of O_2 and some CO_2

▲ **Figure 42.16 The composition of mammalian blood.**

nutrients, metabolic wastes, respiratory gases, and hormones. Plasma has a much higher protein concentration than interstitial fluid, although the two fluids are otherwise similar. (Capillary walls, remember, are not very permeable to proteins.)

Cellular Elements

Blood contains two classes of cells: red blood cells, which transport O_2, and white blood cells, which function in defense (see Figure 42.16). Also suspended in blood plasma are **platelets**, cell fragments that are involved in the clotting process.

Erythrocytes Red blood cells, or **erythrocytes**, are by far the most numerous blood cells. Each microliter (μL, or mm^3) of human blood contains 5–6 million red cells, and there are about 25 trillion of these cells in the body's 5 L of blood. Their main function is O_2 transport, and their structure is closely related to this function. Human erythrocytes are small disks (7–8 μm in diameter) that are biconcave—thinner in the center than at the edges. This shape increases surface area, enhancing the rate of diffusion of O_2 across the plasma membrane. Mature mammalian erythrocytes lack nuclei. This unusual characteristic leaves more space in these tiny cells for **hemoglobin**, the iron-containing protein that transports O_2 (see Figure 5.18). Erythrocytes also lack mitochondria and generate their ATP exclusively by anaerobic metabolism. Oxygen transport would be less efficient if erythrocytes were aerobic and consumed some of the O_2 they carry.

Despite its small size, an erythrocyte contains about 250 million molecules of hemoglobin (Hb). Because each molecule of hemoglobin binds up to four molecules of O_2, one erythrocyte can transport about 1 billion O_2 molecules. As erythrocytes pass through the capillary beds of lungs, gills, or other respiratory organs, O_2 diffuses into the erythrocytes and binds to hemoglobin. In the systemic capillaries, O_2 dissociates from hemoglobin and diffuses into body cells.

In **sickle-cell disease**, an abnormal form of hemoglobin (Hb^S) polymerizes into aggregates. Because the concentration of hemoglobin in erythrocytes is so high, these aggregates are large enough to distort the erythrocyte into an elongated, curved shape that resembles a sickle. This abnormality results from an alteration in the amino acid sequence of hemoglobin at a single position (see Figure 5.19).

Sickle-cell disease significantly impairs the function of the circulatory system. Sickled cells often lodge in arterioles and capillaries, preventing delivery of O_2 and nutrients and removal of CO_2 and wastes. Blood vessel blockage and resulting organ swelling often result in severe pain. In addition, sickled cells frequently rupture, reducing the number of red blood cells available for transporting O_2. The average life span of a sickled erythrocyte is only 20 days—one-sixth

that of a normal erythrocyte. The rate of erythrocyte loss outstrips their production rate. Short-term therapy includes replacement of erythrocytes by blood transfusion; long-term treatments are generally aimed at inhibiting aggregation of Hb^S.

Leukocytes The blood contains five major types of white blood cells, or **leukocytes**. Their function is to fight infections. Some are phagocytic, engulfing and digesting microorganisms as well as debris from the body's own dead cells. Other leukocytes, called lymphocytes, develop into B cells and T cells that mount immune responses against foreign substances (as we'll discuss in Concepts 43.2 and 43.3). Normally, 1 μL of human blood contains about 5,000–10,000 leukocytes; their numbers increase temporarily whenever the body is fighting an infection. Unlike erythrocytes, leukocytes are also found outside the circulatory system, patrolling both interstitial fluid and the lymphatic system.

Platelets Platelets are pinched-off cytoplasmic fragments of specialized bone marrow cells. They are about 2–3 μm in diameter and have no nuclei. Platelets serve both structural and molecular functions in blood clotting.

Stem Cells and the Replacement of Cellular Elements

Erythrocytes, leukocytes, and platelets all develop from a common source: multipotent **stem cells** that are dedicated to replenishing the body's blood cell populations **(Figure 42.17)**.

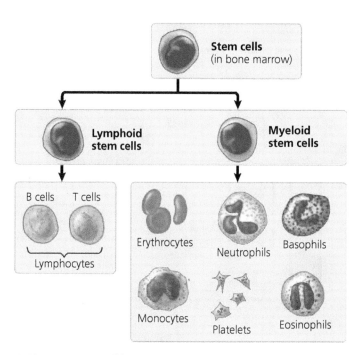

▲ **Figure 42.17 Differentiation of blood cells.** Multipotent stem cells in bone marrow give rise to two specialized sets of stem cells. One set, the lymphoid stem cells, produces B and T cells (lymphocytes), which function in immunity (see Figures 43.9 and 43.11). The other set, the myeloid stem cells, produces all other blood cells, as well as platelets.

The stem cells that produce blood cells are located in the red marrow inside bones, particularly the ribs, vertebrae, sternum, and pelvis. Multipotent stem cells are so named because they have the ability to form multiple types of cells—in this case, the myeloid and lymphoid cell lineages. When a stem cell divides, one daughter cell remains a stem cell while the other takes on a specialized function.

Throughout a person's life, stem cells replace the worn-out cellular elements of blood. Erythrocytes are the shortest-lived, circulating for only 120 days on average before being replaced. A negative-feedback mechanism, sensitive to the amount of O_2 reaching the body's tissues via the blood, controls erythrocyte production. If the tissues do not receive enough O_2, the kidneys synthesize and secrete a hormone called **erythropoietin (EPO)** that stimulates the generation of more erythrocytes. If the blood is delivering more O_2 than the tissues can use, the level of EPO falls and erythrocyte production slows.

Recombinant DNA technology is now used to synthesize EPO in cultured cells. Physicians use recombinant EPO to treat people with health problems such as *anemia*, a condition of lower-than-normal erythrocyte or hemoglobin levels that lowers the oxygen-carrying capacity of the blood. Some athletes inject themselves with EPO to increase their erythrocyte levels, although this practice, a form of blood doping, has been banned by major sports organizations. In recent years, a number of well-known runners and cyclists have been found to have used EPO-related drugs and have forfeited both their records and their right to participate in future competitions.

Blood Clotting

The occasional cut or scrape is not life-threatening because blood components seal the broken blood vessels. A break in a blood vessel wall exposes proteins that attract platelets and initiate coagulation, the conversion of liquid components of blood to a solid clot. The coagulant, or sealant, circulates in an inactive form called fibrinogen. In response to a broken blood vessel, platelets release clotting factors that trigger reactions leading to the formation of thrombin, an enzyme that converts fibrinogen to fibrin. Newly formed fibrin aggregates into threads that form the framework of the clot. Thrombin also activates a factor that catalyzes the formation of more thrombin, driving clotting to completion through positive feedback (see Chapter 40). The steps in the production of a blood clot are diagrammed in **Figure 42.18**. Any genetic mutation that blocks a step in the clotting

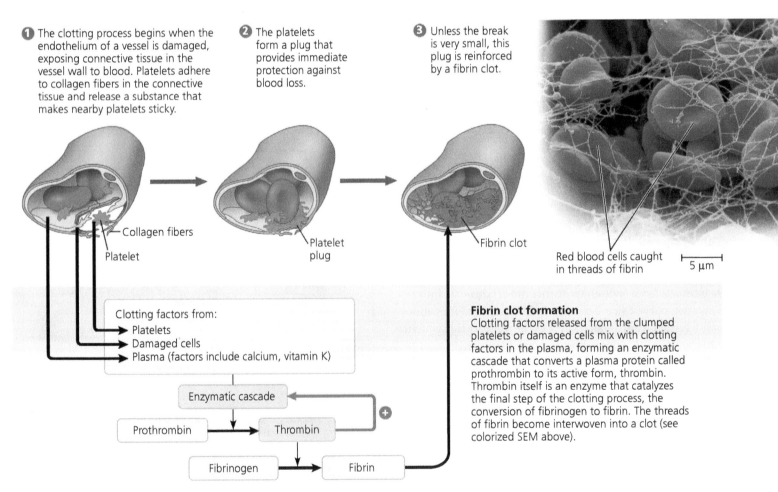

① The clotting process begins when the endothelium of a vessel is damaged, exposing connective tissue in the vessel wall to blood. Platelets adhere to collagen fibers in the connective tissue and release a substance that makes nearby platelets sticky.

② The platelets form a plug that provides immediate protection against blood loss.

③ Unless the break is very small, this plug is reinforced by a fibrin clot.

Collagen fibers

Platelet

Platelet plug

Fibrin clot

Red blood cells caught in threads of fibrin

5 μm

Clotting factors from:
→ Platelets
→ Damaged cells
→ Plasma (factors include calcium, vitamin K)

Enzymatic cascade

Prothrombin → Thrombin (+)

Fibrinogen → Fibrin

Fibrin clot formation
Clotting factors released from the clumped platelets or damaged cells mix with clotting factors in the plasma, forming an enzymatic cascade that converts a plasma protein called prothrombin to its active form, thrombin. Thrombin itself is an enzyme that catalyzes the final step of the clotting process, the conversion of fibrinogen to fibrin. The threads of fibrin become interwoven into a clot (see colorized SEM above).

▲ **Figure 42.18 Blood clotting.**

process can cause hemophilia, a disease characterized by excessive bleeding and bruising from even minor cuts and bumps (see Chapter 15).

Anticlotting factors in the blood normally prevent spontaneous clotting in the absence of injury. Sometimes, however, clots form within a blood vessel, blocking the flow of blood. Such a clot is called a **thrombus** (plural, *thrombi*). We'll explore how thrombi form and the dangers that they pose shortly.

Cardiovascular Disease

Each year, cardiovascular diseases—disorders of the heart and blood vessels—kill more than 750,000 people in the United States. These diseases range from minor disturbances of vein or heart valve function to life-threatening disruptions of blood flow to the heart or brain.

Atherosclerosis, Heart Attacks, and Stroke

Healthy arteries have a smooth inner lining that reduces resistance to blood flow. However, damage or infection can roughen the lining and lead to **atherosclerosis**, the hardening of the arteries by accumulation of fatty deposits. A key player in the development of atherosclerosis is cholesterol, a steroid that is important for maintaining normal membrane fluidity in animal cells (see Chapter 7). Cholesterol travels in blood plasma mainly in particles that consist of thousands of cholesterol molecules and other lipids bound to a protein. One type of particle—**low-density lipoprotein (LDL)**—delivers cholesterol to cells for membrane production. Another type—**high-density lipoprotein (HDL)**—scavenges excess cholesterol for return to the liver. Individuals with a high ratio of LDL to HDL are at substantially increased risk for atherosclerosis.

In atherosclerosis, damage to the arterial lining results in *inflammation*, the body's reaction to injury. Leukocytes are attracted to the inflamed area and begin to take up lipids, including cholesterol. A fatty deposit, called a plaque, grows steadily, incorporating fibrous connective tissue and additional cholesterol. As the plaque grows, the walls of the artery become thick and stiff, and the obstruction of the artery increases. If the plaque ruptures, a thrombus can form in the artery **(Figure 42.19)**.

The result of untreated atherosclerosis is often a heart attack or a stroke. A **heart attack**, also called a *myocardial infarction*, is the damage or death of cardiac muscle tissue resulting from blockage of one or more coronary arteries, which supply oxygen-rich blood to the heart muscle. Because the coronary arteries are small in diameter, they are especially vulnerable to obstruction by atherosclerotic plaques or thrombi. Such blockage can destroy cardiac muscle quickly because the constantly beating heart muscle cannot survive long without O_2. If a large enough portion of the heart is affected, the heart will stop beating, and the victim will die

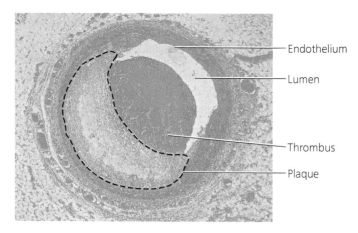

▲ **Figure 42.19 Atherosclerosis.** In atherosclerosis, thickening of an arterial wall by plaque formation can restrict blood flow through the artery. If a plaque ruptures, a thrombus can form, further restricting blood flow. Fragments of a ruptured plaque can also travel via the bloodstream and become lodged in other arteries. If the blockage is in an artery that supplies the heart or brain, the result could be a heart attack or stroke, respectively.

within a few minutes unless a heartbeat is restored by cardiopulmonary resuscitation (CPR) or some other emergency procedure. A **stroke** is the death of nervous tissue in the brain due to a lack of O_2. Strokes usually result from rupture or blockage of arteries in the head. The effects of a stroke and the individual's chance of survival depend on the extent and location of the damaged brain tissue. If a stroke results from arterial blockage by a thrombus, rapid administration of a clot-dissolving drug may help limit the damage.

Although atherosclerosis often isn't detected until critical blood flow is disrupted, there can be warning signs. Partial blockage of the coronary arteries may cause occasional chest pain, a condition known as angina pectoris. The pain is most likely to be felt when the heart is laboring under stress, and it signals that part of the heart is not receiving enough O_2. An obstructed artery may be treated surgically, either by inserting a mesh tube called a stent to expand the artery **(Figure 42.20)** or by transplanting a healthy blood vessel from the chest or a limb to bypass the blockage.

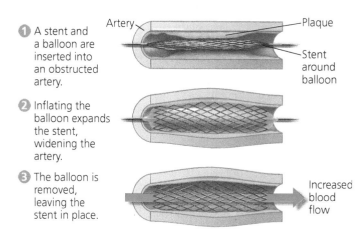

❶ A stent and a balloon are inserted into an obstructed artery.

❷ Inflating the balloon expands the stent, widening the artery.

❸ The balloon is removed, leaving the stent in place.

Artery — Plaque — Stent around balloon — Increased blood flow

▲ **Figure 42.20 Inserting a stent to widen an obstructed artery.**

Risk Factors and Treatment of Cardiovascular Disease

Although the tendency to develop particular cardiovascular diseases is inherited, it is also strongly influenced by lifestyle. For example, exercise decreases the LDL/HDL ratio, reducing the risk of cardiovascular disease. In contrast, smoking and consumption of certain processed vegetable oils called *trans fats* (see Chapter 5) increase the LDL/HDL ratio.

There has been considerable progress in the last decade in preventing cardiovascular disease. For many individuals at high risk, treatment with drugs called statins can lower LDL levels and thereby reduce the risk of heart attacks In the Scientific Skills Exercise, you can interpret the effect of a genetic mutation on blood LDL levels.

The recognition that inflammation plays a central role in atherosclerosis and thrombus formation is also influencing the treatment of cardiovascular disease. For example,

aspirin, which inhibits the inflammatory response, has been found to help prevent the recurrence of heart attacks and stroke. Researchers have also focused on C-reactive protein (CRP), which is produced by the liver and found in the blood during episodes of acute inflammation. Like a high level of LDL cholesterol, the presence of significant amounts of CRP in blood is a useful risk indicator for cardiovascular disease.

Hypertension (high blood pressure) is yet another contributor to heart attack and stroke. According to one hypothesis, chronic high blood pressure damages the endothelium that lines the arteries, promoting plaque formation. The usual definition of hypertension in adults is a systolic pressure above 140 mm Hg or a diastolic pressure above 90 mm Hg. Fortunately, hypertension is simple to diagnose and can usually be controlled by dietary changes, exercise, medication, or a combination of these approaches.

SCIENTIFIC SKILLS EXERCISE

Making and Interpreting Histograms

Does Inactivating the PCSK9 Enzyme Lower LDL Levels?
Researchers interested in genetic factors affecting susceptibility to cardiovascular disease examined the DNA of 15,000 individuals. They found that 3% of the individuals had a mutation that inactivates one copy of the gene for PCSK9, a liver enzyme. Because mutations that *increase* the activity of PCSK9 are known to *increase* levels of LDL cholesterol in the blood, the researchers hypothesized that *inactivating* mutations in this gene would *lower* LDL levels. In this exercise, you will interpret the results of an experiment they carried out to test this hypothesis.

How the Experiment Was Done Researchers measured LDL cholesterol levels in blood plasma from 85 individuals with one copy of the *PCSK9* gene inactivated (the study group) and from 3,278 individuals with two functional copies of the gene (the control group).

Data from the Experiment
The plasma LDL cholesterol levels for the control group and study group are shown in the table at the bottom.

Interpret the Data
1. Graphing often facilitates data interpretation. For this exercise, graph the data in each row of the table as a *histogram* (a type of bar graph). Label the *y*-axis as *Percent of Individuals* and the *x*-axis as *Plasma LDL cholesterol (mg/dl)*. Divide the *x*-axis into twelve equal divisions, one for each range of values (0–25, 26–50, etc). Moving along the *x*-axis, draw a series of twelve vertical bars, with the height of each bar indicating the percentage of samples that fall into the specified range. Note that some bars will be of zero height, such as for a plasma LDL cholesterol level in the 0–25 mg/dL (milligram/deciliter) range. Add the percentages for the relevant bars to calculate the percentage of individuals in the study and control groups that had an LDL cholesterol level of 100 mg/dL or less. (For additional information

about histograms, see the Scientific Skills Review in Appendix F and the Study Area in MasteringBiology.)
2. Comparing the two histograms you drew, do you find support for the researchers' hypothesis? Explain.
3. What if instead of graphing the data you had compared the range of concentrations for plasma LDL cholesterol (low to high) in the control and study groups? How would the conclusions you could draw have differed?
4. Propose an explanation for the fact that the two histograms overlap as much as they do.
5. Consider two individuals with a plasma LDL cholesterol level of 160 mg/dL, one from the study group and one from the control group. What do you predict regarding their relative risk of developing cardiovascular disease? Explain how you arrived at your prediction. What role did the histograms play in helping you make your prediction?

(MB) A version of this Scientific Skills Exercise can be assigned in MasteringBiology.

Data from J. C. Cohen et al., Sequence variations in *PCSK9*, low LDL, and protection against coronary heart disease, *New England Journal of Medicine* 354:1264–1272 (2006).

Plasma LDL Cholesterol (milligrams/deciliter)

	0–25	26–50	51–75	76–100	101–125	126–150	151–175	176–200	201–225	226–250	251-275	276–300
Control Group	0%	1%	4%	13%	23%	23%	18%	10%	5%	2%	1%	0%
Study Group	0%	4%	31%	23%	21%	13%	2%	1%	2%	0%	2%	0%

1. Explain why a physician might order a white cell count for a patient with symptoms of an infection.

2. Clots in arteries can cause heart attacks and strokes. Why, then, does it make sense to treat people with hemophilia by introducing clotting factors into their blood?

3. **WHAT IF?** Nitroglycerin (the key ingredient in dynamite) is sometimes prescribed for heart disease patients. Within the body, the nitroglycerin is converted to nitric oxide. Why would you expect nitroglycerin to relieve chest pain in these patients?

4. **MAKE CONNECTIONS** The allele that encodes Hb^S is codominant with the allele encoding normal hemoglobin (Hb) (see Concept 14.4). What can you deduce about the properties of Hb and Hb^S with regard to aggregate formation and sickling?

5. **MAKE CONNECTIONS** How do stem cells from the bone marrow of an adult differ from embryonic stem cells (see Concept 20.3)?

For suggested answers, see Appendix A.

CONCEPT 42.5

Gas exchange occurs across specialized respiratory surfaces

In the remainder of this chapter, we will focus on the process of **gas exchange**. Although this process is often called respiratory exchange or respiration, it should not be confused with the energy transformations of cellular respiration. Gas exchange is the uptake of molecular O_2 from the environment and the discharge of CO_2 to the environment.

Partial Pressure Gradients in Gas Exchange

To understand the driving forces for gas exchange, we must consider **partial pressure**, which is simply the pressure exerted by a particular gas in a mixture of gases. Once we know partial pressures, we can predict the net movement of a gas at an exchange surface: A gas always undergoes net diffusion from a region of higher partial pressure to a region of lower partial pressure.

To calculate partial pressures, we need to know the pressure that a gas mixture exerts and the fraction of the mixture represented by a particular gas. Let's consider O_2 as an example. At sea level, the atmosphere exerts a downward force equal to that of a column of mercury (Hg) 760 mm high. Atmospheric pressure at sea level is thus 760 mm Hg. Since the atmosphere is 21% O_2 by volume, the partial pressure of O_2 is 0.21×760, or about 160 mm Hg. This value is called the *partial pressure* of O_2 (abbreviated P_{O_2}) because it is the part of atmospheric pressure contributed by O_2. The partial pressure of CO_2 (abbreviated P_{CO_2}) is much less, only 0.29 mm Hg at sea level.

Table 42.1 Comparing Air and Water as Respiratory Media

	Air (Sea Level)	Water (20°C)	Air to Water Ratio
O_2 Partial Pressure	160 mm	160 mm	1 : 1
O_2 Concentration	210 ml/L	7 ml/L	30 : 1
Density	0.0013 kg/L	1 kg/L	1 : 770
Viscosity	0.02 cP	1 cP	1 : 50

Partial pressures also apply to gases dissolved in a liquid, such as water. When water is exposed to air, an equilibrium is reached in which the partial pressure of each gas in the water equals the partial pressure of that gas in the air. Thus, water exposed to air at sea level has a P_{O_2} of 160 mm Hg, the same as in the atmosphere. However, O_2 is much less soluble in water than in air. As a result, air contains much more O_2 than water at the same P_{O_2} **(Table 42.1)**.

Respiratory Media

The conditions for gas exchange vary considerably, depending on whether the respiratory medium—the source of O_2—is air or water. As already noted, O_2 is plentiful in air, making up about 21% of Earth's atmosphere by volume. As shown in Table 42.1, air is much less dense and less viscous than water, so it is easier to move and to force through small passageways. As a result, breathing air is relatively easy and need not be particularly efficient. Humans, for example, extract only about 25% of the O_2 in inhaled air.

Gas exchange with water as the respiratory medium is much more demanding. The amount of O_2 dissolved in a given volume of water varies but is always less than in an equivalent volume of air: Water in many freshwater habitats contains only about 7 mL of dissolved O_2 per liter, a concentration roughly 30 times less than in air. Furthermore, the warmer and saltier the water is, the less dissolved O_2 it can hold. Water's lower O_2 content, greater density, and greater viscosity mean that aquatic animals such as fishes and lobsters must expend considerable energy to carry out gas exchange. In the context of these challenges, adaptations have evolved that enable most aquatic animals to be very efficient in gas exchange. Many of these adaptations involve the organization of the surfaces dedicated to exchange.

Respiratory Surfaces

Specialization for gas exchange is apparent in the structure of the respiratory surface, the part of an animal's body where gas exchange occurs. Like all living cells, the cells that carry out gas exchange have a plasma membrane that must be in contact with an aqueous solution. Respiratory surfaces are therefore always moist.

The movement of O_2 and CO_2 across respiratory surfaces takes place by diffusion. The rate of diffusion is proportional to the surface area across which it occurs and inversely proportional to the square of the distance through which molecules must move. In other words, gas exchange is fast when the area for diffusion is large and the path for diffusion is short. As a result, respiratory surfaces tend to be large and thin.

In some relatively simple animals, such as sponges, cnidarians, and flatworms, every cell in the body is close enough to the external environment that gases can diffuse quickly between any cell and the environment. In many animals, however, the bulk of the body's cells lack immediate access to the environment. The respiratory surface in these animals is a thin, moist epithelium that constitutes a respiratory organ.

In some animals, including earthworms and some amphibians, the skin serves as a respiratory organ. A dense network of capillaries just below the skin facilitates the exchange of gases between the circulatory system and the environment. For most animals, however, the general body surface lacks sufficient area to exchange gases for the whole organism. The evolutionary solution to this limitation is a respiratory organ that is extensively folded or branched, thereby enlarging the available surface area for gas exchange. Gills, tracheae, and lungs are three such organs.

Gills in Aquatic Animals

Gills are outfoldings of the body surface that are suspended in the water. As illustrated in **Figure 42.21**, the distribution of gills over the body can vary considerably. Regardless of

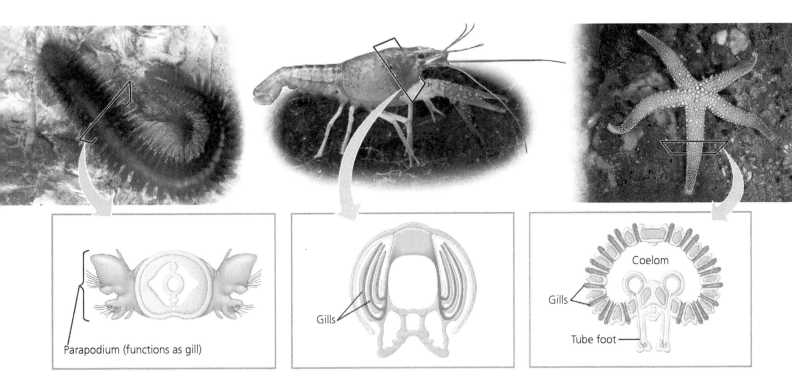

(a) Marine worm. Many polychaetes (marine worms of the phylum Annelida) have a pair of flattened appendages called parapodia on each body segment. The parapodia serve as gills and also function in crawling and swimming.

(b) Crayfish. Crayfish and other crustaceans have long, feathery gills covered by the exoskeleton. Specialized body appendages drive water over the gill surfaces.

(c) Sea star. The gills of a sea star are simple tubular projections of the skin. The hollow core of each gill is an extension of the coelom (body cavity). Gas exchange occurs by diffusion across the gill surfaces, and fluid in the coelom circulates in and out of the gills, aiding gas transport. The tube feet surfaces also function in gas exchange.

▲ **Figure 42.21 Diversity in the structure of gills, external body surfaces that function in gas exchange.**

MAKE CONNECTIONS *Animals with bilateral symmetry are divided into three main lineages (see Figure 32.11). What are those lineages? How many are represented by the animals shown above?*

their distribution, gills often have a total surface area much greater than that of the rest of the body's exterior.

Movement of the respiratory medium over the respiratory surface, a process called **ventilation**, maintains the partial pressure gradients of O_2 and CO_2 across the gill that are necessary for gas exchange. To promote ventilation, most gill-bearing animals either move their gills through the water or move water over their gills. For example, crayfish and lobsters have paddle-like appendages that drive a current of water over the gills, whereas mussels and clams move water with cilia. Octopuses and squids ventilate their gills by taking in and ejecting water, with the side benefit of locomotion by jet propulsion. Fishes use the motion of swimming or coordinated movements of the mouth and gill covers to ventilate their gills. In both cases, a current of water enters the mouth of the fish, passes through slits in the pharynx, flows over the gills, and then exits the body **(Figure 42.22)**.

In fishes, the efficiency of gas exchange is maximized by **countercurrent exchange**, the exchange of a substance or heat between two fluids flowing in opposite directions. In a fish gill, the two fluids are blood and water. Because blood flows in the direction opposite to that of water passing over the gills, at each point in its travel blood is less saturated with O_2 than the water it meets (see Figure 42.22). As blood enters a gill capillary, it encounters water that is completing its passage through the gill. Depleted of much of its dissolved O_2, this water nevertheless has a higher P_{O_2} than the incoming blood, and O_2 transfer takes place. As the blood continues its passage, its P_{O_2} steadily increases, but so does that of the water it encounters, since each successive position in the blood's travel corresponds to an earlier position in the water's passage over the gills. Thus, a partial pressure gradient favoring the diffusion of O_2 from water to blood exists along the entire length of the capillary.

Countercurrent exchange mechanisms are remarkably efficient. In the fish gill, more than 80% of the O_2 dissolved in the water is removed as the water passes over the respiratory surface. In other settings, countercurrent exchange contributes to temperature regulation (see Chapter 40) and to the functioning of the mammalian kidney (see Chapter 44).

Tracheal Systems in Insects

In most terrestrial animals, respiratory surfaces are enclosed within the body, exposed to the atmosphere only through narrow tubes. Although the most familiar example of such an arrangement is the lung, the most common is the insect **tracheal system**, a network of air tubes that branch throughout the body. The largest tubes, called tracheae, open to the outside. The finest branches extend close to the surface of nearly every cell, where gas is exchanged by diffusion across the moist epithelium that lines the tips of the tracheal branches. Because the tracheal system brings air within a very short distance of virtually every body cell in an

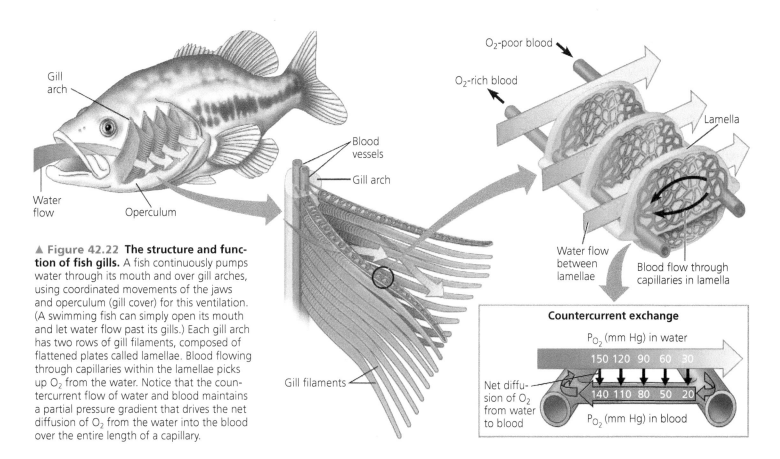

▲ **Figure 42.22 The structure and function of fish gills.** A fish continuously pumps water through its mouth and over gill arches, using coordinated movements of the jaws and operculum (gill cover) for this ventilation. (A swimming fish can simply open its mouth and let water flow past its gills.) Each gill arch has two rows of gill filaments, composed of flattened plates called lamellae. Blood flowing through capillaries within the lamellae picks up O_2 from the water. Notice that the countercurrent flow of water and blood maintains a partial pressure gradient that drives the net diffusion of O_2 from the water into the blood over the entire length of a capillary.

Gill arch

Water flow

Operculum

Blood vessels

Gill arch

Gill filaments

O_2-poor blood

O_2-rich blood

Lamella

Water flow between lamellae

Blood flow through capillaries in lamella

Countercurrent exchange

P_{O_2} (mm Hg) in water

150 120 90 60 30

Net diffusion of O_2 from water to blood

140 110 80 50 20

P_{O_2} (mm Hg) in blood

(a) The respiratory system of an insect consists of branched internal tubes. The largest tubes, called tracheae, connect to external openings spaced along the insect's body surface. Air sacs formed from enlarged portions of the tracheae are found near organs that require a large supply of oxygen.

(b) Rings of chitin keep the tracheae open, allowing air to enter and pass into smaller tubes called tracheoles. The branched tracheoles deliver air directly to cells throughout the body. Tracheoles have closed ends filled with fluid (blue-gray). When the animal is active and using more O_2, most of the fluid is withdrawn into the body. This increases the surface area of air-filled tracheoles in contact with cells.

(c) The TEM above shows cross sections of tracheoles in a tiny piece of insect flight muscle. Each of the numerous mitochondria in the muscle cells lies within about 5 μm of a tracheole.

▲ **Figure 42.23 A tracheal system.**

insect, it can transport O_2 and CO_2 without the participation of the animal's open circulatory system.

For small insects, diffusion through the tracheae brings in enough O_2 and removes enough CO_2 to support cellular respiration. Larger insects meet their higher energy demands by ventilating their tracheal systems with rhythmic body movements that compress and expand the air tubes like bellows. For example, consider an insect in flight, which has a very high metabolic rate, consuming 10 to 200 times more O_2 than it does at rest. In many flying insects, alternating contraction and relaxation of the flight muscles pump air rapidly through the tracheal system. The flight muscle cells are packed with mitochondria that support the high metabolic rate, and the tracheal tubes supply these ATP-generating organelles with ample O_2. Thus, adaptations of tracheal systems are directly related to bioenergetics **(Figure 42.23)**.

Lungs

Unlike tracheal systems, which branch throughout the insect body, **lungs** are localized respiratory organs. Representing an infolding of the body surface, they are typically subdivided into numerous pockets. Because the respiratory surface of a lung is not in direct contact with all other parts of the body, the gap must be bridged by the circulatory system, which transports gases between the lungs and the rest of the body. Lungs have evolved in organisms with open circulatory systems, such as spiders and land snails, as well as in vertebrates.

Among vertebrates that lack gills, the use of lungs for gas exchange varies. Amphibians rely heavily on diffusion across external body surfaces, such as the skin, to carry out gas exchange; lungs, if present, are relatively small. In contrast, most reptiles (including all birds) and all mammals depend entirely on lungs for gas exchange. Turtles are an exception; they supplement lung breathing with gas exchange across moist epithelial surfaces continuous with their mouth or anus. Lungs and air breathing have evolved in a few aquatic vertebrates as adaptations to living in oxygen-poor water or to spending part of their time exposed to air (for instance, when the water level of a pond recedes).

Mammalian Respiratory Systems: A Closer Look

In mammals, a system of branching ducts conveys air to the lungs, which are located in the thoracic cavity **(Figure 42.24)**. Air enters through the nostrils and is then filtered by hairs, warmed, humidified, and sampled for odors as it flows through a maze of spaces in the nasal cavity. The nasal cavity leads to the pharynx, an intersection where the paths for air and food cross. When food is swallowed, the **larynx** (the upper part of the respiratory tract) moves upward and tips the epiglottis over the glottis, which is the opening of the **trachea**, or windpipe. This allows food to go down the esophagus to the stomach (see Figure 41.10). The rest of the time, the glottis is open, enabling breathing.

From the larynx, air passes into the trachea. The cartilage that reinforces the walls of both the larynx and the trachea keeps this part of the airway open. Within the larynx of most mammals, the exhaled air rushes by a pair of elastic bands of muscle called vocal folds, or, in humans, vocal cords. Sounds are produced when muscles in the larynx are tensed, stretching the cords so that they vibrate. High-pitched sounds result from tightly stretched cords vibrating rapidly; low-pitched sounds come from looser cords vibrating slowly.

The trachea branches into two **bronchi** (singular, *bronchus*), one leading to each lung. Within the lung, the bronchi branch repeatedly into finer and finer tubes called **bronchioles**. The entire system of air ducts has the appearance of an inverted tree, the trunk being the trachea. The epithelium lining the major branches of this respiratory tree is covered by cilia and a thin film of mucus. The mucus traps dust, pollen, and other particulate contaminants, and the beating cilia move the mucus upward to the pharynx, where it can be swallowed into the esophagus. This process, sometimes referred to as the "mucus escalator," plays a crucial role in cleansing the respiratory system.

Gas exchange in mammals occurs in **alveoli** (singular, *alveolus*; see Figure 42.24), air sacs clustered at the tips of the tiniest bronchioles. Human lungs contain millions of alveoli, which together have a surface area of about 100 m²—50 times that of the skin. Oxygen in the air entering the alveoli dissolves in the moist film lining their inner surfaces and rapidly diffuses across the epithelium into a web of capillaries that surrounds each alveolus. Net diffusion of carbon dioxide occurs in the opposite direction, from the capillaries across the epithelium of the alveolus and into the air space.

Lacking cilia or significant air currents to remove particles from their surface, alveoli are highly susceptible to contamination. White blood cells patrol the alveoli, engulfing foreign particles. However, if too much particulate matter reaches the alveoli, the defenses can be overwhelmed, leading to inflammation and irreversible damage. For example, particulates from cigarette smoke that enter alveoli can cause a permanent reduction in lung capacity. For coal miners, inhalation of large amounts of coal dust can lead to silicosis, a disabling, irreversible, and sometimes fatal lung disease.

The film of liquid that lines alveoli is subject to surface tension, an attractive force that has the effect of minimizing a liquid's surface area (see Chapter 3). Given their tiny diameter (about 0.25 mm), why don't alveoli collapse under high surface tension? It turns out that alveoli produce a mixture of phospholipids and proteins called **surfactant**, for *surf*ace-*act*ive agent, which coats the alveoli and reduces surface tension.

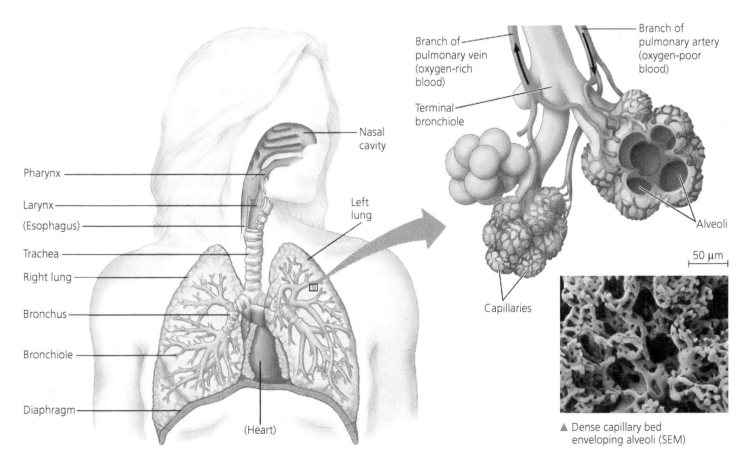

Nasal cavity

Pharynx

Larynx

(Esophagus)

Trachea

Right lung

Bronchus

Bronchiole

Diaphragm

(Heart)

Left lung

Branch of pulmonary vein (oxygen-rich blood)

Terminal bronchiole

Branch of pulmonary artery (oxygen-poor blood)

Alveoli

50 μm

Capillaries

▲ Dense capillary bed enveloping alveoli (SEM)

▲ **Figure 42.24 The mammalian respiratory system.** From the nasal cavity and pharynx, inhaled air passes through the larynx, trachea, and bronchi to the bronchioles, which end in microscopic alveoli lined by a thin, moist epithelium. Branches of the pulmonary arteries convey oxygen-poor blood to the alveoli; branches of the pulmonary veins transport oxygen-rich blood from the alveoli back to the heart.

What causes respiratory distress syndrome?

Experiment Mary Ellen Avery, a research fellow at Harvard University, hypothesized that a lack of surfactant caused respiratory distress syndrome (RDS) in preterm infants. To test this hypothesis, she obtained autopsy samples of lungs from infants who had died of RDS or from other causes. She extracted material from the samples and let it form a film on water. Avery then measured the tension (in dynes per centimeter) across the water surface and recorded the lowest surface tension observed for each sample.

Results Avery noted a pattern when she grouped the samples based on the body mass of the infant: less than 1,200 g (2.7 pounds) and 1,200 g or greater.

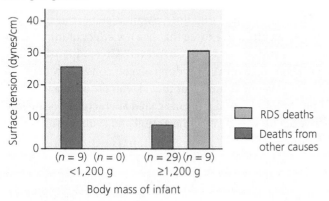

Conclusion For infants with a body mass of 1,200 g or greater, the material from those who had died of RDS exhibited much higher surface tension than the material from those who had died from other causes. Avery inferred that infants' lungs normally contain a surface-tension-reducing substance (now called surfactant) and that a lack of this substance was a likely cause of RDS. The results from infants with a body mass less than 1,200 g were similar to those from infants who had died from RDS, suggesting that surfactant is not normally produced until a fetus reaches this size.

Source: M. E. Avery and J. Mead, Surface properties in relation to atelectasis and hyaline membrane disease, *American Journal of Diseases of Children* 97:517–523 (1959).

WHAT IF? *If the researchers had measured the amount of surfactant in lung samples from the infants, what graph would you expect if the surfactant were plotted against infant body mass?*

In the 1950s, Mary Ellen Avery did the first experiment linking surfactant deficiency to *respiratory distress syndrome (RDS)*, a disease common in infants born 6 weeks or more before their due dates **(Figure 42.25)**. (The average full-term human pregnancy is 38 weeks.) Later studies revealed that surfactant typically appears in the lungs after 33 weeks of development. In the 1950s, RDS killed 10,000 infants annually in the United States, but artificial surfactants are now used successfully to treat early preterm infants. Treated babies with a body mass over 900 g (2 pounds) at birth usually survive without long-term health problems. For her contributions, Avery received the National Medal of Science in 1991.

Having surveyed the route that air follows when we breathe, we'll turn next to the process of breathing itself.

1. Why is the position of lung tissues *within* the body an advantage for terrestrial animals?
2. After a heavy rain, earthworms come to the surface. How would you explain this behavior in terms of an earthworm's requirements for gas exchange?
3. **MAKE CONNECTIONS** Describe the role of countercurrent exchange in facilitating both respiration and thermoregulation (see Concept 40.3).

For suggested answers, see Appendix A.

CONCEPT 42.6

Breathing ventilates the lungs

Like fishes, terrestrial vertebrates rely on ventilation to maintain high O_2 and low CO_2 concentrations at the gas exchange surface. The process that ventilates lungs is **breathing**, the alternating inhalation and exhalation of air. A variety of mechanisms for moving air in and out of lungs have evolved, as we will see by considering breathing in amphibians, birds, and mammals.

How an Amphibian Breathes

An amphibian such as a frog ventilates its lungs by **positive pressure breathing**, inflating the lungs with forced airflow. During the first stage of inhalation, muscles lower the floor of an amphibian's oral cavity, drawing in air through its nostrils. Next, with the nostrils and mouth closed, the floor of the oral cavity rises, forcing air down the trachea. During exhalation, air is forced back out by the elastic recoil of the lungs and by compression of the muscular body wall. When male frogs puff themselves up in aggressive or courtship displays, they disrupt this breathing cycle, taking in air several times without allowing any release.

How a Bird Breathes

To bring fresh air to their lungs, birds use eight or nine air sacs situated on either side of the lungs **(Figure 42.26)**. The air sacs do not function directly in gas exchange but act as bellows that keep air flowing through the lungs. Instead of alveoli, which are dead ends, the sites of gas exchange in bird lungs are tiny channels called *parabronchi*. Passage of air through the entire system—lungs and air sacs—requires two cycles of inhalation and exhalation.

Two features of ventilation in birds make it highly efficient. First, when birds breathe, they pass air over the gas exchange surface in only one direction. Second, incoming fresh air does not mix with air that has already carried out gas exchange.

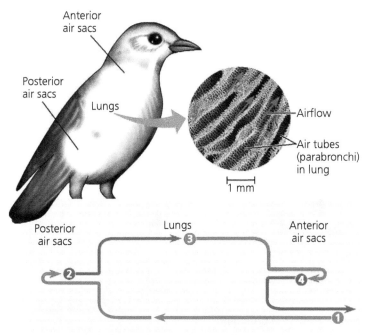

Two cycles of inhalation and exhalation are required to pass one breath through the system:

❶ First inhalation: Air fills the posterior air sacs.

❷ First exhalation: Posterior air sacs contract, pushing air into lungs.

❸ Second inhalation: Air passes through lungs and fills anterior air sacs.

❹ Second exhalation: As anterior air sacs contract, air that entered body at first inhalation is pushed out of body.

▲ **Figure 42.26 The avian respiratory system.** This diagram traces a breath of air through the respiratory system of a bird. As shown, two cycles of inhalation and exhalation are required for the air to pass all the way through the system and out of the bird.

How a Mammal Breathes

Unlike amphibians and birds, mammals employ **negative pressure breathing**—pulling, rather than pushing, air into their lungs **(Figure 42.27)**. Using muscle contraction to actively expand the thoracic cavity, mammals lower air pressure in their lungs below that of the air outside their body. Because gas flows from a region of higher pressure to a region of lower pressure, air rushes through the nostrils and mouth and down the breathing tubes to the alveoli. During exhalation, the muscles controlling the thoracic cavity relax, and the volume of the cavity is reduced. The increased air pressure in the alveoli forces air up the breathing tubes and out of the body. Thus, inhalation is always active and requires work, whereas exhalation is usually passive.

Expanding the thoracic cavity during inhalation involves the animal's rib muscles and the **diaphragm**, a sheet of skeletal muscle that forms the bottom wall of the cavity. Contracting one set of rib muscles expands the rib cage, the front wall of the thoracic cavity, by pulling the ribs upward and the sternum outward. At the same time, the diaphragm

contracts, expanding the thoracic cavity downward. The effect of the descending diaphragm is similar to that of a plunger being drawn out of a syringe.

Within the thoracic cavity, a double membrane surrounds the lungs. The inner layer of this membrane adheres to the outside of the lungs, and the outer layer adheres to the wall of the thoracic cavity. A thin space filled with fluid separates the two layers. Surface tension in the fluid causes the two layers to stick together like two plates of glass separated by a film of water: The layers can slide smoothly past each other, but they cannot be pulled apart easily. Consequently, the volume of the thoracic cavity and the volume of the lungs change in unison.

Depending on activity level, additional muscles may be recruited to aid breathing. The rib muscles and diaphragm are sufficient to change lung volume when a mammal is at rest. During exercise, other muscles of the neck, back, and chest increase the volume of the thoracic cavity by raising the rib cage. In kangaroos and some other mammals, locomotion causes a rhythmic movement of organs in the abdomen, including the stomach and liver. The result is a piston-like pumping motion that pushes and pulls on the diaphragm, further increasing the volume of air moved in and out of the lungs.

The volume of air inhaled and exhaled with each breath is called **tidal volume**. It averages about 500 mL in resting humans. The tidal volume during maximal inhalation and exhalation is the **vital capacity**, which is about 3.4 L and 4.8 L for college-age women and men, respectively. The air that remains after a forced exhalation is called the **residual volume**. With age, the lungs lose their resilience, and residual volume increases at the expense of vital capacity.

❶ INHALATION: Diaphragm contracts (moves down).

❷ EXHALATION: Diaphragm relaxes (moves up).

▲ **Figure 42.27 Negative pressure breathing.** A mammal breathes by changing the air pressure within its lungs relative to the pressure of the outside atmosphere.

WHAT IF? *The walls of alveoli contain elastic fibers that allow the alveoli to expand and contract with each breath. If the alveoli lost their elasticity, how would that affect gas exchange in the lungs?*

Because the lungs in mammals do not completely empty with each breath, and because inhalation occurs through the same airways as exhalation, each inhalation mixes fresh air with oxygen-depleted residual air. As a result, the maximum P_{O_2} in alveoli is always considerably less than in the atmosphere. The maximum P_{O_2} in lungs is also less for mammals than for birds, which have a unidirectional flow of air through the lungs. This is one reason mammals function less well than birds at high altitude. For example, humans have great difficulty obtaining enough O_2 when climbing at high elevations, such as those in the Himalayas. However, bar-headed geese and several other bird species easily fly through high Himalayan passes during their migrations.

NORMAL BLOOD pH (about 7.4)

Blood CO_2 level falls and pH rises.

Blood pH falls due to rising levels of CO_2 in tissues (such as when exercising).

Medulla detects decrease in pH of cerebrospinal fluid.

Cerebrospinal fluid

Carotid arteries

Aorta

Sensors in major blood vessels detect decrease in blood pH.

Signals from medulla to rib muscles and diaphragm increase rate and depth of ventilation.

Medulla oblongata

Medulla receives signals from major blood vessels.

▲ Figure 42.28 **Homeostatic control of breathing.**

WHAT IF? *Suppose a person began breathing very rapidly while resting. Describe the effect on blood CO_2 levels and the steps by which the negative-feedback circuit would restore homeostasis.*

Control of Breathing in Humans

Although you can voluntarily hold your breath or breathe faster and deeper, most of the time your breathing is regulated by involuntary mechanisms. These control mechanisms ensure that gas exchange is coordinated with blood circulation and with metabolic demand.

The neurons mainly responsible for regulating breathing are in the medulla oblongata, near the base of the brain (Figure 42.28). Neural circuits in the medulla form a pair of *breathing control centers* that establish the breathing rhythm. When you breathe deeply, a negative-feedback mechanism prevents the lungs from overexpanding: During inhalation, sensors that detect stretching of the lung tissue send nerve impulses to the control circuits in the medulla, inhibiting further inhalation.

In regulating breathing, the medulla uses the pH of the surrounding tissue fluid as an indicator of blood CO_2 concentration. The reason pH can be used in this way is that blood CO_2 is the main determinant of the pH of cerebrospinal fluid, the fluid surrounding the brain and spinal cord. Carbon dioxide diffuses from the blood to the cerebrospinal fluid, where it reacts with water and forms carbonic acid (H_2CO_3). The H_2CO_3 can then dissociate into a bicarbonate ion (HCO_3^-) and a hydrogen ion (H^+):

$$CO_2 + H_2O \rightleftharpoons H_2CO_3 \rightleftharpoons HCO_3^- + H^+$$

Consider what happens if metabolic activity increases, such as occurs during exercise. Increased metabolism raises the concentration of CO_2 in the blood and cerebrospinal fluid. Through the reactions shown above, the higher CO_2 concentration leads to an increase in the concentration of H^+, lowering pH. Sensors in the medulla as well as in major blood vessels detect this pH change. In response, the medulla's control circuits increase the depth and rate of breathing (see Figure 42.28). Both remain high until the excess CO_2 is eliminated in exhaled air and pH returns to a normal value.

The blood O_2 level usually has little effect on the breathing control centers. However, when the O_2 level drops very low (at high altitudes, for instance), O_2 sensors in the aorta and the carotid arteries in the neck send signals to the breathing control centers, which respond by increasing the breathing rate. The regulation of breathing is modulated by additional neural circuits, primarily in the pons, a part of the brain next to the medulla.

Breathing control is effective only if ventilation is matched to blood flow through alveolar capillaries. During exercise, for instance, such coordination couples an increased breathing rate, which enhances O_2 uptake and CO_2 removal, with an increase in cardiac output.

CONCEPT CHECK 42.6

1. How does an increase in the CO_2 concentration in the blood affect the pH of cerebrospinal fluid?

2. A drop in blood pH causes an increase in heart rate. What is the function of this control mechanism?

3. **WHAT IF?** If an injury tore a small hole in the membranes surrounding your lungs, what effect on lung function would you expect?

For suggested answers, see Appendix A.

Adaptations for gas exchange include pigments that bind and transport gases

The high metabolic demands of many animals necessitate the exchange of large quantities of O_2 and CO_2. Here we'll examine how blood molecules called respiratory pigments facilitate this exchange through their interaction with O_2 and CO_2. We'll also investigate physiological adaptations that enable animals to be active under conditions of high metabolic load or very limiting P_{O_2}. As a basis for exploring these topics, let's summarize the basic gas exchange circuit in humans.

Coordination of Circulation and Gas Exchange

The partial pressures of O_2 and CO_2 in the blood vary as the gases move between air, blood, and other body tissues, as shown in **Figure 42.29**. **1** During inhalation, fresh air mixes with air remaining in the lungs. **2** The resulting mixture formed in the alveoli has a higher P_{O_2} and a lower P_{CO_2} than the blood flowing through the alveolar capillaries. Consequently, there is a net diffusion of O_2 down its partial pressure gradient from the air in the alveoli to the blood. Meanwhile, CO_2 in the blood undergoes net diffusion into the air in the alveoli. **3** By the time the blood leaves the lungs in the pulmonary veins, its P_{O_2} and P_{CO_2} match the values for those gases in the alveoli. After returning to the heart, this blood is pumped through the systemic circuit.

4 In the systemic capillaries, gradients of partial pressure favor the net diffusion of O_2 out of the blood and CO_2 into the blood. These gradients exist because cellular respiration in the mitochondria of cells near each capillary removes O_2 from and adds CO_2 to the surrounding interstitial fluid. **5** After the blood unloads O_2 and loads CO_2, it is returned to the heart and pumped to the lungs again. **6** There, exchange occurs across the alveolar capillaries, resulting in exhaled air enriched in CO_2 and partially depleted of O_2.

Respiratory Pigments

The low solubility of O_2 in water (and thus in blood) poses a problem for animals that rely on the circulatory system to deliver O_2. For example, a person requires almost 2 L of O_2 per minute during intense exercise, and all of it must be carried in the blood from the lungs to the active tissues. At normal body temperature and air pressure, however, only 4.5 mL of O_2 can dissolve into a liter of blood in the lungs. Even if 80% of the dissolved O_2 were delivered to the tissues, the heart would still need to pump 555 L of blood per minute!

In fact, animals transport most of their O_2 bound to proteins called **respiratory pigments**. Respiratory pigments circulate with the blood or hemolymph and are often contained within specialized cells. The pigments greatly increase the amount of O_2 that can be carried in the circulatory fluid (from 4.5 to about 200 mL of O_2 per liter in mammalian blood). In our example of an exercising human with an O_2 delivery rate of 80%, the presence of a respiratory pigment reduces the cardiac output necessary for O_2 transport to a manageable 12.5 L of blood per minute.

A variety of respiratory pigments have evolved in animals. With a few exceptions, these molecules have a distinctive color (hence the term *pigment*) and consist of a metal bound to a protein. One example is the blue pigment *hemocyanin*, which has copper as its oxygen-binding component and is found in arthropods and many molluscs.

The respiratory pigment of almost all vertebrates and many invertebrates is hemoglobin. In vertebrates, it is

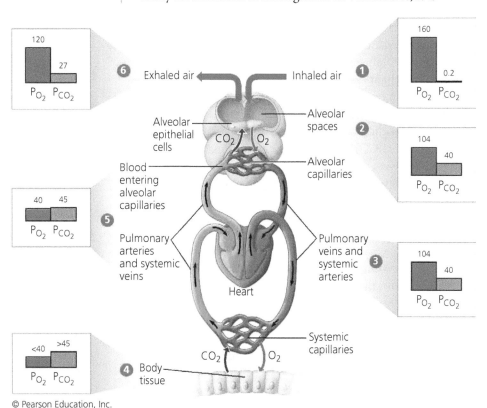

© Pearson Education, Inc.

▲ **Figure 42.29 Loading and unloading of respiratory gases.**

WHAT IF? *If you consciously forced more air out of your lungs each time you exhaled, how would that affect the values shown in the figure?*

ANIMATION **BioFlix** Visit the Study Area in **MasteringBiology** for the BioFlix® 3-D Animation on Gas Exchange. BioFlix Tutorials can also be assigned in MasteringBiology.

contained in erythrocytes and has four subunits (polypeptide chains), each with a cofactor called a heme group that has an iron atom at its center. Each iron atom binds one molecule of O_2, so a hemoglobin molecule can carry four

Hemoglobin

molecules of O_2. Like all respiratory pigments, hemoglobin binds O_2 reversibly, loading O_2 in the lungs or gills and unloading it elsewhere in the body. This process is enhanced by cooperativity between the hemoglobin subunits (see Concept 8.5). When O_2 binds to one subunit, the others change shape slightly, increasing affinity for O_2. When four O_2 molecules are bound and one subunit unloads its O_2, the other three subunits more readily unload O_2, as an associated shape change lowers their affinity for O_2.

Cooperativity in O_2 binding and release is evident in the dissociation curve for hemoglobin (**Figure 42.30a**). Over the range of P_{O_2} where the dissociation curve has a steep slope, even a slight change in P_{O_2} causes hemoglobin to load or unload a substantial amount of O_2. The steep part of the curve corresponds to the range of P_{O_2} found in body tissues. When cells in a particular location begin working harder—during exercise, for instance—P_{O_2} dips in their vicinity as the O_2 is consumed in cellular respiration. Because of subunit cooperativity, a slight drop in P_{O_2} causes a relatively large increase in the amount of O_2 the blood unloads.

The production of CO_2 during cellular respiration promotes the unloading of O_2 by hemoglobin in active tissues. As we have seen, CO_2 reacts with water, forming carbonic acid, which lowers the pH of its surroundings. Low pH, in turn, decreases the affinity of hemoglobin for O_2, an effect called the **Bohr shift** (**Figure 42.30b**). Thus, where CO_2 production is greater, hemoglobin releases more O_2, which can then be used to support more cellular respiration.

Hemoglobin also assists in buffering the blood—that is, preventing harmful changes in pH. And it has a minor role in CO_2 transport, the topic we'll explore next.

Carbon Dioxide Transport

Only about 7% of the CO_2 released by respiring cells is transported in solution in blood plasma. The rest diffuses from plasma into erythrocytes and reacts with water (assisted by the enzyme carbonic anhydrase), forming H_2CO_3. The H_2CO_3 readily dissociates into H^+ and HCO_3^-. Most H^+ binds to hemoglobin and other proteins, minimizing change in blood pH. Most HCO_3^- diffuses out of the erythrocytes and is transported to the lungs in the plasma. The remaining HCO_3^-, representing about 5% of the CO_2, binds to hemoglobin and is transported in erythrocytes.

(a) P_{O_2} and hemoglobin dissociation at pH 7.4. The curve shows the relative amounts of O_2 bound to hemoglobin exposed to solutions with different P_{O_2}. At a P_{O_2} of 100 mm Hg, typical in the lungs, hemoglobin is about 98% saturated with O_2. At a P_{O_2} of 40 mm Hg, common in resting tissues, hemoglobin is about 70% saturated, having unloaded nearly a third of its O_2. As shown in the above graph, hemoglobin can release much more O_2 to metabolically very active tissues, such as muscle tissue during exercise.

(b) pH and hemoglobin dissociation. In very active tissues, CO_2 from cellular respiration reacts with water to form carbonic acid, decreasing pH. Because hydrogen ions affect hemoglobin shape, a drop in pH shifts the O_2 dissociation curve toward the right (the Bohr shift). For a given P_{O_2}, hemoglobin releases more O_2 at a lower pH, supporting increased cellular respiration.

▲ **Figure 42.30 Dissociation curves for hemoglobin at 37°C.**

When blood flows through the lungs, the relative partial pressures of CO_2 favor the net diffusion of CO_2 out of the blood. As CO_2 diffuses into alveoli, the amount of CO_2 in the blood decreases. This decrease shifts the chemical equilibrium in favor of the conversion of HCO_3^- to CO_2, enabling further net diffusion of CO_2 into alveoli. Overall, the P_{CO_2} gradient is sufficient to reduce P_{CO_2} by about 15% during passage of blood through the lungs.

Respiratory Adaptations of Diving Mammals

EVOLUTION Animals vary greatly in their ability to spend time in environments in which there is no access to their normal respiratory medium—for example, when an air-breathing mammal swims underwater. Whereas most humans, even expert divers, cannot hold their breath longer than 2 or 3 minutes or swim deeper than 20 m, the Weddell seal of Antarctica routinely plunges to 200–500 m and remains there for 20 minutes to more than an hour. (Humans can remain submerged for comparable periods, but only with specialized gear and compressed air tanks.) Another diving mammal, the elephant seal, can reach depths of 1,500 m—almost a mile—and stay submerged for as long as 2 hours! One elephant seal carrying a recording device spent 40 days at sea, diving almost continuously with no surface period longer than 6 minutes.

▲ Weddell seal

The ability of seals and other marine mammals to power their bodies during long dives showcases two related phenomena—the response to environmental challenges over the short term by physiological adjustments and adaptation over the long term as a result of natural selection. We'll use the Weddell seal to explore both phenomena.

One adaptation of diving mammals to prolonged stays underwater is a capacity to store large amounts of O_2 in their bodies. Although the Weddell seal has relatively small lungs compared with humans, it has about twice the volume of blood per kilogram of body mass as a human. Furthermore, seals and other diving mammals have a high concentration of an oxygen-storing protein called **myoglobin** in their muscles. As a result, the Weddell seal can store about twice as much O_2 per kilogram of body mass as can a human.

Diving mammals not only have a relatively large O_2 stockpile but also have adaptations that conserve O_2. They swim with little muscular effort and glide passively for prolonged periods. During a dive, their heart rate and O_2 consumption rate decrease, and most blood is routed to the brain, spinal cord, eyes, adrenal glands, and, in pregnant seals, the placenta. Blood supply to the muscles is restricted or, during the longest dives, shut off altogether. During dives of more than about 20 minutes, a Weddell seal's muscles deplete the O_2 stored in myoglobin and then derive their ATP from fermentation instead of respiration (see Chapter 9).

How did these adaptations arise over the course of evolution? All mammals, including humans, have a diving reflex triggered by a plunge or fall into water: When the face contacts cold water, the heart rate immediately decreases and blood flow to body extremities is reduced. Genetic changes that strengthened this reflex would have provided a selective advantage to seal ancestors foraging underwater. Also, genetic variations that increased traits such as blood volume or myoglobin concentration would have improved diving ability and therefore been favored during selection over many generations.

CONCEPT CHECK 42.7

1. What determines whether the net diffusion of O_2 and CO_2 is into or out of the capillaries in the tissues and near the alveoli? Explain.
2. How does the Bohr shift help deliver O_2 to very active tissues?
3. **WHAT IF?** A doctor might give bicarbonate (HCO_3^-) to a patient who is breathing very rapidly. What is the doctor assuming about the patient's blood chemistry?

For suggested answers, see Appendix A.

---

42 Chapter Review

SUMMARY OF KEY CONCEPTS

CONCEPT 42.1

Circulatory systems link exchange surfaces with cells throughout the body (pp. 916–920)

- In animals with simple body plans, a gastrovascular cavity mediates exchange between the environment and cells that can be reached by diffusion. Because diffusion is slow over long distances, most complex animals have a circulatory system that moves fluid between cells and the organs that carry out exchange with the environment. Arthropods and most molluscs have an **open circulatory system**, in which **hemolymph** bathes organs directly. Vertebrates have a **closed circulatory system**, in which **blood** circulates in a closed network of pumps and vessels.

- The closed circulatory system of vertebrates consists of blood, **blood vessels**, and a two- to four-chambered **heart**. Blood pumped by a heart **ventricle** passes to **arteries** and then to the **capillaries**, sites of chemical exchange between blood and interstitial fluid. **Veins** return blood from capillaries to an **atrium**, which passes blood to a ventricle. Fishes, rays, and sharks have a single pump in their circulation. Air-breathing vertebrates have two pumps combined in a single heart. Variations in ventricle number and separation reflect adaptations to different environments and metabolic needs.

? *How does the flow of a fluid in a closed circulatory system differ from the movement of molecules between cells and their environment with regard to distance traveled, direction traveled, and driving force?*

CONCEPT 42.2

Coordinated cycles of heart contraction drive double circulation in mammals (pp. 920–923)

- The right ventricle pumps blood to the lungs, where it loads O_2 and unloads CO_2. Oxygen-rich blood from the lungs enters the heart at the left atrium and is pumped to the body tissues by the left ventricle. Blood returns to the heart through the right atrium.

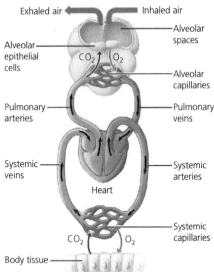

Exhaled air / Inhaled air
Alveolar epithelial cells
Alveolar spaces
CO_2 / O_2
Alveolar capillaries
Pulmonary arteries
Pulmonary veins
Systemic veins
Systemic arteries
Heart
Systemic capillaries
CO_2 / O_2
Body tissue

© Pearson Education, Inc.

- The **cardiac cycle**, a complete sequence of the heart's pumping and filling, consists of a period of contraction, called **systole**, and a period of relaxation, called **diastole**. Heart function can be assessed by measuring the **pulse** (number of times the heart beats each minute) and **cardiac output** (volume of blood pumped by each ventricle per minute).
- The heartbeat originates with impulses at the **sinoatrial (SA) node** (pacemaker) of the right atrium. They trigger atrial contraction, are delayed at the **atrioventricular (AV) node**, and are then conducted along the bundle branches and Purkinje fibers, triggering ventricular contraction. The nervous system, hormones, and body temperature affect pacemaker activity.

? *What changes in cardiac function might you expect after surgical replacement of a defective heart valve?*

CONCEPT 42.3

Patterns of blood pressure and flow reflect the structure and arrangement of blood vessels (pp. 923–927)

- Blood vessels have structures well adapted to function. Capillaries have narrow diameters and thin walls that facilitate exchange. The velocity of blood flow is lowest in the capillary beds as a result of their large total cross-sectional area. Arteries

contain thick elastic walls that maintain blood pressure. Veins contain one-way valves that contribute to the return of blood to the heart. Blood pressure is altered by changes in cardiac output and by variable constriction of arterioles.
- Fluid leaks out of capillaries and is returned to blood by the **lymphatic system**, which also defends against infection.

? *If you placed your forearm on your head, how, if at all, would the blood pressure in that arm change? Explain.*

CONCEPT 42.4

Blood components function in exchange, transport, and defense (pp. 928–933)

- Whole blood consists of cells and cell fragments (**platelets**) suspended in a liquid matrix called **plasma**. Plasma proteins influence blood pH, osmotic pressure, and viscosity, and they function in lipid transport, immunity (antibodies), and blood clotting (fibrinogen). Red blood cells, or **erythrocytes**, transport O_2. Five types of white blood cells, or **leukocytes**, function in defense against microorganisms and foreign substances in the blood. Platelets function in blood clotting, a cascade of reactions that converts plasma fibrinogen to fibrin.
- A variety of diseases impair function of the circulatory system. In **sickle-cell disease**, an aberrant form of **hemoglobin** disrupts erythrocyte shape and function, leading to blockage of small blood vessels and a decrease in the oxygen-carrying capacity of the blood. In cardiovascular disease, inflammation of the arterial lining enhances deposition of lipids and cells, resulting in the potential for life-threatening damage to the heart or brain.

? *In the absence of infection, what percentage of cells in human blood are leukocytes?*

CONCEPT 42.5

Gas exchange occurs across specialized respiratory surfaces (pp. 933–938)

- At all sites of **gas exchange**, a gas undergoes net diffusion from where its **partial pressure** is higher to where it is lower. Air is more conducive to gas exchange than water because air has a higher O_2 content, lower density, and lower viscosity.
- The structure and organization of respiratory surfaces differ among animal species. Gills are outfoldings of the body surface specialized for gas exchange in water. The effectiveness of gas exchange in some gills, including those of fishes, is increased by **ventilation** and **countercurrent exchange** between blood and water. Gas exchange in insects relies on a **tracheal system**, a branched network of tubes that bring O_2 directly to cells. Spiders, land snails, and most terrestrial vertebrates have internal **lungs**. In mammals, air inhaled through the nostrils passes through the pharynx into the **trachea, bronchi, bronchioles**, and dead-end **alveoli**, where gas exchange occurs.

? *Why does altitude have almost no effect on an animal's ability to rid itself of CO_2 through gas exchange?*

CONCEPT 42.6

Breathing ventilates the lungs (pp. 938–940)

- Breathing mechanisms vary substantially among vertebrates. An amphibian ventilates its lungs by **positive pressure breathing**, which forces air down the trachea. Birds use a system of air sacs as bellows to keep air flowing through the lungs in one direction only, preventing the mixing of incoming and outgoing air. Mammals ventilate their lungs by **negative pressure breathing**, which pulls air into the lungs when the rib muscles and

diaphragm contract. Incoming and outgoing air mix, decreasing the efficiency of ventilation.

- Sensors detect the pH of cerebrospinal fluid (reflecting CO_2 concentration in the blood), and a control center in the medulla oblongata adjusts breathing rate and depth to match metabolic demands. Additional input to the control center is provided by sensors in the aorta and carotid arteries that monitor blood levels of O_2 as well as CO_2 (via blood pH).

? *How does air in the lungs differ from the fresh air that enters the body during inspiration?*

CONCEPT 42.7

Adaptations for gas exchange include pigments that bind and transport gases (pp. 941–943)

- In the lungs, gradients of partial pressure favor the net diffusion of O_2 into the blood and CO_2 out of the blood. The opposite situation exists in the rest of the body. **Respiratory pigments** such as hemocyanin and hemoglobin bind O_2, greatly increasing the amount of O_2 transported by the circulatory system.
- Evolutionary adaptations enable some animals to satisfy extraordinary O_2 demands. Deep-diving mammals stockpile O_2 in blood and other tissues and deplete it slowly.

? *How is the role of a respiratory pigment like that of an enzyme?*

TEST YOUR UNDERSTANDING

LEVEL 1: KNOWLEDGE/COMPREHENSION

1. Which of the following respiratory systems is not closely associated with a blood supply?
   a. the lungs of a vertebrate
   b. the gills of a fish
   c. the tracheal system of an insect
   d. the skin of an earthworm

2. Blood returning to the mammalian heart in a pulmonary vein drains first into the
   a. left atrium.   c. left ventricle.
   b. right atrium.   d. right ventricle.

3. Pulse is a direct measure of
   a. blood pressure.   c. cardiac output.
   b. stroke volume.   d. heart rate.

4. When you hold your breath, which of the following blood gas changes first leads to the urge to breathe?
   a. rising O_2 c. rising CO_2
   b. falling O_2 d. falling CO_2

5. One feature that amphibians and humans have in common is
   a. the number of heart chambers.
   b. a complete separation of circuits for circulation.
   c. the number of circuits for circulation.
   d. a low blood pressure in the systemic circuit.

LEVEL 2: APPLICATION/ANALYSIS

6. If a molecule of CO_2 released into the blood in your left toe is exhaled from your nose, it must pass through all of the following except
   a. the pulmonary vein.   c. the right atrium.
   b. the trachea.   d. the right ventricle.

7. Compared with the interstitial fluid that bathes active muscle cells, blood reaching these cells in arterioles has a
   a. higher P_{O_2}.
   b. higher P_{CO_2}.
   c. greater bicarbonate concentration.
   d. lower pH.

LEVEL 3: SYNTHESIS/EVALUATION

8. **DRAW IT** Plot blood pressure against time for one cardiac cycle in humans, drawing separate lines for the pressure in the aorta, the left ventricle, and the right ventricle. Below the time axis, add a vertical arrow pointing to the time when you expect a peak in atrial blood pressure.

9. **EVOLUTION CONNECTION**
   One of the opponents of the movie monster Godzilla is Mothra, a giant mothlike creature with a wingspan of several dozen meters. The largest known insects were Paleozoic dragonflies with half-meter wingspans. Focusing on respiration and gas exchange, explain why giant insects are improbable.

10. **SCIENTIFIC INQUIRY**
    INTERPRET THE DATA
    The hemoglobin of a human fetus differs from adult hemoglobin. Compare the dissociation curves of the two hemoglobins in the graph at right. Describe how they differ, and propose a hypothesis to explain the benefit of this difference.

11. **SCIENCE, TECHNOLOGY, AND SOCIETY**
    Hundreds of studies have linked smoking with cardiovascular and lung disease. According to most health authorities, smoking is the leading cause of preventable, premature death in the United States. What are some arguments in favor of a total ban on cigarette advertising? What are arguments in opposition? Do you favor or oppose such a ban? Explain.

12. **WRITE ABOUT A THEME: INTERACTIONS**
    Some athletes prepare for competition at sea level by sleeping in a tent in which P_{O_2} is kept low. When climbing high peaks, some mountaineers breathe from bottles of pure O_2. In a short essay (100–150 words), relate these behaviors to the mechanism of O_2 transport in the human body and to physiological interactions with our gaseous environment.

13. **SYNTHESIZE YOUR KNOWLEDGE**

The diving bell spider (*Argyroneta aquatica*) stores air underwater in a net of silk. Explain why this adaptation could be more advantageous than having gills, taking into account differences in gas exchange media and gas exchange organs among animals.

For selected answers, see Appendix A.

MasteringBiology®

43

The Immune System

▲ **Figure 43.1 What triggered this attack by an immune cell on a clump of bacteria?**

Recognition and Response

For a **pathogen**—a bacterium, fungus, virus, or other disease-causing agent—the internal environment of an animal is a nearly ideal habitat. The animal body offers a ready source of nutrients, a protected setting, and a means of transport to new environments. From the perspective of a cold or flu virus, we are wonderful hosts. From our vantage point, the situation is not so ideal. Fortunately, adaptations have arisen over the course of evolution that protect animals against many pathogens.

Dedicated immune cells in the body fluids and tissues of most animals specifically interact with and destroy pathogens. For example, **Figure 43.1** shows an immune cell called a macrophage (brown) engulfing rod-shaped bacteria (green). Some immune cells are types of white blood cells called lymphocytes (such as the one shown at left with bacteria). Most lymphocytes recognize and respond to specific types of pathogens. Together, the body's defenses make up the **immune system**, which enables an animal to avoid or limit many infections. A foreign molecule or cell doesn't have to be pathogenic to elicit an immune response, but we'll focus in this chapter on the immune system's role in defending against pathogens.

The first lines of defense offered by immune systems help prevent pathogens from gaining entrance to the body. For example, an outer covering, such as a skin or shell, blocks entry by many pathogens. Sealing off the entire body surface is impossible, however, because gas exchange, nutrition, and reproduction require openings to the environment. Secretions that trap or kill microbes guard the body's entrances and exits, while the linings of the digestive tract, airway, and other exchange surfaces provide additional barriers to infection.

If a pathogen breaches barrier defenses and enters the body, the problem of how to fend off attack changes substantially. Housed within body fluids and tissues, the invader is no longer an outsider. To fight infections, an animal's immune system must detect foreign particles and cells within the body. In other words, a properly functioning immune system distinguishes nonself from self. How is this accomplished? Immune cells produce receptor molecules that bind specifically to molecules from foreign cells or viruses and activate defense responses. The specific binding of immune receptors to foreign molecules is a type of *molecular recognition* and is the central event in identifying nonself particles and cells.

Two types of molecular recognition provide the basis for the two types of immune defense found among animals: innate immunity, which is common to all animals, and adaptive immunity, which is found only in vertebrates. **Figure 43.2** summarizes these two types of immunity, highlighting fundamental similarities and differences.

In **innate immunity**, which includes barrier defenses, molecular recognition relies on a small set of receptor proteins that bind to molecules or structures that are absent from animal bodies but common to a group of viruses, bacteria, or other microbes. Binding of an innate immune receptor to a foreign molecule activates internal defenses, enabling responses to a very broad range of pathogens.

In **adaptive immunity**, molecular recognition relies on a vast arsenal of receptors, each of which recognizes a feature typically found only on a particular part of a particular molecule in a particular pathogen. As a result, recognition and response in adaptive immunity occur with tremendous specificity.

The adaptive immune response, also known as the acquired immune response, is activated after the innate immune response and develops more slowly. The names *adaptive* and *acquired* reflect the fact that this immune response is enhanced by previous exposure to the infecting pathogen. Examples of adaptive responses include the synthesis of proteins that inactivate a bacterial toxin and the targeted killing of a virus-infected body cell.

In this chapter, we'll examine how each type of immunity protects animals from disease. We'll also investigate how pathogens can avoid or overwhelm the immune system and how defects in the immune system can imperil health.

CONCEPT 43.1

In innate immunity, recognition and response rely on traits common to groups of pathogens

Innate immunity is found in all animals (as well as in plants). In exploring innate immunity, we'll begin with invertebrates, which repel and fight infection with only this type of immunity. We'll then turn to vertebrates, in which innate immunity serves both as an immediate defense against infection and as the foundation for adaptive immune defenses.

Innate Immunity of Invertebrates

The great success of insects in terrestrial and freshwater habitats teeming with diverse pathogens highlights the effectiveness of invertebrate innate immunity. In each of these environments, insects rely on their exoskeleton as a first line of defense against infection. Composed largely of the polysaccharide chitin, the exoskeleton provides an effective barrier defense against most pathogens. Chitin also lines the insect intestine, where it blocks infection by many pathogens ingested with food. **Lysozyme**, an enzyme that breaks down bacterial cell walls, further protects the insect digestive system.

Any pathogen that breaches an insect's barrier defenses encounters a number of internal immune defenses. Immune cells called *hemocytes* travel throughout the body in the hemolymph, the insect circulatory fluid. Some hemocytes

Pathogens
(such as bacteria, fungi, and viruses)

INNATE IMMUNITY (all animals)	**Barrier defenses:**
• Recognition of traits shared by broad ranges of pathogens, using a small set of receptors	Skin Mucous membranes Secretions
• Rapid response	**Internal defenses:** Phagocytic cells Natural killer cells Antimicrobial proteins Inflammatory response

ADAPTIVE IMMUNITY (vertebrates only)	**Humoral response:**
• Recognition of traits specific to particular pathogens, using a vast array of receptors	Antibodies defend against infection in body fluids.
• Slower response	**Cell-mediated response:** Cytotoxic cells defend against infection in body cells.

▲ **Figure 43.2 Overview of animal immunity.** Immune responses in animals can be divided into innate and adaptive immunity. Some components of innate immunity contribute to activation of adaptive immune defenses.

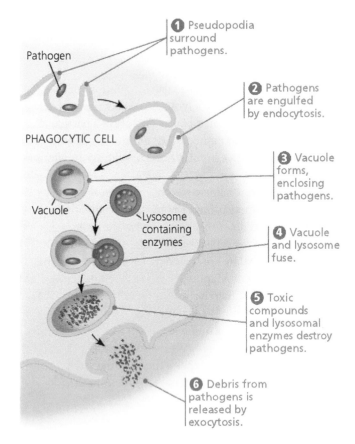

❶ Pseudopodia surround pathogens.

Pathogen

❷ Pathogens are engulfed by endocytosis.

PHAGOCYTIC CELL

❸ Vacuole forms, enclosing pathogens.

Vacuole

Lysosome containing enzymes

❹ Vacuole and lysosome fuse.

❺ Toxic compounds and lysosomal enzymes destroy pathogens.

❻ Debris from pathogens is released by exocytosis.

▲ Figure 43.3 **Phagocytosis.** This diagram depicts events in the ingestion and destruction of pathogens by a typical phagocytic cell.

ingest and break down bacteria and other foreign substances, a process known as **phagocytosis (Figure 43.3).** Other hemocytes release chemicals that kill pathogens and help entrap large parasites, such as *Plasmodium*, the parasite of mosquitoes that causes malaria. In addition, encounters with pathogens in the hemolymph cause hemocytes and certain other cells to secrete *antimicrobial peptides*, which are short chains of amino acids. These peptides circulate throughout the body of the insect **(Figure 43.4)** and inactivate or kill fungi and bacteria by disrupting their plasma membranes.

◀ **Figure 43.4 An inducible innate immune response.** These fruit flies were engineered to express the green fluorescent protein (GFP) gene upon activation of the innate immune response. The fly on the top was injected with bacteria; the fly on the bottom was not. Only the injected fly activates antimicrobial peptide genes, produces GFP, and glows bright green under fluorescent light.

Immune cells of insects bind to molecules found only in the outer layers of fungi or bacteria. Fungal cell walls contain certain unique polysaccharides, whereas bacterial cell walls have polymers containing combinations of sugars and amino acids not found in animal cells. Such macromolecules serve as identity tags in the process of pathogen recognition. Insect immune cells secrete recognition proteins, each of which binds specifically to a macromolecule characteristic of a broad class of bacteria or fungi.

Innate immune responses are distinct for different classes of pathogens. For example, when the fungus *Neurospora crassa* infects a fruit fly, pieces of the fungal cell wall bind to a recognition protein. Together, the complex activates the protein Toll, a receptor on the surface of hemocytes. Signal transduction from the Toll receptor to the cell nucleus leads to synthesis of a set of antimicrobial peptides active against fungi. If the fly is instead infected by the bacterium *Micrococcus luteus*, a different recognition protein is activated, and the fly produces a different set of antimicrobial peptides effective against *M. luteus* and many related bacteria.

Because fruit flies secrete many distinct antimicrobial peptides in response to a single infection, it is difficult to study the activity of any one peptide. To get around this problem, Bruno Lemaitre and fellow researchers used modern genetic techniques to reprogram the fly immune system **(Figure 43.5).** They found that the synthesis of a single type of antimicrobial peptide in the fly's body could provide an effective and specific immune defense.

Innate Immunity of Vertebrates

Among jawed vertebrates, innate immune defenses coexist with the more recently evolved system of adaptive immunity. Because most discoveries regarding vertebrate innate immunity have come from studies of mice and humans, we'll focus here on mammals. In this section, we'll consider first the innate defenses that are similar to those found among invertebrates: barrier defenses, phagocytosis, and antimicrobial peptides. We'll then examine some unique aspects of vertebrate innate immunity, such as natural killer cells, interferons, and the inflammatory response.

Barrier Defenses

In mammals, barrier defenses block the entry of many pathogens. These defenses include the skin and the mucous membranes lining the digestive, respiratory, urinary, and reproductive tracts. The mucous membranes produce *mucus*, a viscous fluid that traps pathogens and other particles. In the airway, ciliated epithelial cells sweep mucus and any entrapped material upward, helping prevent infection of the lungs. Saliva, tears, and mucous secretions that bathe various exposed epithelia provide a washing action that also inhibits colonization by fungi and bacteria.

Can a single antimicrobial peptide protect fruit flies against infection?

Experiment In 2002, Bruno Lemaitre and colleagues in France devised a novel strategy to test the function of a single antimicrobial peptide. They began with a mutant fruit fly strain in which pathogens are recognized but the signaling that would normally trigger innate immune responses is blocked. As a result, the mutant flies do not make any antimicrobial peptides. The researchers then genetically engineered some of the mutant flies to express significant amounts of a single antimicrobial peptide, either drosomycin or defensin. The scientists infected the various flies with the fungus *Neurospora crassa* and monitored survival over a five-day period. They repeated the procedure for infection by the bacterium *Micrococcus luteus*.

Results

Fruit fly survival after infection by *N. crassa* fungi

Fruit fly survival after infection by *M. luteus* bacteria

Conclusion Each of the two antimicrobial peptides provided a protective immune response. Furthermore, the different peptides defended against different pathogens. Drosomycin was effective against *N. crassa*, and defensin was effective against *M. luteus*.

Source: P. Tzou, J. Reichhart, and B. Lemaitre, Constitutive expression of a single antimicrobial peptide can restore wild-type resistance to infection in immunodeficient *Drosophila* mutants, *Proceedings of the National Academy of Sciences USA* 99:2152–2157 (2002).

WHAT IF? *Even if a particular antimicrobial peptide showed no beneficial effect in such an experiment, why might it still be beneficial to flies?*

Beyond their physical role in inhibiting microbial entry, body secretions create an environment that is hostile to many pathogens. Lysozyme in tears, saliva, and mucous secretions destroys the cell walls of susceptible bacteria as they enter the openings around the eyes or the upper respiratory

tract. Microbes in food or water and those in swallowed mucus must also contend with the acidic environment of the stomach, which kills most of them before they can enter the intestines. Similarly, secretions from oil and sweat glands give human skin a pH ranging from 3 to 5, acidic enough to prevent the growth of many bacteria.

Cellular Innate Defenses

Many pathogens that defeat the barrier defenses of mammals are engulfed by phagocytic cells that use several types of receptors to detect viral, fungal, or bacterial components. Some mammalian receptors are very similar to the Toll receptor of insects, a remarkable discovery that was recognized with the Nobel Prize in medicine or physiology in 2011. Each mammalian **Toll-like receptor (TLR)** binds to fragments of molecules normally absent from the vertebrate body but characteristic of a set of pathogens **(Figure 43.6)**. For example, TLR3, on the inner surface of vesicles formed by endocytosis, binds to double-stranded RNA, a form

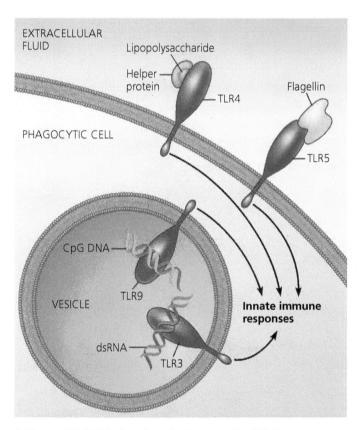

▲ **Figure 43.6 TLR signaling.** Each mammalian Toll-like receptor (TLR) recognizes a molecular pattern characteristic of a group of pathogens. Lipopolysaccharide, flagellin, CpG DNA (DNA containing unmethylated CG sequences), and double-stranded (ds) RNA are all found in bacteria, fungi, or viruses but not in animal cells. Together with other recognition and response factors, TLR proteins trigger internal innate immune defenses.

? *Some TLR proteins are on the cell surface, whereas others are inside vesicles. Suggest a possible benefit of this distribution.*

of nucleic acid characteristic of certain viruses. Similarly, TLR4, located on immune cell plasma membranes, recognizes lipopolysaccharide, a type of molecule found on the surface of many bacteria, and TLR5 recognizes flagellin, the main protein of bacterial flagella.

As in invertebrates, detection of invading pathogens in mammals triggers phagocytosis and destruction. The two main types of phagocytic cells in the mammalian body are neutrophils and macrophages. **Neutrophils**, which circulate in the blood, are attracted by signals from infected tissues and then engulf and destroy the infecting pathogens. **Macrophages** ("big eaters"), like the one shown in Figure 43.1, are larger phagocytic cells. Some migrate throughout the body, whereas others reside permanently in organs and tissues where they are likely to encounter pathogens. For example, some macrophages are located in the spleen, where pathogens in the blood are often trapped.

Two other types of phagocytic cells—dendritic cells and eosinophils—provide additional functions in innate defense. **Dendritic cells** mainly populate tissues, such as skin, that contact the environment. They stimulate adaptive immunity

against pathogens they encounter and engulf, as we'll explore shortly. *Eosinophils*, often found beneath mucosal surfaces, are important in defending against multicellular invaders, such as parasitic worms. Upon encountering such parasites, eosinophils discharge destructive enzymes.

Cellular innate defenses in vertebrates also involve **natural killer cells**. These cells circulate through the body and detect the abnormal array of surface proteins characteristic of some virus-infected and cancerous cells. Natural killer cells do not engulf stricken cells. Instead, they release chemicals that lead to cell death, inhibiting further spread of the virus or cancer.

Many cellular innate defenses in vertebrates involve the lymphatic system, a network that distributes the fluid called lymph throughout the body **(Figure 43.7)**. Some macrophages reside in lymph nodes, where they engulf pathogens that have entered the lymph from the interstitial fluid. Dendritic cells reside outside the lymphatic system but migrate to the lymph nodes after interacting with pathogens. Within the lymph nodes, dendritic cells interact with other immune cells, stimulating adaptive immunity.

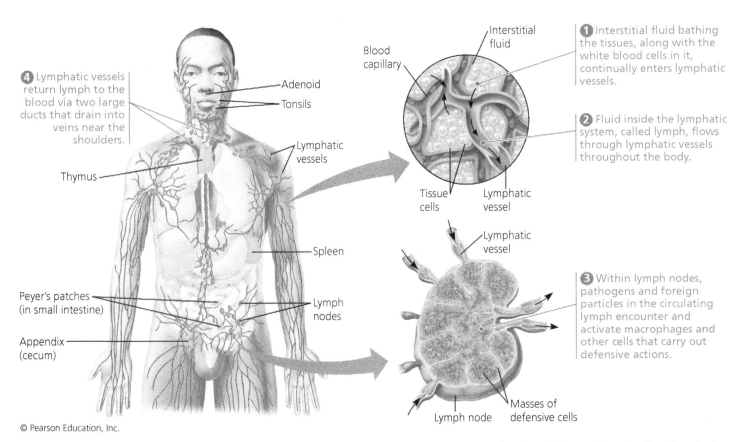

© Pearson Education, Inc.

▲ **Figure 43.7 The human lymphatic system.** The lymphatic system consists of lymphatic vessels (shown in green), through which lymph travels, and structures that trap foreign substances. These structures include lymph nodes (orange) and lymphoid organs (yellow): the adenoids, tonsils, spleen, Peyer's patches, and appendix. Steps 1–4 trace the flow of lymph and illustrate the role of lymph nodes in activating adaptive immunity. (Concept 42.3 will describe the relationship between the lymphatic and circulatory systems.)

Antimicrobial Peptides and Proteins

In mammals, pathogen recognition triggers the production and release of a variety of peptides and proteins that attack pathogens or impede their reproduction. Some of these defense molecules function like the antimicrobial peptides of insects, damaging broad groups of pathogens by disrupting membrane integrity. Others, including the interferons and complement proteins, are unique to vertebrate immune systems.

Interferons are proteins that provide innate defense by interfering with viral infections. Virus-infected body cells secrete interferons, which induce nearby uninfected cells to produce substances that inhibit viral replication. In this way, interferons limit the cell-to-cell spread of viruses in the body, helping control viral infections such as colds and influenza. Some white blood cells secrete a different type of interferon that helps activate macrophages, enhancing their phagocytic ability. Pharmaceutical companies now use recombinant DNA technology to mass-produce interferons to help treat certain viral infections, such as hepatitis C.

The infection-fighting **complement system** consists of roughly 30 proteins in blood plasma. These proteins circulate in an inactive state and are activated by substances on the surface of many microbes. Activation results in a cascade of biochemical reactions that can lead to lysis (bursting) of invading cells. The complement system also functions in the inflammatory response, our next topic, as well as in the adaptive defenses discussed later in the chapter.

Inflammatory Response

The pain and swelling that alert you to a splinter under your skin are the result of a local **inflammatory response**, the changes brought about by signaling molecules released upon injury or infection **(Figure 43.8)**. One important inflammatory signaling molecule is **histamine**, which is stored in densely packed vesicles of **mast cells**, found in connective tissue. Histamine released at sites of damage triggers nearby blood vessels to dilate and become more permeable. The dilated capillaries leak fluid into neighboring tissues, causing localized swelling.

Macrophages and neutrophils also participate in the inflammatory response. Once activated, these cells discharge *cytokines*, signaling molecules that modulate immune responses. The cytokines released by macrophages and neutrophils promote blood flow to the site of injury or infection. The increase in local blood supply produces the redness and increased skin temperature typical of the inflammatory response (from the Latin *inflammare*, to set on fire).

During inflammation, cycles of signaling and response transform the site. Activated complement proteins promote further release of histamine, attracting more phagocytic cells that enter injured tissues (see Figure 43.8) and carry out additional phagocytosis. At the same time, enhanced blood flow to the site helps deliver antimicrobial peptides. The result is an accumulation of *pus*, a fluid rich in white blood cells, dead pathogens, and cell debris from damaged tissue.

① At the injury site, mast cells release histamines, which cause nearby capillaries to dilate. Macrophages release other signaling molecules that increase local blood flow.

② Capillaries widen and become more permeable, allowing fluid containing antimicrobial peptides to enter the tissue. Signals released by immune cells attract neutrophils.

③ Neutrophils digest pathogens and cell debris at the site of injury, and the tissue heals.

▲ **Figure 43.8 Major events in a local inflammatory response.**

A minor injury or infection causes a local inflammatory response, but severe tissue damage or infection may lead to a response that is systemic (throughout the body). Cells in injured or infected tissue often secrete molecules that stimulate the release of additional neutrophils from the bone marrow. In the case of a severe infection, such as meningitis or appendicitis, the number of white blood cells in the bloodstream may increase several-fold within only a few hours.

Another systemic inflammatory response is fever. In response to certain pathogens, substances released by activated macrophages cause the body's thermostat to reset to a higher temperature (see Chapter 40). There is good evidence that fever can be beneficial in fighting certain infections, although the underlying mechanism is still a subject of debate. One hypothesis is that an elevated body temperature may enhance phagocytosis and, by speeding up chemical reactions, accelerate tissue repair.

Certain bacterial infections can induce an overwhelming systemic inflammatory response, leading to a life-threatening condition that is known as *septic shock*. Characterized by very high fever, low blood pressure, and poor blood flow through capillaries, septic shock occurs most often in the very old and the very young. It is fatal in roughly one-third of cases and contributes to the death of more than 200,000 people each year in the United States alone.

Chronic (ongoing) inflammation can also threaten human health. For example, millions of individuals worldwide suffer from Crohn's disease and ulcerative colitis, often debilitating disorders in which an unregulated inflammatory response disrupts intestinal function.

Evasion of Innate Immunity by Pathogens

Adaptations have evolved in some pathogens that enable them to avoid destruction by phagocytic cells. For example, the outer capsule that surrounds certain bacteria interferes with molecular recognition and phagocytosis. One such bacterium, *Streptococcus pneumoniae*, which played a critical role in the discovery that DNA can convey genetic information (see Figure 16.2), can cause ear infections, meningitis, and of course pneumonia.

Some bacteria, after being engulfed by a host cell, resist breakdown within lysosomes. An example is *Mycobacterium tuberculosis*, the bacterium that causes tuberculosis (TB). Figure 43.1 shows a group of *M. tuberculosis* bacteria being engulfed by a macrophage. Rather than being destroyed, however, these bacteria can sometimes grow and reproduce within macrophages, effectively hidden from the body's innate immune defenses. These and other mechanisms that prevent destruction by the innate immune system make certain fungi and bacteria substantial pathogenic threats. Indeed, TB kills more than a million people a year worldwide.

1. Although pus is often seen simply as a sign of infection, it is also an indicator of immune defenses in action. Explain.

2. **MAKE CONNECTIONS** How do the molecules that activate the vertebrate TLR signal transduction pathway differ from the ligands in most other signaling pathways (see Concept 11.2)?

3. **WHAT IF?** Suppose humans were the major host for a bacterial species. What temperature would you predict would be optimal for growth of this species? Explain.

For suggested answers, see Appendix A.

CONCEPT 43.2

In adaptive immunity, receptors provide pathogen-specific recognition

Vertebrates are unique in having both adaptive and innate immunity. The adaptive response relies on T cells and B cells, which are types of white blood cells called **lymphocytes**. Like all blood cells, lymphocytes originate from stem cells in the bone marrow. Some migrate from the bone marrow to the **thymus**, an organ in the thoracic cavity above the heart (see Figure 43.7). These lymphocytes mature into **T cells**. Lymphocytes that remain and mature in the bone marrow develop as **B cells**. (Lymphocytes of a third type remain in the blood and become the natural killer cells active in innate immunity.)

Mature B cell   Mature T cell

Any substance that elicits a B or T cell response is called an **antigen**. In adaptive immunity, recognition occurs when a B cell or T cell binds to an antigen, such as a bacterial or viral protein, via a protein called an **antigen receptor**. Each antigen receptor binds to just one part of one molecule from a particular pathogen, such as a species of bacteria or strain of virus. Although the cells of the immune system produce millions of different antigen receptors, all of the antigen receptors made by a single B or T cell are identical. Infection by a virus, bacterium, or other pathogen triggers activation of B and T cells with antigen receptors specific for parts of that pathogen. B and T cells are shown in this text with only a few antigen receptors, but there are actually about 100,000 antigen receptors on the surface of a single B or T cell.

Antigens are usually foreign and are typically large molecules, either proteins or polysaccharides. Many antigens protrude from the surface of foreign cells or viruses. Other antigens, such as toxins secreted by bacteria, are released into the extracellular fluid.

The small, accessible portion of an antigen that binds to an antigen receptor is called an **epitope**. An example is a group of amino acids in a particular protein. A single antigen usually has several epitopes, each binding a receptor with a different specificity. Because all antigen receptors produced by a single B cell or T cell are identical, they bind to the same epitope. Each B or T cell thus displays *specificity* for a particular epitope, enabling it to respond to any pathogen that produces molecules containing that epitope.

The antigen receptors of B cells and T cells have similar components, but they encounter antigens in different ways. We'll consider the two processes in turn.

Antigen Recognition by B Cells and Antibodies

Each B cell antigen receptor is a Y-shaped molecule consisting of four polypeptide chains: two identical **heavy chains** and two identical **light chains**, with disulfide bridges linking the chains together (Figure 43.9). A transmembrane region near one end of each heavy chain anchors the receptor in the cell's plasma membrane. A short tail region at the end of the heavy chain extends into the cytoplasm.

The light and heavy chains each have a *constant (C) region*, where amino acid sequences vary little among the receptors on different B cells. The C region includes the cytoplasmic tail and transmembrane region of the heavy chain and all of the disulfide bridges. Within the two tips of the Y shape (see Figure 43.9), each chain has a *variable (V) region*, so named because its amino acid sequence varies extensively from one B cell to another. Together, parts of a heavy-chain V region and a light-chain V region form an asymmetric binding site for an antigen. As shown in Figure 43.9, each B cell antigen receptor has two identical antigen-binding sites.

Binding of a B cell antigen receptor to an antigen is an early step in B cell activation, leading to formation of cells that secrete a soluble form of the receptor (Figure 43.10a).

This secreted protein is called an **antibody**, also known as an **immunoglobulin (Ig)**. Antibodies have the same Y-shaped structure as B cell antigen receptors but are secreted rather than membrane bound. It is antibodies, rather than B cells themselves, that actually help defend against pathogens.

The antigen-binding site of a membrane-bound receptor or antibody has a unique shape that provides a lock-and-key fit for a particular epitope. Many noncovalent bonds between an epitope and the surface of the binding site provide a stable and specific interaction. Differences in the amino acid sequences of variable regions provide the variation in binding surfaces that enables this highly specific binding.

B cell antigen receptors and antibodies bind to intact antigens in the blood and lymph. As illustrated in Figure 43.10b for antibodies, they can bind to antigens on the surface of pathogens or free in body fluids. The antigen receptors of T cells function quite differently, as we'll see next.

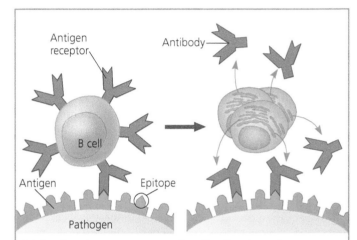

(a) B cell antigen receptors and antibodies. An antigen receptor of a B cell binds to an epitope, a particular part of an antigen. Following binding, the B cell gives rise to cells that secrete a soluble form of the antigen receptor. This soluble receptor, called an antibody, is specific for the same epitope as the original B cell.

(b) Antigen receptor specificity. Different antibodies can recognize distinct epitopes on the same antigen. Furthermore, antibodies can recognize free antigens as well as antigens on a pathogen's surface.

▲ Figure 43.10 **Antigen recognition by B cells and antibodies.**

MAKE CONNECTIONS *The interactions depicted here involve a highly specific binding between antigen and receptor (see Figure 5.17). How is this similar to an enzyme-substrate interaction (see Figure 8.15)?*

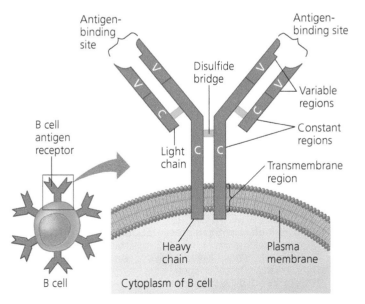

▲ Figure 43.9 **The structure of a B cell antigen receptor.**

Antigen Recognition by T Cells

For a T cell, the antigen receptor consists of two different polypeptide chains, an *α chain* and a *β chain*, linked by a disulfide bridge (**Figure 43.11**). Near the base of the T cell antigen receptor (often called simply a T cell receptor) is a transmembrane region that anchors the molecule in the cell's plasma membrane. At the outer tip of the molecule, the variable (V) regions of the α and β chains together form a single antigen-binding site. The remainder of the molecule is made up of the constant (C) regions.

Whereas the antigen receptors of B cells bind to epitopes of *intact* antigens on pathogens or circulating free in body fluids, those of T cells bind only to fragments of antigens that are displayed, or presented, on the surface of host cells. The host protein that displays the antigen fragment on the cell surface is called a **major histocompatibility complex (MHC) molecule**.

Recognition of protein antigens by T cells begins when a pathogen or part of a pathogen either infects or is taken in by a host cell (**Figure 43.12a**). Inside the host cell, enzymes cleave the antigen into smaller peptides. Each peptide, called an *antigen fragment*, then binds to an MHC molecule inside the cell. Movement of the MHC molecule and bound antigen fragment up to the cell surface results in **antigen presentation**, display of the antigen fragment in an exposed groove of the MHC protein. **Figure 43.12b** shows a close-up view of antigen presentation, a process advertising the fact that a host cell contains a foreign substance. If the cell displaying an antigen fragment encounters a T cell with the right specificity, the antigen receptor on the T cell can bind to both the antigen fragment and the MHC molecule. This interaction of an MHC molecule, an antigen fragment, and an antigen receptor is necessary for a T cell to participate in an adaptive immune response, as you'll see later.

B Cell and T Cell Development

Now that you know how B cells and T cells recognize antigens, let's consider four major characteristics of adaptive immunity. First, there is an immense diversity of lymphocytes and receptors, enabling the immune system to detect pathogens never before encountered. Second, adaptive immunity normally has self-tolerance, the lack of reactivity against an animal's own molecules and cells. Third, cell proliferation triggered by activation greatly increases the number of B and T cells specific for an antigen. Fourth, there is a stronger and more rapid response to an antigen encountered previously, due to a feature known as *immunological memory*, which we'll discuss later in the chapter.

Receptor diversity and self-tolerance arise as a lymphocyte matures. Proliferation of cells and the formation of immunological memory occur later, after a mature lymphocyte encounters and binds to a specific antigen. We'll consider these four characteristics in the order in which they develop.

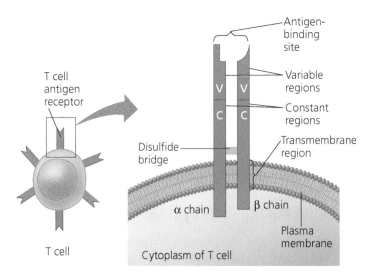

▲ **Figure 43.11 The structure of a T cell antigen receptor.**

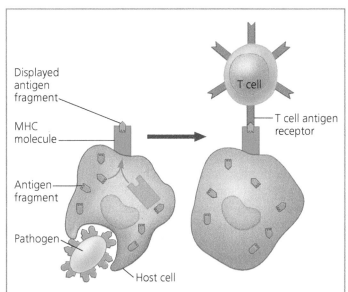

(a) Antigen recognition by a T cell. Inside the host cell, an antigen fragment from a pathogen binds to an MHC molecule and is brought up to the cell surface, where it is displayed. The combination of MHC molecule and antigen fragment is recognized by a T cell.

(b) A closer look at antigen presentation. As shown in this ribbon model, the top of the MHC molecule cradles an antigen fragment, like a bun holding a hot dog. An MHC molecule can display many different antigen fragments, but the antigen receptor of a T cell is specific for a single antigen fragment.

▲ **Figure 43.12 Antigen recognition by T cells.**

Generation of B Cell and T Cell Diversity

Each person makes more than 1 million different B cell antigen receptors and 10 million different T cell antigen receptors. Yet there are only about 20,000 protein-coding genes in the human genome. How, then, do we generate such remarkable diversity in antigen receptors? The answer lies in combinations. Think of selecting a car with a choice of three interior colors and six exterior colors. There are 18 (3×6) color combinations to consider. Similarly, by combining variable elements, the immune system assembles many different receptors from a much smaller collection of parts.

To understand the origin of receptor diversity, let's consider an immunoglobulin (Ig) gene that encodes the light chain of both membrane-bound B cell antigen receptors and secreted antibodies (immunoglobulins). Although we'll analyze only a single Ig light-chain gene, all B and T cell antigen receptor genes undergo very similar transformations.

The capacity to generate diversity is built into the structure of Ig genes. A receptor light chain is encoded by three gene segments: a variable (*V*) segment, a joining (*J*) segment, and a constant (*C*) segment. The *V* and *J* segments together encode the variable region of the receptor chain, while the *C* segment encodes the constant region. The light-chain gene contains a single *C* segment, 40 different *V* segments, and 5 different *J* segments. These alternative copies of the *V* and *J* segments are arranged within the gene in a series (**Figure 43.13**). Because a functional gene is built from one copy of each type of segment, the pieces can be combined in 200 different ways (40 *V* $\times$ 5 *J* $\times$ 1 *C*). The number of different heavy-chain combinations is even greater, resulting in even more diversity.

Assembling a functional Ig gene requires rearranging the DNA. Early in B cell development, an enzyme complex called *recombinase* links one light-chain *V* gene segment to one *J* gene segment. This recombination event eliminates the long stretch of DNA between the segments, forming a single exon that is part *V* and part *J*. Because there is only an intron between the *J* and *C* DNA segments, no further rearrangement of DNA is required. Instead, the *J* and *C*

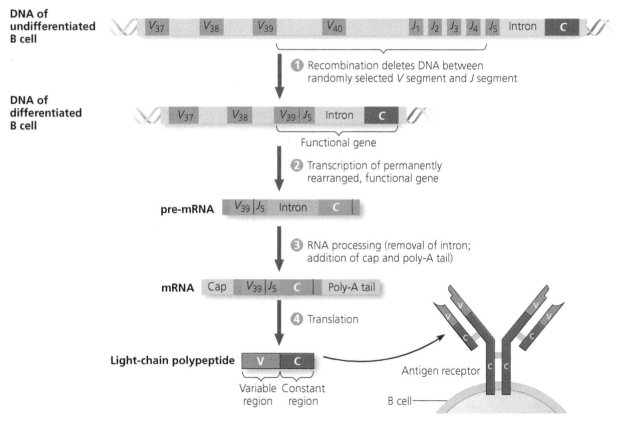

▲ **Figure 43.13 Immunoglobulin (antibody) gene rearrangement.** The joining of randomly selected *V* and *J* gene segments (V_{39} and J_5 in the example shown) results in a functional gene that encodes the light-chain polypeptide of a B cell antigen receptor. Transcription, splicing, and translation result in a light chain that combines with a polypeptide produced from an independently rearranged heavy-chain gene to form a functional receptor. Mature B cells (and T cells) are exceptions to the generalization that all nucleated cells in the body have exactly the same DNA.

MAKE CONNECTIONS *Both alternative splicing and joining of* V *and* J *segments by recombination generate diverse gene products from a limited set of gene segments (see Figure 18.13). How do these processes differ?*

segments of the RNA transcript will be joined when splicing removes the intervening RNA. (See Figure 17.11 to review RNA splicing.)

Recombinase acts randomly, linking any one of the 40 *V* gene segments to any one of the 5 *J* gene segments. Heavy-chain genes undergo a similar rearrangement. In any given cell, however, only one allele of a light-chain gene and one allele of a heavy-chain gene are rearranged. Furthermore, the rearrangements are permanent and are passed on to the daughter cells when the lymphocyte divides.

After both a light-chain and a heavy-chain gene have been rearranged, antigen receptors can be synthesized. The rearranged genes are transcribed, and the transcripts are processed for translation. Following translation, the light chain and heavy chain assemble together, forming an antigen receptor (see Figure 43.13). Each pair of randomly rearranged heavy and light chains results in a different antigen-binding site. For the total population of B cells in a human body, the number of such combinations has been calculated as 3.5×10^6. Furthermore, mutations introduced during *VJ* recombination add additional variation, making the number of possible antigen-binding specificities even greater.

Origin of Self-Tolerance

In adaptive immunity, how does the body distinguish self from nonself? Because antigen receptor genes are randomly rearranged, some immature lymphocytes produce receptors specific for epitopes on the organism's own molecules. If these self-reactive lymphocytes were not eliminated or inactivated, the immune system could not distinguish self from nonself and would attack body proteins, cells, and tissues. Instead, as lymphocytes mature in the bone marrow or thymus, their antigen receptors are tested for self-reactivity. Some B and T cells with receptors specific for the body's own molecules are destroyed by *apoptosis*, which is a programmed cell death (see Chapter 11). The remaining self-reactive lymphocytes are typically rendered nonfunctional, leaving only those that react to foreign molecules. Since the body normally lacks mature lymphocytes that can react against its own components, the immune system is said to exhibit *self-tolerance*.

Proliferation of B Cells and T Cells

Despite the enormous variety of antigen receptors, only a tiny fraction are specific for a given epitope. How then does an effective adaptive response develop? To begin with, an antigen is presented to a steady stream of lymphocytes in the lymph nodes (see Figure 43.7) until a match is made. A successful match between an antigen receptor and an epitope initiates events that activate the lymphocyte bearing the receptor.

Once activated, a B cell or T cell undergoes multiple cell divisions. For each activated cell, the result of this proliferation is a clone, a population of cells that are identical to the original cell. Some cells from this clone become **effector cells**, short-lived cells that take effect immediately against the antigen and any pathogens producing that antigen. The effector forms of B cells are **plasma cells**, which secrete antibodies. The effector forms of T cells are helper T cells and cytotoxic T cells, whose roles we'll explore in Concept 43.3. The remaining cells in the clone become **memory cells**, long-lived cells that can give rise to effector cells if the same antigen is encountered later in the animal's life.

The proliferation of a B cell or T cell into a clone of cells occurs in response to a specific antigen and to immune cell signals. The process is called **clonal selection** because an encounter with an antigen *selects* which lymphocyte will divide to produce a *clonal* population of thousands of cells specific for a particular epitope. Cells that have antigen receptors specific for other antigens do not respond.

Figure 43.14 summarizes the process of clonal selection, using the example of B cells, which generate memory cells and plasma cells. When T cells undergo clonal selection, they generate memory T cells and effector T cells (cytotoxic T cells and helper T cells).

Immunological Memory

Immunological memory is responsible for the long-term protection that a prior infection provides against many diseases, such as chicken pox. This type of protection was noted almost 2,400 years ago by the Greek historian Thucydides. He observed that individuals who had recovered from the plague could safely care for those who were sick or dying, "for the same man was never attacked twice—never at least fatally."

Prior exposure to an antigen alters the speed, strength, and duration of the immune response. The production of effector cells from a clone of lymphocytes during the first exposure to an antigen is the basis for the **primary immune response**. The primary response peaks about 10–17 days after the initial exposure. During this time, selected B cells and T cells give rise to their effector forms. If an individual is exposed again to the same antigen, the response is faster (typically peaking only 2–7 days after exposure), of greater magnitude, and more prolonged. This is the **secondary immune response**, a hallmark of adaptive, or acquired, immunity. Because selected B cells give rise to antibody-secreting effector cells, measuring the concentrations of specific antibodies in blood over time distinguishes the primary and secondary immune responses (**Figure 43.15**).

The secondary immune response relies on the reservoir of T and B memory cells generated following initial exposure to an antigen. Because these cells are long-lived, they provide the basis for immunological memory, which

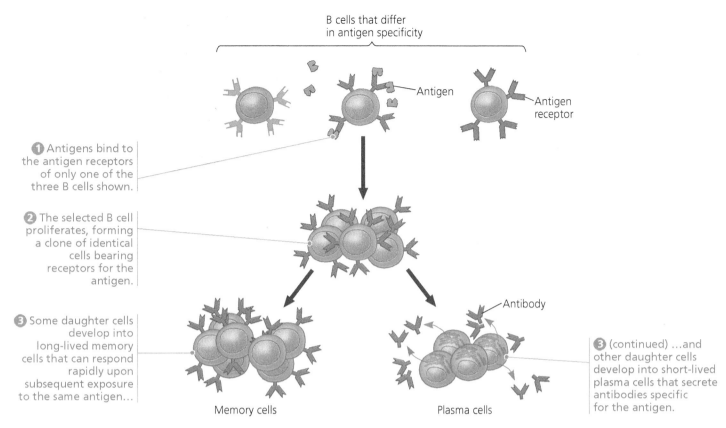

① Antigens bind to the antigen receptors of only one of the three B cells shown.

② The selected B cell proliferates, forming a clone of identical cells bearing receptors for the antigen.

③ Some daughter cells develop into long-lived memory cells that can respond rapidly upon subsequent exposure to the same antigen...

③ (continued) ...and other daughter cells develop into short-lived plasma cells that secrete antibodies specific for the antigen.

B cells that differ in antigen specificity

Antigen

Antigen receptor

Antibody

Memory cells

Plasma cells

▲ Figure 43.14 **Clonal selection of B cells.**

Primary immune response to antigen A produces antibodies to A.

Secondary immune response to antigen A produces antibodies to A; **primary immune response** to antigen B produces antibodies to B.

Antibodies to A

Antibodies to B

Exposure to antigen A

Exposure to antigens A and B

Time (days)

▲ Figure 43.15 **The specificity of immunological memory.** Long-lived memory cells generated in the primary response to antigen A give rise to a heightened secondary response to the same antigen, but they do not affect the primary response to a different antigen (B).

INTERPRET THE DATA *Assume that on average one out of every 10^5 B cells in the body is specific for antigen A on day 16 and that the number of B cells producing a specific antibody is proportional to the concentration of that antibody. What would you predict is the frequency of B cells specific for antigen A on day 36?*

can span many decades. (Effector cells have much shorter life spans, which is why the immune response diminishes after an infection is overcome.) If an antigen is encountered again, memory cells specific for that antigen enable the rapid formation of clones of thousands of effector cells also specific for that antigen, thus generating a greatly enhanced immune defense.

Although the processes for antigen recognition, clonal selection, and immunological memory are similar for B cells and T cells, these two classes of lymphocytes fight infection in different ways and in different settings, as we'll explore in Concept 43.3.

CONCEPT CHECK **43.2**

1. **DRAW IT** Sketch a B cell antigen receptor. Label the V and C regions of the light and heavy chains. Label the antigen-binding sites, disulfide bridges, and transmembrane region. Where are these features located relative to the V and C regions?

2. Explain two advantages of having memory cells when a pathogen is encountered for a second time.

3. **WHAT IF?** If both copies of a light-chain gene and a heavy-chain gene recombined in each (diploid) B cell, how would this affect B cell development and function?

For suggested answers, see Appendix A.

CONCEPT 43.3

Adaptive immunity defends against infection of body fluids and body cells

Having considered how clones of lymphocytes arise, we now explore how these cells help fight infections and minimize damage by pathogens. The defenses provided by B and T lymphocytes can be divided into a humoral immune response and a cell-mediated immune response. The **humoral immune response** occurs in the blood and lymph, which were once called body humors (fluids). In the humoral response, antibodies help neutralize or eliminate toxins and pathogens in the blood and lymph. In the **cell-mediated immune response**, specialized T cells destroy infected host cells. Both responses can include both a primary immune response and a secondary immune response, with memory cells enabling the secondary response.

Helper T Cells: A Response to Nearly All Antigens

A type of T cell called a **helper T cell** triggers both the humoral and cell-mediated immune responses. Helper T cells themselves do not carry out those responses. Instead, signals from helper T cells initiate production of antibodies that neutralize pathogens and activate T cells that will kill the infected cells.

▲ **A dendritic cell** (colorized SEM).

Two requirements must be met for a helper T cell to activate adaptive immune responses. First, a foreign molecule must be present that can bind specifically to the antigen receptor of the T cell. Second, this antigen must be displayed on the surface of an **antigen-presenting cell**. The antigen-presenting cell can be a dendritic cell, macrophage, or B cell.

When host cells are infected, they too display antigens on their surface. What then distinguishes an antigen-presenting cell? The answer lies in the existence of two classes of MHC molecules. Most body cells have only the class I MHC molecules, but antigen-presenting cells have class I and class II MHC molecules. Class II molecules provide a molecular signature by which an antigen-presenting cell is recognized.

A helper T cell and the antigen-presenting cell displaying its specific epitope have a complex interaction (**Figure 43.16**). The antigen receptors on the surface of the helper T cell

❶ An antigen-presenting cell engulfs a pathogen, degrades it, and displays antigen fragments complexed with class II MHC molecules on the cell surface. A specific helper T cell binds to this complex via its antigen receptor and an accessory protein (called CD4).

❷ Binding of the helper T cell promotes secretion of cytokines by the antigen-presenting cell. These cytokines, along with cytokines from the helper T cell itself, activate the helper T cell and stimulate its proliferation.

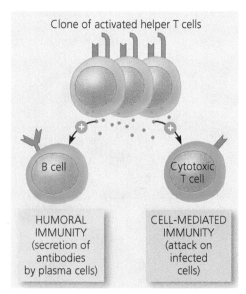

❸ Cell proliferation produces a clone of activated helper T cells. All cells in the clone have receptors for the same antigen fragment complex with the same antigen specificity. These cells secrete other cytokines, which help activate B cells and cytotoxic T cells.

▲ **Figure 43.16 The central role of helper T cells in humoral and cell-mediated immune responses.** In this example, a helper T cell responds to a dendritic cell displaying a microbial antigen.

bind to the antigen fragment and to the class II MHC molecule displaying that fragment on the antigen-presenting cell. At the same time, an accessory protein called CD4 on the helper T cell surface binds to the class II MHC molecule, helping keep the cells joined. As the two cells interact, signals in the form of cytokines are exchanged. For example, the cytokines secreted from a dendritic cell act in combination with the antigen to stimulate the helper T cell, causing it to produce its own set of cytokines. Also, extensive contact between the cell surfaces enables further information exchange.

Antigen-presenting cells interact with helper T cells in several contexts. Antigen presentation by a dendritic cell or macrophage activates a helper T cell, which proliferates, forming a clone of activated cells. In contrast, B cells present antigens to *already* activated helper T cells, which in turn activate the B cells themselves. Activated helper T cells also help stimulate cytotoxic T cells, as we'll discuss next.

Cytotoxic T Cells: A Response to Infected Cells

In the absence of an immune response, pathogens can reproduce in and kill infected cells, as shown at the upper right. In the cell-mediated immune response, **cytotoxic T cells** use toxic proteins to kill cells infected by viruses or other intracellular pathogens before pathogens fully mature. To become active, cytotoxic T cells require signals from helper T cells and interaction with an antigen-presenting cell. Fragments of foreign proteins produced in infected host

▲ **A dying infected cell** (colorized SEM).

cells associate with class I MHC molecules and are displayed on the cell surface, where they can be recognized by cytotoxic T cells **(Figure 43.17)**. As with helper T cells, cytotoxic T cells have an accessory protein that binds to the MHC molecule. This accessory protein, called CD8, helps keep the two cells in contact while the cytotoxic T cell is activated.

The targeted destruction of an infected host cell by a cytotoxic T cell involves the secretion of proteins that disrupt membrane integrity and trigger cell death (apoptosis; see Figure 43.17). The death of the infected cell not only deprives the pathogen of a place to multiply, but also exposes cell contents to circulating antibodies, which mark released antigens for disposal.

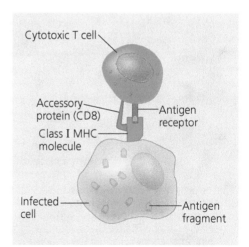

❶ An activated cytotoxic T cell binds to a class I MHC–antigen fragment complex on an infected cell via its antigen receptor and an accessory protein (called CD8).

❷ The T cell releases perforin molecules, which form pores in the infected cell membrane, and granzymes, enzymes that break down proteins. Granzymes enter the infected cell by endocytosis.

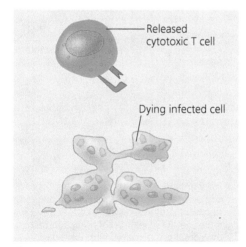

❸ The granzymes initiate apoptosis within the infected cell, leading to fragmentation of the nucleus and cytoplasm and eventual cell death. The released cytotoxic T cell can attack other infected cells.

▲ **Figure 43.17 The killing action of cytotoxic T cells on an infected host cell.** An activated cytotoxic T cell releases molecules that make pores in an infected cell's membrane and enzymes that break down proteins, promoting the cell's death.

B Cells and Antibodies: A Response to Extracellular Pathogens

The secretion of antibodies by B cells is the hallmark of the humoral immune response. It begins with activation of the B cells.

Activation of B Cells

As illustrated in **Figure 43.18**, activation of B cells involves both helper T cells and proteins on the surface of pathogens. Stimulated by both an antigen and cytokines, the B cell proliferates and differentiates into memory B cells and antibody-secreting plasma cells.

The pathway for antigen processing and display in B cells differs from that in other antigen-presenting cells. A macrophage or dendritic cell can present fragments from a wide variety of protein antigens, whereas a B cell presents only the antigen to which it specifically binds. When an antigen first binds to receptors on the surface of a B cell, the cell takes in a few foreign molecules by receptor-mediated endocytosis (see Figure 7.19). The class II MHC protein of the B cell then presents an antigen fragment to a helper T cell. This direct cell-to-cell contact is usually critical to B cell activation (see step 2 in Figure 43.18).

B cell activation leads to a robust humoral immune response: A single activated B cell gives rise to thousands of identical plasma cells. These plasma cells stop expressing a membrane-bound antigen receptor and begin producing and secreting antibodies (see step 3 in Figure 43.18). Each plasma cell secretes approximately 2,000 antibodies every second during its 4- to 5-day life span, nearly a trillion antibody molecules in total. Furthermore, most antigens recognized by B cells contain multiple epitopes. An exposure to a single antigen therefore normally activates a variety of B cells, which give rise to different plasma cells producing antibodies directed against different epitopes on the common antigen.

Antibody Function

Antibodies do not actually kill pathogens, but by binding to antigens, they interfere with pathogen activity or mark pathogens in various ways for inactivation or destruction. Consider, for example, *neutralization*, a process in which antibodies bind to proteins on the surface of a virus **(Figure 43.19a)**. The bound antibodies prevent infection of a host cell, thus neutralizing the virus. Similarly, antibodies sometimes bind to toxins released in body fluids, preventing the toxins from entering body cells.

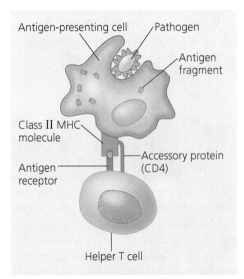

① After an antigen-presenting cell engulfs and degrades a pathogen, it displays an antigen fragment complexed with a class II MHC molecule. A helper T cell that recognizes the complex is activated with the aid of cytokines secreted from the antigen-presenting cell.

② When a B cell with receptors for the same epitope internalizes the antigen, it displays an antigen fragment on the cell surface in a complex with a class II MHC molecule. An activated helper T cell bearing receptors specific for the displayed fragment binds to and activates the B cell.

③ The activated B cell proliferates and differentiates into memory B cells and antibody-secreting plasma cells. The secreted antibodies are specific for the same antigen that initiated the response.

▲ **Figure 43.18 Activation of a B cell in the humoral immune response.** Most protein antigens require activated helper T cells to trigger a humoral response. A macrophage (shown here) or a dendritic cell can activate a helper T cell, which in turn can activate a B cell to give rise to antibody-secreting plasma cells.

[?] *What function do cell-surface antigen receptors play for memory B cells?*

(a) Neutralization	(b) Opsonization	(c) Activation of complement system and pore formation

Antibodies bound to antigens on the surface of a virus neutralize it by blocking its ability to bind to a host cell.

Binding of antibodies to antigens on the surface of bacteria promotes phagocytosis by macrophages and neutrophils.

Binding of antibodies to antigens on the surface of a foreign cell activates the complement system.

Following activation of the complement system, the membrane attack complex forms pores in the foreign cell's membrane, allowing water and ions to rush in. The cell swells and eventually lyses.

In *opsonization*, antibodies bound to antigens on bacteria do not block infection, but instead present a readily recognized structure for macrophages or neutrophils, thereby promoting phagocytosis **(Figure 43.19b)**. Because each antibody has two antigen-binding sites, antibodies can also facilitate phagocytosis by linking bacterial cells, viruses, or other foreign substances into aggregates.

When antibodies facilitate phagocytosis, as in opsonization, they also help fine-tune the humoral immune response. Recall that phagocytosis enables macrophages and dendritic cells to present antigens to and stimulate helper T cells, which in turn stimulate the very B cells whose antibodies contribute to phagocytosis. This positive feedback between innate and adaptive immunity contributes to a coordinated, effective response to infection.

Antibodies sometimes work together with the proteins of the complement system. (The name *complement* reflects the fact that these proteins increase the effectiveness of antibody-directed attacks on bacteria.) Binding of a complement protein to an antigen-antibody complex on a foreign cell triggers the generation of a *membrane attack complex* that forms a pore in the membrane of the cell. Ions and water rush into the cell, causing it to swell and lyse **(Figure 43.19c)**. Whether activated as part of innate or adaptive defenses, this cascade of complement protein activity results in the lysis of foreign cells and produces factors that promote inflammation or stimulate phagocytosis.

Although antibodies are the cornerstones of the response in body fluids, there is also a mechanism by which they can bring about the death of infected body cells. When a virus uses a cell's biosynthetic machinery to produce viral proteins, these viral products can appear on the cell surface. If antibodies specific for epitopes on these viral proteins bind to the exposed proteins, the presence of bound antibody at the cell surface can recruit a natural killer cell. The natural killer cell then releases proteins that cause the infected cell to undergo apoptosis. Thus the activities of the innate and adaptive immune systems are once again closely linked.

B cells can express five types, or *classes*, of immunoglobulin (IgA, IgD, IgE, IgG, and IgM). For a given B cell, each class has an identical antigen-binding specificity but a distinct heavy-chain C region. The B cell antigen receptor, known as IgD, is membrane bound. The other four classes consist of soluble antibodies, including those found in blood, tears, saliva, and breast milk.

Summary of the Humoral and Cell-Mediated Immune Responses

As noted earlier, both the humoral and cell-mediated responses can include primary and secondary immune responses. Memory cells of each type—helper T cell, B cell, and cytotoxic T cell—enable the secondary response. For example, when body fluids are reinfected by a pathogen

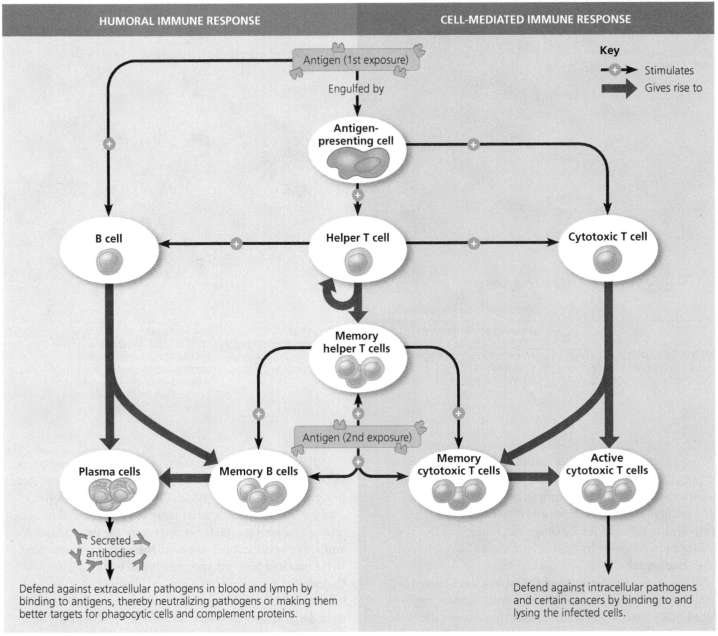

Key
+ → Stimulates
→ Gives rise to

Antigen (1st exposure)

Engulfed by

Antigen-presenting cell

B cell

Helper T cell

Cytotoxic T cell

Memory helper T cells

Antigen (2nd exposure)

Plasma cells

Memory B cells

Memory cytotoxic T cells

Active cytotoxic T cells

Secreted antibodies

Defend against extracellular pathogens in blood and lymph by binding to antigens, thereby neutralizing pathogens or making them better targets for phagocytic cells and complement proteins.

Defend against intracellular pathogens and certain cancers by binding to and lysing the infected cells.

▲ Figure 43.20 An overview of the adaptive immune response.

? *Identify each arrow as representing part of the primary or secondary response.*

ANIMATION **BioFlix** Visit the Study Area in **MasteringBiology** for the BioFlix® 3-D Animation on Immunology.

encountered previously, memory B cells and memory helper T cells initiate a secondary humoral response. **Figure 43.20** summarizes adaptive immunity, reviews the events that initiate humoral and cell-mediated immune responses, and highlights the central role of the helper T cell.

Active and Passive Immunity

Our discussion of adaptive immunity has to this point focused on **active immunity**, the defenses that arise when a pathogen infects the body and prompts a primary or

secondary immune response. A different type of immunity results when the IgG antibodies in the blood of a pregnant female cross the placenta to her fetus. This protection is called **passive immunity** because the antibodies in the recipient (in this case, the fetus) are produced by another individual (the mother). IgA antibodies present in breast milk provide additional passive immunity to the infant's digestive tract while the infant's immune system develops. Because passive immunity does not involve the recipient's B and T cells, it persists only as long as the transferred antibodies last (a few weeks to a few months).

Both active immunity and passive immunity can be induced artificially. Active immunity can develop from the introduction of antigens into the body through **immunization**. In 1796, Edward Jenner noted that milkmaids who had cowpox, a mild disease usually seen only in cows, did not contract smallpox, a far more dangerous disease. In the first documented immunization (or *vaccination*, from the Latin *vacca*, cow), Jenner used the cowpox virus to induce adaptive immunity against the closely related smallpox virus. Today, immunizations are carried out with preparations of antigen (vaccines) obtained from many sources, including inactivated bacterial toxins, killed or weakened pathogens, and even genes encoding microbial proteins. Because all of these agents induce a primary immune response and immunological memory, an encounter with the pathogen from which the vaccine was derived triggers a rapid and strong secondary immune response (see Figure 43.15).

Vaccination programs have been successful against many infectious diseases that once killed or incapacitated large numbers of people. A worldwide vaccination campaign led to eradication of smallpox in the late 1970s. In industrialized nations, routine immunization of infants and children has dramatically reduced the incidence of sometimes devastating diseases, such as polio, measles, and whooping cough. Unfortunately, not all pathogens are easily managed by vaccination. Furthermore, some vaccines are not readily available in impoverished areas of the globe.

Misinformation about vaccine safety and disease risk has led to a substantial and growing public health problem. Consider measles as just one example. Side effects of immunization are remarkably rare, with fewer than one in a million children suffering a significant allergic reaction to the measles vaccine. The disease, however, is quite dangerous, killing more than 200,000 people each year. Declines in measles vaccination rates in parts of the United Kingdom, Russia, and the United States have resulted in a number of recent measles outbreaks and many preventable deaths.

In artificial passive immunization, antibodies from an immune animal are injected into a nonimmune animal. For example, humans bitten by venomous snakes are sometimes treated with antivenin, serum from sheep or horses that have been immunized against a snake venom. When injected immediately after a snakebite, the antibodies in antivenin can neutralize toxins in the venom before the toxins do massive damage.

Antibodies as Tools

Antibodies that an animal produces after exposure to an antigen are the products of many different clones of plasma cells **(Figure 43.21)**, each specific for a different epitope. However, antibodies can also be prepared from a single clone of B cells grown in culture. The **monoclonal antibodies**

Endoplasmic reticulum of plasma cell

▲ **Figure 43.21 A plasma cell.** A plasma cell contains abundant endoplasmic reticulum, a common feature of cells dedicated to making proteins for secretion (TEM).

produced by such a culture are identical and specific for the same epitope on an antigen.

Monoclonal antibodies have provided the basis for many recent advances in medical diagnosis and treatment. For example, home pregnancy test kits use monoclonal antibodies to detect human chorionic gonadotropin (hCG). Because hCG is produced as soon as an embryo implants in the uterus (see Chapter 46), the presence of this hormone in a woman's urine is a reliable indicator for a very early stage of pregnancy. Monoclonal antibodies are also produced in large amounts and injected as a therapy for a number of human diseases, including certain cancers.

Immune Rejection

Like pathogens, cells from another person can be recognized as foreign and attacked by immune defenses. For example, skin transplanted from one person to a genetically nonidentical person will look healthy for a week or so but will then be destroyed (rejected) by the recipient's immune response. Keep in mind that the body's rejection of transplanted tissues or organs or of an incompatible blood transfusion is the expected reaction of a healthy immune system exposed to foreign antigens. (It remains a largely unanswered question why a pregnant woman does not reject her fetus as nonself tissue.)

Blood Groups

To avoid a blood transfusion being recognized as foreign by the recipient's immune system, doctors must take into account a property of the donor and recipient known as the ABO blood group. Red blood cells are designated as type A if they have the A carbohydrate on their surface. Similarly, the B carbohydrate is found on the surface of type B red blood cells; both A and B carbohydrates are found on type AB red blood cells; and neither carbohydrate is found on type O red blood cells (see Figure 14.11).

Why does the immune system recognize particular sugars on red blood cells? It turns out that certain bacteria normally present in the body have epitopes very similar to the A and B carbohydrates. Responding to the bacterial epitope similar to the B carbohydrate, a person with type A blood makes antibodies that will react with the B carbohydrate. That same person doesn't make antibodies against the bacterial epitope similar to the A carbohydrate because lymphocytes reactive with the body's own molecules are inactivated or eliminated during development.

To understand how ABO blood groups affect transfusions, let's consider the immune response of someone with type A blood. If a person with type A blood receives a transfusion of type B blood, the anti-B antibodies in the type A blood cause an immediate and devastating transfusion reaction. The transfused red blood cells undergo lysis, which can lead to chills, fever, shock, and kidney malfunction. By the same token, anti-A antibodies in the donated type B blood will act against the recipient's type A red blood cells. Although such interactions prevent type O individuals from receiving transfusions of any other blood type, the discovery of enzymes that can cleave the A and B carbohydrates from red blood cells may eliminate this problem.

Tissue and Organ Transplants

Each of us expresses MHC proteins from more than a dozen different genes. Furthermore, more than 100 different versions, or alleles, of these genes exist among humans. In transplants or grafts of an organ or a piece of tissue between individuals, these different forms of MHC molecules can act as antigens, stimulating an immune response that leads to rejection. Note that the diversity of MHC molecules almost guarantees that no two people, except identical twins, will have exactly the same set. As a result, some MHC molecules on the donated tissue are foreign to the recipient in the vast majority of grafts and transplants.

To minimize rejection in a graft or transplant operation, physicians use donor tissue bearing MHC molecules that match those of the recipient as closely as possible. In addition, the recipient takes medicines that suppress immune responses (but as a result leave the recipient more susceptible to infections).

Transplants of bone marrow from one person to another can also cause an immune reaction, but for a different reason. Bone marrow transplants are used to treat leukemia and other cancers as well as various hematological (blood cell) diseases. Prior to receiving transplanted bone marrow, the recipient is typically treated with radiation to eliminate his or her own bone marrow cells, thus

destroying the source of abnormal cells. This treatment effectively obliterates the recipient's immune system, leaving little chance of graft rejection. However, lymphocytes in the donated marrow may react against the recipient. This *graft-versus-host reaction* is limited if the MHC molecules of the donor and recipient are well matched. Bone marrow donor programs continually seek volunteers because the great variability of MHC molecules makes a diverse pool of donors essential.

CONCEPT CHECK 43.3

1. If a child were born without a thymus gland, what cells and functions of the immune system would be deficient? Explain.

2. Treatment of antibodies with a particular protease clips the heavy chains in half, releasing the two arms of the Y-shaped molecule. How might the antibodies continue to function?

3. **WHAT IF?** Suppose that a snake handler bitten by a particular venomous snake species was treated with antivenin. Why might the same treatment for a second such bite have different results?

For suggested answers, see Appendix A.

CONCEPT 43.4

Disruptions in immune system function can elicit or exacerbate disease

Although adaptive immunity offers significant protection against a wide range of pathogens, it is not fail-safe. Here we'll first examine the disorders and diseases that arise when adaptive immunity is blocked or misregulated. We'll then turn to some of the evolutionary adaptations of pathogens that diminish the effectiveness of adaptive immune responses in the host.

Exaggerated, Self-Directed, and Diminished Immune Responses

The highly regulated interplay among lymphocytes, other body cells, and foreign substances generates an immune response that provides extraordinary protection against many pathogens. When allergic, autoimmune, or immunodeficiency disorders disrupt this delicate balance, the effects are frequently severe.

Allergies

Allergies are exaggerated (hypersensitive) responses to certain antigens called *allergens*. The most common allergies involve antibodies of the IgE class. Hay fever, for instance, occurs when plasma cells secrete IgE antibodies specific for antigens on the surface of pollen grains (Figure 43.22). Some IgE antibodies attach by their base to mast cells in connective tissues. Pollen grains that enter the body later attach to the antigen-binding sites of these IgE antibodies. Such attachment links adjacent IgE molecules, inducing the mast cell to release histamine and other inflammatory chemicals. Acting on a variety of cell types, these chemicals bring about the typical allergy symptoms: sneezing, runny nose, teary eyes, and smooth muscle contractions in the lungs that can inhibit effective breathing. Drugs known as antihistamines block receptors for histamine, diminishing allergy symptoms (and inflammation).

An acute allergic response sometimes leads to a life-threatening reaction called *anaphylactic shock*. Inflammatory chemicals released from mast cells trigger constriction of bronchioles and sudden dilation of peripheral blood vessels, which causes a precipitous drop in blood pressure. Death may occur within minutes due to the inability to breathe and lack of blood flow. Substances that can cause anaphylactic shock in allergic individuals include bee venom, penicillin, peanuts, and shellfish. People with severe hypersensitivities often carry syringes containing the hormone epinephrine. An injection of epinephrine rapidly counteracts this allergic response, constricting peripheral blood vessels, reducing swelling in the throat, and relaxing muscles in the lungs to help breathing (see Figure 45.8).

IgE

Mast cell

Allergen (second exposure)

1 IgE antibodies produced in response to initial exposure to an allergen bind to receptors on mast cells.

2 On subsequent exposure to the same allergen, IgE molecules attached to a mast cell recognize and bind the allergen.

Vesicle

Histamine

3 Cross-linking of adjacent IgE molecules triggers release of histamine and other chemicals, leading to allergy symptoms.

▲ Figure 43.22 **Mast cells, IgE, and the allergic response.** In this example, pollen grains act as the allergen.

Autoimmune Diseases

In some people, the immune system is active against particular molecules of the body, causing an **autoimmune disease**. Such a loss of self-tolerance has many forms. In systemic lupus erythematosus, commonly called *lupus*, the immune system generates antibodies against histones and DNA released by the normal breakdown of body cells. These self-reactive antibodies cause skin rashes, fever, arthritis, and kidney dysfunction. Other targets of autoimmunity include the insulin-producing beta cells of the pancreas (in type 1 diabetes) and the myelin sheaths that encase many neurons (in multiple sclerosis).

Heredity, gender, and environment all influence susceptibility to autoimmune disorders. For example, members of certain families show an increased susceptibility to particular autoimmune disorders. In addition, many autoimmune diseases afflict females more often than males. Women are nine times as likely as men to suffer from lupus and two to three times as likely to develop *rheumatoid arthritis*, a damaging and painful inflammation of the cartilage and bone in joints (Figure 43.23). The cause of this sex bias, as well as the rise in autoimmune disease frequency in industrialized countries, is an area of active research and debate.

▲ Figure 43.23 **X-ray of hands that are deformed by rheumatoid arthritis.**

Exertion, Stress, and the Immune System

Many forms of exertion and stress influence immune system function. For example, moderate exercise improves immune system function and significantly reduces susceptibility to the common cold and other infections of the upper respiratory tract. In contrast, exercise to the point of exhaustion leads to more frequent infections and more severe symptoms. Studies of marathon runners support the conclusion that exercise intensity is the critical variable. On average, such runners get sick less often than their more sedentary peers during training, a time of moderate exertion, but markedly more often in the period immediately following the grueling race itself. Similarly, psychological stress has been shown to disrupt immune system regulation by altering the interplay of the hormonal, nervous, and immune systems (see Figure 45.20). Research also confirms that rest is important for immunity: Adults who averaged fewer than 7 hours of sleep got sick three times as often when exposed to a cold virus as those who averaged at least 8 hours.

Immunodeficiency Diseases

A disorder in which an immune system response to antigens is defective or absent is called an immunodeficiency. Whatever its cause and nature, an immunodeficiency can lead to frequent and recurrent infections and increased susceptibility to certain cancers.

An *inborn immunodeficiency* results from a genetic or developmental defect in the production of immune system cells or of specific proteins, such as antibodies or the proteins of the complement system. Depending on the specific defect, either innate or adaptive defenses—or both—may be impaired. In severe combined immunodeficiency (SCID), functional lymphocytes are rare or absent. Lacking an adaptive immune response, SCID patients are susceptible to infections, such as pneumonia and meningitis, that can cause death in infancy. Treatments include bone marrow and stem cell transplantation.

Later in life, exposure to chemicals or biological agents can cause an *acquired immunodeficiency*. Drugs used to fight autoimmune diseases or prevent transplant rejection suppress the immune system, leading to an immunodeficient state. Certain cancers also suppress the immune system, especially Hodgkin's disease, which damages the lymphatic system. Acquired immunodeficiencies range from temporary states that may arise from physiological stress to the devastating disease AIDS (acquired immune deficiency syndrome), which we'll discuss in the next section.

Evolutionary Adaptations of Pathogens That Underlie Immune System Avoidance

EVOLUTION Just as immune systems that ward off pathogens have evolved in animals, mechanisms that thwart immune responses have evolved in pathogens. Using human pathogens as examples, we'll examine some common mechanisms: antigenic variation, latency, and direct attack on the immune system.

Antigenic Variation

One mechanism for escaping the body's defenses is for a pathogen to alter how it appears to the immune system. Immunological memory is a record of the foreign epitopes an animal has encountered. If the pathogen that expressed those epitopes no longer does so, it can reinfect or remain in a host without triggering the rapid and robust response that memory cells provide. Such changes in epitope expression are called *antigenic variation*. The parasite that causes sleeping sickness (trypanosomiasis) provides an extreme example, periodically switching at random among 1,000 different versions of the protein found over its entire surface. In the Scientific Skills Exercise, you'll interpret data on this form of antigenic variation and the body's response.

Antigenic variation is the main reason the influenza, or "flu," virus remains a major public health problem. As it replicates in one human host after another, the virus undergoes frequent mutations. Because any change that lessens recognition by the immune system provides a selective advantage, the virus steadily accumulates mutations that change its surface proteins, reducing the effectiveness of the host immune response. As a result, a new flu vaccine must be developed, produced, and distributed each year. In addition, the human influenza virus occasionally forms new strains by exchanging genes with influenza viruses that infect domesticated animals, such as pigs or chickens. When this occurs, the new strain may not be recognized by any of the memory cells in the human population. The resulting outbreak can be deadly: The 1918–1919 influenza outbreak killed more than 20 million people.

In 2009, an influenza virus called H1N1 appeared that contained a novel combination of genes from flu viruses that normally circulate in pigs, birds, and humans. The rapid spread of this flu across the human population caused a *pandemic*, an outbreak of worldwide proportions. Fortunately, a rapidly developed H1N1 vaccine soon provided public health officials with an excellent means of slowing the spread of this virus and reducing the impact of the outbreak.

Latency

Some viruses avoid an immune response by infecting cells and then entering a largely inactive state called *latency*. Because production of most viral proteins and free viruses ceases, latent viruses do not trigger an adaptive immune response. Nevertheless, the viral genome persists in the nuclei of infected cells, either as a separate DNA molecule or as a copy integrated into the host genome. Latency typically persists until conditions arise that are favorable for viral transmission or unfavorable for host survival, such as when the host is infected by another pathogen. Such circumstances trigger the synthesis and release of free viruses that can infect new hosts.

Herpes simplex viruses, which establish themselves in human sensory neurons, provide a good example of latency. The type 1 virus causes most oral herpes infections, whereas the type 2 virus is responsible for most cases of genital herpes. Because sensory neurons express relatively few MHC I molecules, the infected cells are inefficient at presenting viral antigens to circulating lymphocytes. Stimuli such as fever, emotional stress, or menstruation reactivate the virus to replicate and infect surrounding epithelial tissues. Activation of the type 1 virus can result in blisters around the mouth that are inaccurately called "cold" sores. The type 2 virus can cause genital sores, but people infected with either the type 1 or type 2 virus often lack any symptoms. Infections of the type 2 virus, which is sexually transmitted, pose

SCIENTIFIC SKILLS EXERCISE

Comparing Two Variables on a Common x-Axis

How Does the Immune System Respond to a Changing Pathogen? Natural selection favors parasites that are able to maintain a low-level infection in a host for a long time. *Trypanosoma*, the unicellular parasite that causes sleeping sickness, is one example. The glycoproteins covering a trypanosome's surface are encoded by a gene that is duplicated more than a thousand times in the organism's genome. Each copy is slightly different. By periodically switching among these genes, the trypanosome can display a series of surface glycoproteins with different molecular structures. In this exercise, you will interpret two data sets to explore hypotheses about the benefits of the trypanosome's ever-shifting surface glycoproteins and the host's immune response.

▲ Trypanosomes (yellow) and red blood cells

Part A: Data from a Study of Parasite Levels This study measured the abundance of parasites in the blood of one human patient during the first few weeks of a chronic infection.

Day	Number of Parasites (in millions) per mL of Blood
4	0.1
6	0.3
8	1.2
10	0.2
12	0.2
14	0.9
16	0.6
18	0.1
20	0.7
22	1.2
24	0.2

Part A: Interpret the Data

1. Plot the data in the above table as a line graph. Which column is the independent variable, and which is the dependent variable? Put the independent variable on the x-axis. (For additional information about graphs, see the Scientific Skills Review in Appendix F and the Study Area in MasteringBiology.)

2. Visually displaying data in a graph can help make patterns in the data more noticeable. Describe any patterns revealed by your graph.

3. Assume that a drop in parasite abundance reflects an effective immune response by the host. Formulate a hypothesis to explain the pattern you described in question 2.

Part B: Data from a Study of Antibody Levels Many decades after scientists first observed the pattern of *Trypanosoma* abundance over the course of infection, researchers identified antibodies specific to different forms of the parasite's surface glycoprotein. The table below lists the relative abundance of two such antibodies during the early period of chronic infection, using an index ranging from 0 (absent) to 1.

Day	Antibody Specific to Glycoprotein Variant A	Antibody Specific to Glycoprotein Variant B
4	0	0
6	0	0
8	0.2	0
10	0.5	0
12	1	0
14	1	0.1
16	1	0.3
18	1	0.9
20	1	1
22	1	1
24	1	1

Part B: Interpret the Data

4. Note that these data were collected over the same period of infection (days 4–24) as the parasite abundance data you graphed in part A. Therefore, you can incorporate these new data into your first graph, using the same x-axis. However, since the antibody level data are measured in a different way than the parasite abundance data, add a second set of y-axis labels on the right side of your graph. Then, using different colors or sets of symbols, add the data for the two antibody types. Labeling the y-axis two different ways enables you to compare how two dependent variables change relative to a shared independent variable.

5. Describe any patterns you observe by comparing the two data sets over the same period. Do these patterns support your hypothesis from part A? Do they prove that hypothesis? Explain.

6. Scientists can now also distinguish the abundance of trypanosomes recognized specifically by antibodies type A and type B. How would incorporating such information change your graph?

(MB) A version of this Scientific Skills Exercise can be assigned in MasteringBiology.

Data from L. J. Morrison, et al., Probabilistic order in antigenic variation of Trypanosoma brucei, *International Journal for Parasitology* 35:961-972 (2005) and L. J. Morrison, et al.,Antigenic variation in the African trypanosome: molecular mechanisms and phenotypic complexity, *Cellular Microbiology* 1: 1724-1734 (2009).

a serious threat to the babies of infected mothers and can increase transmission of the virus that causes AIDS.

Attack on the Immune System: HIV

The **human immunodeficiency virus (HIV)**, the pathogen that causes AIDS, both escapes and attacks the adaptive immune response. Once introduced into the body, HIV infects helper T cells with high efficiency by binding specifically to the CD4 accessory protein (see Figure 43.16). HIV also infects some cell types that have low levels of CD4, such as macrophages and brain cells. Inside cells, the HIV RNA genome is reverse-transcribed, and the product DNA is integrated into the host cell's genome (see Figure 19.8). In this form, the viral genome can direct the production of new viruses.

Although the body responds to HIV with an immune response sufficient to eliminate most viral infections, some HIV invariably escapes. One reason HIV persists is that it has a very high mutation rate. Altered proteins on the surface of some mutated viruses reduce interaction with antibodies and cytotoxic T cells. Such viruses replicate and mutate further. HIV thus evolves within the body. The continued presence of HIV is also helped by latency while the viral DNA is integrated in the host cell's genome. This latent DNA is shielded from the immune system as well as from antiviral agents currently used against HIV, which attack only actively replicating viruses.

Over time, an untreated HIV infection not only avoids the adaptive immune response but also abolishes it (Figure 43.24). Viral replication and cell death triggered by the virus lead to loss of helper T cells, impairing both humoral and cell-mediated immune responses. The eventual result is **acquired immunodeficiency syndrome (AIDS)**, an impairment in immune responses that leaves the body susceptible to infections and cancers that a healthy immune system would usually defeat. For example, *Pneumocystis carinii*, a common fungus that does not cause disease in healthy individuals, can result in severe pneumonia in people with AIDS. Such opportunistic diseases, as well as nerve damage and body wasting, are the primary causes of death in AIDS patients, not HIV itself.

Transmission of HIV requires the transfer of virus particles or infected cells from person to person via body fluids such as semen, blood, or breast milk. Unprotected sex (that is, without using a condom) and transmission via HIV-contaminated needles (typically among intravenous drug users) cause the vast majority of HIV infections. The virus can enter the body through mucosal linings of the vagina, vulva, penis, or rectum during intercourse or via the mouth during oral sex. People infected with HIV can transmit the disease in the first few weeks of infection, *before* they produce HIV-specific antibodies that can be detected in a blood test. Currently, 10–50% of all new HIV infections appear to be caused by recently infected individuals. Although HIV infection cannot be cured, drugs have been developed that can significantly slow HIV replication and the progression to AIDS.

Cancer and Immunity

When adaptive immunity is inactivated, the frequency of certain cancers increases dramatically. For example, the risk of developing Kaposi's sarcoma is 20,000 times greater for untreated AIDS patients than for healthy people. This observation was unanticipated. If the immune system recognizes only nonself, it should fail to recognize the uncontrolled growth of self cells that is the hallmark of cancer. It turns out, however, that viruses are involved in about 15–20% of all human cancers. Because the immune system can recognize viral proteins as foreign, it can act as a defense against viruses that can cause cancer and against cancer cells that harbor viruses.

Scientists have identified six viruses that can cause cancer in humans. The Kaposi's sarcoma herpesvirus is one such virus. Hepatitis B virus, which can trigger liver cancer, is another. A vaccine introduced in 1986 for hepatitis B virus was the first vaccine shown to help prevent a specific human cancer. Rapid progress on virus-induced cancers continues. In 2006, the release of a vaccine that is derived from human papillomavirus (HPV) marked a major victory against cervical cancer, as well as other cancers that can affect sexually active men or women.

▲ **Human papillomavirus**

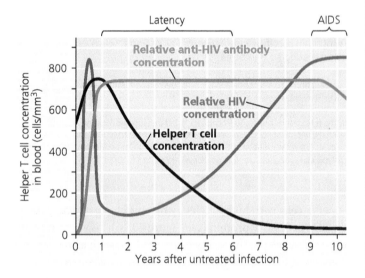

▲ **Figure 43.24 The progress of an untreated HIV infection.**

CONCEPT CHECK **43.4**

1. In the muscular disease myasthenia gravis, antibodies bind to and block certain receptors on muscle cells, preventing muscle contraction. Is this disease best classified as an immunodeficiency disease, an autoimmune disease, or an allergic reaction? Explain.

2. People with herpes simplex type 1 viruses often get mouth sores when they have a cold or similar infection. How might this location benefit the virus?

3. **WHAT IF?** How would a macrophage deficiency likely affect a person's innate and adaptive defenses?

For suggested answers, see Appendix A.

CONCEPT 43.1

In innate immunity, recognition and response rely on traits common to groups of pathogens (pp. 947–952)

- In both invertebrates and vertebrates, innate immunity is mediated by physical and chemical barriers as well as cell-based defenses. Activation of innate immune responses relies on recognition proteins specific for broad classes of pathogens. Microbes that penetrate barrier defenses are ingested by phagocytic cells, which in vertebrates include **macrophages** and **dendritic cells**. Additional cellular defenses include **natural killer cells**, which can induce the death of virus-infected cells. **Complement system** proteins, **interferons**, and other antimicrobial peptides also act against pathogens. In the **inflammatory response**, **histamine** and other chemicals that are released at the injury site promote changes in blood vessels that enhance immune cell access.

- Pathogens sometimes evade innate immune defenses. For example, some bacteria have an outer capsule that prevents recognition, while others are resistant to breakdown within lysosomes.

? *In what ways does innate immunity protect the mammalian digestive tract?*

CONCEPT 43.2

In adaptive immunity, receptors provide pathogen-specific recognition (pp. 952–957)

- **Adaptive immunity** relies on two types of **lymphocytes** that arise from stem cells in the bone marrow: **B cells** and **T cells**. Lymphocytes have cell-surface **antigen receptors** for foreign molecules (**antigens**). All receptor proteins on a single B or T cell are the same, but there are millions of B and T cells in the body that differ in the foreign molecules that their receptors recognize. Upon infection, B and T cells specific for the pathogen are activated. Some T cells help other lymphocytes; others kill infected host cells. B cells called **plasma cells** produce soluble proteins called **antibodies**, which bind to foreign molecules and cells. Activated B and T cells called **memory cells** defend against future infections by the same pathogen.

- Recognition of foreign molecules by B cells and T cells involves the binding of variable regions of receptors to an **epitope**, a small region of an antigen. B cells and antibodies recognize epitopes on the surface of antigens circulating in the blood or lymph. T cells recognize epitopes in small antigen fragments (peptides) that are presented on the surface of host cells by proteins called **major histocompatibility complex (MHC) molecules** This interaction activates a T cell, enabling it to participate in adaptive immunity.

- The four major characteristics of B and T cell development are the generation of cell diversity, self-tolerance, proliferation, and immunological memory. Proliferation and memory are both based on **clonal selection**, illustrated here for B cells:

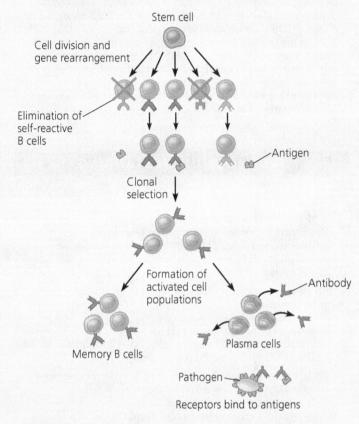

? *Why is the adaptive immune response to an initial infection slower than the innate response?*

CONCEPT 43.3

Adaptive immunity defends against infection of body fluids and body cells (pp. 958–964)

- **Helper T cells** interact with antigen fragments displayed by class II MHC molecules on the surface of **antigen-presenting cells**: dendritic cells, macrophages, and B cells. Activated helper T cells secrete **cytokines** that stimulate other lymphocytes. In the **cell-mediated immune response**, activated **cytotoxic T cells** trigger destruction of infected cells. In the **humoral immune response**, antibodies help eliminate antigens by promoting phagocytosis and complement-mediated lysis.

- **Active immunity** develops in response to infection or to immunization. The transfer of antibodies in **passive immunity** provides immediate, short-term protection.

- Tissues or cells transferred from one person to another are subject to immune rejection. In tissue grafts and organ transplants, MHC molecules stimulate rejection. Lymphocytes in bone marrow transplants may cause a graft-versus-host reaction.

? *Is immunological memory after a natural infection fundamentally different from immunological memory after vaccination? Explain.*

CONCEPT 43.4

Disruptions in immune system function can elicit or exacerbate disease (pp. 964–968)

- In allergies, such as hay fever, the interaction of antibodies and allergens triggers immune cells to release histamine and other mediators that cause vascular changes and allergic symptoms. Loss of self-tolerance can lead to **autoimmune diseases**, such as multiple sclerosis. Inborn immunodeficiencies result from defects that interfere with innate, humoral, or cell-mediated defenses. **AIDS** is an acquired immunodeficiency caused by **HIV**.
- Antigenic variation, latency, and direct assault on the immune system allow some pathogens to thwart immune responses. HIV infection destroys helper T cells, leaving the patient prone to disease. Immune defense against cancer appears to primarily involve action against viruses that can cause cancer and cancer cells that harbor viruses.

? *Is being infected with HIV the same as having AIDS? Explain.*

TEST YOUR UNDERSTANDING

LEVEL 1: KNOWLEDGE/COMPREHENSION

1. Which of these is *not* part of insect immunity?
   a. enzyme activation of pathogen-killing chemicals
   b. activation of natural killer cells
   c. phagocytosis by hemocytes
   d. production of antimicrobial peptides

2. An epitope associates with which part of an antigen receptor or antibody?
   a. the tail
   b. the heavy-chain constant regions only
   c. variable regions of a heavy chain and light chain combined
   d. the light-chain constant regions only

3. Which statement best describes the difference in responses of effector B cells (plasma cells) and cytotoxic T cells?
   a. B cells confer active immunity; cytotoxic T cells confer passive immunity.
   b. B cells respond the first time a pathogen is present; cytotoxic T cells respond subsequent times.
   c. B cells secrete antibodies against a pathogen; cytotoxic T cells kill pathogen-infected host cells.
   d. B cells carry out the cell-mediated response; cytotoxic T cells carry out the humoral response.

LEVEL 2: APPLICATION/ANALYSIS

4. Which of the following statements is *not* true?
   a. An antibody has more than one antigen-binding site.
   b. A lymphocyte has receptors for multiple different antigens.
   c. An antigen can have different epitopes.
   d. A liver cell makes one class of MHC molecule.

5. Which of the following should be the same in identical twins?
   a. the set of antibodies produced
   b. the set of MHC molecules produced
   c. the set of T cell antigen receptors produced
   d. the set of immune cells eliminated as self-reactive

LEVEL 3: SYNTHESIS/EVALUATION

6. Vaccination increases the number of
   a. different receptors that recognize a pathogen.
   b. lymphocytes with receptors that can bind to the pathogen.
   c. epitopes that the immune system can recognize.
   d. MHC molecules that can present an antigen.

7. Which of the following would *not* help a virus avoid triggering an adaptive immune response?
   a. having frequent mutations in genes for surface proteins
   b. infecting cells that produce very few MHC molecules
   c. producing proteins very similar to those of other viruses
   d. infecting and killing helper T cells

8. **DRAW IT** Consider a pencil-shaped protein with two epitopes, Y (the "eraser" end) and Z (the "point" end). They are recognized by antibodies A1 and A2, respectively. Draw and label a picture showing the antibodies linking proteins into a complex that could trigger endocytosis by a macrophage.

9. **MAKE CONNECTIONS** Contrast clonal selection with Lamarck's idea for the inheritance of acquired characteristics (see Concept 22.1).

10. **EVOLUTION CONNECTION** Describe one invertebrate mechanism of defense against pathogens and discuss how it is an evolutionary adaptation retained in vertebrates.

11. **SCIENTIFIC INQUIRY** The presence of bacterial lipopolysaccharide (LPS) in the blood is a major cause of septic shock. Suppose you have available purified LPS and several strains of mice, each with a mutation that inactivates a particular TLR gene. How might you use these mice to test the feasibility of treating septic shock with a drug that blocks TLR signaling?

12. **WRITE ABOUT A THEME: INFORMATION** Among all nucleated body cells, only B and T cells lose DNA during their development and maturation. In a short essay (100–150 words), discuss the relationship between this loss and DNA as heritable biological information, focusing on similarities between cellular and organismal generations.

13. **SYNTHESIZE YOUR KNOWLEDGE**

This photo shows a child receiving an oral vaccine against polio, a disease caused by a virus that infects neurons. Given that the body cannot readily replace most neurons, why is it important that a polio vaccine stimulate not only a cell-mediated response but also a humoral response?

For suggested answers, see Appendix A.

MasteringBiology®

Students Go to **MasteringBiology** for assignments, the eText, and the Study Area with practice tests, animations, and activities.

Instructors Go to **MasteringBiology** for automatically graded tutorials and questions that you can assign to your students, plus Instructor Resources.

44

Osmoregulation and Excretion

▲ Figure 44.1 How does an albatross drink salt water without ill effect?

A Balancing Act

At 3.5 m, the wingspan of a wandering albatross (*Diomedea exulans*) is the largest of any living bird. But the albatross commands attention for more than just its size. This massive bird remains at sea day and night throughout the year, returning to land only to reproduce. A human with only seawater to drink would die of dehydration, but faced with the same conditions, the albatross thrives (Figure 44.1).

For both albatross and human, maintaining the fluid balance of their tissues requires that the relative concentrations of water and solutes be kept within fairly narrow limits. In addition, ions such as sodium and calcium must be maintained at concentrations that permit normal activity of muscles, neurons, and other body cells. Homeostasis thus requires **osmoregulation**, the general term for the processes by which animals control solute concentrations and balance water gain and loss.

A number of mechanisms for water and solute control have arisen during evolution, reflecting the varied and often severe osmoregulatory challenges presented by an animal's surroundings. The arid conditions of a desert, for instance, can quickly deplete an animal of body water. Despite a quite different environment, albatrosses and other marine animals also face potential dehydration. The success of these animals depends on conserving water and, for marine birds and fishes, eliminating excess salts. Freshwater animals face a distinct challenge: an environment that threatens to dilute their body fluids. These organisms survive by conserving solutes and absorbing salts from their surroundings.

In safeguarding their internal fluids, animals must deal with ammonia, a toxic metabolite produced by the dismantling of *nitrogenous* (nitrogen-containing) molecules, chiefly proteins and nucleic acids. Several different mechanisms have evolved for **excretion**, the process that rids the body of nitrogenous metabolites and other metabolic waste products. Because systems for excretion and osmoregulation are structurally and functionally linked in many animals, we'll consider both of these processes in this chapter.

CONCEPT 44.1

Osmoregulation balances the uptake and loss of water and solutes

Just as thermoregulation depends on balancing heat loss and gain (see Concept 40.3), regulating the chemical composition of body fluids depends on balancing the uptake and loss of water and solutes. If water uptake is excessive, animal cells swell and burst; if water loss is substantial, they shrivel and die. Ultimately, the driving force for the movement of both water and solutes—in animals as in all other organisms—is a concentration gradient of one or more solutes across the plasma membrane.

Osmosis and Osmolarity

Water enters and leaves cells by osmosis, which occurs when two solutions separated by a membrane differ in total solute concentration (**Figure 44.2**). The unit of measurement for solute concentration is **osmolarity**, the number of moles of solute per liter of solution. The osmolarity of human blood is about 300 milliosmoles per liter (mOsm/L), whereas that of seawater is about 1,000 mOsm/L.

▲ Figure 44.2 **Solute concentration and osmosis.**

Two solutions with the same osmolarity are said to be *isoosmotic*. If a selectively permeable membrane separates the solutions, water molecules will continually cross the membrane at equal rates in both directions. Thus, there is no *net* movement of water by osmosis between isoosmotic solutions. When two solutions differ in osmolarity, the solution with the higher concentration of solutes is said to be *hyperosmotic*, and the more dilute solution is said to be *hypoosmotic*. Water flows by osmosis from a hypoosmotic solution to a hyperosmotic one (see Figure 44.2).*

Osmoregulatory Challenges and Mechanisms

An animal can maintain water balance in two ways. One is to be an **osmoconformer**: to be isoosmotic with its surroundings. The second is to be an **osmoregulator**: to control internal osmolarity independent of that of the external environment.

All osmoconformers are marine animals. Because an osmoconformer's internal osmolarity is the same as that of its environment, there is no tendency to gain or lose water. Many osmoconformers live in water that has a stable composition and hence have a constant internal osmolarity.

Osmoregulation enables animals to live in environments that are uninhabitable for osmoconformers, such as fresh water and terrestrial habitats, or to move between marine and freshwater environments (**Figure 44.3**). To survive in a hypoosmotic environment, an osmoregulator must discharge excess water. In a hyperosmotic environment, an osmoregulator must instead take in water to offset osmotic loss. Osmoregulation also allows many marine animals

▲ Figure 44.3 **Sockeye salmon (*Oncorhynchus nerka*), osmoregulators that migrate between rivers and the ocean.**

---

*In this chapter, we use the terms *isoosmotic*, *hypoosmotic*, and *hyperosmotic*, which refer specifically to osmolarity, instead of *isotonic*, *hypotonic*, and *hypertonic*. The latter set of terms applies to the response of animal cells— whether they swell or shrink—in solutions of known solute concentrations.

to maintain an internal osmolarity different from that of seawater.

Most animals, whether osmoconformers or osmoregulators, cannot tolerate substantial changes in external osmolarity and are said to be *stenohaline* (from the Greek *stenos*, narrow, and *halos*, salt). In contrast, *euryhaline* animals (from the Greek *eurys*, broad) can survive large fluctuations in external osmolarity. Euryhaline osmoconformers include many barnacles and mussels, which are alternately submerged and exposed by tides; euryhaline osmoregulators include striped bass and the various species of salmon (see Figure 44.3).

Next we'll examine some adaptations for osmoregulation that have evolved in marine, freshwater, and terrestrial animals.

Marine Animals

Most marine invertebrates are osmoconformers. Their osmolarity is the same as that of seawater. They therefore face no substantial challenges in water balance. However, because these animals differ considerably from seawater in the concentrations of *specific* solutes, they must actively transport these solutes to maintain homeostasis. For example, although the concentration of magnesium ions (Mg^{2+}) in seawater is 50 mM (millimolar, or 10^{-3} mol/L), homeostatic mechanisms in the Atlantic lobster (*Homarus americanus*) result in a Mg^{2+} concentration of less than 9 mM in its hemolymph (circulatory fluid).

Many marine vertebrates and some marine invertebrates are osmoregulators. For most of these animals, the ocean is a strongly dehydrating environment. For example, marine fishes, such as the cod in **Figure 44.4a**, constantly lose water by osmosis. Such fishes balance the water loss by drinking large amounts of seawater, and they eliminate the ingested salts through their gills and kidneys.

A distinct osmoregulatory strategy evolved in marine sharks and most other chondrichthyans (cartilaginous animals; see Chapter 34). Like "bony fishes" (as we'll refer collectively to ray-finned and lobe-finned fishes in this chapter), sharks have an internal salt concentration much lower than that of seawater. Thus, salt tends to diffuse into their bodies from the water, especially across their gills. Unlike bony fishes, however, marine sharks are not hypoosmotic to seawater. The explanation is that shark tissue contains high concentrations of urea, a nitrogenous waste product of protein and nucleic acid metabolism (see Figure 44.7). A shark's body fluids also contain trimethylamine oxide (TMAO), an organic molecule that protects proteins from damage by urea. Together, the salts, urea, TMAO, and other compounds maintained in the body fluids of sharks result in an osmolarity very close to that of seawater. For this reason, sharks are often considered osmoconformers. However, because the solute concentration in their body fluids is actually somewhat higher than 1,000 mOsm/L, water slowly *enters* the shark's body by osmosis and in food (sharks do not drink). This small influx of water is disposed of in urine produced by the shark's kidneys. The urine also removes some of the salt that diffuses into the shark's body; the rest is lost in feces or is secreted from a specialized gland.

Freshwater Animals

The osmoregulatory problems of freshwater animals are the opposite of those of marine animals. The body fluids of freshwater animals must be hyperosmotic because animal cells cannot tolerate salt concentrations as low as that of lake or river water. Having internal fluids with an osmolarity higher than that of their surroundings, freshwater animals face the problem of gaining water by osmosis and losing salts by diffusion. Many freshwater animals, including bony fishes such as the perch in **Figure 44.4b**, solve the

▼ Figure 44.4 Osmoregulation in marine and freshwater bony fishes: a comparison.

(a) Osmoregulation in a marine fish

Gain of water and salt ions from food

Excretion of salt ions from gills

Osmotic water **loss** through gills and other parts of body surface

SALT WATER

Gain of water and salt ions from drinking seawater

Excretion of salt ions and small amounts of water in scanty urine from kidneys

Key
⇨ Water
➜ Salt

(b) Osmoregulation in a freshwater fish

Gain of water and some ions in food

Uptake of salt ions by gills

Osmotic water **gain** through gills and other parts of body surface

FRESH WATER

Excretion of salt ions and large amounts of water in dilute urine from kidneys problem of water balance by drinking almost no water and excreting large amounts of very dilute urine. At the same time, salts lost by diffusion and in the urine are replenished by eating. Freshwater fishes also replenish salts by uptake across their gills.

Salmon and other euryhaline fishes that migrate between fresh water and seawater undergo dramatic changes in osmoregulatory status. When living in rivers and streams, salmon osmoregulate like other freshwater fishes, producing large amounts of dilute urine and taking up salt from the dilute environment through their gills. When they migrate to the ocean, salmon acclimatize. They produce more of the steroid hormone cortisol, which increases the number and size of salt-secreting chloride cells. As a result of these and other physiological changes, salmon in salt water excrete excess salt from their gills and produce only small amounts of urine—just like bony fishes that spend their entire lives in salt water.

Animals That Live in Temporary Waters

Extreme dehydration, or *desiccation*, is fatal for most animals. However, a few aquatic invertebrates that live in temporary ponds and in films of water around soil particles can lose almost all their body water and survive. These animals enter a dormant state when their habitats dry up, an adaptation called **anhydrobiosis** ("life without water"). Among the most striking examples are the tardigrades, or water bears, tiny invertebrates less than 1 mm long (Figure 44.5). In their active, hydrated state, they contain about 85% water by weight, but they can dehydrate to less than 2% water and survive in an inactive state, dry as dust, for a decade or more. Just add water, and within hours the rehydrated tardigrades are moving about and feeding.

Anhydrobiosis requires adaptations that keep cell membranes intact. Researchers are just beginning to learn how

(a) Hydrated tardigrade

(b) Dehydrated tardigrade

50 μm

▲ **Figure 44.5 Anhydrobiosis.** Tardigrades (SEM images) inhabit temporary ponds as well as droplets of water in soil and on moist plants.

tardigrades survive drying out, but studies of anhydrobiotic roundworms (phylum Nematoda; see Chapter 33) show that desiccated individuals contain large amounts of sugars. In particular, a disaccharide called trehalose seems to protect the cells by replacing the water that is normally associated with proteins and membrane lipids. Many insects that survive freezing in the winter also use trehalose as a membrane protectant, as do some plants resistant to desiccation.

Recently, scientists began applying lessons learned from the study of anhydrobiosis to the preservation of biological materials. Traditionally, samples of protein, DNA, and cells have been kept in ultracold freezers (−80°C), consuming large amounts of energy and space. Now, however, the manufacture of materials modeled after the protectants found in anhydrobiotic species has enabled such samples to be stored in compact chambers at room temperature.

Land Animals

The threat of dehydration is a major regulatory problem for terrestrial plants and animals. Adaptations that reduce water loss are key to survival on land. Much as a waxy cuticle contributes to the success of land plants, the body coverings of most terrestrial animals help prevent dehydration. Examples are the waxy layers of insect exoskeletons, the shells of land snails, and the layers of dead, keratinized skin cells covering most terrestrial vertebrates, including humans. Many terrestrial animals, especially desert-dwellers, are nocturnal, which reduces evaporative water loss because of the lower temperature and higher humidity of night air.

Despite these and other adaptations, most terrestrial animals lose water through many routes: in urine and feces, across their skin, and from the surfaces of gas exchange organs. Land animals maintain water balance by drinking and eating moist foods and by producing water metabolically through cellular respiration.

A number of desert animals are well enough adapted for minimizing water loss that they can survive for long periods of time without drinking. Camels, for example, can lose 25% of their body water and survive. (In contrast, a human who loses half this amount of body water will die from heart failure.) In the Scientific Skills Exercise, you can examine water balance in another desert species, the sandy inland mouse.

Energetics of Osmoregulation

Maintaining an osmolarity difference between an animal's body and its external environment carries an energy cost. Because diffusion tends to equalize concentrations in a system, osmoregulators must expend energy to maintain the osmotic gradients that cause water to move in or out. They do so by using active transport to manipulate solute concentrations in their body fluids.

Describing and Interpreting Quantitative Data

How Do Desert Mice Maintain Osmotic Homeostasis? The sandy inland mouse, recently reclassified as *Pseudomys hermannsburgensis*, is an Australian desert mammal that can survive indefinitely on a diet of dried seeds without drinking water. To study this species' adaptations to its arid environment, researchers conducted a laboratory experiment in which they controlled access to water. In this exercise, you will analyze some of the data from the experiment.

How the Experiment Was Done Nine captured mice were kept in an environmentally controlled room and given birdseed (10% water by weight) to eat. In part A of the study, the mice had unlimited access to tap water for drinking; in part B of the study, the mice were not given any drinking water for 35 days, similar to conditions in their natural habitat. At the end of parts A and B, the researchers measured the osmolarity and urea concentration of the urine and blood of each mouse. The mice were also weighed three times a week.

Data from the Experiment

Access to Water	Mean Osmolarity (mOsm/L)		Mean Urea Concentration (m*M*)	
	Urine	Blood	Urine	Blood
Part A: Unlimited	490	350	330	7.6
Part B: None	4,700	320	2,700	11

In part A, the mice drank about 33% of their body weight each day. The change in body weight during the study was negligible for all mice.

Interpret the Data

1. In words, describe how the data differ between the unlimited water and no-water conditions for the following: (a) osmolarity of urine; (b) osmolarity of blood; (c) urea concentration in urine; (d) urea concentration in blood. (e) Does this data set provide evidence of homeostatic regulation? Explain.

2. (a) Calculate the ratio of urine osmolarity to blood osmolarity for mice with unlimited access to water. (b) Calculate this ratio for mice with no access to water. (c) What conclusion would you draw from these ratios?

3. If the amount of urine produced were different in the two conditions, how would that affect your calculation? Explain.

(MB) A version of this Scientific Skills Exercise can be assigned in MasteringBiology.

Data from R. E. MacMillen et al., Water economy and energy metabolism of the sandy inland mouse, *Leggadina hermannsburgensis*, *Journal of Mammalogy* 53:529–539 (1972).

The energy cost of osmoregulation depends on how different an animal's osmolarity is from its surroundings, how easily water and solutes can move across the animal's surface, and how much work is required to pump solutes across the membrane. Osmoregulation accounts for 5% or more of the resting metabolic rate of many fishes. For brine shrimp, small crustaceans that live in extremely salty lakes, the gradient between internal and external osmolarity is very large, and the cost of osmoregulation is correspondingly high—as much as 30% of the resting metabolic rate.

The energy cost to an animal of maintaining water and salt balance is minimized by having body fluids that are adapted to the salinity of the animal's habitat. Thus, the body fluids of most animals that live in fresh water (which has an osmolarity of 0.5–15 mOsm/L) have lower solute concentrations than the body fluids of their closest relatives that live in seawater (1,000 mOsm/L). For instance, whereas marine molluscs have body fluids with solute concentrations of approximately 1,000 mOsm/L, some freshwater molluscs maintain the osmolarity of their body fluids at just 40 mOsm/L. In each case, minimizing the osmotic difference between body fluids and the surrounding environment decreases the energy cost of osmoregulation.

Transport Epithelia in Osmoregulation

The ultimate function of osmoregulation is to control solute concentrations in cells, but most animals do this indirectly by managing the solute content of an internal body fluid that bathes the cells. In insects and other animals with an open circulatory system, the fluid surrounding cells is hemolymph. In vertebrates and other animals with a closed circulatory system, the cells are bathed in an interstitial fluid that contains a mixture of solutes controlled indirectly by the blood. Maintaining the composition of such fluids depends on structures ranging from individual cells that regulate solute movement to complex organs such as the vertebrate kidney.

In most animals, osmoregulation and metabolic waste disposal rely on **transport epithelia**—one or more layers of epithelial cells specialized for moving particular solutes in controlled amounts in specific directions. Transport epithelia are typically arranged into complex tubular networks with extensive surface areas. Some transport epithelia face the outside environment directly, while others line channels connected to the outside by an opening on the body surface.

The transport epithelium that enables the albatross and other marine birds to survive on seawater remained undiscovered for many years. To explore this question, researchers gave captive marine birds only seawater to drink. Although very little salt appeared in the birds' urine, fluid dripping from the tip of their beaks was a concentrated solution of salt (NaCl). The source of this solution was a pair of nasal salt glands (Figure 44.6). Salt glands, which are also found in sea turtles and marine iguanas, use active transport of ions to secrete a fluid much saltier than the ocean. Even though drinking seawater brings in a lot of salt, the salt gland enables these marine vertebrates to achieve a net gain of water. By contrast, humans who drink a given volume of seawater must use a *greater* volume of water to excrete the salt load, with the result that they become dehydrated.

Transport epithelia that function in maintaining water balance also often function in disposal of metabolic wastes. We'll see examples of this coordinated function in our upcoming consideration of earthworm and insect excretory systems as well as the vertebrate kidney.

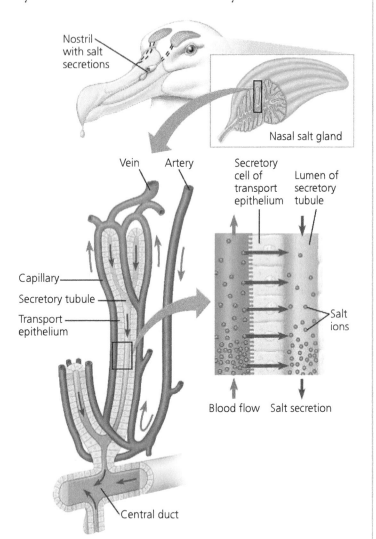

▲ Figure 44.6 **Salt secretion in the nasal glands of a marine bird.** Salt is transported from the blood into secretory tubules, which drain into central ducts leading to the nostrils.

CONCEPT 44.2

An animal's nitrogenous wastes reflect its phylogeny and habitat

Because most metabolic wastes must be dissolved in water to be excreted from the body, the type and quantity of an animal's waste products may have a large impact on its water balance. In this regard, some of the most significant waste products are the nitrogenous breakdown products of proteins and nucleic acids. When proteins and nucleic acids are broken apart for energy or converted to carbohydrates or fats, enzymes remove nitrogen in the form of **ammonia** (NH_3). Ammonia is very toxic, in part because its ion, ammonium (NH_4^+), can interfere with oxidative phosphorylation. Although some animals excrete ammonia directly, many species expend energy to convert it to less toxic compounds prior to excretion.

Forms of Nitrogenous Waste

Animals excrete nitrogenous wastes as ammonia, urea, or uric acid (Figure 44.7). These different forms vary significantly in their toxicity and the energy costs of producing them.

Ammonia

Animals that excrete nitrogenous wastes as ammonia need access to lots of water because ammonia can be tolerated only at very low concentrations. Therefore, ammonia excretion is most common in aquatic species. In many invertebrates, ammonia release occurs across the whole body surface.

Urea

Although ammonia excretion works well in many aquatic species, it is much less suitable for land animals. Ammonia is so toxic that it can be transported and excreted only in large volumes of very dilute solutions. Most terrestrial animals and many marine species simply do not have access to sufficient water to routinely excrete ammonia. Instead, they mainly excrete a different nitrogenous waste, **urea**. In

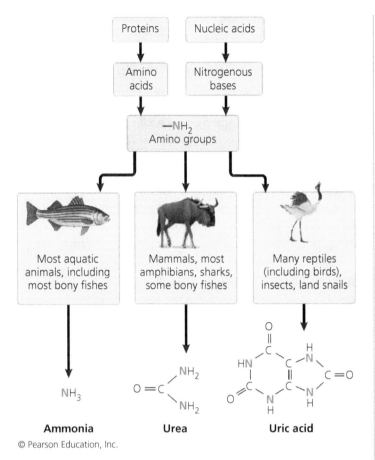

Ammonia   Urea   Uric acid

© Pearson Education, Inc.

▲ **Figure 44.7 Forms of nitrogenous waste.**

vertebrates, urea is the product of a metabolic cycle that combines ammonia with carbon dioxide in the liver.

The main advantage of urea is its very low toxicity. The main disadvantage is its energy cost: Animals must expend energy to produce urea from ammonia. From a bioenergetic standpoint, we would predict that animals that spend part of their lives in water and part on land would switch between excreting ammonia (thereby saving energy) and excreting urea (reducing excretory water loss). Indeed, many amphibians excrete mainly ammonia when they are aquatic tadpoles and switch largely to urea excretion when they become land-dwelling adults.

Uric Acid

Insects, land snails, and many reptiles, including birds, excrete **uric acid** as their primary nitrogenous waste. (Bird droppings, or *guano*, are a mixture of white uric acid and brown feces.) Uric acid is relatively nontoxic and does not readily dissolve in water. It therefore can be excreted as a semisolid paste with very little water loss. However, uric acid is even more energetically expensive than urea, requiring considerable ATP for synthesis from ammonia.

While not primarily uric acid producers, humans and some other animals generate a small amount of uric acid from purine breakdown. Diseases that alter this process reflect problems that can arise when a metabolic product is

insoluble. For example, a genetic defect in purine metabolism predisposes Dalmatian dogs to form uric acid stones in their bladder. In humans, adult males are particularly susceptible to *gout*, a painful joint inflammation caused by deposits of uric acid crystals. Meals containing purine-rich animal tissues can increase the inflammation. Some dinosaurs appear to have been similarly affected: Fossilized bones of *Tyrannosaurus rex* exhibit joint damage characteristic of gout.

The Influence of Evolution and Environment on Nitrogenous Wastes

EVOLUTION In general, the kind of nitrogenous wastes an animal excretes depends on both the species' evolutionary history (phylogeny) and its habitat, especially the availability of water. For example, terrestrial turtles (which often live in dry areas) excrete mainly uric acid, whereas aquatic turtles excrete both urea and ammonia. Another factor affecting the primary type of nitrogenous waste produced by a particular group of animals is the immediate environment of the animal egg. For example, soluble wastes can diffuse out of a shell-less amphibian egg or be carried away from a mammalian embryo by the mother's blood. However, the shelled eggs produced by birds and other reptiles (see Figure 34.25) are permeable to gases but not to liquids, which means that soluble nitrogenous wastes released by an embryo would be trapped within the egg and could accumulate to dangerous levels. (Although urea is much less harmful than ammonia, it is toxic at very high concentrations.) Using uric acid as a waste product conveys a selective advantage because it precipitates out of solution and can be stored within the egg as a harmless solid left behind when the animal hatches.

Regardless of the type of nitrogenous waste, the amount produced is coupled to the animal's energy budget. Endotherms, which use energy at high rates, eat more food and produce more nitrogenous waste than ectotherms. The amount of nitrogenous waste is also linked to diet. Predators, which derive much of their energy from protein, excrete more nitrogen than animals that rely mainly on lipids or carbohydrates as energy sources.

Having surveyed the forms of nitrogenous waste and their interrelationship with evolutionary lineage, habitat, and energy consumption, we'll turn next to the processes and systems animals use to excrete these and other wastes.

CONCEPT CHECK **44.2**

1. What advantage does uric acid offer as a nitrogenous waste in arid environments?

2. **WHAT IF?** Suppose a bird and a human both have gout. Why might reducing purine in their diets help the human much more than the bird?

For suggested answers, see Appendix A.

CONCEPT 44.3

Diverse excretory systems are variations on a tubular theme

Whether an animal lives on land, in salt water, or in fresh water, water balance depends on the regulation of solute movement between internal fluids and the external environment. Much of this movement is handled by excretory systems. These systems are central to homeostasis because they dispose of metabolic wastes and control body fluid composition.

Excretory Processes

Animals across a wide range of species produce a fluid waste called urine through the basic steps shown in **Figure 44.8**. In the first step, body fluid (blood, coelomic fluid, or hemolymph) is brought in contact with the selectively permeable membrane of a transport epithelium. In most cases, hydrostatic pressure (blood pressure in many animals) drives a process of **filtration**. Cells, as well as proteins and other large molecules, cannot cross the epithelial membrane and remain in the body fluid. In contrast, water and small solutes, such as

salts, sugars, amino acids, and nitrogenous wastes, cross the membrane, forming a solution called the **filtrate**.

The filtrate is converted to a waste fluid by the specific transport of materials into or out of the filtrate. The process of selective **reabsorption** recovers useful molecules and water from the filtrate and returns them to the body fluid. Valuable solutes—including glucose, certain salts, vitamins, hormones, and amino acids—are reabsorbed by active transport. Nonessential solutes and wastes are left in the filtrate or are added to it by selective **secretion**, which also occurs by active transport. The pumping of various solutes adjusts the osmotic movement of water into or out of the filtrate. In the last step—excretion—the processed filtrate containing nitrogenous wastes is released from the body as urine.

Survey of Excretory Systems

The systems that perform the basic excretory functions vary widely among animal groups. However, they are generally built on a complex network of tubules that provide a large surface area for the exchange of water and solutes, including nitrogenous wastes. We'll examine the excretory systems of flatworms, earthworms, insects, and vertebrates as examples of evolutionary variations on tubule networks.

Protonephridia

As illustrated in **Figure 44.9**, the excretory systems of flatworms (phylum Platyhelminthes) consist of units called

① Filtration. The excretory tubule collects a filtrate from the blood. Water and solutes are forced by blood pressure across the selectively permeable membranes of a cluster of capillaries and into the excretory tubule.

② Reabsorption. The transport epithelium reclaims valuable substances from the filtrate and returns them to the body fluids.

③ Secretion. Other substances, such as toxins and excess ions, are extracted from body fluids and added to the contents of the excretory tubule.

④ Excretion. The altered filtrate (urine) leaves the system and the body.

Capillary — Filtrate — Excretory tubule — Urine

▲ **Figure 44.8 Key steps of excretory system function: an overview.** Most excretory systems produce a filtrate by pressure-filtering body fluids and then modify the filtrate's contents. This diagram is modeled after the vertebrate excretory system.

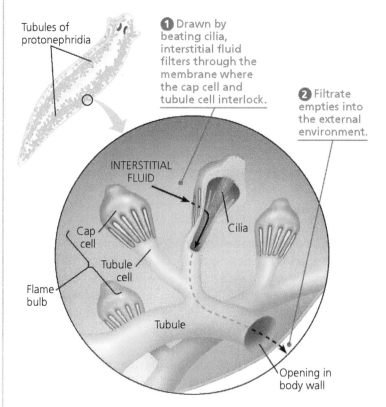

Tubules of protonephridia

① Drawn by beating cilia, interstitial fluid filters through the membrane where the cap cell and tubule cell interlock.

② Filtrate empties into the external environment.

INTERSTITIAL FLUID

Cap cell — Cilia — Tubule cell — Flame bulb — Tubule — Opening in body wall

▲ **Figure 44.9 Protonephridia in a planarian.**

protonephridia (singular, *protonephridium*), which form a network of dead-end tubules. The tubules, which are connected to external openings, branch throughout the flatworm body, which lacks a coelom (body cavity). Cellular units called flame bulbs cap the branches of each protonephridium. Consisting of a tubule cell and a cap cell, each flame bulb has a tuft of cilia projecting into the tubule. During filtration, the beating of the cilia draws water and solutes from the interstitial fluid through the flame bulb, releasing filtrate into the tubule network. (The name *flame bulb* derives from the moving cilia's resemblance to a flickering flame.) The processed filtrate moves outward through the tubules and empties as urine into the environment. The urine of freshwater flatworms is low in solutes, helping balance the osmotic uptake of water from the environment.

Protonephridia are also found in rotifers, some annelids, mollusc larvae, and lancelets (see Figure 34.4). Among these animals, the function of the protonephridia varies. In the freshwater flatworms, protonephridia serve chiefly in osmoregulation. Most metabolic wastes diffuse out of the animal across the body surface or are excreted into the gastrovascular cavity and eliminated through the mouth (see Figure 33.10). However, in some parasitic flatworms, which are isoosmotic to the surrounding fluids of their host organisms, the main function of protonephridia is the disposal of nitrogenous wastes. Natural selection has thus adapted protonephridia to different tasks in different environments.

Metanephridia

Most annelids, such as earthworms, have **metanephridia** (singular, *metanephridium*), excretory organs that collect fluid directly from the coelom (**Figure 44.10**). Each segment

of an annelid has a pair of metanephridia, which are immersed in coelomic fluid and enveloped by a capillary network. A ciliated funnel surrounds the internal opening of each metanephridium. As the cilia beat, fluid is drawn into a collecting tubule, which includes a storage bladder that opens to the outside.

The metanephridia of an earthworm have both excretory and osmoregulatory functions. As urine moves along the tubule, the transport epithelium bordering the lumen reabsorbs most solutes and returns them to the blood in the capillaries. Nitrogenous wastes remain in the tubule and are excreted to the environment. Earthworms inhabit damp soil and therefore usually experience a net uptake of water by osmosis through their skin. Their metanephridia balance the water influx by producing urine that is dilute (hypoosmotic to body fluids).

Malpighian Tubules

Insects and other terrestrial arthropods have organs called **Malpighian tubules** that remove nitrogenous wastes and that also function in osmoregulation (**Figure 44.11**). The Malpighian tubules extend from dead-end tips immersed in hemolymph to openings into the digestive tract. The filtration step common to other excretory systems is absent. Instead, the transport epithelium that lines the tubules secretes certain solutes, including nitrogenous wastes, from the hemolymph into the lumen of the tubule. Water follows the solutes into the tubule by osmosis, and the fluid then

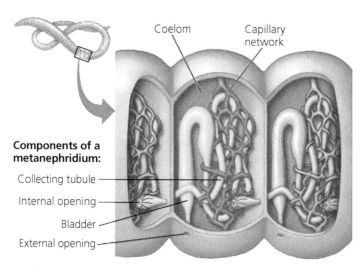

▲ **Figure 44.10 Metanephridia of an earthworm.** Each segment of the worm contains a pair of metanephridia, which collect coelomic fluid from the adjacent anterior segment. The region highlighted in yellow illustrates the organization of one metanephridium of a pair; the other would be behind it.

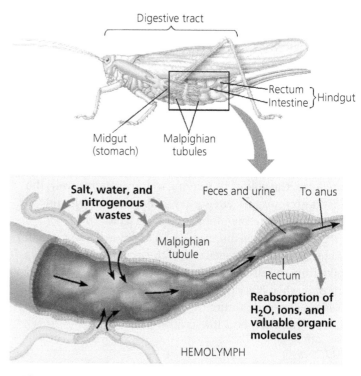

▲ **Figure 44.11 Malpighian tubules of insects.** Malpighian tubules are outpocketings of the digestive tract that remove nitrogenous wastes and function in osmoregulation.

Exploring The Mammalian Excretory System

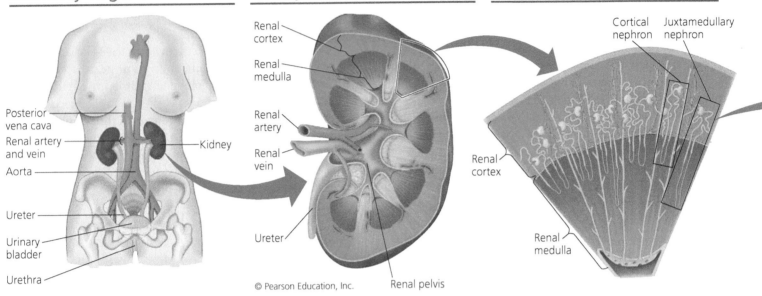

Excretory Organs

In humans, the excretory system consists of **kidneys**, a pair of organs each about 10 cm in length, as well as organs for transporting and storing urine. Urine produced by each kidney exits through a duct called the **ureter**; the two ureters drain into a common sac called the **urinary bladder**. During urination, urine is expelled from the bladder through a tube called the **urethra**, which empties to the outside near the vagina in females and through the penis in males. Sphincter muscles near the junction of the urethra and bladder regulate urination.

Kidney Structure

Each kidney has an outer **renal cortex** and an inner **renal medulla**. Both regions are supplied with blood by a renal artery and drained by a renal vein. Within the cortex and medulla lie tightly packed excretory tubules and associated blood vessels. The excretory tubules carry and process a filtrate produced from the blood entering the kidney. Nearly all of the fluid in the filtrate is reabsorbed into the surrounding blood vessels and exits the kidney in the renal vein. The remaining fluid leaves the excretory tubules as urine, is collected in the inner **renal pelvis**, and exits the kidney via the ureter.

Nephron Types

Weaving back and forth across the renal cortex and medulla are the **nephrons**, the functional units of the vertebrate kidney. Of the roughly 1 million nephrons in a human kidney, 85% are **cortical nephrons**, which reach only a short distance into the medulla. The remainder, the **juxtamedullary nephrons**, extend deep into the medulla. Juxtamedullary nephrons are essential for production of urine that is hyperosmotic to body fluids, a key adaptation for water conservation in mammals.

passes into the rectum. There, most solutes are pumped back into the hemolymph, and water reabsorption by osmosis follows. The nitrogenous wastes—mainly insoluble uric acid—are eliminated as nearly dry matter along with the feces. Capable of conserving water very effectively, the insect excretory system is a key adaptation contributing to these animals' tremendous success on land.

Some terrestrial insects have an additional adaptation for water balance: The rectal end of their gut enables water uptake from the air. Although some species absorb water from air only when it is very humid, others, such as fleas (genus *Xenopsylla*), can capture water from the atmosphere when relative humidity is as low as 50%.

Kidneys

In vertebrates and some other chordates, a specialized organ called the kidney functions in both osmoregulation and excretion. Like the excretory organs of most animal phyla,

kidneys consist of tubules. The numerous tubules of these compact organs are arranged in a highly organized manner and are closely associated with a network of capillaries. The vertebrate excretory system also includes ducts and other structures that carry urine from the tubules out of the kidney and, eventually, the body.

Vertebrate kidneys are typically nonsegmented. However, hagfishes, which are jawless vertebrates (see Chapter 34), have kidneys with segmentally arranged excretory tubules. Because hagfishes and other vertebrates share a common chordate ancestor, it is possible that the excretory structures of vertebrate ancestors also were segmented.

We conclude this introduction to excretory systems with an exploration of the anatomy of the mammalian kidney and associated structures (**Figure 44.12**). Familiarizing yourself with the terms and diagrams in this figure will provide you with a solid foundation for learning about filtrate processing in the kidney, our focus in the next concept.

Nephron Organization

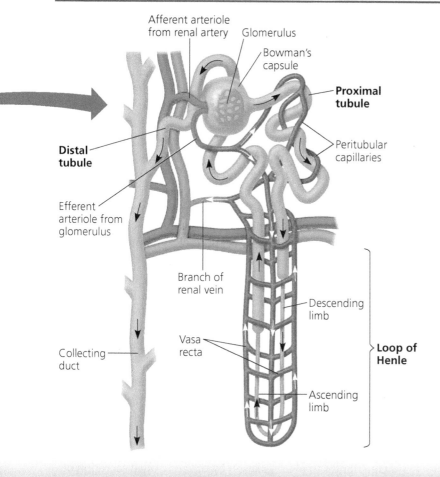

Afferent arteriole
from renal artery

Glomerulus

Bowman's
capsule

**Proximal
tubule**

Peritubular
capillaries

**Distal
tubule**

Efferent
arteriole from
glomerulus

Branch of
renal vein

Descending
limb

Vasa
recta

**Loop of
Henle**

Collecting
duct

Ascending
limb

Each nephron consists of a single long tubule as well as a ball of capillaries called the **glomerulus**. The blind end of the tubule forms a cup-shaped swelling, called **Bowman's capsule**, which surrounds the glomerulus. Filtrate is formed when blood pressure forces fluid from the blood in the glomerulus into the lumen of Bowman's capsule. Processing occurs as the filtrate passes through three major regions of the nephron: the **proximal tubule**, the **loop of Henle** (a hairpin turn with a descending limb and an ascending limb), and the **distal tubule**. A **collecting duct** receives processed filtrate from many nephrons and transports it to the renal pelvis.

Each nephron is supplied with blood by an *afferent arteriole*, an offshoot of the renal artery that branches and forms the capillaries of the glomerulus. The capillaries converge as they leave the glomerulus, forming an *efferent arteriole*. Branches of this vessel form the **peritubular capillaries**, which surround the proximal and distal tubules. Other branches extend downward and form the **vasa recta**, hairpin-shaped capillaries that serve the renal medulla, including the long loop of Henle of juxtamedullary nephrons.

▶ In this SEM of densely packed blood vessels from a human kidney, arterioles and peritubular capillaries appear pink; the glomeruli appear yellow.

200 μm

CONCEPT CHECK 44.3

1. Compare and contrast the ways that metabolic waste products enter the excretory systems of flatworms, earthworms, and insects.

2. What is the function of the filtration step in excretory systems?

3. Where and how does filtrate originate in the vertebrate kidney, and by what two routes do the components of the filtrate exit the kidney?

4. **WHAT IF?** Kidney failure is often treated by hemodialysis, in which blood diverted out of the body is filtered and then allowed to flow on one side of a semipermeable membrane. Fluid called dialysate flows in the opposite direction on the other side of the membrane. In replacing the reabsorption and secretion of solutes in a functional kidney, the makeup of the starting dialysate is critical. What initial solute composition would work well?

For suggested answers, see Appendix A.

CONCEPT 44.4

The nephron is organized for stepwise processing of blood filtrate

We'll continue our exploration of the nephron with a discussion of filtrate processing. We'll then focus on how tubules, capillaries, and surrounding tissue function together.

The porous capillaries and specialized cells of Bowman's capsule are permeable to water and small solutes, but not blood cells or large molecules, such as plasma proteins. Thus, the filtrate produced in the capsule contains salts, glucose, amino acids, vitamins, nitrogenous wastes, and other small molecules. Because such molecules pass freely between glomerular capillaries and Bowman's capsule, the concentrations of these substances in the initial filtrate are the same as those in blood plasma.

From Blood Filtrate to Urine: *A Closer Look*

In this section, we'll follow filtrate along its path in the nephron and collecting duct, examining how each region contributes to the stepwise processing of filtrate into urine. The circled numbers correspond to the numbers in **Figure 44.13**.

❶ Proximal tubule. Reabsorption in the proximal tubule is critical for the recapture of ions, water, and valuable nutrients from the huge volume of initial filtrate. NaCl (salt) in the filtrate enters the cells of the transport epithelium by facilitated diffusion and cotransport mechanisms (see Figures 7.14 and 7.18). The epithelial cells actively transport Na^+ into the interstitial fluid, and this transfer of positive charge out of the tubule drives the passive transport of Cl^-.

As salt moves from the filtrate to the interstitial fluid, water follows by osmosis. The salt and water then diffuse from the interstitial fluid into the peritubular capillaries. Glucose, amino acids, potassium ions (K^+), and other essential substances are also actively or passively transported from the filtrate to the interstitial fluid and then into the peritubular capillaries.

Processing of filtrate in the proximal tubule helps maintain a relatively constant pH in body fluids. Cells of the transport epithelium secrete H^+ into the lumen of the tubule but also synthesize and secrete ammonia, which acts as a buffer to trap H^+ in the form of ammonium ions (NH_4^+). The more acidic the filtrate is, the more ammonia the cells produce and secrete, and a mammal's urine usually contains some ammonia from this source (even though most nitrogenous waste is excreted as urea). The proximal tubules also reabsorb about 90% of the buffer bicarbonate (HCO_3^-) from the filtrate, contributing further to pH balance in body fluids.

As the filtrate passes through the proximal tubule, materials to be excreted become concentrated. Many wastes leave the body fluids during the nonselective filtration process and remain in the filtrate while water and salts are reabsorbed. Urea, for example, is reabsorbed at a much lower rate than are salt and water. In addition, some materials are actively secreted into the filtrate from surrounding tissues. For example, drugs and toxins that have been processed in the liver pass from the peritubular capillaries into the interstitial fluid. These molecules are then actively secreted by the transport epithelium into the lumen of the proximal tubule.

❷ Descending limb of the loop of Henle. Reabsorption of water continues as the filtrate moves into the descending limb of the loop of Henle. Here numerous water channels formed by **aquaporin** proteins make the transport epithelium freely permeable to water. In contrast, there are almost no channels for salt and other small solutes, resulting in very low permeability for these substances.

For water to move out of the tubule by osmosis, the interstitial fluid bathing the tubule must be hyperosmotic to the filtrate. This condition is met along the entire length of the descending limb, because the osmolarity of the interstitial fluid increases progressively from the outer cortex to the inner medulla of the kidney. As a result, the filtrate loses water and increases in solute concentration all along its journey down the descending limb.

❸ Ascending limb of the loop of Henle. The filtrate reaches the tip of the loop and then returns to the cortex in the ascending limb. Unlike the descending limb, the ascending limb has a transport epithelium that lacks water channels. Consequently, the epithelial membrane that faces the filtrate in the ascending limb is impermeable to water.

The ascending limb has two specialized regions: a thin segment near the loop tip and a thick segment adjacent to the distal tubule. As filtrate ascends in the thin segment, NaCl, which became concentrated in the descending limb, diffuses out of the permeable tubule into the interstitial fluid. This movement of NaCl out of the tubule helps maintain the osmolarity of the interstitial fluid in the medulla. In the thick segment of the ascending limb, the movement of NaCl out of the filtrate continues. Here, however, the epithelium actively transports NaCl into the interstitial fluid. As a result of losing salt but not water, the filtrate becomes progressively more dilute as it moves up to the cortex in the ascending limb of the loop.

❹ Distal tubule. The distal tubule plays a key role in regulating the K^+ and NaCl concentration of body fluids. This regulation involves variation in the amount of K^+ secreted into the filtrate as well as the amount of NaCl reabsorbed from the filtrate. Like the proximal tubule, the distal tubule contributes to pH regulation by the controlled secretion of H^+ and reabsorption of HCO_3^-.

❺ Collecting duct. The collecting duct carries the filtrate through the medulla to the renal pelvis. Final processing of the filtrate by the transport epithelium of the collecting duct forms the urine.

Under normal conditions, approximately 1,600 L of blood flows through a pair of human kidneys each day. Processing of this enormous traffic of blood by the nephrons and collecting ducts yields about 180 L of initial filtrate. Of this, about 99% of the water and nearly all of the sugars, amino acids, vitamins, and other organic nutrients are reabsorbed into the blood, leaving only about 1.5 L of urine to be transported to the bladder.

As filtrate passes along the transport epithelium of the collecting duct, hormonal control of permeability and transport determines the extent to which the urine becomes concentrated.

When the kidneys are conserving water, aquaporin channels in the collecting duct allow water molecules to cross the epithelium. At the same time, the epithelium remains impermeable to salt and, in the renal cortex, to urea. As the collecting duct traverses the gradient of osmolarity in the

Filtrate

H_2O
Salts (NaCl and others)
HCO_3^-
H^+
Urea
Glucose, amino acids
Some drugs

Key

→ Active transport
→ Passive transport

▲ **Figure 44.13 The nephron and collecting duct: regional functions of the transport epithelium.** The numbered regions in this diagram are keyed to the circled numbers in the text discussion of kidney function.

? *Some cells lining tubules in the kidney maintain normal cell volume by synthesizing organic solutes. Where in the kidney would you expect to find these cells? Explain.*

kidney, the filtrate becomes increasingly concentrated, losing more and more water by osmosis to the hyperosmotic interstitial fluid. In the inner medulla, the duct becomes permeable to urea. Because of the high urea concentration in the filtrate at this point, some urea diffuses out of the duct and into the interstitial fluid. Along with NaCl, this urea contributes to the high osmolarity of the interstitial fluid in the medulla. The net result is urine that is hyperosmotic to the general body fluids.

When producing dilute rather than concentrated urine, the kidney actively reabsorbs salts without allowing water to follow by osmosis. At these times, the epithelium lacks aquaporin channels, and NaCl is actively transported out of filtrate. As we'll see shortly, the state of the collecting duct epithelium is controlled by hormones that together maintain homeostasis for osmolarity, blood pressure, and blood volume.

Solute Gradients and Water Conservation

The mammalian kidney's ability to conserve water is a key terrestrial adaptation. In humans, the osmolarity of blood is about 300 mOsm/L, but the kidney can excrete urine up to four times as concentrated—about 1,200 mOsm/L. Some mammals can do even better: Australian hopping mice, small marsupials that live in dry desert regions, can produce urine with an osmolarity of 9,300 mOsm/L, 25 times as concentrated as the animal's blood.

In a mammalian kidney, the production of hyperosmotic urine is possible only because considerable energy is expended for the active transport of solutes against concentration gradients. The nephrons—particularly the loops of Henle—can be thought of as energy-consuming machines that produce an osmolarity gradient suitable for extracting water from the filtrate in the collecting duct. The primary solutes affecting osmolarity are NaCl, which is concentrated in the renal medulla by the loop of Henle, and urea, which passes across the epithelium of the collecting duct in the inner medulla.

Concentrating Urine in the Mammalian Kidney

To better understand the physiology of the mammalian kidney as a water-conserving organ, let's retrace the flow of filtrate through the excretory tubule. This time, let's focus on how the juxtamedullary nephrons maintain an osmolarity gradient in the tissues that surround the loop of Henle and how they use that gradient to excrete a hyperosmotic urine (Figure 44.14). Filtrate passing from Bowman's capsule to the proximal tubule has about the same osmolarity as blood. A large amount of water *and* salt is reabsorbed from the filtrate as it flows through the proximal tubule in the renal cortex. As a result, the filtrate's volume decreases substantially, but its osmolarity remains about the same.

As the filtrate flows from cortex to medulla in the descending limb of the loop of Henle, water leaves the tubule by osmosis. Solutes, including NaCl, become more concentrated, increasing the osmolarity of the filtrate. The highest osmolarity (about 1,200 mOsm/L) occurs at the elbow of the loop of Henle. This maximizes the diffusion of salt out of the tubule as the filtrate rounds the curve and enters the ascending limb, which is permeable to salt but not to water. NaCl diffusing from the ascending limb helps maintain a high osmolarity in the interstitial fluid of the renal medulla.

Notice that the loop of Henle has several qualities of a countercurrent system, such as the systems that maximize oxygen absorption by fish gills (see Figure 42.21) or reduce heat loss in endotherms (see Figure 40.13). In those cases, the countercurrent mechanisms involve passive movement along either an oxygen concentration gradient or a heat gradient. In contrast, the countercurrent system involving the loop of Henle expends energy to actively transport NaCl from the filtrate in the upper part of the ascending limb of the loop. Such countercurrent systems, which expend energy to create concentration gradients, are called **countercurrent multiplier systems**. The countercurrent multiplier system involving the loop of Henle maintains a high salt concentration in the interior of the kidney, enabling the kidney to form concentrated urine.

What prevents the capillaries of the vasa recta from dissipating the gradient by carrying away the high concentration of NaCl in the medulla's interstitial fluid? As shown in Figure 44.12, the descending and ascending vessels of the vasa recta carry blood in opposite directions through the kidney's osmolarity gradient. As the descending vessel conveys blood toward the inner medulla, water is lost from the blood and NaCl is gained by diffusion. These net fluxes are reversed as blood flows back toward the cortex in the ascending vessel,

▶ **Figure 44.14 How the human kidney concentrates urine: the two-solute model.** Two solutes contribute to the osmolarity of the interstitial fluid: NaCl (used as shorthand here to refer collectively to Na$^+$ and Cl$^-$) and urea. The loop of Henle maintains the interstitial gradient of NaCl, which increases continuously in concentration from the cortex to the inner medulla. Urea diffuses into the interstitial fluid of the medulla from the collecting duct (although most of the urea in the filtrate remains in the collecting duct and is excreted). The filtrate makes three trips between the cortex and medulla: first down, then up, and then down again in the collecting duct. As the filtrate flows in the collecting duct past interstitial fluid of increasing osmolarity, more water moves out of the duct by osmosis. The loss of water concentrates the solutes, including urea, that will be excreted in the urine.

WHAT IF? *The drug furosemide blocks the cotransporters for Na$^+$ and Cl$^-$ in the ascending limb of the loop of Henle. What effect would you expect this drug to have on urine volume?*

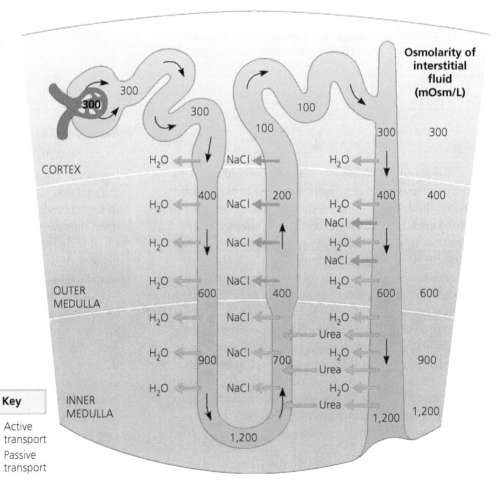

with water reentering the blood and salt diffusing out. Thus, the vasa recta can supply the kidney with nutrients and other important substances carried by the blood without interfering with the osmolarity gradient in the inner and outer medulla.

The countercurrent-like characteristics of the loop of Henle and the vasa recta help to generate the steep osmotic gradient between the medulla and cortex. However, diffusion will eventually eliminate any osmotic gradient within animal tissue unless gradient formation is supported by an expenditure of energy. In the kidney, this expenditure largely occurs in the thick segment of the ascending limb of the loop of Henle, where NaCl is actively transported out of the tubule. Even with the benefits of countercurrent exchange, this process—along with other renal active transport systems—consumes considerable ATP. Thus, for its size, the kidney has one of the highest metabolic rates of any organ.

As a result of active transport of NaCl out of the thick segment of the ascending limb, the filtrate is actually hypoosmotic to body fluids by the time it reaches the distal tubule. Next the filtrate descends again toward the medulla, this time in the collecting duct, which is permeable to water but not to salt. Therefore, osmosis extracts water from the filtrate as it passes from cortex to medulla and encounters interstitial fluid of increasing osmolarity. This process concentrates salt, urea, and other solutes in the filtrate. Some urea passes out of the lower portion of the collecting duct and contributes to the high interstitial osmolarity of the inner medulla. (This urea is recycled by diffusion into the loop of Henle, but continual leakage from the collecting duct maintains a high interstitial urea concentration.) When the kidney concentrates urine maximally, the urine reaches 1,200 mOsm/L, the osmolarity of the interstitial fluid in the inner medulla. Although *isoosmotic* to the inner medulla's interstitial fluid, the urine is *hyperosmotic* to blood and interstitial fluid elsewhere in the body. This high osmolarity allows the solutes remaining in the urine to be excreted from the body with minimal water loss.

Adaptations of the Vertebrate Kidney to Diverse Environments

EVOLUTION Vertebrates occupy habitats ranging from rain forests to deserts and from some of the saltiest bodies of water to the nearly pure waters of high mountain lakes. Variations in nephron structure and function equip the kidneys of different vertebrates for osmoregulation in their various habitats. Of particular importance are the relative numbers of juxtamedullary and cortical nephrons (see Figure 44.12) and the length of the loop of Henle in the juxtamedullary nephrons. The adaptive importance of these variations is made apparent by comparing species that inhabit a wide range of environments or by comparing the responses of different vertebrate groups to similar environmental conditions.

Mammals

The juxtamedullary nephron, with its urine-concentrating features, is a key adaptation to terrestrial life, enabling mammals to get rid of salts and nitrogenous wastes without squandering water. As we have seen, the remarkable ability of the mammalian kidney to produce hyperosmotic urine depends on the precise arrangement of the tubules and collecting ducts in the renal cortex and medulla. In this respect, the kidney is one of the clearest examples of how natural selection links the function of an organ to its structure.

Mammals that excrete the most hyperosmotic urine, such as Australian hopping mice, North American kangaroo rats, and other desert mammals, have many juxtamedullary nephrons with loops of Henle that extend deep into the medulla. Long loops maintain steep osmotic gradients in the kidney, resulting in urine becoming very concentrated as it passes from cortex to medulla in the collecting ducts.

In contrast, beavers, muskrats, and other aquatic mammals that spend much of their time in fresh water and rarely face problems of dehydration have mostly cortical nephrons, resulting in a much lower ability to concentrate urine. Terrestrial mammals living in moist conditions have loops of Henle of intermediate length and the capacity to produce urine intermediate in concentration to that produced by freshwater and desert mammals.

Case Study: *Kidney Function in the Vampire Bat*

The South American vampire bat shown in **Figure 44.15** illustrates the versatility of the mammalian kidney. This species feeds at night on the blood of large birds and mammals. The bat uses its sharp teeth to make a small incision in the prey's skin and then laps up blood from the wound (the prey

▲ **Figure 44.15 A vampire bat (*Desmodus rotundas*), a mammal with unique excretory challenges.**

is typically not seriously harmed). Anticoagulants in the bat's saliva prevent the blood from clotting.

A vampire bat may search for hours and fly long distances to locate a suitable victim. When it does find prey, it benefits from consuming as much blood as possible. Often drinking more than half its body mass, the bat is at risk of becoming too heavy to fly. As it feeds, however, the bat's kidneys excrete large volumes of dilute urine, up to 24% of body mass per hour. Having lost enough weight to take off, the bat can fly back to its roost in a cave or hollow tree, where it spends the day.

In the roost, the vampire bat faces a different regulatory problem. Most of the nutrition it derives from blood comes in the form of protein. Digesting proteins generates large quantities of urea, but roosting bats lack access to the drinking water necessary to dilute it. Instead, their kidneys shift to producing small quantities of highly concentrated urine (up to 4,600 mOsm/L), an adjustment that disposes of the urea load while conserving as much water as possible. The vampire bat's ability to alternate rapidly between producing large amounts of dilute urine and small amounts of very hyperosmotic urine is an essential part of its adaptation to an unusual food source.

Birds and Other Reptiles

Most birds, including the albatross (see Figure 44.1) and the ostrich (Figure 44.16), live in environments that are dehydrating. Like mammals, birds have kidneys with juxtamedullary nephrons that specialize in conserving water. However, the nephrons of birds have loops of Henle that extend less far into the medulla than those of mammals. Thus, bird kidneys cannot concentrate urine to the high osmolarities achieved by mammalian kidneys.

▲ Figure 44.16 An ostrich (*Struthio camelus*), an animal well adapted to its dry environment.

Although birds can produce hyperosmotic urine, their main water conservation adaptation is having uric acid as the nitrogenous waste molecule.

Other reptiles' kidneys have only cortical nephrons and produce urine that is isoosmotic or hypoosmotic to body fluids. However, the epithelium of the cloaca from which urine and feces leave the body conserves fluid by reabsorbing water from these wastes. Also like birds, most other reptiles excrete their nitrogenous wastes as uric acid.

Freshwater Fishes and Amphibians

Freshwater fishes are hyperosmotic to their surroundings, so they must excrete excess water continuously. In contrast to mammals and birds, freshwater fishes produce large volumes of very dilute urine. Their kidneys, which contain many nephrons, produce filtrate at a high rate. Freshwater fishes conserve salts by reabsorbing ions from the filtrate in their distal tubules, leaving water behind.

Amphibian kidneys function much like those of freshwater fishes. When frogs are in fresh water, their kidneys excrete dilute urine while their skin accumulates certain salts from the water by active transport. On land, where dehydration is the most pressing problem of osmoregulation, frogs conserve body fluid by reabsorbing water across the epithelium of the urinary bladder.

Marine Bony Fishes

The tissues of marine bony fishes gain excess salts from their surroundings and lose water. These environmental challenges are opposite to those faced by their freshwater relatives. Compared with freshwater fishes, marine fishes have fewer and smaller nephrons, and their nephrons lack a distal tubule. In addition, their kidneys have small glomeruli or lack glomeruli entirely. In keeping with these features, filtration rates are low and very little urine is excreted.

The main function of kidneys in marine bony fishes is to get rid of divalent ions (those with a charge of 2+ or 2−) such as calcium (Ca^{2+}), magnesium (Mg^{2+}), and sulfate (SO_4^{2-}). Marine fishes take in divalent ions by incessantly drinking seawater. They rid themselves of these ions by secreting them into the proximal tubules of the nephrons and excreting them in urine. Osmoregulation in marine bony fishes also relies on specialized *chloride cells* in the gills. By establishing ion gradients that enable secretion of salt (NaCl) into seawater, the chloride cells maintain proper levels of monovalent ions (charge of 1+ or 1−) such as Na^+ and Cl^-.

The generation of ion gradients and the movement of ions across membranes is central to salt and water balance in marine bony fishes. These events, however, are by no means unique to these organisms nor to homeostasis. As illustrated by the examples in Figure 44.17, osmoregulation by chloride cells is but one of many diverse physiological processes that are driven by the movement of ions across a membrane.

Ion Movement and Gradients

The transport of ions across the plasma membrane of a cell is a fundamental activity of all animals, and indeed of all living things. By generating ion gradients, ion transport provides the potential energy that powers processes ranging from an organism's regulation of salts and gases in internal fluids to its perception of and locomotion through its environment.

Information Processing

In neurons, the opening and closing of channels selective for sodium or other ions underlies the transmission of information as nerve impulses. These signals enable nervous systems to receive and process input and to direct appropriate output, such as this leap of a frog capturing prey. *See Concept 48.3.*

Osmoregulation

In marine bony fishes, ion gradients drive secretion of salt (NaCl), a process essential to avoid dehydration. Within gills, the pumps, cotransporters, and channels of specialized chloride cells function together to drive salt from the blood across the gill epithelium and into the surrounding salt water. *See Concept 44.1.*

Locomotion

A gradient of H^+ ions powers the bacterial flagellum. An electron transport chain generates this gradient, establishing a higher concentration of H^+ outside the bacterial cell. Protons reentering the cell provide a force that causes the flagellar motor to rotate. The rotating motor turns the curved hook, causing the attached filament to propel the cell. *See Concepts 9.4 and 27.1.*

MAKE CONNECTIONS *Explain why the set of forces driving ion movement across the plasma membrane of a cell are described as an electrochemical (electrical and chemical) gradient (see Concept 7.4).*

 ANIMATION *BioFlix* Visit the Study Area in **MasteringBiology** for the BioFlix 3-D Animation on Membrane Transport

Gas Exchange

Ion gradients provide the basis for the opening of plant stomata by surrounding guard cells. Active transport of H^+ out of a guard cell generates a voltage (membrane potential) that drives inward movement of K^+ ions. This uptake of K^+ by guard cells triggers an osmotic influx of water that changes cell shape, bowing the guard cells outward and thereby opening the stoma.

1. What do the number and length of nephrons in a fish's kidney indicate about the fish's habitat? How do they correlate with urine production?

2. Many medications make the epithelium of the collecting duct less permeable to water. How would taking such a medication affect kidney output?

3. **WHAT IF?** If blood pressure in the afferent arteriole leading to a glomerulus decreased, how would the rate of blood filtration within Bowman's capsule be affected? Explain.

For suggested answers, see Appendix A.

CONCEPT 44.5

Hormonal circuits link kidney function, water balance, and blood pressure

In mammals, both the volume and osmolarity of urine are adjusted according to an animal's water and salt balance and its rate of urea production. In situations of high salt intake and low water availability, a mammal can excrete urea and salt in small volumes of hyperosmotic urine with minimal water loss. If salt is scarce and fluid intake is high, the kidney can instead get rid of the excess water with little salt loss by producing large volumes of hypoosmotic urine. At such times, the urine can be as dilute as 70 mOsm/L, less than one fourth the osmolarity of human blood.

How are urine volume and osmolarity regulated so effectively? As we'll explore in this final portion of the chapter, two major control circuits that respond to different stimuli together restore and maintain normal water and salt balance.

Homeostatic Regulation of the Kidney

A combination of nervous and hormonal controls manages the osmoregulatory function of the mammalian kidney. Through their effects on the amount and osmolarity of urine, these controls contribute to homeostasis for both blood pressure and blood volume.

Antidiuretic Hormone

One key hormone in the regulatory circuitry of the kidney is antidiuretic hormone (ADH), also called *vasopressin*. Osmoreceptor cells in the hypothalamus monitor the osmolarity of blood and regulate the release of ADH from the posterior pituitary.

To understand the role of ADH, let's consider first what occurs when blood osmolarity rises, such as after eating salty food or losing water through sweating (Figure 44.18). When osmolarity rises above the set point of 300 mOsm/L, ADH release into the bloodstream increases. Within the kidney, the main targets of ADH are the collecting ducts. There, ADH brings about changes that make the epithelium more permeable to water. The resulting increase in water reabsorption concentrates urine, reduces urine volume, and lowers blood osmolarity back toward the set point. As the osmolarity of the blood falls, a negative-feedback mechanism reduces the activity of osmoreceptor cells in the hypothalamus, and ADH secretion is reduced.

What happens if, instead of ingesting salt or sweating profusely, you drink a large amount of water? The resulting reduction in blood osmolarity below the set point causes a drop in ADH secretion to a very low level. The resulting decrease in permeability of the collecting ducts reduces water reabsorption, resulting in discharge of large volumes

▶ **Figure 44.18 Regulation of fluid retention in the kidney by antidiuretic hormone (ADH).** Osmoreceptors in the hypothalamus monitor blood osmolarity via its effect on the net diffusion of water into or out of the receptor cells. When blood osmolarity increases, signals from the osmoreceptors trigger a release of ADH from the posterior pituitary, as well as thirst. Drinking water reduces blood osmolarity, inhibiting further ADH secretion and thereby completing the feedback circuit.

Osmoreceptors in hypothalamus trigger release of ADH from posterior pituitary.

Hypothalamus

Posterior pituitary

ADH

Hypothalamus generates thirst.

Distal tubule

Drinking water reduces blood osmolarity.

Collecting duct

H₂O reabsorption reduces blood osmolarity.

Blood osmolarity increases (such as after sweating profusely).

NORMAL BLOOD OSMOLARITY (300 mOsm/L)

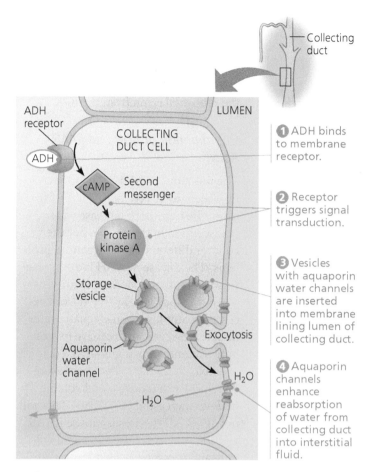

Collecting duct

ADH receptor

COLLECTING DUCT CELL

LUMEN

ADH

cAMP — Second messenger

Protein kinase A

Storage vesicle

Aquaporin water channel

Exocytosis

H_2O

H_2O

1 ADH binds to membrane receptor.

2 Receptor triggers signal transduction.

3 Vesicles with aquaporin water channels are inserted into membrane lining lumen of collecting duct.

4 Aquaporin channels enhance reabsorption of water from collecting duct into interstitial fluid.

▲ **Figure 44.19 ADH response pathway in the collecting duct.**

of dilute urine. (A high level of urine production is called diuresis; ADH is therefore called *anti*diuretic hormone.)

How does ADH influence water uptake in the kidney's collecting ducts? Binding of ADH to receptor molecules leads to a temporary increase in the number of aquaporin proteins inserted in the membranes of collecting duct cells **(Figure 44.19).** Additional aquaporin channels recapture more water, reducing urine volume.

Blood osmolarity, ADH release, and water reabsorption in the kidney are normally linked in a feedback circuit that contributes to homeostasis. Anything that disrupts this circuit can interfere with water balance. For example, alcohol inhibits ADH release, leading to excessive urinary water loss and dehydration (which may cause some of the symptoms of a hangover).

Mutations that prevent ADH production or that inactivate the ADH receptor gene disrupt homeostasis by blocking the insertion of additional aquaporin channels in the collecting duct membrane. The resulting disorder can cause severe dehydration and solute imbalance due to production of copious, dilute urine. These symptoms give the disorder its name: *diabetes insipidus* (from the Greek for "to pass through" and "having no flavor"). Could mutations in an aquaporin gene have a similar effect? **Figure 44.20** describes an experimental approach that addressed this question.

▼ **Figure 44.20** | Inquiry

Can aquaporin mutations cause diabetes?

Experiment Researchers studied a diabetes insipidus patient with a normal ADH receptor gene but two mutant alleles (A and B) of the aquaporin-2 gene. The resulting changes are shown below in an alignment of protein sequences that includes other species.

Source of Aquaporin-2 Gene Sequence	Amino Acids 183–191* in Encoded Protein	Amino Acids 212–220* in Encoded Protein
Frog (*Xenopus laevis*)	MNPARSFAP	GIFASLIYN
Lizard (*Anolis carolinensis*)	MNPARSFGP	AVVASLLYN
Chicken (*Gallus gallus*)	MNPARSFAP	AAAASIIYN
Human (*Homo sapiens*)	MNPARSLAP	AILGSLLYN
Conserved residues	MNPARSxxP	xxxxSxxYN
Patient's gene: allele A	MNPACSLAP	AILGSLLYN
Patient's gene: allele B	MNPARSLAP	AILGPLLYN

*The numbering is based on the human aquaporin-2 protein sequence.

Each mutation changed the protein sequence at a highly conserved position. To test the hypothesis that the changes affect function, researchers used frog oocytes, cells that will express foreign messenger RNA and can be readily collected from adult female frogs.

1 Messenger RNA transcribed from wild-type and mutant aquaporin genes is injected into frog oocytes, where it directs the synthesis of aquaporin proteins.

Wild-type   Allele A   Allele B H_2O (control)

Oocyte

2 The oocytes are transferred from a 200-mOsm to a 10-mOsm solution. The rate of oocyte swelling is measured as an indicator of water permeability.

10-mOsm solution

Results

Source of Injected mRNA	Rate of Swelling (μm/sec)
Human wild type	196
Patient's allele A	17
Patient's allele B	18
None	20

Conclusion Because each mutation inactivates aquaporin as a water channel, the patient's disorder can be attributed to these mutations.

Source: P. M. Deen et al., Requirement of human renal water channel aquaporin-2 for vasopressin-dependent concentration of urine, *Science* 264:92–95 (1994). Reprinted with permission from AAAS.

WHAT IF? *If you measured ADH levels in patients with ADH receptor mutations and in patients with aquaporin mutations, what would you expect to find, compared with wild-type subjects?*

More Na⁺ and H₂O are reabsorbed in distal tubules, increasing blood volume.

Aldosterone

Adrenal gland

Arterioles constrict, increasing blood pressure.

NORMAL BLOOD PRESSURE AND VOLUME

Angiotensin II

ACE

Angiotensin I

Angiotensinogen

Liver

Renin

Blood pressure or blood volume drops (for example, due to dehydration or blood loss).

Distal tubule

JGA releases renin.

Juxtaglomerular apparatus (JGA)

Sensors in JGA detect decrease in pressure or volume.

▲ Figure 44.21 Regulation of blood volume and blood pressure by the renin-angiotensin-aldosterone system (RAAS).

MAKE CONNECTIONS *Compare the activity of renin and ACE in the RAAS with that of the protein kinases in a phosphorylation cascade (such as the one shown in Figure 11.10). How are the roles of these enzymes similar and different in the two regulated response pathways?*

The Renin-Angiotensin-Aldosterone System

A second regulatory mechanism that helps maintain homeostasis by acting on the kidney is the **renin-angiotensin-aldosterone system (RAAS)**. The RAAS involves the **juxtaglomerular apparatus (JGA)**, a specialized tissue consisting of cells of and around the afferent arteriole, which supplies blood to the glomerulus (Figure 44.21). When blood pressure or volume drops in the afferent arteriole (for instance, as a result of dehydration), the JGA releases the enzyme renin. Renin initiates a sequence of steps that cleave a plasma protein called angiotensinogen, ultimately yielding a peptide called **angiotensin II**.

Functioning as a hormone, angiotensin II raises blood pressure by constricting arterioles, which decreases blood flow to capillaries in the kidney (and elsewhere). Angiotensin II also stimulates the adrenal glands to release a hormone called **aldosterone**. Aldosterone causes the nephrons' distal tubules and collecting duct to reabsorb more Na⁺ and water, increasing blood volume and pressure.

Because angiotensin II acts in several ways that increase blood pressure, drugs that block angiotensin II production are widely used to treat hypertension (chronic high blood pressure). Many of these drugs are specific inhibitors of angiotensin converting enzyme (ACE), which catalyzes one of the steps in the production of angiotensin II.

The renin-angiotensin-aldosterone system operates as a feedback circuit. A drop in blood pressure and blood volume triggers renin release. The resulting production of angiotensin II and release of aldosterone cause a rise in blood pressure and volume, reducing the release of renin from the JGA.

Coordination of ADH and RAAS Activity

The functions of ADH and the RAAS may seem to be redundant, but this is not the case. Both increase water reabsorption in the kidney, but they counter different osmoregulatory problems. The release of ADH is a response to an increase in blood osmolarity, as when the body is dehydrated from excessive water loss or inadequate water intake. However, an excessive loss of both salt and body fluids—caused, for example, by a major wound or severe diarrhea—will reduce blood volume *without* increasing osmolarity. This will not affect ADH release, but the RAAS will respond to the drop in blood volume and pressure by increasing water and Na⁺ reabsorption. Thus, ADH and the RAAS are partners in homeostasis. ADH alone would lower blood Na⁺ concentration via water reabsorption in the kidney, but the RAAS helps maintain body fluid osmolarity at the set point by stimulating Na⁺ reabsorption.

Another hormone, **atrial natriuretic peptide (ANP)**, opposes the RAAS. The walls of the atria of the heart release ANP in response to an increase in blood volume and pressure. ANP inhibits the release of renin from the JGA, inhibits NaCl reabsorption by the collecting ducts, and reduces aldosterone release from the adrenal glands. These actions lower blood volume and pressure. Thus, ADH, the RAAS, and ANP provide an elaborate system of checks and balances that regulate the kidney's ability to control the osmolarity, salt concentration, volume, and pressure of blood. The precise regulatory role of ANP is an area of active research.

CONCEPT CHECK 44.5

1. How does alcohol affect regulation of water balance in the body?

2. Why could it be dangerous to drink a very large amount of water in a short period of time?

3. **WHAT IF?** Conn's syndrome is a condition caused by tumors of the adrenal cortex that secrete high amounts of aldosterone in an unregulated manner. What would you expect to be the major symptom of this disorder?

For suggested answers, see Appendix A.

SUMMARY OF KEY CONCEPTS

CONCEPT 44.1

Osmoregulation balances the uptake and loss of water and solutes (pp. 972–976)

Animal	Inflow/Outflow	Urine
Freshwater fish. Lives in water less concentrated than body fluids; fish tends to gain water, lose salt	Does not drink water Salt in (active transport by gills) / H_2O in Salt out	▶ Large volume of urine ▶ Urine is less concentrated than body fluids
Marine bony fish. Lives in water more concentrated than body fluids; fish tends to lose water, gain salt	Drinks water Salt in / H_2O out Salt out (active transport by gills)	▶ Small volume of urine ▶ Urine is slightly less concentrated than body fluids
Terrestrial vertebrate. Terrestrial environment; tends to lose body water to air	Drinks water Salt in (by mouth) H_2O and salt out	▶ Moderate volume of urine ▶ Urine is more concentrated than body fluids

© Pearson Education, Inc.

- Cells balance water gain and loss through **osmoregulation**, a process based on the controlled movement of solutes between internal fluids and the external environment and on the movement of water, which follows by osmosis.
- **Osmoconformers** are isoosmotic with their marine environment and do not regulate their **osmolarity**. In contrast, **osmoregulators** control water uptake and loss in a hypoosmotic or hyperosmotic environment, respectively. Water-conserving excretory organs help terrestrial animals avoid desiccation, which can be life-threatening. Animals that live in temporary waters may enter a dormant state called **anhydrobiosis** when their habitats dry up.
- Transport epithelia contain specialized epithelial cells that control the solute movements required for waste disposal and osmoregulation.

? *Under what environmental conditions does water move into a cell by osmosis?*

CONCEPT 44.2

An animal's nitrogenous wastes reflect its phylogeny and habitat (pp. 976–977)

- Protein and nucleic acid metabolism generates **ammonia**. Most aquatic animals excrete ammonia. Mammals and most adult amphibians convert ammonia to the less toxic **urea**, which is excreted with a minimal loss of water. Insects and many reptiles, including birds, convert ammonia to **uric acid**, a mostly insoluble waste excreted in a paste-like urine.
- The kind of nitrogenous waste excreted depends on an animal's evolutionary history and habitat. The amount excreted is coupled to the animal's energy budget and dietary protein intake.

DRAW IT *Construct a table summarizing the three major types of nitrogenous wastes and their relative toxicity, energy cost to produce, and associated water loss during excretion.*

CONCEPT 44.3

Diverse excretory systems are variations on a tubular theme (pp. 978–981)

- Most excretory systems carry out **filtration, reabsorption, secretion**, and **excretion**. Invertebrate excretory systems include the **protonephridia** of flatworms, the **metanephridia** of earthworms, and the **Malpighian tubules** of insects. **Kidneys** function in both excretion and osmoregulation in vertebrates.
- Excretory tubules (consisting of **nephrons** and **collecting ducts**) and blood vessels pack the mammalian kidney. Blood pressure forces fluid from blood in the **glomerulus** into the lumen of **Bowman's capsule**. Following reabsorption and secretion, filtrate flows into a collecting duct. The **ureter** conveys urine from the **renal pelvis** to the **urinary bladder**.

? *Given that a typical excretory system selectively absorbs and secretes materials, what function does filtration serve?*

CONCEPT 44.4

The nephron is organized for stepwise processing of blood filtrate (pp. 981–988)

- Within the nephron, selective secretion and reabsorption in the **proximal tubule** alter filtrate volume and composition. The *descending limb* of the **loop of Henle** is permeable to water but not salt; water moves by osmosis into the interstitial fluid. The *ascending limb* is permeable to salt but not water; salt leaves by diffusion and by active transport. The **distal tubule** and collecting duct regulate K^+ and NaCl levels in body fluids.
- In mammals, **a countercurrent multiplier system** involving the loop of Henle maintains the gradient of salt concentration in the kidney interior. Urea exiting the collecting duct contributes to the osmotic gradient of the kidney.
- Natural selection has shaped the form and function of nephrons in various vertebrates to the osmoregulatory challenges of the animals' habitats. For example, desert mammals, which excrete the most hyperosmotic urine, have loops of Henle that extend deep into the **renal medulla,** whereas mammals in moist habitats have shorter loops and excrete more dilute urine.

? *How do cortical and juxtamedullary nephrons differ with respect to reabsorbing nutrients and concentrating urine?*

Hormonal circuits link kidney function, water balance, and blood pressure (pp. 988–990)

- The posterior pituitary gland releases antidiuretic hormone (ADH) when blood osmolarity rises above a set point, such as when water intake is inadequate. ADH increases the permeability to water of the collecting ducts by increasing the number of epithelial **aquaporin** channels.
- When blood pressure or blood volume in the afferent arteriole drops, the **juxtaglomerular apparatus** releases renin. **Angiotensin II** formed in response to renin constricts arterioles and triggers release of the hormone **aldosterone**, raising blood pressure and reducing the release of renin. This **renin-angiotensin-aldosterone system** has functions that overlap with those of ADH and are opposed by **atrial natriuretic peptide**.

? *Why can only some patients with diabetes insipidus be treated effectively with ADH?*

TEST YOUR UNDERSTANDING

LEVEL 1: KNOWLEDGE/COMPREHENSION

1. *Unlike* an earthworm's metanephridia, a mammalian nephron
   a. is intimately associated with a capillary network.
   b. functions in both osmoregulation and excretion.
   c. receives filtrate from blood instead of coelomic fluid.
   d. has a transport epithelium.

2. Which process in the nephron is *least* selective?
   a. filtration
   b. reabsorption
   c. active transport
   d. secretion

3. Which of the following animals generally has the lowest volume of urine production?
   a. vampire bat
   b. salmon in fresh water
   c. marine bony fish
   d. freshwater bony fish

LEVEL 2: APPLICATION/ANALYSIS

4. The high osmolarity of the renal medulla is maintained by all of the following *except*
   a. active transport of salt from the upper region of the ascending limb.
   b. the spatial arrangement of juxtamedullary nephrons.
   c. diffusion of urea from the collecting duct.
   d. diffusion of salt from the descending limb of the loop of Henle.

5. Natural selection should favor the highest proportion of juxtamedullary nephrons in which of the following species?
   a. river otter
   b. mouse living in a temperate broadleaf forest
   c. mouse living in a desert
   d. beaver

6. African lungfish, which are often found in small stagnant pools of fresh water, produce urea as a nitrogenous waste. What is the advantage of this adaptation?
   a. Urea takes less energy to synthesize than ammonia.
   b. Small stagnant pools do not provide enough water to dilute ammonia, which is toxic.
   c. Urea forms an insoluble precipitate.
   d. Urea makes lungfish tissue hypoosmotic to the pool.

LEVEL 3: SYNTHESIS/EVALUATION

7. **INTERPRET THE DATA** Use the data below to draw four pie charts for water gain and loss in a kangaroo rat and a human.

	Kangaroo Rat	Human
Water Gain (mL)		
Ingested in food	0.2	750
Ingested in liquid	0	1,500
Derived from metabolism	1.8	250
Water Loss (mL)		
Urine	0.45	1,500
Feces	0.09	100
Evaporation	1.46	900

Which routes of water gain and loss make up a much larger share of the total in a kangaroo rat than in a human?

8. **EVOLUTION CONNECTION**
   Merriam's kangaroo rats (*Dipodomys merriami*) live in North American habitats ranging from moist, cool woodlands to hot deserts. Assuming that natural selection has resulted in differences in water conservation between *D. merriami* populations, propose a hypothesis concerning the relative rates of evaporative water loss by populations that live in moist versus dry environments. Using a humidity sensor to detect this evaporative water loss, how could you test your hypothesis?

9. **SCIENTIFIC INQUIRY**
   You are exploring kidney function in kangaroo rats. You measure urine volume and osmolarity, as well as the amount of chloride (Cl^-) and urea in the urine. If the water source provided to the animals were switched from tap water to a 2% NaCl solution, what change in urine osmolarity would you expect? How would you determine if this change was more likely due to a change in the excretion of Cl^- or urea?

10. **WRITE ABOUT A THEME: ORGANIZATION**
    In a short essay (100–150 words), compare how membrane structures in the loop of Henle and collecting duct of the mammalian kidney enable water to be recovered from filtrate in the process of osmoregulation.

11. **SYNTHESIZE YOUR KNOWLEDGE**

The marine iguana (*Amblyrhynchus cristatus*), which spends long periods under water feeding on seaweed, relies on both salt glands and kidneys for homeostasis of its internal fluids. Describe how these organs together meet the particular osmoregulatory challenges of this animal's environment.

For selected answers, see Appendix A.

MasteringBiology®

Students Go to **MasteringBiology** for assignments, the eText, and the Study Area with practice tests, animations, and activities.

Instructors Go to **MasteringBiology** for automatically graded tutorials and questions that you can assign to your students, plus Instructor Resources.

45

Hormones and the Endocrine System

▲ Figure 45.1 What makes male and female elephant seals look so different?

The Body's Long-Distance Regulators

Although we often distinguish animals of different species by their appearance, in many species the females and males look quite different from each other. Such is the case for the elephant seals (*Mirounga angustirostris*) shown in **Figure 45.1**. The male is much larger than the female, and only he has the prominent proboscis for which the species is named. Males are also far more territorial and aggressive than females. A sex-determining gene on the Y chromosome makes a seal embryo male. But how does the presence of this gene lead to male size, shape, and behavior? The answer to this and many other questions about biological processes involves signaling molecules called **hormones** (from the Greek *horman*, to excite).

In animals, hormones are secreted into the extracellular fluid, circulate in the blood (or hemolymph), and communicate regulatory messages throughout the body. In the case of the elephant seal, increased secretion of particular hormones at puberty triggers sexual maturation, as well as the accompanying changes that distinguish adult females and males. Hormones influence much more than sex and reproduction, however. For example, when seals, humans, and other mammals are stressed, are dehydrated, or have low blood sugar levels, hormones coordinate the physiological responses that restore balance in our bodies.

◀ Male elephant seals sparring

Each hormone binds to specific receptors in the body. Although a given hormone can reach all cells of the body, only some cells have receptors for that hormone. A hormone elicits a response—such as a change in metabolism—in specific *target cells*, those that have the matching receptor. Cells lacking a receptor for that hormone are unaffected.

Chemical signaling by hormones is the function of the **endocrine system**, one of the two basic systems for communication and regulation in the animal body. The other major communication and control system is the **nervous system**, a network of specialized cells—neurons—that transmit signals along dedicated pathways. These signals in turn regulate neurons, muscle cells, and endocrine cells. Because signaling by neurons can regulate the release of hormones, the nervous and endocrine systems often overlap in function.

In this chapter, we'll begin with an overview of the different types of chemical signaling in animals. We'll then explore how hormones regulate target cells, how hormone secretion is regulated, and how hormones help maintain homeostasis. We'll also consider the ways in which endocrine and nervous system activities are coordinated and examine the role of hormones in regulating growth and development.

CONCEPT 45.1

Hormones and other signaling molecules bind to target receptors, triggering specific response pathways

We'll begin our consideration of the endocrine system by examining the diverse ways that animal cells use chemical signals to communicate.

Intercellular Communication

Communication between animal cells via secreted signals is often classified by two criteria: the type of secreting cell and the route taken by the signal in reaching its target. **Figure 45.2** illustrates five forms of signaling distinguished in this manner. We'll explore these forms in turn.

Endocrine Signaling

In endocrine signaling (see Figure 45.2a), hormones secreted into extracellular fluid by endocrine cells reach target cells via the bloodstream (or hemolymph). One function of endocrine signaling is to maintain homeostasis. Hormones regulate properties that include blood pressure and volume, energy metabolism and allocation, and solute concentrations in body fluids. Endocrine signaling also mediates responses to environmental stimuli, regulates growth and development, and, as discussed above, triggers physical and behavioral changes underlying sexual maturity and reproduction.

(a) In **endocrine signaling**, secreted molecules diffuse into the blood-stream and trigger responses in target cells anywhere in the body.

(b) In **paracrine signaling**, secreted molecules diffuse locally and trigger a response in neighboring cells.

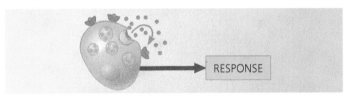

(c) In **autocrine signaling**, secreted molecules diffuse locally and trigger a response in the cells that secrete them.

(d) In **synaptic signaling**, neurotransmitters diffuse across synapses and trigger responses in cells of target tissues (neurons, muscles, or glands).

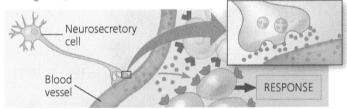

(e) In **neuroendocrine signaling**, neurohormones diffuse into the bloodstream and trigger responses in target cells anywhere in the body.

▲ **Figure 45.2 Intercellular communication by secreted molecules.** In each type of signaling, secreted molecules (•) bind to a specific receptor protein (🥄) expressed by target cells. Some receptors are located inside cells, but for simplicity, here all are drawn on the cell surface.

Paracrine and Autocrine Signaling

Many types of cells produce and secrete **local regulators**, molecules that act over short distances and reach their target cells solely by diffusion. Once secreted, local regulators act on their target cells within seconds or even milliseconds. Local regulators include cytokines, which enable communication between immune cells (see Figure 43.16 and Figure 43.18), and growth factors, which promote the growth, division, and development of many types of cells.

Depending on the target cell, signaling by local regulators can be either paracrine or autocrine. In **paracrine** signaling (from the Greek *para*, to one side of), target cells lie near the secreting cell (see Figure 45.2b). In **autocrine** signaling (from the Greek *auto*, self), the secreting cells themselves are the target cells (see Figure 45.2c).

Paracrine and autocrine signaling play roles in many physiological processes, including blood pressure regulation, nervous system function, and reproduction. Local regulators that mediate such signaling include the **prostaglandins**, so named because they were first discovered in prostate gland secretions that contribute to semen. In the reproductive tract of a female, prostaglandins introduced in semen stimulate the smooth muscles of the uterine wall to contract, helping sperm reach an egg. At the onset of childbirth, prostaglandins produced by the placenta cause the uterine muscles to become more excitable, helping to induce labor (see Figure 46.18).

Prostaglandins also act in the immune system, promoting inflammation and the sensation of pain in response to injury. That is why drugs that block prostaglandin synthesis, such as aspirin and ibuprofen, have both anti-inflammatory and pain-relieving effects. Prostaglandins also help regulate the aggregation of platelets, one step in the formation of blood clots. Because blood clots in vessels that supply the heart can block blood flow, causing a heart attack (see Concept 42.4), some physicians recommend that people at risk for a heart attack take aspirin on a regular basis.

Synaptic and Neuroendocrine Signaling

Secreted molecules are crucial for two types of signaling by neurons. In *synaptic signaling*, neurons form specialized junctions called synapses with target cells, such as other neurons and muscle cells. At most synapses, neurons secrete molecules called **neurotransmitters** that diffuse a very short distance and bind to receptors on the target cells (see Figure 45.2d). Neurotransmitters are central to sensation, memory, cognition, and movement (as we'll explore in Chapters 48–50).

In *neuroendocrine signaling*, specialized neurons called neurosecretory cells secrete **neurohormones**, which diffuse from nerve cell endings into the bloodstream (see Figure 45.2e). One example of a neurohormone is antidiuretic hormone, which is essential to kidney function and water balance (see Concept 44.5). Many neurohormones function in the regulation of endocrine signaling, as we'll discuss later in this chapter.

Signaling by Pheromones

Not all secreted signaling molecules act within the body. Members of a particular animal species sometimes

▲ **Figure 45.3 Signaling by pheromones.** Using their lowered antennae, these Asian army ants (*Leptogenys distinguenda*) follow a pheromone-marked trail as they carry pupae and larvae to a new nest site.

communicate with each other via **pheromones**, chemicals that are released into the external environment. For example, when a foraging ant discovers a new food source, it marks its path back to the nest with a pheromone. Ants also use pheromones for guidance when a colony migrates to a new location **(Figure 45.3)**.

Pheromones serve a wide range of functions that include defining territories, warning of predators, and attracting potential mates. The polyphemus moth (*Antheraea polyphemus*) provides a noteworthy example: The sex pheromone released into the air by a female enables her to attract a male of the species from up to 4.5 km away. You'll read more about pheromone function when we take up the topic of animal behavior in Chapter 51.

Chemical Classes of Local Regulators and Hormones

Molecules used in intercellular signaling vary substantially in size and chemical properties. Let's take a look at some of the most common classes of local regulators and hormones.

Classes of Local Regulators

One group of local regulators, the prostaglandins, are modified fatty acids. Many other local regulators, including cytokines and growth factors, are polypeptides, and some are gases.

Nitric oxide (NO), a gas, functions in the body as both a local regulator and a neurotransmitter. When the level of oxygen in the blood falls, endothelial cells in blood vessel walls synthesize and release NO. After diffusing into the surrounding smooth muscle cells, NO activates an enzyme that relaxes the cells. The result is vasodilation, which increases blood flow to tissues.

In human males, NO's ability to promote vasodilation enables sexual function by increasing blood flow into the penis, producing an erection. The drug Viagra (sildenafil citrate), a

Water-soluble (hydrophilic)	Lipid-soluble (hydrophobic)
Polypeptides	**Steroids**
Insulin 0.8 nm	Cortisol
Amines	
Epinephrine	Thyroxine

▲ **Figure 45.4 Differences in hormone solubility and structure.**

MAKE CONNECTIONS *Cells synthesize epinephrine from the amino acid tyrosine (see Figure 5.14). On the structure of epinephrine shown above, draw an arrow pointing to the position corresponding to the α carbon of tyrosine.*

treatment for male erectile dysfunction, sustains an erection by prolonging activity of the NO response pathway.

Classes of Hormones

Hormones fall into three major chemical classes: polypeptides, steroids, and amines **(Figure 45.4)**. The hormone insulin, for example, is a polypeptide that contains two chains in its active form. Steroid hormones, such as cortisol, are lipids that contain four fused carbon rings. All are derived from the steroid cholesterol (see Figure 5.12). Epinephrine and thyroxine are amine hormones, each synthesized from a single amino acid, either tyrosine or tryptophan.

As Figure 45.4 indicates, hormones vary in their solubility in aqueous and lipid-rich environments. Polypeptides and most amine hormones are water-soluble, whereas steroid hormones and other largely nonpolar (hydrophobic) hormones, such as thyroxine, are lipid-soluble.

Cellular Response Pathways

There are several differences between the response pathways for water-soluble and lipid-soluble signaling molecules.

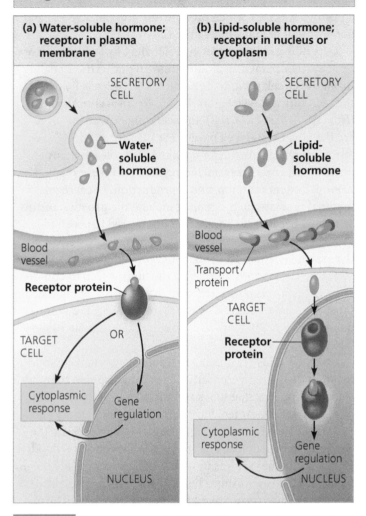

▼ **Figure 45.5 Variation in hormone receptor location.**

(a) Water-soluble hormone; receptor in plasma membrane

(b) Lipid-soluble hormone; receptor in nucleus or cytoplasm

WHAT IF? *Suppose you are studying a cell's response to a particular hormone. You observe that the cell produces the same response to the hormone whether or not the cell is treated with a chemical that blocks transcription. What can you surmise about the hormone and its receptor?*

To focus this and subsequent discussions, we'll restrict our presentation to endocrine signaling.

One difference in cellular hormone response pathways is the location of the target cells' receptor proteins. Water-soluble hormones are secreted by exocytosis and travel freely in the bloodstream. Being insoluble in lipids, they cannot diffuse through the plasma membranes of target cells. Instead, these hormones bind to cell-surface receptors, inducing changes in cytoplasmic molecules and sometimes altering gene transcription **(Figure 45.5a)**. In contrast, lipid-soluble hormones diffuse out across the membranes of endocrine cells. Outside the cell, they bind to transport proteins that keep them soluble in the aqueous environment of the blood. Upon leaving the blood, they diffuse into target cells and typically bind to receptors in the cytoplasm or nucleus **(Figure 45.5b)**. The hormone-bound receptor then triggers changes in gene transcription.

To follow the distinct cellular responses to water-soluble and lipid-soluble hormones, we'll examine the two response pathways in turn.

Pathway for Water-Soluble Hormones

The binding of a water-soluble hormone to a receptor protein triggers events at the plasma membrane that result in a cellular response. The response may be the activation of an enzyme, a change in the uptake or secretion of specific molecules, or a rearrangement of the cytoskeleton. In addition, some cell-surface receptors cause proteins in the cytoplasm to move into the nucleus and alter the transcription of specific genes.

The series of changes in cellular proteins that converts the extracellular chemical signal to a specific intracellular response is called **signal transduction**. A signal transduction pathway typically involves multiple steps, each involving specific molecular interactions (see Chapter 11).

To explore the role of signal transduction in hormone signaling, consider one response to short-term stress. When you are in a stressful situation, perhaps running to catch a bus, the adrenal glands that lie atop your kidneys secrete the hormone **epinephrine**, also known as *adrenaline*. Upon reaching the liver, epinephrine binds to a G protein-coupled receptor in the plasma membrane of target cells **(Figure 45.6)**. The binding of hormone to receptor triggers a cascade of events in liver cells involving synthesis of cyclic AMP (cAMP) as a short-lived *second messenger*. Activation of protein kinase A by cAMP leads to activation of an enzyme required for glycogen breakdown and inactivation of an enzyme needed for glycogen synthesis. The net result is

that the liver releases glucose into the bloodstream, providing the fuel you need to chase the departing bus.

Pathway for Lipid-Soluble Hormones

Intracellular receptors for lipid-soluble hormones perform the entire task of transducing a signal within a target cell. The hormone activates the receptor, which then directly triggers the cell's response. In most cases, the response to a lipid-soluble hormone is a change in gene expression.

Most steroid hormone receptors are predominantly located in the cytosol prior to binding to a hormone. When a steroid hormone binds to its cytosolic receptor, a hormone-receptor complex forms, which moves into the nucleus (see Figure 18.9). There, the receptor portion of the complex alters transcription of particular genes by interacting with a specific DNA-binding protein or response element in the DNA. (In some cell types, steroid hormones trigger additional responses by interacting with other kinds of receptor proteins located at the cell surface).

Among the best-characterized steroid hormone receptors are those that bind to estrogens, steroid hormones necessary for female reproductive function in vertebrates. For example, in female birds and frogs, estradiol, a form of estrogen, binds to a specific cytoplasmic receptor in liver cells. Binding of estradiol to this receptor activates transcription of the gene for the protein vitellogenin **(Figure 45.7)**. Following translation of the messenger RNA, vitellogenin is secreted

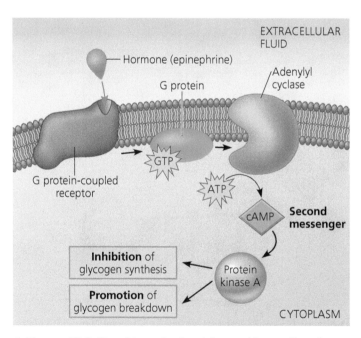

▲ **Figure 45.6 Signal transduction triggered by a cell-surface hormone receptor.**

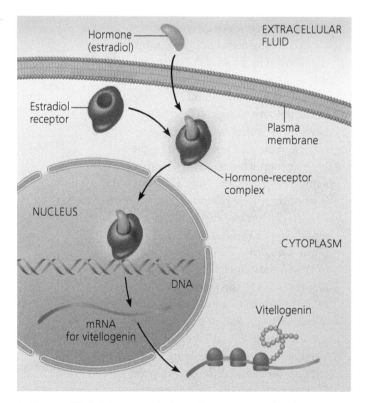

▲ **Figure 45.7 Direct regulation of gene expression by a steroid hormone receptor.**

and transported in the blood to the reproductive system, where it is used to produce egg yolk.

Thyroxine, vitamin D, and other lipid-soluble hormones that are not steroids have receptors that are typically located in the nucleus. These receptors bind to hormone molecules that diffuse from the bloodstream across both the plasma membrane and nuclear envelope. Once bound to a hormone, the receptor binds to specific sites in the cell's DNA and stimulates the transcription of specific genes.

Multiple Effects of Hormones

Many hormones elicit more than one type of response in the body. Consider, for example, epinephrine. As we noted earlier, this hormone triggers glycogen breakdown in the liver. However, epinephrine also *increases* blood flow to major skeletal muscles and *decreases* blood flow to the digestive tract. These varied responses enhance the rapid reactions of the body in emergencies.

How can a hormone such as epinephrine have such widely varying effects? A single hormone can elicit multiple responses if its target cells differ in their receptor type or in the molecules that produce the response. Consider the target cells for epinephrine:

- In liver cells, epinephrine binds to a β-type receptor in the plasma membrane. This receptor activates the enzyme protein kinase A, which in turn regulates enzymes of glycogen metabolism, causing release of glucose into the blood (Figure 45.8a). (Note that this is the signal transduction pathway illustrated in Figure 45.6.)
- In the smooth muscle cells lining blood vessels that supply skeletal muscle, the same kinase activated by the same epinephrine receptor inactivates a muscle-specific enzyme. The result is smooth muscle relaxation, leading to vasodilation and hence increased blood flow to skeletal muscles (Figure 45.8b).
- In the smooth muscle cells lining blood vessels of the intestines, epinephrine binds to an α-type receptor (Figure 45.8c). Rather than activating protein kinase A, this receptor triggers a signaling pathway involving a different G protein and different enzymes. The result is smooth muscle contraction that brings about vasoconstriction, restricting blood flow to the intestines.

Lipid-soluble hormones also exert different effects on different target cells. For example, estradiol, which stimulates a bird's liver to synthesize the yolk protein vitellogenin, stimulates the reproductive system to synthesize proteins that form the egg white.

Endocrine Tissues and Organs

Some endocrine cells are found in organs that are part of other organ systems. For example, the stomach contains isolated endocrine cells that help regulate digestive processes by secreting the hormone gastrin. More often, endocrine cells are grouped in ductless organs called **endocrine glands**, such as the thyroid and parathyroid glands and the gonads, either testes in males or ovaries in females. The endocrine glands of humans are illustrated in **Figure 45.9**. This overview of endocrine glands and the hormones that they produce will serve as a useful point of reference as you move through the chapter.

Note that endocrine glands secrete hormones directly into the surrounding fluid. In contrast, *exocrine glands*,

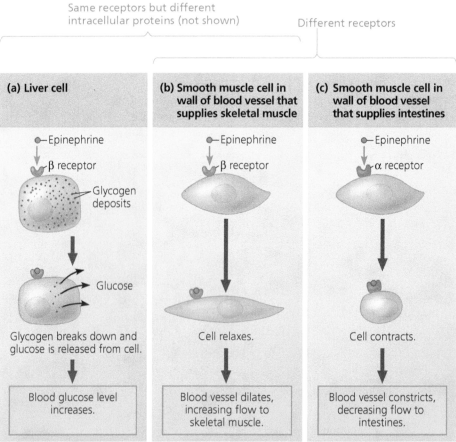

▲ **Figure 45.8 One hormone, different effects.** Epinephrine, the primary "fight-or-flight" hormone, produces different responses in different target cells. Target cells with the same receptor exhibit different responses if they have different signal transduction pathways or effector proteins; compare (a) with (b). Target cells with different receptors for the hormone may also exhibit different responses; compare (b) with (c).

Endocrine gland	Hormones
Pineal gland	• **Melatonin:** Participates in regulation of biological rhythms.
Hypothalamus	• **Hormones released from posterior pituitary (oxytocin and vasopressin)** • **Releasing and inhibiting hormones:** Regulate anterior pituitary
Pituitary gland	
Anterior pituitary	• **Follicle-stimulating hormone (FSH)** and **luteinizing hormone (LH):** Stimulate ovaries and testes • **Thyroid-stimulating hormone (TSH):** Stimulates thyroid gland • **Adrenocorticotropic hormone (ACTH):** Stimulates adrenal cortex • **Prolactin:** Stimulates mammary gland cells • **Growth hormone (GH):** Stimulates growth and metabolic functions
Posterior pituitary	• **Oxytocin:** Stimulates contraction of smooth muscle cells in uterus and mammary glands • **Vasopressin:** (also called **antidiuretic hormone, ADH**): Promotes retention of water by kidneys; influences social behavior and bonding
Thyroid gland	• **Thyroid hormone (T_3 and T_4):** Stimulates and maintains metabolic processes • **Calcitonin:** Lowers blood calcium level
Parathyroid glands	• **Parathyroid hormone (PTH):** Raises blood calcium level
Adrenal glands	
Adrenal medulla	• **Epinephrine** and **norepinephrine:** Raise blood glucose level; increase metabolic activities; constrict certain blood vessels.
Adrenal cortex	• **Glucocorticoids:** Raise blood glucose level • **Mineralocorticoids:** Promote reabsorption of Na^+ and excretion of K^+ in kidneys
Pancreas	• **Insulin:** Lowers blood glucose level • **Glucagon:** Raises blood glucose level
Ovaries (female)	• **Estrogens*:** Stimulate uterine lining growth; promote development and maintenance of female secondary sex characteristics • **Progestins*:** Promote uterine lining growth
Testes (male)	• **Androgens*:** Support sperm formation; promote development and maintenance of male secondary sex characteristics

*Found in both males and females, but with a major role in one sex

such as salivary glands, have ducts that carry secreted substances onto body surfaces or into body cavities. This distinction is reflected in the glands' names: The Greek *endo* (within) and *exo* (out of) refer to secretion into or out of body fluids, while *crine* (from the Greek word meaning "separate") refers to movement away from the secreting cell. In the case of the pancreas, endocrine and exocrine tissues are found in the same gland: Ductless tissues secrete hormones, whereas tissues with ducts secrete enzymes and bicarbonate.

CONCEPT CHECK 45.1

1. How do response mechanisms in target cells differ for water-soluble and lipid-soluble hormones?

2. In what way does one activity described for prostaglandins resemble that of a pheromone?

3. **MAKE CONNECTIONS** How is the action of epinephrine on blood flow to muscles in the fight-or-flight response similar to the action of the plant hormone auxin in apical dominance (see Concept 39.2)?

For suggested answers, see Appendix A.

Feedback regulation and coordination with the nervous system are common in endocrine signaling

So far, we have explored forms of intercellular signaling as well as hormone structure, recognition, and response. We turn now to considering how regulatory pathways that control hormone secretion are organized.

Simple Hormone Pathways

In examining the regulation of hormone secretion, we begin with two basic types of organization—simple endocrine and simple neuroendocrine pathways. In a *simple endocrine pathway*, endocrine cells respond directly to an internal or environmental stimulus by secreting a particular hormone (Figure 45.10). The hormone travels in the bloodstream to target cells, where it interacts with its specific receptors. Signal transduction within target cells brings about a physiological response.

As an example of a simple endocrine pathway, we'll consider the control of pH in the duodenum, the first part of the small intestine. The digestive juices of the stomach are extremely acidic and must be neutralized before further digestion can occur. As the stomach contents enter the duodenum, their low pH stimulates endocrine cells in the lining of the duodenum to secrete the hormone *secretin* into the extracellular fluid (see Figure 45.10). From there, secretin diffuses into the blood. Circulating secretin reaches target cells in the pancreas, which respond by releasing bicarbonate into ducts leading to the duodenum. This response—the release of bicarbonate—raises the pH in the duodenum, neutralizing the stomach acid.

Neuroendocrine pathways include additional steps and involve more than one cell type. In a *simple neuroendocrine pathway*, the stimulus is received by a sensory neuron, which stimulates a neurosecretory cell (Figure 45.11). The neurosecretory cell then secretes a neurohormone, which diffuses into the bloodstream and travels to target cells.

As an example of a simple neuroendocrine pathway, consider the regulation of milk release during nursing in mammals. Suckling by an infant stimulates sensory

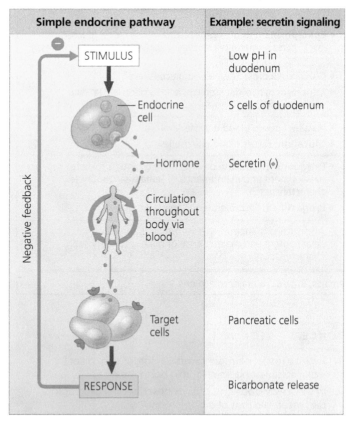

▲ **Figure 45.10 A simple endocrine pathway.** Endocrine cells respond to a change in some internal or external variable—the stimulus—by secreting hormone molecules that trigger a specific response by target cells. In the case of secretin signaling, the simple endocrine pathway is self-limiting because the response to secretin (bicarbonate release) reduces the stimulus (low pH) through negative feedback.

Simple endocrine pathway	Example: secretin signaling
STIMULUS	Low pH in duodenum
Endocrine cell	S cells of duodenum
Hormone	Secretin (•)
Circulation throughout body via blood	
Target cells	Pancreatic cells
RESPONSE	Bicarbonate release

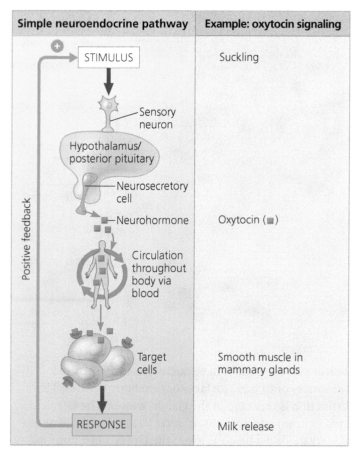

▲ **Figure 45.11 A simple neuroendocrine pathway.** Sensory neurons respond to a stimulus by sending nerve impulses to a neurosecretory cell, triggering secretion of a neurohormone. Upon reaching its target cells, the neurohormone binds to its receptor, triggering a specific response. In oxytocin signaling, the response increases the stimulus, forming a positive-feedback loop that amplifies signaling.

Simple neuroendocrine pathway	Example: oxytocin signaling
STIMULUS	Suckling
Sensory neuron	
Hypothalamus/posterior pituitary	
Neurosecretory cell	
Neurohormone	Oxytocin (■)
Circulation throughout body via blood	
Target cells	Smooth muscle in mammary glands
RESPONSE	Milk release

neurons in the nipples, generating signals in the nervous system that reach the hypothalamus. Nerve impulses from the hypothalamus then trigger the release of the neurohormone **oxytocin** from the posterior pituitary gland (see Figure 45.11). In response to circulating oxytocin, the mammary glands secrete milk.

Feedback Regulation

A feedback loop linking the response back to the initial stimulus is characteristic of control pathways. Often, regulation involves **negative feedback**, in which the response reduces the initial stimulus. For instance, bicarbonate release in response to secretin increases pH in the intestine, eliminating the stimulus and thereby shutting off secretin release (see Figure 45.10). By decreasing hormone signaling, negative-feedback regulation prevents excessive pathway activity.

Whereas negative feedback dampens a stimulus, **positive feedback** reinforces a stimulus, leading to an even greater response. For example, in the oxytocin pathway outlined in Figure 45.11, the mammary glands secrete milk in response to circulating oxytocin. Milk released in response to the oxytocin leads to more suckling and therefore more stimulation. Activation of the pathway is sustained until the baby stops suckling. When mammals give birth, oxytocin induces target cells in the uterine muscles to contract. This pathway is also characterized by positive-feedback regulation, such that it drives the birth process to completion.

While positive feedback amplifies both stimulus and response, negative feedback helps restore a preexisting state. It is not surprising, therefore, that hormone pathways involved in homeostasis typically involve negative feedback. Often such pathways are paired, providing even more balanced control. For example, the regulation of blood glucose levels relies on the antagonistic effects of insulin and glucagon (see Figure 41.21).

Coordination of Endocrine and Nervous Systems

In a wide range of animals, endocrine organs in the brain integrate function of the endocrine system with that of the nervous system. We'll explore the basic principles of such integration in invertebrates and vertebrates.

Invertebrates

The control of development in a moth illustrates neuroendocrine coordination in invertebrates. A moth larva, such as this colorful caterpillar of the giant silk moth (*Hyalophora cecropia*), grows in stages. Because its exoskeleton cannot stretch, the larva must periodically molt, shedding the old exoskeleton and secreting a new one. The endocrine pathway that controls molting originates in the larval brain **(Figure 45.12)**. There, neurosecretory cells

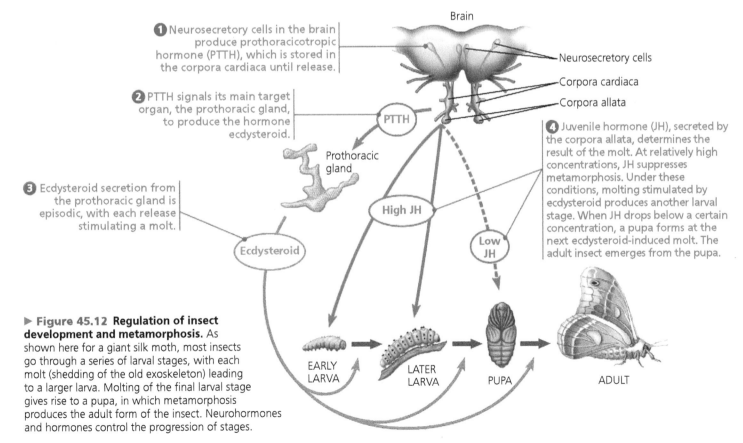

1 Neurosecretory cells in the brain produce prothoracicotropic hormone (PTTH), which is stored in the corpora cardiaca until release.

2 PTTH signals its main target organ, the prothoracic gland, to produce the hormone ecdysteroid.

3 Ecdysteroid secretion from the prothoracic gland is episodic, with each release stimulating a molt.

4 Juvenile hormone (JH), secreted by the corpora allata, determines the result of the molt. At relatively high concentrations, JH suppresses metamorphosis. Under these conditions, molting stimulated by ecdysteroid produces another larval stage. When JH drops below a certain concentration, a pupa forms at the next ecdysteroid-induced molt. The adult insect emerges from the pupa.

Brain

Neurosecretory cells
Corpora cardiaca
Corpora allata

PTTH

Prothoracic gland

High JH

Low JH

Ecdysteroid

EARLY LARVA

LATER LARVA

PUPA

ADULT

▶ **Figure 45.12 Regulation of insect development and metamorphosis.** As shown here for a giant silk moth, most insects go through a series of larval stages, with each molt (shedding of the old exoskeleton) leading to a larger larva. Molting of the final larval stage gives rise to a pupa, in which metamorphosis produces the adult form of the insect. Neurohormones and hormones control the progression of stages.

produce PTTH, a polypeptide neurohormone. When PTTH reaches an endocrine organ called the prothoracic gland, it directs release of a second hormone, *ecdysteroid*. Bursts of ecdysteroid trigger each successive molt.

Ecdysteroid also controls a remarkable change in form called metamorphosis. Within the larva lie islands of tissues that will become the eyes, wings, brain, and other structures of the adult. Once the plump, crawling larva becomes a stationary pupa, these islands of cells take over. They complete their program of development, while many larval tissues undergo programmed cell death. The end result is the transformation of the crawling caterpillar into a free-flying moth.

Given that ecdysteroid can cause molting or metamorphosis, what determines which process takes place? The answer is another signal, juvenile hormone (JH), secreted by a pair of endocrine glands behind the brain. JH modulates the activity of ecdysteroid. As long as the level of JH is high, ecdysteroid stimulates molting (and thus maintains the "juvenile" larval state). When the JH level drops, ecdysteroid induces formation of a pupa, within which metamorphosis occurs.

Understanding the coordination between the nervous system and endocrine system in insects has led to advancements in agricultural pest control. For example, one type of chemical developed to control insect pests is a compound that binds to the ecdysteroid receptor, causing insect larvae to molt prematurely and die.

Vertebrates

In vertebrates, coordination of endocrine signaling relies heavily on a region of the brain called the **hypothalamus** **(Figure 45.13)**. The hypothalamus receives information from nerves throughout the body and, in response, initiates endocrine signaling appropriate to environmental conditions. In many vertebrates, for example, nerve signals from the brain pass sensory information to the hypothalamus about seasonal changes. The hypothalamus, in turn, regulates the release of reproductive hormones required during the breeding season.

Signals from the hypothalamus travel to the **pituitary gland**, a gland located at the base of the hypothalamus (see Figure 45.13). Roughly the size and shape of a lima bean, the pituitary has discrete posterior and anterior parts, or lobes, which are actually two fused glands that perform very different functions. The **posterior pituitary** is an extension of the hypothalamus. Hypothalamic axons that reach into the posterior pituitary secrete neurohormones synthesized in the hypothalamus. In contrast, the **anterior pituitary** is an endocrine gland that synthesizes and secretes hormones in response to hormones from the hypothalamus.

Posterior Pituitary Hormones

Neurosecretory cells of the hypothalamus synthesize the two posterior pituitary hormones: antidiuretic hormone and oxytocin. After traveling to the posterior pituitary within the long axons of the neurosecretory cells, these neurohormones are stored, to be released in response to nerve impulses transmitted by the hypothalamus **(Figure 45.14)**.

▲ Figure 45.13 **Endocrine glands in the human brain.** This side view of the brain indicates the position of the hypothalamus, the pituitary gland, and the pineal gland. (The pineal gland plays a role in regulating biological rhythms.)

Pineal gland
Cerebrum
Thalamus
Hypothalamus
Cerebellum
Pituitary gland
Spinal cord
Posterior pituitary
Hypothalamus
Anterior pituitary

Hypothalamus
Neurosecretory cells of the hypothalamus
Neurohormone
Axons
Posterior pituitary
Anterior pituitary

HORMONE	ADH	Oxytocin
TARGET	Kidney tubules	Mammary glands, uterine muscles

▲ Figure 45.14 **Production and release of posterior pituitary hormones.** The posterior pituitary gland is an extension of the hypothalamus. Certain neurosecretory cells in the hypothalamus make antidiuretic hormone (ADH) and oxytocin, which are transported to the posterior pituitary, where they are stored. Nerve signals from the brain trigger release of these neurohormones.

Antidiuretic hormone (ADH), or *vasopressin*, regulates kidney function. Secretion of ADH increases water retention in the kidneys, helping maintain normal blood osmolarity (see Concept 44.5). ADH also has an important role in social behavior (see Concept 51.4).

Oxytocin has multiple functions related to reproduction. As we have seen, in female mammals oxytocin controls milk secretion by the mammary glands and regulates uterine contractions during birthing. In addition, oxytocin has targets in the brain, where it influences behaviors related to maternal care, pair bonding, and sexual activity.

Anterior Pituitary Hormones

Hormones secreted by the anterior pituitary control a diverse set of processes in the human body, including metabolism, osmoregulation, and reproduction. As illustrated in **Figure 45.15**, many anterior pituitary hormones, but not all, regulate the activity of other endocrine glands or tissues.

Hormones secreted by the hypothalamus control the release of all anterior pituitary hormones. Each hypothalamic hormone is either a *releasing hormone* or an *inhibiting hormone*, reflecting its role in promoting or inhibiting release of one or more specific hormones by the anterior pituitary. *Prolactin-releasing hormone*, for example, is a hypothalamic hormone that stimulates the anterior pituitary to secrete **prolactin**, which has activities that include stimulating milk production. Every anterior pituitary hormone is controlled by at least one releasing hormone. Some, such as prolactin, have both a releasing hormone and an inhibiting hormone.

The hypothalamic releasing and inhibiting hormones are secreted near capillaries at the base of the hypothalamus. The capillaries drain into short blood vessels, called portal vessels, which subdivide into a second capillary bed within the anterior pituitary. Releasing and inhibiting hormones thus have direct access to the gland they control.

Sets of hormones from the hypothalamus, the anterior pituitary, and a target endocrine gland are often organized into a *hormone cascade pathway*. Signals to the brain stimulate the hypothalamus to secrete a hormone that stimulates or inhibits release of an anterior pituitary hormone. The anterior pituitary hormone in turn acts on another endocrine organ, stimulating secretion of yet another hormone, which exerts effects on specific target tissues.

In a sense, hormone cascade pathways redirect signals from the hypothalamus to other endocrine glands. For this reason, the anterior pituitary hormones in these pathways are called **tropic hormones** or *tropins*, from the Greek word for bending or turning. For example, the hormones FSH and LH secreted by the anterior pituitary are called gonadotropins because they convey signals from the hypothalamus to the gonads (testes or ovaries). To learn more about tropic hormones and hormone cascade pathways, we'll turn next to thyroid gland function and regulation.

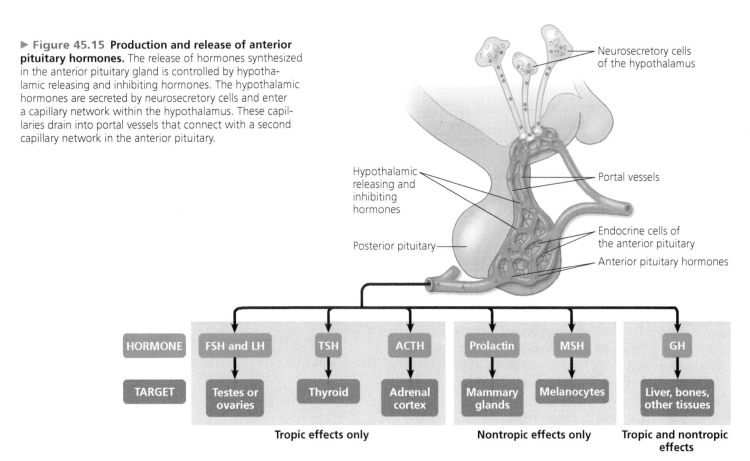

► **Figure 45.15 Production and release of anterior pituitary hormones.** The release of hormones synthesized in the anterior pituitary gland is controlled by hypothalamic releasing and inhibiting hormones. The hypothalamic hormones are secreted by neurosecretory cells and enter a capillary network within the hypothalamus. These capillaries drain into portal vessels that connect with a second capillary network in the anterior pituitary.

Neurosecretory cells of the hypothalamus

Hypothalamic releasing and inhibiting hormones

Portal vessels

Posterior pituitary

Endocrine cells of the anterior pituitary

Anterior pituitary hormones

HORMONE	FSH and LH	TSH	ACTH	Prolactin	MSH	GH
TARGET	Testes or ovaries	Thyroid	Adrenal cortex	Mammary glands	Melanocytes	Liver, bones, other tissues

Tropic effects only   Nontropic effects only   Tropic and nontropic effects

Thyroid Regulation: A Hormone Cascade Pathway

In humans and other mammals, **thyroid hormone** regulates bioenergetics; helps maintain normal blood pressure, heart rate, and muscle tone; and regulates digestive and reproductive functions. If the level of thyroid hormone in the blood drops, the hypothalamus responds by initiating a hormone cascade pathway (**Figure 45.16**). The hypothalamus secretes thyrotropin-releasing hormone (TRH), causing the anterior pituitary to secrete a tropic hormone known as either thyroid-stimulating hormone (TSH) or thyrotropin. TSH stimulates release of thyroid hormone by the **thyroid gland**, an organ in the neck consisting of two lobes on the ventral surface of the trachea. As thyroid hormone accumulates, it increases metabolic rate, while also initiating negative feedback that prevents its overproduction.

Disorders of Thyroid Function and Regulation

Disruption of thyroid hormone production and regulation can result in serious disorders. Hypothyroidism, the secretion of too little thyroid hormone, can cause weight gain, lethargy, and intolerance to cold in adults. In contrast, excessive secretion of thyroid hormone, known as hyperthyroidism, can lead to high body temperature, profuse sweating, weight loss, irritability, and high blood pressure.

The most common form of hyperthyroidism in humans is Graves' disease. Protruding eyes, caused by fluid accumulation behind the eyes, are a typical symptom. In this autoimmune disorder, the body produces antibodies that bind to and activate the receptor for TSH, causing sustained thyroid hormone production.

Some thyroid disorders reflect the unusual chemical makeup of thyroid hormone. The term *thyroid hormone* actually refers to a pair of very similar hormones derived from the amino acid tyrosine. *Triiodothyronine* (T_3) contains three iodine atoms, whereas tetraiodothyronine, or *thyroxine* (T_4), contains four (see Figure 45.4). Because thyroid hormone production requires iodine, it is an essential mineral.

Although iodine is readily obtained from seafood or iodized salt, people in many parts of the world suffer from inadequate iodine in their diet and therefore cannot synthesize adequate amounts of thyroid hormone. The low blood levels of thyroid hormone are insufficient to provide the usual negative feedback on the hypothalamus and anterior pituitary (see Figure 45.16). As a consequence, the pituitary continues to secrete TSH. Elevated TSH levels cause an enlargement of the thyroid gland, resulting in a swelling of the neck known as goiter.

Proper thyroid function is also required for normal development. Humans and other vertebrates require thyroid hormone for the normal functioning of bone-forming cells,

STIMULUS

❶ Thyroid hormone levels drop below the normal range.

Sensory neuron

Hypothalamus

❷ The hypothalamus secretes thyrotropin-releasing hormone (TRH●) into the blood. Portal vessels carry TRH to the anterior pituitary.

Neurosecretory cell

TRH

Negative feedback

❸ TRH causes the anterior pituitary to secrete thyroid-stimulating hormone (TSH, also known as thyrotropin▲) into the circulatory system.

Anterior pituitary

TSH

Circulation throughout body via blood

Thyroid gland

❹ TSH stimulates endocrine cells in the thyroid gland to secrete thyroid hormone (T_3 and T_4 ■) into the circulatory system.

Thyroid hormone

Circulation throughout body via blood

❺ Thyroid hormone levels increase in the blood and body tissues, returning to the normal range. Thyroid hormone acts on target cells throughout the body to control bioenergetics; help maintain normal blood pressure, heart rate, and muscle tone; and regulate digestive and reproductive functions.

RESPONSE

❻ Thyroid hormone blocks TRH release from the hypothalamus and TSH release from the anterior pituitary, forming a negative-feedback loop that prevents overproduction of thyroid hormone.

▲ Figure 45.16 **Regulation of thyroid hormone secretion: a hormone cascade pathway.**

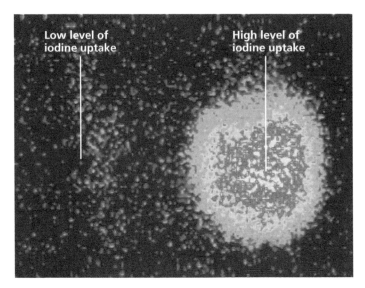

▲ **Figure 45.17 Thyroid scan.** Physicians can use a radioactive isotope of iodine to detect abnormal patterns of iodine uptake that could indicate a thyroid disorder.

as well as for the branching of nerve cells during embryonic development of the brain. In humans, congenital hypothyroidism, an inherited condition of thyroid deficiency, results in markedly retarded skeletal growth and poor mental development. These defects can often be avoided, at least partially, if treatment with thyroid hormone begins early in life. Iodine deficiency in childhood causes the same defects, but it is fully preventable if iodized salt is used in food preparation.

The fact that iodine in the body is dedicated to the production of thyroid hormone provides a novel diagnostic tool for disorders of thyroid function: Radioactive forms of iodine enable specific imaging of the thyroid gland (**Figure 45.17**).

Hormonal Regulation of Growth

Growth hormone (GH), which is secreted by the anterior pituitary, stimulates growth through both tropic and nontropic effects. A major target, the liver, responds to GH by releasing *insulin-like growth factors (IGFs)*, which circulate in the blood and directly stimulate bone and cartilage growth. (IGFs also appear to play a key role in aging in many animal species.) In the absence of GH, the skeleton of an immature animal stops growing. GH also exerts diverse metabolic effects that tend to raise blood glucose levels, thus opposing the effects of insulin.

Abnormal production of GH in humans can result in several disorders, depending on when the problem occurs and whether it involves hypersecretion (too much) or hyposecretion (too little). Hypersecretion of GH during childhood can lead to gigantism, in which the person grows unusually tall but retains relatively normal body proportions (**Figure 45.18**). Excessive GH production in adulthood stimulates bony growth in the few body parts that are still responsive to the hormone—predominantly the face, hands, and feet. The result

▲ **Figure 45.18 Effect of growth hormone overproduction.** Shown here surrounded by his family, Robert Wadlow grew to a height of 2.7 m (8 feet 11 inches) by age 22, making him the tallest man in history. His height was due to excess secretion of growth hormone by his pituitary gland.

is an overgrowth of the extremities called acromegaly (from the Greek *acros*, extreme, and *mega*, large).

Hyposecretion of GH in childhood retards long-bone growth and can lead to pituitary dwarfism. Individuals with this disorder are for the most part properly proportioned but generally reach a height of only about 1.2 m (4 feet). If diagnosed before puberty, pituitary dwarfism can be treated successfully with human GH (also called HGH). Since the mid-1980s, recombinant DNA technology has been used to produce HGH in bacteria (see Concept 20.4). Treatment of affected children with recombinant HGH is now fairly routine.

CONCEPT CHECK **45.2**

1. What are the roles of oxytocin and prolactin in regulating the mammary glands?

2. How do the two fused glands of the pituitary gland differ in function?

3. **WHAT IF?** Propose an explanation for why people with defects in specific endocrine pathways typically have defects in the final gland in the pathway rather than in the hypothalamus or pituitary.

4. **WHAT IF?** Lab tests of two patients, each diagnosed with excessive thyroid hormone production, revealed elevated levels of TSH in one but not the other. Was the diagnosis of one patient necessarily incorrect? Explain.

For suggested answers, see Appendix A.

Endocrine glands respond to diverse stimuli in regulating homeostasis, development, and behavior

In the remainder of this chapter, we'll focus on endocrine function in homeostasis, development, and behavior. We'll begin with another example of a simple hormone pathway, the regulation of calcium ion concentration in the circulatory system.

Parathyroid Hormone and Vitamin D: Control of Blood Calcium

Because calcium ions (Ca^{2+}) are essential to the normal functioning of all cells, homeostatic control of blood calcium level is vital. If the blood Ca^{2+} level falls substantially, skeletal muscles begin to contract convulsively, a potentially fatal condition. If the blood Ca^{2+} level rises substantially, precipitates of calcium phosphate can form in body tissues, leading to widespread organ damage.

In mammals, the **parathyroid glands**, a set of four small structures embedded in the posterior surface of the thyroid (see Figure 45.9), play a major role in blood Ca^{2+} regulation. When the blood Ca^{2+} level falls below a set point of about 10 mg/100 mL, these glands release **parathyroid hormone (PTH)**.

PTH raises the level of blood Ca^{2+} through direct effects in bones and the kidneys and an indirect effect on the intestines (Figure 45.19). In bones, PTH causes the mineralized matrix to break down, releasing Ca^{2+} into the blood. In the kidneys, PTH directly stimulates reabsorption of Ca^{2+} through the renal tubules. In addition, PTH indirectly raises blood Ca^{2+} levels by promoting production of vitamin D. A precursor form of vitamin D is obtained from food or synthesized by skin exposed to sunlight. Conversion of this precursor to active vitamin D begins in the liver. PTH acts in the kidney to stimulate completion of the conversion process. Vitamin D in turn acts on the intestines, stimulating the uptake of Ca^{2+} from food. As the blood Ca^{2+} level rises, a negative-feedback loop inhibits further release of PTH from the parathyroid glands (not shown in Figure 45.19).

The thyroid gland can also contribute to calcium homeostasis. If the blood Ca^{2+} level rises above the set point, the thyroid gland releases **calcitonin**, a hormone that inhibits bone breakdown

and enhances Ca^{2+} excretion by the kidneys. In fishes, rodents, and some other animals, calcitonin is required for Ca^{2+} homeostasis. In humans, however, calcitonin is apparently needed only during the extensive bone growth of childhood.

Adrenal Hormones: Response to Stress

The **adrenal glands** of vertebrates are located atop the kidneys (the *renal* organs). In mammals, each adrenal gland is actually made up of two glands with different cell types, functions, and embryonic origins: the adrenal *cortex*, the outer portion, and the adrenal *medulla*, the central portion. The adrenal cortex consists of true endocrine cells, whereas the secretory cells of the adrenal medulla develop from neural tissue. Thus, like the pituitary gland, each adrenal gland is a fused endocrine and neuroendocrine gland.

Catecholamines from the Adrenal Medulla

Imagine that while walking in the woods at night you hear a growling noise nearby. "A bear?" you wonder. Your heart beats faster, your breathing quickens, your muscles tense, and your thoughts speed up. These and other rapid responses to perceived danger comprise the "fight-or-flight" response. This coordinated set of physiological changes is triggered by two hormones of the adrenal medulla, epinephrine (adrenaline) and **norepinephrine** (also known as noradrenaline). Both are **catecholamines**, a class of amine hormones synthesized from the amino acid tyrosine.

The adrenal medulla secretes epinephrine and norepinephrine in response to short-term stress—whether extreme

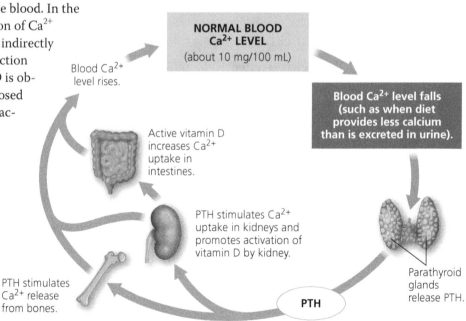

Blood Ca^{2+} level rises.

NORMAL BLOOD Ca^{2+} LEVEL (about 10 mg/100 mL)

Blood Ca^{2+} level falls (such as when diet provides less calcium than is excreted in urine).

Active vitamin D increases Ca^{2+} uptake in intestines.

PTH stimulates Ca^{2+} uptake in kidneys and promotes activation of vitamin D by kidney.

PTH stimulates Ca^{2+} release from bones.

Parathyroid glands release PTH.

PTH

▲ Figure 45.19 The roles of parathyroid hormone (PTH) in regulating blood calcium levels in mammals.

▼ **Figure 45.20 Stress and the adrenal gland.**

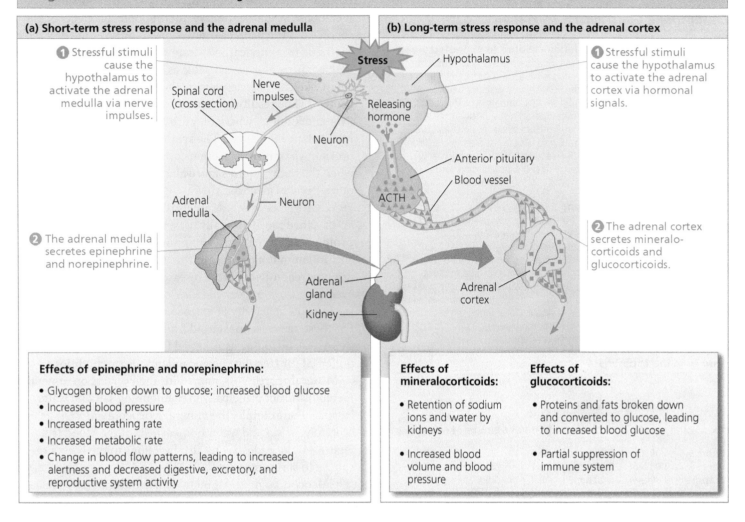

(a) Short-term stress response and the adrenal medulla

1 Stressful stimuli cause the hypothalamus to activate the adrenal medulla via nerve impulses.

Spinal cord (cross section)

Nerve impulses

Stress

Hypothalamus

Releasing hormone

Neuron

2 The adrenal medulla secretes epinephrine and norepinephrine.

Adrenal medulla

Neuron

Effects of epinephrine and norepinephrine:

- Glycogen broken down to glucose; increased blood glucose
- Increased blood pressure
- Increased breathing rate
- Increased metabolic rate
- Change in blood flow patterns, leading to increased alertness and decreased digestive, excretory, and reproductive system activity

(b) Long-term stress response and the adrenal cortex

1 Stressful stimuli cause the hypothalamus to activate the adrenal cortex via hormonal signals.

Anterior pituitary

Blood vessel

ACTH

2 The adrenal cortex secretes mineralo-corticoids and glucocorticoids.

Adrenal gland

Kidney

Adrenal cortex

Effects of mineralocorticoids:

- Retention of sodium ions and water by kidneys
- Increased blood volume and blood pressure

Effects of glucocorticoids:

- Proteins and fats broken down and converted to glucose, leading to increased blood glucose
- Partial suppression of immune system

pleasure or life-threatening danger. A major activity of these hormones is to increase the amount of chemical energy available for immediate use **(Figure 45.20a)**. Both epinephrine and norepinephrine increase the rate of glycogen breakdown in the liver and skeletal muscles, and both promote the release of glucose by liver cells and of fatty acids from fat cells. The released glucose and fatty acids circulate in the blood and can be used by body cells as fuel.

In addition to increasing the availability of energy sources, epinephrine and norepinephrine exert profound effects on the cardiovascular and respiratory systems. For example, they increase heart rate and stroke volume and dilate the bronchioles in the lungs, actions that raise the rate of oxygen delivery to body cells. For this reason, doctors may prescribe epinephrine as a heart stimulant or to open the airways during an asthma attack. These catecholamines also alter blood flow, causing constriction of some blood vessels and dilation of others (see Figure 45.8). The overall effect is to shunt blood away from the skin, digestive organs, and kidneys, while increasing the blood supply to the heart, brain, and skeletal muscles. Epinephrine generally has a

stronger effect on heart and metabolic rates, while norepinephrine primarily modulates blood pressure.

Note that epinephrine and norepinephrine are produced not only in the adrenal medulla, but also in the nervous system. In the latter location they function as neurotransmitters, as you'll read in Chapter 48.

Steroid Hormones from the Adrenal Cortex

Whereas the adrenal medulla responds to short-term stress, the adrenal cortex functions in the body's response to long-term stress **(Figure 45.20b)**. In contrast to the adrenal medulla, which reacts to nervous input, the adrenal cortex responds to endocrine signals. Stressful stimuli cause the hypothalamus to secrete a releasing hormone that stimulates the anterior pituitary to release adrenocorticotropic hormone (ACTH), a tropic hormone. When ACTH reaches the adrenal cortex via the bloodstream, it stimulates the endocrine cells to synthesize and secrete a family of steroids called *corticosteroids*. The two main types of corticosteroids in humans are glucocorticoids and mineralocorticoids.

Designing a Controlled Experiment

How is Nighttime ACTH Secretion Related to Expected Sleep Duration? Humans secrete increasing amounts of adrenocorticotropic hormone (ACTH) during the late stages of normal sleep, with the peak secretion occurring at the time of spontaneous waking. Because ACTH is released in response to stressful stimuli, scientists hypothesized that ACTH secretion prior to waking might be an anticipatory response to the stress associated with transitioning from sleep to a more active state. If so, an individual's expectation of waking at a particular time might influence the timing of ACTH secretion. How can such a hypothesis be tested? In this exercise, you will examine how researchers designed a controlled experiment to study the role of expectation.

How the Experiment Was Done Researchers studied 15 healthy volunteers in their mid-twenties over three nights. Each night each subject was told when he or she would be awakened: 6:00 or 9:00 a.m. The subjects went to sleep at midnight. Subjects in the "short" or "long" protocol group were awakened at the expected time (6:00 or 9:00 a.m., respectively). Subjects in the "surprise" protocol group were told they would be awakened at 9:00 a.m., but were actually awakened three hours early, at 6:00 a.m. At set times, blood samples were drawn to determine plasma levels of ACTH. To determine the change (Δ) in ACTH concentration post-waking, the researchers compared samples drawn at waking and 30 minutes later.

Data from the Experiment

Sleep Protocol	Expected Wake Time	Actual Wake Time	Mean Plasma ACTH Level (pg/mL)		
			1:00 a.m.	6:00 a.m.	Δ in the 30 Minutes Post-waking
Short	6:00 a.m.	6:00 a.m.	9.9	37.3	10.6
Long	9:00 a.m.	9:00 a.m.	8.1	26.5	12.2
Surprise	9:00 a.m.	6:00 a.m.	8.0	25.5	22.1

Interpret the Data

1. Describe the role of the "surprise" protocol in the experimental design.

2. Each subject was given a different protocol on each of the three nights, and the order of the protocols was varied among the subjects that so that one third had each protocol each night. What factors were the researchers attempting to control for with this approach?

3. For subjects in the short protocol, what was the mean ACTH level at waking? Using the data in the last two columns, calculate the mean level 30 minutes later. Was the rate of change faster or slower in that 30-minute period than during the interval from 1:00 to 6:00 a.m.?

4. How does the change in ACTH levels between 1:00 and 6:00 a.m. for the surprise protocol compare to that for the short and long protocols? Does this result support the hypothesis being tested? Explain.

5. Using the data in the last two columns, calculate the mean ACTH concentration 30 minutes post-waking for the surprise protocol and compare to your answer for Question 3. What do your results suggest about a person's physiological response immediately after waking?

6. What are some variables that weren't controlled for in this experiment that could be explored in a follow-up study?

(MB) A version of this Scientific Skills Exercise can be assigned in MasteringBiology.

Data from J. Born, et al., Timing the end of nocturnal sleep, *Nature* 397:29-30 (1999).

As reflected in their name, **glucocorticoids**, such as cortisol (see Figure 45.4), have a primary effect on glucose metabolism. Augmenting the fuel-mobilizing effects of glucagon from the pancreas, glucocorticoids promote glucose synthesis from noncarbohydrate sources, such as proteins, making more glucose available as fuel. Glucocorticoids also act on skeletal muscle, causing the breakdown of muscle proteins. The resulting amino acids are transported to the liver and kidneys, where they are converted to glucose and released into the blood. The synthesis of glucose upon the breakdown of muscle proteins provides circulating fuel when the body requires more glucose than the liver can mobilize from its glycogen stores.

When glucocorticoids are introduced into the body at levels above those normally present, they suppress certain components of the body's immune system. Because of this anti-inflammatory effect, glucocorticoids are sometimes used to treat inflammatory diseases such as arthritis. However, long-term use can have serious side effects, reflecting the potent activity of glucocorticoids on metabolism. For these reasons, nonsteroidal anti-inflammatory drugs (NSAIDs), including aspirin and ibuprofen, are generally preferred for treating chronic inflammatory conditions.

Mineralocorticoids, named for their effects on mineral metabolism, act principally in maintaining salt and water balance. For example, the mineralocorticoid *aldosterone* functions in ion and water homeostasis of the blood (see Figure 44.21). Aldosterone also functions in the body's response to severe stress.

Glucocorticoids and mineralocorticoids not only mediate stress responses, but also participate in homeostatic regulation of metabolism. In the Scientific Skills Exercise, you can explore an experiment investigating changes in ACTH secretion as humans awaken from sleep.

Sex Hormones

Sex hormones affect growth, development, reproductive cycles, and sexual behavior. Whereas the adrenal glands secrete small quantities of these hormones, the gonads (testes of males and ovaries of females) are their principal sources. The gonads produce and secrete three major types of steroid sex hormones: androgens, estrogens, and progestins. All three types are found in both males and females but in different proportions.

The testes primarily synthesize **androgens**, the main one being **testosterone**. In humans, testosterone first functions before birth, promoting development of male reproductive structures **(Figure 45.21)**. Androgens play a major role again at puberty, when they are responsible for the development of male secondary sex characteristics. High concentrations of androgen lead to a low voice and male patterns of hair growth, as well as increases in muscle and bone mass. The

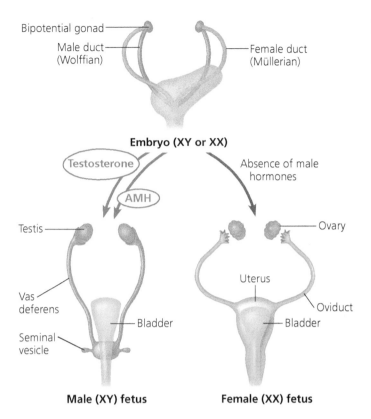

Bipotential gonad

Male duct (Wolffian)

Female duct (Müllerian)

Embryo (XY or XX)

Testosterone

Absence of male hormones

AMH

Testis

Ovary

Vas deferens

Uterus

Seminal vesicle

Bladder

Oviduct

Bladder

Male (XY) fetus

Female (XX) fetus

▲ **Figure 45.21 Sex hormones regulate formation of internal reproductive structures in human development.** In a male (XY) embryo, the bipotential gonads become the testes, which secrete testosterone and anti-Müllerian hormone (AMH). Testosterone directs formation of sperm-carrying ducts (vas deferens and seminal vesicles), while AMH causes the female ducts to degenerate. In the absence of these testis hormones, the male ducts degenerate and female structures form, including the oviduct, uterus, and vagina.

muscle-building, or anabolic, action of testosterone and related steroids has enticed some athletes to take them as supplements, despite prohibitions against their use in nearly all sports. Use of anabolic steroids, while effective in increasing muscle mass, can cause severe acne outbreaks and liver damage, as well as significant decreases in sperm count and testicular size.

Estrogens, of which the most important is **estradiol**, are responsible for the maintenance of the female reproductive system and for the development of female secondary sex characteristics. In mammals, **progestins**, which include **progesterone**, are primarily involved in preparing and maintaining tissues of the uterus required to support the growth and development of an embryo.

Estrogens and other gonadal sex hormones are components of hormone cascade pathways. Synthesis of these hormones is controlled by two gonadotropins from the anterior pituitary gland, follicle-stimulating hormone and luteinizing hormone (see Figure 45.15). Gonadotropin secretion is in turn controlled by GnRH (gonadotropin-releasing hormone), from the hypothalamus. We'll examine the feedback relationships that regulate gonadal hormone secretion in detail when we discuss animal reproduction in Chapter 46.

Endocrine Disruptors

Between 1938 and 1971, some pregnant women at risk for pregnancy complications were prescribed a synthetic estrogen called diethylstilbestrol (DES). What was not known until 1971 was that exposure to DES can alter reproductive system development in the fetus. Daughters of women who took DES are more frequently afflicted with certain reproductive abnormalities, including vaginal and cervical cancer, structural changes in the reproductive organs, and increased risk of miscarriage (spontaneous abortion). DES is now recognized as an *endocrine disruptor*, a foreign molecule that interrupts the normal function of a hormone pathway.

In recent years, some scientists have hypothesized that molecules in the environment also act as endocrine disruptors. For example, bisphenol A, a chemical used in making some plastics, has been studied for potential interference with normal reproduction and development. In addition, it has been suggested that some estrogen-like molecules, such as those present in soybeans and other edible plant products, have the beneficial effect of lowering breast cancer risk. Sorting out such effects, whether harmful or beneficial, has proven quite difficult, in part because enzymes in the liver change the properties of any such molecules entering the body through the digestive system.

Hormones and Biological Rhythms

There is still much to be learned about the hormone **melatonin**, a modified amino acid that regulates functions related to light and the seasons. Melatonin is produced by the **pineal gland**, a small mass of tissue near the center of the mammalian brain (see Figure 45.13).

Although melatonin affects skin pigmentation in many vertebrates, its primary effects relate to biological rhythms associated with reproduction and with daily activity levels (see Figure 40.9). Melatonin is secreted at night, and the amount released depends on the length of the night. In winter, for example, when days are short and nights are long, more melatonin is secreted. There is also good evidence that nightly increases in the levels of melatonin play a significant role in promoting sleep.

The release of melatonin by the pineal gland is controlled by a group of neurons in the hypothalamus called the suprachiasmatic nucleus (SCN). The SCN functions as a biological clock and receives input from specialized light-sensitive neurons in the retina of the eye. Although the SCN regulates melatonin production during the 24-hour light/dark cycle, melatonin also influences SCN activity. We'll consider biological rhythms further in Chapter 49, where we analyze experiments on SCN function.

Evolution of Hormone Function

EVOLUTION Many of the hormones described in this chapter are found in a broad range of animal species. Over the course of evolution, however, the functions of particular hormones have diverged. Thyroid hormone, which regulates metabolism in a number of animals, provides one example. In frogs, thyroid hormone (thyroxine) has taken on an apparently unique function: stimulating tail resorption during metamorphosis, the change in form from tadpole to adult frog (Figure 45.22).

Diverse functions have also evolved for many other vertebrate hormones. Prolactin, a product of the anterior pituitary, has an especially broad range of activities: It stimulates mammary gland growth and milk synthesis in mammals, regulates fat metabolism and reproduction in birds, delays metamorphosis in amphibians, and regulates salt and water balance in freshwater fishes. These varied activities suggest that prolactin is an ancient hormone with functions that have diversified during the evolution of vertebrate groups.

Melanocyte-stimulating hormone (MSH), secreted by the anterior pituitary, provides another example of a hormone with distinct functions in different evolutionary lineages. In amphibians, fishes, and reptiles, MSH regulates skin color by controlling pigment distribution in skin cells called melanocytes. In mammals, MSH functions in hunger and metabolism in addition to skin coloration.

The specialized action of MSH that has evolved in the mammalian brain may prove to be of particular medical importance. Many patients with late-stage cancer, AIDS, tuberculosis, and certain aging disorders suffer from a devastating wasting condition called cachexia. Characterized by weight loss, muscle atrophy, and loss of appetite, cachexia responds poorly to existing therapies. However, it turns out that activation of a brain receptor for MSH produces some of the same changes seen in cachexia. Moreover, in experiments on mice with mutations that cause cancer and consequently cachexia, treatment with drugs that blocked the brain MSH receptor prevented cachexia. Whether such drugs can be used to treat cachexia in humans is an area of active study.

▲ **Adult frog**

◄ **Figure 45.22 Specialized role of a hormone in frog metamorphosis.** The hormone thyroxine is responsible for the resorption of the tadpole's tail as the frog develops into its adult form.

▲ **Tadpole**

CONCEPT CHECK 45.3

1. If a hormone pathway produces a transient response to a stimulus, how would shortening the stimulus duration affect the need for negative feedback?

2. How would a decrease in the number of corticosteroid receptors in the hypothalamus affect levels of corticosteroids in the blood?

3. **WHAT IF?** Suppose you receive an injection of cortisone, a glucocorticoid, in an inflamed joint. What aspect of glucocorticoid activity would you be exploiting? If a glucocorticoid pill were also effective at treating the inflammation, why would it still be preferable to introduce the drug locally?

For suggested answers, see Appendix A.

---

45 Chapter Review

SUMMARY OF KEY CONCEPTS

CONCEPT 45.1

Hormones and other signaling molecules bind to target receptors, triggering specific response pathways (pp. 994–999)

- The forms of signaling between animal cells differ in the type of secreting cell and the route taken by the signal to its target.

Endocrine signals, or **hormones**, are secreted into the extracellular fluid by endocrine cells or ductless glands and reach target cells via circulatory fluids. **Paracrine** signals act on neighboring cells, whereas **autocrine** signals act on the secreting cell itself. **Neurotransmitters** also act locally, but **neurohormones** can act throughout the body. **Pheromones** are released into the environment for communication between animals of the same species.

- **Local regulators**, which carry out paracrine and autocrine signaling, include cytokines and growth factors (polypeptides), **prostaglandins** (modified fatty acids), and **nitric oxide** (a gas).

- Polypeptides, steroids, and amines comprise the major classes of animal hormones. Depending on whether they are water-soluble or lipid-soluble, hormones activate different response pathways.

? *Predict what would happen if you injected a water-soluble hormone directly into the cytosol of a target cell.*

CONCEPT 45.2

Feedback regulation and coordination with the nervous system are common in endocrine signaling (pp. 1000–1005)

- Hormone pathways may be regulated by **negative feedback**, which dampens the stimulus, or **positive feedback**, which amplifies the stimulus and drives the response to completion.
- In insects, molting and development are controlled by three hormones: PTTH; ecdysteroid, whose release is triggered by PTTH; and juvenile hormone. Coordination of signals from the nervous and endocrine systems and modulation of one hormone activity by another bring about the sequence of developmental stages that lead to an adult form.
- In vertebrates, neurosecretory cells in the **hypothalamus** produce two hormones that are secreted by the **posterior pituitary** and that act directly on nonendocrine tissues: **oxytocin**, which induces uterine contractions and release of milk from mammary glands, and **antidiuretic hormone (ADH)**, which enhances water reabsorption in the kidneys.
- Other hypothalamic cells produce hormones that are transported to the **anterior pituitary**, where they stimulate or inhibit the release of particular hormones.
- Often, anterior pituitary hormones act in a cascade. For example, the secretion of thyroid-stimulating hormone (TSH) is regulated by thyrotropin-releasing hormone (TRH). TSH in turn induces the **thyroid gland** to secrete **thyroid hormone**, a combination of the iodine-containing hormones T_3 and T_4. Thyroid hormone stimulates metabolism and influences development and maturation.
- Most anterior pituitary hormones are **tropic hormones**, acting on endocrine tissues or glands to regulate hormone secretion. Tropic hormones of the anterior pituitary include TSH, follicle-stimulating hormone (FSH), luteinizing hormone (LH), and adrenocorticotropic hormone (ACTH). **Growth hormone** (GH) has both tropic and nontropic effects. It promotes growth directly, affects metabolism, and stimulates the production of growth factors by other tissues.

? *Which major endocrine organs described in Figure 45.9 are regulated independently of the hypothalamus and pituitary?*

CONCEPT 45.3

Endocrine glands respond to diverse stimuli in regulating homeostasis, development, and behavior (pp. 1006–1010)

- **Parathyroid hormone** (PTH), secreted by the **parathyroid glands**, causes bone to release Ca^{2+} into the blood and stimulates reabsorption of Ca^{2+} in the kidneys. PTH also stimulates the kidneys to activate vitamin D, which promotes intestinal uptake of Ca^{2+} from food. **Calcitonin**, secreted by the thyroid, has the opposite effects in bones and kidneys as PTH. Calcitonin is important for calcium homeostasis in adults of some vertebrates, but not humans.
- In response to stress, neurosecretory cells in the adrenal medulla release **epinephrine** and **norepinephrine**, which mediate various fight-or-flight responses. The adrenal cortex releases **glucocorticoids**, such as cortisol, which influence glucose metabolism and the immune system. It also releases **mineralocorticoids**, primarily aldosterone, which help regulate salt and water balance.
- Sex hormones regulate growth, development, reproduction, and sexual behavior. Although the adrenal cortex produces small amounts of these hormones, the gonads (testes and ovaries) serve as the major source. All three types—**androgens**, **estrogens**, and **progestins**—are produced in males and females, but in different proportions.
- The **pineal gland**, located within the brain, secretes **melatonin**, which functions in biological rhythms related to reproduction and sleep. Release of melatonin is controlled by the SCN, the region of the brain that functions as a biological clock.
- Hormones have acquired distinct roles in different species over the course of evolution. **Prolactin** stimulates milk production in mammals but has diverse effects in other vertebrates. **Melanocyte-stimulating hormone** (MSH) influences fat metabolism in mammals and skin pigmentation in other vertebrates.

? *ADH and epinephrine act as hormones when released into the bloodstream and as neurotransmitters when released in synapses between neurons. What is similar about the endocrine glands that produce these two molecules?*

TEST YOUR UNDERSTANDING

LEVEL 1: KNOWLEDGE/COMPREHENSION

1. Which of the following is *not* an accurate statement?
   a. Hormones are chemical messengers that travel to target cells through the circulatory system.
   b. Hormones often regulate homeostasis through antagonistic functions.
   c. Hormones of the same chemical class usually have the same function.
   d. Hormones are often regulated through feedback loops.

2. The hypothalamus
   a. synthesizes all of the hormones produced by the pituitary gland.
   b. influences the function of only one lobe of the pituitary gland.
   c. produces only inhibitory hormones.
   d. regulates both reproduction and body temperature.

3. Growth factors are local regulators that
   a. are produced by the anterior pituitary.
   b. are modified fatty acids that stimulate bone and cartilage growth.
   c. are found on the surface of cancer cells and stimulate abnormal cell division.
   d. bind to cell-surface receptors and stimulate growth and development of target cells.

4. Which hormone is *incorrectly* paired with its action?
   a. oxytocin—stimulates uterine contractions during childbirth
   b. thyroxine—inhibits metabolic processes
   c. ACTH—stimulates the release of glucocorticoids by the adrenal cortex
   d. melatonin—affects biological rhythms and seasonal reproduction

LEVEL 2: APPLICATION/ANALYSIS

5. Steroid and peptide hormones typically have in common
   a. their solubility in cell membranes.
   b. their requirement for travel through the bloodstream.
   c. the location of their receptors.
   d. their reliance on signal transduction in the cell.

6. Which of the following is the most likely explanation for hypothyroidism in a patient whose iodine level is normal?
   a. greater production of T_3 than of T_4
   b. hyposecretion of TSH
   c. hypersecretion of MSH
   d. a decrease in the thyroid secretion of calcitonin

7. The relationship between the insect hormones ecdysteroid and PTTH is an example of
   a. an interaction of the endocrine and nervous systems.
   b. homeostasis achieved by positive feedback.
   c. homeostasis maintained by antagonistic hormones.
   d. competitive inhibition of a hormone receptor.

8. **DRAW IT** In mammals, milk production by mammary glands is controlled by prolactin and prolactin-releasing hormone. Draw a simple sketch of this pathway, including glands, tissues, hormones, routes for hormone movement, and effects.

LEVEL 3: SYNTHESIS/EVALUATION

9. **EVOLUTION CONNECTION**
   The intracellular receptors used by all the steroid and thyroid hormones are similar enough in structure that they are all considered members of one "superfamily" of proteins. Propose a hypothesis for how the genes encoding these receptors may have evolved. (*Hint*: See Figure 21.13.) How could you test your hypothesis using DNA sequence data?

10. **SCIENTIFIC INQUIRY**
    INTERPRET THE DATA Chronically high levels of glucocorticoids can result in obesity, muscle weakness, and depression, a combination of symptoms called Cushing's syndrome. Excessive activity of either the pituitary or the adrenal gland can be the cause. To determine which gland has abnormal activity in a particular patient, doctors use the drug dexamethasone, a synthetic glucocorticoid that blocks ACTH release. Based on the graph, which gland is affected in patient X?

Drug administered
- None
- Dexamethasone

(y-axis: Cortisol level in blood; x-axis: Normal, Patient X)

11. **WRITE ABOUT A THEME: INTERACTIONS**
    In a short essay (100–150 words), use specific examples to discuss the role of hormones in an animal's responses to changes in its environment.

12. **SYNTHESIZE YOUR KNOWLEDGE**

The frog on the left was injected with MSH, causing a change in skin color within minutes due to a rapid redistribution of pigment granules in specialized skin cells. Using what you know about neuroendocrine signaling, explain how a frog could use MSH to match its skin coloration to that of its surroundings.

For selected answers, see Appendix A.

MasteringBiology®

Students Go to **MasteringBiology** for assignments, the eText, and the Study Area with practice tests, animations, and activities.

Instructors Go to **MasteringBiology** for automatically graded tutorials and questions that you can assign to your students, plus Instructor Resources.

46

Animal Reproduction

▲ Figure 46.1 How can each of these sea slugs be both male and female?

Pairing Up for Sexual Reproduction

The sea slugs, or nudibranchs (*Nembrotha chamberlaini*), in **Figure 46.1** are mating. If not disturbed, these marine molluscs may remain joined for hours. Sperm will be transferred and will fertilize eggs. A few weeks later, sexual reproduction will be complete. New individuals will hatch, but which parent is the mother? The answer is simple yet probably unexpected: both. In fact, each sea slug produces eggs *and* sperm.

As humans, we tend to think of reproduction in terms of the mating of males and females and the fusion of sperm and eggs. Animal reproduction, however, takes many forms. In some species, individuals change their sex during their lifetime; in other species, such as sea slugs, an individual is both male and female. There are animals that can fertilize their own eggs, as well as others that can reproduce without any form of sex. For certain species, such as honeybees, only a few individuals within a large population reproduce.

A population outlives its members only by reproduction, the generation of new individuals from existing ones. In this chapter, we'll compare the diverse reproductive mechanisms that have evolved among animals. We'll then examine details of mammalian reproduction, with emphasis on the well-studied example of humans. We'll focus on reproduction mostly from the parents' perspective, deferring the details of embryonic development until the next chapter.

Both asexual and sexual reproduction occur in the animal kingdom

There are two modes of animal reproduction—sexual and asexual. In **sexual reproduction**, the fusion of haploid gametes forms a diploid cell, the **zygote**. The animal that develops from a zygote can in turn give rise to gametes by meiosis (see Figure 13.8). The female gamete, the **egg**, is large and nonmotile, whereas the male gamete, the **sperm**, is generally much smaller and motile. In **asexual reproduction**, new individuals are generated without the fusion of egg and sperm. For most asexual animals, reproduction relies entirely on mitotic cell division.

For the vast majority of animals, reproduction is primarily or exclusively sexual. However, there are species that have a primarily asexual mode of reproduction, and in a few all-female species reproduction is exclusively asexual. These include the microscopic bdelloid rotifer (see Figure 13.13), as well as certain species of whiptail lizards, which we'll discuss shortly.

Mechanisms of Asexual Reproduction

Several simple forms of asexual reproduction are found only among invertebrates. One of these is *budding*, in which new individuals arise from outgrowths of existing ones (see Figure 13.2). In stony corals, for example, buds form and remain attached to the parent. The eventual result is a colony more than 1 m across, consisting of thousands of connected individuals. Also common among invertebrates is **fission**, the separation of a parent organism into two individuals of approximately equal size **(Figure 46.2)**.

▲ **Figure 46.2 Asexual reproduction of a sea anemone (*Anthopleura elegantissima*).** The large individual in the center is undergoing fission, dividing into two approximately equal-sized offspring, each a genetic copy of the parent.

Asexual reproduction can be a two-step process: *fragmentation*, the breaking of the body into several pieces, followed by *regeneration*, regrowth of lost body parts. If more than one piece grows and develops into a complete animal, the effect is reproduction. For example, certain annelid worms can split into several fragments, each regenerating a complete worm in less than a week. Numerous sponges, cnidarians, and tunicates also reproduce by fragmentation and regeneration.

A particularly intriguing form of asexual reproduction is **parthenogenesis**, in which an egg develops without being fertilized. Among invertebrates, parthenogenesis occurs in certain species of bees, wasps, and ants. The progeny can be either haploid or diploid. In the case of honeybees, males (drones) are fertile haploid adults that arise by parthenogenesis. In contrast, female honeybees, including both the sterile workers and the fertile queens, are diploid adults that develop from fertilized eggs. Among vertebrates, parthenogenesis has been observed quite rarely (in about one in every thousand species). Zookeepers have discovered parthenogenesis in the Komodo dragon and in a species of hammerhead shark: In both cases, females had been kept isolated from males but nevertheless produced offspring.

Sexual Reproduction: An Evolutionary Enigma

EVOLUTION Sex must enhance reproductive success or survival because it would otherwise rapidly disappear. To see why, consider an animal population in which half the females reproduce sexually and half reproduce asexually **(Figure 46.3)**. We'll assume that the number of offspring per female is a constant, two in this case. The two offspring of an asexual female will both be daughters that will each give birth to two more reproductive daughters. In contrast, half of a sexual female's offspring will be male. The number of sexual offspring will remain the same at each generation, because both a male and a female are required to reproduce. Thus, the asexual condition will increase in frequency at each generation. Yet despite this "twofold cost," sex is maintained even in animal species that can also reproduce asexually.

What advantage does sex provide? The answer remains elusive. Most hypotheses focus on the unique combinations of parental genes formed during meiotic recombination and fertilization. By producing offspring of varied genotypes, sexual reproduction may enhance the reproductive success of parents when environmental factors, such as pathogens, change relatively rapidly. In contrast, asexual reproduction is expected to be most advantageous in stable, favorable environments because it perpetuates successful genotypes precisely.

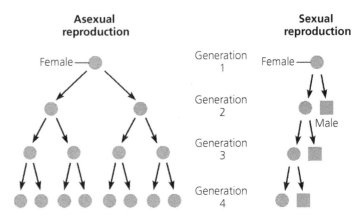

▲ **Figure 46.3 The "reproductive handicap" of sex.** These diagrams contrast asexual versus sexual reproduction over four generations, assuming two surviving offspring per female.

There are a number of reasons why the unique gene combinations formed during sexual reproduction might be advantageous. One is that beneficial gene combinations arising through recombination might speed up adaptation. Although this idea appears straightforward, the theoretical advantage is significant only when the rate of beneficial mutations is high and population size is small. Another idea is that the shuffling of genes during sexual reproduction might allow a population to rid itself of sets of harmful genes more readily.

Reproductive Cycles

Most animals exhibit cycles in reproductive activity, often related to changing seasons. These cycles are controlled by hormones, whose secretion in turn is regulated by environmental cues. In this way, animals conserve resources, reproducing only when sufficient energy sources are available and when environmental conditions favor the survival of offspring. For example, ewes (female sheep) have a reproductive cycle lasting 15–17 days. **Ovulation**, the release of mature eggs, occurs at the midpoint of each cycle. For ewes, reproductive cycles generally occur only during fall and early winter, and the length of any pregnancy is five months. Thus, most lambs are born in the early spring, when their chances of survival are optimal.

Because seasonal changes are often important cues for reproduction, global climate change can decrease reproductive success. Danish researchers have demonstrated just such an effect on caribou (wild reindeer) in Greenland. In spring, caribou migrate to calving grounds to eat sprouting plants, give birth, and care for their new calves. Prior to 1993, the arrival of the caribou at the calving grounds coincided with the brief period during which the plants were nutritious and digestible. Since 1993, however, average spring temperatures in the calving grounds have increased by more than 4°C, and the plants now sprout two weeks earlier. Because caribou migration is triggered by day length, not temperature, there is a mismatch between the timing of new plant growth and caribou birthing. Without adequate nutrition for the nursing females, the number of caribou offspring produced each year declined by 75% in just 14 years.

Reproductive cycles are also found among animals that can reproduce both sexually and asexually. Consider, for instance, the water flea (genus *Daphnia*). A *Daphnia* female can produce eggs of two types. One type of egg requires fertilization to develop, but the other type does not and develops instead by parthenogenesis. Asexual reproduction occurs when environmental conditions are favorable, whereas sexual reproduction occurs during times of environmental stress. As a result, the switch between sexual and asexual reproduction is roughly linked to season.

Some species of whiptail lizards in the genus *Aspidoscelis* exhibit a very different type of reproductive cycle: Reproduction is exclusively asexual, and there are no males.

Nevertheless, these lizards have courtship and mating behaviors very similar to those of sexual species of *Aspidoscelis*. During the breeding season, one female of each mating pair mimics a male **(Figure 46.4a)**. Members of the pair alternate roles two or three times during the season. An individual adopts female behavior when the level of the hormone estradiol is high, and it switches to male-like behavior when the level of the hormone progesterone is high **(Figure 46.4b)**. A female is more likely to ovulate if she is mounted at a critical time of the hormone cycle; isolated lizards lay fewer eggs than those that go through the motions of sex. These findings support the hypothesis that these parthenogenetic lizards evolved from species having two sexes and still require certain sexual stimuli for maximum reproductive success.

(a) Both lizards in this photograph are *A. uniparens* females. The one on top is playing the role of a male. Individuals switch sex roles two or three times during the breeding season.

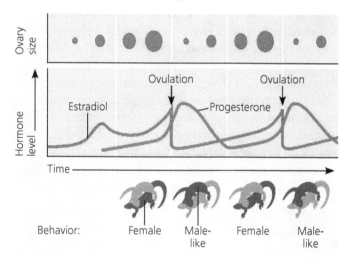

(b) The changes in sexual behavior of *A. uniparens* individuals are correlated with the cycles of ovulation and changing levels of the sex hormones estradiol and progesterone. These drawings track the changes in ovary size, hormone levels, and sexual behavior of one female lizard (shown in brown).

▲ **Figure 46.4 Sexual behavior in parthenogenetic lizards.** The desert-grassland whiptail lizard (*Aspidoscelis uniparens*) is an all-female species. These reptiles reproduce by parthenogenesis, the development of an unfertilized egg, but ovulation is stimulated by mating behavior.

INTERPRET THE DATA *If you plotted hormone levels for the lizard shown in gray, how would your graph differ from the graph in (b)?*

Variation in Patterns of Sexual Reproduction

For many animals, finding a partner for sexual reproduction can be challenging. Adaptations that arose during the evolution of some species meet this challenge in a novel way—by blurring the distinction between male and female. One such adaptation arose among sessile (stationary) animals, such as barnacles; burrowing animals, such as clams; and some parasites, including tapeworms. These animals have a very limited opportunity to find a mate. The evolutionary solution in this case is **hermaphroditism**, in which each individual has both male and female reproductive systems (the term *hermaphrodite* merges the names Hermes and Aphrodite, a Greek god and goddess). Because each hermaphrodite reproduces as both a male and a female, *any* two individuals can mate. Each animal donates and receives sperm during mating, as the sea slugs in Figure 46.1 are doing. In some species, hermaphrodites can also self-fertilize, allowing a form of sexual reproduction that doesn't require any partner.

The bluehead wrasse (*Thalassoma bifasciatum*) provides an example of a quite different variation in sexual reproduction. These coral reef fish live in harems, each consisting of a single male and several females. When the lone male dies, the opportunity for sexual reproduction would appear lost. Instead, the largest female in the harem transforms into a male and within a week begins to produce sperm instead of eggs. What selective pressure in the evolution of the bluehead wrasse resulted in sex reversal for the female with the largest body? Because it is the male wrasse that defends a harem against intruders, a larger size may be particularly important for a male in ensuring successful reproduction.

Certain oyster species also undergo sex reversal. In this case, individuals reproduce as males and then later as females, when their size is greatest. Since the number of gametes produced generally increases with size much more for females than for males, sex reversal in this direction maximizes gamete production. The result is enhanced reproductive success: Because oysters are sedentary animals and release their gametes into the surrounding water rather than mating directly, releasing more gametes tends to result in more offspring.

CONCEPT CHECK 46.1

1. Compare and contrast the outcomes of asexual and sexual reproduction.

2. Parthenogenesis is the most common form of asexual reproduction in animals that at other times reproduce sexually. What characteristic of parthenogenesis might explain this observation?

3. **WHAT IF?** If a hermaphrodite self-fertilizes, will the offspring be identical to the parent? Explain.

4. **MAKE CONNECTIONS** What examples of plant reproduction are most similar to asexual reproduction in animals? (See Concept 38.2.)

For suggested answers, see Appendix A.

Fertilization depends on mechanisms that bring together sperm and eggs of the same species

The union of sperm and egg—**fertilization**—can be either external or internal. In species with *external fertilization*, the female releases eggs into the environment, where the male then fertilizes them (Figure 46.5). Other species have *internal fertilization*: Sperm are deposited in or near the female reproductive tract, and fertilization occurs within the tract. (We'll discuss the cellular and molecular details of fertilization in Chapter 47.)

A moist habitat is almost always required for external fertilization, both to prevent the gametes from drying out and to allow the sperm to swim to the eggs. Many aquatic invertebrates simply shed their eggs and sperm into the surroundings, and fertilization occurs without the parents making physical contact. However, timing is crucial to ensure that mature sperm and eggs encounter one another.

Among some species with external fertilization, individuals clustered in the same area release their gametes into the water at the same time, a process known as *spawning*. In some cases, chemical signals that one individual generates in releasing gametes trigger others to release gametes. In other cases, environmental cues, such as temperature or day length, cause a whole population to release gametes at one time. For example, the palolo worm, native to coral reefs of the South Pacific, times its spawning to both the season and

▲ **Figure 46.5 External fertilization.** Many species of amphibians reproduce by external fertilization. In most of these species, behavioral adaptations ensure that a male is present when the female releases eggs. Here, a female frog (on bottom) has released a mass of eggs in response to being clasped by a male. The male released sperm (not visible) at the same time, and external fertilization has already occurred in the water.

the lunar cycle. In spring, when the moon is in its last quarter, palolo worms break in half, releasing tail segments engorged with sperm or eggs. These packets rise to the ocean surface and burst in such vast numbers that the sea appears milky with gametes. The sperm quickly fertilize the floating eggs, and within hours, the palolo's once-a-year reproductive frenzy is complete.

When external fertilization is not synchronous across a population, individuals may exhibit specific "courtship" behaviors leading to the fertilization of the eggs of one female by one male (see Figure 46.5). By triggering the release of both sperm and eggs, these behaviors increase the probability of successful fertilization.

Internal fertilization is an adaptation that enables sperm to reach an egg even when the environment is dry. It typically requires cooperative behavior that leads to copulation, as well as sophisticated and compatible reproductive systems. The male copulatory organ delivers sperm, and the female reproductive tract often has receptacles for storage and delivery of sperm to mature eggs.

No matter how fertilization occurs, the mating animals may make use of *pheromones*, chemicals released by one organism that can influence the physiology and behavior of other individuals of the same species. Pheromones are small, volatile or water-soluble molecules that disperse into the environment and, like hormones, are active at very low concentrations (see Chapter 45). Many pheromones function as mate attractants, enabling some female insects to be detected by males more than a kilometer away.

There is as yet no good evidence for human pheromones. It was once postulated that female roommates produce pheromones that trigger synchrony in reproductive (menstrual) cycles, but further statistical analyses failed to support this idea.

Ensuring the Survival of Offspring

Internal fertilization is typically associated with the production of fewer gametes than external fertilization but results in the survival of a higher fraction of zygotes. Better zygote survival is due in part to the fact that eggs fertilized internally are sheltered from potential predators. However, internal fertilization is also more often associated with mechanisms that provide greater protection of the embryos and parental care of the young. For example, the internally fertilized eggs of birds and other reptiles have shells and internal membranes that protect against water loss and physical damage during the eggs' external development (see Figure 34.25). In contrast, the eggs of fishes and amphibians have only a gelatinous coat and lack internal membranes.

Rather than secreting a protective eggshell, some animals retain the embryo for a portion of its development within the female's reproductive tract. The offspring of marsupial mammals, such as kangaroos and opossums, spend only a short

◀ **Figure 46.6 Parental care in an invertebrate.** Compared with many other insects, giant water bugs of the genus *Belostoma* produce relatively few offspring but offer much greater parental protection. Following internal fertilization, the female glues her fertilized eggs to the back of the male (shown here). The male carries them for days, frequently fanning water over them to keep the eggs moist, aerated, and free of parasites.

period in the uterus as embryos; they then crawl out and complete development attached to a mammary gland in the mother's pouch. Embryos of eutherian (placental) mammals, such as humans, remain in the uterus throughout fetal development. There they are nourished by the mother's blood supply through a temporary organ, the placenta. The embryos of some fishes and sharks also complete development internally.

When a caribou or kangaroo is born or when a baby eagle hatches out of an egg, the newborn is not yet capable of independent existence. Instead, mammals nurse their offspring and adult birds feed their young. Parental care is in fact widespread among animals, including invertebrates **(Figure 46.6)**.

Gamete Production and Delivery

Sexual reproduction in animals relies on sets of cells that are precursors for eggs and sperm. Cells dedicated to this function are often established early in the formation of the embryo and remain inactive while the body plan takes shape. Cycles of growth and mitosis then increase, or *amplify*, the number of cells available for making eggs or sperm.

In producing gametes from the amplified precursor cells and making them available for fertilization, animals employ a variety of reproductive systems. **Gonads**, organs that produce gametes, are found in many but not all animals. Exceptions include the palolo, discussed above. The palolo and most other polychaete worms (phylum Annelida) have separate sexes but lack distinct gonads; rather, the eggs and sperm develop from undifferentiated cells lining the coelom (body cavity). As the gametes mature, they are released from the body wall and fill the coelom. Depending on the species, mature gametes in these worms may be shed through the excretory opening, or the swelling mass of eggs may split a portion of the body open, spilling the eggs into the environment.

More elaborate reproductive systems include sets of accessory tubes and glands that carry, nourish, and protect the gametes and sometimes the developing embryos. Most insects, for example, have separate sexes with complex reproductive systems (Figure 46.7). In many insect species, the female reproductive system includes one or more **spermathecae** (singular, *spermatheca*), sacs in which sperm may be stored for extended periods, a year or more in some species. Because the female releases male gametes from the spermathecae only in response to the appropriate stimuli, fertilization occurs under conditions likely to be well suited to embryonic development.

Vertebrate reproductive systems display limited but significant variations. In some vertebrates, the uterus is divided into two chambers; in others, including humans and birds, it is a single structure. In many nonmammalian vertebrates, the digestive, excretory, and reproductive systems have a common opening to the outside, the **cloaca**, a structure probably present in the ancestors of all vertebrates. Males of these species lack a well-developed penis and instead release sperm by turning the cloaca inside out. In contrast, mammals generally lack a cloaca and have a separate opening for the digestive tract. In addition, most female mammals have separate openings for the excretory and reproductive systems.

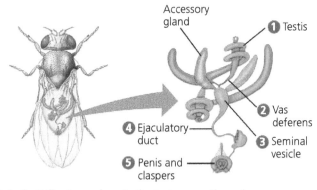

(a) Male fruit fly. Sperm form in the testes, pass through a sperm duct (vas deferens), and are stored in the seminal vesicles. The male ejaculates sperm along with fluid from the accessory glands. (Males of some species of insects and other arthropods have appendages called claspers that grasp the female during copulation.)

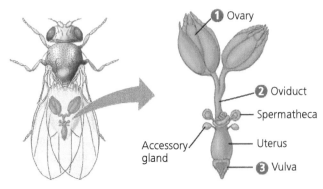

(b) Female fruit fly. Eggs develop in the ovaries and then travel through the oviducts to the uterus. After mating, sperm are stored in the spermathecae, which are connected to the uterus by short ducts. The female uses a stored sperm to fertilize each egg as it enters the uterus before she passes the egg out through the vulva.

▲ **Figure 46.7 Insect reproductive anatomy.** Circled numbers indicate sequences of sperm and egg movement.

Although fertilization involves the union of a single egg and sperm, animals often mate with more than one member of the other sex. Monogamy, the sustained sexual partnership of two individuals, is rare among animals, including most mammals. Mechanisms have evolved, however, that enhance the reproductive success of a male with a particular female and diminish the chance of that female mating successfully with another partner. For example, some male insects transfer secretions that make a female less receptive to courtship, reducing the likelihood of her mating again.

Can females also influence the relative reproductive success of their mates? This question intrigued two scientific collaborators working in Europe. Studying female fruit flies that copulated with one male and then another, the researchers traced the fate of sperm transferred in the first mating. As shown in Figure 46.8, females play a major role in determining the outcome of multiple matings. The processes by which gametes and individuals compete during reproduction remain a vibrant research area.

▼ **Figure 46.8** | **Inquiry**

Why is sperm usage biased when female fruit flies mate twice?

Experiment When a female fruit fly mates twice, 80% of the offspring result from the second mating. Scientists had hypothesized that ejaculate from the second mating displaces sperm from the first mating. To test this hypothesis, Rhonda Snook, at the University of Sheffield, and David Hosken, at the University of Zurich, used mutant males with altered reproductive systems. "No-ejaculate" males mate but do not transfer sperm or fluid to females. "No-sperm" males mate and ejaculate but make no sperm. The researchers allowed females to mate first with wild-type males and then with wild-type males, no-sperm males, or no-ejaculate males. As a control, some females were mated only once (to wild-type males). The scientists then dissected each female under a microscope and recorded whether sperm were absent from the spermathecae, the major sperm storage organs.

Results

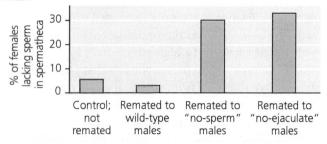

Conclusion Because remating reduces sperm storage when no sperm or fluids are transferred, the hypothesis that ejaculate from a second mating displaces stored sperm is incorrect. Instead, it appears females may get rid of stored sperm in response to remating, perhaps allowing for replacing stored sperm, possibly of diminished fitness, with fresh sperm.

Source: R. R. Snook and D. J. Hosken, Sperm death and dumping in *Drosophila*, *Nature* 428:939–941 (2004).

WHAT IF? *Suppose males in the first mating had a mutant allele for the dominant trait of smaller eyes. What fraction of the females would produce some offspring with smaller eyes?*

1. How does internal fertilization facilitate life on land?
2. What mechanisms have evolved in animals with (a) external fertilization and (b) internal fertilization that help ensure that offspring survive to adulthood?
3. **MAKE CONNECTIONS** What are the shared and distinct functions of the uterus of an insect and the ovary of a flowering plant? (See Figure 38.4.)

For suggested answers, see Appendix A.

CONCEPT 46.3

Reproductive organs produce and transport gametes

Having surveyed some of the general features of animal reproduction, we'll focus in the rest of the chapter on humans, beginning with the reproductive anatomy of each sex.

Human Male Reproductive Anatomy

The human male's external reproductive organs are the scrotum and penis. The internal reproductive organs consist of gonads that produce both sperm and reproductive hormones, accessory glands that secrete products essential to sperm movement, and ducts that carry the sperm and glandular secretions (Figure 46.9).

Testes

The male gonads, or **testes** (singular, *testis*), produce sperm in highly coiled tubes called **seminiferous tubules**. Most mammals produce sperm properly only when the testes are cooler than the rest of the body. In humans and many other mammals, testis temperature is maintained about 2°C below the core body temperature by the **scrotum**, a fold of the body wall.

The testes develop in the abdominal cavity and descend into the scrotum just before birth (a testis within a scrotum is a *testicle*). In many rodents, the testes are drawn back into the cavity between breeding seasons, interrupting sperm maturation. Some mammals whose body temperature is low enough to allow sperm maturation—such as whales and elephants—retain the testes in the abdominal cavity at all times.

Ducts

From the seminiferous tubules of a testis, the sperm pass into the coiled duct of an **epididymis**. In humans, it takes 3 weeks for sperm to travel the 6-m length of this duct, during which time the sperm complete maturation and become motile. During **ejaculation**, the sperm are propelled from each epididymis through a muscular duct, the **vas deferens**. Each vas deferens (one from each epididymis) extends around and behind the urinary bladder, where it joins a duct from the seminal vesicle, forming a short *ejaculatory duct*. The ejaculatory ducts open into the **urethra**, the outlet tube for both the excretory system and the reproductive system.

▲ **Figure 46.9 Reproductive anatomy of the human male.** Some nonreproductive structures are labeled in parentheses for orientation purposes.

The urethra runs through the penis and opens to the outside at the tip of the penis.

Accessory Glands

Three sets of accessory glands—the seminal vesicles, the prostate gland, and the bulbourethral glands—produce secretions that combine with sperm to form **semen**, the fluid that is ejaculated. Two **seminal vesicles** contribute about 60% of the volume of semen. The fluid from the seminal vesicles is thick, yellowish, and alkaline. It contains mucus, the sugar fructose (which provides most of the sperm's energy), a coagulating enzyme, ascorbic acid, and local regulators called prostaglandins (see Chapter 45).

The **prostate gland** secretes its products directly into the urethra through small ducts. Thin and milky, the fluid from this gland contains anticoagulant enzymes and citrate (a sperm nutrient). The prostate undergoes benign (noncancerous) enlargement in more than half of all men over age 40 and in almost all men over 70. In addition, prostate cancer, which most often afflicts men 65 and older, is one of the most common human cancers.

The *bulbourethral glands* are a pair of small glands along the urethra below the prostate. Before ejaculation, they secrete clear mucus that neutralizes any acidic urine remaining in the urethra. There is evidence that bulbourethral fluid carries some sperm released before ejaculation, which may contribute to the high failure rate of the withdrawal method of birth control (coitus interruptus).

Penis

The human **penis** contains the urethra as well as three cylinders of spongy erectile tissue. During sexual arousal, the erectile tissue fills with blood from the arteries. As this tissue fills, the increasing pressure seals off the veins that drain the penis, causing it to engorge with blood. The resulting erection enables the penis to be inserted into the vagina. Alcohol consumption, certain drugs, emotional issues, and aging all can cause an inability to achieve an erection (erectile dysfunction). For individuals with long-term erectile dysfunction, drugs such as Viagra promote the vasodilating action of the local regulator nitric oxide (NO; see Chapter 45); the resulting relaxation of smooth muscles in the blood vessels of the penis enhances blood flow into the erectile tissues. Although all mammals rely on penile erection for mating, the penis of raccoons, walruses, whales, and several other mammals also contains a bone, the baculum, which is thought to further stiffen the penis for mating.

The main shaft of the penis is covered by relatively thick skin. The head, or **glans**, of the penis has a much thinner outer layer and is consequently more sensitive to stimulation. The human glans is surrounded by a fold of skin called the **prepuce**, or foreskin, which is removed if a male is circumcised.

Human Female Reproductive Anatomy

The human female's external reproductive structures are the clitoris and two sets of labia, which surround the clitoris and vaginal opening. The internal organs consist of gonads, which produce eggs and reproductive hormones, and a system of ducts and chambers, which receive and carry gametes and house the embryo and fetus (**Figure 46.10**).

Ovaries

The female gonads are a pair of **ovaries** that flank the uterus and are held in place in the abdominal cavity by ligaments. The outer layer of each ovary is packed with **follicles**, each consisting of an **oocyte**, a partially developed egg, surrounded by support cells. The surrounding cells nourish and protect the oocyte during much of its formation and development.

Oviducts and Uterus

An **oviduct**, or fallopian tube, extends from the uterus toward a funnel-like opening at each ovary. The dimensions of this tube vary along its length, with the inside diameter near the uterus being as narrow as a human hair. Upon ovulation, cilia on the epithelial lining of the oviduct help collect the egg by drawing fluid from the body cavity into the oviduct. Together with wavelike contractions of the oviduct, the cilia convey the egg down the duct to the **uterus**, also known as the womb. The uterus is a thick, muscular organ that can expand during pregnancy to accommodate a 4-kg fetus. The inner lining of the uterus, the **endometrium**, is richly supplied with blood vessels. The neck of the uterus, called the **cervix**, opens into the vagina.

Vagina and Vulva

The **vagina** is a muscular but elastic chamber that is the site for insertion of the penis and deposition of sperm during copulation. The vagina, which also serves as the birth canal through which a baby is born, opens to the outside at the **vulva**, the collective term for the external female genitalia.

A pair of thick, fatty ridges, the **labia majora**, encloses and protects the rest of the vulva. The vaginal opening and the separate opening of the urethra are located within a cavity bordered by a pair of slender skin folds, the **labia minora**. A thin piece of tissue called the *hymen* partly covers the vaginal opening in humans at birth and usually until sexual intercourse or vigorous physical activity ruptures it. Located at the top of the labia minora, the **clitoris** consists of erectile tissue supporting a rounded glans, or head, covered by a small hood of skin, the prepuce. During sexual arousal, the clitoris, vagina, and labia minora all engorge with blood and enlarge. Richly supplied with nerve endings, the clitoris is one of the most sensitive points of sexual stimulation.

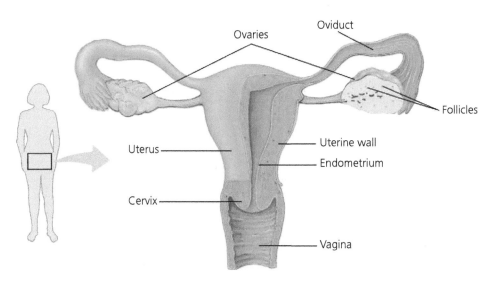

▲ **Figure 46.10 Reproductive anatomy of the human female.** Some nonreproductive structures are labeled in parentheses for orientation purposes.

Sexual arousal also induces the vestibular glands near the vaginal opening to secrete lubricating mucus, thereby facilitating intercourse.

Mammary Glands

The **mammary glands** are present in both sexes, but they normally produce milk only in females. Though not part of the reproductive system, the female mammary glands are important to reproduction. Within the glands, small sacs of epithelial tissue secrete milk, which drains into a series of ducts that open at the nipple. The breasts contain connective and fatty (adipose) tissue in addition to the mammary glands. Because the low level of estradiol in males limits the development of the fat deposits, male breasts usually remain small.

Gametogenesis

With this overview of anatomy in mind, we turn to **gametogenesis**, which is the production of gametes. **Figure 46.11** explores this process in human males and females, highlighting the close relationship between gonadal structure and function.

Spermatogenesis, the formation and development of sperm, is continuous and prolific in adult human males. Cell division and maturation occur throughout the seminiferous tubules coiled within the two testes, producing hundreds of millions of sperm each day. For a single sperm, the process takes about 7 weeks from start to finish.

Oogenesis, the development of mature oocytes (eggs), is a prolonged process in the human female. Immature eggs form in the ovary of the female embryo but do not complete their development until years, and often decades, later.

Spermatogenesis differs from the process of oogenesis in three significant ways:

- Only in spermatogenesis do all four products of meiosis develop into mature gametes. In oogenesis, cytokinesis during meiosis is unequal, with almost all the cytoplasm segregated to a single daughter cell. This large cell is destined to become the egg; the other products of meiosis, smaller cells known as polar bodies, degenerate.
- Spermatogenesis occurs throughout adolescence and adulthood. In contrast, the mitotic divisions that occur in oogenesis in human females are thought to be complete before birth, and the production of mature gametes ceases at about age 50.
- Spermatogenesis produces mature sperm from precursor cells in a continuous sequence, whereas there are long interruptions in oogenesis.

Exploring Human Gametogenesis

Spermatogenesis

Stem cells that give rise to sperm are situated near the outer edge of the seminiferous tubules. Their progeny move inward as they pass through the spermatocyte and spermatid stages, and sperm are released into the lumen (fluid-filled cavity) of the tubule. The sperm travel along the tubule into the epididymis, where they become motile.

The stem cells arise from division and differentiation of primordial germ cells in the embryonic testes. In mature testes, they divide mitotically to form **spermatogonia**, which in turn generate spermatocytes by mitosis. Each spermatocyte gives rise to four spermatids through meiosis, reducing the chromosome number from diploid ($2n = 46$ in humans) to haploid ($n = 23$). Spermatids undergo extensive changes in differentiating into sperm.

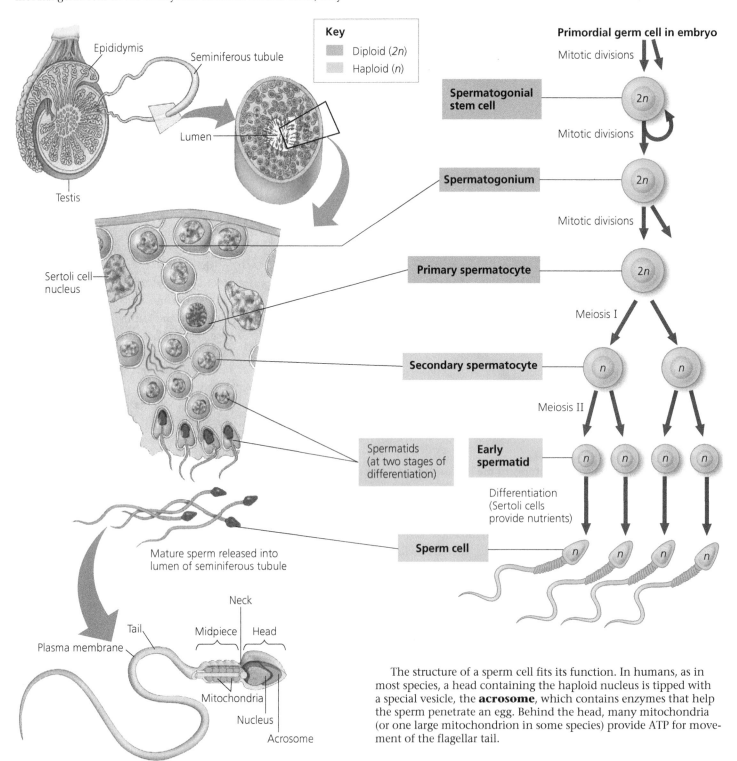

The structure of a sperm cell fits its function. In humans, as in most species, a head containing the haploid nucleus is tipped with a special vesicle, the **acrosome**, which contains enzymes that help the sperm penetrate an egg. Behind the head, many mitochondria (or one large mitochondrion in some species) provide ATP for movement of the flagellar tail.

Oogenesis

Oogenesis begins in the female embryo with the production of **oogonia** from primordial germ cells. The oogonia divide by mitosis to form cells that begin meiosis, but stop the process at prophase I before birth. These developmentally arrested cells, which are **primary oocytes**, each reside within a small follicle, a cavity lined with protective cells. At birth, the ovaries together contain about 1–2 million primary oocytes, of which about 500 fully mature between puberty and menopause.

To the best of our current knowledge, women are born with all the primary oocytes they will ever have. It is worth noting, however, that a similar conclusion regarding most other mammals was overturned in 2004 when researchers discovered that the ovaries of adult mice contain multiplying oogonia that develop into oocytes. If the same turned out to be true of humans, it might be that the marked decline in fertility that occurs as women age results from both a depletion of oogonia and the degeneration of aging oocytes.

Beginning at puberty, follicle-stimulating hormone (FSH) periodically stimulates a small group of follicles to resume growth and development. Typically, only one follicle fully matures each month, with its primary oocyte completing meiosis I. The second meiotic division begins, but stops at metaphase. Thus arrested in meiosis II, the **secondary oocyte** is released at ovulation, when its follicle breaks open. Only if a sperm penetrates the oocyte does meiosis II resume. (In other animal species, the sperm may enter the oocyte at the same stage, earlier, or later.) Each of the two meiotic divisions involves unequal cytokinesis, with the smaller cells becoming polar bodies that eventually degenerate (the first polar body may or may not divide again). As a result, the functional product of complete oogenesis is a single mature egg containing a sperm head. Fertilization is defined strictly as the fusion of the haploid nuclei of the sperm and secondary oocyte, although the term is often used loosely to mean the entry of the sperm head into the egg.

The ruptured follicle left behind after ovulation develops into the corpus luteum. The corpus luteum secretes estradiol as well as progesterone, a hormone that helps maintain the uterine lining during pregnancy. If the egg is not fertilized, the corpus luteum degenerates, and a new follicle matures during the next cycle.

WHAT IF? *Suppose you are analyzing the DNA from the polar bodies formed during human oogenesis. If the woman who produced the oocyte has a mutation in a known disease gene, would analyzing the polar body DNA allow you to infer whether the mutation is present in the mature oocyte? Explain.*

1. Why might frequent use of a hot tub make it harder for a couple to conceive a child?

2. The process of oogenesis is often described as the production of a haploid egg by meiosis, but in some animals, including humans, this is not an entirely accurate description. Explain.

3. **WHAT IF?** If each vas deferens in a male was surgically sealed off, what changes would you expect in sexual response and ejaculate composition?

For suggested answers, see Appendix A.

CONCEPT 46.4

The interplay of tropic and sex hormones regulates mammalian reproduction

In both male and female humans, the coordinated actions of hormones from the hypothalamus, anterior pituitary, and gonads govern reproduction. The hypothalamus secretes *gonadotropin-releasing hormone* (GnRH), which then directs the anterior pituitary to secrete the gonadotropins, **follicle-stimulating hormone (FSH)** and **luteinizing hormone (LH)** (see Figure 45.15). FSH and LH are tropic hormones, meaning that they regulate the activity of endocrine cells or glands. They are called *gonadotropins* because they act on the male and female gonads, and they support gametogenesis, in part by stimulating sex hormone production.

The main sex hormones are steroid hormones. They consist of *androgens*, principally **testosterone**; *estrogens*, principally **estradiol**; and **progesterone**. Males and females differ in their blood concentrations of particular hormones. Testosterone levels are roughly ten times higher in males than in females. In contrast, estradiol levels are about ten times higher in females than in males; females also produce more progesterone. The gonads are the major source of sex hormones, with much smaller amounts being produced by the adrenal glands.

Like gonadotropins, sex hormones regulate gametogenesis both directly and indirectly, but they have other actions as well. For example, androgens are responsible for the territorial songs of male birds and the courtship displays of male lizards **(Figure 46.12)**. In human embryos, androgens promote the appearance of the primary sex characteristics of males, the structures directly involved in reproduction. These include the seminal vesicles and associated ducts, as well as external reproductive structures. In the Scientific Skills Exercise, you can interpret the results of an experiment investigating the development of reproductive structures in mammals.

▲ **Figure 46.12 Androgen-dependent male anatomy and behavior in a lizard.** A male anole (*Norops ortoni*) extends his dewlap, a brightly colored skin flap beneath the throat. Testosterone is required for the dewlap to develop and for the male to display this skin flap when attracting mates and guarding territory.

At puberty, sex hormones in human males and females induce formation of secondary sex characteristics, the physical and behavioral differences between males and females that are not directly related to the reproductive system. In males, androgens cause the voice to deepen, facial and pubic hair to develop, and muscles to grow (by stimulating protein synthesis). Androgens also promote specific sexual behaviors and sex drive, as well as an increase in general aggressiveness. Estrogens similarly have multiple effects in females. At puberty, estradiol stimulates breast and pubic hair development. Estradiol also influences female sexual behavior, induces fat deposition in the breasts and hips, increases water retention, and alters calcium metabolism.

We now turn to the roles of gonadotropins and sex hormones in gametogenesis, beginning with males.

Hormonal Control of the Male Reproductive System

FSH and LH, released by the anterior pituitary in response to GnRH from the hypothalamus, direct spermatogenesis by acting on different types of cells in the testis **(Figure 46.13)**. FSH stimulates *Sertoli cells*, located within the seminiferous tubules, to nourish developing sperm (see Figure 46.11). LH causes *Leydig cells*, scattered in connective tissue between the tubules, to produce testosterone and other androgens, which promote spermatogenesis in the tubules.

Two negative-feedback mechanisms control sex hormone production in males (see Figure 46.13). Testosterone regulates blood levels of GnRH, FSH, and LH through inhibitory effects on the hypothalamus and anterior pituitary. In addition, *inhibin*, a hormone that in males is produced by Sertoli cells, acts on the anterior pituitary gland to reduce FSH secretion. Together, these negative-feedback circuits maintain androgen levels in the normal range.

Making Inferences and Designing an Experiment

What Role Do Hormones Play in Making a Mammal Male or Female? In non-egg-laying mammals, females have two X chromosomes, whereas males have one X chromosome and one Y chromosome. In the 1940s, French physiologist Alfred Jost wondered whether development of mammalian embryos as female or male in accord with their chromosome set requires instructions in the form of hormones produced by the gonads. In this exercise, you will interpret the results of an experiment that Jost performed to answer this question.

How the Experiment Was Done Working with rabbit embryos still in the mother's uterus at a stage before sex differences are observable, Jost surgically removed the portion of each embryo that would form the ovaries or testes. When the baby rabbits were born, he made note of their chromosomal sex and whether their genital structures were male or female.

Data from the Experiment

	Appearance of Genitalia	
Chromosome Set	No Surgery	Embryonic Gonad Removed
XY (male)	Male	Female
XX (female)	Female	Female

Interpret the Data

1. This experiment is an example of a research approach in which scientists infer how something works normally based on what happens when the normal process is blocked. What normal process was blocked in Jost's experiment? From the results, what inference can you make about the role of the gonads in controlling the development of mammalian genitalia?

2. The data in Jost's experiment could be explained if some aspect of the surgery other than gonad removal caused female genitalia to develop. If you were to repeat Jost's experiment, how might you test the validity of such an explanation?

3. What result would Jost have obtained if female development also required a signal from the gonad?

4. Design another experiment to determine whether the signal that controls male development is a hormone. Make sure to identify your hypothesis, prediction, data collection plan, and controls.

(MB) A version of this Scientific Skills Exercise can be assigned in MasteringBiology.

Data from A. Jost, Recherches sur la differenciation sexuelle de l'embryon de lapin (Studies on the sexual differentiation of the rabbit embryo), *Archives d'Anatomie Microscopique et de Morphologie Experimentale* 36:271–316 (1947).

Leydig cells have other roles besides producing testosterone. They in fact secrete small quantities of many other hormones and local regulators, including oxytocin, renin, angiotensin, corticotropin-releasing factor, growth factors, and prostaglandins. These signals coordinate the activity of reproduction with growth, metabolism, homeostasis, and behavior.

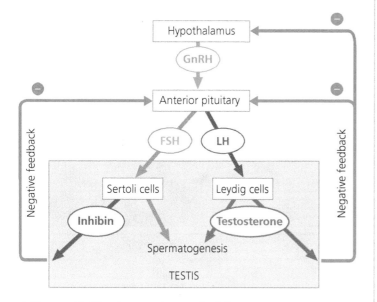

▲ **Figure 46.13 Hormonal control of the testes.**

Hormonal Control of Female Reproductive Cycles

Whereas human males produce sperm continuously, human females produce eggs in cycles. Ovulation occurs only after the endometrium (lining of the uterus) has started to thicken and develop a rich blood supply, preparing the uterus for the possible implantation of an embryo. If pregnancy does not occur, the uterine lining is sloughed off, and another cycle begins. The cyclic shedding of the blood-rich endometrium from the uterus, a process that occurs in a flow through the cervix and vagina, is called **menstruation**.

There are two closely linked reproductive cycles in human females. The term *menstrual cycle* refers specifically to the changes that occur about once a month in the uterus; therefore it is also called the **uterine cycle**. The cyclic changes in the uterus are controlled by the **ovarian cycle**, cyclic events that occur in the ovaries. Thus, the female reproductive cycle is actually one integrated cycle involving two organs, the uterus and the ovaries.

Menstrual cycles average 28 days (although cycles vary, ranging from about 20 to 40 days). Hormone activity links the two cycles, synchronizing ovarian follicle growth and ovulation with the establishment of a uterine lining that can support embryonic development.

Figure 46.14 outlines the major events of the female reproductive cycles, illustrating the close coordination across different tissues in the body.

The Ovarian Cycle

The ovarian cycle begins ❶ with the release from the hypothalamus of GnRH, which stimulates the anterior pituitary to ❷ secrete small amounts of FSH and LH. ❸ Follicle-stimulating hormone (as its name implies) stimulates follicle growth, aided by LH, and ❹ the cells of the growing follicles start to make estradiol. There is a slow rise in estradiol concentration during most of the *follicular phase*, the part of the ovarian cycle during which follicles grow and oocytes mature. (Several follicles begin to grow with each cycle, but usually only one matures; the others disintegrate.) The low levels of estradiol inhibit secretion of the pituitary hormones, keeping the levels of FSH and LH relatively low. During this portion of the cycle, regulation of the hormones controlling reproduction closely parallels the regulation observed in males.

❺ When estradiol secretion by the growing follicle begins to rise steeply, ❻ the FSH and LH levels increase markedly. Why? Whereas a low level of estradiol inhibits the secretion of pituitary gonadotropins, a high concentration has the opposite effect: It stimulates gonadotropin secretion by causing the hypothalamus to increase its output of GnRH. A high estradiol concentration also increases the GnRH sensitivity of LH-releasing cells in the pituitary, resulting in a further increase in LH levels.

❼ The maturing follicle, containing a fluid-filled cavity, enlarges, forming a bulge at the surface of the ovary. The follicular phase ends at ovulation, about a day after the LH surge. In response to both FSH and the peak in LH level, the follicle and adjacent wall of the ovary rupture, releasing the secondary oocyte. At or near the time of ovulation, women sometimes feel a

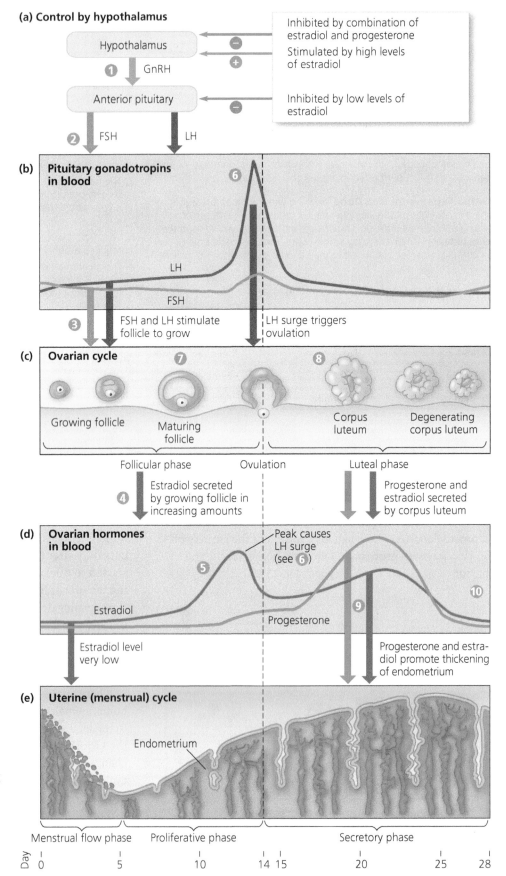

▲ **Figure 46.14 The reproductive cycles of the human female.** This figure shows how **(c)** the ovarian cycle and **(e)** the uterine (menstrual) cycle are regulated by changing hormone levels in the blood, depicted in parts **(a)**, **(b)**, and **(d)**. The time scale at the bottom of the figure applies to parts **(b)–(e)**.

distinctive pain in the lower abdomen, on the same side as the ovary in which the oocyte was released.

The *luteal phase* of the ovarian cycle follows ovulation. ❽ Luteinizing hormone stimulates the follicular tissue left behind in the ovary to transform into a corpus luteum, a glandular structure. Under continued stimulation by LH, the corpus luteum secretes progesterone and estradiol, which in combination exert negative feedback on the hypothalamus and pituitary. This feedback reduces the secretion of LH and FSH to very low levels, preventing another egg from maturing when a pregnancy may already be under way.

If pregnancy does not occur, low gonadotropin levels at the end of the luteal phase cause the corpus luteum to disintegrate, triggering a sharp decline in estradiol and progesterone concentrations. The decreasing levels of ovarian steroid hormones liberate the hypothalamus and pituitary from the negative-feedback effect of these hormones. The pituitary can then begin to secrete enough FSH to stimulate the growth of new follicles in the ovary, initiating the next ovarian cycle.

The Uterine (Menstrual) Cycle

Prior to ovulation, ovarian steroid hormones stimulate the uterus to prepare for support of an embryo. Estradiol secreted in increasing amounts by growing follicles signals the endometrium to thicken. In this way, the follicular phase of the ovarian cycle is coordinated with the *proliferative phase* of the uterine cycle. After ovulation, ❾ the estradiol and progesterone secreted by the corpus luteum stimulate maintenance and further development of the uterine lining, including enlargement of arteries and growth of endometrial glands. These glands secrete a nutrient fluid that can sustain an early embryo even before it implants in the uterine lining. Thus, the luteal phase of the ovarian cycle is coordinated with the *secretory phase* of the uterine cycle.

If an embryo has not implanted in the endometrium by the end of the secretory phase, the corpus luteum disintegrates. The resulting drop ❿ in ovarian hormone levels causes arteries in the endometrium to constrict. Deprived of its circulation, the uterine lining largely disintegrates, releasing blood that is shed along with endometrial tissue and fluid. The result is menstruation—the *menstrual flow phase* of the uterine cycle. During this phase, which usually lasts a few days, a new group of ovarian follicles begin to grow. By convention, the first day of flow is designated day 1 of the new uterine (and ovarian) cycle.

About 7% of women of reproductive age suffer from a disorder called **endometriosis**, in which some cells of the uterine lining migrate to an abdominal location that is abnormal, or **ectopic** (from the Greek *ektopos*, away from a place). Having migrated to a location such as an oviduct, ovary, or large intestine, the ectopic tissue responds to hormones in the bloodstream. Like the uterine endometrium, the ectopic tissue swells and breaks down during each ovarian cycle, resulting in

pelvic pain and bleeding into the abdomen. Researchers have not yet determined why endometriosis occurs, but hormonal therapy or surgery can be used to lessen discomfort.

Menopause

After about 500 cycles, a woman undergoes **menopause**, the cessation of ovulation and menstruation. Menopause usually occurs between the ages of 46 and 54. During this interval, the ovaries lose their responsiveness to FSH and LH, resulting in a decline in estradiol production.

Menopause is an unusual phenomenon. In most other species, females and males can reproduce throughout life. Is there an evolutionary explanation for menopause? One intriguing hypothesis proposes that during early human evolution, undergoing menopause after bearing several children allowed a mother to provide better care for her children and grandchildren, thereby increasing the chances for survival of individuals who share much of her genetic makeup.

Menstrual Versus Estrous Cycles

In all female mammals, the endometrium thickens before ovulation, but only humans and some other primates have menstrual cycles. Other mammals have **estrous cycles**, in which in the absence of a pregnancy, the uterus reabsorbs the endometrium and no extensive fluid flow occurs. Whereas human females may engage in sexual activity throughout the menstrual cycle, mammals with estrous cycles usually copulate only during the period surrounding ovulation. This period, called estrus (from the Latin *oestrus*, frenzy, passion), is the only time the female is receptive to mating. It is often called "heat," and the female's temperature does increase slightly.

The length and frequency of estrous cycles vary widely among mammals. Bears and wolves have one estrous cycle per year; elephants have several. Rats have estrous cycles throughout the year, each lasting just five days.

Human Sexual Response

The arousal of sexual interest in humans is complex, involving a variety of psychological as well as physical factors. Although reproductive structures in the male and female differ in appearance, a number serve similar functions in arousal, reflecting their shared developmental origin. For example, the same embryonic tissues give rise to the scrotum and the labia majora, to the skin on the penis and the labia minora, and to the glans of the penis and the clitoris. Furthermore, the general pattern of human sexual response is similar in males and females. Two types of physiological reactions predominate in both sexes: *vasocongestion*, the filling of a tissue with blood, and *myotonia*, increased muscle tension.

The sexual response cycle can be divided into four phases: excitement, plateau, orgasm, and resolution. An important function of the excitement phase is to prepare the vagina and penis for *coitus* (sexual intercourse). During this phase, vaso-congestion is particularly evident in erection of the penis and clitoris and in enlargement of the testicles, labia, and breasts. The vagina becomes lubricated, and myotonia may occur, as evident in nipple erection or tension of the limbs.

In the plateau phase, sexual responses continue as a result of direct stimulation of the genitalia. In females, the outer third of the vagina becomes vasocongested, while the inner two-thirds slightly expands. This change, coupled with the elevation of the uterus, forms a depression for receiving sperm at the back of the vagina. Breathing quickens and heart rate rises, sometimes to 150 beats per minute—not only in response to the physical effort of sexual activity, but also as an involuntary reaction to stimulation by the autonomic nervous system (see Figure 49.9).

Orgasm is characterized by rhythmic, involuntary contractions of the reproductive structures in both sexes. Male orgasm has two stages. The first, emission, occurs when the glands and ducts of the reproductive tract contract, forcing semen into the urethra. Expulsion, or ejaculation, occurs when the urethra contracts and the semen is expelled. During female orgasm, the uterus and outer vagina contract, but the inner two-thirds of the vagina does not. Orgasm is the shortest phase of the sexual response cycle, usually lasting only a few seconds. In both sexes, contractions occur at about 0.8-second intervals and may also involve the anal sphincter and several abdominal muscles.

The resolution phase completes the cycle and reverses the responses of the earlier stages. Vasocongested organs return to normal size and color, and muscles relax. Most of these changes are completed within 5 minutes, but some may take as long as an hour. Following orgasm, the male typically enters a refractory period, lasting from a few minutes to hours, when erection and orgasm cannot be achieved. Females do not have a refractory period, making possible multiple orgasms within a short period of time.

CONCEPT 46.5

In placental mammals, an embryo develops fully within the mother's uterus

Having surveyed the ovarian and uterine cycles of human females, we turn now to reproduction itself, beginning with the events that transform an egg into a developing embryo.

Conception, Embryonic Development, and Birth

During human copulation, the male delivers 2–5 mL of semen containing hundreds of millions of sperm. When first ejaculated, the semen coagulates, which likely keeps the ejaculate in place until sperm reach the cervix. Soon after, anticoagulants liquefy the semen, and the sperm swim through the uterus and oviducts. Fertilization—also called **conception** in humans—occurs when a sperm fuses with an egg (mature oocyte) in an oviduct **(Figure 46.15)**.

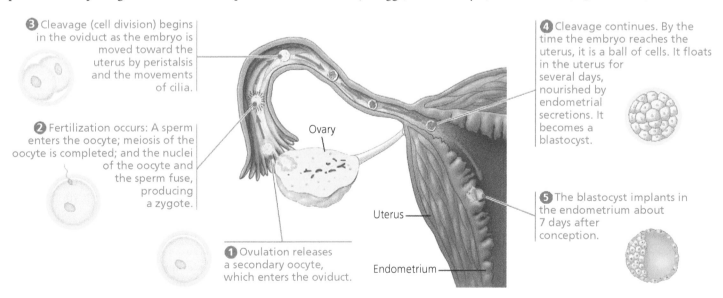

3 Cleavage (cell division) begins in the oviduct as the embryo is moved toward the uterus by peristalsis and the movements of cilia.

2 Fertilization occurs: A sperm enters the oocyte; meiosis of the oocyte is completed; and the nuclei of the oocyte and the sperm fuse, producing a zygote.

1 Ovulation releases a secondary oocyte, which enters the oviduct.

Ovary

Uterus

Endometrium

4 Cleavage continues. By the time the embryo reaches the uterus, it is a ball of cells. It floats in the uterus for several days, nourished by endometrial secretions. It becomes a blastocyst.

5 The blastocyst implants in the endometrium about 7 days after conception.

▲ Figure 46.15 **Formation of a human zygote and early postfertilization events.**

The zygote begins a series of cell divisions called cleavage about 24 hours after fertilization and after an additional 4 days produces a **blastocyst**, a sphere of cells surrounding a central cavity. A few days later, the embryo implants into the endometrium of the uterus. The condition of carrying one or more embryos in the uterus is called **pregnancy**, or **gestation**. Human pregnancy averages 266 days (38 weeks) from fertilization of the egg, or 40 weeks from the start of the last menstrual cycle. In comparison, gestation averages 21 days in many rodents, 270 days in cows, and more than 600 days in elephants. The roughly nine months of human gestation are divided into three *trimesters* of equal length.

First Trimester

During the first trimester, the implanted embryo secretes hormones that signal its presence and regulate the mother's reproductive system. One embryonic hormone, *human chorionic gonadotropin (hCG)*, acts like pituitary LH in maintaining secretion of progesterone and estrogens by the corpus luteum through the first few months of pregnancy. Some hCG passes from the maternal blood to the urine, where it can be detected by the most common early pregnancy tests.

Not all embryos are capable of completing development. Many spontaneously stop developing as a result of chromosomal or developmental abnormalities. Much less often, a fertilized egg lodges in an oviduct (fallopian tube), resulting in a tubal, or ectopic, pregnancy. Such pregnancies cannot be sustained and may rupture the oviduct, resulting in serious internal bleeding. The risk of ectopic pregnancy increases if the oviduct is scarred by bacterial infections arising during childbirth, by medical procedures, or by a sexually transmitted disease.

During its first 2–4 weeks of development, the embryo obtains nutrients directly from the endometrium. Meanwhile, the outer layer of the blastocyst, which is called the **trophoblast**, grows outward and mingles with the endometrium, eventually helping form the **placenta**. This disk-shaped organ, containing both embryonic and maternal blood vessels, can weigh close to 1 kg at birth. Diffusion of material between the maternal and embryonic circulatory systems supplies nutrients, provides immune protection, exchanges respiratory gases, and disposes of metabolic wastes for the embryo. Blood from the embryo travels to the placenta through the arteries of the umbilical cord and returns via the umbilical vein **(Figure 46.16)**.

© Pearson Education, Inc.

▲ **Figure 46.16 Placental circulation.** From the 4th week of development until birth, the placenta, a combination of maternal and embryonic tissues, transports nutrients, respiratory gases, and wastes between the embryo or fetus and the mother. Maternal blood enters the placenta in arteries, flows through blood pools in the endometrium, and leaves via veins. Embryonic or fetal blood, which remains in vessels, enters the placenta through arteries and passes through capillaries in finger-like chorionic villi, where oxygen and nutrients are acquired. Fetal blood leaves the placenta through veins leading back to the fetus. Materials are exchanged by diffusion, active transport, and selective absorption between the fetal capillary bed and the maternal blood pools.

? *In a rare genetic disorder, the absence of a particular enzyme leads to increased testosterone production. When the fetus has this disorder, the mother develops a male-like pattern of body hair during the pregnancy. Explain why.*

Occasionally, an embryo splits during the first month of development, resulting in identical, or *monozygotic* (one-egg), twins. Fraternal, or *dizygotic*, twins arise in a very different way: Two follicles mature in a single cycle, followed by independent fertilization and implantation of two genetically distinct embryos.

The first trimester is the main period of **organogenesis**, the development of the body organs (Figure 46.17a). During organogenesis, the embryo is particularly susceptible to damage. For example, alcohol that passes through the placenta and reaches the developing central nervous system of the embryo can cause fetal alcohol syndrome, a disorder that can result in mental retardation and other serious birth defects. The heart begins beating by the 4th week; a heartbeat can be detected at 8–10 weeks. At 8 weeks, all the major structures of the adult are present in rudimentary form, and the embryo is called a **fetus**. At the end of the first trimester, the fetus, although well differentiated, is only 5 cm long.

Meanwhile, high levels of progesterone bring about rapid changes in the mother: Mucus in the cervix forms a plug that protects against infection, the maternal part of the placenta grows, the breasts and uterus get larger, and both ovulation and menstrual cycling stop. About three-fourths of all pregnant women experience nausea, misleadingly called "morning sickness," during the first trimester.

Second and Third Trimesters

During the second trimester, the fetus grows to about 30 cm in length and is very active (Figure 46.17b and c). The mother may feel fetal movements as early as one month into the second trimester, and fetal activity is typically visible through the abdominal wall one to two months later. Hormone levels stabilize as hCG secretion declines; the corpus luteum deteriorates; and the placenta completely takes over the production of progesterone, the hormone that maintains the pregnancy.

During the third trimester, the fetus grows to about 3–4 kg in weight and 50 cm in length. Fetal activity may decrease as the fetus fills the available space. As the fetus grows and the uterus expands around it, the mother's abdominal organs become compressed and displaced, leading to digestive blockages and a need for frequent urination.

Childbirth begins with *labor*, a series of strong, rhythmic uterine contractions that push the fetus and placenta out of

(a) **5 weeks.** Limb buds, eyes, the heart, the liver, and rudiments of all other organs have started to develop in the embryo, which is only about 1 cm long.

(b) **14 weeks.** Growth and development of the offspring, now called a fetus, continue during the second trimester. This fetus is about 6 cm long.

(c) **20 weeks.** Growth to nearly 20 cm in length requires adoption of the fetal position (head at knees) due to the limited space available.

▲ **Figure 46.17 Some stages of human development during the first and second trimesters.**

▲ Figure 46.18 **Positive feedback in labor.**

? Predict the effect of a single dose of oxytocin on a pregnant woman at the end of 39 weeks gestation.

the body. Once labor begins, local regulators (prostaglandins) and hormones (chiefly estradiol and oxytocin) induce and regulate further contractions of the uterus (**Figure 46.18**). Central to this regulation is a positive-feedback loop (see Concept 45.2) in which uterine contractions stimulate secretion of oxytocin, which in turn stimulates further contractions.

Labor is typically described as having three stages (**Figure 46.19**). The first stage is the thinning and opening up (dilation) of the cervix. The second stage is the expulsion, or delivery, of the baby. Continuous strong contractions force the fetus out of the uterus and through the vagina. The final stage of labor is the delivery of the placenta.

One aspect of postnatal care unique to mammals is *lactation*, the production of mother's milk. In response to suckling by the newborn and changes in estradiol levels after birth, the hypothalamus signals the anterior pituitary to secrete prolactin, which stimulates the mammary glands to produce milk. Suckling also stimulates the secretion of oxytocin from the posterior pituitary, which triggers release of milk from the mammary glands (see Figure 45.14).

Maternal Immune Tolerance of the Embryo and Fetus

Pregnancy is an immunological puzzle. Because half of the embryo's genes are inherited from the father, many of the chemical markers present on the surface of the embryo are foreign to the mother. Why, then, does the mother not reject the embryo as a foreign body, as she would a tissue or organ graft from another person? One intriguing clue comes

1 Dilation of the cervix

2 Expulsion: delivery of the infant

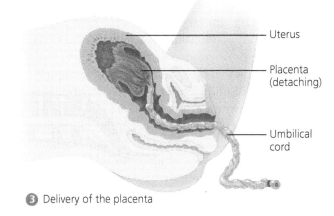

3 Delivery of the placenta

▲ Figure 46.19 **The three stages of labor.**

from the relationship between certain autoimmune disorders and pregnancy. For example, the symptoms of rheumatoid arthritis, an autoimmune disease of the joints, become less severe during pregnancy. Such observations suggest that the overall regulation of the immune system changes during pregnancy. Sorting out these changes and how they might protect the developing fetus is an active area of research for immunologists.

Contraception and Abortion

Contraception, the deliberate prevention of pregnancy, can be achieved in a number of ways. Some contraceptive methods prevent gamete development or release from female or male gonads; others prevent fertilization by keeping sperm and egg apart; and still others prevent implantation of an embryo. For complete information on contraceptive methods, you should consult a health-care provider. The following brief introduction to the biology of the most common methods and the corresponding diagram in **Figure 46.20** make no pretense of being a contraception manual.

Fertilization can be prevented by abstinence from sexual intercourse or by any of several kinds of barriers that keep live sperm from contacting the egg. Temporary abstinence, sometimes called *natural family planning*, depends on refraining from intercourse when conception is most likely. Because the egg can survive in the oviduct for 24–48 hours and sperm for up to 5 days, a couple practicing temporary abstinence should not engage in intercourse for a significant number of days before and after ovulation. Contraceptive methods based on fertility awareness require knowledge of physiological indicators associated with ovulation, such as changes in cervical mucus. Note also that a pregnancy rate of 10–20% is typically reported for couples practicing natural family planning. (In this context, pregnancy rate is the percentage of women who become pregnant in one year while using a particular pregnancy prevention method.)

As a method of preventing fertilization, *coitus interruptus*, or withdrawal (removal of the penis from the vagina before ejaculation), is unreliable. Sperm from a previous ejaculate may be transferred in secretions that precede ejaculation. Furthermore, a split-second lapse in timing or willpower can result in tens of millions of sperm being transferred before withdrawal.

Used properly, several methods of contraception that block sperm from meeting the egg have pregnancy rates of less than 10%. The *condom* is a thin, latex rubber or natural membrane sheath that fits over the penis to collect the semen. For sexually active individuals, latex condoms are the only contraceptives that are highly effective in preventing the spread of AIDS and other *sexually transmitted diseases* (*STDs*), also known as *sexually transmitted infections* (*STIs*). This protection is not absolute, however. Another common barrier device is the *diaphragm*, a dome-shaped rubber cap inserted into the upper portion of the vagina before intercourse. Both of these devices have lower pregnancy rates when used in conjunction with a spermicidal (sperm-killing) foam or jelly. Other barrier devices include the vaginal pouch, or "female condom."

Except for complete abstinence from sexual intercourse or sterilization (discussed later), the most effective means

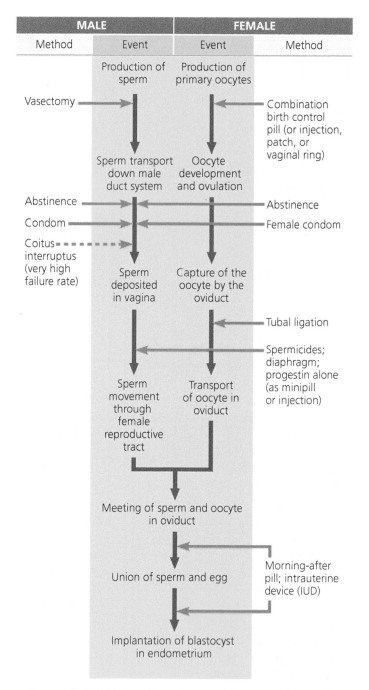

▲ **Figure 46.20 Mechanisms of several contraceptive methods.** Red arrows indicate where these methods, devices, or products interfere with events from the production of sperm and primary oocytes to implantation of a developing embryo.

of birth control are the intrauterine device (IUD) and hormonal contraceptives. The IUD has a pregnancy rate of 1% or less and is the most commonly used reversible method of birth control outside the United States. Placed in the uterus by a doctor, the IUD interferes with fertilization and implantation. Hormonal contraceptives, most often in the form of **birth control pills**, also have pregnancy rates of 1% or less.

The most commonly prescribed hormonal contraceptives combine a synthetic estrogen and a synthetic progestin (progesterone-like hormone). This combination mimics negative feedback in the ovarian cycle, stopping the release of GnRH by the hypothalamus and thus of FSH and LH by the pituitary. The prevention of LH release blocks ovulation. In addition, the inhibition of FSH secretion by the low dose of estrogens in the pills prevents follicles from developing.

Another hormonal contraceptive with a very low pregnancy rate contains only progestin. Progestin causes thickening of a woman's cervical mucus so that it blocks sperm from entering the uterus. Progestin also decreases the frequency of ovulation and causes changes in the endometrium that may interfere with implantation if fertilization occurs. This contraceptive can be administered as injections that last for three months or as a tablet ("minipill") taken daily.

Hormonal contraceptives have both harmful and beneficial side effects. They increase the risk of some cardiovascular disorders slightly for nonsmokers and quite substantially (3- to 10-fold) for women who smoke regularly. At the same time, oral contraceptives eliminate the dangers of pregnancy; women on birth control pills have mortality rates about one-half those of pregnant women. Birth control pills also decrease the risk of ovarian and endometrial cancers. No hormonal contraceptives are available for men.

Sterilization is the permanent prevention of gamete production or release. **Tubal ligation** in women usually involves sealing shut or tying off (ligating) a section of each oviduct to prevent eggs from traveling into the uterus. Similarly, **vasectomy** in men is the cutting and tying off of each vas deferens to prevent sperm from entering the urethra. Sex hormone secretion and sexual function are unaffected by both procedures, with no change in menstrual cycles in females or ejaculate volume in males. Although tubal ligation and vasectomy are considered permanent, both procedures can in many cases be reversed by microsurgery.

The termination of a pregnancy in progress is called **abortion**. Spontaneous abortion, or *miscarriage*, is very common; it occurs in as many as one-third of all pregnancies, often before the woman is even aware she is pregnant. In addition, each year about 850,000 women in the United States choose to have an abortion performed by a physician.

A drug called mifepristone, or RU486, can terminate a pregnancy nonsurgically within the first 7 weeks. RU486 blocks progesterone receptors in the uterus, thus preventing progesterone from maintaining the pregnancy. It is taken with a small amount of prostaglandin to induce uterine contractions.

Modern Reproductive Technologies

Recent scientific and technological advances have made it possible to address many reproductive problems, including genetic diseases and infertility.

Detecting Disorders During Pregnancy

Many developmental problems and genetic diseases can now be diagnosed while the fetus is in the uterus. Ultrasound imaging, which generates images using sound frequencies above the normal hearing range, is commonly used to analyze the fetus's size and condition. In amniocentesis and chorionic villus sampling, a needle is used to obtain fetal cells from fluid or tissue surrounding the embryo; these cells then provide the basis for genetic analysis (see Figure 14.19).

In the newest reproductive technology, a pregnant mother's blood is used to analyze the genome of her fetus. As discussed in Chapter 14, a pregnant woman's blood contains DNA from the growing embryo. How does it get there? The mother's blood reaches the embryo through the placenta. When cells produced by the embryo grow old, die, and break open within the placenta, the released DNA enters the mother's circulation. Although the blood also contains pieces of DNA from the mother, about 10-15% of the DNA circulating in the blood is from the fetus. Both the polymerase chain reaction (PCR) and high throughput sequencing can convert the bits of fetal DNA into useful information.

Unfortunately, almost all detectable disorders remain untreatable in the uterus, and many cannot be corrected even after birth. Genetic testing may leave parents faced with difficult decisions about whether to terminate a pregnancy or to raise a child who may have profound defects and a short life expectancy. These are complex issues that demand careful, informed thought and competent genetic counseling.

Parents will be receiving even more genetic information and confronting further questions in the near future. Indeed, in 2012 we learned of the first infant whose entire genome was known before birth. Nevertheless, completing a genome sequence does not ensure complete information. Consider, for example, Klinefelter syndrome, in which males have an extra X chromosome. This disorder is quite common, affecting 1 in 1,000 men, and can cause reduced testosterone, a feminized appearance, and infertility. However, while some men with an extra X chromosome have a debilitating disorder, others have symptoms so mild that they are unaware of the condition. For other disorders, such as diabetes, heart disease, or cancer, a genome sequence may only indicate the degree of risk. How parents will use this and other information in having and raising children is a question with no clear answers.

Infertility and In Vitro Fertilization

Infertility—an inability to conceive offspring—is quite common, affecting about one in ten couples in the United States and worldwide. The causes of infertility are varied, and the likelihood of a reproductive defect is nearly the same for men and women. For women, however, the risk of reproductive difficulties, as well as genetic abnormalities of the fetus, increases steadily past age 35. Evidence suggests that the prolonged period of time oocytes spend in meiosis is largely responsible for this increased risk.

Among preventable causes of infertility, STDs are the most significant. In women 15–24 years old, approximately 700,000 cases of chlamydia and gonorrhea are reported annually in the United States. The actual number of women infected with the chlamydia or gonorrhea bacterium is considerably higher because most women with these infections have no symptoms and are therefore unaware of their infection. Up to 40% of women who remain untreated for either chlamydia or gonorrhea develop an inflammatory disorder that can lead to infertility or to potentially fatal complications during pregnancy.

Some forms of infertility are treatable. Hormone therapy can sometimes increase sperm or egg production, and surgery can often correct ducts that formed improperly or have become blocked. In some cases, doctors recommend *in vitro* fertilization (IVF), which involves combining oocytes and sperm in the laboratory. Fertilized eggs are incubated until they have formed at least eight cells and are then transferred to the woman's uterus for implantation. If mature sperm are defective or low in number, a whole sperm or a spermatid nucleus is injected directly into an oocyte (Figure 46.21). Though costly, IVF procedures have enabled more than a million couples to conceive children.

By whatever means fertilization occurs, a developmental program follows that transforms the single-celled zygote into a multicellular organism. The mechanisms of this remarkable program of development in humans and other animals are the subject of Chapter 47.

▲ **Figure 46.21 *In vitro* fertilization (IVF).** In this form of IVF, a technician holds the egg in place with a pipette (left) and uses a very fine needle to inject one sperm into the egg cytoplasm (colorized LM).

CONCEPT CHECK 46.5

1. Why does testing for hCG (human chorionic gonadotropin) work as a pregnancy test early in pregnancy but not late in pregnancy? What is the function of hCG in pregnancy?

2. In what ways are tubal ligation and vasectomy similar?

3. **WHAT IF?** If a sperm nucleus is injected into an oocyte, what steps of gametogenesis and conception are bypassed?

For suggested answers, see Appendix A.

46 Chapter Review

SUMMARY OF KEY CONCEPTS

CONCEPT 46.1

Both asexual and sexual reproduction occur in the animal kingdom (pp. 1014–1016)

- **Sexual reproduction** requires the fusion of male and female gametes, forming a diploid **zygote**. **Asexual reproduction** is the production of offspring without gamete fusion. Mechanisms of asexual reproduction include budding, **fission**, and fragmentation with regeneration. Variations on the mode of reproduction are achieved through **parthenogenesis**, **hermaphroditism**, and sex reversal. Hormones and environmental cues control reproductive cycles.

? *Would a pair of haploid offspring produced by parthenogenesis be genetically identical? Explain.*

CONCEPT 46.2

Fertilization depends on mechanisms that bring together sperm and eggs of the same species (pp. 1016–1019)

- **Fertilization** occurs externally, when sperm and eggs are both released outside the body, or internally, when sperm deposited by the male fertilize an egg in the female reproductive system. In either case, fertilization requires coordinated timing, which may be mediated by environmental cues, pheromones, or courtship behavior. Internal fertilization is often associated with relatively fewer offspring and greater protection of offspring by the parents. Systems for gamete production and delivery range from undifferentiated cells in the body cavity to complex systems that include **gonads**, which produce gametes, and accessory tubes and glands that protect or transport gametes and embryos. Although sexual reproduction involves a partnership, it also provides an opportunity for competition between individuals and between gametes.

Complex reproductive systems in fruit flies

Male fruit fly

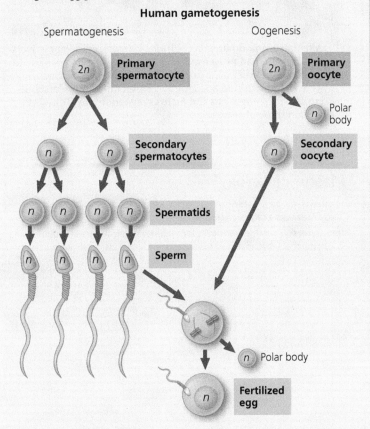

Testis

Vas deferens

Ejaculatory duct

Seminal vesicle

Penis and claspers

Female fruit fly

Ovary

Oviduct

Spermatheca

Accessory gland

Uterus

Vulva

Key to labels:
Gamete production
Gamete protection and transport

? *Identify which of the following, if any, are unique to mammals: a female uterus, a male vas deferens, extended internal development, and parental care of newborns.*

CONCEPT 46.3

Reproductive organs produce and transport gametes (pp. 1019–1024)

- In human males, **sperm** are produced in **testes**, which are suspended outside the body in the **scrotum**. Ducts connect the testes to internal accessory glands and to the **penis**. The reproductive system of the human female consists principally of the **labia** and the **glans** of the **clitoris** externally and the **vagina**, **uterus**, **oviducts**, and **ovaries** internally. **Eggs** are produced in the ovaries and upon fertilization develop in the uterus.
- **Gametogenesis**, or gamete production, consists of the processes of **spermatogenesis** in males and **oogenesis** in females. Human spermatogenesis is continuous and produces four sperm per meiosis. Human oogenesis is discontinuous and cyclic, generating one egg per meiosis.

Human gametogenesis

Spermatogenesis

Oogenesis

2n — Primary spermatocyte

2n — Primary oocyte

n — Polar body

n — Secondary spermatocytes

n — Secondary oocyte

n n n n — Spermatids

n n n n — Sperm

n — Polar body

n — **Fertilized egg**

? *How does the difference in size and cellular contents between sperm and eggs relate to their specific functions in reproduction?*

CONCEPT 46.4

The interplay of tropic and sex hormones regulates mammalian reproduction (pp. 1024–1028)

- In mammals, GnRH from the hypothalamus regulates the release of two hormones, **FSH** and **LH**, from the anterior pituitary. In males, FSH and LH control the secretion of androgens (chiefly **testosterone**) and sperm production. In females, cyclic secretion of FSH and LH orchestrates the **ovarian** and **uterine cycles** via estrogens (primarily **estradiol**) and **progesterone**. The developing **follicle** and the **corpus luteum** also secrete hormones, which help coordinate the uterine and ovarian cycles through positive and negative feedback.

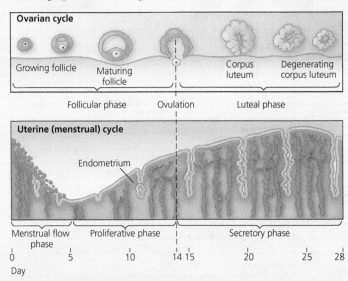

Ovarian cycle

Growing follicle | Maturing follicle | Corpus luteum | Degenerating corpus luteum

Follicular phase | Ovulation | Luteal phase

Uterine (menstrual) cycle

Endometrium

Menstrual flow phase | Proliferative phase | Secretory phase

0   5   10   14 15   20   25   28
Day

- In **estrous cycles**, the lining of the **endometrium** is reabsorbed, and sexual receptivity is limited to a heat period. Reproductive structures with a shared origin in development underlie many features of human sexual arousal and orgasm common to males and females.

? *Why do anabolic steroids lead to reduced sperm counts?*

CONCEPT 46.5

In placental mammals, an embryo develops fully within the mother's uterus (pp. 1028–1034)

- After fertilization and the completion of meiosis in the oviduct, the zygote undergoes a series of cell divisions and develops into a **blastocyst** before implantation in the endometrium. All major organs start developing by 8 weeks. A pregnant woman's acceptance of her "foreign" offspring likely reflects partial suppression of the maternal immune response.
- **Contraception** may prevent release of mature gametes from the gonads, fertilization, or embryo implantation. **Abortion** is the termination of a pregnancy in progress.
- Reproductive technologies can help detect problems before birth and can assist infertile couples. Infertility may be treated through hormone therapy or *in vitro* **fertilization**.

? *What route would oxygen in the mother's blood follow to arrive at a body cell of the fetus?*

TEST YOUR UNDERSTANDING

LEVEL 1: KNOWLEDGE/COMPREHENSION

1. Which of the following characterizes parthenogenesis?
   a. An individual may change its sex during its lifetime.
   b. Specialized groups of cells grow into new individuals.
   c. An organism is first a male and then a female.
   d. An egg develops without being fertilized.

2. In male mammals, excretory and reproductive systems share
   a. the vas deferens.
   b. the urethra.
   c. the seminal vesicle.
   d. the prostate.

3. Which of the following is *not* properly paired?
   a. seminiferous tubule—cervix
   b. vas deferens—oviduct
   c. testosterone—estradiol
   d. scrotum—labia majora

4. Peaks of LH and FSH production occur during
   a. the menstrual flow phase of the uterine cycle.
   b. the beginning of the follicular phase of the ovarian cycle.
   c. the period just before ovulation.
   d. the secretory phase of the menstrual cycle.

5. During human gestation, rudiments of all organs develop
   a. in the first trimester.
   b. in the second trimester.
   c. in the third trimester.
   d. during the blastocyst stage.

LEVEL 2: APPLICATION/ANALYSIS

6. Which of the following is a true statement?
   a. All mammals have menstrual cycles.
   b. The endometrial lining is shed in menstrual cycles but reabsorbed in estrous cycles.
   c. Estrous cycles are more frequent than menstrual cycles.
   d. Ovulation occurs before the endometrium thickens in estrous cycles.

7. For which of the following is the number the same in human males and females?
   a. interruptions in meiotic divisions
   b. functional gametes produced by meiosis
   c. meiotic divisions required to produce each gamete
   d. different cell types produced by meiosis

8. Which statement about human reproduction is false?
   a. Fertilization occurs in the oviduct.
   b. Spermatogenesis and oogenesis require different temperatures.
   c. An oocyte completes meiosis after a sperm penetrates it.
   d. The earliest stages of spermatogenesis occur closest to the lumen of the seminiferous tubules.

LEVEL 3: SYNTHESIS/EVALUATION

9. **DRAW IT** In human spermatogenesis, mitosis of a stem cell gives rise to one cell that remains a stem cell and one cell that becomes a spermatogonium. (a) Draw four rounds of mitosis for a stem cell, and label the daughter cells. (b) For one spermatogonium, draw the cells it would produce from one round of mitosis followed by meiosis. Label the cells, and label mitosis and meiosis. (c) What would happen if stem cells divided like spermatogonia?

10. EVOLUTION CONNECTION
    Hermaphroditism is often found in animals that are fixed to a surface. Motile species are less often hermaphroditic. Why?

11. SCIENTIFIC INQUIRY
    You discover a new egg-laying worm species. You dissect four adults and find both oocytes and sperm in each. Cells outside the gonad contain five chromosome pairs. Lacking genetic variants, how would you determine whether the worms can self-fertilize?

12. WRITE ABOUT A THEME: ENERGY AND MATTER
    In a short essay (100–150 words), discuss how different types of energy investment by females contribute to the reproductive success of a frog, a chicken, and a human.

13. SYNTHESIZE YOUR KNOWLEDGE

A female Komodo dragon (*Varanus komodoensis*) kept in isolation in a zoo had progeny. Each of the offspring had two identical copies of every gene in its genome. However, the offspring were not identical to one another. Based on your understanding of parthenogenesis and meiosis, generate a hypothesis to explain these observations.

For selected answers, see Appendix A.

MasteringBiology®

47

Animal Development

▲ **Figure 47.1 How did a single cell develop into this intricately detailed embryo?**

A Body-Building Plan

The 7-week-old human embryo in **Figure 47.1** has already achieved a remarkable number of milestones in its development. Its heart—the red spot in the center—is beating, and a digestive tract traverses the length of its body. Its brain is forming (at the upper left in the photo), while the blocks of tissue that will give rise to the vertebrae are lined up along its back.

By combining molecular genetics with classical embryology, developmental biologists have learned a great deal about the transformation of a fertilized egg into an adult. Examining embryos from a range of species, such as the chick embryo shown at the left, biologists have long noted common features of early stages, as evident by comparing the human and chick embryos shown on this page. More recently, researchers have demonstrated that specific patterns of gene expression in a developing embryo direct cells to adopt distinct fates. Furthermore, even animals that display widely differing body plans share many basic mechanisms of development and often use a common set of regulatory genes. For example, the gene that specifies heart location in a human embryo (such as the one in Figure 47.1) has a close counterpart with a nearly identical function in the fruit fly *Drosophila melanogaster*. Researchers dubbed the fly gene *tinman*. Why? Embryos in which this gene is defective lack a heart, much like the Tin Man in *The Wizard of Oz*.

In studying development, biologists frequently make use of **model organisms**, species chosen for the ease with which they can be studied in the laboratory. *Drosophila melanogaster*, for example, is a useful model organism: Its life cycle is short, and mutants can be readily identified and studied (see Chapters 15 and 18). In this chapter, we will concentrate on four other model organisms: the sea urchin, the frog, the chick, and the nematode (roundworm). We will also explore some aspects of human embryonic development. Even though humans are not model organisms, we are, of course, intensely interested in our own species.

Development occurs at many points in the life cycle of an animal (**Figure 47.2**). In a frog, for example, a major developmental period is metamorphosis, when the larva (tadpole) undergoes sweeping changes in anatomy in becoming an adult. Development occurs in the adult too, as when stem cells in the gonads produce sperm and eggs (gametes). In this chapter, our focus is on embryonic development.

Across a range of animal species, embryonic development involves common stages that occur in a set order. The first is fertilization, the fusion of sperm and egg. Development proceeds with the cleavage stage, during which a series of cell divisions divide, or cleave, the embryo into many cells. These cleavage divisions, which typically are rapid and lack accompanying cell growth, generate a hollow ball of cells called a blastula. Next, the blastula folds in on itself, rearranging into a multilayered embryo, the gastrula, in a process called gastrulation. During organogenesis, the last major stage of embryonic development, local changes in cell shape and large-scale changes in cell location generate the rudimentary organs from which adult structures grow.

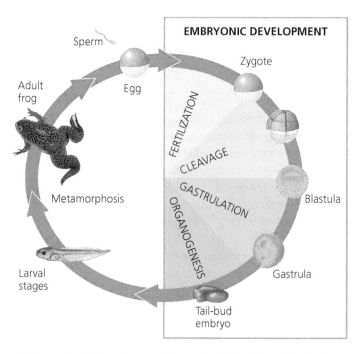

▲ **Figure 47.2 Developmental events in the life cycle of a frog.**

Our exploration of embryonic development will begin with a description of the basic stages common to most animals. We will then look at some of the cellular mechanisms that generate body form. Finally, we will consider how a cell becomes committed to a particular specialized role.

CONCEPT 47.1

Fertilization and cleavage initiate embryonic development

In considering the initiation of embryonic development, we'll begin with the events surrounding **fertilization**, the formation of a diploid zygote from a haploid egg and sperm.

Fertilization

Molecules and events at the egg surface play a crucial role in each step of fertilization. First, sperm dissolve or penetrate any protective layer surrounding the egg to reach the plasma membrane. Next, molecules on the sperm surface bind to receptors on the egg surface, helping ensure that fertilization involves a sperm and egg of the same species. Finally, changes at the surface of the egg prevent *polyspermy*, a condition in which multiple sperm nuclei enter the egg, fatally disrupting development.

The cell surface events that take place during fertilization have been studied most extensively in sea urchins, members of the phylum Echinodermata (see Figure 33.45). Sea urchin gametes are easy to collect, and fertilization is external. As a result, researchers can observe fertilization and subsequent development simply by combining eggs and sperm in seawater in the laboratory. Furthermore, fertilization in sea urchins provides a good general model for the same process in vertebrates.

The Acrosomal Reaction

When sea urchins release their gametes into the water, the jelly coat that surrounds the egg exudes soluble molecules that attract the sperm, which swim toward the egg. As soon as a sperm head contacts the jelly coat of an egg, molecules in the jelly coat trigger the **acrosomal reaction** in the sperm. As detailed in **Figure 47.3**, this reaction begins with the discharge of hydrolytic enzymes from the **acrosome**, a specialized vesicle at the tip of the sperm. These enzymes partially digest the jelly coat, enabling a sperm structure called the *acrosomal process* to elongate and penetrate the coat. Protein molecules on the tip of the extended acrosomal process bind to specific receptor proteins that jut out from the plasma membrane of the egg. This "lock-and-key" recognition is especially important for sea urchins and other species with external fertilization because the water into

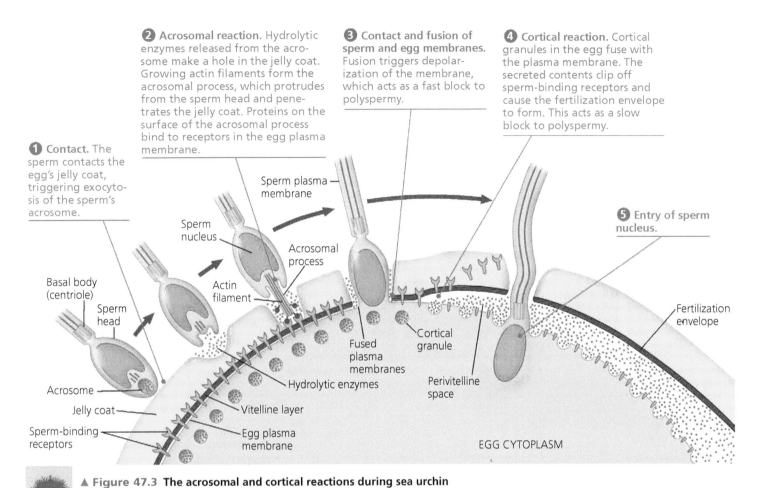

② Acrosomal reaction. Hydrolytic enzymes released from the acrosome make a hole in the jelly coat. Growing actin filaments form the acrosomal process, which protrudes from the sperm head and penetrates the jelly coat. Proteins on the surface of the acrosomal process bind to receptors in the egg plasma membrane.

③ Contact and fusion of sperm and egg membranes. Fusion triggers depolarization of the membrane, which acts as a fast block to polyspermy.

④ Cortical reaction. Cortical granules in the egg fuse with the plasma membrane. The secreted contents clip off sperm-binding receptors and cause the fertilization envelope to form. This acts as a slow block to polyspermy.

① Contact. The sperm contacts the egg's jelly coat, triggering exocytosis of the sperm's acrosome.

Sperm plasma membrane

⑤ Entry of sperm nucleus.

Sperm nucleus

Acrosomal process

Basal body (centriole)

Sperm head

Actin filament

Fertilization envelope

Cortical granule

Acrosome

Fused plasma membranes

Jelly coat

Hydrolytic enzymes

Perivitelline space

Sperm-binding receptors

Vitelline layer

Egg plasma membrane

EGG CYTOPLASM

▲ **Figure 47.3 The acrosomal and cortical reactions during sea urchin fertilization.** The events following contact of a single sperm and egg ensure that the nucleus of only one sperm enters the egg cytoplasm.

The icon above is a simplified drawing of an adult sea urchin. Throughout the chapter, this icon and others representing an adult frog, chicken, nematode, and human indicate the animals whose embryos are featured in certain figures.

which sperm and eggs are released may contain gametes of other species.

The recognition event between the sperm and egg triggers fusion of their plasma membranes. The sperm nucleus then enters the egg cytoplasm as ion channels open in the egg's plasma membrane. Sodium ions diffuse into the egg and cause *depolarization*, a decrease in the membrane potential, the charge difference across the plasma membrane (see Chapter 7). The depolarization occurs within about 1–3 seconds after a sperm binds to an egg. By preventing additional sperm from fusing with the egg's plasma membrane, this depolarization acts as the **fast block to polyspermy**.

The Cortical Reaction

Although membrane depolarization in sea urchins lasts for only a minute or so, there is a longer-lasting change that prevents polyspermy. This **slow block to polyspermy** is established by vesicles that lie just beneath the egg plasma membrane, in the rim of cytoplasm known as the cortex.

Within seconds after a sperm binds to the egg, these vesicles, called cortical granules, fuse with the egg plasma membrane (see Figure 47.3, step 4). Contents of the cortical granules are released into the space between the plasma membrane and the surrounding vitelline layer, a structure formed by the egg's extracellular matrix. Enzymes and other macromolecules from the granules then trigger a *cortical reaction*, which lifts the vitelline layer away from the egg and hardens the layer into a protective fertilization envelope. Additional enzymes clip off and release the external portions of the remaining receptor proteins, along with any attached sperm.

Formation of the fertilization envelope requires a high concentration of calcium ions (Ca^{2+}) in the egg. Does a change in the Ca^{2+} concentration trigger the cortical reaction? To answer this question, researchers used a calcium-sensitive dye to assess how Ca^{2+} is distributed in the egg before and during fertilization. As described in **Figure 47.4**, they found that Ca^{2+} spread across the egg in a wave that correlated with the appearance of the fertilization envelope.

▼ Figure 47.4 Inquiry

Does the distribution of Ca^{2+} in an egg correlate with formation of the fertilization envelope?

Experiment During fertilization, fusion of cortical granules with the egg plasma membrane causes the fertilization envelope to rise and spread around the egg from the point of sperm binding. To produce this series of images, investigators mixed sea urchin eggs with sperm, waited for 10 to 60 seconds, and then added a chemical fixative, freezing cellular structures in place. The researchers then took photomicrographs of each sample. When these images are ordered according to the time of fixation, they illustrate the stages in fertilization membrane formation for a single egg.

Fertilization envelope

10 sec after fertilization   25 sec   35 sec   1 min   500 μm

Calcium ion (Ca^{2+}) signaling was known to be involved in fusion of vesicles with the plasma membrane during neurotransmitter release, insulin secretion, and plant pollen tube formation. Researchers hypothesized that calcium ion signaling is similarly involved in vesicle fusion required for formation of the fertilization envelope. To test this hypothesis, they tracked the release of free Ca^{2+} in sea urchin eggs after sperm binding to see if calcium release correlated with formation of the fertilization envelope. A fluorescent dye that glows when it binds free Ca^{2+} was injected into unfertilized eggs. The scientists then added sea urchin sperm and observed the eggs with a fluorescence microscope as fertilization took place, producing the results shown here.

Results A rise in cytosolic Ca^{2+} concentration began on the side of the egg where the sperm had entered and spread in a wave to the other side of the egg. Soon after the wave passed, the fertilization envelope rose.

Point of sperm nucleus entry   Spreading wave of Ca^{2+}

1 sec before fertilization   10 sec after fertilization   20 sec   30 sec   500 μm

Conclusion The researchers concluded that Ca^{2+} release is correlated with the cortical reaction and formation of the fertilization envelope, supporting their hypothesis that an increase in Ca^{2+} levels triggers cortical granule fusion.

Sources: R. Steinhardt et al., Intracellular calcium release at fertilization in the sea urchin egg, *Developmental Biology* 58:185–197 (1977). M. Hafner et al., Wave of free calcium at fertilization in the sea urchin egg visualized with Fura-2, *Cell Motility and the Cytoskeleton* 9:271–277 (1988).

(MB) See the related Experimental Inquiry Tutorial in MasteringBiology.

WHAT IF? *Suppose you were given a chemical compound that could enter the egg and bind to Ca^{2+}, blocking its function. How would you use this compound to further test the hypothesis that a rise in Ca^{2+} level triggers cortical granule fusion?*

Further studies demonstrated that the binding of sperm to the egg activates a signal transduction pathway that triggers release of Ca^{2+} into the cytosol from the endoplasmic reticulum. The resulting increase in Ca^{2+} levels causes cortical granules to fuse with the plasma membrane. A cortical reaction triggered by Ca^{2+} also occurs in vertebrates such as fishes and mammals.

Egg Activation

Fertilization initiates and speeds up metabolic reactions that trigger the onset of embryonic development, "activating" the egg. There is, for example, a marked increase in the rates of cellular respiration and protein synthesis in the egg following fertilization.

How does fertilization initiate the metabolic steps that activate the egg? A major clue came from experiments demonstrating that the unfertilized eggs of sea urchins and many other species can be activated by an injection of Ca^{2+}. Based on this discovery, researchers concluded that the rise in Ca^{2+} concentration that causes the cortical reaction also causes egg activation. Subsequent experiments revealed that artificial activation is possible even if the nucleus has been removed from the egg. This further finding indicates that the proteins and mRNAs required for activation are already present in the cytoplasm of the unfertilized egg.

Not until about 20 minutes after the sperm nucleus enters the sea urchin egg do the sperm and egg nuclei fuse. DNA synthesis then begins. The first cell division, which occurs after about 90 minutes, marks the end of the fertilization stage.

Fertilization in other species shares many features with the process in sea urchins. However, there are differences, such as the stage of meiosis the egg has reached by the time it is fertilized. Sea urchin eggs have already completed meiosis when they are released from the female. In other species, eggs are arrested at a specific stage of meiosis and do not complete the meiotic divisions until a sperm head enters. Human eggs, for example, are arrested at metaphase of meiosis II prior to sperm entry (see Figure 46.11).

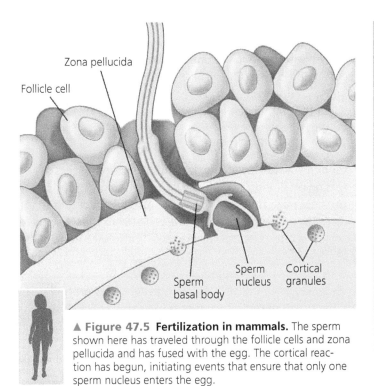

Zona pellucida

Follicle cell

Sperm
basal body

Sperm
nucleus

Cortical
granules

▲ **Figure 47.5 Fertilization in mammals.** The sperm shown here has traveled through the follicle cells and zona pellucida and has fused with the egg. The cortical reaction has begun, initiating events that ensure that only one sperm nucleus enters the egg.

Fertilization in Mammals

Unlike sea urchins and most other marine invertebrates, terrestrial animals, including mammals, fertilize eggs internally. Support cells of the developing follicle surround the mammalian egg before and after ovulation. As shown in **Figure 47.5**, a sperm must travel through this layer of follicle cells before it reaches the **zona pellucida**, the extracellular matrix of the egg. There, the binding of a sperm to a sperm receptor induces an acrosomal reaction, facilitating sperm entry.

As in sea urchin fertilization, sperm binding triggers a cortical reaction, the release of enzymes from cortical granules to the outside of the cell. These enzymes catalyze changes in the zona pellucida, which then functions as the slow block to polyspermy. (No fast block to polyspermy has been identified in mammals.)

Overall, the process of fertilization is much slower in mammals than in sea urchins: The first cell division occurs within 12–36 hours after sperm binding in mammals, compared with about 90 minutes in sea urchins. This cell division marks the end of fertilization and the beginning of the next stage of development, cleavage.

Cleavage

Once fertilization is complete, the zygotes of many animal species undergo a succession of rapid cell divisions that characterize the **cleavage** stage of early development. During cleavage, the cell cycle consists primarily of the S (DNA synthesis) and M (mitosis) phases. The G_1 and G_2 (gap) phases are essentially skipped, and little or no protein synthesis occurs (see Figure 12.6 for a review of the cell cycle). As a result, there is no increase in mass. Instead, cleavage partitions the cytoplasm of the large fertilized egg into many smaller cells called **blastomeres**. The first five to seven cleavage divisions produce a hollow ball of cells, the **blastula**, surrounding a fluid-filled cavity called the **blastocoel** (Figure 47.6).

The pattern of cleavage divisions differs among species. In some cases, as in sand dollars and sea urchins, the division pattern is uniform across the embryo (see Figure 47.6). In others, including frogs, the pattern is asymmetric, with regions of the embryo differing in both the number and size of newly formed cells.

(a) Fertilized egg. Shown here is the zygote shortly before the first cleavage division, surrounded by the fertilization envelope.

(b) Four-cell stage. Remnants of the mitotic spindle can be seen between the two pairs of cells that have just completed the second cleavage division.

(c) Early blastula. After further cleavage divisions, the embryo is a multicellular ball that is still surrounded by the fertilization envelope. The blastocoel has begun to form in the center.

(d) Later blastula. A single layer of cells surrounds a large blastocoel. (Although not visible here, the fertilization envelope is still present at this stage.)

50 μm

▲ **Figure 47.6 Cleavage in an echinoderm embryo.** Cleavage is a series of mitotic cell divisions that transform the fertilized egg into a blastula, a hollow ball composed of cells called blastomeres. These light micrographs show the cleavage stages of a sand dollar embryo, which are virtually identical to those of a sea urchin.

Cleavage Pattern in Frogs

In frogs (and many other animals), cleavage is asymmetric (Figure 47.7), reflecting the asymmetric distribution of **yolk** (stored nutrients) across the egg. Yolk is often concentrated toward one pole, called the **vegetal pole**, and away from the opposite or **animal pole**. As a result, the two halves of the egg, called the animal and vegetal hemispheres, differ in color. As we will see shortly, the yolk greatly affects the pattern of cleavage.

When an animal cell divides, an indentation called a *cleavage furrow* forms in the cell surface as cytokinesis divides the cell in half. As shown in Figure 47.7, the first two cleavage furrows in the frog embryo form parallel to the line (or meridian) connecting the two poles. During these divisions, the main effect of yolk is to slow completion of cytokinesis. As a result, the first cleavage furrow is still dividing the yolky cytoplasm in the vegetal hemisphere when the second cell division begins. Eventually, four blastomeres of equal size extend from the animal pole to the vegetal pole.

During the third division, the yolk begins to affect the relative size of cells produced in the two hemispheres. This division is equatorial (perpendicular to the line connecting the poles) and produces an eight-celled embryo. However, as each of the four blastomeres begins this division, yolk near the vegetal pole displaces the mitotic apparatus toward the animal pole. This in turn displaces the cleavage furrow from the egg equator toward the animal pole, yielding smaller blastomeres in the animal hemisphere than in the vegetal hemisphere. The displacing effect of the yolk persists in subsequent divisions, causing the blastocoel to form entirely in the animal hemisphere (see Figure 47.7).

Cleavage Patterns in Other Animals

Although yolk affects where division occurs in the eggs of frogs and other amphibians, the cleavage furrow still passes entirely through the egg. Cleavage in amphibian development is therefore said to be **holoblastic** (from the Greek *holos*, complete). Holoblastic cleavage is also seen in many other groups of animals, including echinoderms, mammals, and annelids. In those animals whose eggs contain a relatively little amount of yolk, the blastocoel forms centrally and the blastomeres are often of similar size, particularly during the first few divisions of cleavage (see Figure 47.6). This is the case for humans.

Yolk is most plentiful and has its most pronounced effect on cleavage in the eggs of birds, other reptiles, many fishes, and insects. In these animals, the volume of yolk is so great that cleavage furrows cannot pass through it, and only the region of the egg lacking yolk undergoes cleavage. This incomplete cleavage of a yolk-rich egg is said to be **meroblastic** (from the Greek *meros*, partial).

▶ **Figure 47.7 Cleavage in a frog embryo.** The cleavage planes in the first and second divisions extend from the animal pole to the vegetal pole, but the third cleavage is perpendicular to the polar axis. In some species, the first division bisects the gray crescent, a lighter-colored region that appears opposite the site of sperm entry.

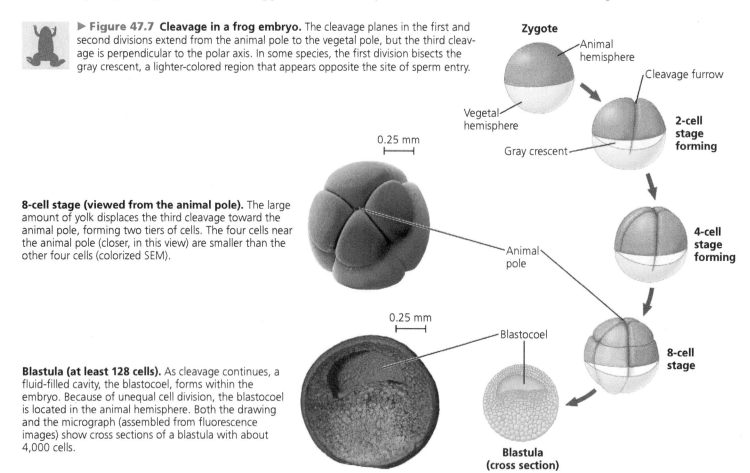

8-cell stage (viewed from the animal pole). The large amount of yolk displaces the third cleavage toward the animal pole, forming two tiers of cells. The four cells near the animal pole (closer, in this view) are smaller than the other four cells (colorized SEM).

Blastula (at least 128 cells). As cleavage continues, a fluid-filled cavity, the blastocoel, forms within the embryo. Because of unequal cell division, the blastocoel is located in the animal hemisphere. Both the drawing and the micrograph (assembled from fluorescence images) show cross sections of a blastula with about 4,000 cells.

0.25 mm

0.25 mm

Zygote — Animal hemisphere — Cleavage furrow — Vegetal hemisphere — Gray crescent — 2-cell stage forming — 4-cell stage forming — Animal pole — 8-cell stage — Blastocoel — Blastula (cross section)

Interpreting a Change in Slope

What Causes the End of Cleavage in a Frog Embryo? During cleavage in a frog embryo, as in many other animals, the cell cycle consists mainly of the S (DNA synthesis) and M (mitosis) phases, and there are no G_1 and G_2 phases. However, after the 12th cell division, G_1 and G_2 phases appear, and the cells grow, producing proteins and cytoplasmic organelles. These and other changes in activity mark the end of cleavage. But what triggers the change in the cell cycle?

How the Experiments Were Done Researchers tested the hypothesis that a mechanism for counting cell divisions determines when cleavage ends. They allowed frog embryos to take up radioactively labeled nucleosides, in one experiment labeling thymidine to measure DNA synthesis and in another experiment labeling uridine to measure RNA synthesis. They then repeated these two experiments in the presence of a toxin that prevents cell division by blocking cleavage furrow formation and cytokinesis.

Data from the Experiments

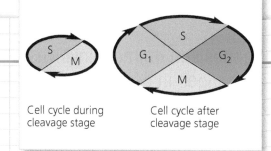

Cell cycle during cleavage stage

Cell cycle after cleavage stage

	Nucleic Acid Synthesis (on scale of 0–100)										
DNA Toxin added	35	48	54	71	83	85	88	87	100	96	
DNA No toxin	10	24	28	31	47	49	49	53	55	55	55
RNA Toxin added			0		6		25	27			33
RNA No toxin			0		3		14	22			27
Time Point (every 35 min)	1	2	3	4	5	6	7	8	9	10	11

Interpret the Data

1. How were the researchers able to independently measure DNA synthesis and RNA synthesis?

2. Use the data in the table to create a graph showing DNA synthesis and RNA synthesis with and without the toxin that prevents cell division. Note that time point 5 corresponds to cell division 12. For the DNA data, draw a straight line to represent the general trend for time points 1–5 and another straight line for time points 5 and later. For RNA, connect each data point with the next. Describe the changes in synthesis that occur at the end of cleavage.

3. The researchers hypothesized that the toxin increases diffusion of thymidine into the embryos. Explain their logic.

4. Do the data support the hypothesis that the timing of the end of cleavage depends on counting cell divisions? Explain.

5. In a separate experiment, researchers disrupted the block to polyspermy, generating embryos with 7 to 10 sperm nuclei. At the end of cleavage, these embryos had the same nucleus-to-cytoplasm ratio as the wild-type embryos, but cleavage ended at the 10th cell division rather than the 12th cell division. What do these results indicate about the timing of the end of cleavage?

(MB) A version of this Scientific Skills Exercise can be assigned in MasteringBiology.

Data from J. Newport and M. Kirschner, A major developmental transition in early *Xenopus* embryos: I. Characterization and timing of cellular changes at the midblastula stage, *Cell* 30:675–686 (1982).

For chickens and other birds, the part of the egg that we commonly call the yolk is actually the entire egg cell. Cell divisions are limited to a small whitish area at the animal pole. These divisions produce a cap of cells that sort into upper and lower layers. The cavity between these two layers is the avian version of the blastocoel.

In *Drosophila* and most other insects, yolk is found throughout the egg. Early in development, multiple rounds of mitosis occur without cytokinesis. In other words, no cell membranes form around the early nuclei. The first several hundred nuclei spread throughout the yolk and later migrate to the outer edge of the embryo. After several more rounds of mitosis, a plasma membrane forms around each nucleus, and the embryo, now the equivalent of a blastula, consists of a single layer of about 6,000 cells surrounding a mass of yolk (see Figure 18.22).

Regulation of Cleavage

The single nucleus in a newly fertilized egg has too little DNA to produce the amount of messenger RNA required to meet the cell's need for new proteins. Instead, initial development is carried out by RNA and proteins deposited in the egg during oogenesis. After cleavage, the egg cytoplasm has been divided among the many blastomeres, each with its own nucleus. Because each blastomere is much smaller than the entire egg, its nucleus can make enough RNA to program the cell's metabolism and further development.

Given that the number of cleavage divisions varies among animals, what mechanism determines the end of the cleavage stage? The Scientific Skills Exercise explores one of the landmark studies that addressed this question.

CONCEPT CHECK 47.1

1. How does the fertilization envelope form in sea urchins? What is its function?

2. **WHAT IF?** Predict what would happen if Ca^{2+} was injected into an unfertilized sea urchin egg.

3. **MAKE CONNECTIONS** Thinking about cell cycle control, would you expect MPF activity to remain steady during cleavage (see Figure 12.16)? Explain your logic.

For suggested answers, see Appendix A.

CONCEPT 47.2

Morphogenesis in animals involves specific changes in cell shape, position, and survival

After cleavage, the rate of cell division slows considerably as the normal cell cycle is restored. The last two stages of embryonic development are responsible for **morphogenesis**, the cellular and tissue-based processes by which the animal body takes shape. During **gastrulation**, a set of cells at or near the surface of the blastula moves to an interior location, cell layers are established, and a primitive digestive tube is formed. Further transformation occurs during **organogenesis**, the formation of organs. We will discuss these two stages in turn, focusing in each case on the development of a few model organisms.

Gastrulation

Gastrulation is a dramatic reorganization of the hollow blastula into a two-layered or three-layered embryo called a **gastrula**. The cell layers produced are collectively called the embryonic **germ layers** (from the Latin *germen*, to sprout or germinate). In the late gastrula, **ectoderm** forms the outer layer and **endoderm** lines the embryonic digestive compartment or tract. In cnidarians and a few other radially symmetrical animals, only these two germ layers form during gastrulation. Such animals are called diploblasts (see Chapter 32). In contrast, vertebrates and other animals with bilateral symmetry are triploblasts, in which a third germ layer, the **mesoderm**, forms between the ectoderm and the endoderm.

Gastrulation in Sea Urchins

As illustrated in **Figure 47.8**, gastrulation in the sea urchin involves cell migration as well as *invagination*, the infolding of a sheet of cells into the embryo. Extensive rearrangement of cells transforms the shallow depression into a deeper, narrower, blind-ended tube called the **archenteron**. The open end of the archenteron, which will become the anus, is called the **blastopore**. A second opening,

which will become the mouth, forms later. Sea urchins and other animals in which the mouth develops from the second opening of the embryo are called *deuterostomes* (from the Greek, meaning "second mouth"). All chordates, including ourselves and other vertebrates, fall in this grouping (see Chapter 32). In contrast, mollusks, annelids, and arthropods are *protostomes*, animals in which the mouth develops from the first opening formed during gastrulation.

Gastrulation in Frogs

Each germ layer contributes to a distinct set of structures in the adult animal, as shown for vertebrates in **Figure 47.9**. Some organs and many organ systems of the adult derive from more than one germ layer. For example, the adrenal glands have both ectodermal and mesoderm tissue, and many other endocrine glands contain endodermal tissue.

① A group of *mesenchyme* cells migrates from the vegetal pole of the blastula into the blastocoel. Some of these cells will eventually secrete calcium carbonate and form a simple internal skeleton.

② Cells at the vegetal plate flatten slightly, causing the vegetal pole of the embryo to buckle inward. This infolding of a sheet of cells is called *invagination*.

③ Endoderm cells form the archenteron, the future digestive tube. New mesenchyme cells at the tip of the archenteron send out thin extensions (filopodia) toward the blastocoel wall (left, LM).

④ The filopodia contract, dragging the archenteron across the blastocoel. The open end of the archenteron, which will become the anus, is called the blastospore.

⑤ Fusion of the archenteron with the blastocoel wall forms the digestive tube, which now has a mouth and an anus. The gastrula has three germ layers and is covered with cilia, which will function in feeding and movement.

▲ **Figure 47.8**
Gastrulation in a sea urchin embryo.

Key

▮	Future ectoderm
▮	Future mesoderm
▯	Future endoderm

Frogs and other bilaterally symmetrical animals have a dorsal (top) side and a ventral (bottom) side, a left side and a right side, and an anterior (front) end and a posterior (back) end. The cell movements that begin gastrulation occur on the dorsal side of the blastula, opposite where the sperm entered the egg (**Figure 47.10**). As in the sea urchin, the frog's anus develops from the blastopore, and the mouth eventually breaks through at the opposite end of the archenteron.

▼ **Figure 47.9 Major derivatives of the three embryonic germ layers in vertebrates.**

ECTODERM (outer layer of embryo)	MESODERM (middle layer of embryo)	ENDODERM (inner layer of embryo)
• Epidermis of skin and its derivatives (including sweat glands, hair follicles) • Nervous and sensory systems • Pituitary gland, adrenal medulla • Jaws and teeth • Germ cells	• Skeletal and muscular systems • Circulatory and lymphatic systems • Excretory and reproductive systems (except germ cells) • Dermis of skin • Adrenal cortex	• Epithelial lining of digestive tract and associated organs (liver, pancreas) • Epithelial lining of respiratory, excretory, and reproductive tracts and ducts • Thymus, thyroid, and parathyroid glands

▼ **Figure 47.10 Gastrulation in a frog embryo.** In the frog blastula, the blastocoel is displaced toward the animal pole and is surrounded by a wall several cells thick.

① Gastrulation begins when cells on the dorsal side invaginate to form a small indented crease, the blastopore. The part above the crease is called the **dorsal lip**. As the blastopore is forming, a sheet of cells begins to spread out of the animal hemisphere, rolls inward over the dorsal lip (involution), and moves into the interior (shown by the dashed arrow). In the interior, these cells will form endoderm and mesoderm, with the endodermal layer on the inside. Meanwhile, cells at the animal pole change shape and begin spreading over the outer surface.

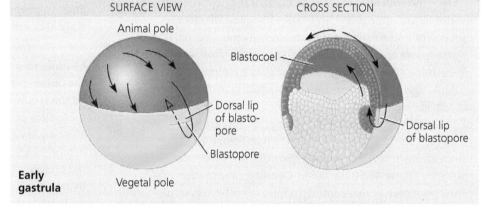

② The blastopore extends around both sides of the embryo as more cells invaginate. When the ends meet, the blastopore forms a circle that becomes smaller as ectoderm spreads downward over the surface. Internally, continued involution expands the endoderm and mesoderm; an archenteron forms and grows as the blastocoel shrinks and eventually disappears.

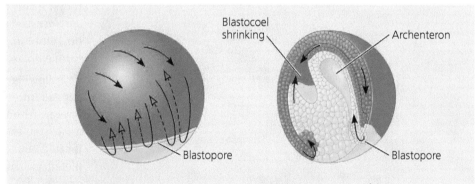

③ Late in gastrulation, the cells remaining on the surface make up the ectoderm. The endoderm is the innermost layer, and the mesoderm lies between the ectoderm and endoderm. The circular blastopore surrounds a plug of yolk-filled cells.

Key	
	Future ectoderm
	Future mesoderm
	Future endoderm

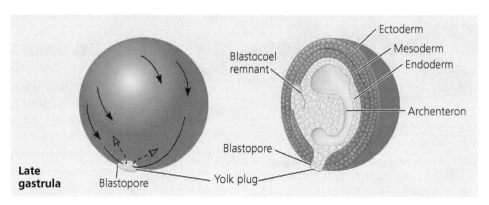

Gastrulation in Chicks

The starting point for gastrulation in chicks is an embryo consisting of upper and lower layers—known as the *epiblast* and *hypoblast*—lying atop a yolk mass. All the cells that will form the embryo come from the epiblast. During gastrulation, some epiblast cells move toward the midline of the blastoderm, detach, and move inward toward the yolk (Figure 47.11). The pileup of cells moving inward at the blastoderm's midline produces a thickening called the **primitive streak**. Some of these cells move downward and form endoderm, pushing aside the hypoblast cells, while others migrate laterally (sideways) and form mesoderm. The cells left behind on the surface of the embryo at the end of gastrulation will become ectoderm. The hypoblast cells later segregate from the endoderm and eventually form part of the sac that surrounds the yolk and also part of the stalk that connects the yolk mass to the embryo.

Over the course of chick gastrulation, the primitive streak lengthens and narrows. This shape change results from a movement and sorting of cells called convergent extension. We'll explore the mechanism of this process shortly, when we examine how form and shape arise in development.

Although different terms describe gastrulation in different vertebrate species, the rearrangements and movements of cells exhibit a number of fundamental similarities. In particular, the primitive streak, shown in Figure 47.11 for the chick embryo, is the counterpart of the blastopore lip, shown in Figure 47.10 for the frog embryo. Formation of a primitive streak is also central to human embryo gastrulation, our next topic.

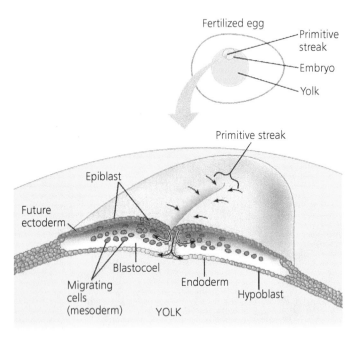

▲ **Figure 47.11 Gastrulation in a chick embryo.** This is a cross section of a gastrulating embryo, looking toward the anterior end.

Gastrulation in Humans

Unlike the large, yolky eggs of many vertebrates, human eggs are quite small, storing little in the way of food reserves. Fertilization takes place in the oviduct, and development begins while the embryo completes its journey down the oviduct to the uterus (see Figure 46.15).

Figure 47.12 outlines development of the human embryo, starting about 6 days after fertilization. This depiction is largely based on observations of embryos from other mammals, such as the mouse, and of very early human embryos following *in vitro* fertilization.

❶ At the end of cleavage, the embryo has more than 100 cells arranged around a central cavity and has reached the uterus. At this stage, the embryo is called a **blastocyst**, the mammalian version of a blastula. Clustered at one end of the blastocyst cavity is a group of cells called the **inner cell mass**, which will develop into the embryo proper. It is the cells of the very early blastocyst stage that are the source of embryonic stem cell lines (see Concept 20.3).

❷ Embryo implantation is initiated by the **trophoblast**, the outer epithelium of the blastocyst. Enzymes secreted by the trophoblast during implantation break down molecules of the endometrium, the lining of the uterus, allowing invasion by the blastocyst. The trophoblast also extends finger-like projections that cause capillaries in the endometrium to spill out blood that can be captured by trophoblast tissues. Around the time the embryo undergoes implantation, the inner cell mass of the blastocyst forms a flat disk with an inner layer of cells, the *epiblast*, and an outer layer, the *hypoblast*. As is true for a bird embryo, the human embryo develops almost entirely from epiblast cells.

❸ Following implantation, the trophoblast continues to expand into the endometrium, and four new membranes appear. Although these **extraembryonic membranes** arise from the embryo, they enclose specialized structures located outside the embryo. As implantation is completed, gastrulation begins. Some epiblast cells remain as ectoderm on the surface, while others move inward through a primitive streak and form mesoderm and endoderm, just as in the chick (see Figure 47.11).

❹ By the end of gastrulation, the embryonic germ layers have formed. Extraembryonic mesoderm and four distinct extraembryonic membranes now surround the embryo. As development proceeds, cells of the invading trophoblast, the epiblast, and the adjacent endometrial tissue all contribute to the formation of the placenta. This vital organ mediates the exchange of nutrients, gases, and nitrogenous wastes between the developing embryo and the mother (see Figure 46.16).

① Blastocyst reaches uterus.

- Endometrial epithelium (uterine lining)
- Inner cell mass
- Trophoblast
- Blastocoel

② Blastocyst implants (7 days after fertilization).

- Maternal blood vessel
- Expanding region of trophoblast
- Epiblast
- Hypoblast
- Trophoblast

③ Extraembryonic membranes start to form (10–11 days), and gastrulation begins (13 days).

- Expanding region of trophoblast
- Amniotic cavity
- Epiblast
- Hypoblast
- Yolk sac (from hypoblast)
- Extraembryonic mesoderm cells (from epiblast)
- Chorion (from trophoblast)

④ Gastrulation has produced a three-layered embryo with four extraembryonic membranes: the amnion, chorion, yolk sac, and allantois.

- Amnion
- Chorion
- Ectoderm
- Mesoderm
- Endoderm
- Yolk sac
- Extraembryonic mesoderm
- Allantois

▲ **Figure 47.12 Four stages in the early embryonic development of a human.** The names of the tissues that develop into the embryo proper are printed in blue.

Developmental Adaptations of Amniotes

EVOLUTION Mammals and reptiles (including birds) form four extraembryonic membranes: the chorion, allantois, amnion, and yolk sac (**Figure 47.13**; see also Figure 34.25). In all these groups, such membranes provide a "life-support system" for further embryonic development. Why did this adaptation appear in the evolutionary history of reptiles and mammals,

- Chorion
- Allantois
- Amnion
- Yolk sac

▲ **Figure 47.13 The four extraembryonic membranes in the shelled egg of a reptile.**

but not other vertebrates, such as fishes and amphibians? We can formulate a reasonable hypothesis by considering a few basic facts about embryonic development. All vertebrate embryos require an aqueous environment for their development. The embryos of fishes and amphibians usually develop in the surrounding sea or pond and need no specialized water-filled enclosure. However, the extensive colonization of land by vertebrates was possible only after the evolution of structures that would allow reproduction in dry environments. Two such structures exist today: (1) the shelled egg of birds and other reptiles as well as a few mammals (the monotremes) and (2) the uterus of marsupial and eutherian mammals. Inside the shell or uterus, the embryos of these animals are surrounded by fluid within a sac formed by one of the extraembryonic membranes, the amnion. Mammals and reptiles, including birds, are therefore called **amniotes** (see Concept 34.5).

For the most part, the extraembryonic membranes have similar functions in mammals and reptiles, consistent with a common evolutionary origin. The chorion is the site of gas exchange, and the fluid within the amnion physically protects the developing embryo. (This amniotic fluid is released from the vagina when a pregnant woman's "water breaks" before childbirth.) The allantois, which disposes of wastes in the reptilian egg, is incorporated into the umbilical cord in mammals. There it forms blood vessels that transport oxygen and nutrients from the placenta to the embryo and rid the embryo of carbon dioxide and nitrogenous wastes. The fourth extraembryonic membrane, the yolk sac, encloses yolk in the eggs of reptiles. In mammals it is a site of early formation of blood cells, which later migrate into the embryo proper. Thus, the extraembryonic membranes common to reptiles and mammals exhibit adaptations specific to development within a shelled egg or a uterus.

After gastrulation is complete and any extraembryonic membranes are formed, the next stage of embryonic development begins: organogenesis, the formation of organs.

Organogenesis

During organogenesis, regions of the three embryonic germ layers develop into the rudiments of organs. Often, cells from two or three germ layers participate in formation of a single organ, with interactions between cells of different germ layers helping to specify cell fates. Adoption of particular developmental fates may in turn cause cells to change shape or, in certain circumstances, migrate to another location in the body. To see how these processes contribute to organogenesis, we'll consider *neurulation*, the early steps in the formation of the brain and spinal cord in vertebrates.

Neurulation

Neurulation begins as cells from the dorsal mesoderm form the **notochord**, a rod that extends along the dorsal side of the chordate embryo, as seen for the frog in **Figure 47.14a**.

Signaling molecules secreted by these mesodermal cells and other tissues cause the ectoderm above the notochord to become the *neural plate*. Formation of the neural plate is thus an example of **induction**, a process in which a group of cells or tissues influences the development of another group through close-range interactions (see Figure 18.17b).

After the neural plate is formed, its cells change shape, curving the structure inward. In this way, the neural plate rolls itself into the **neural tube**, which runs along the anterior-posterior axis of the embryo **(Figure 47.14b)**. The neural tube will become the brain in the head and the spinal cord along the rest of the body. In contrast, the notochord disappears before birth, although parts persist as the inner portions of the disks in the adult spine. (These are the disks that can herniate or rupture, causing back pain.)

Neurulation, like other stages of development, is sometimes imperfect. In humans, an error in neural tube

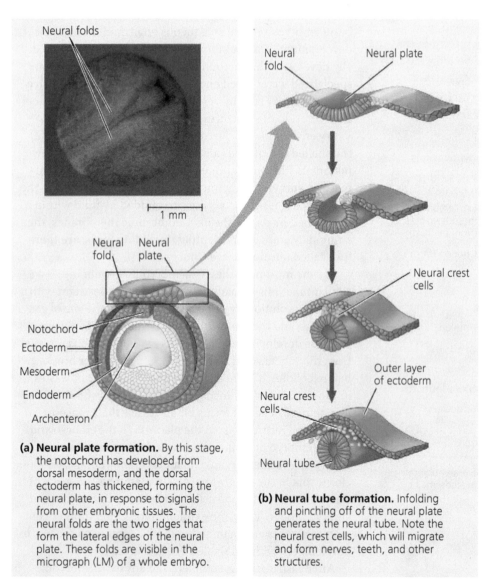

(a) Neural plate formation. By this stage, the notochord has developed from dorsal mesoderm, and the dorsal ectoderm has thickened, forming the neural plate, in response to signals from other embryonic tissues. The neural folds are the two ridges that form the lateral edges of the neural plate. These folds are visible in the micrograph (LM) of a whole embryo.

(b) Neural tube formation. Infolding and pinching off of the neural plate generates the neural tube. Note the neural crest cells, which will migrate and form nerves, teeth, and other structures.

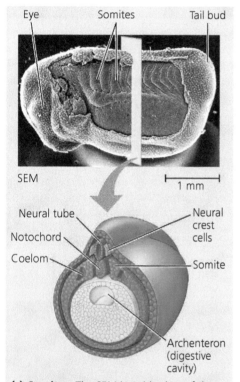

(c) Somites. The SEM is a side view of the whole embryo at the tail-bud stage. Part of the ectoderm has been removed to reveal the somites, blocks of tissue that will give rise to segmental structures such as vertebrae. The drawing shows a similar-stage embryo after formation of the neural tube, as if the embryo in the SEM were cut and viewed in cross section. By this time, the lateral mesoderm has begun to separate into two tissue layers that line the coelom, or body cavity. The somites, formed from mesoderm, flank the notochord.

▲ **Figure 47.14 Neurulation in a frog embryo.**

formation results in *spina bifida*, the most common disabling birth defect in the United States. In spina bifida, a portion of the neural tube fails to develop or close properly, leaving an opening in the spinal column and causing nerve damage. Although the opening can be surgically repaired shortly after birth, the nerve damage is permanent, resulting in varying degrees of leg paralysis.

Cell Migration in Organogenesis

Although organogenesis requires local cellular interactions and activities, some cells undergo long-range migration. For example, two sets of cells that develop near the neural tube of vertebrate embryos migrate in the body before assuming their developmental fate. The first set is a band of cells called the **neural crest**, which develops along the borders where the neural tube pinches off from the ectoderm (see Figure 47.14b). Neural crest cells subsequently migrate to many parts of the embryo, forming a variety of tissues that include peripheral nerves as well as parts of the teeth and skull bones.

A second set of migratory cells is formed when groups of cells located in strips of mesoderm lateral to the notochord separate into blocks called **somites** (Figure 47.14c). The somites are arranged serially on both sides along the length of the notochord. Somites play a significant role in organizing the segmented structure of the vertebrate body. Parts of the somites dissociate into mesenchyme cells, which migrate individually to new locations. Some of these cells form the vertebrae. Somite cells that become mesenchymal also form the muscles associated with the vertebral column and the ribs.

By contributing to formation of vertebrae, ribs, and associated muscles, serially repeating structures of the embryo (somites) form repeated structures in the adult. Chordates, including ourselves, are thus segmented, although in the adult form the segmentation is much less obvious than in shrimp and many other segmented invertebrates.

Organogenesis in Chicks and Insects

Early organogenesis in the chick is quite similar to that in the frog. For example, the borders of the chick blastoderm fold downward and come together, pinching the embryo into a three-layered tube joined under the middle of the body to the yolk (Figure 47.15a). By the time the chick embryo is 3 days old, rudiments of the major organs, including the brain, eyes, and heart, are readily apparent (Figure 47.15b).

In invertebrates, organogenesis is somewhat different, which is not surprising, given that their body plans diverge significantly from those of vertebrates. In insects, for example, tissues of the nervous system form on the ventral side of the insect embryo rather than the dorsal side, as in vertebrates. The mechanism, however, is quite similar to vertebrate neurulation: Ectoderm along the anterior-posterior axis rolls into a tube inside the embryo. Furthermore, the molecular signaling pathways that bring about the events in different locations in the two groups are remarkably similar, underscoring a shared evolutionary history. Likewise, formation of other organs in invertebrates involves many of the same cellular activities observed in vertebrates: inductive interactions, cell shape changes, and cell migration.

As we have seen in our consideration of gastrulation and organogenesis, changes in cell shape and location are essential to early development. We turn now to an exploration of how these changes take place.

► **Figure 47.15 Organogenesis in a chick embryo.**

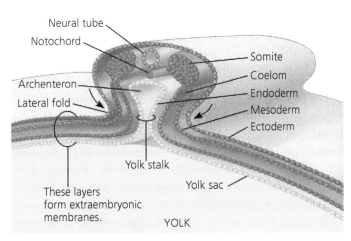

(a) **Early organogenesis.** The archenteron forms when lateral folds pinch the embryo away from the yolk. The embryo remains open to the yolk, attached by the yolk stalk, about midway along its length, as shown in this cross section. The notochord, neural tube, and somites subsequently develop much as they do in the frog. The germ layers lateral to the embryo itself form extraembryonic membranes.

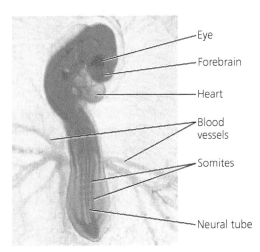

(b) **Late organogenesis.** Rudiments of most major organs have already formed in this chick embryo, which is 3 days old and about 2–3 mm long. The extraembryonic membranes eventually are supplied by blood vessels extending from the embryo; several major blood vessels are seen here in this light micrograph (LM).

Mechanisms of Morphogenesis

Morphogenesis is a major stage of development in both animals and plants, but only in animals does it involve the *movement* of cells. The rigid cell wall that surrounds plant cells prevents complex movements like those that occur during gastrulation and organogenesis. In animals, movement of parts of a cell can bring about changes in cell shape or enable a cell to migrate from one place to another within the embryo. One set of cellular components essential to these events is the collection of microtubules and microfilaments that make up the cytoskeleton (see Table 6.1).

The Cytoskeleton in Morphogenesis

Reorganization of the cytoskeleton is a major force in changing cell shape during development. As an example, let's return to the topic of neurulation. At the onset of neural tube formation, microtubules oriented from dorsal to ventral in a sheet of ectodermal cells help lengthen the cells along that axis (Figure 47.16). At the dorsal end of each cell is a bundle of actin filaments (microfilaments) oriented crosswise. These actin filaments contract, giving the cells a wedge shape that bends the ectoderm layer inward. Similar changes in cell shape occur at the hinge regions where the neural tube is pinching off from the ectoderm. However, the generation of wedge-shaped cells is not limited to neurulation or even to vertebrates. In *Drosophila* gastrulation, for instance, the formation of wedge-shaped cells along the ventral surface is responsible for invagination of a tube of cells that form the mesoderm.

The cytoskeleton also directs a morphogenetic movement called **convergent extension**, a rearrangement that causes a sheet of cells to become narrower (converge) while it becomes longer (extends). It's as if a crowd of people waiting to enter a theater for a concert begin to form a single-file line. The cells elongate, with their ends pointing in the direction they will move, and they then wedge between each other to form fewer columns of cells (Figure 47.17). This is how, for example, the archenteron elongates in the sea urchin embryo (see Figure 47.8). Convergent extension is also important in other settings, such as involution in the frog gastrula. There, convergent extension changes the gastrulating embryo from a spherical shape to the rounded rectangular shape seen in Figure 47.14c.

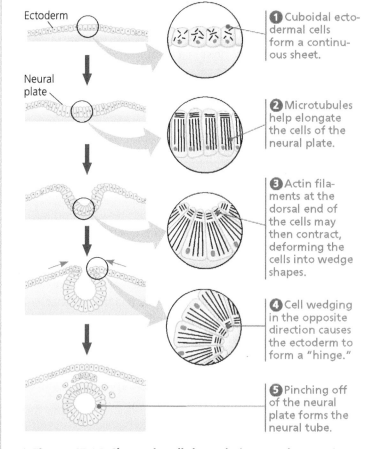

▲ **Figure 47.16 Change in cell shape during morphogenesis.** Reorganization of the cytoskeleton is associated with morphogenetic changes in embryonic tissues, as shown here for the formation of the neural tube in vertebrates.

① Cuboidal ectodermal cells form a continuous sheet.

② Microtubules help elongate the cells of the neural plate.

③ Actin filaments at the dorsal end of the cells may then contract, deforming the cells into wedge shapes.

④ Cell wedging in the opposite direction causes the ectoderm to form a "hinge."

⑤ Pinching off of the neural plate forms the neural tube.

The cytoskeleton is responsible not only for cell shape changes but also for cell migration. During organogenesis in vertebrates, cells from the neural crest and from somites migrate to locations throughout the embryo. Cells "crawl" within the embryo by using cytoskeletal fibers to extend and retract cellular protrusions. This type of motility is akin to amoeboid movement (see Figure 6.26b). Transmembrane glycoproteins called *cell adhesion molecules* play a key role in cell migration by promoting interaction between pairs of cells. Cell migration also involves the *extracellular matrix* (*ECM*), the meshwork of secreted glycoproteins and other macromolecules lying outside the plasma membranes of cells (see Figure 6.28).

▶ **Figure 47.17 Convergent extension of a sheet of cells.** In this simplified diagram, the cells elongate coordinately in a particular direction and crawl between each other (convergence) as the sheet becomes longer and narrower (extension).

Convergence
Cells elongate and crawl between each other.

Extension
The sheet of cells becomes longer and narrower.

The ECM helps to guide cells in many types of movements, such as migration of individual cells and shape changes of cell sheets. Cells that line migration pathways regulate movement of migrating cells by secreting specific molecules into the ECM. For these reasons, there is a substantial effort underway to generate an artificial ECM that can serve as a scaffold for the repair or replacement of damaged tissues or organs. One promising approach involves the use of nanofiber fabrication to produce materials that mimic the essential properties of the natural ECM.

Programmed Cell Death

Just as certain cells of the embryo are programmed to change shape or location, others are programmed to die. A type of *programmed cell death* called **apoptosis** is in fact a common feature of animal development. At various times in development, individual cells, sets of cells, or whole tissues cease to develop, die, and are engulfed by neighboring cells. In some cases, a structure functions in a larval or other immature form of the organism and then is eliminated during later development. One familiar example is provided by the cells in the tail of a tadpole, which undergo apoptosis during frog metamorphosis (see Figure 45.22).

In both nervous and immune system development, large numbers of cells undergo apoptosis. In the vertebrate nervous system, for instance, many more neurons are produced during development than exist in the adult. In general, neurons survive if they make functional connections with other neurons and die if they do not (see Concept 49.4). In the adaptive immune system, cells that are self-reactive are often eliminated by apoptosis, as are effector cells that arise after encountering a pathogen but are no longer required after the infection has been eliminated.

Some cells that undergo apoptosis don't seem to have any function in the developing embryo. Why do such cells form? The answer can be found by considering the evolution of amphibians, birds, and mammals. When these groups began to diverge during evolution, the developmental program for making a vertebrate body was already in place. The differences in present-day body forms arose through modification of that common developmental program (which is why the early embryos of all vertebrates look so similar). As these groups evolved, many structures produced by the ancestral program that no longer offered a selective advantage were targeted for cell death. For example, the shared developmental program generates webbing between the embryonic digits, but in many birds and mammals, including humans, the webbing is eliminated by apoptosis (see Figure 11.21).

As you have seen, cell behavior and the molecular mechanisms underlying it are crucial to the morphogenesis of the embryo. In the next section, you'll learn that a shared set of cellular and genetic processes ensure that the various types of cells end up in the right places in each embryo.

CONCEPT 47.3

Cytoplasmic determinants and inductive signals contribute to cell fate specification

During embryonic development, cells arise by division, take up particular locations in the body, and become specialized in structure and function. Where a cell resides, how it appears, and what it does define its development fate. Developmental biologists use the terms **determination** to refer to the process by which a cell or group of cells becomes committed to a particular fate and **differentiation** to refer to the resulting specialization in structure and function. You may find it a useful analogy to think about determination being equivalent to declaring a major in college and differentiation being comparable to taking the courses required by your major.

Every diploid cell formed during an animal's development has the same genome. With the exception of certain mature immune cells, the collection of genes present in a given cell is the same throughout the cell's life. How, then, do cells acquire different fates? As discussed in Concept 18.4, particular tissues, and often cells within a tissue, differ from one another by expressing distinct sets of genes from their shared genome.

A major focus of developmental biology is to uncover the mechanisms that direct the differences in gene expression underlying developmental fates. As one step toward this goal, scientists often seek to trace tissues and cell types back to their origins in the early embryo.

Fate Mapping

One way to trace the ancestry of embryonic cells is direct observation through the microscope. Such studies produced the first **fate maps**, diagrams showing the structures arising from each region of an embryo. In the 1920s, German embryologist Walther Vogt used this approach to

(a) **Fate map of a frog embryo.** The fates of groups of cells in a frog blastula (left) were determined in part by marking different regions of the blastula surface with nontoxic dyes of various colors. The embryos were sectioned at later stages of development, such as the neural tube stage shown on the right, and the locations of the dyed cells determined. The two embryonic stages shown here represent the result of numerous such experiments.

(b) **Cell lineage analysis in a tunicate.** In lineage analysis, an individual blastomere is injected with a dye during cleavage, as indicated in the drawings of 64-cell embryos of a tunicate, an invertebrate chordate (top). The dark regions in the light micrographs of larvae (bottom) correspond to the cells that developed from the two different blastomeres indicated in the drawings.

▲ **Figure 47.18 Fate mapping for two chordates.**

determine where groups of cells from the blastula end up in the gastrula (**Figure 47.18a**). Later researchers developed techniques that allowed them to mark an individual blastomere during cleavage and then follow the marker as it was distributed to all the mitotic descendants of that cell (**Figure 47.18b**).

A much more comprehensive approach to fate mapping has been carried out on the soil-dwelling nematode *Caenorhabditis elegans*. This roundworm is about 1 mm long, has a simple, transparent body with only a few types of cells, and develops into a mature adult hermaphrodite in only 3½ days in the laboratory. These attributes allowed Sydney Brenner, Robert Horvitz, and John Sulston to determine the complete developmental history, or *lineage*, of every cell in *C. elegans*. They found that every adult hermaphrodite has exactly 959 somatic cells, which arise from the fertilized egg in virtually the same way for every individual. Careful microscopic observations of worms at all stages of development, coupled with experiments in which particular cells or groups of cells were destroyed by a laser beam or through mutations, resulted in the cell lineage diagram shown in **Figure 47.19**. Using this cell lineage

▲ **Figure 47.19 Cell lineage in *Caenorhabditis elegans*.** The *C. elegans* embryo is transparent, making it possible for researchers to trace the lineage of every cell, from the zygote to the adult worm (LM). The diagram shows a detailed lineage only for the intestine, which is derived exclusively from one of the first four cells formed from the zygote.

INTERPRET THE DATA *The pattern of divisions that produces cells of the* C. elegans *intestine is always the same. Is the number of divisions that gives rise to a mature cell always the same?*

diagram, you can identify all of the progeny of a single cell, just as you would use a family history to trace the descendants of one great-great-grandparent.

As an example of a particular cell fate let's consider *germ cells*, the specialized cells that give rise to eggs or sperm. In all animals studied, complexes of RNA and protein are involved in the specification of germ cell fate. In *C. elegans*, such complexes, called *P granules*, can be detected in four cells of the newly hatched larva **(Figure 47.20)** and, later, in the cells of the adult gonad that produce sperm or eggs.

Tracing the position of the P granules provides a dramatic illustration of cell fate specification during development. As shown in **Figure 47.21 ❶** and **❷**, the P granules are distributed throughout the newly fertilized egg but move to the posterior end of the zygote before the first cleavage division. **❸** As a result, only the posterior of the two cells formed by the first division contains P granules. **❹** The P granules continue to be asymmetrically partitioned during subsequent divisions. Thus, the P granules act as cytoplasmic determinants (see Concept 18.4), fixing germ cell fate at the earliest stage of *C. elegans* development.

Fate mapping in *C. elegans* paved the way for major discoveries about programmed cell death. Lineage analysis demonstrated that exactly 131 cells die during normal *C. elegans* development. In the 1980s, researchers found that a mutation inactivating a single gene allows all 131 cells to live. Further research revealed that this gene is part of a pathway that controls and carries out apoptosis in a wide range of animals, including humans. In 2002, Brenner, Horvitz, and Sulston shared a Nobel Prize for their use of the *C. elegans* fate map in studies of programmed cell death and organogenesis.

Having established fate maps for early development, scientists were positioned to answer questions about underlying mechanisms, such as how the basic axes of the embryo are established, a process known as axis formation.

▲ **Figure 47.20 Determination of germ cell fate in *C. elegans*.** Labeling with a fluorescent antibody that is specific for a *C. elegans* P granule protein (green) reveals the incorporation of P granules into four cells of the newly hatched larva (two of the four cells are visible in this view).

|― 20 µm ―|

❶ Newly fertilized egg

❷ Zygote prior to first division

❸ Two-cell embryo

▶ **Figure 47.21 Partitioning of P granules during *C. elegans* development.** The differential interference contrast micrographs (left) highlight the boundaries of nuclei and cells through the first two cell divisions. The fluorescence micrographs (right) show identically staged embryos labeled with a fluorescent antibody specific for a P granule protein.

❹ Four-cell embryo

Axis Formation

A body plan with bilateral symmetry is found across a range of animals, including nematodes, echinoderms, and vertebrates (see Chapter 32). As shown for a frog tadpole in **Figure 47.22a**, this body plan exhibits asymmetry along the dorsal-ventral and anterior-posterior axes. The right-left axis is largely symmetrical, as the two sides are roughly mirror images. When and how are the three axes established?

In the frog, the future position of the anterior-posterior axis is determined during oogenesis. Asymmetry in the egg is apparent in the formation of two distinct hemispheres: Dark melanin granules are embedded in the cortex of the animal hemisphere, whereas a yellow yolk fills the vegetal hemisphere. This animal-vegetal asymmetry dictates where the anterior-posterior axis forms in the embryo. Note, however, that the anterior-posterior and animal-vegetal axes are not the same; that is, the head of the embryo does not coincide with the animal pole.

Surprisingly, the dorsal-ventral axis of the frog embryo is determined at random. Once the sperm and egg fuse, the egg surface—the plasma membrane and associated cortex—rotates with respect to the inner cytoplasm, a movement called *cortical rotation*. From the perspective of the animal pole, this rotation is always toward the point of sperm entry, wherever in the animal hemisphere it occurs (**Figure 47.22b**).

How does cortical rotation establish the dorsal-ventral axis? Cortical rotation allows molecules in one portion of the vegetal cortex to interact with molecules in the inner cytoplasm of the animal hemisphere. These inductive interactions activate regulatory proteins in specific portions of the vegetal cortex, leading to expression of different sets of genes in dorsal and ventral regions of the embryo.

In chicks, gravity is apparently involved in establishing the anterior-posterior axis as the egg travels down the hen's oviduct before being laid. Later, pH differences between the two sides of the blastoderm cells establish the dorsal-ventral axis. If the pH is artificially reversed above and below the blastoderm, the cells' fates will be reversed: The side facing the egg white will become the ventral part of the embryo, whereas the side facing the yolk will become the dorsal part.

In mammals, no polarity is obvious until after cleavage. However, the results of recent experiments suggest that the orientation of the egg and sperm nuclei before they fuse influences the location of the first cleavage plane and thus may play a role in establishing the embryonic axes. In insects, morphogen gradients establish both the anterior-posterior and dorsal-ventral axes (see Chapter 18).

Once the anterior-posterior and dorsal-ventral axes are established, the position of the left-right axis is fixed. Nevertheless, specific molecular mechanisms must establish which side is left and which is right. In vertebrates, there are marked left-right differences in the location of internal organs as well as in the organization and structure of the heart and brain.

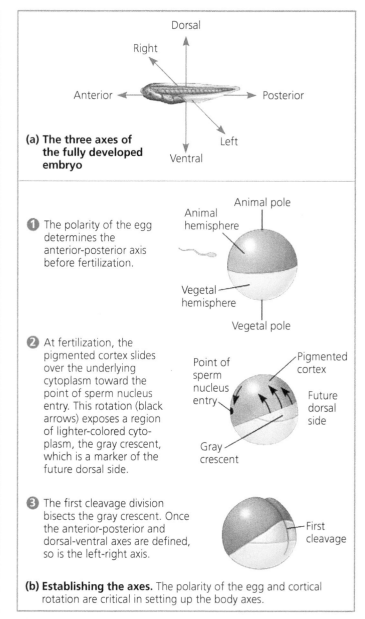

(a) The three axes of the fully developed embryo

❶ The polarity of the egg determines the anterior-posterior axis before fertilization.

Animal pole
Animal hemisphere
Vegetal hemisphere
Vegetal pole

❷ At fertilization, the pigmented cortex slides over the underlying cytoplasm toward the point of sperm nucleus entry. This rotation (black arrows) exposes a region of lighter-colored cytoplasm, the gray crescent, which is a marker of the future dorsal side.

Point of sperm nucleus entry
Pigmented cortex
Future dorsal side
Gray crescent

❸ The first cleavage division bisects the gray crescent. Once the anterior-posterior and dorsal-ventral axes are defined, so is the left-right axis.

First cleavage

(b) Establishing the axes. The polarity of the egg and cortical rotation are critical in setting up the body axes.

▲ **Figure 47.22 The body axes and their establishment in an amphibian.** All three axes are established before the zygote begins to undergo cleavage.

WHAT IF? *When researchers allowed normal cortical rotation to occur, and then forced the opposite rotation, the result was a two-headed embryo. How might you explain this finding, thinking about how cortical rotation influences body axis formation?*

Recent research has revealed that cilia are involved in setting up this left-right asymmetry. We will discuss this and other developmental roles of cilia at the end of this chapter.

Restricting Developmental Potential

Earlier we described determination in terms of commitment to a particular cell fate. The fertilized egg gives rise to all cell fates. How long during development do cells retain this ability? The German zoologist Hans Spemann addressed this question in 1938. By manipulating embryos to perturb normal development and then examining cell fate after the manipulation, he was able to assay a cell's *developmental potential*, the range of structures to which it can give rise **(Figure 47.23)**. The work of Spemann and others demonstrated that the first two blastomeres of the frog embryo are **totipotent**, meaning that they can each develop into all the different cell types of that species.

In mammals, embryonic cells remain totipotent through the eight-cell stage, much longer than in many other animals. Recent work, however, indicates that the very early cells (even the first two) are not actually equivalent in a normal embryo.

Rather, their totipotency when isolated likely means that the cells can regulate their fate in response to their embryonic environment. Once the 16-cell stage is reached, mammalian cells are determined to form the trophoblast or the inner cell mass. Although the cells have a limited developmental potential from this point onward, their nuclei remain totipotent, as demonstrated in transplantation and cloning experiments (see Figures 20.16 and 20.17).

The totipotency of cells early in human embryogenesis is the reason why you or a classmate may have an identical twin. Identical (monozygotic) twins result when cells or groups of cells from a single embryo become separated. If the separation occurs before the trophoblast and inner cell mass become differentiated, two embryos grow, each with its own chorion and amnion. This is the case for about a third of identical twins. For the rest, the two embryos that develop share a chorion and, in very rare cases where separation is particularly late, an amnion as well.

Regardless of how uniform or varied early embryonic cells are in a particular species, the progressive restriction of developmental potential is a general feature of development in all animals. In general, the tissue-specific fates of cells are fixed in a late gastrula, but not always so in an early gastrula. For example, if the dorsal ectoderm of an early amphibian gastrula is experimentally replaced with ectoderm from some other location in the same gastrula, the transplanted tissue forms a neural plate. But if the same experiment is performed on a late-stage gastrula, the transplanted ectoderm does not respond to its new environment and does not form a neural plate.

Cell Fate Determination and Pattern Formation by Inductive Signals

As embryonic development continues, cells influence each other's fates by induction. At the molecular level, the response to an inductive signal is usually to switch on a set of genes that make the receiving cells differentiate into a specific cell type or tissue. Here we will examine examples of this important developmental process in organizing the basic body plan of an embryo and in directing development of a vertebrate limb.

▼ **Figure 47.23** | **Inquiry**

How does distribution of the gray crescent affect the developmental potential of the first two daughter cells?

Experiment Hans Spemann, at the University of Freiburg-im-Breisgau, in Germany, carried out the following experiment in 1938 to test whether substances were located asymmetrically in the gray crescent.

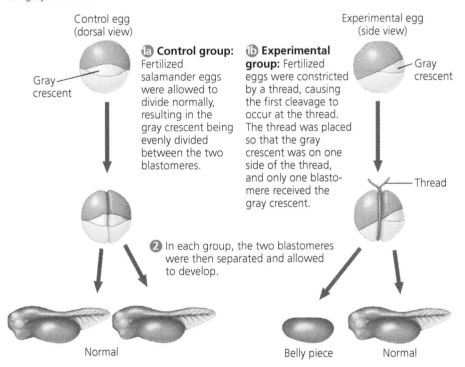

1️⃣a **Control group:** Fertilized salamander eggs were allowed to divide normally, resulting in the gray crescent being evenly divided between the two blastomeres.

1️⃣b **Experimental group:** Fertilized eggs were constricted by a thread, causing the first cleavage to occur at the thread. The thread was placed so that the gray crescent was on one side of the thread, and only one blastomere received the gray crescent.

2️⃣ In each group, the two blastomeres were then separated and allowed to develop.

Results Blastomeres that received half or all of the material in the gray crescent developed into normal embryos, but a blastomere that received none of the gray crescent gave rise to an abnormal embryo without dorsal structures. Spemann called it a "belly piece."

Conclusion The developmental potential of the two blastomeres normally formed during the first cleavage division depends on their acquisition of cytoplasmic determinants localized in the gray crescent.

Source: H. Spemann, Embryonic Development and Induction, Yale University Press, New Haven, CT (1938).

WHAT IF? *In a similar experiment 40 years earlier, embryologist Hans Roux allowed the first cleavage to occur and then used a needle to kill just one blastomere. The embryo that developed from the remaining blastomere (plus remnants of the dead cell) was abnormal, resembling a half-embryo. How might the presence of molecules in the dead cell explain why Roux's result differed from the control result in Spemann's experiment?*

The "Organizer" of Spemann and Mangold

Before his studies of totipotency in the fertilized frog egg, Spemann had investigated cell fate determination during gastrulation. In these experiments, he and his student Hilde Mangold transplanted tissues between early gastrulas. In their most famous such experiment, summarized in **Figure 47.24**, they made a remarkable discovery. Not only

▼ **Figure 47.24** | Inquiry

Can the dorsal lip of the blastopore induce cells in another part of the amphibian embryo to change their developmental fate?

Experiment In 1924, Hans Spemann and Hilde Mangold, at the University of Freiburg-im-Breisgau in Germany, investigated the inductive ability of the dorsal lip. Using newts, they transplanted a piece of the dorsal lip from a pigmented gastrula to the ventral side of a nonpigmented gastrula; cross sections are shown here.

Dorsal lip of blastopore

Pigmented gastrula (donor embryo)

Nonpigmented gastrula (recipient embryo)

Results The recipient embryo formed a second notochord and neural tube in the region of the transplant, and eventually most of a second embryo developed. In the interior of the double embryo, secondary structures were formed partly from recipient tissue.

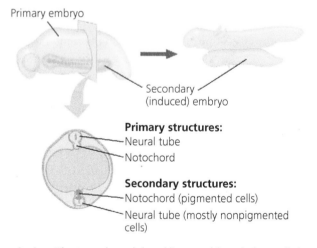

Primary embryo

Secondary (induced) embryo

Primary structures:
— Neural tube
— Notochord

Secondary structures:
— Notochord (pigmented cells)
— Neural tube (mostly nonpigmented cells)

Conclusion The transplanted dorsal lip was able to induce cells in a different region of the recipient to form structures different from their normal fate. In effect, the transplanted dorsal lip "organized" the later development of an entire extra embryo.

Source: H. Spemann and H. Mangold, Induction of embryonic primordia by implantation of organizers from a different species, Trans. V. Hamburger (1924). Reprinted in *International Journal of Developmental Biology* 45:13–38 (2001).

WHAT IF? *Because the transplant caused the recipient tissue to become something it would not have otherwise, a signal must have passed from the dorsal lip. If you identified a protein candidate for the signaling molecule, how would injecting it into ventral cells of a gastrula test its function?*

did a transplanted dorsal lip of the blastopore continue to be a blastopore lip, but it also triggered gastrulation of the surrounding tissue. They concluded that the dorsal lip of the blastopore in the early gastrula functions as an "organizer" of the embryo's body plan, inducing changes in surrounding tissue that direct formation of the notochord, the neural tube, and other organs.

Nearly a century later, developmental biologists are still studying the basis of induction by what is now called *Spemann's organizer.* An important clue has come from studies of a growth factor called bone morphogenetic protein 4 (BMP-4). One major function of the organizer seems to be to inactivate BMP-4 on the dorsal side of the embryo. Inactivation of BMP-4 allows cells on the dorsal side to make dorsal structures, such as the notochord and neural tube. Proteins related to BMP-4 and its inhibitors are found as well in invertebrates such as the fruit fly, where they also function in regulating the dorsal-ventral axis.

Formation of the Vertebrate Limb

Inductive signals play a major role in **pattern formation**, the process governing the arrangement of organs and tissues in their characteristic places in three-dimensional space. The molecular cues that control pattern formation, called **positional information**, tell a cell where it is with respect to the animal's body axes and help to determine how the cell and its descendants will respond to molecular signaling.

In Chapter 18, we discussed pattern formation in the development of *Drosophila*. For the study of pattern formation in vertebrates, a classic model system has been limb development in the chick. The wings and legs of chicks, like all vertebrate limbs, begin as limb buds, bumps of mesodermal tissue covered by a layer of ectoderm **(Figure 47.25a)**. Each component of a chick limb, such as a specific bone or muscle, develops with a precise location and orientation relative to three axes: proximal-distal (shoulder to fingertip), anterior-posterior (thumb to little finger), and dorsal-ventral (knuckle to palm), as shown in **Figure 47.25b**.

Two regions in a limb bud have profound effects on its development. One such region is the **apical ectodermal ridge (AER)**, a thickened area of ectoderm at the tip of the bud (see Figure 47.25a). Surgically removing the AER blocks outgrowth of the limb along the proximal-distal axis. Why? The AER secretes a protein signal called fibroblast growth factor (FGF) that promotes limb-bud outgrowth. If the AER is replaced with beads soaked with FGF, a nearly normal limb develops.

The second major limb-bud regulatory region is the **zone of polarizing activity (ZPA)**, a specialized block of mesodermal tissue (see Figure 47.25a). The ZPA regulates development along the anterior-posterior axis of the limb. Cells nearest the ZPA form posterior structures, such as the most posterior of the chick's digits (equivalent to our little finger);

cells farthest from the ZPA form anterior structures, including the most anterior digit (like our thumb). This model is based on several lines of experiments, including the tissue transplantations outlined in **Figure 47.26**.

Like the AER, the ZPA influences development by secreting a protein signal. The signal secreted by the ZPA is called Sonic hedgehog, named after both a video game character and a similar protein in *Drosophila* that also regulates

development. Implanting cells genetically engineered to produce Sonic hedgehog into the anterior region of a normal limb bud causes formation of a mirror-image limb—just as if a ZPA had been grafted there. Furthermore, experiments with mice reveal that production of Sonic hedgehog in part of the limb bud where it is normally absent can result in extra toes.

The AER and ZPA regulate the axes of a limb bud, but what determines whether the bud develops into a forelimb or hind limb? That information is provided by spatial

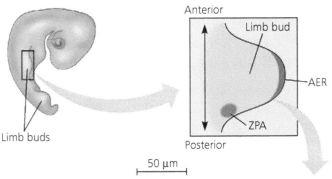

50 μm

(a) Organizer regions.
Vertebrate limbs develop from protrusions called limb buds, each consisting of mesoderm cells covered by a layer of ectoderm. Two regions in each limb bud, the apical ectodermal ridge (AER, shown in this SEM) and the zone of polarizing activity (ZPA), play key roles as organizers in limb pattern formation.

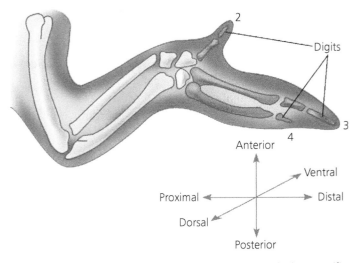

(b) Wing of chick embryo. As the bud develops into a limb, a specific pattern of tissues emerges. In the chick wing, for example, the digits are always present in the arrangement shown here. Pattern formation requires each embryonic cell to receive some kind of positional information indicating location along the three axes of the limb. The AER and ZPA secrete molecules that help provide this information. (Numbers are assigned to the digits based on a convention established for vertebrate limbs. The chicken wing has only four digits; the first digit points backward and is not shown in the diagram.)

▲ **Figure 47.25 Vertebrate limb development.**

▼ **Figure 47.26** | **Inquiry**

What role does the zone of polarizing activity (ZPA) play in limb pattern formation in vertebrates?

Experiment In 1985, researchers were eager to investigate the nature of the zone of polarizing activity. They transplanted ZPA tissue from a donor chick embryo under the ectoderm in the anterior margin of a limb bud in another chick (the host).

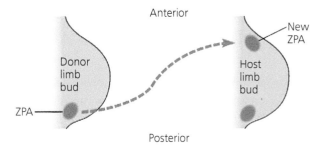

Results The host limb bud developed extra digits from host tissue in a mirror-image arrangement to the normal digits, which also formed (compare with Figure 47.24b, which shows a normal chick wing).

Conclusion The mirror-image duplication observed in this experiment suggests that ZPA cells secrete a signal that diffuses from its source and conveys positional information indicating "posterior." As the distance from the ZPA increases, the signal concentration decreases, and hence more anterior digits develop.

Source: L. S. Honig and D. Summerbell, Maps of strength of positional signaling activity in the developing chick wing bud, *Journal of Embryology and Experimental Morphology* 87:163–174 (1985).

WHAT IF? *Suppose you learned that the ZPA forms after the AER, leading you to develop the hypothesis that the AER is necessary for formation of the ZPA. If you removed the AER and looked for expression of Sonic hedgehog, how would that test your hypothesis?*

patterns of *Hox* genes, which specify different developmental fates in particular body regions (see Figure 21.18).

BMP-4, FGF, hedgehog, and Hox proteins are examples of a much larger set of molecules that govern cell fates in animals. Having mapped out many of the basic functions of these molecules in embryonic development, researchers are now addressing their role in organogenesis, focusing in particular on the development of the brain.

Cilia and Cell Fate

For many years, biologists studying organogenesis largely ignored the cellular organelles known as cilia. That is no longer the case. There is now good evidence that cilia are essential for specifying cell fate in human embryos.

Like other mammals, humans have stationary and motile cilia (see Figure 6.24). Stationary primary cilia, or *monocilia*, jut from the surface of nearly all cells, one per cell. In contrast, motile cilia are restricted to cells that propel fluid over their surface, such as the epithelial cells of airways, and on sperm (as flagella that propel sperm movement). Both stationary and motile cilia play vital roles in development.

Genetic studies provided vital clues to the developmental role of monocilia. In 2003, researchers discovered that certain mutations disrupting development of the mouse nervous system affect genes that function in the assembly of monocilia. Other geneticists found that mutations responsible for a severe kidney disease in mice alter a gene important for the transport of materials up and down monocilia. In addition, mutations in humans that block the function of monocilia were linked to cystic kidney disease.

Given that monocilia are stationary, how do they function in development? The answer is that monocilia act as antennae on the cell surface, receiving signals from multiple signaling proteins, including Sonic hedgehog. Mechanisms that regulate the set of receptor proteins that are present tune the cilium to particular signals. When the monocilia are defective, signaling is disrupted.

Insight into the role of motile cilia in development grew from the identification of Kartagener's syndrome, a particular set of medical conditions that often appear together. These conditions include male infertility due to immotile sperm and infections of the nasal sinuses and bronchi in both males and females. However, by far the most intriguing feature of Kartagener's syndrome is *situs inversus*, a reversal of the normal left-right asymmetry of the organs in the chest and abdomen (**Figure 47.27**). The heart, for example, is on the right side rather than the left. (By itself, situs inversus causes no significant medical problems.)

Scientists studying Kartagener's syndrome came to realize that all of the associated conditions result from a defect that makes cilia immotile. Without motility, sperm tails cannot beat and airway cells cannot sweep mucus and microbes

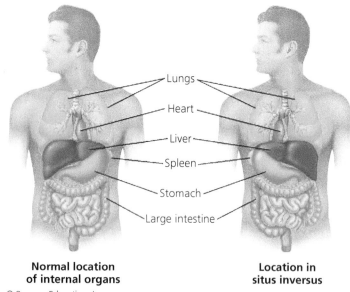

| Normal location of internal organs | Location in situs inversus |

Labels: Lungs, Heart, Liver, Spleen, Stomach, Large intestine

© Pearson Education, Inc.

▲ **Figure 47.27 Situs inversus, a reversal of normal left-right asymmetry in the chest and abdomen.**

out of the airway. But what causes situs inversus in these individuals? The current model proposes that ciliary motion in a particular part of the embryo is essential for normal development. Evidence indicates that movement of the cilia generates a leftward fluid flow, breaking the symmetry between left and right sides. Without that flow, asymmetry along the left-right axis arises randomly, and half of the affected embryos develop situs inversus.

If we step back from the specification of particular cell fates to consider development as a whole, we see a sequence of events marked by cycles of signaling and differentiation. Initial cell asymmetries allow different types of cells to influence each other, resulting in the expression of specific sets of genes. The products of these genes then direct cells to differentiate into specific types. Through pattern formation and morphogenesis, differentiated cells ultimately produce a complex arrangement of tissues and organs, each functioning in its appropriate location and in coordination with other cells, tissues, and organs throughout the organism.

CONCEPT CHECK 47.3

1. How do axis formation and pattern formation differ?

2. **MAKE CONNECTIONS** How does a morphogen gradient differ from cytoplasmic determinants and inductive interactions with regard to the set of cells it affects (see Concept 18.4)?

3. **WHAT IF?** If the ventral cells of an early frog gastrula are experimentally induced to express large amounts of a protein that inhibits BMP-4, could a second embryo develop? Explain.

4. **WHAT IF?** If you removed the ZPA from a limb bud and then placed a bead soaked in Sonic hedgehog in the middle of the bud, what would be the most likely result?

For suggested answers, see Appendix A.

47 Chapter Review

SUMMARY OF KEY CONCEPTS

CONCEPT 47.1

Fertilization and cleavage initiate embryonic development (pp. 1038–1043)

- **Fertilization** forms a diploid zygote and initiates embryonic development. The **acrosomal reaction** releases hydrolytic enzymes from the sperm head that digest material surrounding the egg.

Sperm-egg fusion and depolarization of egg membrane (fast block to polyspermy)

Cortical granule release (cortical reaction)

Formation of fertilization envelope (slow block to polyspermy)

In mammalian fertilization, the cortical reaction modifies the zona pellucida as a **slow block to polyspermy**.

- Fertilization is followed by **cleavage**, a period of rapid cell division without growth, producing a large number of cells called **blastomeres**. The amount and distribution of **yolk** strongly influence the pattern of cleavage. The midblastula transition marks the end of cleavage, which in many species generates a **blastula** containing a fluid-filled cavity, the **blastocoel**.

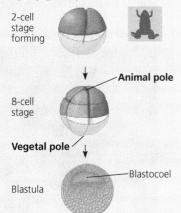

2-cell stage forming

Animal pole

8-cell stage

Vegetal pole

Blastula

Blastocoel

> **?** What cell-surface event would likely fail if a sperm contacted an egg of another species?

CONCEPT 47.2

Morphogenesis in animals involves specific changes in cell shape, position, and survival (pp. 1044–1051)

- **Gastrulation** converts the blastula to a **gastrula**, which has a primitive digestive cavity and three **germ layers: ectoderm** (blue), which forms the outer layer of the embryo, **mesoderm** (red), which forms the middle layer, and **endoderm** (yellow), which gives rise to the innermost tissues.

- Gastrulation and organogenesis in mammals resemble the processes in birds and other reptiles. After fertilization and early cleavage in the oviduct, the **blastocyst** implants in the uterus. The **trophoblast** initiates formation of the fetal portion of the placenta, and the embryo proper develops from a cell layer, the epiblast, within the blastocyst.
- The embryos of birds, other reptiles, and mammals develop within a fluid-filled sac that is contained within a shell or the uterus. In these organisms, the three germ layers produce four **extraembryonic membranes**: the amnion, chorion, yolk sac, and allantois.
- The organs of the animal body develop from specific portions of the three embryonic germ layers. Early events in **organogenesis** in vertebrates include neurulation: formation of the **notochord** by cells of the dorsal mesoderm and development of the **neural tube** from infolding of the ectodermal neural plate.

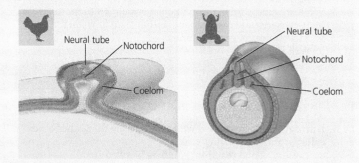

Neural tube
Notochord
Coelom

Neural tube
Notochord
Coelom

- Cytoskeletal rearrangements cause changes in the shape of cells that underlie cell movements in gastrulation and organogenesis, including invaginations and **convergent extension**. The cytoskeleton is also involved in cell migration, which relies on cell adhesion molecules and the extracellular matrix to help cells reach specific destinations. Migratory cells arise both from the neural crest and from somites.

> **?** How does the neural tube form? How do neural crest cells arise?

CONCEPT 47.3

Cytoplasmic determinants and inductive signals contribute to cell fate specification (pp. 1051–1058)

- Experimentally derived **fate maps** of embryos show that specific regions of the zygote or blastula develop into specific parts of older embryos. The complete cell lineage has been worked out for *C. elegans*, revealing that programmed cell death contributes to animal development. In all species, the developmental potential of cells becomes progressively more limited as embryonic development proceeds.
- Cells in a developing embryo receive and respond to **positional information** that varies with location. This information is often in the form of signaling molecules secreted by cells in specific regions of the embryo, such as the dorsal lip of the blastopore in the amphibian gastrula and the **apical ectodermal ridge** and **zone of polarizing activity** of the vertebrate limb bud.

> **?** Suppose you found two classes of mouse mutations, one that affected limb development only and one that affected both limb and kidney development. Which class would be more likely to alter the function of monocilia? Explain.

TEST YOUR UNDERSTANDING

LEVEL 1: KNOWLEDGE/COMPREHENSION

1. The cortical reaction of sea urchin eggs functions directly in
   a. the formation of a fertilization envelope.
   b. the production of a fast block to polyspermy.
   c. the generation of an electrical impulse by the egg.
   d. the fusion of egg and sperm nuclei.

2. Which of the following is common to the development of both birds and mammals?
   a. holoblastic cleavage
   b. epiblast and hypoblast
   c. trophoblast
   d. gray crescent

3. The archenteron develops into
   a. the mesoderm.
   b. the endoderm.
   c. the placenta.
   d. the lumen of the digestive tract.

4. What structural adaptation in chickens allows them to lay their eggs in arid environments rather than in water?
   a. extraembryonic membranes
   b. yolk
   c. cleavage
   d. gastrulation

LEVEL 2: APPLICATION/ANALYSIS

5. If an egg cell were treated with EDTA, a chemical that binds calcium and magnesium ions,
   a. the acrosomal reaction would be blocked.
   b. the fusion of sperm and egg nuclei would be blocked.
   c. the fast block to polyspermy would not occur.
   d. the fertilization envelope would not form.

6. In humans, identical twins are possible because
   a. extraembryonic cells interact with the zygote nucleus.
   b. convergent extension occurs.
   c. early blastomeres can form a complete embryo if isolated.
   d. the gray crescent divides the dorsal-ventral axis into new cells.

7. Cells transplanted from the neural tube of a frog embryo to the ventral part of another embryo develop into nervous system tissues. This result indicates that the transplanted cells were
   a. totipotent.
   b. determined.
   c. differentiated.
   d. mesenchymal.

8. **DRAW IT** Each blue sphere in the figure below represents a cell in a cell lineage. Draw two modified versions of the cell lineage so that each version produces three cells. Use apoptosis in one of the versions, marking any dead cells with an X.

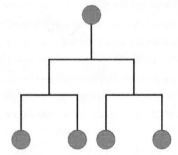

LEVEL 3: SYNTHESIS/EVALUATION

9. **EVOLUTION CONNECTION**
   Evolution in insects and vertebrates has involved the repeated duplication of body segments, followed by fusion of some segments and specialization of their structure and function. What parts of vertebrate anatomy reflect the vertebrate segmentation pattern?

10. **SCIENTIFIC INQUIRY**
    The "snout" of a frog tadpole bears a sucker. A salamander tadpole has a mustache-shaped structure called a balancer in the same area. Suppose that you perform an experiment in which you transplant ectoderm from the side of a young salamander embryo to the snout of a frog embryo. The tadpole that develops has a balancer. When you transplant ectoderm from the side of a slightly older salamander embryo to the snout of a frog embryo, the frog tadpole ends up with a patch of salamander skin on its snout. Suggest a hypothesis to explain these results in terms of developmental mechanisms. How might you test your hypothesis?

11. **SCIENCE, TECHNOLOGY, AND SOCIETY**
    Many scientists think that fetal tissue transplants offer great potential for treating Parkinson's disease, epilepsy, diabetes, Alzheimer's disease, and spinal cord injuries. Why might tissues from a fetus be particularly useful for replacing diseased or damaged cells in patients with such conditions? Some people would allow only tissues from miscarriages to be used in fetal transplant research. However, most researchers prefer to use tissues from surgically aborted fetuses. Why? Explain your position on this controversial issue.

12. **WRITE ABOUT A THEME: ORGANIZATION**
    In a short essay (100–150 words), describe how the emergent properties of the cells of the gastrula direct embryonic development.

13. **SYNTHESIZE YOUR KNOWLEDGE**

Occasionally, two-headed animals are born, such as this turtle. Thinking about the occurrence of identical twins and the property of totipotency, explain how this might occur.

For selected answers, see Appendix A.

MasteringBiology®

Students Go to **MasteringBiology** for assignments, the eText, and the Study Area with practice tests, animations, and activities.

Instructors Go to **MasteringBiology** for automatically graded tutorials and questions that you can assign to your students, plus Instructor Resources.

48

Neurons, Synapses, and Signaling

▲ Ribbon model of one example of a toxic peptide from cone snail venom

▲ Figure 48.1 **What makes this snail such a deadly predator?**

Lines of Communication

The tropical cone snail (*Conus geographus*) in **Figure 48.1** is small and slow-moving, yet it is a dangerous hunter. A carnivore, this marine snail hunts, kills, and dines on fish. Injecting venom with a hollow, harpoon-like tooth, the cone snail paralyzes its free-swimming prey in seconds. The venom is so deadly that unlucky scuba divers have died from just a single injection. What makes cone snail venom so fast acting and lethal? The answer is its mixture of toxin molecules, each with a specific mechanism of disabling **neurons**, the nerve cells that transfer information within the body. Because the venom almost instantaneously disrupts neuronal control of locomotion and respiration, an animal attacked by the cone snail cannot escape, defend itself, or otherwise survive.

Communication by neurons largely consists of long-distance electrical signals and short-distance chemical signals. The specialized structure of neurons allows them to use pulses of electrical current to receive, transmit, and regulate the flow of information over long distances within the body. In transferring information from one cell to another, neurons often rely on chemical signals that act over very short distances. The mixture of molecules in a cone snail's venom is particularly potent because it interferes with both electrical and chemical signaling by neurons.

All neurons transmit electrical signals within the cell in an identical manner. Thus a neuron transmitting sensory input encodes information in the same way as a neuron processing information or triggering movement. The particular connections made by the active neuron are what distinguishes the type of information being transmitted. Interpreting nerve impulses therefore involves sorting neuronal paths and connections. In more complex animals, this processing is carried out largely in groups of neurons organized into a **brain** or into simpler clusters called **ganglia**.

In this chapter, we look closely at the structure of a neuron and explore the molecules and physical principles that govern signaling by neurons. In the remaining chapters in this unit, we will examine nervous systems, information processing, and the systems that detect stimuli and that carry out responses to those stimuli. The unit concludes by looking at how these functions are integrated in producing behavior.

CONCEPT 48.1

Neuron structure and organization reflect function in information transfer

Our starting point for exploring the nervous system is the neuron, a cell type exemplifying the close fit of form and function that often arises over the course of evolution.

Neuron Structure and Function

The ability of a neuron to receive and transmit information is based on a highly specialized cellular organization **(Figure 48.2)**. Most of a neuron's organelles, including its nucleus, are located in the **cell body**. A typical neuron has numerous highly branched extensions called **dendrites** (from the Greek *dendron*, tree). Together with the cell body, the dendrites *receive* signals from other neurons. A neuron also has a single **axon**, an extension that *transmits* signals to other cells. Axons are often much longer than dendrites, and some, such as those that reach from the spinal cord of a giraffe to the muscle cells in its feet, are over a meter long. The cone-shaped base of an axon, called the axon hillock, is typically where signals that travel down the axon are generated. Near its other end, an axon usually divides into many branches.

Each branched end of an axon transmits information to another cell at a junction called a **synapse** (see Figure 48.2). The part of each axon branch that forms this specialized junction is a *synaptic terminal*. At most synapses, chemical messengers called **neurotransmitters** pass information from the transmitting neuron to the receiving cell. In describing a synapse, we refer to the transmitting neuron as the *presynaptic cell* and the neuron, muscle, or gland cell that receives the signal as the *postsynaptic cell*.

The neurons of vertebrates and most invertebrates require supporting cells called **glial cells**, or **glia** (from a Greek word meaning "glue") **(Figure 48.3)**. Glia nourish neurons, insulate the axons of neurons, and regulate the extracellular fluid surrounding neurons. In addition, glia sometimes function in replenishing certain groups of neurons and in transmitting information (as we'll discuss later in this chapter and in Chapter 49). Overall, glia outnumber neurons in the mammalian brain 10- to 50-fold.

◀ **Figure 48.2 Neuron structure.** Arrows illustrate the flow of signals into, along, between, and out of neurons.

8 0 μm   Glia   Cell bodies of neurons

▲ **Figure 48.3 Glia in the mammalian brain.** This micrograph (a fluorescently labeled laser confocal image) shows a region of the rat brain packed with glia and interneurons. The glia are labeled red, the DNA in nuclei is labeled blue, and the dendrites of neurons are labeled green.

Introduction to Information Processing

Information processing by a nervous system occurs in three stages: sensory input, integration, and motor output. As an example, let's consider the cone snail discussed earlier, focusing on the steps involved in identifying and attacking its prey **(Figure 48.4)**. To generate sensory input to the nervous system, the snail surveys its environment with its tubelike siphon, sampling scents that might reveal a nearby fish. During the integration stage, the nervous system processes input to determine if a fish is in fact present and, if so, where the fish is located. Motor output from the processing center then initiates attack, activating neurons that trigger release of the harpoon-like tooth toward the prey.

▲ **Figure 48.4 Summary of information processing.** The cone snail's siphon acts as a sensor, transferring information to the neuronal circuits in the snail's head. If prey is detected, these circuits issue motor commands, triggering release of a harpoon-like tooth from the proboscis.

In all but the simplest animals, specialized populations of neurons handle each stage of information processing.

- **Sensory neurons**, like those in the snail's siphon, transmit information about external stimuli such as light, touch, or smell, or internal conditions such as blood pressure or muscle tension.
- Neurons in the brain or ganglia integrate (analyze and interpret) the sensory input, taking into account the immediate context and the animal's experience. The vast majority of neurons in the brain are **interneurons**, which form the local circuits connecting neurons in the brain.
- Neurons that extend out of the processing centers trigger output in the form of muscle or gland activity. For example, **motor neurons** transmit signals to muscle cells, causing them to contract.

In many animals, the neurons that carry out integration are organized in a **central nervous system (CNS)**. The neurons that carry information into and out of the CNS constitute the **peripheral nervous system (PNS)**. When bundled together, the axons of neurons form **nerves**.

Depending on its role in information processing, the shape of a neuron can vary from simple to quite complex **(Figure 48.5)**. Neurons that transmit information to many target cells do so through highly branched axons. Similarly, neurons that have highly branched dendrites can receive input through tens of thousands of synapses in some interneurons.

▲ **Figure 48.5 Structural diversity of neurons.** In these drawings of neurons, cell bodies and dendrites are black and axons are red.

CONCEPT CHECK 48.1

1. Compare and contrast the structure and function of axons and dendrites.

2. Describe the basic pathway of information flow through neurons that causes you to turn your head when someone calls your name.

3. **WHAT IF?** How might increased branching of an axon help coordinate responses to signals communicated by the nervous system?

For suggested answers, see Appendix A.

CONCEPT 48.2

Ion pumps and ion channels establish the resting potential of a neuron

We turn now to the essential role of ions in neuronal signaling. In neurons, as in other cells, ions are unequally distributed between the interior of cells and the surrounding fluid (see Chapter 7). As a result, the inside of a cell is negatively charged relative to the outside. Because the attraction of opposite charges across the plasma membrane is a source of potential energy, this charge difference, or voltage, is called the **membrane potential**. For a resting neuron—one that is not sending a signal—the membrane potential is called the **resting potential** and is typically between −60 and −80 mV (millivolts).

Inputs from other neurons or specific stimuli cause changes in the neuron's membrane potential that act as signals, transmitting information. Fundamentally, rapid changes in membrane potential are what enable us to see the intricate structure of a spiderweb, hear a song, or ride a bicycle. Thus, to understand how neurons function, we need to examine how chemical and electrical forces form, maintain, and alter membrane potentials.

Formation of the Resting Potential

Potassium ions (K^+) and sodium ions (Na^+) play an essential role in the formation of the resting potential. These ions each have a concentration gradient across the plasma membrane of a neuron (Table 48.1). In most neurons, the

Table 48.1   Ion Concentrations Inside and Outside of Mammalian Neurons

Ion	Intracellular Concentration (mM)	Extracellular Concentration (mM)
Potassium (K^+)	140	5
Sodium (Na^+)	15	150
Chloride (Cl^-)	10	120
Large anions (A^-), such as proteins, inside cell	100	(not applicable)

concentration of K^+ is higher inside the cell, while the concentration of Na^+ is higher outside. The Na^+ and K^+ gradients are maintained by the **sodium-potassium pump** (see Chapter 7). This pump uses the energy of ATP hydrolysis to actively transport Na^+ out of the cell and K^+ into the cell (Figure 48.6). (There are also concentration gradients for chloride ions (Cl^-) and other anions, as shown in Table 48.1, but we can ignore these for now.)

The sodium-potassium pump transports three Na^+ out of the cell for every two K^+ that it transports in. Although this pumping generates a net export of positive charge, the resulting voltage difference is only a few millivolts. Why, then, is there a voltage difference of 60 to 80 mV in a resting neuron? The answer lies in ion movement through **ion channels**, pores formed by clusters of specialized proteins that span the membrane. Ion channels allow ions to diffuse back and forth across the membrane. As ions diffuse through channels, they carry with them units of electrical

Key

▲ **Figure 48.6 The basis of the membrane potential.** The sodium-potassium pump generates and maintains the ionic gradients of Na^+ and K^+ shown in Table 48.1. (Many such pump molecules are located in the plasma membrane of each cell.) Although there is a substantial concentration gradient of sodium across the membrane, very little net diffusion of Na^+ occurs because there are very few open sodium channels. In contrast, the many open potassium channels allow a significant net outflow of K^+. Because the membrane is only weakly permeable to chloride and other anions, this outflow of K^+ results in a net negative charge inside the cell.

charge. Any resulting *net* movement of positive or negative charge will generate a membrane potential, or voltage across the membrane.

The concentration gradients of ions across the plasma membrane represent a chemical form of potential energy that can be harnessed for cellular processes (see Figure 44.17). Ion channels that convert this chemical potential energy to electrical potential energy can do so because they have *selective permeability*, allowing only certain ions to pass. For example, a potassium channel allows K^+ to diffuse freely across the membrane, but not other ions, such as Na^+ or Cl^-.

Diffusion of K^+ through potassium channels that are always open (sometimes called leak channels) is critical for establishing the resting potential. The K^+ concentration is 140 mM inside the cell, but only 5 mM outside. The chemical concentration gradient thus favors a net outflow of K^+. Furthermore, a resting neuron has many open potassium channels, but very few open sodium channels (see Figure 48.6). Because Na^+ and other ions can't readily cross the membrane, K^+ outflow leads to a net negative charge inside the cell. This buildup of negative charge within the neuron is the major source of the membrane potential.

What stops the buildup of negative charge? The excess negative charges inside the cell exert an attractive force that opposes the flow of additional positively charged potassium ions out of the cell. The separation of charge (voltage) thus results in an electrical gradient that counterbalances the chemical concentration gradient of K^+.

Modeling the Resting Potential

The net flow of K^+ out of a neuron proceeds until the chemical and electrical forces are in balance. How well do these two forces account for the resting potential in a mammalian neuron? Consider a simple model consisting of two chambers separated by an artificial membrane (**Figure 48.7a**). To begin, imagine that the membrane contains many open ion channels, all of which allow only K^+ to diffuse across. To produce a K^+ concentration gradient like that of a mammalian neuron, we place a solution of 140 mM potassium chloride (KCl) in the inner chamber and 5 mM KCl in the outer chamber. The K^+ will diffuse down its concentration gradient into the outer chamber. But because the chloride ions (Cl^-) lack a means of crossing the membrane, there will be an excess of negative charge in the inner chamber.

When our model neuron reaches equilibrium, the electrical gradient will exactly balance the chemical gradient, so that no further net diffusion of K^+ occurs across the membrane. The magnitude of the membrane voltage at equilibrium for a particular ion is called that ion's **equilibrium potential (E_{ion})**. For a membrane permeable to a single type of ion, E_{ion} can be calculated using a formula called the Nernst equation. At human body temperature (37°C) and for an ion with a net charge of 1+, such as K^+ or Na^+, the Nernst equation is

$$E_{ion} = 62mV\left(\log\frac{[ion]_{outside}}{[ion]_{inside}}\right)$$

Plugging the K^+ concentrations into the Nernst equation reveals that the equilibrium potential for K^+ (E_K) is −90 mV (see Figure 48.7a). The minus sign indicates that K^+ is at equilibrium when the inside of the membrane is 90 mV more negative than the outside.

While the equilibrium potential for K^+ is −90 mV, the resting potential of a mammalian neuron is somewhat less negative. This difference reflects the small but steady movement of Na^+ across the few open sodium channels in a resting neuron. The concentration gradient of Na^+ has a direction opposite

▶ **Figure 48.7 Modeling a mammalian neuron.** Each container is divided into two chambers by an artificial membrane. Ion channels allow free diffusion for particular ions, resulting in the net ion flow represented by arrows. **(a)** The presence of open potassium channels makes the membrane selectively permeable to K^+, and the inner chamber contains a 28-fold higher concentration of K^+ than the outer chamber; at equilibrium, the inside of the membrane is −90 mV relative to the outside. **(b)** The membrane is selectively permeable to Na^+, and the inner chamber contains a tenfold lower concentration of Na^+ than the outer chamber; at equilibrium, the inside of the membrane is +62 mV relative to the outside.

WHAT IF? *Consider the effect of adding potassium or chloride channels to the membrane in (b). How would the membrane potential be affected in each case?*

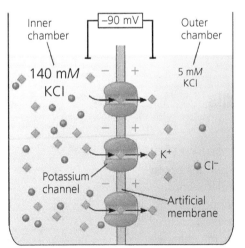

(a) Membrane selectively permeable to K^+

Nernst equation for K^+ equilibrium potential at 37°C:

$$E_K = 62\text{ mV}\left(\log\frac{5\text{ m}M}{140\text{ m}M}\right) = -90\text{ mV}$$

(b) Membrane selectively permeable to Na^+

Nernst equation for Na^+ equilibrium potential at 37°C:

$$E_{Na} = 62\text{ mV}\left(\log\frac{150\text{ m}M}{15\text{ m}M}\right) = +62\text{ mV}$$

to that of K^+ (see Table 48.1). Na^+ therefore diffuses into the cell, making the inside of the cell less negative. If we model a membrane in which the only open channels are selectively permeable to Na^+, we find that a tenfold higher concentration of Na^+ in the outer chamber results in an equilibrium potential (E_{Na}) of +62 mV (Figure 48.7b). In an actual neuron, the resting potential (−60 to −80 mV) is much closer to E_K than to E_{Na} because there are many open potassium channels but only a small number of open sodium channels.

Because neither K^+ nor Na^+ is at equilibrium in a resting neuron, there is a net flow of each ion (a current) across the membrane. The resting potential remains steady, which means that the K^+ and Na^+ currents are equal and opposite. Ion concentrations on either side of the membrane also remain steady. Why? The resting potential arises from the net movement of far fewer ions than would be required to alter the concentration gradients.

Under conditions that allow Na^+ to cross the membrane more readily, the membrane potential will move toward E_{Na} and away from E_K. As you'll see in the next section, this is precisely what happens during the generation of a nerve impulse.

CONCEPT CHECK 48.2

1. Under what circumstances could ions flow through an ion channel from a region of lower ion concentration to a region of higher ion concentration?

2. **WHAT IF?** Suppose a cell's membrane potential shifts from −70 mV to −50 mV. What changes in the cell's permeability to K^+ or Na^+ could cause such a shift?

3. **MAKE CONNECTIONS** Review Figure 7.10, which illustrates the diffusion of dye molecules across a membrane. Could diffusion eliminate the concentration gradient of a dye that has a net charge? Explain.

For suggested answers, see Appendix A.

CONCEPT 48.3

Action potentials are the signals conducted by axons

When a neuron responds to a stimulus, such as the scent of fish detected by a hunting cone snail, the membrane potential changes. Using the technique of intracellular recording, researchers can record these changes as a function of time (Figure 48.8). Changes in the membrane potential occur because neurons contain **gated ion channels**, ion channels that open or close in response to stimuli. The opening or closing of gated ion channels alters the membrane's permeability to particular ions, which in turn alters the membrane potential.

Intracellular Recording

Application Electrophysiologists use intracellular recording to measure the membrane potential of neurons and other cells.

Technique A microelectrode is made from a glass capillary tube filled with an electrically conductive salt solution. One end of the tube tapers to an extremely fine tip (diameter < 1 μm). While looking through a microscope, the experimenter uses a micropositioner to insert the tip of the microelectrode into a cell. A voltage recorder (usually an oscilloscope or a computer-based system) measures the voltage between the microelectrode tip inside the cell and a reference electrode placed in the solution outside the cell.

Hyperpolarization and Depolarization

When gated ion channels are stimulated to open, ions flow across the membrane, changing the membrane potential (Figure 48.9). For example, opening gated potassium channels in a resting neuron increases the membrane's permeability to K^+. Net diffusion of K^+ out of the neuron increases, shifting the membrane potential toward E_K (−90 mV at 37°C). This increase in the magnitude of the membrane potential, called a **hyperpolarization**, makes the inside of the membrane more negative (Figure 48.10a). In a resting neuron, hyperpolarization results from any stimulus that increases the outflow of positive ions or the inflow of negative ions.

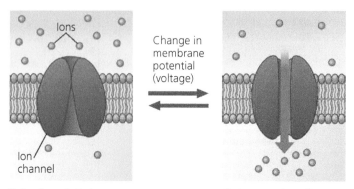

Gate closed: No ions flow across membrane.

Gate open: Ions flow through channel.

▲ Figure 48.9 **Voltage-gated ion channel.** A change in the membrane potential in one direction (indicated by the right-pointing arrow) opens the voltage-gated channel. The opposite change (left-pointing arrow) closes the channel.

(a) **Graded hyperpolarizations produced by two stimuli that increase membrane permeability to K⁺.** The larger stimulus produces a larger hyperpolarization.

(b) **Graded depolarizations produced by two stimuli that increase membrane permeability to Na⁺.** The larger stimulus produces a larger depolarization.

(c) **Action potential triggered by a depolarization that reaches the threshold.**

▲ **Figure 48.10 Graded potentials and an action potential in a neuron.**

DRAW IT *Redraw the graph in (c), extending the y-axis. Then label the positions of E_K and E_{Na}.*

Although opening potassium channels in a resting neuron causes hyperpolarization, opening some other types of ion channels has an opposite effect, making the inside of the membrane less negative **(Figure 48.10b)**. A reduction in the magnitude of the membrane potential is a **depolarization**. In neurons, depolarization often involves gated sodium channels. If a stimulus causes gated sodium channels to open, the membrane's permeability to Na⁺ increases. Na⁺ diffuses into the cell along its concentration gradient, causing a depolarization as the membrane potential shifts toward E_{Na} (+62 mV at 37°C).

Graded Potentials and Action Potentials

Sometimes, the response to hyperpolarization or depolarization is simply a shift in the membrane potential. This shift, called a **graded potential**, has a magnitude that varies with the strength of the stimulus: A larger stimulus causes a greater change in the membrane potential (see Figure 48.10a and b). Graded potentials induce a small electrical current that leaks out of the neuron as it flows along the membrane. Graded potentials thus decay with time and with distance from their source.

If a depolarization shifts the membrane potential sufficiently, the result is a massive change in membrane voltage called an **action potential**. Unlike graded potentials, action potentials have a constant magnitude and can regenerate in adjacent regions of the membrane. Action potentials can

therefore spread along axons, making them well suited for transmitting a signal over long distances.

Action potentials arise because some of the ion channels in neurons are **voltage-gated ion channels**, opening or closing when the membrane potential passes a particular level (see Figure 48.9). If a depolarization opens voltage-gated sodium channels, the resulting flow of Na⁺ into the neuron results in further depolarization. Because the sodium channels are voltage gated, the increased depolarization causes more sodium channels to open, leading to an even greater flow of current. The result is a process of positive feedback that triggers a very rapid opening of many voltage-gated sodium channels and the marked temporary change in membrane potential that defines an action potential **(Figure 48.10c)**.

Action potentials occur whenever a depolarization increases the membrane voltage to a particular value, called the **threshold**. For many mammalian neurons, the threshold is a membrane potential of about −55 mV. Once initiated, the action potential has a magnitude that is independent of the strength of the triggering stimulus. Because action potentials either occur fully or do not occur at all, they represent an *all-or-none* response to stimuli. This all-or-none property reflects the fact that depolarization opens voltage-gated sodium channels, causing further depolarization. The positive-feedback loop of channel opening and depolarization triggers an action potential whenever the membrane potential reaches threshold.

The discovery of how action potentials are generated resulted from the work of British scientists Andrew Huxley and Alan Hodgkin in the 1940s and 1950s. Because no techniques were available for studying electrical events in small cells, they took electrical recordings from the giant neurons of the squid. Their experiments led to the model presented in the next section, which earned them a Nobel Prize.

Generation of Action Potentials: *A Closer Look*

The characteristic shape of the graph of an action potential reflects changes in membrane potential resulting from ion movement through voltage-gated sodium and potassium channels (**Figure 48.11**). Depolarization opens both types of channels, but they respond independently and sequentially. Sodium channels open first, initiating the action potential. As the action potential proceeds, sodium channels become *inactivated*: A loop of the channel protein moves, blocking ion flow through the opening. Sodium channels remain inactivated until after the membrane returns to the resting potential and the channels close. In contrast, potassium channels open more slowly than sodium channels, but remain open and functional until the end of the action potential.

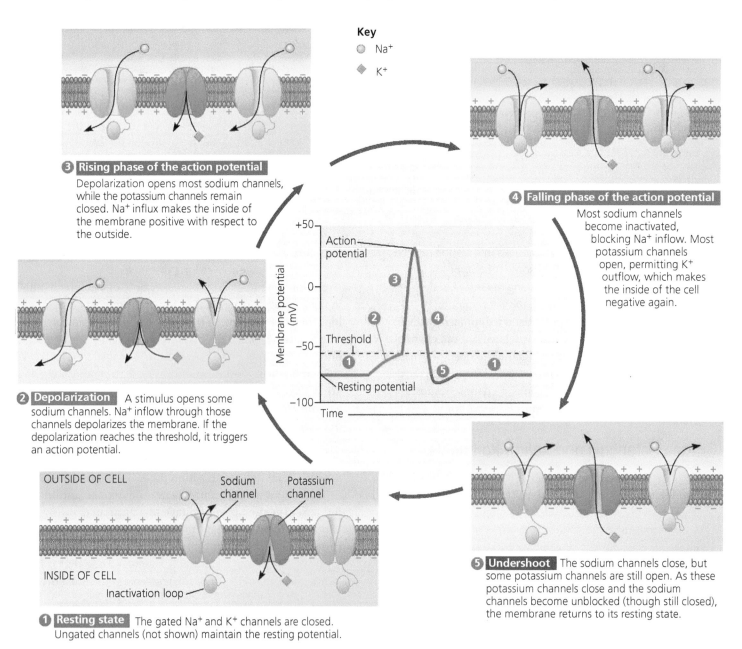

Key
- Na⁺
- K⁺

③ Rising phase of the action potential
Depolarization opens most sodium channels, while the potassium channels remain closed. Na⁺ influx makes the inside of the membrane positive with respect to the outside.

④ Falling phase of the action potential
Most sodium channels become inactivated, blocking Na⁺ inflow. Most potassium channels open, permitting K⁺ outflow, which makes the inside of the cell negative again.

② Depolarization A stimulus opens some sodium channels. Na⁺ inflow through those channels depolarizes the membrane. If the depolarization reaches the threshold, it triggers an action potential.

⑤ Undershoot The sodium channels close, but some potassium channels are still open. As these potassium channels close and the sodium channels become unblocked (though still closed), the membrane returns to its resting state.

OUTSIDE OF CELL
Sodium channel
Potassium channel
INSIDE OF CELL
Inactivation loop

① Resting state The gated Na⁺ and K⁺ channels are closed. Ungated channels (not shown) maintain the resting potential.

▲ **Figure 48.11 The role of voltage-gated ion channels in the generation of an action potential.** The circled numbers on the graph in the center and the colors of the action potential phases correspond to the five diagrams showing voltage-gated sodium and potassium channels in a neuron's plasma membrane. (Ungated ion channels are not illustrated.)

ANIMATION *BioFlix* Visit the Study Area in **MasteringBiology** for the BioFlix® 3-D Animation on How Neurons Work.

To understand further how voltage-gated channels shape the action potential, consider the process as a series of stages, as depicted in Figure 48.11. ❶ When the membrane of the axon is at the resting potential, most voltage-gated sodium channels are closed. Some potassium channels are open, but most voltage-gated potassium channels are closed. ❷ When a stimulus depolarizes the membrane, some gated sodium channels open, allowing more Na$^+$ to diffuse into the cell. The Na$^+$ inflow causes further depolarization, which opens still more gated sodium channels, allowing even more Na$^+$ to diffuse into the cell. ❸ Once the threshold is crossed, the positive-feedback cycle rapidly brings the membrane potential close to E_{Na}. This stage of the action potential is called the *rising phase*. ❹ Two events prevent the membrane potential from actually reaching E_{Na}: Voltage-gated sodium channels inactivate soon after opening, halting Na$^+$ inflow; and most voltage-gated potassium channels open, causing a rapid outflow of K$^+$. Both events quickly bring the membrane potential back toward E_K. This stage is called the *falling phase*. ❺ In the final phase of an action potential, called the *undershoot*, the membrane's permeability to K$^+$ is higher than at rest, so the membrane potential is closer to E_K than it is at the resting potential. The gated potassium channels eventually close, and the membrane potential returns to the resting potential.

The sodium channels remain inactivated during the falling phase and the early part of the undershoot. As a result, if a second depolarizing stimulus occurs during this period, it will be unable to trigger an action potential. The "downtime" when a second action potential cannot be initiated is called the **refractory period**. One consequence of the refractory period is to limit the maximum frequency at which action potentials can be generated. As we will discuss shortly, the refractory period also ensures that all signals in an axon travel in one direction, from the cell body to the axon terminals.

Note that the refractory period is due to the inactivation of sodium channels, not to a change in the ion gradients across the plasma membrane. The flow of charged particles during an action potential involves far too few ions to change the concentration on either side of the membrane significantly.

Conduction of Action Potentials

Having described the events of a single action potential, we'll explore next how a series of action potentials moves a signal along an axon. At the site where an action potential is initiated (usually the axon hillock), Na$^+$ inflow during the rising phase creates an electrical current that depolarizes the neighboring region of the axon membrane (**Figure 48.12**). The depolarization is large enough to reach threshold, causing an action potential in the neighboring region. This process is repeated many times along the length of the axon. Because an

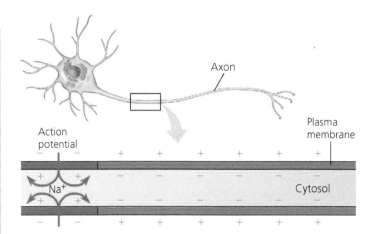

An action potential is generated as Na$^+$ flows inward across the membrane at one location.

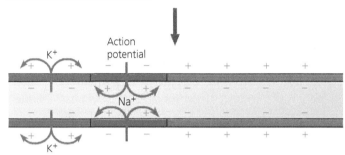

The depolarization of the action potential spreads to the neighboring region of the membrane, reinitiating the action potential there. To the left of this region, the membrane is repolarizing as K$^+$ flows outward.

The depolarization-repolarization process is repeated in the next region of the membrane. In this way, local currents of ions *across* the plasma membrane cause the action potential to be propagated *along* the length of the axon.

▲ **Figure 48.12 Conduction of an action potential.** This figure shows events at three successive times as an action potential passes from left to right. At each point along the axon, voltage-gated ion channels go through the sequence of changes shown in Figure 48.11. Membrane colors correspond to the action potential phases in Figure 48.11.

DRAW IT *For the axon segment shown, consider a point at the left end, a point in the middle, and a point at the right end. Draw a graph for each point showing the change in membrane potential over time at that point as a single nerve impulse moves from left to right across the segment.*

action potential is an all-or-none event, the magnitude and duration of the action potential are the same at each position along the axon. The net result is the movement of a nerve impulse from the cell body to the synaptic terminals, much like the cascade of events triggered by knocking over the first domino in a line.

An action potential that starts at the axon hillock moves along the axon only toward the synaptic terminals. Why? Immediately behind the traveling zone of depolarization caused by Na⁺ inflow is a zone of repolarization caused by K⁺ outflow. In the repolarized zone, the sodium channels remain inactivated. Consequently, the inward current that depolarizes the axon membrane *ahead* of the action potential cannot produce another action potential *behind* it. This prevents action potentials from traveling back toward the cell body.

For most neurons, the interval between the onset of an action potential and the beginning of the undershoot is only 1–2 milliseconds (msec). Because action potentials are so brief, a neuron can produce them as often as hundreds per second. Furthermore, the rate at which action potentials are produced conveys information about the strength of the input signal. In hearing, for example, louder sounds result in more frequent action potentials in neurons connecting the ear to the brain. Similarly, increased frequency of action potentials in a neuron that stimulates skeletal muscle tissue will increase the tension in the contracting muscle. Differences in the number of action potentials in a given time are in fact the only variable in how information is encoded and transmitted along an axon.

Gated ion channels and action potentials have a central role in nervous system activity. As a consequence, mutations in genes that encode ion channel proteins can cause disorders affecting the nerves or brain—or the muscles or heart, depending largely on where in the body the gene for the ion channel protein is expressed. For example, mutations affecting voltage-gated sodium channels in skeletal muscle cells can cause myotonia, a periodic spasming of those muscles. Mutations affecting sodium channels in the brain can cause epilepsy, in which groups of nerve cells fire simultaneously and excessively, producing seizures.

Evolutionary Adaptations of Axon Structure

EVOLUTION The rate at which the axons within nerves conduct action potentials governs how rapidly an animal can react to danger or opportunity. As a consequence, natural selection often results in anatomical adaptations that increase conduction speed. One such adaptation is a wider axon. Axon width matters because resistance to electrical current flow is inversely proportional to the cross-sectional area of a conductor (such as a wire or an axon). In the same way that a wide hose offers less resistance to the flow of water than does a narrow hose, a wide axon provides less resistance to the current associated with an action potential than does a narrow axon.

In invertebrates, conduction speed varies from several centimeters per second in very narrow axons to approximately 30 m/sec in the giant axons of some arthropods and molluscs. These giant axons (up to 1 mm wide) function in rapid behavioral responses, such as the muscle contraction that propels a hunting squid toward its prey.

Vertebrate axons have narrow diameters but can still conduct action potentials at high speed. How is this possible? The evolutionary adaptation that enables fast conduction in vertebrate axons is electrical insulation, analogous to the plastic insulation that encases many electrical wires. Insulation causes the depolarizing current associated with an action potential to travel farther along the axon interior, bringing more distant regions to the threshold sooner.

The electrical insulation that surrounds vertebrate axons is called a **myelin sheath** (Figure 48.13). Myelin sheaths are produced by two types of glia: **oligodendrocytes** in the CNS and **Schwann cells** in the PNS. During development, these specialized glia wrap axons in many layers of membrane. The membranes forming these layers are mostly lipid, which is a poor conductor of electrical current and thus a good insulator.

0.1 μm

▲ **Figure 48.13 Schwann cells and the myelin sheath.** In the PNS, glia called Schwann cells wrap themselves around axons, forming layers of myelin. Gaps between adjacent Schwann cells are called nodes of Ranvier. The TEM shows a cross section through a myelinated axon.

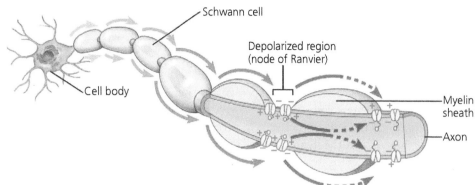

► **Figure 48.14 Saltatory conduction.** In a myelinated axon, the depolarizing current during an action potential at one node of Ranvier spreads along the interior of the axon to the next node (blue arrows), where voltage-gated sodium channels enable reinitiation. Thus, the action potential appears to jump from node to node as it travels along the axon (red arrows).

Labels: Schwann cell; Depolarized region (node of Ranvier); Cell body; Myelin sheath; Axon

In myelinated axons, voltage-gated sodium channels are restricted to gaps in the myelin sheath called **nodes of Ranvier** (see Figure 48.13). Furthermore, the extracellular fluid is in contact with the axon membrane only at the nodes. As a result, action potentials are not generated in the regions between the nodes. Rather, the inward current produced during the rising phase of the action potential at a node travels within the axon all the way to the next node. There, the current depolarizes the membrane and regenerates the action potential **(Figure 48.14)**.

Action potentials propagate more rapidly in myelinated axons because the time-consuming process of opening and closing of ion channels occurs at only a limited number of positions along the axon. This mechanism for propagating action potentials is called **saltatory conduction** (from the Latin *saltare*, to leap) because the action potential appears to jump along the axon from node to node.

The major selective advantage of myelination is its space efficiency. A myelinated axon 20 μm in diameter has a conduction speed faster than that of a squid giant axon with a diameter 40 times greater. Consequently, more than 2,000 of those myelinated axons can be packed into the space occupied by just one giant axon.

For any axon, myelinated or not, the conduction of an action potential to the end of the axon sets the stage for the next step in neuronal signaling—the transfer of information to another cell. This information handoff occurs at synapses, our next topic.

CONCEPT CHECK 48.3

1. How do action potentials and graded potentials differ?
2. In multiple sclerosis (from the Greek *skleros*, hard), a person's myelin sheaths harden and deteriorate. How would this affect nervous system function?
3. How do both negative and positive feedback contribute to the changes in membrane potential during an action potential?
4. **WHAT IF?** Suppose a mutation caused gated sodium channels to remain inactivated longer after an action potential. How would this affect the frequency at which action potentials could be generated? Explain.

For suggested answers, see Appendix A.

CONCEPT 48.4

Neurons communicate with other cells at synapses

In most cases, action potentials are not transmitted from neurons to other cells. However, information is transmitted, and this transmission occurs at synaptic terminals, such as those shown in **Figure 48.15**. Some synapses, called electrical synapses, contain gap junctions (see Figure 6.30), which *do* allow electrical current to flow directly from one neuron to another. In both vertebrates and invertebrates, electrical synapses synchronize the activity of neurons responsible for certain rapid, unvarying behaviors. For example, electrical synapses associated with the giant axons of squids and lobsters facilitate swift escapes from danger. There are also many electrical synapses in the vertebrate brain.

The majority of synapses are chemical synapses, which involve the release of a chemical neurotransmitter by the presynaptic neuron. At each terminal, the presynaptic neuron synthesizes the neurotransmitter and packages it in multiple membrane-enclosed compartments called *synaptic vesicles*. The arrival of an action potential at a synaptic terminal depolarizes the plasma membrane, opening voltage-gated channels that allow Ca^{2+} to diffuse into

Labels: Postsynaptic neuron; Synaptic terminals of presynaptic neurons; 5 μm

▲ **Figure 48.15 Synaptic terminals on the cell body of a postsynaptic neuron (colorized SEM).**

the terminal (**Figure 48.16**). The resulting rise in Ca^{2+} concentration in the terminal causes some of the synaptic vesicles to fuse with the terminal membrane, releasing the neurotransmitter.

Once released, the neurotransmitter diffuses across the *synaptic cleft*, the gap that separates the presynaptic neuron from the postsynaptic cell. Diffusion time is very short because the gap is less than 50 nm across. Upon reaching the postsynaptic membrane, the neurotransmitter binds to and activates a specific receptor in the membrane.

Information transfer is much more readily modified at chemical synapses than at electrical synapses. A variety of factors can affect the amount of neurotransmitter that is released or the responsiveness of the postsynaptic cell. Such modifications underlie an animal's ability to alter its behavior in response to change and form the basis for learning and memory (as you will read in Chapter 49).

Generation of Postsynaptic Potentials

At many chemical synapses, the receptor protein that binds and responds to neurotransmitters is a **ligand-gated ion channel**, often called an *ionotropic receptor*. These receptors are clustered in the membrane of the postsynaptic cell, directly opposite the synaptic terminal. Binding of the neurotransmitter (the receptor's ligand) to a particular part of the receptor opens the channel and allows specific ions to diffuse across the postsynaptic membrane. The result is a *postsynaptic potential*, a graded potential in the postsynaptic cell.

At some synapses, the ligand-gated ion channel is permeable to both K^+ and Na^+ (see Figure 48.16). When this channel opens, the membrane potential depolarizes toward a value roughly midway between E_K and E_{Na}. Because such a depolarization brings the membrane potential

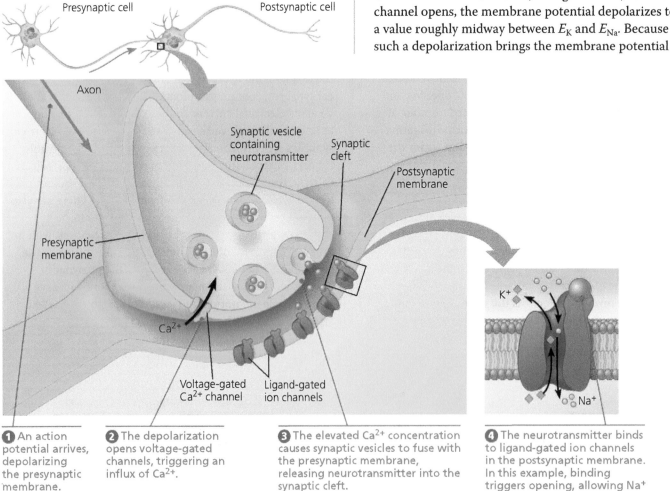

① An action potential arrives, depolarizing the presynaptic membrane.

② The depolarization opens voltage-gated channels, triggering an influx of Ca^{2+}.

③ The elevated Ca^{2+} concentration causes synaptic vesicles to fuse with the presynaptic membrane, releasing neurotransmitter into the synaptic cleft.

④ The neurotransmitter binds to ligand-gated ion channels in the postsynaptic membrane. In this example, binding triggers opening, allowing Na^+ and K^+ to diffuse through.

▲ **Figure 48.16 A chemical synapse.** This figure illustrates the sequence of events that transmits a signal across a chemical synapse. In response to binding of neurotransmitter, ligand-gated ion channels in the postsynaptic membrane open (as shown here) or, less commonly, close. Synaptic transmission ends when the neurotransmitter diffuses out of the synaptic cleft, is taken up by the synaptic terminal or by another cell, or is degraded by an enzyme.

 ANIMATION ***BioFlix*** Visit the Study Area in MasteringBiology for the BioFlix® 3-D Animation on How Synapses Work.

WHAT IF? *If all the Ca^{2+} in the fluid surrounding a neuron were removed, how would this affect the transmission of information within and between neurons?*

toward threshold, it is called an **excitatory postsynaptic potential (EPSP)**.

At other synapses, the ligand-gated ion channel is selectively permeable for only K^+ or Cl^-. When such a channel opens, the postsynaptic membrane hyperpolarizes. A hyperpolarization produced in this manner is an **inhibitory postsynaptic potential (IPSP)** because it moves the membrane potential further from threshold.

Summation of Postsynaptic Potentials

The cell body and dendrites of a postsynaptic neuron may receive inputs from chemical synapses formed with hundreds or even thousands of synaptic terminals (see Figure 48.15). Often, some of these are excitatory and others inhibitory.

The magnitude of the postsynaptic potential at any one synapse varies with a number of factors, including the amount of neurotransmitter released by the presynaptic neuron. As a graded potential, a postsynaptic potential becomes smaller with distance from the synapse. Therefore, by the time a single EPSP reaches the axon hillock, it is usually too small to trigger an action potential (Figure 48.17a).

On some occasions, two EPSPs occur at a single synapse in such rapid succession that the postsynaptic neuron's membrane potential has not returned to the resting potential before the arrival of the second EPSP. When that happens, the EPSPs add together, an effect called **temporal summation** (Figure 48.17b). Moreover, EPSPs produced nearly simultaneously by *different* synapses on the same postsynaptic neuron can also add together, an effect called **spatial summation** (Figure 48.17c). Through spatial and temporal summation, several EPSPs can combine to depolarize the membrane at the axon hillock to threshold, causing the postsynaptic neuron to produce an action potential. Summation applies as well to IPSPs: Two or more IPSPs occurring nearly simultaneously at synapses in the same region or in rapid succession at the same synapse have a larger effect than a single IPSP. Through summation, an IPSP can also counter the effect of an EPSP (Figure 48.17d).

The interplay between multiple excitatory and inhibitory inputs is the essence of integration in the nervous system. The axon hillock is the neuron's integrating center, the region where the membrane potential at any instant represents the summed effect of all EPSPs and IPSPs. Whenever the membrane potential at the axon hillock reaches threshold, an action potential is generated and travels along the axon to its synaptic terminals. After the refractory period, the neuron may produce another action potential, provided the membrane potential at the axon hillock once again reaches threshold.

Modulated Signaling at Synapses

So far, we have focused on synapses where a neurotransmitter binds directly to an ion channel, causing the channel to open. However, there are also synapses in which the receptor for the neurotransmitter is *not* part of an ion channel. At these synapses, the neurotransmitter binds

▲ **Figure 48.17 Summation of postsynaptic potentials.** These graphs trace changes in the membrane potential at a postsynaptic neuron's axon hillock. The arrows indicate times when postsynaptic potentials occur at two excitatory synapses (E_1 and E_2, green in the diagrams above the graphs) and at one inhibitory synapse (I, red). Like most EPSPs, those produced at E_1 or E_2 do not reach the threshold at the axon hillock without summation.

to a *metabotropic receptor*, so called because the resulting opening or closing of ion channels depends on one or more metabolic steps. Binding of a neurotransmitter to a metabotropic receptor activates a signal transduction pathway in the postsynaptic cell involving a second messenger (see Chapter 11). Compared with the postsynaptic potentials produced by ligand-gated channels, the effects of these second-messenger systems have a slower onset but last longer (minutes or even hours). Second messengers modulate the responsiveness of postsynaptic neurons to inputs in diverse ways, such as by altering the number of open potassium channels.

A variety of signal transduction pathways play a role in modulating synaptic transmission. One of the best-studied pathways involves cyclic AMP (cAMP) as a second messenger. For example, when the neurotransmitter norepinephrine binds to its metabotropic receptor, the neurotransmitter–receptor complex activates a G protein, which in turn activates adenylyl cyclase, the enzyme that converts ATP to cAMP (see Figure 11.11). Cyclic AMP activates protein kinase A, which phosphorylates specific ion channel proteins in the postsynaptic membrane, causing them to open or close. Because of the amplifying effect of the signal transduction pathway, the binding of a neurotransmitter molecule to a metabotropic receptor can open or close many channels.

Neurotransmitters

Signaling at a synapse brings about a response that depends on both the neurotransmitter released from the presynaptic membrane and the receptor produced at the postsynaptic membrane. A single neurotransmitter may bind specifically to more than a dozen different receptors, including ionotropic and metabotropic types. Indeed, a particular neurotransmitter can excite postsynaptic cells expressing one receptor and inhibit postsynaptic cells expressing a different receptor.

How is neurotransmitter signaling terminated? Both receptor activation and postsynaptic response cease when neurotransmitter molecules are cleared from the synaptic cleft. The removal of neurotransmitters can occur by simple diffusion or by other mechanisms. For example, some neurotransmitters are inactivated by enzymatic hydrolysis (**Figure 48.18a**). Other neurotransmitters are recaptured into the presynaptic neuron (**Figure 48.18b**). Once this reuptake occurs, neurotransmitters are repackaged in synaptic vesicles or transferred to glia for metabolism or recycling to neurons.

With these basic properties of neurotransmitters in mind, let's now examine some specific examples, beginning with **acetylcholine**, a common neurotransmitter in both invertebrates and vertebrates.

Acetylcholine

Acetylcholine is vital for nervous system functions that include muscle stimulation, memory formation, and learning. In vertebrates, there are two major classes of acetylcholine receptor. One is a ligand-gated ion channel, which functions at the vertebrate *neuromuscular junction*, the site where a motor neuron forms a synapse with a skeletal muscle cell. When acetylcholine released by motor neurons binds this receptor, the ion channel opens, producing an EPSP. This excitatory activity is soon terminated by acetylcholinesterase, an enzyme in the synaptic cleft that hydrolyzes the neurotransmitter.

The acetylcholine receptor active at the neuromuscular junction is also found elsewhere in the PNS, as well as in the CNS. There this ionotropic receptor can bind nicotine, a chemical found in tobacco and tobacco smoke. Nicotine's effects as a physiological and psychological stimulant result from its binding to this receptor.

A metabotropic acetylcholine receptor is found at locations that include the vertebrate CNS and heart. In heart muscle, acetylcholine released by neurons activates a signal transduction pathway. The G proteins in the pathway inhibit adenylyl cyclase and open potassium channels in the muscle cell membrane. Both effects reduce the rate at which the heart pumps. Thus, the effect of acetylcholine in heart muscle is inhibitory rather than excitatory.

(a) Enzymatic breakdown of neurotransmitter in the synaptic cleft

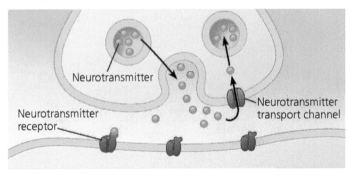

(b) Reuptake of neurotransmitter by presynaptic neuron

▲ **Figure 48.18 Two mechanisms of terminating neurotransmission.**

A number of toxins disrupt neurotransmission by acetylcholine. For example, the nerve gas sarin inhibits acetylcholinesterase, causing a buildup of acetylcholine to levels that trigger paralysis and typically death. In contrast, certain bacteria produce a toxin that inhibits presynaptic release of acetylcholine. This toxin causes a rare but often fatal form of food poisoning called botulism. Untreated botulism is typically fatal because muscles required for breathing fail to contract when acetylcholine release is blocked. Today, injections of the botulinum toxin, known by the trade name Botox, are used cosmetically to minimize wrinkles around the eyes or mouth by blocking transmission at synapses that control particular facial muscles.

Although acetylcholine has many roles, it is just one of more than 100 known neurotransmitters. As shown by the examples in **Table 48.2**, the rest fall into four classes: amino acids, biogenic amines, neuropeptides, and gases.

Amino Acids

Glutamate is one of several amino acids that can act as a neurotransmitter. In invertebrates, glutamate, rather than acetylcholine, is the neurotransmitter at the neuromuscular

junction. In vertebrates, glutamate is the most common neurotransmitter in the CNS. Synapses at which glutamate is the neurotransmitter have a key role in the formation of long-term memory (as we will discuss in Chapter 49).

The amino acid **gamma-aminobutyric acid (GABA)** is the neurotransmitter at most inhibitory synapses in the brain. Binding of GABA to receptors in postsynaptic cells increases membrane permeability to Cl^-, resulting in an IPSP. The widely prescribed drug diazepam (Valium) reduces anxiety through binding to a site on a GABA receptor.

A third amino acid, glycine, acts at inhibitory synapses in parts of the CNS that lie outside of the brain. There, glycine binds to an ionotropic receptor that is inhibited by strychnine, a chemical often used as a rat poison.

Biogenic Amines

The neurotransmitters grouped as **biogenic amines** are synthesized from amino acids and include **norepinephrine**, which is made from tyrosine. Norepinephrine is an excitatory neurotransmitter in the autonomic nervous system, a branch of the PNS. Outside the nervous system, norepinephrine has distinct but related functions as a hormone, as does the chemically similar biogenic amine *epinephrine* (see Chapter 45).

The biogenic amines **dopamine**, made from tyrosine, and **serotonin**, made from tryptophan, are released at many sites in the brain and affect sleep, mood, attention, and learning. Some psychoactive drugs, including LSD and mescaline, apparently produce their hallucinatory effects by binding to brain receptors for these neurotransmitters.

Biogenic amines have a central role in a number of nervous system disorders and treatments (see Chapter 49). The degenerative illness Parkinson's disease is associated with a lack of dopamine in the brain. In addition, depression is often treated with drugs that increase the brain concentrations of biogenic amines. Prozac, for instance, enhances the effect of serotonin by inhibiting its reuptake after release.

Neuropeptides

Several **neuropeptides**, relatively short chains of amino acids, serve as neurotransmitters that operate via metabotropic receptors. Such peptides are typically produced by cleavage of much larger protein precursors. The neuropeptide *substance P* is a key excitatory neurotransmitter that mediates our perception of pain, while other neuropeptides, called **endorphins**, function as natural analgesics, decreasing pain perception.

Endorphins are produced in the brain during times of physical or emotional stress, such as childbirth. In addition to relieving pain, they reduce urine output, decrease respiration, and produce euphoria, as well as other emotional effects. Because opiates (drugs such as morphine and heroin) bind to the same receptor proteins as endorphins, opiates mimic endorphins and produce many of the same

Table 48.2 Major Neurotransmitters

Neurotransmitter	Structure
Acetylcholine	
Amino Acids	
Glutamate	
GABA (gamma-aminobutyric acid)	
Glycine	
Biogenic Amines	
Norepinephrine	
Dopamine	
Serotonin	
Neuropeptides (a very diverse group, only two of which are shown)	
Substance P	Arg—Pro—Lys—Pro—Gln—Gln—Phe—Phe—Gly—Leu—Met
Met-enkephalin (an endorphin)	Tyr—Gly—Gly—Phe—Met
Gases	
Nitric oxide	N=O

Interpreting Data Values Expressed in Scientific Notation

Does the Brain Have Specific Protein Receptors for Opiates?
A team of researchers were looking for opiate receptors in the mammalian brain. Knowing that the drug naloxone blocks the analgesic effect of opiates, they hypothesized that naloxone acts by binding tightly to brain opiate receptors without activating them. In this exercise, you will interpret the results of an experiment that the researchers conducted to test their hypothesis.

How the Experiment Was Done The researchers added radioactive naloxone to a protein mixture prepared from rodent brains. If the mixture contained opiate receptors or other proteins that could bind naloxone, the radioactivity would stably associate with the mixture. To determine whether the binding was due to specific opiate receptors, they tested other drugs, opiate and non-opiate, for their ability to block naloxone binding.

Radioactive naloxone

1. Radioactive naloxone and a test drug are incubated with a protein mixture.

Drug

2. Proteins are trapped on a filter. Bound naloxone is detected by measuring radioactivity.

Data from the Experiment

Drug	Opiate	Lowest Concentration That Blocked Naloxone Binding
Morphine	Yes	$6 \times 10^{-9}\ M$
Methadone	Yes	$2 \times 10^{-8}\ M$
Levorphanol	Yes	$2 \times 10^{-9}\ M$
Phenobarbital	No	No effect at $10^{-4}\ M$
Atropine	No	No effect at $10^{-4}\ M$
Serotonin	No	No effect at $10^{-4}\ M$

Interpret the Data

1. The data above are expressed in scientific notation: a numerical factor times a power of 10. Remember that a negative power of 10 means a number less than 1. For example, $10^{-1}\ M$ (molar) can also be written as 0.1 M. Write the concentrations in the table above for morphine and atropine in this alternative format.

2. Compare the concentrations listed in the table for methadone and phenobarbital. Which concentration is higher? By how much?

3. Would phenobarbital, atropine, or serotonin have blocked naloxone binding at a concentration of $10^{-5}\ M$? Explain why or why not.

4. Which drugs blocked naloxone binding in this experiment? What do these results indicate about the brain receptors for naloxone?

5. If researchers instead used tissue from intestinal muscles rather than brains, they found no naloxone binding. What does that suggest about opiate receptors in mammalian muscle?

(MB) A version of this Scientific Skills Exercise can be assigned in MasteringBiology.

Data from C. B. Pert and S. H. Snyder, Opiate receptor: demonstration in nervous tissue, *Science* 179:1011–1014 (1973).

physiological effects (see Figure 2.16). In the Scientific Skills Exercise, you can interpret data from an experiment designed to search for opiate receptors in the brain.

Gases

Some vertebrate neurons release dissolved gases as neurotransmitters. In human males, for example, certain neurons release nitric oxide (NO) into the erectile tissue of the penis during sexual arousal. The resulting relaxation of smooth muscle in the blood vessel walls of the spongy erectile tissue allows the tissue to fill with blood, producing an erection. The erectile dysfunction drug Viagra works by inhibiting an enzyme that terminates the action of NO.

Unlike most neurotransmitters, NO is not stored in cytoplasmic vesicles but is instead synthesized on demand. NO diffuses into neighboring target cells, produces a change, and is broken down—all within a few seconds. In many of its targets, including smooth muscle cells, NO works like many hormones, stimulating an enzyme to synthesize a second messenger that directly affects cellular metabolism.

Although inhaling the gas carbon monoxide (CO) can be deadly, the vertebrate body uses the enzyme heme oxygenase to produce small amounts of CO, some of which acts as a neurotransmitter. In the brain, CO regulates the release of hypothalamic hormones. In the PNS, it acts as an inhibitory neurotransmitter that hyperpolarizes the plasma membrane of intestinal smooth muscle cells.

In the next chapter, we'll consider how the cellular and biochemical mechanisms we have discussed contribute to nervous system function on the system level.

CONCEPT CHECK 48.4

1. How is it possible for a particular neurotransmitter to produce opposite effects in different tissues?

2. Organophosphate pesticides work by inhibiting acetylcholinesterase, the enzyme that breaks down the neurotransmitter acetylcholine. Explain how these toxins would affect EPSPs produced by acetylcholine.

3. MAKE CONNECTIONS Name one or more membrane activities that occur both in fertilization of an egg and in neurotransmission across a synapse (see Figure 47.3).

For suggested answers, see Appendix A.

CONCEPT 48.1

Neuron structure and organization reflect function in information transfer (pp. 1062–1064)

- Most neurons have branched **dendrites** that receive signals from other neurons and an **axon** that transmits signals to other cells at **synapses**. Neurons rely on **glia** for functions that include nourishment, insulation, and regulation.

- A **central nervous system (CNS)** and a **peripheral nervous system (PNS)** process information in three stages: sensory input, integration, and motor output to effector cells.

? *How would severing an axon affect the flow of information in a neuron?*

CONCEPT 48.2

Ion pumps and ion channels establish the resting potential of a neuron (pp. 1064–1066)

- Ionic gradients generate a voltage difference, or **membrane potential**, across the plasma membrane of cells. The concentration of Na^+ is higher outside than inside; the reverse is true for K^+. In resting neurons, the plasma membrane has many open potassium channels but few open sodium channels. Diffusion of ions, principally K^+, through channels generates a **resting potential**, with the inside more negative than the outside.

? *Suppose you placed an isolated neuron in a solution similar to extracellular fluid and later transferred the neuron to a solution lacking any sodium ions. What change would you expect in the resting potential?*

CONCEPT 48.3

Action potentials are the signals conducted by axons (pp. 1066–1071)

- Neurons have gated ion channels that open or close in response to stimuli, leading to changes in the membrane potential. An increase in the magnitude of the membrane potential is a **hyperpolarization**; a decrease is a **depolarization**. Changes in membrane potential that vary continuously with the strength of a stimulus are known as **graded potentials**.
- An **action potential** is a brief, all-or-none depolarization of a neuron's plasma membrane. When a graded depolarization brings the membrane potential to **threshold**, many **voltage-gated ion channels** open, triggering an inflow of Na^+ that rapidly brings the membrane potential to a positive value. A

negative membrane potential is restored by the inactivation of sodium channels and by the opening of many voltage-gated potassium channels, which increases K^+ outflow. A **refractory period** follows, corresponding to the interval when the sodium channels are inactivated.

- A nerve impulse travels from the axon hillock to the synaptic terminals by propagating a series of action potentials along the axon. The speed of conduction increases with the diameter of the axon and, in many vertebrate axons, with **myelination**. Action potentials in axons insulated by myelination appear to jump from one **node of Ranvier** to the next, a process called **saltatory conduction**.

INTERPRET THE DATA *Assuming a refractory period equal in length to the action potential (see graph above), what is the maximum frequency per unit time at which a neuron could fire action potentials?*

CONCEPT 48.4

Neurons communicate with other cells at synapses (pp. 1071–1076)

- In an electrical **synapse**, electrical current flows directly from one cell to another. In a chemical synapse, depolarization causes synaptic vesicles to fuse with the terminal membrane and release **neurotransmitter** into the synaptic cleft.
- At many synapses, the neurotransmitter binds to **ligand-gated ion channels** in the postsynaptic membrane, producing an **excitatory** or **inhibitory postsynaptic potential** (**EPSP** or **IPSP**). The neurotransmitter then diffuses out of the cleft, is taken up by surrounding cells, or is degraded by enzymes. A single neuron has many synapses on its dendrites and cell body. **Temporal** and **spatial summation** of EPSPs and IPSPs at the axon hillock determine whether a neuron generates an action potential.
- Different receptors for the same neurotransmitter produce different effects. Some neurotransmitter receptors activate signal transduction pathways, which can produce long-lasting changes in postsynaptic cells. Major neurotransmitters include acetylcholine; the amino acids GABA, glutamate, and glycine; biogenic amines; neuropeptides; and gases such as NO.

? *Why are many drugs that are used to treat nervous system diseases or to affect brain function targeted to specific receptors rather than particular neurotransmitters?*

LEVEL 1: KNOWLEDGE/COMPREHENSION

1. What happens when a resting neuron's membrane depolarizes?
   a. There is a net diffusion of Na^+ out of the cell.
   b. The equilibrium potential for K^+ (E_K) becomes more positive.
   c. The neuron's membrane voltage becomes more positive.
   d. The cell's inside is more negative than the outside.

2. A common feature of action potentials is that they
   a. cause the membrane to hyperpolarize and then depolarize.
   b. can undergo temporal and spatial summation.
   c. are triggered by a depolarization that reaches threshold.
   d. move at the same speed along all axons.

3. Where are neurotransmitter receptors located?
   a. the nuclear membrane
   b. the nodes of Ranvier
   c. the postsynaptic membrane
   d. synaptic vesicle membranes

LEVEL 2: APPLICATION/ANALYSIS

4. Why are action potentials usually conducted in one direction?
   a. Ions can flow along the axon in only one direction.
   b. The brief refractory period prevents reopening of voltage-gated Na^+ channels.
   c. The axon hillock has a higher membrane potential than the terminals of the axon.
   d. Voltage-gated channels for both Na^+ and K^+ open in only one direction.

5. Which of the following is the most *direct* result of depolarizing the presynaptic membrane of an axon terminal?
   a. Voltage-gated calcium channels in the membrane open.
   b. Synaptic vesicles fuse with the membrane.
   c. Ligand-gated channels open, allowing neurotransmitters to enter the synaptic cleft.
   d. An EPSP or IPSP is generated in the postsynaptic cell.

6. Suppose a particular neurotransmitter causes an IPSP in postsynaptic cell X and an EPSP in postsynaptic cell Y. A likely explanation is that
   a. the threshold value in the postsynaptic membrane is different for cell X and cell Y.
   b. the axon of cell X is myelinated, but that of cell Y is not.
   c. only cell Y produces an enzyme that terminates the activity of the neurotransmitter.
   d. cells X and Y express different receptor molecules for this particular neurotransmitter.

LEVEL 3: SYNTHESIS/EVALUATION

7. **WHAT IF?** Ouabain, a plant substance used in some cultures to poison hunting arrows, disables the sodium-potassium pump. What change in the resting potential would you expect to see if you treated a neuron with ouabain? Explain.

8. **WHAT IF?** If a drug mimicked the activity of GABA in the CNS, what general effect on behavior might you expect? Explain.

9. **DRAW IT** Suppose a researcher inserts a pair of electrodes at two different positions along the middle of an axon dissected out of a squid. By applying a depolarizing stimulus, the researcher brings the plasma membrane at both positions to threshold. Using the drawing below as a model, create one or more drawings that illustrate where each action potential would terminate.

Electrode

Squid axon

10. **EVOLUTION CONNECTION**
    An action potential is an all-or-none event. This on/off signaling is an evolutionary adaptation of animals that must sense and act in a complex environment. It is possible to imagine a nervous system in which the action potentials are graded, with the amplitude depending on the size of the stimulus. What evolutionary advantage might on/off signaling have over a graded (continuously variable) kind of signaling?

11. **SCIENTIFIC INQUIRY**
    From what you know about action potentials and synapses, propose two or three hypotheses for how various anesthetics might block pain.

12. **WRITE ABOUT A THEME: ORGANIZATION**
    In a short essay (100–150 words), describe how the structure and electrical properties of vertebrate neurons reflect similarities and differences with other animal cells.

13. **SYNTHESIZE YOUR KNOWLEDGE**

The rattlesnake alerts enemies to its presence with a rattle—a set of modified scales at the tip of its tail. Describe the distinct roles of gated ion channels in initiating and moving a signal along the nerve from the snake's head to its tail and then from that nerve to the muscle that shakes the rattle.

For selected answers, see Appendix A.

MasteringBiology®

Students Go to **MasteringBiology** for assignments, the eText, and the Study Area with practice tests, animations, and activities.

Instructors Go to **MasteringBiology** for automatically graded tutorials and questions that you can assign to your students, plus Instructor Resources.

49

Nervous Systems

▲ Figure 49.1 How do scientists identify individual neurons in the brain?

Command and Control Center

What happens in your brain when you solve a math problem or listen to music? Answering such a question was for a long time nearly unimaginable. The human brain contains an estimated 10^{11} (100 billion) neurons. Interconnecting these brain cells are circuits more complex than those of even the most powerful supercomputers. However, thanks in part to several exciting new technologies, scientists have begun to explore the cellular mechanisms that underlie thought and emotion.

One breakthrough came with the development of powerful imaging techniques that reveal activity in the working brain. Researchers can monitor multiple areas of the human brain while a subject is performing various tasks, such as speaking, looking at pictures, or forming a mental image of a person's face. They can use these techniques to look for a correlation between a particular task and activity in specific brain areas.

A more recent advance in exploring the brain relies on a method for expressing random combinations of colored proteins in brain cells—such that each cell shows up in a different color. The result is a "brainbow" like the one in Figure 49.1, which highlights neurons in the brain of a mouse. In this image, each neuron expresses one of more than 90 different color combinations of four fluorescent proteins.

Using the brainbow technology, neuroscientists hope to develop detailed maps of the connections that transfer information between particular regions of the brain.

In this chapter, we'll discuss the organization and evolution of animal nervous systems, exploring how groups of neurons function in specialized circuits dedicated to specific tasks. Next we'll focus on specialization in regions of the vertebrate brain. We'll then turn to the ways in which brain activity makes information storage and organization possible. Finally, we'll consider several disorders of the nervous system that are the subject of intense research today.

CONCEPT 49.1

Nervous systems consist of circuits of neurons and supporting cells

The ability to sense and react originated billions of years ago in prokaryotes, enhancing survival and reproductive success in changing environments. Later in evolution, modification of simple recognition and response processes provided a basis for communication between cells in an animal body. By the time of the Cambrian explosion more than 500 million years ago (see Chapter 32), specialized systems of neurons had appeared that enable animals to sense their surroundings and respond rapidly.

Hydras, jellies, and other cnidarians are the simplest animals with nervous systems. In most cnidarians, interconnected neurons form a diffuse *nerve net* (Figure 49.2a), which controls the contraction and expansion of the gastrovascular cavity. In more complex animals, the axons of multiple neurons are often bundled together, forming **nerves**. These fibrous structures channel and organize information flow along specific routes through the nervous system. For example, sea stars have a set of radial nerves connecting to a central nerve ring (Figure 49.2b). Within each arm of a sea star, the radial nerve is linked to a nerve net from which it receives input and to which it sends signals that control muscle contraction.

Animals that have elongated, bilaterally symmetrical bodies have even more specialized nervous systems. The organization of neurons in such animals reflects *cephalization*, an evolutionary trend toward a clustering of sensory neurons and interneurons at the anterior (front) end of the body. These anterior neurons communicate with cells elsewhere in the body, including neurons located in one or more nerve cords extending toward the posterior (rear) end.

As you learned in Concept 48.1, in many animals neurons that carry out integration form a **central nervous system (CNS)**, and neurons that carry information into and out of the CNS form a **peripheral nervous system (PNS)**. In nonsegmented worms, such as the planarian in Figure 49.2c, a small brain and longitudinal nerve cords constitute the simplest

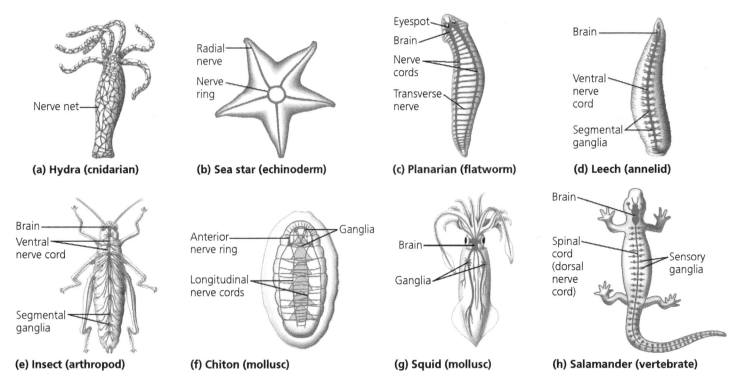

(a) Hydra (cnidarian) (b) Sea star (echinoderm) (c) Planarian (flatworm) (d) Leech (annelid)

(e) Insect (arthropod) (f) Chiton (mollusc) (g) Squid (mollusc) (h) Salamander (vertebrate)

▲ Figure 49.2 Nervous system organization. (a) A hydra contains individual neurons (purple) organized in a diffuse nerve net. (b–h) Animals with more sophisticated nervous systems contain groups of neurons (blue) organized into nerves and often ganglia and a brain.

clearly defined CNS. In some nonsegmented worms, the entire nervous system is constructed from only a small number of cells, as in the case of the nematode *Caenorhabditis elegans*. In this species, an adult worm (hermaphrodite) has exactly 302 neurons, no more and no fewer. More complex invertebrates, such as segmented worms (annelids; Figure 49.2d) and arthropods (Figure 49.2e), have many more neurons. Their behavior is regulated by more complicated brains and by ventral nerve cords containing **ganglia**, segmentally arranged clusters of neurons.

Within an animal group, nervous system organization often correlates with lifestyle. Among the molluscs, for example, sessile and slow-moving species, such as clams and chitons, have relatively simple sense organs and little or no cephalization (Figure 49.2f). In contrast, active predatory molluscs, such as octopuses and squids (Figure 49.2g), have the most sophisticated nervous systems of any invertebrates, rivaling those of some vertebrates. With their large, image-forming eyes and a brain containing millions of neurons, octopuses can learn to discriminate between visual patterns and to perform complex tasks.

In vertebrates (Figure 49.2h), the brain and the spinal cord form the CNS; nerves and ganglia are the key components of the PNS. Regional specialization is a hallmark of both systems, as we will see throughout this chapter.

Glia

As discussed in Chapter 48, the nervous systems of vertebrates and most invertebrates include not only neurons but also **glial cells**, or **glia**. Some examples of glia are the Schwann cells that produce the myelin sheaths surrounding axons in the PNS and oligodendrocytes, their counterparts in the CNS. Figure 49.3 illustrates the major types of glia in the adult vertebrate and provides an overview of the ways in which they nourish, support, and regulate the functioning of neurons.

One of the essential roles of glia is in nervous system development. In embryos, cells called *radial glia* form tracks along which newly formed neurons migrate from the neural tube, the structure that gives rise to the CNS (see Figure 47.14). Later, glia called **astrocytes** participate in formation of the *blood-brain barrier*, a specialization of the walls of brain capillaries that restricts the entry of most substances from the blood into the CNS.

Both radial glia and astrocytes can act as stem cells, which retain the ability to divide indefinitely. While some of their progeny remain undifferentiated, others differentiate into specialized cells. Studies with mice reveal that stem cells in the brain give rise to neurons that mature, migrate to particular locations, and become incorporated into the

Ependymal cells line the ventricles of the brain (see Figure 49.5) and have cilia that promote circulation of the cerebrospinal fluid.

Astrocytes (from the Greek *astron*, star), found in the CNS, facilitate information transfer at synapses and in some instances release neurotransmitters. Astrocytes next to active neurons cause nearby blood vessels to dilate, increasing blood flow and enabling the neurons to obtain oxygen and glucose more quickly. Astrocytes also regulate extracellular concentrations of ions and neurotransmitters.

Oligodendrocytes myelinate axons in the CNS. Myelination greatly increases the conduction speed of action potentials.

Microglia are immune cells in the CNS that protect against pathogens.

Schwann cells myelinate axons in the PNS.

▲ Figure 49.3 **Glia in the vertebrate nervous system.**

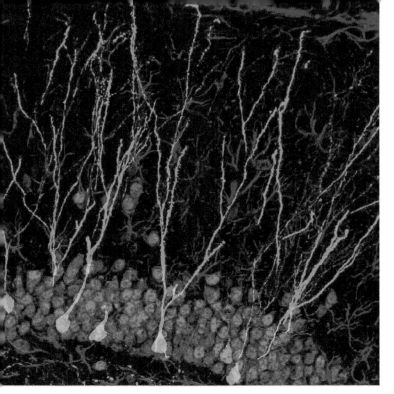

▲ **Figure 49.4 Newly born neurons in the brain of an adult mouse.** In this light micrograph, new neurons derived from adult stem cells are labeled with green fluorescent protein (GFP), and all neurons are labeled with a DNA-binding dye, colored red in this image.

circuitry of the adult nervous system **(Figure 49.4)**. Researchers are now tackling the challenge of finding a way to use neural stem cells as a means of replacing brain tissue that has ceased to function properly.

Organization of the Vertebrate Nervous System

During embryonic development in vertebrates, the central nervous system develops from the hollow dorsal nerve cord— a hallmark of chordates (see Figure 34.3). The cavity of the nerve cord gives rise to the narrow **central canal** of the spinal cord as well as the *ventricles* of the brain **(Figure 49.5)**. Both

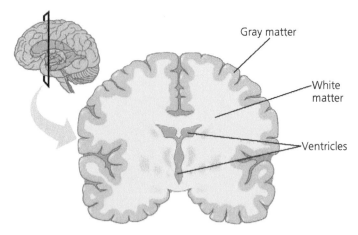

▲ **Figure 49.5 Ventricles, gray matter, and white matter.** Ventricles deep in the brain's interior contain cerebrospinal fluid. Most of the gray matter is on the brain surface, surrounding the white matter.

the canal and ventricles fill with *cerebrospinal fluid,* which is formed in the brain by filtration of arterial blood. The cerebrospinal fluid circulates slowly through the ventricles and central canal and then drains into the veins, supplying the CNS with nutrients and hormones and carrying away wastes.

In addition to these fluid-filled spaces, the brain and spinal cord contain gray matter and white matter (see Figure 49.5). **Gray matter** is primarily made up of neuron cell bodies. **White matter** consists mainly of bundled axons. In the spinal cord, white matter makes up the outer layer, consistent with its function in linking the CNS to sensory and motor neurons of the PNS. In the brain, white matter is predominantly in the interior, where signaling between neurons functions in learning, feeling emotions, processing sensory information, and generating commands.

In vertebrates, the spinal cord runs lengthwise inside the vertebral column, known as the spine **(Figure 49.6)**. The spinal cord conveys information to and from the brain and generates basic patterns of locomotion. It also acts independently of the brain as part of the simple nerve circuits that produce **reflexes**, the body's automatic responses to certain stimuli.

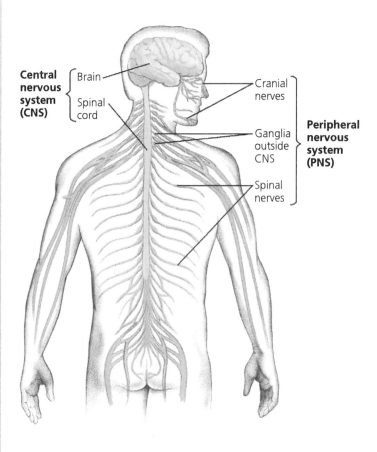

▲ **Figure 49.6 The vertebrate nervous system.** The central nervous system consists of the brain and spinal cord (yellow). Left-right pairs of cranial nerves, spinal nerves, and ganglia make up most of the peripheral nervous system (dark gold).

▶ **Figure 49.7 The knee-jerk reflex.** Many neurons are involved in this reflex, but for simplicity, only a few neurons are shown.

MAKE CONNECTIONS *Using the nerve signals to the hamstring and quadriceps in this reflex as an example, propose a model for regulation of smooth muscle activity in the esophagus during the swallowing reflex (see Figure 41.10).*

1 The reflex is initiated artificially by tapping the tendon connected to the quadriceps muscle.

2 Sensors detect a sudden stretch in the quadriceps, and **sensory neurons** convey the information to the spinal cord.

3 In response to signals from the sensory neurons, **motor neurons** convey signals to the quadriceps, causing it to contract and jerking the lower leg forward.

Cell body of sensory neuron in dorsal root ganglion

Gray matter   White matter

Quadriceps muscle

Spinal cord (cross section)

Hamstring muscle

5 Motor neurons that lead to the hamstring muscle are inhibited by the interneurons. This inhibition prevents contraction of the hamstring, which would resist the action of the quadriceps.

4 Interneurons in the spinal cord also receive signals from sensory neurons.

Key   —● Sensory neuron   —● Motor neuron   —● Interneuron

A reflex protects the body by providing a rapid, involuntary response to a particular stimulus. For example, if you accidentally put your hand on a hot burner, your hand begins to jerk back before your brain processes pain. Similarly, the knee-jerk reflex protects you when you pick up an unexpectedly heavy object. If your legs buckle, the tension across your knees triggers contraction of your thigh muscle (quadriceps), helping you stay upright and support the load. During a physical exam, your doctor may trigger the knee-jerk reflex with a triangular mallet to help assess nervous system function **(Figure 49.7)**.

The Peripheral Nervous System

The PNS transmits information to and from the CNS and plays a large role in regulating both an animal's movement and its internal environment **(Figure 49.8)**. Sensory information reaches the CNS along PNS neurons designated as *afferent* (from the Latin, meaning "to carry toward"). Following information processing within the CNS, instructions then travel to muscles, glands, and endocrine cells along PNS neurons designated as *efferent* (from the Latin, meaning "to carry away"). Most nerves contain both afferent and efferent neurons.

The PNS has two efferent components: the motor system and the autonomic nervous system (see Figure 49.8). The **motor system** consists of neurons that carry signals to skeletal muscles. Motor control can be voluntary, as when you raise your hand to ask a question, or involuntary, as in the knee-jerk reflex controlled by the spinal cord. In contrast, regulation of smooth and cardiac muscles by the **autonomic nervous system** is generally involuntary. The three divisions of the autonomic nervous system—sympathetic, parasympathetic, and enteric—together control the organs of the digestive, cardiovascular, excretory, and endocrine systems. For example, networks of neurons that form the **enteric division** of the autonomic nervous system are active in the digestive tract, pancreas, and gallbladder.

CENTRAL NERVOUS SYSTEM (information processing)

PERIPHERAL NERVOUS SYSTEM

Afferent neurons   Efferent neurons

Sensory receptors

Autonomic nervous system   Motor system

Control of skeletal muscle

Internal and external stimuli

Sympathetic division   Parasympathetic division   Enteric division

Control of smooth muscles, cardiac muscles, glands

▲ **Figure 49.8 Functional hierarchy of the vertebrate peripheral nervous system.**

CHAPTER 49 Nervous Systems   **1083**

The sympathetic and parasympathetic divisions of the autonomic nervous system have largely antagonistic (opposite) functions in regulating organ function (Figure 49.9). Activation of the **sympathetic division** corresponds to arousal and energy generation (the "fight-or-flight" response). For example, the heart beats faster, digestion is inhibited, the liver converts glycogen to glucose, and the adrenal medulla increases secretion of epinephrine (adrenaline). Activation of the **parasympathetic division** generally causes opposite responses that promote calming and a return to self-maintenance functions ("rest and digest"). Thus, heart rate decreases, digestion is enhanced, and glycogen production increases. However, in regulating reproductive activity, a function that is not homeostatic, the parasympathetic division complements rather than antagonizes the sympathetic division (see Figure 49.9).

The two divisions differ not only in overall function but also in organization and signals released. Parasympathetic nerves exit the CNS at the base of the brain or spinal cord and form synapses in ganglia near or within an internal organ (see Figure 49.9). In contrast, sympathetic nerves typically exit the CNS midway along the spinal cord and form synapses in ganglia located just outside of the spinal cord.

In both the sympathetic and parasympathetic divisions, the pathway for information flow frequently involves a preganglionic and a postganglionic neuron. The *preganglionic neurons*, those with cell bodies in the CNS, release acetylcholine as a neurotransmitter. In the case of the *postganglionic neurons*, those of the parasympathetic division release acetycholine, whereas their counterparts in the sympathetic division release norepinephrine. It is this difference in neurotransmitters that enables the sympathetic and parasympathetic divisions to bring about opposite effects in organs such as the lungs, heart, intestines, and bladder.

Homeostasis often relies on cooperation between the motor and autonomic nervous systems. In response to a drop in body temperature, for example, the hypothalamus signals the motor system to cause shivering, which increases heat production. At the same time, the hypothalamus signals the autonomic nervous system to constrict surface blood vessels, reducing heat loss.

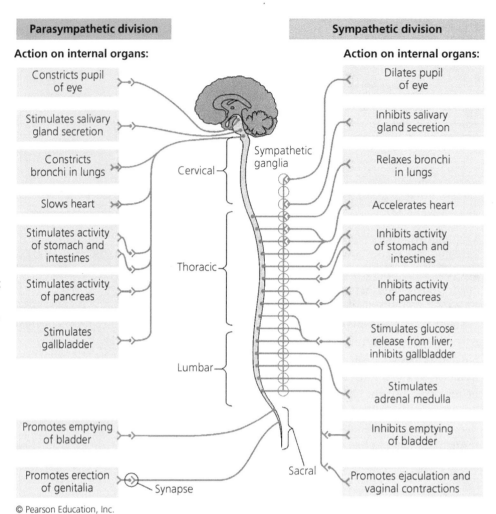

Parasympathetic division

Action on internal organs:
- Constricts pupil of eye
- Stimulates salivary gland secretion
- Constricts bronchi in lungs
- Slows heart
- Stimulates activity of stomach and intestines
- Stimulates activity of pancreas
- Stimulates gallbladder
- Promotes emptying of bladder
- Promotes erection of genitalia

Sympathetic division

Action on internal organs:
- Dilates pupil of eye
- Inhibits salivary gland secretion
- Relaxes bronchi in lungs
- Accelerates heart
- Inhibits activity of stomach and intestines
- Inhibits activity of pancreas
- Stimulates glucose release from liver; inhibits gallbladder
- Stimulates adrenal medulla
- Inhibits emptying of bladder
- Promotes ejaculation and vaginal contractions

Cervical — Thoracic — Lumbar — Sacral

Sympathetic ganglia

Synapse

© Pearson Education, Inc.

▲ Figure 49.9 **The parasympathetic and sympathetic divisions of the autonomic nervous system.** Most pathways in each division involve two neurons. The axon of the first neuron extends from a cell body in the CNS to a set of PNS neurons whose cell bodies are clustered into a ganglion (plural, *ganglia*). The axons of these PNS neurons transmit instructions to internal organs, where they form synapses with smooth muscle, cardiac muscle, or gland cells.

CONCEPT CHECK 49.1

1. Which division of the autonomic nervous system would likely be activated if a student learned that an exam she had forgotten about would start in 5 minutes? Explain your answer.

2. **WHAT IF?** Suppose a person had an accident that severed a small nerve required to move some of the fingers of the right hand. Would you also expect an effect on sensation from those fingers?

3. **MAKE CONNECTIONS** Most tissues regulated by the autonomic nervous system receive both sympathetic and parasympathetic input from postganglionic neurons. Responses are typically local. In contrast, the adrenal medulla receives input only from the sympathetic division and only from preganglionic neurons, yet responses are observed throughout the body. Explain why (see Figure 45.20).

For suggested answers, see Appendix A.

CONCEPT 49.2

The vertebrate brain is regionally specialized

We turn now to the vertebrate brain, which has three major regions: the forebrain, midbrain, and hindbrain (shown here for a ray-finned fish).

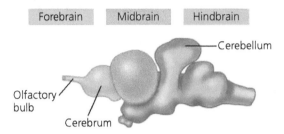

Each region is specialized in function. The **forebrain**, which contains the *olfactory bulb* and *cerebrum*, has activities that include processing of olfactory input (smells), regulation of sleep, learning, and any complex processing. The **midbrain**, located centrally in the brain, coordinates routing of sensory input. The **hindbrain**, part of which forms the *cerebellum*, controls involuntary activities, such as blood circulation, and coordinates motor activities, such as locomotion.

EVOLUTION Comparing vertebrates across a phylogenetic tree, we see that the relative sizes of particular brain regions vary **(Figure 49.10)**. Furthermore, these size differences reflect differences in the importance of particular brain functions. Consider, for example, ray-finned fishes, which explore their environment using olfaction, vision,

and a lateral line system that detects water currents, electrical stimuli, and body position. The olfactory bulb, which detects scents in the water, is relatively large in these fishes. So is the midbrain, which processes input from the visual and lateral line systems. In contrast, the cerebrum, required for complex processing and learning, is relatively small. Evolution has thus resulted in a close match of structure to function, with the size of particular brain regions correlating with their importance for that species in nervous system function and, hence, species survival and reproduction.

The correlation between the size and function of brain regions can also be observed by considering the cerebellum. Free swimming ray-finned fishes, such as the tuna, control movement in three dimensions in the open water and have a relatively large cerebellum. In comparison, the cerebellum is much smaller in species that don't swim actively, such as the lamprey.

If one compares birds and mammals with groups that diverged from the common vertebrate ancestor earlier in evolution, two trends are apparent. First, the forebrain of birds and mammals occupies a larger fraction of the brain than it does in amphibians, fishes, and other vertebrates. Second, birds and mammals have much larger brains relative to body size than do other groups. Indeed, the ratio of brain size to body weight is ten times as large for birds and mammals as for their evolutionary ancestors. These differences in both overall brain size and the relative size of the forebrain reflect the greater capacity of birds and mammals for cognition and higher-order reasoning, traits we will return to later in this chapter.

In the case of humans, it is estimated that the brain contains 100 billion neurons. How are so many cells organized into circuits and networks that can perform highly sophisticated information processing, storage, and retrieval? In addressing this question, let's begin with **Figure 49.11**, which explores the overall architecture of the human brain. You can use this figure to trace how brain structures arise during embryonic development; as a reference for their size, shape, and location in the adult brain; and as an introduction to their best-understood functions.

To learn more about how particular brain structure and brain organization overall relate to brain function in humans, we'll first consider activity cycles of the brain and the physiological basis of emotion. Then, in Concept 49.3, we'll shift our attention to regional specialization within the cerebrum.

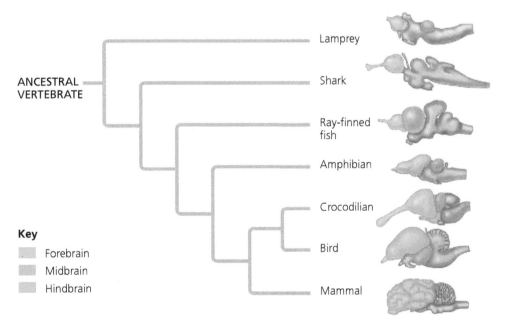

▲ **Figure 49.10 Vertebrate brain structure and evolution.** During evolution, differences arose in the relative size of the major structures common to vertebrate brains. As discussed in the text, size differences correlate with the importance of particular brain functions for particular vertebrate groups.

Exploring The Organization of the Human Brain

The brain is the most complex organ in the human body. Surrounded by the thick bones of the skull, the brain is divided into a set of distinctive structures, some of which are visible in the magnetic resonance image (MRI) of an adult's head shown at right. The diagram below traces the development of these structures in the embryo. Their major functions are explained on the facing page.

Human Brain Development

As a human embryo develops, the neural tube forms three anterior bulges—the forebrain, midbrain, and hindbrain—that together produce the adult brain. The midbrain and portions of the hindbrain give rise to the **brainstem**, a stalk that joins with the spinal cord at the base of the brain. The rest of the hindbrain gives rise to the **cerebellum**, which lies behind the brainstem. The third anterior bulge, the forebrain, develops into the diencephalon, including the neuroendocrine tissues of the brain, and the telencephalon, which becomes the **cerebrum**. Rapid, expansive growth of the telencephalon during the second and third months causes the outer portion, or cortex, of the cerebrum to extend over and around much of the rest of the brain.

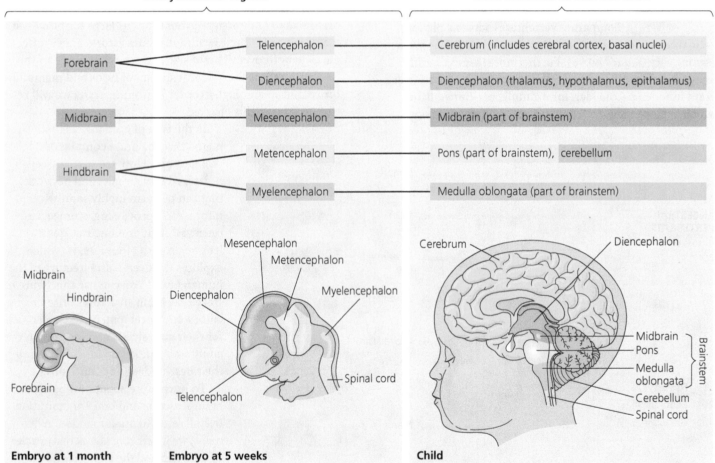

The Cerebrum

The cerebrum controls skeletal muscle contraction and is the center for learning, emotion, memory, and perception. It is divided into right and left **cerebral hemispheres**. The outer layer of the cerebrum is called the **cerebral cortex** and is vital for perception, voluntary movement, and learning. The left side of the cerebral cortex receives information from, and controls the movement of, the right side of the body, and vice versa. A thick band of axons known as the **corpus callosum** enables the right and left cerebral cortices to communicate. Deep within the white matter, clusters of neurons called *basal nuclei* serve as centers for planning and learning movement sequences. Damage to these sites during fetal development can result in cerebral palsy, a disorder resulting from a disruption in the transmission of motor commands to the muscles.

The Cerebellum

The cerebellum coordinates movement and balance and helps in learning and remembering motor skills. The cerebellum receives sensory information about the positions of the joints and the lengths of the muscles, as well as input from the auditory (hearing) and visual systems. It also monitors motor commands issued by the cerebrum. The cerebellum integrates this information as it carries out coordination and error checking during motor and perceptual functions. Hand-eye coordination is an example of cerebellar control; if the cerebellum is damaged, the eyes can follow a moving object, but they will not stop at the same place as the object. Hand movement toward the object will also be erratic.

Adult brain viewed from the rear

The Diencephalon

The diencephalon gives rise to the thalamus, hypothalamus, and epithalamus. The **thalamus** is the main input center for sensory information going to the cerebrum. Incoming information from all the senses, as well as from the cerebral cortex, is sorted in the thalamus and sent to the appropriate cerebral centers for further processing. The thalamus is formed by two masses, each roughly the size and shape of a walnut. A much smaller structure, the **hypothalamus**, constitutes a control center that includes the body's thermostat as well as the central biological clock. Through its regulation of the pituitary gland, the hypothalamus regulates hunger and thirst, plays a role in sexual and mating behaviors, and initiates the fight-or-flight response. The hypothalamus is also the source of posterior pituitary hormones and of releasing hormones that act on the anterior pituitary (see Figures 45.14 and 45.16). The *epithalamus* includes the pineal gland, the source of melatonin. It also contains one of several clusters of capillaries that generate cerebrospinal fluid from blood.

The Brainstem

The brainstem consists of the midbrain, the **pons**, and the **medulla oblongata** (commonly called the *medulla*). The midbrain receives and integrates several types of sensory information and sends it to specific regions of the forebrain. All sensory axons involved in hearing either terminate in the midbrain or pass through it on their way to the cerebrum. In addition, the midbrain coordinates visual reflexes, such as the peripheral vision reflex: The head turns toward an object approaching from the side without the brain having formed an image of the object.

A major function of the pons and medulla is to transfer information between the PNS and the midbrain and forebrain. The pons and medulla also help coordinate large-scale body movements, such as running and climbing. Most axons that carry instructions about these movements cross from one side of the CNS to the other in the medulla. As a result, the right side of the brain controls much of the movement of the left side of the body, and vice versa. An additional function of the medulla is the control of several automatic, homeostatic functions, including breathing, heart and blood vessel activity, swallowing, vomiting, and digestion. The pons also participates in some of these activities; for example, it regulates the breathing centers in the medulla.

Arousal and Sleep

If you've ever drifted off to sleep while listening to a lecture (or reading a book), you know that your attentiveness and mental alertness can change rapidly. Such transitions are regulated by the brainstem and cerebrum, which control arousal and sleep. Arousal is a state of awareness of the external world. Sleep is a state in which external stimuli are received but not consciously perceived.

Contrary to appearances, sleep is an active state, at least for the brain. By placing electrodes at multiple sites on the scalp, we can record patterns of electrical activity called brain waves in an electroencephalogram (EEG). These recordings reveal that brain wave frequencies change as the brain progresses through distinct stages of sleep.

Although sleep is essential for survival, we still know very little about its function. One hypothesis is that sleep and dreams are involved in consolidating learning and memory. Evidence supporting this hypothesis includes the finding that test subjects who are kept awake for 36 hours have a reduced ability to remember when particular events occurred, even if they first "perk up" with caffeine. Other experiments show that regions of the brain that are activated during a learning task can become active again during sleep.

Arousal and sleep are controlled in part by the *reticular formation*, a diffuse network formed primarily by neurons in the midbrain and pons (Figure 49.12). These neurons control the timing of sleep periods characterized by rapid eye movements (REMs) and by vivid dreams. Sleep is also regulated by the biological clock and by regions of the forebrain that regulate sleep intensity and duration.

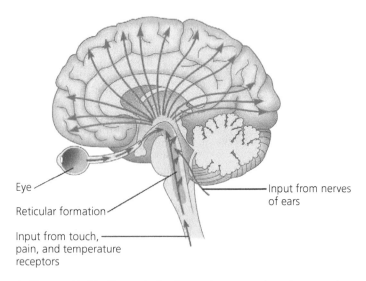

Eye

Reticular formation

Input from touch, pain, and temperature receptors

Input from nerves of ears

▲ **Figure 49.12 The reticular formation.** Once thought to consist of a single diffuse network of neurons, the reticular formation is now recognized as many distinct clusters of neurons. These clusters function in part to filter sensory input (blue arrows), blocking familiar and repetitive information that constantly enters the nervous system before sending the filtered input to the cerebral cortex (green arrows).

Key

〰 Low-frequency waves characteristic of sleep

〜 High-frequency waves characteristic of wakefulness

Location	Time: 0 hours	Time: 1 hour
Left hemisphere		
Right hemisphere		

▲ **Figure 49.13 Dolphins can be asleep and awake at the same time.** EEG recordings were made separately for the two sides of a dolphin's brain. At each time point, low-frequency activity was recorded in one hemisphere while higher-frequency activity typical of being awake was recorded in the other hemisphere.

Some animals have evolutionary adaptations that allow for substantial activity during sleep. Bottlenose dolphins, for example, swim while sleeping, rising to the surface to breathe air on a regular basis. How do they manage this feat? As in other mammals, the forebrain is physically and functionally divided into two halves, the right and left hemispheres. Noting that dolphins sleep with one eye open and one closed, researchers hypothesized that only one side of the brain is asleep at a time. EEG recordings from each hemisphere of sleeping dolphins support this hypothesis (Figure 49.13).

Biological Clock Regulation

Cycles of sleep and wakefulness are an example of a circadian rhythm, a daily cycle of biological activity. Such cycles, which occur in organisms ranging from bacteria to humans, rely on a **biological clock**, a molecular mechanism that directs periodic gene expression and cellular activity. Although biological clocks are typically synchronized to the cycles of light and dark in the environment, they can maintain a roughly 24-hour cycle even in the absence of environmental cues (see Figure 40.9). For example, in a constant environment humans exhibit a sleep/wake cycle of 24.2 hours, with very little variation among individuals.

What normally links an animal's biological clock to environmental cycles of light and dark? In mammals, circadian rhythms are coordinated by a group of neurons in the hypothalamus called the **suprachiasmatic nucleus**, or **SCN**. (Certain clusters of neurons in the CNS are referred to as "nuclei.") In response to sensory information from the eyes, the SCN acts as a pacemaker, synchronizing the biological clock in cells throughout the body to the natural cycles of day length. In the Scientific Skills Exercise, you can interpret data from an experiment and propose experiments to test the role of the SCN in hamster circadian rhythms.

Designing an Experiment Using Genetic Mutants

Does the SCN Control the Circadian Rhythm in Hamsters?
By surgically removing the SCN from laboratory mammals, scientists demonstrated that the SCN is required for circadian rhythms. Those experiments did not, however, reveal whether circadian rhythms originate in the SCN. To answer this question, researchers performed an SCN transplant experiment on wild-type and mutant hamsters (*Mesocricetus auratus*). Whereas wild-type hamsters have a circadian cycle lasting about 24 hours in the absence of external cues, hamsters homozygous for the τ (tau) mutation have a cycle lasting only about 20 hours. In this exercise, you will evaluate the design of this experiment and propose additional experiments to gain further insight.

How the Experiment Was Done
The researchers surgically removed the SCN from wild-type and τ hamsters. Several weeks later, each of these hamsters received a transplant of an SCN from a hamster of the opposite genotype. To determine the periodicity of rhythmic activity for the hamsters before the surgery and after the transplants, the researchers measured activity levels over a three-week period. They plotted the data collected for each day in the manner shown in Figure 40.9a and then calculated the circadian cycle period.

Data from the Experiment
In 80% of the hamsters in which the SCN had been removed, transplanting an SCN from another hamster restored rhythmic activity. For hamsters in which an SCN transplant restored a circadian rhythm, the net effect of the two procedures (SCN removal and replacement) on the circadian cycle period is graphed at the upper right. Each red line connects the two data points for an individual hamster.

Interpret the Data
1. In a controlled experiment, researchers manipulate one variable at a time. What was the variable manipulated in this study? Why did the researchers use more than one hamster for each procedure? What traits of the individual hamsters would likely have been held constant among the treatment groups?
2. For the wild-type hamsters that received τ SCN transplants, what would have been an appropriate experimental control?

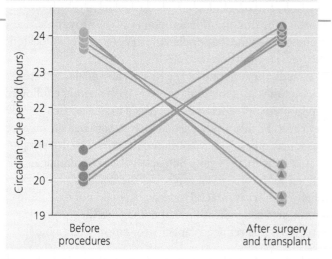

3. What general trends does the graph above reveal about the circadian cycle period of the transplant recipients? Do the trends differ for the wild-type and τ recipients? Based on these data, what can you conclude about the role of the SCN in determining the period of the circadian rhythm?
4. In 20% of the hamsters, there was no restoration of rhythmic activity following the SCN transplant. What are some possible reasons for this finding? Do you think you can be confident of your conclusion about the role of the SCN based on data from 80% of the hamsters?
5. Suppose that researchers identified a mutant hamster that lacked rhythmic activity; that is, its circadian activity cycle had no regular pattern. Propose SCN transplant experiments using such a mutant along with (a) wild-type and (b) τ hamsters. Predict the results of those experiments in light of your conclusion in question 3.

(MB) A version of this Scientific Skills Exercise can be assigned in MasteringBiology.

Data from M. R. Ralph et al., Transplanted suprachiasmatic nucleus determines circadian period, *Science* 247:975–978 (1990). Reprinted with permission from AAAS.

Emotions

Whereas a single structure in the brain controls the biological clock, the generation and experience of emotions depend on many brain structures, including the amygdala, hippocampus, and parts of the thalamus. As shown in **Figure 49.14**, these structures border the brainstem in mammals and are therefore called the *limbic system* (from the Latin *limbus*, border).

Generating emotion and experiencing emotion often require interactions between different regions of the brain. For example, laughing and crying both involve the limbic system interacting with sensory areas of the forebrain. Similarly, structures in the forebrain attach emotional "feelings" to survival-related functions controlled by the brainstem, including aggression, feeding, and sexuality.

Emotional experiences are often stored as memories that can be recalled by similar circumstances. For example, a situation that causes you to remember a frightening event

▲ **Figure 49.14** The limbic system in the human brain.

can trigger a faster heart rate, sweating, and mental state of fear, even if there is currently nothing scary or threatening in your surroundings. The brain structure that is most important for this emotional memory is the **amygdala**, an almond-shaped mass of nuclei (clusters of neurons) located near the base of the cerebrum.

To study the function of the human amygdala, researchers sometimes present adult subjects with an image followed by an unpleasant experience, such as a mild electrical shock. After several trials, study participants experience *autonomic arousal*—as measured by increased heart rate or sweating—if they see the image again. Subjects with brain damage confined to the amygdala can recall the image because their explicit memory is intact. However, they do not exhibit autonomic arousal, indicating that damage to the amygdala has resulted in a reduced capacity for emotional memory.

Functional Imaging of the Brain

Today, the amygdala and other brain structures are being probed and analyzed with functional imaging methods. The first widely used technique was positron-emission tomography (PET), in which injection of radioactive glucose enables a display of metabolic activity. Today, many studies rely on functional magnetic resonance imaging (fMRI). In fMRI, a subject lies with his or her head in the center of a large, doughnut-shaped magnet. Brain activity in a region is detected by changes in the local oxygen concentration. By scanning the brain while the subject performs a task, such as forming a mental image of a person's face, researchers can correlate particular tasks with activity in specific brain areas.

In one experiment using fMRI, researchers mapped brain activity while subjects listened to music that they described as happy or sad (**Figure 49.15**). Listening to happy music led to increased activity in the nucleus accumbens, a brain

Nucleus accumbens   Amygdala

Happy music   **Sad music**

▲ **Figure 49.15 Functional imaging in the working brain.** Functional magnetic resonance imaging (fMRI) was used to reveal brain activity associated with music that listeners described as happy or sad.

WHAT IF? *In the experiment that produced the images shown above, some regions of the brain were active under both conditions. What function might such regions carry out?*

structure important for the perception of pleasure. In contrast, subjects who heard sad music had increased activity in the amygdala.

The range of applications of fMRI includes monitoring recovery from stroke, mapping abnormalities in migraine headaches, and increasing the effectiveness of brain surgery. This technique has even been used to explore sex-based differences in the CNS, demonstrating, for instance, that cerebral blood flow is higher on average in women than in men.

CONCEPT CHECK **49.2**

1. When you wave your right hand, what part of your brain initiates the action?

2. People who are inebriated have difficulty touching their nose with their eyes closed. Which brain region does this observation indicate is one of those impaired by alcohol?

3. **WHAT IF?** Suppose you examine two groups of individuals with CNS damage. In one group, the damage has resulted in a coma (a prolonged state of unconsciousness). In the other group, it has caused paralysis (a loss of skeletal muscle function throughout the body). Relative to the position of the midbrain and pons, where is the likely site of damage in each group? Explain.

For suggested answers, see Appendix A.

CONCEPT 49.3

The cerebral cortex controls voluntary movement and cognitive functions

We turn now to the cerebrum, the part of the brain essential for language, cognition, memory, consciousness, and awareness of our surroundings. As shown in Figure 49.11, the cerebrum is the largest structure in the human brain. Like the brain overall, it exhibits regional specialization. For the most part, cognitive functions reside in the cortex, the outer layer of the cerebrum. Within the cortex, *sensory areas* receive and process sensory information, *association areas* integrate the information, and *motor areas* transmit instructions to other parts of the body.

In discussing the location of particular functions in the cerebral cortex, neurobiologists often use four regions, or *lobes*, as physical landmarks. As shown in **Figure 49.16**, each side of the cerebral cortex has a frontal, temporal, occipital, and parietal lobe (each is named for a nearby bone of the skull).

Information Processing

Broadly speaking, there are two sources of sensory input to the human cerebral cortex. Some sensory input comes from groups of receptors clustered in dedicated sensory organs, such as the eyes and nose. Other sensory input originates

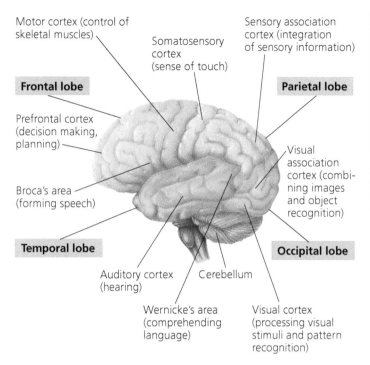

Motor cortex (control of skeletal muscles)

Somatosensory cortex (sense of touch)

Sensory association cortex (integration of sensory information)

Frontal lobe

Parietal lobe

Prefrontal cortex (decision making, planning)

Visual association cortex (combining images and object recognition)

Broca's area (forming speech)

Temporal lobe

Occipital lobe

Auditory cortex (hearing)

Cerebellum

Wernicke's area (comprehending language)

Visual cortex (processing visual stimuli and pattern recognition)

▲ **Figure 49.16 The human cerebral cortex.** Each side of the cerebral cortex is divided into four lobes, and each lobe has specialized functions, some of which are listed here. Some areas on the left side of the brain (shown here) have different functions from those on the right side (not shown).

in individual receptors in the hands, scalp, and elsewhere in the body. These somatic sensory, or *somatosensory*, receptors (from the Greek *soma*, body) provide information about touch, pain, pressure, temperature, and the position of muscles and limbs.

▶ **Figure 49.17 Body part representation in the primary motor and primary somatosensory cortices.** In these cross-sectional maps of the cortices, the cortical surface area devoted to each body part is represented by the relative size of that part in the cartoons.

Most sensory information coming into the cortex is directed via the thalamus to primary sensory areas within the brain lobes. Information received at the primary sensory areas is passed along to nearby association areas, which process particular features in the sensory input. In the occipital lobe, for instance, some groups of neurons in the primary visual area are specifically sensitive to rays of light oriented in a particular direction. In the visual association area, information related to such features is combined in a region dedicated to recognizing complex images, such as faces.

Once processed, sensory information passes to the prefrontal cortex, which helps plan actions and movement. The cerebral cortex may then generate motor commands that cause particular behaviors—moving a limb or saying hello, for example. These commands consist of action potentials produced by neurons in the motor cortex, which lies at the rear of the frontal lobe (see Figure 49.16). The action potentials travel along axons to the brainstem and spinal cord, where they excite motor neurons, which in turn excite skeletal muscle cells.

In the somatosensory cortex and motor cortex, neurons are arranged according to the part of the body that generates the sensory input or receives the motor commands **(Figure 49.17)**. For example, neurons that process sensory information from the legs and feet lie in the region of the somatosensory cortex closest to the midline. Neurons that control muscles in the legs and feet are located in the corresponding region of the motor cortex. Notice in Figure 49.17 that the cortical surface area devoted to each body part is not proportional to the size of the part. Instead, surface area correlates with the extent of neuronal control needed

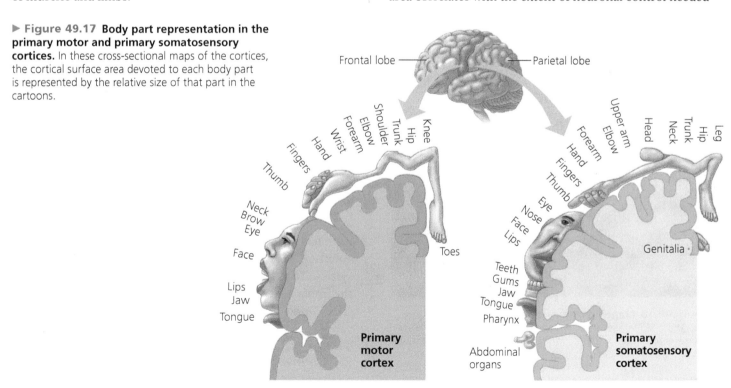

Frontal lobe

Parietal lobe

Thumb
Fingers
Hand
Wrist
Forearm
Elbow
Shoulder
Trunk
Hip
Knee

Neck
Brow
Eye

Face

Lips
Jaw

Tongue

Toes

Primary motor cortex

Upper arm
Forearm
Hand
Fingers
Thumb
Elbow
Head
Neck
Trunk
Hip
Leg

Eye
Nose
Face
Lips

Teeth
Gums
Jaw
Tongue
Pharynx

Abdominal organs

Genitalia

Primary somatosensory cortex

(for the motor cortex) or with the number of sensory neurons that extend axons to that part (for the somatosensory cortex). Thus, the surface area of the motor cortex devoted to the face is much larger than that devoted to the trunk, reflecting the extensive involvement of facial muscles in communication.

Although our focus here is on humans, it is worth noting that the processing sites for sensory information vary among vertebrates. In ray-finned fishes, for example, the relatively large midbrain (see Figure 49.10) serves as the primary center for processing and responding to visual stimuli. Such differences reflect a recognizable evolutionary trend: Following the vertebrate phylogenetic tree from sharks to ray-finned fishes, amphibians, reptiles, and finally mammals, one observes a steadily increasing role for the forebrain in processing sensory information.

Language and Speech

The mapping of cognitive functions within the cortex began in the 1800s when physicians studied the effects of damage to particular regions of the cortex by injuries, strokes, or tumors. Pierre Broca conducted postmortem (after death) examinations of patients who had been able to understand language but unable to speak. He discovered that many had defects in a small region of the left frontal lobe, now known as *Broca's area*. Karl Wernicke found that damage to a posterior portion of the left temporal lobe, now called *Wernicke's area*, abolished the ability to comprehend speech but not the ability to speak. PET studies have now confirmed activity in Broca's area during speech generation and Wernicke's area when speech is heard **(Figure 49.18)**.

▲ **Figure 49.18 Mapping language areas in the cerebral cortex.** These PET images show regions with different activity levels in one person's brain during four activities, all related to speech. Increases in activity are seen in Wernicke's area when hearing words, Broca's area when speaking words, the visual cortex when seeing words, and the frontal lobe when generating words (without reading them).

Lateralization of Cortical Function

Both Broca's area and Wernicke's area reside in the left cortical hemisphere, reflecting a greater role with regard to language for the left side of the cerebrum than for the right side. The left hemisphere is also more adept at math and logical operations. In contrast, the right hemisphere appears to be dominant in the recognition of faces and patterns, spatial relations, and nonverbal thinking. The establishment of these differences in hemisphere function is called **lateralization**.

The two cortical hemispheres normally exchange information through the fibers of the corpus callosum (see Figure 49.11). Severing this connection (a treatment of last resort for the most extreme forms of epilepsy, a seizure disorder) results in a "split-brain" effect. In such patients, the two hemispheres function independently. For example, they cannot read even a familiar word that appears only in their left field of vision: The sensory information that travels from the left field of vision to the right hemisphere cannot reach the language centers in the left hemisphere.

Frontal Lobe Function

In 1848, a horrific accident pointed to the role of the prefrontal cortex in temperament and decision making. Phineas Gage was the foreman of a railroad construction crew when an explosion drove an iron rod through his head. The rod, which was more than 3 cm in diameter at one end, entered his skull just below his left eye and exited through the top of his head, damaging large portions of his frontal lobe. Gage recovered, but his personality changed dramatically. He became emotionally detached, impatient, and erratic in his behavior.

Some frontal lobe tumors cause symptoms similar to those of Gage's brain injury. Intellect and memory seem intact, but decision making is flawed and emotional responses are diminished. In the 1900s, the same problems resulted from frontal lobotomy, a surgical procedure that severs the connection between the prefrontal cortex and the limbic system. Together, these observations provide evidence that the frontal lobes have a substantial influence on what are called "executive functions."

Once a common treatment for severe behavioral disorders, frontal lobotomy is no longer in use. Instead, behavioral disorders are typically treated with medications, as discussed later in this chapter.

Evolution of Cognition in Vertebrates

EVOLUTION In nearly all vertebrates, the brain has the same basic structures (see Figure 49.10). Given this uniform organization, how did a capacity for advanced cognition, the perception and reasoning that constitute knowledge, evolve in certain species? One hypothesis is that higher-order reasoning required evolution of an extensively convoluted cerebral cortex, as is found in humans, other primates, and cetaceans (whales, dolphins, and porpoises). Indeed, in humans the cerebral cortex accounts for about 80% of total brain mass.

Birds, on the other hand, lack a convoluted cerebral cortex and were therefore thought to have much lower intellectual capacity than primates and cetaceans. However, experiments in recent years have refuted this idea. Western scrub jays (*Aphelocoma californica*) can remember which food items they hid first. New Caledonian crows (*Corvus moneduloides*) are highly skilled at making and using tools, an ability otherwise well documented only for humans and some other apes. Furthermore, African gray parrots (*Psittacus erithacus*) understand numerical and abstract concepts, such as "same" and "different" and "none."

The anatomical basis for sophisticated information processing in birds appears to be a clustered organization of neurons within the *pallium*, the top or outer portion of the brain **(Figure 49.19a)**. This arrangement is different from that in the human cerebral cortex, where six parallel layers of neurons are arranged tangential to the brain surface **(Figure 49.19b)**. Thus, evolution has resulted in two types of outer brain organization in vertebrates that support complex and flexible brain function.

How did the bird pallium and human cerebral cortex arise during evolution? The current consensus is that the common ancestor of birds and mammals had a pallium in which neurons were organized into nuclei, as is still found in birds. Early in mammalian evolution, this clustered organization was transformed into a layered one. However, connectivity was maintained such that, for example, the thalamus relays sensory input relating to sights, sounds, and touch to the pallium in birds and the cerebral cortex in mammals.

Sophisticated information processing depends not only on the overall organization of a brain but also on the very small-scale changes that enable learning and encode memory. We'll turn to these changes in the context of humans in the next section.

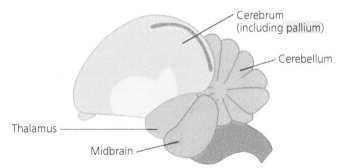

(a) Songbird brain

Cerebrum (including pallium)
Cerebellum
Thalamus
Midbrain

(b) Human brain

Cerebrum (including cerebral cortex)
Thalamus
Midbrain
Cerebellum

▲ **Figure 49.19 Comparison of regions for higher cognition in avian and human brains.** Although structurally different, the pallium of a songbird brain (a) and the cerebral cortex of the human brain (b) play similar roles in higher cognitive activities and make many similar connections with other brain structures.

CONCEPT CHECK **49.3**

1. How can studying individuals with damage to a particular brain region provide insight into the normal function of that region?

2. How do the functions of Broca's area and Wernicke's area each relate to the activity of the surrounding cortex?

3. **WHAT IF?** If a woman with a severed corpus callosum viewed a photograph of a familiar face, first in her left field of vision and then in her right field, why would she find it difficult to put a name to the face?

For suggested answers, see Appendix A.

CONCEPT 49.4

Changes in synaptic connections underlie memory and learning

During embryonic development, regulated gene expression and signal transduction establish the overall structure of the nervous system (see Chapter 47). Two processes then dominate the remaining development and remodeling of the nervous system. The first is a competition among neurons for survival. Neurons compete for growth-supporting factors, which are produced in limited quantities by tissues that direct neuron growth. Cells that don't reach the proper locations fail to receive such factors and undergo programmed cell death. The competition is so severe that half of the neurons formed in the embryo are eliminated. The net effect is the preferential survival of neurons that are located properly within the nervous system.

Synapse elimination is the second major process that shapes the nervous system. A developing neuron forms numerous synapses, more than are required for its proper function. The activity of that neuron then stabilizes some synapses and destabilizes others. By the end of embryonic development, more than half of all synapses have been eliminated.

Together, neuron death and synapse elimination set up the basic network of cells and connections within the nervous system required throughout life.

Neuronal Plasticity

Although the overall organization of the CNS is established during embryonic development, the connections between neurons can be modified. This capacity for the nervous system to be remodeled, especially in response to its own activity, is called **neuronal plasticity**.

Much of the reshaping of the nervous system occurs at synapses. When the activity of a synapse coincides with that of other synapses, changes may occur that reinforce that synaptic connection. Conversely, when the activity of a synapse fails to correlate in this way with that of other synapses, the synaptic connection sometimes becomes weaker. In this way, synapses belonging to circuits that link information in useful ways are maintained, whereas those that convey bits of information lacking any context are lost.

Figure 49.20a illustrates how activity-dependent events can result in either the addition or loss of a synapse. If you think of signals in the nervous system as traffic on a highway, such changes are comparable to adding or removing an entrance ramp. The net effect is to increase signaling between particular pairs of neurons and decrease signaling between other pairs. As shown in **Figure 49.20b**, changes can also strengthen or weaken signaling at a synapse. In our traffic analogy, this would be equivalent to widening or narrowing an entrance ramp.

Research indicates that *autism*, a developmental disorder that first appears early in childhood, involves a disruption of activity-dependent remodeling at synapses. Children affected with autism display impaired communication and social interaction, as well as stereotyped and repetitive behaviors.

Although the underlying causes of autism are unknown, there is a strong genetic contribution to this and related disorders. Extensive research has ruled out a link to vaccine preservatives, once proposed as a potential risk factor. Further understanding of the autism-associated disruption in synaptic plasticity may help efforts to better understand and treat this disorder.

Memory and Learning

Neuronal plasticity is essential to the formation of memories. We are constantly checking what is happening against what just happened. We hold information for a time in **short-term**

(a) Connections between neurons are strengthened or weakened in response to activity. High-level activity at the synapse of the postsynaptic neuron with presynaptic neuron N_1 leads to recruitment of additional axon terminals from that neuron. Lack of activity at the synapse with presynaptic neuron N_2 leads to loss of functional connections with that neuron.

(b) If two synapses on the same postsynaptic cell are often active at the same time, the strength of the postsynaptic response may increase at both synapses.

▲ **Figure 49.20 Neuronal plasticity.** Synaptic connections can change over time, depending on the activity level at the synapse.

memory and then release it if it becomes irrelevant. If we wish to retain knowledge of a name, phone number, or other fact, the mechanisms of **long-term memory** are activated. If we later need to recall the name or number, we fetch it from long-term memory and return it to short-term memory.

Both short-term and long-term memory involve the storage of information in the cerebral cortex. In short-term memory, this information is accessed via temporary links formed in the hippocampus. When memories are made long-term, the links in the hippocampus are replaced by connections within the cerebral cortex itself. As discussed earlier, some of this consolidation of memory is thought to occur during sleep. Furthermore, the reactivation of the hippocampus that is required for memory consolidation likely forms the basis for at least some of our dreams.

According to our current understanding of memory, the hippocampus is essential for acquiring new long-term memories but not for maintaining them. This hypothesis readily explains the symptoms of some individuals who suffer damage to the hippocampus: They cannot form any new lasting memories but can freely recall events from before their injury. In effect, their lack of normal hippocampal function traps them in their past.

What evolutionary advantage might be offered by organizing short-term and long-term memories differently? One hypothesis is that the delay in forming connections in the cerebral cortex allows long-term memories to be integrated gradually into the existing store of knowledge and experience, providing a basis for more meaningful associations. Consistent with this hypothesis, the transfer of information from short-term to long-term memory is enhanced by the association of new data with data previously learned and stored in long-term memory. For example, it's easier to learn a new card game if you already have "card sense" from playing other card games.

Motor skills, such as tying your shoes or writing, are usually learned by repetition. You can perform these skills without consciously recalling the individual steps required to do these tasks correctly. Learning skills and procedures, such as those required to ride a bicycle, appears to involve cellular mechanisms very similar to those responsible for brain growth and development. In such cases, neurons actually make new connections. In contrast, memorizing phone numbers, facts, and places—which can be very rapid and may require only one exposure to the relevant item—may rely mainly on changes in the strength of existing neuronal connections. Next we will consider one way that such changes in strength can take place.

Long-Term Potentiation

In searching for the physiological basis of memory, researchers have concentrated their attention on processes that can alter a synaptic connection, making the flow of communication either more efficient or less efficient. We will focus here on **long-term potentiation (LTP)**, a lasting increase in the strength of synaptic transmission.

First characterized in tissue slices from the hippocampus, LTP involves a presynaptic neuron that releases the excitatory neurotransmitter glutamate. For LTP to occur, there must be a high-frequency series of action potentials in this presynaptic neuron. In addition, these action potentials must arrive at the synaptic terminal at the same time that the postsynaptic cell receives a depolarizing stimulus at another synapse. The net effect is to strengthen a synapse whose activity coincides with that of another input (see Figure 48.17a).

LTP involves two types of glutamate receptors, each named for a molecule—NMDA or AMPA—that can be used to artificially activate that particular receptor. As shown in **Figure 49.21**, the set of receptors present on the postsynaptic membrane changes in response to an active synapse and a depolarizing stimulus. The result is LTP—a stable increase in the size of the postsynaptic potentials at the synapse. Because LTP can last for days or weeks in dissected tissue, it is thought to represent one of the fundamental processes by which memories are stored and learning takes place.

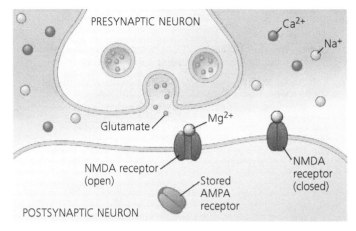

(a) Synapse prior to long-term potentiation (LTP). The NMDA glutamate receptors open in response to glutamate but are blocked by Mg^{2+}.

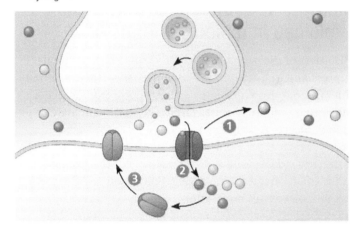

(b) Establishing LTP. Activity at nearby synapses (not shown) depolarizes the postsynaptic membrane, causing ❶ Mg^{2+} release from NMDA receptors. The unblocked receptors respond to glutamate by allowing ❷ an influx of Na^+ and Ca^{2+}. The Ca^{2+} influx triggers ❸ insertion of stored AMPA glutamate receptors into the postsynaptic membrane.

(c) Synapse exhibiting LTP. Glutamate release activates ❶ AMPA receptors that trigger ❷ depolarization. The depolarization unblocks ❸ NMDA receptors. Together, the AMPA and NMDA receptors trigger postsynaptic potentials strong enough to initiate ❹ action potentials without input from other synapses. Additional mechanisms (not shown) contribute to LTP, including receptor modification by protein kinases.

▲ Figure 49.21 **Long-term potentiation in the brain.**

CONCEPT 49.5

Many nervous system disorders can be explained in molecular terms

Disorders of the nervous system, including schizophrenia, depression, drug addiction, Alzheimer's disease, and Parkinson's disease, are a major public health problem. Together, they result in more hospitalizations in the United States than do heart disease or cancer. Until recently, hospitalization was typically the only available treatment, and many affected individuals were institutionalized for the rest of their lives. Today, many disorders that alter mood or behavior can be treated with medication, reducing average hospital stays for these disorders to only a few weeks. Many challenges remain, however, to preventing or treating nervous system disorders, especially for Alzheimer's and other diseases that lead to nervous system degeneration.

Major research efforts are under way to identify genes that cause or contribute to disorders of the nervous system. Identifying such genes offers hope for identifying causes, predicting outcomes, and developing effective treatments. For most nervous system disorders, however, genetic contributions only partially account for which individuals are affected. The other significant contribution to disease comes from environmental factors. Unfortunately, environmental contributions are typically very difficult to identify.

To distinguish between genetic and environmental variables, scientists often carry out family studies. In such studies, researchers track how family members are related genetically, which individuals are affected, and which family members grew up in the same household. These studies are especially informative when one of the affected individuals has either an identical twin or an adopted sibling who is genetically unrelated. The results of family studies indicate that certain nervous system disorders, such as schizophrenia, have a very strong genetic component. However, as shown in Figure 49.22, the disease is also subject to environmental influences, since an individual who shares 100% of his or her genes with a schizophrenic twin has only a 48% chance of developing the disorder.

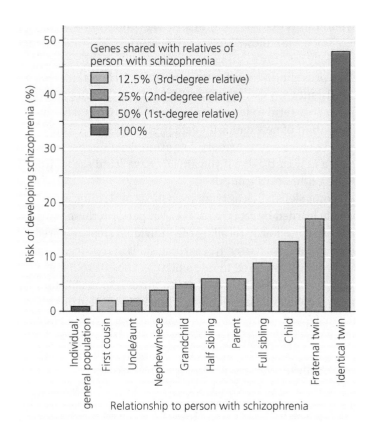

▲ **Figure 49.22 Genetic contribution to schizophrenia.** First cousins, uncles, and aunts of a person with schizophrenia have twice the risk of unrelated members of the population of developing the disease. The risks for closer relatives are many times greater.

INTERPRET THE DATA *What is the likelihood of a person developing schizophrenia if the disorder affects his or her fraternal twin? How would the likelihood change if DNA sequencing revealed that the twins shared the genetic variants that contribute to the disorder?*

Schizophrenia

Approximately 1% of the world's population suffers from **schizophrenia**, a severe mental disturbance characterized by psychotic episodes in which patients have a distorted perception of reality. People with schizophrenia typically experience hallucinations (such as "voices" that only they can hear) and delusions (for example, the idea that others are plotting to harm them). Despite the commonly held notion, schizophrenia does not necessarily result in multiple personalities. Rather, the name *schizophrenia* (from the Greek *schizo*, split, and *phren*, mind) refers to the fragmentation of what are normally integrated brain functions.

Two lines of evidence suggest that schizophrenia affects neuronal pathways that use dopamine as a neurotransmitter. First, the drug amphetamine ("speed"), which stimulates dopamine release, can produce the same set of symptoms as schizophrenia. Second, many of the drugs that alleviate the symptoms of schizophrenia block dopamine receptors. Schizophrenia may also alter glutamate signaling: The street drug "angel dust," or PCP, blocks glutamate receptors and induces strong schizophrenia-like symptoms.

Depression

Depression is a disorder characterized by depressed mood, as well as abnormalities in sleep, appetite, and energy level. Two broad forms of depressive illness are known: major depressive disorder and bipolar disorder. Individuals affected by **major depressive disorder** undergo periods—often lasting many months—during which once enjoyable activities provide no pleasure and provoke no interest. One of the most common nervous system disorders, major depression affects about one in every seven adults at some point, and twice as many women as men.

Bipolar disorder, or manic-depressive disorder, involves extreme swings of mood and affects about 1% of the world's population. The manic phase is characterized by high self-esteem, increased energy, a flow of ideas, overtalkativeness, and increased risk taking. In its milder forms, this phase is sometimes associated with great creativity, and some well-known artists, musicians, and literary figures (Vincent Van Gogh, Robert Schumann, Virginia Woolf, and Ernest Hemingway, to name a few) have had very productive periods during manic phases. The depressive phase comes with lowered ability to feel pleasure, loss of motivation, sleep disturbances, and feelings of worthlessness. These symptoms can be so severe that affected individuals attempt suicide.

Major depressive and bipolar disorders are among the nervous system disorders for which effective therapies are available. Many drugs used to treat depressive illness, including fluoxetine (Prozac), increase the activity of biogenic amines in the brain.

The Brain's Reward System and Drug Addiction

Emotions are strongly influenced by a neuronal circuit in the brain called the *reward system*. The reward system provides motivation for activities that enhance survival and reproduction, such as eating in response to hunger, drinking when thirsty, and engaging in sexual activity when aroused. As shown in **Figure 49.23**, inputs to the reward system are received by neurons in a region near the base of the brain called the *ventral tegmental area (VTA)*. When activated, these neurons release dopamine from their synaptic terminals in specific regions of the cerebrum, including the *nucleus accumbens* (see Figure 49.15).

The brain's reward system is dramatically affected by drug addiction, a disorder characterized by compulsive consumption of a drug and loss of control in limiting intake. Addictive drugs, which range from sedatives to stimulants and include alcohol, cocaine, nicotine, and heroin, enhance the activity of the dopamine pathway (see Figure 49.23). As addiction develops, there are also long-lasting changes in the reward circuitry. The result is a craving for the drug independent of any pleasure associated with consumption.

▲ **Figure 49.23 Effects of addictive drugs on the reward system of the mammalian brain.** Addictive drugs alter the transmission of signals in the pathway formed by neurons of the ventral tegmental area (VTA), a region near the base of the brain.

MAKE CONNECTIONS *What effect would you expect if you depolarized the neurons in the VTA (see Concept 48.3)? Explain.*

Laboratory animals are highly valuable in exploring how the reward system works and how addictive drugs affect its function. For example, Ulrike Heberlein, interviewed at the start of Unit Seven, has shown that the response of fruit flies to alcohol resembles that of humans in several ways, including a loss of coordination and eventually consciousness upon inebriation and a change in responsiveness to alcohol over time. Using fly genetics, she is discovering genes that carry out or control these responses. To study the effects of cocaine or amphetamine in rats, researchers outfit a cage with a dispensing system linked to a lever. In such circumstances, rats exhibit addictive behavior, continuing to self-administer the drug rather than seek food, even to the point of starvation.

As scientists expand their knowledge about the brain's reward system and the various forms of addiction, there is hope that the insights will lead to more effective prevention and treatment.

Alzheimer's Disease

Alzheimer's disease is a mental deterioration, or dementia, characterized by confusion and memory loss. Its incidence

Amyloid plaque   Neurofibrillary tangle   20 μm

▲ Figure 49.24 **Microscopic signs of Alzheimer's disease.**
A hallmark of Alzheimer's disease is the presence in brain tissue of
neurofibrillary tangles surrounding plaques made of β-amyloid (LM).

is age related, rising from about 10% at age 65 to about 35%
at age 85. The disease is progressive, with patients gradually
becoming less able to function and eventually needing to be
dressed, bathed, and fed by others. Moreover, patients with
Alzheimer's disease often lose their ability to recognize people, including their immediate family, and may treat them
with suspicion and hostility.

As shown in **Figure 49.24**, examining the brains of individuals who have died of Alzheimer's disease reveals two
characteristic features: amyloid plaques and neurofibrillary
tangles. There is also often massive shrinkage of brain tissue,
reflecting the death of neurons in many areas of the brain,
including the hippocampus and cerebral cortex.

The plaques are aggregates of β-amyloid, an insoluble
peptide that is cleaved from the extracellular portion of a
membrane protein found in neurons. Membrane enzymes,
called secretases, catalyze the cleavage, causing β-amyloid to
accumulate in plaques outside the neurons. It is these plaques
that appear to trigger the death of surrounding neurons.

The neurofibrillary tangles observed in Alzheimer's
disease are primarily made up of the tau protein. (This protein is unrelated to the tau mutation that affects circadian
rhythm in hamsters.) The tau protein normally helps assemble and maintain microtubules that transport nutrients
along axons. In Alzheimer's disease, tau undergoes changes
that cause it to bind to itself, resulting in neurofibrillary
tangles. There is evidence that changes in tau are associated
with the appearance of early-onset Alzheimer's disease, a
much less common disorder that affects relatively young
individuals.

There is currently no cure for Alzheimer's disease, but an
enormous effort has led to the recent development of drugs
that are partially effective in relieving some symptoms. Doctors are also beginning to use functional brain imaging to diagnose Alzheimer's disease in patients exhibiting early signs
of dementia.

Parkinson's Disease

Symptoms of **Parkinson's disease**, a motor disorder, include muscle tremors, poor balance, a flexed posture, and a
shuffling gait. Facial muscles become rigid, limiting the ability of patients to vary their expressions. Cognitive defects
may also develop. Like Alzheimer's disease, Parkinson's disease is a progressive brain illness and is more common with
advancing age. The incidence of Parkinson's disease is about
1% at age 65 and about 5% at age 85. In the U.S. population,
approximately 1 million people are afflicted.

Parkinson's disease involves the death of neurons in the
midbrain that normally release dopamine at synapses in the
basal nuclei. As with Alzheimer's disease, protein aggregates accumulate. Most cases of Parkinson's disease lack an
identifiable cause; however, a rare form of the disease that
appears in relatively young adults has a clear genetic basis.
Molecular studies of mutations linked to this early-onset
Parkinson's disease reveal disruption of genes required for
certain mitochondrial functions. Researchers are investigating whether mitochondrial defects also contribute to the
more common and later-onset form of the disease.

At present Parkinson's disease can be treated, but not
cured. Approaches used to manage the symptoms include
brain surgery, deep-brain stimulation, and a dopamine-
related drug, L-dopa. Unlike dopamine, L-dopa crosses the
blood-brain barrier. Within the brain, the enzyme dopa
decarboxylase converts the drug to dopamine, reducing the
severity of Parkinson's disease symptoms:

One potential cure is to implant dopamine-secreting neurons, either in the midbrain or in the basal nuclei. Laboratory studies of this strategy show promise: In rats with an
experimentally induced condition that mimics Parkinson's
disease, implanting dopamine-secreting neurons can lead to
a recovery of motor control. Whether this regenerative approach can also work in humans is one of many important
questions in modern brain research.

CONCEPT CHECK **49.5**

1. Compare Alzheimer's disease and Parkinson's disease.
2. How is dopamine activity related to schizophrenia, drug
   addiction, and Parkinson's disease?
3. **WHAT IF?** If you could detect early-stage Alzheimer's
   disease, would you expect to see brain changes that
   were similar to, although less extensive than, those seen
   in patients who have died of this disease? Explain.

For suggested answers, see Appendix A.

CONCEPT 49.1

Nervous systems consist of circuits of neurons and supporting cells (pp. 1080–1084)

- Invertebrate nervous systems range in complexity from simple nerve nets to highly centralized nervous systems having complicated brains and ventral nerve cords.

Hydra (cnidarian)   **Salamander (vertebrate)**

- In vertebrates, the **central nervous system (CNS)**, consisting of the brain and the spinal cord, integrates information, while the **nerves** of the **peripheral nervous system (PNS)** transmit sensory and motor signals between the CNS and the rest of the body. The simplest circuits control **reflex** responses, in which sensory input is linked to motor output without involvement of the brain.

- Afferent neurons carry sensory signals to the CNS. Efferent neurons function in either the **motor system**, which carries signals to skeletal muscles, or the **autonomic nervous system**, which regulates smooth and cardiac muscles. The **sympathetic** and **parasympathetic divisions** of the autonomic nervous system have antagonistic effects on a diverse set of target organs, while the **enteric division** controls the activity of many digestive organs.
- Vertebrate neurons are supported by **glia**, including **astrocytes**, oligodendrocytes, and Schwann cells. Some glia serve as stem cells that can differentiate into mature neurons.

? *How does the circuitry of a reflex facilitate a rapid response?*

CONCEPT 49.2

The vertebrate brain is regionally specialized (pp. 1085–1090)

- The cerebrum has two hemispheres, each of which consists of cortical **gray matter** overlying **white matter** and basal nuclei. The basal nuclei are important in planning and learning movements. The **pons** and **medulla oblongata** are relay stations for information traveling between the PNS and the cerebrum. The reticular formation, a network of neurons within the **brainstem**, regulates sleep and arousal. The **cerebellum** helps coordinate motor, perceptual, and cognitive functions. The **thalamus** is the main center through which sensory information passes to the **cerebrum**. The **hypothalamus** regulates homeostasis and basic survival behaviors. Within the hypothalamus, a group of neurons called the **suprachiasmatic nucleus (SCN)** acts as the pacemaker for circadian rhythms. The **amygdala** plays a key role in recognizing and recalling a number of emotions.

? *What roles do the midbrain, cerebellum, thalamus, and cerebrum play in vision and responses to visual input?*

CONCEPT 49.3

The cerebral cortex controls voluntary movement and cognitive functions (pp. 1090–1093)

- Each side of the **cerebral cortex** has four lobes—frontal, temporal, occipital, and parietal—that contain primary sensory areas and association areas. Association areas integrate information from different sensory areas. Broca's area and Wernicke's area are essential for generating and understanding language. These functions are concentrated in the left **cerebral hemisphere**, as are math and logic operations. The right hemisphere appears to be stronger at pattern recognition and nonverbal thinking.
- In the somatosensory cortex and the motor cortex, neurons are distributed according to the part of the body that generates sensory input or receives motor commands.
- Primates and cetaceans, which are capable of higher cognition, have an extensively convoluted cerebral cortex. In birds, a brain region called the pallium contains clustered nuclei that carry out functions similar to those performed by the cerebral cortex of mammals. Some birds can solve problems and understand abstractions in a manner indicative of higher cognition.

? *A patient has trouble with language and has paralysis on one side of the body. Which side would you expect to be paralyzed? Why?*

CONCEPT 49.4

Changes in synaptic connections underlie memory and learning (pp. 1093–1096)

- During development, more neurons and synapses form than will exist in the adult. The programmed death of neurons and elimination of synapses in embryos establish the basic structure of the nervous system. In the adult, reshaping of the nervous system can involve the loss or addition of synapses or the strengthening or weakening of signaling at synapses. This capacity for remodeling is termed **neuronal plasticity**. **Short-term memory** relies on temporary links in the hippocampus. In **long-term memory**, these temporary links are replaced by connections within the cerebral cortex.

? *Learning multiple languages is typically easier early in childhood than later in life. How does this fit with our understanding of neural development?*

CONCEPT 49.5

Many nervous system disorders can be explained in molecular terms (pp. 1096–1098)

- **Schizophrenia**, which is characterized by hallucinations, delusions, and other symptoms, affects neuronal pathways that use dopamine as a neurotransmitter. Drugs that increase the activity of biogenic amines in the brain can be used to treat **bipolar disorder** and **major depressive disorder**. The compulsive drug use that characterizes addiction reflects altered activity of the brain's reward system, which normally provides motivation for actions that enhance survival or reproduction.
- **Alzheimer's disease** and **Parkinson's disease** are neurodegenerative and typically age related. Alzheimer's disease is a dementia in which neurofibrillary tangles and amyloid plaques form in the brain. Parkinson's disease is a motor disorder caused by the death of dopamine-secreting neurons and associated with the presence of protein aggregates.

? *The fact that both amphetamine and PCP have effects similar to the symptoms of schizophrenia suggests a potentially complex basis for this disease. Explain.*

TEST YOUR UNDERSTANDING

LEVEL 1: KNOWLEDGE/COMPREHENSION

1. Wakefulness is regulated by the reticular formation, which is present in the
   a. basal nuclei.
   b. brainstem.
   c. limbic system.
   d. spinal cord.

2. Which of the following structures or regions is *incorrectly* paired with its function?
   a. limbic system—motor control of speech
   b. medulla oblongata—homeostatic control
   c. cerebellum—coordination of movement and balance
   d. amygdala—emotional memory

3. Patients with damage to Wernicke's area have difficulty
   a. coordinating limb movement.
   b. generating speech.
   c. recognizing faces.
   d. understanding language.

4. The cerebral cortex does *not* play a major role in
   a. short-term memory.   c. circadian rhythm.
   b. long-term memory.   d. breath holding.

LEVEL 2: APPLICATION/ANALYSIS

5. After suffering a stroke, a patient can see objects anywhere in front of him but pays attention only to objects in his right field of vision. When asked to describe these objects, he has difficulty judging their size and distance. What part of the brain was likely damaged by the stroke?
   a. the left frontal lobe   c. the right parietal lobe
   b. the right frontal lobe   d. the corpus callosum

6. Injury localized to the hypothalamus would most likely disrupt
   a. regulation of body temperature.
   b. short-term memory.
   c. executive functions, such as decision making.
   d. sorting of sensory information.

7. **DRAW IT** The reflex that pulls your hand away when you prick your finger on a sharp object relies on a neuronal circuit with two synapses in the spinal cord. (a) Using a circle to represent a cross section of the spinal cord, draw the circuit, labeling the types of neurons, the direction of information flow in each, and the locations of synapses. (b) Draw a simple diagram of the brain indicating where pain would eventually be perceived.

LEVEL 3: SYNTHESIS/EVALUATION

8. **EVOLUTION CONNECTION**
   Scientists often use measures of "higher-order thinking" to assess intelligence in other animals. For example, birds are judged to have sophisticated thought processes because they can use tools and make use of abstract concepts. What problems do you see in defining intelligence in these ways?

9. **SCIENTIFIC INQUIRY**
   Consider an individual who had been fluent in American Sign Language before suffering an injury to his left cerebral hemisphere. After the injury, he could still understand that sign language but could not readily generate sign language that represented his thoughts. What two hypotheses could explain this finding? How might you distinguish between them?

10. **SCIENCE, TECHNOLOGY, AND SOCIETY**
    With increasingly sophisticated methods for scanning brain activity, scientists are developing the ability to detect an individual's particular emotions and thought processes from outside the body. What benefits and problems do you envision when such technology becomes readily available?

11. **WRITE ABOUT A THEME: INFORMATION**
    In a short essay (100–150 words), explain how specification of the adult nervous system by the genome is incomplete.

12. **SYNTHESIZE YOUR KNOWLEDGE**

Imagine you are standing at a microphone in front of a crowd. Checking your notes, you begin speaking. Using the information in this chapter, describe the series of events in particular regions of the brain that enabled you to say the very first word.

MasteringBiology®

Students Go to **MasteringBiology** for assignments, the eText, and the Study Area with practice tests, animations, and activities.

Instructors Go to **MasteringBiology** for automatically graded tutorials and questions that you can assign to your students, plus Instructor Resources.

50
Sensory and Motor Mechanisms

▲ Figure 50.1 **Of what use is a star-shaped nose?**

Sense and Sensibility

Tunneling beneath the wetlands of eastern North America, the star-nosed mole (*Condylura cristata*) lives in almost total darkness. Virtually blind, the mole is nonetheless a remarkably deft predator, capable of detecting and eating its prey in as little as 120 milliseconds. Central to this hunting prowess are 11 pairs of appendages that protrude from its nose, forming a prominent pink star **(Figure 50.1)**. Although they look a bit like fingers, these appendages are not used in grasping. Nor are they used to detect odors. Instead, they are highly specialized to detect touch. Just below their surface lie 25,000 touch-sensitive receptors, more than are found in your whole hand. Over 100,000 neurons relay tactile information from these receptors to the mole's brain.

Detecting and processing sensory information and generating motor responses provide the physiological basis for all animal behavior. In this chapter, we'll explore the processes of sensing and acting in both vertebrates and invertebrates. We'll start with sensory processes that convey information about an animal's external and internal environment to its brain. We'll then consider the structure and function of muscles and skeletons that carry out movements as instructed by the brain. Finally, we'll investigate various mechanisms of animal movement. These topics will lead us naturally to our discussion of animal behavior in Chapter 51.

Sensory receptors transduce stimulus energy and transmit signals to the central nervous system

All sensory processes begin with stimuli, and all stimuli represent forms of energy. A sensory receptor converts stimulus energy to a change in membrane potential, thereby regulating the output of action potentials to the central nervous system (CNS). Decoding of this information within the CNS results in sensation.

When a stimulus is received and processed by the nervous system, a motor response may be generated. One of the simplest stimulus-response circuits is a reflex, such as the knee-jerk reflex shown in Figure 49.7. Many other behaviors rely on more elaborate processing of sensory input. As an example, consider how the star-nosed mole forages (Figure 50.2). When the mole's nose contacts an object in its tunnel, touch receptors in the nose are activated. These receptors transmit sensory information about the object to the mole's brain. Circuits in the brain integrate the input and initiate one of two response pathways, depending on whether food was detected. Motor output commands sent from the brain to skeletal muscles cause the mole to either bite down with its teeth or continue moving along the tunnel.

With this overview in mind, let's examine the general organization and activity of animal sensory systems. We'll focus on four basic functions common to sensory pathways: sensory reception, transduction, transmission, and perception.

Sensory Reception and Transduction

A sensory pathway begins with **sensory reception**, the detection of a stimulus by sensory cells. Some sensory cells are themselves specialized neurons, whereas others are non-neuronal cells that regulate neurons (Figure 50.3). Some exist singly; others are collected in sensory organs, such as the star-shaped nose of the mole in Figure 50.1.

The term **sensory receptor** is used to describe a sensory cell or organ, as well as the subcellular structure that detects stimuli. Many sensory receptors detect stimuli from outside the body, such as heat, light, pressure, or chemicals. However, there are also receptors for stimuli from within the body, such as blood pressure and body position. Activating a sensory receptor does not necessarily require a large amount of stimulus energy. Indeed, some sensory receptors can detect the smallest possible unit of stimulus. Most light receptors, for example, can detect a single quantum (photon) of light.

Although animals use a range of sensory receptors to detect widely varying stimuli, the effect in all cases is to open or close ion channels. Thus, for example, ion channels either

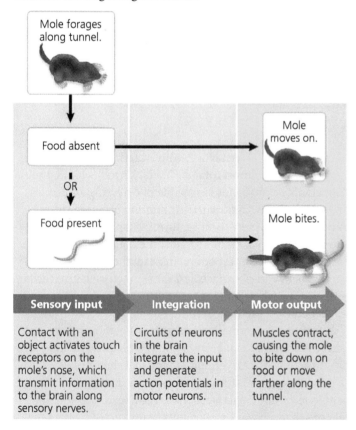

▲ Figure 50.2 A simple response pathway: foraging by a star-nosed mole.

▼ Figure 50.3 Categories of sensory receptors.

open or close when a substance outside the cell binds to a chemical receptor in the plasma membrane. The resulting flow of ions across the membrane changes the membrane potential.

The conversion of a physical or chemical stimulus to a change in the membrane potential of a sensory receptor is called **sensory transduction**, and the change in membrane potential itself is known as a **receptor potential**. Receptor potentials are graded potentials; their magnitude varies with the strength of the stimulus.

Transmission

Sensory information travels through the nervous system as nerve impulses, or action potentials. For many sensory receptors, transducing the energy in a stimulus into a receptor potential initiates action potentials that are transmitted to the CNS.

Neurons that act directly as sensory receptors produce action potentials and have an axon that extends into the CNS (see Figure 50.3). Non-neuronal sensory receptor cells form chemical synapses with sensory (afferent) neurons and typically respond to stimuli by increasing the rate at which the afferent neurons produce action potentials. (One exception is in the vertebrate visual system, discussed in Concept 50.3.)

The size of a receptor potential increases with the intensity of the stimulus. If the receptor is a sensory neuron, a larger receptor potential results in more frequent action potentials **(Figure 50.4)**. If the receptor is not a sensory neuron, a larger receptor potential usually causes more neurotransmitter to be released.

Many sensory neurons spontaneously generate action potentials at a low rate. In these neurons, a stimulus does not switch the production of action potentials on or off, but it does change *how often* an action potential is produced. In this manner, such neurons are also able to alert the nervous system to changes in stimulus intensity.

▲ **Figure 50.4 Coding of stimulus intensity by a single sensory receptor.**

Processing of sensory information can occur before, during, and after transmission of action potentials to the CNS. In many cases, the *integration* of sensory information begins as soon as the information is received. Receptor potentials produced by stimuli delivered to different parts of a sensory receptor cell are integrated through summation, as are postsynaptic potentials in sensory neurons that form synapses with multiple receptors (see Figure 48.15). As we will discuss shortly, sensory structures such as eyes also provide higher levels of integration, and the brain further processes all incoming signals.

Perception

When action potentials reach the brain via sensory neurons, circuits of neurons process this input, generating the **perception** of the stimuli. Perceptions—such as colors, smells, sounds, and tastes—are constructions formed in the brain and do not exist outside it. So, if a tree falls and no animal is present to hear it, is there a sound? The falling tree certainly produces pressure waves in the air, but if sound is defined as a perception, then there is none unless an animal senses the waves and its brain perceives them.

An action potential triggered by light striking the eye has the same properties as an action potential triggered by air vibrating in the ear. How, then, do we distinguish sights, sounds, and other stimuli? The answer lies in the connections that link sensory receptors to the brain. Action potentials from sensory receptors travel along neurons that are dedicated to a particular stimulus; these dedicated neurons synapse with particular neurons in the brain or spinal cord. As a result, the brain distinguishes stimuli such as sight or sound solely by the path along which the action potentials have arrived.

Amplification and Adaptation

The transduction of stimuli by sensory receptors is subject to two types of modification—amplification and adaptation. **Amplification** refers to the strengthening of a sensory signal during transduction. The effect can be considerable. For example, an action potential conducted from the eye to the human brain has about 100,000 times as much energy as the few photons of light that triggered it.

Amplification that occurs in sensory receptor cells often requires signal transduction pathways involving second messengers. Because these pathways include enzyme-catalyzed reactions, they amplify signal strength through the formation of many product molecules by a single enzyme molecule. Amplification may also take place in accessory structures of a complex sense organ, as when the pressure associated with sound waves is enhanced more than 20-fold before reaching receptors in the innermost part of the ear.

Upon continued stimulation, many receptors undergo a decrease in responsiveness termed **sensory adaptation** (not to be confused with the evolutionary term *adaptation*). Without sensory adaptation, you would be constantly aware of feeling every beat of your heart and every bit of clothing on your body. Adaptation also enables you to see, hear, and smell changes in the environment that vary widely in stimulus intensity.

Types of Sensory Receptors

We can classify sensory receptors into five categories based on the nature of the stimuli they transduce: mechanoreceptors, chemoreceptors, electromagnetic receptors, thermoreceptors, and pain receptors.

Mechanoreceptors

Mechanoreceptors sense physical deformation caused by forms of mechanical energy such as pressure, touch, stretch, motion, and sound. Mechanoreceptors typically consist of ion channels that are linked to structures that extend outside the cell, such as "hairs" (cilia), as well as internal cell structures, such as the cytoskeleton. Bending or stretching of the external structure generates tension that alters the permeability of the ion channels. This change in ion permeability alters the membrane potential, resulting in a depolarization or hyperpolarization (see Chapter 48).

The vertebrate stretch receptor, a mechanoreceptor that detects muscle movement, triggers the familiar knee-jerk reflex (see Figure 49.7). Vertebrate stretch receptors are dendrites of sensory neurons that spiral around the middle of certain small skeletal muscle fibers. When the muscle fibers are stretched, the sensory neurons depolarize, triggering nerve impulses that reach the spinal cord, activate motor neurons, and generate a reflex response.

Mechanoreceptors that are the dendrites of sensory neurons are also responsible for the mammalian sense of touch. Touch receptors are often embedded in layers of connective tissue. The structure of the connective tissue and the location of the receptors dramatically affect the type of mechanical energy (light touch, vibration, or strong pressure) that best stimulates them **(Figure 50.5)**. Receptors that detect a light touch or vibration are close to the surface of the skin; they transduce very slight inputs of mechanical energy into receptor potentials. Receptors that respond to stronger pressure and vibrations are in deep skin layers.

Some animals use mechanoreceptors to literally get a feel for their environment. For example, cats as well as many rodents have extremely sensitive mechanoreceptors at the base of their whiskers. Because deflection of different whiskers triggers action potentials that reach different cells in the brain, an animal's whiskers provide detailed information about nearby objects.

Receptors that detect gentle pressure, vibration, and temperature are close to the surface of the skin.

Naked dendrites in the epidermis respond to pain.

Connective tissue
Hair
Epidermis
Dermis
Hypodermis
Nerve

Naked dendrites wind around the base of hairs and detect hair movement.

Receptors that respond to strong pressure are in deep skin layers.

▲ **Figure 50.5 Sensory receptors in human skin.** Most receptors in the dermis are encapsulated by connective tissue. Receptors in the epidermis are naked dendrites, as are hair movement receptors that wind around the base of hairs in the dermis.

Chemoreceptors

Chemoreceptors include both general receptors—those that transmit information about total solute concentration—and specific receptors—those that respond to individual kinds of molecules. Osmoreceptors in the mammalian brain, for example, detect changes in the total solute concentration of the blood and stimulate thirst when osmolarity increases (see Figure 44.18). Most animals also have receptors for specific molecules, including glucose, oxygen, carbon dioxide, and amino acids.

Two of the most sensitive and specific chemoreceptors known are found in the antennae of the male silkworm moth **(Figure 50.6)**; they detect the two chemical components of the female moth sex pheromone. For pheromones and other molecules detected by chemoreceptors, the stimulus molecule binds to the specific receptor on the membrane of the sensory cell and initiates changes in ion permeability.

Electromagnetic Receptors

Electromagnetic receptors detect forms of electromagnetic energy, such as light, electricity, and magnetism. For example, the platypus has electroreceptors on its bill that are

▲ Figure 50.6 **Chemoreceptors in an insect.** The antennae of the male silkworm moth *Bombyx mori* are covered with sensory hairs, visible in the SEM enlargement. The hairs have chemoreceptors that are highly sensitive to the sex pheromone released by the female.

(a) Some migrating animals, such as these beluga whales, apparently sense Earth's magnetic field and use the information, along with other cues, for orientation.

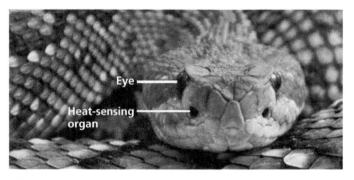

(b) This rattlesnake and other pit vipers have a pair of heat-sensing pit organs, one anterior to and just below each eye. These organs are sensitive enough to detect the infrared radiation emitted by a warm prey a meter away. The snake moves its head from side to side until the radiation is detected equally by the two pit organs, indicating that the prey is straight ahead.

▲ Figure 50.7 **Examples of electromagnetic reception and thermoreception.**

thought to detect the electric field generated by the muscles of crustaceans, small fish, and other prey. In a few cases, the animal detecting the stimulus is also its source: Some fishes generate electric currents and then use electroreceptors to locate prey or other objects that disturb those currents.

Many animals appear to use Earth's magnetic field lines to orient themselves as they migrate **(Figure 50.7a)**, and the iron-containing mineral magnetite may be responsible for this ability. Once collected by sailors to make compasses for navigation, magnetite is found in many vertebrates (including salmon, pigeons, sea turtles, and humans), in bees, in some molluscs, and in certain protists and prokaryotes that orient to Earth's magnetic field.

Thermoreceptors

Thermoreceptors detect heat and cold. For example, certain venomous snakes rely on thermoreceptors to detect the infrared radiation emitted by warm prey. These thermoreceptors are located in a pair of pit organs on the snake's head **(Figure 50.7b)**. Human thermoreceptors, which are located in the skin and in the anterior hypothalamus, send information to the body's thermostat in the posterior hypothalamus. Recently, our understanding of thermoreception has increased substantially, thanks to scientists with an appreciation for fiery foods. Jalapeno and cayenne peppers that we describe as "hot" contain a substance called capsaicin. Applying capsaicin to a sensory neuron causes an influx of calcium ions. When scientists identified the receptor protein

in neurons that binds capsaicin, they made a fascinating discovery: The receptor opens a calcium channel in response not only to capsaicin, but also to high temperatures (42°C or higher). In essence, spicy foods taste "hot" because they activate the same receptors as hot soup and coffee.

Mammals have a variety of thermoreceptors, each specific for a particular temperature range. The capsaicin receptor and at least five other types of thermoreceptors belong to the TRP (transient receptor potential) family of ion channel proteins. Just as the TRP-type receptor specific for high temperature is sensitive to capsaicin, the receptor for temperatures below 28°C can be activated by menthol, a plant product that we perceive to have a "cool" flavor.

Pain Receptors

Extreme pressure or temperature, as well as certain chemicals, can damage animal tissues. To detect stimuli that reflect such noxious (harmful) conditions, animals rely on **nociceptors** (from the Latin *nocere*, to hurt), also called **pain receptors**. By triggering defensive reactions, such as withdrawal from danger, the perception of pain serves an important function.

Chemicals produced in an animal's body sometimes enhance the perception of pain. For example, damaged tissues produce prostaglandins, which act as local regulators of inflammation (see Chapter 45). Prostaglandins worsen pain by increasing nociceptor sensitivity to noxious stimuli. Aspirin and ibuprofen reduce pain by inhibiting the synthesis of prostaglandins.

Next we'll turn our focus to sensory systems, beginning with systems for maintaining balance and detecting sound.

CONCEPT CHECK 50.1

1. Which one of the five categories of sensory receptors is primarily dedicated to external stimuli?

2. Why can eating "hot" peppers cause a person to sweat?

3. **WHAT IF?** If you stimulated a sensory neuron electrically, how would that stimulation be perceived?

For suggested answers, see Appendix A.

CONCEPT 50.2

The mechanoreceptors responsible for hearing and equilibrium detect moving fluid or settling particles

Hearing and the perception of body equilibrium, or balance, are related in most animals. For both senses, mechanoreceptor cells produce receptor potentials in response to deflection of cell-surface structures by settling particles or moving fluid.

Sensing of Gravity and Sound in Invertebrates

To sense gravity and maintain equilibrium, most invertebrates rely on mechanoreceptors located in organs called **statocysts** (Figure 50.8). In a typical statocyst, **statoliths**,

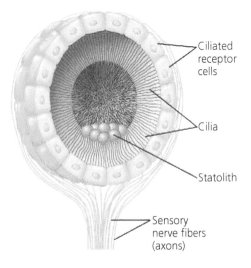

▶ Figure 50.8
The statocyst of an invertebrate.
The settling of granules called statoliths to the low point in the chamber bends cilia on receptor cells in that location, providing the brain with information about the orientation of the body with respect to gravity.

Ciliated receptor cells

Cilia

Statolith

Sensory nerve fibers (axons)

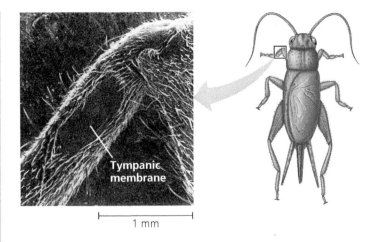

▲ Figure 50.9 **An insect's "ear"—on its leg.** The tympanic membrane, visible in this SEM of a cricket's front leg, vibrates in response to sound waves. The vibrations stimulate mechanoreceptors attached to the inside of the tympanic membrane.

granules formed by grains of sand or other dense materials, sit freely in a chamber lined with ciliated cells. Each time an animal repositions itself, the statoliths resettle, stimulating mechanoreceptors at the low point in the chamber.

How did researchers test the hypothesis that resettling of statoliths informs an invertebrate about its position relative to Earth's gravity? In one key experiment, statoliths were replaced with metal shavings. Researchers then "tricked" crayfish into swimming upside down by using magnets to pull the shavings to the upper end of statocysts at the base of their antennae.

Many (perhaps most) insects have body hairs that vibrate in response to sound waves. Hairs of different stiffnesses and lengths vibrate at different frequencies. For example, fine hairs on the antennae of a male mosquito vibrate in a specific way in response to the hum produced by the beating wings of flying females. The importance of this sensory system in the attraction of males to a potential mate can be demonstrated very simply: A tuning fork vibrating at the same frequency as that of a female's wings will by itself attract males.

Many insects also detect sound by means of vibration-sensitive organs, which consist in some species of a tympanic membrane (eardrum) stretched over an internal air chamber (Figure 50.9). Cockroaches lack such a tympanic membrane, but instead have vibration-sensitive organs that sense air movement, such as that caused by a descending human foot.

Hearing and Equilibrium in Mammals

In mammals, as in most other terrestrial vertebrates, the sensory organs for hearing and equilibrium are closely associated. Figure 50.10 explores the structure and function of these organs in the human ear.

Exploring The Structure of the Human Ear

1 Overview of Ear Structure

The **outer ear** consists of the external pinna and the auditory canal, which collect sound waves and channel them to the **tympanic membrane** (eardrum), which separates the outer ear from the middle ear. In the **middle ear**, three small bones—the malleus (hammer), incus (anvil), and stapes (stirrup)—transmit vibrations to the **oval window**, which is a membrane beneath the stapes. The middle ear also opens into the **Eustachian tube**, which connects to the pharynx and equalizes pressure between the middle ear and the atmosphere. The **inner ear** consists of fluid-filled chambers, including the **semicircular canals**, which function in equilibrium, and the coiled **cochlea** (from the Latin meaning "snail"), a bony chamber that is involved in hearing.

2 The Cochlea

The cochlea has two large canals—an upper vestibular canal and a lower tympanic canal—separated by a smaller cochlear duct. Both canals are filled with fluid.

▲ Bundled hairs projecting from a single mammalian hair cell (SEM). Two shorter rows of hairs lie behind the tall hairs in the foreground.

4 Hair Cell

Projecting from each hair cell is a bundle of rod-shaped "hairs," each containing a core of actin filaments. Vibration of the basilar membrane in response to sound raises and lowers the hair cells, bending the hairs against the surrounding fluid and the tectorial membrane. When the hairs within the bundle are displaced, mechanoreceptors are activated, changing the membrane potential of the hair cell.

3 The Organ of Corti

The floor of the cochlear duct, the basilar membrane, bears the **organ of Corti**, which contains the mechanoreceptors of the ear, hair cells with hairs projecting into the cochlear duct. Many of the hairs are attached to the tectorial membrane, which hangs over the organ of Corti like an awning. Sound waves make the basilar membrane vibrate, which results in bending of the hairs and depolarization of the hair cells.

Hearing

Vibrating objects, such as a plucked guitar string or the vocal cords of a person who is talking, create pressure waves in the surrounding air. In *hearing*, the ear transduces this mechanical stimulus (pressure waves) into nerve impulses that the brain perceives as sound. To hear music, speech, or other sounds in our environment, we rely on **hair cells**, sensory cells with hairlike projections that detect motion.

Before vibration waves reach hair cells, they are amplified and transformed by several accessory structures. The first steps involve structures in the ear that convert the vibrations of moving air to pressure waves in fluid. Moving air that reaches the outer ear causes the tympanic membrane to vibrate. The three bones of the middle ear transmit these vibrations to the oval window, a membrane on the cochlea's surface. When one of those bones, the stapes, vibrates against the oval window, it creates pressure waves in the fluid (called perilymph) inside the cochlea.

Upon entering the vestibular canal, fluid pressure waves push down on the cochlear duct and basilar membrane. In response, the basilar membrane and attached hair cells vibrate up and down. The hairs projecting from the hair cells are deflected by the fixed tectorial membrane, which lies above (see Figure 50.10). With each vibration, the hairs bend first in one direction and then the other, causing ion channels in the hair cells to open or close. Bending in one direction depolarizes hair cells, increasing neurotransmitter release and the frequency of action potentials directed to the brain along the auditory nerve **(Figure 50.11)**. Bending the hairs in the other direction hyperpolarizes hair cells, reducing neurotransmitter release and the frequency of auditory nerve sensations.

What prevents pressure waves from reverberating within the ear and causing prolonged sensation? After propagating through the vestibular canal, pressure waves pass around the apex (tip) of the cochlea and dissipate as they strike the **round window (Figure 50.12a)**. This damping of sound waves resets the apparatus for the next vibrations that arrive.

The ear captures information about two important sound variables: volume and pitch. *Volume* (loudness) is determined by the amplitude, or height, of the sound wave. A large-amplitude wave causes more vigorous vibration of the basilar membrane, greater bending of the hairs on hair cells, and more action potentials in the sensory neurons. *Pitch* is determined by a sound wave's frequency, the number of vibrations per unit time. The detection of sound wave frequency takes place in the cochlea and relies on the asymmetric structure of that organ.

The cochlea can distinguish pitch because the basilar membrane is not uniform along its length: It is relatively narrow and stiff at the base of the cochlea near the oval window and wider and more flexible at the apex. Each region of the basilar membrane is tuned to a different vibration frequency **(Figure 50.12b)**. Furthermore, each region is connected by axons to a different location in the cerebral cortex. Consequently, when a sound wave causes vibration of a particular region of the basilar membrane, a specific site in our cortex is stimulated and we perceive sound of a particular pitch.

(a) No bending of hairs

(b) Bending of hairs in one direction

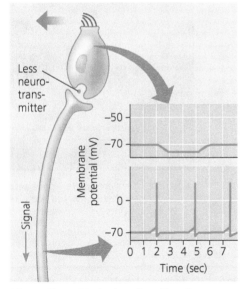

(c) Bending of hairs in other direction

▲ **Figure 50.11 Sensory reception by hair cells.** Vertebrate hair cells required for hearing and balance have "hairs" formed into a bundle that bends when surrounding fluid moves. Each hair cell releases an excitatory neurotransmitter at a synapse with a sensory neuron, which conducts action potentials to the CNS. Bending of the bundle in one direction depolarizes the hair cell, causing it to release more neurotransmitter and increasing the frequency of action potentials in the sensory neuron. Bending in the other direction has the opposite effect.

© Pearson Education, Inc.

(a) Vibrations of the stapes against the oval window produce pressure waves (black arrows) in the fluid (perilymph; blue) of the cochlea. (For purposes of illustration, the cochlea on the right is drawn partially uncoiled.) The waves travel to the apex via the vestibular canal and back towards the base via the tympanic canal. The energy in the waves causes the basilar membrane (pink) to vibrate, stimulating hair cells (not shown). Because the basilar membrane varies in stiffness along its length, each point along the membrane vibrates maximally in response to waves of a particular frequency.

(b) These graphs show the patterns of vibration along the basilar membrane for three different frequencies, high (top), medium (middle), and low (bottom). The higher the frequency, the closer the vibration to the oval window.

▲ **Figure 50.12 Transduction in the cochlea.**

INTERPRET THE DATA *A musical chord consists of several notes, each formed by a sound wave of different frequency. If a chord had notes with frequencies of 100, 1,000, and 6,000 Hz, what would happen to the basilar membrane? How would this result in your hearing a chord?*

Equilibrium

Several organs in the inner ear of humans and most other mammals detect body movement, position, and balance. For example, the chambers called the **utricle** and **saccule** allow us to perceive position with respect to gravity or linear movement **(Figure 50.13)**. Each of these chambers, which are situated in a vestibule behind the oval window, contains hair cells that project into a gelatinous material. Embedded in this gel are small calcium carbonate particles called *otoliths* ("ear stones"). When you tilt your head, the otoliths press on the hairs protruding into the gel. The hair cell receptors transform this deflection into a change in the output of sensory neurons, signaling the brain that your head is at an angle. The otoliths are also responsible for your ability to

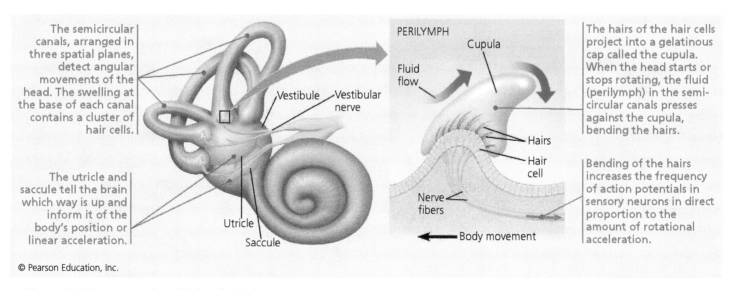

© Pearson Education, Inc.

▲ **Figure 50.13 Organs of equilibrium in the inner ear.**

perceive acceleration, as, for example, when a stationary car in which you are sitting pulls forward.

Three fluid-filled semicircular canals connected to the utricle detect turning of the head and other rotational acceleration. Within each canal, the hair cells form a cluster, with the hairs projecting into a gelatinous cap called a cupula (see Figure 50.13). Because the three canals are arranged in the three spatial planes, they can detect angular motion of the head in any direction. If you spin in place, the fluid in each canal eventually comes to equilibrium and remains in that state until you stop. At that point, the moving fluid encounters a stationary cupula, triggering the false sensation of angular motion that we call dizziness.

Hearing and Equilibrium in Other Vertebrates

Fishes rely on several systems for detecting movement and vibrations in their aquatic environment. One system involves a pair of inner ears that contain otoliths and hair cells. Unlike mammals, fishes have no eardrum, cochlea, or opening to the outside of the body. Instead, the vibrations of the water caused by sound waves are conducted to the inner ear through the skeleton of the head. Some fishes also have a series of bones that conduct vibrations to the inner ear from the swim bladder (see Figure 34.15).

Most fishes and aquatic amphibians are able to detect low-frequency waves by means of a **lateral line system** along both sides of their body (Figure 50.14). As in our semicircular canals, receptors are formed from a cluster of hair cells whose hairs are embedded in a cupula. Water entering the lateral line system through numerous pores bends the cupula, leading to depolarization of the hair cells and production of action potentials. In this way, the fish perceives its movement through water or the direction and velocity of water currents flowing over its body. The lateral line system also detects water movements or vibrations generated by prey, predators, and other moving objects.

In the ear of a frog or toad, sound vibrations in the air are conducted to the inner ear by a tympanic membrane on the body surface and a single middle ear bone. The same is true in birds and other reptiles, although they, like mammals, have a cochlea.

CONCEPT CHECK 50.2

1. How are otoliths adaptive for burrowing mammals, such as the star-nosed mole?

2. **WHAT IF?** Suppose a series of pressure waves in your cochlea caused a vibration of the basilar membrane that moves gradually from the apex toward the base. How would your brain interpret this stimulus?

3. **WHAT IF?** If the stapes became fused to the other middle ear bones or to the oval window, how would this condition affect hearing? Explain.

4. **MAKE CONNECTIONS** Plants use statoliths to detect gravity (see Figure 39.22). How do plants and animals differ with regard to the type of compartment in which statoliths are found and the physiological mechanism for detecting their response to gravity?

For suggested answers, see Appendix A.

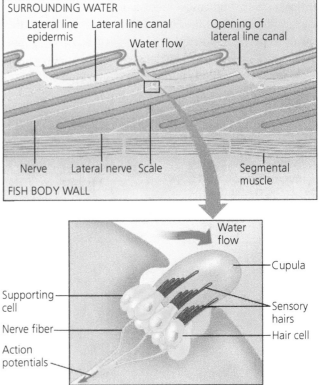

▲ **Figure 50.14 The lateral line system in a fish.** The sensory organs of the lateral line stretch from head to tail along each side of the fish. Water movement into and through the lateral line canals pushes on the gelatinous cupula, bending the hair cells within. In response, the hair cells generate receptor potentials, triggering action potentials that are conveyed to the brain. This information enables a fish to monitor water currents, any pressure waves produced by moving objects, and any low frequency sounds conducted through the water.

CONCEPT 50.3

The diverse visual receptors of animals depend on light-absorbing pigments

The ability to detect light has a central role in the interaction of nearly all animals with their environment. Although the organs used for vision vary considerably among animals, the underlying mechanism for capturing light is the same, suggesting a common evolutionary origin.

Evolution of Visual Perception

EVOLUTION Light detectors in the animal kingdom range from simple clusters of cells that detect only the direction and intensity of light to complex organs that form images. These diverse light detectors all contain **photoreceptors**, sensory cells that contain light-absorbing pigment molecules. Furthermore, the genes that specify where and when photoreceptors arise during embryonic development are shared among flatworms, annelids, arthropods, and vertebrates. It is thus very probable that the genetic underpinnings of all photoreceptors were already present in the earliest bilaterian animals.

Light-Detecting Organs

Most invertebrates have some kind of light-detecting organ. One of the simplest is that of planarians **(Figure 50.15)**. A pair of ocelli (singular, *ocellus*), which are sometimes called eyespots, are located in the head region. Photoreceptors in each ocellus receive light only through an opening where there are no pigmented cells. By comparing the rate of action potentials coming from the two ocelli, the planarian is able to move away from a light source until it reaches a shaded location, where a rock or other object is likely to hide it from predators.

Compound Eyes

Insects and crustaceans have compound eyes, as do some polychaete worms. A **compound eye** consists of up to several thousand light detectors called **ommatidia** (the "facets" of the eye), each with its own light-focusing lens **(Figure 50.16)**. Each ommatidium detects light from a tiny portion of the visual field (the area seen when the eyes point forward). A compound eye is very effective at detecting movement, an important adaptation for flying insects and small animals constantly threatened with predation. Many compound eyes, including those of the fly in Figure 50.16, offer a very wide field of view.

Insects have excellent color vision, and some (including bees) can see into the ultraviolet (UV) range of the electromagnetic spectrum. Because UV light is invisible to humans, we miss seeing differences in the environment that bees and

(a) The planarian's brain directs the body to turn until the sensations from the two ocelli are equal and minimal, causing the animal to move away from light.

(b) Whereas light striking the front of an ocellus excites the photoreceptors, light striking the back is blocked by the screening pigment. In this way, the ocelli indicate the direction of a light source, triggering the light avoidance behavior.

▲ **Figure 50.15 Ocelli and orientation behavior of a planarian.**

(a) The faceted eyes on the head of a fly form a repeating pattern visible in this photomicrograph.

(b) The cornea and crystalline cone of each ommatidium together function as a lens that focuses light on the rhabdom, an organelle formed by and extending inward from a circle of photoreceptors. The rhabdom traps light, serving as the photosensitive part of the ommatidium. Information gathered from different intensities of light entering the many ommatidia from different angles is used to form a visual image.

▲ **Figure 50.16 Compound eyes.**

other insects detect. In studying animal behavior, we cannot simply extrapolate our sensory world to other species; different animals have different sensitivities and different brain organizations.

Single-Lens Eyes

Among invertebrates, **single-lens eyes** are found in some jellies and polychaete worms, as well as in spiders and many molluscs. A single-lens eye works somewhat like a camera. The eye of an octopus or squid, for example, has a small opening, the **pupil**, through which light enters. Like a camera's adjustable aperture, the **iris** contracts or expands, changing the diameter of the pupil to let in more or less light. Behind the pupil, a single lens directs light on a layer of photoreceptors. Similar to a camera's focusing action, muscles in an invertebrate's single-lens eye move the lens forward or backward, focusing on objects at different distances.

▼ **Figure 50.17**

Exploring The Structure of the Human Eye

© Pearson Education, Inc.

1 Overview of Eye Structure

Starting from the outside, the human eye is surrounded by the conjunctiva, a mucous membrane (not shown); the sclera, a connective tissue; and the choroid, a thin, pigmented layer. At the front, the sclera forms the transparent *cornea* and the choroid forms the colored *iris*. By changing size, the iris regulates the amount of light entering the pupil, the hole in the center of the iris. Just inside the choroid, the neurons and photoreceptors of the **retina** form the innermost layer of the eyeball. The optic nerve exits the eye at the optic disk.

The **lens**, a transparent disk of protein, divides the eye into two cavities. In front of the lens lies the *aqueous humor,* a clear watery substance. Blockage of ducts that drain this fluid can produce glaucoma, a condition in which increased pressure in the eye damages the optic nerve, causing vision loss. Behind the lens lies the jellylike *vitreous humor* (illustrated here in the lower portion of the eyeball).

2 The Retina

Light (coming from left in the above view) strikes the retina, passing through largely transparent layers of neurons before reaching the rods and cones, two types of photoreceptors that differ in shape and in function. The neurons of the retina then relay visual information captured by the photoreceptors to the optic nerve and brain along the pathways shown with red arrows. Each *bipolar cell* receives information from several rods or cones, and each *ganglion cell* gathers input from several bipolar cells. *Horizontal* and *amacrine cells* integrate information across the retina.

One region of the retina, the optic disk, lacks photoreceptors. As a result, this region forms a "blind spot" where light is not detected.

The eyes of all vertebrates have a single lens. In fishes, focusing occurs as in invertebrates, with the lens moving forward or backward. In other species, including mammals, focusing is achieved by changing the shape of the lens.

The Vertebrate Visual System

The human eye will serve as our model of vision in vertebrates. As described in **Figure 50.17**, vision begins when photons of light enter the eye and strike the rods and cones. There the energy of each photon is captured by a shift in configuration of a single chemical bond in retinal.

Although light detection in the eye is the first stage in vision, remember that it is actually the brain that "sees." Thus, to understand vision, we must examine how the capture of light by retinal changes the production of action potentials and then follow these signals to the visual centers of the brain, where images are perceived.

© Pearson Education, Inc.

© Pearson Education, Inc.

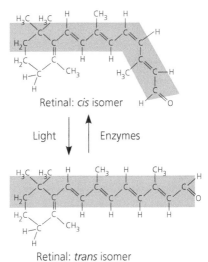

Retinal: *cis* isomer

Light ↓ ↑ Enzymes

Retinal: *trans* isomer

3 Photoreceptor Cells

Humans have two main types of photoreceptor cells: rods and cones. Within the outer segment of a rod or cone is a stack of membranous disks in which *visual pigments* are embedded. **Rods** are more sensitive to light but do not distinguish colors; they enable us to see at night, but only in black and white. **Cones** provide color vision, but, being less sensitive, contribute very little to night vision. There are three types of cones. Each has a different sensitivity across the visible spectrum, providing an optimal response to red, green, or blue light.

In the colorized SEM shown above, cones (green), rods (light tan), and adjacent neurons (purple) are visible. The pigmented epithelium, which was removed in this preparation, would be to the right.

4 Visual Pigments

Vertebrate visual pigments consist of a light-absorbing molecule called **retinal** (a derivative of vitamin A) bound to a membrane protein called an **opsin**. Seven α helices of each opsin molecule span the disk membrane. The visual pigment of rods, shown here, is called **rhodopsin**.

Retinal exists as two isomers. Absorption of light shifts one bond in retinal from a *cis* to a *trans* arrangement, converting the molecule from an angled shape to a straight shape. This change in configuration destabilizes and activates the opsin protein to which retinal is bound.

Sensory Transduction in the Eye

The transduction of visual information to the nervous system begins with the light-induced conversion of *cis*-retinal to *trans*-retinal. As shown in **Figure 50.18**, this conversion activates rhodopsin, which activates a G protein, which in turn activates an enzyme called phosphodiesterase. The substrate for this enzyme is cyclic GMP, which in the dark binds to sodium ion (Na^+) channels and keeps them open. When phosphodiesterase hydrolyzes cyclic GMP, Na^+ channels close, and the cell becomes hyperpolarized.

The signal transduction pathway in photoreceptor cells normally shuts off as enzymes convert retinal back to the *cis* form, returning rhodopsin to its inactive state. In very bright light, however, rhodopsin remains active, and the response in the rods becomes saturated. If the amount of light entering the eyes decreases abruptly, the rods do not regain full responsiveness for several minutes. This is why you are temporarily blinded if you pass quickly from the bright sunshine into a movie theater or other dark environment. (Because light activation changes the color of rhodopsin from purple to yellow, rods in which the light response is saturated are often described as "bleached.")

Processing of Visual Information in the Retina

The processing of visual information begins in the retina itself, where both rods and cones form synapses with bipolar cells (see Figure 50.17). In the dark, rods and cones are depolarized and continually release the neurotransmitter glutamate at these synapses **(Figure 50.19)**. Some bipolar cells depolarize in response to glutamate, whereas others hyperpolarize. When light strikes the rods and cones, they hyperpolarize, shutting off their release of glutamate. In response, the bipolar cells that are depolarized by glutamate hyperpolarize, and those that are hyperpolarized by glutamate depolarize.

Signals from rods and cones can follow several different pathways in the retina. Some information passes directly from photoreceptors to bipolar cells to ganglion cells. In other cases, horizontal cells carry signals from one rod or cone to other photoreceptors and to several bipolar cells.

When an illuminated rod or cone stimulates a horizontal cell, the horizontal cell inhibits more distant photoreceptors and bipolar cells that are not illuminated. The result is that the region receiving light appears lighter and the dark surroundings even darker. This form of integration, called *lateral inhibition*, sharpens edges and enhances contrast in the image. Amacrine cells distribute some information from one bipolar cell to several ganglion cells. Lateral inhibition is repeated by the interactions of the amacrine cells with the ganglion cells and occurs at all levels of visual processing in the brain.

A single ganglion cell receives information from an array of rods and cones, each of which responds to light coming from a particular location. Together, the rods and cones that are feeding information to one ganglion cell define

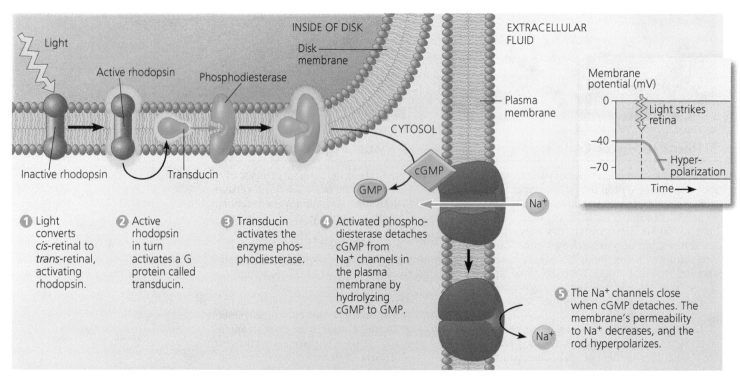

▲ **Figure 50.18 Production of the receptor potential in a rod cell.** In rods (and cones), the receptor potential triggered by light is a hyperpolarization, not a depolarization.

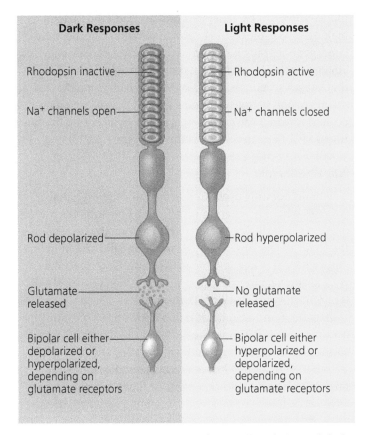

▲ Figure 50.19 Synaptic activity of rod cells in light and dark.

[?] *Like rods, cone cells are depolarized when their opsin molecules are inactive. In the case of a cone, why might it be misleading to call this a dark response?*

a *receptive field*—the part of the visual field to which that ganglion cell can respond. The fewer rods or cones that supply a single ganglion cell, the smaller the receptive field is. A smaller receptive field typically results in a sharper image because the information about where light has struck the retina is more precise.

Processing of Visual Information in the Brain

Axons of ganglion cells form the optic nerves that transmit sensations from the eyes to the brain (**Figure 50.20**). The two optic nerves meet at the *optic chiasm* near the center of the base of the cerebral cortex. Axons in the optic nerves are routed at the optic chiasm such that sensations from the left visual field of both eyes are transmitted to the right side of the brain, and sensations from the right visual field are transmitted to the left side of the brain. (Note that each visual field, whether right or left, involves input from both eyes.)

Within the brain, most ganglion cell axons lead to the *lateral geniculate nuclei*, which have axons that reach the *primary visual cortex* in the cerebrum. Additional neurons carry the information to higher-order visual processing and

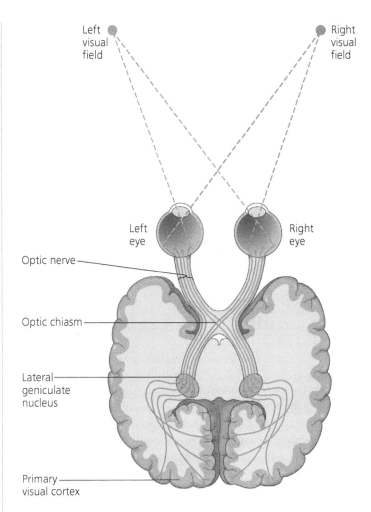

▲ Figure 50.20 Neural pathways for vision. Each optic nerve contains about a million axons that synapse with interneurons in the lateral geniculate nuclei. The nuclei relay sensations to the primary visual cortex, one of many brain centers that cooperate in constructing our visual perceptions.

integrating centers elsewhere in the cortex. Researchers estimate that at least 30% of the cerebral cortex, comprising hundreds of millions of neurons in perhaps dozens of integrating centers, takes part in formulating what we actually "see." Determining how these centers integrate such components of our vision as color, motion, depth, shape, and detail is the focus of much exciting research.

Color Vision

Among vertebrates, most fishes, amphibians, and reptiles, including birds, have very good color vision. Humans and other primates also see color well, but are among the minority of mammals with this ability. Many mammals are nocturnal, and having a high proportion of rods in the retina is an adaptation that gives these animals keen night vision. Cats, for instance, are usually most active at night; they have limited color vision and probably see a pastel world during the day.

In humans, the perception of color is based on three types of cones, each with a different visual pigment—red, green, or blue. The three visual pigments, called *photopsins*, are formed from the binding of retinal to three distinct opsin proteins. Slight differences in the opsin proteins cause each photopsin to absorb light optimally at a different wavelength. Although the visual pigments are designated as red, green, or blue, their absorption spectra in fact overlap. For this reason, the brain's perception of intermediate hues depends on the differential stimulation of two or more classes of cones. For example, when both red and green cones are stimulated, we may see yellow or orange, depending on which class is more strongly stimulated.

Abnormal color vision typically results from mutations in the genes for one or more photopsin proteins. Because the human genes for the red and green pigments are located on the X chromosome, a mutation in one copy of either gene can disrupt color vision in males. For this reason, color blindness is more common in males than in females (5–8% of males, fewer than 1% of females) and nearly always affects perception of red or green. (The human gene for the blue pigment is on chromosome 7.)

Experiments on color vision in the squirrel monkey (*Saimiri sciureus*) enabled a recent breakthrough in the field of gene therapy. These monkeys have only two opsin genes, one sensitive to blue light and the other sensitive to either red or green light, depending on the allele. Because the red/green opsin gene is X-linked, all males have only the red- or green-sensitive version and are red-green color-blind. When researchers injected a virus containing the gene for the missing version into the retina of adult male monkeys, evidence of full color vision was apparent after 20 weeks (Figure 50.21).

The squirrel monkey gene therapy studies demonstrate that the neural circuits required to process visual information can be generated or activated even in adults, making it possible to treat a range of vision disorders. Indeed, gene therapy has been used to treat Leber's congenital amaurosis (LCA), an inherited retinal degenerative disease that causes severe loss of vision. After using gene therapy to restore vision in dogs and mice with LCA, researchers successfully treated the disease in humans by injecting the functional LCA gene in a viral vector (see Figure 20.22).

The Visual Field

The brain not only processes visual information but also controls what information is captured. One important type of control is focusing, which in humans occurs by changing the shape of the lens, as noted earlier and illustrated in **Figure 50.22**. When you focus your eyes on a close object, your lenses become almost spherical. When you view a distant object, your lenses are flattened.

Although our peripheral vision allows us to see objects over a nearly 180° range, the distribution of photoreceptors across the eye limits both what we see and how well we see it. Overall, the human retina contains about 125 million rods and 6 million cones. At the **fovea**, the center of the visual field, there are no rods but a very high density

▲ **Figure 50.21 Gene therapy for vision.** Once color-blind, this adult male monkey treated with gene therapy demonstrates his ability to distinguish red from green.

MAKE CONNECTIONS *Red-green color blindness is X-linked in squirrel monkeys and humans (see Figure 15.7). Why is the inheritance pattern in humans not apparent in squirrel monkeys?*

▼ **Figure 50.22 Focusing in the mammalian eye.** Ciliary muscles control the shape of the lens, which bends light and focuses it on the retina. The thicker the lens, the more sharply the light is bent.

(a) Near vision (accommodation)

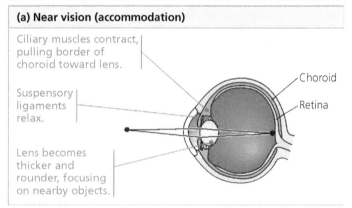

Ciliary muscles contract, pulling border of choroid toward lens.

Suspensory ligaments relax.

Lens becomes thicker and rounder, focusing on nearby objects.

Choroid

Retina

(b) Distance vision

Ciliary muscles relax, and border of choroid moves away from lens.

Suspensory ligaments pull against lens.

Lens becomes flatter, focusing on distant objects.

of cones—about 150,000 cones per square millimeter. The ratio of cones to rods falls with distance from the fovea, with the peripheral regions having only rods. In daylight, you achieve your sharpest vision by looking directly at an object, such that light shines on the tightly packed cones in your fovea. At night, looking directly at a dimly lit object is ineffective, since the rods—the more sensitive light receptors—are absent from the fovea. For this reason you see a dim star best by focusing on a point just to one side of it.

CONCEPT CHECK 50.3

1. Contrast the light-detecting organs of planarians and flies. How is each organ adaptive for the lifestyle of the animal?

2. In a condition called presbyopia, the eyes' lenses lose much of their elasticity and maintain a flat shape. Explain how this condition affects a person's vision.

3. WHAT IF? Our brain receives more action potentials when our eyes are exposed to light even though our photoreceptors release more neurotransmitter in the dark. Propose an explanation.

4. MAKE CONNECTIONS Compare the function of retinal in the eye with that of the pigment chlorophyll in a plant photosystem (see Concept 10.2).

For suggested answers, see Appendix A.

CONCEPT 50.4
The senses of taste and smell rely on similar sets of sensory receptors

Animals use their chemical senses for a wide range of purposes, such as to find mates, to recognize marked territories, and to help navigate during migration. Animals such as ants and bees that live in large social groups rely extensively on chemical "conversation." In all animals, chemical senses are important in feeding behavior. For example, a hydra retracts its tentacles toward its mouth when it detects the compound glutathione, which is released from prey captured by the tentacles.

The perceptions of **gustation** (taste) and **olfaction** (smell) both depend on chemoreceptors. In the case of terrestrial animals, taste is the detection of chemicals called **tastants** that are present in a solution, and smell is the detection of **odorants** that are carried through the air. There is no distinction between taste and smell in aquatic animals.

In insects, taste receptors are located within sensory hairs located on the feet and in mouthparts, where they are used to select food. A tasting hair contains several chemoreceptors, each especially responsive to a particular class of tastant, such as sugar or salt. Insects are also capable of smelling airborne odorants using olfactory hairs, usually located on their antennae (see Figure 50.6). The chemical DEET (*N,N*-diethyl-meta-toluamide), sold as an insect "repellant," actually protects against bites by blocking the olfactory receptor in mosquitoes that detects human scent.

Taste in Mammals

Humans and other mammals perceive five tastes: sweet, sour, salty, bitter, and umami. Umami (Japanese for "delicious") is elicited by the amino acid glutamate. Used as a flavor enhancer, monosodium glutamate (MSG) occurs naturally in foods such as meat and aged cheese. Researchers have identified the receptor proteins for all five tastes.

For decades, many researchers assumed that a taste cell could have more than one type of receptor. An alternative idea is that each taste cell has a single receptor type, programming the cell to recognize only one of the five tastes. Which hypothesis is correct? In 2005, scientists at the University of California, San Diego, used a cloned bitter taste receptor to genetically reprogram gustation in a mouse (Figure 50.23).

▼ Figure 50.23 | Inquiry

How do mammals detect different tastes?

Experiment To investigate the basis of mammalian taste perception, researchers used a chemical called phenyl-β-D-glucopyranoside (PBDG). Humans find PBDG extremely bitter. Mice, however, lack a receptor for PBDG. Mice avoid drinking water containing other bitter tastants but show no aversion to water that contains PBDG.

Using a molecular cloning strategy, Mueller generated mice that made the human PBDG receptor in cells that normally make either a sweet receptor or a bitter receptor. The mice were given a choice of two bottles, one filled with pure water and one filled with water containing PBDG at varying concentrations. The researchers then observed whether the mice had an attraction or an aversion to PBDG.

Results

Relative consumption = (Fluid intake from bottle containing PBDG ÷ Total fluid intake) × 100%

Conclusion The researchers found that the presence of a bitter receptor in sweet taste cells is sufficient to cause mice to be attracted to a bitter chemical. They concluded that the mammalian brain must therefore perceive sweet or bitter taste solely on the basis of which sensory neurons are activated.

Source: K. L. Mueller et al., The receptors and coding logic for bitter taste, *Nature* 434:225–229 (2005).

WHAT IF? *Suppose instead of the PBDG receptor the researchers had used a receptor specific for a sweetener that humans crave but mice ignore. How would the results of the experiment have differed?*

Based on these and other studies, the researchers concluded that an individual taste cell expresses a single receptor type and detects tastants representing only one of the five tastes.

The receptor cells for taste in mammals are modified epithelial cells organized into **taste buds**, which are scattered in several areas of the tongue and mouth (Figure 50.24). Most taste buds on the tongue are associated with nipple-shaped projections called papillae. Any region of the tongue with taste buds can detect any of the five types of taste. (The frequently reproduced "taste maps" of the tongue are thus not accurate.)

The sensation of sweet, umami, and bitter tastes requires a G protein-coupled receptor, or GPCR (see Figure 11.7).

(a) The tongue. Small raised structures called papillae cover the tongue surface. The enlarged cross section shows the side walls of a papilla lined with taste buds.

Key

Sweet   Bitter
Salty   Umami
Sour

(b) A taste bud. Taste buds in all regions of the tongue contain sensory receptor cells specific for each of the five taste types.
© Pearson Education, Inc.

▲ **Figure 50.24 Human taste receptors.**

In humans, there are more than 30 different receptors for bitter taste, and each receptor is able to recognize multiple bitter tastants. In contrast, humans have one type of sweet receptor and one type of umami receptor, each assembled from a different pair of GPCR proteins. Other GPCR proteins are critical for the sense of smell, as we will discuss shortly.

The receptor for sour tastants belongs to the TRP family and is similar to the capsaicin receptor and other thermoreceptor proteins. In taste buds, the TRP proteins of the sour receptor assemble into an ion channel in the plasma membrane of the taste cell. Binding of an acid or other sour-tasting substance to the receptor triggers a change in the ion channel. Depolarization occurs, activating a sensory neuron.

The taste receptor for salt turns out to be a sodium channel. Not surprisingly, it specifically detects sodium salts, such as the NaCl that we use in cooking and flavoring.

Smell in Humans

In olfaction, unlike gustation, the sensory cells are neurons. Olfactory receptor cells line the upper portion of the nasal cavity and send impulses along their axons to the olfactory bulb of the brain (Figure 50.25). The receptive ends of the cells contain cilia that extend into the layer of mucus coating the nasal cavity. When an odorant diffuses into this region, it binds to a specific GPCR protein called an odorant receptor (OR) on the plasma membrane of the olfactory cilia. These events trigger signal transduction leading to the production of cyclic AMP. In olfactory cells, cyclic AMP opens channels in the plasma membrane that are permeable to both Na^+ and Ca^{2+}. The flow of these ions into the receptor cell leads to depolarization of the membrane, generating action potentials.

Humans can distinguish thousands of different odors, each caused by a structurally distinct odorant. This level of sensory discrimination requires many different ORs. In 1991, Richard Axel and Linda Buck, working at Columbia University, discovered a family of more than 1,000 OR genes—about 3% of all human genes. Each olfactory receptor cell appears to express one OR gene. Cells selective for different odorants are interspersed in the nasal cavity. Those cells that express the same OR gene transmit action potentials to the same small region of the olfactory bulb. In 2004, Axel and Buck shared a Nobel Prize for their studies of the gene family and receptors that function in olfaction.

After odorants are detected, information from olfactory receptors is collected and integrated. Genetic studies on mice, worms, and flies have shown that signals from the nervous system regulate this process, dialing the response to particular odorants up or down. As a result, animals can detect the location of food sources even if the concentration of a key odorant is particularly low or high.

▲ **Figure 50.25 Smell in humans.** Odorant molecules bind to specific chemoreceptor proteins in the plasma membrane of olfactory receptor cells, triggering action potentials. Each olfactory receptor cell has just one type of chemoreceptor. As shown, cells that express different chemoreceptors detect different odorants.

WHAT IF? *If you spray an "air freshener" in a musty room, would you be affecting detection, transmission, or perception of the odorants responsible for the musty smell?*

Studies of model organisms also reveal that complex mixtures of odorants are not processed as the simple sum of each input. Rather, the brain integrates olfactory information from different receptors into single sensations. These sensations contribute to the perception of the environment in the present and to the memory of events and emotions.

Although the receptors and neuronal pathways for taste and smell are independent, the two senses do interact. Indeed, much of the complex flavor humans experience when eating is due to our sense of smell. If the olfactory system is blocked, as occurs when you have a head cold, the perception of taste is sharply reduced.

CONCEPT CHECK 50.4

1. Explain why some taste receptor cells and all olfactory receptor cells use G protein-coupled receptors, yet only olfactory receptor cells produce action potentials.

2. Pathways involving G proteins provide an opportunity for an increase in signal strength in the course of signal transduction, a change referred to as amplification. How might this be beneficial in olfaction?

3. **WHAT IF?** If you discovered a mutation in mice that disrupted the ability to taste sweet, bitter, and umami, but not sour or salty, what might you predict about where this mutation acts in the signaling pathways used by these receptors?

For suggested answers, see Appendix A.

CONCEPT 50.5

The physical interaction of protein filaments is required for muscle function

In discussing sensory mechanisms, we have seen some examples of how sensory inputs to the nervous system result in specific behaviors: the touch-guided foraging of a star-nosed mole, the upside-down swimming of a crayfish with manipulated statocysts, and the light-avoiding maneuvers of planarians. Underlying these diverse behaviors are common fundamental mechanisms: Feeding, swimming, and crawling all require muscle activity in response to nervous system motor output.

Muscle cell contraction relies on the interaction between protein structures called thin and thick filaments. The major component of **thin filaments** is the globular protein actin. In thin filaments, two strands of polymerized actin are coiled around one another; similar actin structures called microfilaments function in cell motility. The **thick filaments** are staggered arrays of myosin molecules. Muscle contraction is the product of filament movement powered by chemical energy; muscle extension occurs only passively. To understand how filaments contribute to muscle contraction, we will begin by examining vertebrate skeletal muscle.

Vertebrate Skeletal Muscle

Vertebrate **skeletal muscle**, which moves bones and body, has a hierarchy of smaller and smaller units **(Figure 50.26)**. Within a typical skeletal muscle is a bundle of long fibers running parallel to the length of the muscle. Each fiber is a single cell with multiple nuclei (each nucleus is derived from one of the embryonic cells that fused to form the muscle cell). Inside a muscle cell lies a longitudinal bundle of **myofibrils**, which contain the thin and thick filaments.

▲ **Figure 50.26** **The structure of skeletal muscle.**

The myofibrils in muscle fibers are made up of repeating sections called **sarcomeres**, which are the basic contractile units of skeletal muscle. The borders of the sarcomere line up in adjacent myofibrils, forming a pattern of light and dark bands (striations) visible with a light microscope. For this reason, skeletal muscle is also called *striated muscle*. Thin filaments attach at the Z lines, while thick filaments are anchored at the M lines centered in the sarcomere (see Figure 50.26). In a resting (relaxed) myofibril, thick and thin filaments partially overlap. Near the edge of the sarcomere there are only thin filaments, whereas the zone in the center contains only thick filaments. This arrangement is the key to how the sarcomere, and hence the whole muscle, contracts.

The Sliding-Filament Model of Muscle Contraction

A contracting muscle shortens, but the filaments that bring about contraction stay the same length. To explain this apparent paradox, we'll focus first on a single sarcomere. As shown in **Figure 50.27**, the filaments slide past each other, much like the segments of a telescoping support pole. According to the well-accepted **sliding-filament model**, the thin and thick filaments ratchet past each other, powered by myosin molecules.

Figure 50.28 illustrates the cycles of change in the myosin molecule that form the basis for the longitudinal sliding of the thick and thin filaments. Each myosin molecule has a long "tail" region and a globular "head" region. The tail adheres to the tails of other myosin molecules, binding together the thick filament. The head, which extends to the side, can bind ATP. Hydrolysis of bound ATP converts myosin to a high-energy form that binds to actin, forming a cross-bridge. The myosin head then returns to its low-energy form as it pulls the thin filament toward the center of the sarcomere. When a new molecule of ATP binds to the myosin head, the cross-bridge is broken.

Muscle contraction requires repeated cycles of binding and release. In each cycle, the myosin head freed from a cross-bridge cleaves the newly bound ATP and binds again to actin. Because the thin filament moved toward the center of the sarcomere in the previous cycle, the myosin head now attaches to a new binding site farther along the thin filament. A thick filament contains approximately 350 heads, each of which forms and re-forms about five cross-bridges per second, driving the thick and thin filaments past each other.

At rest, most muscle fibers contain only enough ATP for a few contractions. Powering repetitive contractions requires two other storage compounds: creatine phosphate and glycogen. Transfer of a phosphate group from creatine phosphate to ADP in an enzyme-catalyzed reaction synthesizes additional ATP. In this way, the resting supply of creatine phosphate can sustain contractions for about 15

► **Figure 50.27 The sliding-filament model of muscle contraction.** The drawings on the left show that the lengths of the thick (myosin) filaments (purple) and thin (actin) filaments (orange) remain the same as a muscle fiber contracts.

Sarcomere

Z   M   Z

Relaxed muscle

0.5 µm

Contracting muscle

Fully contracted muscle

Contracted sarcomere

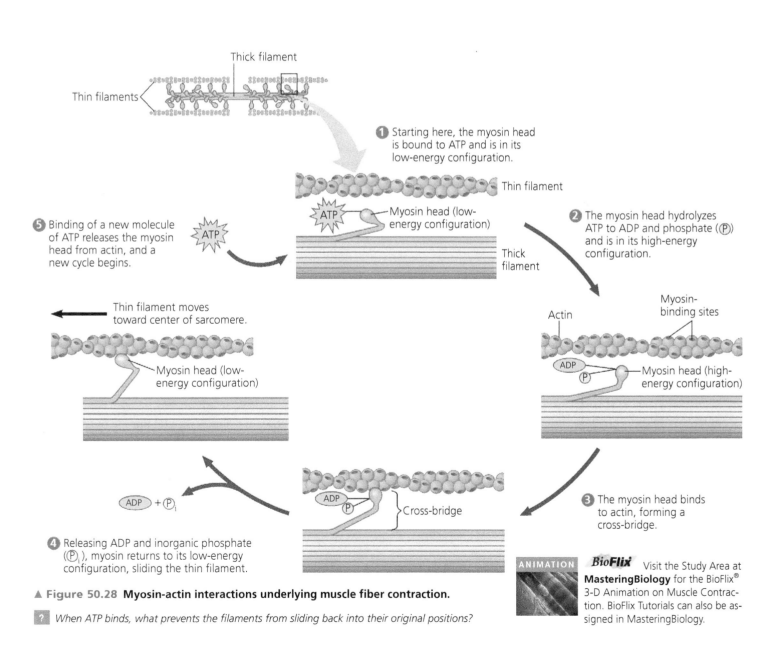

Thick filament

Thin filaments

① Starting here, the myosin head is bound to ATP and is in its low-energy configuration.

Thin filament

ATP

Myosin head (low-energy configuration)

Thick filament

⑤ Binding of a new molecule of ATP releases the myosin head from actin, and a new cycle begins.

ATP

② The myosin head hydrolyzes ATP to ADP and phosphate (Ⓟ) and is in its high-energy configuration.

Actin

Myosin-binding sites

ADP
Ⓟ

Myosin head (high-energy configuration)

Thin filament moves toward center of sarcomere.

Myosin head (low-energy configuration)

ADP + Ⓟᵢ

ADP
Ⓟ

Cross-bridge

③ The myosin head binds to actin, forming a cross-bridge.

④ Releasing ADP and inorganic phosphate (Ⓟᵢ), myosin returns to its low-energy configuration, sliding the thin filament.

▲ **Figure 50.28 Myosin-actin interactions underlying muscle fiber contraction.**

? *When ATP binds, what prevents the filaments from sliding back into their original positions?*

ANIMATION *BioFlix* Visit the Study Area at **MasteringBiology** for the BioFlix® 3-D Animation on Muscle Contraction. BioFlix Tutorials can also be assigned in MasteringBiology.

seconds. ATP stores are also replenished when glycogen is broken down to glucose. During light or moderate muscle activity, this glucose is metabolized by aerobic respiration. This highly efficient metabolic process yields enough power to sustain contractions for nearly an hour. During intense muscle activity, oxygen becomes limiting and ATP is instead generated by lactic acid fermentation (see Chapter 9). This anaerobic pathway, although very rapid, generates much less ATP per glucose molecule and can sustain contraction for only about 1 minute.

The Role of Calcium and Regulatory Proteins

Calcium ions (Ca^{2+}) and proteins bound to actin play crucial roles in muscle contraction and relaxation. **Tropomyosin**, a regulatory protein, and the **troponin complex**, a set of additional regulatory proteins, are bound to the actin strands of thin filaments. In a muscle fiber at rest, tropomyosin covers the myosin-binding sites along the thin filament, preventing actin and myosin from interacting (Figure 50.29a). When Ca^{2+} accumulates in the cytosol, it binds to the troponin complex, causing tropomyosin bound along the actin strands to shift position and expose the myosin-binding sites on the thin filament (Figure 50.29b). Thus, when the Ca^{2+} concentration rises in the cytosol, the thin and thick filaments slide past each other, and the muscle fiber contracts. When the Ca^{2+} concentration falls, the binding sites are covered, and contraction stops.

Motor neurons cause muscle contraction by triggering the release of Ca^{2+} into the cytosol of muscle cells with

(a) Myosin-binding sites blocked

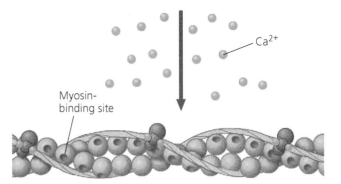

(b) Myosin-binding sites exposed

▲ **Figure 50.29 The role of regulatory proteins and calcium in muscle fiber contraction.** Each thin filament consists of two strands of actin, two long molecules of tropomyosin, and multiple copies of the troponin complex.

which they form synapses. This regulation of Ca^{2+} concentration is a multistep process involving a network of membranes and compartments within the muscle cell. As you read the following description, refer to the overview and diagram in **Figure 50.30**.

The arrival of an action potential at the synaptic terminal of a motor neuron causes release of the neurotransmitter acetylcholine. Binding of acetylcholine to receptors on the muscle fiber leads to a depolarization, triggering an action potential. Within the muscle fiber, the action potential spreads deep into the interior, following infoldings of the plasma membrane called **transverse (T) tubules**. These make close contact with the **sarcoplasmic reticulum (SR)**, a specialized endoplasmic reticulum. As the action potential spreads along the T tubules, it triggers changes in the SR, opening Ca^{2+} channels. Calcium ions stored in the interior of the SR flow through open channels into the cytosol and bind to the troponin complex, initiating the muscle fiber contraction.

When motor neuron input stops, the filaments slide back to their starting position. Relaxation begins as transport proteins in the SR pump Ca^{2+} in from the cytosol. When the Ca^{2+} concentration in the cytosol drops to a low level, the regulatory proteins bound to the thin filament shift back to their starting position, once again blocking the myosin-binding sites. At the same time, the Ca^{2+} pumped from the cytosol accumulates in the SR, providing the stores needed to respond to the next action potential.

Several diseases cause paralysis by interfering with the excitation of skeletal muscle fibers by motor neurons. In amyotrophic lateral sclerosis (ALS), motor neurons in the spinal cord and brainstem degenerate, and muscle fibers atrophy. ALS is progressive and usually fatal within five years after symptoms appear. In myasthenia gravis, a person produces antibodies to the acetylcholine receptors of skeletal muscle. As the disease progresses and the number of receptors decreases, transmission between motor neurons and muscle fibers declines. Myasthenia gravis can generally be controlled with drugs that inhibit acetylcholinesterase or suppress the immune system.

Nervous Control of Muscle Tension

Whereas contraction of a single skeletal muscle fiber is a brief all-or-none twitch, contraction of a whole muscle, such as the biceps in your upper arm, is graded; you can voluntarily alter the extent and strength of its contraction. The nervous system produces graded contractions of whole muscles by varying (1) the number of muscle fibers that contract and (2) the rate at which muscle fibers are stimulated. Let's consider each mechanism in turn.

In vertebrates, each branched motor neuron may synapse with many muscle fibers, although each fiber is controlled by only one motor neuron. A **motor unit** consists of a single motor neuron and all the muscle fibers it controls

Exploring The Regulation of Skeletal Muscle Contraction

The electrical, chemical, and molecular events regulating skeletal muscle contraction are shown in a cutaway view of a muscle cell and in the enlarged diagram below. Action potentials (red arrows) triggered by the motor neuron sweep across the muscle fiber and into it along the transverse (T) tubules, initiating the movements of calcium (green dots) that regulate muscle activity.

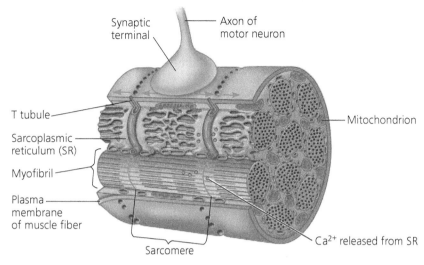

Synaptic terminal

Axon of motor neuron

T tubule

Sarcoplasmic reticulum (SR)

Myofibril

Plasma membrane of muscle fiber

Sarcomere

Mitochondrion

Ca^{2+} released from SR

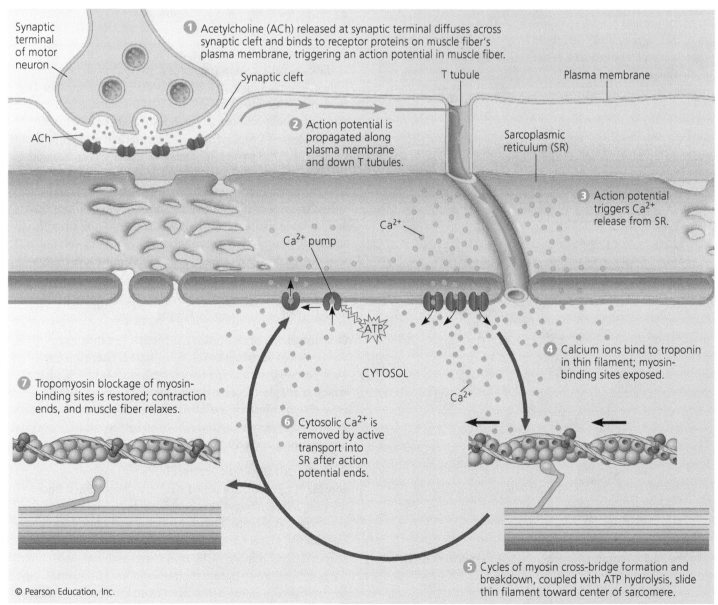

Synaptic terminal of motor neuron

ACh

Synaptic cleft

1 Acetylcholine (ACh) released at synaptic terminal diffuses across synaptic cleft and binds to receptor proteins on muscle fiber's plasma membrane, triggering an action potential in muscle fiber.

2 Action potential is propagated along plasma membrane and down T tubules.

T tubule

Plasma membrane

Sarcoplasmic reticulum (SR)

3 Action potential triggers Ca^{2+} release from SR.

Ca^{2+}

Ca^{2+} pump

ATP

CYTOSOL

Ca^{2+}

4 Calcium ions bind to troponin in thin filament; myosin-binding sites exposed.

7 Tropomyosin blockage of myosin-binding sites is restored; contraction ends, and muscle fiber relaxes.

6 Cytosolic Ca^{2+} is removed by active transport into SR after action potential ends.

5 Cycles of myosin cross-bridge formation and breakdown, coupled with ATP hydrolysis, slide thin filament toward center of sarcomere.

© Pearson Education, Inc.

(Figure 50.31). When a motor neuron produces an action potential, all the muscle fibers in its motor unit contract as a group. The strength of the resulting contraction depends on how many muscle fibers the motor neuron controls. In the whole muscle, there may be hundreds of motor units.

As more and more of the motor neurons controlling the muscle are activated, a process called *recruitment*, the force (tension) developed by a muscle progressively increases Depending on the number of motor neurons your brain recruits and the size of their motor units, you can lift a fork or something much heavier, like your biology textbook. Some muscles, especially those that hold up the body and maintain posture, are almost always partially contracted. In such muscles, the nervous system may alternate activation among the motor units, reducing the length of time any one set of fibers is contracted.

Prolonged contraction can result in muscle fatigue due to the depletion of ATP and dissipation of ion gradients required for normal electrical signaling. Although accumulation of lactate may also contribute to muscle fatigue, recent research actually points to a beneficial effect of lactate on muscle function.

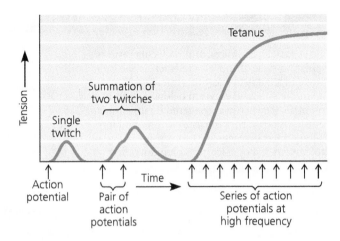

▲ **Figure 50.32 Summation of twitches.** This graph illustrates how the number of action potentials during a short period of time influences the tension developed in a muscle fiber.

> **?** *How could the nervous system cause a skeletal muscle to produce the most forceful contraction it is capable of?*

The nervous system regulates muscle contraction not only by controlling which motor units are activated but also by varying the rate of muscle fiber stimulation. A single action potential produces a twitch lasting about 100 milliseconds or less. If a second action potential arrives before the muscle fiber has completely relaxed, the two twitches add together, resulting in greater tension **(Figure 50.32).** Further summation occurs as the rate of stimulation increases. When the rate is so high that the muscle fiber cannot relax at all between stimuli, the twitches fuse into one smooth, sustained contraction called **tetanus.** (Note that tetanus is also the name of a disease of uncontrolled muscle contraction caused by a bacterial toxin.)

Types of Skeletal Muscle Fibers

Our discussion to this point has focused on the general properties of vertebrate skeletal muscles. There are, however, several distinct types of skeletal muscle fibers, each of which is adapted to a particular set of functions. We typically classify these varied fiber types both by the source of ATP used to power their activity and by the speed of their contraction **(Table 50.1).**

Oxidative and Glycolytic Fibers Fibers that rely mostly on aerobic respiration are called oxidative fibers. Such fibers are specialized in ways that enable them to make use of a steady energy supply: They have many mitochondria, a rich blood supply, and a large amount of an oxygen-storing protein called **myoglobin**. A brownish red pigment, myoglobin binds oxygen more tightly than does hemoglobin, enabling oxidative fibers to extract oxygen from the blood efficiently. In contrast, glycolytic fibers have a larger diameter and less

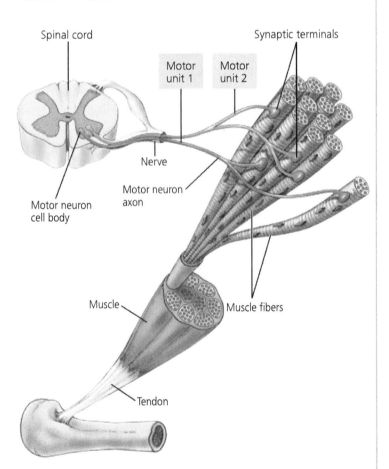

▲ **Figure 50.31 Motor units in a vertebrate skeletal muscle.** Each muscle fiber (cell) forms synapses with only one motor neuron, but each motor neuron typically synapses with many muscle fibers. A motor neuron and all the muscle fibers it controls constitute a motor unit.

Table 50.1	Types of Skeletal Muscle Fibers		
	Slow Oxidative	Fast Oxidative	Fast Glycolytic
Contraction speed	Slow	Fast	Fast
Major ATP source	Aerobic respiration	Aerobic respiration	Glycolysis
Rate of fatigue	Slow	Intermediate	Fast
Mitochondria	Many	Many	Few
Myoglobin content	High (red muscle)	High (red muscle)	Low (white muscle)

▲ **Figure 50.33 Specialization of skeletal muscles.** The male toadfish (*Opsanus tau*) uses superfast muscles to produce its mating call.

myoglobin. Also, glycolytic fibers use glycolysis as their primary source of ATP and fatigue more readily than oxidative fibers. These two fiber types are readily apparent in the muscle of poultry and fish: The dark meat is made up of oxidative fibers rich in myoglobin, and the light meat is composed of glycolytic fibers.

Fast-Twitch and Slow-Twitch Fibers Muscle fibers vary in the speed with which they contract: **Fast-twitch fibers** develop tension two to three times faster than **slow-twitch fibers**. Fast fibers enable brief, rapid, powerful contractions. Compared with a fast fiber, a slow fiber has less sarcoplasmic reticulum and pumps Ca^{2+} more slowly. Because Ca^{2+} remains in the cytosol longer, a muscle twitch in a slow fiber lasts about five times as long as one in a fast fiber.

The difference in contraction speed between slow-twitch and fast-twitch fibers mainly reflects the rate at which their myosin heads hydrolyze ATP. However, there isn't a one-to-one relationship between contraction speed and ATP source. Whereas all slow-twitch fibers are oxidative, fast-twitch fibers can be either glycolytic or oxidative.

Most human skeletal muscles contain both fast-twitch and slow-twitch fibers, although the muscles of the eye and hand are exclusively fast-twitch. In a muscle that has a mixture of fast and slow fibers, the relative proportions of each are genetically determined. However, if such a muscle is used repeatedly for activities requiring high endurance, some fast glycolytic fibers can develop into fast oxidative fibers. Because fast oxidative fibers fatigue more slowly than fast glycolytic fibers, the result will be a muscle that is more resistant to fatigue.

Some vertebrates have skeletal muscle fibers that twitch at rates far faster than any human muscle. For example, super-fast muscles produce a rattlesnake's rattle and a dove's coo. Even faster are the muscles surrounding the gas-filled swim bladder of the male toadfish **(Figure 50.33)**. In producing its "boat whistle" mating call, the toadfish can contract and relax these muscles more than 200 times per second!

Other Types of Muscle

Although all muscles share the same fundamental mechanism of contraction—actin and myosin filaments sliding past each other—there are many different types of muscle. Vertebrates, for example, have cardiac muscle and smooth muscle in addition to skeletal muscle (see Figure 40.5).

Vertebrate **cardiac muscle** is found only in the heart. Like skeletal muscle, cardiac muscle is striated. However, skeletal and cardiac muscle fibers differ in their electrical and membrane properties. Whereas skeletal muscle fibers require motor neuron input to produce action potentials, ion channels in the plasma membrane of cardiac muscle cells cause rhythmic depolarizations that trigger action potentials without nervous system input. Furthermore, these action potentials last up to 20 times longer than those of the skeletal muscle fibers.

Adjacent cardiac muscles cells are electrically coupled by specialized regions called **intercalated disks**. This coupling enables the action potential generated by specialized cells in one part of the heart to spread, causing the whole heart to contract. A long refractory period prevents summation and tetanus.

Smooth muscle in vertebrates is found mainly in the walls of hollow organs, such as blood vessels and organs of the digestive tract. Smooth muscle cells lack striations because their actin and myosin filaments are not regularly arrayed along the length of the cell. Instead, the thick filaments are scattered throughout the cytoplasm, and the thin filaments are attached to structures called dense bodies, some of which are tethered to the plasma membrane. There is less myosin than in striated muscle fibers, and the myosin is not associated with specific actin strands. Some smooth muscle cells contract only when stimulated by neurons of the autonomic nervous system. Others are electrically coupled to one another and can generate action potentials without input from neurons. Smooth muscles contract and relax more slowly than striated muscles.

Although Ca^{2+} regulates smooth muscle contraction, the mechanism for regulation is different from that in skeletal and cardiac muscle. Smooth muscle cells have no troponin complex or T tubules, and their sarcoplasmic reticulum is not well developed. During an action potential, Ca^{2+} enters the cytosol mainly through the plasma membrane. Calcium ions cause contraction by binding to the protein calmodulin, which activates an enzyme that phosphorylates the myosin head, enabling cross-bridge activity.

Invertebrates have muscle cells similar to vertebrate skeletal and smooth muscle cells, and arthropod skeletal muscles are nearly identical to those of vertebrates. However, because the flight muscles of insects are capable of independent, rhythmic contraction, the wings of some insects can actually beat faster than action potentials can arrive from the central nervous system. Another interesting evolutionary adaptation has been discovered in the muscles that hold a clam's shell closed. The thick filaments in these muscles contain a protein called paramyosin that enables the muscles to remain contracted for as long as a month with only a low rate of energy consumption.

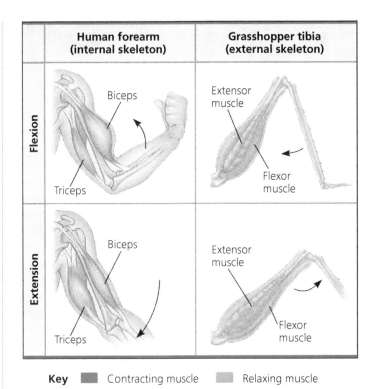

CONCEPT CHECK 50.5

1. Contrast the role of Ca^{2+} in the contraction of a skeletal muscle fiber and a smooth muscle cell.

2. **WHAT IF?** Why are the muscles of an animal that has recently died likely to be stiff?

3. **MAKE CONNECTIONS** How does the activity of tropomyosin and troponin in muscle contraction compare with the activity of a competitive inhibitor in enzyme action? (See Figure 8.18b.)

For suggested answers, see Appendix A.

CONCEPT 50.6

Skeletal systems transform muscle contraction into locomotion

Converting muscle contraction to movement requires a skeleton—a rigid structure to which muscles can attach. An animal changes its shape or location by contracting muscles connecting two parts of its skeleton. Often muscles are anchored to bone indirectly via connective tissue formed into a tendon.

Because muscles exert force only during contraction, moving a body part back and forth typically requires two muscles attached to the same section of the skeleton. We

▲ Figure 50.34 **The interaction of muscles and skeletons in movement.** Back-and-forth movement of a body part is generally accomplished by antagonistic muscles. This arrangement works with either an internal skeleton, as in mammals, or an external skeleton, as in insects.

can see such an arrangement of muscles in the upper portion of a human arm or grasshopper leg **(Figure 50.34)**. Although we call such muscles an antagonistic pair, their function is actually cooperative, coordinated by the nervous system. For example, when you extend your arm, motor neurons trigger your triceps muscle to contract while the absence of neuronal input allows your biceps to relax.

Vital for movement, the skeletons of animals also function in support and protection. Most land animals would collapse if they had no skeleton to support their mass. Even an animal living in water would be formless without a framework to maintain its shape. In many animals, a hard skeleton also protects soft tissues. For example, the vertebrate skull protects the brain, and the ribs of terrestrial vertebrates form a cage around the heart, lungs, and other internal organs.

Types of Skeletal Systems

Although we tend to think of skeletons only as interconnected sets of bones, skeletons come in many different forms. Hardened support structures can be external (as in exoskeletons), internal (as in endoskeletons), or even absent (as in fluid-based, or hydrostatic, skeletons).

Hydrostatic Skeletons

A **hydrostatic skeleton** consists of fluid held under pressure in a closed body compartment. This is the main type of skeleton in most cnidarians, flatworms, nematodes, and annelids (see Chapter 33). These animals control their form and movement by using muscles to change the shape of fluid-filled compartments. Among the cnidarians, for example, a hydra elongates by closing its mouth and constricting its central gastrovascular cavity using contractile cells in its body wall. Because water maintains its volume under pressure, the cavity must elongate when its diameter is decreased.

Worms carry out locomotion in a variety of ways. In planarians and other flatworms, movement results mainly from muscles in the body wall exerting localized forces against the interstitial fluid. In nematodes (roundworms), longitudinal muscles contracting around the fluid-filled body cavity move the animal forward by wavelike motions called undulations. In earthworms and many other annelids, circular and longitudinal muscles act together to change the shape of individual fluid-filled segments, which are divided by septa. These shape changes bring about **peristalsis**, a movement produced by rhythmic waves of muscle contractions passing from front to back (Figure 50.35).

Hydrostatic skeletons are well suited for life in aquatic environments. On land, they provide support for crawling and burrowing and may cushion internal organs from shocks. However, a hydrostatic skeleton cannot support walking or running, in which an animal's body is held off the ground.

Exoskeletons

The clam shell you find on a beach once served as an **exoskeleton**, a hard covering deposited on an animal's surface. The shells of clams and most other molluscs are made of calcium carbonate secreted by the mantle, a sheetlike extension of the body wall (see Figure 33.15). Clams and other bivalves close their hinged shell using muscles attached to the inside of this exoskeleton. As the animal grows, it enlarges its shell by adding to the outer edge.

Insects and other arthropods have a jointed exoskeleton called a *cuticle*, a nonliving coat secreted by the epidermis. About 30–50% of the arthropod cuticle consists of **chitin**, a polysaccharide similar to cellulose (see Figure 5.8). Fibrils of chitin are embedded in a protein matrix, forming a composite material that combines strength and flexibility. The cuticle may be hardened with organic compounds and, in some cases, calcium salts. In body parts that must be flexible, such as leg joints, the cuticle remains unhardened. Muscles are attached to knobs and plates of the cuticle that extend into the interior of the body. With each growth

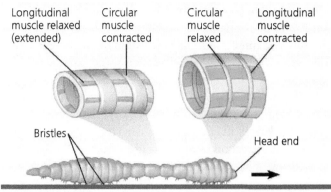

① At the moment depicted, body segments at the earthworm's head end and just in front of the rear end are short and thick (longitudinal muscles contracted; circular muscles relaxed) and are anchored to the ground by bristles. The other segments are thin and elongated (circular muscles contracted; longitudinal muscles relaxed).

② The head has moved forward because circular muscles in the head segments have contracted. Segments behind the head and at the rear are now thick and anchored, thus preventing the worm from slipping backward.

③ The head segments are thick again and anchored in their new positions. The rear segments have released their hold on the ground and have been pulled forward.

▲ **Figure 50.35 Crawling by peristalsis.** Contraction of the longitudinal muscles thickens and shortens the earthworm; contraction of the circular muscles constricts and elongates it.

spurt, an arthropod must shed its exoskeleton (molt) and produce a larger one.

Endoskeletons

Animals ranging from sponges to mammals have a hardened internal skeleton, or **endoskeleton**, buried within their soft tissues. In sponges, the endoskeleton consists of hard needle-like structures of inorganic material or fibers made of protein. Echinoderms' bodies are reinforced by ossicles, hard plates composed of magnesium carbonate and calcium carbonate crystals. Whereas the ossicles of sea urchins are tightly bound, the ossicles of sea stars are more loosely linked, allowing a sea star to change the shape of its arms.

Chordates have an endoskeleton consisting of cartilage, bone, or some combination of these materials (see

Figure 40.5). The mammalian skeleton contains more than 200 bones, some fused together and others connected at joints by ligaments that allow freedom of movement (Figures 50.36 and 50.37). Cells called *osteoblasts* secrete bone matrix and thereby build and repair bone (see Figure 40.5). *Osteoclasts* have an opposite function, resorbing bone components in remodeling of the skeleton.

How thick does an endoskeleton need to be? We can begin to answer this question by applying ideas from civil engineering. The weight of a building increases with the cube of its dimensions. However, the strength of a support depends on its cross-sectional area, which only increases with the square of its diameter. We can thus predict that if we scaled up a mouse

to the size of an elephant, the legs of the giant mouse would be too thin to support its weight. Indeed, large animals have very different body proportions from small ones.

In applying the building analogy, we might also predict that the size of leg bones should be directly proportional to the strain imposed by body weight. Animal bodies, however, are complex and nonrigid. In supporting body weight, it turns out that body posture—the position of the legs relative to the main body—is more important than leg size, at least in mammals and birds. In addition, muscles and tendons, which hold the legs of large mammals relatively straight and positioned under the body, actually bear most of the load.

▼ **Figure 50.36 Bones and joints of the human skeleton.**

▼ **Figure 50.37 Types of joints.**

Ball-and-socket joint

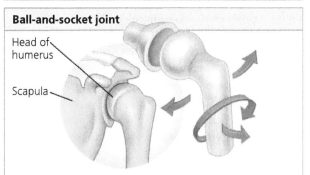

Ball-and-socket joints are found where the humerus contacts the shoulder girdle and where the femur contacts the pelvic girdle. These joints enable the arms and legs to rotate and move in several planes.

Hinge joint

Hinge joints, such as between the humerus and the head of the ulna, restrict movement to a single plane.

Pivot joint

Pivot joints enable rotating the forearm at the elbow and turning the head from side to side.

Types of Locomotion

Movement is a hallmark of animals. Even animals fixed to a surface move their body parts: Sponges use beating flagella to generate water currents that draw and trap small food particles, and sessile cnidarians wave tentacles that capture prey (see Chapter 33). Most animals, however, are mobile and spend a considerable portion of their time and energy actively searching for food, escaping from danger, and seeking mates. These activities involve **locomotion**— active travel from place to place.

Friction and gravity tend to keep an animal stationary and therefore oppose locomotion. To move, an animal must expend energy to overcome these two forces. As we will see next, the amount of energy required to oppose friction or gravity is often reduced by an animal body plan adapted for movement in a particular environment.

▲ **Figure 50.38 Energy-efficient locomotion on land.** Members of the kangaroo family travel from place to place mainly by leaping on their large hind legs. Kinetic energy momentarily stored in tendons after each leap provides a boost for the next leap. In fact, a large kangaroo hopping at 30 km/hr uses no more energy per minute than it does at 6 km/hr. The large tail helps to balance the kangaroo when it leaps as well as when it sits.

Locomotion on Land

On land, a walking, running, hopping, or crawling animal must be able to support itself and move against gravity, but air poses relatively little resistance, at least at moderate speeds. When a land animal walks, runs, or hops, its leg muscles expend energy both to propel it and to keep it from falling down. With each step, the animal's leg muscles must overcome inertia by accelerating a leg from a standing start. For moving on land, powerful muscles and strong skeletal support are therefore more important than a streamlined shape.

Diverse adaptations for traveling on land have evolved in various vertebrates. For example, kangaroos have large, powerful muscles in their hind legs, suitable for locomotion by hopping **(Figure 50.38)**. As a kangaroo lands after each leap, tendons in its hind legs momentarily store energy. The farther the animal hops, the more energy its tendons store. Analogous to the energy in a compressed spring, the energy stored in the tendons is available for the next jump and reduces the total amount of energy the animal must expend to travel. The legs of an insect, dog, or human also retain some energy during walking or running, although a considerably smaller share than those of a kangaroo.

Maintaining balance is another prerequisite for walking, running, or hopping. A kangaroo's large tail helps balance its body during leaps and also forms a stable tripod with its hind legs when the animal sits or moves slowly. Illustrating the same principle, a walking cat, dog, or horse keeps three feet on the ground. Bipedal animals, such as humans

and birds, keep part of at least one foot on the ground when walking. When an animal runs, all four feet (or both feet for bipeds) may be off the ground briefly, but at running speeds it is momentum more than foot contact that keeps the body upright.

Crawling poses a very different challenge. Having much of its body in contact with the ground, a crawling animal must exert considerable effort to overcome friction. As you have read, earthworms crawl by peristalsis. In contrast, many snakes crawl by undulating their entire body from side to side. Assisted by large, movable scales on its underside, a snake's body pushes against the ground, propelling the animal forward. Some snakes, such as boa constrictors and pythons, creep straight forward, driven by muscles that lift belly scales off the ground, tilt the scales forward, and then push them backward against the ground.

Swimming

Because most animals are reasonably buoyant in water, overcoming gravity is less of a problem for swimming animals than for species that move on land or through the air. On the other hand, water is a much denser and more viscous medium than air, and thus drag (friction) is a major problem for aquatic animals. A sleek, fusiform (torpedolike) shape is a common adaptation of fast swimmers (see Figure 40.2).

Most animal phyla include species that swim, but swimming occurs in diverse ways. Many insects and four-legged vertebrates use their legs as oars to push against the water. Squids, scallops, and some cnidarians are jet-propelled, taking in water and squirting it out in bursts. Sharks and bony fishes swim by moving their body and tail from side to side, while whales and dolphins move by undulating their body and tail up and down.

Interpreting a Graph with Log Scales

What Are the Energy Costs of Locomotion? In the 1960s, animal physiologist Knut Schmidt-Nielsen, at Duke University, wondered whether general principles govern the energy costs of different forms of locomotion among diverse animal species. To answer this question, he drew on his own experiments as well as those of other researchers. In this exercise you will analyze the combined results of these studies and evaluate the rationale for plotting the experimental data on a graph with logarithmic scales.

How the Experiments Were Done Researchers measured the rate of oxygen consumption or carbon dioxide production in animals that ran on treadmills, swam in water flumes, or flew in wind tunnels. For example, a tube connected to a plastic face mask collected gases exhaled by a parakeet during flight (see photo at upper right). From these measurements, Schmidt-Nielsen calculated the amount of energy each animal used to transport a given amount of body mass over a given distance (calories/kilogram · meter).

Data from the Experiments Schmidt-Nielsen plotted the cost of running, flying, and swimming versus body mass on a single graph with logarithmic (log) scales for the axes. He then drew a best-fit straight line through the data points for each form of locomotion. (On the graph below, the individual data points are not shown.)

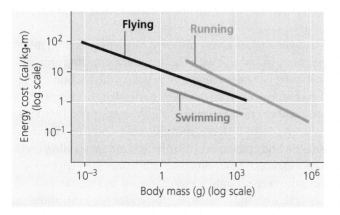

Interpret the Data

1. The body masses of the animals used in these experiments ranged from about 0.001 g to 1,000,000 g, and their rates of energy use ranged from about 0.1 cal/kg · m to 100 cal/kg · m. If you were to plot these data on a graph with linear instead of log scales for the axes, how would you draw the axes so that all of the data would be visible? What is the advantage of using log scales for plotting data with a wide range of values? (For additional information about graphs, see the Scientific Skills Review in Appendix F and in the Study Area in MasteringBiology.)

2. Based on the graph, how much greater is the energy cost of flying for an animal that weighs 10^{-3} g than for an animal that weighs 1 g? For any given form of locomotion, which travels more efficiently, a larger animal or smaller animal?

3. The slopes of the flying and swimming lines are very similar. Based on your answer to question 2, if the energy cost of a 2-g swimming animal is 1.2 cal/kg · m, what is the estimated energy cost of a 2-kg swimming animal?

4. Considering animals with a body mass of about 100 g, rank the three forms of locomotion from highest energy cost to lowest energy cost. Were these the results you expected, based on your own experience? What could explain the energy cost of running compared to that of flying or swimming?

5. Schmidt-Nielson calculated the swimming cost in a mallard duck and found that it was nearly 20 times as high as the swimming cost in a salmon of the same body mass. What could explain the greater swimming efficiency of salmon?

(MB) A version of this Scientific Skills Exercise can be assigned in MasteringBiology.

Data from K. Schmidt-Nielsen, Locomotion: Energy cost of swimming, flying, and running, *Science* 177:222–228 (1972). Reprinted with permission from AAAS.

Flying

Active flight (in contrast to gliding downward from a tree) has evolved in only a few animal groups: insects, reptiles (including birds), and, among the mammals, bats. One group of flying reptiles, the pterosaurs, died out millions of years ago, leaving birds and bats as the only flying vertebrates.

Gravity poses a major problem for a flying animal because its wings must develop enough lift to overcome gravity's downward force. The key to flight is wing shape. All wings act as airfoils—structures whose shape alters air currents in a way that helps animals or airplanes stay aloft. As for the body to which the wings attach, a fusiform shape helps reduce drag in air as it does in water.

Flying animals are relatively light, with body masses ranging from less than a gram for some insects to about 20 kg for the largest flying birds. Many flying animals have structural adaptations that contribute to low body mass. Birds, for example, have no urinary bladder or teeth and have relatively

large bones with air-filled regions that help lessen the bird's weight (see Chapter 34).

Flying, running, and swimming each impose different energetic demands on animals. In the Scientific Skills Exercise, you can interpret a graph that compares the relative energy costs of these three forms of locomotion.

CONCEPT CHECK 50.6

1. In what way are septa an important feature of the earthworm skeleton?

2. Contrast swimming and flying in terms of the main problems they pose and the adaptations that allow animals to overcome those problems.

3. **WHAT IF?** When using your arms to lower yourself into a chair, you bend your arms without using your biceps. Explain how this is possible. (*Hint:* Think about gravity as an antagonistic force.)

For suggested answers, see Appendix A.

CONCEPT 50.1

Sensory receptors transduce stimulus energy and transmit signals to the central nervous system (pp. 1102–1106)

- The detection of a stimulus precedes **sensory transduction**, the change in the membrane potential of a **sensory receptor** in response to a stimulus. The resulting receptor potential controls **transmission** of action potentials to the CNS, where sensory information is integrated to generate **perceptions.** The frequency of action potentials in an axon and the number of axons activated determine stimulus strength. The identity of the axon carrying the signal encodes the nature or quality of the stimulus.
- **Mechanoreceptors** respond to stimuli such as pressure, touch, stretch, motion, and sound. **Chemoreceptors** detect either total solute concentrations or specific molecules. **Electromagnetic receptors** detect different forms of electromagnetic radiation. **Thermoreceptors** signal surface and core temperatures of the body. Pain is detected by a group of **nociceptors** that respond to excess heat, pressure, or specific classes of chemicals.

? *To simplify sensory receptor classification, why might it make sense to eliminate nociceptors as a distinct class?*

CONCEPT 50.2

The mechanoreceptors responsible for hearing and equilibrium detect moving fluid or settling particles (pp. 1106–1100)

- Most invertebrates sense their orientation with respect to gravity by means of **statocysts**. Specialized **hair cells** form the basis for hearing and balance in mammals and for detection of water movement in fishes and aquatic amphibians. In mammals, the **tympanic membrane** (eardrum) transmits sound waves to bones of the middle ear, which transmit the waves through the oval window to the fluid in the coiled **cochlea** of the inner ear. Pressure waves in the fluid vibrate the basilar membrane, depolarizing hair cells and triggering action potentials that travel via the auditory nerve to the brain. Receptors in the inner ear function in balance and equilibrium.

? *How are music volume and pitch encoded in signals to the brain?*

CONCEPT 50.3

The diverse visual receptors of animals depend on light-absorbing pigments (pp. 1111–1117)

- Invertebrates have varied light detectors, including simple light-sensitive eyespots, image-forming compound eyes, and single-lens eyes. In the vertebrate eye, a single lens is used to focus light on **photoreceptors** in the **retina**. Both **rods** and **cones** contain a pigment, **retinal**, bonded to a protein (opsin). Absorption of light by retinal triggers a signal transduction pathway that hyperpolarizes the photoreceptors, causing them to release less neurotransmitter. Synapses transmit information from photoreceptors to cells that integrate information and convey it to the brain along axons that form the optic nerve.

? *How does processing of sensory information sent to the vertebrate brain in vision differ from that in hearing or olfaction?*

CONCEPT 50.4

The senses of taste and smell rely on similar sets of sensory receptors (pp. 1117–1119)

- Taste (**gustation**) and smell (**olfaction**) depend on stimulation of chemoreceptors by small dissolved molecules. In humans, sensory cells in taste buds express a receptor type specific for one of the five taste perceptions: sweet, sour, salty, bitter, and umami (elicited by glutamate). Olfactory receptor cells line the upper part of the nasal cavity. More than 1,000 genes code for membrane proteins that bind to specific classes of odorants, and each receptor cell appears to express only one of those genes.

? *Why do foods taste bland when you have a head cold?*

CONCEPT 50.5

The physical interaction of protein filaments is required for muscle function (pp. 1119–1126)

- The muscle cells (fibers) of vertebrate skeletal muscle contain myofibrils composed of **thin filaments** of (mostly) actin and **thick filaments** of myosin. These filaments are organized into repeating units called **sarcomeres**. Myosin heads, energized by the hydrolysis of ATP, bind to the thin filaments, form cross-bridges, and then release upon binding ATP anew. As this cycle repeats, the thick and thin filaments slide past each other, shortening the sarcomere and contracting the muscle fiber.

- Motor neurons release acetylcholine, triggering action potentials in muscle fibers that stimulate the release of Ca^{2+} from the **sarcoplasmic reticulum**. When the Ca^{2+} binds the **troponin complex, tropomyosin** moves, exposing the myosin-binding sites on actin and thus initiating cross-bridge formation. A **motor unit** consists of a motor neuron and the muscle fibers it controls. A twitch results from one action potential. Skeletal muscle fibers are slow-twitch or fast-twitch and oxidative or glycolytic.
- Cardiac muscle, found in the heart, consists of striated cells electrically connected by intercalated disks and generate action potentials without input from neurons. In smooth muscles, contractions are initiated by the muscles or by stimulation from neurons in the autonomic nervous system.

? *What are two major functions of ATP hydrolysis in skeletal muscle activity?*

Skeletal systems transform muscle contraction into locomotion (pp. 1126–1130)

* Skeletal muscles, often in antagonistic pairs, contract and pull against the skeleton. Skeletons may be **hydrostatic** and maintained by fluid pressure, as in worms; hardened into **exoskeletons**, as in insects; or in the form of **endoskeletons**, as in vertebrates.

* Each form of **locomotion**—swimming, movement on land, or flying—presents a particular challenge. For example, swimmers need to overcome friction, but face less of a challenge from gravity than do animals that move on land or fly.

? *Explain how microscopic and macroscopic anchoring of muscle filaments enables you to bend your elbow.*

TEST YOUR UNDERSTANDING

LEVEL 1: KNOWLEDGE/COMPREHENSION

1. Which of the following sensory receptors is *incorrectly* paired with its category?
   a. hair cell—mechanoreceptor
   b. muscle spindle—mechanoreceptor
   c. taste receptor—chemoreceptor
   d. olfactory receptor—electromagnetic receptor

2. The middle ear converts
   a. air pressure waves to fluid pressure waves.
   b. air pressure waves to nerve impulses.
   c. fluid pressure waves to nerve impulses.
   d. pressure waves to hair cell movements.

3. During the contraction of a vertebrate skeletal muscle fiber, calcium ions
   a. break cross-bridges by acting as a cofactor in the hydrolysis of ATP.
   b. bind with troponin, changing its shape so that the myosin-binding sites on actin are exposed.
   c. transmit action potentials from the motor neuron to the muscle fiber.
   d. spread action potentials through the T tubules.

LEVEL 2: APPLICATION/ANALYSIS

4. Which sensory distinction is *not* encoded by a difference in neuron identity?
   a. white and red
   b. red and green
   c. loud and faint
   d. salty and sweet

5. The transduction of sound waves into action potentials occurs
   a. within the tectorial membrane as it is stimulated by the hair cells.
   b. when hair cells are bent against the tectorial membrane, causing them to depolarize and release neurotransmitter that stimulates sensory neurons.
   c. as the basilar membrane vibrates at different frequencies in response to the varying volume of sounds.
   d. within the middle ear as the vibrations are amplified by the malleus, incus, and stapes.

LEVEL 3: SYNTHESIS/EVALUATION

6. Although some sharks close their eyes just before they bite, their bites are on target. Researchers have noted that sharks often misdirect their bites at metal objects and that they can find batteries buried under sand. This evidence suggests that sharks keep track of their prey during the split second before they bite, in the same way that
   a. a rattlesnake finds a mouse in its burrow.
   b. an insect avoids being stepped on.
   c. a star-nosed mole locates its prey in tunnels.
   d. a platypus locates its prey in a muddy river.

7. **DRAW IT** Based on the information in the text, fill in the following graph. Use one line for rods and another line for cones.

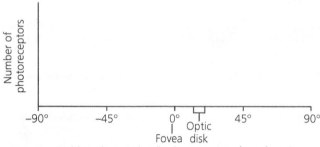

Position along retina (in degrees away from fovea)

8. **EVOLUTION CONNECTION**
   In general, locomotion on land will require more energy than locomotion in water. By integrating what you learned about animal form and function in Unit 7, discuss some of the evolutionary adaptations of mammals that support the high energy requirements for moving on land.

9. **SCIENTIFIC INQUIRY**
   Although skeletal muscles generally fatigue fairly rapidly, clam shell muscles have a protein called paramyosin that allows them to sustain contraction for up to a month. From your knowledge of the cellular mechanism of contraction, propose a hypothesis to explain how paramyosin might work. How would you test your hypothesis experimentally?

10. **WRITE ABOUT A THEME: ORGANIZATION**
    In a short essay (100–150 words), describe at least three ways in which the structure of the lens of the human eye is well adapted to its function in vision.

11. **SYNTHESIZE YOUR KNOWLEDGE**

Bloodhounds, which are adept at following a scent trail even days old, have 1,000 times as many olfactory receptor cells as we have. How might this difference contribute to the tracking ability of these dogs? What differences in brain organization would you expect in comparing a bloodhound and a human?

For selected answers, see Appendix A.

MasteringBiology®

Students Go to **MasteringBiology** for assignments, the eText, and the Study Area with practice tests, animations, and activities.

Instructors Go to **MasteringBiology** for automatically graded tutorials and questions that you can assign to your students, plus Instructor Resources.

51

Animal Behavior

▲ **Figure 51.1 What prompts a male fiddler crab to display his giant claw?**

The How and Why of Animal Activity

Unlike most animals, male fiddler crabs (genus *Uca*) are highly asymmetrical: One claw grows to giant proportions, up to half the mass of the entire body **(Figure 51.1)**. The name *fiddler* comes from the crab's behavior as it feeds on algae from the mudflats where it lives: The smaller of the front claws moves to and from the mouth in front of the enlarged claw. At other times the male waves his large claw in the air. What triggers this behavior? What purpose does it serve?

Claw waving by a male fiddler crab has two functions. Waving the claw, which can be used as a weapon, helps the crab *repel* other males wandering too close to his burrow. Vigorous claw waving also helps him *attract* females, who wander through the crab colony in search of a mate. After the male fiddler crab lures a female to his burrow, he seals her in with mud or sand in preparation for mating.

Animal behavior, be it solitary or social, fixed or variable, is based on physiological systems and processes. An individual **behavior** is an action carried out by muscles under control of the nervous system. Examples include an animal using its throat muscles to produce a song, releasing a scent to mark its territory, or simply waving a claw. Behavior is an essential part of acquiring nutrients and finding a partner for sexual reproduction. Behavior also contributes to homeostasis, as when honeybees huddle to conserve heat (see Concept 40.3). In short, all of animal physiology contributes to behavior, and behavior influences all of physiology.

1133

Being essential for survival and reproduction, behavior is subject to substantial natural selection over time. This evolutionary process of selection also affects anatomy because the recognition and communication that underlie many behaviors depend on body form and appearance. Thus, the enlarged claw of the male fiddler crab is an adaptation that enables the display essential for recognition by other members of the species. Similarly, the positioning of the eyes on stalks held well above the crab's head enables him to see intruders from far off.

In this chapter, we'll examine how behavior is controlled, how it develops during an animal's life, and how it is influenced by genes and the environment. We'll also explore the ways in which behavior evolves over many generations. Shifting our focus from an animal's inner workings to its interactions with the outside world will set the stage for exploring ecology, the subject of Unit Eight.

CONCEPT 51.1

Discrete sensory inputs can stimulate both simple and complex behaviors

What approach do biologists use to determine how behaviors arise and what functions they serve? The Dutch scientist Niko Tinbergen, a pioneer in the study of animal behavior, suggested that understanding any behavior requires answering four questions, which can be summarized as follows:

1. What stimulus elicits the behavior, and what physiological mechanisms mediate the response?
2. How does the animal's experience during growth and development influence the response?
3. How does the behavior aid survival and reproduction?
4. What is the behavior's evolutionary history?

Tinbergen's first two questions ask about *proximate causation*: "how" a behavior occurs or is modified. The last two questions ask about *ultimate causation*: "why" a behavior occurs in the context of natural selection. Thus any given behavior has both proximate and ultimate causes.

Studies on proximate causation by Tinbergen and two other early researchers—Karl von Frisch and Konrad Lorenz—earned the three scientists a Nobel Prize in 1973. We'll consider those experiments in the early part of the chapter. The concept of ultimate causation is central to **behavioral ecology**, the study of the ecological and evolutionary basis for animal behavior. We'll explore this vibrant area of modern biological research in the rest of the chapter.

Fixed Action Patterns

In addressing Tinbergen's first question, the nature of the stimuli that trigger behavior, we'll begin with behavioral

responses to well-defined stimuli, starting with an example from Tinbergen's own experiments.

As part of his research, Tinbergen kept fish tanks containing three-spined sticklebacks (*Gasterosteus aculeatus*). Male sticklebacks, which have red bellies, attack other males that invade their nesting territories. Tinbergen noticed that his male sticklebacks also behaved aggressively when a red truck passed within view of their tank. Inspired by this chance observation, he carried out experiments showing that the red color of an intruder's underside is the proximate cause of the attack behavior. A male stickleback will not attack a fish lacking red coloration (note that female sticklebacks never have red bellies), but will attack even unrealistic models if they contain areas of red color (**Figure 51.2**).

The territorial response of male sticklebacks is an example of a **fixed action pattern**, a sequence of unlearned acts directly linked to a simple stimulus. Fixed action patterns are essentially unchangeable and, once initiated, usually carried to completion. The trigger for the behavior is an

(a) A male stickleback fish attacks other male sticklebacks that invade its nesting territory. The red belly of the intruding male (left) acts as the sign stimulus that releases the aggressive behavior.

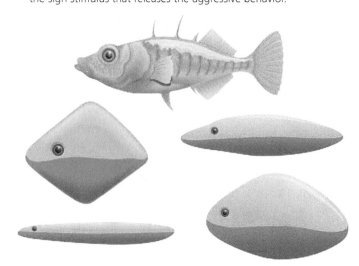

(b) The realistic model at the top, without a red underside, produces no aggressive response in a male three-spined stickleback. The other models, with red undersides, produce strong responses.

▲ Figure 51.2 **Sign stimuli in a classic fixed action pattern.**

? *Suggest an explanation for why this behavior evolved (its ultimate causation).*

external cue called a **sign stimulus**, such as a red object that prompts the male stickleback's aggressive behavior.

Migration

Environmental stimuli not only trigger behaviors but also provide cues that animals use to carry out those behaviors. For example, a wide variety of birds, fishes, and other animals use environmental cues to guide **migration**—a regular, long-distance change in location (**Figure 51.3**). In the course of migration, many animals pass through environments they have not previously encountered. How, then, do they find their way in these foreign settings?

Some migrating animals track their position relative to the sun, even though the sun's position relative to Earth changes throughout the day. Animals can adjust for these changes by means of a *circadian clock*, an internal mechanism that maintains a 24-hour activity rhythm or cycle (see Concept 49.2). For example, experiments have shown that migrating birds orient differently relative to the sun at distinct times of the day. Nocturnal animals can instead use the North Star, which has a constant position in the night sky.

Although the sun and stars can provide useful clues for navigation, these landmarks can be obscured by clouds. How do migrating animals overcome this problem? A simple experiment with homing pigeons provides one answer. On an overcast day, placing a small magnet on the head of

a homing pigeon prevents it from returning efficiently to its roost. Researchers concluded that pigeons sense their position relative to Earth's magnetic field and can thereby navigate without solar or celestial cues.

The way in which animals detect Earth's magnetic field remains a matter of investigation. It is known that the heads of migrating birds (and fishes) contain bits of magnetite, a magnetic iron mineral. There is also evidence that cells in the pigeon's brainstem encode information about magnetic field direction, intensity, and polarity. The search continues for magnetoreceptors, which in migrating birds appear to be located in the eye, beak, and perhaps inner ear.

Behavioral Rhythms

Although the circadian clock plays a small but significant role in navigation by some migrating species, it has a major role in the daily activity of all animals. As discussed in Chapters 40 and 49, the clock is responsible for a circadian rhythm, a daily cycle of rest and activity. The clock is normally synchronized with the light and dark cycles of the environment but can maintain rhythmic activity even under constant environmental conditions, such as during hibernation.

Some behaviors, such as migration and reproduction, reflect biological rhythms with a longer cycle, or period, than the circadian rhythm. Behavioral rhythms linked to the yearly cycle of seasons are called *circannual rhythms*. Although migration and reproduction typically correlate with food availability, these behaviors are not a direct response to changes in food intake. Instead, circannual rhythms, like circadian rhythms, are influenced by the periods of daylight and darkness in the environment. For example, studies with several bird species have shown that an artificial environment with extended daylight can induce out-of-season migratory behavior.

Not all biological rhythms are linked to the light and dark cycles in the environment. Consider, for instance, the fiddler crab shown in Figure 51.1. The male's claw-waving courtship behavior is linked to the timing of the new and full moon. Why? Fiddler crabs begin their lives as plankton, settling in the mudflats after several larval stages. By courting at the time of the new or full moon, crabs link their reproduction to the times of greatest tidal movement. The tides disperse larvae to deeper waters, where they complete early development in relative safety before returning to the tidal flats.

▼ **Figure 51.3 Migration.** Wildebeest herds migrate long distances twice each year, changing their feeding grounds in coordination with the dry and rainy seasons.

Animal Signals and Communication

Claw waving by fiddler crabs during courtship is an example of one animal (the male crab) generating the stimulus that guides the behavior of another animal (the female crab). A stimulus transmitted from one organism to another is called a **signal**. The transmission and reception of signals between animals constitute **communication**, which often has a role in the proximate causation of behavior.

Forms of Animal Communication

Let's consider the courtship behavior of the fruit fly, *Drosophila melanogaster*, as an introduction to the four common modes of animal communication: visual, chemical, tactile, and auditory.

Fruit fly courtship constitutes a *stimulus-response chain*, in which the response to each stimulus is itself the stimulus for the next behavior **(Figure 51.4)**. In the first step, a male detects a female in his field of vision and orients his body toward hers. To confirm she belongs to his species, he uses his olfactory system to detect chemicals she releases into the air. The male then approaches and touches the female with a foreleg. This touching, or tactile communication, alerts the female to the male's presence. In the third stage of courtship, the male extends and vibrates one of his wings, producing a courtship song. This auditory communication informs the female whether the male is of the same species. Only if all of these forms of communication are successful will the female allow the male to attempt copulation.

In general, the form of communication that evolves is closely related to an animal's lifestyle and environment. For example, most terrestrial mammals are nocturnal, which makes visual displays relatively ineffective. Instead, these species use olfactory and auditory signals, which work as well in the dark as in the light. In contrast, most birds are diurnal (active mainly in daytime) and communicate primarily by visual and auditory signals. Humans are also diurnal and, like birds, use primarily visual and auditory communication.

We can thus detect and appreciate the songs and bright colors used by birds to communicate but miss many chemical cues on which other mammals base their behavior.

The information content of animal communication varies considerably. One of the most remarkable examples is the symbolic language of the European honeybee (*Apis mellifera*), discovered in the early 1900s by Austrian researcher Karl von Frisch. Using glass-walled observation hives, he and his students spent several decades observing honeybees. Methodical recordings of bee movements enabled von Frisch to decipher a "dance language" that returning foragers use to inform other bees about the distance and direction of travel to food sources.

A returning bee quickly becomes the center of attention for other bees, called followers **(Figure 51.5a)**. If the food source is close to the hive (less than 50 m away), the returning bee moves in tight circles while moving its abdomen from side to side **(Figure 51.5b)**. This behavior, called the "round dance," motivates the follower bees to leave the hive and search for nearby food.

When the food source is farther from the nest, the returning bee instead performs a "waggle dance." This dance, consisting of a half-circle swing in one direction, a straight run during which the bee waggles its abdomen, and a half-circle swing in the other direction, communicates to the follower bees both the direction and distance of the food source in relation to the hive **(Figure 51.5c)**. The angle of the straight run relative to the hive's vertical surface is the same as the horizontal angle of the food in relation to the sun. For example, if the returning bee runs at a 30° angle to the right of vertical, the follower bees leaving the hive fly 30° to the right of the horizontal direction of the sun. A dance with a longer straight run, and therefore more abdominal waggles per run, indicates a greater distance to the food source. As follower bees exit the hive, they fly almost directly to the area indicated by the waggle dance. By using flower odor and other clues, they locate the food source within this area.

▶ **Figure 51.4 Courtship behavior of the fruit fly.** Fruit fly courtship involves a fixed set of behaviors that follow one another in a rigid order.

Male visually recognizes female.

Female releases chemicals detected by the male's sense of smell.

❶ **Orienting**

Male taps female's abdomen with a foreleg.

❷ **Tapping**

Male extends and vibrates wing, producing a courtship song.

❸ **"Singing"**

(a) Worker bees cluster around a recently returned bee.

(b) The round dance indicates that food is near.

Beehive

Location **A**:
Food source is in same direction as sun.

Location **B**:
Food source is in direction opposite sun.

Location **C**:
Food source is 30° to right of sun.

(c) The waggle dance is performed when food is distant. The waggle dance resembles a figure eight. Distance is indicated by the number of abdominal waggles performed in the straight-run part of the dance. Direction is indicated by the angle (in relation to the vertical surface of the hive) of the straight run.

▲ **Figure 51.5 Honeybee dance language.** Honeybees returning to the hive communicate the location of food sources through the symbolic language of a dance.

Pheromones

Animals that communicate through odors or tastes emit chemical substances called **pheromones**. Pheromones are especially common among mammals and insects and often relate to reproductive behavior. For example, pheromones are the basis for the chemical communication in fruit fly courtship (see Figure 51.4). Pheromones are not limited to short-distance signaling, however. Male silkworm moths have receptors that can detect the pheromone from a female moth from several kilometers away (see Figure 50.6).

In a honeybee colony, pheromones produced by the queen and her daughters, the workers, maintain the hive's complex social order. One pheromone (once called the queen substance) has a particularly wide range of effects. It attracts workers to the queen, inhibits development of ovaries in workers, and attracts males (drones) to the queen during her mating flights out of the hive.

Pheromones can also serve as alarm signals. For example, when a minnow or catfish is injured, a substance released from the fish's skin disperses in the water, inducing a fright response in other fish. These nearby fish become more vigilant and often form tightly packed schools near the river or lake bottom, where they are safer from attack (Figure 51.6). Pheromones can be very effective at remarkably low concentrations. For instance, just 1 cm^2 of skin from a fathead minnow contains sufficient alarm substance to induce a reaction in 58,000 L of water.

So far in this chapter, we have explored the types of stimuli that elicit behaviors—the first part of Tinbergen's first question. The second part of that question—the physiological mechanisms that mediate responses—involves the nervous, muscular, and skeletal systems: Stimuli activate sensory systems, are processed in the central nervous system, and result in motor outputs that constitute behavior. Thus, we are ready to focus on Tinbergen's second question—how experience influences behavior.

❶ Minnows are widely dispersed in an aquarium before an alarm substance is introduced.

❷ Within seconds of the alarm substance being introduced, minnows aggregate near the bottom of the aquarium and reduce their movement.

▲ **Figure 51.6 Minnows responding to the presence of an alarm substance.**

1. If an egg rolls out of the nest, a mother graylag goose will retrieve it by nudging it with her beak and head. If researchers remove the egg or substitute a ball during this process, the goose continues to bob her beak and head while she moves back to the nest. Explain how and why this behavior occurs.

2. **WHAT IF?** Suppose you exposed various fish species from the minnows' environment to the alarm substance from minnows. Thinking about natural selection, suggest why some species might respond like minnows, some might increase their activity, and some might show no change.

3. **MAKE CONNECTIONS** How is the lunar-linked rhythm of fiddler crab courtship similar in mechanism and function to the seasonal timing of plant flowering? (See Concept 39.3.)

For suggested answers, see Appendix A.

CONCEPT 51.2

Learning establishes specific links between experience and behavior

For some behaviors—such as a fixed action pattern, a courtship stimulus-response chain, and pheromone signaling—nearly all individuals in a population behave alike. Behavior that is developmentally fixed in this way is known as **innate behavior**. Other behaviors, however, vary with experience and thus differ between individuals.

Experience and Behavior

Tinbergen's second question asks how an animal's experiences during growth and development influence the response to stimuli. One informative approach to this question is a **cross-fostering study**, in which the young of one species are placed in the care of adults from another species. The extent to which the offspring's behavior changes in such a situation provides a measure of how the social and physical environment influences behavior.

Certain mouse species have behaviors well suited for cross-fostering studies. Male California mice (*Peromyscus californicus*) are highly aggressive toward other mice and provide extensive parental care. In contrast, male white-footed mice (*Peromyscus leucopus*) are less aggressive and engage in little parental care. When the pups of each species were placed in the nests of the other species, the cross-fostering altered some behaviors of both species **(Table 51.1)**. For instance, male California mice raised by white-footed mice were less aggressive toward intruders. Thus, experience during development can strongly influence aggressive behavior in these rodents.

One of the most important findings of the cross-fostering experiments with mice was that the influence of experience

Table 51.1 Influence of Cross-Fostering on Male Mice*

Species	Aggression Toward an Intruder	Aggression In Neutral Situation	Paternal Behavior
California mice fostered by white-footed mice	Reduced	No difference	Reduced
White-footed mice fostered by California mice	No difference	Increased	No difference

*Comparisons are with mice raised by parents of their own species.

on behavior can be passed on to progeny: When the cross-fostered California mice became parents, they spent less time retrieving offspring who wandered off than did California mice raised by their own species. Thus, experience during development can modify physiology in a way that alters parental behavior, extending the influence of environment to a subsequent generation.

For humans, the influence of genetics and environment on behavior can be explored by a **twin study**, in which researchers compare the behavior of identical twins raised apart with the behavior of those raised in the same household. Twin studies have been instrumental in studying disorders, such as schizophrenia, anxiety disorders, and alcoholism, that alter human behavior.

Learning

One powerful way that an animal's environment can influence its behavior is through **learning**, the modification of behavior as a result of specific experiences. The capacity for learning depends on nervous system organization established during development following instructions encoded in the genome. Learning itself involves the formation of memories by specific changes in neuronal connectivity (see Concept 49.4). Therefore, the essential challenge for research into learning is not to decide between nature (genes) and nurture (environment), but rather to explore the contributions of *both* nature and nurture in shaping learning and, more generally, behavior.

Imprinting

In some species, the ability of offspring to recognize and be recognized by a parent is essential for survival. In the young, this learning often takes the form of **imprinting**, the establishment of a long-lasting behavioral response to a particular individual or object. Imprinting can take place only during a specific time period in development, called the **sensitive period**. Among gulls, for instance, the sensitive period for a parent to bond with its young lasts one to two days. During the sensitive period, the young imprint on their parent and learn basic behaviors, while the parent learns to recognize its offspring. If bonding does not occur, the parent will not care for the offspring, leading to the death of the offspring and a decrease in the reproductive success of the parent.

How do the young know on whom—or what—to imprint? Experiments with many species of waterfowl indicate that young birds have no innate recognition of "mother." Rather, they identify with the first object they encounter that has certain key characteristics. In the 1930s, the Austrian researcher Konrad Lorenz showed that the principal imprinting stimulus in graylag geese (*Anser anser*) is a nearby object that is moving away from the young. When incubator-hatched goslings spent their first few hours with Lorenz rather than with a goose, they imprinted on him and steadfastly followed him from then on **(Figure 51.7a)**. Furthermore, they showed no recognition of their biological mother.

Imprinting has become an important component of efforts to save endangered species, such as the whooping crane (*Grus americana*). Scientists tried raising whooping cranes in captivity by using sandhill cranes (*Grus canadensis*) as foster parents. However, because the whooping cranes imprinted on their foster parents, none formed a *pair-bond* (strong attachment) with a whooping crane mate. To avoid such problems, captive breeding programs now isolate young cranes, exposing them to the sights and sounds of members of their own species.

Scientists have made further use of imprinting to teach cranes born in captivity to migrate along safe routes. Young whooping cranes are imprinted on humans in "crane suits" and then allowed to follow these "parents" as they fly ultralight aircraft along selected migration routes **(Figure 51.7b)**. Importantly, these cranes still pair-bond with other whooping cranes, indicating that the crane costumes have the features required to direct "normal" imprinting.

Spatial Learning and Cognitive Maps

Every natural environment has spatial variation, as in locations of nest sites, hazards, food, and prospective mates. Therefore, an organism's fitness may be enhanced by the capacity for **spatial learning**, the establishment of a memory that reflects the environment's spatial structure.

The idea of spatial learning intrigued Tinbergen while he was a graduate student in the Netherlands. At that time, he was studying the female digger wasp (*Philanthus triangulum*), which nests in small burrows dug into sand dunes. When a wasp leaves her nest to go hunting, she hides the entrance from potential intruders by covering it with sand. When she returns, however, she flies directly to her hidden

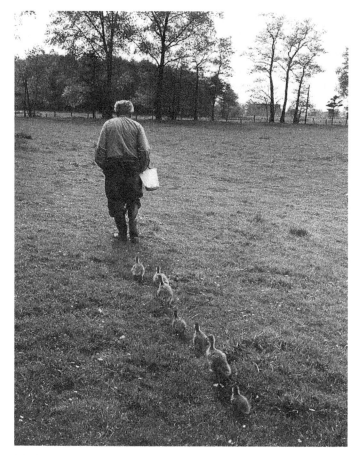

(a) These young greylag geese imprinted on ethologist Konrad Lorenz.

(b) A pilot wearing a crane suit and flying an ultralight plane acts as a surrogate parent to direct the migration of whooping cranes.

▲ **Figure 51.7 Imprinting.** Imprinting can be altered to **(a)** investigate animal behavior or **(b)** direct animal behavior.

WHAT IF? *Suppose the geese following Lorenz were bred to each other. How might their imprinting on Lorenz affect their offspring? Explain.*

nest, despite the presence of hundreds of other burrows in the area. How does she accomplish this feat? Tinbergen hypothesized that a wasp locates her nest by learning its position relative to visible landmarks. To test his hypothesis, he carried out an experiment in the wasps' natural habitat

(Figure 51.8). By manipulating objects around nest entrances, he demonstrated that digger wasps engage in spatial learning. This experiment was so simple and informative that it could be summarized very concisely. In fact, at 32 pages, Tinbergen's Ph.D. thesis from 1932 is still the shortest ever approved at Leiden University.

▼ Figure 51.8 | **Inquiry**

Does a digger wasp use landmarks to find her nest?

Experiment A female digger wasp covers the entrance to her nest while foraging for food, but finds the correct wasp nest reliably upon her return 30 minutes or more later. Niko Tinbergen wanted to test the hypothesis that a wasp learns visual landmarks that mark her nest before she leaves on hunting trips. First, he marked one nest with a ring of pinecones while the wasp was in the burrow. After leaving the nest to forage, the wasp returned to the nest successfully.

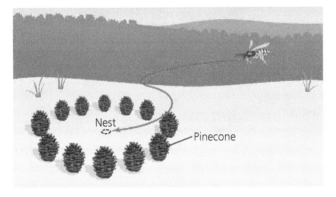

Two days later, after the wasp had again left, Tinbergen shifted the ring of pinecones away from the nest. Then he waited to observe the wasp's behavior.

Results When the wasp returned, she flew to the center of the pinecone circle instead of to the nearby nest. Repeating the experiment with many wasps, Tinbergen obtained the same results.

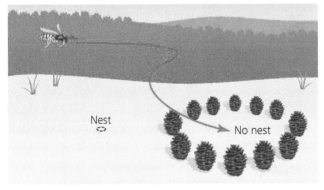

Conclusion The experiment supported the hypothesis that digger wasps use visual landmarks to keep track of their nests.

Source: N. Tinbergen, The Study of Instinct, Clarendon Press, Oxford (1951).

WHAT IF? *Suppose the digger wasp had returned to her original nest site, despite the pinecones having been moved. What alternative hypotheses might you propose regarding how the wasp finds her nest and why the pinecones didn't misdirect the wasp?*

In some animals, spatial learning involves formulating a **cognitive map**, a representation in an animal's nervous system of the spatial relationships between objects in its surroundings. One striking example is found in the Clark's nutcracker (*Nucifraga columbiana*), a relative of ravens, crows, and jays. In the fall, nutcrackers hide pine seeds for retrieval during the winter. By experimentally varying the distance between landmarks in the birds' environment, researchers discovered that the birds kept track of the halfway point between landmarks, rather than a fixed distance, to find their hidden food stores.

Associative Learning

Learning often involves making associations between experiences. Consider, for example, a blue jay (*Cyanocitta cristata*) that ingests a brightly colored monarch butterfly (*Danaus plexippus*). Substances that the monarch accumulates from milkweed plants cause the blue jay to vomit almost immediately (Figure 51.9). Following such experiences, blue jays avoid attacking monarchs and similar-looking butterflies. The ability to associate one environmental feature (such as a color) with another (such as a foul taste) is called **associative learning**.

Associative learning is well suited to study in the laboratory. Such studies typically involve either classical conditioning or operant conditioning. In *classical conditioning*, an arbitrary stimulus becomes associated with a particular outcome. Russian physiologist Ivan Pavlov carried out early experiments in classical conditioning, demonstrating that if he always rang a bell just before feeding a dog, the dog would eventually salivate when the bell sounded, anticipating food. In *operant conditioning*, also called trial-and-error learning, an animal first learns to associate one of its behaviors with a reward or punishment and then tends to repeat or avoid that behavior (see Figure 51.9). B. F. Skinner, an

▲ **Figure 51.9 Associative learning.** Having ingested and vomited a monarch butterfly, a blue jay has probably learned to avoid this species.

American pioneer in the study of operant conditioning, explored this process in the laboratory by, for example, having a rat learn through trial and error to obtain food by pressing a lever.

Studies reveal that animals can learn to link many pairs of features of their environment, but not all. For example, pigeons can learn to associate danger with a sound but not with a color. However, they can learn to associate a color with food. What does this mean? The development and organization of the pigeon's nervous system apparently restrict the associations that can be formed. Moreover, such restrictions are not limited to birds. Rats, for example, can learn to avoid illness-inducing foods on the basis of smells, but not on the basis of sights or sounds.

If we consider how behavior evolves, the fact that some animals can't learn to make particular associations appears logical. The associations an animal can readily form typically reflect relationships likely to occur in nature. Conversely, associations that can't be formed are those unlikely to be of selective advantage in a native environment. In the case of a rat's diet in the wild, for example, a harmful food is far more likely to have a certain odor than to be associated with a particular sound.

Cognition and Problem Solving

The most complex forms of learning involve **cognition**—the process of knowing that involves awareness, reasoning, recollection, and judgment. Although it was once argued that only primates and certain marine mammals have high-level thought processes, many other groups of animals, including insects, appear to exhibit cognition in controlled laboratory studies. For example, an experiment using Y-shaped mazes provided evidence for abstract thinking in honeybees. One maze had different colors, and one had different black-and-white striped patterns, either vertical or horizontal bars. Two groups of honeybees were trained in the color maze. Upon entering, a bee would see a sample color and could then choose between an arm of the maze with the same color or an arm with a different color. Only one arm contained a food reward. The first group of bees were rewarded for flying into the arm with the *same* color as the sample **(Figure 51.10❶)**; the second group were rewarded for choosing the arm with the *different* color. Next, bees from

each group were tested in the bar maze, which had no food reward. After encountering a sample black-and-white pattern of bars, a bee could choose an arm with the same pattern or an arm with a different pattern. The bees in the first group most often chose the arm with the same pattern **(Figure 51.10❷)**, whereas those in the second group typically chose the arm with the different pattern.

The maze experiments provide strong experimental support for the hypothesis that honeybees can distinguish on the basis of "same" and "different." Remarkably, research published in 2010 indicates that honeybees can also learn to distinguish between human faces.

The information-processing ability of a nervous system can also be revealed in **problem solving**, the cognitive activity of devising a method to proceed from one state to another in the face of real or apparent obstacles. For example, if a chimpanzee is placed in a room with several boxes on the floor and a banana hung high out of reach, the chimp can assess the situation and stack the boxes, enabling it to reach the food. Problem-solving behavior is highly developed in some mammals, especially primates and dolphins. Notable examples have also been observed in some bird species, especially corvids. In one study, ravens were confronted with food hanging from a branch by a string. After failing to grab the food in flight, one raven flew to the branch and alternately pulled up and stepped on the string until the food was within reach. A number of other ravens eventually arrived at similar solutions. Nevertheless, some ravens failed to solve the problem, indicating that problem-solving success in this species, as in others, varies with individual experience and abilities.

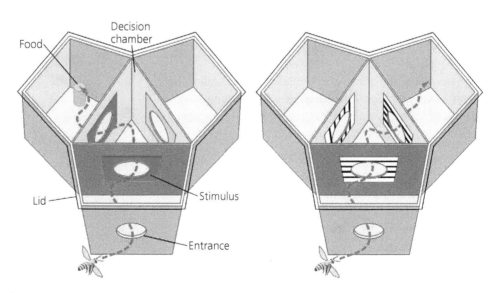

❶ **Bees were trained in a color maze**. As shown here, one group were rewarded for choosing the same color as the stimulus.

❷ **Bees were tested in a pattern maze**. If previously rewarded for choosing the same color, bees most often chose lines oriented the same way as the stimulus.

▲ **Figure 51.10 A maze test of abstract thinking by honeybees.** These mazes are designed to test whether honeybees can distinguish "same" from "different."

Development of Learned Behaviors

Most of the learned behaviors we have discussed develop over a relatively short time. Some behaviors develop more gradually. For example, some bird species learn songs in stages.

In the case of the white-crowned sparrow (*Zonotrichia leucophrys*), the first stage of song learning takes place early in life, when the fledgling sparrow first hears the song. If a fledgling is prevented from hearing real sparrows or recordings of sparrow songs during the first 50 days of its life, it fails to develop the adult song of its species. Although the young bird does not sing during the sensitive period, it memorizes the song of its species by listening to other white-crowned sparrows sing. During the sensitive period, fledglings chirp more in response to songs of their own species than to songs of other species. Thus, although young white-crowned sparrows learn the songs they will sing later on, learning appears to be bounded by genetically controlled preferences.

The sensitive period when a white-crowned sparrow memorizes its species' song is followed by a second learning phase when the juvenile bird sings tentative notes called a subsong. The juvenile bird hears its own singing and compares it with the song memorized during the sensitive period. Once a sparrow's own song matches the one it memorized, the song "crystallizes" as the final song, and the bird sings only this adult song for the rest of its life.

The song-learning process can be quite different in other bird species. Canaries, for example, do not have a single sensitive period for song learning. A young canary begins with a subsong, but the full song does not crystallize in the same way as in white-crowned sparrows. Between breeding seasons, the song becomes flexible again, and an adult male may learn new song "syllables" each year, adding to the song it already sings.

Song learning is one of many examples of how animals learn from other members of their species. In finishing our exploration of learning, we'll look at several more examples that reflect the more general phenomenon of social learning.

Social Learning

Many animals learn to solve problems by observing the behavior of other individuals. Young wild chimpanzees, for example, learn how to crack open oil palm nuts with two stones by copying experienced chimpanzees (Figure 51.11). This type of learning through observing others is called **social learning**.

Another example of how social learning can modify behavior comes from studies of the vervet monkeys (*Cercopithecus aethiops*) in Amboseli National Park, Kenya. Vervet monkeys, which are about the size of a domestic cat, produce a complex set of alarm calls. Amboseli vervets give

▲ Figure 51.11 **A young chimpanzee learning to crack oil palm nuts by observing an experienced elder.**

distinct alarm calls for leopards, eagles, and snakes, all of which prey on vervets. When a vervet sees a leopard, it gives a loud barking sound; when it sees an eagle, it gives a short double-syllable cough; and the snake alarm call is a "chutter." Upon hearing a particular alarm call, other vervets in the group behave in an appropriate way: They run up a tree on hearing the alarm for a leopard (vervets are nimbler than leopards in the trees); look up on hearing the alarm for an eagle; and look down on hearing the alarm for a snake (Figure 51.12).

Infant vervet monkeys give alarm calls, but in a relatively undiscriminating way. For example, they give the "eagle" alarm on seeing any bird, including harmless birds such as

▲ Figure 51.12 **Vervet monkeys learning correct use of alarm calls.** On seeing a python (foreground), vervet monkeys give a distinct "snake" alarm call (inset), and the members of the group stand upright and look down.

bee-eaters. With age, the monkeys improve their accuracy. In fact, adult vervet monkeys give the eagle alarm only on seeing an eagle belonging to either of the two species that eat vervets. Infants probably learn how to give the right call by observing other members of the group and receiving social confirmation. For instance, if the infant gives the call on the right occasion—say, an eagle alarm when there is an eagle overhead—another member of the group will also give the eagle call. But if the infant gives the call when a bee-eater flies by, the adults in the group are silent. Thus, vervet monkeys have an initial, unlearned tendency to give calls upon seeing potentially threatening objects in the environment. Learning fine-tunes the call so that adult vervets give calls only in response to genuine danger and can fine-tune the alarm calls of the next generation.

Social learning forms the roots of **culture**, which can be defined as a system of information transfer through social learning or teaching that influences the behavior of individuals in a population. Cultural transfer of information can alter behavioral phenotypes and thereby influence the fitness of individuals.

Changes in behavior that result from natural selection occur on a much longer time scale than does learning. In Concept 51.3, we'll examine the relationship between particular behaviors and the processes of selection related to survival and reproduction.

CONCEPT CHECK **51.2**

1. How might associative learning explain why different species of distasteful or stinging insects have similar colors?
2. **WHAT IF?** How might you position and manipulate a few objects in a lab to test whether an animal can use a cognitive map to remember the location of a food source?
3. **MAKE CONNECTIONS** How might a learned behavior contribute to speciation? (See Concept 24.1.)

For suggested answers, see Appendix A.

CONCEPT 51.3

Selection for individual survival and reproductive success can explain diverse behaviors

EVOLUTION We turn now to Tinbergen's third question—how behavior enhances survival and reproduction in a population. The focus thus shifts from proximate causation—the "how" questions—to ultimate causation—the "why" questions. We'll begin by considering the activity of gathering food. Food-obtaining behavior, or **foraging**, includes not only eating but also any activities an animal uses to search for, recognize, and capture food items.

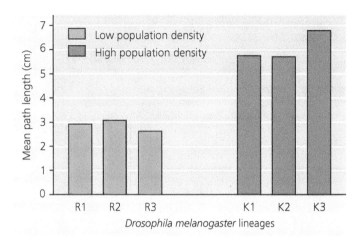

▲ **Figure 51.13 Evolution of foraging behavior by laboratory populations of *Drosophila melanogaster*.** After 74 generations of living at low population density, *D. melanogaster* larvae (populations R1–R3) followed foraging paths significantly shorter than those of *D. melanogaster* larvae that had lived at high density (populations K1–K3).

INTERPRET THE DATA *What alternative hypothesis is ruled out by having three R and K lines, rather than one of each?*

Evolution of Foraging Behavior

The fruit fly allows us to examine one way that foraging behavior might have evolved. Variation in a gene called *forager* (*for*) dictates how far *Drosophila* larvae travel when foraging. On average, larvae carrying the *for*^{R} ("Rover") allele travel nearly twice as far while foraging as do larvae with the *for*^{s} ("sitter") allele.

Both the *for*^{R} and *for*^{s} alleles are present in natural populations. What circumstances might favor one or the other allele? The answer became apparent in experiments that maintained flies at either low or high population densities for many generations. Larvae in populations kept at a low density foraged over shorter distances than those in populations kept at high density **(Figure 51.13)**. Furthermore, the *for*^{s} allele increased in frequency in the low-density populations, whereas the *for*^{R} allele increased in frequency in the high-density group. These changes make sense. At a low population density, short-distance foraging yields sufficient food, while long-distance foraging would result in unnecessary energy expenditure. Under crowded conditions, long-distance foraging could enable larvae to move beyond areas depleted of food. Thus, an interpretable evolutionary change in behavior occurred in the course of the experiment.

Optimal Foraging Model

To study the ultimate causation of foraging strategies, biologists sometimes apply a type of cost-benefit analysis used in economics. This idea proposes that foraging behavior is a compromise between the benefits of nutrition and the costs of obtaining food. These costs might include the energy

Testing a Hypothesis with a Quantitative Model

Do Crows Display Optimal Foraging Behavior? On islands off British Columbia, Canada, Northwestern crows (*Corvus caurinus*) search rocky tide pools for sea snails called whelks. After spotting a whelk, the crow picks it up in its beak, flies upward, and drops the whelk onto the rocks. If the drop is successful, the shell breaks and the crow can dine on the whelk's soft parts. If not, the crow flies up and drops the whelk again and again until the shell breaks. What determines how high the crow flies? If energetic considerations dominated selection for the crow's foraging behavior, the average drop height might reflect a trade-off between the cost of flying higher and the benefit of more frequent success. In this exercise you'll test how well this optimal foraging model predicts the average drop height observed in nature.

How the Experiments Were Done The height of drops made by crows in the wild was measured by referring to a marked pole erected nearby. In the test, the crow's behavior was simulated using a device that dropped a whelk onto the rocks from a fixed platform. The average number of drops required to break whelks from various platform heights was recorded and averaged over many trials with the device. Combining the data for each platform height, total "flight" height was calculated by multiplying the height times the average number of drops required.

Data from the Experiment

Interpret the Data

1. How does the average number of drops required to break open a whelk depend on platform height for a drop of 5 meters or less? For drops of more than 5 meters?

2. Total flight height can be considered to be a measure of the total energy required to break open a whelk. Why is this value lower for a platform set at 5 meters than for one at 2 or 15 meters?

3. Compare the drop height preferred by crows with the graph of total flight height for the platform drops. Are the data consistent with the hypothesis of optimal foraging? Explain.

4. In testing the optimal foraging model, it was assumed that changing the height of the drop only changed the total energy required. Do you think this is a realistic limitation, or might other factors than total energy be affected by height?

5. Researchers observed that the crows only gather and drop the largest whelks. What are some reasons crows might favor larger whelks?

6. It turned out that the probability of a whelk breaking was the same for a whelk dropped for the first time as for an unbroken whelk dropped several times previously. If the probability of breaking instead increased, what change might you predict in the crow's behavior?

(MB) A version of this Scientific Skills Exercise can be assigned in MasteringBiology.

Data from R. Zach, Shell-dropping: Decision-making and optimal foraging in northwestern crows, *Behavior* 68:106–117 (1979).

---

expenditure of foraging as well as the risk of being eaten while foraging. According to this **optimal foraging model**, natural selection should favor a foraging behavior that minimizes the costs of foraging and maximizes the benefits. The Scientific Skills Exercise provides an example of how this model can be applied to animals in the wild.

Balancing Risk and Reward

One of the most significant potential costs to a forager is risk of predation. Maximizing energy gain and minimizing energy costs are of little benefit if the behavior makes the forager a likely meal for a predator. It seems logical,

therefore, that predation risk would influence foraging behavior. Such appears to be the case for the mule deer (*Odocoileus hemionus*), which lives in the mountains of western North America. Researchers found that the food available for mule deer was fairly uniform across the potential foraging areas, although somewhat lower in open, nonforested areas. In contrast, the risk of predation differed greatly; mountain lions (*Puma concolor*), the major predator, killed large numbers of mule deer at forest edges and only a small number in open areas and forest interiors.

How does mule deer foraging behavior reflect the differences in predation risk in particular areas? Mule deer feed predominantly in open areas. Thus, it appears that mule deer foraging behavior reflects the large variation in predation risk and not the smaller variation in food availability. This result underscores the point that behavior typically reflects a compromise between competing selective pressures.

Mating Behavior and Mate Choice

Just as foraging is crucial for individual survival, mating behavior and mate choice play a major role in determining reproductive success. These behaviors include seeking or attracting mates, choosing among potential mates, competing for mates, and caring for offspring.

Mating Systems and Sexual Dimorphism

Although we tend to think of mating simply as the union of a male and female, species vary greatly with regard to *mating systems*, the length and number of relationships between males and females. In some animal species, mating is *promiscuous*, with no strong pair-bonds. In others, mates form a relationship of some duration that is **monogamous** (one male mating with one female) or **polygamous** (an individual of one sex mating with several of the other). Polygamous relationships involve *polygyny*, a single male and many females, or *polyandry*, a single female and multiple males.

The extent to which males and females differ in appearance, a characteristic known as *sexual dimorphism*, typically varies with the type of mating system **(Figure 51.14)**. Among monogamous species, males and females often look very similar. In contrast, among polygamous species, the sex that attracts multiple mating partners is typically showier and larger than the opposite sex. We'll discuss the evolutionary basis of these differences shortly.

Mating Systems and Parental Care

The needs of the young are an important factor constraining the evolution of mating systems. Most newly hatched birds, for instance, cannot care for themselves. Rather, they require a large, continuous food supply, a need that is difficult for a single parent to meet. In such cases, a male that stays with and helps a single mate may ultimately have more viable offspring than it would by going off to seek additional mates. This may explain why many birds are monogamous. In contrast, for birds with young that can feed and care for themselves almost immediately after hatching, the males derive less benefit from staying with their partner. Males of these species, such as pheasants and quail, can maximize their reproductive success by seeking other mates, and polygyny is relatively common in such birds. In the case of mammals, the lactating female is often the only food source for the young, and males usually play no role in raising the young. In mammalian species where males protect the females and young, such as lions, a male or small group of males typically cares for a harem of many females.

▼ **Figure 51.14 Relationship between mating system and male and female forms.**

(a) Monogamy

In monogamous species, such as these western gulls (*Larus occidentalis*), males and females are difficult to distinguish using external characteristics only.

(b) Polygyny

Among polygynous species, such as elk (*Cervus canadensis*), the male (right) is often highly ornamented.

(c) Polyandry

In polyandrous species, such as these red-necked phalaropes (*Phalaropus lobatus*), females (right) are generally more ornamented than males.

▲ Figure 51.15 **Paternal care by a male jawfish.** The male jaw-fish, which lives in tropical marine environments, holds the eggs it has fertilized in its mouth, keeping them aerated and protecting them from egg predators until the young hatch.

Another factor influencing mating behavior and parental care is *certainty of paternity*. Young born to or eggs laid by a female definitely contain that female's genes. However, even within a normally monogamous relationship, a male other than the female's usual mate may have fathered that female's offspring. The certainty of paternity is relatively low in most species with internal fertilization because the acts of mating and birth (or mating and egg laying) are separated over time. This could explain why exclusively male parental care is rare in bird and mammal species. However, the males of many species with internal fertilization engage in behaviors that appear to increase their certainty of paternity. These behaviors include guarding females, removing any sperm from the female reproductive tract before copulation, and introducing large quantities of sperm that displace the sperm of other males.

Certainty of paternity is high when egg laying and mating occur together, as in external fertilization. This may explain why parental care in aquatic invertebrates, fishes, and amphibians, when it occurs at all, is at least as likely to be by males as by females (**Figure 51.15**; see also Figure 46.6). Among fishes and amphibians, parental care occurs in fewer than 10% of species with internal fertilization but in more than half of species with external fertilization.

It is important to point out that certainty of paternity does not mean that animals are aware of those factors when they behave a certain way. Parental behavior correlated with certainty of paternity exists because it has been reinforced over generations by natural selection. The intriguing relationship between certainty of paternity and male parental care remains an area of active research.

Sexual Selection and Mate Choice

Sexual dimorphism results from sexual selection, a form of natural selection in which differences in reproductive

success among individuals are a consequence of differences in mating success (see Concept 23.4). Sexual selection can take the form of *intersexual selection*, in which members of one sex choose mates on the basis of characteristics of the other sex, such as courtship songs, or *intrasexual selection*, which involves competition between members of one sex for mates.

Mate Choice by Females Mate preferences of females may play a central role in the evolution of male behavior and anatomy through intersexual selection. Consider, for example, the courtship behavior of stalk-eyed flies. The eyes of these insects are at the tips of stalks, which are longer in males than in females. During courtship, a male approaches the female headfirst. Researchers have shown that females are more likely to mate with males that have relatively long eyestalks. Why would females favor this seemingly arbitrary trait? Ornaments such as long eyestalks in these flies and bright coloration in birds correlate in general with health and vitality. A female whose mate choice is a healthy male is likely to produce more offspring that survive to reproduce. As a result, males may compete with each other in ritualized contests to attract female attention (**Figure 51.16**).

▲ Figure 51.16 **Male stalk-eyed flies face off for female attention.** In such ritual showdowns, the male whose eyestalk length is smaller usually retreats peacefully.

Mate choice can also be influenced by imprinting, as revealed by experiments carried out with zebra finches. Both male and female zebra finches normally lack any feather crest on their head (**Figure 51.17**). To explore whether parental

▶ Figure 51.17 **Appearance of zebra finches in nature.** The male zebra finch (left) is more highly patterned and colorful than the female zebra finch.

appearance affects mate preference in offspring independent of any genetic influence, researchers provided zebra finches with artificial ornamentation. A 2.5-cm-long red feather was taped to the forehead feathers of either or both zebra finch parents when their chicks were 8 days old, approximately 2 days before they opened their eyes. A control group of zebra finches were raised by unadorned parents. When the chicks matured, they were presented with prospective mates that were either artificially ornamented with a red feather or non-ornamented (Figure 51.18). Males showed no preference. Females raised by a male parent that was not ornamented also showed no preference. However, females raised by an ornamented male parent preferred ornamented males as their own mates. Thus, female finches apparently take cues from their fathers in choosing mates.

Mate-choice copying, a behavior in which individuals in a population copy the mate choice of others, has been studied in the guppy *Poecilia reticulata*. When a female guppy chooses between males with no other females present, the female almost always chooses the male with more orange coloration. To explore if the behavior of other females could influence this preference, an experiment was set up using both living females and artificial model females (Figure 51.19). If a female guppy observed the model "courting" a male with less extensive orange markings, she often copied the preference of the model

▲ **Figure 51.18 Sexual selection influenced by imprinting.** Experiments demonstrated that female zebra finch chicks that had imprinted on artificially ornamented fathers preferred ornamented males as adult mates. For all experimental groups, male offspring showed no preference for either ornamented or non-ornamented female mates.

female. That is, the female chose the male that had been presented in association with a model female rather than a more orange alternative. The exceptions were also informative. Mate-choice behavior typically did not change when the difference in coloration was particularly large. Mate-choice copying can thus mask genetically controlled female preference below a certain threshold of difference, in this case for male color.

▲ **Figure 51.19 Mate choice copying by female guppies (*Poecilia reticulata*).** In the absence of other females (control group), female guppies generally choose males with more orange coloration. However, when a female model is placed near one of the males (experimental group), female guppies often copy the apparent mate choice of the model, even if the male is less colorful than others. Guppy females ignored the mate choice of the model only if an alternative male had much more orange coloration.

Mate-choice copying, a form of social learning, has also been observed in several other fish and bird species. What is the selective pressure for such a mechanism? One possibility is that a female that mates with males that are attractive to other females increases the probability that her male offspring will also be attractive and have high reproductive success.

Male Competition for Mates The previous examples show how female choice can select for one best type of male in a given situation, resulting in low variation among males. Similarly, male competition for mates can reduce variation among males. Such competition may involve *agonistic behavior*, an often-ritualized contest that determines which competitor gains access to a resource, such as food or mates (**Figure 51.20**; see also Figure 51.16).

Despite the potential for male competition to select for reduced variation, behavioral and morphological variation in males is extremely high in some vertebrate species, including species of fish and deer, as well as in a wide variety of invertebrates. In some species, sexual selection has led to the evolution of alternative male mating behavior and morphology. How do scientists analyze situations where more than one mating behavior can result in successful reproduction? One approach relies on the rules that govern games.

▲ **Figure 51.20 Agonistic interaction.** Male eastern grey kangaroos (*Macropus giganteus*) often "box" in contests that determine which male is most likely to mate with an available female. Typically, one male snorts loudly and strikes the other with his forelimbs. If the male under attack does not retreat, the fight may escalate into grappling or the two males balancing on their tails while attempting to kick each other with the sharp toenails of their hind feet.

Applying Game Theory

Often, the fitness of a particular behavioral phenotype is influenced by other behavioral phenotypes in the population. In studying such situations, behavioral ecologists use a range of tools, including game theory. Developed by American mathematician John Nash and others to model human economic behavior, **game theory** evaluates alternative strategies in situations where the outcome depends on the strategies of all the individuals involved.

As an example of applying game theory to mating behavior, let's consider the side-blotched lizard (*Uta stansburiana*) of California. Genetic variations give rise to males with orange, blue, or yellow throats (**Figure 51.21**). One would expect that natural selection would favor one of the three color types, yet all three persist. Why? The answer appears to lie in the fact that each throat color is associated with a different pattern of behavior: Orange-throat males are the most aggressive and defend large territories that contain many females. Blue-throat males are also territorial but defend smaller

▲ **Figure 51.21 Male polymorphism in the side-blotched lizard (*Uta stansburiana*).** An orange-throat male, left; a blue-throat male, center; a yellow-throat male, right.

territories and fewer females. Yellow-throats are nonterritorial males that mimic females and use "sneaky" tactics to gain the chance to mate.

Evidence indicates that the mating success of each male lizard type is influenced by the relative abundance of the other types, an example of frequency-dependent selection. In one study population, the most frequent throat coloration changed over a period of several years from blue to orange to yellow and back to blue.

By comparing the competition between side-blotched lizard males to the children's game of rock-paper-scissors, scientists devised an explanation for the cycles of variation in the lizard population. In the game, paper defeats rock, rock defeats scissors, and scissors defeats paper. Each hand symbol thus wins one matchup but loses the other. Similarly, each type of male lizard has an advantage over one of the other two types. When blue-throats are abundant, they can defend the few females in their territories from the advances of the sneaky yellow-throat males. However, blue-throats cannot defend their territories against the hyperaggressive orange-throats. Once the orange-throats become the most abundant, the larger number of females in each territory provides the opportunity for the yellow-throats to have greater mating success. The yellow-throats become more frequent, but then give way to the blue-throats, whose tactic of guarding small territories once again allows them the most success. Thus, following the population over time, one sees a persistence of all three color types and a periodic shift in which type is most prevalent.

Game theory provides a way to think about complex evolutionary problems in which relative performance (reproductive success relative to other phenotypes), not absolute performance, is the key to understanding the evolution of behavior. This makes game theory an important tool because the relative performance of one phenotype compared with others is a measure of Darwinian fitness.

CONCEPT 51.4

Genetic analyses and the concept of inclusive fitness provide a basis for studying the evolution of behavior

EVOLUTION We'll now explore issues related to Tinbergen's fourth question—the evolutionary history of behaviors. We will first look at the genetic control of a behavior. Next, we will examine the genetic variation underlying the evolution of particular behaviors. Finally, we will see how expanding the definition of fitness beyond individual survival can help explain "selfless" behavior.

Genetic Basis of Behavior

In exploring the genetic basis of behavior, we'll begin with the courtship behavior of the male fruit fly, diagrammed in Figure 51.4. During courtship, the male fly carries out a complex series of actions in response to multiple sensory stimuli. Genetic studies have revealed that a single gene called *fru* controls this entire courtship ritual. If the *fru* gene is mutated to an inactive form, males do not court or mate with females. (The name *fru* is short for *fruitless*, reflecting the absence of offspring from the mutant males.) Normal male and female

flies express distinct forms of the *fru* gene. When females are genetically manipulated to express the male form of *fru*, they court other females, performing the role normally played by the male. How can a single gene control so many different actions? Experiments carried out cooperatively in several laboratories demonstrated that *fru* is a master regulatory gene that directs the expression and activity of many genes with narrower functions. Together, genes that are controlled by the *fru* gene bring about sex-specific development of the fly nervous system. In effect, *fru* programs the fly for male courtship behavior by overseeing a male-specific wiring of the central nervous system.

In many cases, differences in behavior arise not from gene inactivation, but from variation in the activity or amount of a gene product. One striking example comes from the study of two related species of voles, which are small, mouse-like rodents. Male meadow voles (*Microtus pennsylvanicus*) are solitary and do not form lasting relationships with mates. Following mating, they pay little attention to their pups. In contrast, male prairie voles (*Microtus ochrogaster*) form a pair-bond with a single female after they mate **(Figure 51.22)**. Male prairie voles hover over their young pups, licking them and carrying them, while acting aggressively toward intruders.

A peptide neurotransmitter is critical for the partnering and parental behavior of male voles. Known as ADH or vasopressin (see Chapter 44), this peptide is released during mating and binds to a specific receptor in the central nervous system. When male prairie voles are given a drug that inhibits the brain receptor for vasopressin, they fail to form pair-bonds after mating.

◀ **Figure 51.22 A pair of prairie voles (*Microtus ochrogaster*) huddling.** Male North American prairie voles associate closely with their mates, as shown here, and contribute substantially to the care of young.

The vasopressin receptor gene is much more highly expressed in the brain of prairie voles than in the brain of meadow voles. Testing the hypothesis that vasopressin receptor levels in the brain regulate postmating behavior, researchers inserted the vasopressin receptor gene from prairie voles into meadow voles. The male meadow voles carrying this gene not only developed brains with higher levels of the vasopressin receptor but also showed many of the same mating behaviors as male prairie voles, such as pair-bonding. Thus, although many genes influence pair-bonding and parenting in voles, a change in vasopressin receptor levels is sufficient to alter the development of these behaviors.

Genetic Variation and the Evolution of Behavior

Behavioral differences between closely related species, such as meadow and prairie voles, are common. Significant differences in behavior can also be found *within* a species but are often less obvious. When behavioral variation between populations of a species correlates with variation in environmental conditions, it may reflect natural selection.

Case Study: *Variation in Prey Selection*

An example of genetically based behavioral variation within a species involves prey selection by the western garter snake (*Thamnophis elegans*). The natural diet of this species differs widely across its range in California. Coastal populations feed predominantly on banana slugs (*Ariolimax californicus*) (Figure 51.23). Inland populations feed on frogs, leeches, and fish, but not banana slugs. In fact, banana slugs are rare or absent in the inland habitats.

When researchers offered banana slugs to snakes from each wild population, most coastal snakes readily ate them, whereas inland snakes tended to refuse. To what extent does genetic variation contribute to a fondness for banana slugs? To answer this question, researchers collected pregnant snakes from each wild population and housed them in separate cages in the laboratory. While still very young, the offspring were offered a small piece of banana slug on each of ten days. More than 60% of the young snakes from coastal mothers ate banana slugs on eight or more of the ten days. In contrast, fewer than 20% of the young snakes from inland mothers ate a piece of banana slug even once. Perhaps not surprisingly, banana slugs thus appear to be a genetically acquired taste.

How did a genetically determined difference in feeding preference come to match the snakes' habitats so well? It turns out that the coastal and inland populations also vary with respect to their ability to recognize and respond to odor molecules produced by banana slugs. Researchers hypothesize that when inland snakes colonized coastal habitats more than 10,000 years ago, some of them could recognize banana slugs by scent. Because these snakes took advantage

▲ Figure 51.23 **Western garter snake from a coastal habitat eating a banana slug.** Experiments indicate that the preference of these snakes for banana slugs may be influenced more by genetics than by environment.

of this food source, they had higher fitness than snakes in the population that ignored the slugs. Over hundreds or thousands of generations, the capacity to recognize the slugs as prey increased in frequency in the coastal population. The marked variation in behavior observed today between the coastal and inland populations may be evidence of this past evolutionary change.

Case Study: *Variation in Migratory Patterns*

Another species suited to the study of behavioral variation is the blackcap (*Sylvia atricapilla*), a small migratory warbler. Blackcaps that breed in Germany generally migrate southwest to Spain and then south to Africa for the winter. In the 1950s, a few blackcaps began to spend their winters in Britain, and over time the population of blackcaps wintering in Britain grew to many thousands. Leg bands showed that some of these birds had migrated westward from central Germany. Was this change in the pattern of migration the outcome of natural selection? If so, the birds wintering in Britain must have a heritable difference in migratory behavior. To test this hypothesis, researchers at the Max Planck Research Center in Radolfzell, Germany, devised a strategy to study migratory orientation in the laboratory (Figure 51.24). The results demonstrated that the two patterns of migration—to the west and to the southwest—do in fact reflect genetic differences between the two populations.

The study of western European blackcaps indicated that the change in their migratory behavior occurred both recently and rapidly. Before the year 1950, there were no known westward-migrating blackcaps in Germany. By the 1990s, westward migrants made up 7–11% of the blackcap populations of Germany. Once westward migration began,

▼ Figure 51.24 Inquiry

Are differences in migratory orientation within a species genetically determined?

Experiment Peter Berthold and colleagues in southern Germany raised two sets of young birds called blackcaps for their study. One group consisted of the offspring of blackcaps captured while wintering in Britain and then bred in Germany in an outdoor cage. The other group consisted of young birds collected from nests near the laboratory and then raised in cages. In the autumn, Berthold's team placed the blackcaps captured in Britain and the young birds raised in cages in large, glass-covered funnel cages lined with carbon-coated paper for 1.5–2 hours. When the funnels were placed outside at night, the birds moved around, making marks on the paper that indicated the direction in which they were trying to "migrate."

Scratch marks

Results The wintering adult birds captured in Britain and their laboratory-raised offspring both attempted to migrate to the west. In contrast, the young birds collected from nests in southern Germany attempted to migrate to the southwest.

Conclusion The young of the British blackcaps and the young birds from Germany (the control group) were raised under similar conditions but showed very different migratory orientations, indicating that their migratory orientation has a genetic basis.

Source: P. Berthold et al., Rapid microevolution of migratory behavior in a wild bird species, *Nature* 360:668–690 (1992).

WHAT IF? *Suppose the birds had not shown a difference in orientation in these experiments. Could you conclude that the behavior was not genetically based? Explain.*

---

it persisted and increased in frequency, perhaps due to the widespread use of winter bird feeders in Britain, as well as shorter migration distances.

Altruism

We typically assume that behaviors are selfish; that is, they benefit the individual at the expense of others, especially competitors. For example, superior foraging ability by one individual may leave less food for others. The problem comes with "unselfish" behaviors. How can such behaviors arise through natural selection? To answer this question, let's look more closely at some examples of unselfish behavior and consider how they might arise.

In discussing selflessness, we will use the term **altruism** to describe a behavior that reduces an animal's individual fitness but increases the fitness of other individuals in the population. Consider, for example, the Belding's ground squirrel, which lives in the western United States and is vulnerable to predators such as coyotes and hawks. A squirrel that sees a predator approach often gives a high-pitched alarm call that alerts unaware individuals to retreat to their burrows. Note that for the squirrel that warns others, the conspicuous alarm behavior increases the risk of being killed because it brings attention to the caller's location.

Another example of altruistic behavior occurs in honeybee societies, in which the workers are sterile. The workers themselves never reproduce, but they labor on behalf of a single fertile queen. Furthermore, the workers sting intruders, a behavior that helps defend the hive but results in the death of those workers.

Altruism is also observed in naked mole rats (*Heterocephalus glaber*), highly social rodents that live in underground chambers and tunnels in southern and northeastern Africa. The naked mole rat, which is almost hairless and nearly blind, lives in colonies of 75 to 250 or more individuals **(Figure 51.25)**. Each colony has only one reproducing female, the queen, who mates with one to three males, called

▲ **Figure 51.25 Naked mole rats, a species of colonial mammal that exhibits altruistic behavior.** Pictured here is a queen nursing offspring while surrounded by other members of the colony.

kings. The rest of the colony consists of nonreproductive females and males who at times sacrifice themselves to protect the queen or kings from snakes or other predators that invade the colony.

Inclusive Fitness

With these examples from ground squirrels, honeybees, and mole rats in mind, let's return to the question of how altruistic behavior arises during evolution. The easiest case to consider is that of parents sacrificing for their offspring. When parents sacrifice their own well-being to produce and aid offspring, this act actually increases the fitness of the parents because it maximizes their genetic representation in the population. By this logic, altruistic behavior can be maintained by evolution even though it does not enhance the survival and reproductive success of the self-sacrificing individuals.

What about circumstances when individuals help others who are not their offspring? By considering a broader group of relatives than just parents and offspring, Biologist William Hamilton found an answer. He began by proposing that an animal could increase its genetic representation in the next generation by helping close relatives other than its own offspring. Like parents and offspring, full siblings have half their genes in common. Therefore, selection might also favor helping siblings or helping one's parents produce more siblings. This thinking led Hamilton to the idea of **inclusive fitness**, the total effect an individual has on proliferating its genes by producing its own offspring *and* by providing aid that enables other close relatives to produce offspring.

Hamilton's Rule and Kin Selection

The power of Hamilton's hypothesis was that it provided a way to measure, or quantify, the effect of altruism on fitness. According to Hamilton, the three key variables in an act of altruism are the benefit to the recipient, the cost to the altruist, and the coefficient of relatedness. The benefit, B, is the average number of *extra* offspring that the recipient of an altruistic act produces. The cost, C, is how many *fewer* offspring the altruist produces. The **coefficient of relatedness**, r, equals the fraction of genes that, on average, are shared. Natural selection favors altruism when the benefit to the recipient multiplied by the coefficient of relatedness exceeds the cost to the altruist—in other words, when $rB > C$. This statement is called **Hamilton's rule**.

To better understand Hamilton's rule, let's apply it to a human population in which the average individual has two children. We'll imagine that a young man is close to drowning in heavy surf, and his sister risks her life to swim out and pull her sibling to safety. If the young man had drowned, his reproductive output would have been zero; but now, if we use the average, he can father two children. The benefit to the man is thus two offspring ($B = 2$). What cost is incurred by his sister? Let's say that she has a 25% chance of

drowning in attempting the rescue. The cost of the altruistic act to the sister is then 0.25 times 2, the number of offspring she would be expected to have if she had stayed on shore ($C = 0.25 \times 2 = 0.5$). Finally, we note that a brother and sister share half their genes on average ($r = 0.5$). One way to see this is in terms of the segregation of homologous chromosomes that occurs during meiosis of gametes (**Figure 51.26**; see also Chapter 13).

We can now use our values of B, C, and r to evaluate whether natural selection would favor the altruistic act in our imaginary scenario. For the surf rescue, $rB = 0.5 \times 2 = 1$, whereas $C = 0.5$. Because rB is greater than C, Hamilton's rule is satisfied; thus, natural selection would favor this altruistic act.

Averaging over many individuals and generations, any particular gene in a sister faced with the situation described will be passed on to more offspring if she risks the rescue than if she does not. Among the genes propagated in this way may be some that contribute to altruistic behavior. Natural selection that thus favors altruism by enhancing the reproductive success of relatives is called **kin selection**.

Kin selection weakens with hereditary distance. Siblings have an r of 0.5, but between an aunt and her niece, $r = 0.25$ (¼), and between first cousins, $r = 0.125$ (⅛). Notice that as the degree of relatedness decreases, the rB term in the Hamilton inequality also decreases. Would natural selection favor rescuing a cousin? Not unless the surf were less treacherous. For the original conditions, $rB = 0.125 \times 2 = 0.25$, which is only half the value of C (0.5). British geneticist J. B. S. Haldane

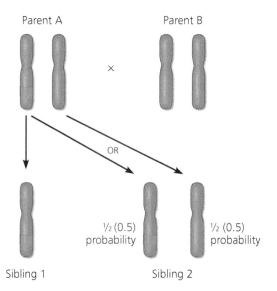

Parent A   Parent B

OR

½ (0.5) probability   ½ (0.5) probability

Sibling 1   Sibling 2

▲ **Figure 51.26 The coefficient of relatedness between siblings.** The red band indicates a particular allele (version of a gene) present on one chromosome, but not its homolog, in parent A. Sibling 1 has inherited the allele from parent A. There is a probability of ½ that sibling 2 will also inherit this allele from parent A. Any allele present on one chromosome of either parent will behave similarly. The coefficient of relatedness between the two siblings is thus ½, or 0.5.

WHAT IF? *The coefficient of relatedness of an individual to a full (nontwin) sibling or to either parent is the same: 0.5. Does this value also hold true in cases of polyandry and polygyny?*

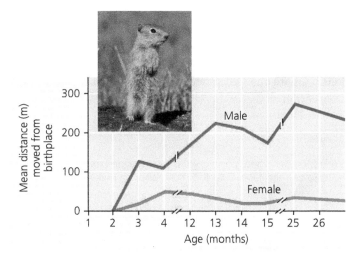

▲ Figure 51.27 Kin selection and altruism in Belding's ground squirrels. This graph helps explain the male-female difference in altruistic behavior of ground squirrels. Once weaned (pups are nursed for about one month), females are more likely than males to live near close relatives. Alarm calls that warn these relatives increase the inclusive fitness of the female altruist.

appears to have anticipated these ideas when he jokingly stated that he would not lay down his life for one brother, but would do so for two brothers or eight cousins.

If kin selection explains altruism, then the examples of unselfish behavior we observe among diverse animal species should involve close relatives. This is apparently the case, but often in complex ways. Like most mammals, female Belding's ground squirrels settle close to their site of birth, whereas males settle at distant sites (Figure 51.27). Since nearly all alarm calls are given by females, they are most likely aiding close relatives. In the case of worker bees, who are all sterile, anything they do to help the entire hive benefits the only permanent member who is reproductively active—the queen, who is their mother.

In the case of naked mole rats, DNA analyses have shown that all the individuals in a colony are closely related. Genetically, the queen appears to be a sibling, daughter, or mother of the kings, and the nonreproductive mole rats are the queen's direct descendants or her siblings. Therefore, when a nonreproductive individual enhances a queen's or king's chances of reproducing, the altruist increases the chance that some genes identical to its own will be passed to the next generation.

Reciprocal Altruism

Some animals occasionally behave altruistically toward others who are not relatives. A baboon may help an unrelated companion in a fight, or a wolf may offer food to another wolf even though they share no kinship. Such behavior can be adaptive if the aided individual returns the favor in the future. This sort of exchange of aid, called **reciprocal altruism**, is commonly invoked to explain altruism that occurs between unrelated humans. Reciprocal altruism is rare in other animals; it is limited largely to species (such as chimpanzees)

with social groups stable enough that individuals have many chances to exchange aid. It is generally thought to occur when individuals are likely to meet again and when there would be negative consequences associated with not returning favors to individuals who had been helpful in the past, a pattern of behavior that behavioral ecologists refer to as "cheating."

Since cheating may benefit the cheater substantially, how could reciprocal altruism evolve? Game theory provides a possible answer in the form of a behavioral strategy called *tit for tat*. In the tit-for-tat strategy, an individual treats another in the same way it was treated the last time they met. Individuals adopting this behavior are always altruistic, or cooperative, on the first encounter with another individual and will remain so as long as their altruism is reciprocated. When their cooperation is not reciprocated, however, individuals employing tit for tat will retaliate immediately but return to cooperative behavior as soon as the other individual becomes cooperative. The tit-for-tat strategy has been used to explain the few apparently reciprocal altruistic interactions observed in animals—ranging from blood sharing between nonrelated vampire bats to social grooming in primates.

Evolution and Human Culture

As animals, humans behave (and, sometimes, misbehave). Just as humans vary extensively in anatomical features, we display substantial variations in behavior. Environment intervenes in the path from genotype to phenotype for physical traits, but does so much more profoundly for behavioral traits. Furthermore, as a consequence of our marked capacity for learning, humans are probably more able than any other animal to acquire new behaviors and skills (Figure 51.28).

Some human activities have a less easily defined function in survival and reproduction than do, for example, foraging or courtship. One of these activities is play, which is sometimes defined as behavior that appears purposeless. We recognize play in children and what we think is play in the young of other vertebrates. Behavioral biologists describe "object play," such as chimps playing with leaves, locomotor play, such as the acrobatics of an antelope, and "social play," such as the interactions and antics of lion cubs. These categories, however, do little to inform us about the function of play. One idea is that, rather than generating specific skills or experience, play serves as preparation

▲ Figure 51.28 Learning a new behavior.

for unexpected events and for circumstances that cannot be controlled.

Human behavior and culture are related to evolutionary theory in the discipline of **sociobiology**. The main premise of sociobiology is that certain behavioral characteristics exist because they are expressions of genes that have been perpetuated by natural selection. In his seminal 1975 book *Sociobiology: The New Synthesis*, E. O. Wilson speculated about the evolutionary basis of certain kinds of social behavior. By including a few examples from human culture, he sparked a debate that continues today.

Over our recent evolutionary history, we have built up structured societies with governments, laws, cultural values, and religions that define what is acceptable behavior and what is not, even when unacceptable behavior might enhance an individual's Darwinian fitness. Perhaps it is our social and cultural institutions that make us distinct and that provide those qualities that at times make less apparent the continuum between humans and other animals. One such quality, our considerable capacity for reciprocal altruism, will be essential as we tackle current challenges, including global climate change, in which individual and collective interests often appear to be in conflict.

CONCEPT CHECK 51.4

1. Explain why geographic variation in garter snake prey choice might indicate that the behavior evolved by natural selection.
2. Suppose an individual organism aids the survival and reproductive success of the offspring of its sibling. How might this behavior result in indirect selection for certain genes carried by that individual?
3. **WHAT IF?** Suppose you applied Hamilton's logic to a situation in which one individual is past reproductive age. Could there still be selection for an altruistic act?

For suggested answers, see Appendix A.

51 Chapter Review

SUMMARY OF KEY CONCEPTS

CONCEPT 51.1

Discrete sensory inputs can stimulate both simple and complex behaviors (pp. 1134–1138)

- **Behavior** is the sum of an animal's responses to external and internal stimuli. In behavior studies, proximate, or "how," questions focus on the stimuli that trigger a behavior and on genetic, physiological, and anatomical mechanisms underlying a behavioral act. Ultimate, or "why," questions address evolutionary significance.
- A **fixed action pattern** is a largely invariant behavior triggered by a simple cue known as a **sign stimulus**. Migratory movements involve navigation, which can be based on orientation relative to the sun, the stars, or Earth's magnetic field. Animal behavior is often synchronized to the circadian cycle of light and dark in the environment or to cues that cycle over the seasons.
- The transmission and reception of signals constitute animal **communication**. Animals use visual, auditory, chemical, and tactile signals. Chemical substances called pheromones transmit species-specific information between members of a species in behaviors ranging from foraging to courtship.

? *How is migration based on circannual rhythms poorly suited for adaptation to global climate change?*

CONCEPT 51.2

Learning establishes specific links between experience and behavior (pp. 1138–1143)

- Cross-fostering studies can be used to measure the influence of social environment and experience on behavior.

- **Learning**, the modification of behavior as a result of experience, can take many forms:

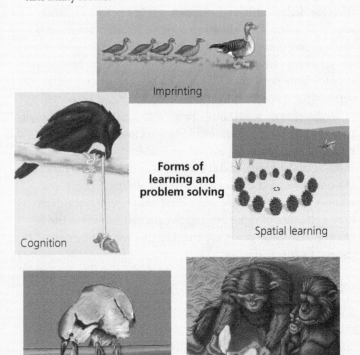

Imprinting

Cognition

Forms of learning and problem solving

Spatial learning

Associative learning

Social learning

? *How do imprinting in geese and song development in sparrows differ with regard to the resulting behavior?*

Selection for individual survival and reproductive success can explain diverse behaviors (pp. 1143–1149)

- Controlled experiments in the laboratory can give rise to interpretable evolutionary changes in behavior.
- An **optimal foraging model** is based on the idea that natural selection should favor foraging behavior that minimizes the costs of foraging and maximizes the benefits.
- Sexual dimorphism correlates with the type of mating relationship between males and females. These include **monogamous** and **polygamous** mating systems. Variations in mating system and mode of fertilization affect certainty of paternity, which in turn has a significant influence on mating behavior and parental care.
- Game theory provides a way of thinking about evolution in situations where the fitness of a particular behavioral phenotype is influenced by other behavioral phenotypes in the population.

? *In some spider species, the female eats the male immediately after copulation. How might you explain this behavior from an evolutionary perspective?*

Genetic analyses and the concept of inclusive fitness provide a basis for studying the evolution of behavior (pp. 1149–1154)

- Genetic studies in insects have revealed the existence of master regulatory genes that control complex behaviors. Within the underlying hierarchy, multiple genes influence specific behaviors, such as a courtship song. Research on voles has revealed that variation in a single gene can determine differences in complex behaviors involved in both mating and parenting.
- When behavioral variation within a species correlates with variation in environmental conditions, it may be evidence of past evolution. Field and laboratory studies have documented the genetic basis for a change in migratory behavior of certain birds and revealed behavioral differences in snakes that correlate with geographic variation in prey availability.
- **Altruism** can be explained by the concept of **inclusive fitness**, the total effect an individual has on proliferating its genes by producing its own offspring *and* by providing aid that enables close relatives to produce offspring. The **coefficient of relatedness** and **Hamilton's rule** provide a way of measuring the strength of the selective forces favoring altruism against the potential cost of the "selfless" behavior. Kin selection favors altruistic behavior by enhancing the reproductive success of relatives.

? *What insight about the genetic basis of behavior emerges from studying the effects of courtship mutations in fruit flies and of pair-bonding in voles?*

TEST YOUR UNDERSTANDING

LEVEL 1: KNOWLEDGE/COMPREHENSION

1. Which of the following is true of innate behaviors?
   a. Their expression is only weakly influenced by genes.
   b. They occur with or without environmental stimuli.
   c. They are expressed in most individuals in a population.
   d. They occur in invertebrates and some vertebrates but not mammals.

2. According to Hamilton's rule,
   a. natural selection does not favor altruistic behavior that causes the death of the altruist.
   b. natural selection favors altruistic acts when the resulting benefit to the recipient, corrected for relatedness, exceeds the cost to the altruist.
   c. natural selection is more likely to favor altruistic behavior that benefits an offspring than altruistic behavior that benefits a sibling.
   d. the effects of kin selection are larger than the effects of direct natural selection on individuals.

3. Female spotted sandpipers aggressively court males and, after mating, leave the clutch of young for the male to incubate. This sequence may be repeated several times with different males until no available males remain, forcing the female to incubate her last clutch. Which of the following terms best describes this behavior?
   a. polygyny
   b. polyandry
   c. promiscuity
   d. certainty of paternity

LEVEL 2: APPLICATION/ANALYSIS

4. A region of the canary forebrain shrinks during the nonbreeding season and enlarges when breeding season begins. This change is probably associated with the annual
   a. addition of new syllables to a canary's song repertoire.
   b. crystallization of subsong into adult songs.
   c. sensitive period in which canary parents imprint on new offspring.
   d. elimination of the memorized template for songs sung the previous year.

5. Although many chimpanzees live in environments containing oil palm nuts, members of only a few populations use stones to crack open the nuts. The likely explanation is that
   a. the behavioral difference is caused by genetic differences between populations.
   b. members of different populations have different nutritional requirements.
   c. the cultural tradition of using stones to crack nuts has arisen in only some populations.
   d. members of different populations differ in learning ability.

6. Which of the following is *not* required for a behavioral trait to evolve by natural selection?
   a. In each individual, the form of the behavior is determined entirely by genes.
   b. The behavior varies among individuals.
   c. An individual's reproductive success depends in part on how the behavior is performed.
   d. Some component of the behavior is genetically inherited.

LEVEL 3: SYNTHESIS/EVALUATION

7. **DRAW IT** You are considering two optimal foraging models for the behavior of a mussel-feeding shorebird, the oystercatcher. In model A, the energetic reward increases solely with mussel size. In model B, you take into consideration that larger mussels are more difficult to open. Draw a graph of reward (energy benefit on a scale of 0–10) versus mussel length (scale of 0–70 mm) for each model. Assume that mussels under 10 mm provide no benefit and are ignored by the birds. Also assume that mussels start becoming difficult to open when they reach 40 mm in length and impossible to open when 70 mm long. Considering the graphs you have drawn, what observations and measurements would you make in this shorebird's habitat to help determine which model is more accurate?

8. **EVOLUTION CONNECTION**

We often explain our behavior in terms of subjective feelings, motives, or reasons, but evolutionary explanations are based on reproductive fitness. What is the relationship between the two kinds of explanation? For instance, is a human explanation for behavior, such as "falling in love," incompatible with an evolutionary explanation?

9. **SCIENTIFIC INQUIRY**

Scientists studying scrub jays found that "helpers" often assist mated pairs of birds in raising their young. The helpers lack territories and mates of their own. Instead, they help the territory owners gather food for their offspring. Propose a hypothesis to explain what advantage there might be for the helpers to engage in this behavior instead of seeking their own territories and mates. How would you test your hypothesis? If it is correct, what results would you expect your tests to yield?

10. **SCIENCE, TECHNOLOGY, AND SOCIETY**

Researchers are very interested in studying identical twins separated at birth and raised apart. So far, the data reveal that such twins frequently have similar personalities, mannerisms, habits, and interests. What general question do you think researchers hope to answer by studying such twins? Why do identical twins make good subjects for this research? What are the potential pitfalls of this research? What abuses might occur if the studies are not evaluated critically?

11. **WRITE ABOUT A THEME: INFORMATION**

Learning is defined as a change in behavior as a result of experience. In a short essay (100–150 words), describe the role of heritable information in the acquisition of learning, using some examples from imprinting and associative learning.

12. **SYNTHESIZE YOUR KNOWLEDGE**

Acorn woodpeckers (*Melanerpes formicivorus*) stash acorns in storage holes they drill in trees. When these woodpeckers breed, the offspring from previous years often help with parental duties. Activities of these nonbreeding helpers include incubating eggs and defending stashed acorns. What are some questions about the proximate and ultimate causation of these behaviors that a behavioral biologist might ask?

For selected answers, see Appendix A.

MasteringBiology®

Students Go to **MasteringBiology** for assignments, the eText, and the Study Area with practice tests, animations, and activities.

Instructors Go to **MasteringBiology** for automatically graded tutorials and questions that you can assign to your students, plus Instructor Resources.

UNIT 8 ECOLOGY

AN INTERVIEW WITH
Monica Turner

As a biology undergraduate at Fordham University in New York, Monica Turner dreamed of becoming either a veterinarian or a forest ranger. A summer internship in Yellowstone National Park steered her toward forest ecology and ultimately changed her life. After graduating *summa cum laude*, Turner obtained her Ph.D. in ecology from the University of Georgia and became a pioneer in the field of landscape ecology. A member of the U.S. National Academy of Sciences, Turner is the Eugene P. Odum Professor of Ecology at the University of Wisconsin, Madison, where she has taught since 1994.

What was it about your first summer in Yellowstone that made you want to be an ecologist?

I had never been out of the eastern United States. So basically take a kid who's going to college in the Bronx, and put them in Yellowstone for a summer, and that's what made the difference. I loved being out of doors. I enjoyed natural history and helping with research. I decided I didn't want to spend my career in a clinical setting.

> " It's so important that we understand the world around us and see the changes that are happening globally and regionally."

You've spent much of your career working in landscape ecology. What is landscape ecology?

Landscape ecology focuses on the causes and consequences of spatial patterning in the environment. Landscape ecologists think about how patches of habitats, and the organisms and processes occurring in them, are arranged and connected. Imagine looking out of an airplane and seeing a mosaic of forest and agricultural patches below you. Across these many patches, you have nutrients flowing, organisms migrating, diseases spreading, and disturbances occurring. How the patches are shaped and arranged makes a world of difference.

You had another transformative moment in Yellowstone that shaped your research. Describe what you saw.

This is one time in my career where I can point to a single event that shaped the direction of my work. I was interested in disturbances because they change landscapes so quickly. In the summer of 1988 fires were burning all over Yellowstone. People thought that the fires had just gone through and burned everything. From a helicopter, I saw instead that the fires had left a mosaic of burned and unburned patches. It was an unparalleled natural experiment. Since then, I've worked to understand what the consequences of fire mosaics and other disturbances are for ecosystems and for species recovery. Despite the extent of the fires, the Yellowstone ecosystem recovered much more quickly than any of us expected. It was incredibly resilient.

How important is it for students to become interested in ecology today?

It's so important that we understand the world around us and see the changes that are happening globally and regionally. We're observing long-term changes in climate. We're seeing disturbances that are becoming larger and more severe. They're happening faster than I think many people had appreciated. We're also learning a lot about ecosystem services, the values and benefits that we gain from nature. Students see changes in the world around them and appreciate ecology as a result. To foster this appreciation, anything that gets young people out to experience nature—whatever nature is around them locally—is a good thing. Having students take a breadth of biology classes as undergraduates is also important. Students need classes in ecology as well as in cell biology and genetics, so that they're not closing off options before they really even know what the breadth of biology is.

(MB) For an extended interview and video clip, go to the Study Area in **MasteringBiology**.

◀ Recovery after the 1988 fires in Yellowstone.

52

An Introduction to Ecology and the Biosphere

▲ Figure 52.1 **What limits the distribution of this tiny frog?**

Discovering Ecology

Kneeling by a stream in Papua New Guinea in 2008, Cornell University undergraduate Michael Grundler heard a series of clicks. He first thought that the sounds must be coming from a nearby cricket. Turning to look, however, he saw instead a tiny frog inflating its vocal sac to call for a mate. Grundler would later learn that he had just discovered the first of two new frog species from the area, *Paedophryne swiftorum* and *Paedophryne amauensis* (Figure 52.1). The entire *Paedophryne* genus is known only from the Papuan Peninsula in eastern New Guinea. Adult frogs of both species are typically only 8 mm (0.3 inch) long and may be the smallest adult vertebrates on Earth.

What environmental factors limit the geographic distribution of *Paedophryne* frogs? How do variations in their food supply or interactions with other species, such as pathogens, affect the size of their population? Questions like these are the subject of **ecology** (from the Greek *oikos*, home, and *logos*, study), the scientific study of the interactions between organisms and the environment. The interactions studied by ecologists can be organized into a hierarchy that ranges in scale from single organisms to the planet (Figure 52.2).

Exploring The Scope of Ecological Research

Ecologists work at different levels of the biological hierarchy, from individual organisms to the planet. Here we present a sample research question for each level of the hierarchy.

Global Ecology

The **biosphere** is the global ecosystem—the sum of all the planet's ecosystems and landscapes. **Global ecology** examines how the regional exchange of energy and materials influences the functioning and distribution of organisms across the biosphere.

◀ How does ocean circulation affect the global distribution of crustaceans?

Landscape Ecology

A **landscape** (or seascape) is a mosaic of connected ecosystems. Research in **landscape ecology** focuses on the factors controlling exchanges of energy, materials, and organisms across multiple ecosystems.

◀ To what extent do the trees lining a river serve as corridors of dispersal for animals?

Ecosystem Ecology

An **ecosystem** is the community of organisms in an area and the physical factors with which those organisms interact. **Ecosystem ecology** emphasizes energy flow and chemical cycling between organisms and the environment.

◀ What factors control photosynthetic productivity in a temperate grassland ecosystem?

Community Ecology

A **community** is a group of populations of different species in an area. **Community ecology** examines how species interactions, such as predation and competition, affect community structure and organization.

◀ What factors influence the diversity of species that make up a forest?

Population Ecology

A **population** is a group of individuals of the same species living in an area. **Population ecology** analyzes factors that affect population size and how and why it changes through time.

◀ What environmental factors affect the reproductive rate of flamingos?

Organismal Ecology

Organismal ecology, which includes the subdisciplines of physiological, evolutionary, and behavioral ecology, is concerned with how an organism's structure, physiology, and behavior meet the challenges posed by its environment.

◀ How do hammerhead sharks select a mate?

Exploring Global Climate Patterns

Latitudinal Variation in Sunlight Intensity

Earth's curved shape causes latitudinal variation in the intensity of sunlight. Because sunlight strikes the **tropics** (those regions that lie between 23.5° north latitude and 23.5° south latitude) most directly, more heat and light per unit of surface area are delivered there. At higher latitudes, sunlight strikes Earth at an oblique angle, and thus the light energy is more diffuse on Earth's surface.

Global Air Circulation and Precipitation Patterns

Intense solar radiation near the equator initiates a global pattern of air circulation and precipitation. High temperatures in the tropics evaporate water from Earth's surface and cause warm, wet air masses to rise (blue arrows) and flow toward the poles. As the rising air masses cool, they release much of their water content, creating abundant precipitation in tropical regions. The high-altitude air masses, now dry, descend (tan arrows) toward Earth around 30° north and south, absorbing moisture from the land and creating an arid climate conducive to the development of the deserts that are common at those latitudes. Some of the descending air then flows toward the poles. At latitudes around 60° north and south, the air masses again rise and release abundant precipitation (though less than in the tropics). Some of the cold, dry rising air then flows to the poles, where it descends and flows back toward the equator, absorbing moisture and creating the comparatively rainless and bitterly cold climates of the polar regions.

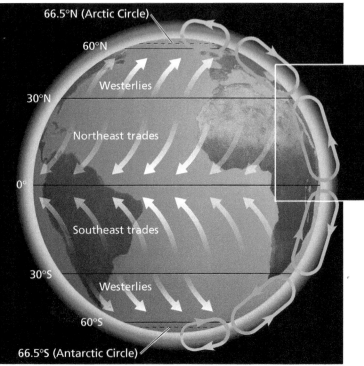

Air flowing close to Earth's surface creates predictable global wind patterns. As Earth rotates on its axis, land near the equator moves faster than that at the poles, deflecting the winds from the vertical paths shown above and creating the more easterly and westerly flows shown at left. Cooling trade winds blow from east to west in the tropics; prevailing westerlies blow from west to east in the temperate zones, defined as the regions between the Tropic of Cancer and the Arctic Circle and between the Tropic of Capricorn and the Antarctic Circle.

Ecology is a rigorous experimental science that requires a breadth of biological knowledge. Ecologists observe nature, generate hypotheses, manipulate environmental variables, and observe outcomes. In this chapter, we'll first consider how Earth's climate and other factors determine the location of major life zones on land and in the oceans. We'll then examine how ecologists investigate what controls the distribution of species. The next four chapters focus on population, community, ecosystem, and global ecology, as we explore how ecologists apply biological knowledge to predict the global consequences of human activities and to conserve Earth's biodiversity.

CONCEPT 52.1

Earth's climate varies by latitude and season and is changing rapidly

The most significant influence on the distribution of organisms on land and in the oceans is **climate**, the long-term prevailing weather conditions in a given area. Four physical factors—temperature, precipitation, sunlight, and wind—are particularly important components of climate. In this section, we'll describe climate patterns at two scales: **macroclimate**, patterns on the global, regional, and landscape level, and **microclimate**, very fine, localized patterns, such as those encountered by the community of organisms that live in the microhabitat beneath a fallen log. First, let's examine Earth's macroclimate.

Global Climate Patterns

Global climate patterns are determined largely by the input of solar energy and Earth's movement in space. The sun warms the atmosphere, land, and water. This warming establishes the temperature variations, cycles of air and water movement, and evaporation of water that cause dramatic latitudinal variations in climate. **Figure 52.3** summarizes Earth's climate patterns and how they are formed.

Regional and Local Effects on Climate

Climate patterns include seasonal variation and can be modified by other factors, such as large bodies of water and mountain ranges. We will examine each of these factors in more detail.

Seasonality

As described in **Figure 52.4**, Earth's tilted axis of rotation and its annual passage around the sun cause strong seasonal cycles in middle to high latitudes. In addition to these global

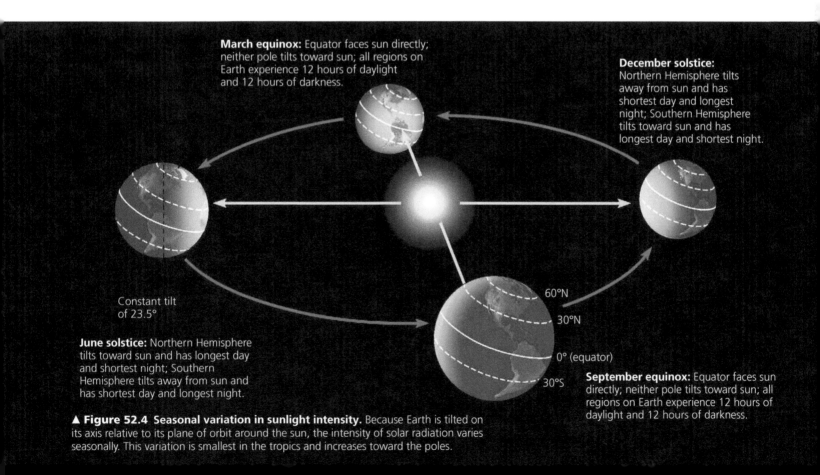

March equinox: Equator faces sun directly; neither pole tilts toward sun; all regions on Earth experience 12 hours of daylight and 12 hours of darkness.

December solstice: Northern Hemisphere tilts away from sun and has shortest day and longest night; Southern Hemisphere tilts toward sun and has longest day and shortest night.

Constant tilt of 23.5°

June solstice: Northern Hemisphere tilts toward sun and has longest day and shortest night; Southern Hemisphere tilts away from sun and has shortest day and longest night.

60°N
30°N
0° (equator)
30°S

September equinox: Equator faces sun directly; neither pole tilts toward sun; all regions on Earth experience 12 hours of daylight and 12 hours of darkness.

▲ **Figure 52.4 Seasonal variation in sunlight intensity.** Because Earth is tilted on its axis relative to its plane of orbit around the sun, the intensity of solar radiation varies seasonally. This variation is smallest in the tropics and increases toward the poles.

changes in day length, solar radiation, and temperature, the changing angle of the sun over the course of the year affects local environments. For example, the belts of wet and dry air on either side of the equator move slightly northward and southward with the changing angle of the sun, producing marked wet and dry seasons around 20° north and 20° south latitude, where many tropical deciduous forests grow. In addition, seasonal changes in wind patterns alter ocean currents, sometimes causing the upwelling of cold water from deep ocean layers. This nutrient-rich water stimulates the growth of surface-dwelling phytoplankton and the organisms that feed on them. These upwelling zones make up only a few percent of ocean area but are responsible for more than a quarter of fish caught globally.

Bodies of Water

Ocean currents influence climate along the coasts of continents by heating or cooling overlying air masses that pass across the land. Coastal regions are also generally wetter than inland areas at the same latitude. The cool, misty climate produced by the cold California Current that flows southward along western North America supports a coniferous rain forest ecosystem along much of the continent's

Pacific coast and large redwood groves farther south. Conversely, the west coast of northern Europe has a mild climate because the Gulf Stream carries warm water from the equator to the North Atlantic (Figure 52.5). As a result, northwestern Europe is warmer during winter than southeastern Canada, which is farther south but is cooled by the Labrador Current flowing south from the coast of Greenland.

Because of the high specific heat of water (see Concept 3.2), oceans and large lakes tend to moderate the climate of nearby land. During a hot day, when land is warmer than the water, air over the land heats up and rises, drawing a cool breeze from the water across the land (Figure 52.6). In contrast, because temperatures drop more quickly over land than over water at night, air over the now warmer water rises, drawing cooler air from the land back out over the water and replacing it with warmer air from offshore. This local moderation of climate can be limited to the coast itself, however. In regions such as southern California and southwestern Australia, cool, dry ocean breezes in summer are warmed when they contact the land, absorbing moisture and creating a hot, arid climate just a few kilometers inland (see Figure 3.5). This climate pattern also occurs around the Mediterranean Sea, which gives it the name *Mediterranean climate*.

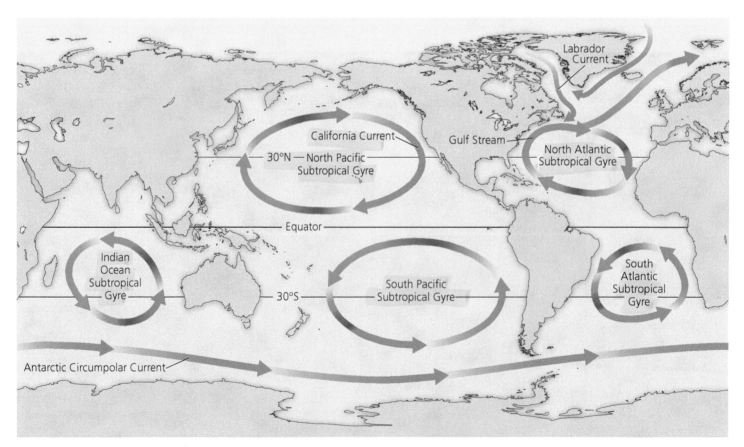

▲ **Figure 52.5 Global circulation of surface water in the oceans.** Water is warmed at the equator and flows north and south toward the poles, where it cools. Note the similarities between the direction of water circulation in the gyres and the direction of the trade winds in Figure 52.3.

▼ **Figure 52.6 How large bodies of water and mountains affect climate.** This figure illustrates what can happen on a hot summer day.

① Cool air flows inland from the water, moderating temperatures near the shore.

② Air that encounters mountains flows upward, cools at higher altitudes, and releases water as precipitation.

③ Less moisture is left in the air reaching the leeward side, which therefore has little precipitation. This rain shadow can create a desert on the back side of the mountain range.

Leeward side of mountains

Mountain range

Ocean

Mountains

Like large bodies of water, mountains influence air flow over land. When warm, moist air approaches a mountain, the air rises and cools, releasing moisture on the windward side of the peak (see Figure 52.6). On the leeward side, cooler, dry air descends, absorbing moisture and producing a "rain shadow." This leeward rain shadow determines where many deserts are found, including the Great Basin and the Mojave Desert of western North America and the Gobi Desert of Asia.

Mountains also affect the amount of sunlight reaching an area and thus the local temperature and rainfall. South-facing slopes in the Northern Hemisphere receive more sunlight than north-facing slopes and are therefore warmer and drier. These physical differences influence species distributions locally. In many mountains of western North America, spruce and other conifers grow on the cooler north-facing slopes, but shrubby, drought-resistant plants inhabit the south-facing slopes. In addition, every 1,000-m increase in elevation produces an average temperature drop of 6°C, equivalent to that produced by an 880-km increase in latitude. This is one reason that high-elevation communities at one latitude can be similar to those at lower elevations much farther from the equator.

Microclimate

Many features in the environment influence microclimate by casting shade, altering evaporation from soil, or changing wind patterns. Forest trees often moderate the microclimate below them. Cleared areas therefore typically experience greater temperature extremes than the forest interior because of greater solar radiation and wind currents that arise from the rapid heating and cooling of open land. Within a forest, low-lying ground is usually wetter than higher ground and tends to be occupied by different tree species. A log or large stone can shelter organisms such as

salamanders, worms, and insects, buffering them from the extremes of temperature and moisture.

Every environment on Earth is characterized by a mosaic of small-scale differences in chemical and physical attributes, such as temperature, light, water, and nutrients. These **abiotic**, or nonliving, factors influence the distribution and abundance of organisms. Later in this chapter, we'll also examine how all of the **biotic**, or living, factors—the other organisms that are part of an individual's environment—similarly influence the distribution and abundance of life on Earth.

Global Climate Change

Because climatic variables affect the geographic ranges of most plants and animals, any large-scale change in Earth's climate profoundly affects the biosphere. In fact, such a large-scale climate "experiment" is already under way, a topic we'll examine in more detail in Concept 56.4. The burning of fossil fuels and deforestation are increasing the concentrations of carbon dioxide and other greenhouse gases in the atmosphere. As a result, Earth has warmed an average of 0.8°C (1.4°F) since 1900 and is projected to warm 1–6°C (2–11°F) more by the year 2100.

One way to predict the possible effects of future climate change on geographic ranges is to look back at the changes that have occurred in temperate regions since the last ice age ended. Until about 16,000 years ago, continental glaciers covered much of North America and Eurasia. As the climate warmed and the glaciers retreated, tree distributions expanded northward. A detailed record of these changes is captured in fossil pollen deposited in lakes and ponds. If researchers can determine the climatic limits of current distributions of organisms, they can make predictions about how those distributions may change with continued climatic warming.

▲ Sugar maple

▲ American beech

A question when applying this approach to plants is whether seeds can disperse quickly enough as climate changes. Fossil pollen shows that species with winged seeds that disperse relatively far from a parent tree, such as the sugar maple (*Acer saccharum*), expanded rapidly northward after the last ice age ended. In contrast, the northward range expansion of the American beech (*Fagus grandifolia*), whose seeds lack wings, was delayed for thousands of years compared with the shift in suitable habitat.

Will plants and other species be able to keep up with the much more rapid warming projected for this century? Ecologists have attempted to answer this question for the American beech. Their models predict that the northern limit of the beech's range may move 700–900 km northward in the next century, and its southern range limit will shift even more. The current and predicted geographic ranges of this species under two different climate-change scenarios are illustrated in **Figure 52.7**. If these predictions are even approximately correct, the beech's range must shift 7–9 km northward per year to keep pace with the warming climate. However, since the end of the last ice age, the beech has moved at a rate of only 0.2 km per year. Without human help in moving to new habitats, species such as the American beech may have much smaller ranges or even become extinct.

Changes in the distributions of species are already evident in many well-studied groups of terrestrial, marine, and freshwater organisms, consistent with the signature of a warmer world. For example, 22 of 35 European butterfly species studied have shifted their ranges farther north by 35–240 km in recent decades. Other research shows that a Pacific diatom species, *Neodenticula seminae*, recently has colonized the Atlantic Ocean for the first time in 800,000 years. As Arctic sea ice has receded in the past decade, the increased flow of water from the Pacific has swept these diatoms around Canada and into the Atlantic, where they quickly became established. In the next section, we'll continue to examine the importance of climate in determining species distributions around the world.

(a) Current range
© 1989 AAAS

(b) 4.5°C warming over next century

(c) 6.5°C warming over next century

▲ **Figure 52.7 Current range and predicted ranges for the American beech under two climate-change scenarios.**

❓ *The predicted range in each scenario is based on climate factors alone. What other factors might alter the distribution of this species?*

CONCEPT CHECK 52.1

1. Explain how the sun's unequal heating of Earth's surface leads to the development of deserts around 30° north and south of the equator.

2. What are some of the differences in microclimate between an unplanted agricultural field and a nearby stream corridor with trees?

3. **WHAT IF?** Changes in Earth's climate at the end of the last ice age happened gradually, taking centuries to thousands of years. If the current global warming happens very quickly, as predicted, how may this rapid climate change affect the evolution of long-lived trees compared with that of annual plants, which have much shorter generation times?

4. **MAKE CONNECTIONS** Focusing just on the effects of temperature, would you expect the global distribution of C_4 plants to expand or contract as Earth becomes warmer? Why? (See Concept 10.4.)

For suggested answers, see Appendix A.

CONCEPT 52.2

The structure and distribution of terrestrial biomes are controlled by climate and disturbance

Throughout this book, you have seen many examples of how climate and other factors influence where individual species are found (see Figure 30.7, for instance). We turn now to the role of climate in determining the nature and location of Earth's **biomes**, major life zones characterized by vegetation type in terrestrial biomes or by the physical environment in aquatic biomes.

Climate and Terrestrial Biomes

Because climate has a strong influence on the distribution of plant species, it is a major factor in determining the locations of terrestrial biomes **(Figure 52.8)**. One way to highlight the importance of climate on the distribution of biomes is to construct a **climograph**, a plot of the annual mean temperature and precipitation in a particular region.

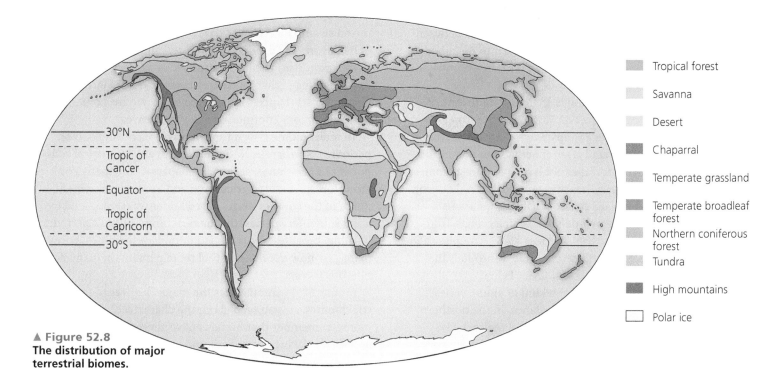

▲ Figure 52.8
The distribution of major terrestrial biomes.

Tropical forest
Savanna
Desert
Chaparral
Temperate grassland
Temperate broadleaf forest
Northern coniferous forest
Tundra
High mountains
Polar ice

Figure 52.9 is a climograph for some of the biomes found in North America. Notice, for instance, that the range of precipitation in northern coniferous and temperate forests is similar but that temperate forests are generally warmer. Grasslands are typically drier than either kind of forest, and deserts are drier still.

Factors other than mean temperature and precipitation also play a role in determining where biomes exist. Some areas in North America with a particular combination of temperature and precipitation support a temperate broadleaf forest, but other areas with similar values for these variables support a coniferous forest (see the overlap in Figure 52.9). How might we explain this variation? One thing to remember is that the climograph is based on annual *averages*. Often, however, the pattern of climatic variation is as important as the average climate. Some areas may receive regular precipitation throughout the year, whereas other areas may have distinct wet and dry seasons.

General Features of Terrestrial Biomes

Most terrestrial biomes are named for major physical or climatic features and for their predominant vegetation. Temperate grasslands, for instance, are generally found in middle latitudes, where the climate is more moderate than in the tropics or polar regions, and are dominated by various grass species (see Figure 52.8). Each biome is also characterized by microorganisms, fungi, and animals adapted to that particular environment. Temperate grasslands are usually more likely than temperate forests to be populated by large grazing mammals and to have arbuscular mycorrhizal fungi (see Figure 37.13).

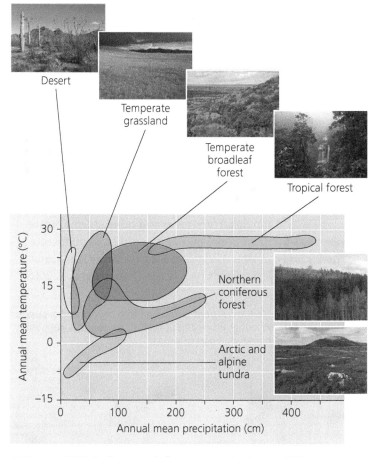

Desert
Temperate grassland
Temperate broadleaf forest
Tropical forest
Northern coniferous forest
Arctic and alpine tundra

▲ **Figure 52.9 A climograph for some major types of biomes in North America.** The areas plotted here encompass the ranges of annual mean temperature and precipitation in the biomes.

INTERPRET THE DATA *Some arctic tundra ecosystems receive as little rainfall as deserts but have much more dense vegetation. What climatic factor might explain this difference? Explain.*

Although Figure 52.8 shows distinct boundaries between the biomes, terrestrial biomes usually grade into neighboring biomes, sometimes over large areas. The area of intergradation, called an **ecotone**, may be wide or narrow.

Vertical layering of vegetation is an important feature of terrestrial biomes. In many forests, the layers from top to bottom consist of the upper **canopy**, the low-tree layer, the shrub understory, the ground layer of herbaceous plants, the forest floor (litter layer), and the root layer. Nonforest biomes have similar, though usually less pronounced, layers. Layering of vegetation provides many different habitats for animals, which sometimes exist in well-defined feeding groups, from the insectivorous birds and bats that feed above canopies to the small mammals, numerous worms, and arthropods that search for food in the litter and root layers below.

The species composition of each kind of biome varies from one location to another. For instance, in the northern coniferous forest (taiga) of North America, red spruce is common in the east but does not occur in most other areas, where black spruce and white spruce are abundant. As Figure 52.10 shows, cacti living in deserts of North and South America appear very similar to plants called euphorbs found in African deserts. But since cacti and euphorbs belong to different evolutionary lineages, their similarities are due to convergent evolution (see Figure 22.18).

Disturbance and Terrestrial Biomes

Biomes are dynamic, and disturbance rather than stability tends to be the rule. In ecological terms, **disturbance** is an event such as a storm, fire, or human activity that changes a community, removing organisms from it and altering resource availability. Frequent fires can kill woody plants and keep a savanna from becoming the woodland that climate alone would support. Hurricanes and other storms create openings for new species in many tropical and temperate forests and can alter forest composition. After Hurricane Katrina struck the Gulf Coast of the United States in 2005,

mixed swamp forests in the area shifted toward a dominance of baldcypress (*Taxodium distichum*) and water tupelo (*Nyssa aquatica*) because these species are less susceptible to wind damage than other tree species found there. As a result of disturbances, biomes are often patchy, containing several different communities in a single area.

In many biomes, even the dominant plants depend on periodic disturbance. Natural wildfires are an integral component of grasslands, savannas, chaparral, and many coniferous forests. Before agricultural and urban development, much of the southeastern United States was dominated by a single conifer species, the longleaf pine. Without periodic burning, broadleaf trees tended to replace the pines. Forest managers now use fire as a tool to help maintain many coniferous forests.

Figure 52.11 summarizes the major features of terrestrial biomes. As you read about the characteristics of each biome, remember that humans have altered much of Earth's surface, replacing natural communities with urban and agricultural ones. The central United States, for example, is classified as grassland and once contained extensive areas of tallgrass prairie. Very little of the original prairie remains today, however, having been converted to agriculture.

CONCEPT CHECK 52.2

1. **INTERPRET THE DATA** Based on the climograph in Figure 52.9, what mainly differentiates temperate grassland from temperate broadleaf forest?

2. Identify the natural biome in which you live, and summarize its abiotic and biotic characteristics. Do these reflect your actual surroundings? Explain.

3. **WHAT IF?** If global warming increases average temperatures on Earth by 4°C in this century, predict which biome is most likely to replace tundra in some locations as a result. Explain your answer.

For suggested answers, see Appendix A.

▼ **Figure 52.10 Convergent evolution in a cactus and a euphorb.** Cacti in the genus *Cereus* are found in the Americas; *Euphorbia canariensis*, a euphorb, is native to the Canary Islands, off the northwest coast of Africa.

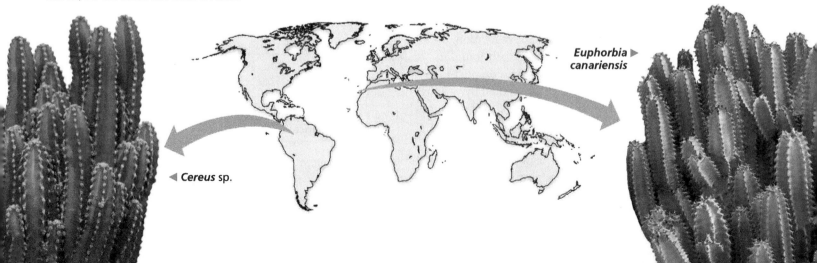

Euphorbia ▶
canariensis

◀ *Cereus* sp.

Exploring Terrestrial Biomes

Tropical Forest

Distribution Tropical forest occurs in equatorial and subequatorial regions.

Precipitation In **tropical rain forests**, rainfall is relatively constant, about 200–400 cm annually. In **tropical dry forests**, precipitation is highly seasonal, about 150–200 cm annually, with a six- to seven-month dry season.

Temperature High year-round, averaging 25–29°C with little seasonal variation.

Plants Tropical forests are vertically layered, and competition for light is intense. Layers in rain forests include trees that grow above a closed canopy, the canopy trees, one or two layers of subcanopy trees, and layers of shrubs and herbs (small, nonwoody plants). There are generally fewer layers in tropical dry forests. Broadleaf evergreen trees are dominant in tropical rain forests, whereas many tropical dry forest trees drop their leaves during the dry season. Epiphytes such as bromeliads and orchids generally cover tropical forest trees but are less abundant in dry forests. Thorny shrubs and succulent plants are common in some tropical dry forests.

Animals Earth's tropical forests are home to millions of species, including an estimated 5–30 million still undescribed species of insects, spiders, and other arthropods. In fact, animal diversity is

A tropical rain forest in Costa Rica

higher in tropical forests than in any other terrestrial biome. The animals, including amphibians, birds and other reptiles, mammals, and arthropods, are adapted to the vertically layered environment and are often inconspicuous.

Human Impact Humans long ago established thriving communities in tropical forests. Rapid population growth leading to agriculture and development is now destroying many tropical forests.

Desert

Distribution **Deserts** occur in bands near 30° north and south latitude or at other latitudes in the interior of continents (for instance, the Gobi Desert of north-central Asia).

Precipitation Precipitation is low and highly variable, generally less than 30 cm per year.

Temperature Temperature is variable seasonally and daily. Maximum air temperature in hot deserts may exceed 50°C; in cold deserts air temperature may fall below –30°C.

Plants Desert landscapes are dominated by low, widely scattered vegetation; the proportion of bare ground is high compared with other terrestrial biomes. The plants include succulents such as cacti or euphorbs, deeply rooted shrubs, and herbs that grow during the infrequent moist periods. Desert plant adaptations include tolerance of heat and dessication, water storage, and reduced leaf surface area. Physical defenses, such as spines, and chemical defenses, such as toxins in the leaves of shrubs, are common. Many of the plants exhibit C_4 or CAM photosynthesis.

Animals Common desert animals include snakes and lizards, scorpions, ants, beetles, migratory and resident birds, and seed-eating rodents. Many species are nocturnal. Water conservation is a common adaptation, with some species surviving solely on water obtained from breaking down carbohydrates in seeds.

Human Impact Long-distance transport of water and deep groundwater wells have allowed humans to maintain substantial populations in deserts. Urbanization and conversion to irrigated agriculture have reduced the natural biodiversity of some deserts.

Organ Pipe Cactus National Monument, Arizona

Exploring Terrestrial Biomes

Savanna

Distribution Savanna occurs in equatorial and subequatorial regions.

Precipitation Seasonal rainfall averages 30–50 cm per year. The dry season can last up to eight or nine months.

Temperature The **savanna** is warm year-round, averaging 24–29°C, but with somewhat more seasonal variation than in tropical forests.

Plants The scattered trees found at different densities in the savanna often are thorny and have small leaves, an apparent adaptation to the relatively dry conditions. Fires are common in the dry season, and the dominant plant species are fire-adapted and tolerant of seasonal drought. Grasses and small nonwoody plants called forbs, which make up most of the ground cover, grow rapidly in response to seasonal rains and are tolerant of grazing by large mammals and other herbivores.

Animals Large plant-eating mammals, such as wildebeests and zebras, and predators, including lions and hyenas, are common inhabitants. However, the dominant herbivores are actually insects, especially termites. During seasonal droughts, grazing mammals often migrate to parts of the savanna with more forage and scattered watering holes.

A savanna in Kenya

Human Impact There is evidence that the earliest humans lived in savannas. Fires set by humans may help maintain this biome, though overly frequent fires reduce tree regeneration by killing the seedlings and saplings. Cattle ranching and overhunting have led to declines in large-mammal populations.

Chaparral

Distribution This biome occurs in midlatitude coastal regions on several continents, and its many names reflect its far-flung distribution: **chaparral** in North America, *matorral* in Spain and Chile, *garigue* and *maquis* in southern France, and *fynbos* in South Africa.

Precipitation Precipitation is highly seasonal, with rainy winters and dry summers. Annual precipitation generally falls within the range of 30–50 cm.

Temperature Fall, winter, and spring are cool, with average temperatures in the range of 10–12°C. Average summer temperature can reach 30°C, and daytime maximum temperature can exceed 40°C.

Plants Chaparral is dominated by shrubs and small trees, along with many kinds of grasses and herbs. Plant diversity is high, with many species confined to a specific, relatively small geographic area. Adaptations of the woody plants to drought include their tough evergreen leaves, which reduce water loss. Adaptations to fire are also prominent. Some of the shrubs produce seeds that will germinate only after a hot fire; food reserves stored in their fire-resistant roots enable them to resprout quickly and use nutrients released by the fire.

Animals Native mammals include browsers, such as deer and goats, that feed on twigs and buds of woody vegetation, and a high diversity of small mammals. Chaparral areas also support many species of amphibians, birds and other reptiles, and insects.

Human Impact Chaparral areas have been heavily settled and reduced through conversion to agriculture and urbanization. Humans contribute to the fires that sweep across the chaparral.

An area of chaparral in California

Temperate Grassland

Distribution The veldts of South Africa, the *puszta* of Hungary, the pampas of Argentina and Uruguay, the steppes of Russia, and the plains and prairies of central North America are examples of **temperate grasslands**.

Precipitation Precipitation is often highly seasonal, with relatively dry winters and wet summers. Annual precipitation generally averages between 30 and 100 cm. Periodic drought is common.

Temperature Winters are generally cold, with average temperatures falling below –10°C. Summers, with average temperatures often approaching 30°C, are hot.

Plants The dominant plants are grasses and forbs, which vary in height from a few centimeters to 2 m in tallgrass prairie. Many grassland plants have adaptations that help them survive periodic, protracted droughts and fire. For example, grasses can sprout quickly following fire. Grazing by large mammals helps prevent establishment of woody shrubs and trees.

A grassland in Mongolia

Animals Native mammals include large grazers such as bison and wild horses. Temperate grasslands are also inhabited by a wide variety of burrowing mammals, such as prairie dogs in North America.

Human Impact Deep, fertile soils make temperate grasslands ideal places for agriculture, especially for growing grains. As a consequence, most grassland in North America and much of Eurasia has been converted to farmland. In some drier grasslands, cattle and other grazers have turned parts of the biome into desert.

Northern Coniferous Forest

Distribution Extending in a broad band across northern North America and Eurasia to the edge of the arctic tundra, the **northern coniferous forest**, or *taiga*, is the largest terrestrial biome on Earth.

Precipitation Annual precipitation generally ranges from 30 to 70 cm, and periodic droughts are common. However, some coastal coniferous forests of the U.S. Pacific Northwest are temperate rain forests that may receive over 300 cm of annual precipitation.

Temperature Winters are usually cold; summers may be hot. Some areas of coniferous forest in Siberia typically range in temperature from –50°C in winter to over 20°C in summer.

Plants Northern coniferous forests are dominated by cone-bearing trees, such as pine, spruce, fir, and hemlock, some of which depend on fire to regenerate. The conical shape of many conifers prevents too much snow from accumulating and breaking their branches, and their needle- or scale-like leaves reduce water loss. The diversity of plants in the shrub and herb layers of these forests is lower than in temperate broadleaf forests.

Animals While many migratory birds nest in northern coniferous forests, other species reside there year-round. The mammals of this biome, which include moose, brown bears, and Siberian tigers, are diverse. Periodic outbreaks of insects that feed on the dominant trees can kill vast tracts of trees.

Human Impact Although they have not been heavily settled by human populations, northern coniferous forests are being logged at an alarming rate, and the old-growth stands of these trees may soon disappear.

A coniferous forest in Norway

Temperate Broadleaf Forest

Distribution Temperate broadleaf forest is found mainly at midlatitudes in the Northern Hemisphere, with smaller areas in Chile, South Africa, Australia, and New Zealand.

Precipitation Precipitation can average from about 70 to over 200 cm annually. Significant amounts fall during all seasons, including summer rain and, in some forests, winter snow.

Temperature Winter temperatures average 0°C. Summers, with temperatures up to 35°C, are hot and humid.

Plants A mature **temperate broadleaf forest** has distinct vertical layers, including a closed canopy, one or two strata of understory trees, a shrub layer, and an herb layer. There are few epiphytes. The dominant plants in the Northern Hemisphere are deciduous trees, which drop their leaves before winter, when low temperatures would reduce photosynthesis and make water uptake from frozen soil difficult. In Australia, evergreen eucalyptus trees dominate these forests.

Animals In the Northern Hemisphere, many mammals hibernate in winter, while many bird species migrate to warmer climates. Mammals, birds, and insects make use of all the vertical layers of the forest.

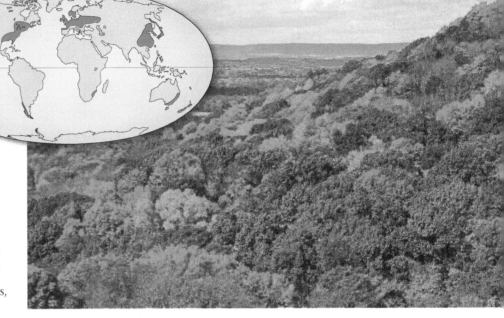

A temperate broadleaf forest in New Jersey

Human Impact Temperate broadleaf forest has been heavily settled on all continents. Logging and land clearing for agriculture and urban development cleared virtually all the original deciduous forests in North America. However, owing to their capacity for recovery, these forests are returning over much of their former range.

Tundra

Distribution **Tundra** covers expansive areas of the Arctic, amounting to 20% of Earth's land surface. High winds and low temperatures produce similar plant communities, called *alpine tundra*, on very high mountaintops at all latitudes, including the tropics.

Precipitation Precipitation averages from 20 to 60 cm annually in arctic tundra but may exceed 100 cm in alpine tundra.

Temperature Winters are cold, with averages in some areas below –30°C. Summer temperatures generally average less than 10°C.

Plants The vegetation of tundra is mostly herbaceous, consisting of a mixture of mosses, grasses, and forbs, along with some dwarf shrubs and trees and lichens. A permanently frozen layer of soil called permafrost restricts the growth of plant roots.

Animals Large grazing musk oxen are resident, while caribou and reindeer are migratory. Predators include bears, wolves, and foxes. Many bird species migrate to the tundra for summer nesting.

Human Impact Tundra is sparsely settled but has become the focus of significant mineral and oil extraction in recent years.

Dovrefjell National Park, Norway, in autumn

CONCEPT 52.3

Aquatic biomes are diverse and dynamic systems that cover most of Earth

Unlike terrestrial biomes, aquatic biomes are characterized primarily by their physical environment. They also show far less latitudinal variation, with all types found across the globe. Ecologists distinguish between freshwater and marine biomes on the basis of physical and chemical differences. Marine biomes generally have salt concentrations that average 3%, whereas freshwater biomes are usually characterized by a salt concentration of less than 0.1%.

The oceans make up the largest marine biome, covering about 75% of Earth's surface. Because of their vast size, they greatly impact the biosphere. Water evaporated from the oceans provides most of the planet's rainfall, and ocean temperatures have a major effect on global climate and wind patterns (see Figure 52.3). Marine algae and photosynthetic bacteria also supply much of the world's oxygen and consume large amounts of atmospheric carbon dioxide.

Freshwater biomes are closely linked to the soils and biotic components of the surrounding terrestrial biome. The particular characteristics of a freshwater biome are also influenced by the patterns and speed of water flow and the climate to which the biome is exposed.

Zonation in Aquatic Biomes

Many aquatic biomes are physically and chemically stratified (layered), vertically and horizontally, as illustrated for both a lake and a marine environment in **Figure 52.12**. Light is absorbed by the water itself and by photosynthetic organisms, so its intensity decreases rapidly with depth. Ecologists distinguish between the upper **photic zone**, where there is sufficient light for photosynthesis, and the lower **aphotic zone**, where little light penetrates. The photic and aphotic zones together make up the **pelagic zone**. Deep in the aphotic zone lies the **abyssal zone**, the part of the ocean 2,000–6,000 m below the surface. At the bottom of all of these aquatic zones, deep or shallow, is the **benthic zone**. Made up of sand and organic and inorganic sediments, the benthic zone is occupied by communities of organisms collectively called the **benthos**. A major source of food for many benthic species is dead organic matter called **detritus**, which "rains" down from the productive surface waters of the photic zone.

Thermal energy from sunlight warms surface waters to whatever depth the sunlight penetrates, but the deeper waters remain quite cold. In the ocean and in most lakes, a narrow layer of abrupt temperature change called a **thermocline**

▼ **Figure 52.12 Zonation in aquatic environments.**

(a) Zonation in a lake

The lake environment is generally classified on the basis of three physical criteria: light penetration (photic and aphotic zones), distance from shore and water depth (littoral and limnetic zones), and whether the environment is open water (pelagic zone) or on the bottom (benthic zone).

(b) Marine zonation

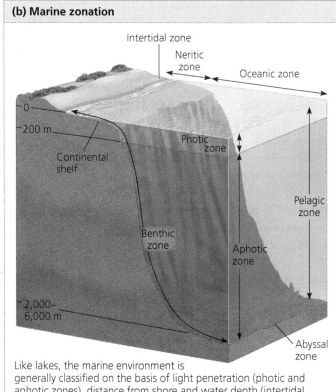

Like lakes, the marine environment is generally classified on the basis of light penetration (photic and aphotic zones), distance from shore and water depth (intertidal, neritic, and oceanic zones), and whether the environment is open water (pelagic zone) or on the bottom (benthic and abyssal zones).

separates the more uniformly warm upper layer from more uniformly cold deeper waters. Lakes tend to be particularly layered with respect to temperature, especially during summer and winter, but many temperate lakes undergo a semiannual mixing of their waters as a result of changing

① In winter, the coldest water in the lake (0°C) lies just below the surface ice; water becomes progressively warmer at deeper levels of the lake, typically 4°C at the bottom.

② In spring, the surface water warms to 4°C and mixes with the layers below, eliminating thermal stratification. Spring winds help mix the water, bringing oxygen to the bottom and nutrients to the surface.

③ In summer, the lake regains a distinctive thermal profile, with warm surface water separated from cold bottom water by a narrow vertical zone of abrupt temperature change, called a thermocline.

④ In autumn, as surface water cools rapidly, it sinks beneath the underlying layers, remixing the water until the surface begins to freeze and the winter temperature profile is reestablished.

▲ **Figure 52.13 Seasonal turnover in lakes with winter ice cover.** Seasonal turnover causes the lake waters to be well oxygenated at all depths in spring and autumn; in winter and summer, when the lake is stratified by temperature, the oxygen concentration decreases with depth.

temperature profiles (**Figure 52.13**). This **turnover**, as it is called, sends oxygenated water from a lake's surface to the bottom and brings nutrient-rich water from the bottom to the surface in both spring and autumn.

In both freshwater and marine environments, communities are distributed according to water depth, degree of light penetration, distance from shore, and whether they are found in open water or near the bottom. Marine communities, in particular, illustrate the limitations on species distribution that result from these abiotic factors. Plankton and many fish species occur in the relatively shallow photic zone (see Figure 52.12b). Because water absorbs light so well and the ocean is so deep, most of the ocean volume is dark (the aphotic zone) and harbors relatively little life.

Figure 52.14 explores the main characteristics of Earth's major aquatic biomes.

CONCEPT CHECK 52.3

1. Why are phytoplankton, and not benthic algae or rooted aquatic plants, the dominant photosynthetic organisms of the oceanic pelagic zone? (See Figure 52.14.)

2. **MAKE CONNECTIONS** Many organisms living in estuaries experience freshwater and saltwater conditions each day with the rising and falling of tides. Explain how these changing conditions challenge the survival of these organisms (see Concept 44.1).

3. **WHAT IF?** Water leaving a reservoir behind a dam is often taken from deep layers of the reservoir. Would you expect fish found in a river below a dam in summer to be species that prefer colder or warmer water than fish found in an undammed river? Explain.

For suggested answers, see Appendix A.

Interactions between organisms and the environment limit the distribution of species

So far in this chapter we've examined Earth's climate and the characteristics of terrestrial and aquatic biomes. We've also introduced the range of biological levels at which ecologists work (see Figure 52.2). In this section, we will examine how ecologists determine what factors control the distribution of species, such as the *Paedophryne* frog shown in Figure 52.1.

Species distributions are a consequence of both ecological and evolutionary interactions through time. The differential survival and reproduction of individuals that lead to evolution occur in *ecological time*, the minute-to-minute time frame of interactions between organisms and the environment. Through natural selection, organisms adapt to their environment over the time frame of many generations, in *evolutionary time*. One example of how events in ecological time have led to evolution is the selection for beak depth in Galápagos finches (see Figures 23.1 and 23.2). On the island of Daphne Major, finches with larger, deeper beaks were better able to survive during a drought because they could eat the large, hard seeds that were available. Finches with shallower beaks, which required smaller, softer seeds that were in short supply, were less likely to survive and reproduce. Because beak depth is hereditary in this species, the generation of finches born after the drought had beaks that were deeper than those of previous generations.

Lakes

Physical Environment Standing bodies of water range from ponds a few square meters in area to lakes covering thousands of square kilometers. Light decreases with depth, creating stratification. Temperate lakes may have a seasonal thermocline; tropical lowland lakes have a thermocline year-round.

Chemical Environment The salinity, oxygen concentration, and nutrient content differ greatly among lakes and can vary with season. **Oligotrophic lakes** are nutrient-poor and generally oxygen-rich; **eutrophic lakes** are nutrient-rich and often depleted of oxygen in the deepest zone in summer and if covered with ice in winter. The amount of decomposable organic matter in bottom sediments is low in oligotrophic lakes and high in eutrophic lakes; high rates of decomposition in deeper layers of eutrophic lakes cause periodic oxygen depletion.

Geologic Features Oligotrophic lakes may become more eutrophic over time as runoff adds sediments and nutrients. They tend to have less surface area relative to their depth than eutrophic lakes.

Photosynthetic Organisms Rooted and floating aquatic plants in lakes live in the

An oligotrophic lake in Jasper National Park, Alberta

littoral zone, the shallow, well-lit waters close to shore. Farther from shore, where water is too deep to support rooted aquatic plants, the **limnetic zone** is inhabited by a variety of phytoplankton, including cyanobacteria.

Heterotrophs In the limnetic zone, small drifting heterotrophs, or zooplankton, graze on the phytoplankton. The benthic zone is inhabited by assorted invertebrates whose species composition depends partly on oxygen levels. Fishes live in all zones with sufficient oxygen.

A eutrophic lake in the Okavango Delta, Botswana

Human Impact Runoff from fertilized land and dumping of wastes lead to nutrient enrichment, which can produce algal blooms, oxygen depletion, and fish kills.

Wetlands

Physical Environment A **wetland** is a habitat that is inundated by water at least some of the time and that supports plants adapted to water-saturated soil. Some wetlands are inundated at all times, whereas others flood infrequently.

Chemical Environment Because of high organic production by plants and decomposition by microbes and other organisms, both the water and the soils are periodically

low in dissolved oxygen. Wetlands have a high capacity to filter dissolved nutrients and chemical pollutants.

Geologic Features *Basin wetlands* develop in shallow basins, ranging from upland depressions to filled-in lakes and ponds. *Riverine wetlands* develop along shallow and periodically flooded banks of rivers and streams. *Fringe wetlands* occur along the coasts of large lakes and seas, where water

flows back and forth because of rising lake levels or tidal action. Thus, fringe wetlands include both freshwater and marine biomes.

Photosynthetic Organisms Wetlands are among the most productive biomes on Earth. Their water-saturated soils favor the growth of plants such as floating pond lilies and emergent cattails, many sedges, bald cypress, and black spruce, which have adaptations enabling them to grow in water or in soil that is periodically anaerobic owing to the presence of unaerated water. Woody plants dominate the vegetation of swamps, while bogs are dominated by sphagnum mosses.

Heterotrophs Wetlands are home to a diverse community of invertebrates, birds, and many other organisms. Herbivores, from crustaceans and aquatic insect larvae to muskrats, consume algae, detritus, and plants. Carnivores are also varied and may include dragonflies, otters, frogs, alligators, and herons.

Human Impact Wetlands help purify water and reduce peak flooding. Draining and filling have destroyed up to 90% of wetlands.

A basin wetland in the United Kingdom

Streams and Rivers

Physical Environment The most prominent physical characteristic of streams and rivers is the speed and volume of their flow. Headwater streams are generally cold, clear, turbulent, and swift. Farther downstream, where numerous tributaries may have joined, forming a river, the water is generally warmer and more turbid because of suspended sediment. Streams and rivers are stratified into vertical zones.

Chemical Environment The salt and nutrient content of streams and rivers increases from the headwaters to the mouth. Headwaters are generally rich in oxygen. Downstream water may also contain substantial oxygen, except where there has been organic enrichment. A large fraction of the organic matter in rivers consists of dissolved or highly fragmented material that is carried by the current from forested streams.

Geologic Features Headwater stream channels are often narrow, have a rocky bottom, and alternate between shallow sections and deeper pools. The downstream stretches of rivers are generally wide and meandering. River bottoms are often silty from sediments deposited over long periods of time.

A headwater stream in Washington

Photosynthetic Organisms Headwater streams that flow through grasslands or deserts may be rich in phytoplankton or rooted aquatic plants.

Heterotrophs A great diversity of fishes and invertebrates inhabit unpolluted rivers and streams, distributed according to, and throughout, the vertical zones. In streams flowing through temperate or tropical forests, organic matter from terrestrial vegetation is the primary source of food for aquatic consumers.

The Loire river in France, far from its headwaters

Human Impact Municipal, agricultural, and industrial pollution degrade water quality and kill aquatic organisms. Damming and flood control impair the natural functioning of stream and river ecosystems and threaten migratory species such as salmon.

Estuaries

Physical Environment An **estuary** is a transition area between river and sea. Seawater flows up the estuary channel during a rising tide and flows back down during the falling tide. Often, higher-density seawater occupies the bottom of the channel and mixes little with the lower-density river water at the surface.

Chemical Environment Salinity varies spatially within estuaries, from nearly that of fresh water to that of seawater. Salinity also varies with the rise and fall of the tides. Nutrients from the river make estuaries, like wetlands, among the most productive biomes.

Geologic Features Estuarine flow patterns combined with the sediments carried by river and tidal waters create a complex network of tidal channels, islands, natural levees, and mudflats.

Photosynthetic Organisms Saltmarsh grasses and algae, including phytoplankton, are the major producers in estuaries.

Heterotrophs Estuaries support an abundance of worms, oysters, crabs, and many fish species that humans consume. Many marine invertebrates and fishes use estuaries as a breeding ground or migrate through them to freshwater habitats upstream. Estuaries are also crucial feeding areas for waterfowl and some marine mammals.

Human Impact Filling, dredging, and pollution from upstream have disrupted estuaries worldwide.

An estuary in southern Spain

Intertidal Zones

Physical Environment An **intertidal zone** is periodically submerged and exposed by the tides, twice daily on most marine shores. Upper zones experience longer exposures to air and greater variations in temperature and salinity. Changes in physical conditions from the upper to the lower intertidal zones limit the distributions of many organisms to particular strata, as shown in the photograph.

Chemical Environment Oxygen and nutrient levels are generally high and are renewed with each turn of the tides. Geologic Features The substrates of intertidal zones, which are generally either rocky or sandy, select for particular behavior and anatomy among intertidal organisms. The configuration of bays or coastlines influences the magnitude of tides and the relative exposure of intertidal organisms to wave action.

Photosynthetic Organisms A high diversity and biomass of attached marine algae inhabit rocky intertidal zones, especially in the lower zone. Sandy intertidal zones exposed to vigorous wave action generally lack attached plants or algae, while sandy intertidal zones in protected bays or lagoons often support rich beds of seagrass and algae.

Heterotrophs Many of the animals in rocky intertidal environments have structural adaptations that enable them to attach to the hard substrate. The composition, density, and diversity of animals change markedly from the upper to the lower intertidal zones. Many of the animals in sandy or muddy intertidal zones, such as worms, clams, and predatory crustaceans, bury themselves and feed as the tides bring sources of food. Other common animals are sponges, sea anemones, echinoderms, and small fishes.

Human Impact Oil pollution has disrupted many intertidal areas. The construction of rock walls and barriers to reduce erosion from waves and storm surges has disrupted this zone in some locations.

A rocky intertidal zone on the Oregon coast

Oceanic Pelagic Zone

Physical Environment The **oceanic pelagic zone** is a vast realm of open blue water, constantly mixed by wind driven oceanic currents. Because of higher water clarity, the photic zone extends to greater depths than in coastal marine waters.

Chemical Environment Oxygen levels are generally high. Nutrient concentrations are generally lower than in coastal waters. Because they are thermally stratified year-round, some tropical areas of the oceanic pelagic zone have lower nutrient concentrations than temperate oceans. Turnover between fall and spring renews nutrients in the photic zones of temperate and high-latitude ocean areas.

Geologic Features This biome covers approximately 70% of Earth's surface and has an average depth of nearly 4,000 m. The deepest point in the ocean is more than 10,000 m beneath the surface.

Photosynthetic Organisms The dominant photosynthetic organisms are phytoplankton, including photosynthetic bacteria, that drift with the oceanic currents. Spring turnover renews nutrients in temperate oceans producing a surge of phytoplankton growth. Because of the large extent of this biome, photosynthetic plankton account for about half of the photosynthetic activity on Earth.

Heterotrophs The most abundant heterotrophs in this biome are zooplankton. These protists, worms, copepods, shrimp-like krill, jellies, and small larvae of invertebrates and fishes graze on photosynthetic plankton. The oceanic pelagic zone also includes numerous free-swimming animals, such as large squids, fishes, sea turtles, and marine mammals.

Human Impact Overfishing has depleted fish stocks in all Earth's oceans, which have also been polluted by waste dumping.

Open ocean near Iceland

Coral Reefs

Physical Environment **Coral reefs** are formed largely from the calcium carbonate skeletons of corals. Shallow reef-building corals live in the photic zone of relatively stable tropical marine environments with high water clarity, primarily near islands and along the edge of some continents. They are sensitive to temperatures below about 18–20°C and above 30°C. Deep-sea coral reefs, found between 200 and 1,500 m deep, are less known than their shallow counterparts but harbor as much diversity as many shallow reefs do.

Chemical Environment Corals require high oxygen levels and are excluded by high inputs of fresh water and nutrients.

Geologic Features Corals require a solid substrate for attachment. A typical coral reef begins as a *fringing reef* on a young, high island, forming an offshore *barrier reef* later in the history of the island and becoming a *coral atoll* as the older island submerges.

A coral reef in the Red Sea

Photosynthetic Organisms Unicellular algae live within the tissues of the corals, forming a mutualistic relationship that provides the corals with organic molecules. Diverse multicellular red and green algae growing on the reef also contribute substantial amounts of photosynthesis.

Heterotrophs Corals, a diverse group of cnidarians, are themselves the predominant animals on coral reefs. However, fish and invertebrate diversity is exceptionally high. Overall animal diversity on coral reefs rivals that of tropical forests.

Human Impact Collecting of coral skeletons and overfishing have reduced populations of corals and reef fishes. Global warming and pollution may be contributing to large-scale coral death. Development of coastal mangroves for aquaculture has also reduced spawning grounds for many species of reef fishes.

Marine Benthic Zone

Physical Environment The **marine benthic zone** consists of the seafloor below the surface waters of the coastal, or **neritic**, zone and the offshore, pelagic zone. Except for shallow, near-coastal areas, the marine benthic zone receives no sunlight. Water temperature declines with depth, while pressure increases. As a result, organisms in the very deep benthic, or abyssal, zone are adapted to continuous cold (about 3°C) and very high water pressure.

Chemical Environment Except in areas of organic enrichment, oxygen is usually present at sufficient concentrations to support diverse animal life.

Geologic Features Soft sediments cover most of the benthic zone. However, there are areas of rocky substrate on reefs, submarine mountains, and new oceanic crust.

Autotrophs Photosynthetic organisms, mainly seaweeds and filamentous algae, are limited to shallow benthic areas with sufficient light to support them. Unique assemblages of organisms, such as those shown in the photo, are found near

deep-sea hydrothermal vents on mid-ocean ridges. In these dark, hot environments, the food producers are chemoautotrophic prokaryotes that obtain energy by oxidizing H_2S formed by a reaction of the hot water with dissolved sulfate (SO_4^{2-}).

Heterotrophs Neritic benthic communities include numerous invertebrates and fishes. Beyond the photic zone, most consumers depend entirely on organic matter raining down from above. Among the animals of the deep-sea hydrothermal vent communities are giant tube worms (pictured at left), some more than 1 m long. They are nourished by chemoautotrophic prokaryotes that live as symbionts within their bodies. Many other invertebrates, including arthropods and echinoderms, are also abundant around the hydrothermal vents.

Human Impact Overfishing has decimated important benthic fish populations, such as the cod of the Grand Banks off Newfoundland. Dumping of organic wastes has created oxygen-deprived benthic areas.

A deep-sea hydrothermal vent community

Biologists have long recognized global and regional patterns in the distribution of organisms (see the discussion of biogeography in Concept 22.3). Ecologists ask not only *where* species occur, but also *why* species occur where they do: What factors determine their distribution? In seeking to answer this question, ecologists focus on both biotic and abiotic factors.

Both kinds of factors often affect the distribution of a species, as we can see for the saguaro (*Carnegiea gigantea*). Saguaro cacti are found almost exclusively in the Sonoran Desert of the southwestern United States and northwestern Mexico (Figure 52.15). To the north, their range is limited by an abiotic factor: temperature. Saguaros tolerate freezing temperatures only briefly, typically for less than a day, and generally cannot survive at temperatures below −4°C (25°F). For the same reason, saguaros are rarely found at elevations above 1,200 m (4,000 feet).

Additional factors must be taken into account to fully explain the distribution of saguaros, however, including why they are missing from the western portion of the Sonoran Desert. Water availability is important because seedling survival typically requires consecutive years of moist conditions, something that may occur only a few times each century. Biotic factors almost certainly influence their distribution as well. Mice and grazers such as goats eat the seedlings, and bats pollinate the large, white flowers that open at night. Saguaros are also vulnerable to a deadly bacterial disease. Thus, for the saguaro, as for most other species, ecologists need to consider multiple factors and alternative hypotheses when attempting to explain the distribution of a species.

To see how ecologists might arrive at such an explanation, let's work our way through the series of questions in the flowchart in Figure 52.16.

▲ Figure 52.15 **Distribution of the saguaro in North America.** Freezing temperatures strongly limit where saguaros are found, but other abiotic and biotic factors are also important.

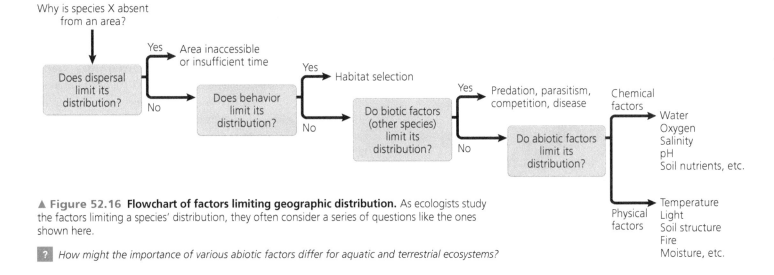

▲ Figure 52.16 **Flowchart of factors limiting geographic distribution.** As ecologists study the factors limiting a species' distribution, they often consider a series of questions like the ones shown here.

? *How might the importance of various abiotic factors differ for aquatic and terrestrial ecosystems?*

Dispersal and Distribution

One factor that contributes greatly to the global distribution of organisms is **dispersal**, the movement of individuals or gametes away from their area of origin or from centers of high population density. A biogeographer who studies the distributions of species in the context of evolutionary theory might consider dispersal in hypothesizing why there are no saguaros in the Sahara Desert of Africa: A barrier may have kept them from reaching the continent. While land-bound saguaros have not reached Africa under their own power, other organisms that disperse more readily, such as some birds, have. The dispersal of organisms is critical to understanding the role of geographic isolation in evolution (see Concept 24.2) as well as the patterns of species distribution we see today, including that of the Pacific diatom discussed earlier in this chapter.

Natural Range Expansions and Adaptive Radiation

EVOLUTION   The importance of dispersal is most evident when organisms reach an area where they did not exist previously. For instance, 200 years ago, the cattle egret (*Bubulcus ibis*) was found only in Africa and southwestern Europe. But in the late 1800s, some of these birds managed to cross the Atlantic Ocean and colonize northeastern South America. From there, cattle egrets gradually spread southward and also northward through Central America and into North America, reaching Florida by 1960 (Figure 52.17).

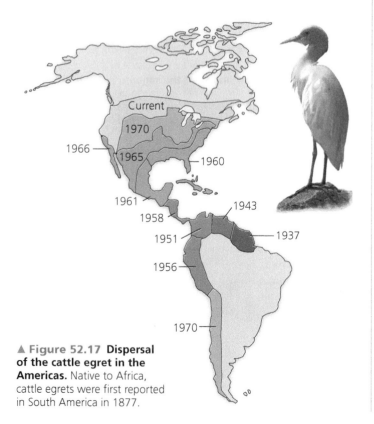

▲ Figure 52.17 Dispersal of the cattle egret in the Americas. Native to Africa, cattle egrets were first reported in South America in 1877.

Today they have breeding populations as far west as the Pacific coast of the United States and as far north as southern Canada.

In rare cases, such long-distance dispersal can lead to adaptive radiation, the rapid evolution of an ancestral species into new species that fill many ecological niches (see Concept 25.4). The incredible diversity of Hawaiian silverswords is an example of adaptive radiation that was possible only with the long-distance dispersal of an ancestral tarweed from North America (see Figure 25.22).

Natural range expansions clearly show the influence of dispersal on distribution. However, opportunities to observe such dispersal directly are rare, so ecologists often turn to experimental methods to better understand the role of dispersal in limiting the distribution of species.

Species Transplants

To determine if dispersal is a key factor limiting the distribution of a species, ecologists may observe the results of intentional or accidental transplants of the species to areas where it was previously absent. For a transplant to be successful, some of the organisms must not only survive in the new area but also reproduce there sustainably. If a transplant is successful, then we can conclude that the *potential* range of the species is larger than its *actual* range; in other words, the species *could* live in certain areas where it currently does not.

Species introduced to new geographic locations often disrupt the communities and ecosystems to which they have been introduced and can spread quickly (see Concept 56.1). Consequently, ecologists rarely move species to new geographic regions. Instead, they document the outcome when a species has been transplanted for other purposes, such as to introduce game animals or predators of pest species, or when a species has been accidentally transplanted or released outside its normal range.

Behavior and Habitat Selection

As transplant experiments show, some organisms do not occupy all of their potential range, even though they may be physically able to disperse into the unoccupied areas. To follow our line of questioning from Figure 52.16, does behavior play a role in limiting distribution in such cases? When individuals seem to avoid certain habitats, even when the habitats are suitable, the organism's distribution may be limited by habitat selection behavior.

Although habitat selection is one of the least understood of all ecological processes, some instances in insects have been closely studied. Female insects often deposit eggs only in response to a very narrow set of stimuli, which may restrict distribution of the insects to certain host plants. Larvae of the European corn borer, for example, can feed on a wide variety of plants but are found almost exclusively on corn (maize) because egg-laying females are attracted by odors produced by the plant. Habitat selection behavior clearly restricts this insect to geographic locations where corn is found.

Biotic Factors

If behavior does not limit the distribution of a species, our next question is whether biotic factors—other species—are responsible. Often, negative interactions with predators (organisms that kill their prey) or herbivores (organisms that eat plants or algae) restrict the ability of a species to survive and reproduce. **Figure 52.18** describes a specific case of an herbivore, a sea urchin, limiting the distribution of a food species. In certain marine ecosystems, there is often an inverse relationship between the abundance of sea urchins and seaweeds (multicellular algae, such as kelp). Where urchins that graze on seaweeds and other algae are common, large stands of seaweeds do not become established. As described in Figure 52.18, Australian researchers have tested the hypothesis that sea urchins are a biotic factor limiting seaweed distribution. When sea urchins were removed from experimental plots, seaweed cover increased dramatically, showing that urchins limited the distribution of seaweeds.

In addition to predation and herbivory, the presence or absence of pollinators, food resources, parasites, pathogens, and competing organisms can act as a biotic limitation on species distribution. Such biotic limitations are common in nature.

Does feeding by sea urchins limit seaweed distribution?

Experiment W. J. Fletcher, of the University of Sydney, Australia, reasoned that if sea urchins are a limiting biotic factor in a particular ecosystem, then more seaweeds should invade an area from which sea urchins have been removed. To isolate the effect of sea urchins from that of a seaweed-eating mollusc, the limpet, he removed only urchins, only limpets, or both from study areas adjacent to a control site.

▼ Limpet

▲ Sea urchin

Results Fletcher observed a large difference in seaweed growth between areas with and without sea urchins.

Removing both limpets and urchins or removing only urchins increased seaweed cover dramatically.

Almost no seaweed grew in areas where both urchins and limpets were present, or where only limpets were removed.

Conclusion Removing both limpets and urchins resulted in the greatest increase in seaweed cover, indicating that both species have some influence on seaweed distribution. But since removing only urchins greatly increased seaweed growth whereas removing only limpets had little effect, Fletcher concluded that sea urchins have a much greater effect than limpets in limiting seaweed distribution.

Source: W. J. Fletcher, Interactions among subtidal Australian sea urchins, gastropods, and algae: effects of experimental removals, *Ecological Monographs* 57:89–109 (1987).

INTERPRET THE DATA *Seaweed cover increased the most when both urchins and limpets were removed. How might you explain this result?*

Abiotic Factors

The last question in the flowchart in Figure 52.16 considers whether abiotic factors, such as temperature, water, oxygen, salinity, sunlight, or soil, might be limiting a species' distribution. If the physical conditions at a site do not allow a species to survive and reproduce, then the species will not be found there. Throughout this discussion, keep in mind that most abiotic factors vary substantially in space and time. Daily and annual fluctuations of abiotic factors may either blur or accentuate regional distinctions. Furthermore, organisms can avoid some stressful conditions temporarily through behaviors such as dormancy or hibernation (see Concept 40.4).

Temperature

Environmental temperature is an important factor in the distribution of organisms because of its effect on biological processes. Cells may rupture if the water they contain freezes (at temperatures below 0°C), and the proteins of most organisms denature at temperatures above 45°C. Most organisms function best within a specific range of environmental temperature. Temperatures outside that range may force some animals to expend energy regulating their internal temperature, as mammals and birds do (see Figure 40.17). Extraordinary adaptations enable certain organisms, such as thermophilic prokaryotes (see Figure 27.17), to live outside the temperature range habitable by other life.

Water and Oxygen

The dramatic variation in water availability among habitats is another important factor in species distribution. Species living at the seashore or in tidal wetlands can desiccate (dry out) as the tide recedes. Terrestrial organisms face a nearly constant threat of desiccation, and the distribution of terrestrial species reflects their ability to obtain and conserve water. Many amphibians, such as the *Paedophryne* frog in Figure 52.1, are particularly vulnerable to drying because they use their moist, delicate skin for gas exchange. Desert organisms exhibit a variety of adaptations for acquiring and conserving water in dry environments, as described in Chapter 44.

Water affects oxygen availability in aquatic environments and in flooded soils, where the slow diffusion of oxygen in water can limit cellular respiration and other physiological processes. Oxygen concentrations can be particularly low in both deep ocean and deep lake waters and sediments where organic matter is abundant. Flooded wetland soils may also have low oxygen content. Mangroves and other trees have specialized roots that project above the water and help the root system obtain oxygen (see Figure 35.4). Unlike many flooded wetlands, the surface waters of streams and rivers tend to be well oxygenated because of rapid exchange of gases with the atmosphere.

Salinity

The salt concentration of water in the environment affects the water balance of organisms through osmosis (see Figure 7.12). Most aquatic organisms are restricted to either freshwater or saltwater habitats by their limited ability to osmoregulate (see Concept 44.1). Although most terrestrial organisms can excrete excess salts from specialized glands or in feces or urine, high-salinity habitats typically have few species of plants or animals. In the Scientific Skills Exercise, you can interpret data from an experiment that investigated the influence of salinity on plant distributions.

Salmon that migrate between freshwater streams and the ocean use both behavioral and physiological mechanisms to osmoregulate. They balance their salt content by adjusting the amount of water they drink and by switching their gills from taking up salt in fresh water to excreting salt in the ocean.

Sunlight

Sunlight provides the energy that drives most ecosystems, and too little sunlight can limit the distribution of

▲ **Figure 52.19 Alpine tree line in Banff National Park, Canada.** Organisms living at high elevations are exposed not only to high levels of ultraviolet radiation but also to freezing temperatures, moisture deficits, and strong winds. Above the tree line, the combination of such factors restricts the growth and survival of trees.

photosynthetic species. In forests, shading by leaves makes competition for light especially intense, particularly for seedlings growing on the forest floor. In aquatic environments, every meter of water depth absorbs about 45% of the red light and about 2% of the blue light passing through it. As a result, most photosynthesis occurs relatively near the water surface.

Too much light can also limit the survival of organisms. In some ecosystems, such as deserts, high light levels can increase temperature stress if animals and plants are unable to avoid the light or to cool themselves through evaporation (see Figure 40.12). At high elevations, the sun's rays are more likely to damage DNA and proteins because the atmosphere is thinner, absorbing less ultraviolet (UV) radiation. Damage from UV radiation, combined with other abiotic stresses, prevents trees from surviving above a certain elevation, resulting in the appearance of a tree line on mountain slopes (Figure 52.19).

Rocks and Soil

In terrestrial environments, the pH, mineral composition, and physical structure of rocks and soil limit the distribution of plants and thus of the animals that feed on them, contributing to the patchiness of terrestrial ecosystems. The pH of soil can limit the distribution of organisms directly, through extreme acidic or basic conditions (see Figure 54.12), or

SCIENTIFIC SKILLS EXERCISE

Making a Bar Graph and a Line Graph to Interpret Data

How Do Salinity and Competition Affect the Distribution of Plants in an Estuary? Many ecologists begin their research by observing the distributions of organisms in the field. For example, field observations show that *Spartina patens* (salt marsh hay) is a dominant plant in salt marshes and *Typha angustifolia* (cattail) is a dominant plant in freshwater marshes. In this exercise, you will graph and interpret data from an experiment that examined the influence of an abiotic factor, salinity, and a biotic factor, competition, on the growth of these two species.

How the Experiment Was Done In a field experiment, researchers planted *S. patens* and *T. angustifolia* in salt marshes and freshwater marshes with and without neighboring plants. After two growing seasons (one and a half years), they measured the biomass of each species in each treatment. The researchers also grew both species in a greenhouse at six salinity levels and measured the biomass at each level after eight weeks.

Data from the Field Experiment Data are averages of 16 replicate samples.

| | Average Biomass (g/100 cm²) | | | |
| | *Spartina patens* | | *Typha angustifolia* | |
	Salt Marshes	Freshwater Marshes	Salt Marshes	Freshwater Marshes
With neighbors	8	3	0	18
Without neighbors	10	20	0	33

Data from the Greenhouse Experiment

Salinity (parts per thousand)	0	20	40	60	80	100
% maximum biomass (*Spartina patens*)	77	40	29	17	9	0
% maximum biomass (*Typha angustifolia*)	80	20	10	0	0	0

▲ *Spartina patens*

▲ *Typha angustifolia*

Interpret the Data

1. Make a bar graph of the data from the field experiment. (For additional information about graphs, see the Scientific Skills Review in Appendix F and in the Study Area in MasteringBiology.) What do these data indicate about the salinity tolerances of *S. patens* and *T. angustifolia*?

2. What do the data from the field experiment indicate about the effect of competition on the growth of these two species? Which species was limited more by competition?

3. Make a line graph of the data from the greenhouse experiment. Decide which values constitute the dependent and independent variables, and use these values to set up the axes of your graph.

4. (a) In the field, *S. patens* is typically absent from freshwater marshes. Based on the data, does this appear to be due to salinity or competition? Explain your answer. (b) *T. angustifolia* does not grow in salt marshes. Does this appear to be due to salinity or competition? Explain your answer.

(MB) A version of this Scientific Skills Exercise can be assigned in MasteringBiology.

Data from C. M. Crain et al., Physical and biotic drivers of plant distribution across estuarine salinity gradients, *Ecology* 85:2539–2549 (2004).

---

indirectly, by affecting the solubility of toxins and nutrients. Soil phosphorus, for instance, is relatively insoluble in basic soils and precipitates into forms unavailable to plants.

In a river, the composition of rocks and soil that make up the substrate (riverbed) can affect water chemistry, which in turn influences the resident organisms. In freshwater and marine environments, the structure of the substrate determines the organisms that can attach to it or burrow into it.

Throughout this chapter, you have seen how the distributions of biomes and organisms depend on abiotic and biotic factors. In the next chapter, we'll continue to work our way through the hierarchy outlined in Figure 52.2, focusing on how abiotic and biotic factors influence the ecology of populations.

CONCEPT CHECK 52.4

1. Give examples of human actions that could expand a species' distribution by changing its (a) dispersal or (b) biotic interactions.

2. **WHAT IF?** You suspect that deer are restricting the distribution of a tree species by preferentially eating the seedlings of the tree. How might you test this hypothesis?

3. **MAKE CONNECTIONS** Hawaiian silverswords underwent a remarkable adaptive radiation after their ancestor reached Hawaii, while the islands were still young (see Figure 25.22). Would you expect the cattle egret to undergo a similar adaptive radiation in the Americas (see Figure 52.17)? Explain.

For suggested answers, see Appendix A.

52 Chapter Review

SUMMARY OF KEY CONCEPTS

CONCEPT 52.1

Earth's climate varies by latitude and season and is changing rapidly (pp. 1161–1164)

- Global **climate** patterns are largely determined by the input of solar energy and Earth's revolution around the sun.
- The changing angle of the sun over the year, bodies of water, and mountains exert seasonal, regional, and local effects on **macroclimate**.
- Fine-scale differences in **abiotic** (nonliving) factors, such as sunlight and temperature, determine **microclimate**.
- Increasing greenhouse gas concentrations in the air are warming Earth and altering the distributions of many species. Some species will not be able to shift their ranges quickly enough to reach suitable habitat in the future.

? *Suppose global air circulation suddenly reversed, with most air ascending at 30° north and south latitude and descending at the equator. At what latitude would you most likely find deserts in this scenario?*

CONCEPT 52.2

The structure and distribution of terrestrial biomes are controlled by climate and disturbance (pp. 1164–1170)

- **Climographs** show that temperature and precipitation are correlated with **biomes**. Because other factors also play roles in biome location, biomes overlap.
- Terrestrial biomes are often named for major physical or climatic factors and for their predominant vegetation. Vertical layering is an important feature of terrestrial biomes.
- **Disturbance**, both natural and human-induced, influences the type of vegetation found in biomes. Humans have altered much of Earth's surface, replacing the natural terrestrial communities described and depicted in Figure 52.11 with urban and agricultural ones.
- The pattern of climatic variation is as important as the average climate in determining where biomes occur.

? *In what ways are disturbances important for savanna ecosystems and the plants in them?*

CONCEPT 52.3

Aquatic biomes are diverse and dynamic systems that cover most of Earth (pp. 1171–1172)

- Aquatic biomes are characterized primarily by their physical environment rather than by climate and are often layered with regard to light penetration, temperature, and community structure. Marine biomes have a higher salt concentration than freshwater biomes.
- In the ocean and in most lakes, an abrupt temperature change called a **thermocline** separates a more uniformly warm upper layer from more uniformly cold deeper waters.
- Many temperate lakes undergo a **turnover** or mixing of water in spring and fall that sends deep, nutrient-rich water to the surface and shallow, oxygen-rich water to deeper layers.

? *In which aquatic biomes might you find an aphotic zone?*

CONCEPT 52.4

Interactions between organisms and the environment limit the distribution of species (pp. 1172–1181)

- Ecologists want to know not only *where* species occur but also *why* those species occur where they do.

? *If you were an ecologist studying the chemical and physical limits to the distributions of species, how might you rearrange the flowchart preceding this question?*

TEST YOUR UNDERSTANDING

LEVEL 1: KNOWLEDGE/COMPREHENSION

1. Which of the following areas of study focuses on the exchange of energy, organisms, and materials between ecosystems?
   a. organismal ecology
   b. landscape ecology
   c. ecosystem ecology
   d. community ecology

2. Which lake zone would be absent in a very shallow lake?
   a. benthic zone
   b. aphotic zone
   c. pelagic zone
   d. littoral zone

3. Which of the following is true with respect to oligotrophic lakes and eutrophic lakes?
   a. Oligotrophic lakes are more subject to oxygen depletion.
   b. Rates of photosynthesis are lower in eutrophic lakes.
   c. Eutrophic lakes are richer in nutrients.
   d. Sediments in oligotrophic lakes contain larger amounts of decomposable organic matter.

LEVEL 2: APPLICATION/ANALYSIS

4. Which of the following is characteristic of most terrestrial biomes?
   a. a distribution predicted almost entirely by rock and soil patterns
   b. clear boundaries between adjacent biomes
   c. vegetation demonstrating vertical layering
   d. cold winter months

5. The oceans affect the biosphere in all of the following ways *except*
   a. producing a substantial amount of the biosphere's oxygen.
   b. removing carbon dioxide from the atmosphere.
   c. moderating the climate of terrestrial biomes.
   d. regulating the pH of freshwater biomes and terrestrial groundwater.

6. Which statement about dispersal is *false*?
   a. Dispersal is a common component of the life cycles of plants and animals.
   b. Colonization of devastated areas after floods or volcanic eruptions depends on dispersal.
   c. Dispersal occurs only on an evolutionary time scale.
   d. The ability to disperse can expand the geographic distribution of a species.

7. When climbing a mountain, we can observe transitions in biological communities that are analogous to the changes
   a. in biomes at different latitudes.
   b. in different depths in the ocean.
   c. in a community through different seasons.
   d. in an ecosystem as it evolves over time.

8. Suppose that the number of bird species is determined mainly by the number of vertical strata found in the environment. If so, in which of the following biomes would you find the greatest number of bird species?
   a. tropical rain forest
   b. savanna
   c. desert
   d. temperate broadleaf forest

LEVEL 3: SYNTHESIS/EVALUATION

9. **WHAT IF?** If the direction of Earth's rotation reversed, the most predictable effect would be
   a. a big change in the length of the year.
   b. winds blowing from west to east along the equator.
   c. a loss of seasonal variation at high latitudes.
   d. the elimination of ocean currents.

10. **INTERPRET THE DATA** After examining Figure 52.18, you decide to study feeding relationships among sea otters, sea urchins, and kelp. You know that sea otters prey on sea urchins and that urchins eat kelp. At four coastal sites, you measure kelp abundance. Then you spend one day at each site and mark whether otters are present or absent every 5 minutes during the day. Make a graph that shows how otter density depends on kelp abundance, using the data below. Then formulate a hypothesis to explain the pattern you observed.

Site	Kelp Abundance (% cover)	Otter Density (# sightings per day)
1	75	98
2	15	18
3	60	85
4	25	36

11. **EVOLUTION CONNECTION**
    Discuss how the concept of time applies to ecological situations and evolutionary changes. Do ecological time and evolutionary time ever overlap? If so, what are some examples?

12. **SCIENTIFIC INQUIRY**
    Jens Clausen and colleagues, at the Carnegie Institution of Washington, studied how the size of yarrow plants (*Achillea lanulosa*) growing on the slopes of the Sierra Nevada varied with elevation. They found that plants from low elevations were generally taller than plants from high elevations, as shown in the diagram.

Source: J. Clausen et al., Experimental studies on the nature of species. III. Environmental responses of climatic races of *Achillea*, Carnegie Institution of Washington Publication No. 581 (1948).

Clausen and colleagues proposed two hypotheses to explain this variation within a species: (1) There are genetic differences between populations of plants found at different elevations. (2) The species has developmental flexibility and can assume tall or short growth forms, depending on local abiotic factors. If you had seeds from yarrow plants found at low and high elevations, what experiments would you perform to test these hypotheses?

13. **WRITE ABOUT A THEME: INTERACTIONS**
    Global warming is occurring rapidly in Arctic marine and terrestrial ecosystems, including tundra and northern coniferous forests. In such locations, reflective white snow and ice cover are melting quickly and extensively, uncovering darker-colored ocean water, plants, and rocks. In a short essay (100–150 words), explain how this process might represent a positive-feedback loop (see Concept 40.2).

14. **SYNTHESIZE YOUR KNOWLEDGE**

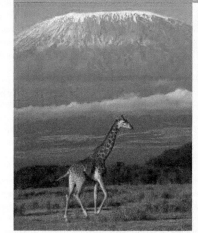

If you were to hike up Mount Kilimanjaro in Tanzania, you would pass through several habitats, including savanna at the base, forest on the slopes, and alpine tundra near the top. Explain how such diverse habitats can be found at one location near the equator.

For selected answers, see Appendix A.

MasteringBiology®

Students Go to **MasteringBiology** for assignments, the eText, and the Study Area with practice tests, animations, and activities.

Instructors Go to **MasteringBiology** for automatically graded tutorials and questions that you can assign to your students, plus Instructor Resources.

53

Population Ecology

▲ **Figure 53.1 What causes the survival of turtle hatchlings to vary each year?**

KEY CONCEPTS

53.1 Biological processes influence population density, dispersion, and demographics

53.2 The exponential model describes population growth in an idealized, unlimited environment

53.3 The logistic model describes how a population grows more slowly as it nears its carrying capacity

53.4 Life history traits are products of natural selection

53.5 Many factors that regulate population growth are density dependent

53.6 The human population is no longer growing exponentially but is still increasing rapidly

Turtle Tracks

Each year in Florida, thousands of loggerhead turtle (*Caretta caretta*) hatchlings break out of their eggshells, dig up through the sand, and crawl down the beach for their first journey to the ocean (**Figure 53.1**). Several factors determine how many turtles will hatch and reach the water. The number of females returning to lay eggs each year varies by a factor of 20. Nest predation by raccoons also varies greatly, ranging from less than 10% in some years to almost 100% in others. Those hatchlings that do manage to dig to the surface can become disoriented by lights and wander away from the ocean or be eaten by birds or crabs before they reach the water.

Why does offspring survival for turtles and other species fluctuate greatly from year to year? To answer this question, we turn to the field of population ecology, the study of populations in relation to their environment. Population ecology explores how biotic and abiotic factors influence the density, distribution, size, and age structure of populations.

Populations evolve as natural selection acts on heritable variations among individuals, changing the frequencies of alleles and traits over time (see Chapter 23). Evolution remains a central theme as we now view populations in the context of ecology.

In this chapter, we will first examine some of the structural and dynamic aspects of populations. We will then explore the tools and models ecologists use to analyze populations and the factors that can regulate the abundance of organisms. Finally, we will apply these basic concepts as we examine recent trends in the size and makeup of the human population.

CONCEPT 53.1

Biological processes influence population density, dispersion, and demographics

A **population** is a group of individuals of a single species living in the same general area. Members of a population rely on the same resources, are influenced by similar environmental factors, and are likely to interact and breed with one another.

Populations are often described by their boundaries and size (the number of individuals living within those boundaries). Ecologists usually begin investigating a population by defining boundaries appropriate to the organism under study and to the questions being asked. A population's boundaries may be natural ones, as in the case of an island or a lake, or they may be arbitrarily defined by an investigator—for example, a specific county in Minnesota for a study of oak trees.

Density and Dispersion

The **density** of a population is the number of individuals per unit area or volume: the number of oak trees per square kilometer in the Minnesota county or the number of *Escherichia coli* bacteria per milliliter in a test tube. **Dispersion** is the pattern of spacing among individuals within the boundaries of the population.

Density: A Dynamic Perspective

In rare cases, population size and density can be determined by counting all individuals within the boundaries of the population. We could count all the sea stars in a tide pool, for instance. Large mammals that live in herds, such as elephants, can sometimes be counted accurately from airplanes. In most cases, however, it is impractical or impossible to count all individuals in a population. Instead, ecologists use various sampling techniques to estimate densities and total population sizes. They might count the number of oak trees in several randomly located 100×100 m plots, calculate the average density in the plots, and then extend the estimate to the population size in the entire area. Such estimates are most accurate when there are many sample plots

and when the habitat is fairly homogeneous. In other cases, instead of counting single organisms, population ecologists estimate density from an indicator of population size, such as the number of nests, burrows, tracks, or fecal droppings. Ecologists also use the **mark-recapture method** to estimate the size of wildlife populations **(Figure 53.2)**.

▼ **Figure 53.2** | **Research Method**

Determining Population Size Using the Mark-Recapture Method

Application Ecologists cannot count all the individuals in a population if the organisms move too quickly or are hidden from view. In such cases, researchers often use the mark-recapture method to estimate population size. Andrew Gormley and his colleagues at the University of Otago applied this method to

Hector's dolphins

a population of endangered Hector's dolphins (*Cephalorhynchus hectori*) near Banks Peninsula, in New Zealand.

Technique Scientists typically begin by capturing a random sample of individuals in a population. They tag, or "mark," each individual and then release it. With some species, researchers can identify individuals without physically capturing them. For example, Gormley and colleagues identified 180 Hector's dolphins by photographing their distinctive dorsal fins from boats.

After waiting for the marked or otherwise identified individuals to mix back into the population, usually a few days or weeks, scientists capture or sample a second set of individuals. At Banks Peninsula, Gormley's team encountered 44 dolphins in their second sampling, 7 of which they had photographed before. The number of marked animals captured in the second sampling (x) divided by the total number of animals captured in the second sampling (n) should equal the number of individuals marked and released in the first sampling (s) divided by the estimated population size (N):

$$\frac{x}{n} = \frac{s}{N} \quad \text{or, solving for population size,} \quad N = \frac{sn}{x}$$

The method assumes that marked and unmarked individuals have the same probability of being captured or sampled, that the marked organisms have mixed completely back into the population, and that no individuals are born, die, immigrate, or emigrate during the resampling interval.

Results Based on these initial data, the estimated population size of Hector's dolphins at Banks Peninsula would be $180 \times 44/7 = 1,131$ individuals. Repeated sampling by Gormley and colleagues suggested a true population size closer to 1,100.

Source: A. M. Gormley et al., Capture-recapture estimates of Hector's dolphin abundance at Banks Peninsula, New Zealand, Marine Mammal Science 21:204–216 (2005).

INTERPRET THE DATA *Suppose that none of the 44 dolphins encountered in the second sampling had been photographed before. Would you be able to solve the equation for N? What might you conclude about population size in this case?*

Births

Births and immigration add individuals to a population.

Immigration

Deaths

Deaths and emigration remove individuals from a population.

Emigration

▲ **Figure 53.3 Population dynamics.**

Density is not a static property but changes as individuals are added to or removed from a population (**Figure 53.3**). Additions occur through birth (which we define here to include all forms of reproduction) and **immigration**, the influx of new individuals from other areas. The factors that remove individuals from a population are death (mortality) and **emigration**, the movement of individuals out of a population and into other locations.

While birth and death rates influence the density of all populations, immigration and emigration also alter the density of many populations. Studies of a population of Hector's dolphins (see Figure 53.2) in New Zealand showed that immigration was approximately 15% of the total population size each year. Emigration of dolphins in the area tends to occur during the winter season when the animals move farther from shore. Both immigration and emigration represent important biological exchanges among populations through time.

Patterns of Dispersion

Within a population's geographic range, local densities may differ substantially, creating contrasting patterns of dispersion. Differences in local density are among the most important characteristics for a population ecologist to study, since they provide insight into the environmental associations and social interactions of individuals in the population.

The most common pattern of dispersion is *clumped*, in which individuals are aggregated in patches. Plants and fungi are often clumped where soil conditions and other environmental factors favor germination and growth. Mushrooms, for instance, may be clumped within and on top of a rotting log. Insects and salamanders may be clumped under the same log because of the higher humidity there. Clumping of animals may also be associated with mating behavior. Sea stars group together in tide pools,

where food is readily available and where they can breed successfully (**Figure 53.4a**). Forming groups may also increase the effectiveness of predation or defense; for example, a wolf pack is more likely than a single wolf to subdue a moose, and a flock of birds is more likely than a single bird to warn of a potential attack.

A *uniform*, or evenly spaced, pattern of dispersion may result from direct interactions between individuals in the population. Some plants secrete chemicals that inhibit the germination and growth of nearby individuals that could compete for resources. Animals often exhibit uniform dispersion as a result of antagonistic social interactions, such as **territoriality**—the defense of a bounded physical space against encroachment by other individuals (**Figure 53.4b**). Uniform patterns are rarer than clumped patterns.

In *random* dispersion (unpredictable spacing), the position of each individual in a population is independent of other individuals. This pattern occurs in the absence of strong attractions or repulsions among individuals or where key physical or chemical factors are relatively constant across the study area. Plants established by windblown seeds, such as dandelions, may be randomly distributed in a fairly uniform habitat (**Figure 53.4c**).

Demographics

The factors that influence population density and dispersion patterns—the ecological needs of a species, structure of the environment, and interactions among individuals within the population—also influence other characteristics of populations. **Demography** is the study of the vital statistics of populations and how they change over time. Of particular interest to demographers are birth rates and death rates. A useful way to summarize some of the vital statistics of a population is to make a life table.

▼ **Figure 53.4 Patterns of dispersion within a population's geographic range.**

(a) Clumped	(b) Uniform	(c) Random

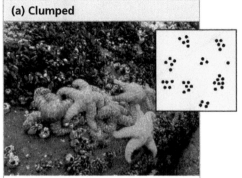

Sea stars group together where food is abundant.

Nesting albatrosses exhibit uniform spacing, maintained by aggressive interactions between neighbors.

Dandelions grow from windblown seeds that land at random and later germinate.

WHAT IF? *Patterns of dispersion can depend on scale. How might the penguin dispersion look from an airplane over the ocean?*

Life Tables

About a century ago, when life insurance first became available, insurance companies began to estimate how long, on average, people of a given age could be expected to live. To do this, demographers developed **life tables**, age-specific summaries of the survival pattern of a population. Population ecologists adapted this approach to the study of populations in general. The best way to construct a life table is to follow the fate of a **cohort**, a group of individuals of the same age, from birth until all of the individuals are dead. To build the life table, we need to determine the number of individuals that die in each age-group and to calculate the proportion of the cohort surviving from one age class to the next. Studies of a population of Belding's ground squirrels produced the life table in **Table 53.1**. The table reveals many things about the population. For instance, the third and eighth columns list, respectively, the proportions of females and males in the cohort that are still alive at each age. A comparison of the fifth and tenth columns reveals that males have higher death rates than females.

Table 53.1 Life Table for Belding's Ground Squirrels (*Spermophilus beldingi*) at Tioga Pass, in the Sierra Nevada of California*

	FEMALES					MALES				
Age (years)	Number Alive at Start of Year	Proportion Alive at Start of Year	Number of Deaths During Year	Death Rate[†]	Average Additional Life Expectancy (years)	Number Alive at Start of Year	Proportion Alive at Start of Year	Number of Deaths During Year	Death Rate[†]	Average Additional Life Expectancy (years)
0–1	337	1.000	207	0.61	1.33	349	1.000	227	0.65	1.07
1–2	252[‡]	0.386	125	0.50	1.56	248[‡]	0.350	140	0.56	1.12
2–3	127	0.197	60	0.47	1.60	108	0.152	74	0.69	0.93
3–4	67	0.106	32	0.48	1.59	34	0.048	23	0.68	0.89
4–5	35	0.054	16	0.46	1.59	11	0.015	9	0.82	0.68
5–6	19	0.029	10	0.53	1.50	2	0.003	2	1.00	0.50
6–7	9	0.014	4	0.44	1.61	0				
7–8	5	0.008	1	0.20	1.50					
8–9	4	0.006	3	0.75	0.75					
9–10	1	0.002	1	1.00	0.50					

Source: P. W. Sherman and M. L. Morton, Demography of Belding's ground squirrel, *Ecology* 65:1617–1628 (1984).

*Females and males have different mortality schedules, so they are tallied separately.
[†]The death rate is the proportion of individuals dying during the specific time interval.
[‡]Includes 122 females and 126 males first captured as 1-year-olds and therefore not included in the count of squirrels age 0–1.

▶ Researchers working with a Belding's ground squirrel

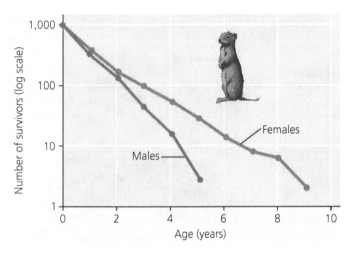

▲ **Figure 53.5 Survivorship curves for male and female Belding's ground squirrels.** The logarithmic scale on the y-axis allows the number of survivors to be visible across the entire range (2–1,000 individuals) on the graph.

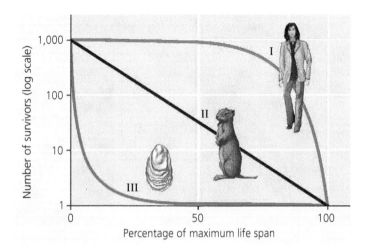

▲ **Figure 53.6 Idealized survivorship curves: Types I, II, and III.** The y-axis is logarithmic and the x-axis is on a relative scale, so that species with widely varying life spans can be presented together on the same graph.

Survivorship Curves

A graphic method of representing some of the data in a life table is a **survivorship curve**, a plot of the proportion or numbers in a cohort still alive at each age. As an example, let's use the data for Belding's ground squirrels in Table 53.1 to draw a survivorship curve for this population. Generally, a survivorship curve begins with a cohort of a convenient size—say, 1,000 individuals. To obtain the other points in the curve for the Belding's ground squirrel population, we multiply the proportion alive at the start of each year (the third and eighth columns of Table 53.1) by 1,000 (the hypothetical beginning cohort). The result is the number alive at the start of each year. Plotting these numbers versus age for female and male Belding's ground squirrels yields **Figure 53.5**. The relatively straight lines of the plots indicate relatively constant rates of death; however, male Belding's ground squirrels have a lower survival rate than females.

Figure 53.5 represents just one of many patterns of survivorship exhibited by natural populations. Though diverse, survivorship curves can be classified into three general types **(Figure 53.6)**. A Type I curve is flat at the start, reflecting low death rates during early and middle life, and then drops steeply as death rates increase among older age-groups. Many large mammals, including humans, that produce few offspring but provide them with good care exhibit this kind of curve. In contrast, a Type III curve drops sharply at the start, reflecting very high death rates for the young, but flattens out as death rates decline for those few individuals that survive the early period of die-off. This type of curve is usually associated with organisms that produce very large numbers of offspring but provide little or no care, such as long-lived plants, many fishes, and most marine invertebrates. An oyster, for example, may release millions of eggs, but most larvae hatched from fertilized eggs die from predation or other causes. Those few offspring that survive long

enough to attach to a suitable substrate and begin growing a hard shell tend to survive for a relatively long time. Type II curves are intermediate, with a constant death rate over the organism's life span. This kind of survivorship occurs in Belding's ground squirrels (see Figure 53.5) and some other rodents, invertebrates, lizards, and annual plants.

Many species fall somewhere between these basic types of survivorship or show more complex patterns. In birds, mortality is often high among the youngest individuals (as in a Type III curve) but fairly constant among adults (as in a Type II curve). Some invertebrates, such as crabs, may show a "stair-stepped" curve, with brief periods of increased mortality during molts, followed by periods of lower mortality when their protective exoskeleton is hard.

In populations not experiencing immigration or emigration, survivorship is one of the two key factors determining changes in population size. The other key factor determining population trends is reproductive rate.

Reproductive Rates

Demographers who study sexually reproducing species generally ignore the males and concentrate on the females in a population because only females produce offspring. Therefore, demographers view populations in terms of females giving rise to new females. The simplest way to describe the reproductive pattern of a population is to ask how reproductive output varies with the number of females and their ages.

Estimating the number of breeding females is one important step in determining reproductive rates for a population or species. Ecologists use many approaches to do this, including direct counts and the mark-recapture method (see Figure 53.2). Increasingly, they also use molecular tools. Scientists working in the state of Georgia collected skin samples from 198 female loggerhead turtles between 2005 and 2009. From these samples, they amplified nuclear short tandem repeats at 14 loci using the polymerase chain reaction (PCR) and produced a genetic profile for each female (Figure 53.7). They then extracted DNA from an eggshell from each turtle nest on the beaches they studied and, using their database of genetic profiles, matched the nest to a specific female. This approach allowed them to determine how many of the 198 females were breeding without having to disturb the females during egg laying.

The age of reproductive females is another important variable for estimating reproductive rates. A **reproductive table**, or fertility schedule, is an age-specific summary of the reproductive rates in a population. It is constructed by measuring the reproductive output of a cohort from birth until death. For a sexual species, the reproductive table tallies the number of female offspring produced by each age-group. Table 53.2 illustrates a reproductive table for Belding's ground squirrels. Reproductive output for sexual organisms such as birds and mammals is the product of the proportion of females of a given age that are breeding and the number of female offspring of those breeding females. Multiplying

Table 53.2 Reproductive Table for Belding's Ground Squirrels at Tioga Pass

Age (years)	Proportion of Females Weaning a Litter	Mean Size of Litters (Males + Females)	Mean Number of Females in a Litter	Average Number of Female Offspring*
0–1	0.00	0.00	0.00	0.00
1–2	0.65	3.30	1.65	1.07
2–3	0.92	4.05	2.03	1.87
3–4	0.90	4.90	2.45	2.21
4–5	0.95	5.45	2.73	2.59
5–6	1.00	4.15	2.08	2.08
6–7	1.00	3.40	1.70	1.70
7–8	1.00	3.85	1.93	1.93
8–9	1.00	3.85	1.93	1.93
9–10	1.00	3.15	1.58	1.58

Source: P. W. Sherman and M. L. Morton, Demography of Belding's ground squirrel, *Ecology* 65:1617–1628 (1984).

*The average number of female offspring is the proportion weaning a litter multiplied by the mean number of females in a litter.

Part 1: Developing the Database:

Skin samples are collected from female loggerhead turtles.

In a lab, DNA is extracted from each skin sample, and short tandem repeats at 14 loci are amplified by PCR.

A genetic profile is determined for each turtle and stored in a database.

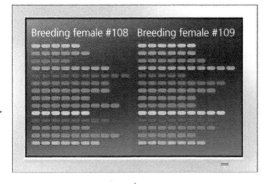

A match identifies the female that laid the eggs in the nest.

Part 2: Comparing Samples to the Database:

An eggshell is collected from a loggerhead turtle nest.

In a lab, DNA is extracted from the eggshell, and short tandem repeats at 14 loci are amplified by PCR.

A genetic profile is determined for each eggshell sample.

The genetic profile of the eggshell is compared with an established database containing genetic profiles of adult female loggerhead turtles.

▲ Figure 53.7 **Using genetic profiles from loggerhead turtle eggshells to identify the eggs' mother.**

? *Which breeding female laid the eggs in the nest that eggshell sample #74 was taken from?*

these numbers gives the average number of female offspring for each female in a given age-group (the last column in Table 53.2). For Belding's ground squirrels, which begin to reproduce at age 1 year, reproductive output rises to a peak at 4 years of age and then falls off in older females.

Reproductive tables vary considerably by species. Squirrels, for example, have a litter of two to six young once a year for less than a decade, whereas oak trees drop thousands of acorns each year for tens or hundreds of years. Mussels and other invertebrates may release millions of eggs and sperm in a spawning cycle. However, a high reproductive rate will not lead to rapid population growth unless conditions are near ideal for the growth and survival of offspring, as you'll learn in the next section.

CONCEPT CHECK 53.1

1. DRAW IT Each female of a particular fish species produces millions of eggs per year. Draw and label the most likely survivorship curve for this species, and explain your choice.

2. WHAT IF? As noted in Figure 53.2, an important assumption of the mark-recapture method is that marked individuals have the same probability of being captured as unmarked individuals. Describe a situation where this assumption might not be valid, and explain how the estimate of population size would be affected.

3. MAKE CONNECTIONS A male stickleback fish attacks other males that invade its nesting territory (see Figure 51.2a). Predict the likely pattern of dispersion for male sticklebacks, and explain your reasoning.

For suggested answers, see Appendix A.

CONCEPT 53.2

The exponential model describes population growth in an idealized, unlimited environment

Populations of all species have the potential to expand greatly when resources are abundant. To appreciate the potential for population increase, consider a bacterium that can reproduce by fission every 20 minutes under ideal laboratory conditions. There would be two bacteria after 20 minutes, four after 40 minutes, and eight after 60 minutes. If reproduction continued at this rate for a day and a half without mortality, there would be enough bacteria to form a layer 30 cm deep over the entire globe. Unlimited growth does not occur for long in nature, where individuals typically have access to fewer resources as a population grows. Nonetheless, ecologists study population growth in ideal, unlimited environments to reveal how fast populations are capable of growing and the conditions under which rapid growth might actually occur.

Per Capita Rate of Increase

Imagine a population consisting of a few individuals living in an ideal, unlimited environment. Under these conditions, there are no external limits on the abilities of individuals to harvest energy, grow, and reproduce. The population will increase in size with every birth and with the immigration of individuals from other populations, and it will decrease in size with every death and with the emigration of individuals out of the population. We can thus define a change in population size during a fixed time interval with the following verbal equation:

$$\begin{array}{c} \text{Change in} \\ \text{population} \\ \text{size} \end{array} = \text{Births} + \begin{array}{c} \text{Immigrants} \\ \text{entering} \\ \text{population} \end{array} - \text{Deaths} - \begin{array}{c} \text{Emigrants} \\ \text{leaving} \\ \text{population} \end{array}$$

For now, we will simplify the equation by ignoring the effects of immigration and emigration.

We can use mathematical notation to express this simplified relationship more concisely. If N represents population size and t represents time, then ΔN is the change in population size and Δt is the time interval (appropriate to the life span or generation time of the species) over which we are evaluating population growth. (The Greek letter delta, Δ, indicates change, such as change in time.) Using B for the number of births in the population during the time interval and D for the number of deaths, we can rewrite the verbal equation:

$$\frac{\Delta N}{\Delta t} = B - D$$

Next, we can convert this simple model to one in which births and deaths are expressed as the average number of births and deaths per individual (per capita) during the specified time interval. The *per capita birth rate* is the number of offspring produced per unit time by an average member of the population. If, for example, there are 34 births per year in a population of 1,000 individuals, then the annual per capita birth rate is 34/1,000, or 0.034. If we know the annual per capita birth rate (symbolized by b), we can use the formula $B = bN$ to calculate the expected number of births per year in a population of any size. For example, if the annual per capita birth rate is 0.034 and the population size is 500,

$$B = bN = 0.034 \times 500 = 17 \text{ per year}$$

Similarly, the *per capita death rate* (symbolized by m, for mortality) allows us to calculate the expected number of deaths per unit time in a population of any size, using the formula $D = mN$. If $m = 0.016$ per year, we would expect 16 deaths per year in a population of 1,000 individuals. For natural populations or those in the laboratory, the per capita birth and death rates can be calculated from estimates of population size and data in life tables and reproductive tables (for example, Tables 53.1 and 53.2).

Now we can revise the population growth equation again, this time using per capita birth and death rates rather than the numbers of births and deaths:

$$\frac{\Delta N}{\Delta t} = bN - mN$$

One final simplification is in order. Population ecologists are most interested in the *difference* between the per capita birth rate and the per capita death rate. This difference is the *per capita rate of increase*, or *r*:

$$r = b - m$$

The value of *r* indicates whether a given population is growing ($r > 0$) or declining ($r < 0$). **Zero population growth (ZPG)** occurs when the per capita birth and death rates are equal ($r = 0$). Births and deaths still occur in such a population, of course, but they balance each other exactly.

Using the per capita rate of increase, we can now rewrite the equation for change in population size as

$$\frac{\Delta N}{\Delta t} = rN$$

Remember that this equation is for a discrete, or fixed, time interval (often one year, as in the previous example) and does not include immigration or emigration. Most ecologists prefer to use differential calculus to express population growth *instantaneously*, as growth rate at a particular instant in time:

$$\frac{dN}{dt} = r_{inst}N$$

In this case r_{inst} is simply the instantaneous per capita rate of increase. If you have not yet studied calculus, don't be intimidated by the last equation; it is similar to the previous one, except that the time intervals Δt are very short and are expressed in the equation as dt. In fact, as Δt becomes shorter, the discrete *r* approaches the instantaneous r_{inst} in value.

Exponential Growth

Earlier we described a population whose members all have access to abundant food and are free to reproduce at their physiological capacity. Population increase under these conditions, called **exponential population growth**, occurs when r_{inst} is greater than zero and is constant at each instant in time. Under ideal conditions, the per capita rate of increase may assume the maximum rate for the species, denoted as r_{max}. The general equation for exponential growth is

$$\frac{dN}{dt} = r_{inst}N$$

The size of a population that is growing exponentially increases at a constant rate, resulting eventually in a J-shaped growth curve when population size is plotted over time (**Figure 53.8**). Although the maximum *rate* of increase is constant, the population accumulates more new individuals per unit of time when it is large than when it is small; thus,

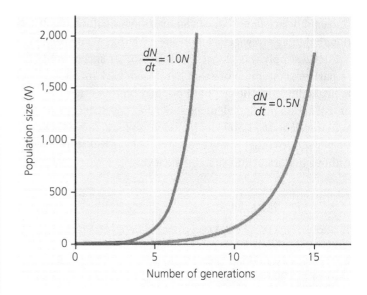

▲ **Figure 53.8 Population growth predicted by the exponential model.** This graph compares growth in two populations with different values of r_{inst}. Increasing the value of r_{inst} from 0.5 to 1.0 increases the rate of rise in population size over time, as reflected by the relative slopes of the curves at any given population size.

the curves in Figure 53.8 get progressively steeper over time. This occurs because population growth depends on *N* as well as r_{inst}, and larger populations experience more births (and deaths) than small ones growing at the same per capita rate. It is also clear from Figure 53.8 that a population with a higher maximum rate of increase ($dN/dt = 1.0N$) will grow faster than one with a lower rate of increase ($dN/dt = 0.5N$).

The J-shaped curve of exponential growth is characteristic of some populations that are introduced into a new environment or whose numbers have been drastically reduced by a catastrophic event and are rebounding. For example, the population of elephants in Kruger National Park, South Africa, grew exponentially for approximately 60 years after they were first protected from hunting (**Figure 53.9**). The

▲ **Figure 53.9 Exponential growth in the African elephant population of Kruger National Park, South Africa.**

increasingly large number of elephants eventually caused enough damage to vegetation in the park that a collapse in their food supply was likely. To protect other species and the park ecosystem before that happened, park managers began limiting the elephant population by using birth control and exporting elephants to other countries. In 2010 there were about 11,500 elephants in the park, more than one per square mile. Many ecologists believe this number to be above historical and sustainable levels.

CONCEPT CHECK 53.2

1. Explain why a constant rate of increase (r_{inst}) for a population produces a growth curve that is J-shaped.

2. Where is exponential growth by a plant population more likely—in an area where a forest was destroyed by fire or in a mature, undisturbed forest? Why?

3. **WHAT IF?** In 2011, the United States had a population of 311 million people. If there were 14 births and 8 deaths per 1,000 people, what was the country's net population growth that year (ignoring immigration and emigration)? What would you need to know to determine whether the population of the United States is currently experiencing exponential growth?

For suggested answers, see Appendix A.

CONCEPT 53.3

The logistic model describes how a population grows more slowly as it nears its carrying capacity

The exponential growth model assumes that resources remain abundant, which is rarely the case in the real world. As population density increases, each individual has access to fewer resources. Ultimately, there is a limit to the number of individuals that can occupy a habitat. Ecologists define the **carrying capacity**, symbolized by K, as the maximum population size that a particular environment can sustain. Carrying capacity varies over space and time with the abundance of limiting resources. Energy, shelter, refuge from predators, nutrient availability, water, and suitable nesting sites can all be limiting factors. For example, the carrying capacity for bats may be high in a habitat with abundant flying insects and roosting sites but lower where there is abundant food but fewer suitable shelters.

Crowding and resource limitation can have a profound effect on population growth rate. If individuals cannot obtain sufficient resources to reproduce, the per capita birth rate (b) will decline. If they cannot consume enough energy to maintain themselves or if disease or parasitism increases with density, the per capita death rate (m) may increase. A decrease in b or an increase in m results in a lower per capita rate of increase (r).

The Logistic Growth Model

We can modify our mathematical model to include changes in growth rate as N increases. In the **logistic population growth** model, the per capita rate of increase approaches zero as the population size nears the carrying capacity.

To construct the logistic model, we start with the exponential population growth model and add an expression that reduces the per capita rate of increase as N increases. If the maximum sustainable population size (carrying capacity) is K, then $K - N$ is the number of additional individuals the environment can support, and $(K - N)/K$ is the fraction of K that is still available for population growth. By multiplying the exponential rate of increase $r_{inst}N$ by $(K - N)/K$, we modify the change in population size as N increases:

$$\frac{dN}{dt} = r_{inst}N\frac{(K - N)}{K}$$

When N is small compared to K, the term $(K - N)/K$ is close to 1, and the per capita rate of increase, $r_{inst}(K - N)/K$, approaches the maximum rate of increase. But when N is large and resources are limiting, then $(K - N)/K$ is close to 0, and the per capita rate of increase is small. When N equals K, the population stops growing. **Table 53.3** shows calculations of population growth rate for a hypothetical population growing according to the logistic model, with $r_{inst} = 1.0$ per individual per year. Notice that the overall population growth rate is highest, +375 individuals per year, when the population size is 750, or half the carrying capacity. At a population size of 750, the per capita rate of increase remains relatively high (one-half the maximum rate), but there are more reproducing individuals (N) in the population than at lower population sizes.

As shown in **Figure 53.10**, the logistic model of population growth produces a sigmoid (S-shaped) growth curve when N is plotted over time (the red line). New individuals

Table 53.3 Logistic Growth of a Hypothetical Population ($K = 1,500$)

Population Size (N)	Maximum Rate of Increase (r_{inst})	$\frac{(K - N)}{K}$	Per Capita Rate of Increase: $r_{inst}\frac{(K - N)}{K}$	Population Growth Rate:* $r_{inst}N\frac{(K - N)}{K}$
25	1.0	0.98	0.98	+25
100	1.0	0.93	0.93	+93
250	1.0	0.83	0.83	+208
500	1.0	0.67	0.67	+333
750	1.0	0.50	0.50	+375
1,000	1.0	0.33	0.33	+333
1,500	1.0	0.00	0.00	0

*Rounded to the nearest whole number.

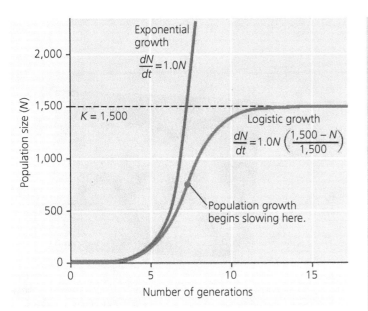

▲ **Figure 53.10 Population growth predicted by the logistic model.** The rate of population growth decreases as population size (N) approaches the carrying capacity (K) of the environment. The red line shows logistic growth in a population where $r_{inst} = 1.0$ and $K = 1,500$ individuals. For comparison, the blue line illustrates a population continuing to grow exponentially with the same r_{inst}.

are added to the population most rapidly at intermediate population sizes, when there is not only a breeding population of substantial size, but also lots of available space and other resources in the environment. The population growth rate decreases dramatically as N approaches K.

Note that we haven't said anything yet about *why* the population growth rate decreases as N approaches K. For a population's growth rate to decrease, the birth rate b must decrease, the death rate m must increase, or both. Later

in the chapter, we'll consider some of the factors affecting these rates, including the presence of disease, predation, and limited amounts of food and other resources. In the Scientific Skills Exercise, you can model what happens to a population if N becomes *greater* than K.

The Logistic Model and Real Populations

The growth of laboratory populations of some small animals, such as beetles and crustaceans, and of some microorganisms, such as bacteria, *Paramecium*, and yeasts, fits an S-shaped curve fairly well under conditions of limited resources (Figure 53.11a). These populations are grown in a constant environment lacking predators and competing species that may reduce growth of the populations, conditions that rarely occur in nature.

Some of the basic assumptions built into the logistic model clearly do not apply to all populations. The logistic model assumes that populations adjust instantaneously to growth and approach carrying capacity smoothly. In reality, there is often a delay before the negative effects of an increasing population are realized. If food becomes limiting for a population, for instance, reproduction will decline eventually, but females may use their energy reserves to continue reproducing for a short time. This may cause the population to overshoot its carrying capacity temporarily, as shown for the water fleas in Figure 53.11b. If the population then drops below carrying capacity, there will be a delay in population growth until the increased number of offspring are actually born. Still other populations fluctuate greatly, making it difficult even to define carrying capacity. We will examine some possible reasons for such fluctuations later in the chapter.

◀ **Figure 53.11 How well do these populations fit the logistic growth model?**

(a) A *Paramecium* population in the lab. The growth (black dots) of *Paramecium aurelia* in a small culture closely approximates logistic growth (red curve) if the researcher maintains a constant environment.

(b) A *Daphnia* population in the lab. The growth (black dots) of a population of water fleas (*Daphnia*) in a small laboratory culture does not correspond well to the logistic model (red curve). This population overshoots the carrying capacity of its artificial environment before it settles down to an approximately stable population size.

SCIENTIFIC SKILLS EXERCISE

Using the Logistic Equation to Model Population Growth

What Happens to the Size of a Population When It Overshoots Its Carrying Capacity? In the logistic population growth model, the per capita rate of population increase approaches zero as the population size (N) approaches the carrying capacity (K). Under some conditions, however, a population in the laboratory or the field can overshoot K, at least temporarily. If food becomes limiting to a population, for instance, there may be a delay before reproduction declines, and N may briefly exceed K. In this exercise, you will use the logistic equation to model the growth of the hypothetical population in Table 53.3 when $N > K$.

Interpret the Data

1. Assuming that $r_{inst} = 1.0$ and $K = 1,500$, calculate the population growth rate for four cases where population size (N) is greater than carrying capacity (K): $N = 1,510$, 1,600, 1,750, and 2,000 individuals. To do this, first write the equation for population growth rate given in Table 53.3. Plug in the values for each of the four cases, starting with $N = 1,510$, and solve the equation for each one. Which population size has the highest growth rate?

2. If r_{inst} is doubled, predict how the population growth rates will change for the four population sizes given in question 1. Now calculate the population growth rate for the same four cases, this time assuming that $r_{inst} = 2.0$ (and with K still $= 1,500$).

▶ *Daphnia*

3. Now let's see how the growth of a real-world population of *Daphnia* corresponds to this model. At what times in Figure 53.11b is the *Daphnia* population changing in ways that correspond to the values you calculated? Hypothesize why the population drops below the carrying capacity briefly late in the experiment.

(MB) A version of this Scientific Skills Exercise can be assigned in MasteringBiology.

In addition to the assumption that populations adjust instantaneously to growth, the logistic model is based on another assumption—that regardless of population density, each individual added to a population has the same negative effect on population growth rate. However, some populations show an *Allee effect* (named after W. C. Allee, of the University of Chicago, who first described it), in which individuals may have a more difficult time surviving or reproducing if the population size is too small. For example, a single plant may be damaged by excessive wind if it is standing alone, but it would be protected in a clump of individuals.

The logistic model is a useful starting point for thinking about how populations grow and for constructing more complex models. The model is also important in conservation biology for predicting how rapidly a particular population might increase in numbers after it has been reduced to a small size and for estimating sustainable harvest rates for wildlife populations. Conservation biologists can use the model to estimate the critical size below which populations of certain organisms, such as the northern subspecies of the white rhinoceros (*Ceratotherium simum*), may become extinct **(Figure 53.12).**

CONCEPT CHECK 53.3

1. Explain why a population that fits the logistic growth model increases more rapidly at intermediate size than at relatively small and large sizes.

2. **WHAT IF?** Given the latitudinal differences in sunlight intensity (see Figure 52.3), how might you expect the carrying capacity of plant species found at the equator to compare with that of plant species found at high latitudes?

3. **MAKE CONNECTIONS** Many viruses are pathogens of animals and plants (see Concept 19.3). How might the presence of pathogens alter the carrying capacity of a population? Explain.

For suggested answers, see Appendix A.

▶ **Figure 53.12 White rhinoceros mother and calf.** The two animals pictured here are members of the southern subspecies, which has a population of more than 20,000 individuals. The northern subspecies is critically endangered, with a population of fewer than 10 known individuals.

CONCEPT 53.4

Life history traits are products of natural selection

EVOLUTION Natural selection favors traits that improve an organism's chances of survival and reproductive success. In every species, there are trade-offs between survival and reproductive traits such as frequency of reproduction, number of offspring (number of seeds produced by plants; litter or clutch size for animals), and investment in parental care. The traits that affect an organism's schedule of reproduction and survival make up its **life history**. Life history traits of an organism are evolutionary outcomes reflected in its development, physiology, and behavior.

Evolution and Life History Diversity

The fundamental idea that evolution accounts for the diversity of life is manifest in a broad range of life histories found in nature. A life history entails three main variables: when reproduction begins (the age at first reproduction or age at maturity), how often the organism reproduces, and how many offspring are produced per reproductive episode. A typical loggerhead turtle is about 30 years old when it first crawls onto a beach to lay eggs (see Figure 53.1). In contrast, the coho salmon (*Oncorhynchus kisutch*) is often only three or four years old when it spawns.

The coho salmon is one example of many organisms that undergo a "one-shot" pattern of big-bang reproduction, or **semelparity** (from the Latin *semel*, once, and *parere*, to beget). It hatches in the headwaters of a freshwater stream and then migrates to the Pacific Ocean, where it typically requires a few years to mature. The salmon eventually returns to the same stream to spawn, producing thousands of eggs in a single reproductive opportunity before it dies. Semelparity also occurs in some plants, such as the agave, or "century plant" **(Figure 53.13a)**. Agaves generally grow in arid climates with unpredictable rainfall and poor soils. An agave grows for years, accumulating nutrients in its tissues, until there is an unusually wet year. It then sends up a large flowering stalk, produces seeds, and dies. This life history is an adaptation to the agave's harsh desert environment.

In contrast to semelparity is **iteroparity** (from the Latin *iterare*, to repeat), or repeated reproduction. For example, a female loggerhead turtle produces four clutches totaling approximately 300 eggs in a year. It then typically waits two to three years before laying more eggs; presumably, the turtles lack sufficient resources to produce that many eggs every year. A mature turtle may lay eggs for 30 years after the first

▶ **Figure 53.13 Semelparity and iteroparity. (a)** An agave (*Agave americana*) is an example of semelparity, or big-bang reproduction. The leaves of the plant are visible at the base of the giant flowering stalk, which is produced only at the end of the agave's life. **(b)** Organisms that reproduce repeatedly, like humans, undergo iteroparity. Such organisms tend to have fewer, larger offspring and take better care of them.

(a) Semelparity, one-time reproducer

(b) Iteroparity, repeat reproducer

clutch. In iteroparity, organisms tend to produce relatively few but large offspring each time they reproduce, and they provide for the offspring better **(Figure 53.13b)**.

What factors contribute to the evolution of semelparity versus iteroparity? Two factors appear to be especially important: the survival rate of the offspring and the likelihood that the adult will survive to reproduce again. Where the survival rate of offspring is low, typically in highly variable or unpredictable environments, semelparity is often favored. Adults are also less likely to survive in such environments, so producing large numbers of offspring should increase the probability that at least some of those offspring will survive. Iteroparity is favored in more dependable environments, where adults are more likely to survive to breed again and where competition for resources may be intense. In this case, a few relatively large, well-provisioned offspring should have a better chance of surviving until they can reproduce.

Nature abounds with life histories that are intermediate between the two extremes of semelparity and iteroparity. Oak trees and sea urchins, for example, can live a long time but repeatedly produce relatively large numbers of offspring.

"Trade-offs" and Life Histories

No organism could produce as many offspring as a semelparous species and provision them as well as an iteroparous species. There is a trade-off between reproduction and

▼ Figure 53.14 | Inquiry

How does caring for offspring affect parental survival in kestrels?

Experiment Cor Dijkstra and colleagues in the Netherlands studied the effects of parental caregiving in Eurasian kestrels over five years. The researchers transferred chicks among nests to produce reduced broods (three or four chicks), normal broods (five or six), and enlarged broods (seven or eight). They then measured the percentage of male and female parent birds that survived the following winter. (Both males and females provide care for chicks.)

Results

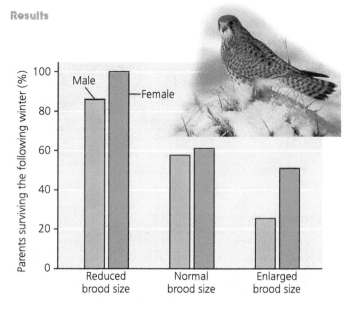

Conclusion The lower survival rates of kestrels with larger broods indicate that caring for more offspring negatively affects survival of the parents.

Source: C. Dijkstra et al., Brood size manipulations in the kestrel (*Falco tinnunculus*): effects on offspring and parent survival, *Journal of Animal Ecology* 59:269–285 (1990).

INTERPRET THE DATA *The males of some bird species provide no parental care. If this were true for the Eurasian kestrel, how would the experimental results differ from those shown above?*

survival. **Figure 53.14** describes a study of Eurasian kestrels that demonstrated a survival cost to parents that care for a large number of young. In another study, in Scotland, researchers found that female red deer that reproduced in a given summer were more likely to die the next winter than were females that did not reproduce.

Selective pressures influence the trade-off between the number and size of offspring. Plants and animals whose young are more likely to die often produce many small offspring. Plants that colonize disturbed environments, for example, usually produce many small seeds, only a few of which may reach a suitable habitat. Small size may also increase the chance of seedling establishment by enabling the seeds to be carried longer distances to a broader range of habitats **(Figure 53.15a)**. Animals that suffer high predation

rates, such as quail, sardines, and mice, also tend to produce many offspring.

In other organisms, extra investment on the part of the parent greatly increases the offspring's chances of survival. Walnut and Brazil nut trees produce large seeds packed with nutrients that help the seedlings become established **(Figure 53.15b)**. Primates generally bear only one or two offspring at a time; parental care and an extended period of learning in the first several years of life are very important to offspring fitness. Such provisioning and extra care can be especially important in habitats with high population densities.

Ecologists have attempted to connect differences in favored traits at different population densities with the logistic growth model discussed in Concept 53.3. Selection for traits that are sensitive to population density and are favored at high densities is known as ***K*-selection**, or density-dependent selection. In contrast, selection for traits that maximize reproductive success in uncrowded environments (low densities) is called ***r*-selection**, or density-independent selection. These names follow from the variables of the logistic equation. *K*-selection is said to operate in populations living at a

(a) Dandelions grow quickly and release a large number of tiny fruits, each containing a single seed. Producing numerous seeds ensures that at least some will grow into plants that eventually produce seeds themselves.

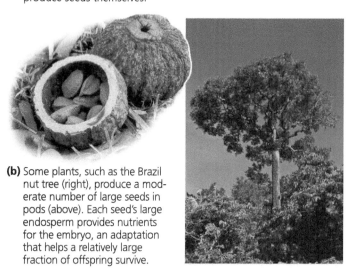

(b) Some plants, such as the Brazil nut tree (right), produce a moderate number of large seeds in pods (above). Each seed's large endosperm provides nutrients for the embryo, an adaptation that helps a relatively large fraction of offspring survive.

▲ **Figure 53.15 Variation in the size of seed crops in plants.**

density near the limit imposed by their resources (the carrying capacity, K), where competition among individuals is stronger. Mature trees growing in an old-growth forest are an example of K-selected organisms. In contrast, r-selection is said to maximize r, the per capita rate of increase, and occurs in environments in which population densities are well below carrying capacity or individuals face little competition. Such conditions are often found in disturbed habitats. Weeds growing in an abandoned agricultural field are an example of r-selected organisms.

The concepts of K- and r-selection represent two extremes in a range of actual life histories. The framework of K- and r-selection, grounded in the idea of carrying capacity, has helped ecologists to propose alternative hypotheses of life history evolution. They have also forced ecologists to address the important question we alluded to earlier: *Why does population growth rate decrease as population size approaches carrying capacity?* Answering this question is the focus of the next section.

CONCEPT CHECK 53.4

1. Consider two rivers: One is spring fed and has a constant water volume and temperature year-round; the other drains a desert landscape and floods and dries out at unpredictable intervals. Which river would you predict is more likely to support many species of iteroparous animals? Why?

2. In the fish called the peacock wrasse (*Symphodus tinca*), females disperse some of their eggs widely and lay other eggs in a nest. Only the latter receive parental care. Explain the trade-offs in reproduction that this behavior illustrates.

3. **WHAT IF?** Mice that experience stress such as a food shortage will sometimes abandon their young. Explain how this behavior might have evolved in the context of reproductive trade-offs and life history.

For suggested answers, see Appendix A.

CONCEPT 53.5

Many factors that regulate population growth are density dependent

What environmental factors keep populations from growing indefinitely? Why are some populations fairly stable in size, while others are not?

Population regulation is an area of ecology that has many practical applications. Farmers may want to reduce the abundance of insect pests or stop the growth of an invasive weed that is spreading rapidly. Conservation ecologists need to know what environmental factors create favorable feeding or breeding habitats for endangered species, such as the white rhinoceros and the whooping crane. Management programs based on population-regulating factors have helped prevent the extinction of many endangered species.

Population Change and Population Density

To understand why a population stops growing, ecologists study how the rates of birth, death, immigration, and emigration change as population density rises. If immigration and emigration offset each other, then a population grows when the birth rate exceeds the death rate and declines when the death rate exceeds the birth rate.

Similar to the case of r-selection, a birth rate or death rate that does *not* change with population density is said to be **density independent**. In a classic study of population regulation, Andrew Watkinson and John Harper, of the University of Wales, found that the mortality of dune fescue grass (*Vulpia fasciculata*) is mainly due to physical factors that kill similar proportions of a local population, regardless of its density. For example, drought stress that arises when the roots of the grass are uncovered by shifting sands is a density-independent factor. In contrast, a death rate that increases with population density or a birth rate that falls with rising density is said to be **density dependent**, a situation similar to K-selection. Watkinson and Harper found that reproduction by dune fescue declines as population density increases, in part because water or nutrients become more scarce. Thus, the key factors regulating birth rate in this population are density dependent, while death rate is largely regulated by density-independent factors. **Figure 53.16** shows how the combination of density-dependent reproduction and density-independent mortality can stop population growth, leading to an equilibrium population density in species such as dune fescue.

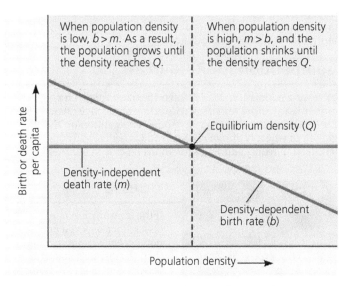

▲ **Figure 53.16 Determining equilibrium for population density.** This simple model considers only birth and death rates. (Immigration and emigration rates are assumed to be either zero or equal.) In this example, the birth rate changes with population density, while the death rate is constant. At the equilibrium density (Q), the birth and death rates are equal.

DRAW IT *Redraw this figure for the case where the birth and death rates are both density dependent, as occurs for many species.*

Mechanisms of Density-Dependent Population Regulation

The principle of feedback regulation applies to population dynamics. Without some type of negative feedback between population density and the rates of birth and death, a population would never stop growing. That feedback is provided by density-dependent regulation, which halts population growth through mechanisms that reduce birth rates or increase death rates. For example, proportional mortality of the kelp perch (*Brachyistius frenatus*) rose as its density increased. Without sufficient kelp to hide in, the perch was vulnerable to predation by a second fish species, the kelp bass (*Paralabrax clathratus*). Proportionally more of the perch were eaten as perch density increased, a result consistent with density-dependent regulation (Figure 53.17). Mechanisms of density-dependent population regulation are described in Figure 53.18.

These various examples of population regulation by negative feedback show how increased densities cause population growth rates to decline by affecting reproduction, growth, and survival. But though negative feedback helps explain why populations stop growing, it does not address why some populations fluctuate dramatically while others remain relatively stable. That is the topic we address next.

▲ Figure 53.17 **Density-dependent regulation by predation.** As the density of kelp perch increased, predation by kelp bass increased, resulting in a higher proportion of kelp perch deaths.

Population Dynamics

All populations show some fluctuation in size. Such population fluctuations from year to year or place to place, called **population dynamics**, are influenced by many factors and in turn affect other species. For example, fluctuations in fish populations influence seasonal harvests of commercially

---

▼ Figure 53.18

Exploring Mechanisms of Density-Dependent Regulation

As population density increases, many density-dependent mechanisms slow or stop population growth by decreasing birth rates or increasing death rates.

Competition for Resources

Increasing population density intensifies competition for nutrients and other resources, reducing reproductive rates. Farmers minimize the effect of resource competition on the growth of wheat (*Triticum aestivum*) and other crops by applying fertilizers to reduce nutrient limitations on crop yield.

Disease

If the transmission rate of a disease increases as a population becomes more crowded, then the disease's impact is density dependent. In humans, the respiratory diseases influenza (flu) and tuberculosis are spread through the air when an infected person sneezes or coughs. Both diseases strike a greater percentage of people in densely populated cities than in rural areas.

Predation

Predation can be an important cause of density-dependent mortality if a predator captures more food as the population density of the prey increases. As a prey population builds up, predators may also feed preferentially on that species. Population increases in the collared lemming (*Dicrostonyx groenlandicus*) lead to density-dependent predation by several predators, including the snowy owl (*Bubo scandiacus*).

important species. The study of population dynamics focuses on the complex interactions between biotic and abiotic factors that cause variation in population sizes.

Stability and Fluctuation

Populations of large mammals were once thought to remain relatively stable, but long-term studies have challenged that idea. For instance, the moose population on Isle Royale in Lake Superior has fluctuated substantially since around 1900. At that time, moose from the Ontario mainland 25 km away colonized the island, likely by swimming to it or by walking across the lake when it was frozen over. Wolves, which rely on moose for most of their food, reached the island around 1950 by walking across the frozen lake. The lake has not frozen over in recent years, and both populations appear to have been isolated from immigration and emigration since then. Despite this isolation, the moose population experienced two major increases and collapses during the last 50 years **(Figure 53.19)**.

What factors cause the size of the moose population to change so dramatically? Harsh weather, particularly cold, wet winters, can weaken moose and reduce food availability, decreasing the population size. When moose numbers are low and the weather is mild, food is readily available and the population grows quickly. Conversely, when moose

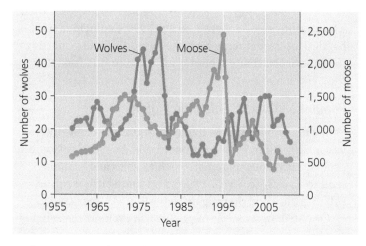

▲ **Figure 53.19 Fluctuations in moose and wolf populations on Isle Royale, 1959–2011.**

 BioFlix Visit the Study Area in **MasteringBiology** for the BioFlix® 3-D Animation on Population Ecology. BioFlix Tutorials can also be assigned in MasteringBiology.

numbers are high, factors such as predation and an increase in the density of ticks and other parasites cause the population to shrink. The effects of some of these factors can be seen in Figure 53.19. The first major collapse coincided with a peak in the numbers of wolves from 1975 to 1980.

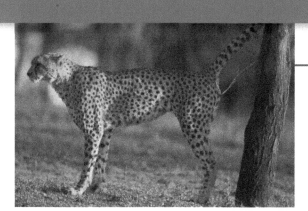

Territoriality

Territoriality can limit population density when space becomes the resource for which individuals compete. Cheetahs (*Acinonyx jubatus*) use a chemical marker in urine to warn other cheetahs of their territorial boundaries. The presence of surplus, or nonbreeding, individuals is a good indication that territoriality is restricting population growth.

Toxic Wastes

Yeasts, such as the brewer's yeast *Saccharomyces cerevisiae*, are used to convert carbohydrates to ethanol in winemaking. The ethanol that accumulates in the wine is toxic to yeasts and contributes to density-dependent regulation of yeast population size. The alcohol content of wine is usually less than 13% because that is the maximum concentration of ethanol that most wine-producing yeast cells can tolerate.

Intrinsic Factors

Intrinsic physiological factors can regulate population size. Reproductive rates of white-footed mice (*Peromyscus leucopus*) in a field enclosure can drop even when food and shelter are abundant. This drop in reproduction at high population density is associated with aggressive interactions and hormonal changes that delay sexual maturation and depress the immune system.

The second major collapse, around 1995, coincided with harsh winter weather, which increased the energy needs of the moose and made it harder for them to find food under the deep snow.

Population Cycles: *Scientific Inquiry*

While many populations fluctuate at unpredictable intervals, others undergo regular boom-and-bust cycles. Some small herbivorous mammals, such as voles and lemmings, tend to have 3- to 4-year cycles, and some birds, such as ruffed grouse and ptarmigans, have 9- to 11-year cycles.

One striking example of population cycles is the roughly 10-year cycling of snowshoe hares (*Lepus americanus*) and lynx (*Lynx canadensis*) in the far northern forests of Canada and Alaska. Lynx are predators that feed predominantly on snowshoe hares, so lynx numbers might be expected to rise and fall with the numbers of hares (Figure 53.20). But why do hare numbers rise and fall in approximately 10-year cycles? Two main hypotheses have been proposed. First, the cycles may be caused by food shortage during winter. Hares eat the terminal twigs of small shrubs such as willow and birch in winter, although why this food supply might cycle in 10-year intervals is uncertain. Second, the cycles may be due to predator-prey interactions. Many predators other than lynx eat hares, and they may overexploit their prey.

▲ **Figure 53.20 Population cycles in the snowshoe hare and lynx.** Population counts are based on the number of pelts sold by trappers to the Hudson Bay Company.

INTERPRET THE DATA *What do you observe about the relative timing of the peaks in lynx numbers and hare numbers? What might explain this observation?*

Let's consider the evidence for the two hypotheses. If hare cycles are due to winter food shortage, then they should stop if extra food is provided to a field population. Researchers conducted such experiments in the Yukon for 20 years—over two hare cycles. They found that hare populations in the areas with extra food increased about three-fold in density but continued to cycle in the same way as the unfed control populations. Therefore, food supplies alone do not cause the hare cycles shown in Figure 53.20, so we can reject the first hypothesis.

To study the effects of predation, ecologists used radio collars to track individual hares to determine why they died. Predators, including lynx, coyotes, hawks, and owls, killed 95% of the hares in such studies. None of the hares appeared to have died of starvation. These data support the second hypothesis. When ecologists set up electric fences to exclude predators from certain areas, the collapse in survival that normally occurs in the decline phase of the cycle was nearly eliminated. Overexploitation by predators thus seems to be an essential part of snowshoe hare cycles; without predators, it is unlikely that hare populations would cycle in northern Canada.

The availability of prey is the major factor influencing population changes for predators such as lynx, great-horned owls, and weasels, each of which depends heavily on a single prey species. When prey become scarce, predators often turn on one another. Coyotes kill both foxes and lynx, and great-horned owls kill smaller birds of prey as well as weasels, accelerating the collapse of the predator populations. Long-term experimental studies help to unravel the causes of such population cycles.

Immigration, Emigration, and Metapopulations

So far, our discussion of population dynamics has focused mainly on the contributions of births and deaths. However, immigration and emigration also influence populations. When a population becomes crowded and resource competition increases (see Figure 53.17), emigration often increases.

Immigration and emigration are particularly important when a number of local populations are linked, forming a **metapopulation**. Local populations in a metapopulation can be thought of as occupying discrete patches of suitable habitat in a sea of otherwise unsuitable habitat. Such patches vary in size, quality, and isolation from other patches, factors that influence how many individuals move among the populations. If one population becomes extinct, the patch it occupied may be recolonized by immigrants from another population.

The Glanville fritillary (*Melitaea cinxia*) illustrates the movement of individuals between populations. This butterfly is found in about 500 meadows across the Åland Islands of Finland, but its potential habitat in the islands is much larger, approximately 4,000 suitable patches. New populations of the butterfly regularly appear and existing

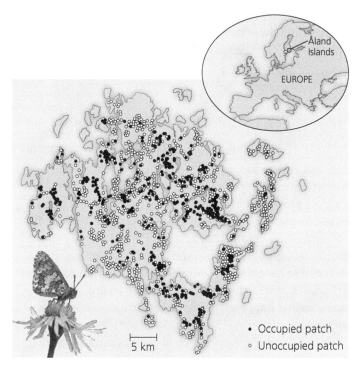

▲ **Figure 53.21 The Glanville fritillary: a metapopulation.** On the Åland Islands, local populations of this butterfly (filled circles) are found in only a fraction of the suitable habitat patches at any given time. Individuals can move between local populations and colonize unoccupied patches (open circles).

populations become extinct, constantly shifting the locations of the 500 colonized patches **(Figure 53.21)**. The species persists in a balance of extinctions and recolonizations.

An individual's ability to move between populations depends on a number of factors, including its genetic makeup. One gene with apparently strong fitness effects on movement in the Glanville fritillary is *Pgi*, which codes for the enzyme phosphoglucoisomerase. This enzyme catalyzes the second step of glycolysis (see Figure 9.9), and its activity correlates with the rate of CO_2 production from respiration by the butterflies. Ecologists studied butterflies known to be heterozygous or homozygous for a single nucleotide polymorphism in *Pgi*. They tracked the movements of individual butterflies using radar and transponders attached to the butterflies that emit an identifying signal. Butterfly movements ranged widely, from 10 m to 4 km, in two-hour periods. Heterozygous individuals flew more than twice as far in the morning and at lower ambient temperatures than homozygous individuals. The results indicated a fitness advantage to the heterozygous genotype in low temperatures and a greater likelihood of heterozygotes colonizing new locations in the metapopulation.

The metapopulation concept underscores the significance of immigration and emigration in the butterfly populations. It also helps ecologists understand population dynamics and gene flow in patchy habitats, providing a framework for the conservation of species living in a network of habitat fragments and reserves.

CONCEPT CHECK **53.5**

1. Describe three attributes of habitat patches that could affect population density and rates of immigration and emigration.

2. **WHAT IF?** Suppose you were studying a species that has a population cycle of about ten years. How long would you need to study the species to determine if its population size were declining? Explain.

3. **MAKE CONNECTIONS** Negative feedback is a process that regulates biological systems (see Concept 40.2). Explain how the density-dependent birth rate of dune fescue grass exemplifies negative feedback.

For suggested answers, see Appendix A.

CONCEPT 53.6

The human population is no longer growing exponentially but is still increasing rapidly

In the last few centuries, the human population has grown at an unprecedented rate, more like the elephant population in Kruger National Park (see Figure 53.9) than the fluctuating populations we considered in Concept 53.5. No population can grow indefinitely, however. In this section of the chapter, we'll apply the concepts of population dynamics to the specific case of the human population.

The Global Human Population

The exponential growth model in Figure 53.8 approximates the explosive growth of the human population over the last four centuries **(Figure 53.22)**. The human population

▲ **Figure 53.22 Human population growth (data as of 2012).** The global human population has grown almost continuously throughout history, but it skyrocketed after the Industrial Revolution. Though it is not apparent at this scale, the rate of population growth has slowed in recent decades, mainly as a result of decreased birth rates throughout the world.

increased relatively slowly until about 1650, at which time approximately 500 million people inhabited Earth. Our population doubled to 1 billion within the next two centuries, doubled again to 2 billion by 1930, and doubled still again by 1975 to more than 4 billion. The global population is now more than 7 billion people and is increasing by about 78 million each year. Currently the population grows by more than 200,000 people each day, the equivalent of adding a city the size of Amarillo, Texas. At this rate, it takes only about four years to add the equivalent of another United States to the world population. Ecologists predict a population of 8.1–10.6 billion people on Earth by the year 2050.

Though the global population is still growing, the *rate* of growth began to slow during the 1960s (Figure 53.23). The annual rate of increase in the global population peaked at 2.2% in 1962 but was only 1.1% in 2011. Current models project a growth rate of 0.5% by 2050, which would add 45 million more people per year if the population climbs to a projected 9 billion. The reduction in annual growth rate already observed is the result of fundamental changes in population dynamics due to diseases, including AIDS, and to voluntary population control.

Regional Patterns of Population Change

We have described changes in the global population, but population dynamics vary widely from region to region. In a stable regional population, birth rate equals death rate

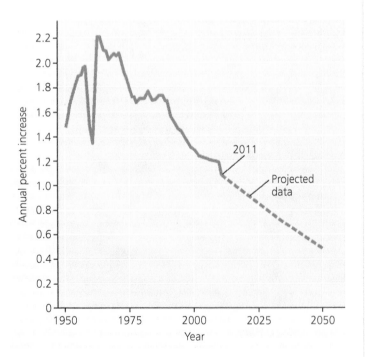

▲ **Figure 53.23 Annual percent increase in the global human population (data as of 2011).** The sharp dip in the 1960s is due mainly to a famine in China in which about 60 million people died.

(disregarding the effects of immigration and emigration). Two possible configurations for a stable population are

Zero population growth = High birth rate − High death rate

or

Zero population growth = Low birth rate − Low death rate

The movement from high birth and death rates toward low birth and death rates, which tends to accompany industrialization and improved living conditions, is called the **demographic transition**. In Sweden, this transition took about 150 years, from 1810 to 1975, when birth rates finally approached death rates. In Mexico, where the human population is still growing rapidly, the transition is projected to take until at least 2050. Demographic transition is associated with an increase in the quality of health care and sanitation as well as improved access to education, especially for women.

After 1950, death rates declined rapidly in most developing countries, but birth rates have declined more variably. Birth rates have fallen most dramatically in China. In 1970, the Chinese birth rate predicted an average of 5.9 children per woman per lifetime (total fertility rate); by 2011, largely because of the government's strict one-child policy, the total fertility rate was 1.6 children. In some countries of Africa, the transition to lower birth rates has also been rapid, though birth rates remain high in most of sub-Saharan Africa. In India, birth rates have fallen more slowly.

How do such variable birth rates affect the growth of the world's population? In industrialized nations, populations are near equilibrium, with reproductive rates near the replacement level (total fertility rate = 2.1 children per female). In many industrialized countries, including Canada, Germany, Japan, and the United Kingdom, total reproductive rates are in fact *below* the replacement level. These populations will eventually decline if there is no immigration and if the birth rate does not change. In fact, the population is already declining in many eastern and central European countries. Most of the current global population growth (1.1% per year) is concentrated in less industrialized countries, where about 80% of the world's people now live.

A unique feature of human population growth is our ability to control family sizes through planning and voluntary contraception. Reduced family size is the key to the demographic transition. Social change and the rising educational and career aspirations of women in many cultures encourage women to delay marriage and postpone reproduction. Delayed reproduction helps to decrease population growth rates and to move a society toward zero population growth under conditions of low birth rates and low death rates. However, there is a great deal of disagreement as to how much support should be provided for global family planning efforts.

Age Structure

Another important demographic variable in present and future growth trends is a country's **age structure**, the relative number of individuals of each age in the population. Age structure is commonly graphed as "pyramids" like those in **Figure 53.24**. For Afghanistan, the pyramid is bottom-heavy, skewed toward young individuals who will grow up and perhaps sustain the explosive growth with their own reproduction. The age structure for the United States is relatively even until the older, postreproductive ages. Although the current total reproductive rate in the United States is 2.1 children per woman—approximately replacement rate—the population is projected to grow slowly through 2050 as a result of immigration. For Italy, the pyramid has a small base, indicating that individuals younger than reproductive age are relatively underrepresented in the population. This situation contributes to the projection of a population decrease in Italy.

Age-structure diagrams not only predict a population's growth trends but also can illuminate social conditions. Based on the diagrams in Figure 53.24, we can predict that employment and education opportunities will continue to be a problem for Afghanistan in the foreseeable future. In the United States and Italy, a decreasing proportion of younger working-age people will soon be supporting an increasing population of retired "boomers." This demographic feature has made the future of Social Security and Medicare a major political issue in the United States. Understanding age structures can help us plan for the future.

Infant Mortality and Life Expectancy

Infant mortality, the number of infant deaths per 1,000 live births, and *life expectancy at birth*, the predicted average length of life at birth, vary widely in different countries. In 2011, for example, the infant mortality rate was 149 (14.9%) in Afghanistan but only 2.8 (0.28%) in Japan. Life expectancy at birth was only 48 years in Afghanistan but 82 years in Japan. These differences reflect the quality of life faced by children at birth and influence the reproductive choices parents make. If infant mortality is high, then parents are likely to have more children to ensure that some reach adulthood.

Although global life expectancy has been increasing since about 1950, it has recently dropped in a number of regions, including countries of the former Soviet Union and in sub-Saharan Africa. In these regions, social upheaval, decaying infrastructure, and infectious diseases such as AIDS and tuberculosis are reducing life expectancy. In the African country of Angola, life expectancy in 2011 was 43 years, about half of that in Japan, Sweden, Italy, and Spain.

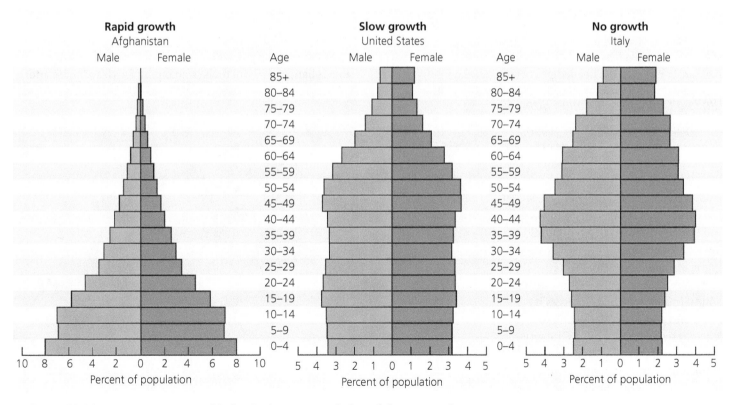

▲ Figure 53.24 **Age-structure pyramids for the human population of three countries (data as of 2010).** The annual growth rate was approximately 2.6% in Afghanistan, 1.0% in the United States, and 0.0% in Italy.

Global Carrying Capacity

No ecological question is more important than the future size of the human population. The projected worldwide population size depends on assumptions about future changes in birth and death rates. As we noted earlier, population ecologists project a global population of approximately 8.1–10.6 billion people in 2050. In other words, an estimated 1–4 billion people will be added to the population in the next four decades because of the momentum of population growth. But just how many humans can the biosphere support? Will the world be overpopulated in 2050? Is it *already* overpopulated?

Estimates of Carrying Capacity

For over three centuries, scientists have attempted to estimate the human carrying capacity of Earth. The first known estimate, 13.4 billion people, was made in 1679 by Anton van Leeuwenhoek, the discoverer of protists (see Chapter 28). Since then, estimates have varied from less than 1 billion to more than 1,000 billion (1 trillion).

Carrying capacity is difficult to estimate, and scientists use different methods to produce their estimates. Some current researchers use curves like that produced by the logistic equation (see Figure 53.10) to predict the future maximum of the human population. Others generalize from existing "maximum" population density and multiply this number by the area of habitable land. Still others base their estimates on a single limiting factor, such as food, and consider variables such as the amount of available farmland, the average yield of crops, the prevalent diet—vegetarian or meat based—and the number of calories needed per person per day.

Limits on Human Population Size

A more comprehensive approach to estimating the carrying capacity of Earth is to recognize that humans have multiple constraints: We need food, water, fuel, building materials, and other resources, such as clothing and transportation. The **ecological footprint** concept summarizes the aggregate land and water area required by each person, city, or nation to produce all the resources it consumes and to absorb all the waste it generates **(Figure 53.25)**. One way to estimate the ecological footprint of the entire human population is to add up all the ecologically productive land on the planet and divide by the population. This calculation yields approximately 2 hectares (ha) per

▲ **Figure 53.25 Ecological footprint.** The resources we use and the waste we produce determine our ecological footprint. Technology castoffs, such as these circuit boards, contribute to our ecological footprint.

person (1 ha = 2.47 acres). Reserving some land for parks and conservation means reducing this allotment to 1.7 ha per person—the benchmark for comparing actual ecological footprints. Anyone who consumes resources that require more than 1.7 ha to produce is said to be using an unsustainable share of Earth's resources. A typical ecological footprint for a person in the United States is about 10 ha.

Ecologists sometimes calculate ecological footprints using other currencies besides land area, such as energy use. Average energy use differs greatly for a person in developed and developing nations **(Figure 53.26)**. A typical person in the United States, Canada, or Norway consumes roughly 30 times the energy that a person in central Africa does. Moreover, fossil fuels, such as oil, coal, and natural gas, are the source of 80% or more of the energy used in most developed nations. As you will see in Chapter 56, this unsustainable reliance on fossil fuels is changing Earth's climate and

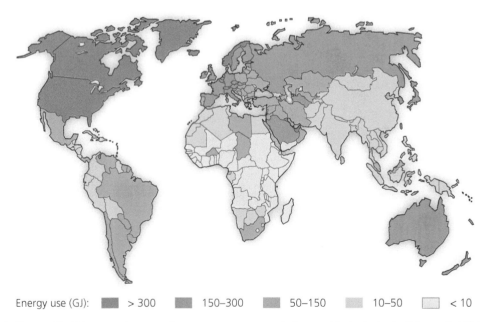

Energy use (GJ): > 300   150–300   50–150   10–50   < 10

▲ **Figure 53.26 Annual per capita energy use around the world.** A gigajoule (GJ) equals 10^9 J. For comparison, leaving a 100-watt lightbulb on continuously for one year would use 3.15 GJ.

increasing the amount of waste that each of us produces. Ultimately, the combination of resource use per person and population density determines our global ecological footprint.

We can only speculate about Earth's ultimate carrying capacity for the human population and about what factors will eventually limit our growth. Perhaps food will be the main limiting factor. Malnutrition and famine are common in some regions, but they result mainly from the unequal distribution of food rather than from inadequate production. So far, technological improvements in agriculture have allowed food supplies to keep up with global population growth.

The demands of many populations have already far exceeded the local and even regional supplies of one renewable resource—fresh water. More than 1 billion people do not have access to sufficient water to meet their basic sanitation needs. The human population may also be limited by the capacity of the environment to absorb its wastes. If so, then Earth's current human occupants could lower the planet's long-term carrying capacity for future generations.

Technology has substantially increased Earth's carrying capacity, but no population can grow indefinitely. After reading this chapter, you should realize that there is no single carrying capacity. How many people our planet can sustain depends on the quality of life each of us enjoys and the distribution of wealth across people and nations, topics of great concern and political debate. We can decide whether zero population growth will be attained through social changes based on human choices or, instead, through increased mortality due to resource limitation, plagues, war, and environmental degradation.

CONCEPT CHECK 53.6

1. How does a human population's age structure affect its growth rate?
2. How has the growth of Earth's human population changed in recent decades? In your answer, discuss growth rate and the number of people added each year.
3. **WHAT IF?** What choices can you make to influence your own ecological footprint?

For suggested answers, see Appendix A.

53 Chapter Review

SUMMARY OF KEY CONCEPTS

CONCEPT 53.1

Biological processes influence population density, dispersion, and demographics (pp. 1185–1190)

- Population **density**—the number of individuals per unit area or volume—reflects the interplay of births, deaths, immigration, and emigration. Environmental and social factors influence the **dispersion** of individuals.

Patterns of dispersion

| Clumped | Uniform | Random |

- Populations increase from births and **immigration** and decrease from deaths and **emigration**. **Life tables**, **survivorship curves**, and **reproductive tables** summarize specific trends in **demography**.

? *Gray whales* (Eschrichtius robustus) *gather each winter near Baja California to give birth. How might such behavior make it easier for ecologists to estimate birth and death rates for the species?*

CONCEPT 53.2

The exponential model describes population growth in an idealized, unlimited environment (pp. 1190–1192)

- If immigration and emigration are ignored, a population's growth rate (the per capita rate of increase) equals its birth rate minus its death rate.
- The **exponential growth** equation $dN/dt = r_{inst}N$ represents a population's growth when resources are relatively abundant, where r_{inst} is the instantaneous per capita rate of increase and N is the number of individuals in the population.

Population size (N) — Number of generations

$$\frac{dN}{dt} = r_{inst}\,N$$

? *Suppose one population has an r_{inst} that is twice as large as the r_{inst} of another population. What is the maximum size that both populations will reach over time, based on the exponential model?*

CONCEPT 53.3

The logistic model describes how a population grows more slowly as it nears its carrying capacity (pp. 1192–1194)

- Exponential growth cannot be sustained for long in any population. A more realistic population model limits growth by incorporating **carrying capacity** (K), the maximum population size the environment can support.
- According to the **logistic growth** equation $dN/dt = r_{inst}N(K - N)/K$, growth levels off as population size approaches the carrying capacity.

- The logistic model fits few real populations perfectly, but it is useful for estimating possible growth.

? *As an ecologist who manages a wildlife preserve, you want to increase the preserve's carrying capacity for a particular endangered species. How might you go about accomplishing this?*

CONCEPT 53.4

Life history traits are products of natural selection (pp. 1195–1197)

- **Life history** traits are evolutionary outcomes reflected in the development, physiology, and behavior of organisms.
- Big-bang, or **semelparous**, organisms reproduce once and die. **Iteroparous** organisms produce offspring repeatedly.
- Life history traits such as brood size, age at maturity, and parental caregiving represent trade-offs between conflicting demands for time, energy, and nutrients. Two hypothetical life history patterns are *K*-**selection**, or density-dependent selection, and *r*-**selection**, or density-independent selection.

? *What two factors likely contribute to the evolution of semelparity versus iteroparity?*

CONCEPT 53.5

Many factors that regulate population growth are density dependent (pp. 1197–1201)

- In **density-dependent** population regulation, death rates rise and birth rates fall with increasing density. In **density-independent** population regulation, birth and death rates do not vary with density.
- Density-dependent changes in birth and death rates curb population increase through negative feedback and can eventually stabilize a population near its carrying capacity. Density-dependent limiting factors include intraspecific competition for limited food or space, increased predation, disease, intrinsic physiological factors, and buildup of toxic substances.
- Because changing environmental conditions periodically disrupt them, all populations exhibit some size fluctuations. Many populations undergo regular boom-and-bust cycles that are

influenced by complex interactions between biotic and abiotic factors. A **metapopulation** is a group of populations linked by immigration and emigration.

? *Give an example of one biotic and one abiotic factor that contribute to yearly fluctuations in the size of the human population.*

CONCEPT 53.6

The human population is no longer growing exponentially but is still increasing rapidly (pp. 1201–1205)

- Since about 1650, the global human population has grown exponentially, but within the last 50 years, the rate of growth has fallen by half. Differences in **age structure** show that while some nations' populations are growing rapidly, those of others are stable or declining in size. Infant mortality rates and life expectancy at birth vary widely in different countries.
- **Ecological footprint** is the aggregate land and water area needed to produce all the resources a person or group of people consume and to absorb all of their wastes. It is one measure of how close we are to the carrying capacity of Earth, which is uncertain. With a world population of more than 7 billion people, we are already using many resources in an unsustainable manner.

? *How are humans different from other species in the ability to "choose" a carrying capacity for their environment?*

TEST YOUR UNDERSTANDING

LEVEL 1: KNOWLEDGE/COMPREHENSION

1. Population ecologists follow the fate of same-age cohorts to
   a. determine a population's carrying capacity.
   b. determine the birth rate and death rate of each group in a population.
   c. determine if a population is regulated by density-dependent processes.
   d. determine the factors that regulate the size of a population.

2. A population's carrying capacity
   a. may change as environmental conditions change.
   b. can be accurately calculated using the logistic growth model.
   c. increases as the per capita growth rate (r) decreases.
   d. can never be exceeded.

3. Scientific study of the population cycles of the snowshoe hare and its predator, the lynx, has revealed that
   a. predation is the dominant factor affecting prey population cycling.
   b. hares and lynx are so mutually dependent that each species cannot survive without the other.
   c. both hare and lynx populations are regulated mainly by abiotic factors.
   d. the hare population is *r*-selected and the lynx population is *K*-selected.

4. Analyzing ecological footprints reveals that
   a. Earth's carrying capacity would increase if per capita meat consumption increased.
   b. current demand by industrialized countries for resources is much smaller than the ecological footprint of those countries.
   c. it is not possible for technological improvements to increase Earth's carrying capacity for humans.
   d. the ecological footprint of the United States is large because per capita resource use is high.

5. Based on current growth rates, Earth's human population in 2015 will be closest to
   a. 2 million.
   c. 7 billion.
   b. 4 billion.
   d. 10 billion.

LEVEL 2: APPLICATION/ANALYSIS

6. The observation that members of a population are uniformly distributed suggests that
   a. resources are distributed unevenly.
   b. the members of the population are competing for access to a resource.
   c. the members of the population are neither attracted to nor repelled by one another.
   d. the density of the population is low.

7. According to the logistic growth equation

$$\frac{dN}{dt} = r_{inst}N\frac{(K - N)}{K}$$

   a. the number of individuals added per unit time is greatest when N is close to zero.
   b. the per capita growth rate (r) increases as N approaches K.
   c. population growth is zero when N equals K.
   d. the population grows exponentially when K is small.

8. Which pair of terms most accurately describes life history traits for a stable population of wolves?
   a. semelparous; r-selected
   b. semelparous; K-selected
   c. iteroparous; r-selected
   d. iteroparous; K-selected

9. During exponential growth, a population always
   a. has a constant, instantaneous per capita growth rate.
   b. quickly reaches its carrying capacity.
   c. cycles through time.
   d. loses some individuals to emigration.

10. Which of the following statements about human population in industrialized countries is *incorrect*?
    a. Life history is r-selected.
    b. Average family size is relatively small.
    c. The population has undergone the demographic transition.
    d. The survivorship curve is Type I.

LEVEL 3: SYNTHESIS/EVALUATION

11. **INTERPRET THE DATA** To estimate which age cohort in a population of females produces the most female offspring, you need information about the number of offspring produced per capita within that cohort and the number of individuals alive in the cohort. Make this estimate for Belding's ground squirrels by multiplying the number of females alive at the start of the year (column 2 in Table 53.1) by the average number of female offspring produced per female (column 5 in Table 53.2). Draw a bar graph with female age in years on the x-axis (0–1, 1–2, and so on) and total number of female offspring produced for each age cohort on the y-axis. Which cohort of female Belding's ground squirrels produces the most female young?

12. EVOLUTION CONNECTION
    Write a paragraph contrasting the conditions that favor the evolution of semelparous (one-time) reproduction versus iteroparous (repeated) reproduction.

13. SCIENTIFIC INQUIRY
    You are testing the hypothesis that increased population density of a particular plant species increases the rate at which a pathogenic fungus infects the plant. Because the fungus causes visible scars on the leaves, you can easily determine whether a plant is infected. Design an experiment to test your hypothesis. Describe your experimental and control groups, how you would collect data, and what results you would see if your hypothesis is correct.

14. SCIENCE, TECHNOLOGY, AND SOCIETY
    Many people regard the rapid population growth of less industrialized countries as our most serious environmental problem. Others think that the population growth in industrialized countries, though smaller, is actually a greater environmental threat. What problems result from population growth in (a) less industrialized countries and (b) industrialized nations? Which do you think is a greater threat, and why?

15. WRITE ABOUT A THEME: INTERACTIONS
    In a short essay (100–150 words), identify the factor or factors in Figure 53.18 that you think may ultimately be most important for density-dependent population regulation in humans, and explain your reasoning.

16. **SYNTHESIZE YOUR KNOWLEDGE**

Locusts (grasshoppers in the family Acrididae) undergo cyclic population outbreaks. Of the mechanisms of density-dependent regulation shown in Figure 53.18, choose the two that you think most apply to locust swarms, and explain why.

For selected answers, see Appendix A.

MasteringBiology®

Students Go to **MasteringBiology** for assignments, the eText, and the Study Area with practice tests, animations, and activities.

Instructors Go to **MasteringBiology** for automatically graded tutorials and questions that you can assign to your students, plus Instructor Resources.

54

Community Ecology

▲ **Figure 54.1 Which species benefits from this interaction?**

Communities in Motion

Deep in the Lembeh Strait of Indonesia, a carrier crab scuttles across the ocean floor holding a large sea urchin on its back **(Figure 54.1)**. When a predatory fish arrives, the crab quickly settles into the sediments and puts its living shield to use. The fish darts in and tries to bite the crab. In response, the crab tilts the spiny sea urchin toward whichever side the fish attacks. The fish eventually gives up and swims away. Carrier crabs use many organisms to protect themselves, including jellies (lower left).

The crab in Figure 54.1 clearly benefits from having the sea urchin on its back. But how does the sea urchin fare in this relationship? Its association with the crab might harm it, help it, or have no effect on its survival and reproduction. Additional observations or experiments would be needed before ecologists could answer this question.

In Chapter 53, you learned how individuals within a population can affect other individuals of the same species. This chapter will examine ecological interactions between populations of different species. A group of populations of different species living close enough to interact is called a biological **community**. Ecologists define the boundaries of a particular community to fit their research questions: They might study the community of decomposers and other organisms living on a rotting log, the benthic community in Lake Superior, or the community of trees and shrubs in Sequoia National Park in California.

We begin this chapter by exploring the kinds of interactions that occur between species in a community, such as the crab and sea urchin in Figure 54.1. We'll then consider several of the factors that are most significant in structuring a community—in determining how many species there are, which particular species are present, and the relative abundance of these species. Finally, we'll apply some of the principles of community ecology to the study of human disease.

CONCEPT 54.1

Community interactions are classified by whether they help, harm, or have no effect on the species involved

Some key relationships in the life of an organism are its interactions with individuals of other species in the community. These **interspecific interactions** include competition, predation, herbivory, symbiosis (including parasitism, mutualism, and commensalism), and facilitation. In this section, we'll define and describe each of these interactions, recognizing that ecologists do not always agree on the precise boundaries of each type of interaction.

We'll use the symbols + and − to indicate how each interspecific interaction affects the survival and reproduction of the two species engaged in the interaction. For example, predation is a +/− interaction, with a positive effect on the survival and reproduction of the predator population and a negative effect on that of the prey population. Mutualism is a +/+ interaction because the survival and reproduction of both species are increased in the presence of the other. A 0 indicates that a population is not affected by the interaction in any known way.

Historically, most ecological research has focused on interactions that have a negative effect on at least one species, such as competition and predation. However, positive interactions are ubiquitous, and their contributions to community structure are the subject of considerable study today.

Competition

Interspecific competition is a −/− interaction that occurs when individuals of different species compete for a resource that limits their growth and survival. Weeds growing in a garden compete with garden plants for soil nutrients and water. Grasshoppers and bison in the Great Plains compete for the grass they both eat. Lynx and foxes in the northern forests of Alaska and Canada compete for prey such as snowshoe hares. In contrast, some resources, such as oxygen, are rarely in short supply on land; most terrestrial species use this resource but do not usually compete for it.

Competitive Exclusion

What happens in a community when two species compete for limited resources? In 1934, Russian ecologist G. F. Gause studied this question using laboratory experiments with two closely related species of ciliated protists, *Paramecium aurelia* and *Paramecium caudatum*. He cultured the species under stable conditions, adding a constant amount of food each day. When Gause grew the two species separately, each population increased rapidly and then leveled off at the apparent carrying capacity of the culture (see Figure 53.11a for an illustration of the logistic growth of *P. aurelia*). But when Gause grew the two species together, *P. caudatum* became extinct in the culture. Gause inferred that *P. aurelia* had a competitive edge in obtaining food. He concluded that two species competing for the same limiting resources cannot coexist permanently in the same place. In the absence of disturbance, one species will use the resources more efficiently and reproduce more rapidly than the other. Even a slight reproductive advantage will eventually lead to local elimination of the inferior competitor, an outcome called **competitive exclusion**.

Paramecium caudatum

25 μm

Ecological Niches and Natural Selection

EVOLUTION The sum of a species' use of the biotic and abiotic resources in its environment is called its **ecological niche**. American ecologist Eugene Odum used the following analogy to explain the niche concept: If an organism's habitat is its "address," the niche is the organism's "profession." The niche of a tropical tree lizard, for instance, includes the temperature range it tolerates, the size of branches on which it perches, the time of day when it is active, and the sizes and kinds of insects it eats. Such factors define the lizard's niche, or ecological role—how it fits into an ecosystem.

We can use the niche concept to restate the principle of competitive exclusion: Two species cannot coexist permanently in a community if their niches are identical. However, ecologically similar species *can* coexist in a community if one or more significant differences in their niches arise through time. Evolution by natural selection can result in one of the species using a different set of resources or similar resources at different times of the day or year. The differentiation of niches that enables similar species

A. distichus perches on fence posts and other sunny surfaces.

A. insolitus usually perches on shady branches.

A. ricordi

A. insolitus
A. christophei

A. aliniger
A. distichus

A. cybotes
A. etheridgei

▲ **Figure 54.2 Resource partitioning among Dominican Republic lizards.** Seven species of *Anolis* lizards live in close proximity, and all feed on insects and other small arthropods. However, competition for food is reduced because each lizard species has a different preferred perch, thus occupying a distinct niche.

to coexist in a community is called **resource partitioning** (Figure 54.2).

As a result of competition, a species' *fundamental niche*, which is the niche potentially occupied by that species, is often different from its *realized niche*, the portion of its fundamental niche that it actually occupies. Ecologists can identify the fundamental niche of a species by testing the range of conditions in which it grows and reproduces in the absence of competitors. They can also test whether a potential competitor limits a species' realized niche by removing the competitor and seeing if the first species expands into the newly available space. The classic experiment depicted in Figure 54.3 clearly showed that competition between two barnacle species kept one species from occupying part of its fundamental niche.

Species can partition their niches not just in space, as lizards and barnacles do, but in time as well. The common spiny mouse (*Acomys cahirinus*) and the golden spiny mouse (*A. russatus*) live in rocky habitats of the Middle East and Africa, sharing similar microhabitats and food sources. Where they coexist, *A. cahirinus* is nocturnal (active at night), while *A. russatus* is diurnal (active during the day). Surprisingly, laboratory research showed that *A. russatus* is naturally nocturnal. To be active during the day, it must **override its** biological clock in **the** presence of *A. cahirinus*. When researchers in Israel removed all *A. cahirinus*

◀ **The golden spiny mouse** (*Acomys russatus*)

▼ **Figure 54.3** Inquiry

Can a species' niche be influenced by interspecific competition?

Experiment Ecologist Joseph Connell studied two barnacle species—*Chthamalus stellatus* and *Balanus balanoides*—that have a stratified distribution on rocks along the coast of Scotland. *Chthamalus* is usually found higher on the rocks than *Balanus*. To determine whether the distribution of *Chthamalus* is the result of interspecific competition with *Balanus*, Connell removed *Balanus* from the rocks at several sites.

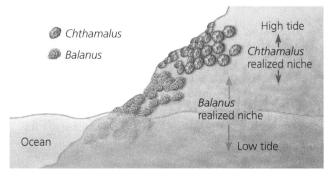

🐚 *Chthamalus*
🐚 *Balanus*

High tide
Chthamalus realized niche
Balanus realized niche
Ocean
Low tide

Results *Chthamalus* spread into the region formerly occupied by *Balanus*.

High tide
Chthamalus fundamental niche
Ocean
Low tide

Conclusion Interspecific competition makes the realized niche of *Chthamalus* much smaller than its fundamental niche.

Source: J. H. Connell, The influence of interspecific competition and other factors on the distribution of the barnacle *Chthamalus stellatus*, *Ecology* 42:710–723 (1961).

(MB) A related Experimental Inquiry Tutorial can be assigned in MasteringBiology.

WHAT IF? *Other observations showed that* Balanus *cannot survive high on the rocks because it dries out during low tides. How would* Balanus's *realized niche compare with its fundamental niche?*

individuals from a site in the species' natural habitat, *A. russatus* individuals at that site became nocturnal, consistent with the laboratory results. This change in behavior suggests that competition exists between the species and that partitioning of their active time helps them coexist.

Character Displacement

Closely related species whose populations are sometimes allopatric (geographically separate; see Chapter 24) and sometimes sympatric (geographically overlapping) provide more evidence for the importance of competition in structuring communities. In some cases, the allopatric populations

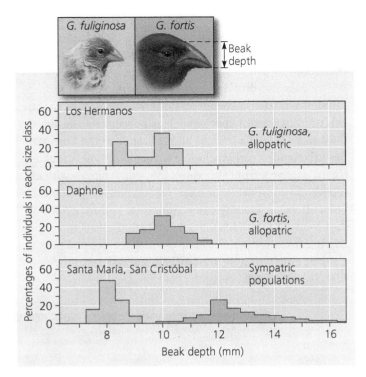

▲ **Figure 54.4 Character displacement: indirect evidence of past competition.** Allopatric populations of *Geospiza fuliginosa* and *Geospiza fortis* on Los Hermanos and Daphne Islands have similar beak morphologies (top two graphs) and presumably eat similarly sized seeds. However, where the two species are sympatric on Santa María and San Cristóbal, *G. fuliginosa* has a shallower, smaller beak and *G. fortis* a deeper, larger one (bottom graph), adaptations that favor eating different-sized seeds.

INTERPRET THE DATA *If the beak length of* G. fortis *is typically 12% longer than the beak depth, what is the predicted beak length of* G. fortis *individuals with the smallest beak depths observed on Santa María and San Cristóbal Islands?*

of such species are morphologically similar and use similar resources. By contrast, sympatric populations, which would potentially compete for resources, show differences in body structures and in the resources they use. This tendency for characteristics to diverge more in sympatric than in allopatric populations of two species is called **character displacement**, as shown for Galápagos finches in **Figure 54.4**.

Predation

Predation refers to a +/− interaction between species in which one species, the predator, kills and eats the other, the prey. Though the term *predation* generally elicits such images as a lion attacking and eating an antelope, it applies to a wide range of interactions. An animal that kills a plant by eating the plant's tissues can also be considered a predator. Because eating and avoiding being eaten are prerequisite to reproductive success, the adaptations of both predators and prey tend to be refined through natural selection. In the Scientific Skills Exercise, you can interpret data from an investigation of a specific predator-prey interaction.

SCIENTIFIC SKILLS EXERCISE

Making a Bar Graph and a Scatter Plot

Can a Native Predator Species Adapt Rapidly to an Introduced Prey Species? Cane toads (*Bufo marinus*), shown above, were introduced to Australia in 1935 in a failed attempt to control an insect pest. Since then, the toads have spread across northeastern Australia, with a population of over 200 million today. Cane toads have glands that produce a toxin that is poisonous to snakes and other potential predators of the toads. In this exercise, you will graph and interpret data from a two-part experiment conducted to determine whether native Australian predators have developed resistance to the cane toad toxin.

How the Experiment Was Done In part 1, researchers collected 12 black snakes (*Pseudechis porphyriacus*) from areas where cane toads had existed for 40–60 years and another 12 from areas free of cane toads. They offered the snakes either a freshly killed native frog (*Limnodynastes peronii*, a species the snakes commonly eat) or a freshly killed cane toad from which the toxin gland had been removed (making the toad nonpoisonous). In part 2, researchers collected snakes from areas where cane toads had been present for 5–60 years. To assess how cane toad toxin affected the physiological activity of these snakes, they injected small amounts of the toxin into the snakes' stomachs and measured the snakes' swimming speed in a small pool.

Data from the Experiment, Part 1

Type of Prey Offered	% of Snakes That Ate Prey Offered in Each Area	
	Cane Toads Present in Area for 40–60 Years	No Cane Toads in Area
Native frog	100	100
Cane toad	0	50

Data from the Experiment, Part 2

Time Since First Exposure to Cane Toads (years)	5	10	10	20	50	60	60	60	60	60
% Reduction in Swimming Speed	52	19	30	30	5	5	9	11	12	22

Interpret the Data

1. Make a bar graph of the data in part 1. (For additional information about graphs, see the Scientific Skills Review in Appendix F and in the Study Area in Mastering Biology.)

2. What do the data represented in the graph suggest about the effects of cane toads on the predatory behavior of black snakes in areas where the toads are and are not currently found?

3. Suppose an enzyme that deactivates the cane toad toxin evolves in black snakes living in areas with cane toads. If the researchers repeated part 1 of this study, predict how the results would change.

4. Identify the dependent and independent variables in part 2 and make a scatter plot. What conclusion would you draw about whether exposure to cane toads is having a selective effect on black snakes? Explain.

5. Explain why a bar graph is appropriate for presenting the data in part 1 and a scatter plot is appropriate for the data in part 2.

(MB) A version of this Scientific Skills Exercise can be assigned in MasteringBiology.

Data from B. L. Phillips and R. Shine, An invasive species induces rapid adaptive change in a native predator: cane toads and black snakes in Australia, *Proceedings of the Royal Society B* 273:1545–1550 (2006).

Many important feeding adaptations of predators are obvious and familiar. Most predators have acute senses that enable them to find and identify potential prey. Rattlesnakes and other pit vipers, for example, find their prey with a pair of heat-sensing organs located between their eyes and nostrils (see Figure 50.7a). Owls have characteristically large eyes that help them see prey at night. Many predators also have adaptations such as claws, fangs, or poison that help them catch and subdue their food. Predators that pursue their prey are generally fast and agile, whereas those that lie in ambush are often disguised in their environments.

Just as predators possess adaptations for capturing prey, potential prey animals have adaptations that help them avoid being eaten. Some common behavioral defenses are hiding, fleeing, and forming herds or schools. Active self-defense is less common, though some large grazing mammals vigorously defend their young from predators such as lions. Other behavioral defenses include alarm calls that summon many individuals of the prey species, which then mob the predator.

Animals also display a variety of morphological and physiological defensive adaptations. Mechanical or chemical defenses protect species such as porcupines and skunks (Figure 54.5a and b). Some animals, such as the European fire salamander, can synthesize toxins; others accumulate toxins passively from the plants they eat. Animals with effective chemical defenses often exhibit bright **aposematic coloration**, or warning coloration, such as that of poison dart frogs (Figure 54.5c). Such coloration seems to be adaptive because predators often avoid brightly colored prey. **Cryptic coloration**, or camouflage, makes prey difficult to see (Figure 54.5d).

▼ Figure 54.5 **Examples of defensive adaptations in animals.**

(a) Mechanical defense

▶ Porcupine

(b) Chemical defense

▶ Skunk

(c) Aposematic coloration: warning coloration

◀ Poison dart frog

(d) Cryptic coloration: camouflage

▶ Canyon tree frog

(e) Batesian mimicry: A harmless species mimics a harmful one.

▲ Venomous green parrot snake

◀ Nonvenomous hawkmoth larva

(f) Müllerian mimicry: Two unpalatable species mimic each other.

◀ Yellow jacket

◀ Cuckoo bee

Some prey species are protected by their resemblance to other species. In **Batesian mimicry**, a palatable or harmless species mimics an unpalatable or harmful one. The larva of the hawkmoth *Hemeroplanes ornatus* puffs up its head and thorax when disturbed, looking like the head of a small venomous snake **(Figure 54.5e)**. In this case, the mimicry even involves behavior; the larva weaves its head back and forth and hisses like a snake. In **Müllerian mimicry**, two or more unpalatable species, such as the cuckoo bee and yellow jacket, resemble each other **(Figure 54.5f)**. Presumably, the more unpalatable prey there are, the more quickly predators learn to avoid prey with that particular appearance. In an example of convergent evolution, unpalatable animals in several different taxa have similar patterns of coloration: Black and yellow or red stripes characterize unpalatable animals as diverse as yellow jackets and coral snakes.

Many predators also use mimicry. The mimic octopus (*Thaumoctopus mimicus*), discovered in 1998, can take on the appearance and movement of more than a dozen marine animals, including crabs, sea stars, sea snakes, fish, and stingrays **(Figure 54.6)**. It uses its mimicry to approach prey—for example, imitating a crab to approach another crab and eat it. It also uses its mimicry to scare predators. When attacked by a damselfish, the octopus quickly mimics a banded sea snake, a known predator of the damselfish.

(a) Mimicking a sea snake

(b) Mimicking a flounder

(c) Mimicking a stingray

▲ **Figure 54.6 The mimic octopus. (a)** After hiding six of its tentacles in a hole in the seafloor, the octopus waves its other two tentacles to mimic a sea snake. **(b)** Flattening its body and arranging its arms to trail behind, the octopus mimics a flounder (a flat fish). **(c)** It can mimic a stingray by flattening most of its tentacles alongside its body while allowing one tentacle to extend behind.

Herbivory

Ecologists use the term **herbivory** to refer to a +/− interaction in which an organism eats parts of a plant or alga. While large mammalian herbivores such as cattle, sheep, and water buffalo may be most familiar, most herbivores are actually invertebrates, such as grasshoppers, caterpillars, and beetles. In the ocean, herbivores include sea urchins, some tropical fishes, and certain mammals **(Figure 54.7)**.

Like predators, herbivores have many specialized adaptations. Many herbivorous insects have chemical sensors on their feet that enable them to distinguish between plants based on their toxicity or nutritional value. Some mammalian herbivores, such as goats, use their sense of smell to examine plants, rejecting some and eating others. They may also eat just a specific part of a plant, such as the flowers. Many herbivores also have specialized teeth or digestive systems adapted for processing vegetation (see Chapter 41).

Unlike prey animals, plants cannot run away to avoid being eaten. Instead, a plant's arsenal against herbivores may feature chemical toxins or structures such as spines and thorns. Among the plant compounds that serve as chemical defenses are the poison strychnine, produced by the tropical vine *Strychnos toxifera*; nicotine, from the tobacco plant; and tannins, from a variety of plant species. Compounds that are not toxic to humans but may be distasteful to many herbivores are responsible for the familiar flavors of cinnamon, cloves, and peppermint. Certain plants produce chemicals that cause abnormal development in some insects that eat them. For more examples of how plants defend themselves, see Figure 39.27, "Make Connections: Levels of Plant Defenses Against Herbivores."

▲ **Figure 54.7 A West Indian manatee (*Trichechus manatus*) in Florida.** This mammalian herbivore is grazing on *Hydrilla*, an introduced plant species.

Symbiosis

When individuals of two or more species live in direct and intimate contact with one another, their relationship is called **symbiosis**. In this book, we define symbiosis to include all such interactions, whether they are harmful, helpful, or neutral. Some biologists define symbiosis more narrowly as a synonym for mutualism, an interaction in which both species benefit.

Parasitism

Parasitism is a +/− symbiotic interaction in which one organism, the **parasite**, derives its nourishment from another organism, its **host**, which is harmed in the process. Parasites that live within the body of their host, such as tapeworms, are called **endoparasites**; parasites that feed on the external surface of a host, such as ticks and lice, are called **ectoparasites**. In one particular type of parasitism, parasitoid insects—usually small wasps—lay eggs on or in living hosts. The larvae then feed on the body of the host, eventually killing it. Some ecologists have estimated that at least one-third of all species on Earth are parasites.

Many parasites have complex life cycles involving multiple hosts. The blood fluke, which currently infects approximately 200 million people around the world, requires two hosts at different times in its development: humans and freshwater snails (see Figure 33.11). Some parasites change the behavior of their current host in ways that increase the likelihood that the parasite will reach its next host. For instance, crustaceans that are parasitized by acanthocephalan (spiny-headed) worms leave protective cover and move into the open, where they are more likely to be eaten by the birds that are the second host in the worm's life cycle.

Parasites can significantly affect the survival, reproduction, and density of their host population, either directly or indirectly. For example, ticks that live as ectoparasites on moose weaken their hosts by withdrawing blood and causing hair breakage and loss. In their weakened condition, the moose have a greater chance of dying from cold stress or predation by wolves (see Figure 53.19).

Mutualism

Mutualistic symbiosis, or **mutualism**, is an interspecific interaction that benefits both species (+/+). We have described many mutualisms in previous chapters: nitrogen fixation by bacteria in the root nodules of legumes; cellulose digestion by microorganisms in the alimentary canals of termites and ruminant mammals; nutrient exchange between fungi and plant roots in mycorrhizae; and photosynthesis by unicellular algae in corals. The interaction between termites and the microorganisms in their digestive system is an example of *obligate mutualism*, in which at least one species has lost the ability to survive on its own. In *facultative mutualism*, as

(a) Certain species of acacia trees in Central and South America have hollow thorns that house stinging ants of the genus *Pseudomyrmex*. The ants feed on nectar produced by the tree and on protein-rich swellings along the bases of leaves.

(b) The acacia benefits because the pugnacious ants, which attack anything that touches the tree, remove fungal spores, small herbivores, and debris. They also clip vegetation that grows close to the acacia.

▲ **Figure 54.8 Mutualism between acacia trees and ants.**

in the acacia-ant example shown in **Figure 54.8**, both species can survive alone.

Mutualisms typically involve the coevolution of related adaptations in both species, with changes in either species likely to affect the survival and reproduction of the other. For example, most flowering plants have adaptations such as nectar or fruit that attract animals that pollinate flowers or disperse seeds (see Concept 38.1). In turn, many animals have adaptations that help them find and consume nectar.

Commensalism

An interaction between species that benefits one of the species but neither harms nor helps the other (+/0) is called **commensalism**. Commensal interactions are difficult to document in nature because any close association between species likely affects both species, even if only slightly. For

▲ **Figure 54.9** A possible example of commensalism between cattle egrets and African buffalo.

instance, "hitchhiking" species, such as algae that live on the shells of aquatic turtles or barnacles that attach to whales, are sometimes considered commensal. The hitchhikers gain a place to grow while having seemingly little effect on their ride. However, they may reduce the hosts' efficiency of movement in searching for food or escaping from predators. Conversely, the hitchhikers may help camouflage the hosts.

Some commensal associations involve one species obtaining food that is inadvertently exposed by another. Cowbirds and cattle egrets feed on insects flushed out of the grass by grazing bison, cattle, horses, and other herbivores. Because the birds increase their feeding rates when following the herbivores, they clearly benefit from the association. Much of the time, the herbivores may be unaffected by the birds **(Figure 54.9)**. However, they, too, may sometimes benefit; the birds occasionally remove and eat ticks and other ecto-parasites from the herbivores or may warn the herbivores of a predator's approach.

Facilitation

Species can have positive effects (+/+ or 0/+) on the survival and reproduction of other species without necessarily living in the direct and intimate contact of a symbiosis. This type of interaction, called **facilitation**, is particularly common in plant ecology. For instance, the black rush *Juncus gerardii* makes the soil more hospitable for other plant species in some zones of New England salt marshes **(Figure 54.10a)**. *Juncus* helps prevent salt buildup in the soil by shading the soil surface, which reduces evaporation. *Juncus* also prevents the salt marsh soils from becoming oxygen depleted as it transports oxygen to its belowground tissues. In one study, when *Juncus* was removed from areas in the upper middle intertidal zone, those areas supported 50% fewer plant species **(Figure 54.10b)**.

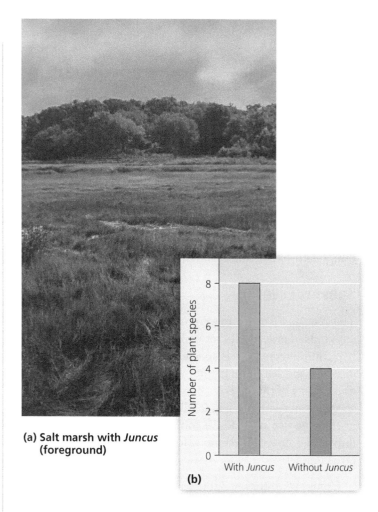

(a) Salt marsh with *Juncus* (foreground)

(b)

▲ **Figure 54.10** Facilitation by black rush (*Juncus gerardii*) in New England salt marshes. Black rush increases the number of plant species that can live in the upper middle zone of the marsh.

All five types of interactions that we have discussed so far—competition, predation, herbivory, symbiosis, and facilitation—strongly influence the structure of communities. You'll see other examples of these interactions throughout this chapter.

CONCEPT CHECK 54.1

1. Explain how interspecific competition, predation, and mutualism differ in their effects on the interacting populations of two species.

2. According to the principle of competitive exclusion, what outcome is expected when two species with identical niches compete for a resource? Why?

3. **MAKE CONNECTIONS** Figure 24.13 illustrates the formation of and possible outcomes for a hybrid zone over time. Imagine that two finch species colonize a new island and are capable of hybridizing. The island contains two plant species, one with large seeds and one with small seeds, growing in isolated habitats. If the two finch species specialize in eating different plant species, would reproductive barriers be reinforced, weakened, or unchanged in this hybrid zone? Explain.

For suggested answers, see Appendix A.

CONCEPT 54.2

Diversity and trophic structure characterize biological communities

Along with the specific interactions described in the previous section, communities are also characterized by more general attributes, including how diverse they are and the feeding relationships of their species. In this section, you'll read why such ecological attributes are important. You'll also learn how a few species sometimes exert strong control on a community's structure, particularly on the composition, relative abundance, and diversity of its species.

Species Diversity

The **species diversity** of a community—the variety of different kinds of organisms that make up the community—has two components. One is **species richness**, the number of different species in the community. The other is the **relative abundance** of the different species, the proportion each species represents of all individuals in the community.

Imagine two small forest communities, each with 100 individuals distributed among four tree species (A, B, C, and D) as follows:

Community 1: 25A, 25B, 25C, 25D
Community 2: 80A, 5B, 5C, 10D

The species richness is the same for both communities because they both contain four species of trees, but the relative abundance is very different (Figure 54.11). You would easily notice the four types of trees in community 1, but you might see only the abundant species A in the second forest. Most observers would intuitively describe community 1 as the more diverse of the two communities.

Ecologists use many tools to compare the diversity of communities across time and space. They often calculate indexes of diversity based on species richness and relative abundance. One widely used index is **Shannon diversity** (H):

$$H = -(p_A \ln p_A + p_B \ln p_B + p_C \ln p_C + \ldots)$$

where A, B, C . . . are the species in the community, p is the relative abundance of each species, and ln is the natural logarithm. A higher value of H indicates a more diverse community. Let's use this equation to calculate the Shannon diversity index of the two communities in Figure 54.11. For community 1, $p = 0.25$ for each species, so

$$H = -4(0.25 \ln 0.25) = 1.39.$$

For community 2,

$$H = -[0.8 \ln 0.8 + 2(0.05 \ln 0.05) + 0.1 \ln 0.1] = 0.71.$$

These calculations confirm our intuitive description of community 1 as more diverse.

Community 1
A: 25% B: 25% C: 25% D: 25%

Community 2
A: 80% B: 5% C: 5% D: 10%

▲ **Figure 54.11 Which forest is more diverse?** Ecologists would say that community 1 has greater species diversity, a measure that includes both species richness and relative abundance.

Determining the number and relative abundance of species in a community can be challenging. Because most species in a community are relatively rare, it may be hard to obtain a sample size large enough to be representative. It can also be difficult to identify the species in the community. If an unknown organism cannot be identified on the basis of morphology alone, it is useful to compare all or part of its genome to a reference database of DNA sequences from known organisms. For example, although the two samples of algae shown at right might appear to be two different species, comparing their sequences of a short standardized section of DNA (a *DNA "barcode"*) to a reference database showed that they belong to the same species. More and more, researchers are using DNA sequencing for species identification as it becomes cheaper and as DNA sequences from more organisms are placed in comparative databases.

It is also difficult to census the highly mobile or less visible members of communities, such as microorganisms, deep-sea creatures, and nocturnal species. The small size of microorganisms makes them particularly difficult to sample, so ecologists now use molecular tools to help determine microbial diversity (Figure 54.12). Despite the challenges, measuring species diversity is essential for understanding community structure and for conserving diversity (as you'll read in Chapter 56).

▼ Figure 54.12 Research Method

Determining Microbial Diversity Using Molecular Tools

Application Ecologists are increasingly using molecular techniques to determine microbial diversity and richness in environmental samples. One such technique produces a DNA profile for microbial taxa based on sequence variations in the DNA that encodes the small subunit of ribosomal RNA. Noah Fierer and Rob Jackson, of Duke University, used this method to compare the diversity of soil bacteria in 98 habitats across North and South America to help identify environmental variables associated with high bacterial diversity.

Technique Researchers first extract and purify DNA from the microbial community in each sample. They use the polymerase chain reaction (PCR; see Figure 20.8) to amplify the ribosomal DNA and label the DNA with a fluorescent dye. Restriction enzymes then cut the amplified, labeled DNA into fragments of different lengths, which are separated by gel electrophoresis. (A gel is shown on the left; see also Figures 20.6 and 20.7.) The number and abundance of these fragments characterize the DNA profile of the sample. Based on their analysis, Fierer and Jackson calculated the Shannon diversity (H) of each sample. They then looked for a correlation between H and several environmental variables, including vegetation type, mean annual temperature and rainfall, and acidity and quality of the soil at each site.

Results The diversity of bacterial communities in soils across North and South America was related almost exclusively to soil pH, with the Shannon diversity being highest in neutral soils and lowest in acidic soils. Amazonian rain forests, which have extremely high plant and animal diversity, had the most acidic soils and the lowest bacterial diversity of the samples tested.

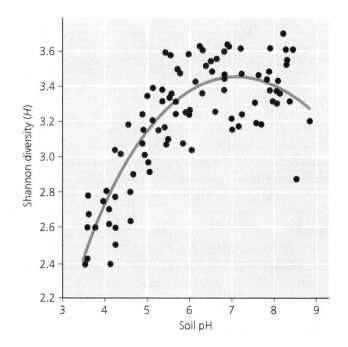

Source: N. Fierer and R. B. Jackson, The diversity and biogeography of soil bacterial communities, *Proceedings of the National Academy of Sciences USA* 103:626–631 (2006).

▶ **Figure 54.13**
Study plots at the Cedar Creek Ecosystem Science Reserve, University of Minnesota, site of long-term experiments on manipulating plant diversity.

Diversity and Community Stability

In addition to measuring species diversity, ecologists manipulate diversity in experimental communities in nature and in the laboratory. They do this to examine the potential benefits of diversity, including increased productivity and stability of biological communities.

Researchers at the Cedar Creek Ecosystem Science Reserve, in Minnesota, have been manipulating plant diversity in experimental communities for more than two decades **(Figure 54.13)**. Higher-diversity communities generally are more productive and are better able to withstand and recover from environmental stresses, such as droughts. More diverse communities are also more stable year to year in their productivity. In one decade-long experiment, for instance, researchers at Cedar Creek created 168 plots, each containing 1, 2, 4, 8, or 16 perennial grassland species. The most diverse plots consistently produced more **biomass** (the total mass of all organisms in a habitat) than the single-species plots each year.

Higher-diversity communities are often more resistant to **invasive species**, which are organisms that become established outside their native range. Scientists working in Long Island Sound, off the coast of Connecticut, created communities of different levels of diversity consisting of sessile marine invertebrates, including tunicates (see Figure 34.5). They then examined how vulnerable these experimental communities were to invasion by an exotic tunicate. They found that the exotic tunicate was four times more likely to survive in lower-diversity communities than in higher-diversity ones. The researchers concluded that relatively diverse communities captured more of the resources available in the system, leaving fewer resources for the invader and decreasing its survival.

Trophic Structure

Experiments like the ones just described often examine the importance of diversity within one trophic level. The structure and dynamics of a community also depend on the feeding relationships between organisms—the **trophic structure** of the community. The transfer of food energy up the trophic levels from its source in plants and other autotrophs (primary producers) through herbivores (primary

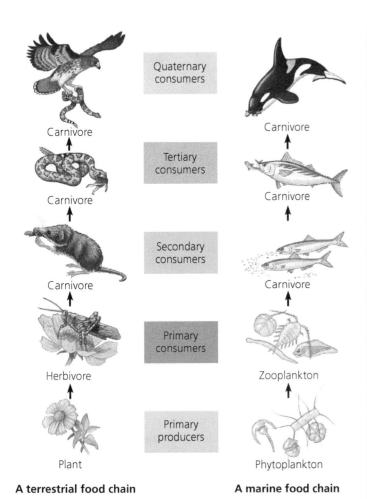

A terrestrial food chain   A marine food chain

▲ Figure 54.14 **Examples of terrestrial and marine food chains.** The arrows trace energy and nutrients that pass through the trophic levels of a community when organisms feed on one another. Decomposers, which "feed" on organisms from all trophic levels, are not shown here.

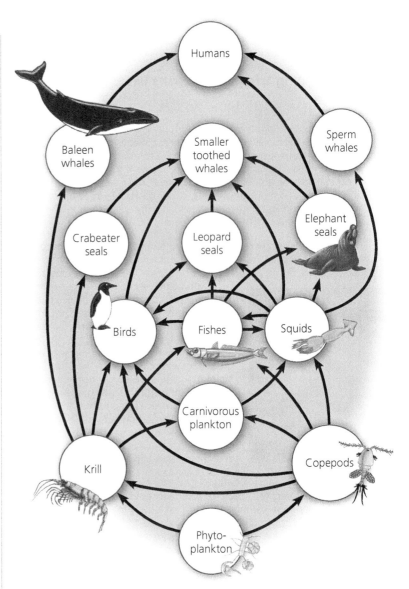

▲ Figure 54.15 **An Antarctic marine food web.** Arrows follow the transfer of food from the producers (phytoplankton) up through the trophic levels. For simplicity, this diagram omits decomposers.

? *How many other organism types does each group eat in this food web? Which two groups are both predator and prey for each other?*

consumers) to carnivores (secondary, tertiary, and quaternary consumers) and eventually to decomposers is referred to as a **food chain** (Figure 54.14).

Food Webs

In the 1920s, Oxford University biologist Charles Elton recognized that food chains are not isolated units but are linked together in **food webs**. Ecologists diagram the trophic relationships of a community using arrows that link species according to who eats whom. In an Antarctic pelagic community, for example, the primary producers are phytoplankton, which serve as food for the dominant grazing zooplankton, especially krill and copepods, both of which are crustaceans (Figure 54.15). These zooplankton species are in turn eaten by various carnivores, including other plankton, penguins, seals, fishes, and baleen whales. Squids, which are carnivores that feed on fish and zooplankton, are another important link in these food webs, as they are in turn eaten by seals and toothed whales. During

the time when whales were commonly hunted for food, humans became the top predator in this food web. Having hunted many whale species to low numbers, humans are now harvesting at lower trophic levels, catching krill as well as fish for food.

How are food chains linked into food webs? A given species may weave into the web at more than one trophic level. In the food web shown in Figure 54.15, krill feed on phytoplankton as well as on other grazing zooplankton, such as copepods. Such "nonexclusive" consumers are also found in terrestrial communities. For instance, foxes are omnivores whose diet includes berries and other plant materials, herbivores such as mice, and other predators, such as weasels. Humans are among the most versatile of omnivores.

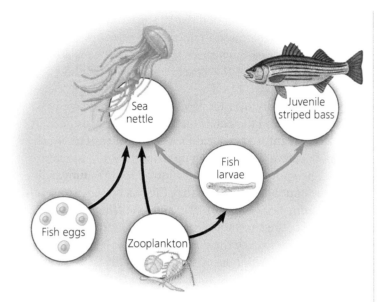

▲ **Figure 54.16 Partial food web for Chesapeake Bay estuary.**
The sea nettle (*Chrysaora quinquecirrha*) and juvenile striped bass
(*Morone saxatilis*) are the main predators of fish larvae (bay anchovy
and several other species). Note that sea nettles are secondary consumers (black arrows) when they eat zooplankton, but tertiary consumers
(red arrows) when they eat fish larvae, which are themselves secondary
consumers of zooplankton.

Complicated food webs can be simplified in two ways for
easier study. First, species with similar trophic relationships
in a given community can be grouped into broad functional
groups. In Figure 54.15, more than 100 phytoplankton species are grouped as the primary producers in the food web.
A second way to simplify a food web for closer study is to
isolate a portion of the web that interacts very little with the
rest of the community. **Figure 54.16** illustrates a partial food
web for sea nettles (a type of cnidarian) and juvenile striped
bass in Chesapeake Bay estuary on the Atlantic coast of the
United States.

Limits on Food Chain Length

Each food chain within a food web is usually only a few links
long. In the Antarctic web of Figure 54.15, there are rarely
more than seven links from the producers to any top-level
predator, and most chains in this web have fewer links. In
fact, most food webs studied to date have chains consisting
of five or fewer links.

Why are food chains relatively short? The most common
explanation, the **energetic hypothesis**, suggests that the
length of a food chain is limited by the inefficiency of energy transfer along the chain. Only about 10% of the energy
stored in the organic matter of each trophic level is converted to organic matter at the next trophic level (see Chapter 55). Thus, a producer level consisting of 100 kg of plant
material can support about 10 kg of herbivore biomass and
1 kg of carnivore biomass. The energetic hypothesis predicts

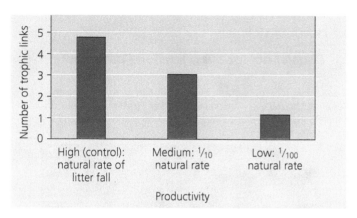

▲ **Figure 54.17 Test of the energetic hypothesis for the restriction of food chain length.** Researchers manipulated the productivity of tree-hole communities in Queensland, Australia, by providing
leaf litter input at three levels. Reducing energy input reduced food
chain length, a result consistent with the energetic hypothesis.

that food chains should be relatively longer in habitats of
higher photosynthetic production, since the amount of energy stored in primary producers is greater than in habitats
with lower photosynthetic production.

Ecologists tested the energetic hypothesis using tree-hole
communities in tropical forests as experimental models.
Many trees have small branch scars that rot, forming holes
in the tree trunk. The holes hold water and provide a habitat for tiny communities consisting of microorganisms and
insects that feed on leaf litter, as well as predatory insects.
Figure 54.17 shows the results of experiments in which researchers manipulated productivity by varying the amount
of leaf litter in tree holes. As predicted by the energetic hypothesis, holes with the most leaf litter, and hence the greatest total food supply at the producer level, supported the
longest food chains.

Another factor that may limit food chain length is that
carnivores in a food chain tend to be larger at successive
trophic levels. The size of a carnivore and its feeding mechanism put some upper limit on the size of food it can take
into its mouth. And except in a few cases, large carnivores
cannot live on very small food items because they cannot
obtain enough food in a given time to meet their metabolic
needs. Among the exceptions are baleen whales, huge filter feeders with adaptations that enable them to consume
enormous quantities of krill and other small organisms (see
Figure 41.6).

Species with a Large Impact

Certain species have an especially large impact on the
structure of entire communities because they are highly
abundant or play a pivotal role in community dynamics. The
impact of these species occurs through trophic interactions
and their influence on the physical environment.

Figure 54.18 Inquiry

Is *Pisaster ochraceus* a keystone predator?

Experiment In rocky intertidal communities of western North America, the relatively uncommon sea star *Pisaster ochraceus* preys on mussels such as *Mytilus californianus*, a dominant species and strong competitor for space.

Robert Paine, of the University of Washington, removed *Pisaster* from an area in the intertidal zone and examined the effect on species richness.

Results In the absence of *Pisaster*, species richness declined as mussels monopolized the rock face and eliminated most other invertebrates and algae. In a control area where *Pisaster* was not removed, species richness changed very little.

Conclusion *Pisaster* acts as a keystone species, exerting an influence on the community that is not reflected in its abundance.

Source: R. T. Paine, Food web complexity and species diversity, *American Naturalist* 100:65–75 (1966).

WHAT IF? *Suppose that an invasive fungus killed most individuals of* Mytilus *at these sites. Predict how species richness would be affected if* Pisaster *were then removed.*

Dominant species in a community are the species that are the most abundant or that collectively have the highest biomass. There is no single explanation for why a species becomes dominant. One hypothesis suggests that dominant species are competitively superior in exploiting limited resources such as water or nutrients. Another hypothesis is that dominant species are most successful at avoiding predation or the impact of disease. The latter idea could explain the high biomass attained in some environments by invasive species. Such species may not face the natural predators or parasites that would otherwise hold their populations in check.

One way to discover the impact of a dominant species is to remove it from the community. The American chestnut was a dominant tree in deciduous forests of eastern North America before 1910, making up more than 40% of mature trees. Then humans accidentally introduced the fungal disease chestnut blight to New York City via nursery stock imported from Asia. Between 1910 and 1950, this fungus killed almost all of the chestnut trees in eastern North America. In this case, removing the dominant species had a relatively small impact on some species but severe effects on others. Oaks, hickories, beeches, and red maples that were already present in the forest increased in abundance and replaced the chestnuts. No mammals or birds seemed to have been harmed by the loss of the chestnut, but seven species of moths and butterflies that fed on the tree became extinct.

In contrast to dominant species, **keystone species** are not usually abundant in a community. They exert strong control on community structure not by numerical might but by their pivotal ecological roles, or niches. **Figure 54.18** highlights the importance of a keystone species, a sea star, in maintaining the diversity of an intertidal community.

Other organisms exert their influence on a community not through trophic interactions but by changing their physical environment. Species that dramatically alter their environment are called **ecosystem engineers** or, to avoid implying conscious intent, "foundation species." A familiar ecosystem engineer is the beaver **(Figure 54.19)**. The effects of ecosystem engineers on other species can be positive or negative, depending on the needs of the other species.

▲ **Figure 54.19 Beavers as ecosystem engineers.** By felling trees, building dams, and creating ponds, beavers can transform large areas of forest into flooded wetlands.

Bottom-Up and Top-Down Controls

Simplified models based on relationships between adjacent trophic levels are useful for describing community organization. Let's consider the three possible relationships between plants (*V* for vegetation) and herbivores (*H*):

$$V \rightarrow H \quad V \leftarrow H \quad V \leftrightarrow H$$

The arrows indicate that a change in the biomass of one trophic level causes a change in the other trophic level. $V \rightarrow H$ means that an increase in vegetation will increase the numbers or biomass of herbivores, but not vice versa. In this situation, herbivores are limited by vegetation, but vegetation is not limited by herbivory. In contrast, $V \leftarrow H$ means that an increase in herbivore biomass will decrease the abundance of vegetation, but not vice versa. A double-headed arrow indicates that each trophic level is sensitive to changes in the biomass of the other.

Two models of community organization are common: the bottom-up model and the top-down model. The $V \rightarrow H$ linkage suggests a **bottom-up model**, which postulates a unidirectional influence from lower to higher trophic levels. In this case, the presence or absence of mineral nutrients (*N*) controls plant (*V*) numbers, which control herbivore (*H*) numbers, which in turn control predator (*P*) numbers. The simplified bottom-up model is thus $N \rightarrow V \rightarrow H \rightarrow P$. To change the community structure of a bottom-up community, you need to alter biomass at the lower trophic levels, allowing those changes to propagate up through the food web. If you add mineral nutrients to stimulate plant growth, then the higher trophic levels should also increase in biomass. If you change predator abundance, however, the effect should not extend down to the lower trophic levels.

In contrast, the **top-down model** postulates the opposite: Predation mainly controls community organization because predators limit herbivores, herbivores limit plants, and plants limit nutrient levels through nutrient uptake. The simplified top-down model, $N \leftarrow V \leftarrow H \leftarrow P$, is also called the *trophic cascade model*. In a lake community with four trophic levels, the model predicts that removing the top carnivores will increase the abundance of primary carnivores, in turn decreasing the number of herbivores, increasing phytoplankton abundance, and decreasing concentrations of mineral nutrients. The effects thus move down the trophic structure as alternating +/− effects.

Ecologists have applied the top-down model to improve water quality in polluted lakes. This approach, called **biomanipulation**, attempts to prevent algal blooms and eutrophication by altering the density of higher-level consumers instead of using chemical treatments. In lakes with three trophic levels, removing fish should improve water quality by increasing zooplankton density, thereby decreasing algal populations. In lakes with four trophic levels,

adding top predators should have the same effect. We can summarize the scenario of three trophic levels with the following diagram:

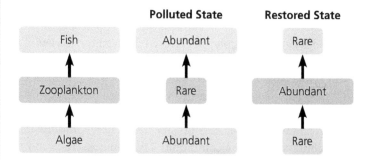

Ecologists in Finland used biomanipulation to help purify Lake Vesijärvi, a large lake that was polluted with city sewage and industrial wastewater until 1976. After pollution controls reduced these inputs, the water quality of the lake began to improve. By 1986, however, massive blooms of cyanobacteria started to occur in the lake. These blooms coincided with an increase in the population of roach, a fish species that eats zooplankton, which otherwise keep the cyanobacteria and algae in check. To reverse these changes, ecologists removed nearly a million kilograms of fish from the lake between 1989 and 1993, reducing roach abundance by about 80%. At the same time, they added a fourth trophic level by stocking the lake with pike perch, a predatory fish that eats roach. The water became clear, and the last cyanobacterial bloom was in 1989. Ecologists continue to monitor the lake for evidence of cyanobacterial blooms and low oxygen availability, but the lake has remained clear, even though roach removal ended in 1993.

▼ Lake Vesijärvi, Finland

As these examples show, communities vary in their degree of bottom-up and top-down control. To manage agricultural landscapes, parks, reservoirs, and fisheries, we need to understand each particular community's dynamics.

CONCEPT CHECK 54.2

1. What two components contribute to species diversity? Explain how two communities with the same number of species can differ in species diversity.

2. How is a food chain different from a food web?

3. **WHAT IF?** Consider a grassland with five trophic levels: grasses, mice, snakes, raccoons, and bobcats. If you released additional bobcats into the grassland, how would grass biomass change if the bottom-up model applied? If the top-down model applied?

For suggested answers, see Appendix A.

Disturbance influences species diversity and composition

Decades ago, most ecologists favored the traditional view that biological communities are at equilibrium, a more or less stable balance, unless seriously disturbed by human activities. The "balance of nature" view focused on interspecific competition as a key factor determining community composition and maintaining stability in communities. *Stability* in this context refers to a community's tendency to reach and maintain a relatively constant composition of species.

One of the earliest proponents of this view, F. E. Clements, of the Carnegie Institution of Washington, argued in the early 1900s that the community of plants at a site had only one stable equilibrium, a *climax community* controlled solely by climate. According to Clements, biotic interactions caused the species in the community to function as an integrated unit—in effect, as a superorganism. His argument was based on the observation that certain species of plants are consistently found together, such as the oaks, maples, birches, and beeches in deciduous forests of the northeastern United States.

Other ecologists questioned whether most communities were at equilibrium or functioned as integrated units. A. G. Tansley, of Oxford University, challenged the concept of a climax community, arguing that differences in soils, topography, and other factors created many potential communities that were stable within a region. H. A. Gleason, of the University of Chicago, saw communities not as superorganisms but more as chance assemblages of species found together because they happen to have similar abiotic requirements—for example, for temperature, rainfall, and soil type. Gleason and other ecologists also realized that disturbance keeps many communities from reaching a state of equilibrium in species diversity or composition. A **disturbance** is an event, such as a storm, fire, flood, drought, or human activity, that changes a community by removing organisms from it or altering resource availability.

This recent emphasis on change has produced the **nonequilibrium model**, which describes most communities as constantly changing after disturbance. Even relatively stable communities can be rapidly transformed into nonequilibrium communities. Let's examine some of the ways that disturbances influence community structure and composition.

Characterizing Disturbance

The types of disturbances and their frequency and severity vary among communities. Storms disturb almost all communities, even those in the oceans through the action of waves.

Fire is a significant disturbance; in fact, chaparral and some grassland biomes require regular burning to maintain their structure and species composition. Many streams and ponds are disturbed by spring flooding and seasonal drying. A high level of disturbance is generally the result of frequent *and* intense disturbance, while low disturbance levels can result from either a low frequency or low intensity of disturbance.

The **intermediate disturbance hypothesis** states that moderate levels of disturbance foster greater species diversity than do high or low levels of disturbance. High levels of disturbance reduce diversity by creating environmental stresses that exceed the tolerances of many species or by disturbing the community so often that slow-growing or slow-colonizing species are excluded. At the other extreme, low levels of disturbance can reduce species diversity by allowing competitively dominant species to exclude less competitive ones. Meanwhile, intermediate levels of disturbance can foster greater species diversity by opening up habitats for occupation by less competitive species. Such intermediate disturbance levels rarely create conditions so severe that they exceed the environmental tolerances or recovery rates of potential community members.

The intermediate disturbance hypothesis is supported by many terrestrial and aquatic studies. In one study, ecologists in New Zealand compared the richness of invertebrates living in the beds of streams exposed to different frequencies and intensities of flooding (Figure 54.20). When floods occurred either very frequently or rarely, invertebrate richness was low. Frequent floods made it difficult for some species to become established in the streambed, while rare floods resulted in species being displaced by superior competitors. Invertebrate richness peaked in streams that had an intermediate frequency or intensity of flooding, as predicted by the hypothesis.

▲ **Figure 54.20 Testing the intermediate disturbance hypothesis.** Researchers identified the taxa (species or genera) of invertebrates at two locations in each of 27 New Zealand streams. They assessed the intensity of flooding at each location using an index of streambed disturbance. The number of invertebrate taxa peaked where the intensity of flooding was at intermediate levels.

(a) **Soon after fire.** The fire has left a patchy landscape. Note the unburned trees in the far distance.

(b) **One year after fire.** The community has begun to recover. Herbaceous plants, different from those in the former forest, cover the ground.

▲ **Figure 54.21 Recovery following a large-scale disturbance.** The 1988 Yellowstone National Park fires burned large areas of forests dominated by lodgepole pines.

Although moderate levels of disturbance appear to maximize species diversity, small and large disturbances often have important effects on community structure. Small-scale disturbances can create patches of different habitats across a landscape, which help maintain diversity in a community. Large-scale disturbances are also a natural part of many communities. Much of Yellowstone National Park, for example, is dominated by lodgepole pine, a tree species that requires the rejuvenating influence of periodic fires. Lodgepole pine cones remain closed until exposed to intense heat. When a forest fire burns the trees, the cones open and the seeds are released. The new generation of lodgepole pines can then thrive on nutrients released from the burned trees and in the sunlight that is no longer blocked by taller trees.

In the summer of 1988, extensive areas of Yellowstone burned during a severe drought. Monica Turner (see the Unit 8 interview before Chapter 52) and other ecologists showed that many burned areas in the park were already covered with new vegetation just one year later, suggesting that the species in this community are adapted to rapid recovery after fire (Figure 54.21). In fact, large-scale fires have periodically swept through the lodgepole pine forests of Yellowstone and other northern areas for thousands of years. In contrast, more southerly pine forests were historically affected by frequent but low-intensity fires. In these forests, a century of human intervention to suppress small fires has allowed an unnatural buildup of fuels in some places and elevated the risk of large, severe fires to which the species are not adapted.

Studies of the Yellowstone forest community and many others indicate that they are nonequilibrium communities, changing continually because of natural disturbances and the internal processes of growth and reproduction.

Mounting evidence suggests that nonequilibrium conditions are in fact the norm for most communities.

Ecological Succession

Changes in the composition and structure of terrestrial communities are most apparent after some severe disturbance, such as a volcanic eruption or a glacier, strips away all the existing vegetation. The disturbed area may be colonized by a variety of species, which are gradually replaced by other species, which are in turn replaced by still other species—a process called **ecological succession**. When this process begins in a virtually lifeless area where soil has not yet formed, such as on a new volcanic island or on the rubble (moraine) left by a retreating glacier, it is called **primary succession**.

During primary succession, the only life-forms initially present are often prokaryotes and protists. Lichens and mosses, which grow from windblown spores, are commonly the first macroscopic photosynthesizers to colonize such areas. Soil develops gradually as rocks weather and organic matter accumulates from the decomposed remains of the early colonizers. Once soil is present, the lichens and mosses are usually overgrown by grasses, shrubs, and trees that sprout from seeds blown in from nearby areas or carried in by animals. Eventually, an area is colonized by plants that become the community's dominant form of vegetation. Producing such a community through primary succession may take hundreds or thousands of years.

Early-arriving species and later-arriving ones may be linked by one of three key processes. The early arrivals may *facilitate* the appearance of the later species by making the environment more favorable—for example, by increasing

① **Pioneer stage**

② *Dryas* **stage**

④ **Spruce stage**

③ **Alder stage**

▲ **Figure 54.22 Glacial retreat and primary succession at Glacier Bay, Alaska.** The different shades of blue on the map show retreat of the glacier since 1760, based on historical descriptions.

the fertility of the soil. Alternatively, the early species may *inhibit* establishment of the later species, so that successful colonization by later species occurs in spite of, rather than because of, the activities of the early species. Finally, the early species may be completely independent of the later species, which *tolerate* conditions created early in succession but are neither helped nor hindered by early species.

Ecologists have conducted some of the most extensive research on primary succession at Glacier Bay in southeastern Alaska, where glaciers have retreated more than 100 km since 1760 **(Figure 54.22)**. By studying the communities at different distances from the mouth of the bay, ecologists can examine different stages in succession. **①** The exposed glacial moraine is colonized first by pioneering species that include liverworts, mosses, fireweed, scattered *Dryas* (a mat-forming shrub), and willows. **②** After about three decades, *Dryas* dominates the plant community. **③** A few decades later, the area is invaded by alder, which forms dense thickets up to 9 m tall. **④** In the next two centuries, these alder stands are overgrown first by Sitka spruce and later by western hemlock and mountain hemlock. In areas of poor drainage, the forest floor of this spruce-hemlock forest is invaded by sphagnum moss, which holds water and acidifies the soil,

eventually killing the trees. Thus, by about 300 years after glacial retreat, the vegetation consists of sphagnum bogs on the poorly drained flat areas and spruce-hemlock forest on the well-drained slopes.

Succession on glacial moraines is related to changes in soil nutrients and other environmental factors caused by transitions in the vegetation. Because the bare soil after glacial retreat is low in nitrogen content, almost all the pioneer plant species begin succession with poor growth and yellow leaves due to limited nitrogen supply. The exceptions are *Dryas* and alder, which have symbiotic bacteria that fix atmospheric nitrogen (see Chapter 37). Soil nitrogen content increases quickly during the alder stage of succession and keeps increasing during the spruce stage **(Figure 54.23)**. By altering soil properties, pioneer plant species can facilitate colonization by new plant species during succession.

In contrast to primary succession, **secondary succession** occurs when an existing community has been cleared by some disturbance that leaves the soil intact, as in Yellowstone following the 1988 fires (see Figure 54.21). Following the disturbance, the area may return to something like its original state. For instance, in a forested area that has been cleared for farming and later abandoned, the earliest plants

▲ **Figure 54.23 Changes in soil nitrogen content during succession at Glacier Bay.**

MAKE CONNECTIONS *Figures 37.10 and 37.11 illustrate two types of atmospheric nitrogen fixation by prokaryotes. At the earliest stages of primary succession, before any plants are present at a site, which type of nitrogen fixation would occur, and why?*

to recolonize are often herbaceous species that grow from windblown or animal-borne seeds. If the area has not been burned or heavily grazed, woody shrubs may in time replace most of the herbaceous species, and forest trees may eventually replace most of the shrubs.

Human Disturbance

Ecological succession is a response to disturbance of the environment, and the strongest disturbances today are human activities. Agricultural development has disrupted what were once the vast grasslands of the North American prairie. Tropical rain forests are quickly disappearing as a result of clear-cutting for lumber, cattle grazing, and farmland. Centuries of overgrazing and agricultural disturbance have contributed to famine in parts of Africa by turning seasonal grasslands into vast barren areas.

Humans disturb marine ecosystems as well as terrestrial ones. The effects of ocean trawling, where boats drag weighted nets across the seafloor, are similar to those of clear-cutting a forest or plowing a field **(Figure 54.24)**. The trawls scrape and scour corals and other life on the seafloor. In a typical year, ships trawl an area about the size of South America, 150 times larger than the area of forests that are clear-cut annually.

Because disturbance by human activities is often severe, it reduces species diversity in many communities. In Chapter 56, we'll take a closer look at how human-caused disturbance is affecting the diversity of life.

◄ Before trawling

After ► trawling

▲ **Figure 54.24 Disturbance of the ocean floor by trawling.** These photos show the seafloor off northwestern Australia before (top) and after (bottom) deep-sea trawlers have passed.

CONCEPT CHECK 54.3

1. Why do high and low levels of disturbance usually reduce species diversity? Why does an intermediate level of disturbance promote species diversity?

2. During succession, how might the early species facilitate the arrival of other species?

3. **WHAT IF?** Most prairies experience regular fires, typically every few years. If these disturbances were relatively modest, how would the species diversity of a prairie likely be affected if no burning occurred for 100 years? Explain your answer.

For suggested answers, see Appendix A.

CONCEPT 54.4

Biogeographic factors affect community diversity

So far, we have examined relatively small-scale or local factors that influence the diversity of communities, including the effects of species interactions, dominant species, and many types of disturbances. Ecologists also recognize that large-scale biogeographic factors contribute to the tremendous range of diversity observed in biological communities. The contributions of two biogeographic factors in particular—the latitude of a community and the area it occupies—have been investigated for more than a century.

Latitudinal Gradients

In the 1850s, both Charles Darwin and Alfred Wallace pointed out that plant and animal life was generally more abundant and diverse in the tropics than in other parts of the globe. Since that time, many researchers have confirmed this observation. One study found that a 6.6-hectare (1 ha = 10,000 m^2) plot in tropical Malaysia contained 711 tree species, while a 2-ha plot of deciduous forest in Michigan typically contained just 10 to 15 tree species. Many groups of animals show similar latitudinal gradients. For instance, there are more than 200 species of ants in Brazil but only 7 in Alaska.

The two key factors in latitudinal gradients of species richness are probably evolutionary history and climate. Over the course of evolutionary time, species richness may increase in a community as more speciation events occur (see Chapter 24). Tropical communities are generally older than temperate or polar communities, which have repeatedly "started over" after major disturbances from glaciations. Also, the growing season in tropical forests is about five times as long as in the tundra communities of high latitudes. In effect, biological time runs about five times as fast in the tropics as near the poles, so intervals between speciation events are shorter in the tropics.

Climate is the other key factor in latitudinal gradients of richness and diversity. In terrestrial communities, the two main climatic factors correlated with diversity are sunlight and precipitation, both of which are relatively abundant in the tropics. These factors can be considered together by measuring a community's rate of **evapotranspiration**, the evaporation of water from soil and plants. Evapotranspiration, a function of solar radiation, temperature, and water availability, is much higher in hot areas with abundant rainfall than in areas with low temperatures or low precipitation. *Potential evapotranspiration*, a measure of potential water loss that assumes that water is readily available, is determined by the amount of solar radiation and temperature and is highest in regions where both are plentiful. The species richness of plants and animals correlates with both measures, as shown for vertebrates and potential evapotranspiration in **Figure 54.25**.

Area Effects

In 1807, naturalist and explorer Alexander von Humboldt described one of the first patterns of species richness to be recognized, the **species-area curve**: All other factors being equal, the larger the geographic area of a community, the more species it has, in part because larger areas offer a greater diversity of habitats and microhabitats. In conservation biology, developing species-area curves for key taxa in a community helps ecologists predict how the loss of a given area of habitat will affect the community's diversity.

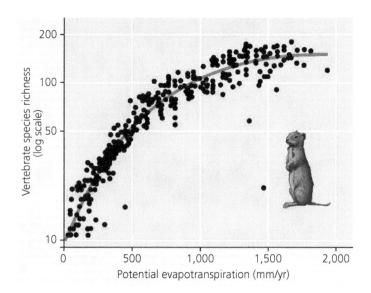

▲ **Figure 54.25 Energy, water, and species richness.** Vertebrate species richness in North America increases most predictably with potential evapotranspiration, expressed as rainfall equivalents (mm/yr).

The first, and still widely used, mathematical description of the species-area relationship was proposed a century ago:

$$S = cA^z$$

where S is the number of species found in a habitat, c is a constant, and A is the area of the habitat. The exponent z tells you how many more species should be found in a habitat as its area increases. In a log-log plot of S versus A, z is the slope of the line through the data points. A value of $z = 1$ would indicate a linear relationship between species number and area, meaning that ten times as many species would be found in a habitat that has ten times the area.

In the 1960s, Robert MacArthur and E. O. Wilson tested the predictions of the species-area relationship by examining the number of animals and plants on different island chains. As one example, in the Sunda Islands of Malaysia, they found that the number of bird species increased with island size, with a value of $z = 0.4$ **(Figure 54.26)**. These and other studies have shown that z is usually between 0.2 and 0.4.

Although the slopes of different species-area curves vary, the basic concept of diversity increasing with increasing area applies in many situations, from surveys of ant diversity in New Guinea to studies of plant species richness on islands of different sizes.

Island Equilibrium Model

Because of their isolation and limited size, islands provide excellent opportunities for studying the biogeographic factors that affect the species diversity of communities. By "islands," we mean not only oceanic islands, but also habitat

▼ Figure 54.26 Inquiry

How does species richness relate to area?

Field Study Ecologists Robert MacArthur and E. O. Wilson studied the number of bird species on the Sunda Islands of Malaysia in relation to the area of the different islands.

Results

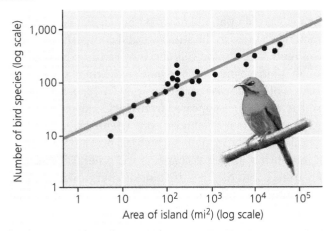

Conclusion Bird species richness increases with island size. The slope of the best-fit line through the data points (the parameter *z*) is about 0.4.

Source: R. H. MacArthur and E. O. Wilson, An equilibrium theory of insular zoogeography, *Evolution* 17:373–387 (1963).

WHAT IF? *Four islands in this study, ranging in area from about 100 to 800 square miles, each contained about 100 bird species. What does such variation tell you about the simple assumptions of the island equilibrium model?*

islands on land, such as lakes, mountain peaks separated by lowlands, or habitat fragments—any patch surrounded by an environment not suitable for the "island" species. While studying the species-area relationship, MacArthur and Wilson developed a general model of island biogeography, identifying the key determinants of species diversity on an island with a given set of physical characteristics.

Consider a newly formed oceanic island that receives colonizing species from a distant mainland. Two factors that determine the number of species on the island are the rate at which new species immigrate to the island and the rate at which species become extinct on the island. At any given time, an island's immigration and extinction rates are affected by the number of species already present. As the number of species on the island increases, the immigration rate of new species decreases, because any individual reaching the island is less likely to represent a species that is not already present. At the same time, as more species inhabit an island, extinction rates on the island increase because of the greater likelihood of competitive exclusion.

▲ **Figure 54.27 A mangrove island in the Florida Keys.** Like this one, most of the islands that Simberloff studied were small, consisting of one or a few mangrove trees. Their small size made it possible for Simberloff to cover each island with a tent to contain the fumigant he used in his experiment.

Two physical features of the island further affect immigration and extinction rates: its size and its distance from the mainland. Small islands generally have lower immigration rates because potential colonizers are less likely to reach a small island than a large one. Small islands also have higher extinction rates because they generally contain fewer resources, have less diverse habitats, and have smaller population sizes. Distance from the mainland is also important; a closer island generally has a higher immigration rate and a lower extinction rate than one farther away. Arriving colonists help sustain the presence of a species on a near island and prevent its extinction.

MacArthur and Wilson's model is called the *island equilibrium model* because an equilibrium will eventually be reached where the rate of species immigration equals the rate of species extinction. The number of species at this equilibrium point is correlated with the island's size and distance from the mainland. Like any ecological equilibrium, this species equilibrium is dynamic; immigration and extinction continue, and the exact species composition may change over time.

MacArthur and Wilson's studies of the diversity of animals and plants on many island chains support the prediction that species richness increases with island size, in keeping with the island equilibrium model (see Figure 54.26). Species counts also fit the prediction that the number of species decreases with increasing remoteness of the island.

In 1967, Dan Simberloff, then a graduate student with E. O. Wilson, tested the island equilibrium model in an experiment on six small mangrove islands in the Florida Keys **(Figure 54.27)**. He first painstakingly identified and counted all of the arthropod species on each island. As predicted by the model, he found more species on islands that were larger and closer to the mainland. He then fumigated four of the islands with methyl bromide to kill all of the arthropods. Within a year or two, the arthropod species richness on these islands increased to near their pre-fumigation values. The island closest to the mainland recovered first, while the island farthest from the mainland was the slowest to recover.

Over long periods, disturbances such as storms, adaptive evolutionary changes, and speciation generally alter the species composition and community structure on islands. Nonetheless, the island equilibrium model is widely applied in ecology. Conservation biologists in particular use it when designing habitat reserves or establishing a starting point for predicting the effects of habitat loss on species diversity.

CONCEPT CHECK 54.4

1. Describe two hypotheses that explain why species diversity is greater in tropical regions than in temperate and polar regions.

2. Describe how an island's size and distance from the mainland affect the island's species richness.

3. WHAT IF? Based on MacArthur and Wilson's island equilibrium model, how would you expect the richness of birds on islands to compare with the richness of snakes and lizards? Explain.

For suggested answers, see Appendix A.

CONCEPT 54.5

Pathogens alter community structure locally and globally

Now that we have examined several important factors that structure biological communities, we'll finish the chapter by examining community interactions involving **pathogens**—disease-causing microorganisms, viruses, viroids, or prions. (Viroids and prions are infectious RNA molecules and proteins, respectively; see Chapter 19.) Scientists have only recently come to appreciate how universal the effects of pathogens are in structuring ecological communities.

Pathogens produce especially clear effects when they are introduced into new habitats, as in the case of chestnut blight and the fungus that causes it (see Concept 54.2). A pathogen can be particularly virulent in a new habitat because new host populations have not had a chance to become resistant to the pathogen through natural selection. The invasive chestnut blight fungus had far stronger effects on the American chestnut, for instance, than it had on Asian chestnut species in the fungus's native habitat. Humans are similarly vulnerable to the effects of emerging diseases spread by our increasingly global economy. Ecologists are applying ecological knowledge to help track and control the pathogens that cause such diseases.

Pathogens and Community Structure

In spite of the potential of pathogens to limit populations, pathogens have until recently been the subject of relatively few ecological studies. This imbalance is now being addressed as events highlight the ecological importance of disease.

Coral reef communities are increasingly susceptible to the influence of newly discovered pathogens. White-band disease, caused by an unknown pathogen, has resulted in dramatic changes in the structure and composition of Caribbean reefs. The disease kills corals by causing their tissue to slough off in a band from the base to the tip of the branches. Because of the disease, staghorn coral (*Acropora cervicornis*) has virtually disappeared from the Caribbean since the 1980s. Populations of elkhorn coral (*Acropora palmata*) have also been decimated. Such corals provide key habitat for lobsters as well as snappers and other fish species. When the corals die, they are quickly overgrown by algae. Surgeonfish and other herbivores that feed on algae come to dominate the fish community. Eventually, the corals topple because of damage from storms and other disturbances. The complex, three-dimensional structure of the reef disappears, and diversity plummets.

Pathogens also influence community structure in terrestrial ecosystems. In the forests and savannas of California, trees of several species are dying from sudden oak death (SOD). This recently discovered disease is caused by the fungus-like protist *Phytophthora ramorum* (see Chapter 28). SOD was first described in California in 1995, when hikers noticed trees dying around San Francisco Bay. By 2012, it had spread more than 1,000 km, from the central California coast to southern Oregon, and killed more than a million oaks and other trees. The loss of the oaks has led to the decreased abundance of at least five bird species, including the acorn woodpecker and the oak titmouse, that rely on oaks for food and habitat.

Human activities are transporting pathogens around the world at unprecedented rates. Genetic analyses using simple sequence DNA (see Chapter 21) suggest that *P. ramorum* likely came to North America from Europe through the horticulture trade. Similarly, the pathogens that cause human diseases are spread by our global economy. H1N1, the virus that causes "swine flu" in humans, was first detected in Veracruz, Mexico, in early 2009. It quickly spread around the world when infected individuals flew on airplanes to other countries. By 2011, the world's first flu pandemic in 40 years had killed more than 18,000 people.

Community Ecology and Zoonotic Diseases

Three-quarters of emerging human diseases and many of the most devastating diseases are caused by **zoonotic**

pathogens—those that are transferred to humans from other animals, either through direct contact with an infected animal or by means of an intermediate species, called a **vector**. The vectors that spread zoonotic diseases are often parasites, including ticks, lice, and mosquitoes.

Identifying the community of hosts and vectors for a pathogen can help prevent illnesses such as Lyme disease, which is spread by ticks. For years, scientists thought that the primary host for the Lyme pathogen was the white-footed mouse. When researchers vaccinated mice against Lyme disease and released them into the wild, however, the number of infected ticks hardly changed. This prompted biologists to look for other hosts for the Lyme pathogen. They first trapped individuals of 11 potential host species in the field and measured the density of larval ticks on the animals (Figure 54.28). They found that each host species transmitted to the ticks a unique set of alleles of a gene that encodes a protein on the pathogen's outer surface. The researchers then collected ticks in the field that were no longer attached to any host and used the genetic database to identify their former hosts. Surprisingly, two inconspicuous shrew species were the source for more than half the ticks collected in the field. Identifying the dominant hosts for a pathogen provides information that may be used to control the hosts most responsible for spreading diseases.

Ecologists also use their knowledge of community interactions to track the spread of zoonotic diseases. One example, avian flu, is caused by highly contagious viruses transmitted through the saliva and feces of birds (see Chapter 19). Most of these viruses affect wild birds mildly, but

▲ **Figure 54.28 Identifying Lyme disease host species.** A student researcher collects ticks from a white-footed mouse. Genetic analysis of the ticks from a variety of hosts enables scientists to identify the former hosts of other ticks collected in the field.

MAKE CONNECTIONS *Concept 23.1 describes genetic variation between populations. How might genetic variation between shrew populations in different locations affect the results of the Lyme disease study described in the text?*

▲ **Figure 54.29 Tracking avian flu.** Graduate student Travis Booms, of Boise State University, bands a young gyrfalcon as part of a project to monitor the spread of avian flu.

they often cause stronger symptoms in domesticated birds, the most common source of human infections. Since 2003, one particular viral strain, called H5N1, has killed hundreds of millions of poultry and more than 300 people.

Control programs that quarantine domestic birds or monitor their transport may be ineffective if avian flu spreads naturally through the movements of wild birds. From 2003 to 2006, the H5N1 strain spread rapidly from southeast Asia into Europe and Africa, but by 2012 it had not appeared in Australia or the Americas. The most likely place for infected wild birds to enter the Americas is Alaska, the entry point for ducks, geese, and shorebirds that migrate across the Bering Sea from Asia every year. Ecologists are studying the spread of the virus by trapping and testing migrating and resident birds in Alaska (Figure 54.29). These ecological detectives are trying to catch the first wave of the disease entering North America.

Community ecology provides the foundation for understanding the life cycles of pathogens and their interactions with hosts. Pathogen interactions are also greatly influenced by changes in the physical environment. To control pathogens and the diseases they cause, scientists need an ecosystem perspective—an intimate knowledge of how the pathogens interact with other species and with all aspects of their environment. Ecosystems are the subject of Chapter 55.

CONCEPT CHECK **54.5**

1. What are pathogens?
2. **WHAT IF?** Rabies, a viral disease in mammals, is not currently found in the British Isles. If you were in charge of disease control there, what practical approaches might you employ to keep the rabies virus from reaching these islands?

For suggested answers, see Appendix A.

SUMMARY OF KEY CONCEPTS

CONCEPT 54.1

Community interactions are classified by whether they help, harm, or have no effect on the species involved (pp. 1209–1215)

- A variety of **interspecific interactions** affect the survival and reproduction of the species that engage in them. These interactions include interspecific competition, predation, herbivory, symbiosis, and facilitation.
- Competitive exclusion states that two species competing for the same resource cannot coexist permanently in the same place. **Resource partitioning** is the differentiation of **ecological niches** that enables species to coexist in a community.

Interspecific Interaction	Description
Interspecific competition (–/–)	Two or more species compete for a resource that is in short supply.
Predation (+/–)	One species, the predator, kills and eats the other, the prey. Predation has led to diverse adaptations, including mimicry.
Herbivory (+/–)	An herbivore eats part of a plant or alga.
Symbiosis	Individuals of two or more species live in close contact with one another. Symbiosis includes parasitism, mutualism, and commensalism.
Parasitism (+/–)	The **parasite** derives its nourishment from a second organism, its **host**, which is harmed.
Mutualism (+/+)	Both species benefit from the interaction.
Commensalism (+/0)	One species benefits from the interaction, while the other is unaffected by it.
Facilitation (+/+ or 0/+)	Species have positive effects on the survival and reproduction of other species without the intimate contact of a symbiosis.

? *Give an example of a pair of species that exhibit each interaction listed in the table above.*

CONCEPT 54.2

Diversity and trophic structure characterize biological communities (pp. 1216–1221)

- **Species diversity** measures the number of species in a community—its **species richness**—and their **relative abundance**.
- More diverse communities typically produce more **biomass** and show less year-to-year variation in growth than less diverse communities and are more resistant to invasion by exotic species.
- **Trophic structure** is a key factor in community dynamics. **Food chains** link the trophic levels from producers to top carnivores. Branching food chains and complex trophic interactions form **food webs**.

- **Dominant species** are the most abundant species in a community. **Keystone species** are usually less abundant species that exert a disproportionate influence on community structure.
- The **bottom-up model** proposes a unidirectional influence from lower to higher trophic levels, in which nutrients and other abiotic factors primarily determine community structure. **The top-down model** proposes that control of each trophic level comes from the trophic level above, with the result that predators control herbivores, which in turn control primary producers.

? *Based on indexes such as Shannon diversity, is a community of higher species richness always more diverse than a community of lower species richness? Explain.*

CONCEPT 54.3

Disturbance influences species diversity and composition (pp. 1222–1225)

- Increasing evidence suggests that **disturbance** and lack of equilibrium, rather than stability and equilibrium, are the norm for most communities. According to the **intermediate disturbance hypothesis**, moderate levels of disturbance can foster higher species diversity than can low or high levels of disturbance.
- **Ecological succession** is the sequence of community and ecosystem changes after a disturbance. **Primary succession** occurs where no soil exists when succession begins; **secondary succession** begins in an area where soil remains after a disturbance.

? *Is the disturbance pictured in Figure 54.24 more likely to initiate primary or secondary succession? Explain.*

CONCEPT 54.4

Biogeographic factors affect community diversity (pp. 1225–1228)

- Species richness generally declines along a latitudinal gradient from the tropics to the poles. The greater age of tropical environments may account for their greater species richness.
- Species richness is directly related to a community's geographic size, a principle formalized in the **species-area curve**.
- Species richness on islands depends on island size and distance from the mainland. The island equilibrium model maintains that species richness on an ecological island reaches an equilibrium where new immigrations are balanced by extinctions.

? *How have periods of glaciation influenced latitudinal patterns of diversity?*

CONCEPT 54.5

Pathogens alter community structure locally and globally (pp. 1228–1229)

- Recent work has highlighted the role that **pathogens** play in structuring terrestrial and marine communities.
- **Zoonotic pathogens** are transferred from other animals to humans and cause the largest class of emerging human diseases. Community ecology provides the framework for identifying key species interactions associated with such pathogens and for helping us track and control their spread.

? *In what way can a **vector** of a zoonotic pathogen differ from a host of the pathogen?*

TEST YOUR UNDERSTANDING

LEVEL 1: KNOWLEDGE/COMPREHENSION

1. The feeding relationships among the species in a community determine the community's
   a. secondary succession.
   c. species richness.
   b. ecological niche.
   d. trophic structure.

2. The principle of competitive exclusion states that
   a. two species cannot coexist in the same habitat.
   b. competition between two species always causes extinction or emigration of one species.
   c. two species that have exactly the same niche cannot coexist in a community.
   d. two species will stop reproducing until one species leaves the habitat.

3. Based on the intermediate disturbance hypothesis, a community's species diversity is increased by
   a. frequent massive disturbance.
   b. stable conditions with no disturbance.
   c. moderate levels of disturbance.
   d. human intervention to eliminate disturbance.

4. According to the island equilibrium model, species richness would be greatest on an island that is
   a. large and remote.
   c. large and close to a mainland.
   b. small and remote.
   d. small and close to a mainland.

LEVEL 2: APPLICATION/ANALYSIS

5. Predators that are keystone species can maintain species diversity in a community if they
   a. competitively exclude other predators.
   b. prey on the community's dominant species.
   c. reduce the number of disruptions in the community.
   d. prey only on the least abundant species in the community.

6. Food chains are sometimes short because
   a. only a single species of herbivore feeds on each plant species.
   b. local extinction of a species causes extinction of the other species in its food chain.
   c. most of the energy in a trophic level is lost as energy passes to the next higher level.
   d. most producers are inedible.

7. Which of the following could qualify as a top-down control on a grassland community?
   a. limitation of plant biomass by rainfall amount
   b. influence of temperature on competition among plants
   c. influence of soil nutrients on the abundance of grasses versus wildflowers
   d. effect of grazing intensity by bison on plant species diversity

8. The most plausible hypothesis to explain why species richness is higher in tropical than in temperate regions is that
   a. tropical communities are younger.
   b. tropical regions generally have more available water and higher levels of solar radiation.
   c. higher temperatures cause more rapid speciation.
   d. diversity increases as evapotranspiration decreases.

9. Community 1 contains 100 individuals distributed among four species: 5A, 5B, 85C, and 5D. Community 2 contains 100 individuals distributed among three species: 30A, 40B, and 30C. Calculate the Shannon diversity (H) for each community. Which community is more diverse?

LEVEL 3: SYNTHESIS/EVALUATION

10. **DRAW IT** An important species in the Chesapeake Bay estuary (see Figure 54.16) is the blue crab (*Callinectes sapidus*). It is an omnivore, eating eelgrass and other primary producers as well as clams. It is also a cannibal. In turn, the crabs are eaten by humans and by the endangered Kemp's Ridley sea turtle. Based on this information, draw a food web that includes the blue crab. Assuming that the top-down model holds for this system, what would happen to the abundance of eelgrass if humans stopped eating blue crabs?

11. **EVOLUTION CONNECTION**
    Explain why adaptations of particular organisms to interspecific competition may not necessarily represent instances of character displacement. What would a researcher have to demonstrate about two competing species to make a convincing case for character displacement?

12. **SCIENTIFIC INQUIRY**
    An ecologist studying desert plants performed the following experiment. She staked out two identical plots, containing sagebrush plants and small annual wildflowers. She found the same five wildflower species in roughly equal numbers on both plots. She then enclosed one plot with a fence to keep out kangaroo rats, the most common grain-eaters of the area. After two years, four of the wildflower species were no longer present in the fenced plot, but one species had become much more abundant. The control plot had not changed in species diversity. Using the principles of community ecology, propose a hypothesis to explain her results. What additional evidence would support your hypothesis?

13. **WRITE ABOUT A THEME: INTERACTIONS**
    In Batesian mimicry, a palatable species gains protection by mimicking an unpalatable one. Imagine that individuals of a palatable, brightly colored fly species are blown to three remote islands. The first island has no predators of that species; the second has predators but no similarly colored, unpalatable species; and the third has both predators and a similarly colored, unpalatable species. In a short essay (100–150 words), predict what might happen to the coloration of the palatable species on each island through evolutionary time if coloration is a genetically controlled trait. Explain your predictions.

14. **SYNTHESIZE YOUR KNOWLEDGE**

Describe two types of interspecific interactions that you can observe in this photo. What morphological adaptation can be seen in the species that is at the highest trophic level in this scene?

For selected answers, see Appendix A.

MasteringBiology®

Students Go to **MasteringBiology** for assignments, the eText, and the Study Area with practice tests, animations, and activities.

Instructors Go to **MasteringBiology** for automatically graded tutorials and questions that you can assign to your students, plus Instructor Resources.

55

Ecosystems and Restoration Ecology

▲ **Figure 55.1 How can a fox transform a grassland into tundra?**

Transformed to Tundra

The arctic fox (*Vulpes lagopus*) is a predator native to arctic regions of North America, Europe, and Asia (**Figure 55.1**). Valued for its fur, it was introduced onto hundreds of islands between Alaska and Russia a century ago in an effort to establish populations that could be easily harvested. The introduction had a surprising effect—it transformed many habitats on the islands from grassland to tundra. How did this remarkable change come about? The foxes fed on seabirds, decreasing their density almost 100-fold compared to that on fox-free islands. Fewer seabirds meant less bird guano, the primary source of nutrients for plants on the islands. The reduction in nutrient availability in turn favored slower-growing forbs and shrubs typical of tundra instead of grasses and sedges, which require more nutrients. To test this explanation, researchers added fertilizer to plots of tundra on one of the fox-infested islands in 2001. Three years later, the fertilized plots had turned back into grassland.

Each of these islands and the community of organisms on it make up an **ecosystem**,

◀ An island ecosystem

▼ A desert spring ecosystem

▲ **Figure 55.2 Ecosystems at different scales.**

the sum of all the organisms living in a given area and the abiotic factors with which they interact. An ecosystem can encompass a vast area, such as a lake, forest, or island, or a microcosm, such as the space under a fallen log or a desert spring **(Figure 55.2).** As with populations and communities, the boundaries of ecosystems are not always discrete. Many ecologists view the entire biosphere as a global ecosystem, a composite of all the local ecosystems on Earth.

Regardless of an ecosystem's size, two key ecosystem processes cannot be fully described by population or community phenomena: energy flow and chemical cycling. Energy enters most ecosystems as sunlight. It is converted to chemical energy by autotrophs, passed to heterotrophs in the organic compounds of food, and dissipated as heat. Chemical elements, such as carbon and nitrogen, are cycled among abiotic and biotic components of the ecosystem. Photosynthetic and chemosynthetic organisms take up these elements in inorganic form from the air, soil, and water and incorporate them into their biomass, some of which is consumed by animals. The elements are returned in inorganic form to the environment by the metabolism of plants and animals and by organisms such as bacteria and fungi that break down organic wastes and dead organisms.

Both energy and matter are transformed in ecosystems through photosynthesis and feeding relationships. But unlike matter, energy cannot be recycled. An ecosystem must be powered by a continuous influx of energy from an external source—in most cases, the sun. Energy flows through ecosystems, whereas matter cycles within and through them.

Resources critical to human survival and welfare, ranging from the food we eat to the oxygen we breathe, are products of ecosystem processes. In this chapter, we'll explore the dynamics of energy flow and chemical cycling, emphasizing the results of ecosystem experiments. One way to study ecosystem processes is to alter environmental factors, such as temperature or the abundance of nutrients, and measure how ecosystems respond. We'll also consider some of the impacts of human activities on energy flow and chemical cycling. Finally, we'll explore the growing science of restoration ecology, which focuses on returning degraded ecosystems to a more natural state.

CONCEPT 55.1

Physical laws govern energy flow and chemical cycling in ecosystems

Cells transform energy and matter, subject to the laws of thermodynamics (see Concept 8.1). Cell biologists study these transformations within organelles and cells and measure the amounts of energy and matter that cross the cells' boundaries. Ecosystem ecologists do the same thing, except in their case the "cell" is a complete ecosystem. By studying the dynamics of populations (see Chapter 53) and by grouping the species in a community into trophic levels of feeding relationships (see Chapter 54), ecologists can follow the transformations of energy in an ecosystem and map the movements of chemical elements.

Conservation of Energy

Because ecosystem ecologists study the interactions of organisms with the physical environment, many ecosystem approaches are based on laws of physics and chemistry. The first law of thermodynamics states that energy cannot be created or destroyed but only transferred or transformed (see Concept 8.1). Plants and other photosynthetic organisms convert solar energy to chemical energy, but the total amount of energy does not change: The amount of energy stored in organic molecules must equal the total solar energy intercepted by the plant minus the amounts reflected and dissipated as heat. Ecosystem ecologists often measure transfers within and across ecosystems, in part to understand how many organisms a habitat can support and the amount of food humans can harvest from a site.

One implication of the second law of thermodynamics, which states that every exchange of energy increases the entropy of the universe, is that energy conversions are inefficient. Some energy is always lost as heat (see Concept 8.1). We can measure the efficiency of ecological energy conversions just as we measure the efficiency of lightbulbs and car engines. Because energy flowing through ecosystems is ultimately dissipated into space as heat, most ecosystems would vanish if the sun were not continuously providing energy to Earth.

Conservation of Mass

Matter, like energy, cannot be created or destroyed. This **law of conservation of mass** is as important for ecosystems as the laws of thermodynamics are. Because mass is conserved, we can determine how much of a chemical element cycles within an ecosystem or is gained or lost by that ecosystem over time.

Unlike energy, chemical elements are continually recycled within ecosystems. A carbon atom in CO_2 is released from the soil by a decomposer, taken up by a grass through photosynthesis, consumed by a grazing animal, and returned to the soil in the animal's waste. Measurement and analysis of chemical cycling are important in ecosystem ecology.

Although most elements are not gained or lost on a global scale, they can be gained by or lost from a particular ecosystem. In a forest, most mineral nutrients—the essential elements that plants obtain from soil—typically enter as dust or as solutes dissolved in rainwater or leached from rocks in the ground. Nitrogen is also supplied through the biological process of nitrogen fixation (see Figure 37.10). In terms of losses, some elements return to the atmosphere as gases, and others are carried out of the ecosystem by moving water or by wind. Like organisms, ecosystems are open systems, absorbing energy and mass and releasing heat and waste products.

In nature, most gains and losses to ecosystems are small compared to the amounts recycled within them. Still, the balance between inputs and outputs determines whether an ecosystem is a source or a sink for a given element. If a mineral nutrient's outputs exceed its inputs, it will eventually limit production in that system. Human activities often change the balance of inputs and outputs considerably, as we'll see later in this chapter and in Chapter 56.

Energy, Mass, and Trophic Levels

Ecologists group species into trophic levels based on their main source of nutrition and energy (see Concept 54.2). The trophic level that ultimately supports all others consists of autotrophs, also called the **primary producers** of the ecosystem. Most autotrophs are photosynthetic organisms that use light energy to synthesize sugars and other organic compounds, which they use as fuel for cellular respiration and as building material for growth. The most common autotrophs are plants, algae, and photosynthetic prokaryotes, although chemosynthetic prokaryotes are the primary producers in ecosystems such as deep-sea hydrothermal vents (see Figure 52.14) and places deep under the ground or ice.

Organisms in trophic levels above the primary producers are heterotrophs, which depend directly or indirectly on the outputs of primary producers for their source of energy. Herbivores, which eat plants and other primary producers,

▼ Fungi decomposing a dead tree

▲ Rod-shaped and spherical bacteria in compost (colorized SEM)

▲ **Figure 55.3** Detritivores.

are **primary consumers**. Carnivores that eat herbivores are **secondary consumers**, and carnivores that eat other carnivores are **tertiary consumers**.

Another group of heterotrophs is the **detritivores**, or **decomposers**, terms used synonymously in this text to refer to consumers that get their energy from detritus. **Detritus** is nonliving organic material, such as the remains of dead organisms, feces, fallen leaves, and wood. Many detritivores are in turn eaten by secondary and tertiary consumers. Two important groups of detritivores are prokaryotes and fungi **(Figure 55.3)**. These organisms secrete enzymes that digest organic material; they then absorb the breakdown products, linking the consumers and primary producers in an ecosystem. In a forest, for instance, birds eat earthworms that have been feeding on leaf litter and its associated prokaryotes and fungi.

Detritivores also play a critical role in recycling chemical elements to primary producers. They convert organic matter from all trophic levels to inorganic compounds usable by primary producers, closing the loop of an ecosystem's chemical cycling. Producers recycle these elements into organic compounds. If decomposition stopped, life would cease as detritus piled up and the supply of ingredients needed to synthesize organic matter was exhausted. **Figure 55.4** summarizes the trophic relationships in an ecosystem.

CONCEPT CHECK **55.1**

1. Why is the transfer of energy in an ecosystem referred to as energy flow, not energy cycling?

2. **WHAT IF?** You are studying nitrogen cycling on the Serengeti Plain in Africa. During your experiment, a herd of migrating wildebeests grazes through your study plot. What would you need to know to measure their effect on nitrogen balance in the plot?

3. **MAKE CONNECTIONS** How does the second law of thermodynamics explain why an ecosystem's energy supply must be continually replenished (see Concept 8.1)?

For suggested answers, see Appendix A.

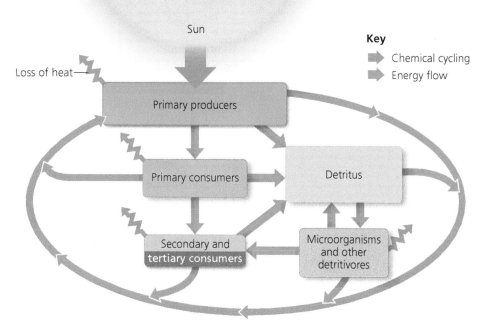

► **Figure 55.4 An overview of energy and nutrient dynamics in an ecosystem.** Energy enters, flows through, and exits an ecosystem, whereas chemical nutrients cycle primarily within it. In this generalized scheme, energy (dark orange arrows) enters from the sun as radiation, moves as chemical energy transfers through the food web, and exits as heat radiated into space. Most transfers of nutrients (blue arrows) through the trophic levels lead eventually to detritus; the nutrients then cycle back to the primary producers.

Key

⟹ Chemical cycling
⟹ Energy flow

Energy and other limiting factors control primary production in ecosystems

The theme of energy transfer underlies all biological interactions (see Concept 1.1). In most ecosystems, the amount of light energy converted to chemical energy—in the form of organic compounds—by autotrophs during a given time period is the ecosystem's **primary production**. These photosynthetic products are the starting point for most studies of ecosystem metabolism and energy flow. In ecosystems where the primary producers are chemoautotrophs, the initial energy input is chemical, and the initial products are the organic compounds synthesized by the microorganisms.

Ecosystem Energy Budgets

In most ecosystems, primary producers use light energy to synthesize energy-rich organic molecules, and consumers acquire their organic fuels secondhand (or even third- or fourthhand) through food webs (see Figure 54.15). Therefore, the total amount of photosynthetic production sets the spending limit for the entire ecosystem's energy budget.

The Global Energy Budget

Each day, Earth's atmosphere is bombarded by about 10^{22} joules of solar radiation (1 J = 0.239 cal). This is enough energy to supply the demands of the entire human population for approximately 20 years at 2010 energy consumption levels. The intensity of the solar energy striking Earth varies with latitude, with the tropics receiving the greatest input (see Figure 52.3). Most incoming solar radiation is absorbed, scattered, or reflected by clouds and dust in the atmosphere. The amount of solar radiation that ultimately reaches Earth's

surface limits the possible photosynthetic output of ecosystems. Only a small fraction of the sunlight that reaches Earth's surface is actually used in photosynthesis. Much of the radiation strikes materials that don't photosynthesize, such as ice and soil. Of the radiation that does reach photosynthetic organisms, only certain wavelengths are absorbed by photosynthetic pigments (see Figure 10.9); the rest is transmitted, reflected, or lost as heat. As a result, only about 1% of the visible light that strikes photosynthetic organisms is converted to chemical energy. Nevertheless, Earth's primary producers create about 150 billion metric tons (1.50×10^{14} kg) of organic material each year.

Gross and Net Production

Total primary production in an ecosystem is known as that ecosystem's **gross primary production (GPP)**—the amount of energy from light (or chemicals, in chemoautotrophic systems) converted to the chemical energy of organic molecules per unit time. Not all of this production is stored as organic material in the primary producers because they use some of the molecules as fuel in their own cellular respiration. **Net primary production (NPP)** is equal to gross primary production minus the energy used by the primary producers for their "autotrophic respiration" (R_a):

$$NPP = GPP - R_a$$

On average, NPP is about one-half of GPP. To ecologists, NPP is the key measurement because it represents the storage of chemical energy that will be available to consumers in the ecosystem.

Net primary production can be expressed as energy per unit area per unit time [J/(m$^2 \cdot$yr)] or as biomass (mass of vegetation) added per unit area per unit time [g/(m$^2 \cdot$yr)]. (Note that biomass is usually expressed in terms of the dry mass of organic material.) An ecosystem's NPP should not be confused with the total biomass of photosynthetic autotrophs present, a measure called the *standing crop*. The net primary production is the amount of *new* biomass added in a given period of time. Although a forest has a large standing crop, its NPP may actually be less than that of some grasslands; grasslands do not accumulate as much biomass as forests because animals consume the plants rapidly and because grasses and herbs decompose more quickly than trees do.

Satellites provide a powerful tool for studying global patterns of primary production (**Figure 55.5**). Images produced from satellite data show that different ecosystems vary considerably in their NPP. Tropical rain forests are among the most productive terrestrial ecosystems and contribute a large portion of the planet's NPP. Estuaries and coral reefs also have very high NPP, but their contribution to the global total is smaller because these ecosystems cover only about one-tenth the area covered by tropical rain forests. In contrast, while the open oceans are relatively unproductive (**Figure 55.6**), their vast size means that together they contribute as much global NPP as terrestrial systems do.

Whereas NPP can be stated as the amount of new biomass added in a given period of time, **net ecosystem production (NEP)** is a measure of the *total biomass accumulation* during that time. Net ecosystem production is defined as gross primary production minus the total respiration of all organisms in the system (R_T)—not just primary producers, as for the calculation of NPP, but decomposers and other heterotrophs as well:

$$NEP = GPP - R_T$$

NEP is useful to ecologists because its value determines whether an ecosystem is gaining or losing carbon over time. A forest may have a positive NPP but still lose carbon if heterotrophs release it as CO_2 more quickly than primary producers incorporate it into organic compounds.

The most common way to estimate NEP is to measure the net flux (flow) of CO_2 or O_2 entering or leaving the ecosystem. If more CO_2 enters than leaves, the system is storing carbon. Because O_2 release is directly coupled to photosynthesis and respiration (see Figure 9.2), a system that is giving

▼ **Figure 55.5**   Research Method

Determining Primary Production with Satellites

Application Because chlorophyll captures visible light (see Figure 10.9), photosynthetic organisms absorb more light at visible wavelengths (about 380–750 nm) than at near-infrared wavelengths (750–1,100 nm). Scientists use this difference in absorption to estimate the rate of photosynthesis in different regions of the globe using satellites.

Technique Most satellites determine what they "see" by comparing the ratios of wavelengths reflected back to them. Vegetation reflects much more near-infrared radiation than visible radiation, producing a reflectance pattern very different from that of snow, clouds, soil, and liquid water.

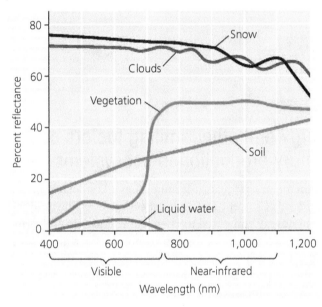

Results Scientists use the satellite data to help produce maps of primary production like the one in Figure 55.6.

off O_2 is also storing carbon. On land, ecologists typically measure only the net flux of CO_2 from ecosystems because detecting small changes in O_2 flux in a large atmospheric O_2 pool is difficult.

Recent research has revealed surprisingly high NEP in some of the nutrient-poor waters that cover much of the

▶ **Figure 55.6 Global net primary production.** The map is based on satellite-collected data, such as amount of sunlight absorbed by vegetation. Note that tropical land areas have the highest rates of production (yellow and red on the map).

Net primary production [kg carbon/(m². yr)]

? *Does this map accurately reflect the importance of some highly productive habitats, such as wetlands, coral reefs, and coastal zones? Explain.*

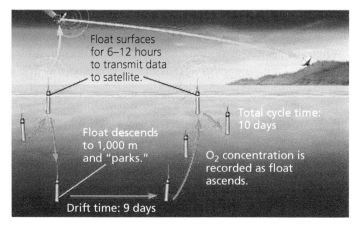

▲ **Figure 55.7 Ocean production revealed.** Oxygen sensors deployed on floats record and transmit data that can be used to calculate net ecosystem production (NEP).

MAKE CONNECTIONS *Consider the role of photosynthetic protists as producers in aquatic ecosystems. (Review the discussion in Concept 28.6.) What factors in addition to light availability are likely to limit primary production in the oceans?*

open ocean. In 2008, scientists measured NEP in the Pacific Ocean using high-resolution oxygen sensors (Figure 55.7). As the floats drifted with the current, they repeatedly moved between the ocean surface and a depth of 1,000 m, recording the O_2 concentration in the water as they ascended. The researchers estimated an average NEP of 25 g C/(m²·yr) over the three-year study, suggesting that phytoplankton in extensive regions of the oceans are more productive than previously thought. Studies like this are giving ecologists a new understanding of Earth's carbon cycle and marine production.

What limits production in ecosystems? To ask this question another way, what factors could we change to increase production for a given ecosystem? We'll address this question first for aquatic ecosystems.

Primary Production in Aquatic Ecosystems

In aquatic (marine and freshwater) ecosystems, both light and nutrients are important in controlling primary production.

Light Limitation

Because solar radiation drives photosynthesis, you would expect light to be a key variable in controlling primary production in oceans. Indeed, the depth of light penetration affects primary production throughout the photic zone of an ocean or lake (see Figure 52.12). About half of the solar radiation is absorbed in the first 15 m of water. Even in "clear" water, only 5–10% of the radiation may reach a depth of 75 m.

If light were the main variable limiting primary production in the ocean, you would expect production to increase along a gradient from the poles toward the equator, which receives the greatest intensity of light. However, you can see in Figure 55.6 that there is no such gradient. Another factor must strongly influence primary production in the ocean.

Nutrient Limitation

More than light, nutrients limit primary production in most oceans and lakes. A **limiting nutrient** is the element that must be added for production to increase. The nutrient most often limiting marine production is either nitrogen or phosphorus. Concentrations of these nutrients are typically low in the photic zone because they are rapidly taken up by phytoplankton and because detritus tends to sink.

As detailed in **Figure 55.8**, nutrient enrichment experiments confirmed that nitrogen was limiting phytoplankton

▼ **Figure 55.8** | Inquiry

Which nutrient limits phytoplankton production along the coast of Long Island?

Experiment Pollution from duck farms concentrated near Moriches Bay adds both nitrogen and phosphorus to the coastal water off Long Island, New York. To determine which nutrient limits phytoplankton growth in this area, John Ryther and William Dunstan, of the Woods Hole Oceanographic Institution, cultured the phytoplankton *Nannochloris atomus* with water collected from several sites, identified as A–G. They added either ammonium (NH_4^+) or phosphate (PO_4^{3-}) to some of the cultures.

Results The addition of ammonium caused heavy phytoplankton growth in the cultures, but the addition of phosphate did not.

Conclusion The researchers concluded that nitrogen is the nutrient that limits phytoplankton growth in this ecosystem because adding phosphorus, which was already in rich supply, did not increase *Nannochloris* growth, whereas adding nitrogen increased phytoplankton density dramatically.

Source: J. H. Ryther and W. M. Dunstan, Nitrogen, phosphorus, and eutrophication in the coastal marine environment, *Science* 171:1008–1013 (1971).‘© 1971 by AAAS. Reprinted with permission.

WHAT IF? *How would you expect the results of this experiment to change if new duck farms substantially increased the amount of pollution in the water? Explain your reasoning.*

growth off the south shore of Long Island, New York. One practical application of this work is in preventing algal "blooms" caused by excess nitrogen runoff that fertilizes the phytoplankton. Prior to this research, phosphate contamination was thought to cause many such blooms in the ocean, but eliminating phosphates alone may not help unless nitrogen pollution is also controlled.

The macronutrients nitrogen and phosphorus are not the only nutrients that limit aquatic production. Several large areas of the ocean have low phytoplankton densities despite relatively high nitrogen concentrations. The Sargasso Sea, a subtropical region of the Atlantic Ocean, has some of the clearest water in the world because of its low phytoplankton density. Nutrient enrichment experiments have revealed that the availability of the micronutrient iron limits primary production there (Table 55.1). Windblown dust from land supplies most of the iron to the oceans but is relatively scarce in this and certain other regions compared to the oceans as a whole.

Areas of upwelling, where deep, nutrient-rich waters circulate to the ocean surface, have exceptionally high primary production. This fact supports the hypothesis that nutrient availability determines marine primary production. Because upwelling stimulates growth of the phytoplankton that form the base of marine food webs, upwelling areas typically host highly productive, diverse ecosystems and are prime fishing locations. The largest areas of upwelling occur in the Southern Ocean (also called the Antarctic Ocean), along the equator, and in the coastal waters off Peru, California, and parts of western Africa.

In freshwater lakes, nutrient limitation is also common. During the 1970s, scientists showed that the sewage and fertilizer runoff from farms and lawns adds considerable nutrients to lakes, promoting the growth of primary producers. When the primary producers die, detritivores decompose them, depleting the water of much or all of its oxygen. The ecological impacts of this process, known as **eutrophication** (from the Greek *eutrophos*, well nourished), include the loss of many fish species from the lakes (see Figure 52.14).

To control eutrophication, scientists need to know which nutrient is responsible. While nitrogen rarely limits primary production in lakes, whole-lake experiments showed that phosphorus availability limited cyanobacterial growth. This and other ecological research led to the use of phosphate-free detergents and other water quality reforms.

Primary Production in Terrestrial Ecosystems

At regional and global scales, temperature and moisture are the main factors controlling primary production in terrestrial ecosystems. Tropical rain forests, with their warm, wet conditions that promote plant growth, are the most productive terrestrial ecosystems (see Figure 55.6). In contrast, low-productivity systems are generally hot and dry, like many deserts, or cold and dry, like arctic tundra. Between these extremes lie the temperate forest and grassland ecosystems, with moderate climates and intermediate productivity.

The climate variables of moisture and temperature are very useful for predicting NPP in terrestrial ecosystems. Primary production is greater in wetter ecosystems, as shown for the plot of NPP and annual precipitation in Figure 55.9. Along with mean annual precipitation, a second useful predictor is *evapotranspiration*, the total amount of water transpired by plants and evaporated from a landscape. Evapotranspiration increases with the temperature and amount of solar energy available to drive evaporation and transpiration.

Table 55.1	Nutrient Enrichment Experiment for Sargasso Sea Samples
Nutrients Added to Experimental Culture	**Relative Uptake of ^{14}C by Cultures***
None (controls)	1.00
Nitrogen (N) + phosphorus (P) only	1.10
N + P + metals excluding iron (Fe)	1.08
N + P + metals including Fe	12.90
N + P + Fe	12.00

*^{14}C uptake by cultures measures primary production.

Source: D. W. Menzel and J. H. Ryther, Nutrients limiting the production of phytoplankton in the Sargasso Sea, with special reference to iron, *Deep Sea Research* 7:276–281 (1961).

INTERPRET THE DATA *The element molybdenum (Mo) is another micronutrient that can limit primary production in the oceans. If the researchers found the following results for additions of Mo, what would you conclude about its relative importance for growth?*

N + P + Mo   6.0
N + P + Fe + Mo   72.0

© Pearson Education, Inc.

▲ **Figure 55.9 A global relationship between net primary production and mean annual precipitation for terrestrial ecosystems.**

Nutrient Limitations and Adaptations That Reduce Them

EVOLUTION Soil nutrients also limit primary production in terrestrial ecosystems. As in aquatic systems, nitrogen and phosphorus are the nutrients that most commonly limit terrestrial production. Globally, nitrogen limits plant growth most. Phosphorus limitations are common in older soils where phosphate molecules have been leached away by water, such as in many tropical ecosystems. Phosphorus availability is also often low in soils of deserts and other ecosystems with a basic pH, where some phosphorus precipitates and becomes unavailable to plants. Adding a nonlimiting nutrient, even one that is scarce, will not stimulate production. Conversely, adding more of the limiting nutrient will increase production until some other nutrient becomes limiting.

▲ Root nodules containing nitrogen-fixing bacteria

Various adaptations have evolved in plants that can increase their uptake of limiting nutrients. One important adaptation is the symbiosis between plant roots and nitrogen-fixing bacteria (see Figure 37.11 and the photo on the left). Another is the mycorrhizal association between plant roots and fungi that supply phosphorus and other limiting elements to plants (see Figure 37.13). Plant roots also have hairs and other anatomical features that increase the area of the soil that roots contact (see Figure 35.3). Many plants release enzymes and other substances into the soil that increase the availability of limiting nutrients; such substances include phosphatases, which cleave a phosphate group from larger molecules, and chelating agents that make micronutrients such as iron more soluble in the soil.

Studies relating nutrients to terrestrial primary production have practical applications in agriculture. Farmers maximize their crop yields by using fertilizers with the right balance of nutrients for the local soil and type of crop. This knowledge of limiting nutrients helps feed billions of people.

CONCEPT CHECK 55.2

1. Why is only a small portion of the solar energy that strikes Earth's atmosphere stored by primary producers?
2. How can ecologists experimentally determine the factor that limits primary production in an ecosystem?
3. **MAKE CONNECTIONS** Explain how nitrogen and phosphorus, the nutrients that most often limit primary production, are necessary for the Calvin cycle to function in photosynthesis (see Concept 10.3).

For suggested answers, see Appendix A.

CONCEPT 55.3

Energy transfer between trophic levels is typically only 10% efficient

The amount of chemical energy in consumers' food that is converted to their own new biomass during a given period is called the **secondary production** of the ecosystem. Consider the transfer of organic matter from primary producers to herbivores, the primary consumers. In most ecosystems, herbivores eat only a small fraction of plant material produced; globally, they consume only about one-sixth of total plant production. Moreover, they cannot digest all the plant material that they *do* eat, as anyone who has walked through a dairy farm will attest. Most of an ecosystem's production is eventually consumed by detritivores. Let's analyze the process of energy transfer and cycling more closely.

Production Efficiency

First we'll examine secondary production in one organism—a caterpillar. When a caterpillar feeds on a leaf, only about 33 J out of 200 J, or one-sixth of the potential energy in the leaf, is used for secondary production, or growth **(Figure 55.10)**. The caterpillar stores some of the remaining energy in organic compounds that will be used for cellular respiration and passes the rest in its feces. The energy in the feces remains in the ecosystem temporarily, but most of it is lost as heat after the feces are consumed by detritivores. The energy used for the caterpillar's respiration is also eventually lost from the ecosystem as heat. This is why energy is said to flow through, not cycle within, ecosystems. Only the chemical energy stored

▲ **Figure 55.10 Energy partitioning within a link of the food chain.**

INTERPRET THE DATA *What percentage of the energy in the caterpillar's food is actually used for secondary production (growth)?*

by herbivores as biomass, through growth or the production of offspring, is available as food to secondary consumers.

We can measure the efficiency of animals as energy transformers using the following equation:

$$\text{Production efficiency} = \frac{\text{Net secondary production} \times 100\%}{\text{Assimilation of primary production}}$$

Net secondary production is the energy stored in biomass represented by growth and reproduction. Assimilation consists of the total energy taken in, not including losses in feces, used for growth, reproduction, and respiration. **Production efficiency**, therefore, is the percentage of energy stored in assimilated food that is *not* used for respiration. For the caterpillar in Figure 55.10, production efficiency is 33%; 67 J of the 100 J of assimilated energy is used for respiration. (The 100 J of energy lost as undigested material in feces does not count toward assimilation.) Birds and mammals typically have low production efficiencies, in the range of 1–3%, because they use so much energy in maintaining a constant, high body temperature. Fishes, which are mainly ectothermic (see Concept 40.3), have production efficiencies around 10%. Insects and microorganisms are even more efficient, with production efficiencies averaging 40% or more.

Trophic Efficiency and Ecological Pyramids

Let's scale up now from the production efficiencies of individual consumers to the flow of energy through trophic levels.

Trophic efficiency is the percentage of production transferred from one trophic level to the next. Trophic efficiencies must always be less than production efficiencies because they take into account not only the energy lost through respiration and contained in feces, but also the energy in organic material in a lower trophic level that is not consumed by the next trophic level. Trophic efficiencies are generally only about 10% and range from approximately 5% to 20% in different ecosystems. In other words, 90% of the energy available at one trophic level typically is *not* transferred to the next. This loss is multiplied over the length of a food chain. If 10% of available energy is transferred from primary producers to primary consumers, such as caterpillars, and 10% of that energy is transferred to secondary consumers (carnivores), then only 1% of net primary production is available to secondary consumers (10% of 10%). In the Scientific Skills Exercise, you can calculate trophic efficiency and other measures of energy flow in a salt marsh ecosystem.

Interpreting Quantitative Data in a Table

How Efficient Is Energy Transfer in a Salt Marsh Ecosystem? In a classic experiment, John Teal studied the flow of energy through the producers, consumers, and detritivores in a salt marsh. In this exercise, you will use the data from this study to calculate some measures of energy transfer between trophic levels in this ecosystem.

How the Study Was Done Teal measured the amount of solar radiation entering a salt marsh in Georgia over a year. He also measured the aboveground biomass of the dominant primary producers, which were grasses, as well as the biomass of the dominant consumers, including insects, spiders, and crabs, and of the detritus that flowed out of the marsh to the surrounding coastal waters. To determine the amount of

energy in each unit of biomass, he dried the biomass, burned it in a calorimeter, and measured the amount of heat produced.

Data from the Study

Form of Energy	kcal/(m² · yr)
Solar radiation	600,000
Gross grass production	34,580
Net grass production	6,585
Gross insect production	305
Net insect production	81
Detritus leaving marsh	3,671

Interpret the Data

1. What proportion of the solar energy that reaches the marsh is incorporated into gross primary production? Into net primary production? (A proportion is the same as a percentage divided by 100. Both measures are useful for comparing relative efficiencies across different ecosystems.)

2. How much energy is lost by primary producers as respiration in this ecosystem? How much is lost as respiration by the insect population?

3. If all of the detritus leaving the marsh is plant material, what proportion of all net primary production leaves the marsh as detritus each year?

(MB) A version of this Scientific Skills Exercise can be assigned in MasteringBiology.

Data from J. M. Teal, Energy flow in the salt marsh ecosystem of Georgia, *Ecology* 43:614–624 (1962).

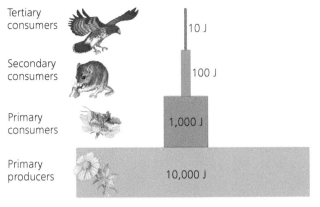

Tertiary consumers — 10 J

Secondary consumers — 100 J

Primary consumers — 1,000 J

Primary producers — 10,000 J

1,000,000 J of sunlight

▲ **Figure 55.11 An idealized pyramid of net production.** This example assumes a trophic efficiency of 10% for each link in the food chain. Notice that primary producers convert only about 1% of the energy available to them to net primary production.

The progressive loss of energy along a food chain severely limits the abundance of top-level carnivores that an ecosystem can support. Only about 0.1% of the chemical energy fixed by photosynthesis can flow all the way through a food web to a tertiary consumer, such as a snake or a shark. This explains why most food webs include only about four or five trophic levels (see Figure 54.14).

The loss of energy with each transfer in a food chain can be represented by a *pyramid of net production*, in which the trophic levels are arranged in tiers **(Figure 55.11)**. The width of each tier is proportional to the net production, expressed in joules, of each trophic level. The highest level, which represents top-level predators, contains relatively few individuals. The small population size typical of top predator species is one reason they tend to be vulnerable to extinction (and to the evolutionary consequences of small population size, discussed in Chapter 23).

One important ecological consequence of low trophic efficiencies is represented in a *biomass pyramid*, in which each tier represents the standing crop (the total dry mass of all organisms) in one trophic level. Most biomass pyramids narrow sharply from primary producers at the base to top-level carnivores at the apex because energy transfers between trophic levels are so inefficient **(Figure 55.12a)**. Certain aquatic ecosystems, however, have inverted biomass pyramids: Primary consumers outweigh the producers **(Figure 55.12b)**. Such inverted biomass pyramids occur because the producers—phytoplankton—grow, reproduce, and are consumed so quickly by the zooplankton that they never develop a large population size, or standing crop. In other words, the phytoplankton have a short **turnover time**, which means they have a small standing crop compared to their production:

$$\text{Turnover time} = \frac{\text{Standing crop (g/m}^2)}{\text{Production [g/(m}^2 \cdot \text{day)]}}$$

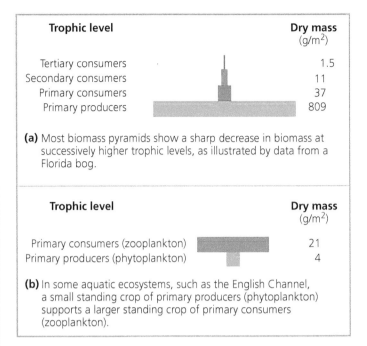

Trophic level	Dry mass (g/m²)
Tertiary consumers	1.5
Secondary consumers	11
Primary consumers	37
Primary producers	809

(a) Most biomass pyramids show a sharp decrease in biomass at successively higher trophic levels, as illustrated by data from a Florida bog.

Trophic level	Dry mass (g/m²)
Primary consumers (zooplankton)	21
Primary producers (phytoplankton)	4

(b) In some aquatic ecosystems, such as the English Channel, a small standing crop of primary producers (phytoplankton) supports a larger standing crop of primary consumers (zooplankton).

▲ **Figure 55.12 Pyramids of biomass (standing crop).** Numbers denote the dry mass of all organisms at each trophic level.

Because the phytoplankton continually replace their biomass at such a rapid rate, they can support a biomass of zooplankton bigger than their own biomass. Nevertheless, because phytoplankton have much higher production than zooplankton, the pyramid of *production* for this ecosystem is still bottom-heavy, like the one in Figure 55.11.

Figure 55.13 illustrates energy transfer, nutrient cycling, and other key processes for an Arctic tundra ecosystem. Note the conceptual similarities between this figure and Figure 10.23 (The Working Cell). The scale of the two figures is different, but the physical laws and biological rules that govern life apply equally to both systems.

In the next section, we'll look at how the transfer of nutrients and energy through food webs is part of a larger picture of chemical cycling in ecosystems.

CONCEPT CHECK 55.3

1. If an insect that eats plant seeds containing 100 J of energy uses 30 J of that energy for respiration and excretes 50 J in its feces, what is the insect's net secondary production? What is its production efficiency?

2. Tobacco leaves contain nicotine, a poisonous compound that is energetically expensive for the plant to make. What advantage might the plant gain by using some of its resources to produce nicotine?

3. **WHAT IF?** Detritivores are consumers that obtain their energy from detritus. How many joules of energy are potentially available to detritivores in the ecosystem represented in Figure 55.11?

For suggested answers, see Appendix A.

The Working Ecosystem

This Arctic tundra ecosystem teems with life in the short two-month growing season each summer. In ecosystems, organisms interact with each other and with the environment around them in diverse ways, including those illustrated here.

1 Caribou

2 Snow geese

1 Populations change in size through births and deaths and through immigration and emigration. Caribou migrate across the tundra to give birth at their calving grounds each year. *See Figure 53.3.*

2 Snow geese and many other species migrate to the Arctic each spring for the abundant food found there in summer. *See Concept 51.1.*

3 Birth and death rates influence the density of all populations. Death in the tundra comes from many causes, including predation, competition for resources, and lack of food in winter. *See Figure 53.18.*

5 Herbivory

Arctic fox

 3

4 Predation

Snow goose

Species Interact in Diverse Ways (Chapter 54)

4 In predation, an individual of one species kills and eats another. *See Concept 54.1.*

5 In herbivory, an individual of one species eats part of a plant or other primary producer, such as a caribou eating a lichen. *See Concept 54.1.*

6 In symbiosis, two or more species live in direct contact. For example, a lichen is a symbiosis between a fungus and an alga or cyanobacterium. *See Concept 54.1 and Figures 31.22 and 31.23.*

7 In competition, individuals seek to acquire the same limiting resources. For example, snow geese and caribou both eat cottongrass. *See Concept 54.1.*

Nitrogen cycle

N₂

Denitrification

Organisms   N fixation

12

Carbon cycle

CO₂

Cellular respiration

Photosynthesis

Organisms Transfer Energy and Matter in Ecosystems (Chapter 55)

8 Primary producers convert the energy in sunlight to chemical energy through photosynthesis. Their growth is often limited by abiotic factors such as low temperatures, scarce soil nutrients, and lack of light in winter. *See Figures 10.6, 52.11, and 55.4.*

9 Food chains are typically short in the tundra because primary production is lower than in most other ecosystems. *See Figure 54.14.*

10 When one organism eats another, the transfer of energy from one trophic level to the next is usually less than 10%. *See Figure 55.11.*

11 Detritivores recycle chemical elements back to primary producers. *See Figures 55.3 and 55.4.*

12 Chemical elements such as carbon and nitrogen move in cycles between the physical environment and organisms. *See Figure 55.14.*

Secondary consumers (wolves)

9

10

Primary consumers (caribou)

Chemical elements

Primary producers (plants and lichens)

Detritivores (soil fungi and prokaryotes)

11

7 **Competition**

8

6 **Symbiosis**

Algal cell
Fungal hyphae } Lichen

MAKE CONNECTIONS *Lichens are important primary producers in the tundra and can comprise more than half the diet of caribou in winter. Why might you predict that lichens would be more abundant in tundra ecosystems than in most other ecosystems around the world? (See Concept 31.5.)*

ANIMATION *BioFlix* For animations of the tundra ecosystem, visit the Study Area in **MasteringBiology** for the BioFlix® 3-D Animations on Population Ecology (Chapter 53) and The Carbon Cycle (Chapter 55). BioFlix Tutorials can also be assigned in MasteringBiology.

CONCEPT 55.4

Biological and geochemical processes cycle nutrients and water in ecosystems

Although most ecosystems receive abundant solar energy, chemical elements are available only in limited amounts. Life therefore depends on the recycling of essential chemical elements. Much of an organism's chemical stock is replaced continuously as nutrients are assimilated and waste products are released. When the organism dies, the atoms in its body are returned to the atmosphere, water, or soil by decomposers. Decomposition replenishes the pools of inorganic nutrients that plants and other autotrophs use to build new organic matter. Because nutrient cycles involve both biotic and abiotic components, they are called **biogeochemical cycles**.

Biogeochemical Cycles

An element's specific route through a biogeochemical cycle depends on the element and the trophic structure of the ecosystem. For convenience, we can recognize two general categories of biogeochemical cycles: global and local. Gaseous forms of carbon, oxygen, sulfur, and nitrogen occur in the atmosphere, and cycles of these elements are essentially global. For example, some of the carbon and oxygen atoms a plant acquires from the air as CO_2 may have been released into the atmosphere by the respiration of an organism in a distant locale. Other elements, including phosphorus, potassium, and calcium, are too heavy to occur as gases at Earth's surface, although they are transported in dust. In terrestrial ecosystems, these elements cycle more locally, absorbed from the soil by plant roots and eventually returned to the soil by decomposers. In aquatic systems, however, they cycle more broadly as dissolved forms carried in currents.

Figure 55.14 provides a detailed look at the cycling of water, carbon, nitrogen, and phosphorus. When you study each cycle, consider which steps are driven primarily by biological processes. For the carbon cycle, for instance, plants, animals, and other organisms control most of the key steps, including photosynthesis and decomposition. For the water cycle, however, purely physical processes control many key steps, such as evaporation from the oceans.

▼ **Figure 55.14**

Exploring Water and Nutrient Cycling

Examine each cycle closely, considering the major reservoirs of water, carbon, nitrogen, and phosphorus and the processes that drive each cycle. The widths of the arrows in the diagrams approximately reflect the relative contribution of each process to the movement of water or a nutrient in the biosphere.

The Water Cycle

Biological importance Water is essential to all organisms, and its availability influences the rates of ecosystem processes, particularly primary production and decomposition in terrestrial ecosystems.

Forms available to life All organisms can exchange water directly with their environment. Liquid water is the primary physical phase in which water is used, though some organisms can harvest water vapor. Freezing of soil water can limit water availability to terrestrial plants.

Reservoirs The oceans contain 97% of the water in the biosphere. Approximately 2% is bound in glaciers and polar ice caps, and the remaining 1% is in lakes, rivers, and groundwater. A negligible amount is in the atmosphere.

Key processes The main processes driving the water cycle are evaporation of liquid water by solar energy, condensation of water vapor into clouds, and precipitation. Transpiration by terrestrial plants also moves large volumes of water into the atmosphere. Surface and groundwater flow returns water to the oceans, completing the water cycle.

The Carbon Cycle

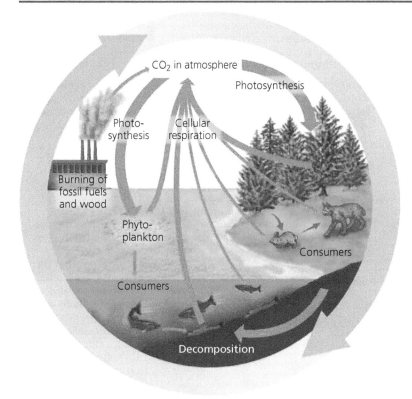

CO$_2$ in atmosphere

Photosynthesis

Photo-synthesis

Cellular respiration

Burning of fossil fuels and wood

Phyto-plankton

Consumers

Consumers

Decomposition

Biological importance   Carbon forms the framework of the organic molecules essential to all organisms.

Forms available to life   Photosynthetic organisms utilize CO$_2$ during photosynthesis and convert the carbon to organic forms that are used by consumers, including animals, fungi, and heterotrophic protists and prokaryotes. All organisms can return carbon directly to their environment as CO$_2$ through respiration.

Reservoirs   The major reservoirs of carbon include fossil fuels, soils, the sediments of aquatic ecosystems, the oceans (dissolved carbon compounds), plant and animal biomass, and the atmosphere (CO$_2$). The largest reservoir is sedimentary rocks such as limestone; however, this pool turns over very slowly.

Key processes   Photosynthesis by plants and phytoplankton removes substantial amounts of atmospheric CO$_2$ each year. This quantity is approximately equaled by CO$_2$ added to the atmosphere through cellular respiration by producers and consumers. The burning of fossil fuels and wood is adding significant amounts of additional CO$_2$ to the atmosphere. Over geologic time, volcanoes are also a substantial source of CO$_2$.

ANIMATION   ***BioFlix***   Visit the Study Area in **MasteringBiology** for the BioFlix® 3-D Animation on The Carbon Cycle. BioFlix Tutorials can also be assigned in MasteringBiology.

The Phosphorus Cycle

Biological importance   Organisms require phosphorus as a major constituent of nucleic acids, phospholipids, and ATP and other energy-storing molecules and as a mineral constituent of bones and teeth.

Forms available to life   The most biologically important inorganic form of phosphorus is phosphate (PO$_4^{3-}$), which plants absorb and use in the synthesis of organic compounds.

Reservoirs   The largest accumulations of phosphorus are in sedimentary rocks of marine origin. There are also large quantities of phosphorus in soil, in the oceans (in dissolved form), and in organisms. Because soil particles bind PO$_4^{3-}$, the recycling of phosphorus tends to be quite localized in ecosystems.

Key processes   Weathering of rocks gradually adds PO$_4^{3-}$ to soil; some leaches into groundwater and surface water and may eventually reach the sea. Phosphate taken up by producers and incorporated into biological molecules may be eaten by consumers. Phosphate is returned to soil or water by either decomposition of biomass or excretion by consumers. Because there are no significant phosphorus-containing gases, only relatively small amounts of phosphorus move through the atmosphere, usually in the forms of dust and sea spray.

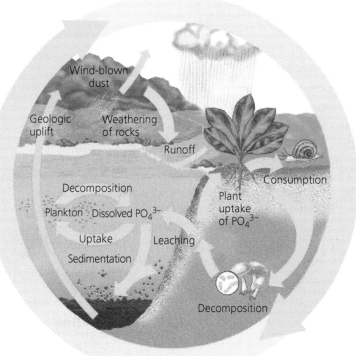

Wind-blown dust

Geologic uplift

Weathering of rocks

Runoff

Consumption

Decomposition

Plankton   Dissolved PO$_4^{3-}$

Plant uptake of PO$_4^{3-}$

Uptake   Leaching

Sedimentation

Decomposition

Continued on next page

The Nitrogen Cycle

Biological importance Nitrogen is part of amino acids, proteins, and nucleic acids and is often a limiting plant nutrient.

Forms available to life Plants can assimilate (use) two inorganic forms of nitrogen—ammonium (NH_4^+) and nitrate (NO_3^-)—and some organic forms, such as amino acids. Various bacteria can use all of these forms as well as nitrite (NO_2^-). Animals can use only organic forms of nitrogen.

Reservoirs The main reservoir of nitrogen is the atmosphere, which is 78% free nitrogen gas (N_2). The other reservoirs of inorganic and organic nitrogen compounds are soils and the sediments of lakes, rivers, and oceans; surface water and groundwater; and the biomass of living organisms.

Key processes The major pathway for nitrogen to enter an ecosystem is via nitrogen fixation, the conversion of N_2 to forms that can be used to synthesize organic nitrogen compounds. Certain bacteria, as well as lightning and volcanic activity, fix nitrogen naturally (see Figures 37.10–37.12). Nitrogen inputs from human activities now outpace natural inputs on land. Two major contributors are industrially produced fertilizers and legume crops that fix nitrogen via bacteria in their root nodules. Other bacteria in soil convert nitrogen to different forms. Some bacteria carry out denitrification, the reduction of nitrate to nitrogen gases. Human activities also release large quantities of reactive nitrogen gases, such as nitrogen oxides, to the atmosphere.

How have ecologists worked out the details of chemical cycling in various ecosystems? Two common methods use isotopes. One method is to follow the movement of naturally occurring, nonradioactive isotopes through the biotic (organic) and abiotic (inorganic) components of an ecosystem. The other method involves adding tiny amounts of radioactive isotopes of specific elements and tracing their progress. Scientists have also been able to make use of radioactive carbon (^{14}C) released into the atmosphere during atom bomb testing in the 1950s and early 1960s. This "spike" of ^{14}C can reveal where and how quickly carbon flows into ecosystem components, including plants, soils, and ocean water.

Decomposition and Nutrient Cycling Rates

The diagrams in Figure 55.14 illustrate the essential role that decomposers (detritivores) play in recycling carbon, nitrogen, and phosphorus. The rates at which these nutrients cycle in different ecosystems vary considerably, mostly as a result of differences in rates of decomposition.

Decomposition is controlled by the same factors that limit primary production in aquatic and terrestrial ecosystems (see Concept 55.2). These factors include temperature, moisture, and nutrient availability. Decomposers usually grow faster and decompose material more quickly in warmer ecosystems (Figure 55.15). In tropical rain forests, most organic material decomposes in a few months to a few years, whereas in temperate forests, decomposition takes four to six years, on average. The difference is largely the result of the higher temperatures and more abundant precipitation in tropical rain forests.

Because decomposition in a tropical rain forest is rapid, relatively little organic material accumulates as leaf litter on the forest floor; about 75% of the nutrients in the ecosystem are present in the woody trunks of trees, and only about 10% is contained in the soil. Thus, the relatively low concentrations of some nutrients in the soil of tropical rain

▼ Figure 55.15 · Inquiry

How does temperature affect litter decomposition in an ecosystem?

Experiment Researchers with the Canadian Forest Service placed identical samples of organic material—litter—on the ground in 21 sites across Canada (marked by letters on the map below). Three years later, they returned to see how much of each sample had decomposed.

Ecosystem type

- Arctic
- Subarctic
- Boreal
- Temperate
- Grassland
- Mountain

Results The mass of litter decreased four times faster in the warmest ecosystem than in the coldest ecosystem.

Conclusion Decomposition rate increases with temperature across much of Canada.

Source: T. R. Moore et al., Litter decomposition rates in Canadian forests, *Global Change Biology* 5:75–82 (1999).

WHAT IF? *What factors other than temperature might also have varied across these 21 sites? How might this variation have affected the interpretation of the results?*

forests result from a short cycling time, not from a lack of these elements in the ecosystem. In temperate forests, where decomposition is much slower, the soil may contain as much as 50% of all the organic material in the ecosystem.

The nutrients that are present in temperate forest detritus and soil may remain there for years before plants assimilate them.

Decomposition on land is also slower when conditions are either too dry for decomposers to thrive or too wet to supply them with enough oxygen. Ecosystems that are both cold and wet, such as peatlands, store large amounts of organic matter (see Figure 29.9a). Decomposers grow poorly there, and net primary production greatly exceeds the rate of decomposition.

In aquatic ecosystems, decomposition in anaerobic muds can take 50 years or longer. Bottom sediments are comparable to the detritus layer in terrestrial ecosystems, but algae and aquatic plants usually assimilate nutrients directly from the water. Thus, the sediments often constitute a nutrient sink, and aquatic ecosystems are very productive only when there is exchange between the bottom layers of water and surface waters (as occurs in the upwelling regions described earlier).

Case Study: Nutrient Cycling in the Hubbard Brook Experimental Forest

Since 1963, ecologist Gene Likens and colleagues have been studying nutrient cycling at the Hubbard Brook Experimental Forest in the White Mountains of New Hampshire. Their research site is a deciduous forest that grows in six small valleys, each drained by a single creek. Impenetrable bedrock underlies the soil of the forest.

The research team first determined the mineral budget for each of six valleys by measuring the input and outflow of several key nutrients. They collected rainfall at several sites to measure the amount of water and dissolved minerals added to the ecosystem. To monitor the loss of water and minerals, they constructed a small concrete dam with a V-shaped spillway across the creek at the bottom of each valley. They found that about 60% of the water added to the ecosystem as rainfall and snow exits through the stream, and the remaining 40% is lost by evapotranspiration.

Preliminary studies confirmed that internal cycling conserved most of the mineral nutrients in the system. For example, only about 0.3% more calcium (Ca^{2+}) leaves a valley via its creek than is added by rainwater, and this small net loss is probably replaced by chemical decomposition of the bedrock. During most years, the forest even registers small net gains of a few mineral nutrients, including nitrogen.

(a) One watershed was clear-cut to study the effects of the loss of vegetation on drainage and nutrient cycling. All of the cut plant material was left in place to decompose.

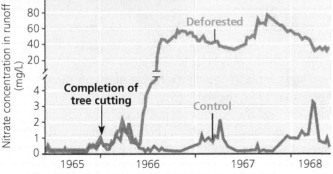

(b) The concentration of nitrate in runoff from the deforested watershed was 60 times greater than in a control (unlogged) watershed.

▶ **Figure 55.16 Nutrient cycling in the Hubbard Brook Experimental Forest: an example of long-term ecological research.**

(MB) *A related Experimental Inquiry Tutorial can be assigned in MasteringBiology.*

Experimental deforestation of a watershed dramatically increased the flow of water and minerals leaving the watershed **(Figure 55.16a)**. Over three years, water runoff from the newly deforested watershed was 30–40% greater than in a control watershed, apparently because there were no plants to absorb and transpire water from the soil. Most remarkable was the loss of nitrate, whose concentration in the creek increased 60-fold, reaching levels considered unsafe for drinking water **(Figure 55.16b)**. The Hubbard Brook deforestation study showed that the amount of nutrients leaving an intact forest ecosystem is controlled mainly by the plants. Retaining nutrients in ecosystems helps to maintain the productivity of the systems and avoid problems, such as algal "blooms," caused by excess nutrient runoff.

CONCEPT CHECK 55.4

1. **DRAW IT** For each of the four biogeochemical cycles in Figure 55.14, draw a simple diagram that shows one possible path for an atom of that chemical from abiotic to biotic reservoirs and back.
2. Why does deforestation of a watershed increase the concentration of nitrates in streams draining the watershed?
3. **WHAT IF?** Why is nutrient availability in a tropical rain forest particularly vulnerable to logging?

For suggested answers, see Appendix A.

Restoration ecologists return degraded ecosystems to a more natural state

Ecosystems can recover naturally from most disturbances (including the experimental deforestation at Hubbard Brook) through the stages of ecological succession (see Chapter 54). Sometimes that recovery takes centuries, though, particularly when humans have degraded the environment. Tropical areas that are cleared for farming may quickly become unproductive because of nutrient losses. Mining activities may last for several decades, and the lands are often abandoned in a degraded state. Ecosystems can also be damaged by salts that build up in soils from irrigation and by toxic chemicals or oil spills. Biologists increasingly are called on to help restore and repair damaged ecosystems.

Restoration ecologists seek to initiate or speed up the recovery of degraded ecosystems. One of the basic assumptions is that environmental damage is at least partly reversible. This optimistic view must be balanced by a second assumption—that ecosystems are not infinitely resilient. Restoration ecologists therefore work to identify and manipulate the processes that most limit recovery of ecosystems from disturbances. Where disturbance is so severe that restoring all of a habitat is impractical, ecologists try to reclaim as much of a habitat or ecological process as possible, within the limits of the time and money available to them.

In extreme cases, the physical structure of an ecosystem may need to be restored before biological restoration can occur. If a stream was straightened to channel water quickly through a suburb, ecologists may reconstruct a meandering channel to slow down the flow of water eroding the stream bank. To restore an open-pit mine, engineers may grade the site with heavy equipment to reestablish a gentle slope, spreading topsoil when the slope is in place **(Figure 55.17)**.

◀ In 1991, before restoration

▶ In 2000, near the completion of restoration

▲ **Figure 55.17 A gravel and clay mine site in New Jersey before and after restoration.**

Once physical reconstruction of the ecosystem is complete—or when it is not needed—biological restoration is the next step. Two key strategies in biological restoration are bioremediation and biological augmentation.

Bioremediation

Using organisms—usually prokaryotes, fungi, or plants—to detoxify polluted ecosystems is known as **bioremediation** (see Chapter 27). Some plants and lichens adapted to soils containing heavy metals can accumulate high concentrations of toxic metals such as lead and cadmium in their tissues. Restoration ecologists can introduce such species to sites polluted by mining and other human activities and then harvest these organisms to remove the metals from the ecosystem. For instance, researchers in the United Kingdom have discovered a lichen species that grows on soil polluted with uranium dust left over from mining. The lichen concentrates uranium in a dark pigment, making it useful as a biological monitor and potentially as a remediator.

Ecologists already use the abilities of many prokaryotes to carry out bioremediation of soils and water. Scientists have sequenced the genomes of at least ten prokaryotic species specifically for their bioremediation potential. One of the species, the bacterium *Shewanella oneidensis*, appears particularly promising. It can metabolize a dozen or more elements under aerobic and anaerobic conditions. In doing so, it converts soluble forms of uranium, chromium, and nitrogen to insoluble forms that are less likely to leach into streams or groundwater. Researchers at Oak Ridge National Laboratory, in Tennessee, stimulated the growth of *Shewanella* and other uranium-reducing bacteria by adding ethanol to groundwater contaminated with uranium; the bacteria can use ethanol as an energy source. In just five months, the concentration of soluble uranium in the ecosystem dropped by 80% (Figure 55.18).

Biological Augmentation

In contrast to bioremediation, which is a strategy for removing harmful substances from an ecosystem, **biological augmentation** uses organisms to *add* essential materials to a degraded ecosystem. To augment ecosystem processes, restoration ecologists need to determine which factors, such as chemical nutrients, have been lost from a system and are limiting its recovery.

Encouraging the growth of plants that thrive in nutrient-poor soils often speeds up succession and ecosystem recovery. In alpine ecosystems of the western United States, nitrogen-fixing plants such as lupines are often planted to raise nitrogen concentrations in soils disturbed by mining and other activities. Once these nitrogen-fixing plants become established, other native species are better able to obtain enough soil nitrogen to survive. In other systems where the soil has been severely disturbed or where topsoil

▲ **Figure 55.18 Bioremediation of groundwater contaminated with uranium at Oak Ridge National Laboratory, Tennessee.** Wastes containing uranium were dumped in four unlined pits for more than 30 years, contaminating soils and groundwater. After ethanol was added, microbial activity decreased the concentration of soluble uranium in groundwater near the pits.

is missing entirely, plant roots may lack the mycorrhizal symbionts that help them meet their nutritional needs (see Chapter 31). Ecologists restoring a tallgrass prairie in Minnesota recognized this limitation and enhanced the recovery of native species by adding mycorrhizal symbionts to the soil they seeded.

Restoring the physical structure and plant community of an ecosystem does not always ensure that animal species will recolonize a site and persist there. Because animals provide critical ecosystem services, including pollination and seed dispersal, restoration ecologists sometimes help wildlife reach and use restored ecosystems. They might release animals at a site or establish habitat corridors that connect a restored site to places where the animals are found. They sometimes establish artificial perches for birds to use at the site. These and other efforts can increase the biodiversity of restored ecosystems and help the community persist.

The long-term objective of restoration is to return an ecosystem as much as possible to its predisturbance state. Figure 55.19 identifies several ambitious and successful restoration projects around the world. The great number of such projects and the dedication of the people engaged in them suggest that restoration ecology will continue to grow as a discipline for many years.

CONCEPT CHECK 55.5

1. Identify the main goal of restoration ecology.

2. **WHAT IF?** In what way is the Kissimmee River project a more complete ecological restoration than the Maungatautari project (see Figure 55.19)?

For suggested answers, see Appendix A.

Exploring Restoration Ecology Worldwide

The examples highlighted on these pages are just a few of the many restoration ecology projects taking place around the world. The color-coded squares on the map indicate the locations of the projects.

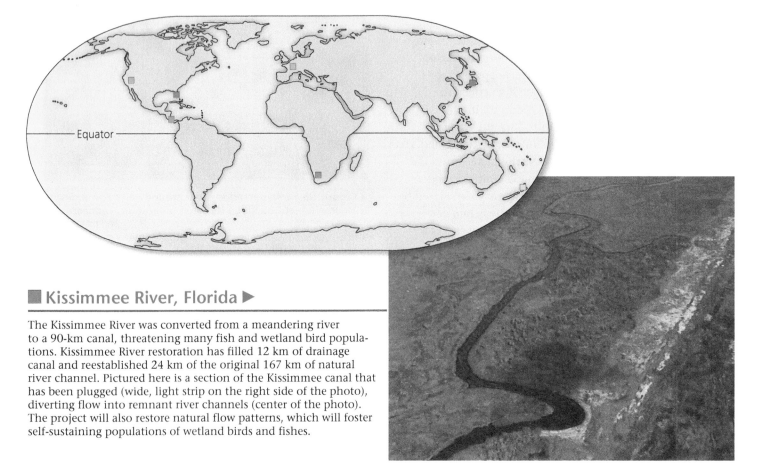

Equator

■ Kissimmee River, Florida ▶

The Kissimmee River was converted from a meandering river to a 90-km canal, threatening many fish and wetland bird populations. Kissimmee River restoration has filled 12 km of drainage canal and reestablished 24 km of the original 167 km of natural river channel. Pictured here is a section of the Kissimmee canal that has been plugged (wide, light strip on the right side of the photo), diverting flow into remnant river channels (center of the photo). The project will also restore natural flow patterns, which will foster self-sustaining populations of wetland birds and fishes.

◀ Truckee River, Nevada ■

Damming and water diversions during the 20th century reduced flow in the Truckee River, leading to declines in riparian (riverside) forests. Restoration ecologists worked with water managers to ensure that sufficient water would be released during the short season of seed release by the native cottonwood and willow trees for seedlings to become established. Nine years of controlled-flow release led to the result shown here: a dramatic recovery of cottonwood-willow riparian forest.

■ Tropical dry forest, Costa Rica ▶

Clearing for agriculture, mainly for livestock grazing, eliminated approximately 98% of tropical dry forest in Central America and Mexico. Reversing this trend, tropical dry forest restoration in Costa Rica has used domestic livestock to disperse the seeds of native trees into open grasslands. The photo shows one of the first trees (right center), dispersed as seed by livestock, to colonize former pastureland. This project is a model for joining restoration ecology with the local economy and educational institutions.

▲ Rhine River, Europe ■

Centuries of dredging and channeling for navigation (see the barges in the wide, main channel on the right side of the photo) have straightened the once-meandering Rhine River and disconnected it from its floodplain and associated wetlands. The countries along the Rhine, particularly France, Germany, Luxembourg, the Netherlands, and Switzerland, are cooperating to reconnect the river to side channels, such as the one shown on the left side of the photo. Such side channels increase the diversity of habitats available to aquatic organisms, improve water quality, and provide flood protection.

▲ Coastal Japan ■

Seaweed and seagrass beds are important nursery grounds for a wide variety of fishes and shellfish. Once extensive but now reduced by development, these beds are being restored in the coastal areas of Japan. Techniques include constructing suitable seafloor habitat, transplanting from natural beds using artificial substrates, and hand seeding (shown in this photograph).

▲ Succulent Karoo, South Africa ■

In this desert region of southern Africa, as in many arid regions, overgrazing by livestock has damaged vast areas. Private landowners and government agencies in South Africa are restoring large areas of this unique region, revegetating the land and employing more sustainable resource management. The photo shows a small sample of the exceptional plant diversity of the Succulent Karoo; its 5,000 plant species include the highest diversity of succulent plants in the world.

▲ Maungatautari, New Zealand ■

Weasels, rats, pigs, and other introduced species pose a serious threat to New Zealand's native plants and animals, including kiwis, a group of flightless, ground-dwelling bird species. The goal of the Maungatautari restoration project is to exclude all exotic mammals from a 3,400-ha reserve located on a forested volcanic cone. A specialized fence around the reserve eliminates the need to continue setting traps and using poisons that can harm native wildlife. In 2006, a pair of critically endangered takahe (a species of flightless rail) were released into the reserve in hopes of reestablishing a breeding population of this colorful bird on New Zealand's North Island.

SUMMARY OF KEY CONCEPTS

CONCEPT 55.1

Physical laws govern energy flow and chemical cycling in ecosystems (pp. 1233–1234)

- An **ecosystem** consists of all the organisms in a community and all the abiotic factors with which they interact. The laws of physics and chemistry apply to ecosystems, particularly regarding the conservation of energy. Energy is conserved but degraded to heat during ecosystem processes.
- Chemical elements enter and leave an ecosystem and cycle within it, subject to the **law of conservation of mass**. Inputs and outputs are generally small compared to recycled amounts, but their balance determines whether the ecosystem gains or loses an element over time.

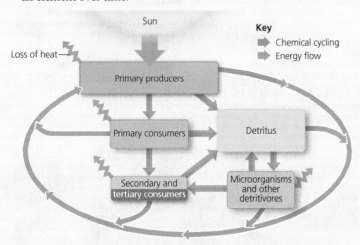

? Considering the second law of thermodynamics, would you expect the typical biomass of primary producers in an ecosystem to be greater than or less than the biomass of secondary producers in the system? Explain your reasoning.

CONCEPT 55.2

Energy and other limiting factors control primary production in ecosystems (pp. 1235–1239)

- **Primary production** sets the spending limit for the global energy budget. **Gross primary production** is the total energy assimilated by an ecosystem in a given period. **Net primary production**, the energy accumulated in autotroph biomass, equals gross primary production minus the energy used by the primary producers for respiration. **Net ecosystem production** is the total biomass accumulation of an ecosystem, defined as the difference between gross primary production and total ecosystem respiration.
- In aquatic ecosystems, light and nutrients limit primary production. In terrestrial ecosystems, climatic factors such as temperature and moisture affect primary production at large scales, but a soil nutrient is often the limiting factor locally.

? If you know NPP, what additional variable do you need to know to estimate NEP? Why might measuring this variable be difficult, for instance, in a sample of ocean water?

CONCEPT 55.3

Energy transfer between trophic levels is typically only 10% efficient (pp. 1239–1243)

- The amount of energy available to each trophic level is determined by the net primary production and the **production efficiency**, the efficiency with which food energy is converted to biomass at each link in the food chain.
- The percentage of energy transferred from one trophic level to the next, called **trophic efficiency**, is typically 10%. Pyramids of net production and biomass reflect low trophic efficiency.

? Why would runners have a lower production efficiency when running a long-distance race than when they are sedentary?

CONCEPT 55.4

Biological and geochemical processes cycle nutrients and water in ecosystems (pp. 1244–1248)

- Water moves in a global cycle driven by solar energy. The carbon cycle primarily reflects the reciprocal processes of photosynthesis and cellular respiration. Nitrogen enters ecosystems through atmospheric deposition and nitrogen fixation by prokaryotes.
- The proportion of a nutrient in a particular form and its cycling in that form vary among ecosystems, largely because of differences in the rate of decomposition.
- Nutrient cycling is strongly regulated by vegetation. The Hubbard Brook case study showed that logging increases water runoff and can cause large losses of minerals.

? If decomposers usually grow faster and decompose material more quickly in warmer ecosystems, why is decomposition in hot deserts so slow?

CONCEPT 55.5

Restoration ecologists return degraded ecosystems to a more natural state (pp. 1248–1251)

- Restoration ecologists harness organisms to detoxify polluted ecosystems through the process of **bioremediation**.
- In **biological augmentation**, ecologists use organisms to add essential materials to ecosystems.

? In preparing a site for surface mining and later restoration, why would engineers separate the topsoil from the deeper soil, rather than removing all soil at once and mixing it in a single pile?

TEST YOUR UNDERSTANDING

LEVEL 1: KNOWLEDGE/COMPREHENSION

1. Which of the following organisms is *incorrectly* paired with its trophic level?
   a. cyanobacterium—primary producer
   b. grasshopper—primary consumer
   c. zooplankton—primary producer
   d. fungus—detritivore

2. Which of these ecosystems has the *lowest* net primary production per square meter?
   a. a salt marsh
   b. an open ocean
   c. a coral reef
   d. a tropical rain forest

3. The discipline that applies ecological principles to returning degraded ecosystems to a more natural state is known as
   a. restoration ecology.
   b. thermodynamics.
   c. eutrophication.
   d. biogeochemistry.

LEVEL 2: APPLICATION/ANALYSIS

4. Nitrifying bacteria participate in the nitrogen cycle mainly by
   a. converting nitrogen gas to ammonia.
   b. releasing ammonium from organic compounds, thus returning it to the soil.
   c. converting ammonium to nitrate, which plants absorb.
   d. incorporating nitrogen into amino acids and organic compounds.

5. Which of the following has the greatest effect on the rate of chemical cycling in an ecosystem?
   a. the rate of decomposition in the ecosystem
   b. the production efficiency of the ecosystem's consumers
   c. the trophic efficiency of the ecosystem
   d. the location of the nutrient reservoirs in the ecosystem

6. The Hubbard Brook watershed deforestation experiment yielded all of the following results *except*:
   a. Most minerals were recycled within a forest ecosystem.
   b. Calcium levels remained high in the soil of deforested areas.
   c. Deforestation increased water runoff.
   d. The nitrate concentration in waters draining the deforested area became dangerously high.

7. Which of the following would be considered an example of bioremediation?
   a. adding nitrogen-fixing microorganisms to a degraded ecosystem to increase nitrogen availability
   b. using a bulldozer to regrade a strip mine
   c. reconfiguring the channel of a river
   d. adding seeds of a chromium-accumulating plant to soil contaminated by chromium

8. If you applied a fungicide to a cornfield, what would you expect to happen to the rate of decomposition and net ecosystem production (NEP)?
   a. Both decomposition rate and NEP would decrease.
   b. Neither would change.
   c. Decomposition rate would increase and NEP would decrease.
   d. Decomposition rate would decrease and NEP would increase.

LEVEL 3: SYNTHESIS/EVALUATION

9. **INTERPRET THE DATA** (a) Draw a simplified global water cycle showing ocean, land, atmosphere, and runoff from the land to the ocean. Add these annual water fluxes to your drawing: ocean evaporation, 425 km³; ocean evaporation that returns to the ocean as precipitation, 385 km³; ocean evaporation that falls as precipitation on land, 40 km³; evapotranspiration from plants and soil that falls as precipitation on land, 70 km³; runoff to the oceans, 40 km³. (b) What is the ratio of ocean evaporation that falls as precipitation on land compared with runoff from land to the oceans? (c) How would this ratio change during an ice age, and why?

10. EVOLUTION CONNECTION
    Some biologists have suggested that ecosystems are emergent, "living" systems capable of evolving. One manifestation of this idea is environmentalist James Lovelock's Gaia hypothesis, which views Earth itself as a living, homeostatic entity—a kind of superorganism. If ecosystems are capable of evolving, would this be a form of Darwinian evolution? Why or why not?

11. SCIENTIFIC INQUIRY
    Using two neighboring ponds in a forest as your study site, design a controlled experiment to measure the effect of falling leaves on net primary production in a pond.

12. WRITE ABOUT A THEME: ENERGY AND MATTER
    Decomposition typically occurs quickly in moist tropical forests. However, waterlogging in the soil of some moist tropical forests results over time in a buildup of organic matter called "peat." In a short essay (100–150 words), discuss the relationship of net primary production, net ecosystem production, and decomposition for such an ecosystem. Are NPP and NEP likely to be positive? What do you think would happen to NEP if a landowner drained the water from a tropical peatland, exposing the organic matter to air?

13. SYNTHESIZE YOUR KNOWLEDGE

    This dung beetle (genus *Scarabaeus*) is burying a ball of dung it has collected from a large mammalian herbivore in Kenya. Explain why this process is important for the cycling of nutrients and for primary production.

For selected answers, see Appendix A.

MasteringBiology®

Students Go to **MasteringBiology** for assignments, the eText, and the Study Area with practice tests, animations, and activities.

Instructors Go to **MasteringBiology** for automatically graded tutorials and questions that you can assign to your students, plus Instructor Resources.

56

Conservation Biology and Global Change

▲ Figure 56.1 **What will be the fate of this newly described lizard species?**

Psychedelic Treasure

Scurrying across a rocky outcrop, a lizard stops abruptly in a patch of sunlight. A conservation biologist senses the motion and turns to find a gecko splashed with rainbow colors, its bright orange legs and tail blending into a striking blue body, its head splotched with yellow and green. The psychedelic rock gecko (*Cnemaspis psychedelica*) was discovered in 2009 during an expedition to the Greater Mekong region of southeast Asia **(Figure 56.1)**. Its known habitat is restricted to Hon Khoai, an island occupying just 8 km² (3 square miles) in southern Vietnam. Other new species found during the same series of expeditions include the Elvis monkey (*Rhinopithecus strykeri*, shown in the lower left in an illustration), which sports a hairdo like that of Elvis Presley. Between 2000 and 2010, biologists identified more than a thousand new species in the Greater Mekong region alone.

To date, scientists have described and formally named about 1.8 million species of organisms. Some biologists think that about 10 million more species currently exist; others estimate the number to be as high as 100 million. Some of the greatest concentrations of species are found in the

1254

▲ Figure 56.2 **Tropical deforestation in Vietnam.**

tropics. Unfortunately, tropical forests are being cleared at an alarming rate to make room for and support a burgeoning human population. Rates of deforestation in Vietnam are among the very highest in the world **(Figure 56.2)**. What will become of the psychedelic rock gecko and other newly discovered species if such activities continue unchecked?

Throughout the biosphere, human activities are altering trophic structures, energy flow, chemical cycling, and natural disturbance—ecosystem processes on which we and all other species depend (see Chapter 55). We have physically altered nearly half of Earth's land surface, and we use over half of all accessible surface fresh water. In the oceans, stocks of most major fisheries are shrinking because of overharvesting. By some estimates, we may be pushing more species toward extinction than the large asteroid that triggered the mass extinctions at the close of the Cretaceous period 65.5 million years ago (see Figure 25.18).

Biology is the science of life. Thus, it is fitting that this chapter applies a global perspective to the changes happening across Earth, focusing in detail on a discipline that seeks to preserve life. **Conservation biology** integrates ecology, physiology, molecular biology, genetics, and evolutionary biology to conserve biological diversity at all levels. Efforts to sustain ecosystem processes and stem the loss of biodiversity also connect the life sciences with the social sciences, economics, and humanities.

In this chapter, we'll take a closer look at the biodiversity crisis and examine some of the conservation strategies being adopted to slow the rate of species loss. We'll also examine how human activities are altering the environment through climate change, ozone depletion, and other global processes. Finally, we'll consider how decisions about long-term conservation priorities could affect life on Earth.

Human activities threaten Earth's biodiversity

Extinction is a natural phenomenon that has been occurring since life first evolved; it is the high *rate* of extinction that is responsible for today's biodiversity crisis (see Concept 25.4). Because we can only estimate the number of species currently existing, we cannot determine the exact rate of species loss. However, we do know that the extinction rate is high and that human activities threaten Earth's biodiversity at all levels.

Three Levels of Biodiversity

Biodiversity—short for biological diversity—can be considered at three main levels: genetic diversity, species diversity, and ecosystem diversity **(Figure 56.3)**.

Genetic diversity in a vole population

Species diversity in a coastal redwood ecosystem

Community and ecosystem diversity across the landscape of an entire region

▲ Figure 56.3 **Three levels of biodiversity.** The oversized chromosomes in the top diagram symbolize the genetic variation within the population.

Genetic Diversity

Genetic diversity comprises not only the individual genetic variation *within* a population, but also the genetic variation *between* populations that is often associated with adaptations to local conditions (see Chapter 23). If one population becomes extinct, then a species may have lost some of the genetic diversity that makes microevolution possible. This erosion of genetic diversity in turn reduces the adaptive potential of the species.

Species Diversity

Public awareness of the biodiversity crisis centers on species diversity—the variety of species in an ecosystem or across the biosphere (see Chapter 54). As more species are lost to extinction, species diversity decreases. The U.S. Endangered Species Act defines an **endangered species** as one that is "in danger of extinction throughout all or a significant portion of its range." **Threatened species** are those considered likely to become endangered in the near future. The following are just a few statistics that illustrate the problem of species loss:

- According to the International Union for Conservation of Nature and Natural Resources (IUCN), 12% of the 10,000 known species of birds and 21% of the 5,500 known species of mammals are threatened.
- A survey by the Center for Plant Conservation showed that of the nearly 20,000 known plant species in the United States, 200 have become extinct since such records have been kept, and 730 are endangered or threatened.
- In North America, at least 123 freshwater animal species have become extinct since 1900, and hundreds more species are threatened. The extinction rate for North American freshwater fauna is about five times as high as that for terrestrial animals.

Extinction of species may also be local; for example, a species may be lost in one river system but survive in an adjacent one. Global extinction of a species means that it is lost from *all* the ecosystems in which it lived, leaving them permanently impoverished (Figure 56.4).

Ecosystem Diversity

The variety of the biosphere's ecosystems is a third level of biological diversity. Because of the many interactions between populations of different species in an ecosystem, the local extinction of one species can have a negative impact on other species in the ecosystem (see Figure 54.18). For instance, bats called "flying foxes" are important pollinators and seed dispersers in the Pacific Islands, where they are increasingly hunted as a luxury food (Figure 56.5). Conservation biologists fear that the extinction of flying foxes would also harm the native plants of the Samoan Islands, where four-fifths of the tree species depend on flying foxes for pollination or seed dispersal.

Philippine eagle

Yangtze River dolphin

▲ **Figure 56.4 A hundred heartbeats from extinction.** These are two members of what Harvard biologist E. O. Wilson calls the Hundred Heartbeat Club, species with fewer than 100 individuals remaining on Earth. The Yangtze River dolphin is likely to be extinct, but a few individuals were reportedly sighted in 2007.

? *To document that a species has actually become extinct, what factors would you need to consider?*

Some ecosystems have already been heavily affected by humans, and others are being altered at a rapid pace. Since European colonization, more than half of the wetlands in the contiguous United States have been drained and converted to agricultural and other uses. In California, Arizona, and New Mexico, roughly 90% of native riparian (streamside) communities have been affected by overgrazing, flood control, water diversions, lowering of water tables, and invasion by non-native plants.

▲ **Figure 56.5 The endangered Marianas "flying fox" bat (*Pteropus mariannus*), an important pollinator.**

Biodiversity and Human Welfare

Why should we care about the loss of biodiversity? One reason is what Harvard biologist E. O. Wilson calls *biophilia*, our sense of connection to nature and all life. The belief that other species are entitled to life is a pervasive theme of many religions and the basis of a moral argument that we should protect biodiversity. There is also a concern for future human generations. Paraphrasing an old proverb, G. H. Brundtland, a former prime minister of Norway, said: "We must consider our planet to be on loan from our children, rather than being a gift from our ancestors." In addition to such philosophical and moral justifications, species and genetic diversity bring us many practical benefits.

Benefits of Species and Genetic Diversity

Many species that are threatened could potentially provide medicines, food, and fibers for human use, making biodiversity a crucial natural resource. Products from aspirin to antibiotics were derived originally from natural sources. In food production, if we lose wild populations of plants closely related to agricultural species, we lose genetic resources that could be used to improve crop qualities, such as disease resistance. For instance, plant breeders responded to devastating outbreaks of the grassy stunt virus in rice (*Oryza sativa*) by screening 7,000 populations of this species and its close relatives for resistance to the virus. One population of a single relative, Indian rice (*Oryza nivara*), was found to be resistant to the virus, and scientists succeeded in breeding the resistance trait into commercial rice varieties. Today, the original disease-resistant population has apparently become extinct in the wild.

In the United States, about 25% of the prescriptions dispensed from pharmacies contain substances originally derived from plants. In the 1970s, researchers discovered that the rosy periwinkle, which grows on the island of Madagascar, off the coast of Africa, contains alkaloids that inhibit cancer cell growth (**Figure 56.6**). This discovery led to

treatments for two deadly forms of cancer, Hodgkin's lymphoma and childhood leukemia, resulting in remission in most cases. Madagascar is also home to five other species of periwinkles, one of which is approaching extinction. Losing these species would mean the loss of any possible medicinal benefits they might offer.

Each species lost means the loss of unique genes, some of which may code for enormously useful proteins. The enzyme Taq polymerase was first extracted from a bacterium, *Thermus aquaticus*, found in hot springs at Yellowstone National Park. This enzyme is essential for the polymerase chain reaction (PCR) because it is stable at the high temperatures required for automated PCR (see Figure 20.8). DNA from many other species of prokaryotes, living in a variety of environments, is used in the mass production of proteins for new medicines, foods, petroleum substitutes, other industrial chemicals, and other products. However, because millions of species may become extinct before we discover them, we stand to lose the valuable genetic potential held in their unique libraries of genes.

Ecosystem Services

The benefits that individual species provide to humans are substantial, but saving individual species is only part of the reason for preserving ecosystems. Humans evolved in Earth's ecosystems, and we rely on these systems and their inhabitants for our survival. **Ecosystem services** encompass all the processes through which natural ecosystems help sustain human life. Ecosystems purify our air and water. They detoxify and decompose our wastes and reduce the impacts of extreme weather and flooding. The organisms in ecosystems pollinate our crops, control pests, and create and preserve our soils. Moreover, these diverse services are provided for free.

Perhaps because we don't attach a monetary value to the services of natural ecosystems, we generally undervalue them. In 1997, ecologist Robert Costanza and his colleagues estimated the value of Earth's ecosystem services at $33 trillion per year, nearly twice the gross national product of all the countries on Earth at the time ($18 trillion). It may be more realistic to do the accounting on a smaller scale. In 1996, New York City invested more than $1 billion to buy land and restore habitat in the Catskill Mountains, the source of much of the city's fresh water. This investment was spurred by increasing pollution of the water by sewage, pesticides, and fertilizers. By harnessing ecosystem services to purify its water naturally, the city saved $8 billion it would have otherwise spent to build a new water treatment plant and $300 million a year to run the plant.

There is growing evidence that the functioning of ecosystems, and hence their capacity to perform services, is linked to biodiversity. As human activities reduce biodiversity, we are reducing the capacity of the planet's ecosystems to perform processes critical to our own survival.

▶ **Figure 56.6**
The rosy periwinkle (*Catharanthus roseus*), a plant that saves lives.

Threats to Biodiversity

Many different human activities threaten biodiversity on local, regional, and global scales. The threats posed by these activities are of four major types: habitat loss, introduced species, overharvesting, and global change.

Habitat Loss

Human alteration of habitat is the single greatest threat to biodiversity throughout the biosphere. Habitat loss has been brought about by factors such as agriculture, urban development, forestry, mining, and pollution. As discussed later in this chapter, global climate change is already altering habitats today and will have an even larger effect later this century. When no alternative habitat is available or a species is unable to move, habitat loss may mean extinction. The IUCN implicates destruction of habitat for 73% of the species that have become extinct, endangered, vulnerable, or rare in the last few hundred years.

Habitat loss and fragmentation may occur over immense regions. Approximately 98% of the tropical dry forests of Central America and Mexico have been cut down. The clearing of tropical rain forest in the state of Veracruz, Mexico, mostly for cattle ranching, has resulted in the loss of more than 90% of the original forest, leaving relatively small, isolated patches of forest. Other natural habitats have also been fragmented by human activities (Figure 56.7).

In almost all cases, habitat fragmentation leads to species loss because the smaller populations in habitat fragments have a higher probability of local extinction. Prairie covered about 800,000 hectares of southern Wisconsin when Europeans first arrived in North America but occupies only 800 hectares today; most of the original prairie in this area is now used to grow crops. Plant diversity surveys of 54 Wisconsin prairie remnants conducted in 1948–1954 and 1987–1988 showed that the remnants lost 8–60% of their plant species in the time between the two surveys.

▲ **Figure 56.7 Habitat fragmentation in the foothills of Los Angeles.** Development in the valleys may confine the organisms that inhabit the narrow strips of hillside.

Habitat loss is also a major threat to aquatic biodiversity. About 70% of coral reefs, among Earth's most species-rich aquatic communities, have been damaged by human activities. At the current rate of destruction, 40–50% of the reefs, home to one-third of marine fish species, could disappear in the next 30 to 40 years. Freshwater habitats are also being lost, often as a result of the dams, reservoirs, channel modification, and flow regulation now affecting most of the world's rivers. For example, the more than 30 dams and locks built along the Mobile River basin in the southeastern United States changed river depth and flow. While providing the benefits of hydroelectric power and increased ship traffic, these dams and locks also helped drive more than 40 species of mussels and snails to extinction.

Introduced Species

Introduced species, also called exotic species, are those that humans move intentionally or accidentally from the species' native locations to new geographic regions. Human travel by ship and airplane has accelerated the transplant of species. Free from the predators, parasites, and pathogens that limit their populations in their native habitats, such transplanted species may spread rapidly through a new region.

Some introduced species disrupt their new community, often by preying on native organisms or outcompeting native organisms for resources. The brown tree snake was accidentally introduced to the island of Guam from other parts of the South Pacific after World War II, as a "stowaway" in military cargo. Since then, 12 species of birds and 6 species of lizards that the snakes ate have become extinct on Guam. The devastating zebra mussel, a filter-feeding mollusc, was introduced into the Great Lakes of North America in 1988, most likely in the ballast water of ships arriving from Europe. Zebra mussels form dense colonies and have disrupted freshwater ecosystems, threatening native aquatic species. They have also clogged water intake structures, causing billions of dollars in damage to domestic and industrial water supplies.

Humans have deliberately introduced many species with good intentions but disastrous effects. An Asian plant called kudzu, which the U.S. Department of Agriculture once introduced in the southern United States to help control erosion, has taken over large areas of the landscape there (Figure 56.8). The European starling was brought intentionally into New York's Central Park in 1890 by a citizens' group intent on introducing all the plants and animals mentioned in Shakespeare's plays. It quickly spread across North America, where its population now exceeds 100 million, displacing many native songbirds.

Introduced species are a worldwide problem, contributing to approximately 40% of the extinctions recorded since 1750 and costing billions of dollars each year in damage and control efforts. There are more than 50,000 introduced species in the United States alone.

▲ **Figure 56.8 Kudzu, an introduced species, thriving in South Carolina.**

Overharvesting

The term *overharvesting* refers generally to the harvesting of wild organisms at rates exceeding the ability of their populations to rebound. Species with restricted habitats, such as small islands, are particularly vulnerable to overharvesting. One such species was the great auk, a large, flightless seabird found on islands in the North Atlantic Ocean. By the 1840s, humans had hunted the great auk to extinction to satisfy demand for its feathers, eggs, and meat.

Also susceptible to overharvesting are large organisms with low reproductive rates, such as elephants, whales, and rhinoceroses. The decline of Earth's largest terrestrial animals, the African elephants, is a classic example of the impact of overhunting. Largely because of the trade in ivory, elephant populations have been declining in most of Africa for the last 50 years. An international ban on the sale of new ivory resulted in increased poaching (illegal hunting), so the ban had little effect in much of central and eastern Africa. Only in South Africa, where once-decimated herds have been well protected for nearly a century, have elephant populations been stable or increasing (see Figure 53.9).

Conservation biologists increasingly use the tools of molecular genetics to track the origins of tissues harvested from endangered species. Researchers at the University of Washington constructed a DNA reference map for the African elephant (*Loxodonta africana*) using DNA isolated from elephant dung. By comparing this reference map with DNA isolated from ivory harvested legally or by poachers, they can determine to within a few hundred kilometers where the elephants were killed (**Figure 56.9**). Such work in Zambia suggested that poaching rates were 30 times higher than previously estimated, leading to improved anti-poaching efforts by the Zambian government. Similarly, biologists using phylogenetic analyses of mitochondrial DNA (mtDNA) showed that some whale meat sold in Japanese fish markets came from illegally harvested species, including fin and humpback whales, which are endangered (see Figure 26.6).

▲ **Figure 56.9 Ecological forensics and elephant poaching.** These severed tusks were part of an illegal shipment of ivory intercepted on its way from Africa to Singapore in 2002. DNA-based evidence showed that the thousands of elephants killed for the tusks came from a relatively narrow east-west band centered in Zambia rather than from across Africa.

MAKE CONNECTIONS *The text and Figure 26.6 describe another example in which conservation biologists used DNA analyses to compare harvested samples of whale meat with a reference DNA database. How are these examples similar, and how are they different? What limitations might there be to using such forensic methods in other suspected cases of poaching?*

Many commercially important fish populations, once thought to be inexhaustible, have been decimated by overfishing. Demands for protein-rich food from an increasing human population, coupled with new harvesting technologies, such as long-line fishing and modern trawlers, have reduced these fish populations to levels that cannot sustain further exploitation. Until the past few decades, the North Atlantic bluefin tuna was considered a sport fish of little commercial value—just a few cents per pound for use in cat food. In the 1980s, however, wholesalers began airfreighting fresh, iced bluefin to Japan for sushi and sashimi. In that market, the fish now brings up to $100 per pound (**Figure 56.10**). With increased harvesting spurred by such high prices, it took just ten years to reduce the western North Atlantic bluefin population to less than 20% of its 1980 size.

▲ **Figure 56.10 Overharvesting.** North Atlantic bluefin tuna are auctioned in a Japanese fish market.

Global Change

The fourth threat to biodiversity, global change, alters the fabric of Earth's ecosystems at regional to global scales. Global change includes alterations in climate, atmospheric chemistry, and broad ecological systems that reduce the capacity of Earth to sustain life.

One of the first types of global change to cause concern was *acid precipitation*, which is rain, snow, sleet, or fog with a pH less than 5.2. The burning of wood and fossil fuels releases oxides of sulfur and nitrogen that react with water in air, forming sulfuric and nitric acids. The acids eventually fall to Earth's surface, harming some aquatic and terrestrial organisms.

In the 1960s, ecologists determined that lake-dwelling organisms in eastern Canada were dying because of air pollution from factories in the Midwestern United States. Newly hatched lake trout, for instance, die when the pH drops below 5.4. Lakes and streams in southern Norway and Sweden were losing fish because of pollution generated in Great Britain and central Europe. By 1980, the pH of precipitation in large areas of North America and Europe averaged 4.0–4.5 and sometimes dropped as low as 3.0. (To review pH, see Concept 3.3.)

Environmental regulations and new technologies have enabled many countries to reduce sulfur dioxide emissions in recent decades. In the United States, sulfur dioxide emissions decreased more than 40% between 1993 and 2008, gradually reducing the acidity of precipitation (Figure 56.11). However, ecologists estimate that it will take decades for aquatic ecosystems to recover. Meanwhile, emissions of nitrogen oxides are increasing in the United States, and emissions of sulfur dioxide and acid precipitation continue to damage forests in central and eastern Europe.

We'll explore the importance of global change for Earth's biodiversity in more detail in Concept 56.4, where we examine such factors as climate change and ozone depletion.

Can Extinct Species Be Resurrected?

To the best of our knowledge, extinction has always been forever. Some scientists are nevertheless trying to use cloning to resurrect species that have become extinct. Resurrecting species is at least theoretically possible because of recent progress in cloning living animals. The most famous case of cloning resulted in the birth of "Dolly" the lamb in 1997 (see Figure 20.17). To create Dolly, Scottish researchers took an egg cell from an adult sheep, removed its nucleus, fused the egg cell with a mammary cell from another sheep, and implanted the fused cell into a surrogate mother.

Spanish researchers used a similar approach on the Pyrenean ibex (*Capra pyrenaica pyrenaica*), one of four subspecies of wild goat endemic to Spain and other countries of the Iberian Peninsula. In 1999, researchers removed a small skin sample from the ear of the last living individual, a female, and froze it. When that individual died a year later, its subspecies became extinct. Using cells from the frozen tissue, the scientists then attempted to resurrect the ibex. Out of hundreds of fused cells and approximately 60 embryos implanted into surrogate mothers (either another species of ibex or a domestic goat), one individual ibex was born in 2009. Sadly, it lived for only 7 minutes before succumbing to lung defects similar to those observed in other cloned animals, including sheep. Nonetheless, this research demonstrated that species recovery may be possible in cases where frozen tissue is available.

Tissue from an extinct species need not be new to be used in cloning. A team of Russian and Japanese scientists is trying to revive the extinct woolly mammoth (*Mammuthus primigenius*) using well-preserved bone marrow from the thigh of a mammoth frozen in Arctic ice (Figure 56.12). Will they succeed? No one knows yet, but eventually someone likely will, with this species and with others. In fact, scientists are already banking frozen tissues from many endangered species so that cells will be available for cloning if those species become extinct. Other scientists are examining whether they can obtain viable cells from museum specimens, such as pelts or feathers. And, of course, some are trying to isolate ancient DNA in soft tissue from dinosaur fossils. Thus far, such attempts have failed.

The quest to resurrect extinct species raises a host of ethical questions. Should scientists be free to resurrect any species for which viable cells or DNA are available? If not, who will decide which species are off-limits? What rules should be put in place before resurrection occurs? Should

▲ **Figure 56.11 Changes in the pH of precipitation at the Hubbard Brook Experimental Forest, New Hampshire.**

MAKE CONNECTIONS *Describe the relationship between pH and acidity. (See Concept 3.3.) Overall, is the precipitation in this forest becoming more acidic or less acidic?*

▲ Figure 56.12 **Collecting a frozen woolly mammoth.** Such specimens are being used in an attempt to resurrect the species through biotechnology.

the species eventually be restored to the wild? Note that, for the Pyrenean ibex, frozen tissue exists for only one female. No males of that subspecies may ever exist again.

Although resurrecting species now seems possible, we still need to preserve species across Earth. For many reasons, including the issue of genetic diversity discussed in Concept 56.2, preservation remains the scientifically and ethically prudent course of action.

CONCEPT CHECK 56.1

1. Explain why it is too narrow to define the biodiversity crisis as simply a loss of species.

2. Identify the four main threats to biodiversity and explain how each damages diversity.

3. **WHAT IF?** Imagine two populations of a fish species, one in the Mediterranean Sea and one in the Caribbean Sea. Now imagine two scenarios: (1) The populations breed separately, and (2) adults of both populations migrate yearly to the North Atlantic to interbreed. Which scenario would result in a greater loss of genetic diversity if the Mediterranean population were harvested to extinction? Explain your answer.

For suggested answers, see Appendix A.

CONCEPT 56.2

Population conservation focuses on population size, genetic diversity, and critical habitat

Biologists who work on conservation at the population and species levels use two main approaches. One approach focuses on populations that are small and hence often vulnerable. The other emphasizes populations that are declining rapidly, even if they are not yet small.

Small-Population Approach

Small populations are particularly vulnerable to overharvesting, habitat loss, and the other threats to biodiversity that you read about in Concept 56.1. After such factors have reduced a population's size to a small number of individuals, the small size itself can push the population to extinction. Conservation biologists who adopt the small-population approach study the various processes that cause extinctions once population sizes have been reduced.

The Extinction Vortex: Evolutionary Implications of Small Population Size

EVOLUTION A small population is vulnerable to inbreeding and genetic drift, which draw the population down an **extinction vortex** toward smaller and smaller population size until no individuals survive **(Figure 56.13).** A key factor driving the extinction vortex is the loss of the genetic variation that enables evolutionary responses to environmental change, such as the appearance of new strains of pathogens. Both inbreeding and genetic drift can cause a loss of genetic variation (see Chapter 23), and their effects become more harmful as a population shrinks. Inbreeding often reduces fitness because offspring are more likely to be homozygous for harmful recessive traits.

Not all small populations are doomed by low genetic diversity, and low genetic variability does not automatically lead to permanently small populations. For instance, overhunting of northern elephant seals in the 1890s reduced the species to only 20 individuals—clearly a bottleneck with reduced genetic variation. Since that time, however, the northern elephant seal populations have rebounded to about 150,000 individuals today, though their genetic variation remains relatively low. Thus, low genetic diversity does not always impede population growth.

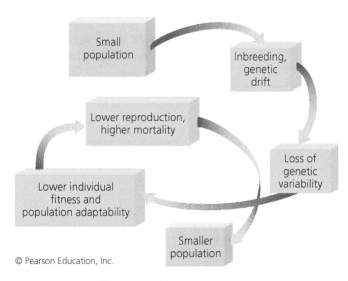

© Pearson Education, Inc.

▲ Figure 56.13 **Processes driving an extinction vortex.**

Case Study: *The Greater Prairie Chicken and the Extinction Vortex*

When Europeans arrived in North America, the greater prairie chicken (*Tympanuchus cupido*) was common from New England to Virginia and across the western prairies of the continent. Land cultivation for agriculture fragmented the populations of this species, and its abundance decreased rapidly (see Figure 23.11). Illinois had millions of greater prairie chickens in the 19th century but fewer than 50 by 1993. Researchers found that the decline in the Illinois population was associated with a decrease in fertility. As a test of the extinction vortex hypothesis, scientists increased genetic variation by importing 271 birds from larger populations elsewhere (Figure 56.14). The Illinois population rebounded, confirming that it had been on its way to extinction until rescued by the transfusion of genetic variation.

Minimum Viable Population Size

How small does a population have to be before it starts down an extinction vortex? The answer depends on the type of organism and other factors. Large predators that feed high on the food chain usually require extensive individual ranges, resulting in low population densities. Therefore, not all rare species concern conservation biologists. All populations, however, require some minimum size to remain viable.

The minimal population size at which a species is able to sustain its numbers is known as the **minimum viable population (MVP)**. MVP is usually estimated for a given species using computer models that integrate many factors. The calculation may include, for instance, an estimate of how many individuals in a small population are likely to be killed by a natural catastrophe such as a storm. Once in the extinction vortex, two or three consecutive years of bad weather could finish off a population that is already below its MVP.

Effective Population Size

Genetic variation is the key issue in the small-population approach. The *total* size of a population may be misleading because only certain members of the population breed successfully and pass their alleles on to offspring. Therefore, a meaningful estimate of MVP requires the researcher to determine the **effective population size**, which is based on the breeding potential of the population.

The following formula incorporates the sex ratio of breeding individuals into the estimate of effective population size, abbreviated N_e:

$$N_e = \frac{4N_f N_m}{N_f + N_m}$$

where N_f and N_m are, respectively, the number of females and the number of males that successfully breed. If we apply

---

▼ **Figure 56.14** | **Inquiry**

What caused the drastic decline of the Illinois greater prairie chicken population?

Experiment Researchers had observed that the population collapse of the greater prairie chicken was mirrored in a reduction in fertility, as measured by the hatching rate of eggs. Comparison of DNA samples from the Jasper County, Illinois, population with DNA from feathers in museum specimens showed that genetic variation had declined in the study population (see Figure 23.11). In 1992, Ronald Westemeier, Jeffrey Brawn, and colleagues began translocating prairie chickens from Minnesota, Kansas, and Nebraska in an attempt to increase genetic variation.

Results After translocation (black arrow), the viability of eggs rapidly increased, and the population rebounded.

(a) Population dynamics

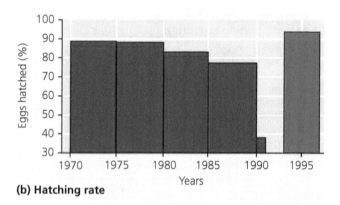

(b) Hatching rate

Conclusion Reduced genetic variation had started the Jasper County population of prairie chickens down the extinction vortex.

Source: R. L. Westemeier et al., Tracking the long-term decline and recovery of an isolated population, *Science* 282:1695–1698 (1998). © 1998 by AAAS. Reprinted with permission.

Inquiry in Action Read and analyze the original paper in *Inquiry in Action: Interpreting Scientific Papers.*

WHAT IF? *Given the success of using transplanted birds as a tool for increasing the percentage of hatched eggs in Illinois, why wouldn't you transplant additional birds immediately to Illinois?*

---

this formula to an idealized population whose total size is 1,000 individuals, N_e will also be 1,000 if every individual breeds and the sex ratio is 500 females to 500 males. In this case, $N_e = (4 \times 500 \times 500)/(500 + 500) = 1,000$. Any deviation from these conditions (not all individuals breed or there is not a 1:1 sex ratio) reduces N_e. For instance, if the total population size is 1,000 but only 400 females and 400 males breed, then $N_e = (4 \times 400 \times 400)/(400 + 400) = 800$, or 80% of the total population size. Numerous life history traits can influence N_e. Alternative formulas for estimating N_e take into account factors such as family size, age at maturation, genetic relatedness among population members, the effects of gene flow between geographically separated populations, and population fluctuations.

In actual study populations, N_e is always some fraction of the total population. Thus, simply determining the total number of individuals in a small population does not provide a good measure of whether the population is large enough to avoid extinction. Whenever possible, conservation programs attempt to sustain total population sizes that include at least the minimum viable number of *reproductively active* individuals. The conservation goal of sustaining effective population size (N_e) above MVP stems from the concern that populations retain enough genetic diversity to adapt as their environment changes.

The MVP of a population is often used in population viability analysis. The objective of this analysis is to predict a population's chances for survival, usually expressed as a specific probability of survival, such as a 95% chance, over a particular time interval, perhaps 100 years. Such modeling approaches allow conservation biologists to explore the potential consequences of alternative management plans.

Case Study: *Analysis of Grizzly Bear Populations*

One of the first population viability analyses was conducted in 1978 by Mark Shaffer, of Duke University, as part of a long-term study of grizzly bears in Yellowstone National Park and its surrounding areas (**Figure 56.15**). A threatened species in the United States, the grizzly bear (*Ursus arctos horribilis*) is currently found in only 4 of the 48 contiguous states. Its populations in those states have been drastically reduced and fragmented. In 1800, an estimated 100,000 grizzlies ranged over about 500 million hectares of habitat, while today only about 1,000 individuals in six relatively isolated populations range over less than 5 million hectares.

Shaffer attempted to determine viable sizes for the Yellowstone grizzly population. Using life history data obtained for individual Yellowstone bears over a 12-year period, he simulated the effects of environmental factors on survival and reproduction. His models predicted that, given a suitable habitat, a Yellowstone grizzly bear population of 70–90 individuals would have about a 95% chance of surviving for 100 years. A slightly larger population of only 100 bears

▲ **Figure 56.15 Long-term monitoring of a grizzly bear population.** The ecologist is fitting this tranquilized bear with a radio collar so that the bear's movements can be compared with those of other grizzlies in the Yellowstone National Park population.

would have a 95% chance of surviving for twice as long, about 200 years.

How does the actual size of the Yellowstone grizzly population compare with Shaffer's predicted MVP? A current estimate puts the total grizzly bear population in the greater Yellowstone ecosystem at about 500 individuals. The relationship of this estimate to the effective population size (N_e) depends on several factors. Usually, only a few dominant males breed, and it may be difficult for them to locate females, since individuals inhabit such large areas. Moreover, females may reproduce only when there is abundant food. As a result, N_e is only about 25% of the total population size, or about 125 bears.

Because small populations tend to lose genetic variation over time, a number of research teams have analyzed proteins, mtDNA, and short tandem repeats (see Chapter 21) to assess genetic variability in the Yellowstone grizzly bear population. All results to date indicate that the Yellowstone population has less genetic variability than other grizzly bear populations in North America.

How might conservation biologists increase the effective size and genetic variation of the Yellowstone grizzly bear population? Migration between isolated populations of grizzlies could increase both effective and total population sizes. Computer models predict that introducing only two unrelated bears each decade into a population of 100 individuals would reduce the loss of genetic variation by about half. For the grizzly bear, and probably for many other species with small populations, finding ways to promote dispersal among populations may be one of the most urgent conservation needs.

This case study and that of the greater prairie chicken bridge small-population models and practical applications in conservation. Next, we look at an alternative approach to understanding the biology of extinction.

Declining-Population Approach

The declining-population approach focuses on threatened and endangered populations that show a downward trend, even if the population is far above its minimum viable population. The distinction between a declining population, which may not be small, and a small population, which may not be declining, is less important than the different priorities of the two approaches. The small-population approach emphasizes smallness itself as an ultimate cause of a population's extinction, especially through the loss of genetic diversity. In contrast, the declining-population approach emphasizes the environmental factors that caused a population decline in the first place. If, for instance, an area is deforested, then species that depend on trees will decline in abundance and become locally extinct, whether or not they retain genetic variation.

Steps for Analysis and Intervention

The declining-population approach requires that researchers carefully evaluate the causes of a decline before taking steps to correct it. If an invasive species such as the brown tree snake in Guam is harming a native bird species, then managers need to reduce or eliminate the invader to restore vulnerable populations of the bird. Although most situations are more complex, we can use the following steps for analyzing declining populations:

1. Confirm, using population data, that the species was more widely distributed or more abundant in the past compared to its current population level.
2. Study the natural history of this and related species, including reviewing the research literature, to determine the species' environmental needs.
3. Develop hypotheses for all possible causes of the decline, including human activities and natural events, and list the predictions of each hypothesis.
4. Because many factors may be correlated with the decline, test the most likely hypothesis first. For example, remove the suspected cause of decline to see if the experimental population rebounds compared to a control population.
5. Apply the results of the diagnosis to manage the threatened species and monitor its recovery.

The following case study is one example of how the declining-population approach has been applied to the conservation of an endangered species.

Case Study: *Decline of the Red-cockaded Woodpecker*

The red-cockaded woodpecker (*Picoides borealis*) is found only in the southeastern United States. It requires mature pine forests, preferably ones dominated by the longleaf pine, for its habitat. Most woodpeckers nest in dead trees, but the red-cockaded woodpecker drills its nest holes in mature, living pine trees. It also drills small holes around the entrance to its nest cavity, which causes resin from the tree to ooze down the trunk. The resin seems to repel predators, such as corn snakes, that eat bird eggs and nestlings.

Another critical habitat factor for the red-cockaded woodpecker is that the undergrowth of plants around the pine trunks must be low **(Figure 56.16a)**. Breeding birds tend to abandon nests when vegetation among the pines is thick and higher than about 4.5 m **(Figure 56.16b)**. Apparently, the birds need a clear flight path between their home

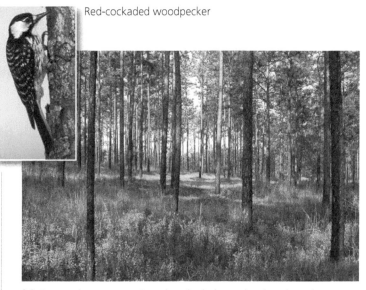

Red-cockaded woodpecker

(a) Forests that can sustain red-cockaded woodpeckers have low undergrowth.

(b) Forests that cannot sustain red-cockaded woodpeckers have high, dense undergrowth that interferes with the woodpeckers' access to feeding grounds.

▲ **Figure 56.16 A habitat requirement of the red-cockaded woodpecker.**

? *How is habitat disturbance absolutely necessary for the long-term survival of the woodpecker?*

trees and the neighboring feeding grounds. Periodic fires have historically swept through longleaf pine forests, keeping the undergrowth low.

One factor leading to decline of the red-cockaded woodpecker has been the destruction or fragmentation of suitable habitats by logging and agriculture. By recognizing key habitat factors, protecting some longleaf pine forests, and using controlled fires to reduce forest undergrowth, conservation managers have helped restore habitat that can support viable populations.

Sometimes conservation managers also help species colonize restored habitats. Because red-cockaded woodpeckers take months to excavate nesting cavities, researchers performed an experiment to see whether providing cavities for the birds would make them more likely to use a site. The researchers constructed cavities in pine trees at 20 sites. The results were dramatic. Cavities in 18 of the 20 sites were colonized by red-cockaded woodpeckers, and new breeding groups formed only in those sites. Based on this experiment, conservationists initiated a habitat maintenance program that included controlled burning and excavation of new nesting cavities, enabling this endangered species to begin to recover.

Weighing Conflicting Demands

Determining population numbers and habitat needs is only part of a strategy to save species. Scientists also need to weigh a species' needs against other conflicting demands. Conservation biology often highlights the relationship between science, technology, and society. For example, an ongoing, sometimes bitter debate in the western United States pits habitat preservation for wolf, grizzly bear, and bull trout populations against job opportunities in the grazing and resource extraction industries. Programs that restocked wolves in Yellowstone National Park remain controversial for people concerned about human safety and for many ranchers concerned with potential loss of livestock outside the park.

Large, high-profile vertebrates are not always the focal point in such conflicts, but habitat use is almost always the issue. Should work proceed on a new highway bridge if it destroys the only remaining habitat of a species of freshwater mussel? If you were the owner of a coffee plantation growing varieties that thrive in bright sunlight, would you be willing to change to shade-tolerant varieties that produce less coffee per hectare but can grow beneath trees that support large numbers of songbirds?

Another important consideration is the ecological role of a species. Because we cannot save every endangered species, we must determine which species are most important for conserving biodiversity as a whole. Identifying keystone species and finding ways to sustain their populations can

be central to maintaining communities and ecosystems. In most situations, conservation biologists must also look beyond single species and consider the whole community and ecosystem as an important unit of biodiversity.

CONCEPT CHECK 56.2

1. How does the reduced genetic diversity of small populations make them more vulnerable to extinction?

2. If there were 100 greater prairie chickens in a population, and 30 females and 10 males bred, what would be the effective population size (N_e)?

3. **WHAT IF?** In 2005, at least ten grizzly bears in the greater Yellowstone ecosystem were killed through contact with people. Three things caused most of these deaths: collisions with automobiles, hunters (of other animals) shooting when charged by a female grizzly bear with cubs nearby, and conservation managers killing bears that attacked livestock repeatedly. If you were a conservation manager, what steps might you take to minimize such encounters in Yellowstone?

For suggested answers, see Appendix A.

CONCEPT 56.3

Landscape and regional conservation help sustain biodiversity

Although conservation efforts historically focused on saving individual species, efforts today often seek to sustain the biodiversity of entire communities, ecosystems, and landscapes. Such a broad view requires applying not just the principles of community, ecosystem, and landscape ecology but aspects of human population dynamics and economics as well. The goals of landscape ecology (see Figure 52.2) include projecting future patterns of landscape use and making biodiversity conservation part of land-use planning.

Landscape Structure and Biodiversity

The biodiversity of a given landscape is in large part a function of the structure of the landscape. Understanding landscape structure is critically important in conservation because many species use more than one kind of ecosystem, and many live on the borders between ecosystems.

Fragmentation and Edges

The boundaries, or *edges*, between ecosystems—such as between a lake and the surrounding forest or between cropland and suburban housing tracts—are defining features of landscapes. An edge has its own set of physical conditions, which differ from those on either side of it. The soil surface of an edge between a forest patch and a burned area receives more sunlight and is usually hotter and drier than the forest

▲ Figure 56.17 **Edges in Yellowstone National Park.**

? *What edges between ecosystems do you see in this photo?*

▲ Figure 56.18 **Amazon rain forest fragments created as part of the Biological Dynamics of Forest Fragments Project.**

interior, but it is cooler and wetter than the soil surface in the burned area. The photo of Yellowstone National Park in **Figure 56.17** shows several edges between ecosystems.

Some organisms thrive in edge communities because they gain resources from both adjacent areas. The ruffed grouse (*Bonasa umbellus*) is a bird that needs forest habitat for nesting, winter food, and shelter, but it also needs forest openings with dense shrubs and herbs for summer food.

Ecosystems in which edges arise from human alterations often have reduced biodiversity and a preponderance of edge-adapted species. For example, white-tailed deer (*Odocoileus virginianus*) thrive in edge habitats, where they can browse on woody shrubs; deer populations often expand when forests are logged and more edges are generated. The brown-headed cowbird (*Molothrus ater*) is an edge-adapted species that lays its eggs in the nests of other birds, often migratory songbirds. Cowbirds need forests, where they can parasitize the nests of other birds, and open fields, where they forage on seeds and insects. Consequently, their populations are growing where forests are being cut and fragmented, creating more edge habitat and open land. Increasing cowbird parasitism and habitat loss are correlated with declining populations of several of the cowbird's host species.

The influence of fragmentation on the structure of communities has been explored since 1979 in the long-term Biological Dynamics of Forest Fragments Project. Located in the heart of the Amazon River basin, the study area consists of isolated fragments of tropical rain forest separated from surrounding continuous forest by distances of 80–1,000 m **(Figure 56.18)**. Numerous researchers working on this project have clearly documented the effects of this fragmentation on organisms ranging from bryophytes to beetles to birds. They have consistently found that species adapted to forest interiors show the greatest declines when patches are the smallest, suggesting that landscapes dominated by small fragments will support fewer species.

Corridors That Connect Habitat Fragments

In fragmented habitats, the presence of a **movement corridor**, a narrow strip or series of small clumps of habitat connecting otherwise isolated patches, can be extremely important for conserving biodiversity. Riparian habitats often serve as corridors, and in some nations, government policy prohibits altering these habitats. In areas of heavy human use, artificial corridors are sometimes constructed. Bridges or tunnels, for instance, can reduce the number of animals killed trying to cross highways **(Figure 56.19)**.

Movement corridors can also promote dispersal and reduce inbreeding in declining populations. Corridors have been shown to increase the exchange of individuals among populations of many organisms, including butterflies, voles,

▲ Figure 56.19 **An artificial corridor.** This bridge in Banff National Park, Canada, helps animals cross a human-created barrier.

and aquatic plants. Corridors are especially important to species that migrate between different habitats seasonally. However, a corridor can also be harmful—for example, by allowing the spread of disease. In a 2003 study, a scientist at the University of Zaragoza, Spain, showed that habitat corridors facilitate the movement of disease-carrying ticks among forest patches in northern Spain. All the effects of corridors are not yet understood, and their impact is an area of active research in conservation biology.

Establishing Protected Areas

Conservation biologists are applying their understanding of landscape dynamics in establishing protected areas to slow biodiversity loss. Currently, governments have set aside about 7% of the world's land in various forms of reserves. Choosing where to place nature reserves and how to design them poses many challenges. Should the reserve be managed to minimize the risks of fire and predation to a threatened species? Or should the reserve be left as natural as possible, with such processes as fires ignited by lightning allowed to play out on their own? This is just one of the debates that arise among people who share an interest in the health of national parks and other protected areas.

Preserving Biodiversity Hot Spots

In deciding which areas are of highest conservation priority, biologists often focus on hot spots of biodiversity. A **biodiversity hot spot** is a relatively small area with numerous endemic species (species found nowhere else in the world) and a large number of endangered and threatened species **(Figure 56.20)**. Nearly 30% of all bird species can be found in hot spots that make up only about 2% of Earth's land area. Together, the "hottest" of the terrestrial biodiversity hot spots total less than 1.5% of Earth's land but are home to more than a third of all species of plants, amphibians, reptiles (including birds), and mammals. Aquatic

ecosystems also have hot spots, such as coral reefs and certain river systems.

Biodiversity hot spots are good choices for nature reserves, but identifying them is not always simple. One problem is that a hot spot for one taxonomic group, such as butterflies, may not be a hot spot for some other taxonomic group, such as birds. Designating an area as a biodiversity hot spot is often biased toward saving vertebrates and plants, with less attention paid to invertebrates and microorganisms. Some biologists are also concerned that the hot-spot strategy places too much emphasis on such a small fraction of Earth's surface.

Global change makes the task of preserving hot spots even more challenging because the conditions that favor a particular community may not be found in the same location in the future. The biodiversity hot spot in the southwest corner of Australia (see Figure 56.20) holds thousands of species of endemic plants and numerous endemic vertebrates. Researchers recently concluded that between 5% and 25% of the plant species they examined may become extinct by 2080 because the plants will be unable to tolerate the increased dryness predicted for this region.

Philosophy of Nature Reserves

Nature reserves are protected "islands" of biodiversity in a sea of habitat altered or degraded by human activity. An earlier policy—that protected areas should be set aside to remain unchanged forever—was based on the concept that ecosystems are balanced, self-regulating units. However, disturbance is common in all ecosystems, and the nonequilibrium model (see Concept 54.3) applies to nature reserves as well as to the larger landscapes around them. Management policies that ignore disturbances or attempt to prevent them have generally failed. For instance, setting aside an area of a fire-dependent community, such as a portion of a tallgrass prairie, chaparral, or dry pine forest, with the intention of saving it is unrealistic if periodic burning is excluded.

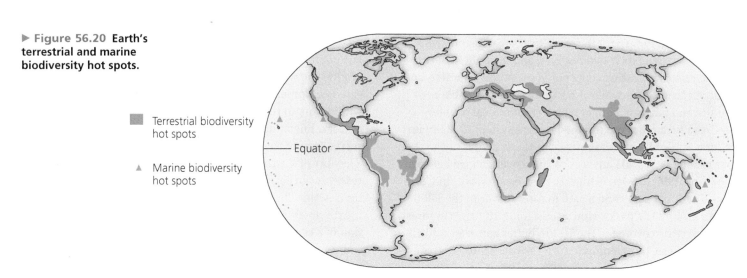

▶ **Figure 56.20 Earth's terrestrial and marine biodiversity hot spots.**

▪ Terrestrial biodiversity hot spots

▲ Marine biodiversity hot spots

Equator

Without the dominant disturbance, the fire-adapted species are usually outcompeted and biodiversity is reduced.

An important conservation question is whether to create numerous small reserves or fewer large reserves. Small, unconnected reserves may slow the spread of disease between populations. One argument for large reserves is that large, far-ranging animals with low-density populations, such as the grizzly bear, require extensive habitats. Large reserves also have proportionately smaller perimeters than small reserves and are therefore less affected by edges.

As conservation biologists have learned more about the requirements for achieving minimum viable populations for endangered species, they have realized that most national parks and other reserves are far too small. The area needed for the long-term survival of the Yellowstone grizzly bear population, for instance, is more than ten times the combined area of Yellowstone and Grand Teton National Parks. Areas of private and public land surrounding reserves will likely have to contribute to biodiversity conservation.

Zoned Reserves

Several nations have adopted a zoned reserve approach to landscape management. A **zoned reserve** is an extensive region that includes areas relatively undisturbed by humans surrounded by areas that have been changed by human activity and are used for economic gain. The key challenge of the zoned reserve approach is to develop a social and economic climate in the surrounding lands that is compatible with the long-term viability of the protected core. These surrounding areas continue to support human activities, but regulations prevent the types of extensive alterations likely to harm the protected area. As a result, the surrounding habitats serve as buffer zones against further intrusion into the undisturbed area.

The small Central American nation of Costa Rica has become a world leader in establishing zoned reserves. An agreement initiated in 1987 reduced Costa Rica's international debt in return for land preservation there. The country is now divided into 11 Conservation Areas, which include national parks and other protected areas, both on land and in the ocean (Figure 56.21). Costa Rica is making progress toward managing its zoned reserves, and the buffer zones provide a steady, lasting supply of forest products, water, and hydroelectric power while also supporting sustainable agriculture and tourism, both of which employ local people.

Costa Rica relies on its zoned reserve system to maintain at least 80% of its native species, but the system is not without problems. A 2003 analysis of land cover change between 1960 and 1997 showed negligible deforestation within Costa Rica's national parks and a gain in forest cover in the 1-km buffer around the parks. However, significant losses in forest cover were discovered in the 10-km buffer zones around all national parks, threatening to turn the parks into isolated habitat islands.

(a) Boundaries of the Conservation Areas are indicated by black outlines.

(b) Tourists marvel at the diversity of life in one of Costa Rica's protected areas.

▲ **Figure 56.21 Protected areas in Costa Rica.**

Although marine ecosystems have also been heavily affected by human exploitation, reserves in the ocean are far less common than reserves on land. Many fish populations around the world have collapsed as increasingly sophisticated equipment puts nearly all potential fishing grounds within human reach. In response, scientists at the University of York, England, have proposed establishing marine reserves around the world that would be off-limits to fishing. They present strong evidence that a patchwork of marine reserves can serve as a means of both increasing fish populations within the reserves and improving fishing success in nearby areas. Their proposed system is a modern application of a centuries-old practice in the Fiji Islands in which some areas have historically remained closed to fishing—a traditional example of the zoned reserve concept.

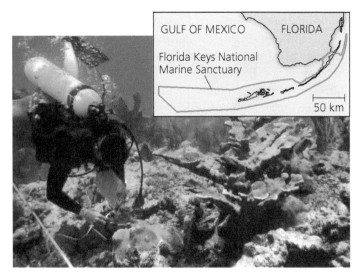

▲ **Figure 56.22 A diver measuring coral in the Florida Keys National Marine Sanctuary.**

The United States adopted such a system in creating a set of 13 national marine sanctuaries, including the Florida Keys National Marine Sanctuary, which was established in 1990 **(Figure 56.22)**. Populations of marine organisms, including fishes and lobsters, recovered quickly after harvests were banned in the 9,500-km^2 reserve. Larger and more abundant fish now produce larvae that help repopulate reefs and improve fishing outside the sanctuary. The increased marine life within the sanctuary also makes it a favorite for recreational divers, increasing the economic value of this zoned reserve.

Urban Ecology

The zoned reserves that you just read about combine habitats that are relatively undisturbed by human activity with those that are used extensively by people for economic gain. Increasingly, ecologists are looking at species preservation even in the context of cities. The field of **urban ecology** examines organisms and their environment in urban settings.

For the first time in history, more than half of the people on Earth live in cities. By the year 2030, 5 billion people are expected to be living in urban environments. As cities expand in number and size, protected areas that were once outside city boundaries become incorporated into urban landscapes. Ecologists are now studying cities as ecological laboratories, seeking to balance species preservation and other ecological needs with the needs of people.

One critical area of research centers on urban streams, including the quality and flow of their water and the organisms living in them. Urban streams tend to rise and fall more quickly after rain than natural streams. This rapid change in water level occurs because of the concrete and other impervious surfaces in cities as well as the drainage systems that route water out of cities as quickly as possible to avoid flooding. Urban streams also tend to have higher concentrations of nutrients and contaminants and are often straightened or even channeled underground.

Near Vancouver, British Columbia, ecologists and volunteers worked to restore a degraded urban stream, Guichon Creek, by planting trees and shrubs along the creek and stabilizing its banks. Their efforts returned the water flow and the communities of invertebrates and fish in the stream much closer to what they had been 50 years before the stream became degraded. A few years ago, ecologists successfully reestablished cutthroat trout in the stream. The trout are now thriving.

As cities continue to expand into the landscapes around them, understanding the ecological effects of this expansion will only increase in importance. Integrating cities into ecological research will grow as a research and conservation field over the coming decades.

CONCEPT CHECK **56.3**

1. What is a biodiversity hot spot?
2. How do zoned reserves provide economic incentives for long-term conservation of protected areas?
3. **WHAT IF?** Suppose a developer proposes to clear-cut a forest that serves as a corridor between two parks. To compensate, the developer also proposes to add the same area of forest to one of the parks. As a professional ecologist, how might you argue for retaining the corridor?

For suggested answers, see Appendix A.

CONCEPT 56.4

Earth is changing rapidly as a result of human actions

As we've discussed, landscape and regional conservation help protect habitats and preserve species. However, environmental changes that result from human activities are creating new challenges. As a consequence of human-caused climate change, for example, the place where a vulnerable species is found today may not be the same place that is needed for preservation in the future. What would happen if *many* habitats on Earth changed so quickly that the locations of preserves today were unsuitable for their species in 10, 50, or 100 years? Such a scenario is increasingly possible.

The rest of this section describes four types of environmental change that humans are bringing about: nutrient enrichment, toxin accumulation, climate change, and ozone depletion. The impacts of these and other changes are evident not just in human-dominated ecosystems, such as cities and farms, but also in the most remote ecosystems on Earth.

Nutrient Enrichment

Human activity often removes nutrients from one part of the biosphere and adds them to another. Someone eating strawberries in Washington, DC, consumes nutrients that only days before were in the soil in California; a short time later, some of these nutrients will be in the Potomac River, having passed through the person's digestive system and a local sewage treatment facility.

Farming is an example of how human activities are altering the environment through the enrichment of nutrients, particularly ones containing nitrogen. After vegetation is cleared from an area, the existing reserve of nutrients in the soil is depleted as nutrients are exported from the area in crop biomass. The "free" period for crop production—when there is no need to replenish nutrients by adding fertilizer to the soil—varies greatly. When some of the early North American prairie lands were first tilled, good crops could be produced for decades because the large store of organic materials in the soil continued to decompose and provide nutrients. By contrast, some cleared land in the tropics can be farmed for only one or two years because so little of the ecosystems' nutrient load is contained in the soil. Despite such variations, in any area under intensive agriculture, the natural store of nutrients eventually becomes exhausted.

Nitrogen is the main nutrient lost through agriculture (see Figure 55.14). Plowing mixes the soil and speeds up decomposition of organic matter, releasing nitrogen that is then removed when crops are harvested. Applied fertilizers make up for the loss of usable nitrogen from agricultural ecosystems (Figure 56.23). However, without plants to take up nitrates from the soil, the nitrates are likely to be leached from the ecosystem (see Figure 55.16).

Recent studies indicate that human activities have more than doubled Earth's supply of fixed nitrogen available to primary producers. Industrial fertilizers provide the largest additional nitrogen source. Fossil fuel combustion also releases nitrogen oxides, which enter the atmosphere and dissolve in rainwater; the nitrogen ultimately enters ecosystems as nitrate. Increased cultivation of legumes, with their nitrogen-fixing symbionts, is a third way in which humans increase the amount of fixed nitrogen in the soil.

A problem arises when the nutrient level in an ecosystem exceeds the **critical load**, the amount of added nutrient, usually nitrogen or phosphorus, that can be absorbed by plants without damaging ecosystem integrity. For example, nitrogenous minerals in the soil that exceed the critical load eventually leach into groundwater or run off into freshwater and marine ecosystems, contaminating water supplies and killing fish. Nitrate concentrations in groundwater are increasing in most agricultural regions, sometimes reaching levels that are unsafe for drinking.

Many rivers contaminated with nitrates and ammonium from agricultural runoff and sewage drain into the Atlantic Ocean, with the highest inputs coming from northern Europe and the central United States. The Mississippi River carries nitrogen pollution to the Gulf of Mexico, fueling a phytoplankton bloom each summer. When the phytoplankton die, their decomposition by oxygen-using organisms creates an extensive "dead zone" of low oxygen levels along the coast (Figure 56.24). Fish and other marine animals disappear from some of the most economically important waters in the United States. To reduce the size of the dead zone, farmers have begun using fertilizers more efficiently, and managers are restoring wetlands in the Mississippi watershed, two changes stimulated by the results of ecosystem experiments.

Nutrient runoff can also lead to the eutrophication of lakes (see Concept 55.2). The bloom and subsequent die-off of algae and cyanobacteria and the ensuing depletion of oxygen are similar to what occurs in a marine dead zone. Such conditions threaten the survival of organisms. For example, eutrophication of Lake Erie coupled with overfishing wiped out commercially important fishes such as blue pike, whitefish, and lake trout by the 1960s. Since then, tighter regulations on the dumping of sewage and other wastes into the lake have enabled some fish populations to rebound, but many native species of fish and invertebrates have not recovered.

▲ **Figure 56.23 Fertilization of a corn (maize) crop.** To replace the nutrients removed in crops, farmers must apply fertilizers—either organic, such as manure or mulch, or synthetic, as shown here.

▶ **Figure 56.24 A phytoplankton bloom arising from nitrogen pollution in the Mississippi basin that leads to a dead zone.** In this satellite image from 2004, red and orange represent high concentrations of phytoplankton in the Gulf of Mexico.

Toxins in the Environment

Humans release an immense variety of toxic chemicals, including thousands of synthetic compounds previously unknown in nature, with little regard for the ecological consequences. Organisms acquire toxic substances from the environment along with nutrients and water. Some of the poisons are metabolized or excreted, but others accumulate in specific tissues, often fat. One of the reasons accumulated toxins are particularly harmful is that they become more concentrated in successive trophic levels of a food web. This phenomenon, called **biological magnification**, occurs because the biomass at any given trophic level is produced from a much larger biomass ingested from the level below (see Concept 55.3). Thus, top-level carnivores tend to be most severely affected by toxic compounds in the environment.

Chlorinated hydrocarbons are a class of industrially synthesized compounds that have demonstrated biological magnification. Chlorinated hydrocarbons include the industrial chemicals called PCBs (polychlorinated biphenyls) and many pesticides, such as DDT. Current research implicates many of these compounds in endocrine system disruption in a large number of animal species, including humans. Biological magnification of PCBs has been found in the food web of the Great Lakes, where the concentration of PCBs in herring gull eggs, at the top of the food web, is nearly 5,000 times that in phytoplankton, at the base of the food web **(Figure 56.25)**.

An infamous case of biological magnification that harmed top-level carnivores involved DDT, a chemical used to control insects such as mosquitoes and agricultural pests. In the decade after World War II, the use of DDT grew rapidly; its ecological consequences were not yet fully understood. By the 1950s, scientists were learning that DDT persists in the environment and is transported by water to areas far from where it is applied. One of the first signs that DDT was a serious environmental problem was a decline in the populations of pelicans, ospreys, and eagles, birds that feed at the top of food webs. The accumulation of DDT (and DDE, a product of its breakdown) in the tissues of these birds interfered with the deposition of calcium in their eggshells. When the birds tried to incubate their eggs, the weight of the parents broke the shells of affected eggs, resulting in catastrophic declines in the birds' reproduction rates. Rachel Carson's book *Silent Spring* helped bring the problem to public attention in the 1960s **(Figure 56.26)**, and DDT was banned in the United States in 1971. A dramatic recovery in populations of the affected bird species followed.

In much of the tropics, DDT is still used to control the mosquitoes that spread malaria and other diseases. Societies there face a trade-off between saving human lives and protecting other species. The best approach seems to be to apply DDT sparingly and to couple its use with mosquito

▲ **Figure 56.25 Biological magnification of PCBs in a Great Lakes food web.** (ppm = parts per million)

INTERPRET THE DATA *If a typical smelt weighs 225 g, what is the total mass of PCBs in a smelt in the Great Lakes? If an average lake trout weighs 4,500 g, what is the total mass of PCBs in a trout in the Great Lakes? Assume that a lake trout from an unpolluted source is introduced into the Great Lakes and smelt are the only source of PCBs in the trout's diet. The new trout would have the same level of PCBs as the existing trout after eating how many smelt? (Assume that the trout retains 100% of the PCBs it consumes.)*

netting and other low-technology solutions. The complicated history of DDT illustrates the importance of understanding the ecological connections between diseases and communities (see Concept 54.5).

Pharmaceuticals make up another group of toxins in the environment, one that is a growing concern among ecologists. The use of over-the-counter and prescription drugs has risen in recent years, particularly in industrialized nations.

◄ **Figure 56.26 Rachel Carson.** Through her writing and her testimony before the U.S. Congress, biologist and author Carson helped promote a new environmental ethic. Her efforts led to a ban on DDT use in the United States and stronger controls on the use of other chemicals.

People who consume such products excrete residual chemicals in their waste and may also dispose of unused drugs improperly, such as in their toilets or sinks. Drugs that are not broken down in sewage treatment plants may then enter rivers and lakes with the material discharged from these plants. Growth-promoting drugs given to farm animals can also enter rivers and lakes with agricultural runoff. As a consequence, many pharmaceuticals are spreading in low concentrations across the world's freshwater ecosystems (Figure 56.27).

▲ Figure 56.27 **Sources and movements of pharmaceuticals in the environment.**

Among the pharmaceuticals that ecologists are studying are the sex steroids, including forms of estrogen used for birth control. Some fish species are so sensitive to certain estrogens that concentrations of a few parts per trillion in their water can alter sexual differentiation and shift the female-to-male sex ratio toward females. Researchers in Ontario, Canada, conducted a seven-year experiment in which they applied the synthetic estrogen used in contraceptives to a lake in very low concentrations (5–6 ng/L). They found that chronic exposure of the fathead minnow (*Pimephales promelas*) to the estrogen led to feminization of males and a near extinction of the species from the lake.

Many toxins cannot be degraded by microorganisms and persist in the environment for years or even decades. In other cases, chemicals released into the environment may be relatively harmless but are converted to more toxic products by reaction with other substances, by exposure to light, or by the metabolism of microorganisms. Mercury, a by-product of plastic production and coal-fired power generation, has been routinely expelled into rivers and the sea in an insoluble form. Bacteria in the bottom mud convert the waste to methylmercury (CH_3Hg^+), an extremely toxic water-soluble compound that accumulates in the tissues of organisms, including humans who consume fish from the contaminated waters.

Greenhouse Gases and Climate Change

Human activities release a variety of gaseous waste products. People once thought that the vast atmosphere could absorb these materials indefinitely, but we now know that such additions can cause fundamental changes to the atmosphere and to its interactions with the rest of the biosphere. In this section, we'll examine how increasing concentrations of carbon dioxide and other greenhouse gases may affect species and ecosystems through a changing climate.

Rising Atmospheric CO₂ Levels

Since the Industrial Revolution, the concentration of CO_2 in the atmosphere has been increasing as a result of the burning of fossil fuels and deforestation. Scientists estimate that the average CO_2 concentration in the atmosphere before 1850 was about 274 ppm. In 1958, a monitoring station began taking very accurate measurements on Hawaii's Mauna Loa peak, a location far from cities and high enough for the atmosphere to be well mixed. At that time, the CO_2 concentration was 316 ppm (Figure 56.28). Today, it is around 400 ppm, an increase of more than 40% since the mid-19th century. In the Scientific Skills Exercise, you can graph and interpret changes in CO_2 concentration that occur during the course of a year and over longer periods.

The marked increase in the concentration of atmospheric CO_2 over the last 150 years concerns scientists because of its link to increased global temperature. Much of the solar radiation that strikes the planet is reflected back into space. Although CO_2, methane, water vapor, and other greenhouse gases in the atmosphere are transparent to visible light, they intercept and absorb much of the infrared radiation Earth emits, re-reflecting some of it back toward Earth. This process retains some of the solar heat. If it were not for this **greenhouse effect**, the average air temperature at Earth's surface would be a frigid −18°C (−0.4°F), and most life as we know it could not exist.

For more than a century, scientists have studied how greenhouse gases warm Earth and how fossil fuel burning could contribute to the warming. Most scientists are convinced that such warming is already occurring and will increase rapidly this century (see Figure 56.28). Global models predict that by the end of the 21st century, the atmospheric

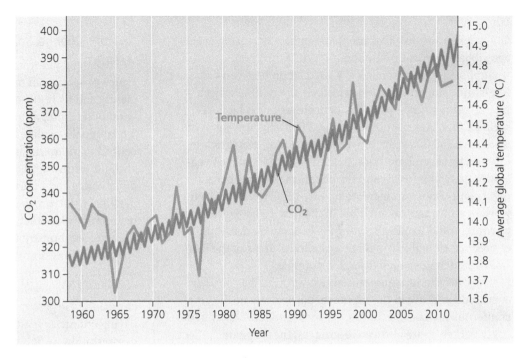

► **Figure 56.28 Increase in atmospheric carbon dioxide concentration at Mauna Loa, Hawaii, and average global temperatures.** Aside from normal seasonal fluctuations, the CO_2 concentration (blue curve) has increased steadily from 1958 to 2013. Though average global temperatures (red curve) fluctuated a great deal over the same period, there is a clear warming trend.

Graphing Cyclic Data

How Does the Atmospheric CO_2 Concentration Change During a Year and from Decade to Decade? The blue curve in Figure 56.28 shows how the concentration of CO_2 in Earth's atmosphere has changed over a span of more than 50 years. For each year in that span, two data points are plotted, one in May and one in November. A more detailed picture of the change in CO_2 concentration can be obtained by looking at measurements made at more frequent intervals. In this exercise, you'll graph monthly CO_2 concentrations for three years over three decades.

Data from the Study The data in the table below are average CO_2 concentrations (in parts per million) at the Mauna Loa monitoring station for each month in 1990, 2000, and 2010.

► A researcher sampling the air at the Mauna Loa monitoring station, Hawaii.

Month	1990	2000	2010
January	353.79	369.25	388.45
February	354.88	369.50	389.82
March	355.65	370.56	391.08
April	356.27	371.82	392.46
May	359.29	371.51	392.95
June	356.32	371.71	392.06
July	354.88	369.85	390.13
August	352.89	368.20	388.15
September	351.28	366.91	386.80
October	351.59	366.91	387.18
November	353.05	366.99	388.59
December	354.27	369.67	389.68

allows you to clearly see the patterns of CO_2 concentration changes, both during each year and from decade to decade. (For additional information about graphs, see the Scientific Skills Review in Appendix F and in the Study Area in MasteringBiology.)

2. Within each year, what is the pattern of change in CO_2 concentration? Why does this pattern occur?

3. The measurements taken at Mauna Loa represent average atmospheric CO_2 concentrations for the Northern Hemisphere. Suppose you could measure CO_2 concentrations under similar conditions in the Southern Hemisphere. What pattern would you expect to see in those measurements over the course of a year? Explain.

4. In addition to the changes within each year, what changes in CO_2 concentration occurred between 1990 and 2010? Calculate the average CO_2 concentration for the 12 months of each year. By what percentage did this average change from 1990 to 2000 and from 1990 to 2010?

(MB) A version of this Scientific Skills Exercise can be assigned in MasteringBiology.

Interpret the Data

1. Plot the data for all three years on one graph. Select a type of graph that is appropriate for these data, and choose a vertical axis scale that

Data from National Oceanic & Atmospheric Administration, Earth System Research Laboratory, Global Monitoring Division.

CO_2 concentration will more than double, increasing average global temperature by about 3°C (5°F).

Supporting these models is a correlation between CO_2 levels and temperatures in prehistoric times. One way climatologists estimate past CO_2 concentrations is by measuring CO_2 levels in bubbles trapped in glacial ice, some of which are 750,000 years old. Prehistoric temperatures are inferred by several methods, including analysis of past vegetation based on fossils and the chemical isotopes in sediments and corals. An increase of only 1.3°C would make the world warmer than at any time in the past 100,000 years. A warming trend would also alter the geographic distribution of precipitation, likely making agricultural areas of the central United States much drier, for example.

The ecosystems where the largest warming has *already* occurred are those in the far north, particularly northern coniferous forests and tundra. As snow and ice melt and uncover darker, more absorptive surfaces, these systems reflect less radiation back to the atmosphere and warm further. Arctic sea ice in the summer of 2012 covered the smallest area on record. Climate models suggest that there may be no summer ice there within a few decades, decreasing habitat for polar bears, seals, and seabirds. Higher temperatures also increase the likelihood of fires. In boreal forests of western North America and Russia, fires have burned twice the usual area in recent decades.

By studying how past periods of global warming and cooling affected plant communities, ecologists are trying to predict the consequences of future changes in temperature and precipitation. Analysis of fossilized pollen indicates that plant communities change dramatically with changes in temperature. Past climate changes occurred gradually, though, and most plant and animal populations had time to migrate into areas where abiotic conditions allowed them to survive.

Many organisms, especially plants that cannot disperse rapidly over long distances, may not be able to survive the rapid climate change projected to result from global warming. Furthermore, many habitats today are more fragmented than ever (see Concept 56.3), further limiting the ability of many organisms to migrate. For these reasons, ecologists are debating **assisted migration**, the translocation of a species to a favorable habitat beyond its native range to protect the species from human-caused threats. Most ecologists consider such an approach only as a last resort, in part because of the dangers of introducing potentially invasive species to new regions. Although scientists have yet to perform assisted migration, activists in 2008 transplanted seedlings of the endangered tree *Torreya taxifolia* hundreds of kilometers north from its native range in Florida to western North Carolina in anticipation of climate change. This "rewilding," as it is sometimes called, appeared to be driven in part by a desire for publicity; no ecological framework yet exists for deciding if, when, and where assisted migration is desirable.

Climate Change Solutions

We will need many approaches to slow global warming. Quick progress can be made by using energy more efficiently and by replacing fossil fuels with renewable solar and wind power and, more controversially, with nuclear power. Today, coal, gasoline, wood, and other organic fuels remain central to industrialized societies and cannot be burned without releasing CO_2. Stabilizing CO_2 emissions will require concerted international effort and changes in both personal lifestyles and industrial processes. International negotiations have yet to reach a global consensus on how to reduce greenhouse gas emissions.

Another important approach to slowing global warming is to reduce deforestation around the world, particularly in the tropics. Deforestation currently accounts for about 10% of greenhouse gas emissions. Recent research shows that paying countries *not* to cut forests could decrease the rate of deforestation by half within 10 to 20 years. Reduced deforestation would not only slow the buildup of greenhouse gases in our atmosphere, but would also sustain native forests and preserve biodiversity, a positive outcome for all.

Depletion of Atmospheric Ozone

Like carbon dioxide and other greenhouse gases, atmospheric ozone (O_3) has also changed in concentration because of human activities. Life on Earth is protected from the damaging effects of ultraviolet (UV) radiation by a layer of ozone located in the stratosphere 17–25 km above Earth's surface. However, satellite studies of the atmosphere show that the springtime ozone layer over Antarctica has thinned substantially since the mid-1970s **(Figure 56.29)**. The

▲ **Figure 56.29 Thickness of the October ozone layer over Antarctica in units called Dobsons.**

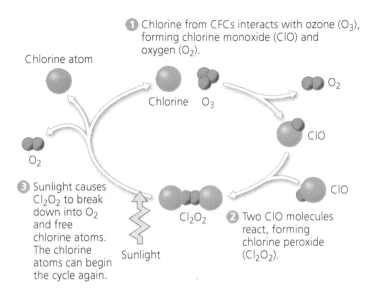

1 Chlorine from CFCs interacts with ozone (O_3), forming chlorine monoxide (ClO) and oxygen (O_2).

Chlorine atom

Chlorine O_3

O_2

ClO

O_2

ClO

3 Sunlight causes Cl_2O_2 to break down into O_2 and free chlorine atoms. The chlorine atoms can begin the cycle again.

Cl_2O_2

Sunlight

2 Two ClO molecules react, forming chlorine peroxide (Cl_2O_2).

▲ Figure 56.30 How free chlorine in the atmosphere destroys ozone.

September 1979   September 2012

▲ Figure 56.31 Erosion of Earth's ozone shield. The ozone hole over Antarctica is visible as the dark blue patch in these images based on atmospheric data.

destruction of atmospheric ozone results primarily from the accumulation of chlorofluorocarbons (CFCs), chemicals once widely used in refrigeration and manufacturing. In the stratosphere, chlorine atoms released from CFCs react with ozone, reducing it to molecular O_2 (Figure 56.30). Subsequent chemical reactions liberate the chlorine, allowing it to react with other ozone molecules in a catalytic chain reaction.

The thinning of the ozone layer is most apparent over Antarctica in spring, where cold, stable air allows the chain reaction to continue (Figure 56.31). The magnitude of ozone depletion and the size of the ozone hole have been slightly smaller in recent years than the average for the last 20 years, but the hole still sometimes extends as far as the southernmost portions of Australia, New Zealand, and South America. At the more heavily populated middle latitudes, ozone levels have decreased 2–10% during the past 20 years.

Decreased ozone levels in the stratosphere increase the intensity of UV rays reaching Earth's surface. The consequences of ozone depletion for life on Earth may be severe for plants, animals, and microorganisms. Some scientists expect increases in both lethal and nonlethal forms of skin cancer and in cataracts among humans, as well as unpredictable effects on crops and natural communities, especially the phytoplankton that are responsible for a large proportion of Earth's primary production.

To study the consequences of ozone depletion, ecologists have conducted field experiments in which they use filters to decrease or block the UV radiation in sunlight. One such experiment, performed on a scrub ecosystem near the tip of South America, showed that when the ozone hole passed over the area, the amount of UV radiation reaching the ground increased sharply, causing more DNA damage in plants that were not protected by filters. Scientists have shown similar DNA damage and a reduction in phytoplankton growth when the ozone hole opens over the Southern Ocean (Antarctic Ocean) each year.

The good news about the ozone hole is how quickly many countries have responded to it. Since 1987, at least 197 nations, including the United States, have signed the Montreal Protocol, a treaty that regulates the use of ozone-depleting chemicals. Most nations, again including the United States, have ended the production of CFCs. As a consequence of these actions, chlorine concentrations in the stratosphere have stabilized and ozone depletion is slowing. Even though CFC emissions are close to zero today, however, chlorine molecules already in the atmosphere will continue to influence stratospheric ozone levels for at least 50 years.

The partial destruction of Earth's ozone shield is one more example of how much humans have been able to disrupt the dynamics of ecosystems and the biosphere. It also highlights our ability to solve environmental problems when we set our minds to it.

CONCEPT CHECK 56.4

1. How can the addition of excess mineral nutrients to a lake threaten its fish population?

2. MAKE CONNECTIONS There are vast stores of organic matter in the soils of northern coniferous forests and tundra around the world. Suggest an explanation for why scientists who study global warming are closely monitoring these stores (see Figure 55.15).

3. MAKE CONNECTIONS Mutagens are chemical and physical agents that induce mutations in DNA (see Concept 17.5). How does reduced ozone concentration in the atmosphere increase the likelihood of mutations in various organisms?

For suggested answers, see Appendix A.

CONCEPT 56.5

Sustainable development can improve human lives while conserving biodiversity

With the increasing loss and fragmentation of habitats, changes in Earth's physical environment and climate, and increasing human population (see Concept 53.6), we face difficult trade-offs in managing the world's resources. Preserving all habitat patches isn't feasible, so biologists must help societies set conservation priorities by identifying which habitat patches are most crucial. Ideally, implementing these priorities should also improve the quality of life for local people. Ecologists use the concept of *sustainability* as a tool to establish long-term conservation priorities.

Sustainable Development

We need to understand the interconnections of the biosphere if we are to protect species from extinction and improve the quality of human life. To this end, many nations, scientific societies, and other groups have embraced the concept of **sustainable development**, economic development that meets the needs of people today without limiting the ability of future generations to meet their needs. The forward-looking Ecological Society of America, the world's largest organization of professional ecologists, endorsed an ongoing research agenda called the Sustainable Biosphere Initiative two decades ago. The goal of this initiative is to define and acquire the basic ecological information needed to develop, manage, and conserve Earth's resources as responsibly as possible. The research agenda includes studies of global change, including interactions between climate and ecological processes; biological diversity and its role in maintaining ecological processes; and the ways in which the productivity of natural and artificial ecosystems can be sustained. This initiative requires a strong commitment of human and economic resources.

Achieving sustainable development is an ambitious goal. To sustain ecosystem processes and stem the loss of biodiversity, we must connect life science with the social sciences, economics, and the humanities. We must also reassess our personal values. Those of us living in wealthier nations have a larger ecological footprint than do people living in developing nations (see Concept 53.6). By including the long-term costs in profit-and-loss calculations, we can learn to value the natural processes that sustain us. The following case study illustrates how the combination of scientific and personal efforts can make a significant difference in creating a truly sustainable world.

Case Study: *Sustainable Development in Costa Rica*

The success of conservation in Costa Rica (see Concept 56.3) has required a partnership between the national government, nongovernment organizations (NGOs), and private citizens. Many nature reserves established by individuals have been recognized by the government as national wildlife reserves and given significant tax benefits. However, conservation and restoration of biodiversity make up only one facet of sustainable development; the other key facet is improving the human condition.

How have the living conditions of the Costa Rican people changed as the country has pursued its conservation goals? Two of the most fundamental indicators of living conditions are infant mortality rate and life expectancy (see Concept 53.6). From 1930 to 2010, the infant mortality rate in Costa Rica declined from 170 to 9 per 1,000 live births; over the same period, life expectancy increased from about 43 years to 79 years (Figure 56.32). Another indicator of living conditions is the literacy rate. The 2004 literacy rate in Costa Rica was 96%, compared to 97% in the United States. Such statistics show that living conditions in Costa Rica have improved greatly over the period in which the country has dedicated itself to conservation and restoration. While this result does not prove that conservation *causes* an improvement in human welfare, we can say with certainty that development in Costa Rica has attended to both nature *and* people.

Costa Rica still faces a number of challenges, particularly a human population growing rapidly at 1.5% per year. Nonetheless, if recent success is any guide, the people of Costa Rica will overcome the challenge of population growth in their quest for sustainable development.

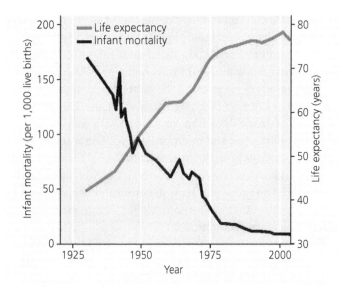

▲ Figure 56.32 **Infant mortality and life expectancy at birth in Costa Rica.**

1276 UNIT EIGHT Ecology

The Future of the Biosphere

Our modern lives are very different from those of early humans, who hunted and gathered to survive. Their reverence for the natural world is evident in the early murals of wildlife they painted on cave walls **(Figure 56.33a)** and in the stylized visions of life they sculpted from bone and ivory **(Figure 56.33b)**.

Our lives reflect remnants of our ancestral attachment to nature and the diversity of life—the concept of *biophilia* that was introduced early in this chapter. We evolved in natural environments rich in biodiversity, and we still have an affinity for such settings **(Figure 56.33 c and d)**. E. O. Wilson makes the case that our biophilia is innate, an evolutionary product of natural selection acting on a brainy species whose survival depended on a close connection to the environment and a practical appreciation of plants and animals.

Our appreciation of life guides the field of biology today. We celebrate life by deciphering the genetic code that makes each species unique. We embrace life by using fossils and DNA to chronicle evolution through time. We preserve life through our efforts to classify and protect the millions of species on Earth. We respect life by using nature responsibly and reverently to improve human welfare.

Biology is the scientific expression of our desire to know nature. We are most likely to protect what we appreciate, and we are most likely to appreciate what we understand. By learning about the processes and diversity of life, we also become more aware of ourselves and our place in the biosphere. We hope this text has served you well in this lifelong adventure.

CONCEPT CHECK 56.5

1. What is meant by the term *sustainable development*?
2. How might biophilia influence us to conserve species and restore ecosystems?
3. **WHAT IF?** Suppose a new fishery is discovered, and you are put in charge of developing it sustainably. What ecological data might you want on the fish population? What criteria would you apply for the fishery's development?

For suggested answers, see Appendix A.

(a) Detail of animals in a 17,000-year-old cave painting, Lascaux, France

(b) A 30,000-year-old ivory carving of a water bird, found in Germany

(c) Nature lovers on a wildlife-watching expedition

▲ **Figure 56.33 Biophilia, past and present.**

(d) A young biologist holding a songbird

SUMMARY OF KEY CONCEPTS

CONCEPT 56.1

Human activities threaten Earth's biodiversity (pp. 1255–1261)

- Biodiversity can be considered at three main levels:

Genetic diversity: source of variations that enable populations to adapt to environmental changes

Species diversity: important in maintaining structure of communities and food webs

Ecosystem diversity: provides life-sustaining services such as nutrient cycling and waste decomposition

- Our biophilia enables us to recognize the value of biodiversity for its own sake. Other species also provide humans with food, fiber, medicines, and **ecosystem services.**
- Four major threats to biodiversity are habitat loss, **introduced species,** overharvesting, and global change.

> **?** *Give at least three examples of key ecosystem services that nature provides for people.*

CONCEPT 56.2

Population conservation focuses on population size, genetic diversity, and critical habitat (pp. 1261–1265)

- When a population drops below a **minimum viable population (MVP)** size, its loss of genetic variation due to nonrandom mating and genetic drift can trap it in an **extinction vortex.**
- The declining-population approach focuses on the environmental factors that cause decline, regardless of absolute population size. It follows a step-by-step conservation strategy.
- Conserving species often requires resolving conflicts between the habitat needs of **endangered species** and human demands.

> **?** *Why is the minimum viable population size smaller for a genetically diverse population than for a less genetically diverse population?*

CONCEPT 56.3

Landscape and regional conservation help sustain biodiversity (pp. 1265–1269)

- The structure of a landscape can strongly influence biodiversity. As habitat fragmentation increases and edges become more extensive, biodiversity tends to decrease. **Movement corridors** can promote dispersal and help sustain populations.
- **Biodiversity hot spots** are also hot spots of extinction and thus prime candidates for protection. Sustaining biodiversity in parks and reserves requires management to ensure that human activities in the surrounding landscape do not harm the protected habitats. The **zoned reserve** model recognizes that conservation efforts often involve working in landscapes that are greatly affected by human activity.
- **Urban ecology** is the study of organisms and their environment in primarily urban settings.

> **?** *Give two examples that show how habitat fragmentation can harm species in the long term.*

CONCEPT 56.4

Earth is changing rapidly as a result of human actions (pp. 1269–1275)

- Agriculture removes plant nutrients from ecosystems, so large supplements are usually required. The nutrients in fertilizer can pollute groundwater and surface-water aquatic ecosystems, where they can stimulate excess algal growth (eutrophication).
- The release of toxic wastes and pharmaceuticals has polluted the environment with harmful substances that often persist for long periods and become increasingly concentrated in successively higher trophic levels of food webs (**biological magnification**).
- Because of human activities, the atmospheric concentration of CO_2 and other greenhouse gases has been steadily increasing. The ultimate effects include significant climate change.
- The ozone layer reduces the penetration of UV radiation through the atmosphere. Human activities, notably the release of chlorine-containing pollutants, have eroded the ozone layer, but government policies are helping to solve the problem.

> **?** *In the face of biological magnification of toxins, is it healthier to feed at a lower or higher trophic level? Explain.*

CONCEPT 56.5

Sustainable development can improve human lives while conserving biodiversity (pp. 1276–1277)

- The goal of the Sustainable Biosphere Initiative is to acquire the ecological information needed for the development, management, and conservation of Earth's resources.
- Costa Rica's success in conserving tropical biodiversity has involved a partnership among the government, other organizations, and private citizens. Human living conditions in Costa Rica have improved along with ecological conservation.
- By learning about biological processes and the diversity of life, we become more aware of our close connection to the environment and the value of other organisms that share it.

> **?** *Why is sustainability such an important goal for conservation biologists?*

TEST YOUR UNDERSTANDING

LEVEL 1: KNOWLEDGE/COMPREHENSION

1. One characteristic that distinguishes a population in an extinction vortex from most other populations is that
   a. it is a rare, top-level predator.
   b. its effective population size is much lower than its total population size.
   c. its genetic diversity is very low.
   d. it is not well adapted to edge conditions.

2. The main cause of the increase in the amount of CO_2 in Earth's atmosphere over the past 150 years is
   a. increased worldwide primary production.
   b. increased worldwide standing crop.
   c. an increase in the amount of infrared radiation absorbed by the atmosphere.
   d. the burning of larger amounts of wood and fossil fuels.

3. What is the single greatest threat to biodiversity?
   a. overharvesting of commercially important species
   b. habitat alteration, fragmentation, and destruction
   c. introduced species that compete with native species
   d. pollution of Earth's air, water, and soil

LEVEL 2: APPLICATION/ANALYSIS

4. Which of the following is a consequence of biological magnification?
   a. Toxic chemicals in the environment pose greater risk to top-level predators than to primary consumers.
   b. Populations of top-level predators are generally smaller than populations of primary consumers.
   c. The biomass of producers in an ecosystem is generally higher than the biomass of primary consumers.
   d. Only a small portion of the energy captured by producers is transferred to consumers.

5. Which of the following strategies would most rapidly increase the genetic diversity of a population in an extinction vortex?
   a. Establish a reserve that protects the population's habitat.
   b. Introduce new individuals transported from other populations of the same species.
   c. Sterilize the least fit individuals in the population.
   d. Control populations of the endangered population's predators and competitors.

6. Of the following statements about protected areas that have been established to preserve biodiversity, which one is *not* correct?
   a. About 25% of Earth's land area is now protected.
   b. National parks are one of many types of protected areas.
   c. Management of a protected area should be coordinated with management of the land surrounding the area.
   d. It is especially important to protect biodiversity hot spots.

LEVEL 3: SYNTHESIS/EVALUATION

7. **DRAW IT** (a) Referring to Figure 56.28, estimate the average CO_2 concentration in 1975 and in 2012. (b) What was the rate of CO_2 concentration increase (ppm/yr) from 1975 to 2012? (c) Assuming that the CO_2 concentration continues to rise as fast as it did from 1975 to 2012, what will be the approximate CO_2 concentration in 2100? (d) Draw a graph of average CO_2 concentration from 1975 to 2012 and then use a dashed line to extend the graph to the year 2100. (e) What ecological factors and human decisions will influence the actual rise in CO_2 concentration? (f) How might additional scientific data help societies predict this value?

8. **EVOLUTION CONNECTION**
   The fossil record indicates that there have been five mass extinction events in the past 500 million years (see Concept 25.4). Many ecologists think we are currently entering a sixth mass extinction event because of the threats to biodiversity described in this chapter. Briefly discuss the history of mass extinctions and the length of time it typically takes for species diversity to recover through the process of evolution. Explain why this should motivate us to slow the loss of biodiversity today.

9. **SCIENTIFIC INQUIRY**
   DRAW IT Suppose that you are managing a forest reserve, and one of your goals is to protect local populations of woodland birds from parasitism by the brown-headed cowbird. You know that female cowbirds usually do not venture more than about 100 m into a forest and that nest parasitism is reduced when woodland birds nest away from forest edges. The reserve you manage extends about 6,000 m from east to west and 1,000 m from north to south. It is surrounded by a deforested pasture on the west, an agricultural field for 500 m in the southwest corner, and intact forest everywhere else. You must build a road, 10 m by 1,000 m, from the north to the south side of the reserve and construct a maintenance building that will take up 100 m^2 in the reserve. Draw a map of the reserve, showing where you would put the road and the building to minimize cowbird intrusion along edges. Explain your reasoning.

10. **WRITE ABOUT A THEME: INTERACTIONS**
    One factor favoring rapid population growth by an introduced species is the absence of the predators, parasites, and pathogens that controlled its population in the region where it evolved. In a short essay (100–150 words), explain how evolution by natural selection would influence the rate at which native predators, parasites, and pathogens in a region of introduction attack an introduced species.

11. **SYNTHESIZE YOUR KNOWLEDGE**

Big cats, such as the Siberian tiger (*Panthera tigris altaica*) shown here, are one of the most endangered groups of mammals in the world. Based on what you've learned in this chapter, discuss some of the approaches you would use to help preserve them.

For selected answers, see Appendix A.

MasteringBiology®

Students Go to **MasteringBiology** for assignments, the eText, and the Study Area with practice tests, animations, and activities.

Instructors Go to **MasteringBiology** for automatically graded tutorials and questions that you can assign to your students, plus Instructor Resources.

Chapter 22

Figure Questions

Figure 22.6 The cactus-eater is more closely related to the seed-eater; Figure 1.22 shows that they share a more recent common ancestor (a seed-eater) than the cactus-eater shares with the insect-eater. **Figure 22.8** The common ancestor lived more than 5.5 million years ago. **Figure 22.12** The colors and body forms of these mantids allow them to blend into their surroundings, providing an example of how organisms are well matched to life in their environments. The mantids also share features with one another (and with all other mantids), such as six legs, grasping forelimbs, and large eyes. These shared features illustrate another key observation about life: the unity that results from descent from a common ancestor. Over time, as these mantids diverged from a common ancestor, they accumulated different adaptations that made them well suited for life in their different environments. Eventually, these differences became large enough that new species were formed, thus contributing to the great diversity of life. **Figure 22.13** These results show that being reared from the egg stage on one plant species or the other did not result in the adult having a beak length appropriate for that host; instead, adult beak lengths were determined primarily by the population from which the eggs were obtained. Because an egg from a balloon vine population likely had long-beaked parents, while an egg from a goldenrain tree population likely had short-beaked parents, these results indicate that beak length is an inherited trait. **Figure 22.14** Both strategies should increase the time that it takes *S. aureus* to become resistant to a new drug. If a drug that harms *S. aureus* does not harm other bacteria, natural selection will not favor resistance to that drug in the other species. This would decrease the chance that *S. aureus* would acquire resistance genes from other bacteria—thus slowing the evolution of resistance. Similarly, selection for resistance to a drug that slows the growth but does not kill *S. aureus* is much weaker than selection for resistance to a drug that kills *S. aureus*—again slowing the evolution of resistance. **Figure 22.17** Based on this evolutionary tree, crocodiles are more closely related to birds than to lizards because they share a more recent common ancestor with birds (ancestor ⑤) than with lizards (ancestor ④). **Figure 22.20** Hind limb structure changed first. *Rodhocetus* lacked flukes, but its pelvic bones and hind limbs had changed substantially from how those bones were shaped and arranged in *Pakicetus*. For example, in *Rodhocetus*, the pelvis and hind limbs appear to be oriented for paddling, whereas they were oriented for walking in *Pakicetus*.

Concept Check 22.1

1. Hutton and Lyell proposed that geologic events in the past were caused by the same processes operating today, at the same gradual rate. This principle suggested that Earth must be much older than a few thousand years, the age that was widely accepted at that time. Hutton's and Lyell's ideas also stimulated Darwin to reason that the slow accumulation of small changes could ultimately produce the profound changes documented in the fossil record. In this context, the age of Earth was important to Darwin, because unless Earth was very old, he could not envision how there would have been enough time for evolution to occur. **2.** By this criterion, Cuvier's explanation of the fossil record and Lamarck's hypothesis of evolution are both scientific. Cuvier thought that species did not evolve over time. He also suggested that sudden, catastrophic events caused extinctions in particular areas and that such regions were later repopulated by a different set of species that immigrated from other areas. These assertions can be tested against the fossil record, and his assertion that species do not evolve has been demonstrated to be incorrect. With respect to Lamarck, his principle of use and disuse can be used to make testable predictions for fossils of groups such as whale ancestors as they adapted to a new habitat. Lamarck's principle of use and disuse and his associated principle of the inheritance of acquired characteristics can also be tested directly in living organisms; these principles have been shown to be incorrect.

Concept Check 22.2

1. Organisms share characteristics (the unity of life) because they share common ancestors; the great diversity of life occurs because new species have repeatedly formed when descendant organisms gradually adapted to different environments, becoming different from their ancestors. **2.** The fossil mammal species (or its ancestors) would most likely have colonized the Andes from within South America, whereas ancestors of mammals currently found in African mountains would most likely have colonized those mountains from other parts of Africa. As a result, the Andes fossil species would share a more recent common ancestor with South American mammals than with mammals in Africa. Thus, for many of its traits, the fossil mammal species would probably more closely resemble mammals that live in South American jungles than mammals that live on African mountains. It is also possible, however, that the fossil mammal species could resemble the African mountain mammals by convergent evolution (even though they were only distantly related to one another). **3.** As long as the white phenotype (encoded by the genotype *pp*) continues to be favored by natural selection, the frequency of the *p* allele will likely increase over time in the population. If the proportion of white individuals increases relative to purple individuals, the frequency of the recessive *p* allele will also increase relative to that of the *P* allele, which only appears in purple individuals (some of which also carry a *p* allele).

Concept Check 22.3

1. An environmental factor such as a drug does not create new traits, such as drug resistance, but rather selects for traits among those that are already present in the population. **2.** (a) Despite their different functions, the forelimbs of different mammals are structurally similar because they all represent modifications of a structure found in the common ancestor. (b) This is a case of convergent evolution. The similarities between the sugar glider and flying squirrel indicate that similar environments selected for similar adaptations despite different ancestry. **3.** At the time that dinosaurs originated, Earth's landmasses formed a single large continent, Pangaea. Because many dinosaurs were large and mobile, it is likely that early members of these groups lived on many different parts of Pangaea. When Pangaea broke apart, fossils of these organisms would have moved with the rocks in which they were deposited. As a result, we would predict that fossils of early dinosaurs would have a broad geographic distribution (this prediction has been upheld).

Summary of Key Concepts Questions

Concept 22.1 Darwin thought that descent with modification occurred as a gradual, steplike process. The age of Earth was important to him because if Earth were only a few thousand years old (as conventional wisdom suggested), there wouldn't have been sufficient time for major evolutionary change. **Concept 22.2** All species have the potential to overreproduce—that is, to produce more offspring than can be supported by the environment. This ensures that there will be what Darwin called a "struggle for existence" in which many of the offspring are eaten, starved, diseased, or unable to reproduce for a variety of other reasons. Members of a population exhibit a range of heritable variations, some of which make it likely that their bearers will leave more offspring than other individuals (for example, the bearer may escape predators more effectively or be more tolerant of the physical conditions of the environment). Over time, natural selection resulting from factors such as predators, lack of food, or the physical conditions of the environment can increase the proportion of individuals with favorable traits in a population (evolutionary adaptation). **Concept 22.3** The hypothesis that cetaceans originated from a terrestrial mammal and are closely related to even-toed ungulates is supported by several lines of evidence. For example, fossils document that early cetaceans had hind limbs, as expected for organisms that descended from a land mammal; these fossils also show that cetacean hind limbs became reduced over time. Other fossils show that early cetaceans had a type of ankle bone that is otherwise found only in even-toed ungulates, providing strong evidence that even-toed ungulates are the land mammals to which cetaceans are most closely related. DNA sequence data also indicate that even-toed ungulates are the land mammals to which cetaceans are most closely related.

Test Your Understanding

1. b **2.** d **3.** c **4.** b **5.** a
7. (a)

(b) The rapid rise in the percentage of mosquitoes resistant to DDT was most likely caused by natural selection in which mosquitoes resistant to DDT could survive and reproduce while other mosquitoes could not. (c) In India—where DDT resistance first appeared—natural selection would have caused the frequency of resistant mosquitoes to increase over time. If resistant mosquitoes then migrated from India (for example, transported by wind or in planes, trains, or ships) to other parts of the world, the frequency of DDT resistance would increase there as well.

Chapter 23

Figure Questions

Figure 23.4 The genetic code is redundant, meaning that more than one codon can specify the same amino acid. As a result, a substitution at a particular site in a coding region of the *Adh* gene might change the codon but not the translated amino

acid, and thus not the resulting protein encoded by the gene. One way an insertion in an exon would not affect the gene produced is if it occurs in an untranslated region of the exon. (This is the case for the insertion at location 1,703.)
Figure 23.8 The predicted frequencies are 36% C^RC^R, 48% C^RC^W, and 16% C^WC^W.
Figure 23.13 Directional selection. Goldenrain tree has smaller fruit than does the native host, balloon vine. Thus, in soapberry bug populations feeding on goldenrain tree, bugs with shorter beaks have an advantage, resulting in directional selection for shorter beak length. **Figure 23.16** Crossing a single female's eggs with both an SC and an LC male's sperm allowed the researchers to directly compare the effects of the males' contribution to the next generation, since both batches of offspring had the same maternal contribution. This isolation of the male's impact enabled researchers to draw conclusions about differences in genetic "quality" between the SC and LC males. **Figure 23.17** Under prolonged low-oxygen conditions, some of the red blood cells of a heterozygote may sickle, leading to harmful effects. This does not occur in individuals with two wild-type hemoglobin alleles, suggesting that there may be selection against heterozygotes in malaria-free regions (where heterozygote advantage does not occur). However, since heterozygotes are healthy under most conditions, selection against them is unlikely to be strong.

Concept Check 23.1

1. Within a population, genetic differences among individuals provide the raw material on which natural selection and other mechanisms can act. Without such differences, allele frequencies could not change over time—and hence the population could not evolve. **2.** Many mutations occur in somatic cells, which do not produce gametes and so are lost when the organism dies. Of mutations that do occur in cell lines that produce gametes, many do not have a phenotypic effect on which natural selection can act. Others have a harmful effect and are thus unlikely to increase in frequency because they decrease the reproductive success of their bearers. **3.** Its genetic variation (whether measured at the level of the gene or at the level of nucleotide sequences) would probably drop over time. During meiosis, crossing over and the independent assortment of chromosomes produce many new combinations of alleles. In addition, a population contains a vast number of possible mating combinations, and fertilization brings together the gametes of individuals with different genetic backgrounds. Thus, via crossing over, independent assortment of chromosomes, and fertilization, sexual reproduction reshuffles alleles into fresh combinations each generation. Without sexual reproduction, the rate of forming new combinations of alleles would be vastly reduced, causing the overall amount of genetic variation to drop.

Concept Check 23.2

1. Each individual has two alleles, so the total number of alleles is 1,400. To calculate the frequency of allele A, note that each of the 85 individuals of genotype AA has two A alleles, each of the 320 individuals of genotype Aa has one A allele, and each of the 295 individuals of genotype aa has zero A alleles. Thus, the frequency (p) of allele A is

$$p = \frac{(2 \times 85) + (1 \times 320) + (0 \times 295)}{1,400} = 0.35$$

There are only two alleles (A and a) in our population, so the frequency of allele a must be $q = 1 - p = 0.65$. **2.** Because the frequency of allele a is 0.45, the frequency of allele A must be 0.55. Thus, the expected genotype frequencies are $p^2 = 0.3025$ for genotype AA, $2pq = 0.495$ for genotype Aa, and $q^2 = 0.2025$ for genotype aa. **3.** There are 120 individuals in the population, so there are 240 alleles. Of these, there are 124 V alleles—32 from the 16 VV individuals and 92 from the 92 Vv individuals. Thus, the frequency of the V allele is $p = 124/240 = 0.52$; hence, the frequency of the v allele is $q = 0.48$. Based on the Hardy-Weinberg equation, if the population were not evolving, the frequency of genotype VV should be $p^2 = 0.52 \times 0.52 = 0.27$; the frequency of genotype Vv should be $2pq = 2 \times 0.52 \times 0.48 = 0.5$; and the frequency of genotype vv should be $q^2 = 0.48 \times 0.48 = 0.23$. In a population of 120 individuals, these expected genotype frequencies lead us to predict that there would be 32 VV individuals (0.27×120), 60 Vv individuals (0.5×120), and 28 vv individuals (0.23×120). The actual numbers for the population (16 VV, 92 Vv, 12 vv) deviate from these expectations (fewer homozygotes and more heterozygotes than expected). This indicates that the population is not in Hardy-Weinberg equilibrium and hence may be evolving at this locus.

Concept Check 23.3

1. Natural selection is more "predictable" in that it alters allele frequencies in a nonrandom way: It tends to increase the frequency of alleles that increase the organism's reproductive success in its environment and decrease the frequency of alleles that decrease the organism's reproductive success. Alleles subject to genetic drift increase or decrease in frequency by chance alone, whether or not they are advantageous. **2.** Genetic drift results from chance events that cause allele frequencies to fluctuate at random from generation to generation; within a population, this process tends to decrease genetic variation over time. Gene flow is the transfer of alleles between populations, a process that can introduce new alleles to a population and hence may increase its genetic variation (albeit slightly, since rates of gene flow are often low). **3.** Selection is not important at this locus; furthermore, the populations are not small, and hence the effects of genetic drift should not be pronounced. Gene flow is occurring via the movement of pollen and seeds. Thus, allele and genotype frequencies in these populations should become more similar over time as a result of gene flow.

Concept Check 23.4

1. Zero, because fitness includes reproductive contribution to the next generation, and a sterile mule cannot produce offspring. **2.** Although both gene flow and genetic drift can increase the frequency of advantageous alleles in a population, they can also decrease the frequency of advantageous alleles or increase the frequency of harmful alleles. Only natural selection *consistently* results in an increase in the frequency of alleles that enhance survival or reproduction. Thus, natural selection is the only mechanism that consistently leads to adaptive evolution. **3.** The three modes of natural selection (directional, stabilizing, and disruptive) are defined in terms of the selective advantage of different *phenotypes*, not different genotypes. Thus, the type of selection represented by heterozygote advantage depends on the phenotype of the heterozygotes. In this question, because heterozygous individuals have a more extreme phenotype than either homozygote, heterozygote advantage represents directional selection.

Summary of Key Concepts Questions

23.1 Much of the nucleotide variability at a genetic locus occurs within introns. Nucleotide variation at these sites typically does not affect the phenotype because introns do not code for the protein product of the gene. (Note: In certain circumstances, it is possible that a change in an intron could affect RNA splicing and ultimately have some phenotypic effect on the organism, but such mechanisms are not covered in this introductory text.) There are also many variable nucleotide sites within exons. However, most of the variable sites within exons reflect changes to the DNA sequence that do not change the sequence of amino acids encoded by the gene (and hence may not affect the phenotype). **23.2** No, this is not an example of circular reasoning. Calculating p and q from observed genotype frequencies does not imply that those genotype frequencies must be in Hardy-Weinberg equilibrium. Consider a population that has 195 individuals of genotype AA, 10 of genotype Aa, and 195 of genotype aa. Calculating p and q from these values yields $p = q = 0.5$. Using the Hardy-Weinberg equation, the predicted equilibrium frequencies are $p^2 = 0.25$ for genotype AA, $2pq = 0.5$ for genotype Aa, and $q^2 = 0.25$ for genotype aa. Since there are 400 individuals in the population, these predicted genotype frequencies indicate that there should be 100 AA individuals, 200 Aa individuals, and 100 aa individuals—numbers that differ greatly from the values that we used to calculate p and q. **23.3** It is unlikely that two such populations would evolve in similar ways. Since their environments are very different, the alleles favored by natural selection would probably differ between the two populations. Although genetic drift may have important effects in each of these small populations, drift causes unpredictable changes in allele frequencies, so it is unlikely that drift would cause the populations to evolve in similar ways. Both populations are geographically isolated, suggesting that little gene flow would occur between them (again making it less likely that they would evolve in similar ways). **23.4** Compared to males, it is likely that the females of such species would be larger, more colorful, endowed with more elaborate ornamentation (for example, a large morphological feature such as the peacock's tail), and more apt to engage in behaviors intended to attract mates or prevent other members of their sex from obtaining mates.

Test Your Understanding

1. d **2.** c **3.** b **4.** a **5.** c
7. The frequency of the lap^{94} allele increases as one moves from southwest to northeast across Long Island Sound. The frequency of the lap^{94} allele is higher at sites 9–11 (open ocean) than it is at sites 1–7 (within the Sound); the northeast edge of the Sound (site 8) has about the same frequency of the lap^{94} allele as do the open ocean sites.

Site	1	2	3	4	5	6
lap^{94}%	13	16	16	25	36	37

Site	7	8	9	10	11
lap^{94}%	39	55	59	59	59

A hypothesis that explains the shape of the graph and accounts for the observations stated in the question is that the frequency of the lap^{94} allele at different sites results from an interaction between selection and gene flow. Under this hypothesis, in the southwest portion of the Sound, salinity is relatively low, and selection against the lap^{94} allele is strong. Moving toward the northeast and into the open ocean, where salinity is relatively high, selection favors a high frequency of the lap^{94} allele. However, because mussel larvae disperse long distances, gene flow prevents the lap^{94} allele from becoming fixed in the open ocean or from declining to zero in the southwestern portion of Long Island Sound.

Chapter 24

Figure Questions

Figure 24.7 If this had not been done, the strong preference of "starch flies" and "maltose flies" to mate with like-adapted flies could have occurred simply because the flies could detect (for example, by sense of smell) what their potential mates had eaten as larvae—and they preferred to mate with flies that had a similar smell to their own. **Figure 24.11** In murky waters where females distinguish colors poorly, females of each species might mate often with males of the other species. Hence, since hybrids between these species are viable and fertile, the gene pools of the two species could become more similar over time. **Figure 24.12** The graph suggests there has been gene flow of some fire-bellied toad alleles into the range of the yellow-bellied toad. Otherwise, all individuals located to the left of the hybrid zone portion of the graph would have allele frequencies close to 1. **Figure 24.13** Because the populations had only just begun to diverge from one another at this point in the process, it is likely that any existing barriers to reproduction would weaken over time. **Figure 24.18** Over time, the chromosomes of the experimental hybrids came to resemble those of *H. anomalus*. This occurred even though conditions in the laboratory differed greatly from conditions in the field, where *H. anomalus* is found, suggesting that selection for laboratory conditions was not strong. Thus, it is unlikely that the observed rise in the fertility of the experimental hybrids was due to selection for life under laboratory conditions. **Figure 24.19** The presence of *M. cardinalis* plants that carry the *M. lewisii yup* allele would make it more likely that bumblebees would transfer pollen between the two monkey flower species. As a result, we would expect the number of hybrid offspring to increase.

Concept Check 24.1

1. (a) All except the biological species concept can be applied to both asexual and sexual species because they define species on the basis of characteristics other than the ability to reproduce. In contrast, the biological species concept can be applied only to sexual species. (b) The easiest species concept to apply in the field would be the morphological species concept because it is based only on the appearance of the organism. Additional information about its ecological habits, evolutionary history, and reproduction is not required. **2.** Because these birds live in fairly similar environments and can breed successfully in captivity, the reproductive barrier in nature is probably prezygotic; given the species' differences in habitat preference, this barrier could result from habitat isolation.

Concept Check 24.2

1. In allopatric speciation, a new species forms while in geographic isolation from its parent species; in sympatric speciation, a new species forms in the absence of geographic isolation. Geographic isolation greatly reduces gene flow between populations, whereas ongoing gene flow is more likely in sympatric populations. As a result, sympatric speciation is less common than allopatric speciation. **2.** Gene flow between subsets of a population that live in the same area can be reduced in a variety of ways. In some species—especially plants—changes in chromosome number can block gene flow and establish reproductive isolation in a single generation. Gene flow can also be reduced in sympatric populations by habitat differentiation (as seen in the apple maggot fly, *Rhagoletis*) and sexual selection (as seen in Lake Victoria cichlids). **3.** Allopatric speciation would be less likely to occur on an island near a mainland than on an isolated island of the same size. The reason we expect this result is that continued gene flow between mainland populations and those on a nearby island reduces the chance that enough genetic divergence will take place for allopatric speciation to occur. **4.** If all of the homologs failed to separate during anaphase I of meiosis, some gametes would end up with an extra set of chromosomes (and others would end up with no chromosomes). If a gamete with an extra set of chromosomes fused with a normal gamete, a triploid would result; if two gametes with an extra set of chromosomes fused with each other, a tetraploid would result.

Concept Check 24.3

1. Hybrid zones are regions in which members of different species meet and mate, producing some offspring of mixed ancestry. Such regions can be viewed as "natural laboratories" in which to study speciation because scientists can directly observe factors that cause (or fail to cause) reproductive isolation. **2.** (a) If hybrids consistently survived and reproduced poorly compared with the offspring of intraspecific matings, reinforcement could occur. If it did, natural selection would cause prezygotic barriers to reproduction between the parent species to strengthen over time, decreasing the production of unfit hybrids and leading to a completion of the speciation process. (b) If hybrid offspring survived and reproduced as well as the offspring of intraspecific matings, indiscriminate mating between the parent species would lead to the production of large numbers of hybrid offspring. As these hybrids mated with each other and with members of both parent species, the gene pools of the parent species could fuse over time, reversing the speciation process.

Concept Check 24.4

1. The time between speciation events includes (1) the length of time that it takes for populations of a newly formed species to begin diverging reproductively from one another and (2) the time it takes for speciation to be complete once this divergence begins. Although speciation can occur rapidly once populations have begun to diverge from one another, it may take millions of years for that divergence to begin. **2.** Investigators transferred alleles at the *yup* locus (which influences flower color) from each parent species to the other. *M. lewisii* plants with an *M. cardinalis yup* allele received many more visits from hummingbirds than usual; hummingbirds usually pollinate *M. cardinalis* but avoid *M. lewisii*. Similarly, *M. cardinalis* plants with an *M. lewisii yup* allele received many more visits from bumblebees than usual; bumblebees usually pollinate *M. lewisii* and avoid *M. cardinalis*. Thus, alleles at the *yup* locus can influence pollinator choice, which in these species provides the primary barrier to interspecific mating. Nevertheless, the experiment does not prove

that the *yup* locus alone controls barriers to reproduction between *M. lewisii* and *M. cardinalis*; other genes might enhance the effect of the *yup* locus (by modifying flower color) or cause entirely different barriers to reproduction (for example, gametic isolation or a postzygotic barrier). **3.** Crossing over. If crossing over did not occur, each chromosome in an experimental hybrid would remain as in the F_1 generation: composed entirely of DNA from one parent species or the other.

Summary of Key Concepts Questions

24.1 According to the biological species concept, a species is a group of populations whose members interbreed and produce viable, fertile offspring; thus, gene flow occurs between populations of a species. In contrast, members of different species do not interbreed and hence no gene flow occurs between their populations. Overall, then, in the biological species concept, species can be viewed as designated by the *absence* of gene flow—making gene flow of central importance to the biological species concept. **24.2** Sympatric speciation can be promoted by factors such as polyploidy, sexual selection, and habitat shifts, all of which can reduce gene flow between the subpopulations of a larger population. But such factors can also occur in allopatric populations and hence can also promote allopatric speciation. **24.3** If the hybrids are selected against, the hybrid zone could persist if individuals from the parent species regularly travel into the zone, where they mate to produce hybrid offspring. If hybrids are not selected against, there is no cost to the continued production of hybrids, and large numbers of hybrid offspring may be produced. However, natural selection for life in different environments may keep the gene pools of the two parent species distinct, thus preventing the loss (by fusion) of the parent species and once again causing the hybrid zone to be stable over time. **24.4** As the goatsbeard plant, Bahamas mosquitofish, and apple maggot fly illustrate, speciation continues to happen today. A new species can begin to form whenever gene flow is reduced between populations of the parent species. Such reductions in gene flow can occur in many ways: A new, geographically isolated population may be founded by a few colonists; some members of the parent species may begin to utilize a new habitat; and sexual selection may isolate formerly connected populations or subpopulations. These and many other such events are happening today.

Test Your Understanding

1. b **2.** c **3.** b **4.** a **5.** d **6.** c **7.** d
8. Here is one possibility:

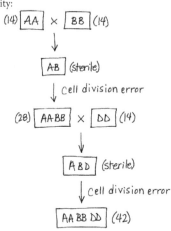

Chapter 25

Figure Questions

Figure 25.2 Proteins are almost always composed of the same 20 amino acids shown in Figure 5.14. However, many other amino acids could potentially form in this or any other experiment. For example, any molecule that had an R group other than those listed in Figure 5.14 yet still contained an α carbon, an amino group, and a carboxyl group would be an amino acid—yet it would not be one of the 20 amino acids commonly found in nature. **Figure 25.6** Because uranium-238 has a half-life of 4.5 billion years, the *x*-axis would be relabeled (in billions of years) as 4.5, 9, 13.5, and 18. **Figure 25.11** You should have circled the node, shown in the tree diagram at approximately 580 million years ago (mya), that leads to the echinoderm/chordate lineage and to the lineage that gave rise to brachiopods, annelids, molluscs, and arthropods. Although the 580 mya date is estimated, this common ancestor must be at least as old as any of its descendants. Since fossil molluscs date to about 560 mya, the common ancestor represented by the circled branch point must be at least 560 million years old. **Figure 25.16** The Australian plate's current direction of movement is roughly similar to the northeasterly direction the continent traveled over the past 65 million years. **Figure 25.26** The coding sequence of the *Pitx1* gene would differ between the marine and lake populations, but patterns of gene expression would not.

Concept Check 25.1

1. The hypothesis that conditions on early Earth could have permitted the synthesis of organic molecules from inorganic ingredients **2.** In contrast to random mingling of molecules in an open solution, segregation of molecular systems by membranes could concentrate organic molecules, assisting biochemical reactions. **3.** Today, genetic information usually flows from DNA to RNA, as when the DNA sequence of a gene is used as a template to synthesize the mRNA encoding a particular protein. However, the life cycle of retroviruses such as HIV shows that genetic information can flow in the reverse direction (from RNA to DNA). In these viruses, the enzyme reverse transcriptase uses RNA as a template for DNA synthesis, suggesting that a similar enzyme could have played a key role in the transition from an RNA world to a DNA world.

Concept Check 25.2

1. 22,920 years (four half-lives: 5,730 × 4)   **2.** The fossil record shows that different groups of organisms dominated life on Earth at different points in time and that many organisms once alive are now extinct; specific examples of these points can be found in Figure 25.5. The fossil record also indicates that new groups of organisms can arise via the gradual modification of previously existing organisms, as illustrated by fossils that document the origin of mammals from their cynodont ancestors.   **3.** The discovery of such a (hypothetical) fossil organism would indicate that aspects of our current understanding of the origin of mammals are not correct because mammals are thought to have originated much more recently (see Figure 25.7). For example, such a discovery could suggest that the dates of previous fossil discoveries are not correct or that the lineages shown in Figure 25.7 shared features with mammals but were not their direct ancestors. Such a discovery would also suggest that radical changes in multiple aspects of the skeletal structure of organisms could arise suddenly—an idea that is not supported by the known fossil record.

Concept Check 25.3

1. Free oxygen attacks chemical bonds and can inhibit enzymes and damage cells. As a result, prokaryotes that had thrived in anaerobic environments would have survived and reproduced poorly in oxygen-rich environments, driving many species to extinction.   **2.** All eukaryotes have mitochondria or remnants of these organelles, but not all eukaryotes have plastids.   **3.** A fossil record of life today would include many organisms with hard body parts (such as vertebrates and many marine invertebrates), but might not include some species we are very familiar with, such as those that have small geographic ranges and/or small population sizes (for example, endangered species such as the giant panda, tiger, and several rhinoceros species).

Concept Check 25.4

1. The theory of plate tectonics describes the movement of Earth's continental plates, which alters the physical geography and climate of Earth, as well as the extent to which organisms are geographically isolated. Because these factors affect extinction and speciation rates, plate tectonics has a major impact on life on Earth.   **2.** Mass extinctions; major evolutionary innovations; the diversification of another group of organisms (which can provide new sources of food); migration to new locations where few competitor species exist   **3.** In theory, fossils of both common and rare species would be present right up to the time of the catastrophic event, then disappear. Reality is more complicated because the fossil record is not perfect. So the most recent fossil for a species might be a million years before the mass extinction—even though the species did not become extinct *until* the mass extinction. This complication is especially likely for rare species because few of their fossils will form and be discovered. Hence, for many rare species, the fossil record would not document that the species was alive immediately before the extinction (even if it was).

Concept Check 25.5

1. Heterochrony can cause a variety of morphological changes. For example, if the onset of sexual maturity changes, a retention of juvenile characteristics (paedomorphosis) may result. Paedomorphosis can be caused by small genetic changes that result in large changes in morphology, as seen in the axolotl salamander.
2. In animal embryos, *Hox* genes influence the development of structures such as limbs and feeding appendages. As a result, changes in these genes—or in the regulation of these genes—are likely to have major effects on morphology.   **3.** From genetics, we know that gene regulation is altered by how well transcription factors bind to noncoding DNA sequences called control elements. Thus, if changes in morphology are often caused by changes in gene regulation, portions of noncoding DNA that contain control elements are likely to be strongly affected by natural selection.

Concept Check 25.6

1. Complex structures do not evolve all at once, but in increments, with natural selection selecting for adaptive variants of the earlier versions.   **2.** Although the myxoma virus is highly lethal, initially some of the rabbits are resistant (0.2% of infected rabbits are not killed). Thus, assuming resistance is an inherited trait, we would expect the rabbit population to show a trend for increased resistance to the virus. We would also expect the virus to show an evolutionary trend toward reduced lethality. We would expect this trend because a rabbit infected with a less lethal virus would be more likely to live long enough for a mosquito to bite it and hence potentially transmit the virus to another rabbit. (A virus that kills its rabbit host before a mosquito transmits the virus to another rabbit dies with its host.)

Summary of Key Concepts Questions

Concept 25.1 Particles of montmorillonite clay may have provided surfaces on which organic molecules became concentrated and hence were more likely to react with one another. Montmorillonite clay particles may also have facilitated the transport of key molecules, such as short strands of RNA, into vesicles. These vesicles can form spontaneously from simple precursor molecules, "reproduce" and "grow" on their own, and maintain internal concentrations of molecules that differ from those in the surrounding environment. These features of vesicles represent key steps in the emergence of protocells and (ultimately) the first living

cells.   **Concept 25.2** One challenge is that organisms do not use radioisotopes that have long half-lives to build their bones or shells. As a result, fossils older than 75,000 years cannot be dated directly. Fossils are often found in sedimentary rock, but those rocks typically contain sediments of different ages, again posing a challenge when trying to date old fossils. To circumvent these challenges, geologists date layers of volcanic rock that surround old fossils and that use radioisotopes with long half-lives. This approach provides minimum and maximum estimates for the ages of fossils sandwiched between two layers of volcanic rock.
Concept 25.3 The "Cambrian explosion" refers to a relatively short interval of time (535–525 million years ago) during which large forms of many present-day animal phyla first appear in the fossil record. The evolutionary changes that occurred during this time, such as the appearance of large predators and well-defended prey, were important because they set the stage for many of the key events in the history of life over the last 500 million years.   **Concept 25.4** The broad evolutionary changes documented by the fossil record reflect the rise and fall of major groups of organisms. In turn, the rise or fall of any particular group results from a balance between speciation and extinction rates: A group increases in size when the rate at which its members produce new species is greater than the rate at which its member species are lost to extinction, while a group shrinks in size if extinction rates are greater than speciation rates.   **Concept 25.5** A change in the sequence or regulation of a developmental gene can produce major morphological changes. In some cases, such morphological changes may enable organisms to perform new functions or live in new environments—thus potentially leading to an adaptive radiation and the formation of a new group of organisms.
Concept 25.6 Evolutionary change results from interactions between organisms and their current environments. No goal is involved in this process. As environments change over time, the features of organisms favored by natural selection may also change. When this happens, what once may have seemed like a "goal" of evolution (for example, improvements in the function of a feature previously favored by natural selection) may cease to be beneficial or may even be harmful.

Test Your Understanding

1. b   **2.** a   **3.** d   **4.** b   **5.** c   **6.** c   **7.** a

Chapter 26

Figure Questions

Figure 26.4 The branching pattern of the tree indicates that the badger and the wolf share a common ancestor that is more recent than the ancestor these two animals share with the leopard.   **Figure 26.5** The new version (shown below) does not alter any of the evolutionary relationships shown in Figure 26.5. For example, B and C remain sister taxa, taxon A is still as closely related to taxon B as it is to taxon C, and so on.

Figure 26.6 Unknown 1b (a portion of sample 1) and Unknowns 9–13 all would have to be located on the branch of the tree that currently leads to Minke (Southern Hemisphere) and Unknowns 1a and 2–8.   **Figure 26.11** You should have circled the branch point that is drawn farthest to the left (the common ancestor of all taxa shown). Both cetaceans and seals descended from terrestrial lineages of mammals, indicating that the cetacean-seal common ancestor lacked a streamlined body form and hence would not be part of the cetacean-seal group.   **Figure 26.12** You should have circled the frog, turtle, and leopard lineages, along with their most recent common ancestor.   **Figure 26.16** The lizard and snake lineage is the most basal taxon shown (closest to the root of the tree). Among the descendants of the common ancestor indicated by the blue dot, the crocodilian lineage is the most basal.   **Figure 26.21** This tree indicates that the sequences of rRNA and other genes in mitochondria are most closely related to those of proteobacteria, while the sequences of chloroplast genes are most closely related to those of cyanobacteria. These gene sequence relationships are what would be predicted from endosymbiont theory, which posits that both mitochondria and chloroplasts originated as engulfed prokaryotic cells.

Concept Check 26.1

1. We are classified the same from the domain level to the class level; both the leopard and human are mammals. Leopards belong to order Carnivora, whereas humans do not.   **2.** The tree in (c) shows a different pattern of evolutionary relationships. In (c), C and B are sister taxa, whereas C and D are sister taxa in (a) and (b).

3.

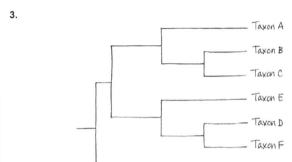

Taxon A
Taxon B
Taxon C
Taxon E
Taxon D
Taxon F
Taxon G

Concept Check 26.2

1. (a) Analogy, since porcupines and cacti are not closely related and since most other animals and plants do not have similar structures; (b) homology, since cats and humans are both mammals and have homologous forelimbs, of which the hand and paw are the lower part; (c) analogy, since owls and hornets are not closely related and since the structure of their wings is very different **2.** Species B and C are more likely to be closely related. Small genetic changes (as between species B and C) can produce divergent physical appearances, but if many genes have diverged greatly (as in species A and B), then the lineages have probably been separate for a long time.

Concept Check 26.3

1. No; hair is a shared ancestral character common to all mammals and thus is not helpful in distinguishing different mammalian subgroups. **2.** The principle of maximum parsimony states that the hypothesis about nature we investigate first should be the simplest explanation found to be consistent with the facts. Actual evolutionary relationships may differ from those inferred by parsimony owing to complicating factors such as convergent evolution. **3.** The traditional classification provides a poor match to evolutionary history, thus violating the basic principle of cladistics—that classification should be based on common descent. Both birds and mammals originated from groups traditionally designated as reptiles, making reptiles (as traditionally delineated) a paraphyletic group. These problems can be addressed by removing *Dimetrodon* and cynodonts from the reptiles and by regarding birds as a group of reptiles (specifically, as a group of dinosaurs).

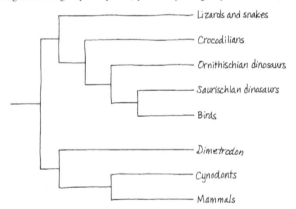

Lizards and snakes
Crocodilians
Ornithischian dinosaurs
Saurischian dinosaurs
Birds
Dimetrodon
Cynodonts
Mammals

Concept Check 26.4

1. Proteins are gene products. Their amino acid sequences are determined by the nucleotide sequences of the DNA that codes for them. Thus, differences between comparable proteins in two species reflect underlying genetic differences that have accumulated as the species diverged from one another. As a result, differences between the proteins can reflect the evolutionary history of the species. **2.** These observations suggest that the evolutionary lineages leading to species 1 and species 2 diverged from one another before a gene duplication event in species 1 produced gene B from gene A. **3.** In RNA processing, the exons or coding regions of a gene can be spliced together in different ways, yielding different mRNAs and hence different protein products. As a result, different proteins could potentially be produced from the same gene in different tissues, thereby enabling the gene to perform different functions in these different tissues.

Concept Check 26.5

1. A molecular clock is a method of estimating the actual time of evolutionary events based on numbers of base changes in orthologous genes. It is based on the assumption that the regions of genomes being compared evolve at constant rates. **2.** There are many portions of the genome that do not code for genes; mutations that alter the sequence of bases in such regions could accumulate through drift without affecting an organism's fitness. Even in coding regions of the genome, some mutations may not have a critical effect on genes or proteins. **3.** The gene

(or genes) used for the molecular clock may have evolved more slowly in these two taxa than in the species used to calibrate the clock; as a result, the clock would underestimate the time at which the taxa diverged from each other.

Concept Check 26.6

1. The kingdom Monera included bacteria and archaea, but we now know that these organisms are in separate domains. Kingdoms are subsets of domains, so a single kingdom (like Monera) that includes taxa from different domains is not valid. **2.** Because of horizontal gene transfer, some genes in eukaryotes are more closely related to bacteria, while others are more closely related to archaea; thus, depending on which genes are used, phylogenetic trees constructed from DNA data can yield conflicting results.

3.

Archaea
Bacteria
Eukarya

Bacteria
Archaea
Eukarya

Eukarya
Bacteria
Archaea

The fossil record indicates that prokaryotes originated long before eukaryotes. This suggests that the third tree, in which the eukaryotic lineage diverged first, is not accurate and hence is not likely to receive support from genetic data.

Summary of Key Concepts Questions

26.1 The fact that humans and chimpanzees are sister species indicates that we share a more recent common ancestor with chimpanzees than we do with any other living primate species. But that does not mean that humans evolved from chimpanzees, or vice versa; instead, it indicates that both humans and chimpanzees are descendants of that common ancestor. **26.2** Homologous characters result from shared ancestry. As organisms diverge over time, some of their homologous characters will also diverge. The homologous characters of organisms that diverged long ago typically differ more than do the homologous characters of organisms that diverged more recently. As a result, differences in homologous characters can be used to infer phylogeny. In contrast, analogous characters result from convergent evolution, not shared ancestry, and hence can give misleading estimates of phylogeny. **26.3** All features of organisms arose at some point in the history of life. In the group in which a new feature first arose, that feature is a shared derived character that is unique to that clade. The group in which each shared derived character first appeared can be determined, and the resulting nested pattern can be used to infer evolutionary history. **26.4** Orthologous genes should be used; for such genes, the homology results from speciation and hence reflects evolutionary history. **26.5** A key assumption of molecular clocks is that nucleotide substitutions occur at fixed rates and hence the number of nucleotide differences between two DNA sequences is proportional to the time since the sequences diverged from each other. Some limitations of molecular clocks: No gene marks time with complete precision; natural selection can favor certain DNA changes over others; nucleotide substitution rates can change over long periods of time (causing molecular clock estimates of when events in the distant past occurred to be highly uncertain); and the same gene can evolve at different rates in different organisms. **26.6** Genetic data indicated that many prokaryotes differed as much from each other as they did from eukaryotes. This indicated that organisms should be grouped into three "super-kingdoms," or domains (Archaea, Bacteria, Eukarya). These data also indicated that the previous kingdom Monera (which had contained all the prokaryotes) did not make biological sense and should be abandoned. Later genetic and morphological data also indicated that the former kingdom Protista (which had primarily contained single-celled organisms) should be abandoned because some protists are more closely related to plants, fungi, or animals than they are to other protists.

Test Your Understanding

1. a **2.** c **3.** b **4.** c **5.** d **6.** a **7.** d

9.

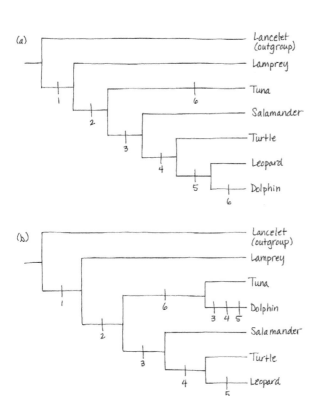

(a) [tree diagram with branches leading to: Lancelet (outgroup), Lamprey, Tuna, Salamander, Turtle, Leopard, Dolphin, with nodes labeled 1, 2, 3, 4, 5, 6]

(b) [tree diagram with branches leading to: Lancelet (outgroup), Lamprey, Tuna, Dolphin, Salamander, Turtle, Leopard, with nodes labeled 1, 2, 3, 4, 5, 6]

(c) The tree in (a) requires seven evolutionary changes, while the tree in (b) requires nine evolutionary changes. Thus, the tree in (a) is more parsimonious, since it requires fewer evolutionary changes.

Chapter 27

Figure Questions

Figure 27.10 It is likely that the expression or sequence of genes that affect glucose metabolism may have changed; genes for metabolic processes no longer needed by the cell also may have changed. **Figure 27.11** Transduction results in horizontal gene transfer when the host and recipient cells are members of different species. **Figure 27.15** Eukarya **Figure 27.17** Thermophiles live in very hot environments, so it is likely that their enzymes can continue to function normally at much higher temperatures than can the enzymes of other organisms. At low temperatures, however, the enzymes of thermophiles may not function as well as the enzymes of other organisms. **Figure 27.18** From the graph, plant uptake can be estimated as 0.7, 0.6, and 0.95 mg K^+ for strains 1, 2, and 3, respectively. These values average to 0.75 mg K^+. If bacteria had no effect, the average plant uptake of K^+ for strains 1, 2, and 3 should be close to 0.5 mg K^+, the value observed for plants grown in bacteria-free soil.

Concept Check 27.1

1. Adaptations include the capsule (shields prokaryotes from the host's immune system) and endospores (enable cells to survive harsh conditions and to revive when the environment becomes favorable). **2.** Prokaryotic cells lack the complex compartmentalization associated with the membrane-enclosed organelles of eukaryotic cells. Prokaryotic genomes have much less DNA than eukaryotic genomes, and most of this DNA is contained in a single ring-shaped chromosome located in the nucleoid rather than within a true membrane-enclosed nucleus. In addition, many prokaryotes also have plasmids, small ring-shaped DNA molecules containing a few genes. **3.** Plastids such as chloroplasts are thought to have evolved from an endosymbiotic photosynthetic prokaryote. More specifically, the phylogenetic tree shown in Figure 26.21 indicates that plastids are closely related to cyanobacteria. Hence, we can hypothesize that the thylakoid membranes of chloroplasts resemble those of cyanobacteria because chloroplasts evolved from a cyanobacterium endosymbiont.

Concept Check 27.2

1. Prokaryotes can have extremely large population sizes, in part because they often have short generation times. The large number of individuals in prokaryotic populations makes it likely that in each generation there will be many individuals that have new mutations at any particular gene, thereby adding considerable genetic diversity to the population. **2.** In transformation, naked, foreign DNA from the environment is taken up by a bacterial cell. In transduction, phages carry bacterial genes from one bacterial cell to another. In conjugation, a bacterial cell directly transfers plasmid or chromosomal DNA to another cell via a mating bridge that temporarily connects the two cells. **3.** The population that includes individuals capable of conjugation would probably be more successful, since some of its members could form recombinant cells whose new gene combinations might

be advantageous in a novel environment. **4.** Yes. Genes for antibiotic resistance could be transferred (by transformation, transduction, or conjugation) from the nonpathogenic bacterium to a pathogenic bacterium; this could make the pathogen an even greater threat to human health. In general, transformation, transduction, and conjugation tend to increase the spread of resistance genes.

Concept Check 27.3

1. A phototroph derives its energy from light, while a chemotroph gets its energy from chemical sources. An autotroph derives its carbon from CO_2, HCO_3^-, or related compounds, while a heterotroph gets its carbon from organic nutrients such as glucose. Thus, there are four nutritional modes: photoautotrophic, photoheterotrophic (unique to prokaryotes), chemoautotrophic (unique to prokaryotes), and chemoheterotrophic. **2.** Chemoheterotrophy; the bacterium must rely on chemical sources of energy, since it is not exposed to light, and it must be a heterotroph if it requires a source of carbon other than CO_2 (or a related compound, such as HCO_3^-). **3.** If humans could fix nitrogen, we could build proteins using atmospheric N_2 and hence would not need to eat high-protein foods such as meat, fish, or soy. Our diet would, however, need to include a source of carbon, along with minerals and water. Thus, a typical meal might consist of carbohydrates as a carbon source, along with fruits and vegetables to provide essential minerals (and additional carbon).

Concept Check 27.4

1. Molecular systematic studies indicate that organisms once classified as bacteria are more closely related to eukaryotes and belong in a domain of their own: Archaea. Such studies have also shown that horizontal gene transfer is common and plays an important role in the evolution of prokaryotes. By not requiring that organisms be cultured in the laboratory, metagenomic studies have revealed an immense diversity of previously unknown prokaryotic species. Over time, the ongoing discovery of new species by metagenomic analyses may alter our understanding of prokaryotic phylogeny greatly. **2.** At present, all known methanogens are archaea in the clade Euryarchaeota; this suggests that this unique metabolic pathway probably arose in ancestral species within Euryarchaeota. Since Bacteria and Archaea have been separate evolutionary lineages for billions of years, the discovery of a methanogen from the domain Bacteria would suggest that adaptations that enabled the use of CO_2 to oxidize H_2 may have evolved twice—once in Archaea (within Euryarchaeota) and once in Bacteria. (It is also possible that a newly discovered bacterial methanogen could have acquired the genes for this metabolic pathway by horizontal gene transfer from a methanogen in domain Archaea. However, horizontal gene transfer is not a likely explanation because of the large number of genes involved and because gene transfers between species in different domains are rare.)

Concept Check 27.5

1. Although prokaryotes are small, their large numbers and metabolic abilities enable them to play key roles in ecosystems by decomposing wastes, recycling chemicals, and affecting the concentrations of nutrients available to other organisms **2.** Cyanobacteria produce oxygen when water is split in the light reactions of photosynthesis. The Calvin cycle incorporates CO_2 from the air into organic molecules, which are then converted to sugars.

Concept Check 27.6

1. Sample answers: eating fermented foods such as yogurt, sourdough bread, or cheese; receiving clean water from sewage treatment; taking medicines produced by bacteria **2.** No. If the poison is secreted as an exotoxin, live bacteria could be transmitted to another person. But the same is true if the poison is an endotoxin— only in this case, the live bacteria that are transmitted may be descendants of the (now-dead) bacteria that produced the poison. **3.** Some of the many different species of prokaryotes that live in the human gut compete with one another for resources (from the food that you eat). Because different prokaryotic species have different adaptations, a change in diet may alter which species can grow most rapidly, thus altering species abundance.

Summary of Key Concepts Questions

27.1 Specific structural features that enable prokaryotes to thrive in diverse environments include their cell walls (which provide shape and protection), flagella (which function in directed movement), and ability to form capsules or endospores (both of which can protect against harsh conditions). Prokaryotes also possess biochemical adaptations for growth in varied conditions, such as those that enable them to tolerate extremely hot or salty environments. **27.2** Many prokaryotic species can reproduce extremely rapidly, and their populations can number in the trillions. As a result, even though mutations are rare, every day many offspring are produced that have new mutations at particular gene loci. In addition, even though prokaryotes reproduce asexually and hence the vast majority of offspring are genetically identical to their parent, the genetic variation of their populations can be increased by transduction, transformation, and conjugation. Each of these (non-reproductive) processes can increase genetic variation by transferring DNA from one cell to another—even among cells that are of different species. **27.3** Prokaryotes have an exceptionally broad range of metabolic adaptations. As a group, prokaryotes perform all four modes of nutrition (photoautotrophy, chemoautotrophy, photoheterotrophy, and chemoheterotrophy), whereas eukaryotes perform only two of these (photoautotrophy and chemoheterotrophy). Prokaryotes are also able to metabolize nitrogen in a wide variety of forms (again unlike eukaryotes), and they frequently cooperate with other prokaryotic cells of the same or different species. **27.4** Phenotypic criteria such as shape, motility, and nutritional mode do not provide a clear picture of the evolutionary history of the prokaryotes. In contrast, molecular data have elucidated relationships among major groups of prokaryotes. Molecular data have also allowed researchers to sample genes directly from the environment; using such genes to construct phylogenies has led to the discovery of major new groups of prokaryotes. **27.5** Prokaryotes play key roles in the chemical cycles on which life depends. For example, prokaryotes are important decomposers, breaking down corpses and waste materials, thereby releasing nutrients to the environment where they can be used by other organisms. Prokaryotes also convert inorganic compounds to forms that other organisms can use. With respect to their ecological interactions, many prokaryotes form life-sustaining mutualisms with other species. In some cases, such as hydrothermal vent communities, the metabolic activities of prokaryotes provide an energy source on which hundreds of other species depend; in the absence of the prokaryotes, the community collapses. **27.6** Human well-being depends on our associations with mutualistic prokaryotes, such as the many species that live in our intestines and digest food that we cannot. Humans also can harness the remarkable metabolic capabilities of prokaryotes to produce a wide range of useful products and to perform key services such as bioremediation. Negative effects of prokaryotes result primarily from bacterial pathogens that cause disease.

Test Your Understanding

1. d **2.** a **3.** c **4.** c **5.** b **6.** a

Chapter 28

Figure Questions

Figure 28.3 Four. The first (and primary) genome is the DNA located in the chlorarachniophyte nucleus. A chlorarachniophyte also contain remnants of a green alga's nuclear DNA, located in the nucleomorph. Finally, mitochondria and chloroplasts contain DNA from the (different) bacteria from which they evolved. These two prokaryotic genomes comprise the third and fourth genomes contained within a chlorarachniophyte. **Figure 28.13** The sperm cells in the diagram are produced by the asexual (mitotic) division of cells in a single male gametophyte, which was itself produced by the asexual (mitotic) division of a single zoospore. Thus, the sperm cells are all derived from a single zoospore and so are genetically identical to one another. **Figure 28.16** Merozoites are produced by the asexual (mitotic) cell division of haploid sporozoites; similarly, gametocytes are produced by the asexual cell division of merozoites. Hence, it is likely that individuals in these three stages have the same complement of genes and that morphological differences between them result from changes in gene expression. **Figure 28.23** The following stage should be circled: step 6, where a mature cell undergoes mitosis and forms four or more daughter cells. In step 7, the zoospores eventually grow into mature haploid cells, but they do not produce new daughter cells. Likewise, in step 2, a mature cell develops into a gamete, but it does not produce new daughter cells. **Figure 28.24** If the assumption is correct, then their results indicate that the fusion of the genes for DHFR and TS may be a derived trait shared by members of three supergroups of eukaryotes (Excavata, SAR clade, and Archaeplastida). However, if the assumption is not correct, the presence or absence of the gene fusion may tell little about phylogenetic history. For example, if the genes fused multiple times, groups could share the trait because of convergent evolution rather than common descent. If instead the genes were secondarily split, a group with such a split could be placed (incorrectly) in Unikonta rather than its correct placement in one of the other three supergroups.

Concept Check 28.1

1. Sample response: Protists include unicellular, colonial, and multicellular organisms; photoautotrophs, heterotrophs, and mixotrophs; species that reproduce asexually, sexually, or both ways; and organisms with diverse physical forms and adaptations. **2.** Strong evidence shows that eukaryotes acquired mitochondria after a host cell (either an archaean or a cell with archaeal ancestors) first engulfed and then formed an endosymbiotic association with an alpha proteobacterium. Similarly, chloroplasts in red and green algae appear to have descended from a photosynthetic cyanobacterium that was engulfed by an ancient heterotrophic eukaryote. Secondary endosymbiosis also played an important role: Various protist lineages acquired plastids by engulfing unicellular red or green algae. **3.** The modified tree would look as follows:

Concept Check 28.2

1. Their mitochondria do not have an electron transport chain and so cannot function in aerobic respiration. **2.** Since the unknown protist is more closely related to diplomonads than to euglenids, it must have originated after the diplomonads and parabasalids diverged from the euglenozoans. In addition, since the unknown species has fully functional mitochondria—yet both diplomonads and parabasalids do not—it is likely that the unknown species originated *before* the last common ancestor of the diplomonads and parabasalids.

Concept Check 28.3

1. Because foram tests are hardened with calcium carbonate, they form long-lasting fossils in marine sediments and sedimentary rocks. **2.** The plastid DNA would likely be more similar to the chromosomal DNA of cyanobacteria based on the well-supported hypothesis that eukaryotic plastids (such as those found in the eukaryote groups listed) originated by an endosymbiosis event in which a eukaryote engulfed a cyanobacterium. If the plastid is derived from the cyanobacterium, its DNA would be derived from the bacterial DNA. **3.** Figure 13.6b. Algae and plants with alternation of generations have a multicellular haploid stage *and* a multicellular diploid stage. In the other two life cycles, either the haploid stage or the diploid stage is unicellular. **4.** During photosynthesis, aerobic algae produce O_2 and use CO_2. O_2 is produced as a by-product of the light reactions, while CO_2 is used as an input to the Calvin cycle (the end products of which are sugars). Aerobic algae also perform cellular respiration, which uses O_2 as an input and produces CO_2 as a waste product.

Concept Check 28.4

1. Many red algae contain a photosynthetic pigment called phycoerythrin, which gives them a reddish color and allows them to carry out photosynthesis in relatively deep coastal water. Also unlike brown algae, red algae have no flagellated stages in their life cycle and must depend on water currents to bring gametes together for fertilization. **2.** *Ulva* contains many cells and its body is differentiated into leaflike blades and a rootlike holdfast. *Caulerpa*'s body is composed of multinucleate filaments without cross-walls, so it is essentially one large cell. **3.** Red algae have no flagellated stages in their life cycle and hence must depend on water currents to bring their gametes together. This feature of their biology might increase the difficulty of reproducing on land. In contrast, the gametes of green algae are flagellated, making it possible for them to swim in thin films of water. In addition, a variety of green algae contain compounds in their cytoplasm, cell wall, or zygote coat that protect against intense sunlight and other terrestrial conditions. Such compounds may have increased the chance that descendants of green algae could survive on land.

Concept Check 28.5

1. Amoebozoans have lobe- or tube-shaped pseudopodia, whereas forams have threadlike pseudopodia. **2.** Slime molds are fungus-like in that they produce fruiting bodies that aid in the dispersal of spores, and they are animal-like in that they are motile and ingest food. However, slime molds are more closely related to tubulinids and entamoebas than to fungi or animals. **3.** Support. Unikonts lack the unique cytoskeletal features shared by many excavates (see Concept 28.2). Thus, if the unikonts were the first group of eukaryotes to diverge from other eukaryotes (as shown in Figure 28.24), it would be unlikely that the eukaryote common ancestor had the cytoskeletal features found today in many excavates. Such a result would strengthen the case that many excavates share cytoskeletal features because they are members of a monophyletic group, the Excavata.

Concept Check 28.6

1. Because photosynthetic protists constitute the base of aquatic food webs, many aquatic organisms depend on them for food, either directly or indirectly. (In addition, a substantial percentage of the oxygen produced by photosynthesis is made by photosynthetic protists.) **2.** Protists form mutualistic and parasitic associations with other organisms. Examples include photosynthetic dinoflagellates that form a mutualistic symbiosis with coral polyps, parabasalids that form a mutualistic symbiosis with termites, and the stramenopile *Phytophthora ramorum*, a parasite of oak trees. **3.** Corals depend on their dinoflagellate symbionts for nourishment, so coral bleaching would probably cause the corals to die. As the corals died, less food would be available for fishes and other species that eat coral. As a result, populations of these species might decline, and that, in turn, might cause populations of their predators to decline. **4.** The two approaches differ in the evolutionary changes they may bring about. A strain of *Wolbachia* that confers resistance to infection by *Plasmodium* and does not harm mosquitoes would spread rapidly through the mosquito population. In this case, natural selection would favor any *Plasmodium* individuals that could overcome the resistance to infection conferred by *Wolbachia*. If insecticides are used, mosquitoes that are resistant to the insecticide would be favored by natural selection. Hence, use of *Wolbachia* could cause evolution in *Plasmodium* populations, while using insecticides could cause evolution in mosquito populations.

Summary of Key Concepts Questions

28.1 Sample response: Protists, plants, animals, and fungi are similar in that their cells have a nucleus and other membrane-enclosed organelles, unlike the cells of prokaryotes. These membrane-enclosed organelles make the cells of eukaryotes more complex than the cells of prokaryotes. Protists and other eukaryotes also differ from prokaryotes in having a well-developed cytoskeleton that enables them to have asymmetric forms and to change in shape as they feed, move, or grow. With respect to differences between protists and other eukaryotes, most protists are unicellular, unlike animals, plants, and most fungi. Protists also have greater nutritional diversity than other eukaryotes. **28.2** Unique cytoskeletal features are shared by many excavates. In addition, some members of Excavata have an "excavated" feeding groove for which the group was named. DNA evidence does not strongly support or refute Excavata as a group. Overall, evidence for the group is relatively weak. **28.3** Stramenopiles and alveolates are hypothesized to have originated by secondary endosymbiosis. Under this hypothesis, we can infer that the common ancestor of these two groups had a plastid, in this case of red algal origin. Thus, we would expect that apicomplexans (and alveolate or stramenopile protists) either would have plastids or would have lost their plastids over the course of evolution.   **28.4** Red algae, green algae, and land plants are placed in the same supergroup because considerable evidence indicates that these organisms all descended from the same ancestor, an ancient heterotrophic protist that acquired a cyanobacterial endosymbiont.   **28.5** The unikonts are a diverse group of eukaryotes that includes many protists, along with animals and fungi. Most of the protists in Unikonta are amoebozoans, a clade of amoebas that have lobe- or tube-shaped pseudopodia (as opposed to the threadlike pseudopodia of rhizarians). Other protists in Unikonta include several groups that are closely related to fungi and several other groups that are closely related to animals.   **28.6** Sample response: Ecologically important protists include photosynthetic dinoflagellates that provide essential sources of energy to their symbiotic partners, the corals that build coral reefs. Other important protistan symbionts include those that enable termites to digest wood and *Plasmodium*, the pathogen that causes malaria. Photosynthetic protists such as diatoms are among the most important producers in aquatic communities; as such, many other species in aquatic environments depend on them for food.

Test Your Understanding
1. d **2.** b **3.** b **4.** d **5.** d **6.** c
7.

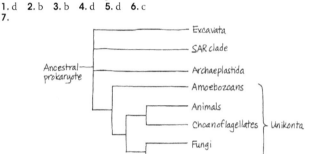

Pathogens that share a relatively recent common ancestor with humans will likely also share metabolic and structural characteristics with humans. Because drugs target the pathogen's metabolism or structure, developing drugs that harm the pathogen but not the patient should be most difficult for pathogens with whom we share the most recent evolutionary history. Working backward in time, we can use the phylogenetic tree to determine the order in which humans shared a common ancestor with pathogens in different taxa. This process leads to the prediction that it should be hardest to develop drugs to combat animal pathogens, followed by choanoflagellate pathogens, fungal and nucleariid pathogens, amoebozoans, other protists, and finally prokaryotes.

Chapter 29

Figure Questions
Figure 29.2 In Figure 29.2, land plants are shown as a sister group to the charophytes, not as members of the charophyte lineage. However, current evidence indicates that land plants emerged from within the charophyte algae, indicating that land plants descended from the common ancestor that gave rise to the charophytes. Hence, when land plants are excluded from the charophytes, the charophytes are a paraphyletic group.   **Figure 29.3** The life cycle in Figure 13.6b has alternation of generations; the others do not. Unlike the animal life cycle (Figure 13.6a), in alternation of generations, meiosis produces spores, not gametes. These spores then divide repeatedly by mitosis, ultimately forming a multicellular haploid individual that produces gametes. There is no multicellular haploid stage in the animal life cycle. An alternation of generations life cycle also has a multicellular diploid stage, whereas the life cycle shown in Figure 13.6c does not. **Figure 29.6** Yes. As shown in the diagram, the sperm cell and the egg cell that fuse each resulted from the mitotic division of spores produced by the same sporophyte. However, these spores would differ genetically from one another because they were produced by meiosis, a cell division process that generates genetic variation among the offspring cells.   **Figure 29.8** Because the moss reduces nitrogen loss from the ecosystem, species that typically colonize the soils after the moss probably experience higher soil nitrogen levels than they otherwise would. The resulting increased availability of nitrogen may benefit these species because nitrogen is an essential nutrient that often is in short supply.   **Figure 29.11** A fern that had wind-dispersed sperm would not require water for fertilization, thus removing a difficulty that ferns face when they live in arid environments. The fern would also be under strong selection to produce sperm above ground (as opposed to the current situation, where some fern gametophytes are located below ground).

Concept Check 29.1
1. Land plants share some key traits only with charophytes: rings of cellulose-synthesizing complexes, similarity in sperm structure, and the formation of a phragmoplast in cell division. Comparisons of nuclear and chloroplast genes also point to a common ancestry.   **2.** Spore walls toughened by sporopollenin (protects against harsh environmental conditions); multicellular, dependent embryos (provide nutrients and protection to the developing embryo); cuticle (reduces

water loss); stomata (control gas exchange and reduce water loss)   **3.** The multicellular diploid stage of the life cycle would not produce gametes. Instead, both males and females would produce haploid spores by meiosis. These spores would give rise to multicellular male and female haploid stages—a major change from the single-celled haploid stages (sperm and eggs) that we actually have. The multicellular haploid stages would produce gametes and reproduce sexually. An individual at the multicellular haploid stage of the human life cycle might look like us, or it might look completely different.   **4.** Land plants, vascular plants, and seed plants are monophyletic because each of these groups includes the common ancestor of the group and all of the descendants of that common ancestor. The other two categories of plants, the nonvascular plants and the seedless vascular plants, are paraphyletic: These groups do not include all of the descendants of the group's most recent common ancestor.

Concept Check 29.2
1. Bryophytes do not have a vascular transport system, and their life cycle is dominated by gametophytes rather than sporophytes.   **2.** Answers may include the following: Large surface area of protonema enhances absorption of water and minerals; the vase-shaped archegonia protect eggs during fertilization and transport nutrients to the embryos via placental transfer cells; the stalk-like seta conducts nutrients from the gametophyte to the capsule, where spores are produced; the peristome enables gradual spore discharge; stomata enable CO_2/O_2 exchange while minimizing water loss; lightweight spores are readily dispersed by wind.   **3.** Effects of global warming on peatlands could result in positive feedback, which occurs when an end product of a process increases its own production. In this case, global warming is expected to lower the water levels of some peatlands. This would expose peat to air and cause it to decompose, thereby releasing stored CO_2 to the atmosphere. The release of more stored CO_2 to the atmosphere could cause additional global warming, which in turn could cause further drops in water levels, the release of still more CO_2 to the atmosphere, additional warming, and so on: an example of positive feedback.

Concept Check 29.3
1. Lycophytes have microphylls, whereas seed plants and monilophytes (ferns and their relatives) have megaphylls. Monilophytes and seed plants also share other traits not found in lycophytes, such as the initiation of new root branches at various points along the length of an existing root.   **2.** Both seedless vascular plants and bryophytes have flagellated sperm that require moisture for fertilization; this shared similarity poses challenges for these species in arid regions. With respect to key differences, seedless vascular plants have lignified, well-developed vascular tissue, a trait that enables the sporophyte to grow tall and that has transformed life on Earth (via the formation of forests). Seedless vascular plants also have true leaves and roots, which, when compared with bryophytes, provide increased surface area for photosynthesis and improve their ability to extract nutrients from soil.   **3.** Three mechanisms contribute to the production of genetic variation in sexual reproduction: independent assortment of chromosomes, crossing over, and random fertilization. If fertilization were to occur between gametes from the same gametophyte, all of the offspring would be genetically identical. This would be the case because all of the cells produced by a gametophyte—including its sperm and egg cells—are the descendants of a single spore and hence are genetically identical. Although crossing over and the independent assortment of chromosomes would continue to generate genetic variation during the production of spores (which ultimately develop into gametophytes), overall the amount of genetic variation produced by sexual reproduction would drop.

Summary of Key Concepts Questions
29.1

29.2 Some mosses colonize bare, sandy soils, leading to the increased retention of nitrogen in these otherwise low-nitrogen environments. Other mosses harbor nitrogen-fixing cyanobacteria that increase the availability of nitrogen in the ecosystem. The moss *Sphagnum* is often a major component of deposits of peat (partially decayed organic material). Boggy regions with thick layers of peat, known as peatlands, cover broad geographic regions and contain large reservoirs of carbon. By storing large amounts of carbon—in effect, removing CO_2 from the atmosphere—peatlands affect the global climate, making them of considerable ecological importance.   **29.3** Lignified vascular tissue provided the strength needed to support a tall plant against gravity, as well as a means to transport water and nutrients to plant parts located high above ground. Roots were another key trait, anchoring the plant to the ground and providing additional structural support for plants that grew tall. Tall plants could shade shorter plants, thereby outcompeting them for light. Because the spores of a tall plant disperse farther than the spores of a short plant, it is also likely that tall plants could colonize new habitats more rapidly than short plants.

Test Your Understanding

1. b **2.** d **3.** c **4.** a **5.** b
6. (a) diploid; (b) haploid; (c) haploid; (d) diploid **7.** Based on our current understanding of the evolution of major plant groups, the phylogeny has the four branch points shown here:

Derived characters unique to the charophyte and land plant clade (indicated by branch point 1) include rings of cellulose-synthesizing complexes, flagellated sperm structure, and a phragmoplast. Derived characters unique to the land plant clade (branch point 2) include alternation of generations; multicellular, dependent embryos; walled spores produced in sporangia; multicellular gametangia; and apical meristems. Derived characters unique to the vascular plant clade (branch point 3) include life cycles with dominant sporophytes, complex vascular systems (xylem and phloem), and well-developed roots and leaves. Derived characters unique to the monilophyte and seed plant clade (branch point 4) include megaphylls and roots that can branch at various points along the length of an existing root.
8. (a)

(b) In the first 40 years after a fire, nitrogen fixation rates were below 0.01 kg per ha per yr, which was less than 1% of the amount of nitrogen deposited from the atmosphere. Thus, in the initial decades after a fire, the moss *Pleurozium* and the nitrogen-fixing bacteria it harbors had relatively little effect on the amount of nitrogen added to the forest. With time, however, *Pleurozium* and its symbiotic, nitrogen-fixing bacteria became increasingly important. By 170 years after a fire, the percentage of the ground surface covered by the moss had increased to about 70%, leading to a corresponding increase in populations of the symbiotic bacteria. As would be predicted from this result, in older forests considerably more nitrogen (130–300%) was added by nitrogen fixation than was deposited from the atmosphere.

Chapter 30

Figure Questions

Figure 30.2 Retaining the gametophyte within the sporophyte shields the egg-containing gametophyte from UV radiation. UV radiation is a mutagen. Hence, we would expect fewer mutations to occur in the egg cells produced by a gametophyte retained in the body of a sporophyte. Most mutations are harmful. Thus, the fitness of embryos should increase because fewer embryos would carry harmful mutations. **Figure 30.3** It contains cells from three generations: (1) the current sporophyte (cells of ploidy 2*n*, found in the seed coat and in the megasporangium remnant that surrounds the spore wall); (2) the female gametophyte (cells of ploidy *n*, found in the food supply); and (3) the sporophyte of the next generation (cells of ploidy 2*n*, found in the embryo). **Figure 30.4** Mitosis. A single haploid megaspore divides by mitosis to produce a multicellular, haploid female gametophyte. (Likewise, a single haploid microspore divides by mitosis to produce a multicellular male gametophyte.) **Figure 30.14** No. The branching order shown could still be correct if *Amborella* and other early angiosperms had originated prior to 150 million years ago, but angiosperm fossils of that age had not yet been discovered. In such a situation, the 140-million-year-old date for the origin of the angiosperms shown on the phylogeny would be incorrect.

Concept Check 30.1

1. To reach the eggs, the flagellated sperm of seedless plants must swim through a film of water, usually over a distance of no more than a few centimeters. In contrast, the sperm of seed plants do not require water because they are produced within pollen grains that can be transported long distances by wind or by animal pollinators. Although flagellated in some species, the sperm of seed plants do not require mobility because pollen tubes convey them from the point at which the pollen grain is deposited (near the ovules) directly to the eggs. **2.** The reduced gametophytes of seed plants are nurtured by sporophytes and protected from stress, such as drought conditions and UV radiation. Pollen grains, with walls containing sporopollenin, provide protection during transport by wind or animals. Seeds have one or two layers of protective tissue, the seed coat, that improve survival by providing more protection from environmental stresses than do the walls of spores. Seeds also contain a stored supply of food, which provides nourishment for growth after dormancy is broken and the embryo emerges as a seedling. **3.** If a seed could not enter dormancy, the embryo would continue to grow after it was fertilized. As a result, the embryo might rapidly become too large to be dispersed, thus limiting its transport. The embryo's chance of survival might also be reduced because it could not delay growth until conditions become favorable.

Concept Check 30.2

1. Although gymnosperms are similar in not having their seeds enclosed in ovaries and fruits, their seed-bearing structures vary greatly. For instance, cycads have large cones, whereas some gymnosperms, such as *Ginkgo* and *Gnetum*, have small cones that look somewhat like berries, even though they are not fruits. Leaf shape also varies greatly, from the needles of many conifers to the palmlike leaves of cycads to *Gnetum* leaves that look like those of flowering plants. **2.** The pine life cycle illustrates heterospory, as ovulate cones produce megaspores and pollen cones produce microspores. The reduced gametophytes are evident in the form of the microscopic pollen grains that develop from microspores and the microscopic female gametophyte that develops from the megaspore. The egg is shown developing within an ovule, and a pollen tube is shown conveying the sperm. The figure also shows the protective and nutritive features of a seed. **3.** No. Fossil evidence indicates that extant gymnosperms originated at least 305 million years ago, but this does not mean that extant angiosperms are that old—only that the most recent common ancestor of extant gymnosperms and extant angiosperms must be that old.

Concept Check 30.3

1. In the oak's life cycle, the tree (the sporophyte) produces flowers, which contain gametophytes in pollen grains and ovules; the eggs in ovules are fertilized; the mature ovaries develop into dry fruits called acorns. We can view the oak's life cycle as starting when the acorn seeds germinate, resulting in embryos giving rise to seedlings and finally to mature trees, which produce flowers—and then more acorns. **2.** Pine cones and flowers both have sporophylls, modified leaves that produce spores. Pine trees have separate pollen cones (with pollen grains) and ovulate cones (with ovules inside cone scales). In flowers, pollen grains are produced by the anthers of stamens, and ovules are within the ovaries of carpels. Unlike pine cones, many flowers produce both pollen and ovules. **3.** The fact that the clade with bilaterally symmetrical flowers had more species establishes a correlation between flower shape and the rate of plant speciation. Flower shape is not necessarily responsible for the result because the shape (that is, bilateral or radial symmetry) may have been correlated with another factor that was the actual cause of the observed result. Note, however, that flower shape was associated with increased speciation rates when averaged across 19 different pairs of plant lineages. Since these 19 lineage pairs were independent of one another, this association suggests—but does not establish—that differences in flower shape cause differences in speciation rates. In general, strong evidence for causation can come from controlled, manipulative experiments, but such experiments are usually not possible for studies of past evolutionary events.

Concept Check 30.4

1. Plant diversity can be considered a resource because plants provide many important benefits to humans; as a resource, plant diversity is nonrenewable because if a species is lost to extinction, that loss is permanent. **2.** A detailed phylogeny of the seed plants would identify many different monophyletic groups of seed plants. Using this phylogeny, researchers could look for clades that contained species in which medicinally useful compounds had already been discovered. Identification of such clades would allow researchers to concentrate their search for new medicinal compounds among clade members—as opposed to searching for new compounds in species that were selected at random from the more than 250,000 existing species of seed plants.

Summary of Key Concepts Questions

30.1 The integument of an ovule develops into the protective coat of a seed. The ovule's megaspore develops into a haploid female gametophyte, and two parts of the seed are related to that gametophyte: The food supply of the seed is derived from haploid gametophyte cells, and the embryo of the seed develops after the female gametophyte's egg cell is fertilized by a sperm cell. A remnant of the ovule's megasporangium surrounds the spore wall that encloses the seed's food supply and embryo. **30.2** Gymnosperms arose about 305 million years ago, making them a successful group in terms of their evolutionary longevity. Gymnosperms have the five derived traits common to all seed plants (reduced gametophytes, heterospory, ovules, pollen, and seeds), making them well adapted for life on land. Finally, because gymnosperms dominate immense geographic regions today, the group is also highly successful in geographic distribution.   **30.3** Darwin was troubled by the relatively sudden and geographically widespread appearance of angiosperms in the fossil record. Fossil evidence shows that angiosperms arose and began to diversify over a period of 20–30 million years, a less rapid event than was suggested by the fossils known during Darwin's lifetime. Fossil discoveries have also uncovered extinct lineages of woody seed plants that may have been closely related to angiosperms; one such group, the Bennettitales, had flowerlike structures that may have been pollinated by insects. Phylogenetic analyses have identified *Amborella* as the most basal angiosperm lineage; *Amborella* is woody, and hence its basal position supports the conclusion (from fossils) that the angiosperm common ancestor was likely woody.   **30.4** The loss of tropical forests could contribute to global warming (which would have negative effects on many human societies). People also depend on Earth's biodiversity for many products and services and hence would be harmed by the loss of species that would occur if the world's remaining tropical forests were cut down. With respect to a possible mass extinction, tropical forests harbor at least 50% of the species on Earth. If the remaining tropical forests were destroyed, large numbers of these species could be driven to extinction, thus rivaling the losses that occurred in the five mass extinction events documented in the fossil record.

Test Your Understanding
1. c   **2.** a   **3.** b   **4.** d   **5.** c
6.

8. (a)

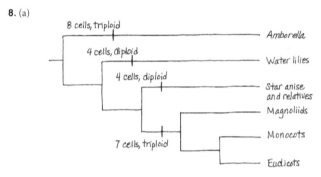

(b) The phylogeny indicates that basal angiosperms differed from other angiosperms in terms of the number of cells in female gametophytes and the ploidy of the endosperm. The ancestral state of the angiosperms cannot be determined from these data alone. It is possible that the common ancestor of angiosperms had seven-celled female gametophytes and triploid endosperm and hence that the eight-celled and four-celled conditions found in basal angiosperms represent derived traits for those lineages. Alternatively, either the eight-celled or four-celled condition may represent the ancestral state.

Chapter 31

Figure Questions
Figure 31.2 DNA from each of these mushrooms would be identical if each mushroom is part of a single hyphal network, as is likely.   **Figure 31.5** The haploid spores produced in the sexual portion of the life cycle develop from haploid nuclei that were produced by meiosis; because genetic recombination occurs during meiosis, these spores will differ genetically from one another. In contrast, the haploid spores produced in the asexual portion of the life cycle develop from nuclei that were produced by mitosis; as a result, these spores are genetically identical to one another.   **Figure 31.15** One or both of the following would apply to each species: DNA analyses would reveal that it is a member of the ascomycete clade, or aspects of its sexual life cycle would indicate that it is an ascomycete (for example, it would produce asci and ascospores).   **Figure 31.20** Two possible controls would be E−P− and E+P−. Results from an E−P− control could be compared with results from the E−P+ experiment, and results from an E+P− control could be compared with results from the E+P+ experiment. Together, these two comparisons would indicate whether the addition of the pathogen causes an increase in leaf mortality. Results from an E−P− experiment could also be compared with results from the second control (E+P−) to determine whether adding the fungal endophytes has a negative effect on the plant

Concept Check 31.1
1. Both a fungus and a human are heterotrophs. Many fungi digest their food externally by secreting enzymes into the food and then absorbing the small molecules that result from digestion. Other fungi absorb such small molecules directly from their environment. In contrast, humans (and most other animals) ingest relatively large pieces of food and digest the food within their bodies.   **2.** The ancestors of such a mutualist most likely secreted powerful enzymes to digest the body of their insect host. Since such enzymes would harm a living host, it is likely that the mutualist would not produce such enzymes or would restrict their secretion and use.   **3.** Carbon that enters the plant through stomata is fixed into sugar through photosynthesis. Some of these sugars are absorbed by the fungus that partners with the plant to form mycorrhizae; others are transported within the plant body and used in the plant. Thus, the carbon may be deposited in either the body of the plant or the body of the fungus.

Concept Check 31.2
1. The majority of the fungal life cycle is spent in the haploid stage, whereas the majority of the human life cycle is spent in the diploid stage.   **2.** The two mushrooms might be reproductive structures of the same mycelium (the same organism). Or they might be parts of two separate organisms that have arisen from a single parent organism through asexual reproduction (for example, from two genetically identical asexual spores) and thus carry the same genetic information.

Concept Check 31.3
1. DNA evidence indicates that fungi, animals, and their protistan relatives form a clade, the opisthokonts. Furthermore, some chytrids and other fungi thought to be members of early diverging lineages have posterior flagella, as do most other opisthokonts. This suggests that other fungal lineages lost their flagella after diverging from ancestors that had flagella.   **2.** Mycorrhizae form extensive networks of hyphae through the soil, enabling nutrients to be absorbed more efficiently than a plant can do on its own; this is true today, and similar associations were probably very important for the earliest land plants (which lacked roots). Evidence for the antiquity of mycorrhizal associations includes fossils showing arbuscular mycorrhizae in the early land plant *Aglaophyton* and molecular results showing that genes required for the formation of mycorrhizae are present in liverworts and other basal plant lineages.   **3.** Fungi are heterotrophs. Prior to the colonization of land by plants, terrestrial fungi would have lived where other organisms (or their remains) were present and provided a source of food. Thus, if fungi colonized land before plants, they could have fed on prokaryotes or protists that lived on land or by the water's edge—but not on the plants or animals on which many fungi feed today.

Concept Check 31.4
1. Flagellated spores; molecular evidence also suggests that chytrids include species that belong to early-diverging fungal lineages.   **2.** Possible answers include the following: In zygomycetes, the sturdy, thick-walled zygosporangium can withstand harsh conditions and then undergo karyogamy and meiosis when the environment is favorable for reproduction. In glomeromycetes, the hyphae have a specialized morphology that enables the fungi to form arbuscular mycorrhizae with plant roots. In ascomycetes, the asexual spores (conidia) are often produced in chains or clusters at the tips of conidiophores, where they are easily dispersed by wind. The often cup-shaped ascocarps house the sexual spore-forming asci. In basidiomycetes, the basidiocarp supports and protects a large surface area of basidia, from which spores are dispersed.   **3.** Such a change to the life cycle of an ascomycete would reduce the number and genetic diversity of ascospores that result from a mating event. Ascospore number would drop because a mating event would lead to the formation of only one ascus. Ascospore genetic diversity would also drop because in ascomycetes, one mating event leads to the formation of asci by many different dikaryotic cells. As a result, genetic recombination and meiosis occur independently many different times—which could not happen if only a single ascus was formed. It is also likely that if such an ascomycete formed an ascocarp, the shape of the ascocarp would differ considerably from that found in its close relatives.

Concept Check 31.5
1. A suitable environment for growth, retention of water and minerals, protection from intense sunlight, and protection from being eaten   **2.** A hardy spore stage enables dispersal to host organisms through a variety of mechanisms; their ability to grow rapidly in a favorable new environment enables them to capitalize on the host's resources.   **3.** Many different outcomes might have occurred. Organisms that currently form mutualisms with fungi might have gained the ability to perform the tasks currently done by their fungal partners, or they might have formed similar mutualisms with other organisms (such as bacteria). Alternatively, organisms that currently form mutualisms with fungi might be less effective at living in their present environments. For example, the colonization of land by plants might have been more difficult. And if plants did eventually colonize land without fungal mutualists, natural selection might have favored plants that formed more highly divided and extensive root systems (in part replacing mycorrhizae).

Summary of Key Concepts Questions
31.1 The body of a multicellular fungus typically consists of thin filaments called hyphae. These filaments form an interwoven mass (mycelium) that penetrates the substrate on which the fungus grows and feeds. Because the individual filaments are thin, the surface-to-volume ratio of the mycelium is maximized, making nutrient absorption highly efficient.

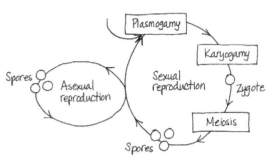

31.3 Phylogenetic analyses show that fungi and animals are more closely related to each other than either is to other multicellular eukaryotes (such as plants or multicellular algae). These analyses also show that fungi are more closely related to single-celled protists called nucleariids than they are to animals, whereas animals are more closely related to a different group of single-celled protists, the choanoflagellates, than they are to fungi. In combination, these results indicate that multicellularity evolved in fungi and animals independently, from different single-celled ancestors.

31.4

31.5 As decomposers, fungi break down the bodies of dead organisms, thereby recycling elements between the living and nonliving environments. Without the activities of fungi and bacterial decomposers, essential nutrients would remain tied up in organic matter, and life would cease. As an example of their key role as mutualists, fungi form mycorrhizal associations with plants. These associations improve the growth and survival of plants, thereby indirectly affecting the many other species (humans included) that depend on plants. As pathogens, fungi harm other species. In some cases, fungal pathogens have caused their host populations to decline across broad geographic regions, as seen for the American chestnut.

Test Your Understanding
1. b 2. d 3. a 4. d

Chapter 32

Figure Questions
Figure 32.3 As described in ❶ and ❷, choanoflagellates and a broad range of animals have collar cells. Since collar cells have never been observed in plants, fungi, or non-choanoflagellate protists, this suggests that choanoflagellates may be more closely related to animals than to other eukaryotes. If choanoflagellates are more closely related to animals than to any other group of eukaryotes, choanoflagellates and animals should share other traits that are not found in other eukaryotes. The data described in ❸ are consistent with this prediction.
Figure 32.10 The cells of an early embryo with deuterostome development typically are not committed to a particular developmental fate, whereas the cells of an early embryo with protostome development typically are committed to a particular developmental fate. As a result, an embryo with deuterostome development would be more likely to contain stem cells that could give rise to cells of any type.
Figure 32.11 Cnidaria is the sister phylum in this tree.

Concept Check 32.1
1. In most animals, the zygote undergoes cleavage, which leads to the formation of a blastula. Next, in gastrulation, one end of the embryo folds inward, producing layers of embryonic tissue. As the cells of these layers differentiate, a wide variety of animal forms are produced. Despite the diversity of animal forms, animal development is controlled by a similar set of *Hox* genes across a broad range of taxa. 2. The imaginary plant would require tissues composed of cells that were analogous to the muscle and nerve cells found in animals: "Muscle" tissue would be necessary for the plant to chase prey, and "nerve" tissue would be required for the plant to coordinate its movements when chasing prey. To digest captured prey, the plant would need to either secrete enzymes into one or more digestive cavities (which could be modified leaves, as in a Venus flytrap) or secrete enzymes outside of its body and feed by absorption. To extract nutrients from the soil—yet be able to chase prey—the plant would need something other than fixed roots, perhaps retractable "roots" or a way to ingest soil. To conduct photosynthesis, the plant would require chloroplasts. Overall, such an imaginary plant would be very similar to an animal that had chloroplasts and retractable roots.

Concept Check 32.2
1. c, b, a, d 2. We cannot infer whether extant animals originated before or after extant fungi. If correct, the date provided for the most recent common ancestor of fungi and animals would indicate that animals originated some time within the last billion years. The fossil record indicates that animals originated at least 560 million years ago. Thus, we could conclude only that animals originated sometime between 1 billion years ago and 560 million years ago. 3. In descent with modification, an organism shares characteristics with its ancestors (due to their shared ancestry), yet it also differs from its ancestors (because organisms accumulate differences over time as they adapt to their surroundings). As an example, consider the evolution of animal cadherin proteins, a key step in the origin of multicellular animals. These proteins illustrate both of these aspects of descent with modification: Animal cadherin proteins share many protein domains with a cadherin-like protein found in their choanoflagellate ancestors, yet they also have a unique "CCD" domain that is not found in choanoflagellates.

Concept Check 32.3
1. Grade-level characteristics are those that multiple lineages share regardless of evolutionary history. Some grade-level characteristics may have evolved multiple times independently. Features that unite clades are derived characteristics that originated in a common ancestor and were passed on to the various descendants. 2. A snail has a spiral and determinate cleavage pattern; a human has radial, indeterminate cleavage. In a snail, the coelomic cavity is formed by splitting of mesoderm masses; in a human, the coelom forms from folds of archenteron. In a snail, the mouth forms from the blastopore; in a human, the anus develops from the blastopore. 3. Most coelomate triploblasts have two openings to their digestive tract, a mouth and an anus. As such, their bodies have a structure that is analogous to that of a doughnut: The digestive tract (the hole of the doughnut) runs from the mouth to the anus and is surrounded by various tissues (the solid part of the doughnut). The doughnut analogy is most obvious at early stages of development (see Figure 32.10c).

Concept Check 32.4
1. Cnidarians possess true tissues, while sponges do not. Also unlike sponges, cnidarians exhibit body symmetry, though it is radial and not bilateral as in other animal phyla.
2.

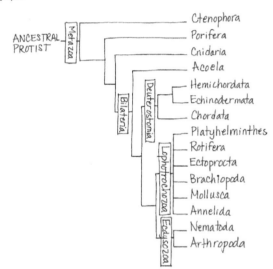

Under the hypothesis that ctenophores are basal metazoans, sponges (which lack true tissues) would be nested within a clade whose other members all have true tissues. As a result, a group composed of animals with true tissues would not form a clade. 3. The phylogeny in Figure 32.11 indicates that molluscs are members of Lophotrochozoa, one of the three main groups of bilaterians (the others being Deuterostomia and Ecdysozoa). As seen in Figure 25.11, the fossil record shows that molluscs were present tens of millions of years before the Cambrian explosion. Thus, long before the Cambrian explosion, the lophotrochozoan clade had formed and was evolving independently of the evolutionary lineages leading to Deuterostomia and Ecdysozoa. Based on the phylogeny in Figure 32.11, we can also conclude that the lineages leading to Deuterostomia and Ecdysozoa were independent of one another before the Cambrian explosion. Since the lineages leading to the three main clades of bilaterians were evolving independently of one another prior to the Cambrian explosion, that explosion could be viewed as consisting of three "explosions," not one.

Summary of Key Concepts Questions
Concept 32.1 Unlike animals, which are heterotrophs that ingest their food, plants are autotrophs, and fungi are heterotrophs that grow on their food and feed by absorption. Animals lack cell walls, which are found in both plants and fungi. Animals also have muscle tissue and nerve tissue, which are not found in either

plants or fungi. In addition, the sperm and egg cells of animals are produced by meiotic division, unlike what occurs in plants and fungi (where reproductive cells such as sperm and eggs are produced by mitotic division). Finally, animals regulate the development of body form with *Hox* genes, a unique group of genes that is not found in either plants or fungi. **Concept 32.2** Current hypotheses about the cause of the Cambrian explosion include new predator-prey relationships, an increase in atmospheric oxygen, and an increase in developmental flexibility provided by the origin of *Hox* genes and other genetic changes. **Concept 32.3** Body plans provide a helpful way to compare and contrast key features of organisms. However, phylogenetic analyses show that similar body plans have arisen independently in different groups of organisms. As such, similar body plans may have arisen by convergent evolution and hence may not be informative about evolutionary relationships. **Concept 32.4** Listed in order from the most to the least inclusive clade, humans belong to Metazoa, Eumetazoa, Bilateria, Deuterostomia, and Chordata.

Test Your Understanding
1. a **2.** d **3.** c **4.** b

Chapter 33

Figure Questions

Figure 33.8 The *Obelia* life cycle is most similar to the life cycle shown in Figure 13.6a. In *Obelia*, both the polyp and the medusa are diploid organisms. Typical of animals, only the single-celled gametes are haploid. By contrast, plants and some algae (Figure 13.6b) have a multicellular haploid generation and a multicellular diploid generation. *Obelia* also differs from fungi and some protists (Figure 13.6c) in that the diploid stage of those organisms is unicellular.
Figure 33.9 Possible examples might include the endoplasmic reticulum (flattening; increases area for biosynthesis), root hairs (projections; increase area for absorption), or cardiovascular systems (branching; increase area for materials exchange in tissues). **Figure 33.11** Adding fertilizer to the water supply would probably increase the abundance of algae, and that, in turn, would likely increase the abundance of snails (which eat algae). If the water was also contaminated with infected human feces, an increase in the number of snails would likely lead to an increase in the abundance of blood flukes (which require snails as an intermediate host). As a result, the occurrence of schistosomiasis might increase.
Figure 33.21 The extinction of freshwater bivalves might lead to an increase in the abundance of photosynthetic protists and bacteria. Because these organisms are at the base of aquatic food webs, increases in their abundance could have major effects on aquatic communities (including both increases and decreases in the abundance of other species). **Figure 33.29** Such a result would be consistent with the *Ubx* and *abd-A Hox* genes having played a major role in the evolution of increased body segment diversity in arthropods. However, by itself, such a result would simply show that the presence of the *Ubx* and *abd-A Hox* genes was *correlated with* an increase in body segment diversity in arthropods; it would not provide direct experimental evidence that the acquisition of the *Ubx* and *abd-A* genes *caused* an increase in arthropod body segment diversity. **Figure 33.34** You should have circled the clade that includes the insects, remipedians, and other crustaceans, along with the branch point that represents their most recent common ancestor.

Concept Check 33.1
1. The flagella of choanocytes draw water through their collars, which trap food particles. The particles are engulfed by phagocytosis and digested, either by choanocytes or by amoebocytes. **2.** The collar cells of sponges bear a striking resemblance to a choanoflagellate cell. This suggests that the last common ancestor of animals and their protist sister group may have resembled a choanoflagellate. Nevertheless, mesomycetozoans could still be the sister group of animals. If this is the case, the lack of collar cells in mesomycetozoans would indicate that over time their structure evolved in ways that caused it to no longer resemble a choanoflagellate cell. It is also possible that choanoflagellates and sponges share similar-looking collar cells as a result of convergent evolution.

Concept Check 33.2
1. Both the polyp and the medusa are composed of an outer epidermis and an inner gastrodermis separated by a gelatinous layer, the mesoglea. The polyp is a cylindrical form that adheres to the substrate by its aboral end; the medusa is a flattened, mouth-down form that moves freely in the water. **2.** Cnidarian stinging cells (cnidocytes) function in defense and prey capture. They contain capsule-like organelles (cnidae), which in turn contain coiled threads. The threads either inject poison or stick to and entangle small prey. **3.** Evolution is not goal oriented; hence, it would not be correct to argue that cnidarians were not "highly evolved" simply because their form had changed relatively little over the past 560 million years. Instead, the fact that cnidarians have persisted for hundreds of millions of years indicates that the cnidarian body plan is a highly successful one.

Concept Check 33.3
1. Tapeworms can absorb food from their environment and release ammonia into their environment through their body surface because their body is very flat, due in part to the lack of a coelom. **2.** The inner tube is the alimentary canal, which runs the length of the body. The outer tube is the body wall. The two tubes are separated by the coelom. **3.** All molluscs have inherited a foot from their common ancestor. However, in different groups of molluscs, the structure of the foot has been modified over time (by natural selection) in ways that reflect how the

foot is used in locomotion by members of each clade. In gastropods, the foot is used as a holdfast or to move slowly on the substrate. In cephalopods, the foot has been modified into part of the tentacles and into an excurrent siphon, through which water is propelled (resulting in movement in the opposite direction).

Concept Check 33.4
1. Nematodes lack body segments and a true coelom; annelids have both. **2.** The arthropod exoskeleton, which had already evolved in the ocean, allows terrestrial species to retain water and support their bodies on land. Wings allow insects to disperse quickly to new habitats and to find food and mates. The tracheal system allows for efficient gas exchange despite the presence of an exoskeleton. **3.** Yes. Under the traditional hypothesis, we would expect body segmentation to be controlled by similar *Hox* genes in annelids and arthropods. However, if annelids are in Lophotrochozoa and arthropods are in Ecdysozoa (as current evidence suggests), body segmentation may have evolved independently in these two groups. In such a case, we might expect that different *Hox* genes would control the development of body segmentation in the two clades.

Concept Check 33.5
1. Each tube foot consists of an ampulla and a podium. When the ampulla squeezes, it forces water into the podium, which causes the podium to expand and contact the substrate. Adhesive chemicals are then secreted from the base of the podium, thereby attaching the podium to the substrate. **2.** Both insects and nematodes are members of Ecdysozoa, one of the three major clades of bilaterians. Therefore, a characteristic shared by *Drosophila* and *Caenorhabditis* may be informative for other members of their clade—but not necessarily for members of Deuterostomia. Instead, Figure 33.2 suggests that a species within Echinodermata or Chordata might be a more appropriate invertebrate model organism from which to draw inferences about humans and other vertebrates. **3.** Echinoderms include species with a wide range of body forms. However, even echinoderms that look very different from one another, such as sea stars and sea cucumbers, share characteristics unique to their phylum, including a water vascular system and tube feet. The differences between echinoderm species illustrate the diversity of life, while the characteristics they share illustrate the unity of life. The match between organisms and their environments can be seen in such echinoderm features as the eversible stomachs of sea stars (enabling them to digest prey that are larger than their mouth) and the complex, jaw-like structure that sea urchins use to eat seaweed.

Summary of Key Concepts Questions
33.1 The sponge body consists of two layers of cells, both of which are in contact with water. As a result, gas exchange and waste removal occur as substances diffuse into and out of the cells of the body. Choanocytes and amoebocytes ingest food particles from the surrounding water. Choanocytes also release food particles to amoebocytes, which then digest the food particles and deliver nutrients to other cells. **33.2** The cnidarian body plan consists of a sac with a central digestive compartment, the gastrovascular cavity. The single opening to this compartment serves as both a mouth and an anus. The two main variations on this body plan are sessile polyps (which adhere to the substrate at the end of the body opposite to the mouth/anus) and motile medusae (which move freely through the water and resemble flattened, mouth-down versions of polyps). **33.3** No. Some lophotrochozoans have a crown of ciliated tentacles that function in feeding (called a lophophore), while others go through a distinctive developmental stage known as trochophore larvae. Many other lophotrochozoans do not have either of these features. As a result, the clade is defined primarily by DNA similarities, not morphological similarities. **33.4** Many nematode species live in soil and in sediments on the bottom of bodies of water. These free-living species play important roles in decomposition and nutrient cycling. Other nematodes are parasites, including many species that attack the roots of plants and some that attack animals (including humans). Arthropods have profound effects on all aspects of ecology. In aquatic environments, crustaceans play key roles as grazers (of algae), scavengers, and predators, and some species, such as krill, are important sources of food for whales and other vertebrates. On land, it is difficult to think of features of the natural world that are not affected in some way by insects and other arthropods, such as spiders and ticks. There are more than 1 million species of insects, many of which have enormous ecological effects as herbivores, predators, parasites, decomposers, and vectors of disease. Insects are also key sources of food for many organisms, including humans in some regions of the world. **33.5** Echinoderms and chordates are both members of Deuterostomia, one of the three main clades of bilaterian animals. As such, chordates (including humans) are more closely related to echinoderms than we are to animals in any of the other phyla covered in this chapter. Nevertheless, echinoderms and chordates have evolved independently for over 500 million years. This statement does not contradict the close relationship of echinoderms and chordates, but it does make clear that "close" is a relative term indicating that these two phyla are more closely related to each other than either is to animal phyla not in Deuterostomia.

Test Your Understanding
1. a **2.** c **3.** b **4.** d **5.** c **6.** d

Chapter 34

Figure Questions

Figure 34.6 Results in these figures suggest that specific *Hox* genes, as well as the order in which they are expressed, have been highly conserved over the course of evolution. **Figure 34.19** *Tiktaalik* was a lobe-fin fish that had both fish and tetrapod characters. Like a fish, *Tiktaalik* had fins, scales, and gills. As described by Darwin's concept of descent with modification, such shared characters can be attributed to descent from ancestral species—in this case, *Tiktaalik's* descent from fish ancestors. *Tiktaalik* also had traits that were unlike a fish but like a tetrapod, including a flat skull, a neck, a full set of ribs, and the skeletal structure of its fin. These characters illustrate the second part of descent with modification, showing how ancestral features had become modified over time.   **Figure 34.20** Sometime between 370 mya and 340 mya. We can infer this because amphibians must have originated after the most recent common ancestor of *Tulerpeton* and living tetrapods (and that ancestor is said to have originated 370 mya), but no later than the date of the earliest known fossils of amphibians (shown in the figure as 340 mya).   **Figure 34.24** Pterosaurs did not descend from the dinosaur common ancestor; hence, pterosaurs are not dinosaurs. However, birds are descendants of the common ancestor of the dinosaurs. As a result, a monophyletic clade of dinosaurs must include birds. In that sense, birds are dinosaurs.   **Figure 34.36** In general, the process of exaptation occurs as a structure that had one function acquires a different function via a series of intermediate stages. Each of these intermediate stages typically has some function in the organism in which it is found. The incorporation of articular and quadrate bones into the mammalian ear illustrates exaptation because these bones originally evolved as part of the jaw, where they functioned as the jaw hinge, but over time they became co-opted for another function, namely, the transmission of sound.   **Figure 34.42** The phylogeny shows humans as the sister group to the lineage that contains chimpanzees and bonobos. This relationship is not consistent with humans as having descended from either chimpanzees or bonobos. If humans had descended from chimpanzees, for example, the human lineage would be nested within the chimpanzee lineage, much as birds are nested within the reptile clade (see Figure 34.24).   **Figure 34.49** Fossil evidence indicates that Neanderthals did not live in Africa; hence there would have been little opportunity for mating (gene flow) between Neanderthals and humans in Africa. However, as humans migrated from Africa, mating may have occurred between Neanderthals and humans in the first region where the two species encountered one another: the Middle East. Humans carrying Neanderthal genes may then have migrated to other locations, explaining why Neanderthals are equally related to humans from France, China, and Papua New Guinea.

Concept Check 34.1

1. The four characters are a notochord; a dorsal, hollow nerve chord; pharyngeal slits or clefts; and a muscular, post-anal tail.   **2.** In humans, these characters are present only in the embryo. The notochord becomes disks between the vertebrae; the dorsal, hollow nerve cord develops into the brain and spinal cord; the pharyngeal clefts develop into various adult structures, and the tail is almost completely lost.   **3.** Not necessarily. It would be possible that the chordate common ancestor had this gene, which was then lost in the lancelet lineage and retained in other chordates. However, it would also be possible that the chordate common ancestor lacked this gene; this could occur if the gene originated after lancelets diverged from other chordates but before tunicates diverged from other chordates.

Concept Check 34.2

1. Lampreys have a round, rasping mouth, which they use to attach to fish. Conodonts had two sets of mineralized dental elements, which may have been used to impale prey and cut it into smaller pieces.   **2.** Such a finding suggests that early organisms with a head were favored by natural selection in several different evolutionary lineages. However, while a logical argument can be made that having a head was advantageous, fossils alone do not constitute proof.   **3.** In armored jawless vertebrates, bone served as external armor that may have provided protection from predators. Some species also had mineralized mouthparts, which could be used for either predation or scavenging.

Concept Check 34.3

1. Both are gnathostomes and have jaws, four clusters of *Hox* genes, enlarged forebrains, and lateral line systems. Shark skeletons consist mainly of cartilage, whereas tuna have bony skeletons. Sharks also have a spiral valve. Tuna have an operculum and a swim bladder, as well as flexible rays supporting their fins.
2. Aquatic gnathostomes have jaws (an adaptation for feeding) and paired fins and a tail (adaptations for swimming). Aquatic gnathostomes also typically have streamlined bodies for efficient swimming and swim bladders or other mechanisms (such as oil storage in sharks) for buoyancy.
3.

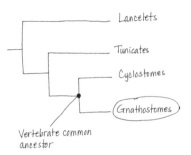

4. Yes, that could have happened. The paired appendages of aquatic gnathostomes other than the lobe-fins could have served as a starting point for the evolution of limbs. The colonization of land by aquatic gnathostomes other than the lobe-fins might have been facilitated in lineages that possessed lungs, as that would have enabled those organisms to breathe air.

Concept Check 34.4

1. Tetrapods are thought to have originated about 365 million years ago when the fins of some lobe-fins evolved into the limbs of tetrapods. In addition to their four limbs with digits—a key derived trait for which the group is named—other derived traits of tetrapods include a neck (consisting of vertebrae that separate the head from the rest of the body), and a pelvic girdle that is fused to the backbone.
2. Some fully aquatic species are paedomorphic, retaining larval features for life in water as adults. Species that live in dry environments may avoid dehydration by burrowing or living under moist leaves, and they protect their eggs with foam nests, viviparity, and other adaptations.   **3.** Many amphibians spend part of their life cycle in aquatic environments and part on land. Thus, they may be exposed to a wide range of environmental problems, including water and air pollution and the loss or degradation of aquatic and/or terrestrial habitats. In addition, amphibians have highly permeable skin, providing relatively little protection from external conditions, and their eggs do not have a protective shell.

Concept Check 34.5

1. The amniotic egg provides protection to the embryo and allows the embryo to develop on land, eliminating the necessity of a watery environment for reproduction. Another key adaptation is rib cage ventilation, which improves the efficiency of air intake and may have allowed early amniotes to dispense with breathing through their skin. Finally, not breathing through their skin allowed amniotes to develop relatively impermeable skin, thereby conserving water.   **2.** Yes. Although snakes lack limbs, they descended from lizards with legs. Some snakes retain vestigial pelvic and leg bones, providing evidence of their descent from an ancestor with legs.   **3.** Birds have weight-saving modifications, including the absence of teeth, a urinary bladder, and a second ovary in females. The wings and feathers are adaptations that facilitate flight, and so are efficient respiratory and circulatory systems that support a high metabolic rate.
4.

Under this convention, the reptiles would consist of all groups in Figure 34.24 except parareptiles and mammals.

Concept Check 34.6

1. Monotremes lay eggs. Marsupials give birth to very small live young that attach to a nipple in the mother's pouch, where they complete development. Eutherians give birth to more developed live young.   **2.** Hands and feet adapted for grasping, flat nails, large brain, forward-looking eyes on a flat face, parental care, and movable big toe and thumb   **3.** Mammals are endothermic, enabling them to live in a wide range of habitats. Milk provides young with a balanced set of nutrients, and hair and a layer of fat under the skin help mammals retain heat. Mammals have differentiated teeth, enabling them to eat many different kinds of food. Mammals also have relatively large brains, and many species are capable learners. Following the mass extinction at the end of the Cretaceous period, the absence of large terrestrial dinosaurs may have opened many new ecological niches to mammals, promoting an adaptive radiation. Continental drift also isolated many groups of mammals from one another, promoting the formation of many new species.

Concept Check 34.7

1. Hominins are a clade within the ape clade that includes humans and all species more closely related to humans than other apes. The derived characters of hominins include bipedal locomotion and relatively larger brains.   **2.** In hominins, bipedal locomotion evolved long before large brain size. *Homo ergaster*, for example, was fully upright, bipedal, and as tall as modern humans, but its brain was significantly smaller than that of modern humans.   **3.** Yes, both can be correct. *Homo sapiens* may have established populations outside of Africa as early as

115,000 years ago, as indicated by the fossil record. However, those populations may have left few or no descendants today. Instead, all living humans may have descended from Africans that spread from Africa roughly 50,000 years ago, as indicated by genetic data.

Summary of Key Concepts Questions

34.1 Lancelets are the most basal group of living chordates, and as adults they have key derived characters of chordates. This suggests that the chordate common ancestor may have resembled a lancelet in having an anterior end with a mouth along with the following four derived characters: a notochord; a dorsal, hollow nerve cord; pharyngeal slits or clefts; and a muscular, post-anal tail.   **34.2** Conodonts, among the earliest vertebrates in the fossil record, were very abundant for 300 million years. While jawless, their well-developed teeth provide early signs of bone formation. Other species of jawless vertebrates developed armor on the outside of their bodies, which probably helped protect them from predators. Like lampreys, these species had paired fins for locomotion and an inner ear with semicircular canals that provided a sense of balance. There were many species of these armored jawless vertebrates, but they all became extinct by the close of the Devonian period, 359 million years ago.   **34.3** The origin of jaws altered how fossil gnathostomes obtained food, which in turn had large effects on ecological interactions. Predators could use their jaws to grab prey or remove chunks of flesh, stimulating the evolution of increasingly sophisticated means of defense in prey species. Evidence for these changes can be found in the fossil record, which includes fossils of 10-m-long predators with remarkably powerful jaws, as well as lineages of well-defended prey species whose bodies were covered by armored plates.   **34.4** Amphibians require water for reproduction; their bodies can lose water rapidly through their moist, highly permeable skin; and amphibian eggs do not have a shell and hence are vulnerable to desiccation.   **34.5** Birds are descended from theropod dinosaurs, and dinosaurs are nested within the archosaur lineage, one of the two main reptile lineages. Thus, the other living archosaur reptiles, the crocodilians, are more closely related to birds than they are to non-archosaur reptiles such as lizards. As a result, birds are considered reptiles. (Note that if reptiles were defined as excluding birds, the reptiles would not form a clade; instead, the reptiles would be a paraphyletic group.)   **34.6** Mammals are members of a group of amniotes called synapsids. Early (nonmammalian) synapsids laid eggs and had a sprawling gait. Fossil evidence shows that mammalian features arose gradually over a period of more than 100 million years. For example, the jaw was modified over time in nonmammalian synapsids, eventually coming to resemble that of a mammal. By 180 million years ago, the first mammals had appeared. There were many species of early mammals, but most of them were small, and they were not abundant or dominant members of their community. Mammals did not rise to ecological dominance until after the extinction of the dinosaurs.   **34.7** The fossil record shows that from 4.5 to 2.5 million years ago, a wide range of hominin species walked upright but had relatively small brain sizes. About 2.5 million years ago, the first members of genus *Homo* emerged. These species used tools and had larger brains than those of earlier hominins. Fossil evidence indicates that multiple members of our genus were alive at any given point in time. Furthermore, until about 1.3 million years ago, these various *Homo* species also coexisted with members of earlier hominin lineages, such as *Paranthropus*. The different hominins alive at the same periods of time varied in body size, body shape, brain size, dental morphology, and the capacity for tool use. Ultimately, except for *Homo sapiens*, all of these species became extinct. Thus, human evolution is viewed not as an evolutionary path leading to *H. sapiens*, but rather as an evolutionary tree with many branches—the only surviving lineage of which is our own.

Test Your Understanding

1. d **2.** c **3.** b **4.** c **5.** d **6.** a

Chapter 35

Figure Questions

Figure 35.17 Pith and cortex are defined, respectively, as ground tissue that is internal and ground tissue that is external to vascular tissue. Since vascular bundles of monocot stems are scattered throughout the ground tissue, there is no clear distinction between internal and external relative to the vascular tissue.
Figure 35.19 The vascular cambium produces growth that increases the diameter of a stem or root. The tissues that are exterior to the vascular cambium cannot keep pace with the growth because their cells no longer divide. As a result, these tissues rupture.   **Figure 35.32** Every root epidermal cell would develop a root hair.   **Figure 35.34** Another example of homeotic gene mutation is the mutation in a *Hox* gene that causes legs to form in place of antennae in *Drosophila* (see Figure 18.20).   **Figure 35.35** The flower would consist of nothing but carpels.

Concept Check 35.1

1. The vascular tissue system connects leaves and roots, allowing sugars to move from leaves to roots in the phloem and allowing water and minerals to move to the leaves in the xylem.   **2.** To get sufficient energy from photosynthesis, we would need lots of surface area exposed to the sun. This large surface-to-volume ratio, however, would create a new problem—evaporative water loss. We would have to be permanently connected to a water source—the soil, also our source of minerals. In short, we would probably look and behave very much like plants.   **3.** As plant cells enlarge, they typically form a huge central vacuole that contains a dilute, watery sap. Central vacuoles enable plant cells to become large with only a minimal investment of new cytoplasm. The orientation of the cellulose microfibrils in plant cell walls affects the growth pattern of cells.

Concept Check 35.2

1. Yes. In a woody plant, secondary growth is occurring in the older parts of the stem and root, while primary growth is occurring at the root and shoot tips.
2. The largest, oldest leaves would be lowest on the shoot. Since they would probably be heavily shaded, they would not photosynthesize much regardless of their size. Determinate growth benefits the plant by keeping it from investing in an ever-increasing amount of resources into organs that provide little photosynthetic product.   **3.** No, the carrot roots will probably be smaller at the end of the second year because the food stored in the roots will be used to produce flowers, fruits, and seeds.

Concept Check 35.3

1. In roots, primary growth occurs in three successive stages, moving away from the tip of the root: the zones of cell division, elongation, and differentiation. In shoots, it occurs at the tip of apical buds, with leaf primordia arising along the sides of an apical meristem. Most growth in length occurs in older internodes below the shoot tip.   **2.** No. Because vertically oriented leaves, such as those of maize, can capture light equally well on both sides of the leaf, you would expect them to have mesophyll cells that are not differentiated into palisade and spongy layers. This is typically the case. Also, vertically oriented leaves usually have stomata on both leaf surfaces.   **3.** Root hairs are cellular extensions that increase the surface area of the root epidermis, thereby enhancing the absorption of minerals and water. Microvilli are extensions that increase the absorption of nutrients by increasing the surface area of the gut.

Concept Check 35.4

1. The sign will still be 2 m above the ground because this part of the tree is no longer growing in length (primary growth); it is now growing only in thickness (secondary growth).   **2.** Stomata must be able to close because evaporation is much more intensive from leaves than from the trunks of woody trees as a result of the higher surface-to-volume ratio in leaves.   **3.** Since there is little seasonal temperature variation in the tropics, the growth rings of a tree from the tropics would be difficult to discern unless the tree came from an area that had pronounced wet and dry seasons.   **4.** The tree would die slowly. Girdling removes an entire ring of secondary phloem (part of the bark), completely preventing transport of sugars and starches from the shoots to the roots. After several weeks, the roots would have used all of their stored carbohydrate reserves and would die.

Concept Check 35.5

1. Although all the living vegetative cells of a plant have the same genome, they develop different forms and functions because of differential gene expression.
2. Plants show indeterminate growth; juvenile and mature phases are found on the same individual plant; and cell differentiation in plants is more dependent on final position than on lineage.   **3.** One hypothesis is that tepals arise if *B* gene activity is present in all three of the outer whorls of the flower.

Summary of Key Concepts Questions

35.1 Here are a few examples: The cuticle of leaves and stems protects these structures from desiccation. Collenchyma and sclerenchyma cells have thick walls that provide support for plants. Strong, branching root systems help anchor plants in the soil.   **35.2** Primary growth arises from apical meristems and involves production and elongation of organs. Secondary growth arises from lateral meristems and adds to the diameter of roots and stems.   **35.3** Lateral roots emerge from the pericycle and destroy plant cells as they emerge. In stems, branches arise from axillary buds and do not destroy any cells.   **35.4** With the evolution of secondary growth, plants were able to grow taller and shade competitors.   **35.5** The orientation of cellulose microfibrils in the innermost layers of the cell wall causes growth along one axis. Microtubules in the cell's outermost cytoplasm play a key role in regulating the axis of cell expansion because it is their orientation that determines the orientation of cellulose microfibrils.

Test Your Understanding

1. d **2.** c **3.** c **4.** a **5.** b **6.** d **7.** d

8.

Chapter 36

Figure Questions

Figure 36.3 The leaves are being produced in a counterclockwise spiral.
Figure 36.4 A higher leaf area index will not necessarily increase photosynthesis because of upper leaves shading lower leaves. **Figure 36.6** A proton pump inhibitor would depolarize (increase) the membrane potential because fewer H^+ ions would be pumped out across the plasma membrane. The immediate effect of an inhibitor of the H^+/sucrose transporter would be to hyperpolarize (decrease) the membrane potential because fewer H^+ ions would be leaking back into the cell through these cotransporters. An inhibitor of the H^+/NO_3^- cotransporter would have no effect on the membrane potential because the simultaneous cotransport of a positively charged ion and a negatively charged ion has no net effect on charge difference across the membrane. An inhibitor of the K^+ ion channels would decrease the membrane potential because additional positively charged ions would not be accumulating outside the cell. **Figure 36.8** The Casparian strip blocks water and minerals from moving between endodermal cells or moving around an endodermal cell via the cell's wall. Therefore, water and minerals must pass through an endodermal cell's plasma membrane. **Figure 36.17** Because the xylem is under negative pressure (tension), excising a stylet that had been inserted into a tracheid or vessel element would probably introduce air into the cell. No xylem sap would exude unless positive root pressure was predominant.

Concept Check 36.1

1. Vascular plants must transport minerals and water absorbed by the roots to all the other parts of the plant. They must also transport sugars from sites of production to sites of use. **2.** Many features of plant architecture affect self-shading, including leaf arrangement, leaf and stem orientation, and leaf area index. **3.** Increased stem elongation would raise the plant's upper leaves. Erect leaves and reduced lateral branching would make the plant less subject to shading by the encroaching neighbors. **4.** Pruning shoot tips removes apical dominance, resulting in lateral shoots (branches) growing from axillary buds (see Chapter 35). This branching produces a bushier plant with a higher leaf area index. **5.** Fungal hyphae are long, thin filaments that form a large, interwoven network in the soil. Their high surface-to-volume ratio is an adaptation that enhances the absorption of materials from the soil.

Concept Check 36.2

1. The cell's Ψ_P is 0.7 MPa. In a solution with a Ψ of -0.4 MPa, the cell's Ψ_P at equilibrium would be 0.3 MPa. **2.** The cell would still adjust to changes in its osmotic environment, but its responses would be slower. Although aquaporins do not affect the water potential gradient across membranes, they allow for more rapid osmotic adjustments. **3.** If tracheids and vessel elements were alive at maturity, their cytoplasm would impede water movement, preventing rapid long-distance transport. **4.** The protoplasts would burst. Because the cytoplasm has many dissolved solutes, water would enter the protoplast continuously without reaching equilibrium. (When present, the cell wall prevents rupturing by limiting expansion of the protoplast.)

Concept Check 36.3

1. Because water-conducting xylem cells are dead at maturity and form essentially hollow tubes, they offer little resistance to water flow, and their thick walls prevent the cells from collapsing from the negative pressure inside. **2.** At dawn, a drop is exuded from the rooted stump because the xylem is under positive pressure due to root pressure. At noon, the xylem is under negative pressure (tension) when it is cut, and the xylem sap is pulled back into the rooted stump. Root pressure cannot keep pace with the increased rate of transpiration at noon. **3.** The endodermis regulates the passage of water-soluble solutes by requiring all such molecules to cross a selectively permeable membrane. Presumably, the inhibitor cannot cross the membrane and therefore never reaches the plant's photosynthetic cells. **4.** Perhaps greater root mass helps compensate for the lower water permeability of the plasma membranes. **5.** The Casparian strip and tight junctions both prevent movement of fluid between cells.

Concept Check 36.4

1. Stomatal opening at dawn is controlled mainly by light, CO_2 concentration, and a circadian rhythm. Environmental stresses such as drought, high temperature, and wind can stimulate stomata to close during the day. Water deficiency can trigger release of the plant hormone abscisic acid, which signals guard cells to close stomata. **2.** The activation of the proton pumps of stomatal cells would cause the guard cells to take up K^+. The increased turgor of the guard cells would lock the stomata open and lead to extreme evaporation from the leaf. **3.** After the flowers are cut, transpiration from any leaves and from the petals (which are modified leaves) will continue to draw water up the xylem. If cut flowers are transferred directly to a vase, air pockets in xylem vessels prevent delivery of water from the vase to the flowers. Cutting stems again underwater, a few centimeters from the original cut, will sever the xylem above the air pocket. The water droplets prevent another air pocket from forming while the flowers are transferred to a vase. **4.** Water molecules are in constant motion, traveling at different speeds. If water molecules gain enough energy, the most energetic molecules near the liquid's surface will have sufficient speed, and therefore sufficient kinetic energy, to leave the liquid in the form of gaseous molecules (water vapor). As the molecules with the highest kinetic energy leave the liquid, the average kinetic energy of the remaining liquid decreases. Because a liquid's temperature is directly related to the average kinetic energy of its molecules, the temperature drops as evaporation proceeds.

Concept Check 36.5

1. In both cases, the long-distance transport is a bulk flow driven by a pressure difference at opposite ends of tubes. Pressure is generated at the source end of a sieve tube by the loading of sugar and resulting osmotic flow of water into the phloem, and this pressure *pushes* sap from the source end to the sink end of the tube. In contrast, transpiration generates a negative pressure potential (tension) that *pulls* the ascent of xylem sap. **2.** The main sources are fully grown leaves (producing sugar by photosynthesis) and fully developed storage organs (producing sugar by breakdown of starch). Roots, buds, stems, expanding leaves, and fruits are powerful sinks because they are actively growing. A storage organ may be a sink in the summer when accumulating carbohydrates but a source in the spring when breaking down starch into sugar for growing shoot tips. **3.** Positive pressure, whether it be in the xylem when root pressure predominates or in the sieve-tube elements of the phloem, requires active transport. Most long-distance transport in the xylem depends on bulk flow driven by the negative pressure potential generated ultimately by the evaporation of water from the leaf and does not require living cells. **4.** The spiral slash prevents optimal bulk flow of the phloem sap to the root sinks. Therefore, more phloem sap can move from the source leaves to the fruit sinks, making them sweeter.

Concept Check 36.6

1. Plasmodesmata, unlike gap junctions, have the ability to pass RNA, proteins, and viruses from cell to cell. **2.** Long-distance signaling is critical for the integrated functioning of all large organisms, but the speed of such signaling is much less critical to plants because their responses to the environment, unlike those of animals, do not typically involve rapid movements. **3.** Although this strategy would eliminate the systemic spread of viral infections, it would also severely impact the development of the plants.

Summary of Key Concepts Questions

36.1 Plants with tall shoots and elevated leaf canopies generally had an advantage over shorter competitors. A consequence of the selective pressure for tall shoots was the further separation of leaves from roots. This separation created problems for the transport of materials between root and shoot systems. Plants with xylem cells were more successful at supplying their shoot systems with soil resources (water and minerals). Similarly, those with phloem cells were more successful at supplying sugar sinks with carbohydrates. **36.2** Xylem sap is usually pulled up the plant by transpiration, much more often than it is pushed up the plant by root pressure. **36.3** Hydrogen bonds are necessary for the cohesion of water molecules to each other and for the adhesion of water to other materials, such as cell walls. Both adhesion and cohesion of water molecules are involved in the ascent of xylem sap under conditions of negative pressure. **36.4** Although stomata account for most of the water lost from plants, they are necessary for exchange of gases—for example, for the uptake of carbon dioxide needed for photosynthesis. The loss of water through stomata also drives the long-distance transport of water that brings soil nutrients from roots to the rest of the plant. **36.5** Although the movement of phloem sap depends on bulk flow, the pressure gradient that drives phloem transport depends on the osmotic uptake of water in response to the loading of sugars into sieve-tube elements at sugar sources. Phloem loading depends on H^+ cotransport processes that ultimately depend on H^+ gradients established by active H^+ pumping. **36.6** Electrical signaling, cytoplasmic pH, cytoplasmic Ca^{2+} concentration, and viral movement proteins all affect symplastic communication, as do developmental changes in the number of plasmodesmata.

Test Your Understanding

1. a **2.** b **3.** b **4.** c **5.** b **6.** c **7.** a **8.** d

Chapter 37

Figure Questions

Figure 37.3 Anions. Because cations are bound to soil particles, they are less likely to be lost from the soil following heavy rains. **Table 37.1** During photosynthesis, CO_2 is fixed into carbohydrates, which contribute to the dry mass. In cellular respiration, O_2 is reduced to H_2O and does not contribute to the dry mass.
Figure 37.11 The legume plants benefit because the bacteria fix nitrogen that is absorbed by their roots. The bacteria benefit because they acquire photosynthetic products from the plants. **Figure 37.12** All three plant tissue systems are affected. Root hairs (dermal tissue) are modified to allow *Rhizobium* penetration. The cortex (ground tissue) and pericycle (vascular tissue) proliferate during nodule formation. The vascular tissue of the nodule connects to the vascular cylinder of the root to allow for efficient nutrient exchange.

Concept Check 37.1

1. Overwatering deprives roots of oxygen. Overfertilizing is wasteful and can lead to soil salinization and water pollution. **2.** As lawn clippings decompose, they restore mineral nutrients to the soil. If they are removed, the minerals lost from the soil must be replaced by fertilization. **3.** Because of their small size and negative charge, clay particles would increase the number of binding sites for cations and water molecules and would therefore increase cation exchange and water retention in the soil. **4.** Due to hydrogen bonding between water molecules, water expands when it freezes, and this causes mechanical fracturing of rocks. Water also coheres to many objects, and this cohesion combined with other forces, such as gravity, can help tug particles from rock. Finally, water, because it is polar, is an excellent solvent that allows many substances, including ions, to become dissolved in solution.

Concept Check 37.2

1. No, because even though macronutrients are required in greater amounts, all essential elements are necessary for the plant to complete its life cycle. **2.** No. The fact that the addition of an element results in an increase in the growth rate of a crop does not mean that the element is strictly required for the plant to complete its life cycle. **3.** Inadequate aeration of the roots of hydroponically grown plants would promote alcohol fermentation, which uses more energy and may lead to the accumulation of ethanol, a toxic byproduct of fermentation.

Concept Check 37.3

1. The rhizosphere is a narrow zone in the soil immediately adjacent to living roots. This zone is especially rich in both organic and inorganic nutrients and has a microbial population that is many times greater than the bulk of the soil. **2.** Soil bacteria and mycorrhizae enhance plant nutrition by making certain minerals more available to plants. For example, many types of soil bacteria are involved in the nitrogen cycle, and the hyphae of mycorrhizae provide a large surface area for the absorption of nutrients, particularly phosphate ions. **3.** Mixotrophy refers to the strategy of using photosynthesis and heterotrophy for nutrition. Euglenids are well-known mixotrophic protists. **4.** Saturating rainfall may deplete the soil of oxygen. A lack of soil oxygen would inhibit nitrogen fixation by the peanut root nodules and decrease the nitrogen available to the plants. Alternatively, heavy rain may leach nitrate from the soil. A symptom of nitrogen deficiency is yellowing of older leaves.

Summary of Key Concepts Questions

37.1 The term *ecosystem* refers to the communities of organisms within a given area and their interactions with the physical environment around them. Soil is teeming with many communities of organisms, including bacteria, fungi, animals, and the root systems of plants. The vigor of these individual communities depends on nonliving factors in the soil environment, such as minerals, oxygen, and water, as well as on interactions, both positive and negative, between different communities of organisms. **37.2** No. Plants can complete their life cycle when grown hydroponically, that is, in aerated salt solutions containing the proper ratios of all the minerals needed by plants. **37.3** No. Some parasitic plants obtain their energy by siphoning off carbon nutrients from other organisms.

Test Your Understanding

1. b **2.** b **3.** a **4.** d **5.** b **6.** b **7.** d **8.** c **9.** d

10.

Chapter 38

Figure Questions

Figure 38.5 Having a specific pollinator is more efficient because less pollen gets delivered to flowers of the wrong species. However, it is also a risky strategy: If the pollinator population suffers to an unusual degree from predation, disease, or climate change, then the plant may not be able to produce seeds. **Figure 38.8** In addition to having a single cotyledon, monocots have leaves with parallel leaf venation, scattered vascular bundles in their stems, a fibrous root system, floral parts in threes or multiples of threes, and pollen grains with only one opening. In contrast, dicots have two cotyledons, netlike leaf venation, vascular bundles in a ring, taproots, floral parts in fours or fives or multiples thereof, and pollen grains with three openings. **Figure 38.9** Beans use a hypocotyl hook to push through the soil. The delicate leaves and shoot apical meristem are also protected by being sandwiched between two large cotyledons. The coleoptile of maize seedlings helps protect the emerging leaves. **Figure 38.18** The crown gall bacterium (*Agrobacterium tumefaciens*) normally causes cancer-like growths in susceptible plants. *Agrobacterium* inserts its own genes into plant cells by means of plasmids. These plasmids have been genetically engineered to retain their ability to insert genes into plant cells without causing cancerous growth.

Concept Check 38.1

1. In angiosperms, pollination is the transfer of pollen from an anther to a stigma. Fertilization is the fusion of the egg and sperm to form the zygote; it cannot occur until after the growth of the pollen tube from the pollen grain. **2.** Seed dormancy prevents the premature germination of seeds. A seed will germinate only when the environmental conditions are optimal for the survival of its embryo as a young seedling. **3.** Long styles help to weed out pollen grains that are genetically inferior and not capable of successfully growing long pollen tubes. **4.** No. The haploid (gametophyte) generation of plants is multicellular and arises from spores. The haploid phase of the animal life cycles is a single-celled gamete (egg or sperm) that arises directly from meiosis: There are no spores.

Concept Check 38.2

1. Flowering plants can avoid self-fertilization by self-incompatibility, having male and female flowers on separate plants (dioecious species), or having stamens and styles of different heights on separate plants ("pin" and "thrum" flowers). **2.** Asexually propagated crops lack genetic diversity. Genetically diverse populations are less likely to become extinct in the face of an epidemic because there is a greater likelihood that a few individuals in the population are resistant.

3. In the short term, selfing may be advantageous in a population that is so dispersed and sparse that pollen delivery is unreliable. In the long term, however, selfing is an evolutionary dead end because it leads to a loss of genetic diversity that may preclude adaptive evolution.

Concept Check 38.3

1. Traditional breeding and genetic engineering both involve artificial selection for desired traits. However, genetic engineering techniques facilitate faster gene transfer and are not limited to transferring genes between closely related varieties or species. **2.** *Bt* maize suffers less insect damage; therefore, *Bt* maize plants are less likely to be infected by fumonisin-producing fungi that infect plants through wounds. **3.** In such species, engineering the transgene into the chloroplast DNA would not prevent its escape in pollen; such a method requires that the chloroplast DNA be found only in the egg. An entirely different method of preventing transgene escape would therefore be needed, such as male sterility, apomixis, or self-pollinating closed flowers.

Summary of Key Concepts Questions

38.1 After pollination and fertilization, a flower changes into a fruit. The petals, sepals, and stamens typically fall off the flower. The stigma of the pistil withers, and the ovary begins to swell. The ovules (embryonic seeds) inside the ovary begin to mature. **38.2** Asexual reproduction can be advantageous in a stable environment because individual plants that are well suited to that environment pass on all their genes to offspring. Also, asexual reproduction generally results in offspring that are less fragile than the seedlings produced by sexual reproduction. However, sexual reproduction offers the advantage of dispersal of tough seeds. Moreover, sexual reproduction produces genetic variety, which may be advantageous in an unstable environment. The likelihood is better that at least one offspring of sexual reproduction will survive in a changed environment. **38.3** "Golden Rice" has been engineered to produce more vitamin A, thereby raising the nutritional value of rice. A protoxin gene from a soil bacterium has been engineered into *Bt* maize. This protoxin is lethal to invertebrates but harmless to vertebrates. *Bt* crops require less pesticide spraying and have lower levels of fungal infection. The nutritional value of cassava is being increased in many ways by genetic engineering. Enriched levels of iron and beta-carotene (a vitamin A precursor) have been achieved, and cyanide-producing chemicals have been almost eliminated from the roots.

Test Your Understanding

1. a **2.** c **3.** b **4.** c **5.** d **6.** d **7.** d
8.

Chapter 39

Figure Questions

Figure 39.4 Panel B in Figure 11.17 shows a branching signal transduction pathway that resembles the branching phytochrome-dependent pathway involved in de-etiolation. **Figure 39.5** To determine which wavelengths of light are most effective in phototropism, you could use a glass prism to split white light into its component colors and see which colors cause the quickest bending (the answer is blue; see Figure 39.15). **Figure 39.6** No. Polar auxin transport depends on the distribution of auxin transport proteins at the basal ends of cells. **Figure 39.16** Yes. The white light, which contains red light, would stimulate seed germination in all treatments. **Figure 39.20** The short-day plant would not flower. The long-day plant would flower. **Figure 39.21** If this were true, florigen would be an inhibitor of flowering, not an inducer. **Figure 39.27** Photosynthetic adaptations can occur at the molecular level, as is apparent in the fact that C_3 plants use rubisco to fix carbon dioxide initially, whereas C_4 and CAM plants use PEP carboxylase. An adaptation at the tissue level is that plants have different stomatal densities based on their genotype and environmental conditions. At the organismal level, plants alter their shoot architectures to make photosynthesis more efficient. For example, self-pruning removes branches and leaves that respire more than they photosynthesize.

Concept Check 39.1

1. Dark-grown seedlings are etiolated: They have long stems, underdeveloped root systems, and unexpanded leaves, and their shoots lack chlorophyll. Etiolated growth is beneficial to seeds sprouting under the dark conditions they would encounter underground. By devoting more energy to stem elongation and less to leaf expansion and root growth, a plant increases the likelihood that the shoot will reach the sunlight before its stored foods run out. **2.** Cycloheximide should inhibit de-etiolation by preventing the synthesis of new proteins necessary for de-etiolation. **3.** No. Applying Viagra, like injecting cyclic GMP as described in the text, should cause only a partial de-etiolation response. Full de-etiolation would require activation of the calcium branch of the signal transduction pathway.

Concept Check 39.2

1. Fusicoccin's ability to cause an increase in plasma H^+ pump activity has an auxin-like effect and promotes stem cell elongation.   **2.** The plant will exhibit a constitutive triple response. Because the kinase that normally prevents the triple response is dysfunctional, the plant will undergo the triple response regardless of whether ethylene is present or the ethylene receptor is functional.   **3.** Since ethylene often stimulates its own synthesis, it is under positive-feedback regulation.

Concept Check 39.3

1. Not necessarily. Many environmental factors, such as temperature and light, change over a 24-hour period in the field. To determine whether the enzyme is under circadian control, a scientist would have to demonstrate that its activity oscillates even when environmental conditions are held constant.   **2.** It is impossible to say. To establish that this species is a short-day plant, it would be necessary to establish the critical night length for flowering and that this species only flowers when the night is longer than the critical night length.   **3.** According to the action spectrum of photosynthesis, red and blue light are the most effective in photosynthesis. Thus, it is not surprising that plants assess their light environment using blue- and red-light-absorbing photoreceptors.

Concept Check 39.4

1. A plant that overproduces ABA would undergo less evaporative cooling because its stomata would not open as widely.   **2.** Plants close to the aisles may be more subject to mechanical stresses caused by passing workers and air currents. The plants nearer to the center of the bench may also be taller as a result of shading and less evaporative stress.   **3.** No. Because root caps are involved in sensing gravity, roots that have their root caps removed are almost completely insensitive to gravity.

Concept Check 39.5

1. Some insects increase plants' productivity by eating harmful insects or aiding in pollination.   **2.** Mechanical damage breaches a plant's first line of defense against infection, its protective dermal tissue.   **3.** No. Pathogens that kill their hosts would soon run out of victims and might themselves go extinct.   **4.** Perhaps the breeze dilutes the local concentration of a volatile defense compound that the plants produce.

Summary of Key Concepts Questions

39.1 Signal transduction pathways often activate protein kinases, enzymes that phosphorylate other proteins. Protein kinases can directly activate certain preexisting enzymes by phosphorylating them, or they can regulate gene transcription (and enzyme production) by phosphorylating specific transcription factors.
39.2 Yes, there is truth to the old adage that one bad apple spoils the whole bunch. Ethylene, a gaseous hormone that stimulates ripening, is produced by damaged, infected, or overripe fruits. Ethylene can diffuse to healthy fruit in the "bunch" and stimulate their rapid ripening.   **39.3** Plant physiologists proposed the existence of a floral-promoting factor (florigen) based on the fact that a plant induced to flower could induce flowering in a second plant to which it was grafted, even though the second plant was not in an environment that would normally induce flowering in that species.   **39.4** Plants subjected to drought stress are often more resistant to freezing stress because the two types of stress are quite similar. Freezing of water in the extracellular spaces causes free water concentrations outside the cell to decrease. This, in turn, causes free water to leave the cell by osmosis, leading to the dehydration of cytoplasm, much like what is seen in drought stress.
39.5 Chewing insects make plants more susceptible to pathogen invasion by disrupting the waxy cuticle of shoots, thereby creating an opening for infection. Moreover, substances released from damaged cells can serve as nutrients for the invading pathogens.

Test Your Understanding

1. b   **2.** c   **3.** d   **4.** e   **5.** b   **6.** b   **7.** c
8.

Chapter 40

Figure Questions

Figure 40.4 Such exchange surfaces are internal in the sense that they are inside the body. However, they are also continuous with openings on the external body surface that contact the environment.   **Figure 40.8** The stimuli (gray boxes) are the room temperature increasing in the top loop or decreasing in the bottom loop.

The responses could include the heater turning off and the temperature decreasing in the top loop and the heater turning on and the temperature increasing in the bottom loop. The sensor/control center is the thermostat. The air conditioner would form a second control circuit, cooling the house when air temperature exceeded the set point. Such opposing, or antagonistic, pairs of control circuits increase the effectiveness of a homeostatic mechanism.   **Figure 40.12** Convection is occurring as the movement of the fan passes air over your skin. Evaporation may also be occurring if your skin is damp with sweat. You also radiate a small amount of heat to the surrounding air at all times.   **Figure 40.16** If a female Burmese python were not incubating eggs, her oxygen consumption would decrease with decreasing temperature, as for any other ectotherm.   **Figure 40.17** The ice water would cool tissues in your head, including blood that would then circulate throughout your body. This effect would accelerate the return to a normal body temperature. If, however, the ice water reached the eardrum and cooled the blood vessel that supplies the hypothalamus, the hypothalamic thermostat would respond by inhibiting sweating and constricting blood vessels in the skin, slowing cooling elsewhere in the body.   **Figure 40.18** The transport of nutrients across membranes and the synthesis of RNA and protein are coupled to ATP hydrolysis. These processes proceed spontaneously because there is an overall drop in free energy, with the excess energy given off as heat. Similarly, less than half of the free energy in glucose is captured in the coupled reactions of cellular respiration. The remainder of the energy is released as heat.   **Figure 40.21** Nothing. Although genes that show a circadian variation in expression during euthermia exhibit constant RNA levels during hibernation, a gene that shows constant expression during hibernation might also show constant expression during euthermia.

Concept Check 40.1

1. All types of epithelia consist of cells that line a surface, are tightly packed, are situated on top of a basal lamina, and form an active and protective interface with the external environment.   **2.** An oxygen molecule must cross a plasma membrane when entering the body at an exchange surface in the respiratory system, in both entering and exiting the circulatory system, and in moving from the interstitial fluid to the cytoplasm of the body cell.   **3.** You need the nervous system to perceive the danger and provoke a split-second muscular response to keep from falling. The nervous system, however, does not make a direct connection with blood vessels or glucose-storing cells in the liver. Instead, the nervous system triggers the release of a hormone (called epinephrine, or adrenaline) by the endocrine system, bringing about a change in these tissues in just a few seconds.

Concept Check 40.2

1. In thermoregulation, the product of the pathway (a change in temperature) decreases pathway activity by reducing the stimulus. In an enzyme-catalyzed biosynthetic process, the product of the pathway (in this case, isoleucine) inhibits the pathway that generated it.   **2.** You would want to put the thermostat close to where you would be spending time, where it would be protected from environmental perturbations, such as direct sunshine, and not right in the path of the output of the heating system. Similarly, the sensors for homeostasis located in the human brain are separated from environmental influences and can monitor conditions in a vital and sensitive tissue.   **3.** In convergent evolution, the same biological trait arises independently in two or more species. Gene analysis can provide evidence for an independent origin. In particular, if the genes responsible for the trait in one species lack significant sequence similarity to the corresponding genes in another species, scientists conclude that there is a separate genetic basis for the trait in the two species and thus an independent origin. In the case of circadian rhythms, the clock genes in cyanobacteria appear unrelated to those in humans.

Concept Check 40.3

1. "Wind chill" involves heat loss through convection, as the moving air contributes to heat loss from the skin surface.   **2.** The hummingbird, being a very small endotherm, has a very high metabolic rate. If by absorbing sunlight certain flowers warm their nectar, a hummingbird feeding on these flowers is saved the metabolic expense of warming the nectar to its body temperature.   **3.** To raise body temperature to the higher range of fever, the hypothalamus triggers heat generation by muscular contractions, or shivering. The person with a fever may in fact say that they feel cold, even though their body temperature is above normal.

Concept Check 40.4

1. The mouse would consume oxygen at a higher rate because it is an endotherm, so its basal metabolic rate is higher than the ectothermic lizard's standard metabolic rate.   **2.** The house cat; smaller animals have a higher metabolic rate per unit body mass and a greater demand for food per unit body mass.   **3.** The alligator's body temperature would decrease along with the air temperature. Its metabolic rate would therefore also decrease as chemical reactions slowed. In contrast, the lion's body temperature would not change. Its metabolic rate would increase as it shivered and produced heat to keep its body temperature constant.

Summary of Key Concepts Questions

40.1 Animals exchange materials with their environment across their body surface, and a spherical shape has the minimum surface area per unit volume. As body size increases, the ratio of surface area to body volume decreases.   **40.2** No; an animal's internal environment fluctuates slightly around set points or within normal ranges. Homeostasis is a dynamic state. Furthermore, there are sometimes programmed changes in set points, such as those resulting in radical increases in hormone levels at particular times in development.   **40.3** Heat exchange across the skin is a primary mechanism for the regulation of body core temperature, with the result that the skin is cooler than the body core.   **40.4** Small animals have a higher BMR per unit mass and therefore consume more oxygen per unit mass than large animals. A higher breathing rate is required to support this increased oxygen consumption.

Test Your Understanding

1. b   2. c   3. a   4. b   5. c   6. b   7. d
8.

Chapter 41

Figure Questions

Figure 41.4 What if? As in the described study, the researchers needed a sample size large enough that they could expect a significant number of neural tube defects in the control group. The information needed to determine the appropriate sample size was the frequency of neural tube defects in first-time pregnancies in the general population. **Figure 41.12** Since enzymes are proteins, and proteins are hydrolyzed in the small intestine, the digestive enzymes in that compartment need to be resistant to enzymatic cleavage other than the cleavage required to activate them. **Figure 41.13** None. Since digestion is completed in the small intestine, tapeworms simply absorb predigested nutrients through their large body surface. **Figure 41.21** Both insulin and glucagon are involved in negative feedback circuits.

Concept Check 41.1

1. The only essential amino acids are those that an animal cannot synthesize from other molecules. **2.** Many vitamins serve as enzyme cofactors, which, like enzymes themselves, are unchanged by the chemical reactions in which they participate. Therefore, only very small amounts of vitamins are needed. **3.** To identify the essential nutrient missing from an animal's diet, a researcher could supplement the diet with individual nutrients and determine which nutrient eliminates the signs of malnutrition.

Concept Check 41.2

1. A gastrovascular cavity is a digestive pouch with a single opening that functions in both ingestion and elimination; an alimentary canal is a digestive tube with a separate mouth and anus at opposite ends. **2.** As long as nutrients are within the cavity of the alimentary canal, they are in a compartment that is continuous with the outside environment via the mouth and anus and have not yet crossed a membrane to enter the body. **3.** Just as food remains outside the body in a digestive tract, gasoline moves from the fuel tank to the engine, and waste products exit through the exhaust without ever entering the passenger compartment of the automobile. In addition, gasoline, like food, is broken down in a specialized compartment, so that the rest of the automobile (or body) is protected from disassembly. In both cases, high-energy fuels are consumed, complex molecules are broken down into simpler ones, and waste products are eliminated.

Concept Check 41.3

1. Because parietal cells in the stomach pump hydrogen ions into the stomach lumen where they combine with chloride ions to form HCl, a proton pump inhibitor reduces the acidity of chyme and thus the irritation that occurs when chyme enters the esophagus. **2.** By releasing sugars from starch or glycogen in the mouth, amylase might allow us to recognize foods that provide a ready source of energy. **3.** Proteins would be denatured and digested into peptides. Further digestion, to individual amino acids, would require enzymatic secretions found in the small intestine. No digestion of carbohydrates or lipids would occur.

Concept Check 41.4

1. The increased time for transit through the alimentary canal allows for more extensive processing, and the increased surface area of the canal provides greater opportunity for absorption. **2.** A mammal's digestive system provides mutualistic microbes with an environment that is protected against other microbes by saliva and gastric juice, that is held at a constant temperature conducive to enzyme action, and that provides a steady source of nutrients. **3.** For the yogurt treatment to be effective, the bacteria from yogurt would have to establish a mutualistic relationship with the small intestine, where disaccharides are broken down and sugars are absorbed. Conditions in the small intestine are likely to be very different from those in a yogurt culture. The bacteria might be killed before they reach the small intestine, or they might not be able to grow there in sufficient numbers to aid in digestion.

Concept Check 41.5

1. Over the long term, the body stores excess calories in fat, whether those calories come from fat, carbohydrate, or protein in food. **2.** In normal individuals, leptin levels decline during fasting. Individuals in the group with low levels of leptin are likely to be defective in leptin production, so leptin levels would remain low regardless of food intake. Individuals in the group with high leptin levels are likely to be defective in responding to leptin, but they still should shut off leptin production as fat stores are used up. **3.** The excess production of insulin will cause blood glucose levels to decrease below normal physiological levels. It will also trigger glycogen synthesis in the liver, further decreasing blood glucose levels. However, low blood glucose levels will stimulate the release of glucagon from alpha cells in the pancreas, which will trigger glycogen breakdown. Thus, there will be antagonistic effects in the liver.

Summary of Key Concepts Questions

41.1 Since the cofactor is necessary in all animals, those animals that do not require it in their diet must be able to synthesize it from other organic molecules. **41.2** A liquid diet containing glucose, amino acids, and other building blocks could be ingested and absorbed without the need for mechanical or chemical digestion. **41.3** The small intestine has a much larger surface area than the stomach. **41.4** The assortment of teeth in our mouth and the short length of our cecum suggest that our ancestors' digestive systems were not specialized for digesting plant material. **41.5** When mealtime arrives, nervous inputs from the brain signal the stomach to prepare to digest food through secretions and churning.

Test Your Understanding

1. b   2. a   3. b   4. c   5. d   6. b
7.

Chapter 42

Figure Questions

Figure 42.2 Although gas exchange might be improved by a steady, one-way flow of fluid, there would likely be inadequate time for food to be digested and nutrients absorbed if fluid flowed through the cavity in this manner. **Figure 42.8** Each feature of the ECG recording, such as the sharp upward spike, occurs once per cardiac cycle. Using the x-axis to measure the time in seconds between successive spikes and dividing that number into 60 would yield the heart rate as the number of cycles per minute. **Figure 42.20** The three main lineages are Deuterostomia, Lophotrochozoa, and Ecdysozoa. All three are represented by the animals shown in Figure 42.22: Polychaetes (phylum Annelida) are lophotrochozoans, crayfish (phylum Arthropoda) are ecdysozoans, and sea stars (phylum Echinodermata) are deuterostomes. **Figure 42.24** The reduction in surface tension results from the presence of surfactant. Therefore, for all the infants who had died of RDS, you would expect the amount of surfactant to be near zero. For infants who had died of other causes, you would expect the amount of surfactant to be near zero for body masses less than 1,200 g but much greater than zero for body masses above 1,200 g. **Figure 42.27** Since exhalation is largely passive, the recoil of the elastic fibers in alveoli helps force air out of the lungs. When alveoli lose their elasticity, as occurs in the disease emphysema, less air is exhaled. Because more air is left in the lungs, less fresh air can be inhaled. With a smaller volume of air exchanged, there is a decrease in the partial pressure gradient that drives gas exchange. **Figure 42.28** Breathing at a rate greater than that needed to meet metabolic demand (hyperventilation) would lower blood CO_2 levels. Sensors in major blood vessels and the medulla would signal the breathing control center to decrease the rate of contraction of the diaphragm and rib muscles, decreasing the breathing rate and restoring normal CO_2 levels in the blood and other tissues. **Figure 42.29** The resulting increase in tidal volume would enhance ventilation within the lungs, increasing P_{O_2} and decreasing P_{CO_2} in the alveoli.

Concept Check 42.1

1. In both an open circulatory system and a fountain, fluid is pumped through a tube and then returns to the pump after collecting in a pool. **2.** The ability to shut off blood supply to the lungs when the animal is submerged **3.** The O_2 content would be abnormally low because some oxygen-depleted blood returned to the right atrium from the systemic circuit would mix with the oxygen-rich blood in the left atrium.

Concept Check 42.2

1. The pulmonary veins carry blood that has just passed through capillary beds in the lungs, where it accumulated O_2. The venae cavae carry blood that has just passed through capillary beds in the rest of the body, where it lost O_2 to the tissues. **2.** The delay allows the atria to empty completely, filling ventricles fully before they contract. **3.** The heart, like any other muscle, becomes stronger through regular exercise. You would expect a stronger heart to have a greater stroke volume, which would allow for the decrease in heart rate.

Concept Check 42.3

1. The large total cross-sectional area of the capillaries **2.** An increase in blood pressure and cardiac output combined with the diversion of more blood to the skeletal muscles would increase the capacity for action by increasing the rate of blood circulation and delivering more O_2 and nutrients to the skeletal muscles. **3.** Additional hearts could be used to improve blood return from the legs. However, it might be difficult to coordinate the activity of multiple hearts and to maintain adequate blood flow to hearts far from the gas exchange organs.

Concept Check 42.4

1. An increase in the number of white blood cells (leukocytes) may indicate that the person is combating an infection. **2.** Clotting factors do not initiate clotting but are essential steps in the clotting process. **3.** The chest pain results from inadequate blood flow in coronary arteries. Vasodilation promoted by nitric oxide from nitroglycerin increases blood flow, providing the heart muscle with additional oxygen and thus relieving the pain. **4.** When a mutant allele is codominant with the wild-type allele, the phenotype of heterozygotes is intermediate between that of wild-type and mutant homozygotes. Therefore, in the presence of wild-type Hb, the aggregation of Hb^S that causes sickling must be significantly reduced. Based on this fact, some therapies for sickle-cell disease are aimed at boosting adult expression of another hemoglobin gene in the body, such as that normally expressed only in the fetus. **5.** Embryonic stem cells are pluripotent rather than multipotent, meaning that they can give rise to many rather than a few different cell types.

Concept Check 42.5

1. Their interior position helps them stay moist. If the respiratory surfaces of lungs extended out into the terrestrial environment, they would quickly dry out, and diffusion of O_2 and CO_2 across these surfaces would stop. **2.** Earthworms need to keep their skin moist for gas exchange, but they need air outside this moist layer. If they stay in their waterlogged tunnels after a heavy rain, they will suffocate because they cannot get as much O_2 from water as from air. **3.** In the gills of fishes, water passes over the gills in the direction opposite to that of blood flowing through the gill capillaries, maximizing the extraction of oxygen from the water along the length of the exchange surface. Similarly, in the extremities of some vertebrates, blood flows in opposite directions in neighboring veins and arteries; this countercurrent arrangement maximizes the recapture of heat from blood leaving the body core in arteries, which is important for thermoregulation in cold environments.

Concept Check 42.6

1. An increase in blood CO_2 concentration causes an increase in the rate of CO_2 diffusion into the cerebrospinal fluid, where the CO_2 combines with water to form carbonic acid. Dissociation of carbonic acid releases hydrogen ions, decreasing the pH of the cerebrospinal fluid. **2.** Increased heart rate increases the rate at which CO_2-rich blood is delivered to the lungs, where CO_2 is removed. **3.** A hole would allow air to enter the space between the inner and outer layers of the double membrane, resulting in a condition called a pneumothorax. The two layers would no longer stick together, and the lung on the side with the hole would collapse and cease functioning.

Concept Check 42.7

1. Differences in partial pressure; the net diffusion of gases occurs from a region of higher partial pressure to a region of lower partial pressure. **2.** The Bohr shift causes hemoglobin to release more O_2 at a lower pH, such as found in the vicinity of tissues with high rates of cellular respiration and CO_2 release. **3.** The doctor is assuming that the rapid breathing is the body's response to low blood pH. Metabolic acidosis, the lowering of blood pH as a result of metabolism, can have many causes, including complications of certain types of diabetes, shock (extremely low blood pressure), and poisoning.

Summary of Key Concepts Questions

42.1 In a closed circulatory system, an ATP-driven muscular pump generally moves fluids in one direction on a scale of millimeters to meters. Exchange between cells and their environment relies on diffusion, which involves random movements of molecules. Concentration gradients of molecules across exchange surfaces can drive rapid net diffusion on a scale of 1 mm or less. **42.2** Replacement of a defective valve should increase stroke volume. A lower heart rate would

therefore be sufficient to maintain the same cardiac output. **42.3** Blood pressure in the arm would fall by 25–30 mm Hg, the same difference as is normally seen between your heart and your brain. **42.4** One microliter of blood contains about 5 million erythrocytes and 5,000 leukocytes, so leukocytes make up only about 0.1% of the cells in the absence of infection. **42.5** Because CO_2 is such a small fraction of atmospheric gas (0.29 mm Hg/760 mm Hg, or less than 0.04%), the partial pressure gradient of CO_2 between the respiratory surface and the environment always strongly favors the release of CO_2 to the atmosphere. **42.6** Because the lungs do not empty completely with each breath, incoming and outgoing air mix, so the air in lungs represents a mixture of fresh and stale air. **42.7** An enzyme speeds up a reaction without changing the equilibrium and without being consumed. Similarly, a respiratory pigment speeds up the exchange of gases between the body and the external environment without changing the equilibrium and without being consumed.

Test Your Understanding

1. c **2.** a **3.** d **4.** c **5.** c **6.** a **7.** a
8.

Chapter 43

Figure Questions

Figure 43.5 The seemingly inactive peptides might offer protection against pathogens other than those studied. Also, some antimicrobial peptides might work best in combination. **Figure 43.6** Cell-surface TLRs recognize molecules on the surface of pathogens, whereas TLRs in vesicles recognize internal molecules of pathogens after the pathogens are broken down. **Figure 43.10** Part of the enzyme or antigen receptor provides a structural "backbone" that maintains overall shape, while interaction occurs at a surface with a close fit to the substrate or antigen. The combined effect of multiple noncovalent interactions at the active site or binding site is a high-affinity interaction of tremendous specificity. **Figure 43.13** After gene rearrangement, a lymphocyte and its daughter cells make a single version of the antigen receptor. In contrast, alternative splicing is not heritable and can give rise to diverse gene products in a single cell. **Figure 43.18** These receptors enable memory cells to present antigen on their cell surface to a helper T cell. This presentation of antigen is required to activate memory cells in a secondary immune response. **Figure 43.20** Primary response: arrows extending from Antigen (1st exposure), Antigen-presenting cell, Helper T cell, B cell, Plasma cells, Cytotoxic T cell, and Active cytotoxic T cells; secondary response: arrows extending from Antigen (2nd exposure), Memory helper T cells, Memory B cells, Memory cytotoxic T cells, Plasma cells, and Active cytotoxic T cells.

Concept Check 43.1

1. Because pus contains white blood cells, fluid, and cell debris, it indicates an active and at least partially successful inflammatory response against invading pathogens. **2.** Whereas the ligand for the TLR receptor is a foreign molecule, the ligand for many signal transduction pathways is a molecule produced by the organism itself. **3.** Bacteria with a human host would likely grow optimally at normal human body temperature or, if fever were often induced, at a temperature a few degrees higher.

Concept Check 43.2

1. See Figure 43.9. The transmembrane regions lie within the C regions, which also form the disulfide bridges. In contrast, the antigen-binding sites are in the V regions. **2.** Generating memory cells ensures both that a receptor specific for a particular epitope will be present and that there will be more lymphocytes with this specificity than in a host that had never encountered the antigen. **3.** If each B cell produced two different light and heavy chains for its antigen receptor, different combinations would make four different receptors. If any one were self-reactive, the lymphocyte would be eliminated in the generation of self-tolerance. For this reason, many more B cells would be eliminated, and those that could respond to a foreign antigen would be less effective at doing so due to the variety of receptors (and antibodies) they express.

Concept Check 43.3

1. A child lacking a thymus would have no functional T cells. Without helper T cells to help activate B cells, the child would be unable to produce antibodies against extracellular bacteria. Furthermore, without cytotoxic T cells or helper T cells, the child's immune system would be unable to kill virus-infected cells.

2. Since the antigen-binding site is intact, the antibody fragments could neutralize viruses and opsonize bacteria. **3.** If the handler developed immunity to proteins in the antivenin, another injection could provoke a severe immune response. The handler's immune system might also now produce antibodies that could neutralize the venom.

Concept Check 43.4

1. Myasthenia gravis is considered an autoimmune disease because the immune system produces antibodies against self molecules (certain receptors on muscle cells). **2.** A person with a cold is likely to produce oral and nasal secretions that facilitate viral transfer. In addition, since sickness can cause incapacitation or death, a virus that is programmed to exit the host when there is a physiological stress has the opportunity to find a new host at a time when the current host may cease to function. **3.** A person with a macrophage deficiency would have frequent infections. The causes would be poor innate responses, due to diminished phagocytosis and inflammation, and poor adaptive responses, due to the lack of macrophages to present antigens to helper T cells.

Summary of Key Concepts Questions

43.1 Lysozyme in saliva destroys bacterial cell walls; the viscosity of mucus helps trap bacteria; acidic pH in the stomach kills many bacteria; and the tight packing of cells lining the gut provides a physical barrier to infection. **43.2** Sufficient numbers of cells to mediate an innate immune response are always present, whereas an adaptive response requires selection and proliferation of an initially very small cell population specific for the infecting pathogen. **43.3** No. Immunological memory after a natural infection and that after vaccination are very similar. There may be minor differences in the particular antigens that can be recognized in a subsequent infection. **43.4** No. AIDS refers to a loss of immune function that can occur over time in an individual infected with HIV. However, certain multidrug combinations ("cocktails") or rare genetic variations usually prevent progression to AIDS in HIV-infected individuals.

Test Your Understanding

1. b **2.** c **3.** c **4.** b **5.** b **6.** b **7.** c
8. One possible answer:

Chapter 44

Figure Questions

Figure 44.13 You would expect to find these cells lining tubules where they pass through the renal medulla. Because the extracellular fluid of the renal medulla has a very high osmolarity, production of organic solutes by tubule cells in this region keeps intracellular osmolarity high, with the result that these cells maintain normal volume. **Figure 44.14** Furosemide increases urine volume. The absence of ion transport in the ascending limb leaves the filtrate too concentrated for substantial volume reduction in the distal tubule and collecting duct. **Figure 44.17** When the concentration of an ion differs across a plasma membrane, the difference in the concentration of ions inside and outside represents chemical potential energy, while the resulting difference in charge inside and outside represents electrical potential energy. **Figure 44.20** The ADH levels would likely be elevated in both sets of patients with mutations because either defect prevents the recapture of water that restores blood osmolarity to normal levels. **Figure 44.21** Each molecule of renin or ACE activates multiple molecules of the next protein in the pathway. The same is true for the protein kinases. The proteases differ from the protein kinases in at least two ways. First, whereas phosphatases can remove the phosphates added to proteins by kinases, cells lack enzymes that can rejoin polypeptides separated by proteases. Second, proteases of this type do not require activation by another enzyme molecule.

Concept Check 44.1

1. Because the salt is moved against its concentration gradient, from low concentration (fresh water) to high concentration (blood) **2.** A freshwater osmoconformer would have body fluids too dilute to carry out life's processes. **3.** Without a layer of insulating fur, the camel must use the cooling effect of

evaporative water loss to maintain body temperature, thus linking thermoregulation and osmoregulation.

Concept Check 44.2

1. Because uric acid is largely insoluble in water, it can be excreted as a semisolid paste, thereby reducing an animal's water loss. **2.** Humans produce uric acid from purine breakdown, and reducing purines in the diet often lessens the severity of gout. Birds, however, produce uric acid as a waste product of general nitrogen metabolism. They would therefore need a diet low in all nitrogen-containing compounds, not just purines.

Concept Check 44.3

1. In flatworms, ciliated cells draw interstitial fluids containing waste products into protonephridia. In earthworms, waste products pass from interstitial fluids into the coelom. From there, cilia move the wastes into metanephridia via a funnel surrounding an internal opening to the metanephridia. In insects, the Malpighian tubules pump fluids from the hemolymph, which receives waste products during exchange with cells in the course of circulation. **2.** Filtration produces a fluid for exchange processes that is free of cells and large molecules, which are of benefit to the animal and could not readily be reabsorbed. **3.** Filtrate is formed when the glomerulus filters blood from the renal artery within Bowman's capsule. Some of the filtrate contents are recovered, enter capillaries, and exit in the renal vein; the rest remain in the filtrate and pass out of the kidney in the ureter. **4.** The presence of Na^+ and other ions (electrolytes) in the dialysate would limit the extent to which they would be removed from the filtrate during dialysis. Adjusting the electrolytes in the starting dialysate can thus lead to the restoration of proper electrolyte concentrations in the plasma. Similarly, the absence of urea and other waste products in the starting dialysate facilitates their removal from the filtrate.

Concept Check 44.4

1. The numerous nephrons and well-developed glomeruli of freshwater fishes produce urine at a high rate, while the small numbers of nephrons and smaller glomeruli of marine fishes produce urine at a low rate. **2.** The kidney medulla would absorb less water; thus, the drug would increase the amount of water lost in the urine. **3.** A decline in blood pressure in the afferent arteriole would reduce the rate of filtration by moving less material through the vessels.

Concept Check 44.5

1. Alcohol inhibits the release of ADH, causing an increase in urinary water loss and increasing the chance of dehydration. **2.** The consumption of a very large amount of water in a short period of time, coupled with an absence of solute intake, can reduce sodium levels in the blood below tolerable levels. This condition, called hyponatremia, leads to disorientation and, sometimes, respiratory distress. It has occurred in some marathon runners who drink water rather than sports drinks. (It has also caused the death of a fraternity pledge as a consequence of a water hazing ritual and the death of a contestant in a water-drinking competition.) **3.** High blood pressure

Summary of Key Concepts Questions

44.1 Water moves into a cell by osmosis when the fluid outside the cells is hypoosmotic (has a lower solute concentration than the cytosol).
44.2

Waste Attribute	Ammonia	Urea	Uric Acid
Toxicity	High	Very low	Low
Energy cost to produce	Low	Moderate	High
Water loss to excretion	High	Moderate	Low

44.3 Filtration retains large molecules that would be difficult to transport across membranes. **44.4** Both types of nephrons have proximal tubules that can reabsorb nutrients, but only juxtamedullary nephrons have loops of Henle that extend deep into the renal medulla. Thus, only kidneys containing juxtamedullary nephrons can produce urine that is more concentrated than the blood. **44.5** Patients who don't produce ADH have symptoms relieved by treatment with the hormone, but many patients with diabetes insipidus lack functional receptors for ADH.

Test Your Understanding

1. c **2.** a **3.** c **4.** d **5.** c **6.** b

Chapter 45

Figure Questions

Figure 45.4

HO—CH—CH₂—NH—CH₃ ... Epinephrine

Epinephrine

Figure 45.5 The hormone is water-soluble and has a cell-surface receptor. Such receptors, unlike those for lipid-soluble hormones, can cause observable changes in cells without hormone-dependent gene transcription.

Concept Check 45.1

1. Water-soluble hormones, which cannot penetrate the plasma membrane, bind to cell-surface receptors. This interaction triggers an intracellular signal transduction pathway that ultimately alters the activity of a preexisting protein in the cytoplasm and/or changes transcription of specific genes in the nucleus. Steroid hormones are lipid-soluble and can cross the plasma membrane into the cell interior, where they bind to receptors located in the cytosol or nucleus. The hormone-receptor complex then functions directly as a transcription factor that changes transcription of specific genes.   **2.** Prostaglandins in semen that induce contractions in the uterus are acting as signaling molecules that are transferred from one individual to another of the same species (like pheromones), thus aiding in reproduction.   **3.** Both hormones produce opposite effects in different target tissues. In the fight-or-flight response, epinephrine increases blood flow to skeletal muscles and reduces blood flow to smooth muscles in the digestive system. In establishing apical dominance, auxin promotes the growth of apical buds and inhibits the growth of lateral buds.

Concept Check 45.2

1. Prolactin regulates milk production, whereas oxytocin regulates milk release.
2. The posterior pituitary, an extension of the hypothalamus that contains the axons of neurosecretory cells, is the storage and release site for two neurohormones, oxytocin and antidiuretic hormone (ADH). The anterior pituitary contains endocrine cells that make at least six different hormones. Secretion of anterior pituitary hormones is controlled by hypothalamic hormones that travel via blood vessels to the anterior pituitary.   **3.** The hypothalamus and pituitary glands function in many different endocrine pathways. Many defects in these glands, such as those affecting growth or organization, would therefore disrupt many hormone pathways. Only a very specific defect, such as a mutation affecting a particular hormone receptor, would alter just one endocrine pathway. The situation is quite different for the final gland in a pathway, such as the thyroid gland. In this case, a wide range of defects that disrupt gland function would disrupt only the one pathway or small set of pathways in which that gland functions.   **4.** Both diagnoses could be correct. In one case, the thyroid gland may produce excess thyroid hormone despite normal hormonal input from the hypothalamus and anterior pituitary. In the other, abnormally elevated hormonal input (elevated TSH levels) may be the cause of the overactive thyroid gland.

Concept Check 45.3

1. If the function of the pathway is to provide a transient response, a short-lived stimulus would be less dependent on negative feedback.   **2.** The levels of these hormones in the blood would become very high. This would be due to the diminished negative feedback on the hypothalamic neurons that secrete the releasing hormone that stimulates the secretion of ACTH by the anterior pituitary.   **3.** You would be exploiting the anti-inflammatory activity of glucocorticoids. Local injection avoids the effects on glucose metabolism that would occur if glucocorticoids were taken orally and transported throughout the body in the bloodstream.

Summary of Key Concepts Questions

45.1 Because receptors for water-soluble hormones are located on the cell surface, facing the extracellular space, injecting the hormone into the cytosol would not trigger a response.   **45.2** The pancreas, parathyroid glands, and pineal gland   **45.3** Both the pituitary and the adrenal glands are formed by fusion of neural and nonneural tissue. ADH is secreted by the neurosecretory portion of the pituitary gland, and epinephrine is secreted by the neurosecretory portion of the adrenal gland.

Test Your Understanding

1. c   **2.** d   **3.** d   **4.** b   **5.** b   **6.** b   **7.** a

8.

Chapter 46

Figure Questions

Figure 46.8 When successfully courted by a second male, regardless of his genotype, about one-third of the females rid themselves of all sperm from the first mating. Thus, two-thirds retained some sperm from the first mating. We would therefore predict that two-thirds of those females would have some offspring exhibiting the small-eye phenotype of the dominant mutation carried by the males with which the females mated first.   **Figure 46.11** The analysis would be informative because the polar bodies contain all of the maternal chromosomes that don't end up in the mature egg. For example, finding two copies of the disease gene in the polar bodies would indicate its absence in the egg. This method of genetic testing is sometimes carried out when oocytes collected from a female are fertilized with sperm in a laboratory dish.   **Figure 46.16** Testosterone can pass from fetal blood to maternal blood via the placental circulation, temporarily upsetting the hormonal balance in the mother.   **Figure 46.18** Oxytocin would most likely induce labor, starting a positive-feedback loop that would direct labor to completion. Synthetic oxytocin is in fact frequently used to induce labor when prolonged pregnancy might endanger the mother or fetus.

Concept Check 46.1

1. The offspring of sexual reproduction are more genetically diverse. However, asexual reproduction can produce more offspring over multiple generations.
2. Unlike other forms of asexual reproduction, parthenogenesis involves gamete production. By controlling whether or not haploid eggs are fertilized, species such as honeybees can readily switch between asexual and sexual reproduction.
3. No. Owing to random assortment of chromosomes during meiosis, the offspring may receive the same copy or different copies of a particular parental chromosome from the sperm and the egg. Furthermore, genetic recombination during meiosis will result in reassortment of genes between pairs of parental chromosomes.   **4.** Both fragmentation and budding in animals have direct counterparts in the asexual reproduction of plants.

Concept Check 46.2

1. Internal fertilization allows sperm to reach the egg without either gamete drying out.   **2.** (a) Animals with external fertilization tend to release many gametes at once, resulting in the production of enormous numbers of zygotes. This increases the chances that some will survive to adulthood. (b) Animals with internal fertilization produce fewer offspring but generally exhibit greater care of the embryos and the young.   **3.** Like the uterus of an insect, the ovary of a plant is the site of fertilization. Unlike the plant ovary, the uterus is not the site of egg production, which occurs in the insect ovary. In addition, the fertilized insect egg is expelled from the uterus, whereas the plant embryo develops within a seed in the ovary.

Concept Check 46.3

1. Spermatogenesis occurs normally only when the testicles are cooler than normal body temperature. Extensive use of a hot tub (or of very tight-fitting underwear) can cause a decrease in sperm quality and number.   **2.** In humans, the secondary oocyte combines with a sperm before it finishes the second meiotic division. Thus, oogenesis is completed after, not before, fertilization.   **3.** The only effect of sealing off each vas deferens is an absence of sperm in the ejaculate. Sexual response and ejaculate volume are unchanged. The cutting and sealing off of these ducts, a *vasectomy*, is a common surgical procedure for men who do not wish to produce any (more) offspring.

Concept Check 46.4

1. In the testis, FSH stimulates the Sertoli cells, which nourish developing sperm. LH stimulates the production of androgens (mainly testosterone), which in turn stimulate sperm production. In both females and males, FSH encourages the growth of cells that support and nourish developing gametes (follicle cells in females and Sertoli cells in males), and LH stimulates the production of sex hormones that promote gametogenesis (estrogens, primarily estradiol, in females and androgens, especially testosterone, in males).   **2.** In estrous cycles, which occur in most female mammals, the endometrium is reabsorbed (rather than shed) if fertilization does not occur. Estrous cycles often occur just once or a few times a year, and the female is usually receptive to copulation only during the period around ovulation. Menstrual cycles are found only in humans and some other primates.   **3.** The combination of estradiol and progesterone would have a negative-feedback effect on the hypothalamus, blocking release of GnRH. This would interfere with LH secretion by the pituitary, thus preventing ovulation. This is in fact one basis of action of the most common hormonal contraceptives. **4.** In the viral replicative cycle, the production of new viral genomes is coordinated with capsid protein expression and with the production of phospholipids for viral coats. In the reproductive cycle of a human female, there is hormonally based coordination of egg maturation with the development of support tissues of the uterus.

Concept Check 46.5

1. The secretion of hCG by the early embryo stimulates the corpus luteum to make progesterone, which helps maintain the pregnancy. During the second trimester, however, hCG production drops, the corpus luteum disintegrates, and the placenta completely takes over progesterone production. **2.** Both tubal ligation and vasectomy block the movement of gametes from the gonads to a site where fertilization could take place. **3.** The introduction of a sperm nucleus directly into an oocyte bypasses the sperm's acquisition of motility in the epididymis, its swimming to meet the egg in the oviduct, and its fusion with the egg.

Summary of Key Concepts Questions

46.1 No. Because parthenogenesis involves meiosis, the mother would pass on to each offspring a random and therefore typically distinct combination of the chromosomes she inherited from her mother and father. **46.2** None **46.3** The small size and lack of cytoplasm characteristic of a sperm are adaptations well suited to its function as a delivery vehicle for DNA. The large size and rich cytoplasmic contents of eggs support the growth and development of the embryo. **46.4** Circulating anabolic steroids mimic the feedback regulation of testosterone, turning off pituitary signaling to the testes and thereby blocking the release of signals required for spermatogenesis. **46.5** Oxygen in maternal blood diffuses from pools in the endometrium into fetal capillaries in the chorionic villi of the placenta, and from there travels throughout the circulatory system of the fetus.

Test Your Understanding

1. d **2.** b **3.** a **4.** c **5.** a **6.** b **7.** c **8.** d
9.

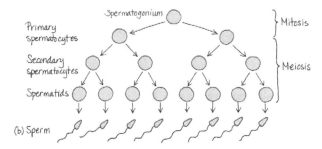

(c) The supply of stem cells would be used up, and spermatogenesis would not be able to continue.

Chapter 47

Figure Questions

Figure 47.4 You could inject the compound into an unfertilized egg, expose the egg to sperm, and see whether the fertilization envelope forms. **Figure 47.22** When the researchers allowed normal cortical rotation to occur, the "back-forming" determinants were activated. When they then forced the opposite rotation to occur, the back was established on the opposite side as well. Because the molecules on the normal side were already activated, forcing the opposite rotation apparently did not "cancel out" the establishment of the back side by the first rotation. **Figure 47.23** In Spemann's control, the two blastomeres were physically separated, and each grew into a whole embryo. In Roux's experiment, remnants of the dead blastomere were still contacting the live blastomere, which developed into a half-embryo. Therefore, molecules present in the dead cell's remnants may have been signaling to the live cell, inhibiting it from making all the embryonic structures. **Figure 47.24** You could inject the isolated protein (or an mRNA encoding it) into ventral cells of an earlier gastrula. If dorsal structures form on the ventral side, that would support the idea that the protein is the signaling molecule secreted or presented by the dorsal lip. You should also do a control experiment to make sure the injection process alone did not cause dorsal structures to form. **Figure 47.26** Either Sonic hedgehog mRNA or protein can serve as a marker of the ZPA. If either was absent after removal of the AER, that would support your hypothesis. You could also block FGF function and see whether the ZPA formed (by looking for Sonic hedgehog).

Concept Check 47.1

1. The fertilization envelope forms after cortical granules release their contents outside the egg, causing the vitelline membrane to rise and harden. The fertilization envelope serves as a barrier to fertilization by more than one sperm. **2.** The increased Ca^{2+} concentration in the egg would cause the cortical granules to fuse with the plasma membrane, releasing their contents and causing a fertilization envelope to form, even though no sperm had entered. This would prevent fertilization. **3.** You would expect it to fluctuate. The fluctuation of MPF drives the transition between DNA replication (S phase) and mitosis (M phase), which is still required in the abbreviated cleavage cell cycle.

Concept Check 47.2

1. The cells of the notochord migrate toward the midline of the embryo (converge), rearranging themselves so there are fewer cells across the notochord, which thus becomes longer overall (extends; see Figure 47.17). **2.** Because microfilaments would not be able to contract and decrease the size of one end of the cell, both the inward bending in the middle of the neural tube and the outward bending of the hinge regions at the edges would be blocked. Therefore, the neural tube probably would not form. **3.** Dietary intake of the vitamin folic acid dramatically reduces the frequency of neural tube defects.

Concept Check 47.3

1. Axis formation establishes the location and polarity of the three axes that provide the coordinates for development. Pattern formation positions particular tissues and organs in the three-dimensional space defined by those coordinates. **2.** Morphogen gradients act by specifying cell fates across a field of cells through variation in the level of a determinant. Morphogen gradients thus act more globally than cytoplasmic determinants or inductive interactions between pairs of cells. **3.** Yes, a second embryo could develop because inhibiting BMP-4 activity would have the same effect as transplanting an organizer. **4.** The limb that developed probably would have a mirror-image duplication, with the most posterior digits in the middle and the most anterior digits at either end.

Summary of Key Concepts Questions

47.1 The binding of a sperm to a receptor on the egg surface is very specific and likely would not occur if the two gametes were from different species. Without sperm binding, the sperm and egg membranes would not fuse. **47.2** The neural tube forms when the neural plate, a band of ectodermal tissue oriented along the anterior-posterior axis on the dorsal side of the embryo, rolls into a tube and pinches off from the rest of the ectoderm. Neural crest cells arise as groups of cells in the regions between the edges of the neural tube and the surrounding ectoderm migrate away from the neural tube. **47.3** Mutations that affected both limb and kidney development would be more likely to alter the function of monocilia because these organelles are important in several signaling pathways. Mutations that affected limb development but not kidney development would more likely alter a single pathway, such as Hedgehog signaling.

Test Your Understanding

1. a **2.** b **3.** d **4.** a **5.** d **6.** c **7.** b
8.

Chapter 48

Figure Questions

Figure 48.7 Adding chloride channels would make the membrane potential less positive. Adding sodium or potassium channels would have no effect, because sodium ions are already at equilibrium and there are no potassium ions present.
Figure 48.10

Figure 48.12

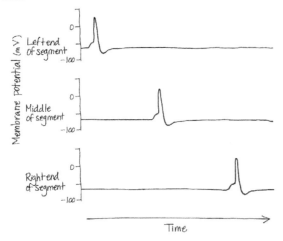

Membrane potential (mV)

Left end of segment

Middle of segment

Right end of segment

Time

Figure 48.16 The production and transmission of action potentials would be unaffected. However, action potentials arriving at chemical synapses would be unable to trigger release of neurotransmitter. Signaling at such synapses would thus be blocked.

Concept Check 48.1

1. Axons and dendrites extend from the cell body and function in information flow. Dendrites transfer information to the cell body, whereas axons transmit information from the cell body. A typical neuron has multiple dendrites and one axon. **2.** Sensors in your ear transmit information to your brain. There the activity of interneurons in processing centers enables you to recognize your name. In response, signals transmitted via motor neurons cause contraction of muscles that turn your neck. **3.** Increased branching would allow control of a greater number of postsynaptic cells, enhancing coordination of responses to nervous system signals.

Concept Check 48.2

1. Ions can flow against a chemical concentration gradient if there is an opposing electrical gradient of greater magnitude. **2.** A decrease in permeability to K^+, an increase in permeability to Na^+, or both **3.** Charged dye molecules could equilibrate only if other charged molecules could also cross the membrane. If not, a membrane potential would develop that would counterbalance the chemical gradient.

Concept Check 48.3

1. A graded potential has a magnitude that varies with stimulus strength, whereas an action potential has an all-or-none magnitude that is independent of stimulus strength. **2.** Loss of the insulation provided by myelin sheaths leads to a disruption of action potential propagation along axons. Voltage-gated sodium channels are restricted to the nodes of Ranvier, and without the insulating effect of myelin, the inward current produced at one node during an action potential cannot depolarize the membrane to the threshold at the next node. **3.** Positive feedback is responsible for the rapid opening of many voltage-gated sodium channels, causing the rapid outflow of sodium ions responsible for the rising phase of the action potential. As the membrane potential becomes positive, voltage-gated potassium channels open in a form of negative feedback that helps bring about the falling phase of the action potential. **4.** The maximum frequency would decrease because the refractory period would be extended.

Concept Check 48.4

1. It can bind to different types of receptors, each triggering a specific response in postsynaptic cells. **2.** These toxins would prolong the EPSPs that acetylcholine produces because the neurotransmitter would remain longer in the synaptic cleft. **3.** Membrane depolarization, exocytosis, and membrane fusion each occur in fertilization and in neurotransmission.

Summary of Key Concepts Questions

48.1 It would prevent information from being transmitted away from the cell body along the axon. **48.2** There are very few open sodium channels in a resting neuron, so the resting potential either would not change or would become slightly more negative (hyperpolarization). **48.4** A given neurotransmitter can have many receptors that differ in their location and activity. Drugs that target receptor activity rather than neurotransmitter release or stability are therefore likely to exhibit greater specificity and potentially have fewer undesirable side effects.

Test Your Understanding

1. c **2.** c **3.** c **4.** b **5.** a **6.** d
7. The activity of the sodium-potassium pump is essential to maintain the resting potential. With the pump inactivated, the sodium and potassium concentration gradients would gradually disappear, resulting in a greatly reduced resting potential. **8.** Since GABA is an inhibitory neurotransmitter in the CNS, this drug would be expected to decrease brain activity. A decrease in brain activity might be expected to slow down or reduce behavioral activity. Many sedative drugs act

in this fashion. **9.** As shown in this pair of drawings, a pair of action potentials would move outward in both directions from each electrode. (Action potentials are unidirectional only if they begin at one end of an axon.) However, because of the refractory period, the two action potentials between the electrodes both stop where they meet. Thus, only one action potential reaches the synaptic terminals.

Chapter 49

Figure Questions

Figure 49.7 During swallowing, muscles along the esophagus alternately contract and relax, resulting in peristalsis. One model to explain this alternation is that each section of muscle receives nerve impulses that alternate between excitation and inhibition, just as the quadriceps and hamstring receive opposing signals in the knee-jerk reflex. **Figure 49.15** Regions you would expect to be active regardless of the type of music played would include ones that are important for processing and interpreting sounds. **Figure 49.23** If the depolarization brings the membrane potential to or past threshold, it should initiate action potentials that cause dopamine release from the VTA neurons. This should mimic natural stimulation of the brain reward system, resulting in positive and perhaps pleasurable sensations.

Concept Check 49.1

1. The sympathetic division would likely be activated. It mediates the "fight-or-flight" response in stressful situations. **2.** Nerves contain bundles of axons, some that belong to motor neurons, which send signals outward from the CNS, and some that belong to sensory neurons, which bring signals into the CNS. Therefore, you would expect effects on both motor control and sensation. **3.** Neurosecretory cells of the adrenal medulla secrete the hormones epinephrine and norepinephrine in response to preganglionic input from sympathetic neurons. These hormones travel in the circulation throughout the body, triggering responses in many tissues.

Concept Check 49.2

1. The cerebral cortex on the left side of the brain initiates voluntary movement of the right side of the body. **2.** Alcohol diminishes function of the cerebellum. **3.** A coma reflects a disruption in the cycles of sleep and arousal regulated by communication between the midbrain and pons (reticular formation) and the cerebrum. You would expect this group to have damage to the midbrain, the pons, the cerebrum, or any part of the brain between these structures. Paralysis reflects an inability to carry out motor commands transmitted from the cerebrum to the spinal cord. You would expect this group to have damage to the portion of the CNS extending from the spinal cord up to but not including the midbrain and pons.

Concept Check 49.3

1. Brain damage that disrupts behavior, cognition, memory, or other functions provides evidence that the portion of the brain affected by the damage is important for the normal activity that is blocked or altered. **2.** Broca's area, which is active during the generation of speech, is located near the motor cortex, which controls skeletal muscles, including those in the face. Wernicke's area, which is active when speech is heard, is located in the posterior part of the temporal lobe, which is involved in hearing. **3.** Each cerebral hemisphere is specialized for different parts of this task—the right for face recognition and the left for language. Without an intact corpus callosum, neither hemisphere can take advantage of the other's processing abilities.

Concept Check 49.4

1. There can be an increase in the number of synapses between the neurons or an increase in the strength of existing synaptic connections. **2.** If consciousness is an emergent property resulting from the interaction of many different regions of the brain, then it is unlikely that localized brain damage will have a discrete effect on consciousness. **3.** The hippocampus is responsible for organizing newly acquired information. Without hippocampal function, the links necessary to retrieve information from the cerebral cortex will be lacking, and no functional memory, short- or long-term, will be formed.

Concept Check 49.5

1. Both are progressive brain diseases whose risk increases with advancing age. Both result from the death of brain neurons and are associated with the accumulation of peptide or protein aggregates. **2.** The symptoms of schizophrenia can be mimicked by a drug that stimulates dopamine-releasing neurons. The brain's reward system, which is involved in drug addiction, is composed of dopamine-releasing neurons that connect the ventral tegmental area to regions in the cerebrum. Parkinson's disease results from the death of dopamine-releasing neurons.   **3.** Not necessarily. It might be that the plaques, tangles, and missing regions of the brain seen at death reflect secondary effects, the consequence of other unseen changes that are actually responsible for the alterations in brain function.

Summary of Key Concepts Questions

49.1 Because reflex circuits involve only a few neurons—the simplest consist of a sensory neuron and a motor neuron—the path for information transfer is short and simple, increasing the speed of the response.   **49.2** The midbrain coordinates visual reflexes; the cerebellum controls coordination of movement that depends on visual input; the thalamus serves as a routing center for visual information; and the cerebrum is essential for converting visual input to a visual image.   **49.3** You would expect the right side of the body to be paralyzed because it is controlled by the left cerebral hemisphere, where language generation and interpretation are localized.   **49.4** Learning a new language likely requires the maintenance of synapses that are formed during early development but are otherwise lost prior to adulthood.   **49.5** Whereas amphetamine stimulates dopamine release, PCP blocks glutamate receptors, suggesting that schizophrenia does not reflect a defect in the function of just one neurotransmitter.

Test Your Understanding

1. b   **2.** a   **3.** d   **4.** c   **5.** c   **6.** a
7.

Chapter 50

Figure Questions

Figure 50.19 Each of the three types of cones is most sensitive to a different wavelength of light. A cone might be fully depolarized when there is light present if the light is of a wavelength far from its optimum.   **Figure 50.21** In humans, an X chromosome with a defect in the red or green opsin gene is much less common than a wild-type X chromosome. Color blindness therefore typically skips a generation as the defective allele passes from an affected male to a carrier daughter and back to an affected grandson. In squirrel monkeys, no X chromosome can confer full color vision. As a result, all males are color-blind and no unusual inheritance pattern is observed.   **Figure 50.23** The results of the experiment would have been identical. What matters is the activation of particular sets of neurons, not the manner in which they are activated. Any signal from a bitter cell will be interpreted by the brain as a bitter taste, regardless of the nature of the compound and the receptor involved.   **Figure 50.25** Only perception. Binding of an odorant to its receptor will cause action potentials to be sent to the brain. Although an excess of that odorant might cause a diminished response through adaptation, another odorant can mask the first only at the level of perception in the brain.   **Figure 50.28** Hundreds of myosin heads participate in sliding each pair of thick and thin filaments past each other. Because cross-bridge formation and breakdown are not synchronized, many myosin heads are exerting force on the thin filaments at all times during muscle contraction.   **Figure 50.32** By causing all of the motor neurons that control the muscle to generate action potentials at a rate high enough to produce tetanus in all of the muscle fibers

Concept Check 50.1

1. Electromagnetic receptors in general detect only external stimuli. Nonelectromagnetic receptors, such as chemoreceptors or mechanoreceptors, can act as either internal or external sensors.   **2.** The capsaicin present in the peppers activates the thermoreceptor for high temperatures. In response to the perceived high temperature, the nervous system triggers sweating to achieve evaporative cooling.   **3.** You would perceive the electrical stimulus as if the sensory receptors that regulate that neuron had been activated. For example, electrical stimulation of the sensory neuron controlled by the thermoreceptor activated by menthol would likely be perceived as a local cooling.

Concept Check 50.2

1. Otoliths detect the animal's orientation with respect to gravity, providing information that is essential in environments such as the tunnel habitat of the star-nosed mole, where light cues are absent.   **2.** As a sound that changes gradually from a very low to a very high pitch   **3.** The stapes and the other middle ear bones transmit vibrations from the tympanic membrane to the oval window. Fusion of these bones (as occurs in a disease called otosclerosis) would block this transmission and result in hearing loss.   **4.** In animals, the statoliths are extracellular. In contrast, the statoliths of plants are found within an intracellular organelle. The methods for detecting their location also differ. In animals, detection is by means of mechanoreceptors on ciliated cells. In plants, the mechanism appears to involve calcium signaling.

Concept Check 50.3

1. Planarians have ocelli that cannot form images but can sense the intensity and direction of light, providing enough information to enable the animals to find protection in shaded places. Flies have compound eyes that form images and excel at detecting movement.   **2.** The person can focus on distant objects but not close objects (without glasses) because close focusing requires the lens to become almost spherical. This problem is common after age 50.   **3.** The signal produced by rod and cone cells is glutamate, and their release of glutamate decreases upon exposure to light. However, a decrease in glutamate production causes other retinal cells to increase the rate at which action potentials are sent to the brain, so that the brain receives more action potentials in light than in dark.   **4.** Absorption of light by retinal converts retinal from its *cis* isomer to its *trans* isomer, initiating the process of light detection. In contrast, a photon absorbed by chlorophyll does not bring about isomerization, but instead boosts an electron to a higher energy orbital, initiating the electron flow that generates ATP and NADPH.

Concept Check 50.4

1. Both taste cells and olfactory cells have receptor proteins in their plasma membrane that bind certain substances, leading to membrane depolarization through a signal transduction pathway involving a G protein. However, olfactory cells are sensory neurons, whereas taste cells are not.   **2.** Since animals rely on chemical signals for behaviors that include finding mates, marking territories, and avoiding dangerous substances, it is adaptive for the olfactory system to have a robust response to a very small number of molecules of a particular odorant.   **3.** Because the sweet, bitter, and umami tastes involve GPCR proteins but the sour taste does not, you might predict that the mutation is in a molecule that acts in the signal transduction pathway common to the different GPCRs.

Concept Check 50.5

1. In a skeletal muscle fiber, Ca^{2+} binds to the troponin complex, which moves tropomyosin away from the myosin-binding sites on actin and allows cross-bridges to form. In a smooth muscle cell, Ca^{2+} binds to calmodulin, which activates an enzyme that phosphorylates the myosin head and thus enables cross-bridge formation.   **2.** *Rigor mortis*, a Latin phrase meaning "stiffness of death," results from the complete depletion of ATP in skeletal muscle. Since ATP is required to release myosin from actin and to pump Ca^{2+} out of the cytosol, muscles become chronically contracted beginning about 3–4 hours after death.   **3.** A competitive inhibitor binds to the same site as the substrate for the enzyme. In contrast, the troponin and tropomyosin complex masks, but does not bind to, the myosin-binding sites on actin.

Concept Check 50.6

1. Septa provide the divisions of the coelom that allow for peristalsis, a form of locomotion requiring independent control of different body segments.   **2.** The main problem in swimming is drag; a fusiform body minimizes drag. The main problem in flying is overcoming gravity; wings shaped like airfoils provide lift, and adaptations such as air-filled bones reduce body mass.   **3.** When you grasp the sides of the chair, you are using a contraction of the triceps to keep your arms extended against the pull of gravity on your body. As you lower yourself slowly into the chair, you gradually decrease the number of motor units in the triceps that are contracted. Contracting your biceps would jerk you down, since you would no longer be opposing gravity.

Summary of Key Concepts Questions

50.1 Nociceptors overlap with other classes of receptors in the type of stimulus they detect. They differ from other receptors only in how a particular stimulus is perceived.   **50.2** Volume is encoded by the frequency of action potentials transmitted to the brain; pitch is encoded by which axons are transmitting action potentials.   **50.3** The major difference is that neurons in the retina integrate information from multiple sensory receptors (photoreceptors) before transmitting information to the central nervous system.   **50.4** Our olfactory sense is responsible for most of what we describe as distinct tastes. A head cold or other source of congestion blocks odorant access to receptors lining portions of the nasal cavity.   **50.5** Hydrolysis of ATP is required to convert myosin to a high-energy configuration for binding to actin and to power the Ca^{2+} pump that removes cytosolic Ca^{2+} during muscle relaxation.   **50.6** Human body movements rely on the contraction of muscles anchored to a rigid endoskeleton. Tendons attach muscles to bones, which in turn are composed of fibers built up from a basic organizational unit, the sarcomere. The thin and thick filaments have separate points of attachment within the sarcomere. In response to nervous system motor output, the formation and breakdown of cross-bridges between myosin heads and actin ratchet the thin and thick filaments past each other. Because the filaments are anchored, this sliding movement shortens the muscle fibers. Furthermore, because the fibers themselves are part of the muscles attached at each end to bones, muscle contraction moves bones of the body relative to each other. In this way, the structural anchoring of muscles and filaments enables muscle function, such as the bending of an elbow by contraction of the biceps.

Test Your Understanding

1. d   **2.** a   **3.** b   **4.** c   **5.** b   **6.** d
7.

The answer shows the actual distribution of rods and cones in the human eye. Your graph may differ, but should have the following properties: Only cones at the fovea; fewer cones and more rods at both ends of the *x*-axis; no photoreceptors in the optic disk.

Chapter 51

Figure Questions

Figure 51.2 The fixed action pattern based on the sign stimulus of a red belly ensures that the male will chase away any invading males of his species. By chasing away such males, the defender decreases the chance that another male will fertilize eggs laid in his nesting territory.   **Figure 51.7** There should be no effect. Imprinting is an innate behavior that is carried out anew in each generation. Assuming the nest was not disturbed, the offspring of the Lorenz followers would imprint on the mother goose.   **Figure 51.8** Perhaps the wasp doesn't use visual cues. It might also be that wasps recognize objects native to their environment, but not foreign objects, such as the pinecones. Tinbergen addressed these ideas before carrying out the pinecone study. When he swept away the pebbles and sticks around the nest, the wasps could no longer find their nests. If he shifted the natural objects in their natural arrangement, the shift in the landmarks caused a shift in the site to which the wasps returned. Finally, if natural objects around the nest site were replaced with pinecones while the wasp was in the burrow, the wasp nevertheless found her way back to the nest site.   **Figure 51.24** It might be that the birds require stimuli during flight to exhibit their migratory preference. If this were true, the birds would show the same orientation in the funnel experiment despite their distinct genetic programming.   **Figure 51.26** It holds true for some, but not all individuals. If a parent has more than one reproductive partner, the offspring of different partners will have a coefficient of relatedness less than 0.5.

Concept Check 51.1

1. The proximate explanation for this fixed action pattern might be that nudging and rolling are released by the sign stimulus of an object outside the nest, and the behavior is carried to completion once initiated. The ultimate explanation might be that ensuring that eggs remain in the nest increases the chance of producing healthy offspring.   **2.** There might be selective pressure for other prey fish to detect an injured fish because the source of the injury might threaten them as well. Among predators, there might be selection for those that are attracted to the alarm substance because they would be more likely to encounter crippled prey. Fish with adequate defenses might show no change because they have a selective advantage if they do not waste energy responding to the alarm substance.   **3.** In both cases, the detection of periodic variation in the environment results in a reproductive cycle timed to environmental conditions that optimize the opportunity for success.

Concept Check 51.2

1. Natural selection would tend to favor convergence in color pattern because a predator learning to associate a pattern with a sting or bad taste would avoid all other individuals with that same color pattern, regardless of species.   **2.** You might move objects around to establish an abstract rule, such as "past landmark A, the same distance as A is from the starting point," while maintaining a minimum of fixed metric relationships, that is, avoiding having the food directly adjacent to or a set distance from a landmark. As you might surmise, designing an informative experiment of this kind is not easy.   **3.** Learned behavior, just like innate behavior, can contribute to reproductive isolation and thus to speciation. For example, learned bird songs contribute to species recognition during courtship, thereby helping ensure that only members of the same species mate.

Concept Check 51.3

1. Certainty of paternity is higher with external fertilization.   **2.** Balancing selection could maintain the two alleles at the *forager* locus if population density fluctuated from one generation to another. At times of low population density, the energy-conserving sitter larvae (carrying the *for^s* allele) would be favored, while at

higher population density, the more mobile Rover larvae (*for^R* allele) would have a selective advantage. Because females would now be present in much larger numbers than males, all three types of males should have some reproductive success. Nevertheless, since the advantage that the blue-throats rely on—a limited number of females in their territory—will be absent, the yellow-throats are likely to increase in frequency in the short term.

Concept Check 51.4

1. Because this geographic variation corresponds to differences in prey availability between two garter snake habitats, it seems likely that snakes with characteristics enabling them to feed on the abundant prey in their locale would have had increased survival and reproductive success. In this way, natural selection would have resulted in the divergent foraging behaviors.   **2.** The fact that the individual shares some genes with the offspring of its sibling (in the case of humans, with the individual's niece or nephew) means that the reproductive success of that niece or nephew increases the representation of those genes in the population (selects for them).   **3.** The older individual cannot be the beneficiary because he or she cannot have extra offspring. However, the cost is low for an older individual performing the altruistic act because that individual has already reproduced (but perhaps is still caring for a child or grandchild). There can therefore be selection for an altruistic act by a postreproductive individual that benefits a young relative.

Summary of Key Concepts Questions

51.1 Circannual rhythms are typically based on the cycles of light and dark in the environment. As the global climate changes, animals that migrate in response to these rhythms may shift to a location before or after local environmental conditions are optimal for reproduction and survival.   **51.2** For the goose, all that is acquired is an object at which the behavior is directed. In the case of the sparrow, learning takes place that will give shape to the behavior itself.   **51.3** Because feeding the female is likely to improve her reproductive success, the genes from the sacrificed male are likely to appear in a greater number of progeny.   **51.4** Studying the genetic basis of these behaviors reveals that changes in a single gene can have large-scale effects on even complex behaviors.

Test Your Understanding

1. c   **2.** b   **3.** b   **4.** a   **5.** c   **6.** a
7.

You could measure the size of mussels that oystercatchers successfully open and compare that with the size distribution in the habitat.

Chapter 52

Figure Questions

Figure 52.7 Dispersal limitations, the activities of people (such as a broad-scale conversion of forests to agriculture or selective harvesting), or many other factors, including those discussed later in the chapter (see Figure 52.16)   **Figure 52.16** Some factors, such as fire, are relevant only for terrestrial systems. At first glance, water availability is primarily a terrestrial factor, too. However, species living along the intertidal zone of oceans or along the edge of lakes also suffer desiccation. Salinity stress is important for species in some aquatic and terrestrial systems. Oxygen availability is an important factor primarily for species in some aquatic systems and in soils and sediments.

Concept Check 52.1

1. In the tropics, high temperatures evaporate water and cause warm, moist air to rise. The rising air cools and releases much of its water as rain over the tropics. The remaining dry air descends at approximately 30° north and south, causing deserts to occur in those regions.   **2.** The microclimate around the stream will be cooler, moister, and shadier than that around the unplanted agricultural field.   **3.** Trees that require a long time to reach reproductive age are likely to evolve more slowly than annual plants in response to climate change, constraining the potential ability of such trees to respond to rapid climate change.   **4.** Plants with C$_4$ photosynthesis are likely to expand their range globally as Earth's climate warms. C$_4$ photosynthesis minimizes photorespiration and enhances sugar production, an advantage that is especially useful in warmer regions where C$_4$ plants are found today.

Concept Check 52.2

2. Answers will vary by location but should be based on the information and maps in Figure 52.11. How much your local area has been altered from its natural state will influence how much it reflects the expected characteristics of your biome, particularly the expected plants and animals.   **3.** Northern coniferous forest is likely to replace tundra along the boundary between these biomes. To see why, note that northern coniferous forest is adjacent to tundra throughout North America, northern Europe, and Asia (see Figure 52.8) and that the temperature range for northern coniferous forest is just above that for tundra (see Figure 52.9).

Concept Check 52.3

1. In the oceanic pelagic zone, the ocean bottom lies below the photic zone, so there is too little light to support benthic algae or rooted plants. **2.** Aquatic organisms either gain or lose water by osmosis if the osmolarity of their environment differs from their internal osmolarity. Water gain can cause cells to swell, and water loss can cause them to shrink. To avoid excessive changes in cell volume, organisms that live in estuaries must be able to compensate for both water gain (under freshwater conditions) and water loss (under saltwater conditions). **3.** In a river below a dam, the fish are more likely to be species that prefer colder water. In summer, the deep layers of a reservoir are colder than the surface layers, so a river below a dam will be colder than an undammed river.

Concept Check 52.4

1. (a) Humans might transplant a species to a new area that it could not previously reach because of a geographic barrier. (b) Humans might eliminate a predator or herbivore species, such as sea urchins, from an area. **2.** One test would be to build a fence around a plot of land in an area that has trees of that species, excluding all deer from the plot. You could then compare the abundance of tree seedlings inside and outside the fenced plot over time. **3.** Because the ancestor of the silverswords reached isolated Hawaii early in the islands' existence, it likely faced little competition and was able to occupy many unfilled niches. The cattle egret, in contrast, arrived in the Americas only recently and has to compete with a well-established group of species. Thus, its opportunities for adaptive radiation have probably been much more limited.

Summary of Key Concepts Questions

52.1 Because dry air would descend at the equator instead of at 30° north and south latitude (where deserts exist today), deserts would be more likely to exist along the equator (see Figure 52.3). **52.2** The dominant plants in savanna ecosystems tend to be adapted to fire and tolerant of seasonal droughts. The savanna biome is maintained by periodic fires, both natural and set by humans, but humans are also clearing savannas for agriculture and other uses. **52.3** An aphotic zone is most likely to be found in the deep waters of a lake, the oceanic pelagic zone, or the marine benthic zone. **52.4** You might arrange a flowchart that begins with abiotic limitations—first determining the physical and chemical conditions under which a species could survive—and then moves through the other factors listed in the flowchart.

Test Your Understanding

1. b **2.** b **3.** c **4.** c **5.** d **6.** c **7.** a **8.** a **9.** b

Chapter 53

Figure Questions

Figure 53.4 The dispersion of the penguins would likely appear clumped as you flew over densely populated islands and sparsely populated ocean.
Figure 53.7 #109
Figure 53.16

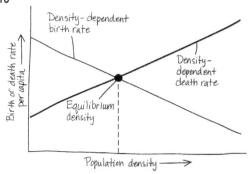

Concept Check 53.1

1.

A Type III survivorship curve is most likely because very few of the young probably survive. **2.** If an animal is captured by attracting it with food, it may be more likely to be recaptured if it seeks the same food. The number of marked animals captured (x) would be an overestimate, and because the population size (N) is equal to sn/x, N would be an underestimate. Alternatively, if an animal has a negative experience during capture and learns from that experience, it may be less likely to be recaptured. In this case, x would be an underestimate and N would be an overestimate. **3.** Male sticklebacks would likely have a uniform pattern of dispersion, with antagonistic interactions maintaining a relatively constant spacing between them.

Concept Check 53.2

1. Though r_{inst} is constant, N, the population size, is increasing. As r_{inst} is applied to an increasingly large N, population growth ($r_{inst}N$) accelerates, producing the J-shaped curve. **2.** Exponential growth is more likely in the area where a forest was destroyed by fire. The first plants that found suitable habitat there would encounter an abundance of space, nutrients, and light. In the undisturbed forest, competition among plants for these resources would be intense. **3.** The net population growth is $\Delta N/\Delta t = bN - mN$. The annual per capita birth rate, b, equals $14/1,000$, or 0.014, and the per capita death rate, m, equals $8/1,000$, or 0.008. Therefore, the net population growth in 2011 was

$$\frac{\Delta N}{\Delta t} = (0.014 \times 311,000,000) - (0.008 \times 311,000,000)$$

or 1.87 million people. To determine whether the population is growing exponentially, you would need to determine whether $r_{inst} > 0$ and if it is constant through time (across multiple years).

Concept Check 53.3

1. When N (population size) is small, there are relatively few individuals producing offspring. When N is large, near the carrying capacity, the per capita growth rate is relatively small because it is limited by available resources. The steepest part of the logistic growth curve corresponds to a population with a number of reproducing individuals that is substantial but not yet near carrying capacity. **2.** All else being equal, you would expect a plant species to have a larger carrying capacity at the equator than at high latitudes because there is more incident sunlight near the equator. **3.** If a population becomes too crowded, the likelihood of disease and mortality may increase because of the effects of pathogens. Thus, pathogens can reduce the long-term carrying capacity of a population.

Concept Check 53.4

1. The constant, spring-fed stream. In more constant physical conditions, populations are more stable and competition for resources is more likely. In such conditions, larger, well-provisioned young typical of iteroparous species have a better chance of surviving. **2.** By preferentially investing in the eggs it lays in the nest, the peacock wrasse increases their probability of survival. The eggs it disperses widely and does not provide care for are less likely to survive, at least some of the time, but require a lower investment by the adults. (In this sense, the adults avoid the risk of placing all their eggs in one basket.) **3.** If a parent's survival is compromised greatly by bearing young during times of stress, the animal's fitness may increase if it abandons its current young and survives to produce healthier young at a later time.

Concept Check 53.5

1. Three attributes are the size, quality, and isolation of patches. A patch that is larger or of higher quality is more likely to attract individuals and to be a source of individuals for other patches. A patch that is relatively isolated will undergo fewer exchanges of individuals with other patches. **2.** You would need to study the population for more than one cycle (longer than 10 years and probably at least 20) before having sufficient data to examine changes through time. Otherwise, it would be impossible to know whether an observed decrease in the population size reflected a long-term trend or was part of the normal cycle. **3.** In negative feedback, the output, or product, of a process slows that process. In populations that have a density-dependent birth rate, such as dune fescue grass, an accumulation of product (more individuals, resulting in a higher population density) slows the process (population growth) by decreasing the birth rate.

Concept Check 53.6

1. A bottom-heavy age structure, with a disproportionate number of young people, portends continuing growth of the population as these young people begin reproducing. In contrast, a more evenly distributed age structure predicts a more stable population size, and a top-heavy age structure predicts a decrease in population size because relatively fewer young people are reproducing. **2.** The growth rate of Earth's human population has dropped by half since the 1960s, from 2.2% in 1962 to 1.1% today. Nonetheless, growth has not slowed much because the smaller growth rate is counterbalanced by increased population size; the number of extra people on Earth each year remains enormous—approximately 78 million.
3. Each of us influences our ecological footprint by how we live—what we eat, how much energy we use, and the amount of waste we generate—as well as by how many children we have. Making choices that reduce our demand for resources makes our ecological footprint smaller.

Summary of Key Concepts Questions

53.1 Ecologists can potentially estimate birth rates by counting the number of young born each year, and they can estimate death rates by seeing how the number of adults changes each year. **53.2** Under the exponential model, both populations will continue to grow to infinite size, regardless of the specific value of r_{inst} (see Figure 53.8).   **53.3** There are many things you can do to increase the carrying capacity of the species, including increasing its food supply, protecting it from predators, and providing more sites for nesting or reproduction.   **53.4** Two key factors appear to be the survival rate of the offspring and the chance that adults will live long enough to reproduce again.   **53.5** An example of a biotic factor would be disease caused by a pathogen; natural disasters, such as floods and storms, are examples of abiotic factors.   **53.6** Humans are unique in our potential ability to reduce global population through contraception and family planning. Humans also are capable of consciously choosing their diet and personal lifestyle, and these choices influence the number of people Earth can support.

Test Your Understanding
1. b   **2.** a   **3.** a   **4.** d   **5.** c   **6.** b   **7.** c   **8.** d   **9.** a   **10.** a

Chapter 54

Figure Questions
Figure 54.3 Its realized and fundamental niches would be similar, unlike those of *Chthamalus*.   **Figure 54.15** The number of other organism types eaten is zero for phytoplankton; one for copepods, crab-eater seals, baleen whales, and sperm whales; two for krill, carnivorous plankton, and elephant seals; three for squids, fishes, leopard seals, and humans; and five for birds and smaller toothed whales. The two groups that both consume and are consumed by each other are fishes and squids.   **Figure 54.18** The death of individuals of *Mytilus*, a dominant species, should open up space for other species and increase species richness even in the absence of *Pisaster*.   **Figure 54.23** At the earliest stages of primary succession, free-living prokaryotes in the soil would reduce atmospheric N_2 to NH_3. Symbiotic nitrogen fixation could not occur until plants were present at the site. **Figure 54.26** Other factors not included in the model must contribute to the number of species.   **Figure 54.28** Shrew populations in different locations and habitats might show substantial genetic variation in their susceptibility to the Lyme pathogen. Further studies would be needed to test the generality of the study's results.

Concept Check 54.1
1. Interspecific competition has negative effects on both species $(-/-)$. In predation, the predator population benefits at the expense of the prey population $(+/-)$. Mutualism is a symbiosis in which both species benefit $(+/+)$.   **2.** One of the competing species will become locally extinct because of the greater reproductive success of the more efficient competitor.   **3.** By specializing in eating seeds of a single plant species, individuals of the two finch species may be less likely to come into contact in the separate habitats, reinforcing a reproductive barrier to hybridization.

Concept Check 54.2
1. Species richness, the number of species in the community, and relative abundance, the proportions of the community represented by the various species, both contribute to species diversity. Compared to a community with a very high proportion of one species, one with a more even proportion of species is considered more diverse.   **2.** A food chain presents a set of one-way transfers of food energy up to successively higher trophic levels. A food web documents how food chains are linked together, with many species weaving into the web at more than one trophic level.   **3.** According to the bottom-up model, adding extra predators would have little effect on lower trophic levels, particularly vegetation. If the top-down model applied, increased bobcat numbers would decrease raccoon numbers, increase snake numbers, decrease mouse numbers, and increase grass biomass.

Concept Check 54.3
1. High levels of disturbance are generally so disruptive that they eliminate many species from communities, leaving the community dominated by a few tolerant species. Low levels of disturbance permit competitively dominant species to exclude other species from the community. But moderate levels of disturbance can facilitate coexistence of a greater number of species in a community by preventing competitively dominant species from becoming abundant enough to eliminate other species from the community.   **2.** Early successional species can facilitate the arrival of other species in many ways, including increasing the fertility or water-holding capacity of soils or providing shelter for seedlings from wind and intense sunlight.   **3.** The absence of fire for 100 years would represent a change to a low level of disturbance. According to the intermediate disturbance hypothesis, this change should cause diversity to decline as competitively dominant species gain sufficient time to exclude less competitive species.

Concept Check 54.4
1. Ecologists propose that the greater species richness of tropical regions is the result of their longer evolutionary history and the greater solar energy input and water availability in tropical regions.   **2.** Immigration of species to islands declines with distance from the mainland and increases with island area. Extinction of species is lower on larger islands and on less isolated islands. Since the number of species on islands is largely determined by the difference between rates of immigration and extinction, the number of species will be highest on large islands near the mainland and lowest on small islands far from the mainland.   **3.** Because of their greater mobility, birds disperse to islands more often than snakes and lizards, so birds should have greater richness.

Concept Check 54.5
1. Pathogens are microorganisms, viruses, viroids, or prions that cause disease.   **2.** To keep the rabies virus out, you could ban imports of all mammals, including pets. Potentially, you could also attempt to vaccinate all dogs in the British Isles against the virus. A more practical approach might be to quarantine all pets brought into the country that are potential carriers of the disease, the approach the British government actually takes.

Summary of Key Concepts Questions
54.1 Note: Sample answers follow; other answers could also be correct. Competition: a fox and a bobcat competing for prey. Predation: an orca eating a sea otter. Herbivory: a bison grazing in a prairie. Parasitism: a parasitoid wasp that lays its eggs on a caterpillar. Mutualism: a fungus and an alga that make up a lichen. Commensalism: a remora attached to a whale. Facilitation: a flowering plant and its pollinator.   **54.2** Not necessarily if the more species-rich community is dominated by only one or a few species   **54.3** Because of the presence of species initially, the disturbance would initiate secondary succession in spite of its severe appearance.   **54.4** Glaciations have severely reduced diversity in northern temperate, boreal, and Arctic ecosystems, compared to tropical ecosystems. **54.5** A host is required to complete the pathogen's life cycle, but a vector is not. Vectors are intermediate species that merely transport a pathogen to its host.

Test Your Understanding
1. d   **2.** c   **3.** c   **4.** c   **5.** b   **6.** c   **7.** d   **8.** b
9. Community 1: $H = -(0.05 \ln 0.05 + 0.05 \ln 0.05 + 0.85 \ln 0.85 + 0.05 \ln 0.05) = 0.59$. Community 2: $H = -(0.30 \ln 0.30 + 0.40 \ln 0.40 + 0.30 \ln 0.30) = 1.1$. Community 2 is more diverse.   **10.** Crab numbers should increase, reducing the abundance of eelgrass.

Chapter 55

Figure Questions
Figure 55.6 Wetlands, coral reefs, and coastal zones cover areas too small to show up clearly on global maps.   **Figure 55.7** The availability of nutrients, particularly nitrogen, phosphorus, and iron, as well as temperature, is likely to limit primary production in the oceans.   **Figure 55.8** If the new duck farms made nitrogen available in rich supply, as phosphorus already is, then adding extra nitrogen in the experiment would not increase phytoplankton density.   **Figure 55.13** The lichen symbiosis allows the photosynthetic symbiont to photosynthesize and, in cases where it is a cyanobacterium, to fix nitrogen. The fungal symbiont provides the photosynthetic symbiont with a protective environment as well as phosphorus and other soil nutrients. Lichens are particularly abundant in nutrient-poor habitats such as those found in the Arctic tundra.   **Figure 55.15** Water availability is probably another factor that varied across the sites. Such factors not included in the experimental design could make the results more difficult to interpret. Multiple factors can also covary in nature, so ecologists must be careful that the factor they are studying is actually causing the observed response and is not just correlated with it.

Concept Check 55.1
1. Energy passes through an ecosystem, entering as sunlight and leaving as heat. It is not recycled within the ecosystem.   **2.** You would need to know how much biomass the wildebeests ate from your plot and how much nitrogen was contained in that biomass. You would also need to know how much nitrogen they deposited in urine or feces.   **3.** The second law states that in any energy transfer or transformation, some of the energy is dissipated to the surroundings as heat. This "escape" of energy from an ecosystem is offset by the continuous influx of solar radiation.

Concept Check 55.2
1. Only a fraction of solar radiation strikes plants or algae, only a portion of that fraction is of wavelengths suitable for photosynthesis, and much energy is lost as a result of reflection or heating of plant tissue.   **2.** By manipulating the level of the factors of interest, such as phosphorus availability or soil moisture, and measuring responses by primary producers   **3.** The enzyme rubisco, which catalyzes the first step in the Calvin cycle, is the most abundant protein on Earth. Photosynthetic organisms require considerable nitrogen to make rubisco. Phosphorus is also needed as a component of several metabolites in the Calvin cycle and as a component of both ATP and NADPH (see Figure 10.19).

Concept Check 55.3

1. 20 J; 40% **2.** Nicotine protects the plant from herbivores. **3.** Total net production is 10,000 + 1,000 + 100 + 10 J = 11,110 J. At steady state, this is the amount of energy theoretically available to detritivores.

Concept Check 55.4

1. For example, for the carbon cycle:

Cycling of a carbon atom

2. Removal of the trees stops nitrogen uptake from the soil, allowing nitrate to accumulate there. The nitrate is washed away by precipitation and enters the streams. **3.** Most of the nutrients in a tropical rain forest are contained in the trees, so removing the trees by logging rapidly depletes nutrients from the ecosystem. The nutrients that remain in the soil are quickly carried away into streams and groundwater by the abundant precipitation.

Concept Check 55.5

1. The main goal is to restore degraded ecosystems to a more natural state.
2. The Kissimmee River project returns the flow of water to the original channel and restores natural flow, a self-sustaining outcome. Ecologists at the Maungatautari reserve will need to maintain the integrity of the fence indefinitely, an outcome that is not self-sustaining in the long term.

Summary of Key Concepts Questions

55.1 Because energy conversions are inefficient, with some energy inevitably lost as heat, you would expect that a given mass of primary producers would support a smaller biomass of secondary producers. **55.2** For estimates of NEP, you need to measure the respiration of all organisms in an ecosystem, not just the respiration of primary producers. In a sample of ocean water, primary producers and other organisms are usually mixed together, making their respective respirations hard to separate. **55.3** Runners use much more energy in respiration when they are running than when they are sedentary, reducing their production efficiency.
55.4 Factors other than temperature, including a shortage of water and nutrients, slow decomposition in hot deserts. **55.5** If the topsoil and deeper soil are kept separate, you could return the deeper soil to the site first and then apply the more fertile topsoil to improve the success of revegetation and other restoration efforts.

Test Your Understanding

1. c **2.** b **3.** a **4.** c **5.** a **6.** b **7.** d **8.** d

Chapter 56

Figure Questions

Figure 56.4 You would need to know the complete range of the species and that it is missing across all of that range. You would also need to be certain that the species isn't hidden, as might be the case for an animal that is hibernating underground or a plant that is present in the form of seeds or spores. **Figure 56.9** The two examples are similar in that segments of DNA from the harvested samples were analyzed and compared with segments from specimens of known origin. One difference is that the whale researchers investigated relatedness at species and population levels to determine whether illegal activity had occurred, whereas the elephant investigators determined relatedness at the population level to determine the precise location of the poaching. Another difference is that mtDNA was used for the whale study, whereas nuclear DNA was used for the elephant study. The primary limitations of such approaches are the need to have (or generate) a reference database and the requirement that the organisms have sufficient variation in their DNA to reveal the relatedness of samples. **Figure 56.11** The higher the pH, the lower the acidity. Thus, the precipitation in this forest is becoming less acidic. **Figure 56.14** Because the population of Illinois birds has a different genetic makeup than birds in other regions, you would want to maintain to the greatest extent possible the frequency of beneficial genes or alleles found only in that population. In restoration, preserving genetic diversity in a species is as important as increasing organism numbers. **Figure 56.16** The natural disturbance regime in this habitat includes frequent fires that clear undergrowth but do not kill mature pine trees. Without these fires, the undergrowth quickly fills in and the habitat becomes unsuitable for red-cockaded woodpeckers. **Figure 56.17** The photo shows edges between forest and grassland ecosystems, grassland and river ecosystems, and grassland and lake ecosystems.

Concept Check 56.1

1. In addition to species loss, the biodiversity crisis includes the loss of genetic diversity within populations and species and the degradation of entire ecosystems. **2.** Habitat destruction, such as deforestation, channelizing of rivers, or conversion of natural ecosystems to agriculture or cities, deprives species of places to live. Introduced species, which are transported by humans to regions outside their native range, where they are not controlled by their natural pathogens or predators, often reduce the population sizes of native species through competition or predation. Overharvesting has reduced populations of plants and animals or driven them to extinction. Finally, global change is altering the environment to the extent that it reduces the capacity of Earth to sustain life. **3.** If both populations breed separately, then gene flow between the populations would not occur and genetic differences between them would be greater. As a result, the loss of genetic diversity would be greater than if the populations interbreed.

Concept Check 56.2

1. Reduced genetic variation decreases the capacity of a population to evolve in the face of change. **2.** The effective population size, N_e, would be 4(30 × 10)/ (30 + 10) = 30 birds. **3.** Because millions of people use the greater Yellowstone ecosystem each year, it would be impossible to eliminate all contact between people and bears. Instead, you might try to reduce the kinds of encounters where bears are killed. You might recommend lower speed limits on roads in the park, adjust the timing or location of hunting seasons (where hunting is allowed outside the park) to minimize contact with mother bears and cubs, and provide financial incentives for livestock owners to try alternative means of protecting livestock, such as using guard dogs.

Concept Check 56.3

1. A small area supporting numerous endemic species as well as a large number of endangered and threatened species **2.** Zoned reserves may provide sustained supplies of forest products, water, hydroelectric power, educational opportunities, and income from tourism. **3.** Habitat corridors can increase the rate of movement or dispersal of organisms between habitat patches and thus the rate of gene flow between subpopulations. They thus help prevent a decrease in fitness attributable to inbreeding. They can also minimize interactions between organisms and humans as the organisms disperse; in cases involving potential predators, such as bears or large cats, minimizing such interactions is desirable.

Concept Check 56.4

1. Adding nutrients causes population explosions of algae and the organisms that feed on them. Increased respiration by algae and consumers, including detritivores, depletes the lake's oxygen, which the fish require. **2.** Because higher temperatures lead to faster decomposition, organic matter in these soils could be quickly decomposed to CO_2, speeding up global warming. **3.** Reduced concentrations of ozone in the atmosphere increase the amount of UV radiation that reaches Earth's surface and the organisms living there. UV radiation can cause mutations by producing disruptive thymine dimers in DNA.

Concept Check 56.5

1. Sustainable development is an approach to development that works toward the long-term prosperity of human societies and the ecosystems that support them, which requires linking the biological sciences with the social sciences, economics, and humanities. **2.** Biophilia, our sense of connection to nature and all forms of life, may act as a significant motivation for the development of an environmental ethic that resolves not to allow species to become extinct or ecosystems to be destroyed. Such an ethic is necessary if we are to become more attentive and effective custodians of the environment. **3.** At a minimum, you would want to know the size of the population and the average reproductive rate of individuals in it. To develop the fishery sustainably, you would seek a harvest rate that maintains the population near its original size and maximizes its harvest in the long term rather than the short term.

Summary of Key Concepts Questions

56.1 Nature provides us with many beneficial services, including a supply of reliable, clean water, the production of food and fiber, and the dilution and detoxification of our pollutants. **56.2** A more genetically diverse population is better able to withstand pressures from disease or environmental change, making it less likely to become extinct over a given period of time. **56.3** Habitat fragmentation can isolate populations, leading to inbreeding and genetic drift, and it can make populations more susceptible to local extinctions resulting from the effects of pathogens, parasites, or predators. **56.4** It's healthier to feed at a lower trophic level because biological magnification increases the concentration of toxins at higher levels. **56.5** One goal of conservation biology is to preserve as many species as possible. Sustainable approaches that maintain the quality of habitats are required for the long-term survival of organisms.

Test Your Understanding

1. c **2.** d **3.** b **4.** a **5.** b **6.** a
7. (a) The average CO_2 concentration was approximately 330 ppm in 1975 and approximately 394 ppm in 2012. (b) The rate of CO_2 concentration increase was (394 ppm − 330 ppm)/(2012 − 1975) = 64 ppm/37 years = 1.73 ppm/yr. (c) If this rate continues, the concentration in 2100 will be approximately 550 ppm (1.73 ppm/yr × 88 yr = 152 ppm for the increase from 2012–2100 + 394 ppm in 2012 = 546 ppm, rounded off to 550 ppm).

(d)

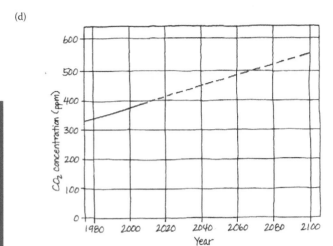

(e) The actual rise in CO_2 concentration could be larger or smaller, depending on Earth's human population, per capita energy use, and the extent to which societies take steps to reduce CO_2 emissions, including replacing fossil fuels with renewable or nuclear fuels. (f) Additional scientific data will be important for many reasons, such as determining how quickly greenhouse gases such as CO_2 are removed from the atmosphere by the biosphere.

9.

To minimize the area of forest into which the cowbirds penetrate, you should locate the road along one edge of the reserve. Any other location would increase the area of affected habitat. Similarly, the maintenance building should be in a corner of the reserve to minimize the area susceptible to cowbirds.

Atomic number (number of protons)

Element symbol

Atomic mass (number of protons plus number of neutrons averaged over all isotopes)

Metals   Metalloids   Nonmetals

Representative elements

Groups: Elements in a vertical column have the same number of electrons in their valence (outer) shell and thus have similar chemical properties.

Periods: Each horizontal row contains elements with the same total number of electron shells. Across each period, elements are ordered by increasing atomic number.

Transition elements

*Lanthanides

†Actinides

Name (Symbol)	Atomic Number	Name (Symbol)	Atomic Number	Name (Symbol)	Atomic Number	Name (Symbol)	Atomic Number	Name (Symbol)	Atomic Number
Actinium (Ac)	89	Copernicium (Cn)	112	Iodine (I)	53	Osmium (Os)	76	Silicon (Si)	14
Aluminum (Al)	13	Copper (Cu)	29	Iridium (Ir)	77	Oxygen (O)	8	Silver (Ag)	47
Americium (Am)	95	Curium (Cm)	96	Iron (Fe)	26	Palladium (Pd)	46	Sodium (Na)	11
Antimony (Sb)	51	Darmstadtium (Ds)	110	Krypton (Kr)	36	Phosphorus (P)	15	Strontium (Sr)	38
Argon (Ar)	18	Dubnium (Db)	105	Lanthanum (La)	57	Platinum (Pt)	78	Sulfur (S)	16
Arsenic (As)	33	Dysprosium (Dy)	66	Lawrencium (Lr)	103	Plutonium (Pu)	94	Tantalum (Ta)	73
Astatine (At)	85	Einsteinium (Es)	99	Lead (Pb)	82	Polonium (Po)	84	Technetium (Tc)	43
Barium (Ba)	56	Erbium (Er)	68	Lithium (Li)	3	Potassium (K)	19	Tellurium (Te)	52
Berkelium (Bk)	97	Europium (Eu)	63	Livermorium (Lv)	116	Praseodymium (Pr)	59	Terbium (Tb)	65
Beryllium (Be)	4	Fermium (Fm)	100	Lutetium (Lu)	71	Promethium (Pm)	61	Thallium (Tl)	81
Bismuth (Bi)	83	Flerovium (Fl)	114	Magnesium (Mg)	12	Protactinium (Pa)	91	Thorium (Th)	90
Bohrium (Bh)	107	Fluorine (F)	9	Manganese (Mn)	25	Radium (Ra)	88	Thulium (Tm)	69
Boron (B)	5	Francium (Fr)	87	Meitnerium (Mt)	109	Radon (Rn)	86	Tin (Sn)	50
Bromine (Br)	35	Gadolinium (Gd)	64	Mendelevium (Md)	101	Rhenium (Re)	75	Titanium (Ti)	22
Cadmium (Cd)	48	Gallium (Ga)	31	Mercury (Hg)	80	Rhodium (Rh)	45	Tungsten (W)	74
Calcium (Ca)	20	Germanium (Ge)	32	Molybdenum (Mo)	42	Roentgenium (Rg)	111	Uranium (U)	92
Californium (Cf)	98	Gold (Au)	79	Neodymium (Nd)	60	Rubidium (Rb)	37	Vanadium (V)	23
Carbon (C)	6	Hafnium (Hf)	72	Neon (Ne)	10	Ruthenium (Ru)	44	Xenon (Xe)	54
Cerium (Ce)	58	Hassium (Hs)	108	Neptunium (Np)	93	Rutherfordium (Rf)	104	Ytterbium (Yb)	70
Cesium (Cs)	55	Helium (He)	2	Nickel (Ni)	28	Samarium (Sm)	62	Yttrium (Y)	39
Chlorine (Cl)	17	Holmium (Ho)	67	Niobium (Nb)	41	Scandium (Sc)	21	Zinc (Zn)	30
Chromium (Cr)	24	Hydrogen (H)	1	Nitrogen (N)	7	Seaborgium (Sg)	106	Zirconium (Zr)	40
Cobalt (Co)	27	Indium (In)	49	Nobelium (No)	102	Selenium (Se)	34		

Metric Prefixes:
10^9 = giga (G)	10^{-2} = centi (c)	10^{-9} = nano (n)
10^6 = mega (M)	10^{-3} = milli (m)	10^{-12} = pico (p)
10^3 = kilo (k)	10^{-6} = micro (μ)	10^{-15} = femto (f)

Measurement	Unit and Abbreviation	Metric Equivalent	Metric-to-English Conversion Factor	English-to-Metric Conversion Factor
Length	1 kilometer (km)	= 1,000 (10^3) meters	1 km = 0.62 mile	1 mile = 1.61 km
	1 meter (m)	= 100 (10^2) centimeters = 1,000 millimeters	1 m = 1.09 yards 1 m = 3.28 feet 1 m = 39.37 inches	1 yard = 0.914 m 1 foot = 0.305 m
	1 centimeter (cm)	= 0.01 (10^{-2}) meter	1 cm = 0.394 inch	1 foot = 30.5 cm 1 inch = 2.54 cm
	1 millimeter (mm)	= 0.001 (10^{-3}) meter	1 mm = 0.039 inch	
	1 micrometer (μm) (formerly micron, μ)	= 10^{-6} meter (10^{-3} mm)		
	1 nanometer (nm) (formerly millimicron, mμ)	= 10^{-9} meter (10^{-3} μm)		
	1 angstrom (Å)	= 10^{-10} meter (10^{-4} μm)		
Area	1 hectare (ha)	= 10,000 square meters	1 ha = 2.47 acres	1 acre = 0.405 ha
	1 square meter (m^2)	= 10,000 square centimeters	1 m^2 = 1.196 square yards 1 m^2 = 10.764 square feet	1 square yard = 0.8361 m^2 1 square foot = 0.0929 m^2
	1 square centimeter (cm^2)	= 100 square millimeters	1 cm^2 = 0.155 square inch	1 square inch = 6.4516 cm^2
Mass	1 metric ton (t)	= 1,000 kilograms	1 t = 1.103 tons	1 ton = 0.907 t
	1 kilogram (kg)	= 1,000 grams	1 kg = 2.205 pounds	1 pound = 0.4536 kg
	1 gram (g)	= 1,000 milligrams	1 g = 0.0353 ounce 1 g = 15.432 grains	1 ounce = 28.35 g
	1 milligram (mg)	= 10^{-3} gram	1 mg = approx. 0.015 grain	
	1 microgram (μg)	= 10^{-6} gram		
Volume (solids)	1 cubic meter (m^3)	= 1,000,000 cubic centimeters	1 m^3 = 1.308 cubic yards 1 m^3 = 35.315 cubic feet	1 cubic yard = 0.7646 m^3 1 cubic foot = 0.0283 m^3
	1 cubic centimeter (cm^3 or cc)	= 10^{-6} cubic meter	1 cm^3 = 0.061 cubic inch	1 cubic inch = 16.387 cm^3
	1 cubic millimeter (mm^3)	= 10^{-9} cubic meter = 10^{-3} cubic centimeter		
Volume (liquids and gases)	1 kiloliter (kL or kl)	= 1,000 liters	1 kL = 264.17 gallons	
	1 liter (L or l)	= 1,000 milliliters	1 L = 0.264 gallon 1 L = 1.057 quarts	1 gallon = 3.785 L 1 quart = 0.946 L
	1 milliliter (mL or ml)	= 10^{-3} liter = 1 cubic centimeter	1 mL = 0.034 fluid ounce 1 mL = approx. ¼ teaspoon 1 mL = approx. 15–16 drops (gtt.)	1 quart = 946 mL 1 pint = 473 mL 1 fluid ounce = 29.57 mL 1 teaspoon = approx. 5 mL
	1 microliter (μL or μl)	= 10^{-6} liter (10^{-3} milliliter)		
Pressure	1 megapascal (MPa)	= 1,000 kilopascals	1 MPa = 10 bars	1 bar = 0.1 MPa
	1 kilopascal (kPa)	= 1,000 pascals	1 kPa = 0.01 bar	1 bar = 100 kPa
	1 pascal (Pa)	= 1 newton/m^2 (N/m^2)	1 Pa = 1.0×10^{-5} bar	1 bar = 1.0×10^5 Pa
Time	1 second (s or sec)	= 1/60 minute		
	1 millisecond (ms or msec)	= 10^{-3} second		
Temperature	Degrees Celsius (°C) (0 K [Kelvin] = −273.15°C)		°F = 9/5°C + 32	°C = 5/9 (°F − 32)

Light Microscope

In light microscopy, light is focused on a specimen by a glass condenser lens; the image is then magnified by an objective lens and an ocular lens for projection on the eye, digital camera, digital video camera, or photographic film.

Electron Microscope

In electron microscopy, a beam of electrons (top of the microscope) is used instead of light, and electromagnets are used instead of glass lenses. The electron beam is focused on the specimen by a condenser lens; the image is magnified by an objective lens and a projector lens for projection on a digital detector, fluorescent screen, or photographic film.

This appendix presents a taxonomic classification for the major extant groups of organisms discussed in this text; not all phyla are included. The classification presented here is based on the three-domain system, which assigns the two major groups of prokaryotes, bacteria and archaea, to separate domains (with eukaryotes making up the third domain).

Various alternative classification schemes are discussed in Unit Five of the text. The taxonomic turmoil includes debates about the number and boundaries of kingdoms and about the alignment of the Linnaean classification hierarchy with the findings of modern cladistic analysis. In this review, asterisks (*) indicate currently recognized phyla thought by some systematists to be paraphyletic.

DOMAIN BACTERIA

- **Proteobacteria**
- **Chlamydia**
- **Spirochetes**
- **Gram-Positive Bacteria**
- **Cyanobacteria**

DOMAIN ARCHAEA

- **Korarchaeota**
- **Euryarchaeota**
- **Crenarchaeota**
- **Nanoarchaeota**

DOMAIN EUKARYA

In the phylogenetic hypothesis we present in Chapter 28, major clades of eukaryotes are grouped together in the four "supergroups" listed in bold type below and on the facing page. Formerly, all the eukaryotes generally called protists were assigned to a single kingdom, Protista. However, advances in systematics have made it clear that some protists are more closely related to plants, fungi, or animals than they are to other protists. As a result, the kingdom Protista has been abandoned.

Excavata
- Diplomonadida (diplomonads)
- Parabasala (parabasalids)
- Euglenozoa (euglenozoans)
    Kinetoplastida (kinetoplastids)
    Euglenophyta (euglenids)

"SAR" Clade
- Stramenopila (stramenopiles)
    Chrysophyta (golden algae)
    Phaeophyta (brown algae)
    Bacillariophyta (diatoms)

- Alveolata (alveolates)
    Dinoflagellata (dinoflagellates)
    Apicomplexa (apicomplexans)
    Ciliophora (ciliates)
- Rhizaria (rhizarians)
    Radiolaria (radiolarians)
    Foraminifera (forams)
    Cercozoa (cercozoans)

Archaeplastida
- Rhodophyta (red algae)
- Chlorophyta (green algae: chlorophytes)
- Charophyta (green algae: charophytes)
- Plantae
    Phylum Hepatophyta (liverworts) ⎫
    Phylum Bryophyta (mosses)   ⎬ Nonvascular plants (bryophytes)
    Phylum Anthocerophyta (hornworts) ⎭
    Phylum Lycophyta (lycophytes)   ⎫ Seedless vascular
    Phylum Monilophyta (ferns, horsetails, ⎬ plants
      whisk ferns)   ⎭
    Phylum Ginkgophyta (ginkgo)   ⎫
    Phylum Cycadophyta (cycads)   ⎬ Gymnosperms ⎫
    Phylum Gnetophyta (gnetophytes)   ⎪   ⎬ Seed
    Phylum Coniferophyta (conifers)   ⎭   ⎪ plants
    Phylum Anthophyta (flowering   ⎫ Angiosperms ⎭
      plants)   ⎭

Unikonta

- Amoebozoa (amoebozoans)
    - Myxogastrida (plasmodial slime molds)
    - Dictyostelida (cellular slime molds)
    - Tubulinea (tubulinids)
    - Entamoeba (entamoebas)
- Nucleariida (nucleariids)
- Fungi
    - *Phylum Chytridiomycota (chytrids)
    - *Phylum Zygomycota (zygomycetes)
    - Phylum Glomeromycota (glomeromycetes)
    - Phylum Ascomycota (ascomycetes)
    - Phylum Basidiomycota (basidiomycetes)

- Choanoflagellata (choanoflagellates)
- Animalia
    - Phylum Porifera (sponges)
    - Phylum Ctenophora (comb jellies)
    - Phylum Cnidaria (cnidarians)
        - Medusozoa (hydrozoans, jellies, box jellies)
        - Anthozoa (sea anemones and most corals)
    - Phylum Acoela (acoel flatworms)
    - Phylum Placozoa (placozoans)
    - <u>Lophotrochozoa (lophotrochozoans)</u>
    - Phylum Platyhelminthes (flatworms)
        - Catenulida (chain worms)
        - Rhabditophora (planarians, flukes, tapeworms)
    - Phylum Nemertea (proboscis worms)
    - Phylum Ectoprocta (ectoprocts)
    - Phylum Brachiopoda (brachiopods)
    - Phylum Rotifera (rotifers)
    - Phylum Cycliophora (cycliophorans)
    - Phylum Mollusca (molluscs)
        - Polyplacophora (chitons)
        - Gastropoda (gastropods)
        - Bivalvia (bivalves)
        - Cephalopoda (cephalopods)
    - Phylum Annelida (segmented worms)
        - Errantia (errantians)
        - Sedentaria (sedentarians)
    - Phylum Acanthocephala (spiny-headed worms)

<u>Ecdysozoa (ecdysozoans)</u>
- Phylum Loricifera (loriciferans)
- Phylum Priapula (priapulans)
- Phylum Nematoda (roundworms)
- Phylum Arthropoda (This survey groups arthropods into a single phylum, but some zoologists now split the arthropods into multiple phyla.)
    - Chelicerata (horseshoe crabs, arachnids)
    - Myriapoda (millipedes, centipedes)
    - Pancrustacea (crustaceans, insects)
- Phylum Tardigrada (tardigrades)
- Phylum Onychophora (velvet worms)

<u>Deuterostomia (deuterostomes)</u>
- Phylum Hemichordata (hemichordates)
- Phylum Echinodermata (echinoderms)
    - Asteroidea (sea stars, sea daisies)
    - Ophiuroidea (brittle stars)
    - Echinoides (sea urchins, sand dollars)
    - Crinoidea (sea lilies)
    - Holothuroidea (sea cucumbers)
- Phylum Chordata (chordates)
    - Cephalochordata (cephalochordates: lancelets)
    - Urochordata (urochordates: tunicates)
    - Cyclostomata (cyclostomes)
        - Myxini (hagfishes)
        - Petromyzontida (lampreys)
    - Gnathostomata (gnathostomes)
        - Chondrichthyes (sharks, rays, chimaeras)
        - Actinopterygii (ray-finned fishes)
        - Actinistia (coelacanths)
        - Dipnoi (lungfishes)
        - Amphibia (amphibians: frogs, salamanders, caecilians)
        - Reptilia (reptiles: tuataras, lizards, snakes, turtles, crocodilians, birds)
        - Mammalia (mammals)

} Vertebrates

Graphs

Graphs provide a visual representation of numerical data. They may reveal patterns or trends in the data that are not easy to recognize in a table. A graph is a diagram that shows how one variable in a data set is related (or perhaps not related) to another variable. If one variable is dependent on the other, the dependent variable is typically plotted on the *y*-axis and the independent variable on the *x*-axis. Types of graphs that are frequently used in biology include scatter plots, line graphs, bar graphs, and histograms.

► A **scatter plot** is used when the data for all variables are numerical and continuous. Each piece of data is represented by a point. In a **line graph**, each data point is connected to the next point in the data set with a straight line, as in the graph to the right. (To practice making and interpreting scatter plots and line graphs, see the Scientific Skills Exercises in Chapters 2, 3, 7, 8, 10, 13, 19, 24, 34, 43, 47, 49, 50, 52, 54, and 56.)

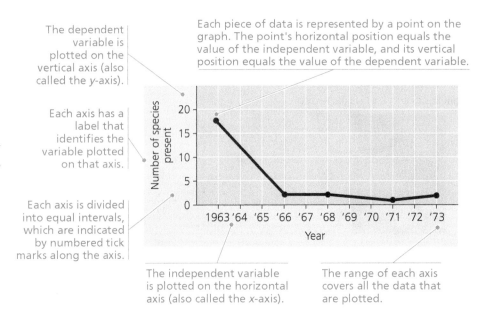

The dependent variable is plotted on the vertical axis (also called the *y*-axis).

Each axis has a label that identifies the variable plotted on that axis.

Each axis is divided into equal intervals, which are indicated by numbered tick marks along the axis.

Each piece of data is represented by a point on the graph. The point's horizontal position equals the value of the independent variable, and its vertical position equals the value of the dependent variable.

The independent variable is plotted on the horizontal axis (also called the *x*-axis).

The range of each axis covers all the data that are plotted.

▼ Two or more data sets can be plotted on the same line graph to show how two dependent variables are related to the same independent variable. (To practice making and interpreting line graphs with two or more data sets, see the Scientific Skills Exercises in Chapters 7, 43, 47, 49, 50, 52, and 56.)

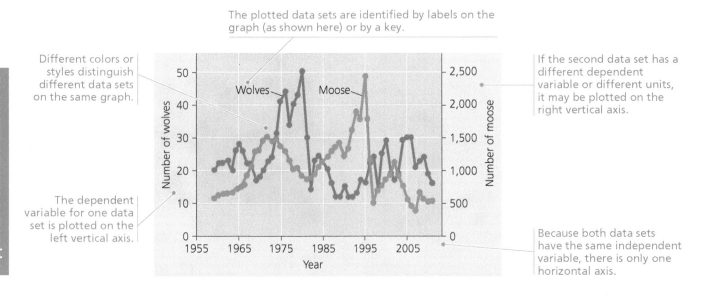

The plotted data sets are identified by labels on the graph (as shown here) or by a key.

Different colors or styles distinguish different data sets on the same graph.

The dependent variable for one data set is plotted on the left vertical axis.

If the second data set has a different dependent variable or different units, it may be plotted on the right vertical axis.

Because both data sets have the same independent variable, there is only one horizontal axis.

▼ In some scatter-plot graphs, a straight or curved line is drawn through the entire data set to show the general trend in the data. A straight line that mathematically fits the data best is called a *regression line.* Alternatively, a mathematical function that best fits the data may describe a curved line, often termed a *best-fit curve.* (To practice making and interpreting regression lines, see the Scientific Skills Exercises in Chapters 3, 10, and 34.)

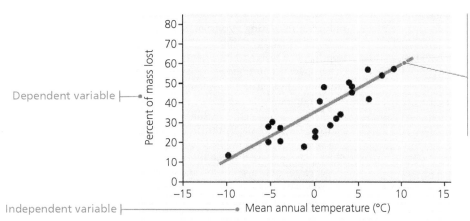

Dependent variable

Independent variable

The regression line can be expressed as a mathematical equation. It allows you to predict the value of the dependent variable for any value of the independent variable within the range of the data set and, less commonly, beyond the range of the data.

▼ A **bar graph** is a kind of graph in which the independent variable represents groups or non-numerical categories and the values of the dependent variable(s) are shown by bars. (To practice making and interpreting bar graphs, see the Scientific Skills Exercises in Chapters 1, 9, 18, 20, 22, 25, 27, 29, 33, 35, 39, 51, 52, and 54.)

As in a line graph or scatter plot, the vertical axis is usually used for the dependent variable.

The axis for the dependent variable is labeled and divided into equal intervals indicated by numbered tick marks.

Each piece of data is represented by a bar on the graph. The top of the bar aligns with the value of the dependent variable.

If multiple data sets are plotted on the same bar graph, they are distinguished by bars of different colors or styles and identified by labels or a key.

The groups or categories of the independent variable are usually spaced equally along the horizontal axis. (In some bar graphs, the horizontal axis is used for the dependent variable and the vertical axis for the independent variable.)

▶ A variant of a bar graph called a **histogram** can be made for numeric data by first grouping, or "binning," the variable plotted on the x-axis into intervals of equal width. The "bins" may be integers or ranges of numbers. In the histogram at right, the intervals are 25 mg/dL wide. The height of each bar shows the percent (or alternatively, the number) of experimental subjects whose characteristics can be described by one of the intervals plotted on the x-axis. (To practice making and interpreting histograms, see the Scientific Skills Exercises in Chapters 12, 14, and 42.)

The height of this bar shows the percent of individuals (about 4%) whose plasma LDL cholesterol levels are in the range indicated on the x-axis.

This interval runs from 50 to 74 mg/dL.

Glossary of Scientific Inquiry Terms

See Concept 1.3 for more discussion of the process of scientific inquiry.

control group In a controlled experiment, a set of subjects that lacks (or does not receive) the specific factor being tested. Ideally, the control group should be identical to the experimental group in other respects.

controlled experiment An experiment in which an experimental group is compared with a control group that varies only in the factor being tested.

data Recorded observations.

deductive reasoning A type of logic in which specific results are predicted from a general premise.

dependent variable A variable whose value is measured during an experiment or other test to see whether it is influenced by changes in another variable (the independent variable).

experiment A scientific test, carried out under controlled conditions, involving manipulation of one or more factors in a system in order to see the effects of those changes.

experimental group A set of subjects that has (or receives) the specific factor being tested in a controlled experiment.

hypothesis A testable explanation for a set of observations based on the available data and guided by inductive reasoning. A hypothesis is narrower in scope than a theory.

independent variable A variable whose value is manipulated or changed during an experiment or other test to reveal possible effects on another variable (the dependent variable).

inductive reasoning A type of logic in which generalizations are based on a large number of specific observations.

inquiry The search for information and explanation, often focusing on specific questions.

model A physical or conceptual representation of a natural phenomenon.

prediction In deductive reasoning, a forecast that follows logically from a hypothesis. By testing predictions, experiments may allow certain hypotheses to be rejected.

theory An explanation that is broader in scope than a hypothesis, generates new hypotheses, and is supported by a large body of evidence.

variable A factor that varies in an experiment or other test.

Chi-Square (χ^2) Distribution Table

To use the table, find the row that corresponds to the degrees of freedom in your data set. (The degrees of freedom is the number of categories of data minus 1.) Move along that row to the pair of values that your calculated χ^2 value lies between. Move up from those numbers to the probabilities at the top of the columns to find the probability range for your χ^2 value. A probability of 0.05 or less is generally considered significant. (To practice using the chi-square test, see the Scientific Skills Exercise in Chapter 15.)

Degrees of Freedom (df)	Probability										
	0.95	0.90	0.80	0.70	0.50	0.30	0.20	0.10	0.05	0.01	0.001
1	0.004	0.02	0.06	0.15	0.45	1.07	1.64	2.71	3.84	6.64	10.83
2	0.10	0.21	0.45	0.71	1.39	2.41	3.22	4.61	5.99	9.21	13.82
3	0.35	0.58	1.01	1.42	2.37	3.66	4.64	6.25	7.82	11.34	16.27
4	0.71	1.06	1.65	2.19	3.36	4.88	5.99	7.78	9.49	13.28	18.47
5	1.15	1.61	2.34	3.00	4.35	6.06	7.29	9.24	11.07	15.09	20.52
6	1.64	2.20	3.07	3.83	5.35	7.23	8.56	10.64	12.59	16.81	22.46
7	2.17	2.83	3.82	4.67	6.35	8.38	9.80	12.02	14.07	18.48	24.32
8	2.73	3.49	4.59	5.53	7.34	9.52	11.03	13.36	15.51	20.09	26.12
9	3.33	4.17	5.38	6.39	8.34	10.66	12.24	14.68	16.92	21.67	27.88
10	3.94	4.87	6.18	7.27	9.34	11.78	13.44	15.99	18.31	23.21	29.59

Mean and Standard Deviation

The **mean** is the sum of all data points in a data set divided by the number of data points. The mean (or average) represents a "typical" or central value around which the data points are clustered. The mean of a variable x (denoted by $\bar{x}$) is calculated from the following equation:

$$\bar{x} = \frac{1}{n}\sum_{i=1}^{n} x_i$$

In this formula, n is the number of observations, and x_i is the value of the ith observation of variable x; the "$\sum$" symbol indicates that the n values of x_i are to be summed. (To practice calculating the mean, see the Scientific Skills Exercises in Chapters 32 and 34.)

The **standard deviation** provides a measure of the variation found in a set of data points. The standard deviation of a variable x (denoted s_x) is calculated from the following equation:

$$s = \sqrt{\frac{\sum_{i=1}^{n}(x_i - \bar{x})^2}{n - 1}}$$

In this formula, n is the number of observations, x_i is the value of the ith observation of variable x, and $\bar{x}$ is the mean of x; the "$\sum$" symbol indicates that the n values of $(x_i - \bar{x})^2$ are to be summed. (To practice calculating standard deviation, see the Scientific Skills Exercises in Chapters 32 and 34.)

Photo Credits

New Content **Unit I** Mark J. Winter/Science Source; **Unit II** Thomas Deerinck and Mark Ellisman, NCMIR; **Unit III** Andrey Prokhorov/E+/Getty Images; **Unit IV** Richard Bizley/Science Source; **Unit V** DOE Photo; **Unit VI** Giuseppe Mazza; **Unit VII** Matthias Wittlinger; **Unit VIII** Jordi Bas Casas/NHPA/Photoshot.

Detailed Contents **p xxxii dandelions** Carola Koserowsky/AGE Fotostock; **gecko** Martin Harvey/Peter Arnold/Getty Images; **p. xxxiii cell** Thomas Deerinck and Mark Ellisman, NCMIR; **ribbon model** Mark J. Winter/Science Source; **p. xxxiv giraffe** Uryadnikov/Shutterstock; **tree** Aflo/Nature Picture Library; **p. xxxv mitosis** George von Dassow; **flower** John Swithinbank/Garden World Images/AGE Fotostock; **p. xxxvi DNA** Andrey Prokhorov/E+/Getty Images; **ribosome** Venki Ramakirshnan; **p. xxxvii viruses** Richard Bizley/Science Source; **membrane model** Dr. Ian Derrington; **pxxxviii caterpillar** Robert Sisson/National Geographic Stock; **tortoise** Pete Oxford/Nature Picture Library; **p. xxxix hot spring** Shaeri Mukherjee; **stentors** Eric V. Grave/Science Source; **p. xl fireweed** Lyn Topinka/USGS; **lizard** Stephen Dalton/Nature Picture Library; **p. xli coral reef** Image Quest Marine; **p. xlii bee** GFC Collection/Alamy; **snowflake plant** Giuseppe Mazza; **p. xliii otter** Jeff Foott/Discovery Channel Images/Getty Images; **elephant seals** Phillip Colla/Oceanlight.com; **p. xlv lizard** Pete Oxford/Nature Picture Library; **synapses** Image by Sebastian Jessberger, Fred H. Gage, Laboratory of Genetics LOG-G, The Salk Institute for Biological Studies; **p. xlvi turtles** Harpe/Robert Harding World Imagery; **p. xlvii fox** Jordi Bas Casas/NHPA/Photoshot.

Unit Opening Interviews **UNIT I p. 27 portrait** Courtesy of Venki Ramakrishnan; **ribosome model** Courtesy of Venki Ramakrishnan. From V. Ramakrishnan, What we have learned from ribosome structures (The Heatley Medal Lecture), *Biochem. Soc. Trans.* 2008 Aug;36(4):567–574 (2008). **UNIT II p. 92 portrait** Haifan Lin; **Piwi protein** Haifan Lin; **UNIT III p. 251 portrait** National Human Genome Research Institute; **villagers** Nigel Pavitt/John Warburton-Lee Photography/Alamy; **UNIT IV p. 461 portrait** Josh Frost, Pearson Education; **mouse** J. B. Miller/Florida Park Service; **UNIT V p. 546 portrait** Josh Frost, Pearson Education; **choanoflagellates** Nicole King; **UNIT VI p. 751 portrait** Jeff Dangl Lab; *Arabidopsis* Daniel Aviv, Jeff Dangl Lab; **UNIT VII p. 866 portrait** Ulrike Heberlein; **laboratory setup** Ulrike Heberlein; **UNIT VIII p. 1157 portrait** Josh Frost, Pearson Education; **recovery after fire** Courtesy of Monica Turner.

Chapter 22 **22.1** Robert Sisson/National Geographic Stock; **p. 462** Corinne Lamontagne; **22.2 fossils** PD image: Skeleton of the Rhinoceros unicorne de Java in the Paris Museum of Natural History. From G. Cuvier, *Recherches sur les ossemens fossiles*, Atlas, pl. 17 (1836); **frog** Alfred Russel Wallace Memorial Fund; **Wallace** The Natural History Museum, London/Alamy; **iguana** Wayne Lynch/AGE Fotostock; **book page** American Museum of Natural History; **22.4** Karen Moskowitz/Stone/Getty Images; **22.5 left** ARCHIV/Science Source; **right** Stanley Owen; **22.6a** Michael Gunther/Science Source; **22.6b** David Hosking/Frank Lane Picture Agency; **22.6c** David Hoskin/Alamy; **22.7** Wikimedia Commons; **22.9 brussels sprouts** Paul Rapson/Alamy; **cabbage** Izaokas Sapiro/iStockphoto; **broccoli** YinYang/iStockphoto; **kale** Robert Sarno/IStockphoto; **kohlrabi** floricica buzlea/iStockphoto; **22.10** Laura Jesse; **22.11** Richard Packwood/Oxford Scientific/Getty Images; **22.12 top to bottom** Edward S. Ross; Gallo Images/the Agency Collection/Getty Images; Mark Taylor/Nature Picture Library; **22.13** Scott P. Carroll; **22.16a** Dr. Keith Wheeler/Science Source; **22.16b** Lennart Nilsson/Scanpix Sweden AB; **22.18 left** ANT Photo Library/Science Source; **right** Joe McDonald/Steve Bloom Images/Alamy; **22.19** Chris Linz, Thewissen Lab, Northeastern Ohio University College of Medicine; **p. 479** John Cancalosi/Nature Picture Library.

Chapter 23 **23.1** Sylvain Cordier/Biosphoto/Science Source; **p. 480** Rosemary B. Grant; **23.3** David Stoecklein/AGE fotostock; **23.5** Erick Greene, University of Montana; **23.6 left** Gary Schultz/Photoshot Holdings; **right** James L. and Roxie Davis; **p. 487** Scott Sinklier/AgStock Images, Inc./Alamy; **23.11** William Ervin/Science Source; **23.12** Jan Visser; **23.14** Bruce Coleman/Photoshot Holdings; **23.15** Dave Blackey/AGE fotostock; **23.17 people** Caroline Penn/Alamy; **blood cells** Eye of Science/Science Source; **mosquito** Kletr/Shutterstock; **p. 499** Thomas & Pat Leeson/Science Source.

Chapter 24 **24.1** Mark Jones/AGE Fotostock; **p. 500** Pete Oxford/Nature Picture Library; **24.2a left** Malcolm Schuyl/Alamy; **right** Wave RF/Getty Images; **24.2b top left to right** Robert Kneschke/iStockphoto; Justin Horrocks/iStockphoto; Ryan McVay/Getty Images; **bottom left to right** Photodisc/Getty Images; Photodisc/Getty Images; Masterfile; **24.3a,b** Joe McDonald/Photoshot; **24.3c** Hogle Zoo; **24.3d** APHIS/USDA; **24.3e** Michael Dietrich/Alamy; **24.3f** Takahiro Asami; **24.3g** William E. Furguson; **24.3h** Charles W. Brown; **24.3i** EyeWire Collection/Getty Images; **23.3j** Corbis; **24.3k** Dawn YL/Fotolia; **24.3l** Kazutoshi Okuno; **24.4 grizzly** CLFProductions/Shutterstock; **polar** Boris Karpinski/Alamy; **hybrid** Troy Maben/AP Images; **24.6** From R. B. Langerhans, Morphology, performance, fitness: Functional insight into a post-Pleistocene radiation of mosquitofish, *Biology Letters* 5(4):488–491 (2009). **24.8 map** Visible Earth (http://visibleearth.nasa.gov/), NASA; **shrimp** Arthur Anker; **p. 507** John Shaw/NHPA/Photoshot; **24.11** Ole Seehausen; **p. 510** Phil Huntley-Franck; **24.12** Jeroen Speybroeck, Research Institute for Nature and Forest, Belgium; **24.15** Ole Seehausen; **24.17** Jason Rick and Loren Rieseberg; **24.19** Reprinted by permission from H. D. Bradshaw and D. W. Schemske, Allele substitution at a flower colour locus produces a pollinator shift in monkeyflowers, *Nature* 426(6963):176–178 (2003), Copyright © 2003. Macmillan Magazines Limited; **p. 518** Thomas Marent/Rolf Nussbaumer Photography/Alamy.

Chapter 25 **25.1** Gerhard Boeggemann; **p. 519** Rebecca Hunt; **25.3** D. S. Kelley, University of Washington; **25.4b** F. M. Menger and Kurt Gabrielson, Emory University; **25.4c** M. Hanczyc; **25.5 left top to bottom** Seelevel.com; Roger Jones; S. M. Awramik/Biological Photo Service; Sinclair Stammers/Science Source; **25.5 right top to bottom** Specimen No. 12478, Markus Moser, Staatliches Museum fur Naturkunde Stuttgart; Ted Daeschler/Academy of Natural Sciences/VIREO; Chip Clark; Lisa-Ann Gershwin, University of California, Berkeley, Museum of Paleontology; Andrew H. Knoll, Harvard University; **25.12** Remy W., Taylor T. N., Hass H., Kerp H./*Proceedings of the National Academy of Sciences*; **p. 532** Biophoto Associates/Science Source; **25.22 top center** Bruce G. Baldwin; **all others** Gerald D. Carr; **25.23** Jean Kern; **25.24** Juniors Bildarchiv/Alamy; **25.26 top** David Horsley; **bottom** Mike Shapiro; **25.27** Sinclair Stammers/Science Source; **p. 545** Solent News/Splash News/Newscom.

Chapter 26 **26.1** John Cancalosi/AGE Fotostock; **26.17a** Courtesy Dept. of Library Services, American Museum of Natural History; **26.17b** Ed Heck; **26.22** Ilias Strachinis/Shutterstock; **p. 564** Nigel Cattlin/Alamy; **p. 566** David Fleetham/Nature Picture Library. Solent News/Splash News/Newscom.

Chapter 27 **27.1** Zastolskiy Victor/Shutterstock; **27.2a** Centers for Disease Control and Prevention (CDC); **27.2b** Kari Lounatmaa/Science Source; **27.2c** Stem Jems/Science Source; **27.3** L. Brent Selinger; **27.4** Dr. Immo Rantala/SPL/Science Source; **27.5** H. S. Pankratz, T. C. Beaman/Biological Photo Service; **27.6** Kwangshin Kim/Science Source; **27.7** Julius Adler; **27.8a** S. W. Watson; **27.8b** N. J. Lang/Biological Photo Service; **27.9** Huntington Potter; **27.12** Charles C. Brinton, Jr.; **27.14** Susan M. Barns, Ph.D.; **27.16 p. 578 top to bottom** L. Evans/Biological Photo Service; Yuichi Suwa; National Library of Medicine; From P. L. Grilione and J. Pangborn, Scanning electron microscopy of fruiting body formation by myxobacteria, *J. Bacteriol.* 124(3):1558–1565 (1975); Science Source; **27.16 p. 579 top to bottom** Moredon Animal Health/SPL/Science Source; CNRI/SPL/Science Source; Culture Collection CCALA, Institute of Botany, Academy of Sciences Dukelska, Czech Republic; Paul Hoskisson, Strathclyde Institute of Pharmacy and Biomedical Sciences, Glasgow, Scotland; David M. Phillips/Science Source; **27.17** Shaeri Mukherjee; **27.18** Pascale Frey-Klett; **27.19** Ken Lucas/Biological Photo Service; **27.20 left to right** Scott Camazine/Science Source; David M. Phillips/Science Source; James Gathany/CDC; **27.21** Metabolix Media; **27.22** ExxonMobil Corporation; **p. 584** igor.stevanovic/Shutterstock; **27.23** Kathleen Spuhler; **p. 586** G. Wanner/ScienceFoto/Getty Images.

Chapter 28 **28.1** Brian S. Leander; **p. 587** Eric V. Grave/Science Source; **p. 589** Marbury/Shutterstock; **28.2** Joel Mancuso, University of California, Berkeley; **28.2 p. 591 left top to bottom** M. I. Walker/NHPA/Photoshot; NOAA; Howard Spero, University of California-Davis; **right top to bottom** David J. Patterson/micro*scope; Kim Taylor/Nature Picture Library; Michael Abbey/Science Source; **28.4** Ken-ichiro Ishida; **28.5** David M. Phillips/Science Source; **28.6** David J. Patterson; **28.7** Oliver Meckes/Science Source; **28.8** David J. Patterson; **28.9** Centers for Disease Control and Prevention; **28.10** Steve Gschmeissner/Science Source; **28.11** Stephen Durr; **28.12** Colin Bates; **28.13** J.R. Waaland/Biological Photo Service; **28.14** Guy Brugerolle; **28.15a** Virginia Institute of Marine Science; **28.15b** Bill Bachman / Science Source; **28.16** Masamichi Aikawa; **28.17** M. I. Walker/Science Source; **28.18** Robert Brons/Biological Photo Service; **28.19** Juan Carlos Munoz/Nature Picture Library; **28.20** Eva Nowack; **28.21 top to bottom** D. P. Wilson, Eric and David Hosking/Science Source; Michael D. Guiry; Biophoto Associates/Science Source; David Murray/DK Images; **28.22a** Laurie Campbell/Photoshot/NHPA Limited; **28.22b** David L. Ballantine; **28.23** William L. Dentler; **28.25** Ken Hickman; **28.26** Robert Kay; **28.27** Kevin Carpenter and Patrick Keeling; **28.28** Dave Rizzo; **p. 611** Biophoto Associates/Science Source.

Chapter 29 **29.1** Exactostock/SuperStock; **p. 612** Belinda Images/SuperStock; **p. 613** S. C. Mueller and R. M. Brown, Jr.; **29.3 multicellular embryos left** Dr. Linda E. Graham; **right** Karen S. Renzaglia; **walled spores left** Alan S. Heilman; **right** Michael Clayton; **multicellular gametangia** David John Jones; **apical meristems left** Centers for Disease Control and Prevention; **right** Ed Reschke/Peter Arnold/Getty Images; **29.4** Charles H. Wellman; **p. 616** Dianne Edwards, Cardiff University, UK; **29.6** Laurie Knight; **29.7 top left to right** Alvin E. Staffan/Science Source; Dr. Linda E. Graham; Hidden Forest; **bottom left to right** Hidden Forest; Tony Wharton/Frank Lane Picture Agency/Corbis Images; **p. 621** Bill and Nancy Malcolm; **29.9a** Brian Lightfoot/AGE Fotostock; **29.9b** Christophe Boisvieux/AGE Fotostock; **p. 623** Richard Becker/FLPA; **29.10** Hans Kerp; **29.12 top** apflora.com; **bottom** www.a-p-h-o-t-o.com; **29.13 top left to right** Jody Banks, Purdue University; Murray Fagg, Australian National Botanic Gardens; Helga and Kurt Rasbach; **bottom left to right** Jon Meier/iStockphoto; Stephen P. Parker/Science Source; Francisco Javier Yeste Garcia; **29.14** Open University, Department of Earth Sciences; **p. 628 top** Ed Reschke/Peter Arnold/Getty Images; **bottom** Michael Clayton; **p. 629** W. Barthlott.

Chapter 30 **30.1** Lyn Topinka/USGS; **p. 630** Marlin Harms 2011; **p. 633** Guy Eisner; **30.6** Copyright ESRF/PNAS/C. Soriano; **30.7 cycad** Johannes Greyling/iStockphoto; **ginkgo seeds** Kurt Stueber; *Welwitschia* **plant** Jeroen Peys/iStockphoto; *Welwitschia* **cones** Thomas Schoepke; *Gnetum* Michael Clayton; *Ephedra* Bob Gibbons/FLPA; **Douglas fir** vincentlouis/Fotolia; **larch** Adam Jones/Getty Images; **sequoia** Tips Images/Tips Italia Srl a socio unico/Alamy; **juniper** Svetlana Tikhonova/Shutterstock; *Wollemia* **fossil** Jaime Plaza, Royal Botanic Gardens Sydney; *Wollemia* **pine** Jaime Plaza, Royal Botanic Gardens Sydney/AP Photo; **bristlecone pine** Russ Bishop/Alamy; **30.9 daffodil** Zee/Fotolia; **orchid** Paul Atkinson/Shutterstock; **stamens** Richard Katz, Flower Essence Society, used by permission; **carpels** www.a-p-h-o-t-o.com; **30.10 tomato** Dave King/DK Images; **grapefruit** Andy Crawford/DK Images; **nectarine** Dave King/DK Images; **hazelnuts** Diana

Taliun/Fotolia; **milkweed** Maria Dryfhout/iStockphoto; **30.11 explosive seed dispersal** Michael J. W. Davis; **maple fruits** PIXTAL/AGE Fotostock; **mouse** Eduard Kyslynskyy/Shutterstock; Derek Hall/DK Images; **dog** Scott Camazine/Science Source; **30.13** David L. Dilcher; **30.15** D. Wilder; **30.17 water lily** Howard Rice/DK Images; **star anise** Jack Scheper, Floridata.com; **Amborella** Joel R. McNeal; **magnolia** Andrew Butler/DK Images; **orchid** Eric Crichton/DK Images; **palm** John Dransfield; **barley** kenjii/Fotolia; **snow pea** Howard Rice/DK Images; **dog rose** Glam/Shutterstock; **oak** Matthew Ward/DK Images; **30.18** NASA images courtesy of USGS Landsat Team; **p. 647** Dartmouth Electron Microscope Facility.

Chapter 31 **31.1** Georg Müller; **p. 648** Philippe Clement/Nature Picture Library; **31.2 top** Nata-Lia/Shutterstock; **bottom** Fred Rhoades; **inset** George Barron; **31.4** G. L. Barron and N. Allin/Biological Photo Service; **p. 651** DOE photo; **31.6 left** Popovaphoto/Dreamstime; **right** Biophoto Associates/Science Source; **31.7** Stephen J. Krons; **31.9** From D. Redecker, R. Kodner, and L. E. Graham, Glomalean: Fungi from the Ordovician, *Science* 289:1920–1921 (2000); **31.10 top to bottom** John Taylor; Ray Watson; Reproduced by permission from E. T. Kiers and M. G. van der Heijden, Mutualistic stability in the arbuscular mycorrhizal symbiosis: Exploring hypotheses of evolutionary cooperation, *Ecology* 87(7):1627–1636 (2006): Fig. 1a. Image by Marcel van der Heijden, Swiss Federal Research Station for Agroecology and Agriculture. Copyright © 2006, Ecological Society of America; Lenz/blickwinkel/Alamy; Phil Dotson/Science Source; **31.11** William E. Barstow; **31.12 left top to bottom** Antonio D'Albore/iStockPhoto; Alena Kubátová; Dr. George L. Barron; **right** Ed Reschke/Peter Arnold/Getty Images; **31.13** G. L. Barron/Biological Photo Service; **31.14** M. F. Brown/Biological Photo Service; **31.15 left** Douglas Adams/iStockphoto; **right** Viard/Jacana/Science Source; **31.16** Fred Spiegel; **31.17 top to bottom** Frank Paul/Alamy; Michael and Patricia Fogden/Terra/Corbis; Fletcher and Baylis/Science Source; **31.18** Biophoto Associates/Science Source; **31.19** University of Tennessee Entomology and Plant Pathology; **31.21** Mark Bowler/Science Source; **31.22 top to bottom** Wild-Worlders of Europe/Nature Picture Library; Geoff Simpson/Nature Picture Library; Ralph Lee Hopkins/Getty Images; **31.23** Eye of Science/Science Source; **31.24a** Scott Camazine/Alamy; **31.24b** Peter Chadwick/DK Images; **31.24c** Hecker-Sauer/AGE Fotostock; **31.25** Vance T. Vredenburg, San Francisco State University; **31.26** From The production of myco-diesel hydrocarbons and their derivatives by the endophytic fungus *Gliocladium roseum* (NRRL 50072). Strobel et al. *Microbiology.* 2008 Nov;154(11:3319-3328. Cover image; **p. 666** Erich G. Vallery, USDA Forest Service - SRS-4452, Bugwood.org.

Chapter 32 **32.1** Stephen Dalton/Nature Picture Library; **p. 667** Nigel Downer/NHPA/Photoshot Holdings Ltd.; **32.5** The Museum Board of South Australia 2004 Photographer: Dr. J. Gehling; **32.6** From S. Bengtson and Y. Zhao, Predatorial borings in late precambrian mineralized exoskeletons, *Science* 257(5068):367–369 (1992), Fig. 3d; **32.7 left** Chip Clark; **right** J. Sibbick/The Natural History Museum, London; **32.12** Kent Wood/Science Source; **p. 679** WaterFrame/Alamy.

Chapter 33 **33.1** Image Quest Marine; **33.3 p. 681 sponge** Andrew J. Martinez/Science Source; **jelly** Robert Brons/Biological Photo Service; **acoel** Teresa Zuberbühler; **placozoan** Stephen Dellaporta; **ctenophore** Gregory G. Dimijian/Science Source; **flatworm** Amar and Isabelle Guillen/Alamy; **ectoproct** Hecker/AGE Fotostock; **rotifer** W. I. Walker/Science Source; **brachiopod** Kåre Telnes/Image Quest Marine; **p. 682 acanthocephalan** Neil Campbell, University of Aberdeen; **ribbon worm** Erling Svensen/UWPhoto ANS; **cycliophoran** Peter Funch; **annelid** Fredrik Pleijel; **octopus** photonimo/iStockphoto; **loriciferan** Reinhart Mobjerg Kristensen; **priapulan** Erling Svensen/UWPhoto ANS; **p. 683 onychophoran** Thomas Stromberg; **roundworm** London Scientific Films/Getty Images; **tardigrades** Andrew Syred/Science Source; **scorpion** Tim Flach/Getty Images; **acorn worm** Leslie Newman and Andrew Flowers/Science Source; **tunicate** Robert Brons/Biological Photo Service; **sea urchin** Robert Harding World Imagery/Alamy; **33.4** Andrew J. Martinez/Science Source; **33.7a left** Robert Brons/Biological Photo Service; **right** David Doubilet/National Geographic Creative/Getty Images; **33.7b left** Neil G. McDaniel/Science Source; **right** Mark Conlin/V&W/Image Quest Marine; **33.8** Robert Brons/Biological Photo Service; **33.9a** Amar and Isabelle Guillen/Alamy; **33.9b** blickwinkel/Alamy; **33.9c** From S. E. Fredrick and E. H. Newcomb, *The Journal of Cell Biology* 43:343 (1969). Provided by E. H. Newcomb; **33.9d** MedicalRF.com/Alamy; **33.11** Centers for Disease Control and Prevention; **33.12** Eye of Science/Science Source; **33.13** W. I. Walker/Science Source; **33.14a** Hecker/AGE Fotostock; **33.14b** Kåre Telnes/Image Quest Marine; **33.16** Dray van Beeck/Image Quest Marine; **33.17a** Amruta Bhelke/Dreamstime LLC; **33.17b** Corbis Images; **p. 694** Christophe Courteau/Nature Picture Library; **33.18** Harold W. Pratt/Biological Photo Service; **33.20 top to bottom** Mark Conlin/V&W/Image Quest Marine; photonimo/iStockphoto; Jonathan Blair/Corbis; **33.21** Photograph courtesy of the U.S. Bureau of Fisheries (1919) and Illinois State Museum; **33.22** Fredrik Pleijel; **33.23** C. Wolcott Henry III/Getty Images; **33.24** Astrid and Hanns-Frieder Michler/Science Source; **33.25** A.N.T./Photoshot/NHPA Limited; **33.26** London Scientific Films/Getty Images; **33.27** SPL/Science Source; **33.28** Collection of Dan Cooper; **33.29** J. K. Grenier et al., Evolution of the entire arthropod Hox gene set predated the origin and radiation of the onychophoran/arthropod clade, *Curr. Biol.* 7(8):547–553 (1997), Fig. 3c; **33.31** Mark Newman/Frank Lane Picture Agency Limited; **33.32 top to bottom** Tim Flach/Getty Images; Andrew Syred/Science Source; Eric Lawton/iStockphoto; **33.33a** PREMAPHOTOS/Nature Picture Library; **33.33b** Tom McHugh/Science Source; **33.35** Maximilian Weinzierl/Alamy; **33.36** Peter Herring/Image Quest Marine; **33.37** Peter Parks/Image Quest Marine; **33.39** Meul/Nature Picture Library; **33.40a,b,d,e** Cathy Keifer/Shutterstock; **33.40c** Jim Zipp/Science Source; **33.41 left top to bottom** PREMAPHOTOS/Nature Picture Library; Bruce Marlin; John Cancalosi/Nature Picture Library; Hans Christoph Kappel/Nature Picture Library; **right top to bottom** Kevin Murphy; Perry Babin; Dante Fenolio/Science Source; Michael and Patricia Fogden/Corbis; **33.42** Andrey Nekrasov/Image Quest Marine; **33.43** Daniel Janies; **33.44** Jeff Rotman/Science Source; **33.45** Robert Harding World Imagery/Alamy; **33.46** Jurgen Freund/Nature Picture Library; **33.47** Hal Beral/Corbis; **p. 711** Lucy Arnold.

Chapter 34 **34.1** Derek Siveter; **34.4** Heather Angel/Natural Visions/Alamy; **34.5** Robert Brons/Biological Photo Service; **34.7** Tom McHugh/Science Source; **34.8** Marevision/AGE Fotostock; **inset** A Hartl/AGE Fotostock; **34.9** Nanjing Institute of Geology and Palaeontology; **34.13** The Field Museum; **34.14a** Carlos Villoch/Image Quest Marine; **34.14b** Masa Ushioda/Image Quest Marine; **34.14c** Andy Murch/Image Quest Marine; **34.16 top to bottom** James D. Watt/Image Quest Marine; Jez Tryner/Image Quest Marine; George Grall/Getty Images; Fred McConnaughey/Science Source; **34.17** From M. Zhu et al., The oldest articulated osteichthyan reveals mosaic gnathostome characters, *Nature* 458(7237):469–474 (2009); **34.18** Arnaz Mehta; **34.19 head, ribs, scales** Ted Daeschler/Academy of Natural Sciences/VIREO; **34.19 fin** Kalliopi Monoyios; **34.21a** Alberto Fernandez/AGE Fotostock; **34.21b** Dr. Paul A. Zahl/Science Source; **34.21c** Bruce Coleman/Photoshot Holdings Ltd.; **34.22a** Stephen Dalton/Science Source; **34.22b** Dave Pressland/FLPA; **34.22c** John Cancalosi/Getty Images; **34.23** Michael and Patricia Fogden/Corbis Images; **34.26** Nobumichi Tamura; **34.27** Michael and Patricia Fogden/Corbis Images; **34.28a** Medford Taylor/National Geographic Stock; **34.28b** Natural Visions/Alamy; **34.28c** Matt T. Lee; **34.28d** Nick Garbutt/Nature Picture Library; **34.28e** Carl and Ann Purcell/Corbis; **34.29 left** Visceralimage/Dreamstime LLC; **right** Janice Sheldon; **34.31** Russell Mountford/Alamy; **34.32** DLILLC/Corbis; **34.33** Yufeng Zhou/iStockphoto; **34.34 left** McPHOTO/AGE Fotostock; **right** paolo barbanera/AGE Fotostock; **34.35** Gianpiero Ferrari/Frank Lane Picture Agency Limited; **34.37 left** clearviewstock/Shutterstock; **right** Mervyn Griffiths/Commonwealth of Scientific and Industrial Research Organization; **34.38a** John Cancalosi/Alamy; **34.38b** Martin Harvey/Alamy; **34.41** J & C Sohns/AGE Fotostock; **34.43a** Kevin Schafer/AGE Fotostock; **34.43b** J & C Sohns/Picture Press/Getty Images; **34.44a** Morales/AGE Fotostock; **34.44b** Anup Shah/Image State/Alamy; **34.44c** T. J. Rick/Nature Picture Library; **34.44d** E. A. Janes/AGE Fotostock; **34.44e** Martin Harvey/Peter Arnold/Getty Images; **34.46** T. White/David L. Brill Photography; **34.47a** John Reader/SPL/Science Source; **34.47b** John Gurche Studios; **p. 745** GOLFX / Shutterstock; **34.48** Prof. Alan Walker; **p. 746** David L. Brill/David L. Brill Photography; **34.50** Professor Chris Henshilwood; **p. 751** Tony Heald/Nature Picture Library.

Chapter 35 **35.1** O. Bellini/Shutterstock; **p. 752** John Walker; **35.3** Dr. Jeremy Burgess/Science Source; **35.4 prop roots** Natalie Bronstein; **storage roots** Rob Walls/Alamy; **pneumatophores** YinYang/iStockphoto; **strangling roots** Piotr Powietrzynski/Travel/Alamy; **buttress roots** Karl Weidmann/Science Source; **35.5 top to bottom** Donald Gregory Clever; DK Images; Aflo Foto Agency/Alamy; **35.7 top to bottom** Neil Cooper/Alamy; Martin Ruegner/Thinkstock; Gusto Production/SPL/Science Source; Mike Zens/Corbis; **p. 756** DK Images; **35.9** Steve Gschmeissner/SPL/Alamy; **35.10 parenchyma** M. I. (Spike) Walker/Alamy; **collenchyma** Clouds Hill Imaging/Last Refuge Limited; **sclerenchyma (both)** Graham Kent; **water conducting cells** N. C. Brown Center for Ultrastructure Studies, SUNY-Environmental Science and Forestry, Syracuse, NY; **micrograph** Brian Gunning; **longitudinal view** Professor Ray F. Evert; **sieve plate** Graham Kent; **35.13** From C. Li et al., *Arabidopsis* TCP20 links regulation of growth and cell division control pathways, *Proc. Natl. Acad. Sci. U S A* 102(36):12978–12983 (2005). Epub 2005 Aug 25. Photo: Peter Doerner; **35.14a top** Ed Reschke/Peter Arnold/Getty Images; **bottom** Natalie Bronstein; **35.15b** Ed Reschke; **35.15** Michael Clayton; **35.16** Michael Clayton; **35.17a** Ed Reschke/Peter Arnold/Getty Images; **35.17b** Ed Reschke/Peter Arnold/Getty Images; **35.18b** Ed Reschke; **35.18c** Ed Reschke/Peter Arnold/Getty Images; **35.19 left** Michael Clayton; **right** Alison W. Roberts; **35.23** California Historical Society Collection (CHS-1177), University of Southern California on behalf of the USC Specialized Libraries and Archival Collections; **p. 770** Reproduced by permission from J. Braam, *Cell* 60 (9 February 1990): Cover. Copyright ©1990 Cell Press. Image courtesy of Elsevier Sciences Ltd.; **35.26** From P. Dhonukshe et al., Microtubule plus-ends reveal essential links between intracellular polarization and localized modulation of endocytosis during division-plane establishment in plant cells, *BMC Biol.* 3:11 (2005); **35.27** From L. G. Smith et al., The tangled-1 mutation alters cell division orientations throughout maize leaf development without altering leaf shape, *Development* 122(2):481–489 (1996); **35.29** From figure 1a in U. Mayer et al., *Development* 117(1):149–162 (1993), © 1993 The Company of Biologists Ltd.; **35.30 left** B. Wells and K. Roberts; **35.30 right** From P. Dhonukshe et al., Microtubule plus-ends reveal essential links between intracellular polarization and localized modulation of endocytosis during division-plane establishment in plant cells, *BMC Biol.* 3:11 (2005); **35.31** Reproduced by permission from figure 1 in D. Hareven et al., *Cell* 84(5):735–744 (1996), Copyright © 1996 by Elsevier Science Ltd.; **35.32** Reproduced by permission from Figure 2g in Hung et al., *Plant Physiology* 117:73–84 (1998), Copyright © 1998 by the American Society of Plant Biologists. Image courtesy from John Schiefelbein/University of Michigan; **35.33** J. B. Friday; **35.34** E. M. Meyerowitz and J. Bowman, *Development* 112:1–231.2 (1991). Division of Biology, California Institute of Technology; **p. 777 left** Peter Kitin; **right** Biophoto Associates/Science Source.

Chapter 36 **36.1** Dennis Frates/Alamy; **p. 778** Bjorn Svensson/Science Source; **36.3** Rolf Rutishauser; **p. 784** Nigel Cattlin/Holt Studios International/Science Source; **36.9** Scott Camazine/Science Source; **36.12** Jeremy Burgess/SPL/Science Source; **36.14 leafless ocotillo** Mlane/Dreamstime; **green ocotillo plant** Kate Shane, Southwest School of Botanical Medicine; **ocotillo leaves** Steven Baskauf, Nature Conservancy Tennessee Chapter Headquarters; **oleander LM** Natalie Bronstein; **oleander flower** Andrew de Lory/DK Images; **cactus** Danita Delimont/Alamy; **36.17** M. H. Zimmermann, courtesy of Professor P. B. Tomlinson, Harvard University; **36.18** From L. Stavolone et al., A coiled-coil interaction mediates cauliflower mosaic virus cell-to-cell movement, *Proc. Natl. Acad. Sci. U S A* 102(17):6219–6224 (2005). Epub 2005 Apr 18; **p. 798** Catalin Petolea/Alamy.

Chapter 37 **37.1** Noah Elhardt; **inset** Wilhelm Barthlott; **p. 799** Bartosz Jan Plachno, Dept. of Plant Cytology and Embryology, Jagiellonian University, Poland; **37.2** USDA/Agricultural Research Service; **37.4** National Oceanic and Atmospheric Administration (NOAA); **37.5** U.S. Geological Survey, Denver; **37.6** Kevin Horan/Getty Images; **p. 806** Nigel Cattlin/Science Source; **37.8** Philip J. White; **37.9** Sarah

Lydia Lebeis; **37.11** Scimat/Science Source; **37.13a left** Hugues B. Massicotte, University of Northern British Columbia Ecosystem Science and Management Program, Prince George, B.C., Canada; **right** Mark Brundrett (http://mycorrhizas.info); **37.13b** Mark Brundrett (http://mycorrhizas.info); **37.14 staghorn fern** David Wall/Alamy; **mistletoe** Ruud de Man/iStockphoto; *Rafflesia* A&J Visage/Alamy; **Indian pipe** Martin Shields/Alamy; **pitcher plants top** Philip Blenkinsop/DK Images; **bottom** Dr. Paul A. Zahl/Science Source; **sundew** Fritz Poking/FLPA/Corbis; **Venus flytraps left** Kim Taylor and Jane Burton/DK Images; **right** Biophoto Associates/Science Source; **p. 814** Wayne Forward/Mode Images/Alamy.

Chapter 38 **38.1** Perennou Nuridsany/Science Source; **p. 815** GFC Collection/Alamy; **38.3 musk mallow** Steve Taylor/ARPS/Alamy; **orchid** Tim Gainey/Alamy; **bloodroot** Marvin Dembinsky Photo Associates/Alamy; *Trillium* Tim Gainey/Alamy; **star of Bethlehem** Tim Gainey/Alamy; **bindweed** Mike Lane/Alamy; **stone plant** blickwinkel/Alamy; **quince** Nigel Cattlin/Alamy; **38.5 hazel flower left** Stephen Dalton/Photoshot/NHPA Limited; **right** WILDLIFE GmbH/Alamy; **dandelions** Bjorn Rorslett; **moth** Doug Backlund; **bat** Merlin D Tuttle, Bat Conservation International, www.batcon.org; **blowfly** Florian Andronache/Shutterstock; **hummingbird** Rolf Nussbaumer/Nature Picture Library; **38.6** W.Rauh, Nees Institute for Biodiversity of Plants; **38.10** blickwinkel/Alamy; **38.12 coconut seed** Kevin Schafer/Alamy; *Alsomitra* Aquiya/Fotolia; **dandelion** Steve Bloom Images/Alamy; **maple** Chrispo/Fotolia; **tumbleweed** Archives/iStockphoto; **puncture vine** California Department of Food and Agriculture's Plant Health and Pest Prevention Services; **squirrel** Alan Williams/Alamy; **feces** Kim A. Cabrera; **ant** Benoit Guénard; **38.13** Dennis Frates/Alamy; **p. 828** Toby Bradshaw; **38.14a** Marcel E. Dorken; **38.14b** Nobumitsu Kawakubo, Gifu University, Japan; **38.15** Meriel G. Jones, University of Liverpool, UK; **38.16** Andrew McRobb/DK Images; **38.17** Gary P. Munkvold; **38.18** Ton Koene/Robert Harding World Imagery; **p. 835** Dartmouth Electron Microscope Facility.

Chapter 39 **39.1** Courtesy of the De Moraes and Mescher Labs (photograph by Jason D. Smith); **39.4** Emilio Ereza/Alamy; **39.2** Natalie Bronstein; **39.6** From L. Galweiler et al., Regulation of polar auxin transport ATPIN1 in *Arabidopsis* vascular tissue, *Science* 282 (1998); **39.8** Malcolm B. Wilkins, University of Glasgow, Glasgow, Scotland, UK; **39.9a** Dr. Richard Amasino; **39.9b** Fred Jensen; **39.11 left** Mia Molvray; **right** Karen E. Koch; **39.13a** Kurt Stepnitz, DOE Plant Research Laboratory, Michigan State University; **39.13b** Joe Kieber, University of North Carolina; **39.14** Ed Reschke; **39.16** Nigel Cattlin/Alamy; **39.18** Martin Shields/Alamy; **39.22** Michael L. Evans; **39.23** Reproduced by permission from J. Braam, *Cell* 60 (1990): Cover. Copyright ©1990 Cell Press. Image courtesy of Elsevier Sciences Ltd.; **39.24** Martin Shields/Science Source; **39.25** J. L. Basq and M. C. Drew; **p. 858** sarsmis/Fotolia; **39.26** New York State Agricultural Experiment Station (NYSAES)/Cornell; **39.27 p. 862 poppy** Johan De Meester/Arterra Picture Library/Alamy; **crystals** David T. Webb, University of Hawaii; **leaf micrograph** Steve Gschmeissner/Science Source; **cactus** Susumu Nishinaga/Science Source; **snowflake plant** Giuseppe Mazza; **egg mimicry** Lawrence E. Gilbert, University of Texas-Austin; **39.27 p. 863 hummingbird** Danny Kessler; **bamboo** KJ/Mode Images/Alamy; **caterpillar and wasp** Custom Life Science Images/Alamy; **p. 866** Gary Crabbe/Alamy.

Chapter 40 **40.1** Matthias Wittlinger; **p. 861** Premaphotos/Alamy; **40.2a** Frank Greenaway/Dorling Kindersley/Getty Images; **40.2b** Duncan Usher/Alamy; **40.2c** Andre Seale/Image Quest Marine; **40.4 left** Eye of Science/Science Source; **top right** Susumu Nishinaga/Science Source; **bottom right** Susumu Nishinaga/Science Source; **40.5 p. 865** Steve Downing; **p. 866 left top to bottom** Nina Zanetti; Alamy; Nina Zanetti; **right top to bottom** Dr. Gopal Murti/SPL/Science Source; Nina Zanetti; Chuck Brown/Science Source; **p. 867 top right to left** Nina Zanetti; Ed Reschke/Peter Arnold/Getty Images; Ed Reschke/Peter Arnold/Getty Images; **bottom left to right** Ulrich Gartner; Thomas Deerinck; **40.7 top** Jeffrey Lepore/Science Source; **bottom** Neil McNicoll/Alamy; **40.10** Meiqianbao/Shutterstock; **40.11a** John Shaw/Science Source; **40.11b** Matt T. Lee; **40.14** Robert Ganz; **40.19** Jeff Rotman/Alamy; **p. 881** Andrew Cooper/Nature Picture Library; **40.21** Phil_Good/Fotolia; **p. 882 sunflowers** Phil_Good/Fotolia; **fly eyes** WildPictures/Alamy; **leaves** irin-k/Shutterstock; **bobcat** Thomas Kitchin and Victoria Hurst/All Canada Photos/AGE Fotostock; **plant** Bogdan Wankowicz/Shutterstock; **molting** Nature's Images/Science Source; **p. 883 xylem** Last Refuge/Robert Harding Picture Library/Alamy; **blood vessels** Susumu Nishinaga/Science Source; **root hairs** Rosanne Quinnell, The University of Sydney; **intestinal lining** David M. Martin, M.D./Science Source; **peas** Scott Rothstein/Shutterstock; **piglets** Walter Hodges/Lithium/AGE Fotostock; **spongy mesophyll** Rosanne Quinnell, The University of Sydney; **alveoli** David M. Phillips/Science Source; **p. 885** Oliver Wien/epa European Pressphoto Agency creative account/Alamy.

Chapter 41 **41.1** Jeff Foott/Discovery Channel Images/Getty Images; **41.3** Stefan Huwiler/Alamy; **41.5** Eric Isselee/Shutterstock; **41.6 whale** Hervey Bay Whale Watch; **caterpillar** Thomas Eisner; **mosquito** Lennart Nilsson/Scanpix Sweden AB; **python** Gunter Ziesler/Getty Images; **41.17 coyote** Fritz Polking/Alamy; **koala** EyeWire Collection/Getty Images; **41.18** Juergen Berger/Science Source; **p. 908** Peter Batson/Image Quest Marine; **p. 912** Jackson Laboratory; **p. 913** Eric Isselee/Shutterstock; **p. 914** Jack Moskovita/Jack Moskovita Photography.

Chapter 42 **42.1** Stephen Dalton/Science Source; **42.2a** Reinhard Dirscherl/WaterFrame/Getty Images; **42.2b** Eric Grave/Alamy; **42.9 top** From Human Histology Photo CD. Image courtesy Indigo Instruments; **bottom** Lennart Nilsson/Scanpix Sweden AB; **42.15** Biophoto Associates/Science Source; **42.18** Eye of Science/Science Source; **42.19** Image Source/SuperStock; **p. 932** Fotolia; **42.21a** Peter Batson/Image Quest Marine; **42.21b** Olgysha/Shutterstock; **42.21c** Jez Tryner/Image Quest Marine; **42.23** Prepared by Dr. Hong Y. Yan, University of Kentucky and Dr. Peng Chai, University of Texas; **42.24** Motta & Macchiarelli/Science Source; **42.26** Prof. Dr. Dr. Hans-Rainer Duncker, University of Giessen, Germany; **p. 943** Doug Allan/Nature Picture Library; **p. 945** Stefan Hetz, Supplied by WENN.com/Newscom.

Chapter 43 **43.1** SPL/Science Source; **p. 946** Juergen Berger/Science Source; **43.4** Dominique Ferrandon; **p. 958** David Scharf/Science Source; **p. 959** Image provided by Vern Carruthers, Bjorn Kafsack, and Sasha Meshinchi, University of Michigan; **43.21** Steve Gschmeissner/Science Source; **43.23** CNRI/Science Source; **p. 967** Eye of Science/Science Source; **p. 968** The Laboratory of Structural Cell Biology, headed by Stephen C. Harrison, Harvard Medical School, HHMI; **p. 970** Tatan Syuflana/AP Images.

Chapter 44 **44.1** David Wall/Alamy; **p. 969** David Wall/Alamy; **44.3** Mark Conlin/Image Quest Marine; **44.5** Eye of Science/Science Source; **p. 973** Jiri Lochman/Lochman Transparencies; **44.12** Steve Gschmeissner/Science Source; **44.15** Michael Fogden/Photoshot; **44.16** VL@/Fotolia; **44.17 fish** Roger Steene / Image Quest Marine; **frog** F1online digitale Bildagentur GmbH / Alamy; **stomata** Power and Syred / Science Source; **bacterium** Eye of Science / Science Source; **p. 990** Steven A. Wasserman.

Chapter 45 **45.1** Phillip Colla/Oceanlight.com; **p. 993** Craig K. Lorenz/Science Source; **45.3** Volker Witte; **p. 1001** George Grall/National Geographic Creative; **45.17** Astier/BSIP/Science Source; **45.18** AP Photo; **45.22a** Photoshot Holdings Ltd/Alamy; **45.22b** Jurgen and Christine Sohns/Frank Lane Picture Agency Limited; **p. 1012** Courtesy of Eric W. Roubos, Radboud University, Nymegen.

Chapter 46 **46.1** Colin Marshall/FLPA; **46.2** David Wrobel; **46.4** P. de Vries, courtesy of David Crews; **46.5** Andy Sands/Nature Picture Library; **46.6** John Cancalosi/Peter Arnold/Getty Images; **46.12** Pete Oxford/Nature Picture Library; **46.17** Lennart Nilsson/Scanpix Sweden AB; **46.21** Phanie/SuperStock; **p. 1036** Dave Thompson/AP Images.

Chapter 47 **47.1** Scanpix Sweden AB; **p. 1037** Oxford Scientific/Getty Images; **47.4 top** From V. D. Vacquier and J. E. Payne, Methods for quantitating sea urchin sperm-egg binding, *Exp. Cell Res.* 82(1):227–235 (1973); **bottom** From M. Hafner et al., Wave of free calcium at fertilization in the sea urchin egg visualized with Fura-2, *Cell Motil. Cytoskel.* 9:271–277 (1988); **47.6** George von Dassow; **47.7a** Jurgen Berger, SpemanMax Planck Campus Tubingen; **47.7b** Andrew J. Ewald, Johns Hopkins Medical School; **47.8** Charles A. Ettensohn; **47.14a** Huw Williams; **47.14c** Thomas Poole, SUNY Health Science Center; **47.15b** Dr. Keith Wheeler/Science Source; **47.18b** From H. Nishida, *Developmental Biology* 121: 526 (1987). Reprinted by permission of Academic Press; **47.20** Adapted from Strome, *International Review of Cytology* 114:81–123 (1989); **47.21** Adapted from Strome, *International Review of Cytology* 114:81–123 (1989); **47.25** Kathryn W. Tosney, University of Michigan; **47.26** Dennis Summerbell; **p. 1060** James Gerholdt/Peter Arnold/Getty Images.

Chapter 48 **48.1** Franco Banfi/Science Source; **48.3** Thomas Deerinck; **48.13** From Bear, Connors, and Paradiso, *Neuroscience: Exploring the Brain* © 1996, p. 43; **48.15** Edwin R. Lewis, Professor Emeritus, University of California-Berkeley; **p. 1078** B.A.E./Alamy.

Chapter 49 **49.1** Image by Tamily Weissman, Harvard University. The Brainbow mouse was produced by J. Livet et al., *Nature* 450:56–62 (2007); **49.4** Image by Sebastian Jessberger. Fred H. Gage, Laboratory of Genetics LOG-G, The Salk Institute for Biological Studies; **49.11** Larry Mulvehill/Corbis; **49.15** From M. T. Mitterschiffthaler et al., A functional MRI study of happy and sad affective states induced by classical music, *Hum. Brain Mapp.* 28(11):1150–1162 (2007); **49.18** Marcus E. Raichle, M.D., Washington University Medical Center; **p. 1092** From H. Bigelow, Dr. Harlow's Case of recovery from the passage of an iron bar through the head, *Am. Journal of the Med. Sci.* July 1850, XXXIX. Images from the History of Medicine (NLM); **49.24** Martin M. Rotker/Science Source; **p. 1100** Eric Delmar/E+/Getty Images.

Chapter 50 **50.1** Kenneth Catania; **50.6 top** R. A. Steinbrecht; **bottom** CSIRO; **50.7a** Michael Nolan/Robert Harding World Imagery; **50.7b** Grischa Georgiew/AGE Fotostock; **50.9** From R. Elzinga, *Fundamentals of Entomology*, 3rd ed., Prentice-Hall, Upper Saddle River, NJ (1987) ©1987, p. 185. Reprinted by permission of Prentice-Hall, Upper Saddle River, NJ; **50.10** SPL/Science Source; **50.16a** USDA/APHIS Animal and Plant Health Inspection Service; **50.17** Steve Gschmeissner/Science Source; **50.21** From K. Mancuso et al., Gene therapy for red-green colour blindness in adult primates, *Nature* 461(7265):784–787 (2009). Photo: Neitz Laboratory; **50.26** Professor Clara Franzini-Armstrong, University of Pennsylvania; **50.28** Dr. H. E. Huxley; **50.33** George Cathcart Photography; **50.38** Dave Watts/NHPA/Science Source; **p. 1130** Vance A. Tucker; **p. 1132** Dogs/Fotolia.

Chapter 51 **51.1** Manamana/Shutterstock; **p. 1133** Ivan Kuzmin/Alamy; **51.3** Denis-Huot/Hemis/Alamy; **51.5** Kenneth Lorenzen, UC Davis; **51.7a** Thomas D. McAvoy/Getty Images; **51.7b** Operation Migration – USA; **51.9** Lincoln Brower, Sweet Briar College; **51.11** Clive Bromhall/Oxford Scientific/Getty Images; **51.12** Richard Wrangham; **inset** Alissa Crandall/Corbis Images; **p. 1144** Matt Goff; **51.14a** Matt T. Lee; **51.14b** David Osborn/Alamy; **51.14c** David Tipling/Frank Lane Picture Agency Limited; **51.15** James D. Watt/Image Quest Marine; **51.16** Courtesy of Gerald S. Wilkinson; from G. S. Wilkinson and G. N. Dodson, In *The Evolution of Mating Systems in Insects and Arachnids*, eds. J. Choe and B. Crespi, Cambridge University Press, Cambridge, pp. 310–328 (1997); **51.17** Cyril Laubscher/DK Images; **51.20** Martin Harvey/Peter Arnold/Getty Images; **51.21** Erik Svensson, Lund University, Sweden; **51.22** Lowell Getz and Lisa Davis; **51.23** Rory Doolin; **51.25** Jennifer Jarvis; **51.27** Marie Read/NHPA/Photoshot; **51.28** Creatas/JupiterImages/Thinkstock/Getty Images; **p. 1156** William Leaman/Alamy.

Chapter 52 **52.1** Christopher C. Austin; **p. 1158** Christopher C. Austin; **52.2 top to bottom** NASA; William D. Bachman/Science Source; B. Tharp/Science Source; Susan Lee Powell; Barrie Britton/Nature Picture Library; James D. Watt/Alamy; **p. 1164 left** Dr. Randall Rosiere; **p. 1164 right** Rick Koval; **52.9 clockwise from top left** Joseph Sohm/AGE Fotostock; David Halbakken/AGE Fotostock; gary718/Shutterstock; Siepmann/Alamy; Bent Nordeng/Shutterstock; Juan Carlos Munoz/Nature Picture Library; **52.10 left** JTB Photo Communications, Inc./Alamy; **right** Krystyna Szulecka/Alamy; **52.11 tropical forest** Siepmann/Alamy; **desert** Joseph

also based on: Figure 1 from "A Kinetic Model of Phanerozoic Taxonomic Diversity. III. Post-Paleozoic Families and Mass Extinctions" by J. John Sepkoski, Jr., from *Paleobiology* Volume 10(2); and Figures 7.3a and 7.6 from *Evolution*, by Douglas J. Futuyma. Sinauer Associates, Inc., 2006; **25.19** Adaptation of Figure 3b from "A Long-Term Association between Global Temperature and Biodiversity, Origination and Extinction in the Fossil Record" by Peter J. Mayhew et al., from *Proceedings of the Royal Society B: Biological Sciences*, January 2008, Volume 275(1630): 47–53. Copyright © 2008 by the Royal Society. Reprinted with permission; **25.20** Adaptation of Figure 3 from "Anatomical and Ecological Constraints on Phanerozoic Animal Diversity in the Marine Realm" by Richard K. Bambach et al., from PNAS, May 2002, Volume 99(10). Copyright © 2002 by National Academy of Sciences. Reprinted with permission; **25.25** Adaptation of Figure 1a from "Hox Protein Mutation and Macroevolution of the Insect Body Plan" by Matthew Ronshaugen et al., from *Nature*, February 2002, Volume 415(6874). Copyright © 2002 by Macmillan Publishers Ltd. Reprinted with permission; **25.26** Source: Based on "Genetic and Developmental Basis of Evolutionary Pelvic Reduction in Threespine Sticklebacks" by Michael D. Shapiro et al., from *Nature*, April 2004, Volume 428(6984); **25.28** Adaptations of figure 3-1(a–d, f) from *Evolution*, 3rd Edition, by Monroe W. Strickberger. Copyright © 2005 by Jones & Bartlett Learning, Burlington, MA. Adapted with permission.

Chapter 26 **26.6** Adaptation of Figure 1 from "Which Whales Are Hunted? A Molecular Genetic Approach to Monitoring Whaling" by C. S. Baker and S. R. Palumbi, from *Science*, September 1994, Volume 265(5178). Copyright © 1994 by AAAS. Reprinted with permission; **26.13** Source: Based on Figure 3 from "The Evolution of the Hedgehog Gene Family in Chordates: Insights from Amphioxus Hedgehog" by Sebastian M. Shimeld, from *Developmental Genes and Evolution*, January 1999, Volume 209(1); **26.19** Adaptation of figure 4.3C from *Molecular Markers, Natural History, and Evolution*, 2nd Edition, by John C. Avise. Copyright © 2004 by Sinauer Associates, Inc. Reprinted with permission; **26.20** Adaptation of figure 1b from "Timing the Ancestor of the HIV-1 Pandemic Strains" by B. Korber et al., from *Science*, June 2000, Volume 288(5472). Copyright © 2000 by AAAS. Reprinted with permission; **26 SSE** Source: Based on "Lateral Transfer of Genes from Fungi Underlies Carotenoid Production in Aphids" by Nancy A. Moran and Tyler Jarvik, from *Science*, April 30, 2010, Volume 328(5978); **26.23** Adaptation of figure 3 from "Phylogenetic Classification and the Universal Tree" by W. Ford Doolittle, from *Science*, June 1999, Volume 284(5423). Copyright © 1999 by AAAS. Reprinted with permission.

Chapter 27 **27.10b** Adaptation of Figure 1 from "The Population Genetics of Ecological Specialization in Evolving *Escherichia coli* Populations" by Vaughn S. Cooper and Richard E. Lenski, from *Nature*, October 12, 2000, Volume 407(679). Copyright © 2000 by Macmillan Publishers Ltd. Reprinted with permission; **27.18** Source: Data from "Root-Associated Bacteria Contribute to Mineral Weathering and to Mineral Nutrition in Trees: A Budgeting Analysis" by Christophe Calvaruso et al., *Applied and Environmental Microbiology*, February 2006, Volume 72(2); **27.UnTable01** Source: Data from "Variation in the Effectiveness of Symbiotic Associations between Native Rhizobia and Temperate Australian *Acacia*: Within-Species Interactions" by J. J. Burdon et al., from *Journal of Applied Ecology*, June 1999, Volume 36(3); **p. 587 Quote** Source: *The Collected Letters of Antoni Van Leeuwenhoek* by Antoni van Leeuwenhoek, edited by a Committee of Dutch scientists. Swets & Zeitlinger, 1939.

Chapter 28 **28 SSE** Table 1 adapted from "Mitochondrial Origins" by D. Yang et al. from *Proceedings of the National Academy of Sciences USA*, July 1985, Volume 82: 4443–4447. Copyright © 1985 by D. Yang et al. Reprinted with permission; **28.2** Adaptation of Figure 2 from "The Number, Speed, and Impact of Plastid Endosymbioses in Eukaryotic Evolution" by Patrick J. Keeling, from *Annual Review of Plant Biology*, April 2013, Volume 64. Copyright © 2002 by Annual Reviews, Inc. Permission to reprint conveyed through Copyright Clearance Center, Inc.; **28.16** Adaptation of illustration by Kenneth X. Probst, from *Microbiology* by R.W. Bauman. Copyright © 2004 by Kenneth X. Probst. Reprinted with permission of the illustrator; **28.24** Source: Based on "Rooting the Eukaryote Tree by Using a Derived Gene Fusion" by Alexandra Stechmann and Thomas Cavalier-Smith, from *Science*, July 2002, Volume 297(5578); **28.30** Source: Based on "Global Phytoplankton Decline over the Past Century" by Daniel G. Boyce et al., from *Nature*, July 29, 2010, Volume 466(7306); and authors' personal communications.

Chapter 29 **29.8** Source: Data from "Inputs, Outputs, and Accumulation of Nitrogen in an Early Successional Moss (*Polytrichum*) Ecosystem" by Richard J. Bowden, from *Ecological Monographs*, June 1991, Volume 61(2); **29 SSE** Source: Data from "First Plants Cooled the Ordovician" by Timothy M. Lenton et al., from *NatureGeoscience*, February 2012, Volume 5(2); **29.UnTable02** Source: Data from "Nitrogen Fixation Increases with Successional Age in Boreal Forests" by O. Zackrisson et al., from *Ecology*, December 2004, Volume 85(12).

Chapter 30 **30 SSE** Source: Data from "Germination, Genetics, and Growth of an Ancient Date Seed" by Sarah Sallon et al., from *Science*, June 2008, Volume 320(5882); **30.14a** Adaptation of Figure 3b from "A Long-Term Association between Global Temperature and Biodiversity, Origination and Extinction in the Figure" adapted from "A Revision of *Williamsoniella*" by T. M. Harris, from *Proceedings of the Royal Society B: Biological Sciences*, October 1944, Volume 231(583): 313–328. Copyright © 2008 by the Royal Society. Reprinted with permission; **30.14b** Adaptation of Figure 2.3 *Phylogeny and Evolution of Angiosperm*, 2nd Edition, by Douglas E. Soltis et al. Copyright © 2005 by Sinauer Associates, Inc. Reprinted with permission.

Chapter 31 **31.UnTable02** Source: Data from "Arbuscular Mycorrhizal Fungi Ameliorate Temperature Stress in Thermophilic Plants" by Rebecca Bunn et al., from *Ecology*, May 2009, Volume 90(5); **31.20a** Adaption of figures 4 and 5 from "Fungal Endophytes Limit Pathogen Damage in a Tropical Tree" by A. Elizabeth Arnold et al., PNAS, December 2003, Volume 100(26). Copyright © 2003 by National Academy of Sciences. Reprinted with permission; **31.25** Adaption of figure 1 from "Reversing Introduced Species Effects: Experimental Removal of Introduced Fish Leads to Rapid Recovery of a Declining Frog" by Vance T. Vredenburg, from PNAS, May 2004, Volume 101(20). Copyright © 2004 by National Academy of Sciences. Reprinted with permission; **31.UnTable01** Source: Data from "Thermotolerance Generated by Plant/Fungal Symbiosis" by Regina S. Redman et al., from *Science*, November 2002, Volume 298(5598).

Chapter 32 **32.UnTable01** Source: Based on "The Mouth, the Anus, and the Blastopore—Open Questions about Questionable Openings" by Andreas Hejnol and Mark Q. Martindale, from *Animal Evolution: Genomes, Fossils, And Trees*, edited by Maximilian J. Telford and D.T.J. Littlewood. Oxford University Press, 2009.

Chapter 33 **33 SSE** Adaptation of Figure 1 from "Interaction between an Invasive Decapod and a Native Gastropod: Predator Foraging Tactics and Prey Architectural Defenses" by Remy Rochette et al., from *Marine Ecology Progress Series*, January 2007, Volume 330. Copyright © 2007 by Inter-Research Science Center. Reprinted with permission; **33.21** Adaptation of figure 3 from "The Global Decline of Nonmarine Mollusks" by Charles Lydeard et al., from *Bioscience*, April 2004, Volume 54(4). Copyright © 2004 by the American Institute of Biological Sciences. Reprinted with permission of the University of California Press; **33.29a** Adaptation of figure 2(a) from "Evolution of the Entire Arthropod Hox Gene Set Predated the Origin and Radiation of the Onychophoran/Arthropod Clade" by Jennifer K. Grenier et al., from *Current Biology*, August 1997, Volume 7(8). Copyright © 1997 by Elsevier. Reprinted with permission; **p. 707 Quote** Source: From T. Eisner, Entomological Society of America 100-Year Anniversary Meeting, November 1989.

Chapter 34 **34 SSE** Data from Dean Falk, Florida State University, 2013; **34.9b** Adaptation of figure 1a from "Fossil Sister Group of Craniates: Predicted and Found" by Jon Mallatt and Jun-yuan Chen, from *Journal of Morphology*, May 15, 2003, Volume 258(1). Copyright © 2003 by Wiley Periodicals Inc. Reprinted with permission of Wiley Inc.; **34.11** Figure adapted from *Vertebrates: Comparative Anatomy, Function, Evolution* by Kenneth Kardong. Copyright © 2002 by The McGraw-Hill Companies, Inc. Reprinted with permission; **34.17** Adaptation of Figure 3 from "The Oldest Articulated Osteichthyan Reveals Mosaic Gnathostome Characters" by Min Zhu et al., from *Nature*, March 26, 2009, Volume 458(7237). Copyright © 2009 by Macmillan Publishers Ltd. Reprinted with permission; **34.20 (right)** Adaptation of figure 4 from "The Pectoral Fin of *Tiktaalik roseae* and the Origin of the Tetrapod Limb" by Neil H. Shubin et al., from *Nature*, April 6, 2006, Volume 440(7085). Copyright © 2006 by Macmillan Publishers Ltd. Reprinted with permission; **34.20 (left)** Adaptation of Figure 27 from "The Devonian Tetrapod *Acanthostega gunnari* Jarvik: Postcranial Anatomy, Basal Tetrapod Relationships and Patterns of Skeletal Evolution" by Michael I. Coates, from *Transactions of the Royal Society Of Edinburgh: Earth Sciences*, Volume 87: 398. Copyright © 1996 by Royal Society of Edinburgh. Reprinted with permission; **34.36a** Sources: Based on many sources including figure 4.10 from *Evolution*, by Douglas J. Futuyma. Sinauer Associates, 2005; and *Vertebrate Paleontology and Evolution* by Robert L. Carroll. W.H. Freeman & Co., 1988; **34.45** Based on many photos of fossils. Some sources are *O. tugenensis* photo in "Early Hominid Sows Division" by Michael Balter, from ScienceNow, Feb. 22, 2001; *A. garhi* and *H. neanderthalensis* based on *The Human Evolution Coloring Book* by Adreienne L. Zihlman and Carla J. Simmons. HarperCollins, 2001; *K. platyops* based on photo in "New Hominin Genus from Eastern Africa Shows Diverse Middle Pliocene Lineages" by Meave Leakey et al., from *Nature*, March 2001, Volume 410(6827); *P. boisei* based on a photo by David Bill; *H. ergaster* based on a photo at www.museumsinhand.com; *S. tchadensis* based on figure 1b from "A New Hominid from the Upper Miocene of Chad, Central Africa" by in Michel Brunet et al., from *Nature*, July 2002, Volume 418(6894); **34.UnTable01** Source: Data from "Big-Brained Birds Survive Better in Nature" by Daniel Sol et al., from *Proceedings of the Royal Society B: Biological Sciences*, March 2007, Volume 274(1611).

Chapter 35 **35 SSE** Source: Based on "Phenotypic Plasticity of Leaf Shape along a Temperature Gradient in *Acer rubrum*" by Dana L. Royer et al., from; **35.21** Adaptation of Figure 2b from "Mongolian Tree Rings and 20th-Century Warming" by Gordon C. Jacoby, Rosanne D. D'Arrigo, and Tsevegyn Davaajamts from *Science*, August 1996, Volume 273(5276). Copyright © 1996 by AAAS. Reprinted with permission.

Chapter 36 **36 SSE** Source: Based on "Temperature Effects on Seed Imbibition and Leakage Mediated by Viscosity and Membranes" by J. Brad Murphy and Thomas L. Noland, from *Plant Physiology*, February 1982, Volume 69(2); **36.17** Source: Based on "Some Evidence for the Existence of Turgor Pressure Gradients in the Sieve Tubes of Willow" by S. Rogers and A. J. Peel, from *Planta*, January 1975, Volume 126(3).

Chapter 37 **37.9** Source: Data from "Defining the Core *Arabidopsis thaliana* Root Microbiome" by Derek S. Lundberg et al., from *Nature*, August 2012, Volume 488(7409).

Chapter 38 **38 SSE** Adaptation of Table 1 from "Trade-offs between Sexual and Asexual Reproduction in the Genus *Mimulus*" by S. Sutherland and R. K. Vickery, Jr., from *Oecologia*, August 1, 1988, Volume 76(3): 332. Copyright © 1988 by Springer. Reprinted with permission of Springer Science+Business Media.

Chapter 39 **39.15a** Source: *Plantwatching: How Plants Remember, Tell Time, Form Relationships and More* by Malcolm Wilkins. Facts on File, 1988; **39.Un02, 39 SSE** Source: Data from "Rumor Has It . . .: Relay Communication of Stress Cues in Plants" by Omer Falik et al., from PLOS ONE, November 2011, Volume 6(11).

Chapter 40 **40.15** Adaptation of figure 7 from "Thermoregulation in Endothermic Insects" by Bernd Heinrich from *Science*, August 1974, Volume 185(4153). Copyright © 1974 by AAAS. Reprinted with permission; **40.16** Adaptation of Figure 2 from "Thermoregulation in a Brooding Female Indian Python, *Python molurus bivittatus*" by Victor H. Hutchison, Herndon G. Dowling, and Allen Vinegar from *Science*, February 1966, Volume 151(3711). Copyright © 1966 by AAAS. Reprinted with permission; **40 SSE** Sources: Data from "Energetics of Foraging in Breeding Adélie Penguins" by Mark A. Chappell et al., from *Ecology*, December 1993, Volume 74(8); "Voluntary Running in Deer Mice: Speed, Distance, Energy Costs, and Temperature Effects" by Mark A. Chappell et al., from *Journal of Experimental Biology*, October 2004, Volume 207(22); and "Metabolism, Temperature Relations, Maternal Behavior, and Reproductive Energetics in the Ball Python (*Python regius*)" by Tamir M. Ellis and Mark A. Chappell, from *Journal of Comparative Physiology B*, 1987, Volume 157(3); **40.21** Adaptation of Figures 2b and 2c from "The Circadian Clock Stops Ticking During Deep Hibernation in the European Hamster" by Florent G. Revel et al., from PNAS, August 2007, Volume 104(24). Copyright © 2007 by National Academy of Sciences. Reprinted with permission.

Chapter 41 **41.4** Source: Based on "Possible Prevention of Neural-Tube Defects by Periconceptional Vitamin Supplementation" by Richard Smithells et al., *Lancet*, February 1980, Volume 315(8164); **41.9** *Human Anatomy and Physiology*, 8th Edition, by Elaine N. Marieb and Katja Hoehn. Copyright © 2010 by Pearson Education. Reprinted and electronically reproduced by permission of Pearson Education, Inc., Upper Saddle River, New Jersey; **41.9b** Figure adapted from *Human Physiology*, 3rd Edition, by R. A. Rhodes. Copyright © 1996 by Brooks/Cole, a part of Cengage Learning, Inc. Reprinted with permission. www.cengage.com/permissions; **41.22** Adaptation of illustration "Appetite Controllers" from "Cellular Warriors at the Battle of the Bulge" by Kathleen Sutliff and Jean Marx, from *Science*, February 2003, Volume 299(5608). Copyright © 2003 by AAAS; **41 SSE** Source: Data from "Effects of Parabiosis of Obese with Diabetes and Normal Mice" by D. L. Coleman, from *Diabetologia*, 1973, Volume 9(4).

Chapter 42 **42 SSE** Source: Based on Figure 1A from "Sequence Variations in PCSK9, Low LDL, and Protection against Coronary Heart Disease" by Jonathan C. Cohen et al., from *New England Journal of Medicine*, March 2006, Volume 354(12); **42.25** Source: Data from "Surface Properties in Relation to Atelectasis and 106 Hyaline Membrane Disease" by M. E. Avery and J. Mead, from *American Journal of Diseases of Children*, May 1959, Volume 97(5, part 1); **42.29, 42.EOC01** Figure adapted from *Human Anatomy and Physiology*, 8th Edition, by Elaine N. Marieb and Katja Hoehn. Copyright © 2010 by Pearson Education, Inc. Adapted and electronically reproduced by permission of Pearson Education, Inc., Upper Saddle River, New Jersey.

Chapter 43 **43.5a** Adaptation of figure 4a from "Constitutive Expression of a Single Antimicrobial Peptide Can Restore Wild-Type Resistance to Infection in Immunodeficient *Drosophila* Mutants" by Phoebe Tzou et al., from PNAS, February 2002, Volume 99(4). Copyright © 2002 by National Academy of Sciences. Reprinted with permission; **43.5b** Adaptation of figure 2a from "Constitutive Expression of a Single Antimicrobial Peptide Can Restore Wild-Type Resistance to Infection in Immunodeficient *Drosophila* Mutants" by Phoebe Tzou et al., from PNAS, February 2002, Volume 99(4). Copyright © 2002 by National Academy of Sciences. Reprinted with permission; **43.7a** Figure adapted from *Human Anatomy and Physiology*, 8th Edition, by Elaine N. Marieb and Katja Hoehn. Copyright © 2010 by Pearson Education, Inc. Adapted and electronically reproduced by permission of Pearson Education, Inc., Upper Saddle River, New Jersey; **43.7b** Figure adapted from *Human Anatomy and Physiology*, 8th Edition, by Elaine N. Marieb and Katja Hoehn. Copyright © 2010 by Pearson Education, Inc. Adapted and electronically reproduced by permission of Pearson Education, Inc., Upper Saddle River, New Jersey; **43.8** Figure adapted from *Microbiology: An Introduction*, 11th Edition, by Gerard J. Tortora, Berdell R. Funke, and Christine L. Case. Copyright © 2012 Pearson Education Inc. Adapted and electronically reproduced by permission of Pearson Education, Inc., Upper Saddle River, New Jersey.

Chapter 44 **44 SSE** Source: Data from "Water Economy and Energy Metabolism of the Sandy Inland Mouse, *Leggadina hermannsburgensis*" by Richard E. MacMillen et al., from *Journal of Mammalogy*, August 1972, Volume 53(3); **44.7** Figure adapted from *Zoology*, 1st Edition, by Lawrence G. Mitchell. Copyright © 1988 by Pearson Education Inc. Adapted and electronically reproduced by permission of Pearson Education, Inc., Upper Saddle River, New Jersey; **44.12b, 44.13** Figure adapted from *Human Anatomy and Physiology*, 8th Edition, by Elaine N. Marieb and Katja Hoehn. Copyright © 2010 by Pearson Education, Inc. Adapted and electronically reproduced by permission of Pearson Education, Inc., Upper Saddle River, New Jersey; **44.20** "Requirement of Human Renal Water Channel Aquaporin-2 for Vasopressin-Dependent Concentration in Urine" by P. M. Deen et al., from *Science*, April 1994, Volume 264(5155). Copyright © 1994 by AAAS. Reprinted with permission; **44.EOC01** Figure adapted from *Life: An Introduction to Biology*, 3rd Edition, by William Samson Beck. Copyright © 1991 by Pearson Education, Inc. Adapted and electronically reproduced by permission of Pearson Education, Inc., Upper Saddle River, New Jersey; **44.Ans01** Source: Data for kangaroo rat from *Animal Physiology: Adaptation and Environment* by Knut Schmidt-Nielsen. Cambridge University Press, 1991.

Chapter 45 **45 SSE** Data from J. Born, et al., "Timing the end of nocturnal sleep," *Nature*, 397:29-30 (1999).

Chapter 46 **46.8** Adaptation of Figure 2 from "Sperm Death and Dumping in *Drosophila*" by Rhonda R. Snook and David J. Hosken, from *Nature*, April 29, 2004, Volume 428(6986). Copyright © 2004 by Macmillan Publishers Ltd. Reprinted with permission; **46 SSE** Source: Data from *"Recherches sur la Différenciation Sexuelle de L'embryon de Lapin* (Studies on the Sexual Differentiation of the Rabbit Embryo)" by Alfred Jost, from *Archives D'anatomie Microscopique Et De Morphologie Experimentale*, 1947, Volume 36; **46.16** Figure adapted from *Human Anatomy and Physiology*, 8th Edition, by Elaine N. Marieb and Katja Hoehn. Copyright © 2010 by Pearson Education, Inc. Adapted and electronically reproduced by permission of Pearson Education, Inc., Upper Saddle River, New Jersey.

Chapter 47 **47.4** Source: Based on "Intracellular Calcium Release at Fertilization in the Sea Urchin Egg" by R. Steinhardt et al., from *Developmental Biology*, July 1977, Volume 58(1); **47.10(b) and 47.14** Figures adapted from "Cell Commitment and Gene Expression in the Axolotl Embryo" by T. J. Mohun, et al., from *Cell*, November 1980, Volume 22(1); **47.17** Adaptation from figure 1.9 and Box 8c from *Principles of Development*, 4th Edition, by Lewis Wolpert. Copyright © 2011 by Oxford University Press. Reprinted with permission; **47.19** Adaptation of figure 21.17 from *Molecular Biology of the Cell*, 4th Edition, by Bruce Alberts et al. Copyright © 2002 by Garland Science/Taylor & Francis LLC. Reprinted with permission; **47.23** Source: Based on *Embryonic Development and Induction* by Hans Spemann. Yale University Press, 1938; **47.24a, b** Adaptation from figure 1.9 and Box 8c from *Principles of Development*, 4th Edition, by Lewis Wolpert. Copyright © 2011 by Oxford University Press. Reprinted with permission; **47.24b** Adaptation of Figure 15.12 from *Developmental Biology* by Scott F. Gilbert. Copyright © 1997 by Sinauer Associates, Inc. Reprinted with permission; **47.26** Source: Based on "Maps of Strength of Positional Signalling Activity in the Developing Chick Wing Bud" by Lawrence S. Honig and Dennis Summerbell, from *Journal of Embryology and Experimental Morphology*, June 1985, Volume 87(1); **47.27** Figure adapted from *Human Anatomy and Physiology*, 8th Edition, by Elaine N. Marieb and Katja Hoehn. Copyright © 2010 by Pearson Education, Inc. Adapted and electronically reproduced by permission of Pearson Education, Inc., Upper Saddle River, New Jersey.

Chapter 48 **48.11f** Source: Based on figure 6-2d from *Cellular Physiology of Nerve and Muscle*, 4th Edition, by Gary G. Matthews. Wiley-Blackwell, 2003; **48 SSE** Source: Data from "Opiate Receptor: Demonstration in Nervous Tissue" by Candace B. Pert and Solomon H. Snyder, from *Science*, March 1973, Volume 179(4077).

Chapter 49 **49.9** *Human Anatomy and Physiology*, 8th Edition, by Elaine N. Marieb and Katja Hoehn. Copyright © 2010 by Pearson Education. Reprinted and electronically reproduced by permission of Pearson Education, Inc., Upper Saddle River, New Jersey; **49.13** Source: Based on "Sleep in Marine Mammals" by L. M. Mukhametov, from *Sleep Mechanisms*, edited by Alexander A. Borberly and J. L. Valatx. Springer, 1984; **49 SSE** Adaptation of Figure 2a from "Transplanted Suprachiasmatic Nucleus Determines Circadian Period" by Martin R. Ralph et al., from *Science*, February 1990, Volume 247(4945). Copyright © 1990 by AAAS. Reprinted with permission; **49.19** Adaptation of figure 1c from "Avian Brains and a New Understanding of Vertebrate Brain Evolution" by Erich D. Jarvis et al., from *Nature Reviews Neuroscience*, February 2005, Volume 6(2). Copyright © 2005 by Macmillan Publishers Ltd. Reprinted with permission; **49.22** Adaptation of figure 10 from *Schizophrenia Genesis: The Origins of Madness* by Irving I. Gottesman. Copyright © 1991 by Irving I. Gottesman. Reprinted by permission of Worth Publishers.

Chapter 50 **50.12** *Human Anatomy and Physiology*, 8th Edition, by Elaine N. Marieb and Katja Hoehn. Copyright © 2010 by Pearson Education. Reprinted and electronically reproduced by permission of Pearson Education, Inc., Upper Saddle River, New Jersey; **50.13** *Human Anatomy and Physiology*, 8th Edition, by Elaine N. Marieb and Katja Hoehn. Copyright © 2010 by Pearson Education. Reprinted and electronically reproduced by permission of Pearson Education, Inc., Upper Saddle River, New Jersey; **50.17a** Figure adapted from *Human Anatomy and Physiology*, 8th Edition, by Elaine N. Marieb and Katja Hoehn. Copyright © 2010 by Pearson Education, Inc. Adapted and electronically reproduced by permission of Pearson Education, Inc., Upper Saddle River, New Jersey; **50.17b** Figure adapted from *Human Anatomy and Physiology*, 8th Edition, by Elaine N. Marieb and Katja Hoehn. Copyright © 2010 by Pearson Education, Inc. Adapted and electronically reproduced by permission of Pearson Education, Inc., Upper Saddle River, New Jersey; **50.23a** Adaptation of figure 4b from "The Receptors and Coding Logic for Bitter Taste" by Ken L. Muller et al., from *Nature*, March 10, 2005, Volume 434(7030). Copyright © 2005 by Macmillan Publishers Ltd. Reprinted with permission; **50.24a** Adaptation of figure 15.23(a) from *Human Anatomy and Physiology*, 8th Edition, by Elaine N. Marieb and Katja Hoehn. Copyright © 2010 by Pearson Education, Inc. Adapted and electronically reproduced by permission of Pearson Education, Inc., Upper Saddle River, New Jersey. Adaptation of figure 15.23(b) from *Human Anatomy and Physiology*, 8th Edition, by Elaine N. Marieb and Katja Hoehn. Copyright © 2010 by Pearson Education, Inc. Adapted and electronically reproduced by permission of Pearson Education, Inc., Upper Saddle River, New Jersey; **50.26** Figure adapted from *Human Anatomy and Physiology*, 8th Edition, by Elaine N. Marieb and Katja Hoehn. Copyright © 2010 by Pearson Education, Inc. Adapted and electronically reproduced by permission of Pearson Education, Inc., Upper Saddle River, New Jersey; **50.30** Figure adapted from *Human Anatomy and Physiology*, 8th Edition, by Elaine N. Marieb and Katja Hoehn. Copyright © 2010 by Pearson Education, Inc. Adapted and electronically reproduced by permission of Pearson Education, Inc., Upper Saddle River, New Jersey; **50 SSE** Adaptation of figure 4 from "Locomotion: Energy Cost of Swimming, Flying, and Running" by Knut Schmidt-Nielsen, from *Science*, July 1972, Volume 177(4045). Copyright © 1972 by AAAS. Reprinted with permission.

Chapter 51 **51.2b** Adaptation of figure 20 from *The Study of Instincts* by Nikolaas Tinbergen. Copyright © 1989 by Oxford University Press. Reprinted with permission. Adaptation of figures 65 and 66 in *Inleiding tot de Diersociologie*, by Nikolaas Tinbergen, © 1946. Reprinted by permission of E. Barendrecht-Tinbergen. **51.4** Adaptation of figure 1 from "*Drosophila*: Genetics Meets Behavior" by Marla B. Sokolowski, from *Nature Reviews: Genetics*, November 2001, Volume 2(11). Copyright © 2001 by Macmillan Publishers Ltd. Reprinted with permission; **51.24b** Adaptation of figure 1 from "Rapid Microevolution of Migratory Behaviour in a Wild Bird Species" by P. Berthold et al., from *Nature*, December 1992, Volume 360(6405). Copyright © 1992 by Macmillan Publishers Ltd. Reprinted with permission; **51.8, 51.EOC** Figure adapted from *Zoology*, 1st Edition, by Lawrence G. Mitchell et al. Pearson Education Inc., 1988; **51.10** Adaptation of figure 3a from "Prospective and Retrospective Learning in Honeybees" by Martin Giurfa and Julie Bernard, from *International Journal of Comparative Psychology*, 2006, Volume 19(3). Copyright © 2006 by International Society for Comparative Psychology. Reprinted with permission; **51.13** Adaptation of figure 2a from "Evolution of Foraging Behavior in *Drosophila* by Density-Dependent Selection" by Maria B. Sokolowski et al., from PNAS, July 8, 1997, Volume 94(14). Copyright © 1997 by National Academy of Sciences, U.S.A. Reprinted with permission; **51 SSE** Source: Data from "Shell Dropping: Decision-Making and Optimal Foraging in Northwestern Crows" by Reto Zach, from *Behaviour*, 1979, Volume 68(1–2); **51.18** Reprinted with the permission of Dr. Klaudia White; **51.24a** Adaptations of photograph by Jonathan Blair from *Animal Behavior: An Evolutionary Approach*, 7th Edition, by John Alcock. Copyright © 2002 by Sinauer Associates, Inc. Reprinted with permission.

Chapter 52 **52.7** Adaptation of figure 2 from "How Fast Can Trees Migrate?" by Leslie Roberts, from *Science*, February 1989, Volume 243(4892). Copyright © 1989 by AAAS. Reprinted with permission; **52.17** Sources: Based on figure 11.19 from *Ecology and Field Biology* by Robert L. Smith. Pearson Education, 1974; and *Sibley Guide to Birds* by David Allen Sibley. Random House, 2000; **52.18** Source: Data from "Interactions Among Subtidal Australian Sea Urchins, Gastropods, and Algae: Effects of Experimental Removals" by W. J. Fletcher, from *Ecological Monographs*, March 1987, Volume 57(1); **52 SSE** Source: Data from "Physical and Biotic Drivers of Plant Distribution across 116 Estuarine Salinity Gradients" by Caitlin M Crain et al., from *Ecology*, September 2004, Volume 85(9); **52.EOC02** Source: Data from *Experimental Studies on the Nature of Species: Iii: Environmental Responses of Climatic Races of Achillea* by Jens C. Clausen et al. Carnegie Institution of Washington, 1948.

Chapter 53 **53.2** Source: Based on "Capture-Recapture Estimates of Hector's Dolphin Abundance at Banks Peninsula, New Zealand" by Andrew M. Gormley et al., from *Marine Mammal Science*, April 2005, Volume 21(2); **Table 53.1** Source: Data from "Demography of Belding's Ground Squirrels" by Paul W. Sherman and Martin

Pronunciation Key

ā	ace
a/ah	ash
ch	chose
ē	meet
e/eh	bet
g	game
ī	ice
i	hit
ks	box
kw	quick
ng	song
ō	robe
o	ox
oy	boy
s	say
sh	shell
th	thin
ū	boot
u/uh	up
z	zoo

ʹ = primary accent
ʹ = secondary accent

5ʹ cap A modified form of guanine nucleotide added onto the 5ʹ end of a pre-mRNA molecule.

ABC hypothesis A model of flower formation identifying three classes of organ identity genes that direct formation of the four types of floral organs.

abiotic (ā′-bī-ot′-ik) Nonliving; referring to the physical and chemical properties of an environment.

abortion The termination of a pregnancy in progress.

abscisic acid (ABA) (ab-sis′-ik) A plant hormone that slows growth, often antagonizing the actions of growth hormones. Two of its many effects are to promote seed dormancy and facilitate drought tolerance.

absorption The third stage of food processing in animals: the uptake of small nutrient molecules by an organism's body.

absorption spectrum The range of a pigment's ability to absorb various wavelengths of light; also a graph of such a range.

abyssal zone (uh-bis′-ul) The part of the ocean's benthic zone between 2,000 and 6,000 m deep.

acanthodian (ak′-an-thō′-dē-un) Any of a group of ancient jawed aquatic vertebrates from the Silurian and Devonian periods.

accessory fruit A fruit, or assemblage of fruits, in which the fleshy parts are derived largely or entirely from tissues other than the ovary.

acclimatization (uh-klī′-muh-tī -zā′-shun) Physiological adjustment to a change in an environmental factor.

acetyl CoA Acetyl coenzyme A; the entry compound for the citric acid cycle in cellular respiration, formed from a two-carbon fragment of pyruvate attached to a coenzyme.

acetylcholine (as′-uh-til-kō′-lēn) One of the most common neurotransmitters; functions by binding to receptors and altering the permeability of the postsynaptic membrane to specific ions, either depolarizing or hyperpolarizing the membrane.

acid A substance that increases the hydrogen ion concentration of a solution.

acoelomate (uh-sē′-lō-māt) A solid-bodied animal lacking a cavity between the gut and outer body wall.

acquired immunodeficiency syndrome (AIDS) The symptoms and signs present during the late stages of HIV infection, defined by a specified reduction in the number of T cells and the appearance of characteristic secondary infections.

acrosomal reaction (ak′-ruh-sōm′-ul) The discharge of hydrolytic enzymes from the acrosome, a vesicle in the tip of a sperm, when the sperm approaches or contacts an egg.

acrosome (ak′-ruh-sōm) A vesicle in the tip of a sperm containing hydrolytic enzymes and other proteins that help the sperm reach the egg.

actin (ak′-tin) A globular protein that links into chains, two of which twist helically about each other, forming microfilaments (actin filaments) in muscle and other kinds of cells.

action potential An electrical signal that propagates (travels) along the membrane of a neuron or other excitable cell as a nongraded (all-or-none) depolarization.

action spectrum A graph that profiles the relative effectiveness of different wavelengths of radiation in driving a particular process.

activation energy The amount of energy that reactants must absorb before a chemical reaction will start; also called free energy of activation.

activator A protein that binds to DNA and stimulates gene transcription. In prokaryotes, activators bind in or near the promoter; in eukaryotes, activators generally bind to control elements in enhancers.

active immunity Long-lasting immunity conferred by the action of B cells and T cells and the resulting B and T memory cells specific for a pathogen. Active immunity can develop as a result of natural infection or immunization.

active site The specific region of an enzyme that binds the substrate and that forms the pocket in which catalysis occurs.

active transport The movement of a substance across a cell membrane against its concentration or electrochemical gradient, mediated by specific transport proteins and requiring an expenditure of energy.

adaptation Inherited characteristic of an organism that enhances its survival and reproduction in a specific environment.

adaptive evolution Evolution that results in a better match between organisms and their environment.

adaptive immunity A vertebrate-specific defense that is mediated by B lymphocytes (B cells) and T lymphocytes (T cells) and that exhibits specificity, memory, and self-nonself recognition; also called acquired immunity.

adaptive radiation Period of evolutionary change in which groups of organisms form many new species whose adaptations allow them to fill different ecological roles in their communities.

addition rule A rule of probability stating that the probability of any one of two or more mutually exclusive events occurring can be determined by adding their individual probabilities.

adenosine triphosphate *See* ATP (adenosine triphosphate).

adenylyl cyclase (uh-den′-uh-lil) An enzyme that converts ATP to cyclic AMP in response to an extracellular signal.

adhesion The clinging of one substance to another, such as water to plant cell walls by means of hydrogen bonds.

adipose tissue A connective tissue that insulates the body and serves as a fuel reserve; contains fat-storing cells called adipose cells.

adrenal gland (uh-drē′-nul) One of two endocrine glands located adjacent to the kidneys in mammals. Endocrine cells in the outer portion (cortex) respond to adrenocorticotropic hormone (ACTH) by secreting steroid hormones that help maintain homeostasis during long-term stress. Neurosecretory cells in the central portion (medulla) secrete epinephrine and norepinephrine in response to nerve signals triggered by short-term stress.

aerobic respiration A catabolic pathway for organic molecules, using oxygen (O_2) as the final electron acceptor in an electron transport chain and ultimately producing ATP. This is the most efficient catabolic pathway and is carried out in most eukaryotic cells and many prokaryotic organisms.

age structure The relative number of individuals of each age in a population.

aggregate fruit A fruit derived from a single flower that has more than one carpel.

AIDS (acquired immunodeficiency syndrome) The symptoms and signs present during the late stages of HIV infection, defined by a specified reduction in the number of T cells and the appearance of characteristic secondary infections.

Glossary

alcohol fermentation Glycolysis followed by the reduction of pyruvate to ethyl alcohol, regenerating NAD^+ and releasing carbon dioxide.

aldosterone (al-dos′-tuh-rōn) A steroid hormone that acts on tubules of the kidney to regulate the transport of sodium ions (Na^+) and potassium ions (K^+).

alga (plural, **algae**) A member of a diverse collection of photosynthetic protists that includes both unicellular and multicellular forms. Algal species are included in three eukaryote supergroups (Excavata, "SAR" clade, and Archaeplastida).

alimentary canal (al′-uh-men′-tuh-rē) A complete digestive tract, consisting of a tube running between a mouth and an anus.

alkaline vent A deep-sea hydrothermal vent that releases water that is warm (40–90°C) rather than hot and that has a high pH (is basic). These vents consist of tiny pores lined with iron and other catalytic minerals that some scientists hypothesize might have been the location of the earliest abiotic synthesis of organic compounds.

allele (uh-lē′-ul) Any of the alternative versions of a gene that may produce distinguishable phenotypic effects.

allopatric speciation (al′-uh-pat′-rik) The formation of new species in populations that are geographically isolated from one another.

allopolyploid (al′-ō-pol′-ē-ployd) A fertile individual that has more than two chromosome sets as a result of two different species interbreeding and combining their chromosomes.

allosteric regulation The binding of a regulatory molecule to a protein at one site that affects the function of the protein at a different site.

alpha (α) helix (al′-fuh hē′-liks) A coiled region constituting one form of the secondary structure of proteins, arising from a specific pattern of hydrogen bonding between atoms of the polypeptide backbone (not the side chains).

alternation of generations A life cycle in which there is both a multicellular diploid form, the sporophyte, and a multicellular haploid form, the gametophyte; characteristic of plants and some algae.

alternative RNA splicing A type of eukaryotic gene regulation at the RNA-processing level in which different mRNA molecules are produced from the same primary transcript, depending on which RNA segments are treated as exons and which as introns.

altruism (al′-trū-iz-um) Selflessness; behavior that reduces an individual's fitness while increasing the fitness of another individual.

alveolates (al-vē′-uh-lets) One of the three major subgroups for which the "SAR" eukaryotic supergroup is named. This clade arose by secondary endosymbiosis; alveolate protists have membrane-enclosed sacs (alveoli) located just under the plasma membrane.

alveolus (al-vē′-uh-lus) (plural, **alveoli**) One of the dead-end air sacs where gas exchange occurs in a mammalian lung.

Alzheimer's disease (alts′-hī-merz) An age-related dementia (mental deterioration) characterized by confusion and memory loss.

amino acid (uh-mēn′-ō) An organic molecule possessing both a carboxyl and an amino group. Amino acids serve as the monomers of polypeptides.

amino group (uh-mēn′-ō) A chemical group consisting of a nitrogen atom bonded to two hydrogen atoms; can act as a base in solution, accepting a hydrogen ion and acquiring a charge of $1+$.

aminoacyl-tRNA synthetase An enzyme that joins each amino acid to the appropriate tRNA.

ammonia A small, toxic molecule (NH_3) produced by nitrogen fixation or as a metabolic waste product of protein and nucleic acid metabolism.

ammonite A member of a group of shelled cephalopods that were important marine predators for hundreds of millions of years until their extinction at the end of the Cretaceous period (65.5 million years ago).

amniocentesis (am′-nē-ō-sen-tē′-sis) A technique associated with prenatal diagnosis in which amniotic fluid is obtained by aspiration from a needle inserted into the uterus. The fluid and the fetal cells it contains are analyzed to detect certain genetic and congenital defects in the fetus.

amniote (am′-nē-ōt) A member of a clade of tetrapods named for a key derived character, the amniotic egg, which contains specialized membranes, including the fluid-filled amnion, that protect the embryo. Amniotes include mammals as well as birds and other reptiles.

amniotic egg An egg that contains specialized membranes that function in protection, nourishment, and gas exchange. The amniotic egg was a major evolutionary innovation, allowing embryos to develop on land in a fluid-filled sac, thus reducing the dependence of tetrapods on water for reproduction.

amoeba (uh-mē′-buh) A protist characterized by the presence of pseudopodia.

amoebocyte (uh-mē′-buh-sīt′) An amoeba-like cell that moves by pseudopodia and is found in most animals. Depending on the species, it may digest and distribute food, dispose of wastes, form skeletal fibers, fight infections, or change into other cell types.

amoebozoan (uh-mē′-buh-zō′-an) A protist in a clade that includes many species with lobe- or tube-shaped pseudopodia.

amphibian A member of the clade of tetrapods that includes salamanders, frogs, and caecilians.

amphipathic (am′-fē-path′-ik) Having both a hydrophilic region and a hydrophobic region.

amplification The strengthening of stimulus energy during transduction.

amygdala (uh-mig′-duh-luh) A structure in the temporal lobe of the vertebrate brain that has a major role in the processing of emotions.

amylase (am′-uh-lās′) An enzyme that hydrolyzes starch (a glucose polymer from plants) and glycogen (a glucose polymer from animals) into smaller polysaccharides and the disaccharide maltose.

anabolic pathway (an′-uh-bol′-ik) A metabolic pathway that consumes energy to synthesize a complex molecule from simpler molecules.

anaerobic respiration (an-er-ō′-bik) A catabolic pathway in which inorganic molecules other than oxygen accept electrons at the "downhill" end of electron transport chains.

analogous Having characteristics that are similar because of convergent evolution, not homology.

analogy (an-al′-uh-jē) Similarity between two species that is due to convergent evolution rather than to descent from a common ancestor with the same trait.

anaphase The fourth stage of mitosis, in which the chromatids of each chromosome have separated and the daughter chromosomes are moving to the poles of the cell.

anatomy The structure of an organism.

anchorage dependence The requirement that a cell must be attached to a substratum in order to initiate cell division.

androgen (an′-drō-jen) Any steroid hormone, such as testosterone, that stimulates the development and maintenance of the male reproductive system and secondary sex characteristics.

aneuploidy (an′-yū-ploy′-dē) A chromosomal aberration in which one or more chromosomes are present in extra copies or are deficient in number.

angiosperm (an′-jē-ō-sperm) A flowering plant, which forms seeds inside a protective chamber called an ovary.

angiotensin II A peptide hormone that stimulates constriction of precapillary arterioles and increases reabsorption of NaCl and water by the proximal tubules of the kidney, increasing blood pressure and volume.

anhydrobiosis (an-hī′-drō-bī-ō′-sis) A dormant state involving loss of almost all body water.

animal pole The point at the end of an egg in the hemisphere where the least yolk is concentrated; opposite of vegetal pole.

anion (an′-ī-on) A negatively charged ion.

anterior Pertaining to the front, or head, of a bilaterally symmetrical animal.

anterior pituitary A portion of the pituitary gland that develops from nonneural tissue; consists of endocrine cells that synthesize and secrete several tropic and nontropic hormones.

anther In an angiosperm, the terminal pollen sac of a stamen, where pollen grains containing sperm-producing male gametophytes form.

antheridium (an-thuh-rid′-ē-um) (plural, **antheridia**) In plants, the male gametangium, a moist chamber in which gametes develop.

anthropoid (an′-thruh-poyd) A member of a primate group made up of the monkeys and the apes (gibbons, orangutans, gorillas, chimpanzees, bonobos, and humans).

antibody A protein secreted by plasma cells (differentiated B cells) that binds to a particular antigen; also called immunoglobulin. All antibodies have the same Y-shaped structure and in their monomer form consist of two identical heavy chains and two identical light chains.

anticodon (an′-tī-kō′-don) A nucleotide triplet at one end of a tRNA molecule that base-pairs

G-2 GLOSSARY

with a particular complementary codon on an mRNA molecule.

antidiuretic hormone (ADH) (an'-tī-dī-yū-ret'-ik) A peptide hormone, also called vasopressin, that promotes water retention by the kidneys. Produced in the hypothalamus and released from the posterior pituitary, ADH also functions in the brain.

antigen (an'-ti-jen) A substance that elicits an immune response by binding to receptors of B or T cells.

antigen presentation (an'-ti-jen) The process by which an MHC molecule binds to a fragment of an intracellular protein antigen and carries it to the cell surface, where it is displayed and can be recognized by a T cell.

antigen-presenting cell (an'-ti-jen) A cell that upon ingesting pathogens or internalizing pathogen proteins generates peptide fragments that are bound by class II MHC molecules and subsequently displayed on the cell surface to T cells. Macrophages, dendritic cells, and B cells are the primary antigen-presenting cells.

antigen receptor (an'-ti-jen) The general term for a surface protein, located on B cells and T cells, that binds to antigens, initiating adaptive immune responses. The antigen receptors on B cells are called B cell receptors, and the antigen receptors on T cells are called T cell receptors.

antiparallel Referring to the arrangement of the sugar-phosphate backbones in a DNA double helix (they run in opposite $5' \rightarrow 3'$ directions).

aphotic zone (ā'-fō'-tik) The part of an ocean or lake beneath the photic zone, where light does not penetrate sufficiently for photosynthesis to occur.

apical bud (ā'-pik-ul) A bud at the tip of a plant stem; also called a terminal bud.

apical dominance (ā'-pik-ul) Tendency for growth to be concentrated at the tip of a plant shoot, because the apical bud partially inhibits axillary bud growth.

apical ectodermal ridge (AER) (ā'-pik-ul) A thickened area of ectoderm at the tip of a limb bud that promotes outgrowth of the limb bud.

apical meristem (ā'-pik-ul mār'-uh-stem) Embryonic plant tissue in the tips of roots and buds of shoots. The dividing cells of an apical meristem enable the plant to grow in length.

apicomplexan (ap'-ē-kom-pleks'-un) A protist in a clade that includes many species that parasitize animals. Some apicomplexans cause human disease.

apomixis (ap'-uh-mik'-sis) The ability of some plant species to reproduce asexually through seeds without fertilization by a male gamete.

apoplast (ap'-ō-plast) Everything external to the plasma membrane of a plant cell, including cell walls, intercellular spaces, and the space within dead structures such as xylem vessels and tracheids.

apoptosis (ā-puh-tō'-sus) A type of programmed cell death, which is brought about by activation of enzymes that break down many chemical components in the cell.

aposematic coloration (ap'-ō-si-mat'-ik) The bright warning coloration of many animals with effective physical or chemical defenses.

appendix A small, finger-like extension of the vertebrate cecum; contains a mass of white blood cells that contribute to immunity.

aquaporin A channel protein in a cellular membrane that specifically facilitates osmosis, the diffusion of free water across the membrane.

aqueous solution (ā'-kwē-us) A solution in which water is the solvent.

arachnid A member of a subgroup of the major arthropod clade Chelicerata. Arachnids have six pairs of appendages, including four pairs of walking legs, and include spiders, scorpions, ticks, and mites.

arbuscular mycorrhiza (ar-bus'-kyū-lur mī'-kō-rī'-zuh) Association of a fungus with a plant root system in which the fungus causes the invagination of the host (plant) cells' plasma membranes.

arbuscular mycorrhizal fungus (ar-bus'-kyū-lur) A symbiotic fungus whose hyphae grow through the cell wall of plant roots and extend into the root cell (enclosed in tubes formed by invagination of the root cell plasma membrane).

Archaea (ar'-kē'-uh) One of two prokaryotic domains, the other being Bacteria.

Archaeplastida (ar'-kē-plas'-tid-uh) One of four supergroups of eukaryotes proposed in a current hypothesis of the evolutionary history of eukaryotes. This monophyletic group, which includes red algae, green algae, and land plants, descended from an ancient protist ancestor that engulfed a cyanobacterium. *See also* Excavata, "SAR" clade, and Unikonta.

archegonium (ar-ki-gō'-nē-um) (plural, **archegonia**) In plants, the female gametangium, a moist chamber in which gametes develop.

archenteron (ar-ken'-tuh-ron) The endoderm-lined cavity, formed during gastrulation, that develops into the digestive tract of an animal.

archosaur (ar'-kō-sōr) A member of the reptilian group that includes crocodiles, alligators and dinosaurs, including birds.

arteriole (ar-ter'-ē-ōl) A vessel that conveys blood between an artery and a capillary bed.

artery A vessel that carries blood away from the heart to organs throughout the body.

arthropod A segmented ecdysozoan with a hard exoskeleton and jointed appendages. Familiar examples include insects, spiders, millipedes, and crabs.

artificial selection The selective breeding of domesticated plants and animals to encourage the occurrence of desirable traits.

ascocarp The fruiting body of a sac fungus (ascomycete).

ascomycete (as'-kuh-mī'-sēt) A member of the fungal phylum Ascomycota, commonly called sac fungus. The name comes from the saclike structure in which the spores develop.

ascus (plural, **asci**) A saclike spore capsule located at the tip of a dikaryotic hypha of a sac fungus.

asexual reproduction The generation of offspring from a single parent that occurs without the fusion of gametes (by budding, division of a single cell, or division of the entire organism into two or more parts). In most cases, the offspring are genetically identical to the parent.

A site One of a ribosome's three binding sites for tRNA during translation. The A site holds the tRNA carrying the next amino acid to be added to the polypeptide chain. (A stands for aminoacyl tRNA.)

assisted migration The translocation of a species to a favorable habitat beyond its native range for the purpose of protecting the species from human-caused threats.

associative learning The acquired ability to associate one environmental feature (such as a color) with another (such as danger).

aster A radial array of short microtubules that extends from each centrosome toward the plasma membrane in an animal cell undergoing mitosis.

astrocyte A glial cell with diverse functions, including providing structural support for neurons, regulating the interstitial environment, facilitating synaptic transmission, and assisting in regulating the blood supply to the brain.

atherosclerosis A cardiovascular disease in which fatty deposits called plaques develop in the inner walls of the arteries, obstructing the arteries and causing them to harden.

atom The smallest unit of matter that retains the properties of an element.

atomic mass The total mass of an atom, numerically equivalent to the mass in grams of 1 mole of the atom. (For an element with more than one isotope, the atomic mass is the average mass of the naturally occurring isotopes, weighted by their abundance.)

atomic nucleus An atom's dense central core, containing protons and neutrons.

atomic number The number of protons in the nucleus of an atom, unique for each element and designated by a subscript.

ATP (adenosine triphosphate) (a-den'-ō-sēn trī-fos'-fāt) An adenine-containing nucleoside triphosphate that releases free energy when its phosphate bonds are hydrolyzed. This energy is used to drive endergonic reactions in cells.

ATP synthase A complex of several membrane proteins that functions in chemiosmosis with adjacent electron transport chains, using the energy of a hydrogen ion (proton) concentration gradient to make ATP. ATP synthases are found in the inner mitochondrial membranes of eukaryotic cells and in the plasma membranes of prokaryotes.

atrial natriuretic peptide (ANP) (ā'-trē-ul na'-trē-yū-ret'-ik) A peptide hormone secreted by cells of the atria of the heart in response to high blood pressure. ANP's effects on the kidney alter ion and water movement and reduce blood pressure.

atrioventricular (AV) node A region of specialized heart muscle tissue between the left and right atria where electrical impulses are delayed for about 0.1 second before spreading to both ventricles and causing them to contract.

atrioventricular (AV) valve A heart valve located between each atrium and ventricle that prevents a backflow of blood when the ventricle contracts.

atrium (ā′-trē-um) (plural, **atria**) A chamber of the vertebrate heart that receives blood from the veins and transfers blood to a ventricle.

autocrine Referring to a secreted molecule that acts on the cell that secreted it.

autoimmune disease An immunological disorder in which the immune system turns against self.

autonomic nervous system (ot′-ō-nom′-ik) An efferent branch of the vertebrate peripheral nervous system that regulates the internal environment; consists of the sympathetic, parasympathetic, and enteric divisions.

autopolyploid (ot′-ō-pol′-ē-ployd) An individual that has more than two chromosome sets that are all derived from a single species.

autosome (ot′-ō-sōm) A chromosome that is not directly involved in determining sex; not a sex chromosome.

autotroph (ot′-ō-trōf) An organism that obtains organic food molecules without eating other organisms or substances derived from other organisms. Autotrophs use energy from the sun or from oxidation of inorganic substances to make organic molecules from inorganic ones.

auxin (ôk′-sin) A term that primarily refers to indoleacetic acid (IAA), a natural plant hormone that has a variety of effects, including cell elongation, root formation, secondary growth, and fruit growth.

axillary bud (ak′-sil-ār-ē) A structure that has the potential to form a lateral shoot, or branch. The bud appears in the angle formed between a leaf and a stem.

axon (ak′-son) A typically long extension, or process, of a neuron that carries nerve impulses away from the cell body toward target cells.

B cells The lymphocytes that complete their development in the bone marrow and become effector cells for the humoral immune response.

Bacteria One of two prokaryotic domains, the other being Archaea.

bacteriophage (bak-tēr′-ē-ō-fāj) A virus that infects bacteria; also called a phage.

bacteroid A form of the bacterium *Rhizobium* contained within the vesicles formed by the root cells of a root nodule.

balancing selection Natural selection that maintains two or more phenotypic forms in a population.

bar graph A graph in which the independent variable represents groups or nonnumerical categories and the values of the dependent variable(s) are shown by bars.

bark All tissues external to the vascular cambium, consisting mainly of the secondary phloem and layers of periderm.

Barr body A dense object lying along the inside of the nuclear envelope in cells of female mammals, representing a highly condensed, inactivated X chromosome.

basal angiosperm A member of one of three clades of early-diverging lineages of extant flowering plants. Examples are *Amborella*, water lilies, and star anise and its relatives.

basal body (bā′-sul) A eukaryotic cell structure consisting of a "9 + 0" arrangement of microtubule triplets. The basal body may organize the microtubule assembly of a cilium or flagellum and is structurally very similar to a centriole.

basal metabolic rate (BMR) The metabolic rate of a resting, fasting, and nonstressed endotherm at a comfortable temperature.

basal taxon In a specified group of organisms, a taxon whose evolutionary lineage diverged early in the history of the group.

base A substance that reduces the hydrogen ion concentration of a solution.

basidiocarp Elaborate fruiting body of a dikaryotic mycelium of a club fungus.

basidiomycete (buh-sid′-ē-ō-mī′-sēt) A member of the fungal phylum Basidiomycota, commonly called club fungus. The name comes from the club-like shape of the basidium.

basidium (plural, **basidia**) (buh-sid′-ē-um, buh-sid′-ē-ah) A reproductive appendage that produces sexual spores on the gills of mushrooms (club fungi).

Batesian mimicry (bāt′-zē-un mim′-uh-krē) A type of mimicry in which a harmless species looks like a species that is poisonous or otherwise harmful to predators.

behavior Individually, an action carried out by muscles or glands under control of the nervous system in response to a stimulus; collectively, the sum of an animal's responses to external and internal stimuli.

behavioral ecology The study of the evolution of and ecological basis for animal behavior.

benign tumor A mass of abnormal cells with specific genetic and cellular changes such that the cells are not capable of surviving at a new site and generally remain at the site of the tumor's origin.

benthic zone The bottom surface of an aquatic environment.

benthos (ben′-thōz) The communities of organisms living in the benthic zone of an aquatic biome.

beta (β) pleated sheet One form of the secondary structure of proteins in which the polypeptide chain folds back and forth. Two regions of the chain lie parallel to each other and are held together by hydrogen bonds between atoms of the polypeptide backbone (not the side chains).

beta oxidation A metabolic sequence that breaks fatty acids down to two-carbon fragments that enter the citric acid cycle as acetyl CoA.

bicoid A maternal effect gene that codes for a protein responsible for specifying the anterior end in *Drosophila melanogaster*.

bilateral symmetry Body symmetry in which a central longitudinal plane divides the body into two equal but opposite halves.

bilaterian (bī′-luh-ter′-ē-uhn) A member of a clade of animals with bilateral symmetry and three germ layers.

bile A mixture of substances that is produced in the liver and stored in the gallbladder; enables formation of fat droplets in water as an aid in the digestion and absorption of fats.

binary fission A method of asexual reproduction by "division in half." In prokaryotes, binary fission does not involve mitosis, but in single-celled eukaryotes that undergo binary fission, mitosis is part of the process.

binomial A common term for the two-part, latinized format for naming a species, consisting of the genus and specific epithet; also called a binomen.

biodiversity hot spot A relatively small area with numerous endemic species and a large number of endangered and threatened species.

bioenergetics (1) The overall flow and transformation of energy in an organism. (2) The study of how energy flows through organisms.

biofilm A surface-coating colony of one or more species of prokaryotes that engage in metabolic cooperation.

biofuel A fuel produced from biomass.

biogenic amine A neurotransmitter derived from an amino acid.

biogeochemical cycle Any of the various chemical cycles, which involve both biotic and abiotic components of ecosystems.

biogeography The scientific study of the past and present geographic distributions of species.

bioinformatics The use of computers, software, and mathematical models to process and integrate biological information from large data sets.

biological augmentation An approach to restoration ecology that uses organisms to add essential materials to a degraded ecosystem.

biological clock An internal timekeeper that controls an organism's biological rhythms. The biological clock marks time with or without environmental cues but often requires signals from the environment to remain tuned to an appropriate period. *See also* circadian rhythm.

biological magnification A process in which retained substances become more concentrated at each higher trophic level in a food chain.

biological species concept Definition of a species as a group of populations whose members have the potential to interbreed in nature and produce viable, fertile offspring but do not produce viable, fertile offspring with members of other such groups.

biology The scientific study of life.

biomanipulation An approach that applies the top-down model of community organization to alter ecosystem characteristics. For example, ecologists can prevent algal blooms and eutrophication by altering the density of higher-level consumers in lakes instead of by using chemical treatments.

biomass The total mass of organic matter comprising a group of organisms in a particular habitat.

biome (bī′-ōm) Any of the world's major ecosystem types, often classified according to the predominant vegetation for terrestrial biomes and the physical environment for aquatic biomes and characterized by adaptations of organisms to that particular environment.

bioremediation The use of organisms to detoxify and restore polluted and degraded ecosystems.

biosphere The entire portion of Earth inhabited by life; the sum of all the planet's ecosystems.

biotechnology The manipulation of organisms or their components to produce useful products.

biotic (bī-ot′-ik) Pertaining to the living factors—the organisms—in an environment.

bipolar disorder A depressive mental illness characterized by swings of mood from high to low; also called manic-depressive disorder.

birth control pill A hormonal contraceptive that inhibits ovulation, retards follicular development, or alters a woman's cervical mucus to prevent sperm from entering the uterus.

blade (1) A leaflike structure of a seaweed that provides most of the surface area for photosynthesis. (2) The flattened portion of a typical leaf.

blastocoel (blas′-tuh-sēl) The fluid-filled cavity that forms in the center of a blastula.

blastocyst (blas′-tuh-sist) The blastula stage of mammalian embryonic development, consisting of an inner cell mass, a cavity, and an outer layer, the trophoblast. In humans, the blastocyst forms 1 week after fertilization.

blastomere An early embryonic cell arising during the cleavage stage of an early embryo.

blastopore (blas′-tō-pōr) In a gastrula, the opening of the archenteron that typically develops into the anus in deuterostomes and the mouth in protostomes.

blastula (blas′-tyū-luh) A hollow ball of cells that marks the end of the cleavage stage during early embryonic development in animals.

blood A connective tissue with a fluid matrix called plasma in which red blood cells, white blood cells, and cell fragments called platelets are suspended.

blue-light photoreceptor A type of light receptor in plants that initiates a variety of responses, such as phototropism and slowing of hypocotyl elongation.

body cavity A fluid- or air-filled space between the digestive tract and the body wall.

body plan In multicellular eukaryotes, a set of morphological and developmental traits that are integrated into a functional whole—the living organism.

Bohr shift A lowering of the affinity of hemoglobin for oxygen, caused by a drop in pH. It facilitates the release of oxygen from hemoglobin in the vicinity of active tissues.

bolus A lubricated ball of chewed food.

bone A connective tissue consisting of living cells held in a rigid matrix of collagen fibers embedded in calcium salts.

book lung An organ of gas exchange in spiders, consisting of stacked plates contained in an internal chamber.

bottleneck effect Genetic drift that occurs when the size of a population is reduced, as by a natural disaster or human actions. Typically, the surviving population is no longer genetically representative of the original population.

bottom-up model A model of community organization in which mineral nutrients influence community organization by controlling plant or phytoplankton numbers, which in turn control herbivore numbers, which in turn control predator numbers.

Bowman's capsule (bō′-munz) A cup-shaped receptacle in the vertebrate kidney that is the initial, expanded segment of the nephron, where filtrate enters from the blood.

brachiopod (bra′-kē-uh-pod′) A marine lophophorate with a shell divided into dorsal and ventral halves; also called lamp shells.

brain Organ of the central nervous system where information is processed and integrated.

brainstem A collection of structures in the vertebrate brain, including the midbrain, the pons, and the medulla oblongata; functions in homeostasis, coordination of movement, and conduction of information to higher brain centers.

branch point The representation on a phylogenetic tree of the divergence of two or more taxa from a common ancestor. A branch point is usually shown as a dichotomy in which a branch representing the ancestral lineage splits (at the branch point) into two branches, one for each of the two descendant lineages.

brassinosteroid A steroid hormone in plants that has a variety of effects, including inducing cell elongation, retarding leaf abscission, and promoting xylem differentiation.

breathing Ventilation of the lungs through alternating inhalation and exhalation.

bronchiole (brong′-kē-ōl′) A fine branch of the bronchi that transports air to alveoli.

bronchus (brong′-kus) (plural, **bronchi**) One of a pair of breathing tubes that branch from the trachea into the lungs.

brown alga A multicellular, photosynthetic protist with a characteristic brown or olive color that results from carotenoids in its plastids. Most brown algae are marine, and some have a plantlike body.

bryophyte (brī′-uh-fīt) An informal name for a moss, liverwort, or hornwort; a nonvascular plant that lives on land but lacks some of the terrestrial adaptations of vascular plants.

buffer A solution that contains a weak acid and its corresponding base. A buffer minimizes changes in pH when acids or bases are added to the solution.

bulk feeder An animal that eats relatively large pieces of food.

bulk flow The movement of a fluid due to a difference in pressure between two locations.

bundle-sheath cell In C_4 plants, a type of photosynthetic cell arranged into tightly packed sheaths around the veins of a leaf.

C_3 plant A plant that uses the Calvin cycle for the initial steps that incorporate CO_2 into organic material, forming a three-carbon compound as the first stable intermediate.

C_4 plant A plant in which the Calvin cycle is preceded by reactions that incorporate CO_2 into a four-carbon compound, the end product of which supplies CO_2 for the Calvin cycle.

calcitonin (kal′-si-tō′-nin) A hormone secreted by the thyroid gland that lowers blood calcium levels by promoting calcium deposition in bone and calcium excretion from the kidneys; nonessential in adult humans.

callus A mass of dividing, undifferentiated cells growing in culture.

calorie (cal) The amount of heat energy required to raise the temperature of 1 g of water by 1°C; also the amount of heat energy that 1 g of water releases when it cools by 1°C. The Calorie (with a capital C), usually used to indicate the energy content of food, is a kilocalorie.

Calvin cycle The second of two major stages in photosynthesis (following the light reactions), involving fixation of atmospheric CO_2 and reduction of the fixed carbon into carbohydrate.

Cambrian explosion A relatively brief time in geologic history when many present-day phyla of animals first appeared in the fossil record. This burst of evolutionary change occurred about 535–525 million years ago and saw the emergence of the first large, hard-bodied animals.

CAM plant A plant that uses crassulacean acid metabolism, an adaptation for photosynthesis in arid conditions. In this process, CO_2 entering open stomata during the night is converted to organic acids, which release CO_2 for the Calvin cycle during the day, when stomata are closed.

canopy The uppermost layer of vegetation in a terrestrial biome.

capillary (kap′-il-ār′-ē) A microscopic blood vessel that penetrates the tissues and consists of a single layer of endothelial cells that allows exchange between the blood and interstitial fluid.

capillary bed (kap′-il-ār′-ē) A network of capillaries in a tissue or organ.

capsid The protein shell that encloses a viral genome. It may be rod-shaped, polyhedral, or more complex in shape.

capsule (1) In many prokaryotes, a dense and well-defined layer of polysaccharide or protein that surrounds the cell wall and is sticky, protecting the cell and enabling it to adhere to substrates or other cells. (2) The sporangium of a bryophyte (moss, liverwort, or hornwort).

carbohydrate (kar′-bō-hī′-drāt) A sugar (monosaccharide) or one of its dimers (disaccharides) or polymers (polysaccharides).

carbon fixation The initial incorporation of carbon from CO_2 into an organic compound by an autotrophic organism (a plant, another photosynthetic organism, or a chemoautotrophic prokaryote).

carbonyl group (kar-buh-nēl′) A chemical group present in aldehydes and ketones and consisting of a carbon atom double-bonded to an oxygen atom.

carboxyl group (kar-bok′-sil) A chemical group present in organic acids and consisting of a single carbon atom double-bonded to an oxygen atom and also bonded to a hydroxyl group.

cardiac cycle (kar′-dē-ak) The alternating contractions and relaxations of the heart.

cardiac muscle (kar'-dē-ak) A type of striated muscle that forms the contractile wall of the heart. Its cells are joined by intercalated disks that relay the electrical signals underlying each heartbeat.

cardiac output (kar'-dē-ak) The volume of blood pumped per minute by each ventricle of the heart.

cardiovascular system A closed circulatory system with a heart and branching network of arteries, capillaries, and veins. The system is characteristic of vertebrates.

carnivore An animal that mainly eats other animals.

carotenoid (kuh-rot'-uh-noyd') An accessory pigment, either yellow or orange, in the chloroplasts of plants and in some prokaryotes. By absorbing wavelengths of light that chlorophyll cannot, carotenoids broaden the spectrum of colors that can drive photosynthesis.

carpel (kar'-pul) The ovule-producing reproductive organ of a flower, consisting of the stigma, style, and ovary.

carrier In genetics, an individual who is heterozygous at a given genetic locus for a recessively inherited disorder. The heterozygote is generally phenotypically normal for the disorder but can pass on the recessive allele to offspring.

carrying capacity The maximum population size that can be supported by the available resources, symbolized as K.

cartilage (kar'-til-ij) A flexible connective tissue with an abundance of collagenous fibers embedded in chondroitin sulfate.

Casparian strip (ka-spär'-ē-un) A water-impermeable ring of wax in the endodermal cells of plants that blocks the passive flow of water and solutes into the stele by way of cell walls.

catabolic pathway (kat'-uh-bol'-ik) A metabolic pathway that releases energy by breaking down complex molecules to simpler molecules.

catalyst (kat'-uh-list) A chemical agent that selectively increases the rate of a reaction without being consumed by the reaction.

catecholamine (kat'-uh-kōl'-uh-mēn) Any of a class of neurotransmitters and hormones, including the hormones epinephrine and norepinephrine, that are synthesized from the amino acid tyrosine.

cation (cat'-ī'-on) A positively charged ion.

cation exchange (cat'-ī'-on) A process in which positively charged minerals are made available to a plant when hydrogen ions in the soil displace mineral ions from the clay particles.

cecum (sē'-kum) (plural, **ceca**) The blind pouch forming one branch of the large intestine.

cell body The part of a neuron that houses the nucleus and most other organelles.

cell cycle An ordered sequence of events in the life of a cell, from its origin in the division of a parent cell until its own division into two. The eukaryotic cell cycle is composed of interphase (including G_1, S, and G_2 subphases) and M phase (including mitosis and cytokinesis).

cell cycle control system A cyclically operating set of molecules in the eukaryotic cell that

both triggers and coordinates key events in the cell cycle.

cell division The reproduction of cells.

cell fractionation The disruption of a cell and separation of its parts by centrifugation at successively higher speeds.

cell-mediated immune response The branch of adaptive immunity that involves the activation of cytotoxic T cells, which defend against infected cells.

cell plate A membrane-bounded, flattened sac located at the midline of a dividing plant cell, inside which the new cell wall forms during cytokinesis.

cellular respiration The catabolic pathways of aerobic and anaerobic respiration, which break down organic molecules and use an electron transport chain for the production of ATP.

cellulose (sel'-yū-lōs) A structural polysaccharide of plant cell walls, consisting of glucose monomers joined by β glycosidic linkages.

cell wall A protective layer external to the plasma membrane in the cells of plants, prokaryotes, fungi, and some protists. Polysaccharides such as cellulose (in plants and some protists), chitin (in fungi), and peptidoglycan (in bacteria) are important structural components of cell walls.

central nervous system (CNS) The portion of the nervous system where signal integration occurs; in vertebrate animals, the brain and spinal cord.

central vacuole In a mature plant cell, a large membranous sac with diverse roles in growth, storage, and sequestration of toxic substances.

centriole (sen'-trē-ōl) A structure in the centrosome of an animal cell composed of a cylinder of microtubule triplets arranged in a "9 + 0" pattern. A centrosome has a pair of centrioles.

centromere (sen'-trō-mēr) In a duplicated chromosome, the region on each sister chromatid where it is most closely attached to the other chromatid by proteins that bind to the centromeric DNA. Other proteins condense the chromatin in that region, so it appears as a narrow "waist" on the duplicated chromosome. (An unduplicated chromosome has a single centromere, identified by the proteins bound there.)

centrosome (sen'-trō-sōm) A structure present in the cytoplasm of animal cells that functions as a microtubule-organizing center and is important during cell division. A centrosome has two centrioles.

cercozoan An amoeboid or flagellated protist that feeds with threadlike pseudopodia.

cerebellum (sār'-ruh-bel'-um) Part of the vertebrate hindbrain located dorsally; functions in unconscious coordination of movement and balance.

cerebral cortex (suh-rē'-brul) The surface of the cerebrum; the largest and most complex part of the mammalian brain, containing nerve cell bodies of the cerebrum; the part of the vertebrate brain most changed through evolution.

cerebral hemisphere (suh-rē'-brul) The right or left side of the cerebrum.

cerebrum (suh-rē'-brum) The dorsal portion of the vertebrate forebrain, composed of right and left hemispheres; the integrating center for memory, learning, emotions, and other highly complex functions of the central nervous system.

cervix (ser'-viks) The neck of the uterus, which opens into the vagina.

chaparral A scrubland biome of dense, spiny evergreen shrubs found at midlatitudes along coasts where cold ocean currents circulate offshore; characterized by mild, rainy winters and long, hot, dry summers.

chaperonin (shap'-er-ō'-nin) A protein complex that assists in the proper folding of other proteins.

character An observable heritable feature that may vary among individuals.

character displacement The tendency for characteristics to be more divergent in sympatric populations of two species than in allopatric populations of the same two species.

checkpoint A control point in the cell cycle where stop and go-ahead signals can regulate the cycle.

chelicera (kē-lih'-suh-ruh) (plural, **chelicerae**) One of a pair of clawlike feeding appendages characteristic of chelicerates.

chelicerate (kē-lih-suh'-rāte) An arthropod that has chelicerae and a body divided into a cephalothorax and an abdomen. Living chelicerates include sea spiders, horseshoe crabs, scorpions, ticks, and spiders.

chemical bond An attraction between two atoms, resulting from a sharing of outer-shell electrons or the presence of opposite charges on the atoms. The bonded atoms gain complete outer electron shells.

chemical energy Energy available in molecules for release in a chemical reaction; a form of potential energy.

chemical equilibrium In a chemical reaction, the state in which the rate of the forward reaction equals the rate of the reverse reaction, so that the relative concentrations of the reactants and products do not change with time.

chemical reaction The making and breaking of chemical bonds, leading to changes in the composition of matter.

chemiosmosis (kem'-ē-oz-mō'-sis) An energy-coupling mechanism that uses energy stored in the form of a hydrogen ion gradient across a membrane to drive cellular work, such as the synthesis of ATP. Under aerobic conditions, most ATP synthesis in cells occurs by chemiosmosis.

chemoautotroph (kē'-mō-ot'-ō-trōf) An organism that obtains energy by oxidizing inorganic substances and needs only carbon dioxide as a carbon source.

chemoheterotroph (kē'-mō-het'-er-ō-trōf) An organism that requires organic molecules for both energy and carbon.

chemoreceptor A sensory receptor that responds to a chemical stimulus, such as a solute or an odorant.

chiasma (plural, **chiasmata**) (kī-az'-muh, kī-az'-muh-tuh) The X-shaped, microscopically visible region where crossing over has occurred earlier in prophase I between homologous nonsister chromatids. Chiasmata become visible after synapsis ends, with the two homologs remaining associated due to sister chromatid cohesion.

chitin (kī'-tin) A structural polysaccharide, consisting of amino sugar monomers, found in many fungal cell walls and in the exoskeletons of all arthropods.

chlorophyll (klôr'-ō-fil) A green pigment located in membranes within the chloroplasts of plants and algae and in the membranes of certain prokaryotes. Chlorophyll *a* participates directly in the light reactions, which convert solar energy to chemical energy.

chlorophyll *a* (klôr'-ō-fil) A photosynthetic pigment that participates directly in the light reactions, which convert solar energy to chemical energy.

chlorophyll *b* (klôr'-ō-fil) An accessory photosynthetic pigment that transfers energy to chlorophyll *a*.

chloroplast (klôr'-ō-plast) An organelle found in plants and photosynthetic protists that absorbs sunlight and uses it to drive the synthesis of organic compounds from carbon dioxide and water.

choanocyte (kō-an'-uh-sīt) A flagellated feeding cell found in sponges. Also called a collar cell, it has a collar-like ring that traps food particles around the base of its flagellum.

cholesterol (kō-les'-tuh-rol) A steroid that forms an essential component of animal cell membranes and acts as a precursor molecule for the synthesis of other biologically important steroids, such as many hormones.

chondrichthyan (kon-drik'-thē-an) A member of the clade Chondrichthyes, vertebrates with skeletons made mostly of cartilage, such as sharks and rays.

chordate A member of the phylum Chordata, animals that at some point during their development have a notochord; a dorsal, hollow nerve cord; pharyngeal slits or clefts; and a muscular, post-anal tail.

chorionic villus sampling (CVS) (kôr'-ē-on'-ik vil'-us) A technique associated with prenatal diagnosis in which a small sample of the fetal portion of the placenta is removed for analysis to detect certain genetic and congenital defects in the fetus.

chromatin (krō'-muh-tin) The complex of DNA and proteins that makes up eukaryotic chromosomes. When the cell is not dividing, chromatin exists in its dispersed form, as a mass of very long, thin fibers that are not visible with a light microscope.

chromosome (krō'-muh-sōm) A cellular structure consisting of one DNA molecule and associated protein molecules. (In some contexts, such as genome sequencing, the term may refer to the DNA alone.) A eukaryotic cell typically has multiple, linear chromosomes, which are located in the nucleus. A prokaryotic cell often has a single, circular chromosome, which is found in the nucleoid, a region that is not enclosed by a membrane. *See also* chromatin.

chromosome theory of inheritance (krō'-muh-sōm) A basic principle in biology stating that genes are located at specific positions (loci) on chromosomes and that the behavior of chromosomes during meiosis accounts for inheritance patterns.

chylomicron (kī'-lō-mī'-kron) A lipid transport globule composed of fats mixed with cholesterol and coated with proteins.

chyme (kīm) The mixture of partially digested food and digestive juices formed in the stomach.

chytrid (kī'-trid) A member of the fungal phylum Chytridiomycota, mostly aquatic fungi with flagellated zoospores that represent an early-diverging fungal lineage.

ciliate (sil'-ē-it) A type of protist that moves by means of cilia.

cilium (sil'-ē-um) (plural, **cilia**) A short appendage containing microtubules in eukaryotic cells. A motile cilium is specialized for locomotion or moving fluid past the cell; it is formed from a core of nine outer doublet microtubules and two inner single microtubules (the "9 + 2" arrangement) ensheathed in an extension of the plasma membrane. A primary cilium is usually nonmotile and plays a sensory and signaling role; it lacks the two inner microtubules (the "9 + 0" arrangement).

circadian rhythm (ser-kā'-dē-un) A physiological cycle of about 24 hours that persists even in the absence of external cues.

***cis-trans* isomer** One of several compounds that have the same molecular formula and covalent bonds between atoms but differ in the spatial arrangements of their atoms owing to the inflexibility of double bonds; formerly called a geometric isomer.

citric acid cycle A chemical cycle involving eight steps that completes the metabolic breakdown of glucose molecules begun in glycolysis by oxidizing acetyl CoA (derived from pyruvate) to carbon dioxide; occurs within the mitochondrion in eukaryotic cells and in the cytosol of prokaryotes; together with pyruvate oxidation, the second major stage in cellular respiration.

clade (klayd) A group of species that includes an ancestral species and all of its descendants. A clade is equivalent to a monophyletic group.

cladistics (kluh-dis'-tiks) An approach to systematics in which organisms are placed into groups called clades based primarily on common descent.

class In Linnaean classification, the taxonomic category above the level of order.

cleavage (1) The process of cytokinesis in animal cells, characterized by pinching of the plasma membrane. (2) The succession of rapid cell divisions without significant growth during early embryonic development that converts the zygote to a ball of cells.

cleavage furrow The first sign of cleavage in an animal cell; a shallow groove around the cell in the cell surface near the old metaphase plate.

climate The long-term prevailing weather conditions at a given place.

climograph A plot of the temperature and precipitation in a particular region.

clitoris (klit'-uh-ris) An organ at the upper intersection of the labia minora that engorges with blood and becomes erect during sexual arousal.

cloaca (klō-ā'-kuh) A common opening for the digestive, urinary, and reproductive tracts found in many nonmammalian vertebrates but in few mammals.

clonal selection The process by which an antigen selectively binds to and activates only those lymphocytes bearing receptors specific for the antigen. The selected lymphocytes proliferate and differentiate into a clone of effector cells and a clone of memory cells specific for the stimulating antigen.

clone (1) A lineage of genetically identical individuals or cells. (2) In popular usage, an individual that is genetically identical to another individual. (3) As a verb, to make one or more genetic replicas of an individual or cell. *See also* gene cloning.

cloning vector In genetic engineering, a DNA molecule that can carry foreign DNA into a host cell and replicate there. Cloning vectors include plasmids and bacterial artificial chromosomes (BACs), which move recombinant DNA from a test tube back into a cell, and viruses that transfer recombinant DNA by infection.

closed circulatory system A circulatory system in which blood is confined to vessels and is kept separate from the interstitial fluid.

cnidocyte (nī'-duh-sīt) A specialized cell unique to the phylum Cnidaria; contains a capsule-like organelle housing a coiled thread that, when discharged, explodes outward and functions in prey capture or defense.

cochlea (kok'-lē-uh) The complex, coiled organ of hearing that contains the organ of Corti.

codominance The situation in which the phenotypes of both alleles are exhibited in the heterozygote because both alleles affect the phenotype in separate, distinguishable ways.

codon (kō'-don) A three-nucleotide sequence of DNA or mRNA that specifies a particular amino acid or termination signal; the basic unit of the genetic code.

coefficient of relatedness The fraction of genes that, on average, are shared by two individuals.

coelom (sē'-lōm) A body cavity lined by tissue derived only from mesoderm.

coelomate (sē'-lō-māt) An animal that possesses a true coelom (a body cavity lined by tissue completely derived from mesoderm).

coenocytic fungus (sē'-no-si'-tic) A fungus that lacks septa and hence whose body is made up of a continuous cytoplasmic mass that may contain hundreds or thousands of nuclei.

coenzyme (kō-en'-zīm) An organic molecule serving as a cofactor. Most vitamins function as coenzymes in metabolic reactions.

coevolution The joint evolution of two interacting species, each in response to selection imposed by the other.

cofactor Any nonprotein molecule or ion that is required for the proper functioning of an enzyme. Cofactors can be permanently bound to the active site or may bind loosely and reversibly, along with the substrate, during catalysis.

cognition The process of knowing that may include awareness, reasoning, recollection, and judgment.

cognitive map A neural representation of the abstract spatial relationships between objects in an animal's surroundings.

cohesion The linking together of like molecules, often by hydrogen bonds.

cohesion-tension hypothesis The leading explanation of the ascent of xylem sap. It states that transpiration exerts pull on xylem sap, putting the sap under negative pressure, or tension, and that the cohesion of water molecules transmits this pull along the entire length of the xylem from shoots to roots.

cohort A group of individuals of the same age in a population.

coleoptile (kō'-lē-op'-tul) The covering of the young shoot of the embryo of a grass seed.

coleorhiza (kō'-lē-uh-rī'-zuh) The covering of the young root of the embryo of a grass seed.

collagen A glycoprotein in the extracellular matrix of animal cells that forms strong fibers, found extensively in connective tissue and bone; the most abundant protein in the animal kingdom.

collecting duct The location in the kidney where processed filtrate, called urine, is collected from the renal tubules.

collenchyma cell (kō-len'-kim-uh) A flexible plant cell type that occurs in strands or cylinders that support young parts of the plant without restraining growth.

colon (kō'-len) The largest section of the vertebrate large intestine; functions in water absorption and formation of feces.

commensalism (kuh-men'-suh-lizm) A symbiotic relationship in which one organism benefits but the other is neither helped nor harmed.

communication In animal behavior, a process involving transmission of, reception of, and response to signals. The term is also used in connection with other organisms, as well as individual cells of multicellular organisms.

community All the organisms that inhabit a particular area; an assemblage of populations of different species living close enough together for potential interaction.

community ecology The study of how interactions between species affect community structure and organization.

companion cell A type of plant cell that is connected to a sieve-tube element by many plasmodesmata and whose nucleus and ribosomes may serve one or more adjacent sieve-tube elements.

competitive exclusion The concept that when populations of two similar species compete for the same limited resources, one population will use the resources more efficiently and have a reproductive advantage that will eventually lead to the elimination of the other population.

competitive inhibitor A substance that reduces the activity of an enzyme by entering the active site in place of the substrate, whose structure it mimics.

complement system A group of about 30 blood proteins that may amplify the inflammatory response, enhance phagocytosis, or directly lyse extracellular pathogens.

complementary DNA (cDNA) A double-stranded DNA molecule made *in vitro* using mRNA as a template and the enzymes reverse transcriptase and DNA polymerase. A cDNA molecule corresponds to the exons of a gene.

complete dominance The situation in which the phenotypes of the heterozygote and dominant homozygote are indistinguishable.

complete flower A flower that has all four basic floral organs: sepals, petals, stamens, and carpels.

complete metamorphosis The transformation of a larva into an adult that looks very different, and often functions very differently in its environment, than the larva.

compound A substance consisting of two or more different elements combined in a fixed ratio.

compound eye A type of multifaceted eye in insects and crustaceans consisting of up to several thousand light-detecting, focusing ommatidia.

concentration gradient A region along which the density of a chemical substance increases or decreases.

conception The fertilization of an egg by a sperm in humans.

cone A cone-shaped cell in the retina of the vertebrate eye, sensitive to color.

conformer An animal for which an internal condition conforms to (changes in accordance with) changes in an environmental variable.

conidium (plural, **conidia**) A haploid spore produced at the tip of a specialized hypha in ascomycetes during asexual reproduction.

conifer A member of the largest gymnosperm phylum. Most conifers are cone-bearing trees, such as pines and firs.

conjugation (kon'-jū-gā'-shun) (1) In prokaryotes, the direct transfer of DNA between two cells that are temporarily joined. When the two cells are members of different species, conjugation results in horizontal gene transfer. (2) In ciliates, a sexual process in which two cells exchange haploid micronuclei but do not reproduce.

connective tissue Animal tissue that functions mainly to bind and support other tissues, having a sparse population of cells scattered through an extracellular matrix.

conodont An early, soft-bodied vertebrate with prominent eyes and dental elements.

conservation biology The integrated study of ecology, evolutionary biology, physiology, molecular biology, and genetics to sustain biological diversity at all levels.

consumer An organism that feeds on producers, other consumers, or nonliving organic material.

contraception The deliberate prevention of pregnancy.

contractile vacuole A membranous sac that helps move excess water out of certain freshwater protists.

control element A segment of noncoding DNA that helps regulate transcription of a gene by serving as a binding site for a transcription factor. Multiple control elements are present in a eukaryotic gene's enhancer.

control group In a controlled experiment, a set of subjects that lacks (or does not receive) the specific factor being tested. Ideally, the control group should be identical to the experimental group in other respects.

controlled experiment An experiment in which an experimental group is compared with a control group that varies only in the factor being tested.

convergent evolution The evolution of similar features in independent evolutionary lineages.

convergent extension A process in which the cells of a tissue layer rearrange themselves in such a way that the sheet of cells becomes narrower (converges) and longer (extends).

cooperativity A kind of allosteric regulation whereby a shape change in one subunit of a protein caused by substrate binding is transmitted to all the other subunits, facilitating binding of additional substrate molecules to those subunits.

coral reef Typically a warm-water, tropical ecosystem dominated by the hard skeletal structures secreted primarily by corals. Some coral reefs also exist in cold, deep waters.

corepressor A small molecule that binds to a bacterial repressor protein and changes the protein's shape, allowing it to bind to the operator and switch an operon off.

cork cambium (kam'-bē-um) A cylinder of meristematic tissue in woody plants that replaces the epidermis with thicker, tougher cork cells.

corpus callosum (kor'-pus kuh-lō'-sum) The thick band of nerve fibers that connects the right and left cerebral hemispheres in mammals, enabling the hemispheres to process information together.

corpus luteum (kor'-pus lū'-tē-um) A secreting tissue in the ovary that forms from the collapsed follicle after ovulation and produces progesterone.

cortex (1) The outer region of cytoplasm in a eukaryotic cell, lying just under the plasma membrane, that has a more gel-like consistency than the inner regions due to the presence of multiple microfilaments. (2) In plants, ground tissue that is between the vascular tissue and dermal tissue in a root or eudicot stem.

cortical nephron In mammals and birds, a nephron with a loop of Henle located almost entirely in the renal cortex.

cotransport The coupling of the "downhill" diffusion of one substance to the "uphill" transport of another against its own concentration gradient.

cotyledon (kot'-uh-lē'-dun) A seed leaf of an angiosperm embryo. Some species have one cotyledon, others two.

countercurrent exchange The exchange of a substance or heat between two fluids flowing in opposite directions. For example, blood in a fish gill flows in the opposite direction of water passing over the gill, maximizing diffusion of oxygen into and carbon dioxide out of the blood.

countercurrent multiplier system A countercurrent system in which energy is expended in active transport to facilitate exchange of materials and generate concentration gradients.

covalent bond (kō-vā′-lent) A type of strong chemical bond in which two atoms share one or more pairs of valence electrons.

crassulacean acid metabolism (CAM) An adaptation for photosynthesis in arid conditions, first discovered in the family Crassulaceae. In this process, a plant takes up CO_2 and incorporates it into a variety of organic acids at night; during the day, CO_2 is released from organic acids for use in the Calvin cycle.

crista (plural, **cristae**) (kris′-tuh, kris′-tē) An infolding of the inner membrane of a mitochondrion. The inner membrane houses electron transport chains and molecules of the enzyme catalyzing the synthesis of ATP (ATP synthase).

critical load The amount of added nutrient, usually nitrogen or phosphorus, that can be absorbed by plants without damaging ecosystem integrity.

crop rotation The practice of growing different crops in succession on the same land chiefly to preserve the productive capacity of the soil.

cross-fostering study A behavioral study in which the young of one species are placed in the care of adults from another species.

crossing over The reciprocal exchange of genetic material between nonsister chromatids during prophase I of meiosis.

cross-pollination In angiosperms, the transfer of pollen from an anther of a flower on one plant to the stigma of a flower on another plant of the same species.

cryptic coloration Camouflage that makes a potential prey difficult to spot against its background.

culture A system of information transfer through social learning or teaching that influences the behavior of individuals in a population.

cuticle (kyū′-tuh-kul) (1) A waxy covering on the surface of stems and leaves that prevents desiccation in terrestrial plants. (2) The exoskeleton of an arthropod, consisting of layers of protein and chitin that are variously modified for different functions. (3) A tough coat that covers the body of a nematode.

cyclic AMP (cAMP) Cyclic adenosine monophosphate, a ring-shaped molecule made from ATP that is a common intracellular signaling molecule (second messenger) in eukaryotic cells. It is also a regulator of some bacterial operons.

cyclic electron flow A route of electron flow during the light reactions of photosynthesis that involves only one photosystem and that produces ATP but not NADPH or O_2.

cyclin (sī′-klin) A cellular protein that occurs in a cyclically fluctuating concentration and that plays an important role in regulating the cell cycle.

cyclin-dependent kinase (Cdk) (sī′-klin) A protein kinase that is active only when attached to a particular cyclin.

cyclostome A member of the vertebrate subgroup lacking jaws. Cyclostomes include hagfishes and lampreys.

cystic fibrosis (sis′-tik fī-brō′-sis) A human genetic disorder caused by a recessive allele for a chloride channel protein; characterized by an excessive secretion of mucus and consequent vulnerability to infection; fatal if untreated.

cytochrome (sī′-tō-krōm) An iron-containing protein that is a component of electron transport chains in the mitochondria and chloroplasts of eukaryotic cells and the plasma membranes of prokaryotic cells.

cytokinesis (sī′-tō-kuh-nē′-sis) The division of the cytoplasm to form two separate daughter cells immediately after mitosis, meiosis I, or meiosis II.

cytokinin (sī′-tō-kī′-nin) Any of a class of related plant hormones that retard aging and act in concert with auxin to stimulate cell division, influence the pathway of differentiation, and control apical dominance.

cytoplasm (sī′-tō-plaz-um) The contents of the cell bounded by the plasma membrane; in eukaryotes, the portion exclusive of the nucleus.

cytoplasmic determinant A maternal substance, such as a protein or RNA, that when placed into an egg influences the course of early development by regulating the expression of genes that affect the developmental fate of cells.

cytoplasmic streaming A circular flow of cytoplasm, involving interactions of myosin and actin filaments, that speeds the distribution of materials within cells.

cytoskeleton A network of microtubules, microfilaments, and intermediate filaments that extend throughout the cytoplasm and serve a variety of mechanical, transport, and signaling functions.

cytosol (sī′-tō-sol) The semifluid portion of the cytoplasm.

cytotoxic T cell A type of lymphocyte that, when activated, kills infected cells as well as certain cancer cells and transplanted cells.

dalton A measure of mass for atoms and subatomic particles; the same as the atomic mass unit, or amu.

data Recorded observations.

day-neutral plant A plant in which flower formation is not controlled by photoperiod or day length.

decomposer An organism that absorbs nutrients from nonliving organic material such as corpses, fallen plant material, and the wastes of living organisms and converts them to inorganic forms; a detritivore.

deductive reasoning A type of logic in which specific results are predicted from a general premise.

deep-sea hydrothermal vent A dark, hot, oxygen-deficient environment associated with volcanic activity on or near the seafloor. The producers in a vent community are chemoautotrophic prokaryotes.

de-etiolation The changes a plant shoot undergoes in response to sunlight; also known informally as greening.

dehydration reaction A chemical reaction in which two molecules become covalently bonded to each other with the removal of a water molecule.

deletion (1) A deficiency in a chromosome resulting from the loss of a fragment through breakage. (2) A mutational loss of one or more nucleotide pairs from a gene.

demographic transition In a stable population, a shift from high birth and death rates to low birth and death rates.

demography The study of changes over time in the vital statistics of populations, especially birth rates and death rates.

denaturation (dē-nā′-chur-ā′-shun) In proteins, a process in which a protein loses its native shape due to the disruption of weak chemical bonds and interactions, thereby becoming biologically inactive; in DNA, the separation of the two strands of the double helix. Denaturation occurs under extreme (noncellular) conditions of pH, salt concentration, or temperature.

dendrite (den′-drīt) One of usually numerous, short, highly branched extensions of a neuron that receive signals from other neurons.

dendritic cell An antigen-presenting cell, located mainly in lymphatic tissues and skin, that is particularly efficient in presenting antigens to helper T cells, thereby initiating a primary immune response.

density The number of individuals per unit area or volume.

density dependent Referring to any characteristic that varies with population density.

density-dependent inhibition The phenomenon observed in normal animal cells that causes them to stop dividing when they come into contact with one another.

density independent Referring to any characteristic that is not affected by population density.

deoxyribonucleic acid (DNA) (dē-ok′-sē-rī′-bō-nū-klā′-ik) A nucleic acid molecule, usually a double-stranded helix, in which each polynucleotide strand consists of nucleotide monomers with a deoxyribose sugar and the nitrogenous bases adenine (A), cytosine (C), guanine (G), and thymine (T); capable of being replicated and determining the inherited structure of a cell's proteins.

deoxyribose (dē-ok′-si-rī′-bōs) The sugar component of DNA nucleotides, having one fewer hydroxyl group than ribose, the sugar component of RNA nucleotides.

dependent variable A variable whose value is measured during an experiment or other test to see whether it is influenced by changes in another variable (the independent variable).

depolarization A change in a cell's membrane potential such that the inside of the membrane is made less negative relative to the outside. For example, a neuron membrane is depolarized if a stimulus decreases its voltage from the resting potential of −70 mV in the direction of zero voltage.

dermal tissue system The outer protective covering of plants.

desert A terrestrial biome characterized by very low precipitation.

desmosome A type of intercellular junction in animal cells that functions as a rivet, fastening cells together.

determinate cleavage A type of embryonic development in protostomes that rigidly casts the developmental fate of each embryonic cell very early.

determinate growth A type of growth characteristic of most animals and some plant organs, in which growth stops after a certain size is reached.

determination The progressive restriction of developmental potential in which the possible fate of each cell becomes more limited as an embryo develops. At the end of determination, a cell is committed to its fate.

detritivore (deh-trī'-tuh-vōr) A consumer that derives its energy and nutrients from nonliving organic material such as corpses, fallen plant material, and the wastes of living organisms; a decomposer.

detritus (di-trī'-tus) Dead organic matter.

deuteromycete (dū'-tuh-rō-mī'-sēt) Traditional classification for a fungus with no known sexual stage.

deuterostome development (dū'-tuh-rō-stōm') In animals, a developmental mode distinguished by the development of the anus from the blastopore; often also characterized by radial cleavage and by the body cavity forming as outpockets of mesodermal tissue.

Deuterostomia (dū'-tuh-rō-stōm'-ē-uh) One of the three main lineages of bilaterian animals. *See also* Ecdysozoa and Lophotrochozoa.

development The events involved in an organism's changing gradually from a simple to a more complex or specialized form.

diabetes mellitus (dī'-uh-bē'-tis mel'-uh-tus) An endocrine disorder marked by an inability to maintain glucose homeostasis. The type 1 form results from autoimmune destruction of insulin-secreting cells; treatment usually requires daily insulin injections. The type 2 form most commonly results from reduced responsiveness of target cells to insulin; obesity and lack of exercise are risk factors.

diacylglycerol (DAG) (dī-a'-sil-glis'-er-ol) A second messenger produced by the cleavage of the phospholipid PIP$_2$ in the plasma membrane.

diaphragm (dī'-uh-fram') (1) A sheet of muscle that forms the bottom wall of the thoracic cavity in mammals. Contraction of the diaphragm pulls air into the lungs. (2) A dome-shaped rubber cup fitted into the upper portion of the vagina before sexual intercourse. It serves as a physical barrier to the passage of sperm into the uterus.

diapsid (dī-ap'-sid) A member of an amniote clade distinguished by a pair of holes on each side of the skull. Diapsids include the lepidosaurs and archosaurs.

diastole (dī-as'-tō-lē) The stage of the cardiac cycle in which a heart chamber is relaxed and fills with blood.

diastolic pressure Blood pressure in the arteries when the ventricles are relaxed.

diatom Photosynthetic protist in the stramenopile clade; diatoms have a unique glass-like wall made of silicon dioxide embedded in an organic matrix.

dicot A term traditionally used to refer to flowering plants that have two embryonic seed leaves, or cotyledons. Recent molecular evidence indicates that dicots do not form a clade; species once classified as dicots are now grouped into eudicots, magnoliids, and several lineages of basal angiosperms.

differential gene expression The expression of different sets of genes by cells with the same genome.

differentiation The process by which a cell or group of cells becomes specialized in structure and function.

diffusion The random thermal motion of particles of liquids, gases, or solids. In the presence of a concentration or electrochemical gradient, diffusion results in the net movement of a substance from a region where it is more concentrated to a region where it is less concentrated.

digestion The second stage of food processing in animals: the breaking down of food into molecules small enough for the body to absorb.

dihybrid (dī'-hī'-brid) An organism that is heterozygous with respect to two genes of interest. All the offspring from a cross between parents doubly homozygous for different alleles are dihybrids. For example, parents of genotypes *AABB* and *aabb* produce a dihybrid of genotype *AaBb*.

dihybrid cross (dī'-hī'-brid) A cross between two organisms that are each heterozygous for both of the characters being followed (or the self-pollination of a plant that is heterozygous for both characters).

dikaryotic (dī'-kār-ē-ot'-ik) Referring to a fungal mycelium with two haploid nuclei per cell, one from each parent.

dinoflagellate (dī'-nō-flaj'-uh-let) A member of a group of mostly unicellular photosynthetic algae with two flagella situated in perpendicular grooves in cellulose plates covering the cell.

dinosaur A member of an extremely diverse clade of reptiles varying in body shape, size, and habitat. Birds are the only extant dinosaurs.

dioecious (dī-ē'-shus) In plant biology, having the male and female reproductive parts on different individuals of the same species.

diploblastic Having two germ layers.

diploid cell (dip'-loyd) A cell containing two sets of chromosomes (2*n*), one set inherited from each parent.

diplomonad A protist that has modified mitochondria, two equal-sized nuclei, and multiple flagella.

directional selection Natural selection in which individuals at one end of the phenotypic range survive or reproduce more successfully than do other individuals.

disaccharide (dī-sak'-uh-rīd) A double sugar, consisting of two monosaccharides joined by a glycosidic linkage formed by a dehydration reaction.

dispersal The movement of individuals or gametes away from their parent location. This movement sometimes expands the geographic range of a population or species.

dispersion The pattern of spacing among individuals within the boundaries of a population.

disruptive selection Natural selection in which individuals on both extremes of a phenotypic range survive or reproduce more successfully than do individuals with intermediate phenotypes.

distal tubule In the vertebrate kidney, the portion of a nephron that helps refine filtrate and empties it into a collecting duct.

disturbance A natural or human-caused event that changes a biological community and usually removes organisms from it. Disturbances, such as fires and storms, play a pivotal role in structuring many communities.

disulfide bridge A strong covalent bond formed when the sulfur of one cysteine monomer bonds to the sulfur of another cysteine monomer.

DNA (deoxyribonucleic acid) (dē-ok'-sē-rī'-bō-nū-klā'-ik) A nucleic acid molecule, usually a double-stranded helix, in which each polynucleotide strand consists of nucleotide monomers with a deoxyribose sugar and the nitrogenous bases adenine (A), cytosine (C), guanine (G), and thymine (T); capable of being replicated and determining the inherited structure of a cell's proteins.

DNA cloning The production of multiple copies of a specific DNA segment.

DNA ligase (lī'-gās) A linking enzyme essential for DNA replication; catalyzes the covalent bonding of the 3' end of one DNA fragment (such as an Okazaki fragment) to the 5' end of another DNA fragment (such as a growing DNA chain).

DNA methylation The presence of methyl groups on the DNA bases (usually cytosine) of plants, animals, and fungi. (The term also refers to the process of adding methyl groups to DNA bases.)

DNA microarray assay A method to detect and measure the expression of thousands of genes at one time. Tiny amounts of a large number of single-stranded DNA fragments representing different genes are fixed to a glass slide and tested for hybridization with samples of labeled cDNA.

DNA polymerase (puh-lim'-er-ās) An enzyme that catalyzes the elongation of new DNA (for example, at a replication fork) by the addition of nucleotides to the 3' end of an existing chain. There are several different DNA polymerases; DNA polymerase III and DNA polymerase I play major roles in DNA replication in *E. coli*.

DNA replication The process by which a DNA molecule is copied; also called DNA synthesis.

DNA sequencing Determining the complete nucleotide sequence of a gene or DNA segment.

DNA technology Techniques for sequencing and manipulating DNA.

domain (1) A taxonomic category above the kingdom level. The three domains are

Archaea, Bacteria, and Eukarya. (2) A discrete structural and functional region of a protein.

dominant allele An allele that is fully expressed in the phenotype of a heterozygote.

dominant species A species with substantially higher abundance or biomass than other species in a community. Dominant species exert a powerful control over the occurrence and distribution of other species.

dopamine A neurotransmitter that is a catecholamine, like epinephrine and norepinephrine.

dormancy A condition typified by extremely low metabolic rate and a suspension of growth and development.

dorsal Pertaining to the top of an animal with radial or bilateral symmetry.

dorsal lip The region above the blastopore on the dorsal side of the amphibian embryo.

double bond A double covalent bond; the sharing of two pairs of valence electrons by two atoms.

double circulation A circulatory system consisting of separate pulmonary and systemic circuits, in which blood passes through the heart after completing each circuit.

double fertilization A mechanism of fertilization in angiosperms in which two sperm cells unite with two cells in the female gametophyte (embryo sac) to form the zygote and endosperm.

double helix The form of native DNA, referring to its two adjacent antiparallel polynucleotide strands wound around an imaginary axis into a spiral shape.

Down syndrome A human genetic disease usually caused by the presence of an extra chromosome 21; characterized by developmental delays and heart and other defects that are generally treatable or non-life-threatening.

Duchenne muscular dystrophy (duh-shen′) A human genetic disease caused by a sex-linked recessive allele; characterized by progressive weakening and a loss of muscle tissue.

duodenum (dū′-uh-dēn′-um) The first section of the small intestine, where chyme from the stomach mixes with digestive juices from the pancreas, liver, and gallbladder as well as from gland cells of the intestinal wall.

duplication An aberration in chromosome structure due to fusion with a fragment from a homologous chromosome, such that a portion of a chromosome is duplicated.

dynein (dī′-nē-un) In cilia and flagella, a large motor protein extending from one microtubule doublet to the adjacent doublet. ATP hydrolysis drives changes in dynein shape that lead to bending of cilia and flagella.

E site One of a ribosome's three binding sites for tRNA during translation. The E site is the place where discharged tRNAs leave the ribosome. (E stands for exit.)

Ecdysozoa (ek′-dē-sō-zō′-uh) One of the three main lineages of bilaterian animals; many ecdysozoans are molting animals. *See also* Deuterostomia and Lophotrochozoa.

echinoderm (i-kī′-nō-derm) A slow-moving or sessile marine deuterostome with a water vascular system and, in larvae, bilateral symmetry. Echinoderms include sea stars, brittle stars, sea urchins, feather stars, and sea cucumbers.

ecological footprint The aggregate land and water area required by a person, city, or nation to produce all of the resources it consumes and to absorb all of the wastes it generates.

ecological niche (nich) The sum of a species' use of the biotic and abiotic resources in its environment.

ecological species concept Definition of a species in terms of ecological niche, the sum of how members of the species interact with the nonliving and living parts of their environment.

ecological succession Transition in the species composition of a community following a disturbance; establishment of a community in an area virtually barren of life.

ecology The study of how organisms interact with each other and their environment.

ecosystem All the organisms in a given area as well as the abiotic factors with which they interact; one or more communities and the physical environment around them.

ecosystem ecology The study of energy flow and the cycling of chemicals among the various biotic and abiotic components in an ecosystem.

ecosystem engineer An organism that influences community structure by causing physical changes in the environment.

ecosystem service A function performed by an ecosystem that directly or indirectly benefits humans.

ecotone The transition from one type of habitat or ecosystem to another, such as the transition from a forest to a grassland.

ectoderm (ek′-tō-durm) The outermost of the three primary germ layers in animal embryos; gives rise to the outer covering and, in some phyla, the nervous system, inner ear, and lens of the eye.

ectomycorrhiza (plural, **ectomycorrhizae**) (ek′-tō-mī′-kō-rī′-zuh, ek′-tō-mī′-kō-rī′-zē) Association of a fungus with a plant root system in which the fungus surrounds the roots but does not cause invagination of the host (plant) cell's plasma membrane.

ectomycorrhizal fungus A symbiotic fungus that forms sheaths of hyphae over the surface of plant roots and also grows into extracellular spaces of the root cortex.

ectoparasite A parasite that feeds on the external surface of a host.

ectopic Occurring in an abnormal location.

ectoproct A sessile, colonial lophophorate; also called a bryozoan.

ectothermic Referring to organisms for which external sources provide most of the heat for temperature regulation.

Ediacaran biota (ē′-dē-uh-keh′-run bī-ō′-tuh) An early group of macroscopic, soft-bodied, multicellular eukaryotes known from fossils that range in age from 635 million to 535 million years old.

effective population size An estimate of the size of a population based on the numbers of females and males that successfully breed; generally smaller than the total population.

effector Pathogen-encoded protein that cripples the host's innate immune system.

effector cell (1) A muscle cell or gland cell that carries out the body's response to stimuli as directed by signals from the brain or other processing center of the nervous system. (2) A lymphocyte that has undergone clonal selection and is capable of mediating an adaptive immune response.

egg The female gamete.

egg-polarity gene A gene that helps control the orientation (polarity) of the egg; also called a maternal effect gene.

ejaculation The propulsion of sperm from the epididymis through the muscular vas deferens, ejaculatory duct, and urethra.

electrocardiogram (ECG or EKG) A record of the electrical impulses that travel through heart muscle during the cardiac cycle.

electrochemical gradient The diffusion gradient of an ion, which is affected by both the concentration difference of an ion across a membrane (a chemical force) and the ion's tendency to move relative to the membrane potential (an electrical force).

electrogenic pump An active transport protein that generates voltage across a membrane while pumping ions.

electromagnetic receptor A receptor of electromagnetic energy, such as visible light, electricity, or magnetism.

electromagnetic spectrum The entire spectrum of electromagnetic radiation, ranging in wavelength from less than a nanometer to more than a kilometer.

electron A subatomic particle with a single negative electrical charge and a mass about 1/2,000 that of a neutron or proton. One or more electrons move around the nucleus of an atom.

electron microscope (EM) A microscope that uses magnets to focus an electron beam on or through a specimen, resulting in a practical resolution that is 100-fold greater than that of a light microscope using standard techniques. A transmission electron microscope (TEM) is used to study the internal structure of thin sections of cells. A scanning electron microscope (SEM) is used to study the fine details of cell surfaces.

electron shell An energy level of electrons at a characteristic average distance from the nucleus of an atom.

electron transport chain A sequence of electron carrier molecules (membrane proteins) that shuttle electrons down a series of redox reactions that release energy used to make ATP.

electronegativity The attraction of a given atom for the electrons of a covalent bond.

electroporation A technique to introduce recombinant DNA into cells by applying a brief electrical pulse to a solution containing the cells. The pulse creates temporary holes in the cells' plasma membranes, through which DNA can enter.

element Any substance that cannot be broken down to any other substance by chemical reactions.

elimination The fourth and final stage of food processing in animals: the passing of undigested material out of the body.

embryo sac (em′-brē-ō) The female gametophyte of angiosperms, formed from the growth and division of the megaspore into a multicellular structure that typically has eight haploid nuclei.

embryonic lethal A mutation with a phenotype leading to death of an embryo or larva.

embryophyte Alternate name for land plants that refers to their shared derived trait of multicellular, dependent embryos.

emergent properties New properties that arise with each step upward in the hierarchy of life, owing to the arrangement and interactions of parts as complexity increases.

emigration The movement of individuals out of a population.

enantiomer (en-an′-tē-ō-mer) One of two compounds that are mirror images of each other and that differ in shape due to the presence of an asymmetric carbon.

endangered species A species that is in danger of extinction throughout all or a significant portion of its range.

endemic (en-dem′-ik) Referring to a species that is confined to a specific geographic area.

endergonic reaction (en′-der-gon′-ik) A nonspontaneous chemical reaction in which free energy is absorbed from the surroundings.

endocrine gland (en′-dō-krin) A ductless gland that secretes hormones directly into the interstitial fluid, from which they diffuse into the bloodstream.

endocrine system (en′-dō-krin) In animals, the internal system of communication involving hormones, the ductless glands that secrete hormones, and the molecular receptors on or in target cells that respond to hormones; functions in concert with the nervous system to effect internal regulation and maintain homeostasis.

endocytosis (en′-dō-sī-tō′-sis) Cellular uptake of biological molecules and particulate matter via formation of vesicles from the plasma membrane.

endoderm (en′-dō-durm) The innermost of the three primary germ layers in animal embryos; lines the archenteron and gives rise to the liver, pancreas, lungs, and the lining of the digestive tract in species that have these structures.

endodermis In plant roots, the innermost layer of the cortex that surrounds the vascular cylinder.

endomembrane system The collection of membranes inside and surrounding a eukaryotic cell, related either through direct physical contact or by the transfer of membranous vesicles; includes the plasma membrane, the nuclear envelope, the smooth and rough endoplasmic reticulum, the Golgi apparatus, lysosomes, vesicles, and vacuoles.

endometriosis (en′-dō-mē-trē-ō′-sis) The condition resulting from the presence of endometrial tissue outside of the uterus.

endometrium (en′-dō-mē′-trē-um) The inner lining of the uterus, which is richly supplied with blood vessels.

endoparasite A parasite that lives within a host.

endophyte A harmless fungus, or occasionally another organism, that lives between cells of a plant part or multicellular alga.

endoplasmic reticulum (ER) (en′-dō-plaz′-mik ruh-tik′-yū-lum) An extensive membranous network in eukaryotic cells, continuous with the outer nuclear membrane and composed of ribosome-studded (rough) and ribosome-free (smooth) regions.

endorphin (en-dōr′-fin) Any of several hormones produced in the brain and anterior pituitary that inhibit pain perception.

endoskeleton A hard skeleton buried within the soft tissues of an animal.

endosperm In angiosperms, a nutrient-rich tissue formed by the union of a sperm with two polar nuclei during double fertilization. The endosperm provides nourishment to the developing embryo in angiosperm seeds.

endospore A thick-coated, resistant cell produced by some bacterial cells when they are exposed to harsh conditions.

endosymbiont theory The theory that mitochondria and plastids, including chloroplasts, originated as prokaryotic cells engulfed by a host cell. The engulfed cell and its host cell then evolved into a single organism. *See also* endosymbiosis.

endosymbiosis A relationship between two species in which one organism lives inside the cell or cells of another organism. *See also* endosymbiont theory.

endothelium (en′-dō-thē′-lē-um) The simple squamous layer of cells lining the lumen of blood vessels.

endothermic Referring to organisms that are warmed by heat generated by their own metabolism. This heat usually maintains a relatively stable body temperature higher than that of the external environment.

endotoxin A toxic component of the outer membrane of certain gram-negative bacteria that is released only when the bacteria die.

energetic hypothesis The concept that the length of a food chain is limited by the inefficiency of energy transfer along the chain.

energy The capacity to cause change, especially to do work (to move matter against an opposing force).

energy coupling In cellular metabolism, the use of energy released from an exergonic reaction to drive an endergonic reaction.

enhancer A segment of eukaryotic DNA containing multiple control elements, usually located far from the gene whose transcription it regulates.

enteric division One of three divisions of the autonomic nervous system; consists of networks of neurons in the digestive tract, pancreas, and gallbladder; normally regulated by the sympathetic and parasympathetic divisions of the autonomic nervous system.

entropy A measure of disorder, or randomness.

enzyme (en′-zīm) A macromolecule serving as a catalyst, a chemical agent that increases the rate of a reaction without being consumed by the reaction. Most enzymes are proteins.

enzyme-substrate complex (en′-zīm) A temporary complex formed when an enzyme binds to its substrate molecule(s).

epicotyl (ep′-uh-kot′-ul) In an angiosperm embryo, the embryonic axis above the point of attachment of the cotyledon(s) and below the first pair of miniature leaves.

epidemic A widespread outbreak of a disease.

epidermis (1) The dermal tissue system of nonwoody plants, usually consisting of a single layer of tightly packed cells. (2) The outermost layer of cells in an animal.

epididymis (ep′-uh-did′-uh-mus) A coiled tubule located adjacent to the mammalian testis where sperm are stored.

epigenetic inheritance Inheritance of traits transmitted by mechanisms that do not involve the nucleotide sequence.

epinephrine (ep′-i-nef′-rin) A catecholamine that, when secreted as a hormone by the adrenal medulla, mediates "fight-or-flight" responses to short-term stresses; also released by some neurons as a neurotransmitter; also called adrenaline.

epiphyte (ep′-uh-fīt) A plant that nourishes itself but grows on the surface of another plant for support, usually on the branches or trunks of trees.

epistasis (ep′-i-stā′-sis) A type of gene interaction in which the phenotypic expression of one gene alters that of another independently inherited gene.

epithelial tissue (ep′-uh-thē′-lē-ul) Sheets of tightly packed cells that line organs and body cavities as well as external surfaces.

epithelium An epithelial tissue.

epitope A small, accessible region of an antigen to which an antigen receptor or antibody binds.

equilibrium potential (E_{ion}) The magnitude of a cell's membrane voltage at equilibrium; calculated using the Nernst equation.

erythrocyte (eh-rith′-ruh-sīt) A blood cell that contains hemoglobin, which transports oxygen; also called a red blood cell.

erythropoietin (EPO) (eh-rith′-rō-poy′-uh-tin) A hormone that stimulates the production of erythrocytes. It is secreted by the kidney when body tissues do not receive enough oxygen.

esophagus (eh-sof′-uh-gus) A muscular tube that conducts food, by peristalsis, from the pharynx to the stomach.

essential amino acid An amino acid that an animal cannot synthesize itself and must be obtained from food in prefabricated form.

essential element A chemical element required for an organism to survive, grow, and reproduce.

essential fatty acid An unsaturated fatty acid that an animal needs but cannot make.

essential nutrient A substance that an organism cannot synthesize from any other material and therefore must absorb in preassembled form.

estradiol (es′-truh-dī′-ol) A steroid hormone that stimulates the development and maintenance of the female reproductive system and secondary sex characteristics; the major estrogen in mammals.

estrogen (es′-trō-jen) Any steroid hormone, such as estradiol, that stimulates the development and maintenance of the female reproductive system and secondary sex characteristics.

estrous cycle (es′-trus) A reproductive cycle characteristic of female mammals except humans and certain other primates, in which the nonpregnant endometrium is reabsorbed rather than shed, and sexual response occurs only during mid-cycle at estrus.

estuary The area where a freshwater stream or river merges with the ocean.

ethylene (eth′-uh-lēn) A gaseous plant hormone involved in responses to mechanical stress, programmed cell death, leaf abscission, and fruit ripening.

etiolation Plant morphological adaptations for growing in darkness.

euchromatin (yū-krō′-muh-tin) The less condensed form of eukaryotic chromatin that is available for transcription.

eudicot (yū-dī′-kot) A member of a clade that contains the vast majority of flowering plants that have two embryonic seed leaves, or cotyledons.

euglenid (yū′-glen-id) A protist, such as *Euglena* or its relatives, characterized by an anterior pocket from which one or two flagella emerge.

euglenozoan A member of a diverse clade of flagellated protists that includes predatory heterotrophs, photosynthetic autotrophs, and pathogenic parasites.

Eukarya (yū-kar′-ē-uh) The domain that includes all eukaryotic organisms.

eukaryotic cell (yū′-ker-ē-ot′-ik) A type of cell with a membrane-enclosed nucleus and membrane-enclosed organelles. Organisms with eukaryotic cells (protists, plants, fungi, and animals) are called eukaryotes.

eumetazoan (yū′-met-uh-zō′-un) A member of a clade of animals with true tissues. All animals except sponges and a few other groups are eumetazoans.

eurypterid (yur-ip′-tuh-rid) An extinct carnivorous chelicerate; also called a water scorpion.

Eustachian tube (yū-stā′-shun) The tube that connects the middle ear to the pharynx.

eutherian (yū-thēr′-ē-un) Placental mammal; mammal whose young complete their embryonic development within the uterus, joined to the mother by the placenta.

eutrophic lake (yū-trōf′-ik) A lake that has a high rate of biological productivity supported by a high rate of nutrient cycling.

eutrophication A process by which nutrients, particularly phosphorus and nitrogen, become highly concentrated in a body of water, leading to increased growth of organisms such as algae or cyanobacteria.

evaporative cooling The process in which the surface of an object becomes cooler during evaporation, a result of the molecules with the greatest kinetic energy changing from the liquid to the gaseous state.

evapotranspiration The total evaporation of water from an ecosystem, including water transpired by plants and evaporated from a landscape, usually measured in millimeters and estimated for a year.

evo-devo Evolutionary developmental biology; a field of biology that compares developmental processes of different multicellular organisms to understand how these processes have evolved and how changes can modify existing organismal features or lead to new ones.

evolution Descent with modification; the idea that living species are descendants of ancestral species that were different from the present-day ones; also defined more narrowly as the change in the genetic composition of a population from generation to generation.

evolutionary tree A branching diagram that reflects a hypothesis about evolutionary relationships among groups of organisms.

Excavata (ex′-kuh-vah′-tuh) One of four supergroups of eukaryotes proposed in a current hypothesis of the evolutionary history of eukaryotes. Excavates have unique cytoskeletal features, and some species have an "excavated" feeding groove on one side of the cell body. *See also* "SAR" clade, Archaeplastida, and Unikonta.

excitatory postsynaptic potential (EPSP) An electrical change (depolarization) in the membrane of a postsynaptic cell caused by the binding of an excitatory neurotransmitter from a presynaptic cell to a postsynaptic receptor; makes it more likely for a postsynaptic cell to generate an action potential.

excretion The disposal of nitrogen-containing metabolites and other waste products.

exergonic reaction (ek′-ser-gon′-ik) A spontaneous chemical reaction in which there is a net release of free energy.

exocytosis (ek′-sō-sī-tō′-sis) The cellular secretion of biological molecules by the fusion of vesicles containing them with the plasma membrane.

exon A sequence within a primary transcript that remains in the RNA after RNA processing; also refers to the region of DNA from which this sequence was transcribed.

exoskeleton A hard encasement on the surface of an animal, such as the shell of a mollusc or the cuticle of an arthropod, that provides protection and points of attachment for muscles.

exotoxin (ek′-sō-tok′-sin) A toxic protein that is secreted by a prokaryote or other pathogen and that produces specific symptoms, even if the pathogen is no longer present.

expansin Plant enzyme that breaks the cross-links (hydrogen bonds) between cellulose microfibrils and other cell wall constituents, loosening the wall's fabric.

experiment A scientific test, carried out under controlled conditions, involving manipulation of one or more factors in a system in order to see the effects of those changes.

experimental group A set of subjects that has (or receives) the specific factor being tested in a controlled experiment.

exponential population growth Growth of a population in an ideal, unlimited environment, represented by a J-shaped curve when population size is plotted over time.

expression vector A cloning vector that contains a highly active bacterial promoter just upstream of a restriction site where a eukaryotic gene can be inserted, allowing the gene to be expressed in a bacterial cell. Expression vectors are also available that have been genetically engineered for use in specific types of eukaryotic cells.

extinction vortex A downward population spiral in which inbreeding and genetic drift combine to cause a small population to shrink and, unless the spiral is reversed, become extinct.

extracellular matrix (ECM) The meshwork surrounding animal cells, consisting of glycoproteins, polysaccharides, and proteoglycans synthesized and secreted by cells.

extraembryonic membrane One of four membranes (yolk sac, amnion, chorion, and allantois) located outside the embryo that support the developing embryo in reptiles and mammals.

extreme halophile An organism that lives in a highly saline environment, such as the Great Salt Lake or the Dead Sea.

extreme thermophile An organism that thrives in hot environments (often 60–80°C or hotter).

extremophile An organism that lives in environmental conditions so extreme that few other species can survive there. Extremophiles include extreme halophiles ("salt lovers") and extreme thermophiles ("heat lovers").

F_1 generation The first filial, hybrid (heterozygous) offspring arising from a parental (P generation) cross.

F_2 generation The offspring resulting from interbreeding (or self-pollination) of the hybrid F_1 generation.

facilitated diffusion The passage of molecules or ions down their electrochemical gradient across a biological membrane with the assistance of specific transmembrane transport proteins, requiring no energy expenditure.

facilitation An interaction in which one species has a positive effect on the survival and reproduction of another species without the intimate association of a symbiosis.

facultative anaerobe (fak′-ul-tā′-tiv an′-uh-rōb) An organism that makes ATP by aerobic respiration if oxygen is present but that switches to anaerobic respiration or fermentation if oxygen is not present.

family In Linnaean classification, the taxonomic category above genus.

fast block to polyspermy The depolarization of the egg plasma membrane that begins within 1–3 seconds after a sperm binds to an egg membrane protein. The depolarization lasts about 1 minute and prevents additional sperm from fusing with the egg during that time.

fast-twitch fiber A muscle fiber used for rapid, powerful contractions.

fat A lipid consisting of three fatty acids linked to one glycerol molecule; also called a triacylglycerol or triglyceride.

fate map A territorial diagram of embryonic development that displays the future derivatives of individual cells and tissues.

fatty acid A carboxylic acid with a long carbon chain. Fatty acids vary in length and in the number and location of double bonds; three fatty acids linked to a glycerol molecule form a fat molecule, also called triacylglycerol or triglyceride.

feces (fē′-sēz) The wastes of the digestive tract.

feedback inhibition A method of metabolic control in which the end product of a metabolic pathway acts as an inhibitor of an enzyme within that pathway.

feedback regulation The regulation of a process by its output or end product.

fermentation A catabolic process that makes a limited amount of ATP from glucose (or other organic molecules) without an electron transport chain and that produces a characteristic end product, such as ethyl alcohol or lactic acid.

fertilization (1) The union of haploid gametes to produce a diploid zygote. (2) The addition of mineral nutrients to the soil.

fetus (fē′-tus) A developing mammal that has all the major structures of an adult. In humans, the fetal stage lasts from the 9th week of gestation until birth.

F factor In bacteria, the DNA segment that confers the ability to form pili for conjugation and associated functions required for the transfer of DNA from donor to recipient. The F factor may exist as a plasmid or be integrated into the bacterial chromosome.

fiber A lignified cell type that reinforces the xylem of angiosperms and functions in mechanical support; a slender, tapered sclerenchyma cell that usually occurs in bundles.

fibroblast (fī′-brō-blast) A type of cell in loose connective tissue that secretes the protein ingredients of the extracellular fibers.

fibronectin An extracellular glycoprotein secreted by animal cells that helps them attach to the extracellular matrix.

filament In an angiosperm, the stalk portion of the stamen, the pollen-producing reproductive organ of a flower.

filter feeder An animal that feeds by using a filtration mechanism to strain small organisms or food particles from its surroundings.

filtrate Cell-free fluid extracted from the body fluid by the excretory system.

filtration In excretory systems, the extraction of water and small solutes, including metabolic wastes, from the body fluid.

fimbria (plural, **fimbriae**) A short, hairlike appendage of a prokaryotic cell that helps it adhere to the substrate or to other cells.

first law of thermodynamics The principle of conservation of energy: Energy can be transferred and transformed, but it cannot be created or destroyed.

fission The separation of an organism into two or more individuals of approximately equal size.

fixed action pattern In animal behavior, a sequence of unlearned acts that is essentially unchangeable and, once initiated, usually carried to completion.

flaccid (flas′-id) Limp. Lacking turgor (stiffness or firmness), as in a plant cell in surroundings where there is a tendency for water to leave the cell. (A walled cell becomes flaccid if it has a higher water potential than its surroundings, resulting in the loss of water.)

flagellum (fluh-jel′-um) (plural, **flagella**) A long cellular appendage specialized for locomotion. Like motile cilia, eukaryotic flagella have a core with nine outer doublet microtubules and two inner single microtubules (the "9 + 2" arrangement) ensheathed in an extension of the plasma membrane. Prokaryotic flagella have a different structure.

florigen A flowering signal, probably a protein, that is made in leaves under certain conditions and that travels to the shoot apical meristems, inducing them to switch from vegetative to reproductive growth.

flower In an angiosperm, a specialized shoot with up to four sets of modified leaves, bearing structures that function in sexual reproduction.

fluid feeder An animal that lives by sucking nutrient-rich fluids from another living organism.

fluid mosaic model The currently accepted model of cell membrane structure, which envisions the membrane as a mosaic of protein molecules drifting laterally in a fluid bilayer of phospholipids.

follicle (fol′-uh-kul) A microscopic structure in the ovary that contains the developing oocyte and secretes estrogens.

follicle-stimulating hormone (FSH) (fol′-uh-kul) A tropic hormone that is produced and secreted by the anterior pituitary and that stimulates the production of eggs by the ovaries and sperm by the testes.

food chain The pathway along which food energy is transferred from trophic level to trophic level, beginning with producers.

food vacuole A membranous sac formed by phagocytosis of microorganisms or particles to be used as food by the cell.

food web The interconnected feeding relationships in an ecosystem.

foot (1) The portion of a bryophyte sporophyte that gathers sugars, amino acids, water, and minerals from the parent gametophyte via transfer cells. (2) One of the three main parts of a mollusc; a muscular structure usually used for movement. *See also* mantle and visceral mass.

foraging The seeking and obtaining of food.

foram (foraminiferan) An aquatic protist that secretes a hardened shell containing calcium carbonate and extends pseudopodia through pores in the shell.

forebrain One of three ancestral and embryonic regions of the vertebrate brain; develops into the thalamus, hypothalamus, and cerebrum.

fossil A preserved remnant or impression of an organism that lived in the past.

founder effect Genetic drift that occurs when a few individuals become isolated from a larger population and form a new population whose gene pool composition is not reflective of that of the original population.

fovea (fō′-vē-uh) The place on the retina at the eye's center of focus, where cones are highly concentrated.

F plasmid The plasmid form of the F factor.

fragmentation A means of asexual reproduction whereby a single parent breaks into parts that regenerate into whole new individuals.

frameshift mutation A mutation occurring when nucleotides are inserted in or deleted from a gene and the number inserted or deleted is not a multiple of three, resulting in the improper grouping of the subsequent nucleotides into codons.

free energy The portion of a biological system's energy that can perform work when temperature and pressure are uniform throughout the system. The change in free energy of a system (ΔG) is calculated by the equation $\Delta G = \Delta H - T\Delta S$, where ΔH is the change in enthalpy (in biological systems, equivalent to total energy), ΔT is the absolute temperature, and ΔS is the change in entropy.

frequency-dependent selection Selection in which the fitness of a phenotype depends on how common the phenotype is in a population.

fruit A mature ovary of a flower. The fruit protects dormant seeds and often functions in their dispersal.

functional group A specific configuration of atoms commonly attached to the carbon skeletons of organic molecules and involved in chemical reactions.

G₀ phase A nondividing state occupied by cells that have left the cell cycle, sometimes reversibly.

G₁ phase The first gap, or growth phase, of the cell cycle, consisting of the portion of interphase before DNA synthesis begins.

G₂ phase The second gap, or growth phase, of the cell cycle, consisting of the portion of interphase after DNA synthesis occurs.

gallbladder An organ that stores bile and releases it as needed into the small intestine.

game theory An approach to evaluating alternative strategies in situations where the outcome of a particular strategy depends on the strategies used by other individuals.

gametangium (gam′-uh-tan′-jē-um) (plural, **gametangia**) Multicellular plant structure in which gametes are formed. Female gametangia are called archegonia, and male gametangia are called antheridia.

gamete (gam′-ēt) A haploid reproductive cell, such as an egg or sperm. Gametes unite during sexual reproduction to produce a diploid zygote.

gametogenesis (guh-mē′-tō-gen′-uh-sis) The process by which gametes are produced.

gametophore (guh-mē′-tō-fōr) The mature gamete-producing structure of a moss gametophyte.

gametophyte (guh-mē′-tō-fīt) In organisms (plants and some algae) that have alternation of generations, the multicellular haploid form that produces haploid gametes by mitosis. The haploid gametes unite and develop into sporophytes.

gamma-aminobutyric acid (GABA) An amino acid that functions as a CNS neurotransmitter in the central nervous system of vertebrates.

ganglion (gang'-glē-uhn) (plural, **ganglia**) A cluster (functional group) of nerve cell bodies in a centralized nervous system.

gap junction A type of intercellular junction in animal cells, consisting of proteins surrounding a pore that allows the passage of materials between cells.

gas exchange The uptake of molecular oxygen from the environment and the discharge of carbon dioxide to the environment.

gastric juice A digestive fluid secreted by the stomach.

gastrovascular cavity A central cavity with a single opening in the body of certain animals, including cnidarians and flatworms, that functions in both the digestion and distribution of nutrients.

gastrula (gas'-trū-luh) An embryonic stage in animal development encompassing the formation of three layers: ectoderm, mesoderm, and endoderm.

gastrulation (gas'-trū-lā'-shun) In animal development, a series of cell and tissue movements in which the blastula-stage embryo folds inward, producing a three-layered embryo, the gastrula.

gated channel A transmembrane protein channel that opens or closes in response to a particular stimulus.

gated ion channel A gated channel for a specific ion. The opening or closing of such channels may alter a cell's membrane potential.

gel electrophoresis (ē-lek'-trō-fōr-ē'-sis) A technique for separating nucleic acids or proteins on the basis of their size and electrical charge, both of which affect their rate of movement through an electric field in a gel made of agarose or another polymer.

gene A discrete unit of hereditary information consisting of a specific nucleotide sequence in DNA (or RNA, in some viruses).

gene annotation Analysis of genomic sequences to identify protein-coding genes and determine the function of their products.

gene cloning The production of multiple copies of a gene.

gene expression The process by which information encoded in DNA directs the synthesis of proteins or, in some cases, RNAs that are not translated into proteins and instead function as RNAs.

gene flow The transfer of alleles from one population to another, resulting from the movement of fertile individuals or their gametes.

gene pool The aggregate of all copies of every type of allele at all loci in every individual in a population. The term is also used in a more restricted sense as the aggregate of alleles for just one or a few loci in a population.

gene therapy The introduction of genes into an afflicted individual for therapeutic purposes.

genetic drift A process in which chance events cause unpredictable fluctuations in allele frequencies from one generation to the next. Effects of genetic drift are most pronounced in small populations.

genetic engineering The direct manipulation of genes for practical purposes.

genetic map An ordered list of genetic loci (genes or other genetic markers) along a chromosome.

genetic profile An individual's unique set of genetic markers, detected most often today by PCR or, previously, by electrophoresis and nucleic acid probes.

genetic recombination General term for the production of offspring with combinations of traits that differ from those found in either parent.

genetic variation Differences among individuals in the composition of their genes or other DNA segments.

genetically modified (GM) organism An organism that has acquired one or more genes by artificial means; also called a transgenic organism.

genetics The scientific study of heredity and hereditary variation.

genome (jē'-nōm) The genetic material of an organism or virus; the complete complement of an organism's or virus's genes along with its noncoding nucleic acid sequences.

genome-wide association study (jē'-nōm) A large-scale analysis of the genomes of many people having a certain phenotype or disease, with the aim of finding genetic markers that correlate with that phenotype or disease.

genomic imprinting (juh-nō'-mik) A phenomenon in which expression of an allele in offspring depends on whether the allele is inherited from the male or female parent.

genomics (juh-nō'-miks) The systematic study of whole sets of genes (or other DNA) and their interactions within a species, as well as genome comparisons between species.

genotype (jē'-nō-tīp) The genetic makeup, or set of alleles, of an organism.

genus (jē'-nus) (plural, **genera**) A taxonomic category above the species level, designated by the first word of a species' two-part scientific name.

geologic record A standard time scale dividing Earth's history into time periods, grouped into four eons—Hadean, Archaean, Proterozoic, and Phanerozoic—and further subdivided into eras, periods, and epochs.

germ layer One of the three main layers in a gastrula that will form the various tissues and organs of an animal body.

gestation (jes-tā'-shun) *See* pregnancy.

gibberellin (jib'-uh-rel'-in) Any of a class of related plant hormones that stimulate growth in the stem and leaves, trigger the germination of seeds and breaking of bud dormancy, and (with auxin) stimulate fruit development.

glans The rounded structure at the tip of the clitoris or penis that is involved in sexual arousal.

glia (glial cells) Cells of the nervous system that support, regulate, and augment the functions of neurons.

global ecology The study of the functioning and distribution of organisms across the biosphere and how the regional exchange of energy and materials affects them.

glomeromycete (glō'-mer-ō-mī'-sēt) A member of the fungal phylum Glomeromycota,

characterized by a distinct branching form of mycorrhizae called arbuscular mycorrhizae.

glomerulus (glō-mār'-yū-lus) A ball of capillaries surrounded by Bowman's capsule in the nephron and serving as the site of filtration in the vertebrate kidney.

glucocorticoid A steroid hormone that is secreted by the adrenal cortex and that influences glucose metabolism and immune function.

glucagon (glū'-kuh-gon) A hormone secreted by pancreatic alpha cells that raises blood glucose levels. It promotes glycogen breakdown and release of glucose by the liver.

glutamate An amino acid that functions as a neurotransmitter in the central nervous system.

glyceraldehyde 3-phosphate (G3P) (glis'-er-al'-de-hīd) A three-carbon carbohydrate that is the direct product of the Calvin cycle; it is also an intermediate in glycolysis.

glycogen (glī'-kō-jen) An extensively branched glucose storage polysaccharide found in the liver and muscle of animals; the animal equivalent of starch.

glycolipid A lipid with one or more covalently attached carbohydrates.

glycolysis (glī-kol'-uh-sis) A series of reactions that ultimately splits glucose into pyruvate. Glycolysis occurs in almost all living cells, serving as the starting point for fermentation or cellular respiration.

glycoprotein A protein with one or more covalently attached carbohydrates.

glycosidic linkage A covalent bond formed between two monosaccharides by a dehydration reaction.

gnathostome (na'-thu-stōm) A member of the vertebrate subgroup possessing jaws. The gnathostomes include sharks and rays, ray-finned fishes, coelacanths, lungfishes, amphibians, reptiles, and mammals.

golden alga A biflagellated, photosynthetic protist named for its color, which results from its yellow and brown carotenoids.

Golgi apparatus (gol'-jē) An organelle in eukaryotic cells consisting of stacks of flat membranous sacs that modify, store, and route products of the endoplasmic reticulum and synthesize some products, notably noncellulose carbohydrates.

gonad (gō'-nad) A male or female gamete-producing organ.

G protein A GTP-binding protein that relays signals from a plasma membrane signal receptor, known as a G protein-coupled receptor, to other signal transduction proteins inside the cell.

G protein-coupled receptor (GPCR) A signal receptor protein in the plasma membrane that responds to the binding of a signaling molecule by activating a G protein. Also called a G protein-linked receptor.

graded potential In a neuron, a shift in the membrane potential that has an amplitude proportional to signal strength and that decays as it spreads.

Gram stain A staining method that distinguishes between two different kinds of bacterial cell walls; may be used to help determine medical response to an infection.

gram-negative Describing the group of bacteria that have a cell wall that is structurally more complex and contains less peptidoglycan than the cell wall of gram-positive bacteria. Gram-negative bacteria are often more toxic than gram-positive bacteria.

gram-positive Describing the group of bacteria that have a cell wall that is structurally less complex and contains more peptidoglycan than the cell wall of gram-negative bacteria. Gram-positive bacteria are usually less toxic than gram-negative bacteria.

granum (gran'-um) (plural, **grana**) A stack of membrane-bounded thylakoids in the chloroplast. Grana function in the light reactions of photosynthesis.

gravitropism (grav'-uh-trō'-pizm) A response of a plant or animal to gravity.

gray matter Regions of clustered neuron cell bodies within the CNS.

green alga A photosynthetic protist, named for green chloroplasts that are similar in structure and pigment composition to the chloroplasts of land plants. Green algae are a paraphyletic group; some members are more closely related to land plants than they are to other green algae.

greenhouse effect The warming of Earth due to the atmospheric accumulation of carbon dioxide and certain other gases, which absorb reflected infrared radiation and reradiate some of it back toward Earth.

gross primary production (GPP) The total primary production of an ecosystem.

ground tissue system Plant tissues that are neither vascular nor dermal, fulfilling a variety of functions, such as storage, photosynthesis, and support.

growth factor (1) A protein that must be present in the extracellular environment (culture medium or animal body) for the growth and normal development of certain types of cells. (2) A local regulator that acts on nearby cells to stimulate cell proliferation and differentiation.

growth hormone (GH) A hormone that is produced and secreted by the anterior pituitary and that has both direct (nontropic) and tropic effects on a wide variety of tissues.

guard cells The two cells that flank the stomatal pore and regulate the opening and closing of the pore.

gustation The sense of taste.

guttation The exudation of water droplets from leaves, caused by root pressure in certain plants.

gymnosperm (jim'-nō-sperm) A vascular plant that bears naked seeds—seeds not enclosed in protective chambers.

hair cell A mechanosensory cell that alters output to the nervous system when hairlike projections on the cell surface are displaced.

half-life The amount of time it takes for 50% of a sample of a radioactive isotope to decay.

halophile *See* extreme halophile.

Hamilton's rule The principle that for natural selection to favor an altruistic act, the benefit

to the recipient, devalued by the coefficient of relatedness, must exceed the cost to the altruist.

haploid cell (hap'-loyd) A cell containing only one set of chromosomes (*n*).

Hardy-Weinberg equilibrium The state of a population in which frequencies of alleles and genotypes remain constant from generation to generation, provided that only Mendelian segregation and recombination of alleles are at work.

haustorium (plural, **haustoria**) (ho-stōr'-ē-um, ho-stōr'-ē-uh) In certain symbiotic fungi, a specialized hypha that can penetrate the tissues of host organisms.

heart A muscular pump that uses metabolic energy to elevate the hydrostatic pressure of the circulatory fluid (blood or hemolymph). The fluid then flows down a pressure gradient through the body and eventually returns to the heart.

heart attack The damage or death of cardiac muscle tissue resulting from prolonged blockage of one or more coronary arteries.

heart murmur A hissing sound that most often results from blood squirting backward through a leaky valve in the heart.

heart rate The frequency of heart contraction (in beats per minute).

heat Thermal energy in transfer from one body of matter to another.

heat of vaporization The quantity of heat a liquid must absorb for 1 g of it to be converted from the liquid to the gaseous state.

heat-shock protein A protein that helps protect other proteins during heat stress. Heat-shock proteins are found in plants, animals, and microorganisms.

heavy chain One of the two types of polypeptide chains that make up an antibody molecule and B cell receptor; consists of a variable region, which contributes to the antigen-binding site, and a constant region.

helicase An enzyme that untwists the double helix of DNA at replication forks, separating the two strands and making them available as template strands.

helper T cell A type of T cell that, when activated, secretes cytokines that promote the response of B cells (humoral response) and cytotoxic T cells (cell-mediated response) to antigens.

hemoglobin (hē'-mō-glō'-bin) An iron-containing protein in red blood cells that reversibly binds oxygen.

hemolymph (hē'-mō-limf') In invertebrates with an open circulatory system, the body fluid that bathes tissues.

hemophilia (hē'-muh-fil'-ē-uh) A human genetic disease caused by a sex-linked recessive allele resulting in the absence of one or more blood-clotting proteins; characterized by excessive bleeding following injury.

hepatic portal vein A large vessel that conveys nutrient-laden blood from the small intestine to the liver, which regulates the blood's nutrient content.

herbivore (hur'-bi-vōr') An animal that mainly eats plants or algae.

herbivory An interaction in which an organism eats part of a plant or alga.

heredity The transmission of traits from one generation to the next.

hermaphrodite (hur-maf'-ruh-dīt') An individual that functions as both male and female in sexual reproduction by producing both sperm and eggs.

hermaphroditism (hur-maf'-rō-dī-tizm) A condition in which an individual has both female and male gonads and functions as both a male and a female in sexual reproduction by producing both sperm and eggs.

heterochromatin (het'-er-ō-krō'-muh-tin) Eukaryotic chromatin that remains highly compacted during interphase and is generally not transcribed.

heterochrony (het'-uh-rok'-ruh-nē) Evolutionary change in the timing or rate of an organism's development.

heterocyst (het'-er-ō-sist) A specialized cell that engages in nitrogen fixation in some filamentous cyanobacteria; also called a heterocyte.

heterokaryon (het'-er-ō-kār'-ē-un) A fungal mycelium that contains two or more haploid nuclei per cell.

heteromorphic (het'-er-ō-mōr'-fik) Referring to a condition in the life cycle of plants and certain algae in which the sporophyte and gametophyte generations differ in morphology.

heterosporous (het-er-os'-pōr-us) Referring to a plant species that has two kinds of spores: microspores, which develop into male gametophytes, and megaspores, which develop into female gametophytes.

heterotroph (het'-er-ō-trōf) An organism that obtains organic food molecules by eating other organisms or substances derived from them.

heterozygote advantage Greater reproductive success of heterozygous individuals compared with homozygotes; tends to preserve variation in a gene pool.

heterozygous (het'-er-ō-zī'-gus) Having two different alleles for a given gene.

hibernation A long-term physiological state in which metabolism decreases, the heart and respiratory system slow down, and body temperature is maintained at a lower level than normal.

high-density lipoprotein (HDL) A particle in the blood made up of thousands of cholesterol molecules and other lipids bound to a protein. HDL scavenges excess cholesterol.

hindbrain One of three ancestral and embryonic regions of the vertebrate brain; develops into the medulla oblongata, pons, and cerebellum.

histamine (his'-tuh-mēn) A substance released by mast cells that causes blood vessels to dilate and become more permeable in inflammatory and allergic responses.

histogram A variant of a bar graph that is made for numeric data by first grouping, or "binning," the variable plotted on the *x*-axis into intervals of equal width. The "bins" may be integers or ranges of numbers. The height of each bar shows the percent or number of experimental subjects whose characteristics can be described by one of the intervals plotted on the *x*-axis.

histone (his'-tōn) A small protein with a high proportion of positively charged amino acids that binds to the negatively charged DNA and plays a key role in chromatin structure.

histone acetylation (his'-tōn) The attachment of acetyl groups to certain amino acids of histone proteins.

HIV (human immunodeficiency virus) The infectious agent that causes AIDS. HIV is a retrovirus.

holdfast A rootlike structure that anchors a seaweed.

holoblastic (hō'-lō-blas'-tik) Referring to a type of cleavage in which there is complete division of the egg; occurs in eggs that have little yolk (such as those of the sea urchin) or a moderate amount of yolk (such as those of the frog).

homeobox (hō'-mē-ō-boks') A 180-nucleotide sequence within homeotic genes and some other developmental genes that is widely conserved in animals. Related sequences occur in plants and yeasts.

homeostasis (hō'-mē-ō-stā'-sis) The steady-state physiological condition of the body.

homeotic gene (hō-mē-o'-tik) Any of the master regulatory genes that control placement and spatial organization of body parts in animals, plants, and fungi by controlling the developmental fate of groups of cells.

hominin (hō'-mi-nin) A member of the human branch of the evolutionary tree. Hominins include *Homo sapiens* and our ancestors, a group of extinct species that are more closely related to us than to chimpanzees.

homologous chromosomes (or **homologs**) (hō-mol'-uh-gus) A pair of chromosomes of the same length, centromere position, and staining pattern that possess genes for the same characters at corresponding loci. One homologous chromosome is inherited from the organism's father, the other from the mother. Also called a homologous pair.

homologous structures (hō-mol'-uh-gus) Structures in different species that are similar because of common ancestry.

homology (hō-mol'-ō-jē) Similarity in characteristics resulting from a shared ancestry.

homoplasy (hō'-muh-play'-zē) A similar (analogous) structure or molecular sequence that has evolved independently in two species.

homosporous (hō-mos'-puh-rus) Referring to a plant species that has a single kind of spore, which typically develops into a bisexual gametophyte.

homozygous (hō'-mō-zī'-gus) Having two identical alleles for a given gene.

horizontal gene transfer The transfer of genes from one genome to another through mechanisms such as transposable elements, plasmid exchange, viral activity, and perhaps fusions of different organisms.

hormone In multicellular organisms, one of many types of secreted chemicals that are formed in specialized cells, travel in body fluids, and act on specific target cells in other parts of the organism, changing the target cells' functioning.

hornwort A small, herbaceous, nonvascular plant that is a member of the phylum Anthocerophyta.

host The larger participant in a symbiotic relationship, often providing a home and food source for the smaller symbiont.

host range The limited number of species whose cells can be infected by a particular virus.

Human Genome Project An international collaborative effort to map and sequence the DNA of the entire human genome.

human immunodeficiency virus (HIV) The infectious agent that causes AIDS (acquired immunodeficiency syndrome). HIV is a retrovirus.

humoral immune response (hyū'-mer-ul) The branch of adaptive immunity that involves the activation of B cells and that leads to the production of antibodies, which defend against bacteria and viruses in body fluids.

humus (hyū'-mus) Decomposing organic material that is a component of topsoil.

Huntington's disease A human genetic disease caused by a dominant allele; characterized by uncontrollable body movements and degeneration of the nervous system; usually fatal 10 to 20 years after the onset of symptoms.

hybrid Offspring that results from the mating of individuals from two different species or from two true-breeding varieties of the same species.

hybrid zone A geographic region in which members of different species meet and mate, producing at least some offspring of mixed ancestry.

hybridization In genetics, the mating, or crossing, of two true-breeding varieties.

hydration shell The sphere of water molecules around a dissolved ion.

hydrocarbon An organic molecule consisting only of carbon and hydrogen.

hydrogen bond A type of weak chemical bond that is formed when the slightly positive hydrogen atom of a polar covalent bond in one molecule is attracted to the slightly negative atom of a polar covalent bond in another molecule or in another region of the same molecule.

hydrogen ion A single proton with a charge of 1+. The dissociation of a water molecule (H_2O) leads to the generation of a hydroxide ion (OH^-) and a hydrogen ion (H^+); in water, H^+ is not found alone but associates with a water molecule to form a hydronium ion.

hydrolysis (hī-drol'-uh-sis) A chemical reaction that breaks bonds between two molecules by the addition of water; functions in disassembly of polymers to monomers.

hydronium ion A water molecule that has an extra proton bound to it; H_3O^+, commonly represented as H^+.

hydrophilic (hī'-drō-fil'-ik) Having an affinity for water.

hydrophobic (hī'-drō-fō-bik) Having no affinity for water; tending to coalesce and form droplets in water.

hydrophobic interaction (hī'-drō-fō'-bik) A type of weak chemical interaction caused when molecules that do not mix with water coalesce to exclude water.

hydroponic culture A method in which plants are grown in mineral solutions rather than in soil.

hydrostatic skeleton A skeletal system composed of fluid held under pressure in a closed body compartment; the main skeleton of most cnidarians, flatworms, nematodes, and annelids.

hydrothermal vent An area on the deep sea-floor where heated water and minerals from Earth's interior gush into the seawater.

hydroxide ion A water molecule that has lost a proton; OH^-.

hydroxyl group (hī-drok'-sil) A chemical group consisting of an oxygen atom joined to a hydrogen atom. Molecules possessing this group are soluble in water and are called alcohols.

hyperpolarization A change in a cell's membrane potential such that the inside of the membrane becomes more negative relative to the outside. Hyperpolarization reduces the chance that a neuron will transmit a nerve impulse.

hypersensitive response A plant's localized defense response to a pathogen, involving the death of cells around the site of infection.

hypertension A disorder in which blood pressure remains abnormally high.

hypertonic Referring to a solution that, when surrounding a cell, will cause the cell to lose water.

hypha (plural, **hyphae**) (hī'-fuh, hī'-fē) One of many connected filaments that collectively make up the mycelium of a fungus.

hypocotyl (hī'-puh-cot'-ul) In an angiosperm embryo, the embryonic axis below the point of attachment of the cotyledon(s) and above the radicle.

hypothalamus (hī'-pō-thal'-uh-mus) The ventral part of the vertebrate forebrain; functions in maintaining homeostasis, especially in coordinating the endocrine and nervous systems; secretes hormones of the posterior pituitary and releasing factors that regulate the anterior pituitary.

hypothesis (hī-poth'-uh-sis) A testable explanation for a set of observations based on the available data and guided by inductive reasoning. A hypothesis is narrower in scope than a theory.

hypotonic Referring to a solution that, when surrounding a cell, will cause the cell to take up water.

imbibition The physical adsorption of water onto the internal surfaces of structures.

immigration The influx of new individuals into a population from other areas.

immune system An organism's system of defenses against agents that cause disease.

immunization The process of generating a state of immunity by artificial means. In vaccination, an inactive or weakened form of a pathogen is administered, inducing B and T cell responses and immunological memory. In passive immunization, antibodies specific for a particular pathogen are administered, conferring immediate but temporary protection.

immunoglobulin (Ig) (im'-yū-nō-glob'-yū-lin) *See* antibody.

imprinting In animal behavior, the formation at a specific stage in life of a long-lasting behavioral response to a specific individual or object. *See also* genomic imprinting.

inclusive fitness The total effect an individual has on proliferating its genes by producing its own offspring and by providing aid that enables other close relatives to increase production of their offspring.

incomplete dominance The situation in which the phenotype of heterozygotes is intermediate between the phenotypes of individuals homozygous for either allele.

incomplete flower A flower in which one or more of the four basic floral organs (sepals, petals, stamens, or carpels) are either absent or nonfunctional.

incomplete metamorphosis A type of development in certain insects, such as grasshoppers, in which the young (called nymphs) resemble adults but are smaller and have different body proportions. The nymph goes through a series of molts, each time looking more like an adult, until it reaches full size.

independent variable A variable whose value is manipulated or changed during an experiment or other test to reveal possible effects on another variable (the dependent variable).

indeterminate cleavage A type of embryonic development in deuterostomes in which each cell produced by early cleavage divisions retains the capacity to develop into a complete embryo.

indeterminate growth A type of growth characteristic of plants, in which the organism continues to grow as long as it lives.

induced fit Caused by entry of the substrate, the change in shape of the active site of an enzyme so that it binds more snugly to the substrate.

inducer A specific small molecule that binds to a bacterial repressor protein and changes the repressor's shape so that it cannot bind to an operator, thus switching an operon on.

induction A process in which a group of cells or tissues influences the development of another group through close-range interactions.

inductive reasoning A type of logic in which generalizations are based on a large number of specific observations.

inflammatory response An innate immune defense triggered by physical injury or infection of tissue involving the release of substances that promote swelling, enhance the infiltration of white blood cells, and aid in tissue repair and destruction of invading pathogens.

inflorescence A group of flowers tightly clustered together.

ingestion The first stage of food processing in animals: the act of eating.

ingroup A species or group of species whose evolutionary relationships are being examined in a given analysis.

inhibitory postsynaptic potential (IPSP) An electrical change (usually hyperpolarization) in the membrane of a postsynaptic neuron caused by the binding of an inhibitory neurotransmitter from a presynaptic cell to a postsynaptic receptor; makes it more difficult for a postsynaptic neuron to generate an action potential.

innate behavior Animal behavior that is developmentally fixed and under strong genetic control. Innate behavior is exhibited in virtually the same form by all individuals in a population despite internal and external environmental differences during development and throughout their lifetimes.

innate immunity A form of defense common to all animals that is active immediately upon exposure to a pathogen and that is the same whether or not the pathogen has been encountered previously.

inner cell mass An inner cluster of cells at one end of a mammalian blastocyst that subsequently develops into the embryo proper and some of the extraembryonic membranes.

inositol trisphosphate (IP$_3$) (in-ō'-suh-tol) A second messenger that functions as an intermediate between certain signaling molecules and a subsequent second messenger, Ca^{2+}, by causing a rise in cytoplasmic Ca^{2+} concentration.

inquiry The search for information and explanation, often focusing on specific questions.

insertion A mutation involving the addition of one or more nucleotide pairs to a gene.

in situ hybridization A technique using nucleic acid hybridization with a labeled probe to detect the location of a specific mRNA in an intact organism.

insulin (in'-suh-lin) A hormone secreted by pancreatic beta cells that lowers blood glucose levels. It promotes the uptake of glucose by most body cells and the synthesis and storage of glycogen in the liver and also stimulates protein and fat synthesis.

integral protein A transmembrane protein with hydrophobic regions that extend into and often completely span the hydrophobic interior of the membrane and with hydrophilic regions in contact with the aqueous solution on one or both sides of the membrane (or lining the channel in the case of a channel protein).

integrin (in'-tuh-grin) In animal cells, a transmembrane receptor protein with two subunits that interconnects the extracellular matrix and the cytoskeleton.

integument (in-teg'-yū-ment) Layer of sporophyte tissue that contributes to the structure of an ovule of a seed plant.

integumentary system The outer covering of a mammal's body, including skin, hair, and nails, claws, or hooves.

intercalated disk (in-ter'-kuh-lā'-ted) A specialized junction between cardiac muscle cells that provides direct electrical coupling between the cells.

interferon (in'-ter-fēr'-on) A protein that has antiviral or immune regulatory functions. Interferon-α and interferon-β, secreted by virus-infected cells, help nearby cells resist viral infection; interferon-γ, secreted by T cells, helps activate macrophages.

intermediate disturbance hypothesis The concept that moderate levels of disturbance can foster greater species diversity than low or high levels of disturbance.

intermediate filament A component of the cytoskeleton that includes filaments intermediate in size between microtubules and microfilaments.

interneuron An association neuron; a nerve cell within the central nervous system that forms synapses with sensory and/or motor neurons and integrates sensory input and motor output.

internode A segment of a plant stem between the points where leaves are attached.

interphase The period in the cell cycle when the cell is not dividing. During interphase, cellular metabolic activity is high, chromosomes and organelles are duplicated, and cell size may increase. Interphase often accounts for about 90% of the cell cycle.

intersexual selection A form of natural selection in which individuals of one sex (usually the females) are choosy in selecting their mates from the other sex; also called mate choice.

interspecific competition Competition for resources between individuals of two or more species when resources are in short supply.

interspecific interaction A relationship between individuals of two or more species in a community.

interstitial fluid The fluid filling the spaces between cells in most animals.

intertidal zone The shallow zone of the ocean adjacent to land and between the high- and low-tide lines.

intrasexual selection A form of natural selection in which there is direct competition among individuals of one sex for mates of the opposite sex.

introduced species A species moved by humans, either intentionally or accidentally, from its native location to a new geographic region; also called non-native or exotic species.

intron (in'-tron) A noncoding, intervening sequence within a primary transcript that is removed from the transcript during RNA processing; also refers to the region of DNA from which this sequence was transcribed.

invasive species A species, often introduced by humans, that takes hold outside its native range.

inversion An aberration in chromosome structure resulting from reattachment of a chromosomal fragment in a reverse orientation to the chromosome from which it originated.

invertebrate An animal without a backbone. Invertebrates make up 95% of animal species.

in vitro fertilization (IVF) (vē'-trō) Fertilization of oocytes in laboratory containers followed by artificial implantation of the early embryo in the mother's uterus.

in vitro mutagenesis A technique used to discover the function of a gene by cloning it, introducing specific changes into the cloned gene's sequence, reinserting the mutated gene into a cell, and studying the phenotype of the mutant.

ion (ī′-on) An atom or group of atoms that has gained or lost one or more electrons, thus acquiring a charge.

ion channel (ī′-on) A transmembrane protein channel that allows a specific ion to diffuse across the membrane down its concentration or electrochemical gradient.

ionic bond (ī-on′-ik) A chemical bond resulting from the attraction between oppositely charged ions.

ionic compound (ī-on′-ik) A compound resulting from the formation of an ionic bond; also called a salt.

iris The colored part of the vertebrate eye, formed by the anterior portion of the choroid.

isomer (ī′-sō-mer) One of several compounds with the same molecular formula but different structures and therefore different properties. The three types of isomers are structural isomers, *cis-trans* isomers, and enantiomers.

isomorphic Referring to alternating generations in plants and certain algae in which the sporophytes and gametophytes look alike, although they differ in chromosome number.

isotonic (ī′-sō-ton′-ik) Referring to a solution that, when surrounding a cell, causes no net movement of water into or out of the cell.

isotope (ī′-sō-tōp′) One of several atomic forms of an element, each with the same number of protons but a different number of neutrons, thus differing in atomic mass.

iteroparity Reproduction in which adults produce offspring over many years; also called repeated reproduction.

jasmonate Any of a class of plant hormones that regulate a wide range of developmental processes in plants and play a key role in plant defense against herbivores.

joule (J) A unit of energy: 1 J = 0.239 cal; 1 cal = 4.184 J.

juxtaglomerular apparatus (JGA) (juks′-tuh-gluh-mār′-yū-ler) A specialized tissue in nephrons that releases the enzyme renin in response to a drop in blood pressure or volume.

juxtamedullary nephron In mammals and birds, a nephron with a loop of Henle that extends far into the renal medulla.

karyogamy (kār′-ē-og′-uh-mē) In fungi, the fusion of haploid nuclei contributed by the two parents; occurs as one stage of sexual reproduction, preceded by plasmogamy.

karyotype (kār′-ē-ō-tīp) A display of the chromosome pairs of a cell arranged by size and shape.

keystone species A species that is not necessarily abundant in a community yet exerts strong control on community structure by the nature of its ecological role or niche.

kidney In vertebrates, one of a pair of excretory organs where blood filtrate is formed and processed into urine.

kilocalorie (kcal) A thousand calories; the amount of heat energy required to raise the temperature of 1 kg of water by 1°C.

kinetic energy (kuh-net′-ik) The energy associated with the relative motion of objects.

Moving matter can perform work by imparting motion to other matter.

kinetic energy (kuh-net′-ik) The energy associated with the relative motion of objects. Moving matter can perform work by imparting motion to other matter.

kinetochore (kuh-net′-uh-kōr) A structure of proteins attached to the centromere that links each sister chromatid to the mitotic spindle.

kinetoplastid A protist, such as a trypanosome, that has a single large mitochondrion that houses an organized mass of DNA.

kingdom A taxonomic category, the second broadest after domain.

kin selection Natural selection that favors altruistic behavior by enhancing the reproductive success of relatives.

K-selection Selection for life history traits that are sensitive to population density; also called density-dependent selection.

labia majora A pair of thick, fatty ridges that encloses and protects the rest of the vulva.

labia minora A pair of slender skin folds that surrounds the openings of the vagina and urethra.

lacteal (lak′-tē-ul) A tiny lymph vessel extending into the core of an intestinal villus and serving as the destination for absorbed chylomicrons.

lactic acid fermentation Glycolysis followed by the reduction of pyruvate to lactate, regenerating NAD^+ with no release of carbon dioxide.

lagging strand A discontinuously synthesized DNA strand that elongates by means of Okazaki fragments, each synthesized in a $5' \rightarrow 3'$ direction away from the replication fork.

lancelet A member of the clade Cephalochordata, small blade-shaped marine chordates that lack a backbone.

landscape An area containing several different ecosystems linked by exchanges of energy, materials, and organisms.

landscape ecology The study of how the spatial arrangement of habitat types affects the distribution and abundance of organisms and ecosystem processes.

large intestine The portion of the vertebrate alimentary canal between the small intestine and the anus; functions mainly in water absorption and the formation of feces.

larva (lar′-vuh) (plural, **larvae**) A free-living, sexually immature form in some animal life cycles that may differ from the adult animal in morphology, nutrition, and habitat.

larynx (lār′-inks) The portion of the respiratory tract containing the vocal cords; also called the voice box.

lateralization Segregation of functions in the cortex of the left and right cerebral hemispheres.

lateral line system A mechanoreceptor system consisting of a series of pores and receptor units along the sides of the body in fishes and aquatic amphibians; detects water movements made by the animal itself and by other moving objects.

lateral meristem (mār′-uh-stem) A meristem that thickens the roots and shoots of woody

plants. The vascular cambium and cork cambium are lateral meristems.

lateral root A root that arises from the pericycle of an established root.

law of conservation of mass A physical law stating that matter can change form but cannot be created or destroyed. In a closed system, the mass of the system is constant.

law of independent assortment Mendel's second law, stating that each pair of alleles segregates, or assorts, independently of each other pair during gamete formation; applies when genes for two characters are located on different pairs of homologous chromosomes or when they are far enough apart on the same chromosome to behave as though they are on different chromosomes.

law of segregation Mendel's first law, stating that the two alleles in a pair segregate (separate from each other) into different gametes during gamete formation.

leading strand The new complementary DNA strand synthesized continuously along the template strand toward the replication fork in the mandatory $5' \rightarrow 3'$ direction.

leaf The main photosynthetic organ of vascular plants.

leaf primordium (plural, **primordia**) A finger-like projection along the flank of a shoot apical meristem, from which a leaf arises.

learning The modification of behavior as a result of specific experiences.

lens The structure in an eye that focuses light rays onto the photoreceptors.

lenticel (len′-ti-sel) A small raised area in the bark of stems and roots that enables gas exchange between living cells and the outside air.

lepidosaur (leh-pid′-uh-sōr) A member of the reptilian group that includes lizards, snakes, and two species of New Zealand animals called tuataras.

leukocyte (lū′-kō-sīt′) A blood cell that functions in fighting infections; also called a white blood cell.

lichen The mutualistic association between a fungus and a photosynthetic alga or cyanobacterium.

life cycle The generation-to-generation sequence of stages in the reproductive history of an organism.

life history The traits that affect an organism's schedule of reproduction and survival.

life table An age-specific summary of the survival pattern of a population.

ligament A fibrous connective tissue that joins bones together at joints.

ligand (lig′-und) A molecule that binds specifically to another molecule, usually a larger one.

ligand-gated ion channel (lig′-und) A transmembrane protein containing a pore that opens or closes as it changes shape in response to a signaling molecule (ligand), allowing or blocking the flow of specific ions; also called an ionotropic receptor.

light chain One of the two types of polypeptide chains that make up an antibody molecule and B cell receptor; consists of a variable region, which contributes to the antigen-binding site, and a constant region.

light-harvesting complex A complex of proteins associated with pigment molecules (including chlorophyll *a*, chlorophyll *b*, and carotenoids) that captures light energy and transfers it to reaction-center pigments in a photosystem.

light microscope (LM) An optical instrument with lenses that refract (bend) visible light to magnify images of specimens.

light reactions The first of two major stages in photosynthesis (preceding the Calvin cycle). These reactions, which occur on the thylakoid membranes of the chloroplast or on membranes of certain prokaryotes, convert solar energy to the chemical energy of ATP and NADPH, releasing oxygen in the process.

lignin (lig'-nin) A strong polymer embedded in the cellulose matrix of the secondary cell walls of vascular plants that provides structural support in terrestrial species.

limiting nutrient An element that must be added for production to increase in a particular area.

limnetic zone In a lake, the well-lit, open surface waters far from shore.

linear electron flow A route of electron flow during the light reactions of photosynthesis that involves both photosystems (I and II) and produces ATP, NADPH, and O_2. The net electron flow is from H_2O to $NADP^+$.

line graph A graph in which each data point is connected to the next point in the data set with a straight line.

linkage map A genetic map based on the frequencies of recombination between markers during crossing over of homologous chromosomes.

linked genes Genes located close enough together on a chromosome that they tend to be inherited together.

lipid (lip'-id) Any of a group of large biological molecules, including fats, phospholipids, and steroids, that mix poorly, if at all, with water.

littoral zone In a lake, the shallow, well-lit waters close to shore.

liver A large internal organ in vertebrates that performs diverse functions, such as producing bile, maintaining blood glucose level, and detoxifying poisonous chemicals in the blood.

liverwort A small, herbaceous, nonvascular plant that is a member of the phylum Hepatophyta.

loam The most fertile soil type, made up of roughly equal amounts of sand, silt, and clay.

lobe-fin A member of the vertebrate clade Sarcopterygii, osteichthyans with rod-shaped muscular fins, including coelacanths, lungfishes, and tetrapods.

local regulator A secreted molecule that influences cells near where it is secreted.

locomotion Active motion from place to place.

locus (lō'-kus) (plural, **loci**) (lō'-sī) A specific place along the length of a chromosome where a given gene is located.

logistic population growth Population growth that levels off as population size approaches carrying capacity.

long-day plant A plant that flowers (usually in late spring or early summer) only when the light period is longer than a critical length.

long-term memory The ability to hold, associate, and recall information over one's lifetime.

long-term potentiation (LTP) An enhanced responsiveness to an action potential (nerve signal) by a receiving neuron.

loop of Henle (hen'-lē) The hairpin turn, with a descending and ascending limb, between the proximal and distal tubules of the vertebrate kidney; functions in water and salt reabsorption.

lophophore (lof'-uh-fōr) In some lophotrochozoan animals, including brachiopods, a crown of ciliated tentacles that surround the mouth and function in feeding.

Lophotrochozoa (lo-phah'-truh-kō-zō'-uh) One of the three main lineages of bilaterian animals; lophotrochozoans include organisms that have lophophores or trochophore larvae. *See also* Deuterostomia and Ecdysozoa.

low-density lipoprotein (LDL) A particle in the blood made up of thousands of cholesterol molecules and other lipids bound to a protein. LDL transports cholesterol from the liver for incorporation into cell membranes.

lung An infolded respiratory surface of a terrestrial vertebrate, land snail, or spider that connects to the atmosphere by narrow tubes.

luteinizing hormone (LH) (lū'-tē-uh-nī'-zing) A tropic hormone that is produced and secreted by the anterior pituitary and that stimulates ovulation in females and androgen production in males.

lycophyte (lī'-kuh-fīt) An informal name for a member of the phylum Lycophyta, which includes club mosses, spike mosses, and quillworts.

lymph The colorless fluid, derived from interstitial fluid, in the lymphatic system of vertebrates.

lymph node An organ located along a lymph vessel. Lymph nodes filter lymph and contain cells that attack viruses and bacteria.

lymphatic system A system of vessels and nodes, separate from the circulatory system, that returns fluid, proteins, and cells to the blood.

lymphocyte A type of white blood cell that mediates immune responses. The two main classes are B cells and T cells.

lysogenic cycle (lī'-sō-jen'-ik) A type of phage replicative cycle in which the viral genome becomes incorporated into the bacterial host chromosome as a prophage, is replicated along with the chromosome, and does not kill the host.

lysosome (lī'-suh-sōm) A membrane-enclosed sac of hydrolytic enzymes found in the cytoplasm of animal cells and some protists.

lysozyme (lī'-sō-zīm) An enzyme that destroys bacterial cell walls; in mammals, it is found in sweat, tears, and saliva.

lytic cycle (lit'-ik) A type of phage replicative cycle resulting in the release of new phages by lysis (and death) of the host cell.

macroclimate Large-scale patterns in climate; the climate of an entire region.

macroevolution Evolutionary change above the species level. Examples of macroevolutionary change include the origin of a new group of organisms through a series of speciation events and the impact of mass extinctions on the diversity of life and its subsequent recovery.

macromolecule A giant molecule formed by the joining of smaller molecules, usually by a dehydration reaction. Polysaccharides, proteins, and nucleic acids are macromolecules.

macronutrient An essential element that an organism must obtain in relatively large amounts. *See also* micronutrient.

macrophage (mak'-rō-fāj) A phagocytic cell present in many tissues that functions in innate immunity by destroying microbes and in acquired immunity as an antigen-presenting cell.

magnoliid A member of the angiosperm clade that is most closely related to the combined eudicot and monocot clades. Extant examples are magnolias, laurels, and black pepper plants.

major depressive disorder A mood disorder characterized by feelings of sadness, lack of self-worth, emptiness, or loss of interest in nearly all things.

major histocompatibility complex (MHC) molecule A host protein that functions in antigen presentation. Foreign MHC molecules on transplanted tissue can trigger T cell responses that may lead to rejection of the transplant.

malignant tumor A cancerous tumor containing cells that have significant genetic and cellular changes and are capable of invading and surviving in new sites. Malignant tumors can impair the functions of one or more organs.

Malpighian tubule (mal-pig'-ē-un) A unique excretory organ of insects that empties into the digestive tract, removes nitrogenous wastes from the hemolymph, and functions in osmoregulation.

mammal A member of the clade Mammalia, amniotes that have hair and mammary glands (glands that produce milk).

mammary gland An exocrine gland that secretes milk for nourishing the young. Mammary glands are characteristic of mammals.

mantle One of the three main parts of a mollusc; a fold of tissue that drapes over the mollusc's visceral mass and may secrete a shell. *See also* foot and visceral mass.

mantle cavity A water-filled chamber that houses the gills, anus, and excretory pores of a mollusc.

map unit A unit of measurement of the distance between genes. One map unit is equivalent to a 1% recombination frequency.

marine benthic zone The ocean floor.

mark-recapture method A sampling technique used to estimate the size of animal populations.

marsupial (mar-sū'-pē-ul) A mammal, such as a koala, kangaroo, or opossum, whose young complete their embryonic development inside a maternal pouch called the marsupium.

mass extinction The elimination of a large number of species throughout Earth, the result of global environmental changes.

mass number The sum of the number of protons and neutrons in an atom's nucleus.

mast cell A vertebrate body cell that produces histamine and other molecules that trigger inflammation in response to infection and in allergic reactions.

mate-choice copying Behavior in which individuals in a population copy the mate choice of others, apparently as a result of social learning.

maternal effect gene A gene that, when mutant in the mother, results in a mutant phenotype in the offspring, regardless of the offspring's genotype. Maternal effect genes, also called egg-polarity genes, were first identified in *Drosophila melanogaster.*

matter Anything that takes up space and has mass.

maximum likelihood As applied to DNA sequence data, a principle that states that when considering multiple phylogenetic hypotheses, one should take into account the hypothesis that reflects the most likely sequence of evolutionary events, given certain rules about how DNA changes over time.

maximum parsimony A principle that states that when considering multiple explanations for an observation, one should first investigate the simplest explanation that is consistent with the facts.

mean The sum of all data points in a data set divided by the number of data points.

mechanoreceptor A sensory receptor that detects physical deformation in the body's environment associated with pressure, touch, stretch, motion, or sound.

medulla oblongata (meh-dul'-uh ōb'-long-go'-tuh) The lowest part of the vertebrate brain, commonly called the medulla; a swelling of the hindbrain anterior to the spinal cord that controls autonomic, homeostatic functions, including breathing, heart and blood vessel activity, swallowing, digestion, and vomiting.

medusa (plural, **medusae**) (muh-dū'-suh) The floating, flattened, mouth-down version of the cnidarian body plan. The alternate form is the polyp.

megapascal (MPa) (meg'-uh-pas-kal') A unit of pressure equivalent to about 10 atmospheres of pressure.

megaphyll (meh'-guh-fil) A leaf with a highly branched vascular system, characteristic of the vast majority of vascular plants. *See also* microphyll.

megaspore A spore from a heterosporous plant species that develops into a female gametophyte.

meiosis (mī-ō'-sis) A modified type of cell division in sexually reproducing organisms consisting of two rounds of cell division but only one round of DNA replication. It results in cells with half the number of chromosome sets as the original cell.

meiosis I (mī-ō'-sis) The first division of a two-stage process of cell division in sexually reproducing organisms that results in cells with half the number of chromosome sets as the original cell.

meiosis II (mī-ō'-sis) The second division of a two-stage process of cell division in sexually reproducing organisms that results in cells with half the number of chromosome sets as the original cell.

melanocyte-stimulating hormone (MSH) A hormone produced and secreted by the anterior pituitary with multiple activities, including regulating the behavior of pigment-containing cells in the skin of some vertebrates.

melatonin A hormone that is secreted by the pineal gland and that is involved in the regulation of biological rhythms and sleep.

membrane potential The difference in electrical charge (voltage) across a cell's plasma membrane due to the differential distribution of ions. Membrane potential affects the activity of excitable cells and the transmembrane movement of all charged substances.

memory cell One of a clone of long-lived lymphocytes, formed during the primary immune response, that remains in a lymphoid organ until activated by exposure to the same antigen that triggered its formation. Activated memory cells mount the secondary immune response.

menopause The cessation of ovulation and menstruation marking the end of a human female's reproductive years.

menstrual cycle (men'-strŭ-ul) *See* uterine cycle.

menstruation The shedding of portions of the endometrium during a uterine (menstrual) cycle.

meristem (mār'-uh-stem) Plant tissue that remains embryonic as long as the plant lives, allowing for indeterminate growth.

meristem identity gene (mār'-uh-stem) A plant gene that promotes the switch from vegetative growth to flowering.

meroblastic (mār'-ō-blas'-tik) Referring to a type of cleavage in which there is incomplete division of a yolk-rich egg, characteristic of avian development.

mesoderm (mez'-ō-derm) The middle primary germ layer in a triploblastic animal embryo; develops into the notochord, the lining of the coelom, muscles, skeleton, gonads, kidneys, and most of the circulatory system in species that have these structures.

mesohyl (mez'-ō-hīl) A gelatinous region between the two layers of cells of a sponge.

mesophyll (mez'-ō-fil) Leaf cells specialized for photosynthesis. In C_3 and CAM plants, mesophyll cells are located between the upper and lower epidermis; in C_4 plants, they are located between the bundle-sheath cells and the epidermis.

messenger RNA (mRNA) A type of RNA, synthesized using a DNA template, that attaches to ribosomes in the cytoplasm and specifies the primary structure of a protein. (In eukaryotes, the primary RNA transcript must undergo RNA processing to become mRNA.)

metabolic pathway A series of chemical reactions that either builds a complex molecule (anabolic pathway) or breaks down a complex molecule to simpler molecules (catabolic pathway).

metabolic rate The total amount of energy an animal uses in a unit of time.

metabolism (muh-tab'-uh-lizm) The totality of an organism's chemical reactions, consisting of catabolic and anabolic pathways, which manage the material and energy resources of the organism.

metagenomics The collection and sequencing of DNA from a group of species, usually an environmental sample of microorganisms. Computer software sorts partial sequences and assembles them into genome sequences of individual species making up the sample.

metamorphosis (met'-uh-mōr'-fuh-sis) A developmental transformation that turns an animal larva into either an adult or an adult-like stage that is not yet sexually mature.

metanephridium (met'-uh-nuh-frid'-ē-um) (plural, **metanephridia**) An excretory organ found in many invertebrates that typically consists of tubules connecting ciliated internal openings to external openings.

metaphase The third stage of mitosis, in which the spindle is complete and the chromosomes, attached to microtubules at their kinetochores, are all aligned at the metaphase plate.

metaphase plate An imaginary structure located at a plane midway between the two poles of a cell in metaphase on which the centromeres of all the duplicated chromosomes are located.

metapopulation A group of spatially separated populations of one species that interact through immigration and emigration.

metastasis (muh-tas'-tuh-sis) The spread of cancer cells to locations distant from their original site.

methanogen (meth-an'-ō-jen) An organism that produces methane as a waste product of the way it obtains energy. All known methanogens are in domain Archaea.

methyl group A chemical group consisting of a carbon bonded to three hydrogen atoms. The methyl group may be attached to a carbon or to a different atom.

microclimate Climate patterns on a very fine scale, such as the specific climatic conditions underneath a log.

microevolution Evolutionary change below the species level; change in the allele frequencies in a population over generations.

microfilament A cable composed of actin proteins in the cytoplasm of almost every eukaryotic cell, making up part of the cytoskeleton and acting alone or with myosin to cause cell contraction; also called an actin filament.

micronutrient An essential element that an organism needs in very small amounts. *See also* macronutrient.

microphyll (mī'-krō-fil) In lycophytes, a small leaf with a single unbranched vein. *See also* megaphyll.

micropyle A pore in the integuments of an ovule.

microRNA (miRNA) A small, single-stranded RNA molecule, generated from a double-stranded RNA precursor. The miRNA associates with one or more proteins in a complex that can degrade or prevent translation of an mRNA with a complementary sequence.

microspore A spore from a heterosporous plant species that develops into a male gametophyte.

microtubule A hollow rod composed of tubulin proteins that makes up part of the cytoskeleton in all eukaryotic cells and is found in cilia and flagella.

microvillus (plural, **microvilli**) One of many fine, finger-like projections of the epithelial cells in the lumen of the small intestine that increase its surface area.

midbrain One of three ancestral and embryonic regions of the vertebrate brain; develops into sensory integrating and relay centers that send sensory information to the cerebrum.

middle lamella (luh-mel'-uh) In plants, a thin layer of adhesive extracellular material, primarily pectins, found between the primary walls of adjacent young cells.

migration A regular, long-distance change in location.

mineral In nutrition, a simple nutrient that is inorganic and therefore cannot be synthesized in the body.

mineralocorticoid A steroid hormone secreted by the adrenal cortex that regulates salt and water homeostasis.

minimum viable population (MVP) The smallest population size at which a species is able to sustain its numbers and survive.

mismatch repair The cellular process that uses specific enzymes to remove and replace incorrectly paired nucleotides.

missense mutation A nucleotide-pair substitution that results in a codon that codes for a different amino acid.

mitochondrial matrix The compartment of the mitochondrion enclosed by the inner membrane and containing enzymes and substrates for the citric acid cycle, as well as ribosomes and DNA.

mitochondrion (mī'-tō-kon'-drē-un) (plural, **mitochondria**) An organelle in eukaryotic cells that serves as the site of cellular respiration; uses oxygen to break down organic molecules and synthesize ATP.

mitosis (mī-tō'-sis) A process of nuclear division in eukaryotic cells conventionally divided into five stages: prophase, prometaphase, metaphase, anaphase, and telophase. Mitosis conserves chromosome number by allocating replicated chromosomes equally to each of the daughter nuclei.

mitotic (M) phase The phase of the cell cycle that includes mitosis and cytokinesis.

mitotic spindle An assemblage of microtubules and associated proteins that is involved in the movement of chromosomes during mitosis.

mixotroph An organism that is capable of both photosynthesis and heterotrophy.

model A physical or conceptual representation of a natural phenomenon.

model organism A particular species chosen for research into broad biological principles because it is representative of a larger group and usually easy to grow in a lab.

molarity A common measure of solute concentration, referring to the number of moles of solute per liter of solution.

mold Informal term for a fungus that grows as a filamentous fungus, producing haploid spores by mitosis and forming a visible mycelium.

mole (mol) The number of grams of a substance that equals its molecular or atomic mass in daltons; a mole contains Avogadro's number of the molecules or atoms in question.

molecular clock A method for estimating the time required for a given amount of evolutionary change, based on the observation that some regions of genomes evolve at constant rates.

molecular mass The sum of the masses of all the atoms in a molecule; sometimes called molecular weight.

molecule Two or more atoms held together by covalent bonds.

molting A process in ecdysozoans in which the exoskeleton is shed at intervals, allowing growth by the production of a larger exoskeleton.

monilophyte An informal name for a member of the phylum Monilophyta, which includes ferns, horsetails, and whisk ferns and their relatives.

monoclonal antibody (mon'-ō-klōn'-ul) Any of a preparation of antibodies that have been produced by a single clone of cultured cells and thus are all specific for the same epitope.

monocot A member of a clade consisting of flowering plants that have one embryonic seed leaf, or cotyledon.

monogamous (muh-nog'-uh-mus) Referring to a type of relationship in which one male mates with just one female.

monohybrid An organism that is heterozygous with respect to a single gene of interest. All the offspring from a cross between parents homozygous for different alleles are monohybrids. For example, parents of genotypes *AA* and *aa* produce a monohybrid of genotype *Aa*.

monohybrid cross A cross between two organisms that are heterozygous for the character being followed (or the self-pollination of a heterozygous plant).

monomer (mon'-uh-mer) The subunit that serves as the building block of a polymer.

monophyletic (mon'-ō-fī-let'-ik) Pertaining to a group of taxa that consists of a common ancestor and all of its descendants. A monophyletic taxon is equivalent to a clade.

monosaccharide (mon'-ō-sak'-uh-rīd) The simplest carbohydrate, active alone or serving as a monomer for disaccharides and polysaccharides. Also called simple sugars, monosaccharides have molecular formulas that are generally some multiple of CH_2O.

monosomic Referring to a diploid cell that has only one copy of a particular chromosome instead of the normal two.

monotreme An egg-laying mammal, such as a platypus or echidna. Like all mammals, monotremes have hair and produce milk, but they lack nipples.

morphogen A substance, such as Bicoid protein in *Drosophila*, that provides positional information in the form of a concentration gradient along an embryonic axis.

morphogenesis (mōr'-fō-jen'-uh-sis) The development of the form of an organism and its structures.

morphological species concept Definition of a species in terms of measurable anatomical criteria.

moss A small, herbaceous, nonvascular plant that is a member of the phylum Bryophyta.

motor neuron A nerve cell that transmits signals from the brain or spinal cord to muscles or glands.

motor protein A protein that interacts with cytoskeletal elements and other cell components, producing movement of the whole cell or parts of the cell.

motor system An efferent branch of the vertebrate peripheral nervous system composed of motor neurons that carry signals to skeletal muscles in response to external stimuli.

motor unit A single motor neuron and all the muscle fibers it controls.

movement corridor A series of small clumps or a narrow strip of quality habitat (usable by organisms) that connects otherwise isolated patches of quality habitat.

MPF Maturation-promoting factor (or M-phase-promoting factor); a protein complex required for a cell to progress from late interphase to mitosis. The active form consists of cyclin and a protein kinase.

mucus A viscous and slippery mixture of glycoproteins, cells, salts, and water that moistens and protects the membranes lining body cavities that open to the exterior.

Müllerian mimicry (myū-lār'-ē-un mim'-uh-krē) Reciprocal mimicry by two unpalatable species.

multifactorial Referring to a phenotypic character that is influenced by multiple genes and environmental factors.

multigene family A collection of genes with similar or identical sequences, presumably of common origin.

multiple fruit A fruit derived from an entire inflorescence.

multiplication rule A rule of probability stating that the probability of two or more independent events occurring together can be determined by multiplying their individual probabilities.

muscle tissue Tissue consisting of long muscle cells that can contract, either on its own or when stimulated by nerve impulses.

mutagen (myū'-tuh-jen) A chemical or physical agent that interacts with DNA and can cause a mutation.

mutation (myū-tā'-shun) A change in the nucleotide sequence of an organism's DNA or in the DNA or RNA of a virus.

mutualism (myū'-chū-ul-izm) A symbiotic relationship in which both participants benefit.

mycelium (mī-sē'-lē-um) The densely branched network of hyphae in a fungus.

mycorrhiza (plural, **mycorrhizae**) (mī′-kō-rī′-zuh, mī′-kō-rī′-zē) A mutualistic association of plant roots and fungus.

mycosis (mī-kō′-sis) General term for a fungal infection.

myelin sheath (mī′-uh-lin) Wrapped around the axon of a neuron, an insulating coat of cell membranes from Schwann cells or oligodendrocytes. It is interrupted by nodes of Ranvier, where action potentials are generated.

myofibril (mī′-ō-fī′-bril) A longitudinal bundle in a muscle cell (fiber) that contains thin filaments of actin and regulatory proteins and thick filaments of myosin.

myoglobin (mī′-uh-glō′-bin) An oxygen-storing, pigmented protein in muscle cells.

myosin (mī′-uh-sin) A type of motor protein that associates into filaments that interact with actin filaments to cause cell contraction.

myriapod (mir′-ē-uh-pod′) A terrestrial arthropod with many body segments and one or two pairs of legs per segment. Millipedes and centipedes are the two major groups of living myriapods.

NAD⁺ Nicotinamide adenine dinucleotide, a coenzyme that cycles easily between oxidized (NAD^+) and reduced (NADH) states, thus acting as an electron carrier.

NADP⁺ Nicotinamide adenine dinucleotide phosphate, an electron acceptor that, as NADPH, temporarily stores energized electrons produced during the light reactions.

natural killer cell A type of white blood cell that can kill tumor cells and virus-infected cells as part of innate immunity.

natural selection A process in which individuals that have certain inherited traits tend to survive and reproduce at higher rates than other individuals because of those traits.

negative feedback A form of regulation in which accumulation of an end product of a process slows the process; in physiology, a primary mechanism of homeostasis, whereby a change in a variable triggers a response that counteracts the initial change.

negative pressure breathing A breathing system in which air is pulled into the lungs.

nematocyst (nem′-uh-tuh-sist′) In a cnidocyte of a cnidarian, a capsule-like organelle containing a coiled thread that when discharged can penetrate the body wall of the prey.

nephron (nef′-ron) The tubular excretory unit of the vertebrate kidney.

neritic zone The shallow region of the ocean overlying the continental shelf.

nerve A fiber composed primarily of the bundled axons of neurons.

nervous system In animals, the fast-acting internal system of communication involving sensory receptors, networks of nerve cells, and connections to muscles and glands that respond to nerve signals; functions in concert with the endocrine system to effect internal regulation and maintain homeostasis.

nervous tissue Tissue made up of neurons and supportive cells.

net ecosystem production (NEP) The gross primary production of an ecosystem minus the energy used by all autotrophs and heterotrophs for respiration.

net primary production (NPP) The gross primary production of an ecosystem minus the energy used by the producers for respiration.

neural crest In vertebrates, a region located along the sides of the neural tube where it pinches off from the ectoderm. Neural crest cells migrate to various parts of the embryo and form pigment cells in the skin and parts of the skull, teeth, adrenal glands, and peripheral nervous system.

neural tube A tube of infolded ectodermal cells that runs along the anterior-posterior axis of a vertebrate, just dorsal to the notochord. It will give rise to the central nervous system.

neurohormone A molecule that is secreted by a neuron, travels in body fluids, and acts on specific target cells, changing their functioning.

neuron (nyūr′-on) A nerve cell; the fundamental unit of the nervous system, having structure and properties that allow it to conduct signals by taking advantage of the electrical charge across its plasma membrane.

neuronal plasticity The capacity of a nervous system to change with experience.

neuropeptide A relatively short chain of amino acids that serves as a neurotransmitter.

neurotransmitter A molecule that is released from the synaptic terminal of a neuron at a chemical synapse, diffuses across the synaptic cleft, and binds to the postsynaptic cell, triggering a response.

neutral variation Genetic variation that does not provide a selective advantage or disadvantage.

neutron A subatomic particle having no electrical charge (electrically neutral), with a mass of about 1.7×10^{-24} g, found in the nucleus of an atom.

neutrophil The most abundant type of white blood cell. Neutrophils are phagocytic and tend to self-destruct as they destroy foreign invaders, limiting their life span to a few days.

nitric oxide (NO) A gas produced by many types of cells that functions as a local regulator and as a neurotransmitter.

nitrogen cycle The natural process by which nitrogen, either from the atmosphere or from decomposed organic material, is converted by soil bacteria to compounds assimilated by plants. This incorporated nitrogen is then taken in by other organisms and subsequently released, acted on by bacteria, and made available again to the nonliving environment.

nitrogen fixation The conversion of atmospheric nitrogen (N_2) to ammonia (NH_3). Biological nitrogen fixation is carried out by certain prokaryotes, some of which have mutualistic relationships with plants.

nociceptor (nō′-si-sep′-tur) A sensory receptor that responds to noxious or painful stimuli; also called a pain receptor.

node A point along the stem of a plant at which leaves are attached.

node of Ranvier (ron′-vē-ā′) Gap in the myelin sheath of certain axons where an action potential may be generated. In saltatory conduction, an action potential is regenerated at each node, appearing to "jump" along the axon from node to node.

nodule A swelling on the root of a legume. Nodules are composed of plant cells that contain nitrogen-fixing bacteria of the genus *Rhizobium*.

noncompetitive inhibitor A substance that reduces the activity of an enzyme by binding to a location remote from the active site, changing the enzyme's shape so that the active site no longer effectively catalyzes the conversion of substrate to product.

nondisjunction An error in meiosis or mitosis in which members of a pair of homologous chromosomes or a pair of sister chromatids fail to separate properly from each other.

nonequilibrium model A model that maintains that communities change constantly after being buffeted by disturbances.

nonpolar covalent bond A type of covalent bond in which electrons are shared equally between two atoms of similar electronegativity.

nonsense mutation A mutation that changes an amino acid codon to one of the three stop codons, resulting in a shorter and usually nonfunctional protein.

norepinephrine A catecholamine that is chemically and functionally similar to epinephrine and acts as a hormone or neurotransmitter; also called noradrenaline.

northern coniferous forest A terrestrial biome characterized by long, cold winters and dominated by cone-bearing trees.

no-till agriculture A plowing technique that minimally disturbs the soil, thereby reducing soil loss.

notochord (nō′-tuh-kord′) A longitudinal, flexible rod made of tightly packed mesodermal cells that runs along the anterior-posterior axis of a chordate in the dorsal part of the body.

nuclear envelope In a eukaryotic cell, the double membrane that surrounds the nucleus, perforated with pores that regulate traffic with the cytoplasm. The outer membrane is continuous with the endoplasmic reticulum.

nuclear lamina A netlike array of protein filaments that lines the inner surface of the nuclear envelope and helps maintain the shape of the nucleus.

nucleariid A member of a group of unicellular, amoeboid protists that are more closely related to fungi than they are to other protists.

nuclease An enzyme that cuts DNA or RNA, either removing one or a few bases or hydrolyzing the DNA or RNA completely into its component nucleotides.

nucleic acid (nū-klā′-ik) A polymer (polynucleotide) consisting of many nucleotide monomers; serves as a blueprint for proteins and, through the actions of proteins, for all cellular activities. The two types are DNA and RNA.

nucleic acid hybridization (nū-klā′-ik) The base pairing of one strand of a nucleic acid to the complementary sequence on a strand from *another* nucleic acid molecule.

nucleic acid probe (nū-klā′-ik) In DNA technology, a labeled single-stranded nucleic acid molecule used to locate a specific nucleotide sequence in a nucleic acid sample. Molecules of the probe hydrogen-bond to the complementary sequence wherever it occurs; radioactive, fluorescent, or other labeling of the probe allows its location to be detected.

nucleoid (nū'-klē-oyd) A non-membrane-enclosed region in a prokaryotic cell where its chromosome is located.

nucleolus (nū-klē'-ō-lus) (plural, **nucleoli**) A specialized structure in the nucleus, consisting of chromosomal regions containing ribosomal RNA (rRNA) genes along with ribosomal proteins imported from the cytoplasm; site of rRNA synthesis and ribosomal subunit assembly. *See also* ribosome.

nucleosome (nū'-klē-ō-sōm') The basic, bead-like unit of DNA packing in eukaryotes, consisting of a segment of DNA wound around a protein core composed of two copies of each of four types of histone.

nucleotide (nū'-klē-ō-tīd') The building block of a nucleic acid, consisting of a five-carbon sugar covalently bonded to a nitrogenous base and one or more phosphate groups.

nucleotide excision repair (nū'-klē-ō-tīd') A repair system that removes and then correctly replaces a damaged segment of DNA using the undamaged strand as a guide.

nucleotide-pair substitution (nū'-klē-ō-tīd') A type of point mutation in which one nucleotide in a DNA strand and its partner in the complementary strand are replaced by another pair of nucleotides.

nucleus (1) An atom's central core, containing protons and neutrons. (2) The organelle of a eukaryotic cell that contains the genetic material in the form of chromosomes, made up of chromatin. (3) A cluster of neurons.

nutrition The process by which an organism takes in and makes use of food substances.

obligate aerobe (ob'-lig-et âr'-ōb) An organism that requires oxygen for cellular respiration and cannot live without it.

obligate anaerobe (ob'-lig-et an'-uh-rōb) An organism that carries out only fermentation or anaerobic respiration. Such organisms cannot use oxygen and in fact may be poisoned by it.

ocean acidification Decreasing pH of ocean waters due to absorption of excess atmospheric CO_2 from the burning of fossil fuels.

oceanic pelagic zone Most of the ocean's waters far from shore, constantly mixed by ocean currents.

odorant A molecule that can be detected by sensory receptors of the olfactory system.

Okazaki fragment (ō'-kah-zah'-kē) A short segment of DNA synthesized away from the replication fork on a template strand during DNA replication. Many such segments are joined together to make up the lagging strand of newly synthesized DNA.

olfaction The sense of smell.

oligodendrocyte A type of glial cell that forms insulating myelin sheaths around the axons of neurons in the central nervous system.

oligotrophic lake A nutrient-poor, clear lake with few phytoplankton.

ommatidium (ōm'-uh-tid'-ē-um) (plural, **ommatidia**) One of the facets of the compound eye of arthropods and some polychaete worms.

omnivore An animal that regularly eats animals as well as plants or algae.

oncogene (on'-kō-jēn) A gene found in viral or cellular genomes that is involved in triggering molecular events that can lead to cancer.

oocyte (ō'-uh-sīt) A cell in the female reproductive system that differentiates to form an egg.

oogenesis (ō'-uh-jen'-uh-sis) The process in the ovary that results in the production of female gametes.

oogonium (ō'-uh-gō'-nē-em) (plural, **oogonia**) A cell that divides mitotically to form oocytes.

open circulatory system A circulatory system in which fluid called hemolymph bathes the tissues and organs directly and there is no distinction between the circulating fluid and the interstitial fluid.

operator In bacterial and phage DNA, a sequence of nucleotides near the start of an operon to which an active repressor can attach. The binding of the repressor prevents RNA polymerase from attaching to the promoter and transcribing the genes of the operon.

operculum (ō-per'-kyuh-lum) In aquatic osteichthyans, a protective bony flap that covers and protects the gills.

operon (op'-er-on) A unit of genetic function found in bacteria and phages, consisting of a promoter, an operator, and a coordinately regulated cluster of genes whose products function in a common pathway.

opisthokont (uh-pis'-thuh-kont') A member of an extremely diverse clade of eukaryotes that includes fungi, animals, and several closely-related groups of protists.

opposable thumb A thumb that can touch the ventral surface of the fingertips of all four fingers.

opsin A membrane protein bound to a light-absorbing pigment molecule.

optimal foraging model The basis for analyzing behavior as a compromise between feeding costs and feeding benefits.

oral cavity The mouth of an animal.

orbital The three-dimensional space where an electron is found 90% of the time.

order In Linnaean classification, the taxonomic category above the level of family.

organ A specialized center of body function composed of several different types of tissues.

organ identity gene A plant homeotic gene that uses positional information to determine which emerging leaves develop into which types of floral organs.

organ of Corti (kor'-tē) The actual hearing organ of the vertebrate ear, located in the floor of the cochlear duct in the inner ear; contains the receptor cells (hair cells) of the ear.

organ system A group of organs that work together in performing vital body functions.

organelle (ōr-guh-nel') Any of several membrane-enclosed structures with specialized functions, suspended in the cytosol of eukaryotic cells.

organic chemistry The study of carbon compounds (organic compounds).

organismal ecology The branch of ecology concerned with the morphological,

physiological, and behavioral ways in which individual organisms meet the challenges posed by their biotic and abiotic environments.

organogenesis (ōr-gan'-ō-jen'-uh-sis) The process in which organ rudiments develop from the three germ layers after gastrulation.

origin of replication Site where the replication of a DNA molecule begins, consisting of a specific sequence of nucleotides.

orthologous genes Homologous genes that are found in different species because of speciation.

osculum (os'-kyuh-lum) A large opening in a sponge that connects the spongocoel to the environment.

osmoconformer An animal that is isoosmotic with its environment.

osmolarity (oz'-mō-lâr'-uh-tē) Solute concentration expressed as molarity.

osmoregulation Regulation of solute concentrations and water balance by a cell or organism.

osmoregulator An animal that controls its internal osmolarity independent of the external environment.

osmosis (oz-mō'-sis) The diffusion of free water across a selectively permeable membrane.

osteichthyan (os'-tē-ik'-thē-an) A member of a vertebrate clade with jaws and mostly bony skeletons.

outgroup A species or group of species from an evolutionary lineage that is known to have diverged before the lineage that contains the group of species being studied. An outgroup is selected so that its members are closely related to the group of species being studied, but not as closely related as any study-group members are to each other.

oval window In the vertebrate ear, a membrane-covered gap in the skull bone, through which sound waves pass from the middle ear to the inner ear.

ovarian cycle (ō-vār'-ē-un) The cyclic recurrence of the follicular phase, ovulation, and the luteal phase in the mammalian ovary, regulated by hormones.

ovary (ō'-vuh-rē) (1) In flowers, the portion of a carpel in which the egg-containing ovules develop. (2) In animals, the structure that produces female gametes and reproductive hormones.

oviduct (ō'-vuh-duct) A tube passing from the ovary to the vagina in invertebrates or to the uterus in vertebrates, where it is also called a fallopian tube.

oviparous (ō-vip'-uh-rus) Referring to a type of development in which young hatch from eggs laid outside the mother's body.

ovoviviparous (ō'-vō-vī-vip'-uh-rus) Referring to a type of development in which young hatch from eggs that are retained in the mother's uterus.

ovulation The release of an egg from an ovary. In humans, an ovarian follicle releases an egg during each uterine (menstrual) cycle.

ovule (o'-vyūl) A structure that develops within the ovary of a seed plant and contains the female gametophyte.

oxidation The complete or partial loss of electrons from a substance involved in a redox reaction.

oxidative phosphorylation (fos′-fōr-uh-lā′-shun) The production of ATP using energy derived from the redox reactions of an electron transport chain; the third major stage of cellular respiration.

oxidizing agent The electron acceptor in a redox reaction.

oxytocin (ok′-si-tō′-sen) A hormone produced by the hypothalamus and released from the posterior pituitary. It induces contractions of the uterine muscles during labor and causes the mammary glands to eject milk during nursing.

p53 gene A tumor-suppressor gene that codes for a specific transcription factor that promotes the synthesis of proteins that inhibit the cell cycle.

paedomorphosis (pē′-duh-mōr′-fuh-sis) The retention in an adult organism of the juvenile features of its evolutionary ancestors.

pain receptor A sensory receptor that responds to noxious or painful stimuli; also called a nociceptor.

paleoanthropology The study of human origins and evolution.

paleontology (pā′-lē-un-tol′-ō-jē) The scientific study of fossils.

pancreas (pan′-krē-us) A gland with exocrine and endocrine tissues. The exocrine portion functions in digestion, secreting enzymes and an alkaline solution into the small intestine via a duct; the ductless endocrine portion functions in homeostasis, secreting the hormones insulin and glucagon into the blood.

pancrustacean A member of a diverse arthropod clade that includes lobsters, crabs, barnacles and other crustaceans, as well as insects and their six-legged terrestrial relatives.

pandemic A global epidemic.

Pangaea (pan-jē′-uh) The supercontinent that formed near the end of the Paleozoic era, when plate movements brought all the landmasses of Earth together.

parabasalid A protist, such as a trichomonad, with modified mitochondria.

paracrine Referring to a secreted molecule that acts on a neighboring cell.

paralogous genes Homologous genes that are found in the same genome as a result of gene duplication.

paraphyletic (pār′-uh-fī-let′-ik) Pertaining to a group of taxa that consists of a common ancestor and some, but not all, of its descendants.

parareptile A basal group of reptiles, consisting mostly of large, stocky quadrupedal herbivores. Parareptiles died out in the late Triassic period.

parasite (pār′-uh-sīt) An organism that feeds on the cell contents, tissues, or body fluids of another species (the host) while in or on the host organism. Parasites harm but usually do not kill their host.

parasitism (pār′-uh-sit-izm) A symbiotic relationship in which one organism, the parasite, benefits at the expense of another, the host, by living either within or on the host.

parasympathetic division One of three divisions of the autonomic nervous system; generally enhances body activities that gain and conserve energy, such as digestion and reduced heart rate.

parathyroid gland One of four small endocrine glands, embedded in the surface of the thyroid gland, that secrete parathyroid hormone.

parathyroid hormone (PTH) A hormone secreted by the parathyroid glands that raises blood calcium level by promoting calcium release from bone and calcium retention by the kidneys.

parenchyma cell (puh-ren′-ki-muh) A relatively unspecialized plant cell type that carries out most of the metabolism, synthesizes and stores organic products, and develops into a more differentiated cell type.

parental type An offspring with a phenotype that matches one of the true-breeding parental (P generation) phenotypes; also refers to the phenotype itself.

Parkinson's disease A progressive brain disease characterized by difficulty in initiating movements, slowness of movement, and rigidity.

parthenogenesis (par′-thuh-nō′-jen′-uh-sis) A form of asexual reproduction in which females produce offspring from unfertilized eggs.

partial pressure The pressure exerted by a particular gas in a mixture of gases (for instance, the pressure exerted by oxygen in air).

passive immunity Short-term immunity conferred by the transfer of antibodies, as occurs in the transfer of maternal antibodies to a fetus or nursing infant.

passive transport The diffusion of a substance across a biological membrane with no expenditure of energy.

pathogen An organism or virus that causes disease.

pathogen-associated molecular patterns (PAMPs) Short molecular sequences that typify certain groups of pathogens and that are recognized by cells of the innate immune system.

pattern formation The development of a multicellular organism's spatial organization, the arrangement of organs and tissues in their characteristic places in three-dimensional space.

peat Extensive deposits of partially decayed organic material often formed primarily from the wetland moss *Sphagnum*.

pedigree A diagram of a family tree with conventional symbols, showing the occurrence of heritable characters in parents and offspring over multiple generations.

pelagic zone The open-water component of aquatic biomes.

penis The copulatory structure of male mammals.

PEP carboxylase An enzyme that adds CO_2 to phosphoenolpyruvate (PEP) to form oxaloacetate in mesophyll cells of C_4 plants. It acts prior to photosynthesis.

pepsin An enzyme present in gastric juice that begins the hydrolysis of proteins.

pepsinogen The inactive form of pepsin secreted by chief cells located in gastric pits of the stomach.

peptide bond The covalent bond between the carboxyl group on one amino acid and the amino group on another, formed by a dehydration reaction.

peptidoglycan (pep′-tid-ō-glī′-kan) A type of polymer in bacterial cell walls consisting of modified sugars cross-linked by short polypeptides.

perception The interpretation of sensory system input by the brain.

pericycle The outermost layer in the vascular cylinder, from which lateral roots arise.

periderm (pār′-uh-derm′) The protective coat that replaces the epidermis in woody plants during secondary growth, formed of the cork and cork cambium.

peripheral nervous system (PNS) The sensory and motor neurons that connect to the central nervous system.

peripheral protein A protein loosely bound to the surface of a membrane or to part of an integral protein and not embedded in the lipid bilayer.

peristalsis (pār′-uh-stal′-sis) (1) Alternating waves of contraction and relaxation in the smooth muscles lining the alimentary canal that push food along the canal. (2) A type of movement on land produced by rhythmic waves of muscle contractions passing from front to back, as in many annelids.

peristome (pār′-uh-stōme′) A ring of interlocking, tooth-like structures on the upper part of a moss capsule (sporangium), often specialized for gradual spore discharge.

peritubular capillary One of the tiny blood vessels that form a network surrounding the proximal and distal tubules in the kidney.

peroxisome (puh-rok′-suh-sōm′) An organelle containing enzymes that transfer hydrogen atoms from various substrates to oxygen (O_2), producing and then degrading hydrogen peroxide (H_2O_2).

petal A modified leaf of a flowering plant. Petals are the often colorful parts of a flower that advertise it to insects and other pollinators.

petiole (pet′-ē-ōl) The stalk of a leaf, which joins the leaf to a node of the stem.

P generation The true-breeding (homozygous) parent individuals from which F_1 hybrid offspring are derived in studies of inheritance; P stands for "parental."

pH A measure of hydrogen ion concentration equal to $-\log [H^+]$ and ranging in value from 0 to 14.

phage (fāj) A virus that infects bacteria; also called a bacteriophage.

phagocytosis (fag′-ō-sī-tō′-sis) A type of endocytosis in which large particulate substances or small organisms are taken up by a cell. It is carried out by some protists and by certain immune cells of animals (in mammals, mainly macrophages, neutrophils, and dendritic cells).

pharyngeal cleft (fuh-rin'-jē-ul) In chordate embryos, one of the grooves that separate a series of arches along the outer surface of the pharynx and may develop into a pharyngeal slit.

pharyngeal slit (fuh-rin'-jē-ul) In chordate embryos, one of the slits that form from the pharyngeal clefts and open into the pharynx, later developing into gill slits in many vertebrates.

pharynx (fãr'-inks) (1) An area in the vertebrate throat where air and food passages cross. (2) In flatworms, the muscular tube that protrudes from the ventral side of the worm and ends in the mouth.

phase change (1) A shift from one developmental phase to another. (2) In plants, a morphological change that arises from a transition in shoot apical meristem activity.

phenotype (fē'-nō-tīp) The observable physical and physiological traits of an organism, which are determined by its genetic makeup.

pheromone (fãr'-uh-mōn) In animals and fungi, a small molecule released into the environment that functions in communication between members of the same species. In animals, it acts much like a hormone in influencing physiology and behavior.

phloem (flō'-em) Vascular plant tissue consisting of living cells arranged into elongated tubes that transport sugar and other organic nutrients throughout the plant.

phloem sap (flō'-em) The sugar-rich solution carried through a plant's sieve tubes.

phosphate group A chemical group consisting of a phosphorus atom bonded to four oxygen atoms; important in energy transfer.

phospholipid (fos'-fō-lip'-id) A lipid made up of glycerol joined to two fatty acids and a phosphate group. The hydrocarbon chains of the fatty acids act as nonpolar, hydrophobic tails, while the rest of the molecule acts as a polar, hydrophilic head. Phospholipids form bilayers that function as biological membranes.

phosphorylated intermediate (fos'-fōr-uh-lā'-ted) A molecule (often a reactant) with a phosphate group covalently bound to it, making it more reactive (less stable) than the unphosphorylated molecule.

phosphorylation cascade (fos'-fōr-uh-lā'-shun) A series of protein phosphorylations occurring sequentially in which each protein kinase phosphorylates the next, activating it; often found in signaling pathways.

photic zone (fō'-tic) The narrow top layer of an ocean or lake, where light penetrates sufficiently for photosynthesis to occur.

photoautotroph (fō'-tō-ot'-ō-trōf) An organism that harnesses light energy to drive the synthesis of organic compounds from carbon dioxide.

photoheterotroph (fō'-tō-het'-er-ō-trōf) An organism that uses light to generate ATP but must obtain carbon in organic form.

photomorphogenesis Effects of light on plant morphology.

photon (fō'-ton) A quantum, or discrete quantity, of light energy that behaves as if it were a particle.

photoperiodism (fō'-tō-pĕr'-ē-ō-dizm) A physiological response to photoperiod, the interval in a 24-hour period during which an organism is exposed to light. An example of photoperiodism is flowering.

photophosphorylation (fō'-tō-fos'-fōr-uh-lā'-shun) The process of generating ATP from ADP and phosphate by means of chemiosmosis, using a proton-motive force generated across the thylakoid membrane of the chloroplast or the membrane of certain prokaryotes during the light reactions of photosynthesis.

photoreceptor An electromagnetic receptor that detects the radiation known as visible light.

photorespiration A metabolic pathway that consumes oxygen and ATP, releases carbon dioxide, and decreases photosynthetic output. Photorespiration generally occurs on hot, dry, bright days, when stomata close and the O_2/CO_2 ratio in the leaf increases, favoring the binding of O_2 rather than CO_2 by rubisco.

photosynthesis (fō'-tō-sin'-thi-sis) The conversion of light energy to chemical energy that is stored in sugars or other organic compounds; occurs in plants, algae, and certain prokaryotes.

photosystem A light-capturing unit located in the thylakoid membrane of the chloroplast or in the membrane of some prokaryotes, consisting of a reaction-center complex surrounded by numerous light-harvesting complexes. There are two types of photosystems, I and II; they absorb light best at different wavelengths.

photosystem I (PS I) A light-capturing unit in a chloroplast's thylakoid membrane or in the membrane of some prokaryotes; it has two molecules of P700 chlorophyll *a* at its reaction center.

photosystem II (PS II) One of two light-capturing units in a chloroplast's thylakoid membrane or in the membrane of some prokaryotes; it has two molecules of P680 chlorophyll *a* at its reaction center.

phototropism (fō'-tō-trō'-pizm) Growth of a plant shoot toward or away from light.

phyllotaxy (fil'-uh-tak'-sē) The pattern of leaf attachment to the stem of a plant.

phylogenetic species concept Definition of a species as the smallest group of individuals that share a common ancestor, forming one branch on the tree of life.

phylogenetic tree A branching diagram that represents a hypothesis about the evolutionary history of a group of organisms.

phylogeny (fī-loj'-uh-nē) The evolutionary history of a species or group of related species.

phylum (fī'-lum) (plural, **phyla**) In Linnaean classification, the taxonomic category above class.

physiology The processes and functions of an organism.

phytochrome (fī'-tuh-krōm) A type of light receptor in plants that mostly absorbs red light and regulates many plant responses, such as seed germination and shade avoidance.

phytoremediation An emerging technology that seeks to reclaim contaminated areas by taking advantage of some plant species' ability to extract heavy metals and other pollutants from the soil and to concentrate them in easily harvested portions of the plant.

pilus (plural, **pili**) (pī'-lus, pī'-lī) In bacteria, a structure that links one cell to another at the start of conjugation; also called a sex pilus or conjugation pilus.

pineal gland (pī'-nē-ul) A small gland on the dorsal surface of the vertebrate forebrain that secretes the hormone melatonin.

pinocytosis (pī'-nō-sī-tō'-sis) A type of endocytosis in which the cell ingests extracellular fluid and its dissolved solutes.

pistil A single carpel or a group of fused carpels.

pith Ground tissue that is internal to the vascular tissue in a stem; in many monocot roots, parenchyma cells that form the central core of the vascular cylinder.

pituitary gland (puh-tū'-uh-tār'-ē) An endocrine gland at the base of the hypothalamus; consists of a posterior lobe, which stores and releases two hormones produced by the hypothalamus, and an anterior lobe, which produces and secretes many hormones that regulate diverse body functions.

placenta (pluh-sen'-tuh) A structure in the uterus of a pregnant eutherian mammal that nourishes the fetus with the mother's blood supply; formed from the uterine lining and embryonic membranes.

placoderm A member of an extinct group of fishlike vertebrates that had jaws and were enclosed in a tough outer armor.

planarian A free-living flatworm found in ponds and streams.

plasma (plaz'-muh) The liquid matrix of blood in which the blood cells are suspended.

plasma cell (plaz'-muh) The antibody-secreting effector cell of humoral immunity. Plasma cells arise from antigen-stimulated B cells.

plasma membrane (plaz'-muh) The membrane at the boundary of every cell that acts as a selective barrier, regulating the cell's chemical composition.

plasmid (plaz'-mid) A small, circular, double-stranded DNA molecule that carries accessory genes separate from those of a bacterial chromosome; in DNA cloning, plasmids are used as vectors carrying up to about 10,000 base pairs (10 kb) of DNA. Plasmids are also found in some eukaryotes, such as yeasts.

plasmodesma (plaz'-mō-dez'-muh) (plural, **plasmodesmata**) An open channel through the cell wall that connects the cytoplasm of adjacent plant cells, allowing water, small solutes, and some larger molecules to pass between the cells.

plasmogamy (plaz-moh'-guh-mē) In fungi, the fusion of the cytoplasm of cells from two individuals; occurs as one stage of sexual reproduction, followed later by karyogamy.

plasmolysis (plaz-mol'-uh-sis) A phenomenon in walled cells in which the cytoplasm shrivels and the plasma membrane pulls away from the cell wall; occurs when the cell loses water to a hypertonic environment.

plastid One of a family of closely related organelles that includes chloroplasts, chromoplasts, and amyloplasts. Plastids are found in cells of photosynthetic eukaryotes.

plate tectonics The theory that the continents are part of great plates of Earth's crust that float on the hot, underlying portion of the mantle. Movements in the mantle cause the continents to move slowly over time.

platelet A pinched-off cytoplasmic fragment of a specialized bone marrow cell. Platelets circulate in the blood and are important in blood clotting.

pleiotropy (plī'-o-truh-pē) The ability of a single gene to have multiple effects.

pluripotent Describing a cell that can give rise to many, but not all, parts of an organism.

point mutation A change in a single nucleotide pair of a gene.

polar covalent bond A covalent bond between atoms that differ in electronegativity. The shared electrons are pulled closer to the more electronegative atom, making it slightly negative and the other atom slightly positive.

polar molecule A molecule (such as water) with an uneven distribution of charges in different regions of the molecule.

polarity A lack of symmetry; structural differences in opposite ends of an organism or structure, such as the root end and shoot end of a plant.

pollen grain In seed plants, a structure consisting of the male gametophyte enclosed within a pollen wall.

pollen tube A tube that forms after germination of the pollen grain and that functions in the delivery of sperm to the ovule.

pollination (pol'-uh-nā'-shun) The transfer of pollen to the part of a seed plant containing the ovules, a process required for fertilization.

poly-A tail A sequence of 50–250 adenine nucleotides added onto the 3′ end of a pre-mRNA molecule.

polygamous Referring to a type of relationship in which an individual of one sex mates with several of the other.

polygenic inheritance (pol'-ē-jen'-ik) An additive effect of two or more genes on a single phenotypic character.

polymer (pol'-uh-mer) A long molecule consisting of many similar or identical monomers linked together by covalent bonds.

polymerase chain reaction (PCR) (puh-lim'-uh-rās) A technique for amplifying DNA *in vitro* by incubating it with specific primers, a heat-resistant DNA polymerase, and nucleotides.

polynucleotide (pol'-ē-nū'-klē-ō-tīd) A polymer consisting of many nucleotide monomers in a chain. The nucleotides can be those of DNA or RNA.

polyp The sessile variant of the cnidarian body plan. The alternate form is the medusa.

polypeptide (pol'-ē-pep'-tīd) A polymer of many amino acids linked together by peptide bonds.

polyphyletic (pol'-ē-fī-let'-ik) Pertaining to a group of taxa that includes distantly related organisms but does not include their most recent common ancestor.

polyploidy (pol'-ē-ploy'-dē) A chromosomal alteration in which the organism possesses more than two complete chromosome sets. It is the result of an accident of cell division.

polyribosome (polysome) (pol'-ē-rī'-buh-sōm') A group of several ribosomes attached to, and translating, the same messenger RNA molecule.

polysaccharide (pol'-ē-sak'-uh-rīd) A polymer of many monosaccharides, formed by dehydration reactions.

polytomy (puh-lit'-uh-mē) In a phylogenetic tree, a branch point from which more than two descendant taxa emerge. A polytomy indicates that the evolutionary relationships between the descendant taxa are not yet clear.

pons A portion of the brain that participates in certain automatic, homeostatic functions, such as regulating the breathing centers in the medulla.

population A group of individuals of the same species that live in the same area and interbreed, producing fertile offspring.

population dynamics The study of how complex interactions between biotic and abiotic factors influence variations in population size.

population ecology The study of populations in relation to their environment, including environmental influences on population density and distribution, age structure, and variations in population size.

positional information Molecular cues that control pattern formation in an animal or plant embryonic structure by indicating a cell's location relative to the organism's body axes. These cues elicit a response by genes that regulate development.

positive feedback A form of regulation in which an end product of a process speeds up that process; in physiology, a control mechanism in which a change in a variable triggers a response that reinforces or amplifies the change.

positive pressure breathing A breathing system in which air is forced into the lungs.

posterior Pertaining to the rear, or tail end, of a bilaterally symmetrical animal.

posterior pituitary An extension of the hypothalamus composed of nervous tissue that secretes oxytocin and antidiuretic hormone made in the hypothalamus; a temporary storage site for these hormones.

postzygotic barrier (pōst'-zī-got'-ik) A reproductive barrier that prevents hybrid zygotes produced by two different species from developing into viable, fertile adults.

potential energy The energy that matter possesses as a result of its location or spatial arrangement (structure).

predation An interaction between species in which one species, the predator, eats the other, the prey.

prediction In deductive reasoning, a forecast that follows logically from a hypothesis. By testing predictions, experiments may allow certain hypotheses to be rejected.

pregnancy The condition of carrying one or more embryos in the uterus; also called gestation.

prepuce (prē'-pyūs) A fold of skin covering the head of the clitoris or penis.

pressure potential (Ψ_p) A component of water potential that consists of the physical pressure on a solution, which can be positive, zero, or negative.

prezygotic barrier (prē-zī-got'-ik) A reproductive barrier that impedes mating between species or hinders fertilization if interspecific mating is attempted.

primary cell wall In plants, a relatively thin and flexible layer that surrounds the plasma membrane of a young cell.

primary consumer An herbivore; an organism that eats plants or other autotrophs.

primary electron acceptor In the thylakoid membrane of a chloroplast or in the membrane of some prokaryotes, a specialized molecule that shares the reaction-center complex with a pair of chlorophyll *a* molecules and that accepts an electron from them.

primary growth Growth produced by apical meristems, lengthening stems and roots.

primary immune response The initial adaptive immune response to an antigen, which appears after a lag of about 10–17 days.

primary oocyte (ō'-uh-sīt) An oocyte prior to completion of meiosis I.

primary producer An autotroph, usually a photosynthetic organism. Collectively, autotrophs make up the trophic level of an ecosystem that ultimately supports all other levels.

primary production The amount of light energy converted to chemical energy (organic compounds) by the autotrophs in an ecosystem during a given time period.

primary structure The level of protein structure referring to the specific linear sequence of amino acids.

primary succession A type of ecological succession that occurs in an area where there were originally no organisms present and where soil has not yet formed.

primary transcript An initial RNA transcript from any gene; also called pre-mRNA when transcribed from a protein-coding gene.

primase An enzyme that joins RNA nucleotides to make a primer during DNA replication, using the parental DNA strand as a template.

primer A short stretch of RNA with a free 3′ end, bound by complementary base pairing to the template strand and elongated with DNA nucleotides during DNA replication.

primitive streak A thickening along the future anterior-posterior axis on the surface of an early avian or mammalian embryo, caused by a piling up of cells as they congregate at the midline before moving into the embryo.

prion An infectious agent that is a misfolded version of a normal cellular protein. Prions appear to increase in number by converting correctly folded versions of the protein to more prions.

problem solving The cognitive activity of devising a method to proceed from one state to another in the face of real or apparent obstacles.

producer An organism that produces organic compounds from CO_2 by harnessing light energy (in photosynthesis) or by oxidizing inorganic chemicals (in chemosynthetic reactions carried out by some prokaryotes).

product A material resulting from a chemical reaction.

production efficiency The percentage of energy stored in assimilated food that is not used for respiration or eliminated as waste.

progesterone A steroid hormone that prepares the uterus for pregnancy; the major progestin in mammals.

progestin Any steroid hormone with progesterone-like activity.

prokaryotic cell (prō′-kăr′-ē-ot′-ik) A type of cell lacking a membrane-enclosed nucleus and membrane-enclosed organelles. Organisms with prokaryotic cells (bacteria and archaea) are called prokaryotes.

prolactin A hormone produced and secreted by the anterior pituitary with a great diversity of effects in different vertebrate species. In mammals, it stimulates growth of and milk production by the mammary glands.

prometaphase The second stage of mitosis, in which the nuclear envelope fragments and the spindle microtubules attach to the kinetochores of the chromosomes.

promoter A specific nucleotide sequence in the DNA of a gene that binds RNA polymerase, positioning it to start transcribing RNA at the appropriate place.

prophage (prō′-fāj) A phage genome that has been inserted into a specific site on a bacterial chromosome.

prophase The first stage of mitosis, in which the chromatin condenses into discrete chromosomes visible with a light microscope, the mitotic spindle begins to form, and the nucleolus disappears but the nucleus remains intact.

prostaglandin (pros′-tuh-glan′-din) One of a group of modified fatty acids that are secreted by virtually all tissues and that perform a wide variety of functions as local regulators.

prostate gland (pros′-tāt) A gland in human males that secretes an acid-neutralizing component of semen.

protease (prō′-tē-āz) An enzyme that digests proteins by hydrolysis.

protein (prō′-tēn) A biologically functional molecule consisting of one or more polypeptides folded and coiled into a specific three-dimensional structure.

protein kinase (prō′-tēn) An enzyme that transfers phosphate groups from ATP to a protein, thus phosphorylating the protein.

protein phosphatase (prō′-tēn) An enzyme that removes phosphate groups from (dephosphorylates) proteins, often functioning to reverse the effect of a protein kinase.

proteoglycan (prō′-tē-ō-glī′-kan) A large molecule consisting of a small core protein with many carbohydrate chains attached, found in the extracellular matrix of animal cells. A proteoglycan may consist of up to 95% carbohydrate.

proteome The entire set of proteins expressed by a given cell or group of cells.

proteomics (prō′-tē-ō′-miks) The systematic study of sets of proteins and their properties, including their abundance, chemical modifications, and interactions.

protist An informal term applied to any eukaryote that is not a plant, animal, or fungus. Most protists are unicellular, though some are colonial or multicellular.

protocell An abiotic precursor of a living cell that had a membrane-like structure and that maintained an internal chemistry different from that of its surroundings.

proton (prō′-ton) A subatomic particle with a single positive electrical charge, with a mass of about 1.7×10^{-24} g, found in the nucleus of an atom.

protonema (prō′-tuh-nē′-muh) (plural, **protonemata**) A mass of green, branched, one-cell-thick filaments produced by germinating moss spores.

protonephridium (prō′-tō-nuh-frid′-ē-um) (plural, **protonephridia**) An excretory system, such as the flame bulb system of flatworms, consisting of a network of tubules lacking internal openings.

proton-motive force (prō′-ton) The potential energy stored in the form of a proton electrochemical gradient, generated by the pumping of hydrogen ions (H^+) across a biological membrane during chemiosmosis.

proton pump (prō′-ton) An active transport protein in a cell membrane that uses ATP to transport hydrogen ions out of a cell against their concentration gradient, generating a membrane potential in the process.

proto-oncogene (prō′-tō-on′-kō-jēn) A normal cellular gene that has the potential to become an oncogene.

protoplast The living part of a plant cell, which also includes the plasma membrane.

protostome development In animals, a developmental mode distinguished by the development of the mouth from the blastopore; often also characterized by spiral cleavage and by the body cavity forming when solid masses of mesoderm split.

provirus A viral genome that is permanently inserted into a host genome.

proximal tubule In the vertebrate kidney, the portion of a nephron immediately downstream from Bowman's capsule that conveys and helps refine filtrate.

pseudocoelomate (sū′-dō-sē′-lō-māt) An animal whose body cavity is lined by tissue derived from mesoderm and endoderm.

pseudogene (sū′-dō-jēn) A DNA segment that is very similar to a real gene but does not yield a functional product; a DNA segment that formerly functioned as a gene but has become inactivated in a particular species because of mutation.

pseudopodium (sū′-dō-pō′-dē-um) (plural, **pseudopodia**) A cellular extension of amoeboid cells used in moving and feeding.

P site One of a ribosome's three binding sites for tRNA during translation. The P site holds the tRNA carrying the growing polypeptide chain. (P stands for peptidyl tRNA.)

pterosaur Winged reptile that lived during the Mesozoic era.

pulse The rhythmic bulging of the artery walls with each heartbeat.

punctuated equilibria In the fossil record, long periods of apparent stasis, in which a species undergoes little or no morphological change, interrupted by relatively brief periods of sudden change.

Punnett square A diagram used in the study of inheritance to show the predicted genotypic results of random fertilization in genetic crosses between individuals of known genotype.

pupil The opening in the iris, which admits light into the interior of the vertebrate eye. Muscles in the iris regulate its size.

purine (pyŭ′-rēn) One of two types of nitrogenous bases found in nucleotides, characterized by a six-membered ring fused to a five-membered ring. Adenine (A) and guanine (G) are purines.

pyrimidine (puh-rim′-uh-dēn) One of two types of nitrogenous bases found in nucleotides, characterized by a six-membered ring. Cytosine (C), thymine (T), and uracil (U) are pyrimidines.

quantitative character A heritable feature that varies continuously over a range rather than in an either-or fashion.

quaternary structure (kwot′-er-nār′-ē) The particular shape of a complex, aggregate protein, defined by the characteristic three-dimensional arrangement of its constituent subunits, each a polypeptide.

radial cleavage A type of embryonic development in deuterostomes in which the planes of cell division that transform the zygote into a ball of cells are either parallel or perpendicular to the vertical axis of the embryo, thereby aligning tiers of cells one above the other.

radial symmetry Symmetry in which the body is shaped like a pie or barrel (lacking a left side and a right side) and can be divided into mirror-imaged halves by any plane through its central axis.

radicle An embryonic root of a plant.

radioactive isotope An isotope (an atomic form of a chemical element) that is unstable; the nucleus decays spontaneously, giving off detectable particles and energy.

radiolarian A protist, usually marine, with a shell generally made of silica and pseudopodia that radiate from the central body.

radiometric dating A method for determining the absolute age of rocks and fossils, based on the half-life of radioactive isotopes.

radula A straplike scraping organ used by many molluscs during feeding.

***ras* gene** A gene that codes for Ras, a G protein that relays a growth signal from a growth factor receptor on the plasma membrane to a cascade of protein kinases, ultimately resulting in stimulation of the cell cycle.

ratite (rat′-īt) A member of the group of flightless birds.

ray-finned fish A member of the clade Actinopterygii, aquatic osteichthyans with fins supported by long, flexible rays, including tuna, bass, and herring.

reabsorption In excretory systems, the recovery of solutes and water from filtrate.

reactant A starting material in a chemical reaction.

reaction-center complex A complex of proteins associated with a special pair of chlorophyll *a* molecules and a primary electron acceptor. Located centrally in a photosystem, this complex triggers the light reactions of photosynthesis. Excited by light energy, the pair of chlorophylls donates an electron to the primary electron acceptor, which passes an electron to an electron transport chain.

reading frame On an mRNA, the triplet grouping of ribonucleotides used by the translation machinery during polypeptide synthesis.

receptacle The base of a flower; the part of the stem that is the site of attachment of the floral organs.

reception In cellular communication, the first step of a signaling pathway in which a signaling molecule is detected by a receptor molecule on or in the cell.

receptor-mediated endocytosis (en′-dō-sī-tō′-sis) The movement of specific molecules into a cell by the infolding of vesicles containing proteins with receptor sites specific to the molecules being taken in; enables a cell to acquire bulk quantities of specific substances.

receptor potential An initial response of a receptor cell to a stimulus, consisting of a change in voltage across the receptor membrane proportional to the stimulus strength.

receptor tyrosine kinase (RTK) A receptor protein spanning the plasma membrane, the cytoplasmic (intracellular) part of which can catalyze the transfer of a phosphate group from ATP to a tyrosine on another protein. Receptor tyrosine kinases often respond to the binding of a signaling molecule by dimerizing and then phosphorylating a tyrosine on the cytoplasmic portion of the other receptor in the dimer.

recessive allele An allele whose phenotypic effect is not observed in a heterozygote.

reciprocal altruism Altruistic behavior between unrelated individuals, whereby the altruistic individual benefits in the future when the beneficiary reciprocates.

recombinant chromosome A chromosome created when crossing over combines DNA from two parents into a single chromosome.

recombinant DNA A DNA molecule made *in vitro* with segments from different sources.

recombinant type (recombinant) An offspring whose phenotype differs from that of the true-breeding P generation parents; also refers to the phenotype itself.

rectum The terminal portion of the large intestine, where the feces are stored prior to elimination.

red alga A photosynthetic protist, named for its color, which results from a red pigment that masks the green of chlorophyll. Most red algae are multicellular and marine.

redox reaction (rē′-doks) A chemical reaction involving the complete or partial transfer of one or more electrons from one reactant to another; short for **red**uction-**ox**idation reaction.

reducing agent The electron donor in a redox reaction.

reduction The complete or partial addition of electrons to a substance involved in a redox reaction.

reflex An automatic reaction to a stimulus, mediated by the spinal cord or lower brain.

refractory period (rē-frakt′-ōr-ē) The short time immediately after an action potential in which the neuron cannot respond to another stimulus, owing to the inactivation of voltage-gated sodium channels.

regulator An animal for which mechanisms of homeostasis moderate internal changes in a particular variable in the face of external fluctuation of that variable.

regulatory gene A gene that codes for a protein, such as a repressor, that controls the transcription of another gene or group of genes.

reinforcement In evolutionary biology, a process in which natural selection strengthens prezygotic barriers to reproduction, thus reducing the chances of hybrid formation. Such a process is likely to occur only if hybrid offspring are less fit than members of the parent species.

relative abundance The proportional abundance of different species in a community.

relative fitness The contribution an individual makes to the gene pool of the next generation, relative to the contributions of other individuals in the population.

renal cortex The outer portion of the vertebrate kidney.

renal medulla The inner portion of the vertebrate kidney, beneath the renal cortex.

renal pelvis The funnel-shaped chamber that receives processed filtrate from the vertebrate kidney's collecting ducts and is drained by the ureter.

renin-angiotensin-aldosterone system (RAAS) A hormone cascade pathway that helps regulate blood pressure and blood volume.

repetitive DNA Nucleotide sequences, usually noncoding, that are present in many copies in a eukaryotic genome. The repeated units may be short and arranged tandemly (in series) or long and dispersed in the genome.

replication fork A Y-shaped region on a replicating DNA molecule where the parental strands are being unwound and new strands are being synthesized.

repressor A protein that inhibits gene transcription. In prokaryotes, repressors bind to the DNA in or near the promoter. In eukaryotes, repressors may bind to control elements within enhancers, to activators, or to other proteins in a way that blocks activators from binding to DNA.

reproductive isolation The existence of biological factors (barriers) that impede members of two species from producing viable, fertile offspring.

reproductive table An age-specific summary of the reproductive rates in a population.

reptile A member of the clade of amniotes that includes tuataras, lizards, snakes, turtles, crocodilians, and birds.

residual volume The amount of air that remains in the lungs after forceful exhalation.

resource partitioning The division of environmental resources by coexisting species such that the niche of each species differs by one or more significant factors from the niches of all coexisting species.

respiratory pigment A protein that transports oxygen in blood or hemolymph.

response (1) In cellular communication, the change in a specific cellular activity brought about by a transduced signal from outside the cell. (2) In feedback regulation, a physiological activity triggered by a change in a variable.

resting potential The membrane potential characteristic of a nonconducting excitable cell, with the inside of the cell more negative than the outside.

restriction enzyme An endonuclease (type of enzyme) that recognizes and cuts DNA molecules foreign to a bacterium (such as phage genomes). The enzyme cuts at specific nucleotide sequences (restriction sites).

restriction fragment A DNA segment that results from the cutting of DNA by a restriction enzyme.

restriction site A specific sequence on a DNA strand that is recognized and cut by a restriction enzyme.

retina (ret′-i-nuh) The innermost layer of the vertebrate eye, containing photoreceptor cells (rods and cones) and neurons; transmits images formed by the lens to the brain via the optic nerve.

retinal The light-absorbing pigment in rods and cones of the vertebrate eye.

retrotransposon (re′-trō-trans-pō′-zon) A transposable element that moves within a genome by means of an RNA intermediate, a transcript of the retrotransposon DNA.

retrovirus (re′-trō-vī′-rus) An RNA virus that replicates by transcribing its RNA into DNA and then inserting the DNA into a cellular chromosome; an important class of cancer-causing viruses.

reverse transcriptase (tran-skrip′-tās) An enzyme encoded by certain viruses (retroviruses) that uses RNA as a template for DNA synthesis.

reverse transcriptase–polymerase chain reaction (RT-PCR) A technique for determining expression of a particular gene. It uses reverse transcriptase and DNA polymerase to synthesize cDNA from all the mRNA in a sample and then subjects the cDNA to PCR amplification using primers specific for the gene of interest.

Rhizaria (rī-za′-rē-uh) One of the three major subgroups for which the "SAR" eukaryotic supergroup is named. Many species in this clade are amoebas characterized by threadlike pseudopodia.

rhizobacterium A soil bacterium whose population size is much enhanced in the rhizosphere, the soil region close to a plant's roots.

rhizoid (rī′-zoyd) A long, tubular single cell or filament of cells that anchors bryophytes to the ground. Unlike roots, rhizoids are not composed of tissues, lack specialized conducting cells, and do not play a primary role in water and mineral absorption.

rhizosphere The soil region close to plant roots and characterized by a high level of microbiological activity.

rhodopsin (rō-dop′-sin) A visual pigment consisting of retinal and opsin. Upon absorbing light, the retinal changes shape and dissociates from the opsin.

ribonucleic acid (RNA) (rī′-bō-nū-klā′-ik) A type of nucleic acid consisting of a polynucleotide made up of nucleotide monomers with a ribose sugar and the nitrogenous bases adenine (A), cytosine (C), guanine (G), and uracil (U); usually single-stranded; functions in protein synthesis, in gene regulation, and as the genome of some viruses.

ribose The sugar component of RNA nucleotides.

ribosomal RNA (rRNA) (rī′-buh-sō′-mul) RNA molecules that, together with proteins, make up ribosomes; the most abundant type of RNA.

ribosome (rī′-buh-sōm) A complex of rRNA and protein molecules that functions as a site of protein synthesis in the cytoplasm; consists of a large and a small subunit. In eukaryotic cells, each subunit is assembled in the nucleolus. *See also* nucleolus.

ribozyme (rī′-buh-zīm) An RNA molecule that functions as an enzyme, such as an intron that catalyzes its own removal during RNA splicing.

RNA interference (RNAi) A mechanism for silencing the expression of specific genes. In RNAi, double-stranded RNA molecules that match the sequence of a particular gene are processed into siRNAs that either block translation or trigger the degradation of the gene's messenger RNA. This happens naturally in some cells, and can be carried out in laboratory experiments as well.

RNA polymerase An enzyme that links ribonucleotides into a growing RNA chain during transcription, based on complementary binding to nucleotides on a DNA template strand.

RNA processing Modification of RNA primary transcripts, including splicing out of introns, joining together of exons, and alteration of the 5′ and 3′ ends.

RNA splicing After synthesis of a eukaryotic primary RNA transcript, the removal of portions of the transcript (introns) that will not be included in the mRNA and the joining together of the remaining portions (exons).

rod A rodlike cell in the retina of the vertebrate eye, sensitive to low light intensity.

root An organ in vascular plants that anchors the plant and enables it to absorb water and minerals from the soil.

root cap A cone of cells at the tip of a plant root that protects the apical meristem.

root hair A tiny extension of a root epidermal cell, growing just behind the root tip and increasing surface area for absorption of water and minerals.

root pressure Pressure exerted in the roots of plants as the result of osmosis, causing exudation from cut stems and guttation of water from leaves.

root system All of a plant's roots, which anchor it in the soil, absorb and transport minerals and water, and store food.

rooted Describing a phylogenetic tree that contains a branch point (often, the one farthest to the left) representing the most recent common ancestor of all taxa in the tree.

rough ER That portion of the endoplasmic reticulum with ribosomes attached.

round window In the mammalian ear, the point of contact where vibrations of the stapes create a traveling series of pressure waves in the fluid of the cochlea.

R plasmid A bacterial plasmid carrying genes that confer resistance to certain antibiotics.

r-selection Selection for life history traits that maximize reproductive success in uncrowded environments; also called density-independent selection.

rubisco (rū-bis′-kō) Ribulose bisphosphate (RuBP) carboxylase-oxygenase, the enzyme that normally catalyzes the first step of the Calvin cycle (the addition of CO_2 to RuBP). When excess O_2 is present or CO_2 levels are low, rubisco can bind oxygen, resulting in photorespiration.

saccule In the vertebrate ear, a chamber in the vestibule behind the oval window that participates in the sense of balance.

salicylic acid (sal′-i-sil′-ik) A signaling molecule in plants that may be partially responsible for activating systemic acquired resistance to pathogens.

salivary gland A gland associated with the oral cavity that secretes substances that lubricate food and begin the process of chemical digestion.

salt A compound resulting from the formation of an ionic bond; also called an ionic compound.

saltatory conduction (sol′-tuh-tōr′-ē) Rapid transmission of a nerve impulse along an axon, resulting from the action potential jumping from one node of Ranvier to another, skipping the myelin-sheathed regions of membrane.

"SAR" clade One of four supergroups of eukaryotes proposed in a current hypothesis of the evolutionary history of eukaryotes. This supergroup contains a large, extremely diverse collection of protists from three major subgroups: stramenopiles, alveolates, and rhizarians. *See also* Excavata, Archaeplastida, and Unikonta.

sarcomere (sar′-kō-mēr) The fundamental, repeating unit of striated muscle, delimited by the Z lines.

sarcoplasmic reticulum (SR) (sar′-kō-plaz′-mik ruh-tik′-yū-lum) A specialized endoplasmic reticulum that regulates the calcium concentration in the cytosol of muscle cells.

saturated fatty acid A fatty acid in which all carbons in the hydrocarbon tail are connected by single bonds, thus maximizing the number of hydrogen atoms that are attached to the carbon skeleton.

savanna A tropical grassland biome with scattered individual trees and large herbivores and maintained by occasional fires and drought.

scaffolding protein A type of large relay protein to which several other relay proteins are simultaneously attached, increasing the efficiency of signal transduction.

scanning electron microscope (SEM) A microscope that uses an electron beam to scan the surface of a sample, coated with metal atoms, to study details of its topography.

scatter plot A graph in which each piece of data is represented by a point. A scatter plot is used when the data for all variables are numerical and continuous.

schizophrenia (skit′-suh-frē′-nē-uh) A severe mental disturbance characterized by psychotic episodes in which patients have a distorted perception of reality.

Schwann cell A type of glial cell that forms insulating myelin sheaths around the axons of neurons in the peripheral nervous system.

science An approach to understanding the natural world.

scion (sī′-un) The twig grafted onto the stock when making a graft.

sclereid (sklār′-ē-id) A short, irregular sclerenchyma cell in nutshells and seed coats. Sclereids are scattered throughout the parenchyma of some plants.

sclerenchyma cell (skluh-ren′-kim-uh) A rigid, supportive plant cell type usually lacking a protoplast and possessing thick secondary walls strengthened by lignin at maturity.

scrotum A pouch of skin outside the abdomen that houses the testes; functions in maintaining the testes at the lower temperature required for spermatogenesis.

second law of thermodynamics The principle stating that every energy transfer or transformation increases the entropy of the universe. Usable forms of energy are at least partly converted to heat.

second messenger A small, nonprotein, water-soluble molecule or ion, such as a calcium ion (Ca^{2+}) or cyclic AMP, that relays a signal to a cell's interior in response to a signaling molecule bound by a signal receptor protein.

secondary cell wall In plant cells, a strong and durable matrix that is often deposited in several laminated layers around the plasma membrane and provides protection and support.

secondary consumer A carnivore that eats herbivores.

secondary endosymbiosis A process in eukaryotic evolution in which a heterotrophic eukaryotic cell engulfed a photosynthetic eukaryotic cell, which survived in a symbiotic relationship inside the heterotrophic cell.

secondary growth Growth produced by lateral meristems, thickening the roots and shoots of woody plants.

secondary immune response The adaptive immune response elicited on second or subsequent exposures to a particular antigen. The secondary immune response is more rapid, of greater magnitude, and of longer duration than the primary immune response.

secondary oocyte (ō'-uh-sīt) An oocyte that has completed meiosis I.

secondary production The amount of chemical energy in consumers' food that is converted to their own new biomass during a given time period.

secondary structure Regions of repetitive coiling or folding of the polypeptide backbone of a protein due to hydrogen bonding between constituents of the backbone (not the side chains).

secondary succession A type of succession that occurs where an existing community has been cleared by some disturbance that leaves the soil or substrate intact.

secretion (1) The discharge of molecules synthesized by a cell. (2) The active transport of wastes and certain other solutes from the body fluid into the filtrate in an excretory system.

seed An adaptation of some terrestrial plants consisting of an embryo packaged along with a store of food within a protective coat.

seed coat A tough outer covering of a seed, formed from the outer coat of an ovule. In a flowering plant, the seed coat encloses and protects the embryo and endosperm.

seedless vascular plant An informal name for a plant that has vascular tissue but lacks seeds. Seedless vascular plants form a paraphyletic group that includes the phyla Lycophyta (club mosses and their relatives) and Monilophyta (ferns and their relatives).

selective permeability A property of biological membranes that allows them to regulate the passage of substances across them.

self-incompatibility The ability of a seed plant to reject its own pollen and sometimes the pollen of closely related individuals.

semelparity (seh'-mel-pār'-i-tē) Reproduction in which an organism produces all of its offspring in a single event; also called big-bang reproduction.

semen (sē'-mun) The fluid that is ejaculated by the male during orgasm; contains sperm and secretions from several glands of the male reproductive tract.

semicircular canals A three-part chamber of the inner ear that functions in maintaining equilibrium.

semiconservative model Type of DNA replication in which the replicated double helix consists of one old strand, derived from the parental molecule, and one newly made strand.

semilunar valve A valve located at each exit of the heart, where the aorta leaves the left ventricle and the pulmonary artery leaves the right ventricle.

seminal vesicle (sem'-i-nul ves'-i-kul) A gland in males that secretes a fluid component of semen that lubricates and nourishes sperm.

seminiferous tubule (sem'-i-nif'-er-us) A highly coiled tube in the testis in which sperm are produced.

senescence (se-nes'-ens) The growth phase in a plant or plant part (as a leaf) from full maturity to death.

sensitive period A limited phase in an animal's development when learning of particular behaviors can take place; also called a critical period.

sensor In homeostasis, a receptor that detects a stimulus.

sensory adaptation The tendency of sensory neurons to become less sensitive when they are stimulated repeatedly.

sensory neuron A nerve cell that receives information from the internal or external environment and transmits signals to the central nervous system.

sensory reception The detection of a stimulus by sensory cells.

sensory receptor A specialized structure or cell that responds to a stimulus from an animal's internal or external environment.

sensory transduction The conversion of stimulus energy to a change in the membrane potential of a sensory receptor cell.

sepal (sē'-pul) A modified leaf in angiosperms that helps enclose and protect a flower bud before it opens.

septum (plural, **septa**) One of the cross-walls that divide a fungal hypha into cells. Septa generally have pores large enough to allow ribosomes, mitochondria, and even nuclei to flow from cell to cell.

serial endosymbiosis A hypothesis for the origin of eukaryotes consisting of a sequence of endosymbiotic events in which mitochondria, chloroplasts, and perhaps other cellular structures were derived from small prokaryotes that had been engulfed by larger cells.

serotonin (ser'-uh-tō'-nin) A neurotransmitter, synthesized from the amino acid tryptophan, that functions in the central nervous system.

set point In homeostasis in animals, a value maintained for a particular variable, such as body temperature or solute concentration.

seta (sē'-tuh) (plural, **setae**) The elongated stalk of a bryophyte sporophyte.

sex chromosome A chromosome responsible for determining the sex of an individual.

sex-linked gene A gene located on either sex chromosome. Most sex-linked genes are on the X chromosome and show distinctive patterns of inheritance; there are very few genes on the Y chromosome.

sexual dimorphism (dī-mōr'-fizm) Differences between the secondary sex characteristics of males and females of the same species.

sexual reproduction A type of reproduction in which two parents give rise to offspring that have unique combinations of genes inherited from both parents via the gametes.

sexual selection A form of natural selection in which individuals with certain inherited characteristics are more likely than other individuals to obtain mates.

Shannon diversity An index of community diversity symbolized by H and represented by the equation $H = -(p_A \ln p_A + p_B \ln p_B + p_C \ln p_C + \ldots)$, where A, B, C . . . are species, p is the relative abundance of each species, and ln is the natural logarithm.

shared ancestral character A character, shared by members of a particular clade, that originated in an ancestor that is not a member of that clade.

shared derived character An evolutionary novelty that is unique to a particular clade.

shoot system The aerial portion of a plant body, consisting of stems, leaves, and (in angiosperms) flowers.

short tandem repeat (STR) Simple sequence DNA containing multiple tandemly repeated units of two to five nucleotides. Variations in STRs act as genetic markers in STR analysis, used to prepare genetic profiles.

short-day plant A plant that flowers (usually in late summer, fall, or winter) only when the light period is shorter than a critical length.

short-term memory The ability to hold information, anticipations, or goals for a time and then release them if they become irrelevant.

sickle-cell disease A recessively inherited human blood disorder in which a single nucleotide change in the β-globin gene causes hemoglobin to aggregate, changing red blood cell shape and causing multiple symptoms in afflicted individuals.

sieve plate An end wall in a sieve-tube element, which facilitates the flow of phloem sap in angiosperm sieve tubes.

sieve-tube element A living cell that conducts sugars and other organic nutrients in the phloem of angiosperms; also called a sieve-tube member. Connected end to end, they form sieve tubes.

sign stimulus An external sensory cue that triggers a fixed action pattern by an animal.

signal In animal behavior, transmission of a stimulus from one animal to another. The term is also used in the context of communication in other kinds of organisms and in cell-to-cell communication in all multicellular organisms.

signal peptide A sequence of about 20 amino acids at or near the leading (amino) end of a polypeptide that targets it to the endoplasmic reticulum or other organelles in a eukaryotic cell.

signal-recognition particle (SRP) A protein-RNA complex that recognizes a signal peptide as it emerges from a ribosome and helps direct the ribosome to the endoplasmic reticulum (ER) by binding to a receptor protein on the ER.

signal transduction The linkage of a mechanical, chemical, or electromagnetic stimulus to a specific cellular response.

signal transduction pathway A series of steps linking a mechanical, chemical, or electrical stimulus to a specific cellular response.

silent mutation A nucleotide-pair substitution that has no observable effect on the phenotype; for example, within a gene, a mutation that results in a codon that codes for the same amino acid.

simple fruit A fruit derived from a single carpel or several fused carpels.

simple sequence DNA A DNA sequence that contains many copies of tandemly repeated short sequences.

single bond A single covalent bond; the sharing of a pair of valence electrons by two atoms.

single circulation A circulatory system consisting of a single pump and circuit, in which blood passes from the sites of gas exchange to the rest of the body before returning to the heart.

single-lens eye The camera-like eye found in some jellies, polychaete worms, spiders, and many molluscs.

single nucleotide polymorphism (SNP) A single base-pair site in a genome where nucleotide variation is found in at least 1% of the population.

single-strand binding protein A protein that binds to the unpaired DNA strands during DNA replication, stabilizing them and holding them apart while they serve as templates for the synthesis of complementary strands of DNA.

sinoatrial (sī′-nō-ā′-trē-uhl) **(SA) node** A region in the right atrium of the heart that sets the rate and timing at which all cardiac muscle cells contract; the pacemaker.

sister chromatids Two copies of a duplicated chromosome attached to each other by proteins at the centromere and, sometimes, along the arms. While joined, two sister chromatids make up one chromosome. Chromatids are eventually separated during mitosis or meiosis II.

sister taxa Groups of organisms that share an immediate common ancestor and hence are each other's closest relatives.

skeletal muscle A type of striated muscle that is generally responsible for the voluntary movements of the body.

sliding-filament model The idea that muscle contraction is based on the movement of thin (actin) filaments along thick (myosin) filaments, shortening the sarcomere, the basic unit of muscle organization.

slow block to polyspermy The formation of the fertilization envelope and other changes in an egg's surface that prevent fusion of the egg with more than one sperm. The slow block begins about 1 minute after fertilization.

slow-twitch fiber A muscle fiber that can sustain long contractions.

small interfering RNA (siRNA) One of multiple small, single-stranded RNA molecules generated by cellular machinery from a long, linear, double-stranded RNA molecule. The siRNA associates with one or more proteins in a complex that can degrade or prevent translation of an mRNA with a complementary sequence.

small intestine The longest section of the alimentary canal, so named because of its small diameter compared with that of the large intestine; the principal site of the enzymatic hydrolysis of food macromolecules and the absorption of nutrients.

smooth ER That portion of the endoplasmic reticulum that is free of ribosomes.

smooth muscle A type of muscle lacking the striations of skeletal and cardiac muscle because of the uniform distribution of myosin filaments in the cells; responsible for involuntary body activities.

social learning Modification of behavior through the observation of other individuals.

sociobiology The study of social behavior based on evolutionary theory.

sodium-potassium pump A transport protein in the plasma membrane of animal cells that actively transports sodium out of the cell and potassium into the cell.

soil horizon A soil layer with physical characteristics that differ from those of the layers above or beneath.

solute (sol′-yūt) A substance that is dissolved in a solution.

solute potential (Ψ_S) A component of water potential that is proportional to the molarity of a solution and that measures the effect of solutes on the direction of water movement; also called osmotic potential, it can be either zero or negative.

solution A liquid that is a homogeneous mixture of two or more substances.

solvent The dissolving agent of a solution. Water is the most versatile solvent known.

somatic cell (sō-mat′-ik) Any cell in a multicellular organism except a sperm or egg or their precursors.

somite One of a series of blocks of mesoderm that exist in pairs just lateral to the notochord in a vertebrate embryo.

soredium (suh-rē′-dē-um) (plural, **soredia**) In lichens, a small cluster of fungal hyphae with embedded algae.

sorus (plural, **sori**) A cluster of sporangia on a fern sporophyll. Sori may be arranged in various patterns, such as parallel lines or dots, which are useful in fern identification.

spatial learning The establishment of a memory that reflects the environment's spatial structure.

spatial summation A phenomenon of neural integration in which the membrane potential of the postsynaptic cell is determined by the combined effect of EPSPs or IPSPs produced nearly simultaneously by different synapses.

speciation (spē′-sē-ā′-shun) An evolutionary process in which one species splits into two or more species.

species (spē′-sēz) A population or group of populations whose members have the potential to interbreed in nature and produce viable, fertile offspring but do not produce viable, fertile offspring with members of other such groups.

species-area curve (spē′-sēz) The biodiversity pattern that shows that the larger the geographic area of a community is, the more species it has.

species diversity (spē′-sēz) The number and relative abundance of species in a biological community.

species richness (spē′-sēz) The number of species in a biological community.

specific heat The amount of heat that must be absorbed or lost for 1 g of a substance to change its temperature by 1°C.

spectrophotometer An instrument that measures the proportions of light of different wavelengths absorbed and transmitted by a pigment solution.

sperm The male gamete.

spermatheca (sper′-muh-thē′-kuh) (plural, **spermathecae**) In many insects, a sac in the female reproductive system where sperm are stored.

spermatogenesis (sper-ma′-tō-gen′-uh-sis) The continuous and prolific production of mature sperm in the testis.

spermatogonium (sper-ma′-tō-gō′-nē-um) (plural, **spermatogonia**) A cell that divides mitotically to form spermatocytes.

S phase The synthesis phase of the cell cycle; the portion of interphase during which DNA is replicated.

sphincter (sfink′-ter) A ringlike band of muscle fibers that controls the size of an opening in the body, such as the passage between the esophagus and the stomach.

spiral cleavage A type of embryonic development in protostomes in which the planes of cell division that transform the zygote into a ball of cells are diagonal to the vertical axis of the embryo. As a result, the cells of each tier sit in the grooves between cells of adjacent tiers.

spliceosome (splī′-sō-sōm) A large complex made up of proteins and RNA molecules that splices RNA by interacting with the ends of an RNA intron, releasing the intron and joining the two adjacent exons.

spongocoel (spon′-jō-sēl) The central cavity of a sponge.

spontaneous process A process that occurs without an overall input of energy; a process that is energetically favorable.

sporangium (spōr-an′-jē-um) (plural, **sporangia**) A multicellular organ in fungi and plants in which meiosis occurs and haploid cells develop.

spore (1) In the life cycle of a plant or alga undergoing alternation of generations, a haploid cell produced in the sporophyte by meiosis. A spore can divide by mitosis to develop into a multicellular haploid individual, the gametophyte, without fusing with another cell. (2) In fungi, a haploid cell, produced either sexually or asexually, that produces a mycelium after germination.

sporophyll (spō′-ruh-fil) A modified leaf that bears sporangia and hence is specialized for reproduction.

sporophyte (spō-ruh-fīt′) In organisms (plants and some algae) that have alternation of generations, the multicellular diploid form that results from the union of gametes. The sporophyte produces haploid spores by meiosis that develop into gametophytes.

sporopollenin (spōr-uh-pol′-eh-nin) A durable polymer that covers exposed zygotes of charophyte algae and forms the walls of plant spores, preventing them from drying out.

stabilizing selection Natural selection in which intermediate phenotypes survive or reproduce more successfully than do extreme phenotypes.

stamen (stā′-men) The pollen-producing reproductive organ of a flower, consisting of an anther and a filament.

standard deviation A measure of the variation found in a set of data points.

standard metabolic rate (SMR) Metabolic rate of a resting, fasting, and nonstressed ectotherm at a particular temperature.

starch A storage polysaccharide in plants, consisting entirely of glucose monomers joined by α glycosidic linkages.

start point In transcription, the nucleotide position on the promoter where RNA polymerase begins synthesis of RNA.

statocyst (stat′-uh-sist′) A type of mechanoreceptor that functions in equilibrium in invertebrates by use of statoliths, which stimulate hair cells in relation to gravity.

statolith (stat′-uh-lith′) (1) In plants, a specialized plastid that contains dense starch grains and may play a role in detecting gravity. (2) In invertebrates, a dense particle that settles in response to gravity and is found in sensory organs that function in equilibrium.

stele (stēl) The vascular tissue of a stem or root.

stem A vascular plant organ consisting of an alternating system of nodes and internodes that support the leaves and reproductive structures.

stem cell Any relatively unspecialized cell that can produce, during a single division, one identical daughter cell and one more specialized daughter cell that can undergo further differentiation.

steroid A type of lipid characterized by a carbon skeleton consisting of four fused rings with various chemical groups attached.

sticky end A single-stranded end of a double-stranded restriction fragment.

stigma (plural, **stigmata**) The sticky part of a flower's carpel, which receives pollen grains.

stimulus In feedback regulation, a fluctuation in a variable that triggers a response.

stipe A stemlike structure of a seaweed.

stock The plant that provides the root system when making a graft.

stoma (stō′-muh) (plural, **stomata**) A microscopic pore surrounded by guard cells in the epidermis of leaves and stems that allows gas exchange between the environment and the interior of the plant.

stomach An organ of the digestive system that stores food and performs preliminary steps of digestion.

Stramenopila (strah′-men-ō′-pē-lah) One of the three major subgroups for which the "SAR" eukaryotic supergroup is named. This clade arose by secondary endosymbiosis and includes diatoms and brown algae.

stratum (strah′-tum) (plural, **strata**) A rock layer formed when new layers of sediment cover older ones and compress them.

strigolactone Any of a class of plant hormones that inhibit shoot branching, trigger the germination of parasitic plant seeds, and stimulate the association of plant roots with mycorrhizal fungi.

strobilus (strō-bī′-lus) (plural, **strobili**) The technical term for a cluster of sporophylls known commonly as a cone, found in most gymnosperms and some seedless vascular plants.

stroke The death of nervous tissue in the brain, usually resulting from rupture or blockage of arteries in the head.

stroke volume The volume of blood pumped by a heart ventricle in a single contraction.

stroma (strō′-muh) The dense fluid within the chloroplast surrounding the thylakoid membrane and containing ribosomes and DNA; involved in the synthesis of organic molecules from carbon dioxide and water.

stromatolite Layered rock that results from the activities of prokaryotes that bind thin films of sediment together.

structural isomer One of several compounds that have the same molecular formula but differ in the covalent arrangements of their atoms.

style The stalk of a flower's carpel, with the ovary at the base and the stigma at the top.

substrate The reactant on which an enzyme works.

substrate feeder An animal that lives in or on its food source, eating its way through the food.

substrate-level phosphorylation The enzyme-catalyzed formation of ATP by direct transfer of a phosphate group to ADP from an intermediate substrate in catabolism.

sugar sink A plant organ that is a net consumer or storer of sugar. Growing roots, shoot tips, stems, and fruits are examples of sugar sinks supplied by phloem.

sugar source A plant organ in which sugar is being produced by either photosynthesis or the breakdown of starch. Mature leaves are the primary sugar sources of plants.

sulfhydryl group A chemical group consisting of a sulfur atom bonded to a hydrogen atom.

suprachiasmatic nucleus (SCN) (sūp′-ruh-kē′-as-ma-tik) A group of neurons in the hypothalamus of mammals that functions as a biological clock.

surface tension A measure of how difficult it is to stretch or break the surface of a liquid. Water has a high surface tension because of the hydrogen bonding of surface molecules.

surfactant A substance secreted by alveoli that decreases surface tension in the fluid that coats the alveoli.

survivorship curve A plot of the number of members of a cohort that are still alive at each age; one way to represent age-specific mortality.

suspension feeder An animal that feeds by removing suspended food particles from the surrounding medium by a capture, trapping, or filtration mechanism.

sustainable agriculture Long-term productive farming methods that are environmentally safe.

sustainable development Development that meets the needs of people today without limiting the ability of future generations to meet their needs.

swim bladder In aquatic osteichthyans, an air sac that enables the animal to control its buoyancy in the water.

symbiont (sim′-bē-ont) The smaller participant in a symbiotic relationship, living in or on the host.

symbiosis An ecological relationship between organisms of two different species that live together in direct and intimate contact.

sympathetic division One of three divisions of the autonomic nervous system; generally increases energy expenditure and prepares the body for action.

sympatric speciation (sim-pat′-rik) The formation of new species in populations that live in the same geographic area.

symplast In plants, the continuum of cytoplasm connected by plasmodesmata between cells.

synapse (sin′-aps) The junction where a neuron communicates with another cell across a narrow gap via a neurotransmitter or an electrical coupling.

synapsid (si-nap′-sid) A member of an amniote clade distinguished by a single hole on each side of the skull. Synapsids include the mammals.

synapsis (si-nap′-sis) The pairing and physical connection of duplicated homologous chromosomes during prophase I of meiosis.

synaptonemal (si-nap′-tuh-nē′-muhl) **complex** A zipper-like structure composed of proteins, which connects two homologous chromosomes tightly along their lengths.

systematics A scientific discipline focused on classifying organisms and determining their evolutionary relationships.

systemic acquired resistance A defensive response in infected plants that helps protect healthy tissue from pathogenic invasion.

systemic circuit The branch of the circulatory system that supplies oxygenated blood to and carries deoxygenated blood away from organs and tissues throughout the body.

systems biology An approach to studying biology that aims to model the dynamic behavior of whole biological systems based on a study of the interactions among the system's parts.

systole (sis′-tō-lē) The stage of the cardiac cycle in which a heart chamber contracts and pumps blood.

systolic pressure Blood pressure in the arteries during contraction of the ventricles.

taproot A main vertical root that develops from an embryonic root and gives rise to lateral (branch) roots.

tastant Any chemical that stimulates the sensory receptors in a taste bud.

taste bud A collection of modified epithelial cells on the tongue or in the mouth that are receptors for taste in mammals.

TATA box A DNA sequence in eukaryotic promoters crucial in forming the transcription initiation complex.

taxis (tak′-sis) An oriented movement toward or away from a stimulus.

taxon (plural, **taxa**) A named taxonomic unit at any given level of classification.

taxonomy (tak-son′-uh-mē) A scientific discipline concerned with naming and classifying the diverse forms of life.

Tay-Sachs disease A human genetic disease caused by a recessive allele for a dysfunctional enzyme, leading to accumulation of certain lipids in the brain. Seizures, blindness, and degeneration of motor and mental performance usually become manifest a few months after birth, followed by death within a few years.

T cells The class of lymphocytes that mature in the thymus; they include both effector cells for the cell-mediated immune response and helper cells required for both branches of adaptive immunity.

technology The application of scientific knowledge for a specific purpose, often involving industry or commerce but also including uses in basic research.

telomere (tel′-uh-mēr) The tandemly repetitive DNA at the end of a eukaryotic chromosome's DNA molecule. Telomeres protect the organism's genes from being eroded during successive rounds of replication. *See also* repetitive DNA.

telophase The fifth and final stage of mitosis, in which daughter nuclei are forming and cytokinesis has typically begun.

temperate broadleaf forest A biome located throughout midlatitude regions where there is sufficient moisture to support the growth of large, broadleaf deciduous trees.

temperate grassland A terrestrial biome that exists at midlatitude regions and is dominated by grasses and forbs.

temperate phage A phage that is capable of replicating by either a lytic or lysogenic cycle.

temperature A measure in degrees of the average kinetic energy (thermal energy) of the atoms and molecules in a body of matter.

template strand The DNA strand that provides the pattern, or template, for ordering, by complementary base pairing, the sequence of nucleotides in an RNA transcript.

temporal summation A phenomenon of neural integration in which the membrane potential of the postsynaptic cell in a chemical synapse is determined by the combined effect of EPSPs or IPSPs produced in rapid succession.

tendon A fibrous connective tissue that attaches muscle to bone.

terminator In bacteria, a sequence of nucleotides in DNA that marks the end of a gene and signals RNA polymerase to release the newly made RNA molecule and detach from the DNA.

territoriality A behavior in which an animal defends a bounded physical space against encroachment by other individuals, usually of its own species.

tertiary consumer (ter′-shē-ār′-ē) A carnivore that eats other carnivores.

tertiary structure (ter′-shē-ār′-ē) The overall shape of a protein molecule due to interactions of amino acid side chains, including hydrophobic interactions, ionic bonds, hydrogen bonds, and disulfide bridges.

test In foram protists, a porous shell that consists of a single piece of organic material hardened with calcium carbonate.

testcross Breeding an organism of unknown genotype with a homozygous recessive individual to determine the unknown genotype. The ratio of phenotypes in the offspring reveals the unknown genotype.

testis (plural, **testes**) The male reproductive organ, or gonad, in which sperm and reproductive hormones are produced.

testosterone A steroid hormone required for development of the male reproductive system, spermatogenesis, and male secondary sex characteristics; the major androgen in mammals.

tetanus (tet′-uh-nus) The maximal, sustained contraction of a skeletal muscle, caused by a very high frequency of action potentials elicited by continual stimulation.

tetrapod A vertebrate clade whose members have limbs with digits. Tetrapods include mammals, amphibians, and birds and other reptiles.

thalamus (thal′-uh-mus) An integrating center of the vertebrate forebrain. Neurons with cell bodies in the thalamus relay neural input to specific areas in the cerebral cortex and regulate what information goes to the cerebral cortex.

theory An explanation that is broader in scope than a hypothesis, generates new hypotheses, and is supported by a large body of evidence.

thermal energy Kinetic energy due to the random motion of atoms and molecules; energy in its most random form. *See also* heat.

thermocline A narrow stratum of abrupt temperature change in the ocean and in many temperate-zone lakes.

thermodynamics (ther′-mō-dī-nam′-iks) The study of energy transformations that occur in a collection of matter. *See also* first law of thermodynamics and second law of thermodynamics.

thermophile *See* extreme thermophile.

thermoreceptor A receptor stimulated by either heat or cold.

thermoregulation The maintenance of internal body temperature within a tolerable range.

theropod A member of a group of dinosaurs that were bipedal carnivores.

thick filament A filament composed of staggered arrays of myosin molecules; a component of myofibrils in muscle fibers.

thigmomorphogenesis (thig′-mō-mor′-phō-gen′-uh-sis) A response in plants to chronic mechanical stimulation, resulting from increased ethylene production. An example is thickening stems in response to strong winds.

thigmotropism (thig-mō′-truh-pizm) A directional growth of a plant in response to touch.

thin filament A filament consisting of two strands of actin and two strands of regulatory protein coiled around one another; a component of myofibrils in muscle fibers.

threatened species A species that is considered likely to become endangered in the foreseeable future.

threshold The potential that an excitable cell membrane must reach for an action potential to be initiated.

thrombus A fibrin-containing clot that forms in a blood vessel and blocks the flow of blood.

thylakoid (thī′-luh-koyd) A flattened, membranous sac inside a chloroplast. Thylakoids often exist in stacks called grana that are interconnected; their membranes contain molecular "machinery" used to convert light energy to chemical energy.

thymus (thī′-mus) A small organ in the thoracic cavity of vertebrates where maturation of T cells is completed.

thyroid gland An endocrine gland, located on the ventral surface of the trachea, that secretes two iodine-containing hormones, triiodothyronine (T$_3$) and thyroxine (T$_4$), as well as calcitonin.

thyroid hormone Either of two iodine-containing hormones (triiodothyronine and thyroxine) that are secreted by the thyroid gland and that help regulate metabolism, development, and maturation in vertebrates.

thyroxine (T$_4$) One of two iodine-containing hormones that are secreted by the thyroid gland and that help regulate metabolism, development, and maturation in vertebrates.

tidal volume The volume of air a mammal inhales and exhales with each breath.

tight junction A type of intercellular junction between animal cells that prevents the leakage of material through the space between cells.

tissue An integrated group of cells with a common structure, function, or both.

tissue system One or more tissues organized into a functional unit connecting the organs of a plant.

Toll-like receptor (TLR) A membrane receptor on a phagocytic white blood cell that recognizes fragments of molecules common to a set of pathogens.

tonicity The ability of a solution surrounding a cell to cause that cell to gain or lose water.

top-down model A model of community organization in which predation influences community organization by controlling herbivore numbers, which in turn control plant or phytoplankton numbers, which in turn control nutrient levels; also called the trophic cascade model.

topoisomerase A protein that breaks, swivels, and rejoins DNA strands. During DNA replication, topoisomerase helps to relieve strain in the double helix ahead of the replication fork.

topsoil A mixture of particles derived from rock, living organisms, and decaying organic material (humus).

torpor A physiological state in which activity is low and metabolism decreases.

totipotent (tō′-tuh-pōt′-ent) Describing a cell that can give rise to all parts of the embryo and adult, as well as extraembryonic membranes in species that have them.

trace element An element indispensable for life but required in extremely minute amounts.

trachea (trā′-kē-uh) The portion of the respiratory tract that passes from the larynx to the bronchi; also called the windpipe.

tracheal system In insects, a system of branched, air-filled tubes that extends throughout the body and carries oxygen directly to cells.

tracheid (trā′-kē-id) A long, tapered water-conducting cell found in the xylem of nearly all vascular plants. Functioning tracheids are no longer living.

trait One of two or more detectable variants in a genetic character.

trans fat An unsaturated fat, formed artificially during hydrogenation of oils, containing one or more *trans* double bonds.

transcription The synthesis of RNA using a DNA template.

transcription factor A regulatory protein that binds to DNA and affects transcription of specific genes.

transcription initiation complex The completed assembly of transcription factors and RNA polymerase bound to a promoter.

transcription unit A region of DNA that is transcribed into an RNA molecule.

transduction (1) A process in which phages (viruses) carry bacterial DNA from one bacterial cell to another. When these two cells are members of different species, transduction results in horizontal gene transfer. (2) In cellular communication, the conversion of a signal from outside the cell to a form that can bring about a specific cellular response; also called signal transduction.

transfer RNA (tRNA) An RNA molecule that functions as a translator between nucleic acid and protein languages by carrying specific amino acids to the ribosome, where they recognize the appropriate codons in the mRNA.

transformation (1) The conversion of a normal cell into a cell that is able to divide indefinitely in culture, thus behaving like a cancer cell. (Malignant transformation may also describe the series of changes in a normal cell in an organism that change it into a malignant (cancerous) cell.) (2) A change in genotype and phenotype due to the assimilation of external DNA by a cell. When the external DNA is from a member of a different species, transformation results in horizontal gene transfer.

transgenic Pertaining to an organism whose genome contains a gene introduced from another organism of the same or a different species.

translation The synthesis of a polypeptide using the genetic information encoded in an mRNA molecule. There is a change of "language" from nucleotides to amino acids.

translocation (1) An aberration in chromosome structure resulting from attachment of a chromosomal fragment to a nonhomologous chromosome. (2) During protein synthesis, the third stage in the elongation cycle, when the RNA carrying the growing polypeptide moves from the A site to the P site on the ribosome. (3) The transport of organic nutrients in the phloem of vascular plants.

transmission The passage of a nerve impulse along axons.

transmission electron microscope (TEM) A microscope that passes an electron beam through very thin sections stained with metal atoms and is primarily used to study the internal ultrastructure of cells.

transpiration The evaporative loss of water from a plant.

transport epithelium One or more layers of specialized epithelial cells that carry out and regulate solute movement.

transport protein A transmembrane protein that helps a certain substance or class of closely related substances to cross the membrane.

transport vesicle A small membranous sac in a eukaryotic cell's cytoplasm carrying molecules produced by the cell.

transposable element A segment of DNA that can move within the genome of a cell by means of a DNA or RNA intermediate; also called a transposable genetic element.

transposon A transposable element that moves within a genome by means of a DNA intermediate.

transverse (T) tubule An infolding of the plasma membrane of skeletal muscle cells.

triacylglycerol (trī-as′-ul-glis′-uh-rol) A lipid consisting of three fatty acids linked to one glycerol molecule; also called a fat or triglyceride.

triple response A plant growth maneuver in response to mechanical stress, involving slowing of stem elongation, thickening of the stem, and a curvature that causes the stem to start growing horizontally.

triplet code A genetic information system in which sets of three-nucleotide-long words specify the amino acids for polypeptide chains.

triploblastic Possessing three germ layers: the endoderm, mesoderm, and ectoderm. All bilaterian animals are triploblastic.

trisomic Referring to a diploid cell that has three copies of a particular chromosome instead of the normal two.

trochophore larva (trō′-kuh-fōr) Distinctive larval stage observed in some lophotrochozoan animals, including some annelids and molluscs.

trophic efficiency The percentage of production transferred from one trophic level to the next higher trophic level.

trophic structure The different feeding relationships in an ecosystem, which determine the route of energy flow and the pattern of chemical cycling.

trophoblast The outer epithelium of a mammalian blastocyst. It forms the fetal part of the placenta, supporting embryonic development but not forming part of the embryo proper.

tropic hormone A hormone that has an endocrine gland or endocrine cells as a target.

tropical dry forest A terrestrial biome characterized by relatively high temperatures and precipitation overall but with a pronounced dry season.

tropical rain forest A terrestrial biome characterized by relatively high precipitation and temperatures year-round.

tropics Latitudes between 23.5° north and south.

tropism A growth response that results in the curvature of whole plant organs toward or away from stimuli due to differential rates of cell elongation.

tropomyosin The regulatory protein that blocks the myosin-binding sites on actin molecules.

troponin complex The regulatory proteins that control the position of tropomyosin on the thin filament.

true-breeding Referring to organisms that produce offspring of the same variety over many generations of self-pollination.

tubal ligation A means of sterilization in which a woman's two oviducts (fallopian tubes) are tied closed and a segment of each is removed to prevent eggs from reaching the uterus.

tube foot One of numerous extensions of an echinoderm's water vascular system. Tube feet function in locomotion and feeding.

tumor-suppressor gene A gene whose protein product inhibits cell division, thereby preventing the uncontrolled cell growth that contributes to cancer.

tundra A terrestrial biome at the extreme limits of plant growth. At the northernmost limits, it is called arctic tundra, and at high altitudes, where plant forms are limited to low shrubby or matlike vegetation, it is called alpine tundra.

tunicate A member of the clade Urochordata, sessile marine chordates that lack a backbone.

turgid (ter′-jid) Swollen or distended, as in plant cells. (A walled cell becomes turgid if it has a lower water potential than its surroundings, resulting in entry of water.)

turgor pressure The force directed against a plant cell wall after the influx of water and swelling of the cell due to osmosis.

turnover The mixing of waters as a result of changing water-temperature profiles in a lake.

turnover time The time required to replace the standing crop of a population or group of populations (for example, of phytoplankton), calculated as the ratio of standing crop to production.

twin study A behavioral study in which researchers compare the behavior of identical twins raised apart with that of identical twins raised in the same household.

tympanic membrane Another name for the eardrum, the membrane between the outer and middle ear.

Unikonta (yū′-ni-kon′-tuh) One of four supergroups of eukaryotes proposed in a current hypothesis of the evolutionary history of eukaryotes. This clade, which is supported by studies of myosin proteins and DNA, consists of amoebozoans and opisthokonts. *See also* Excavata, "SAR" clade, and Archaeplastida.

unsaturated fatty acid A fatty acid that has one or more double bonds between carbons in the hydrocarbon tail. Such bonding reduces the number of hydrogen atoms attached to the carbon skeleton.

urban ecology The study of organisms and their environment in urban and suburban settings.

urea A soluble nitrogenous waste produced in the liver by a metabolic cycle that combines ammonia with carbon dioxide.

ureter (yū-rĕ′-ter) A duct leading from the kidney to the urinary bladder.

urethra (yū-rē′-thruh) A tube that releases urine from the mammalian body near the vagina in females and through the penis in males; also serves in males as the exit tube for the reproductive system.

uric acid A product of protein and purine metabolism and the major nitrogenous waste product of insects, land snails, and many reptiles. Uric acid is relatively nontoxic and largely insoluble in water.

urinary bladder The pouch where urine is stored prior to elimination.

uterine cycle In humans and certain other primates, a type of reproductive cycle in which the nonpregnant endometrium is shed through the cervix into the vagina; also called the menstrual cycle.

uterus A female organ where eggs are fertilized and/or development of the young occurs.

utricle (yū′-trih-kuhl) In the vertebrate ear, a chamber in the vestibule behind the oval window that opens into the three semicircular canals.

vaccine A harmless variant or derivative of a pathogen that stimulates a host's immune system to mount defenses against the pathogen.

vacuole (vak′-yū-ōl′) A membrane-bounded vesicle whose specialized function varies in different kinds of cells.

vagina Part of the female reproductive system between the uterus and the outside opening; the birth canal in mammals. During copulation, the vagina accommodates the male's penis and receives sperm.

valence The bonding capacity of a given atom; usually equals the number of unpaired electrons required to complete the atom's outermost (valence) shell.

valence electron An electron in the outermost electron shell.

valence shell The outermost energy shell of an atom, containing the valence electrons involved in the chemical reactions of that atom.

van der Waals interactions Weak attractions between molecules or parts of molecules that result from transient local partial charges.

variable A factor that varies in an experiment or other test.

variation Differences between members of the same species.

vas deferens In mammals, the tube in the male reproductive system in which sperm travel from the epididymis to the urethra.

vasa recta The capillary system in the kidney that serves the loop of Henle.

vascular cambium A cylinder of meristematic tissue in woody plants that adds layers of secondary vascular tissue called secondary xylem (wood) and secondary phloem.

vascular plant A plant with vascular tissue. Vascular plants include all living plant species except liverworts, mosses, and hornworts.

vascular tissue Plant tissue consisting of cells joined into tubes that transport water and nutrients throughout the plant body.

vascular tissue system A transport system formed by xylem and phloem throughout a vascular plant. Xylem transports water and minerals; phloem transports sugars, the products of photosynthesis.

vasectomy The cutting and sealing of each vas deferens to prevent sperm from entering the urethra.

vasoconstriction A decrease in the diameter of blood vessels caused by contraction of smooth muscles in the vessel walls.

vasodilation An increase in the diameter of blood vessels caused by relaxation of smooth muscles in the vessel walls.

vector An organism that transmits pathogens from one host to another.

vegetal pole The point at the end of an egg in the hemisphere where most yolk is concentrated; opposite of animal pole.

vegetative propagation Asexual reproduction in plants that is facilitated or induced by humans.

vegetative reproduction Asexual reproduction in plants.

vein (1) In animals, a vessel that carries blood toward the heart. (2) In plants, a vascular bundle in a leaf.

ventilation The flow of air or water over a respiratory surface.

ventral Pertaining to the underside, or bottom, of an animal with radial or bilateral symmetry.

ventricle (ven′-tri-kul) (1) A heart chamber that pumps blood out of the heart. (2) A space in the vertebrate brain, filled with cerebrospinal fluid.

venule (ven′-yūl) A vessel that conveys blood between a capillary bed and a vein.

vernalization The use of cold treatment to induce a plant to flower.

vertebrate A chordate animal with vertebrae, the series of bones that make up the backbone.

vesicle (ves′-i-kul) A membranous sac in the cytoplasm of a eukaryotic cell.

vessel A continuous water-conducting micropipe found in most angiosperms and a few nonflowering vascular plants.

vessel element A short, wide water-conducting cell found in the xylem of most angiosperms and a few nonflowering vascular plants. Dead at maturity, vessel elements are aligned end to end to form micropipes called vessels.

vestigial structure A feature of an organism that is a historical remnant of a structure that served a function in the organism's ancestors.

villus (plural, **villi**) (1) A finger-like projection of the inner surface of the small intestine. (2) A finger-like projection of the chorion of the mammalian placenta. Large numbers of villi increase the surface areas of these organs.

viral envelope A membrane, derived from membranes of the host cell, that cloaks the capsid, which in turn encloses a viral genome.

viroid (vī′-royd) A plant pathogen consisting of a molecule of naked, circular RNA a few hundred nucleotides long.

virulent phage A phage that replicates only by a lytic cycle.

virus An infectious particle incapable of replicating outside of a cell, consisting of an RNA or DNA genome surrounded by a protein coat (capsid) and, for some viruses, a membranous envelope.

visceral mass One of the three main parts of a mollusc; the part containing most of the internal organs. *See also* foot and mantle.

visible light That portion of the electromagnetic spectrum that can be detected as various colors by the human eye, ranging in wavelength from about 380 nm to about 750 nm.

vital capacity The maximum volume of air that a mammal can inhale and exhale with each breath.

vitamin An organic molecule required in the diet in very small amounts. Many vitamins serve as coenzymes or parts of coenzymes.

viviparous (vī-vip′-uh-rus) Referring to a type of development in which the young are born alive after having been nourished in the uterus by blood from the placenta.

voltage-gated ion channel A specialized ion channel that opens or closes in response to changes in membrane potential.

vulva Collective term for the female external genitalia.

water potential (Ψ) The physical property predicting the direction in which water will flow, governed by solute concentration and applied pressure.

water vascular system A network of hydraulic canals unique to echinoderms that branches into extensions called tube feet, which function in locomotion and feeding.

wavelength The distance between crests of waves, such as those of the electromagnetic spectrum.

wetland A habitat that is inundated by water at least some of the time and that supports plants adapted to water-saturated soil.

white matter Tracts of axons within the CNS.

whole-genome shotgun approach Procedure for genome sequencing in which the genome is randomly cut into many overlapping short segments that are sequenced; computer software then assembles the complete sequence.

wild type The phenotype most commonly observed in natural populations; also refers to the individual with that phenotype.

wilting The drooping of leaves and stems as a result of plant cells becoming flaccid.

wobble Flexibility in the base-pairing rules in which the nucleotide at the 5′ end of a tRNA anticodon can form hydrogen bonds with more than one kind of base in the third position (3′ end) of a codon.

xerophyte (zir′-ō-fīt′) A plant adapted to an arid climate.

X-linked gene A gene located on the X chromosome; such genes show a distinctive pattern of inheritance.

X-ray crystallography A technique used to study the three-dimensional structure of molecules. It depends on the diffraction of an X-ray beam by the individual atoms of a crystallized molecule.

xylem (zī′-lum) Vascular plant tissue consisting mainly of tubular dead cells that conduct most of the water and minerals upward from the roots to the rest of the plant.

xylem sap (zī′-lum) The dilute solution of water and minerals carried through vessels and tracheids.

yeast Single-celled fungus. Yeasts reproduce asexually by binary fission or by the pinching of small buds off a parent cell. Many fungal species can grow both as yeasts and as a network of filaments; relatively few species grow only as yeasts.

yolk Nutrients stored in an egg.

zero population growth (ZPG) A period of stability in population size, when additions to the population through births and immigration are balanced by subtractions through deaths and emigration.

zona pellucida The extracellular matrix surrounding a mammalian egg.

zoned reserve An extensive region that includes areas relatively undisturbed by humans surrounded by areas that have been changed by human activity and are used for economic gain.

zone of polarizing activity (ZPA) A block of mesoderm located just under the ectoderm where the posterior side of a limb bud is attached to the body; required for proper pattern formation along the anterior-posterior axis of the limb.

zoonotic pathogen A disease-causing agent that is transmitted to humans from other animals.

zoospore Flagellated spore found in chytrid fungi and some protists.

zygomycete (zī′-guh-mī′-sēt) A member of the fungal phylum Zygomycota, characterized by the formation of a sturdy structure called a zygosporangium during sexual reproduction.

zygosporangium (zī′-guh-spōr-an′-jē-um) (plural, **zygosporangia**) In zygomycete fungi, a sturdy multinucleate structure in which karyogamy and meiosis occur.

zygote (zī′-gōt) The diploid cell produced by the union of haploid gametes during fertilization; a fertilized egg.

Developmental biology, 1037f–1038f
Developmental genes. *See* Homeotic genes; *Hox* genes
Developmental plasticity, 769f
Developmental potential, cell fate and, 1054–1055f
Diabetes
    aquaporin mutations as causes of diabetes insipidus, 989f
    autoimmunity and, 965
    disruption of glucose homeostasis in, 910–911
    genetic engineering of insulin to treat, 430
Diabetes mellitus, **910**–911
Diacodexis, 476
Diacylglycerol (DAG), **222**f
Diagnosis
    antibodies as tools in, 963
    biotechnology in, 428
Diaphragm, birth control, 1032f
Diaphragm, breathing and, **939**f
Diapsids, **730**
Diarrhea, 136–137, 221, 583, 590f, 905
Diastole phase, **921**f
Diastolic pressure, **924**–925f
Diatomaceous earth, 596
Diatoms, 242f, 591f, **595**f–596, 1164
Diazepam, 1075
Dicots, **643**f–644f
Dictyostelium discoideum, 606, 607f
Dideoxy (dideoxyribonucleotide) chain termination DNA sequencing, 409f–410f, 437
Diencephalon, 1087f
Diets. *See also* Food
    adaptations of vertebrate digestive systems for, 906f–908f
    assessing nutritional needs in, 896–897
    catabolism and human, 180f–181
    deficiencies in, 895f–896f
    essential nutrients for, 893f, 894t–895t
    genetic variation in prey selection and, 1150f
    nonheritable variation and, 482f
    phenylketonuria and, 486
    typical and opportunistic, 892f–893
Differential centrifugation, 96f
Differential gene expression, **365**. *See also* Gene regulation
    cytoplasmic determinants and induction in, 377f–378
    in eukaryotic gene regulation, 365f–366
    in gene regulation, 360f
    in pattern formation of body plans, 379–380f, 381f–382f, 383
    in processes of embryonic development, 376f–377 (*see also* Embryonic development)
    sequential regulation of, during cellular differentiation, 378–379f
Differential-interference microscopy, **95**f
Differential reproductive success, 264–265f
Differential speciation success, 542–543
Differentiation, cell, **376**
    cytokinins in, 844
    as embryonic development process, 376f–377 (*see also* Embryonic development)
    plant development and, 757, 769, 773f
    sequential gene regulation in, 378–379f
    stem cells and, 425f (*see also* Stem cells)
Differentiation, determination vs., **1051**
Diffusion, **131**
    body surface area and, 689f
    effects on water balance of osmosis as, 131f–133f
    free energy change and, 146f
    interpreting scatter plots on glucose uptake as, 134
    as passive transport, 130–131f
    in plant cells, 207f
    proteins and facilitated, 133f
    of water across plant plasma membranes, 782–784, 785f
    of water and minerals into root cells, 786
Digestion, **897**
    in animal food processing, 897f
    digestive compartments in, 897f–899f, 900
    digestive systems and, 869f
    extracellular, 899f–900
    feeding mechanisms and, 898f
    fungal, 649, 662

hydrolysis in, 67
intracellular, 899
lysosomes in intracellular, 107f–108
regulation of animal, 908–909f
sea star, 707–708f
in small intestine, 902–903f, 904f–905f
in stomach, 901–902f
vertebrate adaptations for, 906f–908f
Digestive enzymes, 76f
Digestive systems
    adaptations of, 906f–908f
    alimentary canal of, 900f
    feedback regulation of, 908–909f
    internal exchange surfaces and, 869f
    large intestine in, 905f–906
    oral cavity, pharynx, and esophagus in, 900–901f
    small intestine in, 902–903f, 904f–905f
    stomach in, 901–902f
Digger wasps, 1140f
Dihybrid crosses, **273**–274f
Dihybrids, **273**–274f
Dihydrofolate reductase (DHFR), 605f
Dihydroxyacetone, 68f
Dijkstra, Cor, 1196f
Dikaryotic mycelia, **651**
Dimers, tubulin, 114
Dimetrodon fossil, 523f
Dimorphism, sexual, 1145f
Dinoflagellates, 141f, 242f, **598**f
Dinosaurs, **730**
    blood pressure of, 925
    C. Darwin and, 12f
    disappearance of, 673
    as early reptiles, 730
    flying, 1130
    in fossil record, 519f–520, 523f, 558f
    mass extinction of, 535f, 536
    in Mesozoic era, 526
Dioecious species, **828**–829f
Diphtheria, 398
Diploblastic animals, **674**
Diploid cells, **255**
    genetic variation preserved in recessive alleles of, 494
    haploid cells vs., 255
    mitosis vs. meiosis in, 260–261f, 262
    in sexual life cycles, 256f–257
Diplomonads, **593**
Dipnoi (lungfishes), 723–724
Diptera, 706f
Direct contact, cell signaling by, 212f
Direct inhibition hypothesis, 844
Directionality, DNA replication, 322–323f, 324f
Directional selection, **492**f
Disaccharides, **69**f
Diseases, animal
    density-dependent population regulation by, 1198f
    movement corridors and spread of, 1267
    viral, 394f, 401f, 402–403f, 404–405, 406f
Diseases, plant
    community structure and pathogens in, 1228
    density-dependent population regulation by, 1198f
    disease-resistant genes and, 860
    disease-suppressive soil and, 584
    prokaryotes in protection against, 584
    viral, 393f, 394f, 405
Diseases and disorders, human
    adenoviruses and, 394f–395
    alkaptonuria, 334
    allergies, 964–965f
    Alzheimer's disease, 406, 1097–1098f
    amebic dysentery, 607
    amytrophic lateral sclerosis (ALS), 1122
    antibiotic resistance and, 472f–473
    asthma, 62
    atherosclerosis, 74, 75, 137, 931f–932
    autism, 1094
    autoimmune, 965f
    bacterial, 398, 568–569f, 570, 583f
    biotechnology in diagnosis and treatment of, 428–429f, 430f
    cachexia, 1010
    cancer (*see* Cancer)

cardiovascular diseases, 74, 931f–932
cholera, 221
color blindness, 297f, 1116f
community ecology, pathogens, and, 1228–1229f
cri du chat and chronic myelogenous leukemia (CML), 307f
cystic fibrosis, 284
cystic kidney disease, 1058
density-dependent population regulation by, 1198f
detecting fetal, during pregnancy, 1033
diabetes (*see* Diabetes)
diarrhea, 136–137
dominantly inherited, 285f
Down syndrome, 305, 306f–307
drug addiction, 1097f
Duchenne muscular dystrophy, 297
due to chromosomal alterations, 304–305f, 306f–307f
emerging viruses and, 402f–403, 404–405, 406f
endocrine disruptors and, 1009
endometriosis, 1027
epilepsy, 1092
erectile dysfunction, 1076
familial cardiomyopathy, 355f
faulty apoptosis in nervous system and, 229
faulty cell-surface receptors and, 214, 215f, 217
flatworm parasites and, 690f–691f
flesh-eating disease, 472f–473
fungal, 664
gastric ulcers and acid reflux, 902
genetic (*see* Genetic disorders)
genomics and proteomics in, 88f, 251
gonorrhea, 570
gout, 977
growth-related, 1005f
heart murmurs, 922
hemophilia, 297–298, 931
HIV/AIDS (*see* AIDS (acquired immunodeficiency syndrome); HIV (human immunodeficiency virus))
Hodgkin's disease, 966
Huntington's disease, 285
hypercholesterolemia, 137
hypertension, 932
immune system disruptions and, 964–965f, 966–968f
immunization against, 963
immunodeficiency, 966
influenza, 394f–395, 402–403f, 404–405
insects as carriers of, 707
iodine deficiency and goiter, 29
Kartagener's syndrome, 1058f
karyotypes and, 254f
Klinefelter syndrome, 307
Leber's congenital amaurosis (LCA), 1116
lymphatic system and, 927
major depressive disorder and bipolar disorder, 1097
malaria (*see* Malaria)
mitochondrial, 309
mosaicism, 298
multifactorial, 285
mutations and, 355f–356f, 357
myasthenia gravis, 1122
myotonia and epilepsy, 1070
nematode parasites and trichinosis, 699f–700
of nervous system, 1096–1099
neurodegenerative, 406
neurotransmitters and, 1074–1076
from ozone depletion, 1275
parasitic (*see* Parasites)
Parkinson's disease, 406, 1075, 1098
phenylketonuria, 486–487
pleiotropy and inherited, 278–279
pneumonia, 313f, 573
polydactyly, 278
protein misfolding and, 83
protists and, 590f–591f
recessively inherited, 283f–284f, 285
respiratory distress syndrome (RDS), 938f
retinitis pigmentosa, 489
schizophrenia, 1096f
sexually transmitted diseases (STDs) (*see* Sexually transmitted diseases (STDs))

Human population
  biosphere carrying capacity for global, 1201*f*–
    1204*f*, 1205
  density-dependent population regulation of, by
    diseases, 1198*f*
  survivorship curves for, 1188*f*
Human reproduction. *See also* Animal reproduction
  conception, embryonic development, and birth in,
    1028*f*–1031*f*
  contraception and abortion in, 1032*f*–1033
  endocrine disruptors and, 1009
  female reproductive organs of, 1020–1021*f*
  hormonal regulation of, 1024*f*–1027*f*
  as iteroparity, 1195*f*
  male reproductive organs of, 1019*f*–1020
  maternal immune tolerance of embryo and fetus
    in, 1031
  oogenesis in, 1023*f*
  prostaglandins and, 999
  reproductive technologies and, 1033–1034*f*
  sexual response in, 1027–1028
  spermatogenesis in, 1022*f*
Hummingbird hawkmoth, 706*f*
Hummingbirds, 4, 516, 734*f*, 821*f*
Humoral immune response, 947*f*, **958*f*–959*f***
Humpback whales, 898*f*
Humus, **800**, 801
Hundred Heartbeat Club species, 1256*f*
Hunger, transgenic crops and reducing human,
  831–832*f*
Huntington's disease, **285**, 426
Hurricane Katrina, 1166
Hutton, James, 463*f*, 464
Huxley, Andrew, 1068
Hybrid breakdown, 503*f*
Hybridization, **269**, 831, 833–834
Hybrid orbitals, 39*f*–40
Hybrids, **501**
  bears, 504*f*
  reproductive barriers and sterility of, 503*f*
  speciation rates and, 514–515*f*
  sterility of, 516
Hybrid zones, **510**–511*f*, 512*f*–513*f*
Hydrangea, 280*f*
Hydras, 253*f*, 685–686*f*, 687*f*, 899*f*, 1080*f*
Hydration shells, **49**
Hydrocarbons, **60**–61*f*, 665*f*
Hydrocarbon tail, chlorophyll, 192*f*
Hydrochloric acid, 51, 901–902*f*
Hydrogen
  covalent bonding and, 36*f*–37*f*
  as essential element, 29*t*, 56, 64
  in organic compounds, 59*f*
  oxidation of organic molecules containing,
    164–165*f*
  in plant composition, 803
  in saturated and unsaturated fats, 73*f*–74
Hydrogen bonds, **39*f***
  in DNA structure, 86–87*f*
  floating of ice and, 48
  in water molecules, 45*f*
  as weak chemical bonds, 39*f*
Hydrogen ions, **51**–52*f*, 53
Hydrogenosomes, 593
Hydrogen peroxide, 111
Hydrogen sulfide gas, 534–535
Hydrolysis, **67**
  of ATP, 149*f*–151*f*
  disassembling of polymers to monomers by, 67*f*
  enzymatic, 897
  by lysosomes, 107*f*–108
Hydrolytic enzymes, fungal, 649
Hydronium ions, **51**–52*f*, 53
Hydrophilic substances, **49**, 76–77*f*, 125*f*–126
Hydrophobic interaction, **81***f*
Hydrophobic substances, **49**, 76–77*f*, 125*f*–126
Hydroponic culture, **804***f*
Hydrostatic skeletons, **1127***f*
Hydrothermal vents, **520**–21*f*, 580, 582, 908*f*
Hydroxide ions, **51**–52*f*, 53
Hydroxyl group, **63***f*
Hydrozoans, 686*f*–687*f*
Hymen, 1020
Hymenoptera, 706*f*

Hypercholesterolemia, 137
Hypermastigote, 608*f*
Hyperosmotic solutions, 972*f*, 985
Hyperpolarization, **1066***f*–1067*f*
Hypersensitive response, plant, **860**, 861
Hypertension, **932**
Hypertonic solutions, **132***f*
Hyphae, fungal, **649***f*–650*f*, 651, 811
Hypoblast cells, 1046*f*–1047*f*
Hypocotyl, **822**–823*f*, 824*f*
Hypoosmotic solutions, 972*f*
Hypothalamus, **882**, **1002**, **1087**
  in homeostasis, 1084
  in human brain, 1087*f*
  in human endocrine system, 999*f*
  in kidney regulation, 988*f*–989*f*
  in neuroendocrine signaling, 1002*f*–1005*f*
  in regulation of mammalian reproduction,
    1024*f*–1026*f*, 1027
  in sex hormone cascades, 1009
  in stress responses, 1007*f*
  suparchiasmatic nucleus (SCN) in, 1088–1089
  in thermoregulation, 882–883*f*
Hypotheses, **16**. *See also* Inquiry Figures; Scientific
    Skills Exercises
  forming and testing of, in science, 16–17*f*, 18*f*–19
  phylogenetic trees as, 558*f*
  theories and, 21, 477–478
Hypothyroidism, 1004
Hypotonic solutions, **132***f*
Hyracoidea, 739*f*
Hyracotherium, 542–543*f*

I

Ibex, 1260–1261
Ibuprofen, 62*f*, 1008, 1106
Ice
  floating of, on liquid water, 48*f*
  on Mars, 50*f*
  as solid water, 44
Icosahedral viruses, 394*f*–395
Identical DNA sequences, 447*f*
Identical twins, 1030, 1055
Idioblasts, 862*f*
IgE antibodies, 964
Iguanas, 883
Ileum, 904
Imaging, brain, 1079*f*–1080, 1090*f*
Imaging techniques, fetal testing, 287
Imatinib, 429–430
Imbibition, **823**
Immigration, population dynamics of, **1186***f*,
    1190–1191*f*, 1200–1201*f*, 1227
Immune defenses, plant, 751, 859–860
Immune response
  primary and secondary, 956–957*f*
  trypanosome evasion of, 594
Immune systems, **946**
  adaptations of pathogens to evade, 965–968*f*
  diseases of, 227
  disruptions of, 964–965*f*, 966
  HIV/AIDS and, 392*f*, 400 (*see also* AIDS (acquired
    immunodeficiency syndrome); HIV (human
    immunodeficiency virus))
  immune rejection by, 962–963
  immune responses by adaptive immunity in,
    958*f*–963*f*, 964
  immune responses by innate immunity in,
    947–948*f*, 949*f*–951*f*, 952
  immunization and, 961–962, 967*f*
  leukocytes in, 929
  lymphatic systems and, 927*f*
  maternal immune tolerance of embryo and fetus
    during pregnancy, 1031
  membrane carbohydrate cell-cell recognition in,
    128–129
  pathogen-specific recognition by adaptive
    immunity in, 952–953*f*, 954–955*f*, 956–957*f*
  in plants, 751, 859–860
  prostaglandins in, 995
  recognition and response functions of innate and
    adaptive immunity in, 946*f*–947*f*
  stem cells and, 426
  trematode camouflage and, 690*f*

Immunity
  active and passive, and immunization, 962–963
  maternal immune tolerance of embryo and fetus
    during pregnancy, 1031
Immunization, **963**
Immunodeficiency diseases, 966
Immunoglobulin (Ig), **953***f*, 955*f*–956*f*, 961
Immunological memory, 954, 956–957*f*
Impala, 219*f*
Imprinting, **1138**–1139*f*, 1146*f*–1147*f*
Inactivation, cell-signaling, 227
Inborn immunodeficiency, 966
Inclusive fitness, **1152***f*–1153*f*
Incomplete dominance, **277***f*
Incomplete flowers, **638***f*, 816
Incomplete metamorphosis, **705**, 706*f*
Independent assortment, law of, 272–**273**, 274*f*,
    293*f*–294, 300
Independent assortment of chromosomes, 263*f*
Independent variables, **21**, 507
Indeterminate cleavage, **675***f*–676
Indeterminate growth, **760***f*–761*f*
Indian corn, 445*f*
Indian Ocean Subtropical Gyre, 1162*f*
Indian pipe, 812*f*
Indian rice, 1257
Indoleacetic acid (IAA), 842. *See also* Auxin
Indolebutyric acid (IBA), 843
Induced fit, 153*f*–**154**
Induced pluripotent stem cells, 426–427*f*
Inducers, **363***f*–364
Inducible enzymes, 363*f*–364
Inducible innate immune response, 948*f*, 949*f*
Inducible operons, **363***f*–364
Induction, 377*f*–**378**, **1048**
Inductive reasoning, **16**
Inductive signals, cell fate determination and pattern
    formation by, 1055–1056*f*, 1057*f*–1058
Industrialization, human population growth and,
    1201*f*–1202
Inert elements, 35
Infant mortality, 1203, 1276*f*
Infection
  bacterial, 215*f*
  cytotoxic T cell response to, 959*f*
  fungal, 664
  inflammatory response and, 951–952
Infection thread, bacterial, 809*f*
Inferences, 1025
Infertility, 1033–1034*f*
Inflammation, 578*f*, 931*f*–932, 1008, 1106
Inflammatory response, **951***f*–952
Inflorescences, **816**
Influenza viruses
  antibody proteins and, 79*f*
  antigenic variation of, 966
  in density-dependent population regulation, 1198*f*
  as emerging viruses, 402–403*f*, 404–405
  structure of, 394*f*–395
  as zoonotic, 1228–1229*f*
Information, as theme of biology, 2, 5*f*–6*f*, 7
Information processing
  cerebral cortex in, 1090–1091*f*
  ion movements and gradients and, 987*f*
  neuron, 1061–1062, 1063*f*
  problem solving and, 1141*f*
Infrared receptors, 1104–1105*f*
Ingestion, **897***f*
Ingroups, **555**
Inhalation, 938–939*f*, 940*f*
Inheritance. *See also* Mendelian inheritance; Sexual
    life cycles
  blending hypothesis vs. particulate hypothesis on,
    267–68
  of cancer predisposition, 388
  chromosomal basis of (*see* Chromosomal basis of
    inheritance)
  of chromosomes and genes, 253
  C. Darwin on, 13*f*–15*f*
  Darwinian theory on, 469*f*–470
  epigenetic, 367
  expression and transmission of genetic
    information in, 5*f*–6*f*, 7

Index

in sex determination, 1025
smooth ER synthesis of, 104–105
as steroids, 75f, 1008–1009f
Sex-linked genes, 296f, **297**–298f
Sex pili, 570, 574f–575
Sex reversal, 1016
Sexual dimorphism, **493f**, 1145f
Sexual intercourse, human, 1027–1028, 1032–1033, 1076
Sexual life cycles. *See also* Life cycles
  alternation of fertilization and meiosis in, 254f–256f, 257
  angiosperm, 818–819f
  asexual reproduction vs., 253f
  chromosomal basis of Mendelian inheritance in, 292f–293f, 294 (*see also* Chromosomal basis of inheritance)
  evolution from genetic variation produced in, 263f–265f
  genetics of heredity and genetic variation in, 252f
  graphing DNA changes in meiosis of, 262
  human chromosome sets in, 254f–255f, 256
  inheritance of chromosomes and genes in, 253
  karyotypes of chromosomes in, 254f
  mitosis vs. meiosis in, 260–261f, 262
  protist, 588
  stages of meiosis in, 257f–260f
  varieties of, 256f–257
Sexually transmitted diseases (STDs), 579f, 593f, 1029, 1032f, 1034. *See also* AIDS (acquired immunodeficiency syndrome); HIV (human immunodeficiency virus)
Sexually transmitted infections (STIs), 1032
Sexual reproduction, **253**. *See also* Sexual life cycles
  in angiosperms (*see* Angiosperm reproduction)
  in animals, 668f–669 (*see also* Animal reproduction)
  asexual reproduction vs., 253f, 827–828
  in bryophytes, 618–619f, 620f–621
  flowers and angiosperm, 638f
  in fungi, 652f
  microevolution from sexual selection in, 493f–494f
  as source of genetic variation, 483
Sexual reproduction, animal, **1014**. *See also* Animal reproduction; Human reproduction
  asexual reproduction vs., 1014f–1015
  as evolutionary enigma, 1014f–1015
  fertilization mechanisms in, 1016f–1018f
  reproductive cycles in, 1015f
  variations in patterns of, 1016
Sexual response, human, 1027–1028
Sexual selection, 493f–494f, 509f, 1146f–1147f, 1148
S genes, 829
Shade avoidance, plant, 851
Shaffer, Mark, 1263f
Shannon diversity, **1216f**
Shapes
  cell, 116, 117
  enzyme, 153f–154, 158f–159f, 220
  insect pollinators and flower, 643f
  molecular, 39f–40
  morphogenesis and cell, 1050f–1051
  of organic compounds, 59f
  prokaryotic, 568f
Shapiro, Michael, 540f
Shared ancestral characters, **554f**–555
Shared derived characters, **554f**–555
Sharks, 720–721f, 973
Shelf fungi, 659f
Shell drilling adaptation, 536
Shells, electron, 32f–35f
Shigella bacteria, 575
Shivering thermogenesis, 882f
Shoots, 842f
  apical meristems of land plant, 615f
  light capture and architecture of, 780f–781f
  primary growth of, 763f–765f
  transport of water and minerals from roots to, via xylem, 786–787f, 788f–789f, 790
Shoot systems, 753f
Short-day plants, **853f**
Short tandem repeats (STRs), **431**, **446**

Short-term memory, **1094**–1095
Shrimp, 458f, 506–507f, 703
Sickle-cell disease, **82**, **284**, **929**
  abnormal hemoglobin in, 929
  evolution of, 497f
  heterozygote advantage in, 494–495
  pleiotropy and, 278–279
  point mutations and, 355f, 482, 496f
  protein primary structure changes and, 82f
  as recessively inherited, 284f–285
Side-blotched lizards, 1148f
Side chains, amino acid, 75–77f
Sidedness, cellular membrane, 129f
Sieve plates, **759f**, 793–794
Sieve-tube elements, **759f**
Sieve tubes, 793–794, 795f
Signaling molecules, 994f–995f. *See also* Animal hormones; Neurohormones; Neurotransmitters
Signal peptides, **351f**
Signal-recognition particles (SRPs), **351f**
Signals, animal, **1136f**–1137f
Signal transduction, **997**
  in hormone pathways, 997f
  membrane proteins and, 128f
Signal transduction pathways, **214**
  cancer and interference with normal, 384–385f, 386
  in cell signaling, 210, 213f–214, 218–219
  coordinate control of, 371
  differential gene expression and induction in, 377–378
  evolution of, 211
  linking signal reception to plant responses, 837f–838f, 840
  neurotransmitters and, 1074
  second messengers in, 220f–221f, 222f
  in sensory amplification, 1103–1104
  in visual sensory transduction, 1114f
Sign stimulus, 1134f–**1135**
Silencing, gene expression, 421–422f
Silencing, transcription, 369
Silent mutations, **355**–356f
Silent Spring (book), 1271f
Silk, 80f, 702
Silk moth, 1001f–1002
Silkworm moths, 1104, 1105f
Silverfish, 706f
Silversword plants, 537f–538, 551
Simberloff, Dan, 1227f–1228
Simple columnar epithelium, 871f
Simple endocrine pathway, 1000f
Simple fruits, **825f**
Simple leaves, 755f
Simple neuroendocrine pathway, 1000f–1001
Simple sequence DNA, **446**
Simple squamous epithelium, 871f
Singing, fruit fly, 1136f
Single bonds, 36–37
Single-celled organisms, 526, 528f–529f, 588. *See also* Protists
Single circulation, **918**, 919f
Single-lens eyes, **1112f**–1113
Single nucleotide polymorphisms (SNPs), **422f**, 428, 456
Single-strand binding proteins, **321f**, 325t
Single-stranded DNA (ssDNA) viruses, 398t
Single-stranded RNA (ssRNA) viruses, 398t, 399f–400
Sinoatrial (SA) node, **922f**
Sirenia, 739f
Sister cells, 233
Sister chromatid cohesion, 234, 257
Sister chromatids, **234f**–235, 255f, 258f–261f, 262, 264f
Sister species, 506
Sister taxa, **550f**
Situs inversus, 1058f
Sixth mass extinction, 535f–536
Size
  brain, 1085f
  carrying capacity and population, 1192t–1194f
  determining population, using mark-recapture method, 1185f
  ecosystem, 1232–1233

evolution of axon, 1070f–1071f
  of genomes, 442t–443
  of global human population, 1201f–1204f, 1205
  Hardy-Weinberg equilibrium and population, 486
  Homo floresiensis, 748
  of hormones, 212
  individual survival and population, 1194
  locomotion costs and, 1130
  metabolic rate and animal body, 885f
  of offspring litter or clutch as life history trait, 1195f–1196f, 1197
  of plasmodesmatal pores, 796
  prokaryotic cell, 568
  of prokaryotic vs. eukaryotic cells, 4f–5, 98
  protist, 587
  of skeletons, 1128
Skeletal muscle, **873f**, **1120**. *See also* Muscle
  in human breathing, 939f–940f
  locomotion from contraction of, in skeletal systems, 1126f–1129f, 1130
  muscle fibers of, 1124–1125t
  regulation of contraction of, 1122f–1124f
  sliding-filament model of contraction of, 1120–1121f, 1122
  structure of, 1119, 1120f
Skeletal systems
  bones and joints of human, 1128f
  cartilage, 718, 720
  energy costs of locomotion by, 1130
  locomotion from interaction of muscles and skeletons in, 1126f, 1129f–1130
  origins of, 719
  types of, 1126f–1127f
Skeletons, carbon, 60f–61f, 62f
Skills, scientific. *See* Scientific Skills Exercises
Skin
  cancer of, 326, 1275
  coloration, 1010
  heat exchange and, in animals, 879
  mechanoreceptors in human, 1104f
  pigmentation of human, 279–280f
Skinner, B. F., 1140–1141
Skulls, human vs. chimpanzee, 538f, 552
Sleep, ACTH secretion during, 1008
Sleep, brain functions and, 1088f
Sleeping sickness, 594f, 707, 967
Sleep movements, plant, 851–852f
Sliding-filament model, **1120**–1121f, 1122f
Slime, hagfish, 717
Slime bacteria, 211f
Slime layer, 569
Slime molds, 605–606f, 607f
Slope in Scientific Skills Exercises, 155, 1043
Slow block to polyspermy, **1039**
Slow-twitch fibers, **1125**
Slugs, 692
Small interfering RNAs (siRNAs), **374**–375f, 376
Small intestine, 689f, **902**
  absorption in, 904f–905f
  adaptations of, 906–907f
  digestion in, 902–903f, 904
Small-population approach, population conservation, 1261f–1263f
Smallpox, 402, 963
Smart plants, 806f
Smithells, Richard, 896f
Smithies, Oliver, 421
Smooth ER, 100f, 101f, **104**–105f
Smooth muscle, **873f**, **1126**–1127
Smuts, 659
Snails, 502f, 515–516, 532, 692, 696f, 1061f, 1063f
Snakes, 493f, 729f, 731f–732, 963, 1104–1105f, 1150f, 1258
Snapdragons, 277f
Snapping shrimp, 506–507f
Snook, Rhonda, 1018f
Snow pea, 644f
Snowshoe hares, 1200f
Snowy owls, 1198f
Soapberry bugs, 471f–472
Social behavior, 1153f–1154
Social learning, **1142f**–1143, 1148